**Be sure to keep up-to-** date in 2010!

Register now and we'll notify you when the newest cost index is available free online.

Please provide your name, address, and email below
and return this card by mail or
Fax: 1-800-632-6732.

To register online:  www.rsmeans411.com/register

Name _____

email _____

Company _____

Street _____

City/Town _____ State/Prov. _____ Zip/Postal Code _____

RS**Means**

RSMeans
Quarterly Updates
63 Smiths Lane
Kingston, MA 02364-3008
USA

$144.95 per copy (in United States)
Price is subject to change without prior notice.

0170

# RSMeans
# Residential
# Cost Data

## 29TH ANNUAL EDITION

# 2010

**RSMeans**
A division of Reed Construction Data
*Construction Publishers & Consultants*
*63 Smiths Lane*
*Kingston, MA 02364-3008*
**(781) 422-5000**

Copyright©2009 by RSMeans
A division of Reed Construction Data
All rights reserved.

Printed in the United States of America
ISSN 0738-1239
ISBN 978-0-87629-828-2

**Senior Editor**
Bob Mewis, CCC

**Contributing Editors**
Christopher Babbitt
Ted Baker
Barbara Balboni
Robert A. Bastoni
John H. Chiang, PE
Gary W. Christensen
David G. Drain, PE
Cheryl Elsmore
Robert J. Kuchta
Robert C. McNichols
Melville J. Mossman, PE
Jeannene D. Murphy
Stephen C. Plotner
Eugene R. Spencer
Marshall J. Stetson
Phillip R. Waier, PE

**Book Design**
Norman R. Forgit

**President & CEO**
Iain Melville

**Vice President,
Product & Development**
Richard Remington

**Vice President of
Operations**
David C. Walsh

**Vice President of Sales**
Thomas Kesler

**Director, Cost Products**
Daimon Bridge

**Marketing Director**
John M. Shea

**Engineering Manager**
Bob Mewis, CCC

**Cover Design**
Paul Robertson
Wayne Engebretson

**Production Manager**
Michael Kokernak

**Production Coordinator**
Jill Goodman

**Production**
Paula Reale-Camelio
Sheryl A. Rose
Jonathan Forgit
Debbie Panarelli
Mary Lou Geary

**Technical Support**
A.K. Dash
Tom Dion
Roger Hancock
Gary L. Hoitt
Genevieve Medeiros
Kathryn S. Rodriguez
Sharon Proulx

PRINTED WITH
SOY INK

# Foreword

## Our Mission

Since 1942, RSMeans has been actively engaged in construction cost publishing and consulting throughout North America.

Today, more than 65 years after RSMeans began, our primary objective remains the same: to provide you, the construction and facilities professional, with the most current and comprehensive construction cost data possible.

Whether you are a contractor, owner, architect, engineer, facilities manager, or anyone else who needs a reliable construction cost estimate, you'll find this publication to be a highly useful and necessary tool.

With the constant flow of new construction methods and materials today, it's difficult to find the time to look at and evaluate all the different construction cost possibilities. In addition, because labor and material costs keep changing, last year's cost information is not a reliable basis for today's estimate or budget.

That's why so many construction professionals turn to RSMeans. We keep track of the costs for you, along with a wide range of other key information, from city cost indexes . . . to productivity rates . . . to crew composition . . . to contractor's overhead and profit rates.

RSMeans performs these functions by collecting data from all facets of the industry and organizing it in a format that is instantly accessible to you. From the preliminary budget to the detailed unit price estimate, you'll find the data in this book useful for all phases of construction cost determination.

## The Staff, the Organization, and Our Services

When you purchase one of RSMeans' publications, you are, in effect, hiring the services of a full-time staff of construction and engineering professionals.

Our thoroughly experienced and highly qualified staff works daily at collecting, analyzing, and disseminating comprehensive cost information for your needs. These staff members have years of practical construction experience and engineering training prior to joining the firm. As a result, you can count on them not only for accurate cost figures, but also for additional background reference information that will help you create a realistic estimate.

The RSMeans organization is always prepared to help you solve construction problems through its variety of data solutions, including online, CD, and print book formats, as well as cost estimating expertise available via our business solutions, training, and seminars.

Besides a full array of construction cost estimating books, RSMeans also publishes a number of other reference works for the construction industry. Subjects include construction estimating and project and business management, special topics such as green building and job order contracting, and a library of facility management references.

In addition, you can access all of our construction cost data electronically using *Means CostWorks*® CD or on the Web using **MeansCostWorks.com.**

What's more, you can increase your knowledge and improve your construction estimating and management performance with an RSMeans construction seminar or in-house training program. These two-day seminar programs offer unparalleled opportunities for everyone in your organization to become updated on a wide variety of construction-related issues.

RSMeans is also a worldwide provider of construction cost management and analysis services for commercial and government owners.

In short, RSMeans can provide you with the tools and expertise for constructing accurate and dependable construction estimates and budgets in a variety of ways.

## Robert Snow Means Established a Tradition of Quality That Continues Today

Robert Snow Means spent years building RSMeans, making certain he always delivered a quality product.

Today, at RSMeans, we do more than talk about the quality of our data and the usefulness of our books. We stand behind all of our data, from historical cost indexes to construction materials and techniques to current costs.

If you have any questions about our products or services, please call us toll-free at 1-800-334-3509. Our customer service representatives will be happy to assist you. You can also visit our Web site at **www.rsmeans.com.**

# Table of Contents

# Related RSMeans Products and Services

The engineers at RSMeans suggest the following products and services as companion information resources to *RSMeans Residential Cost Data:*

## Construction Cost Data Books
*Open Shop Building Construction Cost Data 2010*
*Light Commerical Cost Data 2010*

## Reference Books
*ADA Compliance Pricing Guide*
*Designing & Building with the IBC*
*Estimating Building Costs*
*Exterior Home Improvement Costs*
*Home Addition & Renovation Project Costs*
*Interior Home Improvement Costs*
*Kitchen & Bath Project Costs*
*Plan Reading & Material Takeoff*
*Project Scheduling and Management for Construction*
*Unit Price Estimating Methods*

## Seminars and In-House Training
Unit Price Estimating
*Means CostWorks®* Training
Means Data for Job Order Contracting (JOC)
Plan Reading & Material Takeoff
Scheduling & Project Management
Mechanical & Electrical Estimating

## RSMeans on the Internet
Visit RSMeans at **www.rsmeans.com** for a one-stop portal for the most reliable and current resources available on the market. Here you can request or download **FREE** estimating software demos, visit our bookstore for convenient ordering, and learn more about new publications and companion products.
Also visit **www.reedconstructiondata.com** for RSMeans business solutions, seminars, training, and more.

## RSMeans Electronic Data
Get the information found in RSMeans cost books electronically on *Means CostWorks®* CD or on the Web at **MeansCostWorks.com.**

## RSMeans Business Solutions
Cost engineers and analysts conduct facility life cycle and benchmark research studies and predictive cost modeling, as well as offer consultation services for conceptual estimating, real property management, and job order contracting. Research studies are designed with the application of proprietary cost and project data from Reed Construction Data and RSMeans' extensive North American databases. Analysts offer building product manufacturers qualitative and quantitative market research, as well as time/motion studies for new products, and Web-based dashboards for market opportunity analysis. Clients are from both the public and private sectors, including federal, state, and municipal agencies, corporations, institutions, construction management firms, hospitals, and associations.

## RSMeans for Job Order Contracting (JOC)
Best practice job order contracting (JOC) services support the owner in the development of their program. RSMeans develops all required contracting documents, works with stakeholders, and develops qualified and experienced contractor lists. Means JOCWorks™ software is the best of class in the functional tools that meet JOC specific requirements. RSMeans data is organized to meet JOC cost estimating requirements.

## Construction Costs for Software Applications
Over 25 unit price and assemblies cost databases are available through a number of leading estimating and facilities management software providers (listed below). For more information see the "Other RSMeans Products" pages at the back of this publication.
MeansData™ is also available to federal, state, and local government agencies as multi-year, multi-seat licenses.

- 4Clicks-Solutions, LLC
- ArenaSoft Estimating
- Beck Technology
- BSD – Building Systems Design, Inc.
- CMS – Construction Management Software
- Corecon Technologies, Inc.
- CorVet Systems
- Estimating Systems, Inc.
- Hard Dollar Corporation
- MC$^2$
- Parsons Corporation
- Sage Timberline Office
- UDA Technologies, Inc.
- US Cost, Inc.
- VFA – Vanderweil Facility Advisers
- WinEstimator, Inc.

# How the Book Is Built: An Overview

The Construction Specifications Institute (CSI) and Construction Specifications Canada (CSC) have produced the 2004 edition of MasterFormat, a system of titles and numbers used extensively to organize construction information.

All unit price data in the RSMeans cost data books is now arranged in the 50-division MasterFormat 2004 system.

## A Powerful Construction Tool

You have in your hands one of the most powerful construction tools available today. A successful project is built on the foundation of an accurate and dependable estimate. This book will enable you to construct just such an estimate.

For the casual user the book is designed to be:

- quickly and easily understood so you can get right to your estimate.
- filled with valuable information so you can understand the necessary factors that go into the cost estimate.

For the regular user, the book is designed to be:

- a handy desk reference that can be quickly referred to for key costs.
- a comprehensive, fully reliable source of current construction costs and productivity rates, so you'll be prepared to estimate any project.
- a source book for preliminary project cost, product selections, and alternate materials and methods.

To meet all of these requirements we have organized the book into the following clearly defined sections.

## New: Quick Start

See our new "Quick Start" instructions on the following page to get started right away.

## Estimating with RSMeans Unit Price Cost Data

Please refer to these steps for guidance on completing an estimate using RSMeans unit price cost data.

## Square Foot Cost Section

This section lists Square Foot costs for typical residential construction projects. The organizational format used divides the projects into basic building classes. These classes are defined at the beginning of the section. The individual projects are further divided into ten common components of construction.

A Table of Contents, an explanation of square foot prices, and an outline of a typical page layout are located at the beginning of this section.

## Assemblies Cost Section

This section uses an "Assemblies" (sometimes referred to as "systems") format grouping all the functional elements of a building into 9 construction divisions.

At the top of each "Assembly" cost table is an illustration, a brief description, and the design criteria used to develop the cost. Each of the components and its contributing cost to the system is shown.

**Material:** These cost figures include a standard 10% markup for "handling". They are national average material costs as of January of the current year and include delivery to the job site.

**Installation:** The installation costs include labor and equipment, plus a markup for the installing contractor's overhead and profit.

For a complete breakdown and explanation of a typical "Assemblies" page, see "How To Use the Assemblies Cost Tables" at the beginning of the Assemblies Section.

## Unit Price Section

All cost data has been divided into the 50 divisions according to the MasterFormat system of classification and numbering. For a listing of these divisions and an outline of their subdivisions, see the Unit Price Section Table of Contents.

*Estimating tips are included at the beginning of each division.*

## Reference Section

This section includes information on Equipment Rental Costs, Crew Listings, Location Factors, Reference Tables, and a listing of Abbreviations.

**Equipment Rental Costs:** This section contains the average costs to rent and operate hundreds of pieces of construction equipment.

**Crew Listings:** This section lists all the crews referenced in the book. For the purposes of this book, a crew is composed of more than one trade classification and/or the addition of power equipment to any trade classification. Power equipment is included in the cost of the crew. Costs are shown both with the bare labor rates and with the installing contractor's overhead and profit added. For each, the total crew cost per eight-hour day and the composite cost per labor-hour are listed.

**Location Factors:** You can adjust total project costs to over 900 locations throughout the U.S. and Canada by using the data in this section.

**Reference Tables:** At the beginning of selected major classifications in the Unit Price section are "reference numbers" shown in a shaded box. These numbers refer you to related information in the Reference Section. In this section, you'll find reference tables, explanations, and estimating information that support how we develop the unit price data, technical data, and estimating procedures.

**Abbreviations:** A listing of abbreviations used throughout this book, along with the terms they represent, is included in this section.

## Index

A comprehensive listing of all terms and subjects in this book will help you quickly find what you need when you are not sure where it falls in MasterFormat.

## The Scope of This Book

This book is designed to be as comprehensive and as easy to use as possible. To that end we have made certain assumptions and limited its scope in two key ways:

1. We have established material prices based on a national average.
2. We have computed labor costs based on a 7 major region average of residential wage rates.

## Project Size/Type

The material prices in Means data cost books are "contractor's prices." They are the prices that contractors can expect to pay at the lumberyards, suppliers/distributers warehouses, etc. Small orders of speciality items would be higher than the costs shown, while very large orders, such as truckload lots, would be less. The variation would depend on the size, timing, and negotiating power of the contractor. The labor costs are primarily for new construction or major renovations rather than repairs or minor alterations. **With reasonable exercise of judgment, the figures can be used for any building work.**

# Absolute Essentials for a Quick Start

If you feel you are ready to use this book and don't think you will need the detailed instructions that begin on the following page, this Absolute Essentials for a Quick Start page is for you. These steps will allow you to get started estimating in a matter of minutes.

## 1 Scope

Think through the project that you will be estimating, and identify the many individual work tasks that will need to be covered in your estimate.

## 2 Quantify

Determine the number of units that will be required for each work task that you identified.

## 3 Pricing

Locate individual Unit Price line items that match the work tasks you identified. The Unit Price Section Table of Contents that begins on page 1 and the Index in the back of the book will help you find these line items.

## 4 Multiply

Multiply the Total Incl O&P cost for a Unit Price line item in the book by your quantity for that item. The price you calculate will be an estimate for a completed item of work performed by a subcontractor. Keep adding line items in this manner to build your estimate.

## 5 Project Overhead

Include project overhead items in your estimate. These items are needed to make the job run and are typically, but not always, provided by the General Contractor. They can be found in Division 1. An alternate method of estimating project overhead costs is to apply a percentage of the total project cost.

Include rented tools not included in crews, waste, rubbish handling, and cleanup.

## 6 Estimate Summary

Include General Contractor's markup on subcontractors, General Contractor's office overhead and profit, and sales tax on materials and equipment.

Adjust your estimate to the project's location by using the City Cost Indexes or Location Factors found in the Reference Section.

---

*Editors' Note: We urge you to spend time reading and understanding the supporting material in the front of this book. An accurate estimate requires experience, knowledge, and careful calculation. The more you know about how we at RSMeans developed the data, the more accurate your estimate will be. In addition, it is important to take into consideration the reference material in the back of the book such as Equipment Listings, Crew Listings, City Cost Indexes, Location Factors, and Reference Numbers.*

# Estimating with RSMeans Unit Price Cost Data

Following these steps will allow you to complete an accurate estimate using RSMeans Unit Price cost data.

## 1 Scope out the project

- Identify the individual work tasks that will need to be covered in your estimate.
- The Unit Price data inside this book has been divided into 44 Divisions according to the CSI MasterFormat 2004—their titles are listed on the back cover of your book.
- Think through the project that you will be estimating, and identify those CSI Divisions that you will need to use in your estimate.
- The Unit Price Section Table of Contents that begins on page 1 may also be helpful when scoping out your project.
- Experienced estimators find it helpful to begin an estimate with Division 2, estimating Division 1 after the full scope of the project is known.

## 2 Quantify

- Determine the number of units that will be required for each work task that you previously identified.
- Experienced estimators will include an allowance for waste in their quantities. (Waste is not included in RSMeans Unit Price line items unless so stated.)

## 3 Price the quantities

- Use the Unit Price Table of Contents, and the Index, to locate the first individual Unit Price line item for your estimate.
- Reference Numbers indicated within a Unit Price section refer to additional information that you may find useful.
- The crew indicates who is performing the work for that task. Crew codes are expanded in the Crew Listings in the Reference Section to include all trades and equipment that comprise the crew.
- The Daily Output is the amount of work the crew is expected to do in one day.

- The Labor-Hours value is the amount of time it will take for the average crew member to install one unit of measure.
- The abbreviated Unit designation indicates the unit of measure upon which the crew, productivity, and prices are based.
- Bare Costs are shown for materials, labor, and equipment needed to complete the Unit Price line item. Bare costs do not include waste, project overhead, payroll insurance, payroll taxes, main office overhead, or profit.
- The Total Incl O&P cost is the billing rate or invoice amount of the installing contractor or subcontractor who performs the work for the Unit Price line item.

## 4 Multiply

- Multiply the total number of units needed for your project by the Total Incl O&P cost for the Unit Price line item.
- Be careful that the final unit of measure for your quantity of units matches the unit of measure in the Unit column in the book.
- The price you calculate will be an estimate for a completed item of work.
- Keep scoping individual tasks, determining the number of units required for those tasks, matching them up with individual Unit Price line items in the book, and multiplying quantities by Total Incl O&P costs. In this manner, keep building your estimate.
- An estimate completed to this point, in this manner, will be priced as if a subcontractor, or set of subcontractors, will perform the work. The estimate does not yet include Project Overhead or Estimate Summary components such as General Contractor markups on subcontracted and self-performed work, General Contractor office overhead and profit, contingency, and location factor.

## 5 Project Overhead

- Include project overhead items from Division 1 – General Requirements.
- These are items that will be needed to make the job run. These are typically, but not always, provided by the General Contractor. They include, but are not limited to, such items as field personnel, insurance, performance bond, permits, testing, temporary utilities, field office and storage facilities, temporary scaffolding and platforms, equipment mobilization and demobilization, temporary roads and sidewalks, winter protection, temporary barricades and fencing, temporary security, temporary signs, field engineering and layout, final cleaning and commissioning.
- These items should be scoped, quantified, matched to individual Unit Price line items in Division 1, priced and added to your estimate.
- An alternate method of estimating project overhead costs is to apply a percentage of the total project cost, usually 5% to 15% with an average of 10% (see General Conditions, page ix).
- Include other project related expenses in your estimate such as:
  - Rented equipment not itemized in the Crew Listings
  - Rubbish handling throughout the project (see 02 41 19.23)

# 6 Estimate Summary

- Includes sales tax on materials and equipment.
  *Note: Sales tax must be added for materials in subcontracted work.*

- Include the General Contractor's markup on self-performed work, usually 5% to 15% with an average of 10%.

- Include the General Contractor's markup on subcontracted work, usually 5% to 15% with an average of 10%.

- Include General Contractor's main office overhead and profit.

- RSMeans gives general guidelines on the General Contractor's main office overhead (see section 01 31 13.50 and Reference Number R013113-50).

- RSMeans gives no guidance on the General Contractor's profit.

- Markups will depend on the size of the General Contractor's operations, his projected annual revenue, the level of risk he is taking on, and on the level of competitiveness in the local area and for this project in particular.

- Include a contingency, usually 3% to 5%.

- Adjust your estimate to the project's location by using the City Cost Indexes or the Location Factors in the Reference Section.

- Look at the rules on the pages for How to Use the City Cost Indexes to see how to apply the Indexes for your location.

- When the proper Index or Factor has been identified for the project's location, convert it to a multiplier by dividing it by 100, then multiply that multiplier by your estimate total cost. Your original estimate total cost will now be adjusted up or down from the national average to a total that is appropriate for your location.

*Editors' Notes:*

1) *We urge you to spend time reading and understanding the supporting material in the front of this book. An accurate estimate requires experience, knowledge, and careful calculation. The more you know about how we at RSMeans developed the data, the more accurate your estimate will be. In addition, it is important to take into consideration the reference material in the back of the book such as Equipment Listings, Crew Listings, City Cost Indexes, Location Factors, and Reference Numbers.*

2) *Contractors who are bidding or are involved in JOC, DOC, SABER, or IDIQ type contracts are cautioned that workers' compensation insurance, federal and state payroll taxes, waste, project supervision, project overhead, main office overhead, and profit are not included in bare costs. Your coefficient or multiplier must cover these costs.*

# How to Use the Book: The Details

## What's Behind the Numbers? The Development of Cost Data

The staff at RSMeans continuously monitors developments in the construction industry in order to ensure reliable, thorough, and up-to-date cost information.

While *overall* construction costs may vary relative to general economic conditions, price fluctuations within the industry are dependent upon many factors. Individual price variations may, in fact, be opposite to overall economic trends. Therefore, costs are continually monitored and complete updates are published yearly. Also, new items are frequently added in response to changes in materials and methods.

## Costs—$ (U.S.)

All costs represent U.S. national averages and are given in U.S. dollars. The RSMeans Location Factors can be used to adjust costs to a particular location. The Location Factors for Canada can be used to adjust U.S. national averages to local costs in Canadian dollars. No exchange rate conversion is necessary.

G  The processes or products identified by the green symbol in this publication have been determined to be environmentally responsible and/or resource-efficient solely by the RSMeans engineering staff. The inclusion of the green symbol does not represent compliance with any specific industry association or standard.

## Material Costs

The RSMeans staff contacts manufacturers, dealers, distributors, and contractors all across the U.S. and Canada to determine national average material costs. If you have access to current material costs for your specific location, you may wish to make adjustments to reflect differences from the national average. Included within material costs are fasteners for a normal installation. RSMeans engineers use

manufacturers' recommendations, written specifications, and/or standard construction practice for size and spacing of fasteners. Adjustments to material costs may be required for your specific application or location. Material costs do not include sales tax.

## Labor Costs

Labor costs are based on the average of residential wages from across the U.S. for the current year. Rates, along with overhead and profit markups, are listed on the inside back cover of this book.

- If wage rates in your area vary from those used in this book, or if rate increases are expected within a given year, labor costs should be adjusted accordingly.

Labor costs reflect productivity based on actual working conditions. In addition to actual installation, these figures include time spent during a normal workday on tasks such as, material receiving and handling, mobilization at site, site movement, breaks, and cleanup.

Productivity data is developed over an extended period so as not to be influenced by abnormal variations and reflects a typical average.

## Equipment Costs

Equipment costs include not only rental, but also operating costs for equipment under normal use. The operating costs include parts and labor for routine servicing such as repair and replacement of pumps, filters, and worn lines. Normal operating expendables, such as fuel, lubricants, tires, and electricity (where applicable), are also included. Extraordinary operating expendables with highly variable wear patterns, such as diamond bits and blades, are excluded. These costs are included under materials. Equipment rental rates are obtained from industry sources throughout North America—contractors, suppliers, dealers, manufacturers, and distributors.

Equipment costs do not include operators' wages; nor do they include the cost to move equipment to a job site (mobilization) or from a job site (demobilization).

**Equipment Cost/Day**—The cost of power equipment required for each crew is included in the Crew Listings in the Reference Section (small tools that are considered as essential

everyday tools are not listed out separately). The Crew Listings itemize specialized tools and heavy equipment along with labor trades. The daily cost of itemized equipment included in a crew is based on dividing the weekly bare rental rate by 5 (number of working days per week) and then adding the hourly operating cost times 8 (the number of hours per day). This Equipment Cost/Day is shown in the last column of the Equipment Rental Cost pages in the Reference Section.

**Mobilization/Demobilization**—The cost to move construction equipment from an equipment yard or rental company to the job site and back again is not included in equipment costs. Mobilization (to the site) and demobilization (from the site) costs can be found in the Unit Price Section. If a piece of equipment is already at the job site, it is not appropriate to utilize mobil./demob. costs again in an estimate.

## Factors Affecting Costs

Costs can vary depending upon a number of variables. Here's how we have handled the main factors affecting costs.

**Quality**—The prices for materials and the workmanship upon which productivity is based represent sound construction work. They are also in line with U.S. government specifications.

**Overtime**—We have made no allowance for overtime. If you anticipate premium time or work beyond normal working hours, be sure to make an appropriate adjustment to your labor costs.

**Productivity**—The productivity, daily output, and labor-hour figures for each line item are based on working an eight-hour day in daylight hours in moderate temperatures. For work that extends beyond normal work hours or is performed under adverse conditions, productivity may decrease. (See the section in "How To Use the Unit Price Pages" for more on productivity.)

**Size of Project**—The size, scope of work, and type of construction project will have a significant impact on cost. Economies of scale can reduce costs for large projects. Unit costs can often run higher for small projects. Costs in this book are intended for the size and type of project as previously described in "How the Book Is Built: An Overview." Costs for projects of a significantly different size or type should be adjusted accordingly.

**Location**—Material prices in this book are for metropolitan areas. However, in dense urban areas, traffic and site storage limitations may increase costs. Beyond a 20-mile radius of large cities, extra trucking or transportation charges may also increase the material costs slightly. On the other hand, lower wage rates may be in effect. Be sure to consider both of these factors when preparing an estimate, particularly if the job site is located in a central city or remote rural location.

In addition, highly specialized subcontract items may require travel and per-diem expenses for mechanics.

**Other Factors**—
- season of year
- contractor management
- weather conditions
- local union restrictions
- building code requirements
- availability of:
  - adequate energy
  - skilled labor
  - building materials
- owner's special requirements/restrictions
- safety requirements
- environmental considerations

**General Conditions**—The "Square Foot" and "Assemblies" sections of this book use costs that include the installing contractor's overhead and profit (O&P). The Unit Price Section presents cost data in two ways: Bare Costs and Total Cost including O&P (Overhead and Profit). General Conditions, when applicable, should also be added to the Total Cost including O&P. The costs for General Conditions are listed in Division 1 of the Unit Price Section and the Reference Section of this book. General Conditions for the *Installing Contractor* may range from 0% to 10% of the Total Cost including O&P. For

the *General* or *Prime Contractor*, costs for General Conditions may range from 5% to 15% of the Total Cost including O&P, with a figure of 10% as the most typical allowance.

**Overhead & Profit**—Total Cost, including O&P, for the *Installing Contractor* is shown in the last column on both the Unit Price and the Assemblies pages of this book. This figure is the sum of the bare material cost plus 10% for profit, the bare labor cost plus overhead and profit, and the bare equipment cost plus 10% for profit. Details for the calculation of Overhead and Profit on labor are shown on the inside back cover and in the Reference Section of this book. (See the "How to Use the Unit Price Pages" for an example of this calculation.)

**Unpredictable Factors**—General business conditions influence "in-place" costs of all items. Substitute materials and construction methods may have to be employed. These may affect the installed cost and/or life cycle costs. Such factors may be difficult to evaluate and cannot necessarily be predicted on the basis of the job's location in a particular section of the country. Thus, where these factors apply, you may find significant, but unavoidable cost variations for which you will have to apply a measure of judgment to your estimate.

## Rounding of Costs

In general, all unit prices in excess of $5.00 have been rounded to make them easier to use and still maintain adequate precision of the results. The rounding rules we have chosen are in the following table.

| Prices from . . . | Rounded to the nearest . . . |
|---|---|
| $.01 to $5.00 | $.01 |
| $5.01 to $20.00 | $.05 |
| $20.01 to $100.00 | $.50 |
| $100.01 to $300.00 | $1.00 |
| $300.01 to $1,000.00 | $5.00 |
| $1,000.01 to $10,000.00 | $25.00 |
| $10,000.01 to $50,000.00 | $100.00 |
| $50,000.01 and above | $500.00 |

## Final Checklist

Estimating can be a straightforward process provided you remember the basics. Here's a checklist of some of the steps you should remember to complete before finalizing your estimate.

Did you remember to . . .

- factor in the Location Factor for your locale?
- take into consideration which items have been marked up and by how much?
- mark up the entire estimate sufficiently for your purposes?
- read the background information on techniques and technical matters that could impact your project time span and cost?
- include all components of your project in the final estimate?
- double check your figures for accuracy?
- call RSMeans if you have any questions about your estimate or the data you've found in our publications?

Remember, RSMeans stands behind its publications. If you have any questions about your estimate . . . about the costs you've used from our books . . . or even about the technical aspects of the job that may affect your estimate, feel free to call the RSMeans editors at 1-800-334-3509.

# Square Foot Cost Section

## Table of Contents

# Introduction to Square Foot Cost Section

The Square Foot Cost Section of this manual contains costs per square foot for four classes of construction in seven building types. Costs are listed for various exterior wall materials which are typical of the class and building type. There are cost tables for Wings and Ells with modification tables to adjust the base cost of each class of building. Non-standard items can easily be added to the standard structures.

Cost estimating for a residence is a three-step process:
- (1) Identification
- (2) Listing dimensions
- (3) Calculations

Guidelines and a sample cost estimating procedure are shown on the following pages.

## Identification

To properly identify a residential building, the class of construction, type, and exterior wall material must be determined. Page 8 has drawings and guidelines for determining the class of construction. There are also detailed specifications and additional drawings at the beginning of each set of tables to further aid in proper building class and type identification.

Sketches for eight types of residential buildings and their configurations are shown on pages 10 and 11. Definitions of living area are next to each sketch. Sketches and definitions of garage types are on page 12.

## Living Area

Base cost tables are prepared as costs per square foot of living area. The living area of a residence is that area which is suitable and normally designed for full time living. It does not include basement recreation rooms or finished attics, although these areas are often considered full time living areas by the owners.

Living area is calculated from the exterior dimensions without the need to adjust for exterior wall thickness. When calculating the living area of a 1-1/2 story, two story, three story or tri-level residence, overhangs and other differences in size and shape between floors must be considered.

Only the floor area with a ceiling height of six feet or more in a 1-1/2 story residence is considered living area. In bi-levels and tri-levels, the areas that are below grade are considered living area, even when these areas may not be completely finished.

## Base Tables and Modifications

Base cost tables show the base cost per square foot without a basement, with one full bath and one full kitchen for economy and average homes, and an additional half bath for custom and luxury models. Adjustments for finished and unfinished basements are part of the base cost tables. Adjustments for multi-family residences, additional bathrooms, townhouses, alternative roofs, and air conditioning and heating systems are listed in Modifications, Adjustments and Alternatives tables below the base cost tables.

Costs for other modifications, adjustments and alternatives, including garages, breezeways and site improvements, are on pages 93 to 96.

## Listing of Dimensions

To use this section of the manual, only the dimensions used to calculate the horizontal area of the building and additions, modifications, adjustments and alternatives are needed. The dimensions, normally the length and width, can come from drawings or field measurements. For ease in calculation, consider measuring in tenths of feet, i.e., 9 ft. 6 in. = 9.5 ft., 9 ft. 4 in. = 9.3 ft.

In all cases, make a sketch of the building. Any protrusions or other variations in shape should be noted on the sketch with dimensions.

## Calculations

The calculations portion of the estimate is a two-step activity:
- (1) The selection of appropriate costs from the tables
- (2) Computations

## Selection of Appropriate Costs

To select the appropriate cost from the base tables, the following information is needed:
- (1) Class of construction
  - (a) Economy
  - (b) Average
  - (c) Custom
  - (d) Luxury
- (2) Type of residence
  - (a) One story
  - (b) 1-1/2 story
  - (c) 2 story
  - (d) 3 story
  - (e) Bi-level
  - (f) Tri-level
- (3) Occupancy
  - (a) One family
  - (b) Two family
  - (c) Three family
- (4) Building configuration
  - (a) Detached
  - (b) Town/Row house
  - (c) Semi-detached
- (5) Exterior wall construction
  - (a) Wood frame
  - (b) Brick veneer
  - (c) Solid masonry
- (6) Living areas

Modifications, adjustments and alternatives are classified by class, type and size.

## Computations

The computation process should take the following sequence:
- (1) Multiply the base cost by the area.
- (2) Add or subtract the modifications, adjustments, and alternatives.
- (3) Apply the location modifier.

When selecting costs, interpolate or use the cost that most nearly matches the structure under study. This applies to size, exterior wall construction, and class.

# How to Use the Residential Square Foot Cost Pages

The following is a detailed explanation of a sample entry in the Residential Square Foot Cost Section. Each bold number below corresponds to the item described on the facing page with the appropriate component of the sample entry following in parentheses.

Prices listed are costs that include overhead and profit of the installing contractor. Total model costs include an additional mark-up for General Contractors' overhead and profit and fees specific to class of construction.

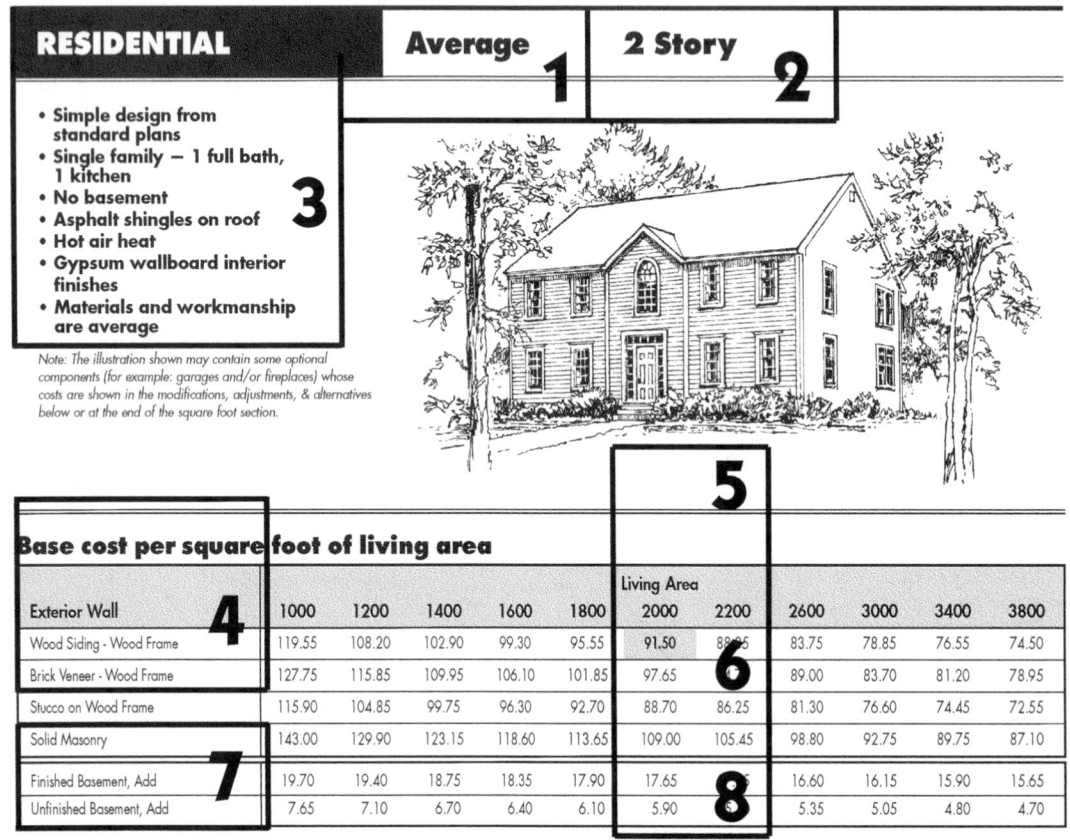

**RESIDENTIAL** | **Average** 1 | **2 Story** 2

- Simple design from standard plans
- Single family — 1 full bath, 1 kitchen
- No basement
- Asphalt shingles on roof
- Hot air heat
- Gypsum wallboard interior finishes
- Materials and workmanship are average

3

Note: The illustration shown may contain some optional components (for example: garages and/or fireplaces) whose costs are shown in the modifications, adjustments, & alternatives below or at the end of the square foot section.

## Base cost per square foot of living area

| Exterior Wall | 1000 | 1200 | 1400 | 1600 | 1800 | Living Area 2000 | 2200 | 2600 | 3000 | 3400 | 3800 |
|---|---|---|---|---|---|---|---|---|---|---|---|
| Wood Siding - Wood Frame | 119.55 | 108.20 | 102.90 | 99.30 | 95.55 | 91.50 | 88.95 | 83.75 | 78.85 | 76.55 | 74.50 |
| Brick Veneer - Wood Frame | 127.75 | 115.85 | 109.95 | 106.10 | 101.85 | 97.65 | | 89.00 | 83.70 | 81.20 | 78.95 |
| Stucco on Wood Frame | 115.90 | 104.85 | 99.75 | 96.30 | 92.70 | 88.70 | 86.25 | 81.30 | 76.60 | 74.45 | 72.55 |
| Solid Masonry | 143.00 | 129.90 | 123.15 | 118.60 | 113.65 | 109.00 | 105.45 | 98.80 | 92.75 | 89.75 | 87.10 |
| Finished Basement, Add | 19.70 | 19.40 | 18.75 | 18.35 | 17.90 | 17.65 | | 16.60 | 16.15 | 15.90 | 15.65 |
| Unfinished Basement, Add | 7.65 | 7.10 | 6.70 | 6.40 | 6.10 | 5.90 | | 5.35 | 5.05 | 4.80 | 4.70 |

(labels 4, 5, 6, 7, 8 point into the table)

## Modifications

Add to the total cost

| | |
|---|---|
| Upgrade Kitchen Cabinets | $ + 3521 |
| Solid Surface Countertops (Included) | |
| Full Bath - including plumbing, wall and floor finishes | + 5993 |
| Half Bath - including plumbing, wall and floor finishes | + 3570 |
| One Car Attached Garage | + 12,676 |
| One Car Detached Garage | + 16,871 |
| Fireplace & Chimney | + 5836 |

9

## Adjustments

For multi family - add to total cost

| | |
|---|---|
| Additional Kitchen | $ + 6796 |
| Additional Bath | + 5993 |
| Additional Entry & Exit | + 1640 |
| Separate Heating | + 1409 |
| Separate Electric | + 1915 |

For Townhouse/Rowhouse - Multiply cost per square foot by

| | |
|---|---|
| Inner Unit | + .90 |
| End Unit | + .95 |

10

## Alternatives

Add to or deduct from the cost per square foot of living area

| | |
|---|---|
| Cedar Shake Roof | + 1.95 |
| Clay Tile Roof | + 2.25 |
| Slate Roof | + 3.30 |
| Upgrade Walls to Skim Coat Plaster | + .49 |
| Upgrade Ceilings to Textured Finish | + .48 |
| Air Conditioning, in Heating Ductwork | + 2.54 |
| In Separate Ductwork | + 6.36 |
| Heating Systems, Hot Water | + 2.01 |
| Heat Pump | + 3.11 |
| Electric Heat | − .80 |
| Not Heated | − 3.55 |

11

## Additional upgrades or components

| | |
|---|---|
| Kitchen Cabinets & Countertops | Page 93 |
| Bathroom Vanities | 94 |
| Fireplaces & Chimneys | 94 |
| Windows, Skylights & Dormers | 94 |
| Appliances | 95 |
| Breezeways & Porches | 95 |
| Finished Attic | 95 |
| Garages | 96 |
| Site Improvements | 96 |
| Wings & Ells | 56 |

12

## 1 Class of Construction (Average)

The class of construction depends upon the design and specifications of the plan. The four classes are economy, average, custom, and luxury.

## 2 Type of Residence (2 Story)

The building type describes the number of stories or levels in the model. The seven building types are 1 story, 1-1/2 story, 2 story, 2-1/2 story, 3 story, bi-level, and tri-level.

## 3 Specification Highlights (Hot Air Heat)

These specifications include information concerning the components of the model, including the number of baths, roofing types, HVAC systems, and materials and workmanship. If the components listed are not appropriate, modifications can be made by consulting the information shown lower on the page or the Assemblies Section.

## 4 Exterior Wall System (Wood Siding - Wood Frame)

This section includes the types of exterior wall systems and the structural frame used. The exterior wall systems shown are typical of the class of construction and the building type shown.

## 5 Living Areas (2000 SF)

The living area is that area of the residence which is suitable and normally designed for full time living. It does not include basement recreation rooms or finished attics. Living area is calculated from the exterior dimensions without the need to adjust for exterior wall thickness. When calculating the living area of a 1-1/2 story, 2 story, 3 story, or tri-level residence, overhangs and other differences in size and shape between floors must be considered. Only the floor area with a ceiling height of six feet or more in a 1-1/2 story residence is considered living area. In bi-levels and tri-levels, the areas that are below grade are considered living area, even when these areas may not be completely finished. A range of various living areas for the residential model are shown to aid in selection of values from the matrix.

## 6 Base Costs per Square Foot of Living Area ($91.50)

Base cost tables show the cost per square foot of living area without a basement, with one full bath and one full kitchen for economy and average homes, and an additional half bath for custom and luxury models. When selecting costs, interpolate or use the cost that most nearly matches the residence under consideration for size, exterior wall system,

and class of construction. Prices listed are costs that include overhead and profit of the installing contractor, a general contractor markup, and an allowance for plans that vary by class of construction. For additional information on contractor overhead and architectural fees, see the Reference Section.

## 7 Basement Types (Finished)

The two types of basements are finished and unfinished. The specifications and components for both are shown on the Building Classes page in the Introduction to this section.

## 8 Additional Costs for Basements ($17.65)

These values indicate the additional cost per square foot of living area for either a finished or an unfinished basement.

## 9 Modifications and Adjustments (Upgrade Kitchen Cabinets $3521)

Modifications and Adjustments are costs added to or subtracted from the total cost of the residence. The total cost of the residence is equal to the cost per square foot of living area times the living area. Typical modifications and adjustments include kitchens, baths, garages and fireplaces.

## 10 Multiplier for Townhouse/ Rowhouse (Inner Unit .90)

The multipliers shown adjust the base costs per square foot of living area for the common wall condition encountered in townhouses or rowhouses.

## 11 Alternatives (Skim Coat Plaster $.49)

Alternatives are costs added to or subtracted from the base cost per square foot of living area. Typical alternatives include variations in kitchens, baths, roofing, and air conditioning and heating systems.

## 12 Additional Upgrades or Components (Wings & Ells page 56)

Costs for additional upgrades or components, including wings or ells, breezeways, porches, finished attics, and site improvements, are shown in other locations in the Residential Square Foot Cost Section.

**2**

| | | Cost Per Square Foot Of Living Area | | | % of Total |
|---|---|---|---|---|---|
| | | Mat. | Inst. | Total | (rounded) |
| **1 Site Work** | Site preparation for slab; 4' deep trench excavation for foundation wall. | | .72 | .72 | 0.8% |
| **2 Foundation** | Continuous reinforced concrete footing 8" deep x 18" wide; dampproofed and insulated reinforced concrete foundation wall, 8" thick, 4' deep, 4" concrete slab on 4" crushed stone base and polyethylene vapor barrier, trowel finish. | 2.97 | 3.73 | 6.70 | 7.3% |
| **3 Framing** | Exterior walls - 2" x 4" wood studs, 16" O.C.; 1/2" plywood sheathing; 2" x 6" rafters 16" O.C. with 1/2" plywood sheathing, 4 in 12 pitch; 2" x 6" ceiling joists 16" O.C.; 2" x 8" floor joists 16" O.C. with 5/8" plywood subfloor; 1/2" plywood subfloor on 1" x 2" wood sleepers 16" O.C. | 4.96 | 8.27 | 13.23 | 14.5% |
| **4 Exterior Walls** | Beveled wood siding and building paper on insulated wood frame walls; 6" attic insulation; double hung windows; 3 flush solid core wood exterior doors with storms. | 12.67 | 5.25 | 17.92 | 19.6% |
| **5 Roofing** | 25 year asphalt shingles; #15 felt building paper; aluminum gutters, downspouts, drip edge and flashings. | .96 | 1.11 | 2.07 | 2.3% |
| **6 Interiors** | Walls and ceilings, 1/2" taped and finished gypsum wallboard, primed and painted with 2 coats; painted baseboard and trim, finished hardwood floor 40%, carpet with 1/2" underlayment 40%, vinyl tile with 1/2" underlayment 15%, ceramic tile with 1/2" underlayment 5%; hollow core and louvered doors. | 12.71 | 13.38 | 26.09 | 28.5% |
| **7 Specialties** | Average grade kitchen cabinets - 14 L.F. wall and base with solid surface counter top and kitchen sink; 40 gallon electric water heater. | 2.26 | .83 | 3.09 | 3.4% |
| **8 Mechanical** | 1 lavatory, white, wall hung; 1 water closet, white; 1 bathtub with shower; enameled steel, white; gas fired warm air heat. | 3.02 | 2.68 | 5.70 | 6.2% |
| **9 Electrical** | 200 Amp. service; romex wiring; incandescent lighting fixtures, switches, receptacles. | 1.13 | 1.54 | 2.67 | 2.9% |
| **10 Overhead** | Contractor's overhead and profit and plans. | 6.92 | 6.39 | 13.31 | 14.5% |
| **Total** | | 47.60 | 43.90 | 91.50 | |

Numbered callout boxes: **4** **5** **6** **7** (Foundation/Framing columns), **3** (Exterior Walls description), **8** **9** (Overhead row)

## 1 Specifications

The parameters for an example dwelling from the previous pages are listed here. Included are the square foot dimensions of the proposed building. Living Area takes into account the number of floors and other factors needed to define a building's total square footage. Perimeter dimensions are defined in terms of linear feet.

## 2 Building Type

This is a sketch of a cross section view through the dwelling. It is shown to help define the living area for the building type. For more information, see the Building Types pages in the Introduction.

## 3 Components (4 Exterior Walls)

This page contains the ten components needed to develop the complete square foot cost of the typical dwelling specified. All components are defined with a description of the materials and/or task involved. Use cost figures from each component to estimate the cost per square foot of that section of the project. The components listed on this page are typical of all sizes of residences from the facing page. Specific quantities of components required would vary with the size of the dwelling and the exterior wall system.

## 4 Materials (4.96)

This column gives the amount needed to develop the cost of materials. The figures given here are not bare costs. Ten percent has been added to bare material cost for profit.

## 5 Installation (8.27)

Installation includes labor and equipment costs. The labor rates included here incorporate the total overhead and profit costs for the installing contractor. The average mark-up used to create these figures is 72.0% over and above bare labor costs. The equipment rates include 10% for profit.

## 6 Total (13.23)

This column lists the sum of two figures. Use this total to determine the sum of material cost plus installation cost. The result is a convenient total cost for each of the ten components.

## 7 % of Total (rounded) (14.5%)

This column represents the percent of the total cost for this component group.

## 8 Overhead

The costs in components 1 through 9 include overhead and profit for the installing contractor. Item 10 is overhead and profit for the general contractor. This is typically a percentage mark-up of all other costs. The amount depends on size and type of dwelling, building class, and economic conditions. An allowance for plans or design has been included where appropriate.

## 9 Bottom Line Total (91.50)

This figure is the complete square foot cost for the construction project and equals the sum of total material and total labor costs. To determine total project cost, multiply the bottom line total by the living area.

# Building Classes

## Economy Class

An economy class residence is usually built from stock plans. The materials and workmanship are sufficient to satisfy building codes. Low construction cost is more important than distinctive features. The overall shape of the foundation and structure is seldom other than square or rectangular.

An unfinished basement includes 7' high 8" thick foundation wall composed of either concrete block or cast-in-place concrete.

Included in the finished basement cost are inexpensive paneling or drywall as the interior finish on the foundation walls, a low cost sponge backed carpeting adhered to the concrete floor, a drywall ceiling, and overhead lighting.

## Custom Class

A custom class residence is usually built from plans and specifications with enough features to give the building a distinction of design. Materials and workmanship are generally above average with obvious attention given to construction details. Construction normally exceeds building code requirements.

An unfinished basement includes a 7'-6" high 10" thick cast-in-place concrete foundation wall or a 7'-6" high 12" thick concrete block foundation wall.

A finished basement includes painted drywall on insulated 2" x 4" wood furring as the interior finish to the concrete walls, a suspended ceiling, carpeting adhered to the concrete floor, overhead lighting and heating.

## Average Class

An average class residence is a simple design and built from standard plans. Materials and workmanship are average, but often exceed minimum building codes. There are frequently special features that give the residence some distinctive characteristics.

An unfinished basement includes 7'-6" high 8" thick foundation wall composed of either cast-in-place concrete or concrete block.

Included in the finished basement are plywood paneling or drywall on furring that is fastened to the foundation walls, sponge backed carpeting adhered to the concrete floor, a suspended ceiling, overhead lighting and heating.

## Luxury Class

A luxury class residence is built from an architect's plan for a specific owner. It is unique both in design and workmanship. There are many special features, and construction usually exceeds all building codes. It is obvious that primary attention is placed on the owner's comfort and pleasure. Construction is supervised by an architect.

An unfinished basement includes 8' high 12" thick foundation wall that is composed of cast-in-place concrete or concrete block.

A finished basement includes painted drywall on 2" x 4" wood furring as the interior finish, suspended ceiling, tackless carpet on wood subfloor with sleepers, overhead lighting and heating.

# Configurations

## Detached House

This category of residence is a free-standing separate building with or without an attached garage. It has four complete walls.

## Semi-Detached House

This category of residence has two living units side-by-side. The common wall is a fireproof wall. Semi-detached residences can be treated as a row house with two end units. Semi-detached residences can be any of the building types.

## Town/Row House

This category of residence has a number of attached units made up of inner units and end units. The units are joined by common walls. The inner units have only two exterior walls. The common walls are fireproof. The end units have three walls and a common wall. Town houses/row houses can be any of the building types.

# Building Types

## One Story

This is an example of a one-story dwelling. The living area of this type of residence is confined to the ground floor. The headroom in the attic is usually too low for use as a living area.

## One-and-a-half Story

The living area in the upper level of this type of residence is 50% to 90% of the ground floor. This is made possible by a combination of this design's high-peaked roof and/or dormers. Only the upper level area with a ceiling height of 6 feet or more is considered living area. The living area of this residence is the sum of the ground floor area plus the area on the second level with a ceiling height of 6 feet or more.

## One Story with Finished Attic

The main living area in this type of residence is the ground floor. The upper level or attic area has sufficient headroom for comfortable use as a living area. This is made possible by a high peaked roof. The living area in the attic is less than 50% of the ground floor. The living area of this type of residence is the ground floor area only. The finished attic is considered an adjustment.

## Two Story

This type of residence has a second floor or upper level area which is equal or nearly equal to the ground floor area. The upper level of this type of residence can range from 90% to 110% of the ground floor area, depending on setbacks or overhangs. The living area is the sum of the ground floor area and the upper level floor area.

## Two-and-one-half Story

This type of residence has two levels of equal or nearly equal area and a third level which has a living area that is 50% to 90% of the ground floor. This is made possible by a high peaked roof, extended wall heights and/or dormers. Only the upper level area with a ceiling height of 6 feet or more is considered living area. The living area of this residence is the sum of the ground floor area, the second floor area and the area on the third level with a ceiling height of 6 feet or more.

## Bi-level

This type of residence has two living areas, one above the other. One area is about 4 feet below grade and the second is about 4 feet above grade. Both areas are equal in size. The lower level in this type of residence is originally designed and built to serve as a living area and not as a basement. Both levels have full ceiling heights. The living area is the sum of the lower level area and the upper level area.

## Three Story

This type of residence has three levels which are equal or nearly equal. As in the 2 story residence, the second and third floor areas may vary slightly depending on setbacks or overhangs. The living area is the sum of the ground floor area and the two upper level floor areas.

## Tri-level

This type of residence has three levels of living area: one at grade level, one about 4 feet below grade, and one about 4 feet above grade. All levels are originally designed to serve as living areas. All levels have full ceiling heights. The living area is a sum of the areas of each of the three levels.

# Garage Types

## Attached Garage

Shares a common wall with the dwelling. Access is typically through a door between dwelling and garage.

## Basement Garage

Constructed under the roof of the dwelling but below the living area.

## Built-In Garage

Constructed under the second floor living space and above basement level of dwelling. Reduces gross square feet of living area.

## Detached Garage

Constructed apart from the main dwelling. Shares no common area or wall with the dwelling.

# Building Components

1. Excavation
2. Sill Plate
3. Basement Window
4. Floor Joist
5. Shoe Plate
6. Studs
7. Drywall
8. Plate
9. Ceiling Joists
10. Rafters

11. Collar Ties
12. Ridge Rafter
13. Roof Sheathing
14. Roof Felt
15. Roof Shingles
16. Flashing
17. Flue Lining
18. Chimney
19. Roof Shingles
20. Gutter

21. Fascia
22. Downspout
23. Shutter
24. Window
25. Wall Shingles
26. Building Paper
27. Wall Sheathing
28. Fire Stop
29. Dampproofing
30. Foundation Wall

31. Backfill
32. Drainage Stone
33. Drainage Tile
34. Wall Footing
35. Gravel
36. Concrete Slab
37. Column Footing
38. Pipe Column
39. Expansion Joint
40. Girder

41. Sub-floor
42. Finish Floor
43. Attic Insulation
44. Soffit
45. Ceiling Strapping
46. Wall Insulation
47. Cross Bridging
48. Bulkhead Stairs

# Exterior Wall Construction

## Typical Frame Construction

Typical wood frame construction consists of wood studs with insulation between them. A typical exterior surface is made up of sheathing, building paper and exterior siding consisting of wood, vinyl, aluminum or stucco over the wood sheathing.

## Brick Veneer

Typical brick veneer construction consists of wood studs with insulation between them. A typical exterior surface is sheathing, building paper and an exterior of brick tied to the sheathing, with metal strips.

## Stone

Typical solid masonry construction consists of a stone or block wall covered on the exterior with brick, stone or other masonry.

# Residential Cost Estimate Worksheet

## Worksheet Instructions

The residential cost estimate worksheet can be used as an outline for developing a residential construction or replacement cost. It is also useful for insurance appraisals. The design of the worksheet helps eliminate errors and omissions. To use the worksheet, follow the example below.

1. Fill out the owner's name, residence address, the estimator or appraiser's name, some type of project identifying number or code, and the date.

2. Determine from the plans, specifications, owner's description, photographs or any other means possible the class of construction. The models in this book use economy, average, custom and luxury as classes. Fill in the appropriate box.

3. Fill in the appropriate box for the residence type, configuration, occupancy, and exterior wall. If you require clarification, the pages preceding this worksheet describe each of these.

4. Next, the living area of the residence must be established. The heated or air conditioned space of the residence, not including the basement, should be measured. It is easiest to break the structure up into separate components as shown in the example. The main house (A), a one-and-one-half story wing (B), and a one story wing (C). The breezeway (D), garage (E), and open covered porch (F) will be treated differently. Data entry blocks for the living area are included on the worksheet for your use. Keep each level of each component separate, and fill out the blocks as shown.

5. By using the information on the worksheet, find the model, wing or ell in the following square foot cost pages that best matches the class, type, exterior finish and size of the residence being estimated. Use the *Modifications, Adjustments, and Alternatives* to determine the adjusted cost per square foot of living area for each component.

6. For each component, multiply the cost per square foot by the living area square footage. If the residence is a townhouse/rowhouse, a multiplier should be applied based upon the configuration.

7. The second page of the residential cost estimate worksheet has space for the additional components of a house. The cost for additional bathrooms, finished attic space, breezeways, porches, fireplaces, appliance or cabinet upgrades, and garages should be added on this page. The information for each of these components is found with the model being used, or in the *Modifications, Adjustments, and Alternatives* pages.

8. Add the total from page one of the estimate worksheet and the items listed on page two. The sum is the adjusted total building cost.

9. Depending on the use of the final estimated cost, one of the remaining two boxes should be filled out. Any additional items or exclusions should be added or subtracted at this time. The data contained in this book is a national average. Construction costs are different throughout the country. To allow for this difference, a location factor based upon the first three digits of the residence's zip code must be applied. The location factor is a multiplier that increases or decreases the adjusted total building cost. Find the appropriate location factor and calculate the local cost. If depreciation is a concern, a dollar figure should be subtracted at this point.

10. No residence will match a model exactly. Many differences will be found. At this level of estimating, a variation of plus or minus 10% should be expected.

# Adjustments Instructions

No residence matches a model exactly in shape, material, or specifications.

The common differences are:

1. Two or more exterior wall systems:
   a. Partial basement
   b. Partly finished basement
2. Specifications or features that are between two classes
3. Crawl space instead of a basement

## EXAMPLES

Below are quick examples. See pages 17-19 for complete examples of cost adjustments for these differences:

1. Residence "A" is an average one-story structure with 1,600 S.F. of living area and no basement. Three walls are wood siding on wood frame, and the fourth wall is brick veneer on wood frame. The brick veneer wall is 35% of the exterior wall area.

   Use page 38 to calculate the Base Cost per S.F. of Living Area.
   Wood Siding for 1,600 S.F.   =   $94.05 per S.F.
   Brick Veneer for 1,600 S.F.   =   $108.35 per S.F.
   .65 ($94.05) + .35 ($108.35) = $99.05 per S.F. of Living Area.

2. a. Residence "B" is the same as Residence "A"; However, it has an unfinished basement under 50% of the building. To adjust the $99.05 per S.F. of living area for this partial basement, use page 38.

   $99.05 + .50 ($9.50) = $103.80 per S.F. of Living Area.

   b. Residence "C" is the same as Residence "A"; However, it has a full basement under the entire building. 640 S.F. or 40% of the basement area is finished.

   Using Page 38:

   $99.05 + .40 ($27.95) + .60 ($9.50) = $115.93 per S.F. of Living Area.

3. When specifications or features of a building are between classes, estimate the percent deviation, and use two tables to calculate the cost per S.F.

   A two-story residence with wood siding and 1,800 S.F. of living area has features 30% better than Average, but 70% less than Custom.

   From pages 42 and 64:

   Custom 1,800 S.F. Base Cost   =   $116.70 per S.F.
   Average 1,800 S.F. Base Cost   =   $95.55 per S.F.
   DIFFERENCE   =   $21.15 per S.F.

   Cost is $95.55 + .30 ($21.15) = $101.90 per S.F. of Living Area.

4. To add the cost of a crawl space, use the cost of an unfinished basement as a maximum. For specific costs of components to be added or deducted, such as vapor barrier, underdrain, and floor, see the "Assemblies" section, pages 97 to 281.

# Model Residence Example

**First Floor Plan**

18'

24'

E    D    C

8'

12'

12'

F

16'

12'

A

28'

20'

24'    12'    12'    46'

B

18'

**Second Floor Plan**

46'

28'

A

20'

5'

5'

B

5'    13'

**A** = Main House
**B** = 1-1/2 Story Wing
**C** = 1 Story Wing
**D** = Breezeway
**E** = Garage
**F** = Open Covered Porch

17

## RESIDENTIAL COST ESTIMATE

| | | | |
|---|---|---|---|
| OWNERS NAME: | **Albert Westenberg** | APPRAISER: | **Nicole Wojtowicz** |
| RESIDENCE ADDRESS: | **300 Sygiel Road** | PROJECT: | **# 55** |
| CITY, STATE, ZIP CODE: | **Three Rivers, MA 01080** | DATE: | **Jan. 1, 2010** |

| CLASS OF CONSTRUCTION | RESIDENCE TYPE | CONFIGURATION | EXTERIOR WALL SYSTEM |
|---|---|---|---|
| ☐ ECONOMY | ☐ 1 STORY | ☑ DETACHED | ☑ WOOD SIDING - WOOD FRAME |
| ☑ AVERAGE | ☐ 1 1/2 STORY | ☐ TOWN/ROW HOUSE | ☐ BRICK VENEER - WOOD FRAME |
| ☐ CUSTOM | ☑ 2 STORY | ☐ SEMI-DETACHED | ☐ STUCCO ON WOOD FRAME |
| ☐ LUXURY | ☐ 2 1/2 STORY | | ☐ PAINTED CONCRETE BLOCK |
| | ☐ 3 STORY | OCCUPANCY | ☐ SOLID MASONRY (AVERAGE & CUSTOM) |
| | ☐ BI-LEVEL | ☑ ONE FAMILY | ☐ STONE VENEER - WOOD FRAME |
| | ☐ TRI-LEVEL | ☐ TWO FAMILY | ☐ SOLID BRICK (LUXURY) |
| | | ☐ THREE FAMILY | ☐ SOLID STONE (LUXURY) |
| | | ☐ OTHER | |

| * LIVING AREA (Main Building) | | | * LIVING AREA (Wing or Ell) | ( **B** ) | | * LIVING AREA (Wing or Ell) | ( **C** ) |
|---|---|---|---|---|---|---|---|
| First Level | **1288** | S.F. | First Level | **360** | S.F. | First Level | **192** | S.F. |
| Second level | **1288** | S.F. | Second level | **310** | S.F. | Second Level | | S.F. |
| Third Level | | S.F. | Third Level | | S.F. | Third Level | | S.F. |
| Total | **2576** | S.F. | Total | **670** | S.F. | Total | **192** | S.F. |

* Basement Area is not part of living area.

| MAIN BUILDING | | | COSTS PER S.F. LIVING AREA | |
|---|---|---|---|---|
| Cost per Square Foot of Living Area, from Page | **42** | | $ | **83.75** |
| Basement Addition: _____ % Finished, | **100** | % Unfinished | + | **5.35** |
| Roof Cover Adjustment: **Cedar Shake** Type, Page | **42** | (Add or Deduct) | ( ) | **1.95** |
| Central Air Conditioning: ☐ Separate Ducts ☑ Heating Ducts, Page | **42** | | + | **2.54** |
| Heating System Adjustment: _____ Type, Page _____ | | (Add or Deduct) | ( ) | _____ |
| Main Building: Adjusted Cost per S.F. of Living Area | | | $ # | **93.59** |

| MAIN BUILDING TOTAL COST | $ **93.59** /S.F. | x | **2,576** S.F. | x | _____ | = | $ **241,088** |
|---|---|---|---|---|---|---|---|
| | Cost per S.F. Living Area | | Living Area | | Town/Row House Multiplier (Use 1 for Detached) | | TOTAL COST |

| WING OR ELL (B) | **1 - 1/2** STORY | COSTS PER S.F. LIVING AREA | |
|---|---|---|---|
| Cost per Square Foot of Living Area, from Page **56** | | $ | **78.20** |
| Basement Addition: **100** % Finished, _____ % Unfinished | | + | **24.75** |
| Roof Cover Adjustment: _____ Type, Page _____ (Add or Deduct) | | ( ) | — |
| Central Air Conditioning: ☐ Separate Ducts ☑ Heating Ducts, Page **42** | | + | **2.54** |
| Heating System Adjustment: _____ Type, Page _____ (Add or Deduct) | | ( ) | _____ |
| Wing or Ell ( **B** ): Adjusted Cost per S.F. of Living Area | | $ | **105.49** |

| WING OR ELL (B) TOTAL COST | $ **105.49** /S.F. | x | **670** S.F. | | = | $ **70,678** |
|---|---|---|---|---|---|---|
| | Cost per S.F. Living Area | | Living Area | | | TOTAL COST |

| WING OR ELL (C) | **1** STORY | COSTS PER S.F. LIVING AREA | |
|---|---|---|---|
| Cost per Square Foot of Living Area, from Page **# 56** | **(WOOD SIDING)** | $ | **118.75** |
| Basement Addition: _____ % Finished, _____ % Unfinished | | + | — |
| Roof Cover Adjustment: _____ Type, Page _____ (Add or Deduct) | | ( ) | — |
| Central Air Conditioning: ☐ Separate Ducts ☐ Heating Ducts, Page _____ | | + | — |
| Heating System Adjustment: _____ Type, Page _____ (Add or Deduct) | | ( ) | — |
| Wing or Ell (C) Adjusted Cost per S.F. of Living Area | | $ | **118.75** |

| WING OR ELL (C) TOTAL COST | $ **118.75** /S.F. | x | **192** S.F. | | = | $ **22,800** |
|---|---|---|---|---|---|---|
| | Cost per S.F. Living Area | | Living Area | | | TOTAL COST |

| | | |
|---|---|---|
| | TOTAL THIS PAGE | **334,566** |

## RESIDENTIAL
## COST ESTIMATE

| | | | | | QUANTITY | | UNIT COST | | |
|---|---|---|---|---|---|---|---|---|---|
| Total Page 1 | | | | | | | | $ | 334,566 |
| Additional Bathrooms: | **2** | Full, | **1** | Half **2 @ 5993** **1 @ 3570** | | | | + | 15,556 |
| Finished Attic: | **N/A** | Ft. x | | Ft. | | S.F. | | | |
| Breezeway: ☑ Open ☐ closed | **12** | Ft. x | **12** | Ft. | 144 | S.F. | 23.52 | + | 3,387 |
| Covered Porch: ☑ Open ☐ Enclosed | **18** | Ft. x | **12** | Ft. | 216 | S.F. | 34.85 | + | 7,528 |
| Fireplace: ☑ Interior Chimney ☐ Exterior Chimney | | | | | | | | | |
| ☑ No. of Flues ( **2** ) ☑ Additional Fireplaces **1 - 2nd Story** | | | | | | | | + | 9,853 |
| Appliances: | | | | | | | | + | — |
| Kitchen Cabinets Adjustments: | | | | (±) | | | | | — |
| ☑ Garage ☐ Carport **2** Car(s) Description **Wood, Attached** (±) | | | | | | | | | 21,272 |
| Miscellaneous: | | | | | | | | + | |

| | | |
|---|---|---|
| ADJUSTED TOTAL BUILDING COST | $ | 392,162 |

| REPLACEMENT COST | | |
|---|---|---|
| ADJUSTED TOTAL BUILDING COST | $ | 392,162 |
| Site Improvements | | |
| (A) Paving & Sidewalks | $ | |
| (B) Landscaping | $ | |
| (C) Fences | $ | |
| (D) Swimming Pools | $ | |
| (E) Miscellaneous | $ | |
| TOTAL | $ | 392,162 |
| Location Factor | x | **1.040** |
| Location Replacement Cost | $ | 407,848 |
| Depreciation | -$ | 40,785 |
| LOCAL DEPRECIATED COST | $ | 367,063 |

| INSURANCE COST | | |
|---|---|---|
| ADJUSTED TOTAL BUILDING COST | $ | |
| Insurance Exclusions | | |
| (A) Footings, sitework, Underground Piping | -$ | |
| (B) Architects Fees | -$ | |
| Total Building Cost Less Exclusion | $ | |
| Location Factor | x | |
| LOCAL INSURABLE REPLACEMENT COST | $ | |

### SKETCH AND ADDITIONAL CALCULATIONS

## 1 Story

© Home Planners, Inc.

## 1-1/2 Story

## 2 Story

## Bi-Level

## Tri-Level

©Design Basics, Inc.

- **Mass produced from stock plans**
- **Single family — 1 full bath, 1 kitchen**
- **No basement**
- **Asphalt shingles on roof**
- **Hot air heat**
- **Gypsum wallboard interior finishes**
- **Materials and workmanship are sufficient to meet codes**

*Note: The illustration shown may contain some optional components (for example: garages and/or fireplaces) whose costs are shown in the modifications, adjustments, & alternatives below or at the end of the square foot section.*

©Home Planners, Inc.

## Base cost per square foot of living area

| Exterior Wall | Living Area | | | | | | | | | | |
|---|---|---|---|---|---|---|---|---|---|---|---|
| | 600 | 800 | 1000 | 1200 | 1400 | 1600 | 1800 | 2000 | 2400 | 2800 | 3200 |
| Wood Siding - Wood Frame | 113.20 | 102.25 | 94.05 | 87.30 | 81.50 | 77.80 | 75.95 | 73.45 | 68.45 | 64.80 | 62.30 |
| Brick Veneer - Wood Frame | 118.40 | 106.90 | 98.30 | 91.10 | 85.00 | 81.05 | 79.10 | 76.40 | 71.15 | 67.30 | 64.55 |
| Stucco on Wood Frame | 106.90 | 96.65 | 89.00 | 82.75 | 77.35 | 73.90 | 72.20 | 69.95 | 65.25 | 61.85 | 59.50 |
| Painted Concrete Block | 112.10 | 101.25 | 93.15 | 86.50 | 80.75 | 77.10 | 75.30 | 72.85 | 67.90 | 64.30 | 61.80 |
| Finished Basement, Add | 27.90 | 26.30 | 25.10 | 24.00 | 23.20 | 22.60 | 22.30 | 21.85 | 21.15 | 20.70 | 20.25 |
| Unfinished Basement, Add | 12.30 | 10.95 | 10.05 | 9.15 | 8.45 | 8.00 | 7.80 | 7.40 | 6.90 | 6.50 | 6.15 |

## Modifications

*Add to the total cost*

| | |
|---|---|
| Upgrade Kitchen Cabinets | $ + 803 |
| Solid Surface Countertops | + 576 |
| Full Bath - including plumbing, wall and floor finishes | + 4775 |
| Half Bath - including plumbing, wall and floor finishes | + 2845 |
| One Car Attached Garage | + 11,273 |
| One Car Detached Garage | + 14,630 |
| Fireplace & Chimney | + 5267 |

## Adjustments

*For multi family - add to total cost*

| | |
|---|---|
| Additional Kitchen | $ + 3709 |
| Additional Bath | + 4775 |
| Additional Entry & Exit | + 1640 |
| Separate Heating | + 1409 |
| Separate Electric | + 1066 |

*For Townhouse/Rowhouse - Multiply cost per square foot by*

| | |
|---|---|
| Inner Unit | + .95 |
| End Unit | + .97 |

## Alternatives

*Add to or deduct from the cost per square foot of living area*

| | |
|---|---|
| Composition Roll Roofing | − 1.05 |
| Cedar Shake Roof | + 4.20 |
| Upgrade Walls and Ceilings to Skim Coat Plaster | + .65 |
| Upgrade Ceilings to Textured Finish | + .48 |
| Air Conditioning, in Heating Ductwork | + 4.05 |
| In Separate Ductwork | + 7.72 |
| Heating Systems, Hot Water | + 2.11 |
| Heat Pump | + 2.56 |
| Electric Heat | − 1.81 |
| Not Heated | − 4.56 |

## Additional upgrades or components

| | |
|---|---|
| Kitchen Cabinets & Countertops | Page 93 |
| Bathroom Vanities | 94 |
| Fireplaces & Chimneys | 94 |
| Windows, Skylights & Dormers | 94 |
| Appliances | 95 |
| Breezeways & Porches | 95 |
| Finished Attic | 95 |
| Garages | 96 |
| Site Improvements | 96 |
| Wings & Ells | 34 |

**Important: See the Reference Section for Location Factors (to adjust for your city) and Estimating Forms**

# Economy 1 Story

**Living Area - 1200 S.F.**
**Perimeter - 146 L.F.**

| | | | Cost Per Square Foot Of Living Area | | | % of Total |
|---|---|---|---|---|---|---|
| | | | Mat. | Inst. | Total | (roun |
| **1** | **Site Work** | Site preparation for slab; 4' deep trench excavation for foundation wall. | | 1.17 | 1.17 | 1.4% |
| **2** | **Foundation** | Continuous reinforced concrete footing, 8" deep x 18" wide; dampproofed and insulated 8" thick reinforced concrete block foundation wall, 4' deep; 4" concrete slab on 4" crushed stone base and polyethylene vapor barrier, trowel finish. | 5.39 | 6.67 | 12.06 | 14.6% |
| **3** | **Framing** | Exterior walls - 2" x 4" wood studs, 16" O.C.; 1/2" insulation board sheathing; wood truss roof frame, 24" O.C. with 1/2" plywood sheathing, 4 in 12 pitch. | 3.97 | 5.73 | 9.70 | 11.7% |
| **4** | **Exterior Walls** | Metal lath reinforced stucco exterior on insulated wood frame walls; 6" attic insulation; sliding sash wood windows; 2 flush solid core wood exterior doors with storms. | 6.73 | 6.05 | 12.78 | 15.4% |
| **5** | **Roofing** | 20 year asphalt shingles; #15 felt building paper; aluminum gutters, downspouts, drip edge and flashings. | 1.85 | 2.16 | 4.01 | 4.8% |
| **6** | **Interiors** | Walls and ceilings, 1/2" taped and finished gypsum wallboard, primed and painted with 2 coats; painted baseboard and trim; rubber backed carpeting 80%, asphalt tile 20%; hollow core wood interior doors. | 8.32 | 11.18 | 19.50 | 23.6% |
| **7** | **Specialties** | Economy grade kitchen cabinets - 6 L.F. wall and base with plastic laminate counter top and kitchen sink; 30 gallon electric water heater. | 2.36 | .89 | 3.25 | 3.9% |
| **8** | **Mechanical** | 1 lavatory, white, wall hung; 1 water closet, white; 1 bathtub, enameled steel, white; gas fired warm air heat. | 4.06 | 3.16 | 7.22 | 8.7% |
| **9** | **Electrical** | 100 Amp. service; romex wiring; incandescent lighting fixtures, switches, receptacles. | .89 | 1.38 | 2.27 | 2.7% |
| **10** | **Overhead** | Contractor's overhead and profit. | 5.03 | 5.76 | 10.79 | 13.0% |
| | **Total** | | 38.60 | 44.15 | **82.75** | |

- Mass produced from stock plans
- Single family — 1 full bath, 1 kitchen
- No basement
- Asphalt shingles on roof
- Hot air heat
- Gypsum wallboard interior finishes
- Materials and workmanship are sufficient to meet codes

*Note: The illustration shown may contain some optional components (for example: garages and/or fireplaces) whose costs are shown in the modifications, adjustments, & alternatives below or at the end of the square foot section.*

## Base cost per square foot of living area

| Exterior Wall | Living Area | | | | | | | | | | |
|---|---|---|---|---|---|---|---|---|---|---|---|
| | 600 | 800 | 1000 | 1200 | 1400 | 1600 | 1800 | 2000 | 2400 | 2800 | 3200 |
| Wood Siding - Wood Frame | 129.30 | 107.15 | 95.65 | 90.25 | 86.40 | 80.55 | 77.65 | 74.60 | 68.45 | 66.00 | 63.50 |
| Brick Veneer - Wood Frame | 136.55 | 112.45 | 100.60 | 94.85 | 90.80 | 84.50 | 81.40 | 78.15 | 71.60 | 69.00 | 66.25 |
| Stucco on Wood Frame | 120.50 | 100.80 | 89.80 | 84.80 | 81.15 | 75.80 | 73.10 | 70.30 | 64.65 | 62.45 | 60.20 |
| Painted Concrete Block | 127.75 | 106.05 | 94.65 | 89.30 | 85.45 | 79.70 | 76.85 | 73.85 | 67.75 | 65.40 | 62.90 |
| Finished Basement, Add | 21.55 | 18.25 | 17.45 | 16.80 | 16.35 | 15.70 | 15.35 | 15.00 | 14.30 | 14.00 | 13.65 |
| Unfinished Basement, Add | 10.90 | 8.30 | 7.65 | 7.15 | 6.80 | 6.25 | 6.00 | 5.70 | 5.15 | 4.95 | 4.60 |

## Modifications

*Add to the total cost*

| | |
|---|---|
| Upgrade Kitchen Cabinets | $  + 803 |
| Solid Surface Countertops | + 576 |
| Full Bath - including plumbing, wall and floor finishes | + 4775 |
| Half Bath - including plumbing, wall and floor finishes | + 2845 |
| One Car Attached Garage | + 11,273 |
| One Car Detached Garage | + 14,630 |
| Fireplace & Chimney | + 5267 |

## Adjustments

*For multi family - add to total cost*

| | |
|---|---|
| Additional Kitchen | $  + 3709 |
| Additional Bath | + 4775 |
| Additional Entry & Exit | + 1640 |
| Separate Heating | + 1409 |
| Separate Electric | + 1066 |

*For Townhouse/Rowhouse - Multiply cost per square foot by*

| | |
|---|---|
| Inner Unit | + .95 |
| End Unit | + .97 |

## Alternatives

*Add to or deduct from the cost per square foot of living area*

| | |
|---|---|
| Composition Roll Roofing | – .70 |
| Cedar Shake Roof | + 3.05 |
| Upgrade Walls and Ceilings to Skim Coat Plaster | + .66 |
| Upgrade Ceilings to Textured Finish | + .48 |
| Air Conditioning, in Heating Ductwork | + 3.03 |
| In Separate Ductwork | + 6.79 |
| Heating Systems, Hot Water | + 2.01 |
| Heat Pump | + 2.82 |
| Electric Heat | – 1.44 |
| Not Heated | – 4.20 |

## Additional upgrades or components

| | |
|---|---|
| Kitchen Cabinets & Countertops | Page 93 |
| Bathroom Vanities | 94 |
| Fireplaces & Chimneys | 94 |
| Windows, Skylights & Dormers | 94 |
| Appliances | 95 |
| Breezeways & Porches | 95 |
| Finished Attic | 95 |
| Garages | 96 |
| Site Improvements | 96 |
| Wings & Ells | 34 |

| | | | Cost Per Square Foot Of Living Area | | | % of Total |
|---|---|---|---|---|---|---|
| | | | Mat. | Inst. | Total | (roun |
| 1 | Site Work | Site preparation for slab; 4' deep trench excavation for foundation wall. | | .88 | .88 | 1.1% |
| 2 | Foundation | Continuous reinforced concrete footing, 8" deep x 18" wide; dampproofed and insulated 8" thick reinforced concrete block foundation wall, 4' deep; 4" concrete slab on 4" crushed stone base and polyethylene vapor barrier, trowel finish. | 3.61 | 4.53 | 8.14 | 10.1% |
| 3 | Framing | Exterior walls - 2" x 4" wood studs, 16" O.C.; 1/2" insulation board sheathing; 2" x 6" rafters, 16" O.C. with 1/2" plywood sheathing, 8 in 12 pitch; 2" x 8" floor joists 16" O.C. with bridging and 5/8" plywood subfloor. | 3.91 | 6.43 | 10.34 | 12.8% |
| 4 | Exterior Walls | Beveled wood siding and building paper on insulated wood frame walls; 6" attic insulation; double hung windows; 2 flush solid core wood exterior doors with storms. | 11.54 | 4.79 | 16.33 | 20.3% |
| 5 | Roofing | 20 year asphalt shingles; #15 felt building paper; aluminum gutters, downspouts, drip edge and flashings. | 1.16 | 1.35 | 2.51 | 3.1% |
| 6 | Interiors | Walls and ceilings, 1/2" taped and finished gypsum wallboard, primed and painted with 2 coats; painted baseboard and trim; rubber backed carpeting 80%, asphalt tile 20%; hollow core wood interior doors. | 9.34 | 11.85 | 21.19 | 26.3% |
| 7 | Specialties | Economy grade kitchen cabinets - 6 L.F. wall and base with plastic laminate counter top and kitchen sink; 30 gallon electric water heater. | 1.77 | .67 | 2.44 | 3.0% |
| 8 | Mechanical | 1 lavatory, white, wall hung; 1 water closet, white; 1 bathtub, enameled steel, white; gas fired warm air heat. | 3.33 | 2.83 | 6.16 | 7.6% |
| 9 | Electrical | 100 Amp. service; romex wiring; incandescent lighting fixtures, switches, receptacles. | .81 | 1.24 | 2.05 | 2.5% |
| 10 | Overhead | Contractor's overhead and profit. | 5.33 | 5.18 | 10.51 | 13.0% |
| | **Total** | | 40.80 | 39.75 | **80.55** | |

- **Mass produced from stock plans**
- **Single family — 1 full bath, 1 kitchen**
- **No basement**
- **Asphalt shingles on roof**
- **Hot air heat**
- **Gypsum wallboard interior finishes**
- **Materials and workmanship are sufficient to meet codes**

*Note: The illustration shown may contain some optional components (for example: garages and/or fireplaces) whose costs are shown in the modifications, adjustments, & alternatives below or at the end of the square foot section.*

## Base cost per square foot of living area

| Exterior Wall | Living Area | | | | | | | | | | |
|---|---|---|---|---|---|---|---|---|---|---|---|
| | 1000 | 1200 | 1400 | 1600 | 1800 | 2000 | 2200 | 2600 | 3000 | 3400 | 3800 |
| Wood Siding - Wood Frame | 101.65 | 91.80 | 87.20 | 84.10 | 80.90 | 77.30 | 74.90 | 70.40 | 66.05 | 64.05 | 62.30 |
| Brick Veneer - Wood Frame | 107.30 | 97.00 | 92.10 | 88.70 | 85.30 | 81.55 | 78.95 | 74.05 | 69.45 | 67.20 | 65.30 |
| Stucco on Wood Frame | 94.95 | 85.55 | 81.35 | 78.50 | 75.65 | 72.25 | 70.05 | 66.05 | 62.05 | 60.25 | 58.65 |
| Painted Concrete Block | 100.45 | 90.75 | 86.20 | 83.10 | 80.00 | 76.40 | 74.05 | 69.65 | 65.35 | 63.35 | 61.65 |
| Finished Basement, Add | 14.65 | 14.05 | 13.50 | 13.20 | 12.80 | 12.60 | 12.35 | 11.85 | 11.50 | 11.25 | 11.05 |
| Unfinished Basement, Add | 6.70 | 6.15 | 5.75 | 5.50 | 5.25 | 5.05 | 4.85 | 4.45 | 4.15 | 4.00 | 3.80 |

## Modifications
*Add to the total cost*

| | |
|---|---|
| Upgrade Kitchen Cabinets | $ + 803 |
| Solid Surface Countertops | + 576 |
| Full Bath - including plumbing, wall and floor finishes | + 4775 |
| Half Bath - including plumbing, wall and floor finishes | + 2845 |
| One Car Attached Garage | + 11,273 |
| One Car Detached Garage | + 14,630 |
| Fireplace & Chimney | + 5820 |

## Adjustments
*For multi family - add to total cost*

| | |
|---|---|
| Additional Kitchen | $ + 3709 |
| Additional Bath | + 4775 |
| Additional Entry & Exit | + 1640 |
| Separate Heating | + 1409 |
| Separate Electric | + 1066 |

*For Townhouse/Rowhouse - Multiply cost per square foot by*

| | |
|---|---|
| Inner Unit | + .93 |
| End Unit | + .96 |

## Alternatives
*Add to or deduct from the cost per square foot of living area*

| | |
|---|---|
| Composition Roll Roofing | – .50 |
| Cedar Shake Roof | + 2.10 |
| Upgrade Walls and Ceilings to Skim Coat Plaster | + .67 |
| Upgrade Ceilings to Textured Finish | + .48 |
| Air Conditioning, in Heating Ductwork | + 2.45 |
| In Separate Ductwork | + 6.21 |
| Heating Systems, Hot Water | + 1.96 |
| Heat Pump | + 3 |
| Electric Heat | – 1.26 |
| Not Heated | – 3.96 |

## Additional upgrades or components

| | |
|---|---|
| Kitchen Cabinets & Countertops | Page 93 |
| Bathroom Vanities | 94 |
| Fireplaces & Chimneys | 94 |
| Windows, Skylights & Dormers | 94 |
| Appliances | 95 |
| Breezeways & Porches | 95 |
| Finished Attic | 95 |
| Garages | 96 |
| Site Improvements | 96 |
| Wings & Ells | 34 |

| | | | Cost Per Square Foot Of Living Area | | | % of Total |
|---|---|---|---|---|---|---|
| | | | Mat. | Inst. | Total | (roun |
| **1** | **Site Work** | Site preparation for slab; 4' deep trench excavation for foundation wall. | | .70 | .70 | 0.9% |
| **2** | **Foundation** | Continuous reinforced concrete footing, 8" deep x 18" wide; dampproofed and insulated 8" thick reinforced concrete block foundation wall, 4' deep; 4" concrete slab on 4" crushed stone base and polyethylene vapor barrier, trowel finish. | 2.89 | 3.63 | 6.52 | 8.4% |
| **3** | **Framing** | Exterior walls - 2" x 4" wood studs, 16" O.C.; 1/2" insulation board sheathing; wood truss roof frame, 24" O.C. with 1/2" plywood sheathing, 4 in 12 pitch; 2" x 8" floor joists 16" O.C. with bridging and 5/8" plywood subfloor. | 3.94 | 6.77 | 10.71 | 13.9% |
| **4** | **Exterior Walls** | Beveled wood siding and building paper on insulated wood frame walls; 6" attic insulation; double hung windows; 2 flush solid core wood exterior doors with storms. | 11.90 | 4.89 | 16.79 | 21.7% |
| **5** | **Roofing** | 20 year asphalt shingles; #15 felt building paper; aluminum gutters, downspouts, drip edge and flashings. | .93 | 1.08 | 2.01 | 2.6% |
| **6** | **Interiors** | Walls and ceilings, 1/2" taped and finished gypsum wallboard, primed and painted with 2 coats; painted baseboard and trim; rubber backed carpeting 80%, asphalt tile 20%; hollow core wood interior doors. | 9.24 | 11.87 | 21.11 | 27.3% |
| **7** | **Specialties** | Economy grade kitchen cabinets - 6 L.F. wall and base with plastic laminate counter top and kitchen sink; 30 gallon electric water heater. | 1.42 | .53 | 1.95 | 2.5% |
| **8** | **Mechanical** | 1 lavatory, white, wall hung; 1 water closet, white; 1 bathtub, enameled steel, white; gas fired warm air heat. | 2.88 | 2.63 | 5.51 | 7.1% |
| **9** | **Electrical** | 100 Amp. service; romex wiring; incandescent lighting fixtures; switches, receptacles. | .76 | 1.16 | 1.92 | 2.5% |
| **10** | **Overhead** | Contractor's overhead and profit. | 5.09 | 4.99 | 10.08 | 13.0% |
| | **Total** | | 39.05 | 38.25 | **77.30** | |

- **Mass produced from stock plans**
- **Single family — 1 full bath, 1 kitchen**
- **No basement**
- **Asphalt shingles on roof**
- **Hot air heat**
- **Gypsum wallboard interior finishes**
- **Materials and workmanship are sufficient to meet codes**

*Note: The illustration shown may contain some optional components (for example: garages and/or fireplaces) whose costs are shown in the modifications, adjustments, & alternatives below or at the end of the square foot section.*

## Base cost per square foot of living area

| Exterior Wall | Living Area | | | | | | | | | | |
|---|---|---|---|---|---|---|---|---|---|---|---|
| | 1000 | 1200 | 1400 | 1600 | 1800 | 2000 | 2200 | 2600 | 3000 | 3400 | 3800 |
| Wood Siding - Wood Frame | 94.20 | 84.90 | 80.75 | 77.85 | 75.10 | 71.70 | 69.60 | 65.55 | 61.60 | 59.80 | 58.25 |
| Brick Veneer - Wood Frame | 98.40 | 88.80 | 84.40 | 81.40 | 78.35 | 74.85 | 72.60 | 68.25 | 64.10 | 62.20 | 60.50 |
| Stucco on Wood Frame | 89.15 | 80.15 | 76.35 | 73.70 | 71.15 | 67.85 | 65.95 | 62.30 | 58.55 | 56.90 | 55.50 |
| Painted Concrete Block | 93.30 | 84.05 | 79.95 | 77.15 | 74.40 | 71.00 | 68.95 | 65.00 | 61.10 | 59.30 | 57.75 |
| Finished Basement, Add | 14.65 | 14.05 | 13.50 | 13.20 | 12.80 | 12.60 | 12.35 | 11.85 | 11.50 | 11.25 | 11.05 |
| Unfinished Basement, Add | 6.70 | 6.15 | 5.75 | 5.50 | 5.25 | 5.05 | 4.85 | 4.45 | 4.15 | 4.00 | 3.80 |

## Modifications

*Add to the total cost*

| | |
|---|---|
| Upgrade Kitchen Cabinets | $ + 803 |
| Solid Surface Countertops | + 576 |
| Full Bath - including plumbing, wall and floor finishes | + 4775 |
| Half Bath - including plumbing, wall and floor finishes | + 2845 |
| One Car Attached Garage | + 11,273 |
| One Car Detached Garage | + 14,630 |
| Fireplace & Chimney | + 5267 |

## Adjustments

*For multi family - add to total cost*

| | |
|---|---|
| Additional Kitchen | $ + 3709 |
| Additional Bath | + 4775 |
| Additional Entry & Exit | + 1640 |
| Separate Heating | + 1409 |
| Separate Electric | + 1066 |

*For Townhouse/Rowhouse -*
*Multiply cost per square foot by*

| | |
|---|---|
| Inner Unit | + .94 |
| End Unit | + .97 |

## Alternatives

*Add to or deduct from the cost per square foot of living area*

| | |
|---|---|
| Composition Roll Roofing | – .50 |
| Cedar Shake Roof | + 2.10 |
| Upgrade Walls and Ceilings to Skim Coat Plaster | + .63 |
| Upgrade Ceilings to Textured Finish | + .48 |
| Air Conditioning, in Heating Ductwork | + 2.45 |
| In Separate Ductwork | + 6.21 |
| Heating Systems, Hot Water | + 1.96 |
| Heat Pump | + 3 |
| Electric Heat | – 1.26 |
| Not Heated | – 3.96 |

## Additional upgrades or components

| | |
|---|---|
| Kitchen Cabinets & Countertops | Page 93 |
| Bathroom Vanities | 94 |
| Fireplaces & Chimneys | 94 |
| Windows, Skylights & Dormers | 94 |
| Appliances | 95 |
| Breezeways & Porches | 95 |
| Finished Attic | 95 |
| Garages | 96 |
| Site Improvements | 96 |
| Wings & Ells | 34 |

**Important: See the Reference Section for Location Factors (to adjust for your city) and Estimating Forms**

| | | Cost Per Square Foot Of Living Area | | | % of Total |
|---|---|---|---|---|---|
| | | Mat. | Inst. | Total | (roun |
| **1** Site Work | Excavation for lower level, 4' deep. Site preparation for slab. | | .70 | .70 | 1.0% |
| **2** Foundation | Continuous reinforced concrete footing, 8" deep x 18" wide; dampproofed and insulated 8" thick reinforced concrete block foundation wall, 4' deep; 4" concrete slab on 4" crushed stone base and polyethylene vapor barrier, trowel finish. | 2.89 | 3.63 | 6.52 | 9.1% |
| **3** Framing | Exterior walls - 2" x 4" wood studs, 16" O.C.; 1/2" insulation board sheathing; wood truss roof frame, 24" O.C. with 1/2" plywood sheathing, 4 in 12 pitch; 2" x 8" floor joists 16" O.C. with bridging and 5/8" plywood subfloor. | 3.73 | 6.36 | 10.09 | 14.1% |
| **4** Exterior Walls | Beveled wood siding and building paper on insulated wood frame walls; 6" attic insulation; double hung windows; 2 flush solid core wood exterior doors with storms. | 9.25 | 3.84 | 13.09 | 18.3% |
| **5** Roofing | 20 year asphalt shingles; #15 felt building paper; aluminum gutters, downspouts, drip edge and flashings. | .93 | 1.08 | 2.01 | 2.8% |
| **6** Interiors | Walls and ceilings, 1/2" taped and finished gypsum wallboard, primed and painted with 2 coats; painted baseboard and trim, rubber backed carpeting 80%, asphalt tile 20%; hollow core wood interior doors. | 9.04 | 11.49 | 20.53 | 28.6% |
| **7** Specialties | Economy grade kitchen cabinets - 6 L.F. wall and base with plastic laminate counter top and kitchen sink; 30 gallon electric water heater. | 1.42 | .53 | 1.95 | 2.7% |
| **8** Mechanical | 1 lavatory, white, wall hung; 1 water closet, white; 1 bathtub, enameled steel, white; gas fired warm air heat. | 2.88 | 2.63 | 5.51 | 7.7% |
| **9** Electrical | 100 Amp. service; romex wiring; incandescent lighting fixtures; switches, receptacles. | .76 | 1.16 | 1.92 | 2.7% |
| **10** Overhead | Contractor's overhead and profit. | 4.65 | 4.73 | 9.38 | 13.1% |
| **Total** | | 35.55 | 36.15 | **71.70** | |

- **Mass produced from stock plans**
- **Single family — 1 full bath, 1 kitchen**
- **No basement**
- **Asphalt shingles on roof**
- **Hot air heat**
- **Gypsum wallboard interior finishes**
- **Materials and workmanship are sufficient to meet codes**

*Note: The illustration shown may contain some optional components (for example: garages and/or fireplaces) whose costs are shown in the modifications, adjustments, & alternatives below or at the end of the square foot section.*

©Design Basics, Inc.

## Base cost per square foot of living area

| Exterior Wall | Living Area | | | | | | | | | | |
|---|---|---|---|---|---|---|---|---|---|---|---|
| | 1200 | 1500 | 1800 | 2000 | 2200 | 2400 | 2800 | 3200 | 3600 | 4000 | 4400 |
| Wood Siding - Wood Frame | 86.90 | 79.75 | 74.35 | 72.15 | 69.00 | 66.45 | 64.50 | 61.80 | 58.55 | 57.45 | 55.00 |
| Brick Veneer - Wood Frame | 90.75 | 83.25 | 77.50 | 75.15 | 71.90 | 69.15 | 67.10 | 64.20 | 60.80 | 59.65 | 57.05 |
| Stucco on Wood Frame | 82.30 | 75.50 | 70.50 | 68.50 | 65.50 | 63.20 | 61.35 | 58.85 | 55.90 | 54.85 | 52.55 |
| Solid Masonry | 86.10 | 78.95 | 73.65 | 71.50 | 68.35 | 65.90 | 63.95 | 61.20 | 58.05 | 57.05 | 54.60 |
| Finished Basement, Add* | 17.50 | 16.70 | 16.00 | 15.70 | 15.40 | 15.05 | 14.80 | 14.45 | 14.10 | 13.95 | 13.70 |
| Unfinished Basement, Add* | 7.30 | 6.70 | 6.15 | 5.85 | 5.60 | 5.35 | 5.15 | 4.85 | 4.60 | 4.50 | 4.30 |

*Basement under middle level only.

## Modifications

*Add to the total cost*

| | |
|---|---|
| Upgrade Kitchen Cabinets | $ + 803 |
| Solid Surface Countertops | + 576 |
| Full Bath - including plumbing, wall and floor finishes | + 4775 |
| Half Bath - including plumbing, wall and floor finishes | + 2845 |
| One Car Attached Garage | + 11,273 |
| One Car Detached Garage | + 14,630 |
| Fireplace & Chimney | + 5267 |

## Adjustments

*For multi family - add to total cost*

| | |
|---|---|
| Additional Kitchen | $ + 3709 |
| Additional Bath | + 4775 |
| Additional Entry & Exit | + 1640 |
| Separate Heating | + 1409 |
| Separate Electric | + 1066 |

*For Townhouse/Rowhouse - Multiply cost per square foot by*

| | |
|---|---|
| Inner Unit | + .93 |
| End Unit | + .96 |

## Alternatives

*Add to or deduct from the cost per square foot of living area*

| | |
|---|---|
| Composition Roll Roofing | – .70 |
| Cedar Shake Roof | + 3.05 |
| Upgrade Walls and Ceilings to Skim Coat Plaster | + .57 |
| Upgrade Ceilings to Textured Finish | + .48 |
| Air Conditioning, in Heating Ductwork | + 2.10 |
| In Separate Ductwork | + 5.78 |
| Heating Systems, Hot Water | + 1.88 |
| Heat Pump | + 3.11 |
| Electric Heat | – 1.09 |
| Not Heated | – 3.84 |

## Additional upgrades or components

| | |
|---|---|
| Kitchen Cabinets & Countertops | Page 93 |
| Bathroom Vanities | 94 |
| Fireplaces & Chimneys | 94 |
| Windows, Skylights & Dormers | 94 |
| Appliances | 95 |
| Breezeways & Porches | 95 |
| Finished Attic | 95 |
| Garages | 96 |
| Site Improvements | 96 |
| Wings & Ells | 34 |

**Important: See the Reference Section for Location Factors (to adjust for your city) and Estimating Forms**

| | | | Cost Per Square Foot Of Living Area | | | % of Total |
|---|---|---|---|---|---|---|
| | | | Mat. | Inst. | Total | (roun |
| **1** | **Site Work** | Site preparation for slab; 4' deep trench excavation for foundation wall, excavation for lower level, 4' deep. | | .58 | .58 | 0.9% |
| **2** | **Foundation** | Continuous reinforced concrete footing, 8" deep x 18" wide; dampproofed and insulated 8" thick reinforced concrete block foundation wall, 4' deep; 4" concrete slab on 4" crushed stone base and polyethylene vapor barrier, trowel finish. | 3.26 | 3.94 | 7.20 | 10.8% |
| **3** | **Framing** | Exterior walls - 2" x 4" wood studs, 16" O.C.; 1/2" insulation board sheathing; wood truss roof frame, 24" O.C. with 1/2" plywood sheathing, 4 in 12 pitch; 2" x 8" floor joists 16" O.C. with bridging and 5/8" plywood subfloor. | 3.61 | 5.71 | 9.32 | 14.0% |
| **4** | **Exterior Walls** | Beveled wood siding and building paper on insulated wood frame walls; 6" attic insulation; double hung windows; 2 flush solid core wood exterior doors with storms. | 7.98 | 3.33 | 11.31 | 17.0% |
| **5** | **Roofing** | 20 year asphalt shingles; #15 felt building paper; aluminum gutters, downspouts, drip edge and flashings. | 1.23 | 1.44 | 2.67 | 4.0% |
| **6** | **Interiors** | Walls and ceilings, 1/2" taped and finished gypsum wallboard, primed and painted with 2 coats; painted baseboard and trim, rubber backed carpeting 80%, asphalt tile 20%; hollow core wood interior doors. | 7.97 | 10.21 | 18.18 | 27.4% |
| **7** | **Specialties** | Economy grade kitchen cabinets - 6 L.F. wall and base with plastic laminate counter top and kitchen sink; 30 gallon electric water heater. | 1.17 | .45 | 1.62 | 2.4% |
| **8** | **Mechanical** | 1 lavatory, white, wall hung; 1 water closet, white; 1 bathtub, enameled steel, white; gas fired warm air heat. | 2.60 | 2.49 | 5.09 | 7.7% |
| **9** | **Electrical** | 100 Amp. service; romex wiring; incandescent lighting fixtures, switches, receptacles. | .72 | 1.10 | 1.82 | 2.7% |
| **10** | **Overhead** | Contractor's overhead and profit. | 4.26 | 4.40 | 8.66 | 13.0% |
| | **Total** | | 32.80 | 33.65 | **66.45** | |

## 1 Story     Base cost per square foot of living area

| Exterior Wall | Living Area | | | | | | | |
|---|---|---|---|---|---|---|---|---|
| | 50 | 100 | 200 | 300 | 400 | 500 | 600 | 700 |
| Wood Siding - Wood Frame | 157.10 | 119.20 | 102.75 | 84.95 | 79.60 | 76.35 | 74.25 | 74.80 |
| Brick Veneer - Wood Frame | 170.25 | 128.60 | 110.65 | 90.15 | 84.30 | 80.75 | 78.40 | 78.85 |
| Stucco on Wood Frame | 141.35 | 107.95 | 93.40 | 78.70 | 74.00 | 71.10 | 69.15 | 69.95 |
| Painted Concrete Block | 154.35 | 117.20 | 101.15 | 83.90 | 78.60 | 75.40 | 73.35 | 73.90 |
| Finished Basement, Add | 42.80 | 34.90 | 31.55 | 26.05 | 24.95 | 24.30 | 23.85 | 23.55 |
| Unfinished Basement, Add | 23.70 | 17.55 | 14.95 | 10.70 | 9.80 | 9.30 | 8.95 | 8.70 |

## 1-1/2 Story     Base cost per square foot of living area

| Exterior Wall | Living Area | | | | | | | |
|---|---|---|---|---|---|---|---|---|
| | 100 | 200 | 300 | 400 | 500 | 600 | 700 | 800 |
| Wood Siding - Wood Frame | 124.70 | 99.95 | 84.90 | 75.60 | 71.05 | 68.85 | 66.10 | 65.30 |
| Brick Veneer - Wood Frame | 136.45 | 109.35 | 92.75 | 81.70 | 76.70 | 74.15 | 71.05 | 70.25 |
| Stucco on Wood Frame | 110.60 | 88.70 | 75.50 | 68.25 | 64.35 | 62.50 | 60.05 | 59.30 |
| Painted Concrete Block | 122.15 | 98.00 | 83.20 | 74.35 | 69.90 | 67.75 | 64.95 | 64.20 |
| Finished Basement, Add | 28.55 | 25.25 | 23.00 | 20.60 | 19.95 | 19.50 | 19.10 | 19.05 |
| Unfinished Basement, Add | 14.50 | 11.95 | 10.25 | 8.35 | 7.80 | 7.50 | 7.15 | 7.15 |

## 2 Story     Base cost per square foot of living area

| Exterior Wall | Living Area | | | | | | | |
|---|---|---|---|---|---|---|---|---|
| | 100 | 200 | 400 | 600 | 800 | 1000 | 1200 | 1400 |
| Wood Siding - Wood Frame | 127.10 | 94.10 | 79.70 | 65.30 | 60.65 | 57.75 | 55.90 | 56.70 |
| Brick Veneer - Wood Frame | 140.25 | 103.50 | 87.55 | 70.55 | 65.35 | 62.20 | 60.10 | 60.75 |
| Stucco on Wood Frame | 111.35 | 82.85 | 70.35 | 59.05 | 55.00 | 52.55 | 50.90 | 51.85 |
| Painted Concrete Block | 124.35 | 92.10 | 78.10 | 64.20 | 59.65 | 56.90 | 55.05 | 55.85 |
| Finished Basement, Add | 21.45 | 17.45 | 15.85 | 13.10 | 12.55 | 12.20 | 12.00 | 11.80 |
| Unfinished Basement, Add | 11.90 | 8.80 | 7.50 | 5.35 | 4.95 | 4.70 | 4.45 | 4.35 |

Base costs do not include bathroom or kitchen facilities. Use Modifications/Adjustments/Alternatives on pages 93–96 where appropriate.

## 1 Story

eHome Planners, Inc.

## 1 - 1/2 Story

© By Designer

## 2 Story

## 2-1/2 Story

## Bi-Level

## Tri-Level

eDesign Basics, Inc.

- **Simple design from standard plans**
- **Single family — 1 full bath, 1 kitchen**
- **No basement**
- **Asphalt shingles on roof**
- **Hot air heat**
- **Gypsum wallboard interior finishes**
- **Materials and workmanship are average**

*Note: The illustration shown may contain some optional components (for example: garages and/or fireplaces) whose costs are shown in the modifications, adjustments, & alternatives below or at the end of the square foot section.*

eHome Planners, Inc.

## Base cost per square foot of living area

| Exterior Wall | Living Area | | | | | | | | | | |
|---|---|---|---|---|---|---|---|---|---|---|---|
| | 600 | 800 | 1000 | 1200 | 1400 | 1600 | 1800 | 2000 | 2400 | 2800 | 3200 |
| Wood Siding - Wood Frame | 135.60 | 122.45 | 112.70 | 104.85 | 98.30 | 94.05 | 91.75 | 88.85 | 83.15 | 78.95 | 76.10 |
| Brick Veneer - Wood Frame | 152.80 | 138.85 | 128.50 | 120.05 | 112.95 | 108.35 | 105.95 | 102.75 | 96.70 | 92.20 | 89.10 |
| Stucco on Wood Frame | 141.80 | 129.05 | 119.55 | 112.00 | 105.65 | 101.50 | 99.35 | 96.50 | 91.05 | 86.95 | 84.20 |
| Solid Masonry | 166.85 | 151.40 | 139.85 | 130.30 | 122.25 | 117.10 | 114.35 | 110.65 | 103.95 | 98.90 | 95.30 |
| Finished Basement, Add | 33.95 | 32.80 | 31.25 | 29.85 | 28.75 | 27.95 | 27.60 | 27.00 | 26.10 | 25.50 | 24.90 |
| Unfinished Basement, Add | 13.90 | 12.50 | 11.55 | 10.65 | 9.95 | 9.50 | 9.20 | 8.85 | 8.30 | 7.90 | 7.60 |

## Modifications

*Add to the total cost*

| | |
|---|---|
| Upgrade Kitchen Cabinets | $  + 3521 |
| Solid Surface Countertops (Included) | |
| Full Bath - including plumbing, wall and floor finishes | + 5993 |
| Half Bath - including plumbing, wall and floor finishes | + 3570 |
| One Car Attached Garage | + 12,676 |
| One Car Detached Garage | + 16,871 |
| Fireplace & Chimney | + 5234 |

## Adjustments

*For multi family - add to total cost*

| | |
|---|---|
| Additional Kitchen | $  + 6796 |
| Additional Bath | + 5993 |
| Additional Entry & Exit | + 1640 |
| Separate Heating | + 1409 |
| Separate Electric | + 1915 |

*For Townhouse/Rowhouse - Multiply cost per square foot by*

| | |
|---|---|
| Inner Unit | + .92 |
| End Unit | + .96 |

## Alternatives

*Add to or deduct from the cost per square foot of living area*

| | |
|---|---|
| Cedar Shake Roof | + 3.85 |
| Clay Tile Roof | + 4.55 |
| Slate Roof | + 6.65 |
| Upgrade Walls to Skim Coat Plaster | + .41 |
| Upgrade Ceilings to Textured Finish | + .48 |
| Air Conditioning, in Heating Ductwork | + 4.19 |
| In Separate Ductwork | + 8.02 |
| Heating Systems, Hot Water | + 2.16 |
| Heat Pump | + 2.66 |
| Electric Heat | – 1.01 |
| Not Heated | – 3.80 |

## Additional upgrades or components

| | |
|---|---|
| Kitchen Cabinets & Countertops | Page 93 |
| Bathroom Vanities | 94 |
| Fireplaces & Chimneys | 94 |
| Windows, Skylights & Dormers | 94 |
| Appliances | 95 |
| Breezeways & Porches | 95 |
| Finished Attic | 95 |
| Garages | 96 |
| Site Improvements | 96 |
| Wings & Ells | 56 |

# Average 1 Story

**Living Area - 1600 S.F.**
**Perimeter - 163 L.F.**

| | | | Cost Per Square Foot Of Living Area | | | % of Total |
|---|---|---|---|---|---|---|
| | | | Mat. | Inst. | Total | (roun |
| **1** | **Site Work** | Site preparation for slab; 4' deep trench excavation for foundation wall. | | .90 | .90 | 1.0% |
| **2** | **Foundation** | Continuous reinforced concrete footing 8" deep x 18" wide; dampproofed and insulated reinforced concrete foundation wall, 8" thick, 4' deep; 4" concrete slab on 4" crushed stone base and polyethylene vapor barrier, trowel finish. | 5.02 | 6.07 | 11.09 | 11.8% |
| **3** | **Framing** | Exterior walls - 2" x 4" wood studs, 16" O.C.; 1/2" plywood sheathing; 2" x 6" rafters 16" O.C. with 1/2" plywood sheathing, 4 in 12 pitch; 2" x 6" ceiling joists 16" O.C.; 1/2" plywood subfloor on 1" x 2" wood sleepers 16" O.C. | 4.39 | 8.56 | 12.95 | 13.8% |
| **4** | **Exterior Walls** | Beveled wood siding and building paper on insulated wood frame walls; 6" attic insulation; double hung windows; 3 flush solid core wood exterior doors with storms. | 10.53 | 4.51 | 15.04 | 16.0% |
| **5** | **Roofing** | 25 year asphalt shingles; #15 felt building paper; aluminum gutters, downspouts, drip edge and flashings. | 1.90 | 2.22 | 4.12 | 4.4% |
| **6** | **Interiors** | Walls and ceilings, 1/2" taped and finished gypsum wallboard, primed and painted with 2 coats; painted baseboard and trim, finished hardwood floor 40%, carpet with 1/2" underlayment 40%, vinyl tile with 1/2" underlayment 15%, ceramic tile with 1/2" underlayment 5%; hollow core and louvered doors. | 11.16 | 11.93 | 23.09 | 24.6% |
| **7** | **Specialties** | Average grade kitchen cabinets - 14 L.F. wall and base with solid surface counter top and kitchen sink; 40 gallon electric water heater. | 2.83 | 1.05 | 3.88 | 4.1% |
| **8** | **Mechanical** | 1 lavatory, white, wall hung; 1 water closet, white; 1 bathtub with shower, enameled steel, white; gas fired warm air heat. | 3.50 | 2.87 | 6.37 | 6.8% |
| **9** | **Electrical** | 200 Amp. service; romex wiring; incandescent lighting fixtures, switches, receptacles. | 1.25 | 1.68 | 2.93 | 3.1% |
| **10** | **Overhead** | Contractor's overhead and profit and plans. | 6.92 | 6.76 | 13.68 | 14.5% |
| | **Total** | | 47.50 | 46.55 | **94.05** | |

- **Simple design from standard plans**
- **Single family — 1 full bath, 1 kitchen**
- **No basement**
- **Asphalt shingles on roof**
- **Hot air heat**
- **Gypsum wallboard interior finishes**
- **Materials and workmanship are average**

*Note: The illustration shown may contain some optional components (for example: garages and/or fireplaces) whose costs are shown in the modifications, adjustments, & alternatives below or at the end of the square foot section.*

©By Designer

## Base cost per square foot of living area

| Exterior Wall | Living Area | | | | | | | | | | |
|---|---|---|---|---|---|---|---|---|---|---|---|
| | 600 | 800 | 1000 | 1200 | 1400 | 1600 | 1800 | 2000 | 2400 | 2800 | 3200 |
| Wood Siding - Wood Frame | 151.70 | 126.70 | 113.30 | 106.95 | 102.40 | 95.75 | 92.40 | 88.90 | 82.05 | 79.25 | 76.35 |
| Brick Veneer - Wood Frame | 162.30 | 134.35 | 120.45 | 113.60 | 108.75 | 101.55 | 97.85 | 94.10 | 86.60 | 83.60 | 80.35 |
| Stucco on Wood Frame | 146.95 | 123.20 | 110.15 | 103.95 | 99.55 | 93.15 | 89.95 | 86.60 | 79.95 | 77.30 | 74.50 |
| Solid Masonry | 181.90 | 148.55 | 133.55 | 125.90 | 120.45 | 112.20 | 107.95 | 103.70 | 95.10 | 91.65 | 87.80 |
| Finished Basement, Add | 27.80 | 24.25 | 23.20 | 22.40 | 21.85 | 20.95 | 20.45 | 20.10 | 19.15 | 18.80 | 18.30 |
| Unfinished Basement, Add | 12.10 | 9.45 | 8.70 | 8.20 | 7.85 | 7.30 | 7.00 | 6.75 | 6.20 | 5.90 | 5.65 |

## Modifications

*Add to the total cost*

| | |
|---|---|
| Upgrade Kitchen Cabinets | $ + 3521 |
| Solid Surface Countertops (Included) | |
| Full Bath - including plumbing, wall and floor finishes | + 5993 |
| Half Bath - including plumbing, wall and floor finishes | + 3570 |
| One Car Attached Garage | + 12,676 |
| One Car Detached Garage | + 16,871 |
| Fireplace & Chimney | + 5234 |

## Adjustments

*For multi family - add to total cost*

| | |
|---|---|
| Additional Kitchen | $ + 6796 |
| Additional Bath | + 5993 |
| Additional Entry & Exit | + 1640 |
| Separate Heating | + 1409 |
| Separate Electric | + 1915 |

*For Townhouse/Rowhouse - Multiply cost per square foot by*

| | |
|---|---|
| Inner Unit | + .92 |
| End Unit | + .96 |

## Alternatives

*Add to or deduct from the cost per square foot of living area*

| | |
|---|---|
| Cedar Shake Roof | + 2.80 |
| Clay Tile Roof | + 3.30 |
| Slate Roof | + 4.80 |
| Upgrade Walls to Skim Coat Plaster | + .47 |
| Upgrade Ceilings to Textured Finish | + .48 |
| Air Conditioning, in Heating Ductwork | + 3.19 |
| In Separate Ductwork | + 7.01 |
| Heating Systems, Hot Water | + 2.05 |
| Heat Pump | + 2.96 |
| Electric Heat | - .91 |
| Not Heated | - 3.67 |

## Additional upgrades or components

| | |
|---|---|
| Kitchen Cabinets & Countertops | Page 93 |
| Bathroom Vanities | 94 |
| Fireplaces & Chimneys | 94 |
| Windows, Skylights & Dormers | 94 |
| Appliances | 95 |
| Breezeways & Porches | 95 |
| Finished Attic | 95 |
| Garages | 96 |
| Site Improvements | 96 |
| Wings & Ells | 56 |

# Average 1-1/2 Story

**Living Area - 1800 S.F.**
**Perimeter - 144 L.F.**

| | | Cost Per Square Foot Of Living Area | | | % of Total |
|---|---|---|---|---|---|
| | | Mat. | Inst. | Total | (roun |
| **1 Site Work** | Site preparation for slab; 4' deep trench excavation for foundation wall. | | .80 | .80 | 0.9% |
| **2 Foundation** | Continuous reinforced concrete footing 8" deep x 18" wide; dampproofed and insulated reinforced concrete foundation wall, 8" thick, 4' deep; 4" concrete slab on 4" crushed stone base and polyethylene vapor barrier, trowel finish. | 3.57 | 4.46 | 8.03 | 8.7% |
| **3 Framing** | Exterior walls - 2" x 4" wood studs, 16" O.C.; 1/2" plywood sheathing; 2" x 6" rafters 16" O.C. with 1/2" plywood sheathing, 8 in 12 pitch; 2" x 8" floor joists 16" O.C. with 5/8" plywood subfloor; 1/2" plywood subfloor on 1" x 2" wood sleepers 16" O.C. | 4.67 | 7.99 | 12.66 | 13.7% |
| **4 Exterior Walls** | Beveled wood siding and building paper on insulated wood frame walls; 6" attic insulation; double hung windows; 3 flush solid core wood exterior doors with storms. | 11.59 | 4.83 | 16.42 | 17.8% |
| **5 Roofing** | 25 year asphalt shingles; #15 felt building paper; aluminum gutters, downspouts, drip edge and flashings. | 1.19 | 1.39 | 2.58 | 2.8% |
| **6 Interiors** | Walls and ceilings, 1/2" taped and finished gypsum wallboard, primed and painted with 2 coats; painted baseboard and trim, finished hardwood floor 40%, carpet with 1/2" underlayment 40%, vinyl tile with 1/2" underlayment 15%, ceramic tile with 1/2" underlayment 5%; hollow core and louvered doors. | 12.87 | 13.38 | 26.25 | 28.4% |
| **7 Specialties** | Average grade kitchen cabinets - 14 L.F. wall and base with solid surface counter top and kitchen sink; 40 gallon electric water heater. | 2.52 | .93 | 3.45 | 3.7% |
| **8 Mechanical** | 1 lavatory, white, wall hung; 1 water closet, white; 1 bathtub with shower, enameled steel, white; gas fired warm air heat. | 3.24 | 2.76 | 6.00 | 6.5% |
| **9 Electrical** | 200 Amp. service; romex wiring; incandescent lighting fixtures, switches, receptacles. | 1.18 | 1.61 | 2.79 | 3.0% |
| **10 Overhead** | Contractor's overhead and profit and plans. | 6.92 | 6.50 | 13.42 | 14.5% |
| | **Total** | 47.75 | 44.65 | 92.40 | |

- **Simple design from standard plans**
- **Single family — 1 full bath, 1 kitchen**
- **No basement**
- **Asphalt shingles on roof**
- **Hot air heat**
- **Gypsum wallboard interior finishes**
- **Materials and workmanship are average**

*Note: The illustration shown may contain some optional components (for example: garages and/or fireplaces) whose costs are shown in the modifications, adjustments, & alternatives below or at the end of the square foot section.*

## Base cost per square foot of living area

| Exterior Wall | Living Area | | | | | | | | | | |
|---|---|---|---|---|---|---|---|---|---|---|---|
| | 1000 | 1200 | 1400 | 1600 | 1800 | 2000 | 2200 | 2600 | 3000 | 3400 | 3800 |
| Wood Siding - Wood Frame | 119.55 | 108.20 | 102.90 | 99.30 | 95.55 | 91.50 | 88.85 | 83.75 | 78.85 | 76.55 | 74.50 |
| Brick Veneer - Wood Frame | 127.75 | 115.85 | 109.95 | 106.10 | 101.85 | 97.65 | 94.70 | 89.00 | 83.70 | 81.20 | 78.95 |
| Stucco on Wood Frame | 115.90 | 104.85 | 99.75 | 96.30 | 92.70 | 88.70 | 86.25 | 81.30 | 76.60 | 74.45 | 72.55 |
| Solid Masonry | 143.00 | 129.90 | 123.15 | 118.60 | 113.65 | 109.00 | 105.45 | 98.80 | 92.75 | 89.75 | 87.10 |
| Finished Basement, Add | 19.70 | 19.40 | 18.75 | 18.35 | 17.90 | 17.65 | 17.25 | 16.60 | 16.15 | 15.90 | 15.65 |
| Unfinished Basement, Add | 7.65 | 7.10 | 6.70 | 6.40 | 6.10 | 5.90 | 5.70 | 5.35 | 5.05 | 4.80 | 4.70 |

## Modifications

*Add to the total cost*

| | |
|---|---|
| Upgrade Kitchen Cabinets | $ + 3521 |
| Solid Surface Countertops (Included) | |
| Full Bath - including plumbing, wall and floor finishes | + 5993 |
| Half Bath - including plumbing, wall and floor finishes | + 3570 |
| One Car Attached Garage | + 12,676 |
| One Car Detached Garage | + 16,871 |
| Fireplace & Chimney | + 5836 |

## Adjustments

*For multi family - add to total cost*

| | |
|---|---|
| Additional Kitchen | $ + 6796 |
| Additional Bath | + 5993 |
| Additional Entry & Exit | + 1640 |
| Separate Heating | + 1409 |
| Separate Electric | + 1915 |

*For Townhouse/Rowhouse -
Multiply cost per square foot by*

| | |
|---|---|
| Inner Unit | + .90 |
| End Unit | + .95 |

## Alternatives

*Add to or deduct from the cost per square foot of living area*

| | |
|---|---|
| Cedar Shake Roof | + 1.95 |
| Clay Tile Roof | + 2.25 |
| Slate Roof | + 3.30 |
| Upgrade Walls to Skim Coat Plaster | + .49 |
| Upgrade Ceilings to Textured Finish | + .48 |
| Air Conditioning, in Heating Ductwork | + 2.54 |
| In Separate Ductwork | + 6.36 |
| Heating Systems, Hot Water | + 2.01 |
| Heat Pump | + 3.11 |
| Electric Heat | − .80 |
| Not Heated | − 3.55 |

## Additional upgrades or components

| | |
|---|---|
| Kitchen Cabinets & Countertops | Page 93 |
| Bathroom Vanities | 94 |
| Fireplaces & Chimneys | 94 |
| Windows, Skylights & Dormers | 94 |
| Appliances | 95 |
| Breezeways & Porches | 95 |
| Finished Attic | 95 |
| Garages | 96 |
| Site Improvements | 96 |
| Wings & Ells | 56 |

# Average 2 Story

**Living Area - 2000 S.F.**
**Perimeter - 135 L.F.**

| | | Cost Per Square Foot Of Living Area | | | % of Total |
|---|---|---|---|---|---|
| | | Mat. | Inst. | Total | (roun |
| **1 Site Work** | Site preparation for slab; 4' deep trench excavation for foundation wall. | | .72 | .72 | 0.8% |
| **2 Foundation** | Continuous reinforced concrete footing 8″ deep x 18″ wide; dampproofed and insulated reinforced concrete foundation wall, 8″ thick, 4' deep, 4″ concrete slab on 4″ crushed stone base and polyethylene vapor barrier, trowel finish. | 2.97 | 3.73 | 6.70 | 7.3% |
| **3 Framing** | Exterior walls - 2″ x 4″ wood studs, 16″ O.C.; 1/2″ plywood sheathing; 2″ x 6″ rafters 16″ O.C. with 1/2″ plywood sheathing, 4 in 12 pitch; 2″ x 6″ ceiling joists 16″ O.C.; 2″ x 8″ floor joists 16″ O.C. with 5/8″ plywood subfloor; 1/2″ plywood subfloor on 1″ x 2″ wood sleepers 16″ O.C. | 4.96 | 8.27 | 13.23 | 14.5% |
| **4 Exterior Walls** | Beveled wood siding and building paper on insulated wood frame walls; 6″ attic insulation; double hung windows; 3 flush solid core wood exterior doors with storms. | 12.67 | 5.25 | 17.92 | 19.6% |
| **5 Roofing** | 25 year asphalt shingles; #15 felt building paper; aluminum gutters, downspouts, drip edge and flashings. | .96 | 1.11 | 2.07 | 2.3% |
| **6 Interiors** | Walls and ceilings, 1/2″ taped and finished gypsum wallboard, primed and painted with 2 coats; painted baseboard and trim, finished hardwood floor 40%, carpet with 1/2″ underlayment 40%, vinyl tile with 1/2″ underlayment 15%, ceramic tile with 1/2″ underlayment 5%; hollow core and louvered doors. | 12.71 | 13.38 | 26.09 | 28.5% |
| **7 Specialties** | Average grade kitchen cabinets - 14 L.F. wall and base with solid surface counter top and kitchen sink; 40 gallon electric water heater. | 2.26 | .83 | 3.09 | 3.4% |
| **8 Mechanical** | 1 lavatory, white, wall hung; 1 water closet, white; 1 bathtub with shower; enameled steel, white; gas fired warm air heat. | 3.02 | 2.68 | 5.70 | 6.2% |
| **9 Electrical** | 200 Amp. service; romex wiring; incandescent lighting fixtures, switches, receptacles. | 1.13 | 1.54 | 2.67 | 2.9% |
| **10 Overhead** | Contractor's overhead and profit and plans. | 6.92 | 6.39 | 13.31 | 14.5% |
| **Total** | | 47.60 | 43.90 | 91.50 | |

43

- **Simple design from standard plans**
- **Single family — 1 full bath, 1 kitchen**
- **No basement**
- **Asphalt shingles on roof**
- **Hot air heat**
- **Gypsum wallboard interior finishes**
- **Materials and workmanship are average**

*Note: The illustration shown may contain some optional components (for example: garages and/or fireplaces) whose costs are shown in the modifications, adjustments, & alternatives below or at the end of the square foot section.*

## Base cost per square foot of living area

| Exterior Wall | Living Area | | | | | | | | | | |
|---|---|---|---|---|---|---|---|---|---|---|---|
| | 1200 | 1400 | 1600 | 1800 | 2000 | 2400 | 2800 | 3200 | 3600 | 4000 | 4400 |
| Wood Siding - Wood Frame | 118.55 | 111.25 | 101.50 | 99.60 | 95.95 | 90.20 | 85.75 | 81.10 | 78.80 | 74.55 | 73.25 |
| Brick Veneer - Wood Frame | 127.20 | 119.10 | 108.75 | 106.90 | 102.80 | 96.40 | 91.65 | 86.50 | 83.85 | 79.25 | 77.85 |
| Stucco on Wood Frame | 114.60 | 107.75 | 98.25 | 96.35 | 92.90 | 87.45 | 83.10 | 78.75 | 76.45 | 72.45 | 71.20 |
| Solid Masonry | 143.45 | 133.70 | 122.15 | 120.35 | 115.45 | 107.85 | 102.55 | 96.35 | 93.20 | 88.05 | 86.25 |
| Finished Basement, Add | 16.70 | 16.30 | 15.75 | 15.70 | 15.25 | 14.65 | 14.35 | 13.85 | 13.60 | 13.30 | 13.15 |
| Unfinished Basement, Add | 6.35 | 5.80 | 5.50 | 5.40 | 5.15 | 4.75 | 4.55 | 4.25 | 4.10 | 3.90 | 3.85 |

## Modifications

*Add to the total cost*

| | |
|---|---|
| Upgrade Kitchen Cabinets | $ + 3521 |
| Solid Surface Countertops (Included) | |
| Full Bath - including plumbing, wall and floor finishes | + 5993 |
| Half Bath - including plumbing, wall and floor finishes | + 3570 |
| One Car Attached Garage | + 12,676 |
| One Car Detached Garage | + 16,871 |
| Fireplace & Chimney | + 6634 |

## Adjustments

*For multi family - add to total cost*

| | |
|---|---|
| Additional Kitchen | $ + 6796 |
| Additional Bath | + 5993 |
| Additional Entry & Exit | + 1640 |
| Separate Heating | + 1409 |
| Separate Electric | + 1915 |

*For Townhouse/Rowhouse - Multiply cost per square foot by*

| | |
|---|---|
| Inner Unit | + .90 |
| End Unit | + .95 |

## Alternatives

*Add to or deduct from the cost per square foot of living area*

| | |
|---|---|
| Cedar Shake Roof | + 1.70 |
| Clay Tile Roof | + 1.95 |
| Slate Roof | + 2.90 |
| Upgrade Walls to Skim Coat Plaster | + .47 |
| Upgrade Ceilings to Textured Finish | + .48 |
| Air Conditioning, in Heating Ductwork | + 2.31 |
| In Separate Ductwork | + 6.14 |
| Heating Systems, Hot Water | + 1.81 |
| Heat Pump | + 3.19 |
| Electric Heat | – 1.40 |
| Not Heated | – 4.15 |

## Additional upgrades or components

| | |
|---|---|
| Kitchen Cabinets & Countertops | Page 93 |
| Bathroom Vanities | 94 |
| Fireplaces & Chimneys | 94 |
| Windows, Skylights & Dormers | 94 |
| Appliances | 95 |
| Breezeways & Porches | 95 |
| Finished Attic | 95 |
| Garages | 96 |
| Site Improvements | 96 |
| Wings & Ells | 56 |

**Important: See the Reference Section for Location Factors (to adjust for your city) and Estimating Forms**

| | | Cost Per Square Foot Of Living Area | | | % of Total |
| | | Mat. | Inst. | Total | (roun |
|---|---|---|---|---|---|
| **1 Site Work** | Site preparation for slab; 4' deep trench excavation for foundation wall. | | .45 | .45 | 0.6% |
| **2 Foundation** | Continuous reinforced concrete footing 8" deep x 18" wide, dampproofed and insulated reinforced concrete foundation wall, 8" thick, 4' deep; 4" concrete slab on 4" crushed stone base and polyethylene vapor barrier, trowel finish. | 2.14 | 2.65 | 4.79 | 5.9% |
| **3 Framing** | Exterior walls - 2" x 4" wood studs, 16" O.C.; 1/2" plywood sheathing; 2" x 6" rafters 16" O.C. with 1/2" plywood sheathing, 4 in 12 pitch; 2" x 6" ceiling joists 16" O.C.; 2" x 8" floor joists 16" O.C. with 5/8" plywood subfloor; 1/2" plywood subfloor on 1" x 2" wood sleepers 16" O.C. | 5.00 | 8.08 | 13.08 | 16.1% |
| **4 Exterior Walls** | Beveled wood siding and building paper on insulated wood frame walls; 6" attic insulation; double hung windows; 3 flush solid core wood exterior doors with storms. | 10.71 | 4.41 | 15.12 | 18.6% |
| **5 Roofing** | 25 year asphalt shingles; #15 felt building paper; aluminum gutters, downspouts, drip edge and flashings. | .73 | .85 | 1.58 | 1.9% |
| **6 Interiors** | Walls and ceilings, 1/2" taped and finished gypsum wallboard, primed and painted with 2 coats; painted baseboard and trim, finished hardwood floor 40%, carpet with 1/2" underlayment 40%, vinyl tile with 1/2" underlayment 15%, ceramic tile with 1/2" underlayment 5%; hollow core and louvered doors. | 12.44 | 12.93 | 25.37 | 31.3% |
| **7 Specialties** | Average grade kitchen cabinets - 14 L.F. wall and base with solid surface counter top and kitchen sink; 40 gallon electric water heater. | 1.42 | .51 | 1.93 | 2.4% |
| **8 Mechanical** | 1 lavatory, white, wall hung; 1 water closet, white; 1 bathtub with shower, enameled steel, white; gas fired warm air heat. | 2.33 | 2.38 | 4.71 | 5.8% |
| **9 Electrical** | 200 Amp. service; romex wiring; incandescent lighting fixtures, switches, receptacles. | .97 | 1.35 | 2.32 | 2.9% |
| **10 Overhead** | Contractor's overhead and profit and plans. | 6.06 | 5.69 | 11.75 | 14.5% |
| | **Total** | 41.80 | 39.30 | **81.10** | |

- Simple design from standard plans
- Single family — 1 full bath, 1 kitchen
- No basement
- Asphalt shingles on roof
- Hot air heat
- Gypsum wallboard interior finishes
- Materials and workmanship are average

*Note: The illustration shown may contain some optional components (for example: garages and/or fireplaces) whose costs are shown in the modifications, adjustments, & alternatives below or at the end of the square foot section.*

## Base cost per square foot of living area

| Exterior Wall | Living Area | | | | | | | | | | |
|---|---|---|---|---|---|---|---|---|---|---|---|
| | 1500 | 1800 | 2100 | 2500 | 3000 | 3500 | 4000 | 4500 | 5000 | 5500 | 6000 |
| Wood Siding - Wood Frame | 109.85 | 99.65 | 95.10 | 91.60 | 85.00 | 82.05 | 77.95 | 73.60 | 72.25 | 70.55 | 68.85 |
| Brick Veneer - Wood Frame | 118.00 | 107.30 | 102.20 | 98.40 | 91.15 | 87.90 | 83.25 | 78.50 | 77.00 | 75.10 | 73.15 |
| Stucco on Wood Frame | 106.20 | 96.30 | 91.95 | 88.60 | 82.30 | 79.45 | 75.55 | 71.40 | 70.10 | 68.50 | 67.00 |
| Solid Masonry | 133.25 | 121.30 | 115.35 | 110.90 | 102.55 | 98.65 | 93.05 | 87.55 | 85.70 | 83.55 | 81.10 |
| Finished Basement, Add | 14.35 | 14.20 | 13.80 | 13.50 | 13.05 | 12.70 | 12.40 | 12.00 | 11.95 | 11.75 | 11.60 |
| Unfinished Basement, Add | 5.15 | 4.80 | 4.55 | 4.35 | 4.05 | 3.85 | 3.60 | 3.40 | 3.30 | 3.25 | 3.15 |

## Modifications

*Add to the total cost*

| | |
|---|---|
| Upgrade Kitchen Cabinets | $ + 3521 |
| Solid Surface Countertops (Included) | |
| Full Bath - including plumbing, wall and floor finishes | + 5993 |
| Half Bath - including plumbing, wall and floor finishes | + 3570 |
| One Car Attached Garage | + 12,676 |
| One Car Detached Garage | + 16,871 |
| Fireplace & Chimney | + 6634 |

## Adjustments

*For multi family - add to total cost*

| | |
|---|---|
| Additional Kitchen | $ + 6796 |
| Additional Bath | + 5993 |
| Additional Entry & Exit | + 1640 |
| Separate Heating | + 1409 |
| Separate Electric | + 1915 |

*For Townhouse/Rowhouse - Multiply cost per square foot by*

| | |
|---|---|
| Inner Unit | + .88 |
| End Unit | + .94 |

## Alternatives

*Add to or deduct from the cost per square foot of living area*

| | |
|---|---|
| Cedar Shake Roof | + 1.30 |
| Clay Tile Roof | + 1.50 |
| Slate Roof | + 2.20 |
| Upgrade Walls to Skim Coat Plaster | + .49 |
| Upgrade Ceilings to Textured Finish | + .48 |
| Air Conditioning, in Heating Ductwork | + 2.31 |
| In Separate Ductwork | + 6.14 |
| Heating Systems, Hot Water | + 1.81 |
| Heat Pump | + 3.19 |
| Electric Heat | − 1.09 |
| Not Heated | − 3.85 |

## Additional upgrades or components

| | |
|---|---|
| Kitchen Cabinets & Countertops | Page 93 |
| Bathroom Vanities | 94 |
| Fireplaces & Chimneys | 94 |
| Windows, Skylights & Dormers | 94 |
| Appliances | 95 |
| Breezeways & Porches | 95 |
| Finished Attic | 95 |
| Garages | 96 |
| Site Improvements | 96 |
| Wings & Ells | 56 |

| | | | Cost Per Square Foot Of Living Area | | | % of Total |
|---|---|---|---|---|---|---|
| | | | Mat. | Inst. | Total | (roun |
| **1** | **Site Work** | Site preparation for slab; 4' deep trench excavation for foundation wall. | | .48 | .48 | 0.6% |
| **2** | **Foundation** | Continuous reinforced concrete footing 8" deep x 18" wide, dampproofed and insulated reinforced concrete foundation wall, 8" thick, 4' deep; 4" concrete slab on 4" crushed stone base and polyethylene vapor barrier, trowel finish. | 1.99 | 2.49 | 4.48 | 5.3% |
| **3** | **Framing** | Exterior walls - 2" x 4" wood studs, 16" O.C.; 1/2" plywood sheathing; 2" x 6" rafters 16" O.C. with 1/2" plywood sheathing, 4 in 12 pitch; 2" x 6" ceiling joists 16" O.C.; 2" x 8" floor joists 16" O.C. with 5/8" plywood subfloor; 1/2" plywood subfloor on 1" x 2" wood sleepers 16" O.C. | 5.18 | 8.36 | 13.54 | 15.9% |
| **4** | **Exterior Walls** | Horizontal beveled wood siding; building paper; 3-1/2" batt insulation; wood double hung windows; 3 flush solid core wood exterior doors; storms and screens. | 12.21 | 5.04 | 17.25 | 20.3% |
| **5** | **Roofing** | 25 year asphalt shingles; #15 felt building paper; aluminum gutters, downspouts, drip edge and flashings. | .64 | .74 | 1.38 | 1.6% |
| **6** | **Interiors** | Walls and ceilings, 1/2" taped and finished gypsum wallboard, primed and painted with 2 coats; painted baseboard and trim, finished hardwood floor 40%, carpet with 1/2" underlayment 40%, vinyl tile with 1/2" underlayment 15%, ceramic tile with 1/2" underlayment 5%; hollow core and louvered doors. | 12.88 | 13.38 | 26.26 | 30.9% |
| **7** | **Specialties** | Average grade kitchen cabinets - 14 L.F. wall and base with solid surface counter top and kitchen sink; 40 gallon electric water heater. | 1.53 | .57 | 2.10 | 2.5% |
| **8** | **Mechanical** | 1 lavatory, white, wall hung; 1 water closet, white; 1 bathtub with shower, enameled steel, white; gas fired warm air heat. | 2.42 | 2.41 | 4.83 | 5.7% |
| **9** | **Electrical** | 200 Amp. service; romex wiring; incandescent lighting fixtures, switches, receptacles. | .98 | 1.37 | 2.35 | 2.8% |
| **10** | **Overhead** | Contractor's overhead and profit and plans. | 6.42 | 5.91 | 12.33 | 14.5% |
| | **Total** | | 44.25 | 40.75 | **85.00** | |

- Simple design from standard plans
- Single family — 1 full bath, 1 kitchen
- No basement
- Asphalt shingles on roof
- Hot air heat
- Gypsum wallboard interior finishes
- Materials and workmanship are average

*Note: The illustration shown may contain some optional components (for example: garages and/or fireplaces) whose costs are shown in the modifications, adjustments, & alternatives below or at the end of the square foot section.*

## Base cost per square foot of living area

| Exterior Wall | Living Area | | | | | | | | | | |
|---|---|---|---|---|---|---|---|---|---|---|---|
| | 1000 | 1200 | 1400 | 1600 | 1800 | 2000 | 2200 | 2600 | 3000 | 3400 | 3800 |
| Wood Siding - Wood Frame | 111.50 | 100.75 | 95.90 | 92.60 | 89.25 | 85.40 | 83.10 | 78.45 | 74.00 | 72.00 | 70.10 |
| Brick Veneer - Wood Frame | 117.65 | 106.45 | 101.25 | 97.70 | 94.00 | 90.00 | 87.50 | 82.45 | 77.70 | 75.45 | 73.45 |
| Stucco on Wood Frame | 108.75 | 98.20 | 93.50 | 90.30 | 87.05 | 83.35 | 81.15 | 76.75 | 72.35 | 70.40 | 68.70 |
| Solid Masonry | 129.05 | 117.00 | 111.05 | 107.10 | 102.80 | 98.50 | 95.60 | 89.80 | 84.45 | 81.85 | 79.60 |
| Finished Basement, Add | 19.70 | 19.40 | 18.75 | 18.35 | 17.90 | 17.65 | 17.25 | 16.60 | 16.15 | 15.90 | 15.65 |
| Unfinished Basement, Add | 7.65 | 7.10 | 6.70 | 6.40 | 6.10 | 5.90 | 5.70 | 5.35 | 5.05 | 4.80 | 4.70 |

## Modifications

*Add to the total cost*

| | |
|---|---|
| Upgrade Kitchen Cabinets | $  + 3521 |
| Solid Surface Countertops (Included) | |
| Full Bath - including plumbing, wall and floor finishes | + 5993 |
| Half Bath - including plumbing, wall and floor finishes | + 3570 |
| One Car Attached Garage | + 12,676 |
| One Car Detached Garage | + 16,871 |
| Fireplace & Chimney | + 5234 |

## Adjustments

*For multi family - add to total cost*

| | |
|---|---|
| Additional Kitchen | $  + 6796 |
| Additional Bath | + 5993 |
| Additional Entry & Exit | + 1640 |
| Separate Heating | + 1409 |
| Separate Electric | + 1915 |

*For Townhouse/Rowhouse -*
*Multiply cost per square foot by*

| | |
|---|---|
| Inner Unit | + .91 |
| End Unit | + .96 |

## Alternatives

*Add to or deduct from the cost per square foot of living area*

| | |
|---|---|
| Cedar Shake Roof | + 1.95 |
| Clay Tile Roof | + 2.25 |
| Slate Roof | + 3.30 |
| Upgrade Walls to Skim Coat Plaster | + .45 |
| Upgrade Ceilings to Textured Finish | + .48 |
| Air Conditioning, in Heating Ductwork | + 2.54 |
| In Separate Ductwork | + 6.36 |
| Heating Systems, Hot Water | + 2.01 |
| Heat Pump | + 3.11 |
| Electric Heat | – .80 |
| Not Heated | – 3.55 |

## Additional upgrades or components

| | |
|---|---|
| Kitchen Cabinets & Countertops | Page 93 |
| Bathroom Vanities | 94 |
| Fireplaces & Chimneys | 94 |
| Windows, Skylights & Dormers | 94 |
| Appliances | 95 |
| Breezeways & Porches | 95 |
| Finished Attic | 95 |
| Garages | 96 |
| Site Improvements | 96 |
| Wings & Ells | 56 |

# Average Bi-Level

### Living Area - 2000 S.F.
### Perimeter - 135 L.F.

| | Description | Cost Per Square Foot Of Living Area | | | % of Total |
|---|---|---|---|---|---|
| | | Mat. | Inst. | Total | (roun |
| **1** Site Work | Excavation for lower level, 4' deep. Site preparation for slab. | | .72 | .72 | 0.8% |
| **2** Foundation | Continuous reinforced concrete footing 8" deep x 18" wide, dampproofed and insulated reinforced concrete foundation wall, 8" thick, 4' deep; 4" concrete slab on 4" crushed stone base and polyethylene vapor barrier, trowel finish. | 2.97 | 3.73 | 6.70 | 7.8% |
| **3** Framing | Exterior walls - 2" x 4" wood studs, 16" O.C.; 1/2" plywood sheathing; 2" x 6" rafters 16" O.C. with 1/2" plywood sheathing, 4 in 12 pitch; 2" x 6" ceiling joists 16" O.C.; 2" x 8" floor joists 16" O.C. with 5/8" plywood subfloor; 1/2" plywood subfloor on 1" x 2" wood sleepers 16" O.C. | 4.75 | 7.84 | 12.59 | 14.7% |
| **4** Exterior Walls | Horizontal beveled wood siding; building paper; 3-1/2" batt insulation; wood double hung windows; 3 flush solid core wood exterior doors; storms and screens. | 9.83 | 4.11 | 13.94 | 16.3% |
| **5** Roofing | 25 year asphalt shingles; #15 felt building paper; aluminum gutters, downspouts, drip edge and flashings. | .96 | 1.11 | 2.07 | 2.4% |
| **6** Interiors | Walls and ceilings, 1/2" taped and finished gypsum wallboard, primed and painted with 2 coats; painted baseboard and trim, finished hardwood floor 40%, carpet with 1/2" underlayment 40%, vinyl tile with 1/2" underlayment 15%, ceramic tile with 1/2" underlayment 5%; hollow core and louvered doors. | 12.51 | 12.99 | 25.50 | 29.9% |
| **7** Specialties | Average grade kitchen cabinets - 14 L.F. wall and base with solid surface counter top and kitchen sink; 40 gallon electric water heater. | 2.26 | .83 | 3.09 | 3.6% |
| **8** Mechanical | 1 lavatory, white, wall hung; 1 water closet, white; 1 bathtub with shower, enameled steel, white; gas fired warm air heat. | 3.02 | 2.68 | 5.70 | 6.7% |
| **9** Electrical | 200 Amp. service; romex wiring; incandescent lighting fixtures, switches, receptacles. | 1.13 | 1.54 | 2.67 | 3.1% |
| **10** Overhead | Contractor's overhead and profit and plans. | 6.37 | 6.05 | 12.42 | 14.5% |
| **Total** | | 43.80 | 41.60 | **85.40** | |

- Simple design from standard plans
- Single family — 1 full bath, 1 kitchen
- No basement
- Asphalt shingles on roof
- Hot air heat
- Gypsum wallboard interior finishes
- Materials and workmanship are average

*Note: The illustration shown may contain some optional components (for example: garages and/or fireplaces) whose costs are shown in the modifications, adjustments, & alternatives below or at the end of the square foot section.*

©Design Basics, Inc.

## Base cost per square foot of living area

| Exterior Wall | Living Area | | | | | | | | | | |
|---|---|---|---|---|---|---|---|---|---|---|---|
| | 1200 | 1500 | 1800 | 2100 | 2400 | 2700 | 3000 | 3400 | 3800 | 4200 | 4600 |
| Wood Siding - Wood Frame | 105.90 | 97.55 | 91.35 | 86.00 | 82.50 | 80.50 | 78.35 | 76.25 | 72.80 | 70.00 | 68.65 |
| Brick Veneer - Wood Frame | 111.55 | 102.70 | 95.95 | 90.20 | 86.45 | 84.25 | 81.90 | 79.70 | 76.05 | 73.00 | 71.55 |
| Stucco on Wood Frame | 103.35 | 95.25 | 89.25 | 84.10 | 80.75 | 78.80 | 76.75 | 74.70 | 71.40 | 68.60 | 67.35 |
| Solid Masonry | 122.00 | 112.15 | 104.55 | 97.95 | 93.70 | 91.30 | 88.55 | 86.10 | 82.00 | 78.55 | 76.90 |
| Finished Basement, Add* | 22.50 | 22.10 | 21.15 | 20.35 | 19.95 | 19.65 | 19.25 | 19.00 | 18.60 | 18.25 | 18.10 |
| Unfinished Basement, Add* | 8.40 | 7.75 | 7.20 | 6.70 | 6.40 | 6.25 | 6.00 | 5.80 | 5.55 | 5.35 | 5.25 |

*Basement under middle level only.

## Modifications

### Add to the total cost

| | |
|---|---|
| Upgrade Kitchen Cabinets | $ + 3521 |
| Solid Surface Countertops (Included) | |
| Full Bath - including plumbing, wall and floor finishes | + 5993 |
| Half Bath - including plumbing, wall and floor finishes | + 3570 |
| One Car Attached Garage | + 12,676 |
| One Car Detached Garage | + 16,871 |
| Fireplace & Chimney | + 5234 |

## Adjustments

### For multi family - add to total cost

| | |
|---|---|
| Additional Kitchen | $ + 6796 |
| Additional Bath | + 5993 |
| Additional Entry & Exit | + 1640 |
| Separate Heating | + 1409 |
| Separate Electric | + 1915 |

### For Townhouse/Rowhouse - Multiply cost per square foot by

| | |
|---|---|
| Inner Unit | + .90 |
| End Unit | + .95 |

## Alternatives

### Add to or deduct from the cost per square foot of living area

| | |
|---|---|
| Cedar Shake Roof | + 2.80 |
| Clay Tile Roof | + 3.30 |
| Slate Roof | + 4.80 |
| Upgrade Walls to Skim Coat Plaster | + .39 |
| Upgrade Ceilings to Textured Finish | + .48 |
| Air Conditioning, in Heating Ductwork | + 2.14 |
| In Separate Ductwork | + 6 |
| Heating Systems, Hot Water | + 1.94 |
| Heat Pump | + 3.23 |
| Electric Heat | − .65 |
| Not Heated | − 3.43 |

## Additional upgrades or components

| | |
|---|---|
| Kitchen Cabinets & Countertops | Page 93 |
| Bathroom Vanities | 94 |
| Fireplaces & Chimneys | 94 |
| Windows, Skylights & Dormers | 94 |
| Appliances | 95 |
| Breezeways & Porches | 95 |
| Finished Attic | 95 |
| Garages | 96 |
| Site Improvements | 96 |
| Wings & Ells | 56 |

| | | Cost Per Square Foot Of Living Area | | | % of Total |
|---|---|---|---|---|---|
| | | Mat. | Inst. | Total | (roun |
| **1** Site Work | Site preparation for slab; 4' deep trench excavation for foundation wall, excavation for lower level, 4' deep. | | .60 | .60 | 0.7% |
| **2** Foundation | Continuous reinforced concrete footing 8" deep x 18" wide; dampproofed and insulated reinforced concrete foundation wall, 8" thick, 4' deep; 4" concrete slab on 4" crushed stone base and polyethylene vapor barrier, trowel finish. | 3.35 | 4.05 | 7.40 | 9.0% |
| **3** Framing | Exterior walls - 2" x 4" wood studs, 16" O.C.; 1/2" plywood sheathing; 2" x 6" rafters 16" O.C. with 1/2" plywood sheathing, 4 in 12 pitch; 2" x 6" ceiling joists 16" O.C.; 2" x 8" floor joists 16" O.C. with 5/8" plywood subfloor; 1/2" plywood subfloor on 1" x 2" wood sleepers 16" O.C. | 4.35 | 7.37 | 11.72 | 14.2% |
| **4** Exterior Walls | Horizontal beveled wood siding: building paper; 3-1/2" batt insulation; wood double hung windows; 3 flush solid core wood exterior doors; storms and screens. | 8.49 | 3.57 | 12.06 | 14.6% |
| **5** Roofing | 25 year asphalt shingles; #15 felt building paper; aluminum gutters, downspouts, drip edge and flashings. | 1.26 | 1.48 | 2.74 | 3.3% |
| **6** Interiors | Walls and ceilings, 1/2" taped and finished gypsum wallboard, primed and painted with 2 coats; painted baseboard and trim, finished hardwood floor 40%, carpet with 1/2" underlayment 40%, vinyl tile with 1/2" underlayment 15%, ceramic tile with 1/2" underlayment 5%; hollow core and louvered doors. | 12.97 | 12.72 | 25.69 | 31.1% |
| **7** Specialties | Average grade kitchen cabinets - 14 L.F. wall and base with solid surface counter top and kitchen sink; 40 gallon electric water heater. | 1.89 | .70 | 2.59 | 3.1% |
| **8** Mechanical | 1 lavatory, white, wall hung; 1 water closet, white; 1 bathtub with shower, enameled steel, white; gas fired warm air heat. | 2.65 | 2.53 | 5.18 | 6.3% |
| **9** Electrical | 200 Amp. service; romex wiring; incandescent lighting fixtures, switches, receptacles. | 1.06 | 1.46 | 2.52 | 3.1% |
| **10** Overhead | Contractor's overhead and profit and plans. | 6.13 | 5.87 | 12.00 | 14.5% |
| **Total** | | 42.15 | 40.35 | **82.50** | |

- Post and beam frame
- Log exterior walls
- Simple design from standard plans
- Single family — 1 full bath, 1 kitchen
- No basement
- Asphalt shingles on roof
- Hot air heat
- Gypsum wallboard interior finishes
- Materials and workmanship are average

*Note: The illustration shown may contain some optional components (for example: garages and/or fireplaces) whose costs are shown in the modifications, adjustments, & alternatives below or at the end of the square foot section.*

## Base cost per square foot of living area

| Exterior Wall | Living Area | | | | | | | | | | |
|---|---|---|---|---|---|---|---|---|---|---|---|
| | 600 | 800 | 1000 | 1200 | 1400 | 1600 | 1800 | 2000 | 2400 | 2800 | 3200 |
| 6" Log - Solid Wall | 152.60 | 138.45 | 128.00 | 119.40 | 112.20 | 107.60 | 105.10 | 101.85 | 95.75 | 91.20 | 88.05 |
| 8" Log - Solid Wall | 143.40 | 130.20 | 120.50 | 112.65 | 106.15 | 101.85 | 99.55 | 96.65 | 90.95 | 86.80 | 84.00 |
| Finished Basement, Add | 33.95 | 32.80 | 31.25 | 29.85 | 28.75 | 27.95 | 27.60 | 27.00 | 26.10 | 25.50 | 24.90 |
| Unfinished Basement, Add | 13.90 | 12.50 | 11.55 | 10.65 | 9.95 | 9.50 | 9.20 | 8.85 | 8.30 | 7.90 | 7.60 |

## Modifications

*Add to the total cost*

| | |
|---|---|
| Upgrade Kitchen Cabinets | $ + 3521 |
| Solid Surface Countertops (Included) | |
| Full Bath - including plumbing, wall and floor finishes | + 5993 |
| Half Bath - including plumbing, wall and floor finishes | + 3570 |
| One Car Attached Garage | + 12,676 |
| One Car Detached Garage | + 16,871 |
| Fireplace & Chimney | + 5234 |

## Adjustments

*For multi family - add to total cost*

| | |
|---|---|
| Additional Kitchen | $ + 6796 |
| Additional Bath | + 5993 |
| Additional Entry & Exit | + 1640 |
| Separate Heating | + 1409 |
| Separate Electric | + 1915 |

*For Townhouse/Rowhouse - Multiply cost per square foot by*

| | |
|---|---|
| Inner Unit | + .92 |
| End Unit | + .96 |

## Alternatives

*Add to or deduct from the cost per square foot of living area*

| | |
|---|---|
| Cedar Shake Roof | + 3.85 |
| Air Conditioning, in Heating Ductwork | + 4.19 |
| In Separate Ductwork | + 8 |
| Heating Systems, Hot Water | + 2.16 |
| Heat Pump | + 2.65 |
| Electric Heat | − 1.04 |
| Not Heated | − 3.80 |

## Additional upgrades or components

| | |
|---|---|
| Kitchen Cabinets & Countertops | Page 93 |
| Bathroom Vanities | 94 |
| Fireplaces & Chimneys | 94 |
| Windows, Skylights & Dormers | 94 |
| Appliances | 95 |
| Breezeways & Porches | 95 |
| Finished Attic | 95 |
| Garages | 96 |
| Site Improvements | 96 |
| Wings & Ells | 56 |

| | | Cost Per Square Foot Of Living Area | | | % of Total |
| --- | --- | --- | --- | --- | --- |
| | | Mat. | Inst. | Total | (roun |
| **1 Site Work** | Site preparation for slab; 4' deep trench excavation for foundation wall. | | .90 | .90 | 0.8% |
| **2 Foundation** | Continuous reinforced concrete footing 8" deep x 18" wide; dampproofed and insulated reinforced concrete foundation wall, 8" thick, 4' deep; 4" concrete slab on 4" crushed stone base and polyethylene vapor barrier, trowel finish. | 5.02 | 6.07 | 11.09 | 10.3% |
| **3 Framing** | Exterior walls - Precut traditional log home. Handcrafted white cedar or pine logs. Delivery included. | 20.33 | 13.19 | 33.52 | 31.2% |
| **4 Exterior Walls** | Wood double hung windows, solid wood exterior doors. | 5.26 | 2.61 | 7.87 | 7.3% |
| **5 Roofing** | 25 year asphalt shingles; #15 felt building paper; aluminum gutters, downspouts, drip edge and flashings. | 1.90 | 2.22 | 4.12 | 3.8% |
| **6 Interiors** | Walls and ceilings, 1/2" taped and finished gypsum wallboard, primed and painted with 2 coats; painted baseboard and trim, finished hardwood floor 40%, carpet with 1/2" underlayment 40%, vinyl tile with 1/2" underlayment 15%, ceramic tile with 1/2" underlayment 5%, hollow core and louvered doors. | 10.53 | 10.74 | 21.27 | 19.8% |
| **7 Specialties** | Average grade kitchen cabinets - 14 L.F. wall and base with solid surface counter top and kitchen sink; 40 gallon electric water heater. | 2.83 | 1.05 | 3.88 | 3.6% |
| **8 Mechanical** | 1 lavatory, white, wall hung; 1 water closet, white; 1 bathtub with shower, enameled steel, white; gas fired warm air heat. | 3.50 | 2.87 | 6.37 | 5.9% |
| **9 Electrical** | 200 Amp. service; romex wiring; incandescent lighting fixtures, switches, receptacles. | 1.25 | 1.68 | 2.93 | 2.7% |
| **10 Overhead** | Contractor's overhead and profit and plans. | 8.63 | 7.02 | 15.65 | 14.5% |
| **Total** | | 59.25 | 48.35 | **107.60** | |

- Post and beam frame
- Log exterior walls
- Simple design from standard plans
- Single family — 1 full bath, 1 kitchen
- No basement
- Asphalt shingles on roof
- Hot air heat
- Gypsum wallboard interior finishes
- Materials and workmanship are average

*Note: The illustration shown may contain some optional components (for example: garages and/or fireplaces) whose costs are shown in the modifications, adjustments, & alternatives below or at the end of the square foot section.*

## Base cost per square foot of living area

| Exterior Wall | Living Area | | | | | | | | | | |
|---|---|---|---|---|---|---|---|---|---|---|---|
| | 1000 | 1200 | 1400 | 1600 | 1800 | 2000 | 2200 | 2600 | 3000 | 3400 | 3800 |
| 6" Log-Solid | 135.50 | 123.40 | 117.50 | 113.50 | 109.20 | 104.90 | 101.95 | 96.10 | 90.70 | 88.20 | 85.90 |
| 8" Log-Solid | 125.50 | 114.20 | 108.85 | 105.25 | 101.45 | 97.40 | 94.85 | 89.70 | 84.75 | 82.55 | 80.50 |
| Finished Basement, Add | 19.70 | 19.40 | 18.75 | 18.35 | 17.90 | 17.65 | 17.25 | 16.60 | 16.15 | 15.90 | 15.65 |
| Unfinished Basement, Add | 7.65 | 7.10 | 6.70 | 6.40 | 6.10 | 5.90 | 5.70 | 5.35 | 5.05 | 4.80 | 4.70 |

## Modifications

*Add to the total cost*

| | |
|---|---|
| Upgrade Kitchen Cabinets | $ + 3521 |
| Solid Surface Countertops (Included) | |
| Full Bath - including plumbing, wall and floor finishes | + 5993 |
| Half Bath - including plumbing, wall and floor finishes | + 3570 |
| One Car Attached Garage | + 12,676 |
| One Car Detached Garage | + 16,871 |
| Fireplace & Chimney | + 5836 |

## Adjustments

*For multi family - add to total cost*

| | |
|---|---|
| Additional Kitchen | $ + 6796 |
| Additional Bath | + 5993 |
| Additional Entry & Exit | + 1640 |
| Separate Heating | + 1409 |
| Separate Electric | + 1915 |

*For Townhouse/Rowhouse - Multiply cost per square foot by*

| | |
|---|---|
| Inner Unit | + .92 |
| End Unit | + .96 |

## Alternatives

*Add to or deduct from the cost per square foot of living area*

| | |
|---|---|
| Cedar Shake Roof | + 2.80 |
| Air Conditioning, in Heating Ductwork | + 2.54 |
| In Separate Ductwork | + 6.36 |
| Heating Systems, Hot Water | + 2.01 |
| Heat Pump | + 3.11 |
| Electric Heat | − .80 |
| Not Heated | − 3.55 |

## Additional upgrades or components

| | |
|---|---|
| Kitchen Cabinets & Countertops | Page 93 |
| Bathroom Vanities | 94 |
| Fireplaces & Chimneys | 94 |
| Windows, Skylights & Dormers | 94 |
| Appliances | 95 |
| Breezeways & Porches | 95 |
| Finished Attic | 95 |
| Garages | 96 |
| Site Improvements | 96 |
| Wings & Ells | 56 |

# Solid Wall 2 Story

**Living Area - 2000 S.F.**
**Perimeter - 135 L.F.**

| | | Cost Per Square Foot Of Living Area | | | % of Total |
|---|---|---|---|---|---|
| | | Mat. | Inst. | Total | (roun |
| **1 Site Work** | Site preparation for slab; 4' deep trench excavation for foundation wall. | | .72 | .72 | 0.7% |
| **2 Foundation** | Continuous reinforced concrete footing 8" deep x 18" wide; dampproofed and insulated reinforced concrete foundation wall, 8" thick, 4' deep, 4" concrete slab on 4" crushed stone base and polyethylene vapor barrier, trowel finish. | 2.97 | 3.73 | 6.70 | 6.4% |
| **3 Framing** | Exterior walls - Precut traditional log home. Handcrafted white cedar or pine logs. Delivery included. | 22.72 | 13.68 | 36.40 | 34.7% |
| **4 Exterior Walls** | Wood double hung windows, solid wood exterior doors. | 5.81 | 2.79 | 8.60 | 8.2% |
| **5 Roofing** | 25 year asphalt shingles; #15 felt building paper; aluminum gutters, downspouts, drip edge and flashings. | .96 | 1.11 | 2.07 | 2.0% |
| **6 Interiors** | Walls and ceilings, 1/2" taped and finished gypsum wallboard, primed and painted with 2 coats; painted baseboard and trim, finished hardwood floor 40%, carpet with 1/2" underlayment 40%, vinyl tile with 1/2" underlayment 15%, ceramic tile with 1/2" underlayment 5%; hollow core and louvered doors. | 11.89 | 11.83 | 23.72 | 22.6% |
| **7 Specialties** | Average grade kitchen cabinets - 14 L.F. wall and base with solid surface counter top and kitchen sink; 40 gallon electric water heater. | 2.26 | .83 | 3.09 | 2.9% |
| **8 Mechanical** | 1 lavatory, white, wall hung; 1 water closet, white; 1 bathtub with shower; enameled steel, white; gas fired warm air heat. | 3.02 | 2.68 | 5.70 | 5.4% |
| **9 Electrical** | 200 Amp. service; romex wiring; incandescent lighting fixtures, switches, receptacles. | 1.13 | 1.54 | 2.67 | 2.5% |
| **10 Overhead** | Contractor's overhead and profit and plans. | 8.64 | 6.59 | 15.23 | 14.5% |
| **Total** | | 59.40 | 45.50 | **104.90** | |

## 1 Story — Base cost per square foot of living area

| Exterior Wall | Living Area | | | | | | | |
|---|---|---|---|---|---|---|---|---|
| | 50 | 100 | 200 | 300 | 400 | 500 | 600 | 700 |
| Wood Siding - Wood Frame | 178.60 | 136.90 | 118.75 | 99.85 | 93.95 | 90.35 | 88.00 | 88.90 |
| Brick Veneer - Wood Frame | 188.10 | 140.95 | 120.55 | 97.85 | 91.15 | 87.10 | 84.45 | 85.10 |
| Stucco on Wood Frame | 169.85 | 130.55 | 113.40 | 96.30 | 90.65 | 87.30 | 85.05 | 86.05 |
| Solid Masonry | 233.15 | 175.90 | 151.20 | 121.50 | 113.45 | 108.50 | 106.90 | 106.95 |
| Finished Basement, Add | 54.20 | 44.95 | 40.45 | 32.90 | 31.40 | 30.55 | 29.90 | 29.50 |
| Unfinished Basement, Add | 25.55 | 19.20 | 16.60 | 12.20 | 11.30 | 10.80 | 10.40 | 10.15 |

## 1-1/2 Story — Base cost per square foot of living area

| Exterior Wall | Living Area | | | | | | | |
|---|---|---|---|---|---|---|---|---|
| | 100 | 200 | 300 | 400 | 500 | 600 | 700 | 800 |
| Wood Siding - Wood Frame | 144.50 | 115.95 | 98.90 | 88.95 | 83.75 | 81.35 | 78.20 | 77.25 |
| Brick Veneer - Wood Frame | 198.15 | 147.90 | 122.45 | 106.90 | 99.25 | 95.15 | 90.70 | 89.05 |
| Stucco on Wood Frame | 173.40 | 128.05 | 105.95 | 94.10 | 87.40 | 83.95 | 80.10 | 78.60 |
| Solid Masonry | 229.75 | 173.15 | 143.55 | 123.40 | 114.45 | 109.45 | 104.25 | 102.50 |
| Finished Basement, Add | 36.60 | 33.10 | 30.15 | 26.80 | 25.95 | 25.30 | 24.75 | 24.65 |
| Unfinished Basement, Add | 16.00 | 13.30 | 11.60 | 9.60 | 9.10 | 8.75 | 8.40 | 8.40 |

## 2 Story — Base cost per square foot of living area

| Exterior Wall | Living Area | | | | | | | |
|---|---|---|---|---|---|---|---|---|
| | 100 | 200 | 400 | 600 | 800 | 1000 | 1200 | 1400 |
| Wood Siding - Wood Frame | 144.30 | 107.80 | 91.75 | 76.45 | 71.25 | 68.05 | 66.00 | 67.10 |
| Brick Veneer - Wood Frame | 201.90 | 140.70 | 112.80 | 90.45 | 82.90 | 78.25 | 75.25 | 75.70 |
| Stucco on Wood Frame | 174.20 | 120.90 | 96.25 | 79.50 | 73.00 | 69.10 | 66.50 | 67.25 |
| Solid Masonry | 237.35 | 165.95 | 133.90 | 104.50 | 95.50 | 90.05 | 86.50 | 86.55 |
| Finished Basement, Add | 29.05 | 24.45 | 22.15 | 18.45 | 17.65 | 17.25 | 16.95 | 16.75 |
| Unfinished Basement, Add | 13.00 | 9.80 | 8.45 | 6.25 | 5.80 | 5.55 | 5.40 | 5.25 |

Base costs do not include bathroom or kitchen facilities. Use Modifications/Adjustments/Alternatives on pages 93–96 where appropriate.

## 1 Story

## 1 - 1/2 Story

## 2 Story

## 2 - 1/2 Story

## Bi-Level

## Tri-Level

- **A distinct residence from designer's plans**
- **Single family — 1 full bath, 1 half bath, 1 kitchen**
- **No basement**
- **Asphalt shingles on roof**
- **Forced hot air heat/air conditioning**
- **Gypsum wallboard interior finishes**
- **Materials and workmanship are above average**

*Note: The illustration shown may contain some optional components (for example: garages and/or fireplaces) whose costs are shown in the modifications, adjustments, & alternatives below or at the end of the square foot section.*

eDesign Basics, Inc.

## Base cost per square foot of living area

| Exterior Wall | Living Area | | | | | | | | | | |
|---|---|---|---|---|---|---|---|---|---|---|---|
| | 800 | 1000 | 1200 | 1400 | 1600 | 1800 | 2000 | 2400 | 2800 | 3200 | 3600 |
| Wood Siding - Wood Frame | 161.95 | 146.65 | 134.40 | 124.60 | 117.80 | 114.15 | 109.80 | 101.65 | 95.70 | 91.55 | 87.25 |
| Brick Veneer - Wood Frame | 180.80 | 164.70 | 151.65 | 141.15 | 133.95 | 130.10 | 125.30 | 116.75 | 110.45 | 105.90 | 101.30 |
| Stone Veneer - Wood Frame | 185.65 | 169.10 | 155.60 | 144.80 | 137.35 | 133.35 | 128.40 | 119.55 | 113.05 | 108.35 | 103.55 |
| Solid Masonry | 190.20 | 173.15 | 159.30 | 148.15 | 140.50 | 136.45 | 131.25 | 122.10 | 115.45 | 110.55 | 105.60 |
| Finished Basement, Add | 50.70 | 50.50 | 48.40 | 46.60 | 45.50 | 44.85 | 43.90 | 42.60 | 41.60 | 40.75 | 39.95 |
| Unfinished Basement, Add | 20.90 | 19.65 | 18.50 | 17.60 | 17.00 | 16.65 | 16.20 | 15.50 | 14.95 | 14.50 | 14.10 |

## Modifications

*Add to the total cost*

| | |
|---|---|
| Upgrade Kitchen Cabinets | $  + 1108 |
| Solid Surface Countertops (Included) | |
| Full Bath - including plumbing, wall and floor finishes | + 7102 |
| Half Bath - including plumbing, wall and floor finishes | + 4230 |
| Two Car Attached Garage | + 21,916 |
| Two Car Detached Garage | + 25,336 |
| Fireplace & Chimney | + 5760 |

## Adjustments

*For multi family - add to total cost*

| | |
|---|---|
| Additional Kitchen | $  + 14,160 |
| Additional Full Bath & Half Bath | + 11,332 |
| Additional Entry & Exit | + 1640 |
| Separate Heating & Air Conditioning | + 6271 |
| Separate Electric | + 1915 |

*For Townhouse/Rowhouse - Multiply cost per square foot by*

| | |
|---|---|
| Inner Unit | + .90 |
| End Unit | + .95 |

## Alternatives

*Add to or deduct from the cost per square foot of living area*

| | |
|---|---|
| Cedar Shake Roof | + 3.45 |
| Clay Tile Roof | + 4.10 |
| Slate Roof | + 6.20 |
| Upgrade Ceilings to Textured Finish | + .48 |
| Air Conditioning, in Heating Ductwork | Base System |
| Heating Systems, Hot Water | + 2.21 |
| Heat Pump | + 2.64 |
| Electric Heat | − 2.95 |
| Not Heated | − 4.77 |

## Additional upgrades or components

| | |
|---|---|
| Kitchen Cabinets & Countertops | Page 93 |
| Bathroom Vanities | 94 |
| Fireplaces & Chimneys | 94 |
| Windows, Skylights & Dormers | 94 |
| Appliances | 95 |
| Breezeways & Porches | 95 |
| Finished Attic | 95 |
| Garages | 96 |
| Site Improvements | 96 |
| Wings & Ells | 74 |

| | | Cost Per Square Foot Of Living Area | | | % of Total |
|---|---|---|---|---|---|
| | | Mat. | Inst. | Total | (roun |
| **1 Site Work** | Site preparation for slab; 4' deep trench excavation for foundation wall. | | .71 | .71 | 0.7% |
| **2 Foundation** | Continuous reinforced concrete footing 8" deep x 18" wide; dampproofed and insulated reinforced concrete foundation wall, 8" thick, 4' deep, 4" concrete slab on 4" crushed stone base and polyethylene vapor barrier, trowel finish. | 5.60 | 6.71 | 12.31 | 12.1% |
| **3 Framing** | Exterior walls - 2" x 6" wood studs, 16" O.C.; 1/2" plywood sheathing; 2" x 8" rafters 16" O.C. with 1/2" plywood sheathing, 4 in 12 pitch; 2" x 6" ceiling joists 16" O.C.; 5/8" plywood subfloor on 1" x 3" wood sleepers 16" O.C. | 2.92 | 6.21 | 9.13 | 9.0% |
| **4 Exterior Walls** | Horizontal beveled wood siding; building paper; 6" batt insulation; wood double hung windows; 3 solid core wood exterior doors; storms and screens. | 9.13 | 3.14 | 12.27 | 12.1% |
| **5 Roofing** | 30 year asphalt shingles; #15 felt building paper; aluminum gutters, downspouts and drip edge; copper flashings. | 4.66 | 3.25 | 7.91 | 7.8% |
| **6 Interiors** | Walls and ceilings - 5/8" gypsum wallboard, skim coat plaster, painted with primer and 2 coats; hardwood baseboard and trim, sanded and finished; hardwood floor 70%, ceramic tile with underlayment 20%, vinyl tile with underlayment 10%; wood panel interior doors, primed and painted with 2 coats. | 12.54 | 11.77 | 24.31 | 23.9% |
| **7 Specialties** | Custom grade kitchen cabinets - 20 L.F. wall and base with solid surface counter top and kitchen sink; 4 L.F. bathroom vanity; 75 gallon electric water heater, medicine cabinet. | 5.04 | 1.18 | 6.22 | 6.1% |
| **8 Mechanical** | Gas fired warm air heat/air conditioning; one full bath including: bathtub, corner shower, built in lavatory and water closet; one 1/2 bath including: built in lavatory and water closet. | 6.04 | 2.96 | 9.00 | 8.9% |
| **9 Electrical** | 200 Amp. service; romex wiring; fluorescent and incandescent lighting fixtures, switches, receptacles. | 1.19 | 1.66 | 2.85 | 2.8% |
| **10 Overhead** | Contractor's overhead and profit and design. | 9.43 | 7.51 | 16.94 | 16.7% |
| **Total** | | 56.55 | 45.10 | 101.65 | |

- **A distinct residence from designer's plans**
- **Single family — 1 full bath, 1 half bath, 1 kitchen**
- **No basement**
- **Asphalt shingles on roof**
- **Forced hot air heat/air conditioning**
- **Gypsum wallboard interior finishes**
- **Materials and workmanship are above average**

*Note: The illustration shown may contain some optional components (for example: garages and/or fireplaces) whose costs are shown in the modifications, adjustments, & alternatives below or at the end of the square foot section.*

©Donald A. Gardner Architects, Inc.

## Base cost per square foot of living area

| Exterior Wall | Living Area | | | | | | | | | | |
|---|---|---|---|---|---|---|---|---|---|---|---|
| | 1000 | 1200 | 1400 | 1600 | 1800 | 2000 | 2400 | 2800 | 3200 | 3600 | 4000 |
| Wood Siding - Wood Frame | 145.30 | 135.10 | 127.80 | 119.10 | 114.10 | 109.20 | 99.85 | 95.55 | 91.55 | 88.55 | 84.30 |
| Brick Veneer - Wood Frame | 154.60 | 143.80 | 136.15 | 126.65 | 121.25 | 115.90 | 105.80 | 101.25 | 96.85 | 93.65 | 89.00 |
| Stone Veneer - Wood Frame | 159.75 | 148.60 | 140.65 | 130.80 | 125.15 | 119.70 | 109.10 | 104.35 | 99.70 | 96.45 | 91.60 |
| Solid Masonry | 164.50 | 153.05 | 144.90 | 134.60 | 128.75 | 123.10 | 112.15 | 107.25 | 102.35 | 99.00 | 94.00 |
| Finished Basement, Add | 33.65 | 33.90 | 32.95 | 31.60 | 30.90 | 30.15 | 28.80 | 28.15 | 27.50 | 27.05 | 26.50 |
| Unfinished Basement, Add | 14.15 | 13.45 | 13.05 | 12.30 | 11.90 | 11.55 | 10.85 | 10.50 | 10.15 | 9.95 | 9.60 |

## Modifications

**Add to the total cost**

| | |
|---|---|
| Upgrade Kitchen Cabinets | $ + 1108 |
| Solid Surface Countertops (Included) | |
| Full Bath - including plumbing, wall and floor finishes | + 7102 |
| Half Bath - including plumbing, wall and floor finishes | + 4230 |
| Two Car Attached Garage | + 21,916 |
| Two Car Detached Garage | + 25,336 |
| Fireplace & Chimney | + 5760 |

## Adjustments

**For multi family - add to total cost**

| | |
|---|---|
| Additional Kitchen | $ + 14,160 |
| Additional Full Bath & Half Bath | + 11,332 |
| Additional Entry & Exit | + 1640 |
| Separate Heating & Air Conditioning | + 6271 |
| Separate Electric | + 1915 |

**For Townhouse/Rowhouse - Multiply cost per square foot by**

| | |
|---|---|
| Inner Unit | + .90 |
| End Unit | + .95 |

## Alternatives

**Add to or deduct from the cost per square foot of living area**

| | |
|---|---|
| Cedar Shake Roof | + 2.50 |
| Clay Tile Roof | + 2.95 |
| Slate Roof | + 4.50 |
| Upgrade Ceilings to Textured Finish | + .48 |
| Air Conditioning, in Heating Ductwork | Base System |
| Heating Systems, Hot Water | + 2.10 |
| Heat Pump | + 2.77 |
| Electric Heat | − 2.60 |
| Not Heated | − 4.40 |

## Additional upgrades or components

| | |
|---|---|
| Kitchen Cabinets & Countertops | Page 93 |
| Bathroom Vanities | 94 |
| Fireplaces & Chimneys | 94 |
| Windows, Skylights & Dormers | 94 |
| Appliances | 95 |
| Breezeways & Porches | 95 |
| Finished Attic | 95 |
| Garages | 96 |
| Site Improvements | 96 |
| Wings & Ells | 74 |

**Important: See the Reference Section for Location Factors (to adjust for your city) and Estimating Forms**

| | | Cost Per Square Foot Of Living Area | | | % of Total |
|---|---|---|---|---|---|
| | | Mat. | Inst. | Total | (roun |
| **1 Site Work** | Site preparation for slab; 4' deep trench excavation for foundation wall. | | .61 | .61 | 0.6% |
| **2 Foundation** | Continuous reinforced concrete footing 8" deep x 18" wide; dampproofed and insulated reinforced concrete foundation wall, 8" thick, 4' deep, 4" concrete slab on 4" crushed stone base and polyethylene vapor barrier, trowel finish. | 3.91 | 4.78 | 8.69 | 9.1% |
| **3 Framing** | Exterior walls - 2" x 6" wood studs, 16" O.C.; 1/2" plywood sheathing; 2" x 8" rafters 16" O.C. with 1/2" plywood sheathing, 8 in 12 pitch; 2" x 10" floor joists 16" O.C. with 5/8" plywood subfloor; 5/8" plywood subfloor on 1" x 3" wood sleepers 16" O.C. | 3.80 | 6.54 | 10.34 | 10.8% |
| **4 Exterior Walls** | Horizontal beveled wood siding; building paper; 6" batt insulation; wood double hung windows; 3 solid core wood exterior doors; storms and screens. | 9.17 | 3.18 | 12.35 | 12.9% |
| **5 Roofing** | 30 year asphalt shingles; #15 felt building paper; aluminum gutters, downspouts and drip edge; copper flashings. | 2.92 | 2.03 | 4.95 | 5.2% |
| **6 Interiors** | Walls and ceilings - 5/8" gypsum wallboard, skim coat plaster, painted with primer and 2 coats; hardwood baseboard and trim, sanded and finished; hardwood floor 70%, ceramic tile with underlayment 20%, vinyl tile with underlayment 10%; wood panel interior doors, primed and painted with 2 coats. | 13.81 | 12.80 | 26.61 | 27.8% |
| **7 Specialties** | Custom grade kitchen cabinets - 20 L.F. wall and base with solid surface counter top and kitchen sink; 4 L.F. bathroom vanity; 75 gallon electric water heater, medicine cabinet. | 4.32 | 1.01 | 5.33 | 5.6% |
| **8 Mechanical** | Gas fired warm air heat/air conditioning; one full bath including: bathtub, corner shower, built in lavatory and water closet; one 1/2 bath including: built in lavatory and water closet. | 5.25 | 2.78 | 8.03 | 8.4% |
| **9 Electrical** | 200 Amp. service; romex wiring; fluorescent and incandescent lighting fixtures, switches, receptacles. | 1.12 | 1.60 | 2.72 | 2.8% |
| **10 Overhead** | Contractor's overhead and profit and design. | 8.85 | 7.07 | 15.92 | 16.7% |
| **Total** | | 53.15 | 42.40 | **95.55** | |

- **A distinct residence from designer's plans**
- **Single family — 1 full bath, 1 half bath, 1 kitchen**
- **No basement**
- **Asphalt shingles on roof**
- **Forced hot air heat/air conditioning**
- **Gypsum wallboard interior finishes**
- **Materials and workmanship are above average**

*Note: The illustration shown may contain some optional components (for example: garages and/or fireplaces) whose costs are shown in the modifications, adjustments, & alternatives below or at the end of the square foot section.*

## Base cost per square foot of living area

| Exterior Wall | Living Area | | | | | | | | | | |
|---|---|---|---|---|---|---|---|---|---|---|---|
| | 1200 | 1400 | 1600 | 1800 | 2000 | 2400 | 2800 | 3200 | 3600 | 4000 | 4400 |
| Wood Siding - Wood Frame | 135.85 | 127.55 | 121.75 | 116.70 | 111.20 | 103.20 | 96.50 | 92.00 | 89.40 | 86.55 | 84.20 |
| Brick Veneer - Wood Frame | 145.80 | 136.90 | 130.60 | 125.10 | 119.25 | 110.45 | 103.10 | 98.15 | 95.30 | 92.15 | 89.55 |
| Stone Veneer - Wood Frame | 151.25 | 141.95 | 135.45 | 129.60 | 123.65 | 114.45 | 106.70 | 101.55 | 98.60 | 95.20 | 92.55 |
| Solid Masonry | 156.35 | 146.70 | 140.00 | 133.90 | 127.70 | 118.10 | 110.05 | 104.70 | 101.65 | 98.05 | 95.30 |
| Finished Basement, Add | 27.05 | 27.25 | 26.50 | 25.75 | 25.35 | 24.25 | 23.40 | 22.85 | 22.45 | 22.00 | 21.75 |
| Unfinished Basement, Add | 11.30 | 10.80 | 10.45 | 10.05 | 9.85 | 9.25 | 8.80 | 8.50 | 8.35 | 8.10 | 7.95 |

## Modifications

*Add to the total cost*

| | |
|---|---|
| Upgrade Kitchen Cabinets | $ + 1108 |
| Solid Surface Countertops (Included) | |
| Full Bath - including plumbing, wall and floor finishes | + 7102 |
| Half Bath - including plumbing, wall and floor finishes | + 4230 |
| Two Car Attached Garage | + 21,916 |
| Two Car Detached Garage | + 25,336 |
| Fireplace & Chimney | + 6502 |

## Adjustments

*For multi family - add to total cost*

| | |
|---|---|
| Additional Kitchen | $ + 14,160 |
| Additional Full Bath & Half Bath | + 11,332 |
| Additional Entry & Exit | + 1640 |
| Separate Heating & Air Conditioning | + 6271 |
| Separate Electric | + 1915 |

*For Townhouse/Rowhouse - Multiply cost per square foot by*

| | |
|---|---|
| Inner Unit | + .87 |
| End Unit | + .93 |

## Alternatives

*Add to or deduct from the cost per square foot of living area*

| | |
|---|---|
| Cedar Shake Roof | + 1.70 |
| Clay Tile Roof | + 2.05 |
| Slate Roof | + 3.10 |
| Upgrade Ceilings to Textured Finish | + .48 |
| Air Conditioning, in Heating Ductwork | Base System |
| Heating Systems, Hot Water | + 2.05 |
| Heat Pump | + 3.08 |
| Electric Heat | – 2.60 |
| Not Heated | – 4.16 |

## Additional upgrades or components

| | |
|---|---|
| Kitchen Cabinets & Countertops | Page 93 |
| Bathroom Vanities | 94 |
| Fireplaces & Chimneys | 94 |
| Windows, Skylights & Dormers | 94 |
| Appliances | 95 |
| Breezeways & Porches | 95 |
| Finished Attic | 95 |
| Garages | 96 |
| Site Improvements | 96 |
| Wings & Ells | 74 |

**Living Area - 2800 S.F.**
**Perimeter - 156 L.F.**

| | | Cost Per Square Foot Of Living Area | | | % of Total |
|---|---|---|---|---|---|
| | | Mat. | Inst. | Total | (roun |
| **1 Site Work** | Site preparation for slab; 4' deep trench excavation for foundation wall. | | .61 | .61 | 0.6% |
| **2 Foundation** | Continuous reinforced concrete footing 8" deep x 18" wide; dampproofed and insulated reinforced concrete foundation wall, 8" thick, 4' deep, 4" concrete slab on 4" crushed stone base and polyethylene vapor barrier, trowel finish. | 3.31 | 4.09 | 7.40 | 7.7% |
| **3 Framing** | Exterior walls - 2" x 6" wood studs, 16" O.C.; 1/2" plywood sheathing; 2" x 8" rafters 16" O.C. with 1/2" plywood sheathing, 6 in 12 pitch; 2" x 8" ceiling joists 16" O.C.; 2" x 10" floor joists 16" O.C. with 5/8" plywood subfloor; 5/8" plywood subfloor on 1" x 3" wood sleepers 16" O.C. | 4.17 | 6.74 | 10.91 | 11.3% |
| **4 Exterior Walls** | Horizontal beveled wood siding; building paper; 6" batt insulation; wood double hung windows; 3 solid core wood exterior doors; storms and screens. | 10.46 | 3.64 | 14.10 | 14.6% |
| **5 Roofing** | 30 year asphalt shingles; #15 felt building paper; aluminum gutters, downspouts and drip edge; copper flashings. | 2.33 | 1.63 | 3.96 | 4.1% |
| **6 Interiors** | Walls and ceilings - 5/8" gypsum wallboard, skim coat plaster, painted with primer and 2 coats; hardwood baseboard and trim, sanded and finished; hardwood floor 70%, ceramic tile with underlayment 20%, vinyl tile with underlayment 10%; wood panel interior doors, primed and painted with 2 coats. | 14.06 | 13.10 | 27.16 | 28.1% |
| **7 Specialties** | Custom grade kitchen cabinets - 20 L.F. wall and base with solid surface counter top and kitchen sink; 4 L.F. bathroom vanity; 75 gallon electric water heater, medicine cabinet. | 4.32 | 1.01 | 5.33 | 5.5% |
| **8 Mechanical** | Gas fired warm air heat/air conditioning; one full bath including: bathtub, corner shower; built in lavatory and water closet; one 1/2 bath including: built in lavatory and water closet. | 5.39 | 2.82 | 8.21 | 8.5% |
| **9 Electrical** | 200 Amp. service; romex wiring; fluorescent and incandescent lighting fixtures, switches, receptacles. | 1.12 | 1.60 | 2.72 | 2.8% |
| **10 Overhead** | Contractor's overhead and profit and design. | 9.04 | 7.06 | 16.10 | 16.7% |
| **Total** | | 54.20 | 42.30 | **96.50** | |

- **A distinct residence from designer's plans**
- **Single family — 1 full bath, 1 half bath, 1 kitchen**
- **No basement**
- **Asphalt shingles on roof**
- **Forced hot air heat/air conditioning**
- **Gypsum wallboard interior finishes**
- **Materials and workmanship are above average**

*Note: The illustration shown may contain some optional components (for example: garages and/or fireplaces) whose costs are shown in the modifications, adjustments, & alternatives below or at the end of the square foot section.*

## Base cost per square foot of living area

| Exterior Wall | Living Area | | | | | | | | | | |
|---|---|---|---|---|---|---|---|---|---|---|---|
| | 1500 | 1800 | 2100 | 2400 | 2800 | 3200 | 3600 | 4000 | 4500 | 5000 | 5500 |
| Wood Siding - Wood Frame | 133.30 | 119.90 | 112.00 | 107.30 | 101.15 | 95.30 | 92.05 | 87.00 | 84.30 | 81.90 | 79.45 |
| Brick Veneer - Wood Frame | 143.65 | 129.40 | 120.50 | 115.35 | 108.85 | 102.30 | 98.65 | 93.10 | 90.10 | 87.45 | 84.70 |
| Stone Veneer - Wood Frame | 149.30 | 134.65 | 125.20 | 119.80 | 113.15 | 106.15 | 102.30 | 96.45 | 93.30 | 90.50 | 87.60 |
| Solid Masonry | 154.55 | 139.50 | 129.55 | 123.90 | 117.05 | 109.70 | 105.65 | 99.65 | 96.30 | 93.30 | 90.25 |
| Finished Basement, Add | 21.50 | 21.50 | 20.35 | 19.80 | 19.35 | 18.65 | 18.20 | 17.70 | 17.30 | 17.05 | 16.80 |
| Unfinished Basement, Add | 9.10 | 8.60 | 8.00 | 7.75 | 7.50 | 7.15 | 6.90 | 6.65 | 6.45 | 6.35 | 6.15 |

## Modifications

*Add to the total cost*

| | |
|---|---|
| Upgrade Kitchen Cabinets | $ + 1108 |
| Solid Surface Countertops (Included) | |
| Full Bath - including plumbing, wall and floor finishes | + 7102 |
| Half Bath - including plumbing, wall and floor finishes | + 4230 |
| Two Car Attached Garage | + 21,916 |
| Two Car Detached Garage | + 25,336 |
| Fireplace & Chimney | + 7342 |

## Adjustments

*For multi family - add to total cost*

| | |
|---|---|
| Additional Kitchen | $ + 14,160 |
| Additional Full Bath & Half Bath | + 11,332 |
| Additional Entry & Exit | + 1640 |
| Separate Heating & Air Conditioning | + 6271 |
| Separate Electric | + 1915 |

*For Townhouse/Rowhouse - Multiply cost per square foot by*

| | |
|---|---|
| Inner Unit | + .87 |
| End Unit | + .94 |

## Alternatives

*Add to or deduct from the cost per square foot of living area*

| | |
|---|---|
| Cedar Shake Roof | + 1.50 |
| Clay Tile Roof | + 1.80 |
| Slate Roof | + 2.70 |
| Upgrade Ceilings to Textured Finish | + .48 |
| Air Conditioning, in Heating Ductwork | Base System |
| Heating Systems, Hot Water | + 1.85 |
| Heat Pump | + 3.19 |
| Electric Heat | – 4.56 |
| Not Heated | – 4.16 |

## Additional upgrades or components

| | |
|---|---|
| Kitchen Cabinets & Countertops | Page 93 |
| Bathroom Vanities | 94 |
| Fireplaces & Chimneys | 94 |
| Windows, Skylights & Dormers | 94 |
| Appliances | 95 |
| Breezeways & Porches | 95 |
| Finished Attic | 95 |
| Garages | 96 |
| Site Improvements | 96 |
| Wings & Ells | 74 |

# Custom 2-1/2 Story

**Living Area - 3200 S.F.**
**Perimeter - 150 L.F.**

| | | Cost Per Square Foot Of Living Area | | | % of Total |
|---|---|---|---|---|---|
| | | Mat. | Inst. | Total | (roun |
| **1 Site Work** | Site preparation for slab; 4' deep trench excavation for foundation wall. | | .53 | .53 | 0.6% |
| **2 Foundation** | Continuous reinforced concrete footing 8" deep x 18" wide; dampproofed and insulated reinforced concrete foundation wall, 8" thick, 4' deep, 4" concrete slab on 4" crushed stone base and polyethylene vapor barrier, trowel finish. | 2.72 | 3.41 | 6.13 | 6.4% |
| **3 Framing** | Exterior walls - 2" x 6" wood studs, 16" O.C.; 1/2" plywood sheathing; 2" x 8" rafters 16" O.C. with 1/2" plywood sheathing, 6 in 12 pitch; 2" x 8" ceiling joists 16" O.C.; 2" x 10" floor joists 16" O.C. with 5/8" plywood subfloor; 5/8" plywood subfloor on 1" x 3" wood sleepers 16" O.C. | 4.52 | 7.03 | 11.55 | 12.1% |
| **4 Exterior Walls** | Horizontal beveled wood siding; building paper; 6" batt insulation; wood double hung windows; 3 solid core wood exterior doors; storms and screens. | 10.81 | 3.78 | 14.59 | 15.3% |
| **5 Roofing** | 30 year asphalt shingles; #15 felt building paper; aluminum gutters, downspouts and drip edge; copper flashings. | 1.79 | 1.25 | 3.04 | 3.2% |
| **6 Interiors** | Walls and ceilings - 5/8" gypsum wallboard, skim coat plaster, painted with primer and 2 coats; hardwood baseboard and trim, sanded and finished; hardwood floor 70%, ceramic tile with underlayment 20%, vinyl tile with underlayment 10%; wood panel interior doors, primed and painted with 2 coats. | 14.82 | 13.88 | 28.70 | 30.1% |
| **7 Specialties** | Custom grade kitchen cabinets - 20 L.F. wall and base with solid surface counter top and kitchen sink; 4 L.F. bathroom vanity; 75 gallon electric water heater, medicine cabinet. | 3.79 | .88 | 4.67 | 4.9% |
| **8 Mechanical** | Gas fired warm air heat/air conditioning; one full bath including: bathtub, corner shower; built in lavatory and water closet; one 1/2 bath including: built in lavatory and water closet. | 4.89 | 2.70 | 7.59 | 8.0% |
| **9 Electrical** | 200 Amp. service; romex wiring; fluorescent and incandescent lighting fixtures, switches, receptacles. | 1.09 | 1.54 | 2.63 | 2.8% |
| **10 Overhead** | Contractor's overhead and profit and design. | 8.87 | 7.00 | 15.87 | 16.7% |
| **Total** | | 53.30 | 42.00 | **95.30** | |

- A distinct residence from designer's plans
- Single family — 1 full bath, 1 half bath, 1 kitchen
- No basement
- Asphalt shingles on roof
- Forced hot air heat/air conditioning
- Gypsum wallboard interior finishes
- Materials and workmanship are above average

*Note: The illustration shown may contain some optional components (for example: garages and/or fireplaces) whose costs are shown in the modifications, adjustments, & alternatives below or at the end of the square foot section.*

## Base cost per square foot of living area

| Exterior Wall | Living Area | | | | | | | | | | |
|---|---|---|---|---|---|---|---|---|---|---|---|
| | 1500 | 1800 | 2100 | 2500 | 3000 | 3500 | 4000 | 4500 | 5000 | 5500 | 6000 |
| Wood Siding - Wood Frame | 132.75 | 119.45 | 112.95 | 107.60 | 99.40 | 95.25 | 90.20 | 84.90 | 83.00 | 80.95 | 78.80 |
| Brick Veneer - Wood Frame | 143.45 | 129.40 | 122.25 | 116.45 | 107.45 | 102.85 | 97.15 | 91.30 | 89.15 | 86.85 | 84.40 |
| Stone Veneer - Wood Frame | 149.35 | 134.85 | 127.35 | 121.30 | 111.90 | 107.00 | 100.95 | 94.80 | 92.60 | 90.15 | 87.45 |
| Solid Masonry | 154.80 | 139.90 | 132.05 | 125.85 | 115.95 | 110.90 | 104.45 | 98.05 | 95.75 | 93.20 | 90.30 |
| Finished Basement, Add | 18.85 | 18.85 | 18.10 | 17.60 | 16.85 | 16.40 | 15.80 | 15.30 | 15.15 | 14.90 | 14.65 |
| Unfinished Basement, Add | 7.95 | 7.50 | 7.20 | 6.90 | 6.50 | 6.30 | 6.00 | 5.75 | 5.65 | 5.55 | 5.35 |

## Modifications

*Add to the total cost*

| | |
|---|---|
| Upgrade Kitchen Cabinets | $ + 1108 |
| Solid Surface Countertops (Included) | |
| Full Bath - including plumbing, wall and floor finishes | + 7102 |
| Half Bath - including plumbing, wall and floor finishes | + 4230 |
| Two Car Attached Garage | + 21,916 |
| Two Car Detached Garage | + 25,336 |
| Fireplace & Chimney | + 7342 |

## Adjustments

*For multi family - add to total cost*

| | |
|---|---|
| Additional Kitchen | $ + 14,160 |
| Additional Full Bath & Half Bath | + 11,332 |
| Additional Entry & Exit | + 1640 |
| Separate Heating & Air Conditioning | + 6271 |
| Separate Electric | + 1915 |

*For Townhouse/Rowhouse - Multiply cost per square foot by*

| | |
|---|---|
| Inner Unit | + .85 |
| End Unit | + .93 |

## Alternatives

*Add to or deduct from the cost per square foot of living area*

| | |
|---|---|
| Cedar Shake Roof | + 1.15 |
| Clay Tile Roof | + 1.35 |
| Slate Roof | + 2.05 |
| Upgrade Ceilings to Textured Finish | + .48 |
| Air Conditioning, in Heating Ductwork | Base System |
| Heating Systems, Hot Water | + 1.85 |
| Heat Pump | + 3.19 |
| Electric Heat | – 4.56 |
| Not Heated | – 4.03 |

## Additional upgrades or components

| | |
|---|---|
| Kitchen Cabinets & Countertops | Page 93 |
| Bathroom Vanities | 94 |
| Fireplaces & Chimneys | 94 |
| Windows, Skylights & Dormers | 94 |
| Appliances | 95 |
| Breezeways & Porches | 95 |
| Finished Attic | 95 |
| Garages | 96 |
| Site Improvements | 96 |
| Wings & Ells | 74 |

# Custom 3 Story

**Living Area - 3000 S.F.**
**Perimeter - 135 L.F.**

| | | Cost Per Square Foot Of Living Area | | | % of Total |
|---|---|---|---|---|---|
| | | Mat. | Inst. | Total | (roun |
| **1 Site Work** | Site preparation for slab; 4' deep trench excavation for foundation wall. | | .56 | .56 | 0.6% |
| **2 Foundation** | Continuous reinforced concrete footing 8" deep x 18" wide; dampproofed and insulated reinforced concrete foundation wall, 8" thick, 4' deep, 4" concrete slab on 4" crushed stone base and polyethylene vapor barrier, trowel finish. | 2.55 | 3.22 | 5.77 | 5.8% |
| **3 Framing** | Exterior walls - 2" x 6" wood studs, 16" O.C.; 1/2" plywood sheathing; 2" x 8" rafters 16" O.C. with 1/2" plywood sheathing, 6 in 12 pitch; 2" x 8" ceiling joists 16" O.C.; 2" x 10" floor joists 16" O.C. with 5/8" plywood subfloor; 5/8" plywood subfloor on 1" x 3" wood sleepers 16" O.C. | 4.74 | 7.25 | 11.99 | 12.1% |
| **4 Exterior Walls** | Horizontal beveled wood siding; building paper; 6" batt insulation; wood double hung windows; 3 solid core wood exterior doors; storms and screens. | 12.34 | 4.33 | 16.67 | 16.8% |
| **5 Roofing** | 30 year asphalt shingles; #15 felt building paper; aluminum gutters, downspouts and drip edge; copper flashings. | 1.56 | 1.09 | 2.65 | 2.7% |
| **6 Interiors** | Walls and ceilings - 5/8" gypsum wallboard, skim coat plaster, painted with primer and 2 coats; hardwood baseboard and trim, sanded and finished; hardwood floor 70%, ceramic tile with underlayment 20%, vinyl tile with underlayment 10%; wood panel interior doors, primed and painted with 2 coats. | 15.31 | 14.37 | 29.68 | 29.9% |
| **7 Specialties** | Custom grade kitchen cabinets - 20 L.F. wall and base with solid surface counter top and kitchen sink; 4 L.F. bathroom vanity; 75 gallon electric water heater, medicine cabinet. | 4.03 | .94 | 4.97 | 5.0% |
| **8 Mechanical** | Gas fired warm air heat/air conditioning; one full bath including: bathtub, corner shower; built in lavatory and water closet; one 1/2 bath including: built in lavatory and water closet. | 5.12 | 2.76 | 7.88 | 7.9% |
| **9 Electrical** | 200 Amp. service; romex wiring; fluorescent and incandescent lighting fixtures, switches, receptacles. | 1.10 | 1.57 | 2.67 | 2.7% |
| **10 Overhead** | Contractor's overhead and profit and design. | 9.35 | 7.21 | 16.56 | 16.7% |
| **Total** | | 56.10 | 43.30 | **99.40** | |

- A distinct residence from designer's plans
- Single family — 1 full bath, 1 half bath, 1 kitchen
- No basement
- Asphalt shingles on roof
- Forced hot air heat/air conditioning
- Gypsum wallboard interior finishes
- Materials and workmanship are above average

*Note: The illustration shown may contain some optional components (for example: garages and/or fireplaces) whose costs are shown in the modifications, adjustments, & alternatives below or at the end of the square foot section.*

## Base cost per square foot of living area

| Exterior Wall | Living Area | | | | | | | | | | |
|---|---|---|---|---|---|---|---|---|---|---|---|
| | 1200 | 1400 | 1600 | 1800 | 2000 | 2400 | 2800 | 3200 | 3600 | 4000 | 4400 |
| Wood Siding - Wood Frame | 128.45 | 120.70 | 115.20 | 110.45 | 105.15 | 97.80 | 91.50 | 87.30 | 84.95 | 82.35 | 80.05 |
| Brick Veneer - Wood Frame | 135.85 | 127.65 | 121.80 | 116.75 | 111.25 | 103.20 | 96.40 | 91.95 | 89.40 | 86.55 | 84.15 |
| Stone Veneer - Wood Frame | 139.95 | 131.45 | 125.45 | 120.15 | 114.50 | 106.20 | 99.15 | 94.50 | 91.85 | 88.85 | 86.35 |
| Solid Masonry | 143.80 | 135.00 | 128.85 | 123.35 | 117.55 | 108.95 | 101.65 | 96.80 | 94.10 | 91.05 | 88.45 |
| Finished Basement, Add | 27.05 | 27.25 | 26.50 | 25.75 | 25.35 | 24.25 | 23.40 | 22.85 | 22.45 | 22.00 | 21.75 |
| Unfinished Basement, Add | 11.30 | 10.80 | 10.45 | 10.05 | 9.85 | 9.25 | 8.80 | 8.50 | 8.35 | 8.10 | 7.95 |

## Modifications

*Add to the total cost*

| | |
|---|---|
| Upgrade Kitchen Cabinets | $ + 1108 |
| Solid Surface Countertops (Included) | |
| Full Bath - including plumbing, wall and floor finishes | + 7102 |
| Half Bath - including plumbing, wall and floor finishes | + 4230 |
| Two Car Attached Garage | + 21,916 |
| Two Car Detached Garage | + 25,336 |
| Fireplace & Chimney | + 5760 |

## Adjustments

*For multi family - add to total cost*

| | |
|---|---|
| Additional Kitchen | $ + 14,160 |
| Additional Full Bath & Half Bath | + 11,332 |
| Additional Entry & Exit | + 1640 |
| Separate Heating & Air Conditioning | + 6271 |
| Separate Electric | + 1915 |

*For Townhouse/Rowhouse - Multiply cost per square foot by*

| | |
|---|---|
| Inner Unit | + .89 |
| End Unit | + .95 |

## Alternatives

*Add to or deduct from the cost per square foot of living area*

| | |
|---|---|
| Cedar Shake Roof | + 1.70 |
| Clay Tile Roof | + 2.05 |
| Slate Roof | + 3.10 |
| Upgrade Ceilings to Textured Finish | + .48 |
| Air Conditioning, in Heating Ductwork | Base System |
| Heating Systems, Hot Water | + 2.05 |
| Heat Pump | + 3.08 |
| Electric Heat | – 2.60 |
| Not Heated | – 4.03 |

## Additional upgrades or components

| | |
|---|---|
| Kitchen Cabinets & Countertops | Page 93 |
| Bathroom Vanities | 94 |
| Fireplaces & Chimneys | 94 |
| Windows, Skylights & Dormers | 94 |
| Appliances | 95 |
| Breezeways & Porches | 95 |
| Finished Attic | 95 |
| Garages | 96 |
| Site Improvements | 96 |
| Wings & Ells | 74 |

| | | Cost Per Square Foot Of Living Area | | | % of Total |
| --- | --- | --- | --- | --- | --- |
| | | Mat. | Inst. | Total | (roun |
| **1 Site Work** | Excavation for lower level, 4' deep. Site preparation for slab. | | .61 | .61 | 0.7% |
| **2 Foundation** | Continuous reinforced concrete footing 8" deep x 18" wide; dampproofed and insulated reinforced concrete foundation wall, 8" thick, 4' deep, 4" concrete slab on 4" crushed stone base and polyethylene vapor barrier, trowel finish. | 3.31 | 4.09 | 7.40 | 8.1% |
| **3 Framing** | Exterior walls - 2" x 6" wood studs, 16" O.C.; 1/2" plywood sheathing; 2" x 8" rafters 16" O.C. with 1/2" plywood sheathing, 6 in 12 pitch; 2" x 8" ceiling joists 16" O.C.; 2" x 10" floor joists 16" O.C. with 5/8" plywood subfloor; 5/8" plywood subfloor on 1" x 3" wood sleepers 16" O.C. | 3.98 | 6.43 | 10.41 | 11.4% |
| **4 Exterior Walls** | Horizontal beveled wood siding; building paper; 6" batt insulation; wood double hung windows; 3 solid core wood exterior doors; storms and screens. | 8.17 | 2.82 | 10.99 | 12.0% |
| **5 Roofing** | 30 year asphalt shingles; #15 felt building paper; aluminum gutters, downspouts and drip edge; copper flashings. | 2.33 | 1.63 | 3.96 | 4.3% |
| **6 Interiors** | Walls and ceilings - 5/8" gypsum wallboard, skim coat plaster, painted with primer and 2 coats; hardwood baseboard and trim, sanded and finished; hardwood floor 70%, ceramic tile with underlayment 20%, vinyl tile with underlayment 10%; wood panel interior doors, primed and painted with 2 coats. | 13.87 | 12.74 | 26.61 | 29.1% |
| **7 Specialties** | Custom grade kitchen cabinets - 20 L.F. wall and base with solid surface counter top and kitchen sink; 4 L.F. bathroom vanity; 75 gallon electric water heater, medicine cabinet. | 4.32 | 1.01 | 5.33 | 5.8% |
| **8 Mechanical** | Gas fired warm air heat/air conditioning; one full bath including: bathtub, corner shower, built in lavatory and water closet; one 1/2 bath including: built in lavatory and water closet. | 5.39 | 2.82 | 8.21 | 9.0% |
| **9 Electrical** | 200 Amp. service; romex wiring; fluorescent and incandescent lighting fixtures, switches, receptacles. | 1.12 | 1.60 | 2.72 | 3.0% |
| **10 Overhead** | Contractor's overhead and profit and design. | 8.51 | 6.75 | 15.26 | 16.7% |
| **Total** | | 51.00 | 40.50 | **91.50** | |

- **A distinct residence from designer's plans**
- **Single family — 1 full bath, 1 half bath, 1 kitchen**
- **No basement**
- **Asphalt shingles on roof**
- **Forced hot air heat/air conditioning**
- **Gypsum wallboard interior finishes**
- **Materials and workmanship are above average**

*Note: The illustration shown may contain some optional components (for example: garages and/or fireplaces) whose costs are shown in the modifications, adjustments, & alternatives below or at the end of the square foot section.*

eDesign Basics, Inc.

## Base cost per square foot of living area

| Exterior Wall | Living Area | | | | | | | | | | |
|---|---|---|---|---|---|---|---|---|---|---|---|
| | 1200 | 1500 | 1800 | 2100 | 2400 | 2800 | 3200 | 3600 | 4000 | 4500 | 5000 |
| Wood Siding - Wood Frame | 132.40 | 120.30 | 111.05 | 103.45 | 98.30 | 94.60 | 90.20 | 85.55 | 83.60 | 79.25 | 76.85 |
| Brick Veneer - Wood Frame | 139.80 | 127.00 | 117.10 | 108.90 | 103.45 | 99.55 | 94.80 | 89.80 | 87.75 | 83.10 | 80.45 |
| Stone Veneer - Wood Frame | 143.85 | 130.70 | 120.40 | 111.95 | 106.30 | 102.30 | 97.35 | 92.15 | 90.05 | 85.15 | 82.40 |
| Solid Masonry | 147.60 | 134.05 | 123.45 | 114.70 | 108.90 | 104.80 | 99.65 | 94.30 | 92.15 | 87.10 | 84.20 |
| Finished Basement, Add* | 33.80 | 33.65 | 32.25 | 31.05 | 30.30 | 29.80 | 29.10 | 28.40 | 28.15 | 27.50 | 27.05 |
| Unfinished Basement, Add* | 13.95 | 13.10 | 12.35 | 11.75 | 11.30 | 11.10 | 10.70 | 10.35 | 10.20 | 9.85 | 9.60 |

*Basement under middle level only.

## Modifications

*Add to the total cost*

| | |
|---|---|
| Upgrade Kitchen Cabinets | $ + 1108 |
| Solid Surface Countertops (Included) | |
| Full Bath - including plumbing, wall and floor finishes | + 7102 |
| Half Bath - including plumbing, wall and floor finishes | + 4230 |
| Two Car Attached Garage | + 21,916 |
| Two Car Detached Garage | + 25,336 |
| Fireplace & Chimney | + 5760 |

## Adjustments

*For multi family - add to total cost*

| | |
|---|---|
| Additional Kitchen | $ + 14,160 |
| Additional Full Bath & Half Bath | + 11,332 |
| Additional Entry & Exit | + 1640 |
| Separate Heating & Air Conditioning | + 6271 |
| Separate Electric | + 1915 |

*For Townhouse/Rowhouse - Multiply cost per square foot by*

| | |
|---|---|
| Inner Unit | + .87 |
| End Unit | + .94 |

## Alternatives

*Add to or deduct from the cost per square foot of living area*

| | |
|---|---|
| Cedar Shake Roof | + 2.50 |
| Clay Tile Roof | + 2.95 |
| Slate Roof | + 4.50 |
| Upgrade Ceilings to Textured Finish | + .48 |
| Air Conditioning, in Heating Ductwork | Base System |
| Heating Systems, Hot Water | + 1.99 |
| Heat Pump | + 3.22 |
| Electric Heat | − 2.31 |
| Not Heated | − 4.03 |

## Additional upgrades or components

| | |
|---|---|
| Kitchen Cabinets & Countertops | Page 93 |
| Bathroom Vanities | 94 |
| Fireplaces & Chimneys | 94 |
| Windows, Skylights & Dormers | 94 |
| Appliances | 95 |
| Breezeways & Porches | 95 |
| Finished Attic | 95 |
| Garages | 96 |
| Site Improvements | 96 |
| Wings & Ells | 74 |

| | | Cost Per Square Foot Of Living Area | | | % of Total |
|---|---|---|---|---|---|
| | | Mat. | Inst. | Total | (roun |
| **1 Site Work** | Site preparation for slab; 4' deep trench excavation for foundation wall, excavation for lower level, 4' deep. | | .53 | .53 | 0.6% |
| **2 Foundation** | Continuous reinforced concrete footing 8" deep x 18" wide; dampproofed and insulated reinforced concrete foundation wall, 8" thick, 4' deep, 4" concrete slab on 4" crushed stone base and polyethylene vapor barrier, trowel finish. | 3.91 | 4.72 | 8.63 | 9.6% |
| **3 Framing** | Exterior walls - 2" x 6" wood studs, 16" O.C.; 1/2" plywood sheathing; 2" x 8" rafters 16" O.C. with 1/2" plywood sheathing, 6 in 12 pitch; 2" x 8" ceiling joists 16" O.C.; 2" x 10" floor joists 16" O.C. with 5/8" plywood subfloor; 5/8" plywood subfloor on 1" x 3" wood sleepers 16" O.C. | 3.58 | 6.31 | 9.89 | 11.0% |
| **4 Exterior Walls** | Horizontal beveled wood siding; building paper; 6" batt insulation; wood double hung windows; 3 solid core wood exterior doors; storms and screens. | 7.88 | 2.73 | 10.61 | 11.8% |
| **5 Roofing** | 30 year asphalt shingles; #15 felt building paper; aluminum gutters, downspouts and drip edge; copper flashings. | 3.10 | 2.16 | 5.26 | 5.8% |
| **6 Interiors** | Walls and ceilings - 5/8" gypsum wallboard, skim coat plaster, painted with primer and 2 coats; hardwood baseboard and trim, sanded and finished; hardwood floor 70%, ceramic tile with underlayment 20%, vinyl tile with underlayment 10%; wood panel interior doors, primed and painted with 2 coats. | 13.18 | 12.20 | 25.38 | 28.1% |
| **7 Specialties** | Custom grade kitchen cabinets - 20 L.F. wall and base with solid surface counter top and kitchen sink; 4 L.F. bathroom vanity; 75 gallon electric water heater, medicine cabinet. | 3.79 | .88 | 4.67 | 5.2% |
| **8 Mechanical** | Gas fired warm air heat/air conditioning; one full bath including: bathtub, corner shower, built in lavatory and water closet; one 1/2 bath including: built in lavatory and water closet. | 4.89 | 2.70 | 7.59 | 8.4% |
| **9 Electrical** | 200 Amp. service; romex wiring; fluorescent and incandescent lighting fixtures, switches, receptacles. | 1.09 | 1.54 | 2.63 | 2.9% |
| **10 Overhead** | Contractor's overhead and profit and design. | 8.28 | 6.73 | 15.01 | 16.6% |
| **Total** | | 49.70 | 40.50 | **90.20** | |

## 1 Story  Base cost per square foot of living area

| Exterior Wall | Living Area | | | | | | | |
|---|---|---|---|---|---|---|---|---|
| | 50 | 100 | 200 | 300 | 400 | 500 | 600 | 700 |
| Wood Siding - Wood Frame | 210.95 | 164.35 | 144.15 | 122.55 | 115.95 | 111.95 | 109.35 | 110.25 |
| Brick Veneer - Wood Frame | 235.90 | 182.20 | 159.05 | 132.55 | 124.95 | 120.35 | 117.35 | 117.90 |
| Stone Veneer - Wood Frame | 249.65 | 192.00 | 167.20 | 137.95 | 129.80 | 124.90 | 121.65 | 122.05 |
| Solid Masonry | 262.40 | 201.15 | 174.80 | 143.05 | 134.35 | 129.20 | 125.75 | 126.00 |
| Finished Basement, Add | 80.90 | 69.05 | 62.60 | 51.90 | 49.75 | 48.50 | 47.60 | 47.00 |
| Unfinished Basement, Add | 59.60 | 40.75 | 32.00 | 24.30 | 22.25 | 21.00 | 20.20 | 19.60 |

## 1-1/2 Story  Base cost per square foot of living area

| Exterior Wall | Living Area | | | | | | | |
|---|---|---|---|---|---|---|---|---|
| | 100 | 200 | 300 | 400 | 500 | 600 | 700 | 800 |
| Wood Siding - Wood Frame | 169.35 | 139.35 | 121.15 | 110.40 | 104.85 | 102.25 | 98.90 | 97.85 |
| Brick Veneer - Wood Frame | 191.65 | 157.25 | 136.05 | 122.05 | 115.60 | 112.45 | 108.45 | 107.35 |
| Stone Veneer - Wood Frame | 203.95 | 167.05 | 144.25 | 128.40 | 121.50 | 118.00 | 113.65 | 112.55 |
| Solid Masonry | 215.30 | 176.15 | 151.85 | 134.30 | 126.95 | 123.10 | 118.60 | 117.35 |
| Finished Basement, Add | 54.05 | 50.10 | 45.80 | 41.05 | 39.80 | 38.95 | 38.10 | 38.00 |
| Unfinished Basement, Add | 35.35 | 26.65 | 22.50 | 19.05 | 17.80 | 17.00 | 16.30 | 16.05 |

## 2 Story  Base cost per square foot of living area

| Exterior Wall | Living Area | | | | | | | |
|---|---|---|---|---|---|---|---|---|
| | 100 | 200 | 400 | 600 | 800 | 1000 | 1200 | 1400 |
| Wood Siding - Wood Frame | 168.45 | 129.20 | 112.00 | 95.55 | 89.95 | 86.60 | 84.40 | 85.55 |
| Brick Veneer - Wood Frame | 193.45 | 147.10 | 126.90 | 105.50 | 98.90 | 95.00 | 92.35 | 93.25 |
| Stone Veneer - Wood Frame | 207.20 | 156.85 | 135.10 | 110.95 | 103.80 | 99.50 | 96.70 | 97.45 |
| Solid Masonry | 219.95 | 166.00 | 142.65 | 116.10 | 108.40 | 103.80 | 100.75 | 101.35 |
| Finished Basement, Add | 40.45 | 34.55 | 31.35 | 26.00 | 24.95 | 24.25 | 23.90 | 23.55 |
| Unfinished Basement, Add | 29.85 | 20.35 | 16.00 | 12.15 | 11.10 | 10.55 | 10.10 | 9.85 |

Base costs do not include bathroom or kitchen facilities. Use Modifications/Adjustments/Alternatives on pages 93–96 where appropriate.

## 1 Story

## 1 - 1/2 Story

## 2 Story

## 2 - 1/2 Story

## Bi-Level

## Tri-Level

- **Unique residence built from an architect's plan**
- **Single family — 1 full bath, 1 half bath, 1 kitchen**
- **No basement**
- **Cedar shakes on roof**
- **Forced hot air heat/air conditioning**
- **Gypsum wallboard interior finishes**
- **Many special features**
- **Extraordinary materials and workmanship**

Note: The illustration shown may contain some optional components (for example: garages and/or fireplaces) whose costs are shown in the modifications, adjustments, & alternatives below or at the end of the square foot section.

©Home Planners, Inc.

## Base cost per square foot of living area

| Exterior Wall | Living Area | | | | | | | | | | |
|---|---|---|---|---|---|---|---|---|---|---|---|
| | 1000 | 1200 | 1400 | 1600 | 1800 | 2000 | 2400 | 2800 | 3200 | 3600 | 4000 |
| Wood Siding - Wood Frame | 185.40 | 170.80 | 159.15 | 151.00 | 146.60 | 141.40 | 131.70 | 124.80 | 119.85 | 114.85 | 110.75 |
| Brick Veneer - Wood Frame | 194.65 | 179.10 | 166.70 | 158.10 | 153.45 | 147.80 | 137.55 | 130.25 | 124.85 | 119.50 | 115.15 |
| Solid Brick | 210.80 | 193.70 | 179.90 | 170.60 | 165.45 | 159.10 | 147.90 | 139.70 | 133.65 | 127.75 | 122.80 |
| Solid Stone | 208.45 | 191.55 | 178.05 | 168.75 | 163.70 | 157.40 | 146.35 | 138.35 | 132.35 | 126.50 | 121.70 |
| Finished Basement, Add | 48.80 | 52.45 | 50.30 | 48.85 | 48.00 | 46.90 | 45.30 | 44.05 | 42.95 | 42.00 | 41.25 |
| Unfinished Basement, Add | 21.40 | 20.05 | 18.90 | 18.25 | 17.80 | 17.20 | 16.40 | 15.80 | 15.20 | 14.70 | 14.30 |

## Modifications

*Add to the total cost*

| | |
|---|---|
| Upgrade Kitchen Cabinets | $ + 1462 |
| Solid Surface Countertops (Included) | |
| Full Bath - including plumbing, wall and floor finishes | + 8238 |
| Half Bath - including plumbing, wall and floor finishes | + 4907 |
| Two Car Attached Garage | + 26,381 |
| Two Car Detached Garage | + 30,256 |
| Fireplace & Chimney | + 8141 |

## Adjustments

*For multi family - add to total cost*

| | |
|---|---|
| Additional Kitchen | $ + 18,138 |
| Additional Full Bath & Half Bath | + 13,145 |
| Additional Entry & Exit | + 2342 |
| Separate Heating & Air Conditioning | + 6271 |
| Separate Electric | + 1915 |

*For Townhouse/Rowhouse - Multiply cost per square foot by*

| | |
|---|---|
| Inner Unit | + .90 |
| End Unit | + .95 |

## Alternatives

*Add to or deduct from the cost per square foot of living area*

| | |
|---|---|
| Heavyweight Asphalt Shingles | – 3.45 |
| Clay Tile Roof | + .65 |
| Slate Roof | + 2.75 |
| Upgrade Ceilings to Textured Finish | + .48 |
| Air Conditioning, in Heating Ductwork | Base System |
| Heating Systems, Hot Water | + 2.39 |
| Heat Pump | + 2.86 |
| Electric Heat | – 2.60 |
| Not Heated | – 5.21 |

## Additional upgrades or components

| | |
|---|---|
| Kitchen Cabinets & Countertops | Page 93 |
| Bathroom Vanities | 94 |
| Fireplaces & Chimneys | 94 |
| Windows, Skylights & Dormers | 94 |
| Appliances | 95 |
| Breezeways & Porches | 95 |
| Finished Attic | 95 |
| Garages | 96 |
| Site Improvements | 96 |
| Wings & Ells | 92 |

| | | | Cost Per Square Foot Of Living Area | | | % of Total |
|---|---|---|---|---|---|---|
| | | | Mat. | Inst. | Total | (roun |
| **1** | **Site Work** | Site preparation for slab; 4' deep trench excavation for foundation wall. | | .66 | .66 | 0.5% |
| **2** | **Foundation** | Continuous reinforced concrete footing 8" deep x 18" wide; dampproofed and insulated reinforced concrete foundation wall, 12" thick, 4' deep, 4" concrete slab on 4" crushed stone base and polyethylene vapor barrier, trowel finish. | 6.60 | 6.97 | 13.57 | 10.9% |
| **3** | **Framing** | Exterior walls - 2" x 6" wood studs, 16" O.C.; 5/8" plywood sheathing; 2" x 10" rafters 16" O.C. with 5/8" plywood sheathing, 6 in 12 pitch; 2" x 8" ceiling joists 16" O.C.; 5/8" plywood subfloor on 1" x 3" wood sleepers 16" O.C. | 7.94 | 12.74 | 20.68 | 16.6% |
| **4** | **Exterior Walls** | Horizontal beveled wood siding; building paper; 6" batt insulation; wood double hung windows; 3 solid core wood exterior doors; storms and screens. | 9.17 | 3.04 | 12.21 | 9.8% |
| **5** | **Roofing** | Red cedar shingles; #15 felt building paper; aluminum gutters, downspouts and drip edge; copper flashings. | 5.45 | 3.80 | 9.25 | 7.4% |
| **6** | **Interiors** | Walls and ceilings - 5/8" gypsum wallboard, skim coat plaster, painted with primer and 2 coats; hardwood baseboard and trim, sanded and finished; hardwood floor 70%, ceramic tile with underlayment 20%, vinyl tile with underlayment 10%; wood panel interior doors, primed and painted with 2 coats. | 11.91 | 12.93 | 24.84 | 19.9% |
| **7** | **Specialties** | Luxury grade kitchen cabinets - 25 L.F. wall and base with solid surface counter top and kitchen sink; 6 L.F. bathroom vanity; 75 gallon electric water heater; medicine cabinet. | 5.60 | 1.29 | 6.89 | 5.5% |
| **8** | **Mechanical** | Gas fired warm air heat/air conditioning; one full bath including: bathtub, corner shower; built in lavatory and water closet; one 1/2 bath including: built in lavatory and water closet. | 6.17 | 3.12 | 9.29 | 7.4% |
| **9** | **Electrical** | 200 Amp. service; romex wiring; fluorescent and incandescent lighting fixtures; intercom, switches, receptacles. | 1.34 | 1.91 | 3.25 | 2.6% |
| **10** | **Overhead** | Contractor's overhead and profit and architect's fees. | 13.02 | 11.14 | 24.16 | 19.4% |
| | **Total** | | 67.20 | 57.60 | **124.80** | |

- **Unique residence built from an architect's plan**
- **Single family — 1 full bath, 1 half bath, 1 kitchen**
- **No basement**
- **Cedar shakes on roof**
- **Forced hot air heat/air conditioning**
- **Gypsum wallboard interior finishes**
- **Many special features**
- **Extraordinary materials and workmanship**

*Note: The illustration shown may contain some optional components (for example: garages and/or fireplaces) whose costs are shown in the modifications, adjustments, & alternatives below or at the end of the square foot section.*

*©Larry E. Belk Designs*

## Base cost per square foot of living area

| Exterior Wall | Living Area | | | | | | | | | | |
|---|---|---|---|---|---|---|---|---|---|---|---|
| | 1000 | 1200 | 1400 | 1600 | 1800 | 2000 | 2400 | 2800 | 3200 | 3600 | 4000 |
| Wood Siding - Wood Frame | 172.45 | 159.95 | 151.00 | 140.65 | 134.60 | 128.70 | 117.65 | 112.65 | 107.80 | 104.25 | 99.30 |
| Brick Veneer - Wood Frame | 183.10 | 169.95 | 160.55 | 149.25 | 142.80 | 136.50 | 124.55 | 119.15 | 113.85 | 110.05 | 104.70 |
| Solid Brick | 201.80 | 187.50 | 177.25 | 164.50 | 157.20 | 150.20 | 136.65 | 130.60 | 124.40 | 120.30 | 114.15 |
| Solid Stone | 199.05 | 184.95 | 174.75 | 162.20 | 155.10 | 148.15 | 134.85 | 128.90 | 122.85 | 118.80 | 112.75 |
| Finished Basement, Add | 34.35 | 37.30 | 36.10 | 34.50 | 33.55 | 32.75 | 31.05 | 30.30 | 29.30 | 28.85 | 28.15 |
| Unfinished Basement, Add | 15.55 | 14.75 | 14.25 | 13.40 | 12.95 | 12.55 | 11.65 | 11.30 | 10.75 | 10.55 | 10.15 |

## Modifications

*Add to the total cost*

| | |
|---|---|
| Upgrade Kitchen Cabinets | $ + 1462 |
| Solid Surface Countertops (Included) | |
| Full Bath - including plumbing, wall and floor finishes | + 8238 |
| Half Bath - including plumbing, wall and floor finishes | + 4907 |
| Two Car Attached Garage | + 26,381 |
| Two Car Detached Garage | + 30,256 |
| Fireplace & Chimney | + 8141 |

## Adjustments

*For multi family - add to total cost*

| | |
|---|---|
| Additional Kitchen | $ + 18,138 |
| Additional Full Bath & Half Bath | + 13,145 |
| Additional Entry & Exit | + 2342 |
| Separate Heating & Air Conditioning | + 6271 |
| Separate Electric | + 1915 |

*For Townhouse/Rowhouse - Multiply cost per square foot by*

| | |
|---|---|
| Inner Unit | + .90 |
| End Unit | + .95 |

## Alternatives

*Add to or deduct from the cost per square foot of living area*

| | |
|---|---|
| Heavyweight Asphalt Shingles | – 2.85 |
| Clay Tile Roof | + .50 |
| Slate Roof | + 2 |
| Upgrade Ceilings to Textured Finish | + .48 |
| Air Conditioning, in Heating Ductwork | Base System |
| Heating Systems, Hot Water | + 2.27 |
| Heat Pump | + 3.17 |
| Electric Heat | – 2.60 |
| Not Heated | – 4.80 |

## Additional upgrades or components

| | |
|---|---|
| Kitchen Cabinets & Countertops | Page 93 |
| Bathroom Vanities | 94 |
| Fireplaces & Chimneys | 94 |
| Windows, Skylights & Dormers | 94 |
| Appliances | 95 |
| Breezeways & Porches | 95 |
| Finished Attic | 95 |
| Garages | 96 |
| Site Improvements | 96 |
| Wings & Ells | 92 |

| | | | Cost Per Square Foot Of Living Area | | | % of Total |
|---|---|---|---|---|---|---|
| | | | Mat. | Inst. | Total | (roun |
| **1** | **Site Work** | Site preparation for slab; 4' deep trench excavation for foundation wall. | | .66 | .66 | 0.6% |
| **2** | **Foundation** | Continuous reinforced concrete footing 8" deep x 18" wide; dampproofed and insulated reinforced concrete foundation wall, 12" thick, 4' deep, 4" concrete slab on 4" crushed stone base and polyethylene vapor barrier, trowel finish. | 4.76 | 5.26 | 10.02 | 8.9% |
| **3** | **Framing** | Exterior walls - 2" x 6" wood studs, 16" O.C.; 5/8" plywood sheathing; 2" x 10" rafters 16" O.C. with 5/8" plywood sheathing, 8 in 12 pitch; 2" x 8" ceiling joists 16" O.C.; 2" x 12" floor joists 16" O.C. with 5/8" plywood subfloor; 5/8" plywood subfloor on 1" x 3" wood sleepers 16" O.C. | 4.73 | 8.28 | 13.01 | 11.5% |
| **4** | **Exterior Walls** | Horizontal beveled wood siding; building paper; 6" batt insulation; wood double hung windows; 3 solid core wood exterior doors; storms and screens. | 10.17 | 3.42 | 13.59 | 12.1% |
| **5** | **Roofing** | Red cedar shingles; #15 felt building paper; aluminum gutters, downspouts and drip edge; copper flashings. | 3.40 | 2.37 | 5.77 | 5.1% |
| **6** | **Interiors** | Walls and ceilings - 5/8" gypsum wallboard, skim coat plaster, painted with primer and 2 coats; hardwood baseboard and trim, sanded and finished; hardwood floor 70%, ceramic tile with underlayment 20%, vinyl tile with underlayment 10%; wood panel interior doors, primed and painted with 2 coats. | 13.69 | 14.64 | 28.33 | 25.1% |
| **7** | **Specialties** | Luxury grade kitchen cabinets - 25 L.F. wall and base with solid surface counter top and kitchen sink; 6 L.F. bathroom vanity; 75 gallon electric water heater; medicine cabinet. | 5.60 | 1.29 | 6.89 | 6.1% |
| **8** | **Mechanical** | Gas fired warm air heat/air conditioning; one full bath including: bathtub, corner shower; built in lavatory and water closet; one 1/2 bath including: built in lavatory and water closet. | 6.17 | 3.12 | 9.29 | 8.2% |
| **9** | **Electrical** | 200 Amp. service; romex wiring; fluorescent and incandescent lighting fixtures; intercom, switches, receptacles. | 1.34 | 1.91 | 3.25 | 2.9% |
| **10** | **Overhead** | Contractor's overhead and profit and architect's fees. | 11.99 | 9.85 | 21.84 | 19.4% |
| | **Total** | | 61.85 | 50.80 | **112.65** | |

- **Unique residence built from an architect's plan**
- **Single family — 1 full bath, 1 half bath, 1 kitchen**
- **No basement**
- **Cedar shakes on roof**
- **Forced hot air heat/air conditioning**
- **Gypsum wallboard interior finishes**
- **Many special features**
- **Extraordinary materials and workmanship**

*Note: The illustration shown may contain some optional components (for example: garages and/or fireplaces) whose costs are shown in the modifications, adjustments, & alternatives below or at the end of the square foot section.*

## Base cost per square foot of living area

| Exterior Wall | Living Area | | | | | | | | | | |
|---|---|---|---|---|---|---|---|---|---|---|---|
| | 1200 | 1400 | 1600 | 1800 | 2000 | 2400 | 2800 | 3200 | 3600 | 4000 | 4400 |
| Wood Siding - Wood Frame | 159.45 | 149.60 | 142.50 | 136.45 | 129.95 | 120.50 | 112.65 | **107.30** | 104.25 | 100.90 | 98.05 |
| Brick Veneer - Wood Frame | 170.85 | 160.25 | 152.65 | 146.00 | 139.15 | 128.80 | 120.20 | 114.40 | 111.05 | 107.30 | 104.25 |
| Solid Brick | 190.90 | 178.95 | 170.50 | 162.80 | 155.40 | 143.40 | 133.50 | 126.85 | 123.10 | 118.65 | 115.25 |
| Solid Stone | 187.95 | 176.15 | 167.90 | 160.35 | 153.00 | 141.25 | 131.55 | 125.05 | 121.35 | 116.90 | 113.55 |
| Finished Basement, Add | 27.65 | 29.95 | 29.10 | 28.15 | 27.60 | 26.30 | 25.15 | 24.45 | 24.10 | 23.50 | 23.15 |
| Unfinished Basement, Add | 12.45 | 11.85 | 11.50 | 11.00 | 10.75 | 10.00 | 9.50 | 9.15 | 8.95 | 8.60 | 8.40 |

## Modifications

*Add to the total cost*

| | |
|---|---|
| Upgrade Kitchen Cabinets | $ + 1462 |
| Solid Surface Countertops (Included) | |
| Full Bath - including plumbing, wall and floor finishes | + 8238 |
| Half Bath - including plumbing, wall and floor finishes | + 4907 |
| Two Car Attached Garage | + 26,381 |
| Two Car Detached Garage | + 30,256 |
| Fireplace & Chimney | + 8924 |

## Adjustments

*For multi family - add to total cost*

| | |
|---|---|
| Additional Kitchen | $ + 18,138 |
| Additional Full Bath & Half Bath | + 13,145 |
| Additional Entry & Exit | + 2342 |
| Separate Heating & Air Conditioning | + 6271 |
| Separate Electric | + 1915 |

*For Townhouse/Rowhouse -
Multiply cost per square foot by*

| | |
|---|---|
| Inner Unit | + .86 |
| End Unit | + .93 |

## Alternatives

*Add to or deduct from the cost per square foot of living area*

| | |
|---|---|
| Heavyweight Asphalt Shingles | – 1.70 |
| Clay Tile Roof | + .35 |
| Slate Roof | + 1.40 |
| Upgrade Ceilings to Textured Finish | + .48 |
| Air Conditioning, in Heating Ductwork | Base System |
| Heating Systems, Hot Water | + 2.21 |
| Heat Pump | + 3.34 |
| Electric Heat | – 2.34 |
| Not Heated | – 4.54 |

## Additional upgrades or components

| | |
|---|---|
| Kitchen Cabinets & Countertops | Page 93 |
| Bathroom Vanities | 94 |
| Fireplaces & Chimneys | 94 |
| Windows, Skylights & Dormers | 94 |
| Appliances | 95 |
| Breezeways & Porches | 95 |
| Finished Attic | 95 |
| Garages | 96 |
| Site Improvements | 96 |
| Wings & Ells | 92 |

## Luxury 2 Story

**Living Area - 3200 S.F.**
**Perimeter - 163 L.F.**

| | | | Cost Per Square Foot Of Living Area | | | % of Total |
|---|---|---|---|---|---|---|
| | | | Mat. | Inst. | Total | (roun |
| **1** | **Site Work** | Site preparation for slab; 4' deep trench excavation for foundation wall. | | .58 | .58 | 0.5% |
| **2** | **Foundation** | Continuous reinforced concrete footing 8" deep x 18" wide; dampproofed and insulated reinforced concrete foundation wall, 12" thick, 4' deep, 4" concrete slab on 4" crushed stone base and polyethylene vapor barrier, trowel finish. | 3.85 | 4.27 | 8.12 | 7.6% |
| **3** | **Framing** | Exterior walls - 2" x 6" wood studs, 16" O.C.; 5/8" plywood sheathing; 2" x 10" rafters 16" O.C. with 5/8" plywood sheathing, 6 in 12 pitch; 2" x 8" ceiling joists 16" O.C.; 2" x 12" floor joists 16" O.C. with 5/8" plywood subfloor; 5/8" plywood subfloor on 1" x 3" wood sleepers 16" O.C. | 4.81 | 8.19 | 13.00 | 12.1% |
| **4** | **Exterior Walls** | Horizontal beveled wood siding, building paper; 6" batt insulation; wood double hung windows; 3 solid core wood exterior doors; storms and screens. | 10.78 | 3.65 | 14.43 | 13.4% |
| **5** | **Roofing** | Red cedar shingles; #15 felt building paper; aluminum gutters, downspouts and drip edge; copper flashings. | 2.72 | 1.90 | 4.62 | 4.3% |
| **6** | **Interiors** | Walls and ceilings - 5/8" gypsum wallboard, skim coat plaster, painted with primer and 2 coats; hardwood baseboard and trim, sanded and finished; hardwood floor 70%, ceramic tile with underlayment 20%, vinyl tile with underlayment 10%; wood panel interior doors, primed and painted with 2 coats. | 13.48 | 14.57 | 28.05 | 26.1% |
| **7** | **Specialties** | Luxury grade kitchen cabinets - 25 L.F. wall and base with solid surface counter top and kitchen sink; 6 L.F. bathroom vanity; 75 gallon electric water heater; medicine cabinet. | 4.90 | 1.10 | 6.00 | 5.6% |
| **8** | **Mechanical** | Gas fired warm air heat/air conditioning; one full bath including: bathtub, corner shower; built in lavatory and water closet; one 1/2 bath including: built in lavatory and water closet. | 5.57 | 3.00 | 8.57 | 8.0% |
| **9** | **Electrical** | 200 Amp. service; romex wiring; fluorescent and incandescent lighting fixtures; intercom, switches, receptacles. | 1.31 | 1.85 | 3.16 | 2.9% |
| **10** | **Overhead** | Contractor's overhead and profit and architect's fee. | 11.38 | 9.39 | 20.77 | 19.4% |
| | **Total** | | 58.80 | 48.50 | **107.30** | |

- Unique residence built from an architect's plan
- Single family — 1 full bath, 1 half bath, 1 kitchen
- No basement
- Cedar shakes on roof
- Forced hot air heat/air conditioning
- Gypsum wallboard interior finishes
- Many special features
- Extraordinary materials and workmanship

*Note: The illustration shown may contain some optional components (for example: garages and/or fireplaces) whose costs are shown in the modifications, adjustments, & alternatives below or at the end of the square foot section.*

©Larry W. Garnett & Associates, Inc

## Base cost per square foot of living area

| Exterior Wall | Living Area | | | | | | | | | | |
|---|---|---|---|---|---|---|---|---|---|---|---|
| | 1500 | 1800 | 2100 | 2500 | 3000 | 3500 | 4000 | 4500 | 5000 | 5500 | 6000 |
| Wood Siding - Wood Frame | 155.05 | 139.30 | 129.95 | 123.10 | 113.75 | 106.95 | 100.45 | 97.40 | 94.45 | 91.60 | 88.60 |
| Brick Veneer - Wood Frame | 166.90 | 150.25 | 139.70 | 132.30 | 122.10 | 114.55 | 107.50 | 104.05 | 100.80 | 97.65 | 94.40 |
| Solid Brick | 187.70 | 169.40 | 156.90 | 148.50 | 136.80 | 127.90 | 119.85 | 115.80 | 112.00 | 108.30 | 104.60 |
| Solid Stone | 184.65 | 166.60 | 154.25 | 146.10 | 134.65 | 126.00 | 118.05 | 114.05 | 110.30 | 106.70 | 103.15 |
| Finished Basement, Add | 22.05 | 23.75 | 22.40 | 21.65 | 20.60 | 19.70 | 19.05 | 18.65 | 18.30 | 17.90 | 17.65 |
| Unfinished Basement, Add | 10.05 | 9.50 | 8.80 | 8.45 | 7.90 | 7.45 | 7.15 | 6.95 | 6.75 | 6.55 | 6.40 |

## Modifications

*Add to the total cost*

| | |
|---|---|
| Upgrade Kitchen Cabinets | $ + 1462 |
| Solid Surface Countertops (Included) | |
| Full Bath - including plumbing, wall and floor finishes | + 8238 |
| Half Bath - including plumbing, wall and floor finishes | + 4907 |
| Two Car Attached Garage | + 26,381 |
| Two Car Detached Garage | + 30,256 |
| Fireplace & Chimney | + 9765 |

## Adjustments

*For multi family - add to total cost*

| | |
|---|---|
| Additional Kitchen | $ + 18,138 |
| Additional Full Bath & Half Bath | + 13,145 |
| Additional Entry & Exit | + 2342 |
| Separate Heating & Air Conditioning | + 6271 |
| Separate Electric | + 1915 |

*For Townhouse/Rowhouse - Multiply cost per square foot by*

| | |
|---|---|
| Inner Unit | + .86 |
| End Unit | + .93 |

## Alternatives

*Add to or deduct from the cost per square foot of living area*

| | |
|---|---|
| Heavyweight Asphalt Shingles | – 1.50 |
| Clay Tile Roof | + .30 |
| Slate Roof | + 1.20 |
| Upgrade Ceilings to Textured Finish | + .48 |
| Air Conditioning, in Heating Ductwork | Base System |
| Heating Systems, Hot Water | + 2 |
| Heat Pump | + 3.44 |
| Electric Heat | – 4.60 |
| Not Heated | – 4.54 |

## Additional upgrades or components

| | |
|---|---|
| Kitchen Cabinets & Countertops | Page 93 |
| Bathroom Vanities | 94 |
| Fireplaces & Chimneys | 94 |
| Windows, Skylights & Dormers | 94 |
| Appliances | 95 |
| Breezeways & Porches | 95 |
| Finished Attic | 95 |
| Garages | 96 |
| Site Improvements | 96 |
| Wings & Ells | 92 |

# Luxury 2-1/2 Story

**Living Area - 3000 S.F.**
**Perimeter - 148 L.F.**

| | | | Cost Per Square Foot Of Living Area | | | % of Total |
|---|---|---|---|---|---|---|
| | | | Mat. | Inst. | Total | (roun |
| **1** | **Site Work** | Site preparation for slab; 4' deep trench excavation for foundation wall. | | .61 | .61 | 0.5% |
| **2** | **Foundation** | Continuous reinforced concrete footing 8" deep x 18" wide; dampproofed and insulated reinforced concrete foundation wall, 12" thick, 4' deep, 4" concrete slab on 4" crushed stone base and polyethylene vapor barrier, trowel finish. | 3.38 | 3.88 | 7.26 | 6.4% |
| **3** | **Framing** | Exterior walls - 2" x 6" wood studs, 16" O.C.; 5/8" plywood sheathing; 2" x 10" rafters 16" O.C. with 5/8" plywood sheathing, 8 in 12 pitch; 2" x 8" ceiling joists 16" O.C.; 2" x 12" floor joists 16" O.C. with 5/8" plywood subfloor; 5/8" plywood subfloor on 1" x 3" wood sleepers 16" O.C. | 5.00 | 8.48 | 13.48 | 11.9% |
| **4** | **Exterior Walls** | Horizontal beveled wood siding; building paper; 6" batt insulation; wood double hung windows; 3 solid core wood exterior doors; storms and screens. | 12.57 | 4.23 | 16.80 | 14.8% |
| **5** | **Roofing** | Red cedar shingles; #15 felt building paper; aluminum gutters, downspouts and drip edge; copper flashings. | 2.09 | 1.46 | 3.55 | 3.1% |
| **6** | **Interiors** | Walls and ceilings - 5/8" gypsum wallboard, skim coat plaster, painted with primer and 2 coats; hardwood baseboard and trim, sanded and finished; hardwood floor 70%, ceramic tile with underlayment 20%, vinyl tile with underlayment 10%; wood panel interior doors, primed and painted with 2 coats. | 15.28 | 16.23 | 31.51 | 27.7% |
| **7** | **Specialties** | Luxury grade kitchen cabinets - 25 L.F. wall and base with solid surface counter top and kitchen sink; 6 L.F. bathroom vanity; 75 gallon electric water heater; medicine cabinet. | 5.22 | 1.18 | 6.40 | 5.6% |
| **8** | **Mechanical** | Gas fired warm air heat/air conditioning; one full bath including: bathtub, corner shower; built in lavatory and water closet; one 1/2 bath including: built in lavatory and water closet. | 5.87 | 3.05 | 8.92 | 7.8% |
| **9** | **Electrical** | 200 Amp. service; romex wiring; fluorescent and incandescent lighting fixtures; intercom, switches, receptacles. | 1.32 | 1.87 | 3.19 | 2.8% |
| **10** | **Overhead** | Contractor's overhead and profit and architect's fee. | 12.17 | 9.86 | 22.03 | 19.4% |
| | **Total** | | 62.90 | 50.85 | **113.75** | |

- **Unique residence built from an architect's plan**
- **Single family — 1 full bath, 1 half bath, 1 kitchen**
- **No basement**
- **Cedar shakes on roof**
- **Forced hot air heat/air conditioning**
- **Gypsum wallboard interior finishes**
- **Many special features**
- **Extraordinary materials and workmanship**

*Note: The illustration shown may contain some optional components (for example: garages and/or fireplaces) whose costs are shown in the modifications, adjustments, & alternatives below or at the end of the square foot section.*

## Base cost per square foot of living area

| Exterior Wall | Living Area | | | | | | | | | | |
|---|---|---|---|---|---|---|---|---|---|---|---|
| | 1500 | 1800 | 2100 | 2500 | 3000 | 3500 | 4000 | 4500 | 5000 | 5500 | 6000 |
| Wood Siding - Wood Frame | 153.95 | 138.35 | 130.60 | 124.15 | 114.55 | 109.65 | 103.70 | 97.65 | 95.30 | 92.90 | 90.45 |
| Brick Veneer - Wood Frame | 166.25 | 149.75 | 141.25 | 134.35 | 123.75 | 118.35 | 111.65 | 105.00 | 102.40 | 99.75 | 96.90 |
| Solid Brick | 187.85 | 169.75 | 159.95 | 152.15 | 140.00 | 133.70 | 125.55 | 117.85 | 114.85 | 111.70 | 108.20 |
| Solid Stone | 184.60 | 166.80 | 157.15 | 149.55 | 137.55 | 131.40 | 123.55 | 115.95 | 113.05 | 110.00 | 106.50 |
| Finished Basement, Add | 19.35 | 20.80 | 19.95 | 19.35 | 18.40 | 17.85 | 17.10 | 16.50 | 16.25 | 16.00 | 15.60 |
| Unfinished Basement, Add | 8.85 | 8.30 | 7.90 | 7.60 | 7.15 | 6.85 | 6.55 | 6.15 | 6.10 | 5.95 | 5.75 |

## Modifications

*Add to the total cost*

| | |
|---|---|
| Upgrade Kitchen Cabinets | $ + 1462 |
| Solid Surface Countertops (Included) | |
| Full Bath - including plumbing, wall and floor finishes | + 8238 |
| Half Bath - including plumbing, wall and floor finishes | + 4907 |
| Two Car Attached Garage | + 26,381 |
| Two Car Detached Garage | + 30,256 |
| Fireplace & Chimney | + 9765 |

## Adjustments

*For multi family - add to total cost*

| | |
|---|---|
| Additional Kitchen | $ + 18,138 |
| Additional Full Bath & Half Bath | + 13,145 |
| Additional Entry & Exit | + 2342 |
| Separate Heating & Air Conditioning | + 6271 |
| Separate Electric | + 1915 |

*For Townhouse/Rowhouse - Multiply cost per square foot by*

| | |
|---|---|
| Inner Unit | + .84 |
| End Unit | + .92 |

## Alternatives

*Add to or deduct from the cost per square foot of living area*

| | |
|---|---|
| Heavyweight Asphalt Shingles | – 1.15 |
| Clay Tile Roof | + .20 |
| Slate Roof | + .90 |
| Upgrade Ceilings to Textured Finish | + .48 |
| Air Conditioning, in Heating Ductwork | Base System |
| Heating Systems, Hot Water | + 2 |
| Heat Pump | + 3.44 |
| Electric Heat | – 4.60 |
| Not Heated | – 4.40 |

## Additional upgrades or components

| | |
|---|---|
| Kitchen Cabinets & Countertops | Page 93 |
| Bathroom Vanities | 94 |
| Fireplaces & Chimneys | 94 |
| Windows, Skylights & Dormers | 94 |
| Appliances | 95 |
| Breezeways & Porches | 95 |
| Finished Attic | 95 |
| Garages | 96 |
| Site Improvements | 96 |
| Wings & Ells | 92 |

# Luxury 3 Story

**Living Area - 3000 S.F.**
**Perimeter - 135 L.F.**

| | | | Cost Per Square Foot Of Living Area | | | % of Total |
|---|---|---|---|---|---|---|
| | | | Mat. | Inst. | Total | (roun |
| **1** | **Site Work** | Site preparation for slab; 4' deep trench excavation for foundation wall. | | .61 | .61 | 0.5% |
| **2** | **Foundation** | Continuous reinforced concrete footing 8" deep x 18" wide; dampproofed and insulated reinforced concrete foundation wall, 12" thick, 4' deep, 4" concrete slab on 4" crushed stone base and polyethylene vapor barrier, trowel finish. | 3.04 | 3.52 | 6.56 | 5.7% |
| **3** | **Framing** | Exterior walls - 2" x 6" wood studs, 16" O.C.; 5/8" plywood sheathing; 2" x 10" rafters 16" O.C. with 5/8" plywood sheathing, 6 in 12 pitch; 2" x 8" ceiling joists 16" O.C.; 2" x 12" floor joists 16" O.C. with 5/8" plywood subfloor; 5/8" plywood subfloor on 1" x 3" wood sleepers 16" O.C. | 5.10 | 8.54 | 13.64 | 11.9% |
| **4** | **Exterior Walls** | Horizontal beveled wood siding; building paper; 6" batt insulation; wood double hung windows; 3 solid core wood exterior doors; storms and screens. | 13.69 | 4.65 | 18.34 | 16.0% |
| **5** | **Roofing** | Red cedar shingles; #15 felt building paper; aluminum gutters, downspouts and drip edge; copper flashings. | 1.82 | 1.27 | 3.09 | 2.7% |
| **6** | **Interiors** | Walls and ceilings - 5/8" gypsum wallboard, skim coat plaster, painted with primer and 2 coats; hardwood baseboard and trim, sanded and finished; hardwood floor 70%, ceramic tile with underlayment 20%, vinyl tile with underlayment 10%; wood panel interior doors, primed and painted with 2 coats. | 15.29 | 16.34 | 31.63 | 27.6% |
| **7** | **Specialties** | Luxury grade kitchen cabinets - 25 L.F. wall and base with solid surface counter top and kitchen sink; 6 L.F. bathroom vanity; 75 gallon electric water heater; medicine cabinet. | 5.22 | 1.18 | 6.40 | 5.6% |
| **8** | **Mechanical** | Gas fired warm air heat/air conditioning; one full bath including: bathtub, corner shower; built in lavatory and water closet; one 1/2 bath including: built in lavatory and water closet. | 5.87 | 3.05 | 8.92 | 7.8% |
| **9** | **Electrical** | 200 Amp. service; romex wiring; fluorescent and incandescent lighting fixtures; intercom, switches, receptacles. | 1.32 | 1.87 | 3.19 | 2.8% |
| **10** | **Overhead** | Contractor's overhead and profit and architect's fees. | 12.30 | 9.87 | 22.17 | 19.4% |
| | **Total** | | 63.65 | 50.90 | **114.55** | |

- **Unique residence built from an architect's plan**
- **Single family — 1 full bath, 1 half bath, 1 kitchen**
- **No basement**
- **Cedar shakes on roof**
- **Forced hot air heat/air conditioning**
- **Gypsum wallboard interior finishes**
- **Many special features**
- **Extraordinary materials and workmanship**

*Note: The illustration shown may contain some optional components (for example: garages and/or fireplaces) whose costs are shown in the modifications, adjustments, & alternatives below or at the end of the square foot section.*

## Base cost per square foot of living area

| Exterior Wall | Living Area | | | | | | | | | | |
|---|---|---|---|---|---|---|---|---|---|---|---|
|  | 1200 | 1400 | 1600 | 1800 | 2000 | 2400 | 2800 | 3200 | 3600 | 4000 | 4400 |
| Wood Siding - Wood Frame | 150.85 | 141.60 | 134.85 | 129.20 | 123.05 | 114.15 | 106.85 | 101.85 | 99.05 | 96.05 | 93.40 |
| Brick Veneer - Wood Frame | 159.40 | 149.55 | 142.45 | 136.35 | 129.95 | 120.40 | 112.55 | 107.20 | 104.20 | 100.85 | 98.05 |
| Solid Brick | 174.40 | 163.55 | 155.85 | 148.95 | 142.10 | 131.30 | 122.55 | 116.55 | 113.25 | 109.25 | 106.20 |
| Solid Stone | 172.20 | 161.50 | 153.90 | 147.15 | 140.30 | 129.70 | 121.05 | 115.20 | 111.85 | 108.05 | 105.00 |
| Finished Basement, Add | 27.65 | 29.95 | 29.10 | 28.15 | 27.60 | 26.30 | 25.15 | 24.45 | 24.10 | 23.50 | 23.15 |
| Unfinished Basement, Add | 12.45 | 11.85 | 11.50 | 11.00 | 10.75 | 10.00 | 9.50 | 9.15 | 8.95 | 8.60 | 8.40 |

## Modifications

*Add to the total cost*

| | |
|---|---|
| Upgrade Kitchen Cabinets | $ + 1462 |
| Solid Surface Countertops (Included) | |
| Full Bath - including plumbing, wall and floor finishes | + 8238 |
| Half Bath - including plumbing, wall and floor finishes | + 4907 |
| Two Car Attached Garage | + 26,381 |
| Two Car Detached Garage | + 30,256 |
| Fireplace & Chimney | + 8141 |

## Adjustments

*For multi family - add to total cost*

| | |
|---|---|
| Additional Kitchen | $ + 18,138 |
| Additional Full Bath & Half Bath | + 13,145 |
| Additional Entry & Exit | + 2342 |
| Separate Heating & Air Conditioning | + 6271 |
| Separate Electric | + 1915 |

*For Townhouse/Rowhouse -*
*Multiply cost per square foot by*

| | |
|---|---|
| Inner Unit | + .89 |
| End Unit | + .94 |

## Alternatives

*Add to or deduct from the cost per square foot of living area*

| | |
|---|---|
| Heavyweight Asphalt Shingles | – 1.70 |
| Clay Tile Roof | + .35 |
| Slate Roof | + 1.40 |
| Upgrade Ceilings to Textured Finish | + .48 |
| Air Conditioning, in Heating Ductwork | Base System |
| Heating Systems, Hot Water | + 2.21 |
| Heat Pump | + 3.34 |
| Electric Heat | – 2.34 |
| Not Heated | – 4.54 |

## Additional upgrades or components

| | |
|---|---|
| Kitchen Cabinets & Countertops | Page 93 |
| Bathroom Vanities | 94 |
| Fireplaces & Chimneys | 94 |
| Windows, Skylights & Dormers | 94 |
| Appliances | 95 |
| Breezeways & Porches | 95 |
| Finished Attic | 95 |
| Garages | 96 |
| Site Improvements | 96 |
| Wings & Ells | 92 |

# Luxury Bi-Level

**Living Area - 3200 S.F.**
**Perimeter - 163 L.F.**

| | | Cost Per Square Foot Of Living Area | | | % of Total |
| --- | --- | --- | --- | --- | --- |
| | | Mat. | Inst. | Total | (roun |
| **1 Site Work** | Excavation for lower level, 4' deep. Site preparation for slab. | | .58 | .58 | 0.6% |
| **2 Foundation** | Continuous reinforced concrete footing 8" deep x 18" wide; dampproofed and insulated reinforced concrete foundation wall, 12" thick, 4' deep, 4" concrete slab on 4" crushed stone base and polyethylene vapor barrier, trowel finish. | 3.85 | 4.27 | 8.12 | 8.0% |
| **3 Framing** | Exterior walls - 2" x 6" wood studs, 16" O.C.; 5/8" plywood sheathing; 2" x 10" rafters 16" O.C. with 5/8" plywood sheathing, 6 in 12 pitch; 2" x 8" ceiling joists 16" O.C.; 2" x 12" floor joists 16" O.C. with 5/8" plywood subfloor; 5/8" plywood subfloor on 1" x 3" wood sleepers 16" O.C. | 4.60 | 7.80 | 12.40 | 12.2% |
| **4 Exterior Walls** | Horizontal beveled wood siding; building paper; 6" batt insulation; wood double hung windows; 3 solid core wood exterior doors; storms and screens. | 8.40 | 2.80 | 11.20 | 11.0% |
| **5 Roofing** | Red cedar shingles; #15 felt building paper; aluminum gutters, downspouts and drip edge; copper flashings. | 2.72 | 1.90 | 4.62 | 4.5% |
| **6 Interiors** | Walls and ceilings - 5/8" gypsum wallboard, skim coat plaster, painted with primer and 2 coats; hardwood baseboard and trim, sanded and finished; hardwood floor 70%, ceramic tile with underlayment 20%; vinyl tile with underlayment 10%; wood panel interior doors, primed and painted with 2 coats. | 13.30 | 14.22 | 27.52 | 27.0% |
| **7 Specialties** | Luxury grade kitchen cabinets - 25 L.F. wall and base with solid surface counter top and kitchen sink; 6 L.F. bathroom vanity; 75 gallon electric water heater; medicine cabinet. | 4.90 | 1.10 | 6.00 | 5.9% |
| **8 Mechanical** | Gas fired warm air heat/air conditioning; one full bath including: bathtub, corner shower; built in lavatory and water closet; one 1/2 bath including: built in lavatory and water closet. | 5.57 | 3.00 | 8.57 | 8.4% |
| **9 Electrical** | 200 Amp. service; romex wiring; fluorescent and incandescent lighting fixtures; intercom, switches, receptacles. | 1.31 | 1.85 | 3.16 | 3.1% |
| **10 Overhead** | Contractor's overhead and profit and architect's fees. | 10.70 | 8.98 | 19.68 | 19.3% |
| **Total** | | 55.35 | 46.50 | **101.85** | |

- **Unique residence built from an architect's plan**
- **Single family — 1 full bath, 1 half bath, 1 kitchen**
- **No basement**
- **Cedar shakes on roof**
- **Forced hot air heat/air conditioning**
- **Gypsum wallboard interior finishes**
- **Many special features**
- **Extraordinary materials and workmanship**

*Note: The illustration shown may contain some optional components (for example: garages and/or fireplaces) whose costs are shown in the modifications, adjustments, & alternatives below or at the end of the square foot section.*

©Home Planners, Inc.

## Base cost per square foot of living area

| Exterior Wall | Living Area | | | | | | | | | | |
|---|---|---|---|---|---|---|---|---|---|---|---|
| | 1500 | 1800 | 2100 | 2400 | 2800 | 3200 | 3600 | 4000 | 4500 | 5000 | 5500 |
| Wood Siding - Wood Frame | 142.05 | 131.05 | 121.95 | 115.95 | 111.55 | 106.30 | 100.95 | 98.60 | 93.55 | 90.65 | 87.60 |
| Brick Veneer - Wood Frame | 149.75 | 138.00 | 128.30 | 121.85 | 117.25 | 111.60 | 105.85 | 103.35 | 97.90 | 94.80 | 91.50 |
| Solid Brick | 163.25 | 150.15 | 139.40 | 132.25 | 127.20 | 120.85 | 114.40 | 111.70 | 105.55 | 102.00 | 98.30 |
| Solid Stone | 161.25 | 148.30 | 137.75 | 130.75 | 125.70 | 119.50 | 113.10 | 110.45 | 104.45 | 100.90 | 97.30 |
| Finished Basement, Add* | 32.50 | 35.00 | 33.50 | 32.60 | 32.00 | 31.10 | 30.20 | 29.85 | 29.05 | 28.50 | 28.05 |
| Unfinished Basement, Add* | 14.25 | 13.35 | 12.65 | 12.20 | 11.85 | 11.35 | 10.95 | 10.75 | 10.30 | 10.05 | 9.80 |

*Basement under middle level only.

## Modifications

*Add to the total cost*

| | |
|---|---|
| Upgrade Kitchen Cabinets | $ + 1462 |
| Solid Surface Countertops (Included) | |
| Full Bath - including plumbing, wall and floor finishes | + 8238 |
| Half Bath - including plumbing, wall and floor finishes | + 4907 |
| Two Car Attached Garage | + 26,381 |
| Two Car Detached Garage | + 30,256 |
| Fireplace & Chimney | + 8141 |

## Adjustments

*For multi family - add to total cost*

| | |
|---|---|
| Additional Kitchen | $ + 18,138 |
| Additional Full Bath & Half Bath | + 13,145 |
| Additional Entry & Exit | + 2342 |
| Separate Heating & Air Conditioning | + 6271 |
| Separate Electric | + 1915 |

*For Townhouse/Rowhouse - Multiply cost per square foot by*

| | |
|---|---|
| Inner Unit | + .86 |
| End Unit | + .93 |

## Alternatives

*Add to or deduct from the cost per square foot of living area*

| | |
|---|---|
| Heavyweight Asphalt Shingles | – 2.50 |
| Clay Tile Roof | + .50 |
| Slate Roof | + 2 |
| Upgrade Ceilings to Textured Finish | + .48 |
| Air Conditioning, in Heating Ductwork | Base System |
| Heating Systems, Hot Water | + 2.15 |
| Heat Pump | + 3.48 |
| Electric Heat | – 2.06 |
| Not Heated | – 4.40 |

## Additional upgrades or components

| | |
|---|---|
| Kitchen Cabinets & Countertops | Page 93 |
| Bathroom Vanities | 94 |
| Fireplaces & Chimneys | 94 |
| Windows, Skylights & Dormers | 94 |
| Appliances | 95 |
| Breezeways & Porches | 95 |
| Finished Attic | 95 |
| Garages | 96 |
| Site Improvements | 96 |
| Wings & Ells | 92 |

**Important: See the Reference Section for Location Factors (to adjust for your city) and Estimating Forms**

| | | | Cost Per Square Foot Of Living Area | | | % of Total |
| --- | --- | --- | --- | --- | --- | --- |
| | | | Mat. | Inst. | Total | (roun |
| **1** | **Site Work** | Site preparation for slab; 4' deep trench excavation for foundation wall, excavation for lower level, 4' deep. | | .51 | .51 | 0.5% |
| **2** | **Foundation** | Continuous reinforced concrete footing 8" deep x 18" wide; dampproofed and insulated reinforced concrete foundation wall, 12" thick, 4' deep, 4" concrete slab on 4" crushed stone base and polyethylene vapor barrier, trowel finish. | 4.59 | 4.92 | 9.51 | 9.4% |
| **3** | **Framing** | Exterior walls - 2" x 6" wood studs, 16" O.C.; 5/8" plywood sheathing; 2" x 10" rafters 16" O.C. with 5/8" plywood sheathing, 6 in 12 pitch; 2" x 8" ceiling joists 16" O.C.; 2" x 12" floor joists 16" O.C. with 5/8" plywood subfloor; 5/8" plywood subfloor on 1" x 3" wood sleepers 16" O.C. | 4.48 | 7.83 | 12.31 | 12.2% |
| **4** | **Exterior Walls** | Horizontal beveled wood siding; building paper; 6" batt insulation; wood double hung windows; 3 solid core wood exterior doors; storms and screens. | 8.05 | 2.68 | 10.73 | 10.6% |
| **5** | **Roofing** | Red cedar shingles; #15 felt building paper; aluminum gutters, downspouts and drip edge; copper flashings. | 3.63 | 2.53 | 6.16 | 6.1% |
| **6** | **Interiors** | Walls and ceilings - 5/8" gypsum wallboard, skim coat plaster, painted with primer and 2 coats; hardwood baseboard and trim, sanded and finished; hardwood floor 70%, ceramic tile with underlayment 20%, vinyl tile with underlayment 10%; wood panel interior doors, primed and painted with 2 coats. | 12.44 | 13.30 | 25.74 | 25.5% |
| **7** | **Specialties** | Luxury grade kitchen cabinets - 25 L.F. wall and base with solid surface counter top and kitchen sink; 6 L.F. bathroom vanity; 75 gallon electric water heater; medicine cabinet. | 4.37 | .99 | 5.36 | 5.3% |
| **8** | **Mechanical** | Gas fired warm air heat/air conditioning; one full bath including: bathtub, corner shower; built in lavatory and water closet; one 1/2 bath including: built in lavatory and water closet. | 5.12 | 2.88 | 8.00 | 7.9% |
| **9** | **Electrical** | 200 Amp. service; romex wiring; fluorescent and incandescent lighting fixtures; intercom, switches, receptacles. | 1.26 | 1.81 | 3.07 | 3.0% |
| **10** | **Overhead** | Contractor's overhead and profit and architect's fees. | 10.56 | 9.00 | 19.56 | 19.4% |
| | | **Total** | 54.50 | 46.45 | **100.95** | |

## 1 Story    Base cost per square foot of living area

| Exterior Wall | Living Area | | | | | | | |
|---|---|---|---|---|---|---|---|---|
| | 50 | 100 | 200 | 300 | 400 | 500 | 600 | 700 |
| Wood Siding - Wood Frame | 229.75 | 176.80 | 153.85 | 129.05 | 121.60 | 117.00 | 114.00 | 114.95 |
| Brick Veneer - Wood Frame | 258.50 | 197.30 | 170.95 | 140.45 | 131.85 | 126.60 | 123.15 | 123.75 |
| Solid Brick | 308.95 | 233.30 | 200.90 | 160.45 | 149.80 | 143.35 | 139.15 | 139.15 |
| Solid Stone | 301.50 | 228.00 | 196.50 | 157.55 | 147.20 | 140.90 | 136.80 | 136.85 |
| Finished Basement, Add | 87.35 | 79.10 | 70.90 | 57.25 | 54.60 | 52.90 | 51.85 | 51.05 |
| Unfinished Basement, Add | 45.65 | 35.00 | 30.50 | 23.15 | 21.65 | 20.75 | 20.15 | 19.75 |

## 1-1/2 Story    Base cost per square foot of living area

| Exterior Wall | Living Area | | | | | | | |
|---|---|---|---|---|---|---|---|---|
| | 100 | 200 | 300 | 400 | 500 | 600 | 700 | 800 |
| Wood Siding - Wood Frame | 183.15 | 149.05 | 128.30 | 115.85 | 109.60 | 106.60 | 102.70 | 101.55 |
| Brick Veneer - Wood Frame | 208.80 | 169.55 | 145.40 | 129.20 | 121.90 | 118.20 | 113.65 | 112.45 |
| Solid Brick | 253.80 | 205.55 | 175.45 | 152.60 | 143.45 | 138.60 | 132.95 | 131.60 |
| Solid Stone | 247.10 | 200.25 | 171.00 | 149.10 | 140.20 | 135.60 | 130.10 | 128.80 |
| Finished Basement, Add | 57.45 | 56.70 | 51.30 | 45.25 | 43.65 | 42.55 | 41.55 | 41.40 |
| Unfinished Basement, Add | 28.85 | 24.40 | 21.45 | 18.20 | 17.30 | 16.70 | 16.15 | 16.10 |

## 2 Story    Base cost per square foot of living area

| Exterior Wall | Living Area | | | | | | | |
|---|---|---|---|---|---|---|---|---|
| | 100 | 200 | 400 | 600 | 800 | 1000 | 1200 | 1400 |
| Wood Siding - Wood Frame | 180.20 | 135.40 | 115.90 | 96.80 | 90.45 | 86.60 | 84.05 | 85.30 |
| Brick Veneer - Wood Frame | 208.90 | 155.90 | 133.00 | 108.20 | 100.70 | 96.15 | 93.15 | 94.10 |
| Solid Brick | 259.35 | 191.90 | 163.00 | 128.20 | 118.65 | 112.95 | 109.15 | 109.50 |
| Solid Stone | 251.90 | 186.65 | 158.50 | 125.25 | 116.00 | 110.45 | 106.75 | 107.20 |
| Finished Basement, Add | 43.70 | 39.60 | 35.50 | 28.65 | 27.30 | 26.45 | 25.95 | 25.55 |
| Unfinished Basement, Add | 22.80 | 17.50 | 15.30 | 11.60 | 10.85 | 10.35 | 10.10 | 9.90 |

Base costs do not include bathroom or kitchen facilities. Use Modifications/Adjustments/Alternatives on pages 93–96 where appropriate.

## Kitchen cabinets - Base units, hardwood (Cost per Unit)

| | Economy | Average | Custom | Luxury |
|---|---|---|---|---|
| **24" deep, 35" high,** | | | | |
| One top drawer, | | | | |
| One door below | | | | |
| 12" wide | $ 213 | $ 284 | $ 378 | $ 497 |
| 15" wide | 221 | 295 | 392 | 516 |
| 18" wide | 240 | 320 | 426 | 560 |
| 21" wide | 251 | 335 | 446 | 586 |
| 24" wide | 285 | 380 | 505 | 665 |
| Four drawers | | | | |
| 12" wide | 222 | 296 | 394 | 518 |
| 15" wide | 225 | 300 | 399 | 525 |
| 18" wide | 248 | 330 | 439 | 578 |
| 24" wide | 278 | 370 | 492 | 648 |
| Two top drawers, | | | | |
| Two doors below | | | | |
| 27" wide | 300 | 400 | 532 | 700 |
| 30" wide | 326 | 435 | 579 | 761 |
| 33" wide | 345 | 460 | 612 | 805 |
| 36" wide | 360 | 480 | 638 | 840 |
| 42" wide | 383 | 510 | 678 | 893 |
| 48" wide | 409 | 545 | 725 | 954 |
| **Range or sink base** | | | | |
| (Cost per unit) | | | | |
| Two doors below | | | | |
| 30" wide | 278 | 370 | 492 | 648 |
| 33" wide | 300 | 400 | 532 | 700 |
| 36" wide | 315 | 420 | 559 | 735 |
| 42" wide | 334 | 445 | 592 | 779 |
| 48" wide | 349 | 465 | 618 | 814 |
| **Corner Base Cabinet** | | | | |
| (Cost per unit) | | | | |
| 36" wide | 480 | 640 | 851 | 1120 |
| **Lazy Susan** (Cost per unit) | | | | |
| With revolving door | 634 | 845 | 1124 | 1479 |

## Kitchen cabinets - Wall cabinets, hardwood (Cost per Unit)

| | Economy | Average | Custom | Luxury |
|---|---|---|---|---|
| **12" deep, 2 doors** | | | | |
| 12" high | | | | |
| 30" wide | $ 193 | $ 257 | $ 342 | $ 450 |
| 36" wide | 223 | 297 | 395 | 520 |
| 15" high | | | | |
| 30" wide | 161 | 214 | 285 | 375 |
| 33" wide | 212 | 283 | 376 | 495 |
| 36" wide | 224 | 299 | 398 | 523 |
| 24" high | | | | |
| 30" wide | 255 | 340 | 452 | 595 |
| 36" wide | 278 | 370 | 492 | 648 |
| 42" wide | 315 | 420 | 559 | 735 |
| 30" high, 1 door | | | | |
| 12" wide | 180 | 240 | 319 | 420 |
| 15" wide | 199 | 265 | 352 | 464 |
| 18" wide | 218 | 290 | 386 | 508 |
| 24" wide | 248 | 330 | 439 | 578 |
| 30" high, 2 doors | | | | |
| 27" wide | 274 | 365 | 485 | 639 |
| 30" wide | 281 | 375 | 499 | 656 |
| 36" wide | 319 | 425 | 565 | 744 |
| 42" wide | 349 | 465 | 618 | 814 |
| 48" wide | 390 | 520 | 692 | 910 |
| Corner wall, 30" high | | | | |
| 24" wide | 225 | 300 | 399 | 525 |
| 30" wide | 251 | 335 | 446 | 586 |
| 36" wide | 281 | 375 | 499 | 656 |
| **Broom closet** | | | | |
| 84" high, 24" deep | | | | |
| 18" wide | 536 | 715 | 951 | 1251 |
| **Oven Cabinet** | | | | |
| 84" high, 24" deep | | | | |
| 27" wide | 788 | 1050 | 1397 | 1838 |

## Kitchen countertops (Cost per L.F.)

| | Economy | Average | Custom | Luxury |
|---|---|---|---|---|
| Solid Surface | | | | |
| 24" wide, no backsplash | 92 | 123 | 164 | 215 |
| with backsplash | 100 | 133 | 177 | 233 |
| Stock plastic laminate, 24" wide | | | | |
| with backsplash | 17 | 23 | 31 | 40 |
| Custom plastic laminate, no splash | | | | |
| 7/8" thick, alum. molding | 27 | 36 | 48 | 63 |
| 1-1/4" thick, no splash | 36 | 48 | 64 | 84 |
| Marble | | | | |
| 1/2" - 3/4" thick w/splash | 48 | 64 | 86 | 113 |
| Maple, laminated | | | | |
| 1-1/2" thick w/splash | 72 | 95 | 127 | 167 |
| Stainless steel | | | | |
| (per S.F.) | 130 | 173 | 230 | 303 |
| Cutting blocks, recessed | | | | |
| 16" x 20" x 1" (each) | 97 | 129 | 172 | 226 |

## Vanity bases *(Cost per Unit)*

| 2 door, 30" high, 21" deep | Economy | Average | Custom | Luxury |
|---|---|---|---|---|
| 24" wide | 217 | 289 | 384 | 506 |
| 30" wide | 251 | 335 | 446 | 586 |
| 36" wide | 334 | 445 | 592 | 779 |
| 48" wide | 398 | 530 | 705 | 928 |

## Solid surface vanity tops *(Cost Each)*

| Center bowl | Economy | Average | Custom | Luxury |
|---|---|---|---|---|
| 22" x 25" | $ 261 | $ 282 | $ 305 | $ 329 |
| 22" x 31" | 298 | 322 | 348 | 376 |
| 22" x 37" | 340 | 367 | 396 | 428 |
| 22" x 49" | 420 | 454 | 490 | 529 |

## Fireplaces & Chimneys *(Cost per Unit)*

| | 1-1/2 Story | 2 Story | 3 Story |
|---|---|---|---|
| **Economy (prefab metal)** | | | |
| Exterior chimney & 1 fireplace | $ 5266 | $ 5819 | $ 6382 |
| Interior chimney & 1 fireplace | 5046 | 5610 | 5869 |
| **Average (masonry)** | | | |
| Exterior chimney & 1 fireplace | 5233 | 5835 | 6633 |
| Interior chimney & 1 fireplace | 4902 | 5503 | 5992 |
| For more than 1 flue, add | 376 | 640 | 1073 |
| For more than 1 fireplace, add | 3710 | 3710 | 3710 |
| **Custom (masonry)** | | | |
| Exterior chimney & 1 fireplace | 5759 | 6501 | 7341 |
| Interior chimney & 1 fireplace | 5400 | 6112 | 6588 |
| For more than 1 flue, add | 451 | 782 | 1060 |
| For more than 1 fireplace, add | 4137 | 4137 | 4137 |
| **Luxury (masonry)** | | | |
| Exterior chimney & 1 fireplace | 8140 | 8923 | 9764 |
| Interior chimney & 1 fireplace | 7766 | 8490 | 8987 |
| For more than 1 flue, add | 672 | 1121 | 1566 |
| For more than 1 fireplace, add | 6416 | 6416 | 6416 |

## Windows and Skylights *(Cost Each)*

| | Economy | Average | Custom | Luxury |
|---|---|---|---|---|
| **Fixed Picture Windows** | | | | |
| 3'-6" x 4'-0" | $ 344 | $ 458 | $ 610 | $ 803 |
| 4'-0" x 6'-0" | 606 | 808 | 1075 | 1414 |
| 5'-0" x 6'-0" | 677 | 902 | 1200 | 1579 |
| 6'-0" x 6'-0" | 677 | 902 | 1200 | 1579 |
| **Bay/Bow Windows** | | | | |
| 8'-0" x 5'-0" | 860 | 1146 | 1525 | 2007 |
| 10'-0" x 5'-0" | 916 | 1221 | 1625 | 2138 |
| 10'-0" x 6'-0" | 1452 | 1936 | 2575 | 3388 |
| 12'-0" x 6'-0" | 1889 | 2518 | 3350 | 4408 |
| **Palladian Windows** | | | | |
| 3'-2" x 6'-4" | | 1466 | 1950 | 2566 |
| 4'-0" x 6'-0" | | 1710 | 2275 | 2993 |
| 5'-5" x 6'-10" | | 2236 | 2975 | 3914 |
| 8'-0" x 6'-0" | | 2650 | 3525 | 4638 |
| **Skylights** | | | | |
| 46" x 21-1/2" | 416 | 450 | 590 | 637 |
| 46" x 28" | 453 | 490 | 625 | 675 |
| 57" x 44" | 550 | 595 | 735 | 793 |

## Dormers *(Cost/S.F. of plan area )*

| | Economy | Average | Custom | Luxury |
|---|---|---|---|---|
| **Framing and Roofing Only** | | | | |
| Gable dormer, 2" x 6" roof frame | $ 26 | $ 29 | $ 31 | $ 51 |
| 2" x 8" roof frame | 27 | 30 | 32 | 54 |
| Shed dormer, 2" x 6" roof frame | 16 | 18 | 20 | 33 |
| 2" x 8" roof frame | 18 | 19 | 21 | 34 |
| 2" x 10" roof frame | 19 | 21 | 22 | 35 |

## Appliances *(Cost per Unit)*

| | Economy | Average | Custom | Luxury |
|---|---|---|---|---|
| **Range** | | | | |
| 30" free standing, 1 oven | $ 440 | $ 1345 | $ 1798 | $ 2250 |
| 2 oven | 1575 | 1700 | 1763 | 1825 |
| 30" built-in, 1 oven | 820 | 1435 | 1743 | 2050 |
| 2 oven | 1900 | 2185 | 2328 | 2470 |
| 21" free standing | | | | |
| 1 oven | 420 | 468 | 492 | 515 |
| **Counter Top Ranges** | | | | |
| 4 burner standard | 400 | 603 | 704 | 805 |
| As above with griddle | 1600 | 2713 | 3269 | 3825 |
| **Microwave Oven** | 228 | 452 | 564 | 675 |
| **Compactor** | | | | |
| 4 to 1 compaction | 665 | 858 | 954 | 1050 |
| **Deep Freeze** | | | | |
| 15 to 23 C.F. | 645 | 745 | 795 | 845 |
| 30 C.F. | 990 | 1108 | 1167 | 1225 |
| **Dehumidifier,** portable, auto. | | | | |
| 15 pint | 170 | 196 | 209 | 221 |
| 30 pint | 188 | 216 | 230 | 244 |
| **Washing Machine,** automatic | 540 | 1058 | 1317 | 1575 |
| **Water Heater** | | | | |
| **Electric,** glass lined | | | | |
| 30 gal. | 680 | 828 | 902 | 975 |
| 80 gal. | 1300 | 1638 | 1807 | 1975 |
| **Water Heater, Gas,** glass lined | | | | |
| 30 gal. | 1075 | 1300 | 1413 | 1525 |
| 50 gal. | 1275 | 1575 | 1725 | 1875 |
| **Dishwasher,** built-in | | | | |
| 2 cycles | 375 | 503 | 567 | 630 |
| 4 or more cycles | 445 | 550 | 988 | 1425 |
| **Dryer,** automatic | 625 | 1200 | 1488 | 1775 |
| **Garage Door Opener** | 500 | 605 | 658 | 710 |
| **Garbage Disposal** | 135 | 201 | 234 | 266 |
| **Heater, Electric,** built-in | | | | |
| 1250 watt ceiling type | 212 | 264 | 290 | 315 |
| 1250 watt wall type | 277 | 301 | 313 | 325 |
| Wall type w/blower | | | | |
| 1500 watt | 277 | 319 | 340 | 360 |
| 3000 watt | 490 | 564 | 601 | 637 |
| **Hood For Range,** 2 speed | | | | |
| 30" wide | 172 | 636 | 868 | 1100 |
| 42" wide | 370 | 1298 | 1762 | 2225 |
| **Humidifier,** portable | | | | |
| 7 gal. per day | 182 | 210 | 224 | 237 |
| 15 gal. per day | 218 | 251 | 267 | 283 |
| **Ice Maker,** automatic | | | | |
| 13 lb. per day | 1025 | 1179 | 1256 | 1333 |
| 51 lb. per day | 1600 | 1840 | 1960 | 2080 |
| **Refrigerator,** no frost | | | | |
| 10-12 C.F. | 550 | 570 | 580 | 590 |
| 14-16 C.F. | 585 | 740 | 818 | 895 |
| 18-20 C.F. | 725 | 1038 | 1194 | 1350 |
| 21-29 C.F. | 1100 | 2338 | 2957 | 3575 |
| **Sump Pump,** 1/3 H.P. | 281 | 398 | 457 | 515 |

## Breezeway *(Cost per S.F.)*

| Class | Type | Area (S.F.) | | | |
|---|---|---|---|---|---|
| | | 50 | 100 | 150 | 200 |
| Economy | Open | $ 23.18 | $ 19.70 | $ 16.53 | $ 16.26 |
| | Enclosed | 111.19 | 85.87 | 71.31 | 62.46 |
| Average | Open | 30.49 | 26.89 | 23.52 | 21.37 |
| | Enclosed | 119.08 | 88.74 | 72.58 | 63.89 |
| Custom | Open | 40.58 | 35.72 | 31.08 | 28.44 |
| | Enclosed | 166.68 | 124.00 | 101.37 | 89.12 |
| Luxury | Open | 42.69 | 37.42 | 33.72 | 32.75 |
| | Enclosed | 171.90 | 127.49 | 103.13 | 92.32 |

## Porches *(Cost per S.F.)*

| Class | Type | Area (S.F.) | | | | |
|---|---|---|---|---|---|---|
| | | 25 | 50 | 100 | 200 | 300 |
| Economy | Open | $ 66.45 | $ 44.46 | $ 34.75 | $ 29.41 | $ 25.09 |
| | Enclosed | 132.79 | 92.53 | 69.94 | 54.56 | 46.71 |
| Average | Open | 85.84 | 54.65 | 41.93 | 34.85 | 34.85 |
| | Enclosed | 155.77 | 105.54 | 79.83 | 61.81 | 52.37 |
| Custom | Open | 103.63 | 68.76 | 51.76 | 45.22 | 40.52 |
| | Enclosed | 206.04 | 140.77 | 107.12 | 83.42 | 71.87 |
| Luxury | Open | 113.02 | 73.88 | 54.57 | 49.03 | 43.72 |
| | Enclosed | 221.26 | 155.39 | 115.28 | 89.58 | 77.11 |

## Finished attic *(Cost per S.F.)*

| Class | Area (S.F.) | | | | |
|---|---|---|---|---|---|
| | 400 | 500 | 600 | 800 | 1000 |
| Economy | $ 17.73 | $ 17.14 | $ 16.42 | $ 16.15 | $ 15.54 |
| Average | 26.66 | 26.08 | 25.44 | 25.12 | 24.42 |
| Custom | 33.03 | 32.29 | 31.56 | 31.08 | 30.44 |
| Luxury | 42.43 | 41.40 | 40.43 | 39.47 | 38.82 |

## Alarm system *(Cost per System)*

| | Burglar Alarm | Smoke Detector |
|---|---|---|
| Economy | $ 405 | $ 67 |
| Average | 460 | 81 |
| Custom | 793 | 178 |
| Luxury | 1150 | 242 |

## Sauna, prefabricated
*(Cost per unit, including heater and controls—7' high)*

| Size | Cost |
|---|---|
| 6' x 4' | $ 5250 |
| 6' x 5' | 5850 |
| 6' x 6' | 6225 |
| 6' x 9' | 7625 |
| 8' x 10' | 10,100 |
| 8' x 12' | 11,700 |
| 10' x 12' | 12,200 |

## Garages *

(Costs include exterior wall systems comparable with the quality of the residence. Included in the cost is an allowance for one personnel door, manual overhead door(s) and electrical fixture.)

| Class | Type | | | | | | | | | |
|---|---|---|---|---|---|---|---|---|---|---|
| | Detached | | | Attached | | | Built-in | | Basement | |
| | One Car | Two Car | Three Car | One Car | Two Car | Three Car | One Car | Two Car | One Car | Two Car |
| **Economy** | | | | | | | | | | |
| Wood | $14,630 | $22,195 | $29,761 | $11,273 | $19,305 | $26,871 | $-1477 | $-2953 | $1277 | $1666 |
| Masonry | 19,785 | 28,647 | 37,510 | 14,499 | 23,828 | 32,690 | -2110 | -4220 | | |
| **Average** | | | | | | | | | | |
| Wood | 16,871 | 25,001 | 33,130 | 12,676 | 21,272 | 29,401 | -1752 | -3504 | 1472 | 2056 |
| Masonry | 20,570 | 29,630 | 38,689 | 14,991 | 24,516 | 33,576 | -2206 | -3652 | | |
| **Custom** | | | | | | | | | | |
| Wood | 16,887 | 25,336 | 33,785 | 12,844 | 21,916 | 30,365 | -3574 | -4365 | 1366 | 1845 |
| Masonry | 21,566 | 31,191 | 40,816 | 15,771 | 26,020 | 35,646 | -4148 | -5514 | | |
| **Luxury** | | | | | | | | | | |
| Wood | 19,802 | 30,256 | 40,710 | 15,304 | 26,381 | 36,835 | -3723 | -4664 | 2259 | 3216 |
| Masonry | 25,168 | 36,971 | 48,774 | 18,661 | 31,088 | 42,891 | -4382 | -5982 | | |

*See the Introduction to this section for definitions of garage types.

## Swimming pools  *(Cost per S.F.)*

| | | |
|---|---|---|
| **Residential** | | (includes equipment) |
| In-ground | | $ 25.00 - 64.50 |
| Deck equipment | | 1.30 |
| **Paint pool,** preparation & 3 coats (epoxy) | | 4.75 |
| Rubber base paint | | 4.03 |
| **Pool Cover** | | .88 |
| **Swimming Pool Heaters** | | |
| (not including wiring, external piping, base or pad) | | |
| **Gas** | | |
| 155 MBH | | $ 2525.00 |
| 190 MBH | | 3050.00 |
| 500 MBH | | 10,900.00 |
| **Electric** | | |
| 15 KW | 7200 gallon pool | 2700.00 |
| 24 KW | 9600 gallon pool | 3125.00 |
| 54 KW | 24,000 gallon pool | 4850.00 |

## Wood and coal stoves

| | | |
|---|---|---|
| **Wood Only** | | |
| Free Standing (minimum) | $ | 1825 |
| Fireplace Insert (minimum) | | 1915 |
| **Coal Only** | | |
| Free Standing | $ | 2164 |
| Fireplace Insert | | 2369 |
| **Wood and Coal** | | |
| Free Standing | $ | 4450 |
| Fireplace Insert | | 4561 |

## Sidewalks  *(Cost per S.F.)*

| | | |
|---|---|---|
| Concrete, 3000 psi with wire mesh | 4" thick | $ 3.51 |
| | 5" thick | 4.27 |
| | 6" thick | 4.80 |
| Precast concrete patio blocks (natural) | 2" thick | 10.60 |
| Precast concrete patio blocks (colors) | 2" thick | 11.20 |
| Flagstone, bluestone | 1" thick | 15.15 |
| Flagstone, bluestone | 1-1/2" thick | 20.15 |
| Slate (natural, irregular) | 3/4" thick | 15.25 |
| Slate (random rectangular) | 1/2" thick | 23.30 |
| **Seeding** | | |
| Fine grading & seeding includes lime, fertilizer & seed  per S.Y. | | 2.44 |
| **Lawn Sprinkler System** | per S.F. | .89 |

## Fencing  *(Cost per L.F.)*

| | |
|---|---|
| Chain Link, 4' high, galvanized | $ 16.60 |
| Gate, 4' high (each) | 157.00 |
| Cedar Picket, 3' high, 2 rail | 12.25 |
| Gate (each) | 186.00 |
| 3 Rail, 4' high | 15.30 |
| Gate (each) | 197.00 |
| Cedar Stockade, 3 Rail, 6' high | 15.45 |
| Gate (each) | 197.00 |
| Board & Battens, 2 sides 6' high, pine | 21.00 |
| 6' high, cedar | 29.00 |
| No. 1 Cedar, basketweave, 6' high | 16.90 |
| Gate, 6' high (each) | 225.00 |

## Carport  *(Cost per S.F.)*

| | |
|---|---|
| Economy | $ 8.24 |
| Average | 12.26 |
| Custom | 18.03 |
| Luxury | 20.86 |

# Assemblies Section

## Table of Contents

# How to Use the Assemblies Cost Tables

The following is a detailed explanation of a sample Assemblies Cost Table. Included are an illustration and accompanying system descriptions. Additionally, related systems and price sheets may be included. Next to each bold number below is the item being described with the appropriate component of the sample entry following in parenthesis. General contractors should add an additional markup to the figures shown in the Assemblies section. Note: Throughout this section, the words assembly and system are used interchangeably.

## 1 System Identification (3 Framing 12)

Each Assemblies section has been assigned a unique identification number, component category, system number and system description.

**3 | FRAMING    12   Gable End Roof Framing Systems**

**1**

Labels: Sheathing, Ridge Board, Rafters, Rafter Tie, Ceiling Joists, Furring Strips, Soffit Nailer, Fascia Board

**2**

| System Description | QUAN. | UNIT | LABOR HOURS | COST PER S.F. MAT. | COST PER S.F. INST. | COST PER S.F. TOTAL |
|---|---|---|---|---|---|---|
| **2" X 6" RAFTERS, 16" O.C., 4/12 PITCH** | **4** | **5** | **6** | | **7** | |
| Rafters, 2" x 6", 16" O.C., 4/12 pitch | 1.170 | L.F. | .019 | .48 | .91 | 1.39 |
| Ceiling joists, 2" x 4", 16" O.C. | 1.000 | L.F. | .013 | .27 | .63 | .90 |
| Ridge board, 2" x 6" | .050 | L.F. | .002 | .02 | .08 | .10 |
| Fascia board, 2" x 6" | .100 | L.F. | .005 | .05 | .26 | .31 |
| Rafter tie, 1" x 4", 4' O.C. | .060 | L.F. | .001 | .03 | .06 | .09 |
| Soffit nailer (outrigger), 2" x 4", 24" O.C. | .170 | L.F. | .004 | .05 | .21 | .26 |
| Sheathing, exterior, plywood, CDX, 1/2" thick | 1.170 | S.F. | .013 | .54 | .66 | 1.20 |
| Furring strips, 1" x 3", 16" O.C. | 1.000 | L.F. | .023 | .38 | 1.12 | 1.50 |
| **3** | | | | | | |
| TOTAL | | S.F. | .080 | 1.82 | 3.93 | 5.75 |
| **2" X 8" RAFTERS, 16" O.C., 4/12 PITCH** | | | | | | **11** |
| Rafters, 2" x 8", 16" O.C., 4/12 pitch | 1.170 | L.F. | .020 | .71 | .96 | 1.67 |
| Ceiling joists, 2" x 6", 16" O.C. | 1.000 | L.F. | .013 | .41 | .63 | 1.04 |
| Ridge board, 2" x 8" | .050 | L.F. | .002 | .03 | .09 | .12 |
| Fascia board, 2" x 8" | .100 | L.F. | .007 | .06 | .35 | .41 |
| Rafter tie, 1" x 4", 4' O.C. | .060 | L.F. | .001 | .03 | .06 | .09 |
| Soffit nailer (outrigger), 2" x 4", 24" O.C. | .170 | L.F. | .004 | .05 | .21 | .26 |
| Sheathing, exterior, plywood, CDX, 1/2" thick | 1.170 | S.F. | .013 | .54 | .66 | 1.20 |
| Furring strips, 1" x 3", 16" O.C. | 1.000 | L.F. | .023 | .38 | 1.12 | 1.50 |
| **8** | | | **9** | **10** | | |
| TOTAL | | S.F. | .083 | 2.21 | 4.08 | 6.29 |

The cost of this system is based on the square foot of plan area.
All quantities have been adjusted accordingly.

| Description | QUAN. | UNIT | LABOR HOURS | COST PER S.F. MAT. | COST PER S.F. INST. | COST PER S.F. TOTAL |
|---|---|---|---|---|---|---|
| **12** | | | | | | |
| | | | | | | |
| | | | | | | |
| | | | | | | |
| | | | | | | |

## 2 Illustration

At the top of most assembly pages is an illustration with individual components labeled. Elements involved in the total system function are shown.

## 3 System Description (2" x 6" Rafters, 16" O.C., 4/12 Pitch)

The components of a typical system are listed separately to show what has been included in the development of the total system price. Each page includes a brief outline of any special conditions to be used when pricing a system. Alternative components can be found on the opposite page. Simply insert any chosen new element into the chart to develop a custom system.

## 4 Quantities for Each Component

Each material in a system is shown with the quantity required for the system unit. For example, there are 1.170 L.F. of rafter per S.F. of plan area.

## 5 Unit of Measure for Each Component

The abbreviated designation indicates the unit of measure, as defined by industry standards, upon which the individual component has been priced. In this example, items are priced by the linear foot (L.F.) or the square foot (S.F.).

## 6 Labor Hours

This is the amount of time it takes to install the quantity of the individual component.

## 7 Unit of Measure (Cost per S.F.)

In the three right-hand columns, each cost figure is adjusted to agree with the unit of measure for the entire system. In this case, cost per S.F. is the common unit of measure.

## 8 Labor Hours (.083)

The labor hours column shows the amount of time necessary to install the system per the unit of measure. For example, it takes .083 labor hours to install one square foot (plan area) of this roof framing system.

## 9 Materials (2.21)

This column contains the material cost of each element. These cost figures include 10% for profit.

## 10 Installation (4.08)

This column contains labor and equipment costs. Labor rates include bare cost and the installing contractor's overhead and profit. On the average, the labor cost will be 69.5% over the bare labor cost. Equipment costs include 10% for profit.

## 11 Totals (6.29)

The figure in this column is the sum of the material and installation costs.

## 12 Work Sheet

Using the selective price sheet on the page opposite each system, it is possible to create estimates with alternative items for any number of systems.

Backfill

Excavate

| System Description | QUAN. | UNIT | LABOR HOURS | COST EACH | | |
|---|---|---|---|---|---|---|
| | | | | MAT. | INST. | TOTAL |
| **BUILDING, 24' X 38', 4' DEEP** | | | | | | |
| Cut & chip light trees to 6" diam. | .190 | Acre | 9.120 | | 646 | 646 |
| Excavator, hydraulic, crawler mtd., 1 C.Y. cap. = 100 C.Y./hr. | 174.000 | C.Y. | 3.480 | | 341.04 | 341.04 |
| Backfill, dozer, 4" lifts, no compaction | 87.000 | C.Y. | .580 | | 122.67 | 122.67 |
| Rough grade, dozer, 30' from building | 87.000 | C.Y. | .580 | | 122.67 | 122.67 |
| TOTAL | | Ea. | 13.760 | | 1,232.38 | 1,232.38 |
| **BUILDING, 26' X 46', 4' DEEP** | | | | | | |
| Cut & chip light trees to 6" diam. | .210 | Acre | 10.080 | | 714 | 714 |
| Excavator, hydraulic, crawler mtd., 1 C.Y. cap. = 100 C.Y./hr. | 201.000 | C.Y. | 4.020 | | 393.96 | 393.96 |
| Backfill, dozer, 4" lifts, no compaction | 100.000 | C.Y. | .667 | | 141 | 141 |
| Rough grade, dozer, 30' from building | 100.000 | C.Y. | .667 | | 141 | 141 |
| TOTAL | | Ea. | 15.434 | | 1,389.96 | 1,389.96 |
| **BUILDING, 26' X 60', 4' DEEP** | | | | | | |
| Cut & chip light trees to 6" diam. | .240 | Acre | 11.520 | | 816 | 816 |
| Excavator, hydraulic, crawler mtd., 1 C.Y. cap. = 100 C.Y./hr. | 240.000 | C.Y. | 4.800 | | 470.40 | 470.40 |
| Backfill, dozer, 4" lifts, no compaction | 120.000 | C.Y. | .800 | | 169.20 | 169.20 |
| Rough grade, dozer, 30' from building | 120.000 | C.Y. | .800 | | 169.20 | 169.20 |
| TOTAL | | Ea. | 17.920 | | 1,624.80 | 1,624.80 |
| **BUILDING, 30' X 66', 4' DEEP** | | | | | | |
| Cut & chip light trees to 6" diam. | .260 | Acre | 12.480 | | 884 | 884 |
| Excavator, hydraulic, crawler mtd., 1 C.Y. cap. = 100 C.Y./hr. | 268.000 | C.Y. | 5.360 | | 525.28 | 525.28 |
| Backfill, dozer, 4" lifts, no compaction | 134.000 | C.Y. | .894 | | 188.94 | 188.94 |
| Rough grade, dozer, 30' from building | 134.000 | C.Y. | .894 | | 188.94 | 188.94 |
| TOTAL | | Ea. | 19.628 | | 1,787.16 | 1,787.16 |

The costs in this system are on a cost each basis.
Quantities are based on 1'-0" clearance on each side of footing.

| Description | QUAN. | UNIT | LABOR HOURS | COST EACH | | |
|---|---|---|---|---|---|---|
| | | | | MAT. | INST. | TOTAL |
| | | | | | | |
| | | | | | | |
| | | | | | | |

| Footing Excavation Price Sheet | QUAN. | UNIT | LABOR HOURS | COST EACH | | |
|---|---|---|---|---|---|---|
| | | | | MAT. | INST. | TOTAL |
| Clear and grub, medium brush, 30' from building, 24' x 38' | .190 | Acre | 9.120 | | 645 | 645 |
| 26' x 46' | .210 | Acre | 10.080 | | 715 | 715 |
| 26' x 60' | .240 | Acre | 11.520 | | 815 | 815 |
| 30' x 66' | .260 | Acre | 12.480 | | 885 | 885 |
| Light trees, to 6" dia. cut & chip, 24' x 38' | .190 | Acre | 9.120 | | 645 | 645 |
| 26' x 46' | .210 | Acre | 10.080 | | 715 | 715 |
| 26' x 60' | .240 | Acre | 11.520 | | 815 | 815 |
| 30' x 66' | .260 | Acre | 12.480 | | 885 | 885 |
| Medium trees, to 10" dia. cut & chip, 24' x 38' | .190 | Acre | 13.029 | | 930 | 930 |
| 26' x 46' | .210 | Acre | 14.400 | | 1,025 | 1,025 |
| 26' x 60' | .240 | Acre | 16.457 | | 1,175 | 1,175 |
| 30' x 66' | .260 | Acre | 17.829 | | 1,275 | 1,275 |
| Excavation, footing, 24' x 38', 2' deep | 68.000 | C.Y. | .906 | | 134 | 134 |
| 4' deep | 174.000 | C.Y. | 2.319 | | 340 | 340 |
| 8' deep | 384.000 | C.Y. | 5.119 | | 750 | 750 |
| 26' x 46', 2' deep | 79.000 | C.Y. | 1.053 | | 155 | 155 |
| 4' deep | 201.000 | C.Y. | 2.679 | | 395 | 395 |
| 8' deep | 404.000 | C.Y. | 5.385 | | 790 | 790 |
| 26' x 60', 2' deep | 94.000 | C.Y. | 1.253 | | 184 | 184 |
| 4' deep | 240.000 | C.Y. | 3.199 | | 470 | 470 |
| 8' deep | 483.000 | C.Y. | 6.438 | | 945 | 945 |
| 30' x 66', 2' deep | 105.000 | C.Y. | 1.400 | | 207 | 207 |
| 4' deep | 268.000 | C.Y. | 3.572 | | 525 | 525 |
| 8' deep | 539.000 | C.Y. | 7.185 | | 1,050 | 1,050 |
| Backfill, 24' x 38', 2" lifts, no compaction | 34.000 | C.Y. | .227 | | 48 | 48 |
| Compaction, air tamped, add | 34.000 | C.Y. | 2.267 | | 420 | 420 |
| 4" lifts, no compaction | 87.000 | C.Y. | .580 | | 123 | 123 |
| Compaction, air tamped, add | 87.000 | C.Y. | 5.800 | | 1,075 | 1,075 |
| 8" lifts, no compaction | 192.000 | C.Y. | 1.281 | | 271 | 271 |
| Compaction, air tamped, add | 192.000 | C.Y. | 12.801 | | 2,375 | 2,375 |
| 26' x 46', 2" lifts, no compaction | 40.000 | C.Y. | .267 | | 56.50 | 56.50 |
| Compaction, air tamped, add | 40.000 | C.Y. | 2.667 | | 490 | 490 |
| 4" lifts, no compaction | 100.000 | C.Y. | .667 | | 141 | 141 |
| Compaction, air tamped, add | 100.000 | C.Y. | 6.667 | | 1,225 | 1,225 |
| 8" lifts, no compaction | 202.000 | C.Y. | 1.347 | | 285 | 285 |
| Compaction, air tamped, add | 202.000 | C.Y. | 13.467 | | 2,500 | 2,500 |
| 26' x 60', 2" lifts, no compaction | 47.000 | C.Y. | .313 | | 66 | 66 |
| Compaction, air tamped, add | 47.000 | C.Y. | 3.133 | | 580 | 580 |
| 4" lifts, no compaction | 120.000 | C.Y. | .800 | | 170 | 170 |
| Compaction, air tamped, add | 120.000 | C.Y. | 8.000 | | 1,475 | 1,475 |
| 8" lifts, no compaction | 242.000 | C.Y. | 1.614 | | 340 | 340 |
| Compaction, air tamped, add | 242.000 | C.Y. | 16.134 | | 2,975 | 2,975 |
| 30' x 66', 2" lifts, no compaction | 53.000 | C.Y. | .354 | | 75 | 75 |
| Compaction, air tamped, add | 53.000 | C.Y. | 3.534 | | 655 | 655 |
| 4" lifts, no compaction | 134.000 | C.Y. | .894 | | 189 | 189 |
| Compaction, air tamped, add | 134.000 | C.Y. | 8.934 | | 1,650 | 1,650 |
| 8" lifts, no compaction | 269.000 | C.Y. | 1.794 | | 380 | 380 |
| Compaction, air tamped, add | 269.000 | C.Y. | 17.934 | | 3,300 | 3,300 |
| Rough grade, 30' from building, 24' x 38' | 87.000 | C.Y. | .580 | | 123 | 123 |
| 26' x 46' | 100.000 | C.Y. | .667 | | 141 | 141 |
| 26' x 60' | 120.000 | C.Y. | .800 | | 170 | 170 |
| 30' x 66' | 134.000 | C.Y. | .894 | | 189 | 189 |
| | | | | | | |
| | | | | | | |
| | | | | | | |
| | | | | | | |

Backfill

Excavate

| System Description | QUAN. | UNIT | LABOR HOURS | COST EACH | | |
|---|---|---|---|---|---|---|
| | | | | MAT. | INST. | TOTAL |
| **BUILDING, 24' X 38', 8' DEEP** | | | | | | |
| Medium clearing | .190 | Acre | 2.027 | | 251.75 | 251.75 |
| Excavate, track loader, 1-1/2 C.Y. bucket | 550.000 | C.Y. | 7.860 | | 847 | 847 |
| Backfill, dozer, 8″ lifts, no compaction | 180.000 | C.Y. | 1.201 | | 253.80 | 253.80 |
| Rough grade, dozer, 30' from building | 280.000 | C.Y. | 1.868 | | 394.80 | 394.80 |
| TOTAL | | Ea. | 12.956 | | 1,747.35 | 1,747.35 |
| **BUILDING, 26' X 46', 8' DEEP** | | | | | | |
| Medium clearing | .210 | Acre | 2.240 | | 278.25 | 278.25 |
| Excavate, track loader, 1-1/2 C.Y. bucket | 672.000 | C.Y. | 9.603 | | 1,034.88 | 1,034.88 |
| Backfill, dozer, 8″ lifts, no compaction | 220.000 | C.Y. | 1.467 | | 310.20 | 310.20 |
| Rough grade, dozer, 30' from building | 340.000 | C.Y. | 2.268 | | 479.40 | 479.40 |
| TOTAL | | Ea. | 15.578 | | 2,102.73 | 2,102.73 |
| **BUILDING, 26' X 60', 8' DEEP** | | | | | | |
| Medium clearing | .240 | Acre | 2.560 | | 318 | 318 |
| Excavate, track loader, 1-1/2 C.Y. bucket | 829.000 | C.Y. | 11.846 | | 1,276.66 | 1,276.66 |
| Backfill, dozer, 8″ lifts, no compaction | 270.000 | C.Y. | 1.801 | | 380.70 | 380.70 |
| Rough grade, dozer, 30' from building | 420.000 | C.Y. | 2.801 | | 592.20 | 592.20 |
| TOTAL | | Ea. | 19.008 | | 2,567.56 | 2,567.56 |
| **BUILDING, 30' X 66', 8' DEEP** | | | | | | |
| Medium clearing | .260 | Acre | 2.773 | | 344.50 | 344.50 |
| Excavate, track loader, 1-1/2 C.Y. bucket | 990.000 | C.Y. | 14.147 | | 1,524.60 | 1,524.60 |
| Backfill dozer, 8″ lifts, no compaction | 320.000 | C.Y. | 2.134 | | 451.20 | 451.20 |
| Rough grade, dozer, 30' from building | 500.000 | C.Y. | 3.335 | | 705 | 705 |
| TOTAL | | Ea. | 22.389 | | 3,025.30 | 3,025.30 |

The costs in this system are on a cost each basis.
Quantities are based on 1'-0″ clearance beyond footing projection.

| Description | QUAN. | UNIT | LABOR HOURS | COST EACH | | |
|---|---|---|---|---|---|---|
| | | | | MAT. | INST. | TOTAL |
| | | | | | | |
| | | | | | | |
| | | | | | | |

| Foundation Excavation Price Sheet | QUAN. | UNIT | LABOR HOURS | COST EACH | | |
|---|---|---|---|---|---|---|
| | | | | MAT. | INST. | TOTAL |
| Clear & grub, medium brush, 30' from building, 24' x 38' | .190 | Acre | 2.027 | | 252 | 252 |
| 26' x 46' | .210 | Acre | 2.240 | | 279 | 279 |
| 26' x 60' | .240 | Acre | 2.560 | | 320 | 320 |
| 30' x 66' | .260 | Acre | 2.773 | | 345 | 345 |
| Light trees, to 6" dia. cut & chip, 24' x 38' | .190 | Acre | 9.120 | | 645 | 645 |
| 26' x 46' | .210 | Acre | 10.080 | | 715 | 715 |
| 26' x 60' | .240 | Acre | 11.520 | | 815 | 815 |
| 30' x 66' | .260 | Acre | 12.480 | | 885 | 885 |
| Medium trees, to 10" dia. cut & chip, 24' x 38' | .190 | Acre | 13.029 | | 930 | 930 |
| 26' x 46' | .210 | Acre | 14.400 | | 1,025 | 1,025 |
| 26' x 60' | .240 | Acre | 16.457 | | 1,175 | 1,175 |
| 30' x 66' | .260 | Acre | 17.829 | | 1,275 | 1,275 |
| Excavation, basement, 24' x 38', 2' deep | 98.000 | C.Y. | 1.400 | | 151 | 151 |
| 4' deep | 220.000 | C.Y. | 3.144 | | 340 | 340 |
| 8' deep | 550.000 | C.Y. | 7.860 | | 850 | 850 |
| 26' x 46', 2' deep | 123.000 | C.Y. | 1.758 | | 190 | 190 |
| 4' deep | 274.000 | C.Y. | 3.915 | | 420 | 420 |
| 8' deep | 672.000 | C.Y. | 9.603 | | 1,025 | 1,025 |
| 26' x 60', 2' deep | 157.000 | C.Y. | 2.244 | | 241 | 241 |
| 4' deep | 345.000 | C.Y. | 4.930 | | 530 | 530 |
| 8' deep | 829.000 | C.Y. | 11.846 | | 1,275 | 1,275 |
| 30' x 66', 2' deep | 192.000 | C.Y. | 2.744 | | 295 | 295 |
| 4' deep | 419.000 | C.Y. | 5.988 | | 645 | 645 |
| 8' deep | 990.000 | C.Y. | 14.147 | | 1,525 | 1,525 |
| Backfill, 24' x 38', 2" lifts, no compaction | 32.000 | C.Y. | .213 | | 45.50 | 45.50 |
| Compaction, air tamped, add | 32.000 | C.Y. | 2.133 | | 395 | 395 |
| 4" lifts, no compaction | 72.000 | C.Y. | .480 | | 102 | 102 |
| Compaction, air tamped, add | 72.000 | C.Y. | 4.800 | | 890 | 890 |
| 8" lifts, no compaction | 180.000 | C.Y. | 1.201 | | 254 | 254 |
| Compaction, air tamped, add | 180.000 | C.Y. | 12.001 | | 2,225 | 2,225 |
| 26' x 46', 2" lifts, no compaction | 40.000 | C.Y. | .267 | | 56.50 | 56.50 |
| Compaction, air tamped, add | 40.000 | C.Y. | 2.667 | | 490 | 490 |
| 4" lifts, no compaction | 90.000 | C.Y. | .600 | | 127 | 127 |
| Compaction, air tamped, add | 90.000 | C.Y. | 6.000 | | 1,100 | 1,100 |
| 8" lifts, no compaction | 220.000 | C.Y. | 1.467 | | 310 | 310 |
| Compacton, air tamped, add | 220.000 | C.Y. | 14.667 | | 2,700 | 2,700 |
| 26' x 60', 2" lifts, no compaction | 50.000 | C.Y. | .334 | | 70.50 | 70.50 |
| Compaction, air tamped, add | 50.000 | C.Y. | 3.334 | | 615 | 615 |
| 4" lifts, no compaction | 110.000 | C.Y. | .734 | | 155 | 155 |
| Compaction, air tamped, add | 110.000 | C.Y. | 7.334 | | 1,350 | 1,350 |
| 8" lifts, no compaction | 270.000 | C.Y. | 1.801 | | 380 | 380 |
| Compaction, air tamped, add | 270.000 | C.Y. | 18.001 | | 3,350 | 3,350 |
| 30' x 66', 2" lifts, no compaction | 60.000 | C.Y. | .400 | | 84.50 | 84.50 |
| Compaction, air tamped, add | 60.000 | C.Y. | 4.000 | | 740 | 740 |
| 4" lifts, no compaction | 130.000 | C.Y. | .867 | | 184 | 184 |
| Compaction, air tamped, add | 130.000 | C.Y. | 8.667 | | 1,600 | 1,600 |
| 8" lifts, no compaction | 320.000 | C.Y. | 2.134 | | 450 | 450 |
| Compaction, air tamped, add | 320.000 | C.Y. | 21.334 | | 3,950 | 3,950 |
| Rough grade, 30' from building, 24' x 38' | 280.000 | C.Y. | 1.868 | | 395 | 395 |
| 26' x 46' | 340.000 | C.Y. | 2.268 | | 480 | 480 |
| 26' x 60' | 420.000 | C.Y. | 2.801 | | 595 | 595 |
| 30' x 66' | 500.000 | C.Y. | 3.335 | | 705 | 705 |

Backfill

Bedding

Sewer Pipe

Excavation

| System Description | QUAN. | UNIT | LABOR HOURS | COST PER L.F. | | |
|---|---|---|---|---|---|---|
| | | | | MAT. | INST. | TOTAL |
| **2' DEEP** | | | | | | |
| Excavation, backhoe | .296 | C.Y. | .032 | | 2.07 | 2.07 |
| Alternate pricing method, 4" deep | .111 | C.Y. | .044 | 2.33 | 1.86 | 4.19 |
| Utility, sewer, 6" cast iron | 1.000 | L.F. | .283 | 20.21 | 13.80 | 34.01 |
| Compaction in 12" layers, hand tamp, add to above | .185 | C.Y. | .044 | | 1.57 | 1.57 |
| TOTAL | | L.F. | .403 | 22.54 | 19.30 | 41.84 |
| **4' DEEP** | | | | | | |
| Excavation, backhoe | .889 | C.Y. | .095 | | 6.22 | 6.22 |
| Alternate pricing method, 4" deep | .111 | C.Y. | .044 | 2.33 | 1.86 | 4.19 |
| Utility, sewer, 6" cast iron | 1.000 | L.F. | .283 | 20.21 | 13.80 | 34.01 |
| Compaction in 12" layers, hand tamp, add to above | .778 | C.Y. | .183 | | 6.61 | 6.61 |
| TOTAL | | L.F. | .605 | 22.54 | 28.49 | 51.03 |
| **6' DEEP** | | | | | | |
| Excavation, backhoe | 1.770 | C.Y. | .189 | | 12.39 | 12.39 |
| Alternate pricing method, 4" deep | .111 | C.Y. | .044 | 2.33 | 1.86 | 4.19 |
| Utility, sewer, 6" cast iron | 1.000 | L.F. | .283 | 20.21 | 13.80 | 34.01 |
| Compaction in 12" layers, hand tamp, add to above | 1.660 | C.Y. | .391 | | 14.11 | 14.11 |
| TOTAL | | L.F. | .907 | 22.54 | 42.16 | 64.70 |
| **8' DEEP** | | | | | | |
| Excavation, backhoe | 2.960 | C.Y. | .316 | | 20.72 | 20.72 |
| Alternate pricing method, 4" deep | .111 | C.Y. | .044 | 2.33 | 1.86 | 4.19 |
| Utility, sewer, 6" cast iron | 1.000 | L.F. | .283 | 20.21 | 13.80 | 34.01 |
| Compaction in 12" layers, hand tamp, add to above | 2.850 | C.Y. | .671 | | 24.23 | 24.23 |
| TOTAL | | L.F. | 1.314 | 22.54 | 60.61 | 83.15 |

The costs in this system are based on a cost per linear foot of trench,
and based on 2' wide at bottom of trench up to 6' deep.

| Description | QUAN. | UNIT | LABOR HOURS | COST PER L.F. | | |
|---|---|---|---|---|---|---|
| | | | | MAT. | INST. | TOTAL |
| | | | | | | |
| | | | | | | |
| | | | | | | |

| Utility Trenching Price Sheet | QUAN. | UNIT | LABOR HOURS | COST PER UNIT | | |
|---|---|---|---|---|---|---|
| | | | | MAT. | INST. | TOTAL |
| Excavation, bottom of trench 2' wide, 2' deep | .296 | C.Y. | .032 | | 2.07 | 2.07 |
| 4' deep | .889 | C.Y. | .095 | | 6.20 | 6.20 |
| 6' deep | 1.770 | C.Y. | .142 | | 9.75 | 9.75 |
| 8' deep | 2.960 | C.Y. | .105 | | 18.90 | 18.90 |
| Bedding, sand, bottom of trench 2' wide, no compaction, pipe, 2" diameter | .070 | C.Y. | .028 | 1.47 | 1.18 | 2.65 |
| 4" diameter | .084 | C.Y. | .034 | 1.76 | 1.41 | 3.17 |
| 6" diameter | .105 | C.Y. | .042 | 2.21 | 1.77 | 3.98 |
| 8" diameter | .122 | C.Y. | .049 | 2.56 | 2.05 | 4.61 |
| Compacted, pipe, 2" diameter | .074 | C.Y. | .030 | 1.55 | 1.24 | 2.79 |
| 4" diameter | .092 | C.Y. | .037 | 1.93 | 1.55 | 3.48 |
| 6" diameter | .111 | C.Y. | .044 | 2.33 | 1.86 | 4.19 |
| 8" diameter | .129 | C.Y. | .052 | 2.71 | 2.17 | 4.88 |
| 3/4" stone, bottom of trench 2' wide, pipe, 4" diameter | .082 | C.Y. | .033 | 1.72 | 1.37 | 3.09 |
| 6" diameter | .099 | C.Y. | .040 | 2.08 | 1.66 | 3.74 |
| 3/8" stone, bottom of trench 2' wide, pipe, 4" diameter | .084 | C.Y. | .034 | 1.76 | 1.41 | 3.17 |
| 6" diameter | .102 | C.Y. | .041 | 2.14 | 1.71 | 3.85 |
| Utilities, drainage & sewerage, corrugated plastic, 6" diameter | 1.000 | L.F. | .069 | 4 | 2.56 | 6.56 |
| 8" diameter | 1.000 | L.F. | .072 | 8.65 | 2.67 | 11.32 |
| Bituminous fiber, 4" diameter | 1.000 | L.F. | .064 | 1.85 | 2.39 | 4.24 |
| 6" diameter | 1.000 | L.F. | .069 | 4 | 2.56 | 6.56 |
| 8" diameter | 1.000 | L.F. | .072 | 8.65 | 2.67 | 11.32 |
| Concrete, non-reinforced, 6" diameter | 1.000 | L.F. | .181 | 6.90 | 8.35 | 15.25 |
| 8" diameter | 1.000 | L.F. | .214 | 7.55 | 9.90 | 17.45 |
| PVC, SDR 35, 4" diameter | 1.000 | L.F. | .064 | 1.85 | 2.39 | 4.24 |
| 6" diameter | 1.000 | L.F. | .069 | 4 | 2.56 | 6.56 |
| 8" diameter | 1.000 | L.F. | .072 | 8.65 | 2.67 | 11.32 |
| Vitrified clay, 4" diameter | 1.000 | L.F. | .091 | 1.98 | 3.38 | 5.36 |
| 6" diameter | 1.000 | L.F. | .120 | 3.32 | 4.47 | 7.79 |
| 8" diameter | 1.000 | L.F. | .140 | 4.71 | 6.25 | 10.96 |
| Gas & service, polyethylene, 1-1/4" diameter | 1.000 | L.F. | .059 | 2.82 | 2.60 | 5.42 |
| Steel sched.40, 1" diameter | 1.000 | L.F. | .107 | 8.55 | 5.90 | 14.45 |
| 2" diameter | 1.000 | L.F. | .114 | 13.40 | 6.35 | 19.75 |
| Sub-drainage, PVC, perforated, 3" diameter | 1.000 | L.F. | .064 | 1.85 | 2.39 | 4.24 |
| 4" diameter | 1.000 | L.F. | .064 | 1.85 | 2.39 | 4.24 |
| 5" diameter | 1.000 | L.F. | .069 | 4 | 2.56 | 6.56 |
| 6" diameter | 1.000 | L.F. | .069 | 4 | 2.56 | 6.56 |
| Porous wall concrete, 4" diameter | 1.000 | L.F. | .072 | 3.74 | 2.67 | 6.41 |
| Vitrified clay, perforated, 4" diameter | 1.000 | L.F. | .120 | 3.52 | 5.55 | 9.07 |
| 6" diameter | 1.000 | L.F. | .152 | 5.85 | 7.05 | 12.90 |
| Water service, copper, type K, 3/4" | 1.000 | L.F. | .083 | 5.10 | 4.70 | 9.80 |
| 1" diameter | 1.000 | L.F. | .093 | 6.75 | 5.25 | 12 |
| PVC, 3/4" | 1.000 | L.F. | .121 | 1.60 | 6.80 | 8.40 |
| 1" diameter | 1.000 | L.F. | .134 | 1.85 | 7.55 | 9.40 |
| Backfill, bottom of trench 2' wide no compact, 2' deep, pipe, 2" diameter | .226 | L.F. | .053 | | 1.92 | 1.92 |
| 4" diameter | .212 | L.F. | .050 | | 1.80 | 1.80 |
| 6" diameter | .185 | L.F. | .044 | | 1.57 | 1.57 |
| 4' deep, pipe, 2" diameter | .819 | C.Y. | .193 | | 6.95 | 6.95 |
| 4" diameter | .805 | C.Y. | .189 | | 6.85 | 6.85 |
| 6" diameter | .778 | C.Y. | .183 | | 6.60 | 6.60 |
| 6' deep, pipe, 2" diameter | 1.700 | C.Y. | .400 | | 14.45 | 14.45 |
| 4" diameter | 1.690 | C.Y. | .398 | | 14.35 | 14.35 |
| 6" diameter | 1.660 | C.Y. | .391 | | 14.10 | 14.10 |
| 8' deep, pipe, 2" diameter | 2.890 | C.Y. | .680 | | 24.50 | 24.50 |
| 4" diameter | 2.870 | C.Y. | .675 | | 24.50 | 24.50 |
| 6" diameter | 2.850 | C.Y. | .671 | | 24 | 24 |

Asphalt — Brick Edge — Gravel Fill

| System Description | QUAN. | UNIT | LABOR HOURS | COST PER S.F. | | |
|---|---|---|---|---|---|---|
| | | | | MAT. | INST. | TOTAL |
| **ASPHALT SIDEWALK SYSTEM, 3′ WIDE WALK** | | | | | | |
| Gravel fill, 4″ deep | 1.000 | S.F. | .001 | .35 | .05 | .40 |
| Compact fill | .012 | C.Y. | | | .02 | .02 |
| Handgrade | 1.000 | S.F. | .004 | | .15 | .15 |
| Walking surface, bituminous paving, 2″ thick | 1.000 | S.F. | .007 | .84 | .31 | 1.15 |
| Edging, brick, laid on edge | .670 | L.F. | .079 | 2.06 | 3.45 | 5.51 |
| TOTAL | | S.F. | .091 | 3.25 | 3.98 | 7.23 |
| **CONCRETE SIDEWALK SYSTEM, 3′ WIDE WALK** | | | | | | |
| Gravel fill, 4″ deep | 1.000 | S.F. | .001 | .35 | .05 | .40 |
| Compact fill | .012 | C.Y. | | | .02 | .02 |
| Handgrade | 1.000 | S.F. | .004 | | .15 | .15 |
| Walking surface, concrete, 4″ thick | 1.000 | S.F. | .040 | 1.78 | 1.73 | 3.51 |
| Edging, brick, laid on edge | .670 | L.F. | .079 | 2.06 | 3.45 | 5.51 |
| TOTAL | | S.F. | .124 | 4.19 | 5.40 | 9.59 |
| **PAVERS, BRICK SIDEWALK SYSTEM, 3′ WIDE WALK** | | | | | | |
| Sand base fill, 4″ deep | 1.000 | S.F. | .001 | .43 | .08 | .51 |
| Compact fill | .012 | C.Y. | | | .02 | .02 |
| Handgrade | 1.000 | S.F. | .004 | | .15 | .15 |
| Walking surface, brick pavers | 1.000 | S.F. | .160 | 3.30 | 6.95 | 10.25 |
| Edging, redwood, untreated, 1″ x 4″ | .670 | L.F. | .032 | 1.66 | 1.58 | 3.24 |
| TOTAL | | S.F. | .197 | 5.39 | 8.78 | 14.17 |

The costs in this system are based on a cost per square foot of sidewalk area. Concrete used is 3000 p.s.i.

| Description | QUAN. | UNIT | LABOR HOURS | COST PER S.F. | | |
|---|---|---|---|---|---|---|
| | | | | MAT. | INST. | TOTAL |
| | | | | | | |
| | | | | | | |
| | | | | | | |
| | | | | | | |
| | | | | | | |

| Sidewalk Price Sheet | QUAN. | UNIT | LABOR HOURS | COST PER S.F. | | |
|---|---|---|---|---|---|---|
| | | | | MAT. | INST. | TOTAL |
| Base, crushed stone, 3" deep | 1.000 | S.F. | .001 | .41 | .09 | .50 |
| 6" deep | 1.000 | S.F. | .001 | .83 | .10 | .93 |
| 9" deep | 1.000 | S.F. | .002 | 1.21 | .12 | 1.33 |
| 12" deep | 1.000 | S.F. | .002 | 1.71 | .16 | 1.87 |
| Bank run gravel, 6" deep | 1.000 | S.F. | .001 | .52 | .07 | .59 |
| 9" deep | 1.000 | S.F. | .001 | .76 | .10 | .86 |
| 12" deep | 1.000 | S.F. | .001 | 1.05 | .12 | 1.17 |
| Compact base, 3" deep | .009 | C.Y. | .001 | | .01 | .01 |
| 6" deep | .019 | C.Y. | .001 | | .03 | .03 |
| 9" deep | .028 | C.Y. | .001 | | .04 | .04 |
| Handgrade | 1.000 | S.F. | .004 | | .15 | .15 |
| Surface, brick, pavers dry joints, laid flat, running bond | 1.000 | S.F. | .160 | 3.30 | 6.95 | 10.25 |
| Basket weave | 1.000 | S.F. | .168 | 3.84 | 7.35 | 11.19 |
| Herringbone | 1.000 | S.F. | .174 | 3.84 | 7.55 | 11.39 |
| Laid on edge, running bond | 1.000 | S.F. | .229 | 3.50 | 9.95 | 13.45 |
| Mortar jts. laid flat, running bond | 1.000 | S.F. | .192 | 3.96 | 8.35 | 12.31 |
| Basket weave | 1.000 | S.F. | .202 | 4.61 | 8.80 | 13.41 |
| Herringbone | 1.000 | S.F. | .209 | 4.61 | 9.05 | 13.66 |
| Laid on edge, running bond | 1.000 | S.F. | .274 | 4.20 | 11.95 | 16.15 |
| Bituminous paving, 1-1/2" thick | 1.000 | S.F. | .006 | .63 | .23 | .86 |
| 2" thick | 1.000 | S.F. | .007 | .84 | .31 | 1.15 |
| 2-1/2" thick | 1.000 | S.F. | .008 | 1.07 | .34 | 1.41 |
| Sand finish, 3/4" thick | 1.000 | S.F. | .001 | .36 | .11 | .47 |
| 1" thick | 1.000 | S.F. | .001 | .44 | .13 | .57 |
| Concrete, reinforced, broom finish, 4" thick | 1.000 | S.F. | .040 | 1.78 | 1.73 | 3.51 |
| 5" thick | 1.000 | S.F. | .044 | 2.37 | 1.90 | 4.27 |
| 6" thick | 1.000 | S.F. | .047 | 2.77 | 2.03 | 4.80 |
| Crushed stone, white marble, 3" thick | 1.000 | S.F. | .009 | .24 | .34 | .58 |
| Bluestone, 3" thick | 1.000 | S.F. | .009 | .26 | .34 | .60 |
| Flagging, bluestone, 1" | 1.000 | S.F. | .198 | 6.55 | 8.60 | 15.15 |
| 1-1/2" | 1.000 | S.F. | .188 | 11.95 | 8.20 | 20.15 |
| Slate, natural cleft, 3/4" | 1.000 | S.F. | .174 | 7.70 | 7.55 | 15.25 |
| Random rect., 1/2" | 1.000 | S.F. | .152 | 16.65 | 6.65 | 23.30 |
| Granite blocks | 1.000 | S.F. | .174 | 11.05 | 7.55 | 18.60 |
| Edging, corrugated aluminum, 4", 3' wide walk | .666 | L.F. | .008 | .53 | .40 | .93 |
| 4' wide walk | .500 | L.F. | .006 | .40 | .30 | .70 |
| 6", 3' wide walk | .666 | L.F. | .010 | .66 | .47 | 1.13 |
| 4' wide walk | .500 | L.F. | .007 | .50 | .36 | .86 |
| Redwood-cedar-cypress, 1" x 4", 3' wide walk | .666 | L.F. | .021 | .85 | 1.05 | 1.90 |
| 4' wide walk | .500 | L.F. | .016 | .64 | .79 | 1.43 |
| 2" x 4", 3' wide walk | .666 | L.F. | .032 | 1.66 | 1.58 | 3.24 |
| 4' wide walk | .500 | L.F. | .024 | 1.25 | 1.19 | 2.44 |
| Brick, dry joints, 3' wide walk | .666 | L.F. | .079 | 2.06 | 3.45 | 5.51 |
| 4' wide walk | .500 | L.F. | .059 | 1.54 | 2.58 | 4.12 |
| Mortar joints, 3' wide walk | .666 | L.F. | .095 | 2.48 | 4.14 | 6.62 |
| 4' wide walk | .500 | L.F. | .071 | 1.85 | 3.09 | 4.94 |
| | | | | | | |
| | | | | | | |
| | | | | | | |
| | | | | | | |
| | | | | | | |

109

| System Description | QUAN. | UNIT | LABOR HOURS | COST PER S.F. | | |
|---|---|---|---|---|---|---|
| | | | | MAT. | INST. | TOTAL |
| **ASPHALT DRIVEWAY TO 10' WIDE** | | | | | | |
| Excavation, driveway to 10' wide, 6" deep | .019 | C.Y. | | | .04 | .04 |
| Base, 6" crushed stone | 1.000 | S.F. | .001 | .83 | .10 | .93 |
| Handgrade base | 1.000 | S.F. | .004 | | .15 | .15 |
| 2" thick base | 1.000 | S.F. | .002 | .84 | .18 | 1.02 |
| 1" topping | 1.000 | S.F. | .001 | .44 | .13 | .57 |
| Edging, brick pavers | .200 | L.F. | .024 | .62 | 1.03 | 1.65 |
| TOTAL | | S.F. | .032 | 2.73 | 1.63 | 4.36 |
| **CONCRETE DRIVEWAY TO 10' WIDE** | | | | | | |
| Excavation, driveway to 10' wide, 6" deep | .019 | C.Y. | | | .04 | .04 |
| Base, 6" crushed stone | 1.000 | S.F. | .001 | .83 | .10 | .93 |
| Handgrade base | 1.000 | S.F. | .004 | | .15 | .15 |
| Surface, concrete, 4" thick | 1.000 | S.F. | .040 | 1.78 | 1.73 | 3.51 |
| Edging, brick pavers | .200 | L.F. | .024 | .62 | 1.03 | 1.65 |
| TOTAL | | S.F. | .069 | 3.23 | 3.05 | 6.28 |
| **PAVERS, BRICK DRIVEWAY TO 10' WIDE** | | | | | | |
| Excavation, driveway to 10' wide, 6" deep | .019 | C.Y. | | | .04 | .04 |
| Base, 6" sand | 1.000 | S.F. | .001 | .68 | .13 | .81 |
| Handgrade base | 1.000 | S.F. | .004 | | .15 | .15 |
| Surface, pavers, brick laid flat, running bond | 1.000 | S.F. | .160 | 3.30 | 6.95 | 10.25 |
| Edging, redwood, untreated, 2" x 4" | .200 | L.F. | .010 | .50 | .47 | .97 |
| TOTAL | | S.F. | .175 | 4.48 | 7.74 | 12.22 |

| Description | QUAN. | UNIT | LABOR HOURS | COST PER S.F. | | |
|---|---|---|---|---|---|---|
| | | | | MAT. | INST. | TOTAL |
| | | | | | | |
| | | | | | | |
| | | | | | | |
| | | | | | | |
| | | | | | | |

| Driveway Price Sheet | QUAN. | UNIT | LABOR HOURS | COST PER S.F. | | |
|---|---|---|---|---|---|---|
| | | | | MAT. | INST. | TOTAL |
| Excavation, by machine, 10' wide, 6" deep | .019 | C.Y. | .001 | | .04 | .04 |
| 12" deep | .037 | C.Y. | .001 | | .07 | .07 |
| 18" deep | .055 | C.Y. | .001 | | .11 | .11 |
| 20' wide, 6" deep | .019 | C.Y. | .001 | | .04 | .04 |
| 12" deep | .037 | C.Y. | .001 | | .07 | .07 |
| 18" deep | .055 | C.Y. | .001 | | .11 | .11 |
| Base, crushed stone, 10' wide, 3" deep | 1.000 | S.F. | .001 | .42 | .06 | .48 |
| 6" deep | 1.000 | S.F. | .001 | .83 | .10 | .93 |
| 9" deep | 1.000 | S.F. | .002 | 1.21 | .12 | 1.33 |
| 20' wide, 3" deep | 1.000 | S.F. | .001 | .42 | .06 | .48 |
| 6" deep | 1.000 | S.F. | .001 | .83 | .10 | .93 |
| 9" deep | 1.000 | S.F. | .002 | 1.21 | .12 | 1.33 |
| Bank run gravel, 10' wide, 3" deep | 1.000 | S.F. | .001 | .26 | .04 | .30 |
| 6" deep | 1.000 | S.F. | .001 | .52 | .07 | .59 |
| 9" deep | 1.000 | S.F. | .001 | .76 | .10 | .86 |
| 20' wide, 3" deep | 1.000 | S.F. | .001 | .26 | .04 | .30 |
| 6" deep | 1.000 | S.F. | .001 | .52 | .07 | .59 |
| 9" deep | 1.000 | S.F. | .001 | .76 | .10 | .86 |
| Handgrade, 10' wide | 1.000 | S.F. | .004 | | .15 | .15 |
| 20' wide | 1.000 | S.F. | .004 | | .15 | .15 |
| Surface, asphalt, 10' wide, 3/4" topping, 1" base | 1.000 | S.F. | .002 | 1.01 | .24 | 1.25 |
| 2" base | 1.000 | S.F. | .003 | 1.20 | .29 | 1.49 |
| 1" topping, 1" base | 1.000 | S.F. | .002 | 1.09 | .26 | 1.35 |
| 2" base | 1.000 | S.F. | .003 | 1.28 | .31 | 1.59 |
| 20' wide, 3/4" topping, 1" base | 1.000 | S.F. | .002 | 1.01 | .24 | 1.25 |
| 2" base | 1.000 | S.F. | .003 | 1.20 | .29 | 1.49 |
| 1" topping, 1" base | 1.000 | S.F. | .002 | 1.09 | .26 | 1.35 |
| 2" base | 1.000 | S.F. | .003 | 1.28 | .31 | 1.59 |
| Concrete, 10' wide, 4" thick | 1.000 | S.F. | .040 | 1.78 | 1.73 | 3.51 |
| 6" thick | 1.000 | S.F. | .047 | 2.77 | 2.03 | 4.80 |
| 20' wide, 4" thick | 1.000 | S.F. | .040 | 1.78 | 1.73 | 3.51 |
| 6" thick | 1.000 | S.F. | .047 | 2.77 | 2.03 | 4.80 |
| Paver, brick 10' wide dry joints, running bond, laid flat | 1.000 | S.F. | .160 | 3.30 | 6.95 | 10.25 |
| Laid on edge | 1.000 | S.F. | .229 | 3.50 | 9.95 | 13.45 |
| Mortar joints, laid flat | 1.000 | S.F. | .192 | 3.96 | 8.35 | 12.31 |
| Laid on edge | 1.000 | S.F. | .274 | 4.20 | 11.95 | 16.15 |
| 20' wide, running bond, dry jts., laid flat | 1.000 | S.F. | .160 | 3.30 | 6.95 | 10.25 |
| Laid on edge | 1.000 | S.F. | .229 | 3.50 | 9.95 | 13.45 |
| Mortar joints, laid flat | 1.000 | S.F. | .192 | 3.96 | 8.35 | 12.31 |
| Laid on edge | 1.000 | S.F. | .274 | 4.20 | 11.95 | 16.15 |
| Crushed stone, 10' wide, white marble, 3" | 1.000 | S.F. | .009 | .24 | .34 | .58 |
| Bluestone, 3" | 1.000 | S.F. | .009 | .26 | .34 | .60 |
| 20' wide, white marble, 3" | 1.000 | S.F. | .009 | .24 | .34 | .58 |
| Bluestone, 3" | 1.000 | S.F. | .009 | .26 | .34 | .60 |
| Soil cement, 10' wide | 1.000 | S.F. | .007 | .41 | .88 | 1.29 |
| 20' wide | 1.000 | S.F. | .007 | .41 | .88 | 1.29 |
| Granite blocks, 10' wide | 1.000 | S.F. | .174 | 11.05 | 7.55 | 18.60 |
| 20' wide | 1.000 | S.F. | .174 | 11.05 | 7.55 | 18.60 |
| Asphalt block, solid 1-1/4" thick | 1.000 | S.F. | .119 | 8.60 | 5.15 | 13.75 |
| Solid 3" thick | 1.000 | S.F. | .123 | 12.05 | 5.35 | 17.40 |
| Edging, brick, 10' wide | .200 | L.F. | .024 | .62 | 1.03 | 1.65 |
| 20' wide | .100 | L.F. | .012 | .31 | .52 | .83 |
| Redwood, untreated 2" x 4", 10' wide | .200 | L.F. | .010 | .50 | .47 | .97 |
| 20' wide | .100 | L.F. | .005 | .25 | .24 | .49 |
| Granite, 4 1/2" x 12" straight, 10' wide | .200 | L.F. | .032 | 1.33 | 1.85 | 3.18 |
| 20' wide | .100 | L.F. | .016 | .67 | .93 | 1.60 |
| Finishes, asphalt sealer, 10' wide | 1.000 | S.F. | .023 | 1.16 | .85 | 2.01 |
| 20' wide | 1.000 | S.F. | .023 | 1.16 | .85 | 2.01 |
| Concrete, exposed aggregate 10' wide | 1.000 | S.F. | .013 | .25 | .57 | .82 |
| 20' wide | 1.000 | S.F. | .013 | .25 | .57 | .82 |

| System Description | QUAN. | UNIT | LABOR HOURS | COST EACH | | |
|---|---|---|---|---|---|---|
| | | | | MAT. | INST. | TOTAL |
| **SEPTIC SYSTEM WITH 1000 S.F. LEACHING FIELD, 1000 GALLON TANK** | | | | | | |
| Tank, 1000 gallon, concrete | 1.000 | Ea. | 3.500 | 825 | 156 | 981 |
| Distribution box, concrete | 1.000 | Ea. | 1.000 | 88 | 36 | 124 |
| 4" PVC pipe | 25.000 | L.F. | 1.600 | 46.25 | 59.75 | 106 |
| Tank and field excavation | 119.000 | C.Y. | 13.130 | | 1,179.29 | 1,179.29 |
| Crushed stone backfill | 76.000 | C.Y. | 12.160 | 2,584 | 671.08 | 3,255.08 |
| Backfill with excavated material | 36.000 | C.Y. | .240 | | 50.76 | 50.76 |
| Building paper | 125.000 | S.Y. | 2.430 | 67.50 | 123.75 | 191.25 |
| 4" PVC perforated pipe | 145.000 | L.F. | 9.280 | 268.25 | 346.55 | 614.80 |
| 4" pipe fittings | 2.000 | Ea. | 1.939 | 22.20 | 98 | 120.20 |
| TOTAL | | | 45.279 | 3,901.20 | 2,721.18 | 6,622.38 |
| **SEPTIC SYSTEM WITH 1000 S.F. LEACHING FIELD, 1500 GALLON TANK** | | | | | | |
| Tank, 1500 gallon, concrete | 1.000 | Ea. | 4.000 | 1,275 | 177.50 | 1,452.50 |
| Distribution box, concrete | 1.000 | Ea. | 1.000 | 88 | 36 | 124 |
| 4" PVC pipe | 25.000 | L.F. | 1.600 | 46.25 | 59.75 | 106 |
| Tank and field excavation | 119.000 | C.Y. | 13.130 | | 1,179.29 | 1,179.29 |
| Crushed stone backfill | 76.000 | C.Y. | 12.160 | 2,584 | 671.08 | 3,255.08 |
| Backfill with excavated material | 36.000 | C.Y. | .240 | | 50.76 | 50.76 |
| Building paper | 125.000 | S.Y. | 2.430 | 67.50 | 123.75 | 191.25 |
| 4" PVC perforated pipe | 145.000 | L.F. | 9.280 | 268.25 | 346.55 | 614.80 |
| 4" pipe fittings | 2.000 | Ea. | 1.939 | 22.20 | 98 | 120.20 |
| TOTAL | | | 45.779 | 4,351.20 | 2,742.68 | 7,093.88 |
| **SEPTIC SYSTEM WITH 2 LEACHING PITS, 1000 GALLON TANK** | | | | | | |
| Tank, 1000 gallon, concrete | 1.000 | Ea. | 3.500 | 825 | 156 | 981 |
| Distribution box, concrete | 1.000 | Ea. | 1.000 | 88 | 36 | 124 |
| 4" PVC pipe | 75.000 | L.F. | 4.800 | 138.75 | 179.25 | 318 |
| Excavation for tank only | 20.000 | C.Y. | 2.207 | | 198.20 | 198.20 |
| Crushed stone backfill | 10.000 | C.Y. | 1.600 | 340 | 88.30 | 428.30 |
| Backfill with excavated material | 55.000 | C.Y. | .367 | | 77.55 | 77.55 |
| Pits, 6' diameter, including excavation and stone backfill | 2.000 | Ea. | | 2,300 | | 2,300 |
| TOTAL | | Ea. | 13.474 | 3,691.75 | 735.30 | 4,427.05 |

The costs in this system include all necessary piping and excavation.

| Septic Systems Price Sheet | QUAN. | UNIT | LABOR HOURS | COST EACH | | |
|---|---|---|---|---|---|---|
| | | | | MAT. | INST. | TOTAL |
| Tank, precast concrete, 1000 gallon | 1.000 | Ea. | 3.500 | 825 | 156 | 981 |
| 2000 gallon | 1.000 | Ea. | 5.600 | 1,850 | 250 | 2,100 |
| Distribution box, concrete, 5 outlets | 1.000 | Ea. | 1.000 | 88 | 36 | 124 |
| 12 outlets | 1.000 | Ea. | 2.000 | 490 | 72.50 | 562.50 |
| 4″ pipe, PVC, solid | 25.000 | L.F. | 1.600 | 46.50 | 60 | 106.50 |
| Tank and field excavation, 1000 S.F. field | 119.000 | C.Y. | 6.565 | | 1,175 | 1,175 |
| 2000 S.F. field | 190.000 | C.Y. | 10.482 | | 1,875 | 1,875 |
| Tank excavation only, 1000 gallon tank | 20.000 | C.Y. | 1.103 | | 198 | 198 |
| 2000 gallon tank | 32.000 | C.Y. | 1.765 | | 315 | 315 |
| Backfill, crushed stone 1000 S.F. field | 76.000 | C.Y. | 12.160 | 2,575 | 675 | 3,250 |
| 2000 S.F. field | 140.000 | C.Y. | 22.400 | 4,750 | 1,225 | 5,975 |
| Backfill with excavated material, 1000 S.F. field | 36.000 | C.Y. | .240 | | 50.50 | 50.50 |
| 2000 S.F. field | 60.000 | C.Y. | .400 | | 84.50 | 84.50 |
| 6′ diameter pits | 55.000 | C.Y. | .367 | | 77.50 | 77.50 |
| 3′ diameter pits | 42.000 | C.Y. | .280 | | 59.50 | 59.50 |
| Building paper, 1000 S.F. field | 125.000 | S.Y. | 2.376 | 66 | 121 | 187 |
| 2000 S.F. field | 250.000 | S.Y. | 4.860 | 135 | 248 | 383 |
| 4″ pipe, PVC, perforated, 1000 S.F. field | 145.000 | L.F. | 9.280 | 268 | 345 | 613 |
| 2000 S.F. field | 265.000 | L.F. | 16.960 | 490 | 635 | 1,125 |
| Pipe fittings, bituminous fiber, 1000 S.F. field | 2.000 | Ea. | 1.939 | 22 | 98 | 120 |
| 2000 S.F. field | 4.000 | Ea. | 3.879 | 44.50 | 196 | 240.50 |
| Leaching pit, including excavation and stone backfill, 3′ diameter | 1.000 | Ea. | | 865 | | 865 |
| 6′ diameter | 1.000 | Ea. | | 1,150 | | 1,150 |
| | | | | | | |
| | | | | | | |
| | | | | | | |
| | | | | | | |
| | | | | | | |
| | | | | | | |
| | | | | | | |
| | | | | | | |
| | | | | | | |
| | | | | | | |
| | | | | | | |
| | | | | | | |
| | | | | | | |
| | | | | | | |
| | | | | | | |
| | | | | | | |
| | | | | | | |
| | | | | | | |

| System Description | QUAN. | UNIT | LABOR HOURS | MAT. | INST. | TOTAL |
|---|---|---|---|---|---|---|
| Chain link fence | | | | | | |
| Galv.9ga. wire, 1-5/8"post 10'O.C., 1-3/8"top rail, 2"corner post, 3'hi | 1.000 | L.F. | .130 | 9.45 | 4.84 | 14.29 |
| 4' high | 1.000 | L.F. | .141 | 11.35 | 5.25 | 16.60 |
| 6' high | 1.000 | L.F. | .209 | 12.85 | 7.80 | 20.65 |
| Add for gate 3' wide 1-3/8" frame 3' high | 1.000 | Ea. | 2.000 | 69 | 74.50 | 143.50 |
| 4' high | 1.000 | Ea. | 2.400 | 67 | 89.50 | 156.50 |
| 6' high | 1.000 | Ea. | 2.400 | 72.50 | 89.50 | 162 |
| Add for gate 4' wide 1-3/8" frame 3' high | 1.000 | Ea. | 2.667 | 70.50 | 99.50 | 170 |
| 4' high | 1.000 | Ea. | 2.667 | 76 | 99.50 | 175.50 |
| 6' high | 1.000 | Ea. | 3.000 | 190 | 112 | 302 |
| Alum.9ga. wire, 1-5/8"post, 10'O.C., 1-3/8"top rail, 2"corner post,3'hi | 1.000 | L.F. | .130 | 11.20 | 4.84 | 16.04 |
| 4' high | 1.000 | L.F. | .141 | 12.75 | 5.25 | 18 |
| 6' high | 1.000 | L.F. | .209 | 16.35 | 7.80 | 24.15 |
| Add for gate 3' wide 1-3/8" frame 3' high | 1.000 | Ea. | 2.000 | 109 | 74.50 | 183.50 |
| 4' high | 1.000 | Ea. | 2.400 | 149 | 89.50 | 238.50 |
| 6' high | 1.000 | Ea. | 2.400 | 223 | 89.50 | 312.50 |
| Add for gate 4' wide 1-3/8" frame 3' high | 1.000 | Ea. | 2.400 | 149 | 89.50 | 238.50 |
| 4' high | 1.000 | Ea. | 2.667 | 198 | 99.50 | 297.50 |
| 6' high | 1.000 | Ea. | 3.000 | 310 | 112 | 422 |
| Vinyl 9ga. wire, 1-5/8"post 10'O.C., 1-3/8"top rail, 2"corner post,3'hi | 1.000 | L.F. | .130 | 9.90 | 4.84 | 14.74 |
| 4' high | 1.000 | L.F. | .141 | 14.90 | 5.25 | 20.15 |
| 6' high | 1.000 | L.F. | .209 | 17 | 7.80 | 24.80 |
| Add for gate 3' wide 1-3/8" frame 3' high | 1.000 | Ea. | 2.000 | 106 | 74.50 | 180.50 |
| 4' high | 1.000 | Ea. | 2.400 | 138 | 89.50 | 227.50 |
| 6' high | 1.000 | Ea. | 2.400 | 213 | 89.50 | 302.50 |
| Add for gate 4' wide 1-3/8" frame 3' high | 1.000 | Ea. | 2.400 | 145 | 89.50 | 234.50 |
| 4' high | 1.000 | Ea. | 2.667 | 192 | 99.50 | 291.50 |
| 6' high | 1.000 | Ea. | 3.000 | 277 | 112 | 389 |
| Tennis court, chain link fence, 10' high | | | | | | |
| Galv.11ga.wire, 2"post 10'O.C., 1-3/8"top rail, 2-1/2"corner post | 1.000 | L.F. | .253 | 21.50 | 9.40 | 30.90 |
| Add for gate 3' wide 1-3/8" frame | 1.000 | Ea. | 2.400 | 266 | 89.50 | 355.50 |
| Alum.11ga.wire, 2"post 10'O.C., 1-3/8"top rail, 2-1/2"corner post | 1.000 | L.F. | .253 | 34.50 | 9.40 | 43.90 |
| Add for gate 3' wide 1-3/8" frame | 1.000 | Ea. | 2.400 | 395 | 89.50 | 484.50 |
| Vinyl 11ga.wire,2"post 10' O.C.,1-3/8"top rail,2-1/2"corner post | 1.000 | L.F. | .253 | 26.50 | 9.40 | 35.90 |
| Add for gate 3' wide 1-3/8" frame | 1.000 | Ea. | 2.400 | 400 | 89.50 | 489.50 |
| Railings, commercial | | | | | | |
| Aluminum balcony rail, 1-1/2" posts with pickets | 1.000 | L.F. | .164 | 66.50 | 10.75 | 77.25 |
| With expanded metal panels | 1.000 | L.F. | .164 | 85.50 | 10.75 | 96.25 |
| With porcelain enamel panel inserts | 1.000 | L.F. | .164 | 76.50 | 10.75 | 87.25 |
| Mild steel, ornamental rounded top rail | 1.000 | L.F. | .164 | 62.50 | 10.75 | 73.25 |
| As above, but pitch down stairs | 1.000 | L.F. | .183 | 67.50 | 11.95 | 79.45 |
| Steel pipe, welded, 1-1/2" round, painted | 1.000 | L.F. | .160 | 25 | 10.50 | 35.50 |
| Galvanized | 1.000 | L.F. | .160 | 35 | 10.50 | 45.50 |
| Residential, stock units, mild steel, deluxe | 1.000 | L.F. | .102 | 14.25 | 6.65 | 20.90 |
| Economy | 1.000 | L.F. | .102 | 10.70 | 6.65 | 17.35 |

| System Description | QUAN. | UNIT | LABOR HOURS | COST PER UNIT | | |
|---|---|---|---|---|---|---|
| | | | | MAT. | INST. | TOTAL |
| Basketweave, 3/8"x4" boards, 2"x4" stringers on spreaders, 4"x4" posts | | | | | | |
| No. 1 cedar, 6' high | 1.000 | L.F. | .150 | 9.70 | 7.20 | 16.90 |
| Treated pine, 6' high | 1.000 | L.F. | .160 | 11.70 | 7.70 | 19.40 |
| | | | | | | |
| Board fence, 1"x4" boards, 2"x4" rails, 4"x4" posts | | | | | | |
| Preservative treated, 2 rail, 3' high | 1.000 | L.F. | .166 | 7.20 | 8 | 15.20 |
| 4' high | 1.000 | L.F. | .178 | 7.90 | 8.55 | 16.45 |
| 3 rail, 5' high | 1.000 | L.F. | .185 | 8.95 | 8.90 | 17.85 |
| 6' high | 1.000 | L.F. | .192 | 10.35 | 9.25 | 19.60 |
| Western cedar, No. 1, 2 rail, 3' high | 1.000 | L.F. | .166 | 7.85 | 8 | 15.85 |
| 3 rail, 4' high | 1.000 | L.F. | .178 | 9.40 | 8.55 | 17.95 |
| 5' high | 1.000 | L.F. | .185 | 10.85 | 8.90 | 19.75 |
| 6' high | 1.000 | L.F. | .192 | 11.85 | 9.25 | 21.10 |
| No. 1 cedar, 2 rail, 3' high | 1.000 | L.F. | .166 | 11.90 | 8 | 19.90 |
| 4' high | 1.000 | L.F. | .178 | 13.45 | 8.55 | 22 |
| 3 rail, 5' high | 1.000 | L.F. | .185 | 15.85 | 8.90 | 24.75 |
| 6' high | 1.000 | L.F. | .192 | 17.70 | 9.25 | 26.95 |
| | | | | | | |
| Shadow box, 1"x6" boards, 2"x4" rails, 4"x4" posts | | | | | | |
| Fir, pine or spruce, treated, 3 rail, 6' high | 1.000 | L.F. | .160 | 13.25 | 7.70 | 20.95 |
| No. 1 cedar, 3 rail, 4' high | 1.000 | L.F. | .185 | 16.25 | 8.90 | 25.15 |
| 6' high | 1.000 | L.F. | .192 | 20 | 9.25 | 29.25 |
| Open rail, split rails, No. 1 cedar, 2 rail, 3' high | 1.000 | L.F. | .150 | 6.60 | 7.20 | 13.80 |
| 3 rail, 4' high | 1.000 | L.F. | .160 | 8.80 | 7.70 | 16.50 |
| No. 2 cedar, 2 rail, 3' high | 1.000 | L.F. | .150 | 5.20 | 7.20 | 12.40 |
| 3 rail, 4' high | 1.000 | L.F. | .160 | 6.20 | 7.70 | 13.90 |
| Open rail, rustic rails, No. 1 cedar, 2 rail, 3' high | 1.000 | L.F. | .150 | 4.25 | 7.20 | 11.45 |
| 3 rail, 4' high | 1.000 | L.F. | .160 | 5.75 | 7.70 | 13.45 |
| No. 2 cedar, 2 rail, 3' high | 1.000 | L.F. | .150 | 4.21 | 7.20 | 11.41 |
| 3 rail, 4' high | 1.000 | L.F. | .160 | 4.38 | 7.70 | 12.08 |
| Rustic picket, molded pine pickets, 2 rail, 3' high | 1.000 | L.F. | .171 | 5.85 | 8.25 | 14.10 |
| 3 rail, 4' high | 1.000 | L.F. | .197 | 6.75 | 9.50 | 16.25 |
| No. 1 cedar, 2 rail, 3' high | 1.000 | L.F. | .171 | 7.85 | 8.25 | 16.10 |
| 3 rail, 4' high | 1.000 | L.F. | .197 | 9.05 | 9.50 | 18.55 |
| Picket fence, fir, pine or spruce, preserved, treated | | | | | | |
| 2 rail, 3' high | 1.000 | L.F. | .171 | 4.91 | 8.25 | 13.16 |
| 3 rail, 4' high | 1.000 | L.F. | .185 | 5.80 | 8.90 | 14.70 |
| Western cedar, 2 rail, 3' high | 1.000 | L.F. | .171 | 6.15 | 8.25 | 14.40 |
| 3 rail, 4' high | 1.000 | L.F. | .185 | 6.30 | 8.90 | 15.20 |
| No. 1 cedar, 2 rail, 3' high | 1.000 | L.F. | .171 | 12.30 | 8.25 | 20.55 |
| 3 rail, 4' high | 1.000 | L.F. | .185 | 14.30 | 8.90 | 23.20 |
| | | | | | | |
| Stockade, No. 1 cedar, 3-1/4" rails, 6' high | 1.000 | L.F. | .150 | 11.55 | 7.20 | 18.75 |
| 8' high | 1.000 | L.F. | .155 | 14.95 | 7.45 | 22.40 |
| No. 2 cedar, treated rails, 6' high | 1.000 | L.F. | .150 | 11.55 | 7.20 | 18.75 |
| Treated pine, treated rails, 6' high | 1.000 | L.F. | .150 | 11.30 | 7.20 | 18.50 |
| Gates, No. 2 cedar, picket, 3'-6" wide 4' high | 1.000 | Ea. | 2.667 | 61 | 129 | 190 |
| No. 2 cedar, rustic round, 3' wide, 3' high | 1.000 | Ea. | 2.667 | 85 | 129 | 214 |
| No. 2 cedar, stockade screen, 3'-6" wide, 6' high | 1.000 | Ea. | 3.000 | 68 | 144 | 212 |
| General, wood, 3'-6" wide, 4' high | 1.000 | Ea. | 2.400 | 64.50 | 115 | 179.50 |
| 6' high | 1.000 | Ea. | 3.000 | 80.50 | 144 | 224.50 |
| | | | | | | |
| | | | | | | |

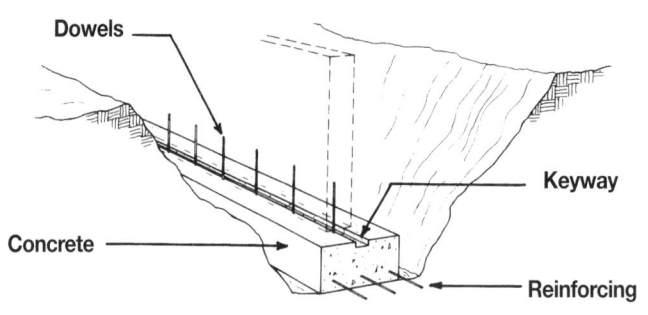

| System Description | QUAN. | UNIT | LABOR HOURS | COST PER L.F. | | |
|---|---|---|---|---|---|---|
| | | | | MAT. | INST. | TOTAL |
| **8″ THICK BY 18″ WIDE FOOTING** | | | | | | |
| Concrete, 3000 psi | .040 | C.Y. | | 4.28 | | 4.28 |
| Place concrete, direct chute | .040 | C.Y. | .016 | | .63 | .63 |
| Forms, footing, 4 uses | 1.330 | SFCA | .103 | .73 | 4.38 | 5.11 |
| Reinforcing, 1/2″ diameter bars, 2 each | 1.380 | Lb. | .011 | .63 | .58 | 1.21 |
| Keyway, 2″ x 4″, beveled, 4 uses | 1.000 | L.F. | .015 | .15 | .74 | .89 |
| Dowels, 1/2″ diameter bars, 2′ long, 6′ O.C. | .166 | Ea. | .006 | .11 | .30 | .41 |
| TOTAL | | L.F. | .151 | 5.90 | 6.63 | 12.53 |
| **12″ THICK BY 24″ WIDE FOOTING** | | | | | | |
| Concrete, 3000 psi | .070 | C.Y. | | 7.49 | | 7.49 |
| Place concrete, direct chute | .070 | C.Y. | .028 | | 1.11 | 1.11 |
| Forms, footing, 4 uses | 2.000 | SFCA | .155 | 1.10 | 6.58 | 7.68 |
| Reinforcing, 1/2″ diameter bars, 2 each | 1.380 | Lb. | .011 | .63 | .58 | 1.21 |
| Keyway, 2″ x 4″, beveled, 4 uses | 1.000 | L.F. | .015 | .15 | .74 | .89 |
| Dowels, 1/2″ diameter bars, 2′ long, 6′ O.C. | .166 | Ea. | .006 | .11 | .30 | .41 |
| TOTAL | | L.F. | .215 | 9.48 | 9.31 | 18.79 |
| **12″ THICK BY 36″ WIDE FOOTING** | | | | | | |
| Concrete, 3000 psi | .110 | C.Y. | | 11.77 | | 11.77 |
| Place concrete, direct chute | .110 | C.Y. | .044 | | 1.74 | 1.74 |
| Forms, footing, 4 uses | 2.000 | SFCA | .155 | 1.10 | 6.58 | 7.68 |
| Reinforcing, 1/2″ diameter bars, 2 each | 1.380 | Lb. | .011 | .63 | .58 | 1.21 |
| Keyway, 2″ x 4″, beveled, 4 uses | 1.000 | L.F. | .015 | .15 | .74 | .89 |
| Dowels, 1/2″ diameter bars, 2′ long, 6′ O.C. | .166 | Ea. | .006 | .11 | .30 | .41 |
| TOTAL | | L.F. | .231 | 13.76 | 9.94 | 23.70 |

The footing costs in this system are on a cost per linear foot basis

| Description | QUAN. | UNIT | LABOR HOURS | COST PER S.F. | | |
|---|---|---|---|---|---|---|
| | | | | MAT. | INST. | TOTAL |
| | | | | | | |
| | | | | | | |
| | | | | | | |
| | | | | | | |
| | | | | | | |

| Footing Price Sheet | QUAN. | UNIT | LABOR HOURS | COST PER L.F. | | |
|---|---|---|---|---|---|---|
| | | | | MAT. | INST. | TOTAL |
| Concrete, 8″ thick by 18″ wide footing | | | | | | |
| 2000 psi concrete | .040 | C.Y. | | 4.04 | | 4.04 |
| 2500 psi concrete | .040 | C.Y. | | 4.12 | | 4.12 |
| 3000 psi concrete | .040 | C.Y. | | 4.28 | | 4.28 |
| 3500 psi concrete | .040 | C.Y. | | 4.40 | | 4.40 |
| 4000 psi concrete | .040 | C.Y. | | 4.52 | | 4.52 |
| 12″ thick by 24″ wide footing | | | | | | |
| 2000 psi concrete | .070 | C.Y. | | 7.05 | | 7.05 |
| 2500 psi concrete | .070 | C.Y. | | 7.20 | | 7.20 |
| 3000 psi concrete | .070 | C.Y. | | 7.50 | | 7.50 |
| 3500 psi concrete | .070 | C.Y. | | 7.70 | | 7.70 |
| 4000 psi concrete | .070 | C.Y. | | 7.90 | | 7.90 |
| 12″ thick by 36″ wide footing | | | | | | |
| 2000 psi concrete | .110 | C.Y. | | 11.10 | | 11.10 |
| 2500 psi concrete | .110 | C.Y. | | 11.35 | | 11.35 |
| 3000 psi concrete | .110 | C.Y. | | 11.75 | | 11.75 |
| 3500 psi concrete | .110 | C.Y. | | 12.10 | | 12.10 |
| 4000 psi concrete | .110 | C.Y. | | 12.45 | | 12.45 |
| Place concrete, 8″ thick by 18″ wide footing, direct chute | .040 | C.Y. | .016 | | .63 | .63 |
| Pumped concrete | .040 | C.Y. | .017 | | .90 | .90 |
| Crane & bucket | .040 | C.Y. | .032 | | 1.89 | 1.89 |
| 12″ thick by 24″ wide footing, direct chute | .070 | C.Y. | .028 | | 1.11 | 1.11 |
| Pumped concrete | .070 | C.Y. | .030 | | 1.58 | 1.58 |
| Crane & bucket | .070 | C.Y. | .056 | | 3.31 | 3.31 |
| 12″ thick by 36″ wide footing, direct chute | .110 | C.Y. | .044 | | 1.74 | 1.74 |
| Pumped concrete | .110 | C.Y. | .047 | | 2.48 | 2.48 |
| Crane & bucket | .110 | C.Y. | .088 | | 5.20 | 5.20 |
| Forms, 8″ thick footing, 1 use | 1.330 | SFCA | .140 | 2.26 | 5.95 | 8.21 |
| 4 uses | 1.330 | SFCA | .103 | .73 | 4.38 | 5.11 |
| 12″ thick footing, 1 use | 2.000 | SFCA | .211 | 3.40 | 8.95 | 12.35 |
| 4 uses | 2.000 | SFCA | .155 | 1.10 | 6.60 | 7.70 |
| Reinforcing, 3/8″ diameter bar, 1 each | .400 | Lb. | .003 | .18 | .17 | .35 |
| 2 each | .800 | Lb. | .006 | .37 | .34 | .71 |
| 3 each | 1.200 | Lb. | .009 | .55 | .50 | 1.05 |
| 1/2″ diameter bar, 1 each | .700 | Lb. | .005 | .32 | .29 | .61 |
| 2 each | 1.380 | Lb. | .011 | .63 | .58 | 1.21 |
| 3 each | 2.100 | Lb. | .016 | .97 | .88 | 1.85 |
| 5/8″ diameter bar, 1 each | 1.040 | Lb. | .008 | .48 | .44 | .92 |
| 2 each | 2.080 | Lb. | .016 | .96 | .87 | 1.83 |
| Keyway, beveled, 2″ x 4″, 1 use | 1.000 | L.F. | .030 | .30 | 1.48 | 1.78 |
| 2 uses | 1.000 | L.F. | .023 | .23 | 1.11 | 1.34 |
| 2″ x 6″, 1 use | 1.000 | L.F. | .032 | .42 | 1.56 | 1.98 |
| 2 uses | 1.000 | L.F. | .024 | .32 | 1.17 | 1.49 |
| Dowels, 2 feet long, 6′ O.C., 3/8″ bar | .166 | Ea. | .005 | .06 | .28 | .34 |
| 1/2″ bar | .166 | Ea. | .006 | .11 | .30 | .41 |
| 5/8″ bar | .166 | Ea. | .006 | .17 | .34 | .51 |
| 3/4″ bar | .166 | Ea. | .006 | .17 | .34 | .51 |

| System Description | QUAN. | UNIT | LABOR HOURS | COST PER S.F. | | |
|---|---|---|---|---|---|---|
| | | | | MAT. | INST. | TOTAL |
| **8″ WALL, GROUTED, FULL HEIGHT** | | | | | | |
| Concrete block, 8″ x 16″ x 8″ | 1.000 | S.F. | .094 | 3.19 | 4.18 | 7.37 |
| Masonry reinforcing, every second course | .750 | L.F. | .002 | .14 | .10 | .24 |
| Parging, plastering with portland cement plaster, 1 coat | 1.000 | S.F. | .014 | .25 | .64 | .89 |
| Dampproofing, bituminous coating, 1 coat | 1.000 | S.F. | .012 | .22 | .53 | .75 |
| Insulation, 1″ rigid polystyrene | 1.000 | S.F. | .010 | .56 | .49 | 1.05 |
| Grout, solid, pumped | 1.000 | S.F. | .059 | 1.21 | 2.57 | 3.78 |
| Anchor bolts, 1/2″ diameter, 8″ long, 4′ O.C. | .060 | Ea. | .002 | .05 | .12 | .17 |
| Sill plate, 2″ x 4″, treated | .250 | L.F. | .007 | .10 | .36 | .46 |
| TOTAL | | S.F. | .200 | 5.72 | 8.99 | 14.71 |
| **12″ WALL, GROUTED, FULL HEIGHT** | | | | | | |
| Concrete block, 8″ x 16″ x 12″ | 1.000 | S.F. | .160 | 4.38 | 6.95 | 11.33 |
| Masonry reinforcing, every second course | .750 | L.F. | .003 | .14 | .14 | .28 |
| Parging, plastering with portland cement plaster, 1 coat | 1.000 | S.F. | .014 | .25 | .64 | .89 |
| Dampproofing, bituminous coating, 1 coat | 1.000 | S.F. | .012 | .22 | .53 | .75 |
| Insulation, 1″ rigid polystyrene | 1.000 | S.F. | .010 | .56 | .49 | 1.05 |
| Grout, solid, pumped | 1.000 | S.F. | .063 | 1.97 | 2.74 | 4.71 |
| Anchor bolts, 1/2″ diameter, 8″ long, 4′ O.C. | .060 | Ea. | .002 | .05 | .12 | .17 |
| Sill plate, 2″ x 4″, treated | .250 | L.F. | .007 | .10 | .36 | .46 |
| TOTAL | | S.F. | .271 | 7.67 | 11.97 | 19.64 |

The costs in this system are based on a square foot of wall. Do not subtract for window or door openings.

| Description | QUAN. | UNIT | LABOR HOURS | COST PER S.F. | | |
|---|---|---|---|---|---|---|
| | | | | MAT. | INST. | TOTAL |
| | | | | | | |
| | | | | | | |
| | | | | | | |
| | | | | | | |
| | | | | | | |

| Block Wall Systems | QUAN. | UNIT | LABOR HOURS | COST PER S.F. | | |
|---|---|---|---|---|---|---|
| | | | | MAT. | INST. | TOTAL |
| Concrete, block, 8″ x 16″ x, 6″ thick | 1.000 | S.F. | .089 | 2.87 | 3.91 | 6.78 |
| 8″ thick | 1.000 | S.F. | .093 | 3.19 | 4.18 | 7.37 |
| 10″ thick | 1.000 | S.F. | .095 | 3.90 | 5.10 | 9 |
| 12″ thick | 1.000 | S.F. | .122 | 4.38 | 6.95 | 11.33 |
| Solid block, 8″ x 16″ x, 6″ thick | 1.000 | S.F. | .091 | 2.94 | 4.04 | 6.98 |
| 8″ thick | 1.000 | S.F. | .096 | 4.16 | 4.28 | 8.44 |
| 10″ thick | 1.000 | S.F. | .096 | 4.16 | 4.28 | 8.44 |
| 12″ thick | 1.000 | S.F. | .126 | 6 | 5.95 | 11.95 |
| Masonry reinforcing, wire strips, to 8″ wide, every course | 1.500 | L.F. | .004 | .27 | .20 | .47 |
| Every 2nd course | .750 | L.F. | .002 | .14 | .10 | .24 |
| Every 3rd course | .500 | L.F. | .001 | .09 | .07 | .16 |
| Every 4th course | .400 | L.F. | .001 | .07 | .05 | .12 |
| Wire strips to 12″ wide, every course | 1.500 | L.F. | .006 | .29 | .29 | .58 |
| Every 2nd course | .750 | L.F. | .003 | .14 | .14 | .28 |
| Every 3rd course | .500 | L.F. | .002 | .10 | .10 | .20 |
| Every 4th course | .400 | L.F. | .002 | .08 | .08 | .16 |
| Parging, plastering with portland cement plaster, 1 coat | 1.000 | S.F. | .014 | .25 | .64 | .89 |
| 2 coats | 1.000 | S.F. | .022 | .39 | .99 | 1.38 |
| Dampproofing, bituminous, brushed on, 1 coat | 1.000 | S.F. | .012 | .22 | .53 | .75 |
| 2 coats | 1.000 | S.F. | .016 | .44 | .70 | 1.14 |
| Sprayed on, 1 coat | 1.000 | S.F. | .010 | .22 | .42 | .64 |
| 2 coats | 1.000 | S.F. | .016 | .43 | .70 | 1.13 |
| Troweled on, 1/16″ thick | 1.000 | S.F. | .016 | .47 | .70 | 1.17 |
| 1/8″ thick | 1.000 | S.F. | .020 | .83 | .88 | 1.71 |
| 1/2″ thick | 1.000 | S.F. | .023 | 2.68 | 1.01 | 3.69 |
| | | | | | | |
| Insulation, rigid, fiberglass, 1.5#/C.F., unfaced | | | | | | |
| 1-1/2″ thick R 6.2 | 1.000 | S.F. | .008 | .70 | .39 | 1.09 |
| 2″ thick R 8.5 | 1.000 | S.F. | .008 | .76 | .39 | 1.15 |
| 3″ thick R 13 | 1.000 | S.F. | .010 | .88 | .49 | 1.37 |
| Foamglass, 1-1/2″ thick R 2.64 | 1.000 | S.F. | .010 | 1.54 | .49 | 2.03 |
| 2″ thick R 5.26 | 1.000 | S.F. | .011 | 3.80 | .54 | 4.34 |
| Perlite, 1″ thick R 2.77 | 1.000 | S.F. | .010 | .33 | .49 | .82 |
| 2″ thick R 5.55 | 1.000 | S.F. | .011 | .66 | .54 | 1.20 |
| Polystyrene, extruded, 1″ thick R 5.4 | 1.000 | S.F. | .010 | .56 | .49 | 1.05 |
| 2″ thick R 10.8 | 1.000 | S.F. | .011 | 1.54 | .54 | 2.08 |
| Molded 1″ thick R 3.85 | 1.000 | S.F. | .010 | .40 | .49 | .89 |
| 2″ thick R 7.7 | 1.000 | S.F. | .011 | 1.19 | .54 | 1.73 |
| Grout, concrete block cores, 6″ thick | 1.000 | S.F. | .044 | .91 | 1.93 | 2.84 |
| 8″ thick | 1.000 | S.F. | .059 | 1.21 | 2.57 | 3.78 |
| 10″ thick | 1.000 | S.F. | .061 | 1.59 | 2.65 | 4.24 |
| 12″ thick | 1.000 | S.F. | .063 | 1.97 | 2.74 | 4.71 |
| Anchor bolts, 2′ on center, 1/2″ diameter, 8″ long | .120 | Ea. | .005 | .11 | .23 | .34 |
| 12″ long | .120 | Ea. | .005 | .20 | .24 | .44 |
| 3/4″ diameter, 8″ long | .120 | Ea. | .006 | .42 | .29 | .71 |
| 12″ long | .120 | Ea. | .006 | .53 | .31 | .84 |
| 4′ on center, 1/2″ diameter, 8″ long | .060 | Ea. | .002 | .05 | .12 | .17 |
| 12″ long | .060 | Ea. | .003 | .10 | .12 | .22 |
| 3/4″ diameter, 8″ long | .060 | Ea. | .003 | .21 | .14 | .35 |
| 12″ long | .060 | Ea. | .003 | .26 | .15 | .41 |
| Sill plates, treated, 2″ x 4″ | .250 | L.F. | .007 | .10 | .36 | .46 |
| 4″ x 4″ | .250 | L.F. | .007 | .42 | .34 | .76 |
| | | | | | | |
| | | | | | | |
| | | | | | | |

| System Description | QUAN. | UNIT | LABOR HOURS | COST PER S.F. | | |
|---|---|---|---|---|---|---|
| | | | | MAT. | INST. | TOTAL |
| **8″ THICK, POURED CONCRETE WALL** | | | | | | |
| Concrete, 8″ thick , 3000 psi | .025 | C.Y. | | 2.68 | | 2.68 |
| Forms, prefabricated plywood, up to 8′ high | 2.000 | SFCA | .120 | 3.18 | 5.18 | 8.36 |
| Reinforcing, light | .670 | Lb. | .004 | .31 | .19 | .50 |
| Placing concrete, direct chute | .025 | C.Y. | .013 | | .53 | .53 |
| Dampproofing, brushed on, 2 coats | 1.000 | S.F. | .016 | .44 | .70 | 1.14 |
| Rigid insulation, 1″ polystyrene | 1.000 | S.F. | .010 | .56 | .49 | 1.05 |
| Anchor bolts, 1/2″ diameter, 12″ long, 4′ O.C. | .060 | Ea. | .003 | .10 | .12 | .22 |
| Sill plates, 2″ x 4″, treated | .250 | L.F. | .007 | .10 | .36 | .46 |
| TOTAL | | S.F. | .173 | 7.37 | 7.57 | 14.94 |
| **12″ THICK, POURED CONCRETE WALL** | | | | | | |
| Concrete, 12″ thick, 3000 psi | .040 | C.Y. | | 4.28 | | 4.28 |
| Forms, prefabricated plywood, up to 8′ high | 2.000 | SFCA | .120 | 3.18 | 5.18 | 8.36 |
| Reinforcing, light | 1.000 | Lb. | .005 | .46 | .29 | .75 |
| Placing concrete, direct chute | .040 | C.Y. | .019 | | .76 | .76 |
| Dampproofing, brushed on, 2 coats | 1.000 | S.F. | .016 | .44 | .70 | 1.14 |
| Rigid insulation, 1″ polystyrene | 1.000 | S.F. | .010 | .56 | .49 | 1.05 |
| Anchor bolts, 1/2″ diameter, 12″ long, 4′ O.C. | .060 | Ea. | .003 | .10 | .12 | .22 |
| Sill plates, 2″ x 4″ treated | .250 | L.F. | .007 | .10 | .36 | .46 |
| TOTAL | | S.F. | .180 | 9.12 | 7.90 | 17.02 |

The costs in this system are based on sq. ft. of wall. Do not subtract
for window and door openings. The costs assume a 4′ high wall.

| Description | QUAN. | UNIT | LABOR HOURS | COST PER S.F. | | |
|---|---|---|---|---|---|---|
| | | | | MAT. | INST. | TOTAL |
| | | | | | | |
| | | | | | | |
| | | | | | | |
| | | | | | | |
| | | | | | | |

| Concrete Wall Price Sheet | QUAN. | UNIT | LABOR HOURS | COST PER S.F. | | |
|---|---|---|---|---|---|---|
| | | | | MAT. | INST. | TOTAL |
| Formwork, prefabricated plywood, up to 8' high | 2.000 | SFCA | .081 | 3.18 | 5.20 | 8.38 |
| Over 8' to 16' high | 2.000 | SFCA | .076 | 3.24 | 6.90 | 10.14 |
| Job built forms, 1 use per month | 2.000 | SFCA | .320 | 4.94 | 11.20 | 16.14 |
| 4 uses per month | 2.000 | SFCA | .221 | 1.80 | 8.20 | 10 |
| Reinforcing, 8" wall, light reinforcing | .670 | Lb. | .004 | .31 | .19 | .50 |
| Heavy reinforcing | 1.500 | Lb. | .008 | .69 | .44 | 1.13 |
| 10" wall, light reinforcing | .850 | Lb. | .005 | .39 | .25 | .64 |
| Heavy reinforcing | 2.000 | Lb. | .011 | .92 | .58 | 1.50 |
| 12" wall light reinforcing | 1.000 | Lb. | .005 | .46 | .29 | .75 |
| Heavy reinforcing | 2.250 | Lb. | .012 | 1.04 | .65 | 1.69 |
| Placing concrete, 8" wall, direct chute | .025 | C.Y. | .013 | | .53 | .53 |
| Pumped concrete | .025 | C.Y. | .016 | | .85 | .85 |
| Crane & bucket | .025 | C.Y. | .023 | | 1.33 | 1.33 |
| 10" wall, direct chute | .030 | C.Y. | .016 | | .64 | .64 |
| Pumped concrete | .030 | C.Y. | .019 | | 1.01 | 1.01 |
| Crane & bucket | .030 | C.Y. | .027 | | 1.60 | 1.60 |
| 12" wall, direct chute | .040 | C.Y. | .019 | | .76 | .76 |
| Pumped concrete | .040 | C.Y. | .023 | | 1.24 | 1.24 |
| Crane & bucket | .040 | C.Y. | .032 | | 1.89 | 1.89 |
| Dampproofing, bituminous, brushed on, 1 coat | 1.000 | S.F. | .012 | .22 | .53 | .75 |
| 2 coats | 1.000 | S.F. | .016 | .44 | .70 | 1.14 |
| Sprayed on, 1 coat | 1.000 | S.F. | .010 | .22 | .42 | .64 |
| 2 coats | 1.000 | S.F. | .016 | .43 | .70 | 1.13 |
| Troweled on, 1/16" thick | 1.000 | S.F. | .016 | .47 | .70 | 1.17 |
| 1/8" thick | 1.000 | S.F. | .020 | .83 | .88 | 1.71 |
| 1/2" thick | 1.000 | S.F. | .023 | 2.68 | 1.01 | 3.69 |
| Insulation rigid, fiberglass, 1.5#/C.F., unfaced | | | | | | |
| 1-1/2" thick, R 6.2 | 1.000 | S.F. | .008 | .70 | .39 | 1.09 |
| 2" thick, R 8.3 | 1.000 | S.F. | .008 | .76 | .39 | 1.15 |
| 3" thick, R 12.4 | 1.000 | S.F. | .010 | .88 | .49 | 1.37 |
| Foamglass, 1-1/2" thick R 2.64 | 1.000 | S.F. | .010 | 1.54 | .49 | 2.03 |
| 2" thick R 5.26 | 1.000 | S.F. | .011 | 3.80 | .54 | 4.34 |
| Perlite, 1" thick R 2.77 | 1.000 | S.F. | .010 | .33 | .49 | .82 |
| 2" thick R 5.55 | 1.000 | S.F. | .011 | .66 | .54 | 1.20 |
| Polystyrene, extruded, 1" thick R 5.40 | 1.000 | S.F. | .010 | .56 | .49 | 1.05 |
| 2" thick R 10.8 | 1.000 | S.F. | .011 | 1.54 | .54 | 2.08 |
| Molded, 1" thick R 3.85 | 1.000 | S.F. | .010 | .40 | .49 | .89 |
| 2" thick R 7.70 | 1.000 | S.F. | .011 | 1.19 | .54 | 1.73 |
| Anchor bolts, 2' on center, 1/2" diameter, 8" long | .120 | Ea. | .005 | .11 | .23 | .34 |
| 12" long | .120 | Ea. | .005 | .20 | .24 | .44 |
| 3/4" diameter, 8" long | .120 | Ea. | .006 | .42 | .29 | .71 |
| 12" long | .120 | Ea. | .006 | .53 | .31 | .84 |
| Sill plates, treated lumber, 2" x 4" | .250 | L.F. | .007 | .10 | .36 | .46 |
| 4" x 4" | .250 | L.F. | .007 | .42 | .34 | .76 |

123

Sheathing — Top Plates
Asphalt Paper — Studs
Vapor Barrier — Insulation
Bottom Plate

| System Description | QUAN. | UNIT | LABOR HOURS | COST PER S.F. | | |
|---|---|---|---|---|---|---|
| | | | | MAT. | INST. | TOTAL |
| **2″ X 4″ STUDS, 16″ O.C., WALL** | | | | | | |
| Studs, 2″ x 4″, 16″ O.C., treated | 1.000 | L.F. | .015 | .38 | .71 | 1.09 |
| Plates, double top plate, single bottom plate, treated, 2″ x 4″ | .750 | L.F. | .011 | .29 | .53 | .82 |
| Sheathing, 1/2″, exterior grade, CDX, treated | 1.000 | S.F. | .014 | 1.12 | .70 | 1.82 |
| Asphalt paper, 15# roll | 1.100 | S.F. | .002 | .07 | .12 | .19 |
| Vapor barrier, 4 mil polyethylene | 1.000 | S.F. | .002 | .06 | .11 | .17 |
| Insulation, batts, fiberglass, 3-1/2″ thick, R 11 | 1.000 | S.F. | .006 | .36 | .29 | .65 |
| TOTAL | | S.F. | .050 | 2.28 | 2.46 | 4.74 |
| **2″ X 6″ STUDS, 16″ O.C., WALL** | | | | | | |
| Studs, 2″ x 6″, 16″ O.C., treated | 1.000 | L.F. | .016 | .61 | .78 | 1.39 |
| Plates, double top plate, single bottom plate, treated, 2″ x 6″ | .750 | L.F. | .012 | .46 | .59 | 1.05 |
| Sheathing, 5/8″ exterior grade, CDX, treated | 1.000 | S.F. | .015 | 1.71 | .75 | 2.46 |
| Asphalt paper, 15# roll | 1.100 | S.F. | .002 | .07 | .12 | .19 |
| Vapor barrier, 4 mil polyethylene | 1.000 | S.F. | .002 | .06 | .11 | .17 |
| Insulation, batts, fiberglass, 6″ thick, R 19 | 1.000 | S.F. | .006 | .47 | .29 | .76 |
| TOTAL | | S.F. | .053 | 3.38 | 2.64 | 6.02 |
| **2″ X 8″ STUDS, 16″ O.C., WALL** | | | | | | |
| Studs, 2″ x 8″, 16″ O.C. treated | 1.000 | L.F. | .018 | 1.14 | .87 | 2.01 |
| Plates, double top plate, single bottom plate, treated, 2″ x 8″ | .750 | L.F. | .013 | .86 | .65 | 1.51 |
| Sheathing, 3/4″ exterior grade, CDX, treated | 1.000 | S.F. | .016 | 1.87 | .80 | 2.67 |
| Asphalt paper, 15# roll | 1.100 | S.F. | .002 | .07 | .12 | .19 |
| Vapor barrier, 4 mil polyethylene | 1.000 | S.F. | .002 | .06 | .11 | .17 |
| Insulation, batts, fiberglass, 9″ thick, R 30 | 1.000 | S.F. | .006 | .77 | .29 | 1.06 |
| TOTAL | | S.F. | .057 | 4.77 | 2.84 | 7.61 |

The costs in this system are based on a sq. ft. of wall area. Do not subtract for window or door openings. The costs assume a 4′ high wall.

| Description | QUAN. | UNIT | LABOR HOURS | COST PER S.F. | | |
|---|---|---|---|---|---|---|
| | | | | MAT. | INST. | TOTAL |
| | | | | | | |
| | | | | | | |
| | | | | | | |
| | | | | | | |
| | | | | | | |

| Wood Wall Foundation Price Sheet | QUAN. | UNIT | LABOR HOURS | COST PER S.F. | | |
|---|---|---|---|---|---|---|
| | | | | MAT. | INST. | TOTAL |
| Studs, treated, 2″ x 4″, 12″ O.C. | 1.250 | L.F. | .018 | .48 | .89 | 1.37 |
| 16″ O.C. | 1.000 | L.F. | .015 | .38 | .71 | 1.09 |
| 2″ x 6″, 12″ O.C. | 1.250 | L.F. | .020 | .76 | .98 | 1.74 |
| 16″ O.C. | 1.000 | L.F. | .016 | .61 | .78 | 1.39 |
| 2″ x 8″, 12″ O.C. | 1.250 | L.F. | .022 | 1.43 | 1.09 | 2.52 |
| 16″ O.C. | 1.000 | L.F. | .018 | 1.14 | .87 | 2.01 |
| Plates, treated double top single bottom, 2″ x 4″ | .750 | L.F. | .011 | .29 | .53 | .82 |
| 2″ x 6″ | .750 | L.F. | .012 | .46 | .59 | 1.05 |
| 2″ x 8″ | .750 | L.F. | .013 | .86 | .65 | 1.51 |
| | | | | | | |
| Sheathing, treated exterior grade CDX, 1/2″ thick | 1.000 | S.F. | .014 | 1.12 | .70 | 1.82 |
| 5/8″ thick | 1.000 | S.F. | .015 | 1.71 | .75 | 2.46 |
| 3/4″ thick | 1.000 | S.F. | .016 | 1.87 | .80 | 2.67 |
| | | | | | | |
| Asphalt paper, 15# roll | 1.100 | S.F. | .002 | .07 | .12 | .19 |
| | | | | | | |
| Vapor barrier, polyethylene, 4 mil | 1.000 | S.F. | .002 | .04 | .11 | .15 |
| 10 mil | 1.000 | S.F. | .002 | .07 | .11 | .18 |
| Insulation, rigid, fiberglass, 1.5#/C.F., unfaced | 1.000 | S.F. | .008 | .48 | .39 | .87 |
| 1-1/2″ thick, R 6.2 | 1.000 | S.F. | .008 | .70 | .39 | 1.09 |
| 2″ thick, R 8.3 | 1.000 | S.F. | .008 | .76 | .39 | 1.15 |
| 3″ thick, R 12.4 | 1.000 | S.F. | .010 | .90 | .50 | 1.40 |
| Foamglass 1 1/2″ thick, R 2.64 | 1.000 | S.F. | .010 | 1.54 | .49 | 2.03 |
| 2″ thick, R 5.26 | 1.000 | S.F. | .011 | 3.80 | .54 | 4.34 |
| Perlite 1″ thick, R 2.77 | 1.000 | S.F. | .010 | .33 | .49 | .82 |
| 2″ thick, R 5.55 | 1.000 | S.F. | .011 | .66 | .54 | 1.20 |
| Polystyrene, extruded, 1″ thick, R 5.40 | 1.000 | S.F. | .010 | .56 | .49 | 1.05 |
| 2″ thick, R 10.8 | 1.000 | S.F. | .011 | 1.54 | .54 | 2.08 |
| Molded 1″ thick, R 3.85 | 1.000 | S.F. | .010 | .40 | .49 | .89 |
| 2″ thick, R 7.7 | 1.000 | S.F. | .011 | 1.19 | .54 | 1.73 |
| Non rigid, batts, fiberglass, paper backed, 3-1/2″ thick roll, R 11 | 1.000 | S.F. | .005 | .36 | .29 | .65 |
| 6″, R 19 | 1.000 | S.F. | .006 | .47 | .29 | .76 |
| 9″, R 30 | 1.000 | S.F. | .006 | .77 | .29 | 1.06 |
| 12″, R 38 | 1.000 | S.F. | .006 | 1.10 | .29 | 1.39 |
| Mineral fiber, paper backed, 3-1/2″, R 13 | 1.000 | S.F. | .005 | .42 | .24 | .66 |
| 6″, R 19 | 1.000 | S.F. | .005 | .53 | .24 | .77 |
| 10″, R 30 | 1.000 | S.F. | .006 | .80 | .29 | 1.09 |
| | | | | | | |
| | | | | | | |
| | | | | | | |
| | | | | | | |
| | | | | | | |
| | | | | | | |
| | | | | | | |
| | | | | | | |
| | | | | | | |
| | | | | | | |
| | | | | | | |
| | | | | | | |

Concrete Slab — Expansion Material — Bank Run Gravel — Welded Wire Fabric — Vapor Barrier

| System Description | QUAN. | UNIT | LABOR HOURS | COST PER S.F. | | |
|---|---|---|---|---|---|---|
| | | | | MAT. | INST. | TOTAL |
| **4″ THICK SLAB** | | | | | | |
| Concrete, 4″ thick, 3000 psi concrete | .012 | C.Y. | | 1.28 | | 1.28 |
| Place concrete, direct chute | .012 | C.Y. | .005 | | .21 | .21 |
| Bank run gravel, 4″ deep | 1.000 | S.F. | .001 | .39 | .05 | .44 |
| Polyethylene vapor barrier, .006″ thick | 1.000 | S.F. | .002 | .06 | .11 | .17 |
| Edge forms, expansion material | .100 | L.F. | .005 | .03 | .23 | .26 |
| Welded wire fabric, 6 x 6, 10/10 (W1.4/W1.4) | 1.100 | S.F. | .005 | .14 | .28 | .42 |
| Steel trowel finish | 1.000 | S.F. | .014 | | .61 | .61 |
| TOTAL | | S.F. | .032 | 1.90 | 1.49 | 3.39 |
| **6″ THICK SLAB** | | | | | | |
| Concrete, 6″ thick, 3000 psi concrete | .019 | C.Y. | | 2.03 | | 2.03 |
| Place concrete, direct chute | .019 | C.Y. | .008 | | .33 | .33 |
| Bank run gravel, 4″ deep | 1.000 | S.F. | .001 | .39 | .05 | .44 |
| Polyethylene vapor barrier, .006″ thick | 1.000 | S.F. | .002 | .06 | .11 | .17 |
| Edge forms, expansion material | .100 | L.F. | .005 | .03 | .23 | .26 |
| Welded wire fabric, 6 x 6, 10/10 (W1.4/W1.4) | 1.100 | S.F. | .005 | .14 | .28 | .42 |
| Steel trowel finish | 1.000 | S.F. | .014 | | .61 | .61 |
| TOTAL | | S.F. | .035 | 2.65 | 1.61 | 4.26 |

The slab costs in this section are based on a cost per square foot of floor area.

| Description | QUAN. | UNIT | LABOR HOURS | COST PER S.F. | | |
|---|---|---|---|---|---|---|
| | | | | MAT. | INST. | TOTAL |
| | | | | | | |

| Floor Slab Price Sheet | QUAN. | UNIT | LABOR HOURS | COST PER S.F. | | |
|---|---|---|---|---|---|---|
| | | | | MAT. | INST. | TOTAL |
| Concrete, 4" thick slab, 2000 psi concrete | .012 | C.Y. | | 1.21 | | 1.21 |
| 2500 psi concrete | .012 | C.Y. | | 1.24 | | 1.24 |
| 3000 psi concrete | .012 | C.Y. | | 1.28 | | 1.28 |
| 3500 psi concrete | .012 | C.Y. | | 1.32 | | 1.32 |
| 4000 psi concrete | .012 | C.Y. | | 1.36 | | 1.36 |
| 4500 psi concrete | .012 | C.Y. | | 1.39 | | 1.39 |
| 5" thick slab, 2000 psi concrete | .015 | C.Y. | | 1.52 | | 1.52 |
| 2500 psi concrete | .015 | C.Y. | | 1.55 | | 1.55 |
| 3000 psi concrete | .015 | C.Y. | | 1.61 | | 1.61 |
| 3500 psi concrete | .015 | C.Y. | | 1.65 | | 1.65 |
| 4000 psi concrete | .015 | C.Y. | | 1.70 | | 1.70 |
| 4500 psi concrete | .015 | C.Y. | | 1.74 | | 1.74 |
| 6" thick slab, 2000 psi concrete | .019 | C.Y. | | 1.92 | | 1.92 |
| 2500 psi concrete | .019 | C.Y. | | 1.96 | | 1.96 |
| 3000 psi concrete | .019 | C.Y. | | 2.03 | | 2.03 |
| 3500 psi concrete | .019 | C.Y. | | 2.09 | | 2.09 |
| 4000 psi concrete | .019 | C.Y. | | 2.15 | | 2.15 |
| 4500 psi concrete | .019 | C.Y. | | 2.20 | | 2.20 |
| Place concrete, 4" slab, direct chute | .012 | C.Y. | .005 | | .21 | .21 |
| Pumped concrete | .012 | C.Y. | .006 | | .31 | .31 |
| Crane & bucket | .012 | C.Y. | .008 | | .46 | .46 |
| 5" slab, direct chute | .015 | C.Y. | .007 | | .26 | .26 |
| Pumped concrete | .015 | C.Y. | .007 | | .39 | .39 |
| Crane & bucket | .015 | C.Y. | .010 | | .58 | .58 |
| 6" slab, direct chute | .019 | C.Y. | .008 | | .33 | .33 |
| Pumped concrete | .019 | C.Y. | .009 | | .50 | .50 |
| Crane & bucket | .019 | C.Y. | .012 | | .74 | .74 |
| Gravel, bank run, 4" deep | 1.000 | S.F. | .001 | .39 | .05 | .44 |
| 6" deep | 1.000 | S.F. | .001 | .52 | .07 | .59 |
| 9" deep | 1.000 | S.F. | .001 | .76 | .10 | .86 |
| 12" deep | 1.000 | S.F. | .001 | 1.05 | .12 | 1.17 |
| 3/4" crushed stone, 3" deep | 1.000 | S.F. | .001 | .42 | .06 | .48 |
| 6" deep | 1.000 | S.F. | .001 | .83 | .10 | .93 |
| 9" deep | 1.000 | S.F. | .002 | 1.21 | .12 | 1.33 |
| 12" deep | 1.000 | S.F. | .002 | 1.71 | .16 | 1.87 |
| Vapor barrier polyethylene, .004" thick | 1.000 | S.F. | .002 | .04 | .11 | .15 |
| .006" thick | 1.000 | S.F. | .002 | .06 | .11 | .17 |
| Edge forms, expansion material, 4" thick slab | .100 | L.F. | .004 | .02 | .15 | .17 |
| 6" thick slab | .100 | L.F. | .005 | .03 | .23 | .26 |
| Welded wire fabric 6 x 6, 10/10 (W1.4/W1.4) | 1.100 | S.F. | .005 | .14 | .28 | .42 |
| 6 x 6, 6/6 (W2.9/W2.9) | 1.100 | S.F. | .006 | .29 | .33 | .62 |
| 4 x 4, 10/10 (W1.4/W1.4) | 1.100 | S.F. | .006 | .22 | .31 | .53 |
| Finish concrete, screed finish | 1.000 | S.F. | .009 | | .25 | .25 |
| Float finish | 1.000 | S.F. | .011 | | .25 | .25 |
| Steel trowel, for resilient floor | 1.000 | S.F. | .013 | | .79 | .79 |
| For finished floor | 1.000 | S.F. | .015 | | .61 | .61 |
| | | | | | | |
| | | | | | | |
| | | | | | | |

127

| System Description | QUAN. | UNIT | LABOR HOURS | COST PER S.F. | | |
|---|---|---|---|---|---|---|
| | | | | MAT. | INST. | TOTAL |
| **2″ X 8″, 16″ O.C.** | | | | | | |
| Wood joists, 2″ x 8″, 16″ O.C. | 1.000 | L.F. | .015 | .61 | .71 | 1.32 |
| Bridging, 1″ x 3″, 6′ O.C. | .080 | Pr. | .005 | .04 | .24 | .28 |
| Box sills, 2″ x 8″ | .150 | L.F. | .002 | .09 | .11 | .20 |
| Concrete filled steel column, 4″ diameter | .125 | L.F. | .002 | .20 | .12 | .32 |
| Girder, built up from three 2″ x 8″ | .125 | L.F. | .013 | .23 | .65 | .88 |
| Sheathing, plywood, subfloor, 5/8″ CDX | 1.000 | S.F. | .012 | .56 | .58 | 1.14 |
| Furring, 1″ x 3″, 16″ O.C. | 1.000 | L.F. | .023 | .38 | 1.12 | 1.50 |
| TOTAL | | S.F. | .072 | 2.11 | 3.53 | 5.64 |
| **2″ X 10″, 16″ O.C.** | | | | | | |
| Wood joists, 2″ x 10″, 16″ OC | 1.000 | L.F. | .018 | .80 | .87 | 1.67 |
| Bridging, 1″ x 3″, 6′ OC | .080 | Pr. | .005 | .04 | .24 | .28 |
| Box sills, 2″ x 10″ | .150 | L.F. | .003 | .12 | .13 | .25 |
| Concrete filled steel column, 4″ diameter | .125 | L.F. | .002 | .20 | .12 | .32 |
| Girder, built up from three 2″ x 10″ | .125 | L.F. | .014 | .30 | .70 | 1 |
| Sheathing, plywood, subfloor, 5/8″ CDX | 1.000 | S.F. | .012 | .56 | .58 | 1.14 |
| Furring, 1″ x 3″,16″ OC | 1.000 | L.F. | .023 | .38 | 1.12 | 1.50 |
| TOTAL | | S.F. | .077 | 2.40 | 3.76 | 6.16 |
| **2″ X 12″, 16″ O.C.** | | | | | | |
| Wood joists, 2″ x 12″, 16″ O.C. | 1.000 | L.F. | .018 | 1.17 | .90 | 2.07 |
| Bridging, 1″ x 3″, 6′ O.C. | .080 | Pr. | .005 | .04 | .24 | .28 |
| Box sills, 2″ x 12″ | .150 | L.F. | .003 | .18 | .14 | .32 |
| Concrete filled steel column, 4″ diameter | .125 | L.F. | .002 | .20 | .12 | .32 |
| Girder, built up from three 2″ x 12″ | .125 | L.F. | .015 | .44 | .74 | 1.18 |
| Sheathing, plywood, subfloor, 5/8″ CDX | 1.000 | S.F. | .012 | .56 | .58 | 1.14 |
| Furring, 1″ x 3″, 16″ O.C. | 1.000 | L.F. | .023 | .38 | 1.12 | 1.50 |
| TOTAL | | S.F. | .078 | 2.97 | 3.84 | 6.81 |

Floor costs on this page are given on a cost per square foot basis.

| Description | QUAN. | UNIT | LABOR HOURS | COST PER S.F. | | |
|---|---|---|---|---|---|---|
| | | | | MAT. | INST. | TOTAL |
| | | | | | | |
| | | | | | | |
| | | | | | | |
| | | | | | | |

| Floor Framing Price Sheet (Wood) | QUAN. | UNIT | LABOR HOURS | COST PER S.F. | | |
|---|---|---|---|---|---|---|
| | | | | MAT. | INST. | TOTAL |
| Joists, #2 or better, pine, 2" x 4", 12" O.C. | 1.250 | L.F. | .016 | .34 | .79 | 1.13 |
| 16" O.C. | 1.000 | L.F. | .013 | .27 | .63 | .90 |
| 2" x 6", 12" O.C. | 1.250 | L.F. | .016 | .51 | .79 | 1.30 |
| 16" O.C. | 1.000 | L.F. | .013 | .41 | .63 | 1.04 |
| 2" x 8", 12" O.C. | 1.250 | L.F. | .018 | .76 | .89 | 1.65 |
| 16" O.C. | 1.000 | L.F. | .015 | .61 | .71 | 1.32 |
| 2" x 10", 12" O.C. | 1.250 | L.F. | .022 | 1 | 1.09 | 2.09 |
| 16" O.C. | 1.000 | L.F. | .018 | .80 | .87 | 1.67 |
| 2" x 12", 12" O.C. | 1.250 | L.F. | .023 | 1.46 | 1.13 | 2.59 |
| 16" O.C. | 1.000 | L.F. | .018 | 1.17 | .90 | 2.07 |
| Bridging, wood 1" x 3", joists 12" O.C. | .100 | Pr. | .006 | .06 | .30 | .36 |
| 16" O.C. | .080 | Pr. | .005 | .04 | .24 | .28 |
| Metal, galvanized, joists 12" O.C. | .100 | Pr. | .006 | .17 | .30 | .47 |
| 16" O.C. | .080 | Pr. | .005 | .14 | .24 | .38 |
| Compression type, joists 12" O.C. | .100 | Pr. | .004 | .18 | .20 | .38 |
| 16" O.C. | .080 | Pr. | .003 | .14 | .16 | .30 |
| Box sills, #2 or better pine, 2" x 4" | .150 | L.F. | .002 | .04 | .09 | .13 |
| 2" x 6" | .150 | L.F. | .002 | .06 | .09 | .15 |
| 2" x 8" | .150 | L.F. | .002 | .09 | .11 | .20 |
| 2" x 10" | .150 | L.F. | .003 | .12 | .13 | .25 |
| 2" x 12" | .150 | L.F. | .003 | .18 | .14 | .32 |
| Girders, including lally columns, 3 pieces spiked together, 2" x 8" | .125 | L.F. | .015 | .43 | .77 | 1.20 |
| 2" x 10" | .125 | L.F. | .016 | .50 | .82 | 1.32 |
| 2" x 12" | .125 | L.F. | .017 | .64 | .86 | 1.50 |
| Solid girders, 3" x 8" | .040 | L.F. | .004 | .30 | .20 | .50 |
| 3" x 10" | .040 | L.F. | .004 | .33 | .21 | .54 |
| 3" x 12" | .040 | L.F. | .004 | .36 | .22 | .58 |
| 4" x 8" | .040 | L.F. | .004 | .33 | .22 | .55 |
| 4" x 10" | .040 | L.F. | .004 | .37 | .23 | .60 |
| 4" x 12" | .040 | L.F. | .004 | .48 | .24 | .72 |
| Steel girders, bolted & including fabrication, wide flange shapes | | | | | | |
| 12" deep, 14#/l.f. | .040 | L.F. | .003 | .88 | .26 | 1.14 |
| 10" deep, 15#/l.f. | .040 | L.F. | .003 | .88 | .26 | 1.14 |
| 8" deep, 10#/l.f. | .040 | L.F. | .003 | .58 | .26 | .84 |
| 6" deep, 9#/l.f. | .040 | L.F. | .003 | .52 | .26 | .78 |
| 5" deep, 16#/l.f. | .040 | L.F. | .003 | .88 | .26 | 1.14 |
| Sheathing, plywood exterior grade CDX, 1/2" thick | 1.000 | S.F. | .011 | .46 | .56 | 1.02 |
| 5/8" thick | 1.000 | S.F. | .012 | .56 | .58 | 1.14 |
| 3/4" thick | 1.000 | S.F. | .013 | .64 | .63 | 1.27 |
| Boards, 1" x 8" laid regular | 1.000 | S.F. | .016 | 1.47 | .78 | 2.25 |
| Laid diagonal | 1.000 | S.F. | .019 | 1.47 | .92 | 2.39 |
| 1" x 10" laid regular | 1.000 | S.F. | .015 | 1.62 | .71 | 2.33 |
| Laid diagonal | 1.000 | S.F. | .018 | 1.62 | .87 | 2.49 |
| Furring, 1" x 3", 12" O.C. | 1.250 | L.F. | .029 | .48 | 1.40 | 1.88 |
| 16" O.C. | 1.000 | L.F. | .023 | .38 | 1.12 | 1.50 |
| 24" O.C. | .750 | L.F. | .017 | .29 | .84 | 1.13 |
| | | | | | | |
| | | | | | | |
| | | | | | | |
| | | | | | | |
| | | | | | | |

| System Description | QUAN. | UNIT | LABOR HOURS | COST PER S.F. | | |
|---|---|---|---|---|---|---|
| | | | | MAT. | INST. | TOTAL |
| **9-1/2″ COMPOSITE WOOD JOISTS, 16″ O.C.** | | | | | | |
| CWJ, 9-1/2″, 16″ O.C., 15′ span | 1.000 | L.F. | .018 | 1.73 | .87 | 2.60 |
| Temp. strut line, 1″ x 4″, 8′ O.C. | .160 | L.F. | .003 | .08 | .16 | .24 |
| CWJ rim joist, 9-1/2″ | .150 | L.F. | .003 | .26 | .13 | .39 |
| Concrete filled steel column, 4″ diameter | .125 | L.F. | .002 | .20 | .12 | .32 |
| Girder, built up from three 2″ x 8″ | .125 | L.F. | .013 | .23 | .65 | .88 |
| Sheathing, plywood, subfloor, 5/8″ CDX | 1.000 | S.F. | .012 | .56 | .58 | 1.14 |
| | | | | | | |
| TOTAL | | S.F. | .051 | 3.06 | 2.51 | 5.57 |
| **11-1/2″ COMPOSITE WOOD JOISTS, 16″ O.C.** | | | | | | |
| CWJ, 11-1/2″, 16″ O.C., 18′ span | 1.000 | L.F. | .018 | 1.85 | .89 | 2.74 |
| Temp. strut line, 1″ x 4″, 8′ O.C. | .160 | L.F. | .003 | .08 | .16 | .24 |
| CWJ rim joist, 11-1/2″ | .150 | L.F. | .003 | .28 | .13 | .41 |
| Concrete filled steel column, 4″ diameter | .125 | L.F. | .002 | .20 | .12 | .32 |
| Girder, built up from three 2″ x 10″ | .125 | L.F. | .014 | .30 | .70 | 1 |
| Sheathing, plywood, subfloor, 5/8″ CDX | 1.000 | S.F. | .012 | .56 | .58 | 1.14 |
| | | | | | | |
| TOTAL | | S.F. | .052 | 3.27 | 2.58 | 5.85 |
| **14″ COMPOSITE WOOD JOISTS, 16″ O.C.** | | | | | | |
| CWJ, 14″, 16″ O.C., 22′ span | 1.000 | L.F. | .020 | 2.58 | .96 | 3.54 |
| Temp. strut line, 1″ x 4″, 8′ O.C. | .160 | L.F. | .003 | .08 | .16 | .24 |
| CWJ rim joist, 14″ | .150 | L.F. | .003 | .39 | .14 | .53 |
| Concrete filled steel column, 4″ diameter | .600 | L.F. | .002 | .20 | .12 | .32 |
| Girder, built up from three 2″ x 12″ | .600 | L.F. | .015 | .44 | .74 | 1.18 |
| Sheathing, plywood, subfloor, 5/8″ CDX | 1.000 | S.F. | .012 | .56 | .58 | 1.14 |
| | | | | | | |
| TOTAL | | S.F. | .055 | 4.25 | 2.70 | 6.95 |

Floor costs on this page are given on a cost per square foot basis.

| Description | QUAN. | UNIT | LABOR HOURS | COST PER S.F. | | |
|---|---|---|---|---|---|---|
| | | | | MAT. | INST. | TOTAL |
| | | | | | | |
| | | | | | | |
| | | | | | | |

| Floor Framing Price Sheet (Wood) | QUAN. | UNIT | LABOR HOURS | COST PER S.F. | | |
|---|---|---|---|---|---|---|
| | | | | MAT. | INST. | TOTAL |
| Composite wood joist 9-1/2″ deep, 12″ O.C. | 1.250 | L.F. | .022 | 2.16 | 1.09 | 3.25 |
| 16″ O.C. | 1.000 | L.F. | .018 | 1.73 | .87 | 2.60 |
| 11-1/2″ deep, 12″ O.C. | 1.250 | L.F. | .023 | 2.31 | 1.11 | 3.42 |
| 16″ O.C. | 1.000 | L.F. | .018 | 1.85 | .89 | 2.74 |
| 14″ deep, 12″ O.C. | 1.250 | L.F. | .024 | 3.22 | 1.19 | 4.41 |
| 16″ O.C. | 1.000 | L.F. | .020 | 2.58 | .96 | 3.54 |
| 16 ″ deep, 12″ O.C. | 1.250 | L.F. | .026 | 4.22 | 1.25 | 5.47 |
| 16″ O.C. | 1.000 | L.F. | .021 | 3.38 | 1 | 4.38 |
| CWJ rim joist, 9-1/2″ | .150 | L.F. | .003 | .26 | .13 | .39 |
| 11-1/2″ | .150 | L.F. | .003 | .28 | .13 | .41 |
| 14″ | .150 | L.F. | .003 | .39 | .14 | .53 |
| 16″ | .150 | L.F. | .003 | .51 | .15 | .66 |
| Girders, including lally columns, 3 pieces spiked together, 2″ x 8″ | .125 | L.F. | .015 | .43 | .77 | 1.20 |
| 2″ x 10″ | .125 | L.F. | .016 | .50 | .82 | 1.32 |
| 2″ x 12″ | .125 | L.F. | .017 | .64 | .86 | 1.50 |
| Solid girders, 3″ x 8″ | .040 | L.F. | .004 | .30 | .20 | .50 |
| 3″ x 10″ | .040 | L.F. | .004 | .33 | .21 | .54 |
| 3″ x 12″ | .040 | L.F. | .004 | .36 | .22 | .58 |
| 4″ x 8″ | .040 | L.F. | .004 | .33 | .22 | .55 |
| 4″ x 10″ | .040 | L.F. | .004 | .37 | .23 | .60 |
| 4″ x 12″ | .040 | L.F. | .004 | .48 | .24 | .72 |
| Steel girders, bolted & including fabrication, wide flange shapes | | | | | | |
| 12″ deep, 14#/l.f. | .040 | L.F. | .061 | 20 | 5.85 | 25.85 |
| 10″ deep, 15#/l.f. | .040 | L.F. | .067 | 22 | 6.35 | 28.35 |
| 8″ deep, 10#/l.f. | .040 | L.F. | .067 | 14.50 | 6.35 | 20.85 |
| 6″ deep, 9#/l.f. | .040 | L.F. | .067 | 13.05 | 6.35 | 19.40 |
| 5″ deep, 16#/l.f. | .040 | L.F. | .064 | 21.50 | 6.15 | 27.65 |
| Sheathing, plywood exterior grade CDX, 1/2″ thick | 1.000 | S.F. | .011 | .46 | .56 | 1.02 |
| 5/8″ thick | 1.000 | S.F. | .012 | .56 | .58 | 1.14 |
| 3/4″ thick | 1.000 | S.F. | .013 | .64 | .63 | 1.27 |
| Boards, 1″ x 8″ laid regular | 1.000 | S.F. | .016 | 1.47 | .78 | 2.25 |
| Laid diagonal | 1.000 | S.F. | .019 | 1.47 | .92 | 2.39 |
| 1″ x 10″ laid regular | 1.000 | S.F. | .015 | 1.62 | .71 | 2.33 |
| Laid diagonal | 1.000 | S.F. | .018 | 1.62 | .87 | 2.49 |
| Furring, 1″ x 3″, 12″ O.C. | 1.250 | L.F. | .029 | .48 | 1.40 | 1.88 |
| 16″ O.C. | 1.000 | L.F. | .023 | .38 | 1.12 | 1.50 |
| 24″ O.C. | .750 | L.F. | .017 | .29 | .84 | 1.13 |
| | | | | | | |
| | | | | | | |
| | | | | | | |
| | | | | | | |
| | | | | | | |
| | | | | | | |

Cont. 2" x 4" Ribbon — Plywood Sheathing — Girder — Wood Floor Trusses

| System Description | QUAN. | UNIT | LABOR HOURS | COST PER S.F. | | |
|---|---|---|---|---|---|---|
| | | | | MAT. | INST. | TOTAL |
| **12" OPEN WEB JOISTS, 16" O.C.** | | | | | | |
| OWJ 12", 16" O.C., 21' span | 1.000 | L.F. | .018 | 3.05 | .89 | 3.94 |
| Continuous ribbing, 2" x 4" | .150 | L.F. | .002 | .04 | .09 | .13 |
| Concrete filled steel column, 4" diameter | .125 | L.F. | .002 | .20 | .12 | .32 |
| Girder, built up from three 2" x 8" | .125 | L.F. | .013 | .23 | .65 | .88 |
| Sheathing, plywood, subfloor, 5/8" CDX | 1.000 | S.F. | .012 | .56 | .58 | 1.14 |
| Furring, 1" x 3", 16" O.C. | 1.000 | L.F. | .023 | .38 | 1.12 | 1.50 |
| TOTAL | | S.F. | .070 | 4.46 | 3.45 | 7.91 |
| **14" OPEN WEB WOOD JOISTS, 16" O.C.** | | | | | | |
| OWJ 14", 16" O.C., 22' span | 1.000 | L.F. | .020 | 3.28 | .96 | 4.24 |
| Continuous ribbing, 2" x 4" | .150 | L.F. | .002 | .04 | .09 | .13 |
| Concrete filled steel column, 4" diameter | .125 | L.F. | .002 | .20 | .12 | .32 |
| Girder, built up from three 2" x 10" | .125 | L.F. | .014 | .30 | .70 | 1 |
| Sheathing, plywood, subfloor, 5/8" CDX | 1.000 | S.F. | .012 | .56 | .58 | 1.14 |
| Furring, 1" x 3", 16" O.C. | 1.000 | L.F. | .023 | .38 | 1.12 | 1.50 |
| TOTAL | | S.F. | .073 | 4.76 | 3.57 | 8.33 |
| **16" OPEN WEB WOOD JOISTS, 16" O.C.** | | | | | | |
| OWJ 16", 16" O.C., 24' span | 1.000 | L.F. | .021 | 3.25 | 1 | 4.25 |
| Continuous ribbing, 2" x 4" | .150 | L.F. | .002 | .04 | .09 | .13 |
| Concrete filled steel column, 4" diameter | .125 | L.F. | .002 | .20 | .12 | .32 |
| Girder, built up from three 2" x 12" | .125 | L.F. | .015 | .44 | .74 | 1.18 |
| Sheathing, plywood, subfloor, 5/8" CDX | 1.000 | S.F. | .012 | .56 | .58 | 1.14 |
| Furring, 1" x 3", 16" O.C. | 1.000 | L.F. | .023 | .38 | 1.12 | 1.50 |
| TOTAL | | S.F. | .075 | 4.87 | 3.65 | 8.52 |

Floor costs on this page are given on a cost per square foot basis.

| Description | QUAN. | UNIT | LABOR HOURS | COST PER S.F. | | |
|---|---|---|---|---|---|---|
| | | | | MAT. | INST. | TOTAL |
| | | | | | | |
| | | | | | | |
| | | | | | | |

# Floor Framing Price Sheet (Wood)

| Floor Framing Price Sheet (Wood) | QUAN. | UNIT | LABOR HOURS | COST PER S.F. MAT. | COST PER S.F. INST. | COST PER S.F. TOTAL |
|---|---|---|---|---|---|---|
| Open web joists, 12" deep, 12" O.C. | 1.250 | L.F. | .023 | 3.81 | 1.11 | 4.92 |
| 16" O.C. | 1.000 | L.F. | .018 | 3.05 | .89 | 3.94 |
| 14" deep, 12" O.C. | 1.250 | L.F. | .024 | 4.09 | 1.19 | 5.28 |
| 16" O.C. | 1.000 | L.F. | .020 | 3.28 | .96 | 4.24 |
| 16 " deep, 12" O.C. | 1.250 | L.F. | .026 | 4.06 | 1.25 | 5.31 |
| 16" O.C. | 1.000 | L.F. | .021 | 3.25 | 1 | 4.25 |
| 18" deep, 12" O.C. | 1.250 | L.F. | .027 | 4.38 | 1.31 | 5.69 |
| 16" O.C. | 1.000 | L.F. | .022 | 3.50 | 1.05 | 4.55 |
| Continuous ribbing, 2" x 4" | .150 | L.F. | .002 | .04 | .09 | .13 |
| 2" x 6" | .150 | L.F. | .002 | .06 | .09 | .15 |
| 2" x 8" | .150 | L.F. | .002 | .09 | .11 | .20 |
| 2" x 10" | .150 | L.F. | .003 | .12 | .13 | .25 |
| 2" x 12" | .150 | L.F. | .003 | .18 | .14 | .32 |
| Girders, including lally columns, 3 pieces spiked together, 2" x 8" | .125 | L.F. | .015 | .43 | .77 | 1.20 |
| 2" x 10" | .125 | L.F. | .016 | .50 | .82 | 1.32 |
| 2" x 12" | .125 | L.F. | .017 | .64 | .86 | 1.50 |
| Solid girders, 3" x 8" | .040 | L.F. | .004 | .30 | .20 | .50 |
| 3" x 10" | .040 | L.F. | .004 | .33 | .21 | .54 |
| 3" x 12" | .040 | L.F. | .004 | .36 | .22 | .58 |
| 4" x 8" | .040 | L.F. | .004 | .33 | .22 | .55 |
| 4" x 10" | .040 | L.F. | .004 | .37 | .23 | .60 |
| 4" x 12" | .040 | L.F. | .004 | .48 | .24 | .72 |
| Steel girders, bolted & including fabrication, wide flange shapes | | | | | | |
| 12" deep, 14#/l.f. | .040 | L.F. | .061 | 20 | 5.85 | 25.85 |
| 10" deep, 15#/l.f. | .040 | L.F. | .067 | 22 | 6.35 | 28.35 |
| 8" deep, 10#/l.f. | .040 | L.F. | .067 | 14.50 | 6.35 | 20.85 |
| 6" deep, 9#/l.f. | .040 | L.F. | .067 | 13.05 | 6.35 | 19.40 |
| 5" deep, 16#/l.f. | .040 | L.F. | .064 | 21.50 | 6.15 | 27.65 |
| Sheathing, plywood exterior grade CDX, 1/2" thick | 1.000 | S.F. | .011 | .46 | .56 | 1.02 |
| 5/8" thick | 1.000 | S.F. | .012 | .56 | .58 | 1.14 |
| 3/4" thick | 1.000 | S.F. | .013 | .64 | .63 | 1.27 |
| Boards, 1" x 8" laid regular | 1.000 | S.F. | .016 | 1.47 | .78 | 2.25 |
| Laid diagonal | 1.000 | S.F. | .019 | 1.47 | .92 | 2.39 |
| 1" x 10" laid regular | 1.000 | S.F. | .015 | 1.62 | .71 | 2.33 |
| Laid diagonal | 1.000 | S.F. | .018 | 1.62 | .87 | 2.49 |
| Furring, 1" x 3", 12" O.C. | 1.250 | L.F. | .029 | .48 | 1.40 | 1.88 |
| 16" O.C. | 1.000 | L.F. | .023 | .38 | 1.12 | 1.50 |
| 24" O.C. | .750 | L.F. | .017 | .29 | .84 | 1.13 |
| | | | | | | |
| | | | | | | |
| | | | | | | |
| | | | | | | |
| | | | | | | |

Sheathing →

Top Plates

Studs

Bottom Plate →

Corner Bracing

| System Description | QUAN. | UNIT | LABOR HOURS | COST PER S.F. | | |
|---|---|---|---|---|---|---|
| | | | | MAT. | INST. | TOTAL |
| **2″ X 4″, 16″ O.C.** | | | | | | |
| 2″ x 4″ studs, 16″ O.C. | 1.000 | L.F. | .015 | .27 | .71 | .98 |
| Plates, 2″ x 4″, double top, single bottom | .375 | L.F. | .005 | .10 | .27 | .37 |
| Corner bracing, let-in, 1″ x 6″ | .063 | L.F. | .003 | .04 | .16 | .20 |
| Sheathing, 1/2″ plywood, CDX | 1.000 | S.F. | .011 | .46 | .56 | 1.02 |
| TOTAL | | S.F. | .034 | .87 | 1.70 | 2.57 |
| **2″ X 4″, 24″ O.C.** | | | | | | |
| 2″ x 4″ studs, 24″ O.C. | .750 | L.F. | .011 | .20 | .53 | .73 |
| Plates, 2″ x 4″, double top, single bottom | .375 | L.F. | .005 | .10 | .27 | .37 |
| Corner bracing, let-in, 1″ x 6″ | .063 | L.F. | .002 | .04 | .11 | .15 |
| Sheathing, 1/2″ plywood, CDX | 1.000 | S.F. | .011 | .46 | .56 | 1.02 |
| TOTAL | | S.F. | .029 | .80 | 1.47 | 2.27 |
| **2″ X 6″, 16″ O.C.** | | | | | | |
| 2″ x 6″ studs, 16″ O.C. | 1.000 | L.F. | .016 | .41 | .78 | 1.19 |
| Plates, 2″ x 6″, double top, single bottom | .375 | L.F. | .006 | .15 | .29 | .44 |
| Corner bracing, let-in, 1″ x 6″ | .063 | L.F. | .003 | .04 | .16 | .20 |
| Sheathing, 1/2″ plywood, CDX | 1.000 | S.F. | .014 | .46 | .70 | 1.16 |
| TOTAL | | S.F. | .039 | 1.06 | 1.93 | 2.99 |
| **2″ X 6″, 24″ O.C.** | | | | | | |
| 2″ x 6″ studs, 24″ O.C. | .750 | L.F. | .012 | .31 | .59 | .90 |
| Plates, 2″ x 6″, double top, single bottom | .375 | L.F. | .006 | .15 | .29 | .44 |
| Corner bracing, let-in, 1″ x 6″ | .063 | L.F. | .002 | .04 | .11 | .15 |
| Sheathing, 1/2″ plywood, CDX | 1.000 | S.F. | .011 | .46 | .56 | 1.02 |
| TOTAL | | S.F. | .031 | .96 | 1.55 | 2.51 |

The wall costs on this page are given in cost per square foot of wall.
For window and door openings see below.

| Description | QUAN. | UNIT | LABOR HOURS | COST PER S.F. | | |
|---|---|---|---|---|---|---|
| | | | | MAT. | INST. | TOTAL |
| | | | | | | |
| | | | | | | |
| | | | | | | |

| Exterior Wall Framing Price Sheet | QUAN. | UNIT | LABOR HOURS | COST PER S.F. | | |
|---|---|---|---|---|---|---|
| | | | | MAT. | INST. | TOTAL |
| Studs, #2 or better, 2" x 4", 12" O.C. | 1.250 | L.F. | .018 | .34 | .89 | 1.23 |
| 16" O.C. | 1.000 | L.F. | .015 | .27 | .71 | .98 |
| 24" O.C. | .750 | L.F. | .011 | .20 | .53 | .73 |
| 32" O.C. | .600 | L.F. | .009 | .16 | .43 | .59 |
| 2" x 6", 12" O.C. | 1.250 | L.F. | .020 | .51 | .98 | 1.49 |
| 16" O.C. | 1.000 | L.F. | .016 | .41 | .78 | 1.19 |
| 24" O.C. | .750 | L.F. | .012 | .31 | .59 | .90 |
| 32" O.C. | .600 | L.F. | .010 | .25 | .47 | .72 |
| 2" x 8", 12" O.C. | 1.250 | L.F. | .025 | 1.14 | 1.23 | 2.37 |
| 16" O.C. | 1.000 | L.F. | .020 | .91 | .98 | 1.89 |
| 24" O.C. | .750 | L.F. | .015 | .68 | .74 | 1.42 |
| 32" O.C. | .600 | L.F. | .012 | .55 | .59 | 1.14 |
| Plates, #2 or better, double top, single bottom, 2" x 4" | .375 | L.F. | .005 | .10 | .27 | .37 |
| 2" x 6" | .375 | L.F. | .006 | .15 | .29 | .44 |
| 2" x 8" | .375 | L.F. | .008 | .34 | .37 | .71 |
| Corner bracing, let-in 1" x 6" boards, studs, 12" O.C. | .070 | L.F. | .004 | .05 | .18 | .23 |
| 16" O.C. | .063 | L.F. | .003 | .04 | .16 | .20 |
| 24" O.C. | .063 | L.F. | .002 | .04 | .11 | .15 |
| 32" O.C. | .057 | L.F. | .002 | .04 | .10 | .14 |
| Let-in steel ("T" shape), studs, 12" O.C. | .070 | L.F. | .001 | .06 | .05 | .11 |
| 16" O.C. | .063 | L.F. | .001 | .05 | .04 | .09 |
| 24" O.C. | .063 | L.F. | .001 | .05 | .04 | .09 |
| 32" O.C. | .057 | L.F. | .001 | .05 | .04 | .09 |
| Sheathing, plywood CDX, 3/8" thick | 1.000 | S.F. | .010 | .40 | .51 | .91 |
| 1/2" thick | 1.000 | S.F. | .011 | .46 | .56 | 1.02 |
| 5/8" thick | 1.000 | S.F. | .012 | .56 | .60 | 1.16 |
| 3/4" thick | 1.000 | S.F. | .013 | .64 | .65 | 1.29 |
| Boards, 1" x 6", laid regular | 1.000 | S.F. | .025 | 1.53 | 1.21 | 2.74 |
| Laid diagonal | 1.000 | S.F. | .027 | 1.53 | 1.34 | 2.87 |
| 1" x 8", laid regular | 1.000 | S.F. | .021 | 1.47 | 1.02 | 2.49 |
| Laid diagonal | 1.000 | S.F. | .025 | 1.47 | 1.21 | 2.68 |
| Wood fiber, regular, no vapor barrier, 1/2" thick | 1.000 | S.F. | .013 | .62 | .65 | 1.27 |
| 5/8" thick | 1.000 | S.F. | .013 | .78 | .65 | 1.43 |
| Asphalt impregnated 25/32" thick | 1.000 | S.F. | .013 | .31 | .65 | .96 |
| 1/2" thick | 1.000 | S.F. | .013 | .22 | .65 | .87 |
| Polystyrene, regular, 3/4" thick | 1.000 | S.F. | .010 | .56 | .49 | 1.05 |
| 2" thick | 1.000 | S.F. | .011 | 1.54 | .54 | 2.08 |
| Fiberglass, foil faced, 1" thick | 1.000 | S.F. | .008 | 1.01 | .39 | 1.40 |
| 2" thick | 1.000 | S.F. | .009 | 1.88 | .44 | 2.32 |

| Window & Door Openings | QUAN. | UNIT | LABOR HOURS | COST EACH | | |
|---|---|---|---|---|---|---|
| | | | | MAT. | INST. | TOTAL |
| The following costs are to be added to the total costs of the wall for each opening. Do not subtract the area of the openings. | | | | | | |
| Headers, 2" x 6" double, 2' long | 4.000 | L.F. | .178 | 1.64 | 8.70 | 10.34 |
| 3' long | 6.000 | L.F. | .267 | 2.46 | 13.10 | 15.56 |
| 4' long | 8.000 | L.F. | .356 | 3.28 | 17.45 | 20.73 |
| 5' long | 10.000 | L.F. | .444 | 4.10 | 22 | 26.10 |
| 2" x 8" double, 4' long | 8.000 | L.F. | .376 | 4.88 | 18.40 | 23.28 |
| 5' long | 10.000 | L.F. | .471 | 6.10 | 23 | 29.10 |
| 6' long | 12.000 | L.F. | .565 | 7.30 | 27.50 | 34.80 |
| 8' long | 16.000 | L.F. | .753 | 9.75 | 37 | 46.75 |
| 2" x 10" double, 4' long | 8.000 | L.F. | .400 | 6.40 | 19.60 | 26 |
| 6' long | 12.000 | L.F. | .600 | 9.60 | 29.50 | 39.10 |
| 8' long | 16.000 | L.F. | .800 | 12.80 | 39 | 51.80 |
| 10' long | 20.000 | L.F. | 1.000 | 16 | 49 | 65 |
| 2" x 12" double, 8' long | 16.000 | L.F. | .853 | 18.70 | 42 | 60.70 |
| 12' long | 24.000 | L.F. | 1.280 | 28 | 62.50 | 90.50 |

| System Description | QUAN. | UNIT | LABOR HOURS | COST PER S.F. | | |
|---|---|---|---|---|---|---|
| | | | | MAT. | INST. | TOTAL |
| **2″ X 6″ RAFTERS, 16″ O.C., 4/12 PITCH** | | | | | | |
| Rafters, 2″ x 6″, 16″ O.C., 4/12 pitch | 1.170 | L.F. | .019 | .48 | .91 | 1.39 |
| Ceiling joists, 2″ x 4″, 16″ O.C. | 1.000 | L.F. | .013 | .27 | .63 | .90 |
| Ridge board, 2″ x 6″ | .050 | L.F. | .002 | .02 | .08 | .10 |
| Fascia board, 2″ x 6″ | .100 | L.F. | .005 | .05 | .26 | .31 |
| Rafter tie, 1″ x 4″, 4′ O.C. | .060 | L.F. | .001 | .03 | .06 | .09 |
| Soffit nailer (outrigger), 2″ x 4″, 24″ O.C. | .170 | L.F. | .004 | .05 | .21 | .26 |
| Sheathing, exterior, plywood, CDX, 1/2″ thick | 1.170 | S.F. | .013 | .54 | .66 | 1.20 |
| Furring strips, 1″ x 3″, 16″ O.C. | 1.000 | L.F. | .023 | .38 | 1.12 | 1.50 |
| TOTAL | | S.F. | .080 | 1.82 | 3.93 | 5.75 |
| **2″ X 8″ RAFTERS, 16″ O.C., 4/12 PITCH** | | | | | | |
| Rafters, 2″ x 8″, 16″ O.C., 4/12 pitch | 1.170 | L.F. | .020 | .71 | .96 | 1.67 |
| Ceiling joists, 2″ x 6″, 16″ O.C. | 1.000 | L.F. | .013 | .41 | .63 | 1.04 |
| Ridge board, 2″ x 8″ | .050 | L.F. | .002 | .03 | .09 | .12 |
| Fascia board, 2″ x 8″ | .100 | L.F. | .007 | .06 | .35 | .41 |
| Rafter tie, 1″ x 4″, 4′ O.C. | .060 | L.F. | .001 | .03 | .06 | .09 |
| Soffit nailer (outrigger), 2″ x 4″, 24″ O.C. | .170 | L.F. | .004 | .05 | .21 | .26 |
| Sheathing, exterior, plywood, CDX, 1/2″ thick | 1.170 | S.F. | .013 | .54 | .66 | 1.20 |
| Furring strips, 1″ x 3″, 16″ O.C. | 1.000 | L.F. | .023 | .38 | 1.12 | 1.50 |
| TOTAL | | S.F. | .083 | 2.21 | 4.08 | 6.29 |

The cost of this system is based on the square foot of plan area.
All quantities have been adjusted accordingly.

| Description | QUAN. | UNIT | LABOR HOURS | COST PER S.F. | | |
|---|---|---|---|---|---|---|
| | | | | MAT. | INST. | TOTAL |
| | | | | | | |
| | | | | | | |
| | | | | | | |
| | | | | | | |
| | | | | | | |

| Gable End Roof Framing Price Sheet | QUAN. | UNIT | LABOR HOURS | COST PER S.F. | | |
|---|---|---|---|---|---|---|
| | | | | MAT. | INST. | TOTAL |
| Rafters, #2 or better, 16″ O.C., 2″ x 6″, 4/12 pitch | 1.170 | L.F. | .019 | .48 | .91 | 1.39 |
| 8/12 pitch | 1.330 | L.F. | .027 | .55 | 1.30 | 1.85 |
| 2″ x 8″, 4/12 pitch | 1.170 | L.F. | .020 | .71 | .96 | 1.67 |
| 8/12 pitch | 1.330 | L.F. | .028 | .81 | 1.38 | 2.19 |
| 2″ x 10″, 4/12 pitch | 1.170 | L.F. | .030 | .94 | 1.45 | 2.39 |
| 8/12 pitch | 1.330 | L.F. | .043 | 1.06 | 2.10 | 3.16 |
| 24″ O.C., 2″ x 6″, 4/12 pitch | .940 | L.F. | .015 | .39 | .73 | 1.12 |
| 8/12 pitch | 1.060 | L.F. | .021 | .43 | 1.04 | 1.47 |
| 2″ x 8″, 4/12 pitch | .940 | L.F. | .016 | .57 | .77 | 1.34 |
| 8/12 pitch | 1.060 | L.F. | .023 | .65 | 1.10 | 1.75 |
| 2″ x 10″, 4/12 pitch | .940 | L.F. | .024 | .75 | 1.17 | 1.92 |
| 8/12 pitch | 1.060 | L.F. | .034 | .85 | 1.67 | 2.52 |
| Ceiling joist, #2 or better, 2″ x 4″, 16″ O.C. | 1.000 | L.F. | .013 | .27 | .63 | .90 |
| 24″ O.C. | .750 | L.F. | .010 | .20 | .47 | .67 |
| 2″ x 6″, 16″ O.C. | 1.000 | L.F. | .013 | .41 | .63 | 1.04 |
| 24″ O.C. | .750 | L.F. | .010 | .31 | .47 | .78 |
| 2″ x 8″, 16″ O.C. | 1.000 | L.F. | .015 | .61 | .71 | 1.32 |
| 24″ O.C. | .750 | L.F. | .011 | .46 | .53 | .99 |
| 2″ x 10″, 16″ O.C. | 1.000 | L.F. | .018 | .80 | .87 | 1.67 |
| 24″ O.C. | .750 | L.F. | .013 | .60 | .65 | 1.25 |
| Ridge board, #2 or better, 1″ x 6″ | .050 | L.F. | .001 | .04 | .07 | .11 |
| 1″ x 8″ | .050 | L.F. | .001 | .05 | .07 | .12 |
| 1″ x 10″ | .050 | L.F. | .002 | .06 | .08 | .14 |
| 2″ x 6″ | .050 | L.F. | .002 | .02 | .08 | .10 |
| 2″ x 8″ | .050 | L.F. | .002 | .03 | .09 | .12 |
| 2″ x 10″ | .050 | L.F. | .002 | .04 | .10 | .14 |
| Fascia board, #2 or better, 1″ x 6″ | .100 | L.F. | .004 | .03 | .19 | .22 |
| 1″ x 8″ | .100 | L.F. | .005 | .04 | .22 | .26 |
| 1″ x 10″ | .100 | L.F. | .005 | .04 | .25 | .29 |
| 2″ x 6″ | .100 | L.F. | .006 | .05 | .28 | .33 |
| 2″ x 8″ | .100 | L.F. | .007 | .06 | .35 | .41 |
| 2″ x 10″ | .100 | L.F. | .004 | .16 | .17 | .33 |
| Rafter tie, #2 or better, 4′ O.C., 1″ x 4″ | .060 | L.F. | .001 | .03 | .06 | .09 |
| 1″ x 6″ | .060 | L.F. | .001 | .03 | .06 | .09 |
| 2″ x 4″ | .060 | L.F. | .002 | .04 | .08 | .12 |
| 2″ x 6″ | .060 | L.F. | .002 | .05 | .10 | .15 |
| Soffit nailer (outrigger), 2″ x 4″, 16″ O.C. | .220 | L.F. | .006 | .06 | .28 | .34 |
| 24″ O.C. | .170 | L.F. | .004 | .05 | .21 | .26 |
| 2″ x 6″, 16″ O.C. | .220 | L.F. | .006 | .07 | .32 | .39 |
| 24″ O.C. | .170 | L.F. | .005 | .05 | .25 | .30 |
| Sheathing, plywood CDX, 4/12 pitch, 3/8″ thick. | 1.170 | S.F. | .012 | .47 | .60 | 1.07 |
| 1/2″ thick | 1.170 | S.F. | .013 | .54 | .66 | 1.20 |
| 5/8″ thick | 1.170 | S.F. | .014 | .66 | .70 | 1.36 |
| 8/12 pitch, 3/8″ | 1.330 | S.F. | .014 | .53 | .68 | 1.21 |
| 1/2″ thick | 1.330 | S.F. | .015 | .61 | .74 | 1.35 |
| 5/8″ thick | 1.330 | S.F. | .016 | .74 | .80 | 1.54 |
| Boards, 4/12 pitch roof, 1″ x 6″ | 1.170 | S.F. | .026 | 1.79 | 1.26 | 3.05 |
| 1″ x 8″ | 1.170 | S.F. | .021 | 1.72 | 1.05 | 2.77 |
| 8/12 pitch roof, 1″ x 6″ | 1.330 | S.F. | .029 | 2.03 | 1.44 | 3.47 |
| 1″ x 8″ | 1.330 | S.F. | .024 | 1.96 | 1.20 | 3.16 |
| Furring, 1″ x 3″, 12″ O.C. | 1.200 | L.F. | .027 | .46 | 1.34 | 1.80 |
| 16″ O.C. | 1.000 | L.F. | .023 | .38 | 1.12 | 1.50 |
| 24″ O.C. | .800 | L.F. | .018 | .30 | .90 | 1.20 |
| | | | | | | |
| | | | | | | |
| | | | | | | |

Sheathing

Trusses

Fascia Board

Furring

| System Description | QUAN. | UNIT | LABOR HOURS | COST PER S.F. | | |
|---|---|---|---|---|---|---|
| | | | | MAT. | INST. | TOTAL |
| **TRUSS, 16″ O.C., 4/12 PITCH, 1′ OVERHANG, 26′ SPAN** | | | | | | |
| Truss, 40# loading, 16″ O.C., 4/12 pitch, 26′ span | .030 | Ea. | .021 | 2.64 | 1.31 | 3.95 |
| Fascia board, 2″ x 6″ | .100 | L.F. | .005 | .05 | .26 | .31 |
| Sheathing, exterior, plywood, CDX, 1/2″ thick | 1.170 | S.F. | .013 | .54 | .66 | 1.20 |
| Furring, 1″ x 3″, 16″ O.C. | 1.000 | L.F. | .023 | .38 | 1.12 | 1.50 |
| TOTAL | | S.F. | .062 | 3.61 | 3.35 | 6.96 |
| **TRUSS, 16″ O.C., 8/12 PITCH, 1′ OVERHANG, 26′ SPAN** | | | | | | |
| Truss, 40# loading, 16″ O.C., 8/12 pitch, 26′ span | .030 | Ea. | .023 | 3.33 | 1.44 | 4.77 |
| Fascia board, 2″ x 6″ | .100 | L.F. | .005 | .05 | .26 | .31 |
| Sheathing, exterior, plywood, CDX, 1/2″ thick | 1.330 | S.F. | .015 | .61 | .74 | 1.35 |
| Furring, 1″ x 3″, 16″ O.C. | 1.000 | L.F. | .023 | .38 | 1.12 | 1.50 |
| TOTAL | | S.F. | .066 | 4.37 | 3.56 | 7.93 |
| **TRUSS, 24″ O.C., 4/12 PITCH, 1′ OVERHANG, 26′ SPAN** | | | | | | |
| Truss, 40# loading, 24″ O.C., 4/12 pitch, 26′ span | .020 | Ea. | .014 | 1.76 | .87 | 2.63 |
| Fascia board, 2″ x 6″ | .100 | L.F. | .005 | .05 | .26 | .31 |
| Sheathing, exterior, plywood, CDX, 1/2″ thick | 1.170 | S.F. | .013 | .54 | .66 | 1.20 |
| Furring, 1″ x 3″, 16″ O.C. | 1.000 | L.F. | .023 | .38 | 1.12 | 1.50 |
| TOTAL | | S.F. | .055 | 2.73 | 2.91 | 5.64 |
| **TRUSS, 24″ O.C., 8/12 PITCH, 1′ OVERHANG, 26′ SPAN** | | | | | | |
| Truss, 40# loading, 24″ O.C., 8/12 pitch, 26′ span | .020 | Ea. | .015 | 2.22 | .96 | 3.18 |
| Fascia board, 2″ x 6″ | .100 | L.F. | .005 | .05 | .26 | .31 |
| Sheathing, exterior, plywood, CDX, 1/2″ thick | 1.330 | S.F. | .015 | .61 | .74 | 1.35 |
| Furring, 1″ x 3″, 16″ O.C. | 1.000 | L.F. | .023 | .38 | 1.12 | 1.50 |
| TOTAL | | S.F. | .058 | 3.26 | 3.08 | 6.34 |

The cost of this system is based on the square foot of plan area.
A one foot overhang is included.

| Description | QUAN. | UNIT | LABOR HOURS | COST PER S.F. | | |
|---|---|---|---|---|---|---|
| | | | | MAT. | INST. | TOTAL |
| | | | | | | |
| | | | | | | |
| | | | | | | |

# Truss Roof Framing Price Sheet

| Truss Roof Framing Price Sheet | QUAN. | UNIT | LABOR HOURS | COST PER S.F. MAT. | COST PER S.F. INST. | COST PER S.F. TOTAL |
|---|---|---|---|---|---|---|
| Truss, 40# loading, including 1' overhang, 4/12 pitch, 24' span, 16" O.C. | .033 | Ea. | .022 | 2.92 | 1.37 | 4.29 |
| 24" O.C. | .022 | Ea. | .015 | 1.95 | .91 | 2.86 |
| 26' span, 16" O.C. | .030 | Ea. | .021 | 2.64 | 1.31 | 3.95 |
| 24" O.C. | .020 | Ea. | .014 | 1.76 | .87 | 2.63 |
| 28' span, 16" O.C. | .027 | Ea. | .020 | 2.61 | 1.27 | 3.88 |
| 24" O.C. | .019 | Ea. | .014 | 1.83 | .90 | 2.73 |
| 32' span, 16" O.C. | .024 | Ea. | .019 | 2.88 | 1.20 | 4.08 |
| 24" O.C. | .016 | Ea. | .013 | 1.92 | .80 | 2.72 |
| 36' span, 16" O.C. | .022 | Ea. | .019 | 3.59 | 1.20 | 4.79 |
| 24" O.C. | .015 | Ea. | .013 | 2.45 | .82 | 3.27 |
| 8/12 pitch, 24' span, 16" O.C. | .033 | Ea. | .024 | 3.53 | 1.49 | 5.02 |
| 24" O.C. | .022 | Ea. | .016 | 2.35 | .99 | 3.34 |
| 26' span, 16" O.C. | .030 | Ea. | .023 | 3.33 | 1.44 | 4.77 |
| 24" O.C. | .020 | Ea. | .015 | 2.22 | .96 | 3.18 |
| 28' span, 16" O.C. | .027 | Ea. | .022 | 3.32 | 1.37 | 4.69 |
| 24" O.C. | .019 | Ea. | .016 | 2.34 | .96 | 3.30 |
| 32' span, 16" O.C. | .024 | Ea. | .021 | 3.53 | 1.33 | 4.86 |
| 24" O.C. | .016 | Ea. | .014 | 2.35 | .88 | 3.23 |
| 36' span, 16" O.C. | .022 | Ea. | .021 | 4.03 | 1.34 | 5.37 |
| 24" O.C. | .015 | Ea. | .015 | 2.75 | .91 | 3.66 |
| Fascia board, #2 or better, 1" x 6" | .100 | L.F. | .004 | .03 | .19 | .22 |
| 1" x 8" | .100 | L.F. | .005 | .04 | .22 | .26 |
| 1" x 10" | .100 | L.F. | .005 | .04 | .25 | .29 |
| 2" x 6" | .100 | L.F. | .006 | .05 | .28 | .33 |
| 2" x 8" | .100 | L.F. | .007 | .06 | .35 | .41 |
| 2" x 10" | .100 | L.F. | .009 | .08 | .44 | .52 |
| Sheathing, plywood CDX, 4/12 pitch, 3/8" thick | 1.170 | S.F. | .012 | .47 | .60 | 1.07 |
| 1/2" thick | 1.170 | S.F. | .013 | .54 | .66 | 1.20 |
| 5/8" thick | 1.170 | S.F. | .014 | .66 | .70 | 1.36 |
| 8/12 pitch, 3/8" thick | 1.330 | S.F. | .014 | .53 | .68 | 1.21 |
| 1/2" thick | 1.330 | S.F. | .015 | .61 | .74 | 1.35 |
| 5/8" thick | 1.330 | S.F. | .016 | .74 | .80 | 1.54 |
| Boards, 4/12 pitch, 1" x 6" | 1.170 | S.F. | .026 | 1.79 | 1.26 | 3.05 |
| 1" x 8" | 1.170 | S.F. | .021 | 1.72 | 1.05 | 2.77 |
| 8/12 pitch, 1" x 6" | 1.330 | S.F. | .029 | 2.03 | 1.44 | 3.47 |
| 1" x 8" | 1.330 | S.F. | .024 | 1.96 | 1.20 | 3.16 |
| Furring, 1" x 3", 12" O.C. | 1.200 | L.F. | .027 | .46 | 1.34 | 1.80 |
| 16" O.C. | 1.000 | L.F. | .023 | .38 | 1.12 | 1.50 |
| 24" O.C. | .800 | L.F. | .018 | .30 | .90 | 1.20 |

Ceiling Joists — 

Sheathing —

Fascia Board —

Jack Rafters —

Hip Rafter —

| System Description | QUAN. | UNIT | LABOR HOURS | COST PER S.F. | | |
|---|---|---|---|---|---|---|
| | | | | MAT. | INST. | TOTAL |
| **2″ X 6″, 16″ O.C., 4/12 PITCH** | | | | | | |
| Hip rafters, 2″ x 8″, 4/12 pitch | .160 | L.F. | .004 | .10 | .17 | .27 |
| Jack rafters, 2″ x 6″, 16″ O.C., 4/12 pitch | 1.430 | L.F. | .038 | .59 | 1.87 | 2.46 |
| Ceiling joists, 2″ x 6″, 16″ O.C. | 1.000 | L.F. | .013 | .41 | .63 | 1.04 |
| Fascia board, 2″ x 8″ | .220 | L.F. | .016 | .13 | .77 | .90 |
| Soffit nailer (outrigger), 2″ x 4″, 24″ O.C. | .220 | L.F. | .006 | .06 | .28 | .34 |
| Sheathing, 1/2″ exterior plywood, CDX | 1.570 | S.F. | .018 | .72 | .88 | 1.60 |
| Furring strips, 1″ x 3″, 16″ O.C. | 1.000 | L.F. | .023 | .38 | 1.12 | 1.50 |
| TOTAL | | S.F. | .118 | 2.39 | 5.72 | 8.11 |
| **2″ X 8″, 16″ O.C., 4/12 PITCH** | | | | | | |
| Hip rafters, 2″ x 10″, 4/12 pitch | .160 | L.F. | .004 | .13 | .22 | .35 |
| Jack rafters, 2″ x 8″, 16″ O.C., 4/12 pitch | 1.430 | L.F. | .047 | .87 | 2.29 | 3.16 |
| Ceiling joists, 2″ x 6″, 16″ O.C. | 1.000 | L.F. | .013 | .41 | .63 | 1.04 |
| Fascia board, 2″ x 8″ | .220 | L.F. | .012 | .10 | .59 | .69 |
| Soffit nailer (outrigger), 2″ x 4″, 24″ O.C. | .220 | L.F. | .006 | .06 | .28 | .34 |
| Sheathing, 1/2″ exterior plywood, CDX | 1.570 | S.F. | .018 | .72 | .88 | 1.60 |
| Furring strips, 1″ x 3″, 16″ O.C. | 1.000 | L.F. | .023 | .38 | 1.12 | 1.50 |
| TOTAL | | S.F. | .123 | 2.67 | 6.01 | 8.68 |

The cost of this system is based on S.F. of plan area. Measurement is area under the hip roof only. See gable roof system for added costs.

| Description | QUAN. | UNIT | LABOR HOURS | COST PER S.F. | | |
|---|---|---|---|---|---|---|
| | | | | MAT. | INST. | TOTAL |
| | | | | | | |
| | | | | | | |
| | | | | | | |
| | | | | | | |
| | | | | | | |

# Hip Roof Framing Price Sheet

| Hip Roof Framing Price Sheet | QUAN. | UNIT | LABOR HOURS | COST PER S.F. | | |
|---|---|---|---|---|---|---|
| | | | | MAT. | INST. | TOTAL |
| Hip rafters, #2 or better, 2" x 6", 4/12 pitch | .160 | L.F. | .003 | .07 | .16 | .23 |
| 8/12 pitch | .210 | L.F. | .006 | .09 | .28 | .37 |
| 2" x 8", 4/12 pitch | .160 | L.F. | .004 | .10 | .17 | .27 |
| 8/12 pitch | .210 | L.F. | .006 | .13 | .30 | .43 |
| 2" x 10", 4/12 pitch | .160 | L.F. | .004 | .13 | .22 | .35 |
| 8/12 pitch roof | .210 | L.F. | .008 | .17 | .37 | .54 |
| Jack rafters, #2 or better, 16" O.C., 2" x 6", 4/12 pitch | 1.430 | L.F. | .038 | .59 | 1.87 | 2.46 |
| 8/12 pitch | 1.800 | L.F. | .061 | .74 | 2.97 | 3.71 |
| 2" x 8", 4/12 pitch | 1.430 | L.F. | .047 | .87 | 2.29 | 3.16 |
| 8/12 pitch | 1.800 | L.F. | .075 | 1.10 | 3.65 | 4.75 |
| 2" x 10", 4/12 pitch | 1.430 | L.F. | .051 | 1.14 | 2.49 | 3.63 |
| 8/12 pitch | 1.800 | L.F. | .082 | 1.44 | 4.03 | 5.47 |
| 24" O.C., 2" x 6", 4/12 pitch | 1.150 | L.F. | .031 | .47 | 1.51 | 1.98 |
| 8/12 pitch | 1.440 | L.F. | .048 | .59 | 2.38 | 2.97 |
| 2" x 8", 4/12 pitch | 1.150 | L.F. | .038 | .70 | 1.84 | 2.54 |
| 8/12 pitch | 1.440 | L.F. | .060 | .88 | 2.92 | 3.80 |
| 2" x 10", 4/12 pitch | 1.150 | L.F. | .041 | .92 | 2 | 2.92 |
| 8/12 pitch | 1.440 | L.F. | .066 | 1.15 | 3.23 | 4.38 |
| Ceiling joists, #2 or better, 2" x 4", 16" O.C. | 1.000 | L.F. | .013 | .27 | .63 | .90 |
| 24" O.C. | .750 | L.F. | .010 | .20 | .47 | .67 |
| 2" x 6", 16" O.C. | 1.000 | L.F. | .013 | .41 | .63 | 1.04 |
| 24" O.C. | .750 | L.F. | .010 | .31 | .47 | .78 |
| 2" x 8", 16" O.C. | 1.000 | L.F. | .015 | .61 | .71 | 1.32 |
| 24" O.C. | .750 | L.F. | .011 | .46 | .53 | .99 |
| 2" x 10", 16" O.C. | 1.000 | L.F. | .018 | .80 | .87 | 1.67 |
| 24" O.C. | .750 | L.F. | .013 | .60 | .65 | 1.25 |
| Fascia board, #2 or better, 1" x 6" | .220 | L.F. | .009 | .07 | .42 | .49 |
| 1" x 8" | .220 | L.F. | .010 | .09 | .49 | .58 |
| 1" x 10" | .220 | L.F. | .011 | .10 | .55 | .65 |
| 2" x 6" | .220 | L.F. | .013 | .11 | .61 | .72 |
| 2" x 8" | .220 | L.F. | .016 | .13 | .77 | .90 |
| 2" x 10" | .220 | L.F. | .020 | .18 | .96 | 1.14 |
| Soffit nailer (outrigger), 2" x 4", 16" O.C. | .280 | L.F. | .007 | .08 | .35 | .43 |
| 24" O.C. | .220 | L.F. | .006 | .06 | .28 | .34 |
| 2" x 8", 16" O.C. | .280 | L.F. | .007 | .13 | .33 | .46 |
| 24" O.C. | .220 | L.F. | .005 | .10 | .27 | .37 |
| Sheathing, plywood CDX, 4/12 pitch, 3/8" thick | 1.570 | S.F. | .016 | .63 | .80 | 1.43 |
| 1/2" thick | 1.570 | S.F. | .018 | .72 | .88 | 1.60 |
| 5/8" thick | 1.570 | S.F. | .019 | .88 | .94 | 1.82 |
| 8/12 pitch, 3/8" thick | 1.900 | S.F. | .020 | .76 | .97 | 1.73 |
| 1/2" thick | 1.900 | S.F. | .022 | .87 | 1.06 | 1.93 |
| 5/8" thick | 1.900 | S.F. | .023 | 1.06 | 1.14 | 2.20 |
| Boards, 4/12 pitch, 1" x 6" boards | 1.450 | S.F. | .032 | 2.22 | 1.57 | 3.79 |
| 1" x 8" boards | 1.450 | S.F. | .027 | 2.13 | 1.31 | 3.44 |
| 8/12 pitch, 1" x 6" boards | 1.750 | S.F. | .039 | 2.68 | 1.89 | 4.57 |
| 1" x 8" boards | 1.750 | S.F. | .032 | 2.57 | 1.58 | 4.15 |
| Furring, 1" x 3", 12" O.C. | 1.200 | L.F. | .027 | .46 | 1.34 | 1.80 |
| 16" O.C. | 1.000 | L.F. | .023 | .38 | 1.12 | 1.50 |
| 24" O.C. | .800 | L.F. | .018 | .30 | .90 | 1.20 |
| | | | | | | |
| | | | | | | |
| | | | | | | |
| | | | | | | |

| System Description | QUAN. | UNIT | LABOR HOURS | COST PER S.F. | | |
|---|---|---|---|---|---|---|
| | | | | MAT. | INST. | TOTAL |
| **2″ X 6″ RAFTERS, 16″ O.C.** | | | | | | |
| Roof rafters, 2″ x 6″, 16″ O.C. | 1.430 | L.F. | .029 | .59 | 1.40 | 1.99 |
| Ceiling joists, 2″ x 6″, 16″ O.C. | .710 | L.F. | .009 | .29 | .45 | .74 |
| Stud wall, 2″ x 4″, 16″ O.C., including plates | .790 | L.F. | .012 | .21 | .61 | .82 |
| Furring strips, 1″ x 3″, 16″ O.C. | .710 | L.F. | .016 | .27 | .80 | 1.07 |
| Ridge board, 2″ x 8″ | .050 | L.F. | .002 | .03 | .09 | .12 |
| Fascia board, 2″ x 6″ | .100 | L.F. | .006 | .05 | .28 | .33 |
| Sheathing, exterior grade plywood, 1/2″ thick | 1.450 | S.F. | .017 | .67 | .81 | 1.48 |
| TOTAL | | S.F. | .091 | 2.11 | 4.44 | 6.55 |
| **2″ X 8″ RAFTERS, 16″ O.C.** | | | | | | |
| Roof rafters, 2″ x 8″, 16″ O.C. | 1.430 | L.F. | .031 | .87 | 1.49 | 2.36 |
| Ceiling joists, 2″ x 6″, 16″ O.C. | .710 | L.F. | .009 | .29 | .45 | .74 |
| Stud wall, 2″ x 4″, 16″ O.C., including plates | .790 | L.F. | .012 | .21 | .61 | .82 |
| Furring strips, 1″ x 3″, 16″ O.C. | .710 | L.F. | .016 | .27 | .80 | 1.07 |
| Ridge board, 2″ x 8″ | .050 | L.F. | .002 | .03 | .09 | .12 |
| Fascia board, 2″ x 8″ | .100 | L.F. | .007 | .06 | .35 | .41 |
| Sheathing, exterior grade plywood, 1/2″ thick | 1.450 | S.F. | .017 | .67 | .81 | 1.48 |
| TOTAL | | S.F. | .094 | 2.40 | 4.60 | 7 |

The cost of this system is based on the square foot of plan area on the first floor.

| Description | QUAN. | UNIT | LABOR HOURS | COST PER S.F. | | |
|---|---|---|---|---|---|---|
| | | | | MAT. | INST. | TOTAL |
| | | | | | | |
| | | | | | | |
| | | | | | | |
| | | | | | | |
| | | | | | | |
| | | | | | | |

| Gambrel Roof Framing Price Sheet | QUAN. | UNIT | LABOR HOURS | COST PER S.F. | | |
|---|---|---|---|---|---|---|
| | | | | MAT. | INST. | TOTAL |
| Roof rafters, #2 or better, 2″ x 6″, 16″ O.C. | 1.430 | L.F. | .029 | .59 | 1.40 | 1.99 |
| 24″ O.C. | 1.140 | L.F. | .023 | .47 | 1.12 | 1.59 |
| 2″ x 8″, 16″ O.C. | 1.430 | L.F. | .031 | .87 | 1.49 | 2.36 |
| 24″ O.C. | 1.140 | L.F. | .024 | .70 | 1.19 | 1.89 |
| 2″ x 10″, 16″ O.C. | 1.430 | L.F. | .046 | 1.14 | 2.26 | 3.40 |
| 24″ O.C. | 1.140 | L.F. | .037 | .91 | 1.80 | 2.71 |
| Ceiling joist, #2 or better, 2″ x 4″, 16″ O.C. | .710 | L.F. | .009 | .19 | .45 | .64 |
| 24″ O.C. | .570 | L.F. | .007 | .15 | .36 | .51 |
| 2″ x 6″, 16″ O.C. | .710 | L.F. | .009 | .29 | .45 | .74 |
| 24″ O.C. | .570 | L.F. | .007 | .23 | .36 | .59 |
| 2″ x 8″, 16″ O.C. | .710 | L.F. | .010 | .43 | .50 | .93 |
| 24″ O.C. | .570 | L.F. | .008 | .35 | .40 | .75 |
| Stud wall, #2 or better, 2″ x 4″, 16″ O.C. | .790 | L.F. | .012 | .21 | .61 | .82 |
| 24″ O.C. | .630 | L.F. | .010 | .17 | .49 | .66 |
| 2″ x 6″, 16″ O.C. | .790 | L.F. | .014 | .32 | .70 | 1.02 |
| 24″ O.C. | .630 | L.F. | .011 | .26 | .55 | .81 |
| Furring, 1″ x 3″, 16″ O.C. | .710 | L.F. | .016 | .27 | .80 | 1.07 |
| 24″ O.C. | .590 | L.F. | .013 | .22 | .66 | .88 |
| Ridge board, #2 or better, 1″ x 6″ | .050 | L.F. | .001 | .04 | .07 | .11 |
| 1″ x 8″ | .050 | L.F. | .001 | .05 | .07 | .12 |
| 1″ x 10″ | .050 | L.F. | .002 | .06 | .08 | .14 |
| 2″ x 6″ | .050 | L.F. | .002 | .02 | .08 | .10 |
| 2″ x 8″ | .050 | L.F. | .002 | .03 | .09 | .12 |
| 2″ x 10″ | .050 | L.F. | .002 | .04 | .10 | .14 |
| Fascia board, #2 or better, 1″ x 6″ | .100 | L.F. | .004 | .03 | .19 | .22 |
| 1″ x 8″ | .100 | L.F. | .005 | .04 | .22 | .26 |
| 1″ x 10″ | .100 | L.F. | .005 | .04 | .25 | .29 |
| 2″ x 6″ | .100 | L.F. | .006 | .05 | .28 | .33 |
| 2″ x 8″ | .100 | L.F. | .007 | .06 | .35 | .41 |
| 2″ x 10″ | .100 | L.F. | .009 | .08 | .44 | .52 |
| Sheathing, plywood, exterior grade CDX, 3/8″ thick | 1.450 | S.F. | .015 | .58 | .74 | 1.32 |
| 1/2″ thick | 1.450 | S.F. | .017 | .67 | .81 | 1.48 |
| 5/8″ thick | 1.450 | S.F. | .018 | .81 | .87 | 1.68 |
| 3/4″ thick | 1.450 | S.F. | .019 | .93 | .94 | 1.87 |
| Boards, 1″ x 6″, laid regular | 1.450 | S.F. | .032 | 2.22 | 1.57 | 3.79 |
| Laid diagonal | 1.450 | S.F. | .036 | 2.22 | 1.75 | 3.97 |
| 1″ x 8″, laid regular | 1.450 | S.F. | .027 | 2.13 | 1.31 | 3.44 |
| Laid diagonal | 1.450 | S.F. | .032 | 2.13 | 1.57 | 3.70 |

Labels: Hip Rafters, Sheathing, Rafters, Ridge Board, Rafters, Top Plates, Furring, Ceiling Joists, Bottom Plate

| System Description | QUAN. | UNIT | LABOR HOURS | COST PER S.F. | | |
|---|---|---|---|---|---|---|
| | | | | MAT. | INST. | TOTAL |
| **2" X 6" RAFTERS, 16" O.C.** | | | | | | |
| Roof rafters, 2" x 6", 16" O.C. | 1.210 | L.F. | .033 | .50 | 1.61 | 2.11 |
| Rafter plates, 2" x 6", double top, single bottom | .364 | L.F. | .010 | .15 | .48 | .63 |
| Ceiling joists, 2" x 4", 16" O.C. | .920 | L.F. | .012 | .25 | .58 | .83 |
| Hip rafter, 2" x 6" | .070 | L.F. | .002 | .03 | .11 | .14 |
| Jack rafter, 2" x 6", 16" O.C. | 1.000 | L.F. | .039 | .41 | 1.91 | 2.32 |
| Ridge board, 2" x 6" | .018 | L.F. | .001 | .01 | .03 | .04 |
| Sheathing, exterior grade plywood, 1/2" thick | 2.210 | S.F. | .025 | 1.02 | 1.24 | 2.26 |
| Furring strips, 1" x 3", 16" O.C. | .920 | L.F. | .021 | .35 | 1.03 | 1.38 |
| | | | | | | |
| TOTAL | | S.F. | .143 | 2.72 | 6.99 | 9.71 |
| **2" X 8" RAFTERS, 16" O.C.** | | | | | | |
| Roof rafters, 2" x 8", 16" O.C. | 1.210 | L.F. | .036 | .74 | 1.75 | 2.49 |
| Rafter plates, 2" x 8", double top, single bottom | .364 | L.F. | .011 | .22 | .53 | .75 |
| Ceiling joists, 2" x 6", 16" O.C. | .920 | L.F. | .012 | .38 | .58 | .96 |
| Hip rafter, 2" x 8" | .070 | L.F. | .002 | .04 | .12 | .16 |
| Jack rafter, 2" x 8", 16" O.C. | 1.000 | L.F. | .048 | .61 | 2.34 | 2.95 |
| Ridge board, 2" x 8" | .018 | L.F. | .001 | .01 | .03 | .04 |
| Sheathing, exterior grade plywood, 1/2" thick | 2.210 | S.F. | .025 | 1.02 | 1.24 | 2.26 |
| Furring strips, 1" x 3", 16" O.C. | .920 | L.F. | .021 | .35 | 1.03 | 1.38 |
| | | | | | | |
| TOTAL | | S.F. | .156 | 3.37 | 7.62 | 10.99 |

The cost of this system is based on the square foot of plan area.

| Description | QUAN. | UNIT | LABOR HOURS | COST PER S.F. | | |
|---|---|---|---|---|---|---|
| | | | | MAT. | INST. | TOTAL |
| | | | | | | |
| | | | | | | |
| | | | | | | |
| | | | | | | |
| | | | | | | |
| | | | | | | |

| Mansard Roof Framing Price Sheet | QUAN. | UNIT | LABOR HOURS | COST PER S.F. | | |
|---|---|---|---|---|---|---|
| | | | | MAT. | INST. | TOTAL |
| Roof rafters, #2 or better, 2" x 6", 16" O.C. | 1.210 | L.F. | .033 | .50 | 1.61 | 2.11 |
| 24" O.C. | .970 | L.F. | .026 | .40 | 1.29 | 1.69 |
| 2" x 8", 16" O.C. | 1.210 | L.F. | .036 | .74 | 1.75 | 2.49 |
| 24" O.C. | .970 | L.F. | .029 | .59 | 1.41 | 2 |
| 2" x 10", 16" O.C. | 1.210 | L.F. | .046 | .97 | 2.23 | 3.20 |
| 24" O.C. | .970 | L.F. | .037 | .78 | 1.78 | 2.56 |
| Rafter plates, #2 or better double top single bottom, 2" x 6" | .364 | L.F. | .010 | .15 | .48 | .63 |
| 2" x 8" | .364 | L.F. | .011 | .22 | .53 | .75 |
| 2" x 10" | .364 | L.F. | .014 | .29 | .67 | .96 |
| Ceiling joist, #2 or better, 2" x 4", 16" O.C. | .920 | L.F. | .012 | .25 | .58 | .83 |
| 24" O.C. | .740 | L.F. | .009 | .20 | .47 | .67 |
| 2" x 6", 16" O.C. | .920 | L.F. | .012 | .38 | .58 | .96 |
| 24" O.C. | .740 | L.F. | .009 | .30 | .47 | .77 |
| 2" x 8", 16" O.C. | .920 | L.F. | .013 | .56 | .65 | 1.21 |
| 24" O.C. | .740 | L.F. | .011 | .45 | .53 | .98 |
| Hip rafter, #2 or better, 2" x 6" | .070 | L.F. | .002 | .03 | .11 | .14 |
| 2" x 8" | .070 | L.F. | .002 | .04 | .12 | .16 |
| 2" x 10" | .070 | L.F. | .003 | .06 | .14 | .20 |
| Jack rafter, #2 or better, 2" x 6", 16" O.C. | 1.000 | L.F. | .039 | .41 | 1.91 | 2.32 |
| 24" O.C. | .800 | L.F. | .031 | .33 | 1.53 | 1.86 |
| 2" x 8", 16" O.C. | 1.000 | L.F. | .048 | .61 | 2.34 | 2.95 |
| 24" O.C. | .800 | L.F. | .038 | .49 | 1.87 | 2.36 |
| Ridge board, #2 or better, 1" x 6" | .018 | L.F. | .001 | .01 | .02 | .03 |
| 1" x 8" | .018 | L.F. | .001 | .02 | .03 | .05 |
| 1" x 10" | .018 | L.F. | .001 | .02 | .03 | .05 |
| 2" x 6" | .018 | L.F. | .001 | .01 | .03 | .04 |
| 2" x 8" | .018 | L.F. | .001 | .01 | .03 | .04 |
| 2" x 10" | .018 | L.F. | .001 | .01 | .04 | .05 |
| Sheathing, plywood exterior grade CDX, 3/8" thick | 2.210 | S.F. | .023 | .88 | 1.13 | 2.01 |
| 1/2" thick | 2.210 | S.F. | .025 | 1.02 | 1.24 | 2.26 |
| 5/8" thick | 2.210 | S.F. | .027 | 1.24 | 1.33 | 2.57 |
| 3/4" thick | 2.210 | S.F. | .029 | 1.41 | 1.44 | 2.85 |
| Boards, 1" x 6", laid regular | 2.210 | S.F. | .049 | 3.38 | 2.39 | 5.77 |
| Laid diagonal | 2.210 | S.F. | .054 | 3.38 | 2.67 | 6.05 |
| 1" x 8", laid regular | 2.210 | S.F. | .040 | 3.25 | 1.99 | 5.24 |
| Laid diagonal | 2.210 | S.F. | .049 | 3.25 | 2.39 | 5.64 |
| Furring, 1" x 3", 12" O.C. | 1.150 | L.F. | .026 | .44 | 1.29 | 1.73 |
| 24" O.C. | .740 | L.F. | .017 | .28 | .83 | 1.11 |

| System Description | QUAN. | UNIT | LABOR HOURS | COST PER S.F. | | |
|---|---|---|---|---|---|---|
| | | | | MAT. | INST. | TOTAL |
| **2″ X 6″,16″ O.C., 4/12 PITCH** | | | | | | |
| Rafters, 2″ x 6″, 16″ O.C., 4/12 pitch | 1.170 | L.F. | .019 | .48 | .91 | 1.39 |
| Fascia, 2″ x 6″ | .100 | L.F. | .006 | .05 | .28 | .33 |
| Bridging, 1″ x 3″, 6′ O.C. | .080 | Pr. | .005 | .04 | .24 | .28 |
| Sheathing, exterior grade plywood, 1/2″ thick | 1.230 | S.F. | .014 | .57 | .69 | 1.26 |
| TOTAL | | S.F. | .044 | 1.14 | 2.12 | 3.26 |
| **2″ X 6″, 24″ O.C., 4/12 PITCH** | | | | | | |
| Rafters, 2″ x 6″, 24″ O.C., 4/12 pitch | .940 | L.F. | .015 | .39 | .73 | 1.12 |
| Fascia, 2″ x 6″ | .100 | L.F. | .006 | .05 | .28 | .33 |
| Bridging, 1″ x 3″, 6′ O.C. | .060 | Pr. | .004 | .03 | .18 | .21 |
| Sheathing, exterior grade plywood, 1/2″ thick | 1.230 | S.F. | .014 | .57 | .69 | 1.26 |
| TOTAL | | S.F. | .039 | 1.04 | 1.88 | 2.92 |
| **2″ X 8″, 16″ O.C., 4/12 PITCH** | | | | | | |
| Rafters, 2″ x 8″, 16″ O.C., 4/12 pitch | 1.170 | L.F. | .020 | .71 | .96 | 1.67 |
| Fascia, 2″ x 8″ | .100 | L.F. | .007 | .06 | .35 | .41 |
| Bridging, 1″ x 3″, 6′ O.C. | .080 | Pr. | .005 | .04 | .24 | .28 |
| Sheathing, exterior grade plywood, 1/2″ thick | 1.230 | S.F. | .014 | .57 | .69 | 1.26 |
| TOTAL | | S.F. | .046 | 1.38 | 2.24 | 3.62 |
| **2″ X 8″, 24″ O.C., 4/12 PITCH** | | | | | | |
| Rafters, 2″ x 8″, 24″ O.C., 4/12 pitch | .940 | L.F. | .016 | .57 | .77 | 1.34 |
| Fascia, 2″ x 8″ | .100 | L.F. | .007 | .06 | .35 | .41 |
| Bridging, 1″ x 3″, 6′ O.C. | .060 | Pr. | .004 | .03 | .18 | .21 |
| Sheathing, exterior grade plywood, 1/2″ thick | 1.230 | S.F. | .014 | .57 | .69 | 1.26 |
| TOTAL | | S.F. | .041 | 1.23 | 1.99 | 3.22 |

The cost of this system is based on the square foot of plan area.
A 1′ overhang is assumed. No ceiling joists or furring are included.

| Description | QUAN. | UNIT | LABOR HOURS | COST PER S.F. | | |
|---|---|---|---|---|---|---|
| | | | | MAT. | INST. | TOTAL |
| | | | | | | |
| | | | | | | |
| | | | | | | |

| Shed/Flat Roof Framing Price Sheet | QUAN. | UNIT | LABOR HOURS | COST PER S.F. | | |
|---|---|---|---|---|---|---|
| | | | | MAT. | INST. | TOTAL |
| Rafters, #2 or better, 16" O.C., 2" x 4", 0 - 4/12 pitch | 1.170 | L.F. | .014 | .36 | .68 | 1.04 |
| 5/12 - 8/12 pitch | 1.330 | L.F. | .020 | .41 | .98 | 1.39 |
| 2" x 6", 0 - 4/12 pitch | 1.170 | L.F. | .019 | .48 | .91 | 1.39 |
| 5/12 - 8/12 pitch | 1.330 | L.F. | .027 | .55 | 1.30 | 1.85 |
| 2" x 8", 0 - 4/12 pitch | 1.170 | L.F. | .020 | .71 | .96 | 1.67 |
| 5/12 - 8/12 pitch | 1.330 | L.F. | .028 | .81 | 1.38 | 2.19 |
| 2" x 10", 0 - 4/12 pitch | 1.170 | L.F. | .030 | .94 | 1.45 | 2.39 |
| 5/12 - 8/12 pitch | 1.330 | L.F. | .043 | 1.06 | 2.10 | 3.16 |
| 24" O.C., 2" x 4", 0 - 4/12 pitch | .940 | L.F. | .011 | .29 | .55 | .84 |
| 5/12 - 8/12 pitch | 1.060 | L.F. | .021 | .43 | 1.04 | 1.47 |
| 2" x 6", 0 - 4/12 pitch | .940 | L.F. | .015 | .39 | .73 | 1.12 |
| 5/12 - 8/12 pitch | 1.060 | L.F. | .021 | .43 | 1.04 | 1.47 |
| 2" x 8", 0 - 4/12 pitch | .940 | L.F. | .016 | .57 | .77 | 1.34 |
| 5/12 - 8/12 pitch | 1.060 | L.F. | .023 | .65 | 1.10 | 1.75 |
| 2" x 10", 0 - 4/12 pitch | .940 | L.F. | .024 | .75 | 1.17 | 1.92 |
| 5/12 - 8/12 pitch | 1.060 | L.F. | .034 | .85 | 1.67 | 2.52 |
| Fascia, #2 or better,, 1" x 4" | .100 | L.F. | .003 | .02 | .14 | .16 |
| 1" x 6" | .100 | L.F. | .004 | .03 | .19 | .22 |
| 1" x 8" | .100 | L.F. | .005 | .04 | .22 | .26 |
| 1" x 10" | .100 | L.F. | .005 | .04 | .25 | .29 |
| 2" x 4" | .100 | L.F. | .005 | .04 | .24 | .28 |
| 2" x 6" | .100 | L.F. | .006 | .05 | .28 | .33 |
| 2" x 8" | .100 | L.F. | .007 | .06 | .35 | .41 |
| 2" x 10" | .100 | L.F. | .009 | .08 | .44 | .52 |
| Bridging, wood 6' O.C., 1" x 3", rafters, 16" O.C. | .080 | Pr. | .005 | .04 | .24 | .28 |
| 24" O.C. | .060 | Pr. | .004 | .03 | .18 | .21 |
| Metal, galvanized, rafters, 16" O.C. | .080 | Pr. | .005 | .14 | .24 | .38 |
| 24" O.C. | .060 | Pr. | .003 | .11 | .17 | .28 |
| Compression type, rafters, 16" O.C. | .080 | Pr. | .003 | .14 | .16 | .30 |
| 24" O.C. | .060 | Pr. | .002 | .11 | .12 | .23 |
| Sheathing, plywood, exterior grade, 3/8" thick, flat 0 - 4/12 pitch | 1.230 | S.F. | .013 | .49 | .63 | 1.12 |
| 5/12 - 8/12 pitch | 1.330 | S.F. | .014 | .53 | .68 | 1.21 |
| 1/2" thick, flat 0 - 4/12 pitch | 1.230 | S.F. | .014 | .57 | .69 | 1.26 |
| 5/12 - 8/12 pitch | 1.330 | S.F. | .015 | .61 | .74 | 1.35 |
| 5/8" thick, flat 0 - 4/12 pitch | 1.230 | S.F. | .015 | .69 | .74 | 1.43 |
| 5/12 - 8/12 pitch | 1.330 | S.F. | .016 | .74 | .80 | 1.54 |
| 3/4" thick, flat 0 - 4/12 pitch | 1.230 | S.F. | .016 | .79 | .80 | 1.59 |
| 5/12 - 8/12 pitch | 1.330 | S.F. | .018 | .85 | .86 | 1.71 |
| Boards, 1" x 6", laid regular, flat 0 - 4/12 pitch | 1.230 | S.F. | .027 | 1.88 | 1.33 | 3.21 |
| 5/12 - 8/12 pitch | 1.330 | S.F. | .041 | 2.03 | 2.01 | 4.04 |
| Laid diagonal, flat 0 - 4/12 pitch | 1.230 | S.F. | .030 | 1.88 | 1.49 | 3.37 |
| 5/12 - 8/12 pitch | 1.330 | S.F. | .044 | 2.03 | 2.17 | 4.20 |
| 1" x 8", laid regular, flat 0 - 4/12 pitch | 1.230 | S.F. | .022 | 1.81 | 1.11 | 2.92 |
| 5/12 - 8/12 pitch | 1.330 | S.F. | .034 | 1.96 | 1.64 | 3.60 |
| Laid diagonal, flat 0 - 4/12 pitch | 1.230 | S.F. | .027 | 1.81 | 1.33 | 3.14 |
| 5/12 - 8/12 pitch | 1.330 | S.F. | .044 | 2.03 | 2.17 | 4.20 |
| | | | | | | |
| | | | | | | |
| | | | | | | |
| | | | | | | |
| | | | | | | |
| | | | | | | |

| System Description | QUAN. | UNIT | LABOR HOURS | COST PER S.F. | | |
|---|---|---|---|---|---|---|
| | | | | MAT. | INST. | TOTAL |
| **2″ X 6″, 16″ O.C.** | | | | | | |
| Dormer rafter, 2″ x 6″, 16″ O.C. | 1.330 | L.F. | .036 | .55 | 1.77 | 2.32 |
| Ridge board, 2″ x 6″ | .280 | L.F. | .009 | .11 | .44 | .55 |
| Trimmer rafters, 2″ x 6″ | .880 | L.F. | .014 | .36 | .69 | 1.05 |
| Wall studs & plates, 2″ x 4″, 16″ O.C. | 3.160 | L.F. | .056 | .85 | 2.75 | 3.60 |
| Fascia, 2″ x 6″ | .220 | L.F. | .012 | .10 | .59 | .69 |
| Valley rafter, 2″ x 6″, 16″ O.C. | .280 | L.F. | .009 | .11 | .43 | .54 |
| Cripple rafter, 2″ x 6″, 16″ O.C. | .560 | L.F. | .022 | .23 | 1.07 | 1.30 |
| Headers, 2″ x 6″, doubled | .670 | L.F. | .030 | .27 | 1.46 | 1.73 |
| Ceiling joist, 2″ x 4″, 16″ O.C. | 1.000 | L.F. | .013 | .27 | .63 | .90 |
| Sheathing, exterior grade plywood, 1/2″ thick | 3.610 | S.F. | .041 | 1.66 | 2.02 | 3.68 |
| | | | | | | |
| TOTAL | | S.F. | .242 | 4.51 | 11.85 | 16.36 |
| **2″ X 8″, 16″ O.C.** | | | | | | |
| Dormer rafter, 2″ x 8″, 16″ O.C. | 1.330 | L.F. | .039 | .81 | 1.93 | 2.74 |
| Ridge board, 2″ x 8″ | .280 | L.F. | .010 | .17 | .49 | .66 |
| Trimmer rafter, 2″ x 8″ | .880 | L.F. | .015 | .54 | .72 | 1.26 |
| Wall studs & plates, 2″ x 4″, 16″ O.C. | 3.160 | L.F. | .056 | .85 | 2.75 | 3.60 |
| Fascia, 2″ x 8″ | .220 | L.F. | .016 | .13 | .77 | .90 |
| Valley rafter, 2″ x 8″, 16″ O.C. | .280 | L.F. | .010 | .17 | .47 | .64 |
| Cripple rafter, 2″ x 8″, 16″ O.C. | .560 | L.F. | .027 | .34 | 1.31 | 1.65 |
| Headers, 2″ x 8″, doubled | .670 | L.F. | .032 | .41 | 1.54 | 1.95 |
| Ceiling joist, 2″ x 4″, 16″ O.C. | 1.000 | L.F. | .013 | .27 | .63 | .90 |
| Sheathing,, exterior grade plywood, 1/2″ thick | 3.610 | S.F. | .041 | 1.66 | 2.02 | 3.68 |
| | | | | | | |
| TOTAL | | S.F. | .259 | 5.35 | 12.63 | 17.98 |

The cost in this system is based on the square foot of plan area.
The measurement being the plan area of the dormer only.

| Description | QUAN. | UNIT | LABOR HOURS | COST PER S.F. | | |
|---|---|---|---|---|---|---|
| | | | | MAT. | INST. | TOTAL |
| | | | | | | |
| | | | | | | |
| | | | | | | |
| | | | | | | |
| | | | | | | |
| | | | | | | |

| Gable Dormer Framing Price Sheet | QUAN. | UNIT | LABOR HOURS | COST PER S.F. | | |
|---|---|---|---|---|---|---|
| | | | | MAT. | INST. | TOTAL |
| Dormer rafters, #2 or better, 2" x 4", 16" O.C. | 1.330 | L.F. | .029 | .44 | 1.42 | 1.86 |
| 24" O.C. | 1.060 | L.F. | .023 | .35 | 1.13 | 1.48 |
| 2" x 6", 16" O.C. | 1.330 | L.F. | .036 | .55 | 1.77 | 2.32 |
| 24" O.C. | 1.060 | L.F. | .029 | .43 | 1.41 | 1.84 |
| 2" x 8", 16" O.C. | 1.330 | L.F. | .039 | .81 | 1.93 | 2.74 |
| 24" O.C. | 1.060 | L.F. | .031 | .65 | 1.54 | 2.19 |
| Ridge board, #2 or better, 1" x 4" | .280 | L.F. | .006 | .16 | .29 | .45 |
| 1" x 6" | .280 | L.F. | .007 | .20 | .37 | .57 |
| 1" x 8" | .280 | L.F. | .008 | .26 | .40 | .66 |
| 2" x 4" | .280 | L.F. | .007 | .09 | .35 | .44 |
| 2" x 6" | .280 | L.F. | .009 | .11 | .44 | .55 |
| 2" x 8" | .280 | L.F. | .010 | .17 | .49 | .66 |
| Trimmer rafters, #2 or better, 2" x 4" | .880 | L.F. | .011 | .29 | .55 | .84 |
| 2" x 6" | .880 | L.F. | .014 | .36 | .69 | 1.05 |
| 2" x 8" | .880 | L.F. | .015 | .54 | .72 | 1.26 |
| 2" x 10" | .880 | L.F. | .022 | .70 | 1.09 | 1.79 |
| Wall studs & plates, #2 or better, 2" x 4" studs, 16" O.C. | 3.160 | L.F. | .056 | .85 | 2.75 | 3.60 |
| 24" O.C. | 2.800 | L.F. | .050 | .76 | 2.44 | 3.20 |
| 2" x 6" studs, 16" O.C. | 3.160 | L.F. | .063 | 1.30 | 3.10 | 4.40 |
| 24" O.C. | 2.800 | L.F. | .056 | 1.15 | 2.74 | 3.89 |
| Fascia, #2 or better, 1" x 4" | .220 | L.F. | .006 | .05 | .31 | .36 |
| 1" x 6" | .220 | L.F. | .008 | .07 | .38 | .45 |
| 1" x 8" | .220 | L.F. | .009 | .08 | .45 | .53 |
| 2" x 4" | .220 | L.F. | .011 | .09 | .52 | .61 |
| 2" x 6" | .220 | L.F. | .014 | .12 | .66 | .78 |
| 2" x 8" | .220 | L.F. | .016 | .13 | .77 | .90 |
| Valley rafter, #2 or better, 2" x 4" | .280 | L.F. | .007 | .09 | .34 | .43 |
| 2" x 6" | .280 | L.F. | .009 | .11 | .43 | .54 |
| 2" x 8" | .280 | L.F. | .010 | .17 | .47 | .64 |
| 2" x 10" | .280 | L.F. | .012 | .22 | .58 | .80 |
| Cripple rafter, #2 or better, 2" x 4", 16" O.C. | .560 | L.F. | .018 | .18 | .86 | 1.04 |
| 24" O.C. | .450 | L.F. | .014 | .15 | .69 | .84 |
| 2" x 6", 16" O.C. | .560 | L.F. | .022 | .23 | 1.07 | 1.30 |
| 24" O.C. | .450 | L.F. | .018 | .18 | .86 | 1.04 |
| 2" x 8", 16" O.C. | .560 | L.F. | .027 | .34 | 1.31 | 1.65 |
| 24" O.C. | .450 | L.F. | .021 | .27 | 1.05 | 1.32 |
| Headers, #2 or better double header, 2" x 4" | .670 | L.F. | .024 | .22 | 1.18 | 1.40 |
| 2" x 6" | .670 | L.F. | .030 | .27 | 1.46 | 1.73 |
| 2" x 8" | .670 | L.F. | .032 | .41 | 1.54 | 1.95 |
| 2" x 10" | .670 | L.F. | .034 | .54 | 1.64 | 2.18 |
| Ceiling joist, #2 or better, 2" x 4", 16" O.C. | 1.000 | L.F. | .013 | .27 | .63 | .90 |
| 24" O.C. | .800 | L.F. | .010 | .22 | .50 | .72 |
| 2" x 6", 16" O.C. | 1.000 | L.F. | .013 | .41 | .63 | 1.04 |
| 24" O.C. | .800 | L.F. | .010 | .33 | .50 | .83 |
| Sheathing, plywood exterior grade, 3/8" thick | 3.610 | S.F. | .038 | 1.44 | 1.84 | 3.28 |
| 1/2" thick | 3.610 | S.F. | .041 | 1.66 | 2.02 | 3.68 |
| 5/8" thick | 3.610 | S.F. | .044 | 2.02 | 2.17 | 4.19 |
| 3/4" thick | 3.610 | S.F. | .048 | 2.31 | 2.35 | 4.66 |
| Boards, 1" x 6", laid regular | 3.610 | S.F. | .089 | 5.50 | 4.37 | 9.87 |
| Laid diagonal | 3.610 | S.F. | .099 | 5.50 | 4.84 | 10.34 |
| 1" x 8", laid regular | 3.610 | S.F. | .076 | 5.30 | 3.68 | 8.98 |
| Laid diagonal | 3.610 | S.F. | .089 | 5.30 | 4.37 | 9.67 |
| | | | | | | |
| | | | | | | |
| | | | | | | |
| | | | | | | |

Sheathing
Ceiling Joists
Fascia Board
Rafters
Studs & Plates
Trimmer Rafters

| System Description | QUAN. | UNIT | LABOR HOURS | COST PER S.F. | | |
|---|---|---|---|---|---|---|
| | | | | MAT. | INST. | TOTAL |
| **2″ X 6″ RAFTERS, 16″ O.C.** | | | | | | |
| Dormer rafter, 2″ x 6″, 16″ O.C. | 1.080 | L.F. | .029 | .44 | 1.44 | 1.88 |
| Trimmer rafter, 2″ x 6″ | .400 | L.F. | .006 | .16 | .31 | .47 |
| Studs & plates, 2″ x 4″, 16″ O.C. | 2.750 | L.F. | .049 | .74 | 2.39 | 3.13 |
| Fascia, 2″ x 6″ | .250 | L.F. | .014 | .12 | .66 | .78 |
| Ceiling joist, 2″ x 4″, 16″ O.C. | 1.000 | L.F. | .013 | .27 | .63 | .90 |
| Sheathing, exterior grade plywood, CDX, 1/2″ thick | 2.940 | S.F. | .034 | 1.35 | 1.65 | 3 |
| TOTAL | | S.F. | .145 | 3.08 | 7.08 | 10.16 |
| **2″ X 8″ RAFTERS, 16″ O.C.** | | | | | | |
| Dormer rafter, 2″ x 8″, 16″ O.C. | 1.080 | L.F. | .032 | .66 | 1.57 | 2.23 |
| Trimmer rafter, 2″ x 8″ | .400 | L.F. | .007 | .24 | .33 | .57 |
| Studs & plates, 2″ x 4″, 16″ O.C. | 2.750 | L.F. | .049 | .74 | 2.39 | 3.13 |
| Fascia, 2″ x 8″ | .250 | L.F. | .018 | .15 | .87 | 1.02 |
| Ceiling joist, 2″ x 6″, 16″ O.C. | 1.000 | L.F. | .013 | .41 | .63 | 1.04 |
| Sheathing, exterior grade plywood, CDX, 1/2″ thick | 2.940 | S.F. | .034 | 1.35 | 1.65 | 3 |
| TOTAL | | S.F. | .153 | 3.55 | 7.44 | 10.99 |
| **2″ X 10″ RAFTERS, 16″ O.C.** | | | | | | |
| Dormer rafter, 2″ x 10″, 16″ O.C. | 1.080 | L.F. | .041 | .86 | 1.99 | 2.85 |
| Trimmer rafter, 2″ x 10″ | .400 | L.F. | .010 | .32 | .50 | .82 |
| Studs & plates, 2″ x 4″, 16″ O.C. | 2.750 | L.F. | .049 | .74 | 2.39 | 3.13 |
| Fascia, 2″ x 10″ | .250 | L.F. | .022 | .20 | 1.09 | 1.29 |
| Ceiling joist, 2″ x 6″, 16″ O.C. | 1.000 | L.F. | .013 | .41 | .63 | 1.04 |
| Sheathing, exterior grade plywood, CDX, 1/2″ thick | 2.940 | S.F. | .034 | 1.35 | 1.65 | 3 |
| TOTAL | | S.F. | .169 | 3.88 | 8.25 | 12.13 |

The cost in this system is based on the square foot of plan area.
The measurement is the plan area of the dormer only.

| Description | QUAN. | UNIT | LABOR HOURS | COST PER S.F. | | |
|---|---|---|---|---|---|---|
| | | | | MAT. | INST. | TOTAL |
| | | | | | | |
| | | | | | | |
| | | | | | | |
| | | | | | | |
| | | | | | | |

| Shed Dormer Framing Price Sheet | QUAN. | UNIT | LABOR HOURS | COST PER S.F. | | |
|---|---|---|---|---|---|---|
| | | | | MAT. | INST. | TOTAL |
| Dormer rafters, #2 or better, 2" x 4", 16" O.C. | 1.080 | L.F. | .023 | .35 | 1.15 | 1.50 |
| 24" O.C. | .860 | L.F. | .019 | .28 | .92 | 1.20 |
| 2" x 6", 16" O.C. | 1.080 | L.F. | .029 | .44 | 1.44 | 1.88 |
| 24" O.C. | .860 | L.F. | .023 | .35 | 1.14 | 1.49 |
| 2" x 8", 16" O.C. | 1.080 | L.F. | .032 | .66 | 1.57 | 2.23 |
| 24" O.C. | .860 | L.F. | .025 | .52 | 1.25 | 1.77 |
| 2" x 10", 16" O.C. | 1.080 | L.F. | .041 | .86 | 1.99 | 2.85 |
| 24" O.C. | .860 | L.F. | .032 | .69 | 1.58 | 2.27 |
| Trimmer rafter, #2 or better, 2" x 4" | .400 | L.F. | .005 | .13 | .25 | .38 |
| 2" x 6" | .400 | L.F. | .006 | .16 | .31 | .47 |
| 2" x 8" | .400 | L.F. | .007 | .24 | .33 | .57 |
| 2" x 10" | .400 | L.F. | .010 | .32 | .50 | .82 |
| Studs & plates, #2 or better, 2" x 4", 16" O.C. | 2.750 | L.F. | .049 | .74 | 2.39 | 3.13 |
| 24" O.C. | 2.200 | L.F. | .039 | .59 | 1.91 | 2.50 |
| 2" x 6", 16" O.C. | 2.750 | L.F. | .055 | 1.13 | 2.70 | 3.83 |
| 24" O.C. | 2.200 | L.F. | .044 | .90 | 2.16 | 3.06 |
| Fascia, #2 or better, 1" x 4" | .250 | L.F. | .006 | .05 | .31 | .36 |
| 1" x 6" | .250 | L.F. | .008 | .07 | .38 | .45 |
| 1" x 8" | .250 | L.F. | .009 | .08 | .45 | .53 |
| 2" x 4" | .250 | L.F. | .011 | .09 | .52 | .61 |
| 2" x 6" | .250 | L.F. | .014 | .12 | .66 | .78 |
| 2" x 8" | .250 | L.F. | .018 | .15 | .87 | 1.02 |
| Ceiling joist, #2 or better, 2" x 4", 16" O.C. | 1.000 | L.F. | .013 | .27 | .63 | .90 |
| 24" O.C. | .800 | L.F. | .010 | .22 | .50 | .72 |
| 2" x 6", 16" O.C. | 1.000 | L.F. | .013 | .41 | .63 | 1.04 |
| 24" O.C. | .800 | L.F. | .010 | .33 | .50 | .83 |
| 2" x 8", 16" O.C. | 1.000 | L.F. | .015 | .61 | .71 | 1.32 |
| 24" O.C. | .800 | L.F. | .012 | .49 | .57 | 1.06 |
| Sheathing, plywood exterior grade, 3/8" thick | 2.940 | S.F. | .031 | 1.18 | 1.50 | 2.68 |
| 1/2" thick | 2.940 | S.F. | .034 | 1.35 | 1.65 | 3 |
| 5/8" thick | 2.940 | S.F. | .036 | 1.65 | 1.76 | 3.41 |
| 3/4" thick | 2.940 | S.F. | .039 | 1.88 | 1.91 | 3.79 |
| Boards, 1" x 6", laid regular | 2.940 | S.F. | .072 | 4.50 | 3.56 | 8.06 |
| Laid diagonal | 2.940 | S.F. | .080 | 4.50 | 3.94 | 8.44 |
| 1" x 8", laid regular | 2.940 | S.F. | .062 | 4.32 | 3 | 7.32 |
| Laid diagonal | 2.940 | S.F. | .072 | 4.32 | 3.56 | 7.88 |
| | | | | | | |
| | | | | | | |
| | | | | | | |

| Window Openings | QUAN. | UNIT | LABOR HOURS | COST EACH | | |
|---|---|---|---|---|---|---|
| | | | | MAT. | INST. | TOTAL |
| The following are to be added to the total cost of the dormers for window openings. Do not subtract window area from the stud wall quantities. | | | | | | |
| Headers, 2" x 6" doubled, 2' long | 4.000 | L.F. | .178 | 1.64 | 8.70 | 10.34 |
| 3' long | 6.000 | L.F. | .267 | 2.46 | 13.10 | 15.56 |
| 4' long | 8.000 | L.F. | .356 | 3.28 | 17.45 | 20.73 |
| 5' long | 10.000 | L.F. | .444 | 4.10 | 22 | 26.10 |
| 2" x 8" doubled, 4' long | 8.000 | L.F. | .376 | 4.88 | 18.40 | 23.28 |
| 5' long | 10.000 | L.F. | .471 | 6.10 | 23 | 29.10 |
| 6' long | 12.000 | L.F. | .565 | 7.30 | 27.50 | 34.80 |
| 8' long | 16.000 | L.F. | .753 | 9.75 | 37 | 46.75 |
| 2" x 10" doubled, 4' long | 8.000 | L.F. | .400 | 6.40 | 19.60 | 26 |
| 6' long | 12.000 | L.F. | .600 | 9.60 | 29.50 | 39.10 |
| 8' long | 16.000 | L.F. | .800 | 12.80 | 39 | 51.80 |
| 10' long | 20.000 | L.F. | 1.000 | 16 | 49 | 65 |

| System Description | | QUAN. | UNIT | LABOR HOURS | COST PER S.F. | | |
|---|---|---|---|---|---|---|---|
| | | | | | MAT. | INST. | TOTAL |
| **2″ X 4″, 16″ O.C.** | | | | | | | |
| 2″ x 4″ studs, #2 or better, 16″ O.C. | | 1.000 | L.F. | .015 | .27 | .71 | .98 |
| Plates, double top, single bottom | | .375 | L.F. | .005 | .10 | .27 | .37 |
| Cross bracing, let-in, 1″ x 6″ | | .080 | L.F. | .004 | .06 | .21 | .27 |
| | TOTAL | | S.F. | .024 | .43 | 1.19 | 1.62 |
| **2″ X 4″, 24″ O.C.** | | | | | | | |
| 2″ x 4″ studs, #2 or better, 24″ O.C. | | .800 | L.F. | .012 | .22 | .57 | .79 |
| Plates, double top, single bottom | | .375 | L.F. | .005 | .10 | .27 | .37 |
| Cross bracing, let-in, 1″ x 6″ | | .080 | L.F. | .003 | .06 | .14 | .20 |
| | TOTAL | | S.F. | .020 | .38 | .98 | 1.36 |
| **2″ X 6″, 16″ O.C.** | | | | | | | |
| 2″ x 6″ studs, #2 or better, 16″ O.C. | | 1.000 | L.F. | .016 | .41 | .78 | 1.19 |
| Plates, double top, single bottom | | .375 | L.F. | .006 | .15 | .29 | .44 |
| Cross bracing, let-in, 1″ x 6″ | | .080 | L.F. | .004 | .06 | .21 | .27 |
| | TOTAL | | S.F. | .026 | .62 | 1.28 | 1.90 |
| **2″ X 6″, 24″ O.C.** | | | | | | | |
| 2″ x 6″ studs, #2 or better, 24″ O.C. | | .800 | L.F. | .013 | .33 | .62 | .95 |
| Plates, double top, single bottom | | .375 | L.F. | .006 | .15 | .29 | .44 |
| Cross bracing, let-in, 1″ x 6″ | | .080 | L.F. | .003 | .06 | .14 | .20 |
| | TOTAL | | S.F. | .022 | .54 | 1.05 | 1.59 |

The costs in this system are based on a square foot of wall area. Do not subtract for door or window openings.

| Description | QUAN. | UNIT | LABOR HOURS | COST PER S.F. | | |
|---|---|---|---|---|---|---|
| | | | | MAT. | INST. | TOTAL |
| | | | | | | |
| | | | | | | |
| | | | | | | |
| | | | | | | |

# Partition Framing Price Sheet

| Partition Framing Price Sheet | QUAN. | UNIT | LABOR HOURS | COST PER S.F. | | |
|---|---|---|---|---|---|---|
| | | | | MAT. | INST. | TOTAL |
| Wood studs, #2 or better, 2" x 4", 12" O.C. | 1.250 | L.F. | .018 | .34 | .89 | 1.23 |
| 16" O.C. | 1.000 | L.F. | .015 | .27 | .71 | .98 |
| 24" O.C. | .800 | L.F. | .012 | .22 | .57 | .79 |
| 32" O.C. | .650 | L.F. | .009 | .18 | .46 | .64 |
| 2" x 6", 12" O.C. | 1.250 | L.F. | .020 | .51 | .98 | 1.49 |
| 16" O.C. | 1.000 | L.F. | .016 | .41 | .78 | 1.19 |
| 24" O.C. | .800 | L.F. | .013 | .33 | .62 | .95 |
| 32" O.C. | .650 | L.F. | .010 | .27 | .51 | .78 |
| Plates, #2 or better double top single bottom, 2" x 4" | .375 | L.F. | .005 | .10 | .27 | .37 |
| 2" x 6" | .375 | L.F. | .006 | .15 | .29 | .44 |
| 2" x 8" | .375 | L.F. | .005 | .23 | .27 | .50 |
| Cross bracing, let-in, 1" x 6" boards studs, 12" O.C. | .080 | L.F. | .005 | .07 | .26 | .33 |
| 16" O.C. | .080 | L.F. | .004 | .06 | .21 | .27 |
| 24" O.C. | .080 | L.F. | .003 | .06 | .14 | .20 |
| 32" O.C. | .080 | L.F. | .002 | .04 | .11 | .15 |
| Let-in steel (T shaped) studs, 12" O.C. | .080 | L.F. | .001 | .08 | .07 | .15 |
| 16" O.C. | .080 | L.F. | .001 | .07 | .05 | .12 |
| 24" O.C. | .080 | L.F. | .001 | .07 | .05 | .12 |
| 32" O.C. | .080 | L.F. | .001 | .05 | .04 | .09 |
| Steel straps studs, 12" O.C. | .080 | L.F. | .001 | .09 | .06 | .15 |
| 16" O.C. | .080 | L.F. | .001 | .09 | .05 | .14 |
| 24" O.C. | .080 | L.F. | .001 | .09 | .05 | .14 |
| 32" O.C. | .080 | L.F. | .001 | .08 | .05 | .13 |
| Metal studs, load bearing 24" O.C., 20 ga. galv., 2-1/2" wide | 1.000 | S.F. | .015 | .62 | .73 | 1.35 |
| 3-5/8" wide | 1.000 | S.F. | .015 | .74 | .75 | 1.49 |
| 4" wide | 1.000 | S.F. | .016 | .78 | .76 | 1.54 |
| 6" wide | 1.000 | S.F. | .016 | .98 | .78 | 1.76 |
| 16 ga., 2-1/2" wide | 1.000 | S.F. | .017 | .72 | .84 | 1.56 |
| 3-5/8" wide | 1.000 | S.F. | .017 | .86 | .85 | 1.71 |
| 4" wide | 1.000 | S.F. | .018 | .91 | .87 | 1.78 |
| 6" wide | 1.000 | S.F. | .018 | 1.14 | .89 | 2.03 |
| Non-load bearing 24" O.C., 25 ga. galv., 1-5/8" wide | 1.000 | S.F. | .011 | .19 | .52 | .71 |
| 2-1/2" wide | 1.000 | S.F. | .011 | .23 | .52 | .75 |
| 3-5/8" wide | 1.000 | S.F. | .011 | .26 | .53 | .79 |
| 4" wide | 1.000 | S.F. | .011 | .27 | .53 | .80 |
| 6" wide | 1.000 | S.F. | .011 | .40 | .54 | .94 |
| 20 ga., 2-1/2" wide | 1.000 | S.F. | .013 | .30 | .65 | .95 |
| 3-5/8" wide | 1.000 | S.F. | .014 | .33 | .66 | .99 |
| 4" wide | 1.000 | S.F. | .014 | .39 | .66 | 1.05 |
| 6" wide | 1.000 | S.F. | .014 | .46 | .68 | 1.14 |

| Window & Door Openings | QUAN. | UNIT | LABOR HOURS | COST EACH | | |
|---|---|---|---|---|---|---|
| | | | | MAT. | INST. | TOTAL |
| The following costs are to be added to the total costs of the walls. | | | | | | |
| Do not subtract openings from total wall area. | | | | | | |
| Headers, 2" x 6" double, 2' long | 4.000 | L.F. | .178 | 1.64 | 8.70 | 10.34 |
| 3' long | 6.000 | L.F. | .267 | 2.46 | 13.10 | 15.56 |
| 4' long | 8.000 | L.F. | .356 | 3.28 | 17.45 | 20.73 |
| 5' long | 10.000 | L.F. | .444 | 4.10 | 22 | 26.10 |
| 2" x 8" double, 4' long | 8.000 | L.F. | .376 | 4.88 | 18.40 | 23.28 |
| 5' long | 10.000 | L.F. | .471 | 6.10 | 23 | 29.10 |
| 6' long | 12.000 | L.F. | .565 | 7.30 | 27.50 | 34.80 |
| 8' long | 16.000 | L.F. | .753 | 9.75 | 37 | 46.75 |
| 2" x 10" double, 4' long | 8.000 | L.F. | .400 | 6.40 | 19.60 | 26 |
| 6' long | 12.000 | L.F. | .600 | 9.60 | 29.50 | 39.10 |
| 8' long | 16.000 | L.F. | .800 | 12.80 | 39 | 51.80 |
| 10' long | 20.000 | L.F. | 1.000 | 16 | 49 | 65 |
| 2" x 12" double, 8' long | 16.000 | L.F. | .853 | 18.70 | 42 | 60.70 |
| 12' long | 24.000 | L.F. | 1.280 | 28 | 62.50 | 90.50 |

155

| System Description | QUAN. | UNIT | LABOR HOURS | COST PER S.F. | | |
|---|---|---|---|---|---|---|
| | | | | MAT. | INST. | TOTAL |
| **6″ THICK CONCRETE BLOCK WALL** | | | | | | |
| 6″ thick concrete block, 6″ x 8″ x 16″ | 1.000 | S.F. | .100 | 2.29 | 4.44 | 6.73 |
| Masonry reinforcing, truss strips every other course | .625 | L.F. | .002 | .11 | .08 | .19 |
| Furring, 1″ x 3″, 16″ O.C. | 1.000 | L.F. | .016 | .38 | .79 | 1.17 |
| Masonry insulation, poured vermiculite | 1.000 | S.F. | .013 | .64 | .65 | 1.29 |
| Stucco, 2 coats | 1.000 | S.F. | .069 | .21 | 3.08 | 3.29 |
| Masonry paint, 2 coats | 1.000 | S.F. | .016 | .19 | .67 | .86 |
| TOTAL | | S.F. | .216 | 3.82 | 9.71 | 13.53 |
| **8″ THICK CONCRETE BLOCK WALL** | | | | | | |
| 8″ thick concrete block, 8″ x 8″ x 16″ | 1.000 | S.F. | .107 | 2.60 | 4.74 | 7.34 |
| Masonry reinforcing, truss strips every other course | .625 | L.F. | .002 | .11 | .08 | .19 |
| Furring, 1″ x 3″, 16″ O.C. | 1.000 | L.F. | .016 | .38 | .79 | 1.17 |
| Masonry insulation, poured vermiculite | 1.000 | S.F. | .018 | .85 | .86 | 1.71 |
| Stucco, 2 coats | 1.000 | S.F. | .069 | .21 | 3.08 | 3.29 |
| Masonry paint, 2 coats | 1.000 | S.F. | .016 | .19 | .67 | .86 |
| TOTAL | | S.F. | .228 | 4.34 | 10.22 | 14.56 |
| **12″ THICK CONCRETE BLOCK WALL** | | | | | | |
| 12″ thick concrete block, 12″ x 8″ x 16″ | 1.000 | S.F. | .141 | 3.76 | 6.15 | 9.91 |
| Masonry reinforcing, truss strips every other course | .625 | L.F. | .003 | .12 | .12 | .24 |
| Furring, 1″ x 3″, 16″ O.C. | 1.000 | L.F. | .016 | .38 | .79 | 1.17 |
| Masonry insulation, poured vermiculite | 1.000 | S.F. | .026 | 1.25 | 1.27 | 2.52 |
| Stucco, 2 coats | 1.000 | S.F. | .069 | .21 | 3.08 | 3.29 |
| Masonry paint, 2 coats | 1.000 | S.F. | .016 | .19 | .67 | .86 |
| TOTAL | | S.F. | .271 | 5.91 | 12.08 | 17.99 |

Costs for this system are based on a square foot of wall area. Do not subtract for window openings.

| Description | QUAN. | UNIT | LABOR HOURS | COST PER S.F. | | |
|---|---|---|---|---|---|---|
| | | | | MAT. | INST. | TOTAL |
| | | | | | | |
| | | | | | | |
| | | | | | | |
| | | | | | | |

## Masonry Block Price Sheet

| Masonry Block Price Sheet | QUAN. | UNIT | LABOR HOURS | COST PER S.F. MAT. | COST PER S.F. INST. | COST PER S.F. TOTAL |
|---|---|---|---|---|---|---|
| Block concrete, 8" x 16" regular, 4" thick | 1.000 | S.F. | .093 | 1.61 | 4.13 | 5.74 |
| 6" thick | 1.000 | S.F. | .100 | 2.29 | 4.44 | 6.73 |
| 8" thick | 1.000 | S.F. | .107 | 2.60 | 4.74 | 7.34 |
| 10" thick | 1.000 | S.F. | .111 | 3.30 | 4.94 | 8.24 |
| 12" thick | 1.000 | S.F. | .141 | 3.76 | 6.15 | 9.91 |
| Solid block, 4" thick | 1.000 | S.F. | .096 | 2 | 4.28 | 6.28 |
| 6" thick | 1.000 | S.F. | .104 | 2.36 | 4.62 | 6.98 |
| 8" thick | 1.000 | S.F. | .111 | 3.57 | 4.94 | 8.51 |
| 10" thick | 1.000 | S.F. | .133 | 4.82 | 5.75 | 10.57 |
| 12" thick | 1.000 | S.F. | .148 | 5.35 | 6.40 | 11.75 |
| Lightweight, 4" thick | 1.000 | S.F. | .093 | 1.61 | 4.13 | 5.74 |
| 6" thick | 1.000 | S.F. | .100 | 2.29 | 4.44 | 6.73 |
| 8" thick | 1.000 | S.F. | .107 | 2.60 | 4.74 | 7.34 |
| 10" thick | 1.000 | S.F. | .111 | 3.30 | 4.94 | 8.24 |
| 12" thick | 1.000 | S.F. | .141 | 3.76 | 6.15 | 9.91 |
| Split rib profile, 4" thick | 1.000 | S.F. | .116 | 3.48 | 5.15 | 8.63 |
| 6" thick | 1.000 | S.F. | .123 | 4 | 5.45 | 9.45 |
| 8" thick | 1.000 | S.F. | .131 | 4.58 | 5.95 | 10.53 |
| 10" thick | 1.000 | S.F. | .157 | 4.91 | 6.85 | 11.76 |
| 12" thick | 1.000 | S.F. | .175 | 5.45 | 7.60 | 13.05 |
| Masonry reinforcing, wire truss strips, every course, 8" block | 1.375 | L.F. | .004 | .25 | .18 | .43 |
| 12" block | 1.375 | L.F. | .006 | .26 | .26 | .52 |
| Every other course, 8" block | .625 | L.F. | .002 | .11 | .08 | .19 |
| 12" block | .625 | L.F. | .003 | .12 | .12 | .24 |
| Furring, wood, 1" x 3", 12" O.C. | 1.250 | L.F. | .020 | .48 | .99 | 1.47 |
| 16" O.C. | 1.000 | L.F. | .016 | .38 | .79 | 1.17 |
| 24" O.C. | .800 | L.F. | .013 | .30 | .63 | .93 |
| 32" O.C. | .640 | L.F. | .010 | .24 | .51 | .75 |
| Steel, 3/4" channels, 12" O.C. | 1.250 | L.F. | .034 | .34 | 1.42 | 1.76 |
| 16" O.C. | 1.000 | L.F. | .030 | .31 | 1.26 | 1.57 |
| 24" O.C. | .800 | L.F. | .023 | .20 | .95 | 1.15 |
| 32" O.C. | .640 | L.F. | .018 | .16 | .76 | .92 |
| Masonry insulation, vermiculite or perlite poured 4" thick | 1.000 | S.F. | .009 | .41 | .42 | .83 |
| 6" thick | 1.000 | S.F. | .013 | .64 | .65 | 1.29 |
| 8" thick | 1.000 | S.F. | .018 | .85 | .86 | 1.71 |
| 10" thick | 1.000 | S.F. | .021 | 1.03 | 1.04 | 2.07 |
| 12" thick | 1.000 | S.F. | .026 | 1.25 | 1.27 | 2.52 |
| Block inserts polystyrene, 6" thick | 1.000 | S.F. | | 1.99 | | 1.99 |
| 8" thick | 1.000 | S.F. | | 1.99 | | 1.99 |
| 10" thick | 1.000 | S.F. | | 2.34 | | 2.34 |
| 12" thick | 1.000 | S.F. | | 2.46 | | 2.46 |
| Stucco, 1 coat | 1.000 | S.F. | .057 | .18 | 2.53 | 2.71 |
| 2 coats | 1.000 | S.F. | .069 | .21 | 3.08 | 3.29 |
| 3 coats | 1.000 | S.F. | .081 | .25 | 3.62 | 3.87 |
| Painting, 1 coat | 1.000 | S.F. | .011 | .13 | .47 | .60 |
| 2 coats | 1.000 | S.F. | .016 | .19 | .67 | .86 |
| Primer & 1 coat | 1.000 | S.F. | .013 | .21 | .55 | .76 |
| 2 coats | 1.000 | S.F. | .018 | .28 | .76 | 1.04 |
| Lath, metal lath expanded 2.5 lb/S.Y., painted | 1.000 | S.F. | .010 | .50 | .44 | .94 |
| Galvanized | 1.000 | S.F. | .012 | .55 | .48 | 1.03 |
| | | | | | | |
| | | | | | | |

| System Description | QUAN. | UNIT | LABOR HOURS | COST PER S.F. | | |
|---|---|---|---|---|---|---|
| | | | | MAT. | INST. | TOTAL |
| **SELECT COMMON BRICK** | | | | | | |
| Brick, select common, running bond | 1.000 | S.F. | .174 | 3.97 | 7.75 | 11.72 |
| Wall ties, 7/8" x 7", 22 gauge | 1.000 | Ea. | .008 | .11 | .37 | .48 |
| Building paper, spunbonded polypropylene | 1.100 | S.F. | .002 | .15 | .11 | .26 |
| Trim, pine, painted | .125 | L.F. | .004 | .06 | .20 | .26 |
| TOTAL | | S.F. | .188 | 4.29 | 8.43 | 12.72 |
| **RED FACED COMMON BRICK** | | | | | | |
| Brick, common, red faced, running bond | 1.000 | S.F. | .182 | 5.15 | 8.10 | 13.25 |
| Wall ties, 7/8" x 7", 22 gauge | 1.000 | Ea. | .008 | .11 | .37 | .48 |
| Building paper, spundbonded polypropylene | 1.100 | S.F. | .002 | .15 | .11 | .26 |
| Trim, pine, painted | .125 | L.F. | .004 | .06 | .20 | .26 |
| TOTAL | | S.F. | .196 | 5.47 | 8.78 | 14.25 |
| **BUFF OR GREY FACE BRICK** | | | | | | |
| Brick, buff or grey | 1.000 | S.F. | .182 | 5.45 | 8.10 | 13.55 |
| Wall ties, 7/8" x 7", 22 gauge | 1.000 | Ea. | .008 | .11 | .37 | .48 |
| Building paper, spundbonded polypropylene | 1.100 | S.F. | .002 | .15 | .11 | .26 |
| Trim, pine, painted | .125 | L.F. | .004 | .06 | .20 | .26 |
| TOTAL | | S.F. | .196 | 5.77 | 8.78 | 14.55 |
| **STONE WORK, ROUGH STONE, AVERAGE** | | | | | | |
| Field stone veneer | 1.000 | S.F. | .223 | 7.34 | 9.92 | 17.26 |
| Wall ties, 7/8" x 7", 22 gauge | 1.000 | Ea. | .008 | .11 | .37 | .48 |
| Building paper, spundbonded polypropylene | 1.000 | S.F. | .002 | .15 | .11 | .26 |
| Trim, pine, painted | .125 | L.F. | .004 | .06 | .20 | .26 |
| TOTAL | | S.F. | .237 | 7.66 | 10.60 | 18.26 |

The costs in this system are based on a square foot of wall area. Do not subtract area for window & door openings.

| Description | QUAN. | UNIT | LABOR HOURS | COST PER S.F. | | |
|---|---|---|---|---|---|---|
| | | | | MAT. | INST. | TOTAL |
| | | | | | | |
| | | | | | | |
| | | | | | | |

| Brick/Stone Veneer Price Sheet | QUAN. | UNIT | LABOR HOURS | COST PER S.F. | | |
|---|---|---|---|---|---|---|
| | | | | MAT. | INST. | TOTAL |
| Brick | | | | | | |
| Select common, running bond | 1.000 | S.F. | .174 | 3.97 | 7.75 | 11.72 |
| Red faced, running bond | 1.000 | S.F. | .182 | 5.15 | 8.10 | 13.25 |
| Buff or grey faced, running bond | 1.000 | S.F. | .182 | 5.45 | 8.10 | 13.55 |
| Header every 6th course | 1.000 | S.F. | .216 | 6 | 9.60 | 15.60 |
| English bond | 1.000 | S.F. | .286 | 7.65 | 12.70 | 20.35 |
| Flemish bond | 1.000 | S.F. | .195 | 5.40 | 8.65 | 14.05 |
| Common bond | 1.000 | S.F. | .267 | 6.80 | 11.85 | 18.65 |
| Stack bond | 1.000 | S.F. | .182 | 5.45 | 8.10 | 13.55 |
| Jumbo, running bond | 1.000 | S.F. | .092 | 5.35 | 4.09 | 9.44 |
| Norman, running bond | 1.000 | S.F. | .125 | 6.25 | 5.55 | 11.80 |
| Norwegian, running bond | 1.000 | S.F. | .107 | 4.56 | 4.74 | 9.30 |
| Economy, running bond | 1.000 | S.F. | .129 | 4.61 | 5.75 | 10.36 |
| Engineer, running bond | 1.000 | S.F. | .154 | 3.79 | 6.85 | 10.64 |
| Roman, running bond | 1.000 | S.F. | .160 | 6.35 | 7.10 | 13.45 |
| Utility, running bond | 1.000 | S.F. | .089 | 4.96 | 3.95 | 8.91 |
| Glazed, running bond | 1.000 | S.F. | .190 | 13.15 | 8.45 | 21.60 |
| Stone work, rough stone, average | 1.000 | S.F. | .179 | 7.35 | 9.90 | 17.25 |
| Maximum | 1.000 | S.F. | .267 | 10.95 | 14.80 | 25.75 |
| Wall ties, galvanized, corrugated 7/8″ x 7″, 22 gauge | 1.000 | Ea. | .008 | .11 | .37 | .48 |
| 16 gauge | 1.000 | Ea. | .008 | .26 | .37 | .63 |
| Cavity wall, every 3rd course 6″ long Z type, 1/4″ diameter | 1.330 | L.F. | .010 | .55 | .47 | 1.02 |
| 3/16″ diameter | 1.330 | L.F. | .010 | .29 | .47 | .76 |
| 8″ long, Z type, 1/4″ diameter | 1.330 | L.F. | .010 | .64 | .47 | 1.11 |
| 3/16″ diameter | 1.330 | L.F. | .010 | .33 | .47 | .80 |
| Building paper, aluminum and kraft laminated foil, 1 side | 1.000 | S.F. | .002 | .10 | .11 | .21 |
| 2 sides | 1.000 | S.F. | .002 | .10 | .11 | .21 |
| #15 asphalt paper | 1.100 | S.F. | .002 | .07 | .12 | .19 |
| Polyethylene, .002″ thick | 1.000 | S.F. | .002 | .01 | .11 | .12 |
| .004″ thick | 1.000 | S.F. | .002 | .04 | .11 | .15 |
| .006″ thick | 1.000 | S.F. | .002 | .06 | .11 | .17 |
| .010″ thick | 1.000 | S.F. | .002 | .07 | .11 | .18 |
| Trim, 1″ x 4″, cedar | .125 | L.F. | .005 | .16 | .25 | .41 |
| Fir | .125 | L.F. | .005 | .11 | .25 | .36 |
| Redwood | .125 | L.F. | .005 | .16 | .25 | .41 |
| White pine | .125 | L.F. | .005 | .11 | .25 | .36 |
| | | | | | | |
| | | | | | | |
| | | | | | | |
| | | | | | | |
| | | | | | | |
| | | | | | | |
| | | | | | | |
| | | | | | | |
| | | | | | | |

Trim

Building Paper

Beveled Cedar Siding

| System Description | QUAN. | UNIT | LABOR HOURS | COST PER S.F. | | |
|---|---|---|---|---|---|---|
| | | | | MAT. | INST. | TOTAL |
| **1/2″ X 6″ BEVELED CEDAR SIDING, ″A″ GRADE** | | | | | | |
| 1/2″ x 6″ beveled cedar siding | 1.000 | S.F. | .027 | 5.20 | 1.33 | 6.53 |
| Building wrap, spunbonded polypropylene | 1.100 | S.F. | .002 | .15 | .11 | .26 |
| Trim, cedar | .125 | L.F. | .005 | .16 | .25 | .41 |
| Paint, primer & 2 coats | 1.000 | S.F. | .017 | .18 | .72 | .90 |
| TOTAL | | S.F. | .051 | 5.69 | 2.41 | 8.10 |
| **1/2″ X 8″ BEVELED CEDAR SIDING, ″A″ GRADE** | | | | | | |
| 1/2″ x 8″ beveled cedar siding | 1.000 | S.F. | .024 | 6.10 | 1.19 | 7.29 |
| Building wrap, spunbonded polypropylene | 1.100 | S.F. | .002 | .15 | .11 | .26 |
| Trim, cedar | .125 | L.F. | .005 | .16 | .25 | .41 |
| Paint, primer & 2 coats | 1.000 | S.F. | .017 | .18 | .72 | .90 |
| TOTAL | | S.F. | .048 | 6.59 | 2.27 | 8.86 |
| **1″ X 4″ TONGUE & GROOVE, REDWOOD, VERTICAL GRAIN** | | | | | | |
| Redwood, clear, vertical grain, 1″ x 10″ | 1.000 | S.F. | .020 | 5.32 | .95 | 6.27 |
| Building wrap, spunbonded polypropylene | 1.100 | S.F. | .002 | .15 | .11 | .26 |
| Trim, redwood | .125 | L.F. | .005 | .16 | .25 | .41 |
| Sealer, 1 coat, stain, 1 coat | 1.000 | S.F. | .013 | .12 | .56 | .68 |
| TOTAL | | S.F. | .040 | 5.75 | 1.87 | 7.62 |
| **1″ X 6″ TONGUE & GROOVE, REDWOOD, VERTICAL GRAIN** | | | | | | |
| Redwood, clear, vertical grain, 1″ x 10″ | 1.000 | S.F. | .020 | 5.47 | .98 | 6.45 |
| Building wrap, spunbonded polypropylene | 1.100 | S.F. | .002 | .15 | .11 | .26 |
| Trim, redwood | .125 | L.F. | .005 | .16 | .25 | .41 |
| Sealer, 1 coat, stain, 1 coat | 1.000 | S.F. | .013 | .12 | .56 | .68 |
| TOTAL | | S.F. | .040 | 5.90 | 1.90 | 7.80 |

The costs in this system are based on a square foot of wall area.
Do not subtract area for door or window openings.

| Description | QUAN. | UNIT | LABOR HOURS | COST PER S.F. | | |
|---|---|---|---|---|---|---|
| | | | | MAT. | INST. | TOTAL |
| | | | | | | |
| | | | | | | |
| | | | | | | |

# Wood Siding Price Sheet

| Wood Siding Price Sheet | QUAN. | UNIT | LABOR HOURS | COST PER S.F. | | |
|---|---|---|---|---|---|---|
| | | | | MAT. | INST. | TOTAL |
| Siding, beveled cedar, "A" grade, 1/2" x 6" | 1.000 | S.F. | .028 | 5.20 | 1.33 | 6.53 |
| 1/2" x 8" | 1.000 | S.F. | .023 | 6.10 | 1.19 | 7.29 |
| "B" grade, 1/2" x 6" | 1.000 | S.F. | .032 | 5.80 | 1.48 | 7.28 |
| 1/2" x 8" | 1.000 | S.F. | .029 | 6.80 | 1.32 | 8.12 |
| Clear grade, 1/2" x 6" | 1.000 | S.F. | .028 | 6.50 | 1.66 | 8.16 |
| 1/2" x 8" | 1.000 | S.F. | .023 | 7.65 | 1.49 | 9.14 |
| Redwood, clear vertical grain, 1/2" x 6" | 1.000 | S.F. | .036 | 3.41 | 1.33 | 4.74 |
| 1/2" x 8" | 1.000 | S.F. | .032 | 3.56 | 1.19 | 4.75 |
| Clear all heart vertical grain, 1/2" x 6" | 1.000 | S.F. | .028 | 3.79 | 1.48 | 5.27 |
| 1/2" x 8" | 1.000 | S.F. | .023 | 3.96 | 1.32 | 5.28 |
| Siding board & batten, cedar, "B" grade, 1" x 10" | 1.000 | S.F. | .031 | 4.33 | .93 | 5.26 |
| 1" x 12" | 1.000 | S.F. | .031 | 4.33 | .93 | 5.26 |
| Redwood, clear vertical grain, 1" x 6" | 1.000 | S.F. | .043 | 3.41 | 1.33 | 4.74 |
| 1" x 8" | 1.000 | S.F. | .018 | 3.56 | 1.19 | 4.75 |
| White pine, #2 & better, 1" x 10" | 1.000 | S.F. | .029 | 2.42 | 1.19 | 3.61 |
| 1" x 12" | 1.000 | S.F. | .029 | 2.42 | 1.19 | 3.61 |
| Siding vertical, tongue & groove, cedar "B" grade, 1" x 4" | 1.000 | S.F. | .033 | 2.72 | .95 | 3.67 |
| 1" x 6" | 1.000 | S.F. | .024 | 2.79 | .98 | 3.77 |
| 1" x 8" | 1.000 | S.F. | .024 | 2.87 | 1.01 | 3.88 |
| 1" x 10" | 1.000 | S.F. | .021 | 2.96 | 1.04 | 4 |
| "A" grade, 1" x 4" | 1.000 | S.F. | .033 | 2.49 | .87 | 3.36 |
| 1" x 6" | 1.000 | S.F. | .024 | 2.55 | .90 | 3.45 |
| 1" x 8" | 1.000 | S.F. | .024 | 2.62 | .92 | 3.54 |
| 1" x 10" | 1.000 | S.F. | .021 | 2.69 | .95 | 3.64 |
| Clear vertical grain, 1" x 4" | 1.000 | S.F. | .033 | 2.29 | .81 | 3.10 |
| 1" x 6" | 1.000 | S.F. | .024 | 2.35 | .83 | 3.18 |
| 1" x 8" | 1.000 | S.F. | .024 | 2.41 | .85 | 3.26 |
| 1" x 10" | 1.000 | S.F. | .021 | 2.47 | .87 | 3.34 |
| Redwood, clear vertical grain, 1" x 4" | 1.000 | S.F. | .033 | 5.30 | .95 | 6.25 |
| 1" x 6" | 1.000 | S.F. | .024 | 5.45 | .98 | 6.43 |
| 1" x 8" | 1.000 | S.F. | .024 | 5.65 | 1.01 | 6.66 |
| 1" x 10" | 1.000 | S.F. | .021 | 5.80 | 1.04 | 6.84 |
| Clear all heart vertical grain, 1" x 4" | 1.000 | S.F. | .033 | 4.87 | .87 | 5.74 |
| 1" x 6" | 1.000 | S.F. | .024 | 5 | .90 | 5.90 |
| 1" x 8" | 1.000 | S.F. | .024 | 5.15 | .92 | 6.07 |
| 1" x 10" | 1.000 | S.F. | .021 | 5.25 | .95 | 6.20 |
| White pine, 1" x 10" | 1.000 | S.F. | .024 | 1.82 | 1.04 | 2.86 |
| Siding plywood, texture 1-11 cedar, 3/8" thick | 1.000 | S.F. | .024 | 1.32 | 1.16 | 2.48 |
| 5/8" thick | 1.000 | S.F. | .024 | 2.67 | 1.16 | 3.83 |
| Redwood, 3/8" thick | 1.000 | S.F. | .024 | 1.32 | 1.16 | 2.48 |
| 5/8" thick | 1.000 | S.F. | .024 | 2.11 | 1.16 | 3.27 |
| Fir, 3/8" thick | 1.000 | S.F. | .024 | .84 | 1.16 | 2 |
| 5/8" thick | 1.000 | S.F. | .024 | 1.51 | 1.16 | 2.67 |
| Southern yellow pine, 3/8" thick | 1.000 | S.F. | .024 | .84 | 1.16 | 2 |
| 5/8" thick | 1.000 | S.F. | .024 | 1.31 | 1.16 | 2.47 |
| Paper, #15 asphalt felt | 1.100 | S.F. | .002 | .07 | .12 | .19 |
| Trim, cedar | .125 | L.F. | .005 | .16 | .25 | .41 |
| Fir | .125 | L.F. | .005 | .11 | .25 | .36 |
| Redwood | .125 | L.F. | .005 | .16 | .25 | .41 |
| White pine | .125 | L.F. | .005 | .11 | .25 | .36 |
| Painting, primer, & 1 coat | 1.000 | S.F. | .013 | .12 | .56 | .68 |
| 2 coats | 1.000 | S.F. | .017 | .18 | .72 | .90 |
| Stain, sealer, & 1 coat | 1.000 | S.F. | .017 | .13 | .73 | .86 |
| 2 coats | 1.000 | S.F. | .019 | .21 | .79 | 1 |

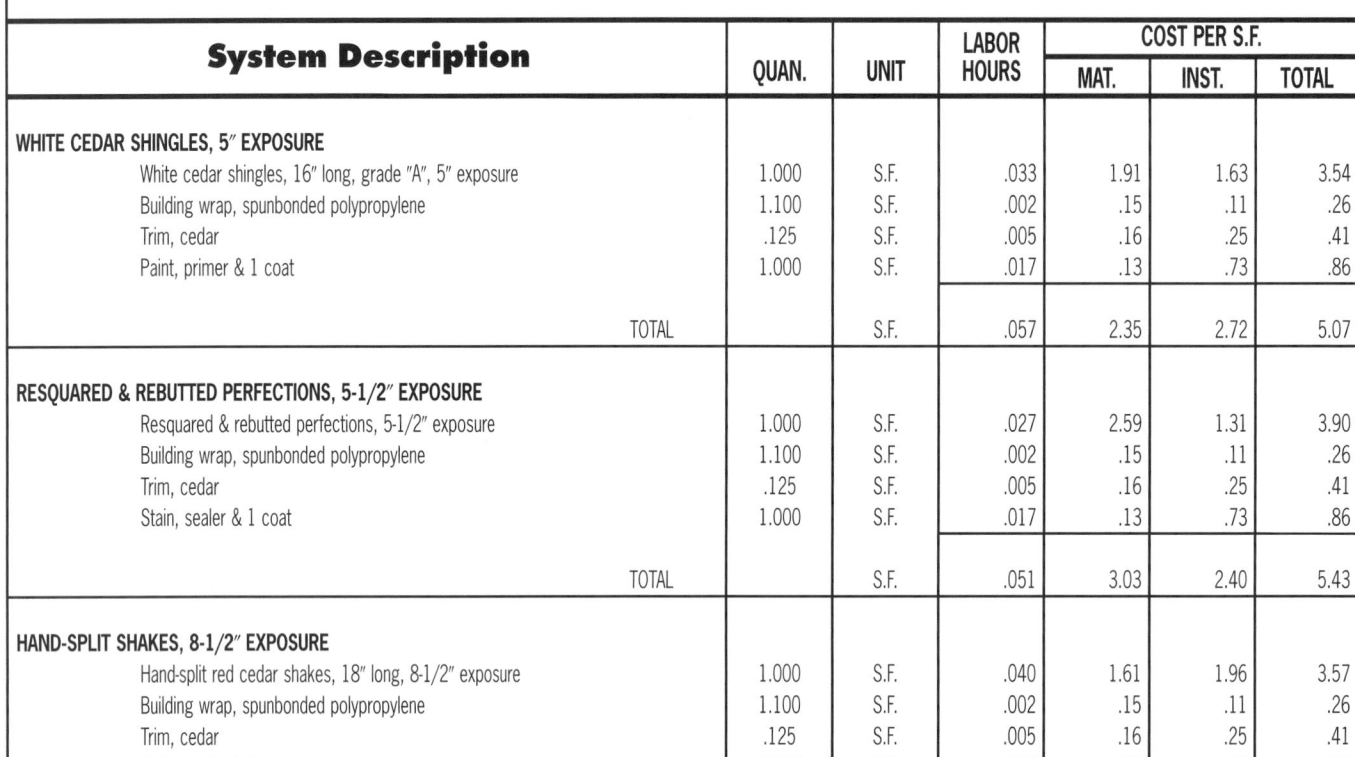

| System Description | QUAN. | UNIT | LABOR HOURS | COST PER S.F. | | |
|---|---|---|---|---|---|---|
| | | | | MAT. | INST. | TOTAL |
| **WHITE CEDAR SHINGLES, 5″ EXPOSURE** | | | | | | |
| White cedar shingles, 16″ long, grade "A", 5″ exposure | 1.000 | S.F. | .033 | 1.91 | 1.63 | 3.54 |
| Building wrap, spunbonded polypropylene | 1.100 | S.F. | .002 | .15 | .11 | .26 |
| Trim, cedar | .125 | S.F. | .005 | .16 | .25 | .41 |
| Paint, primer & 1 coat | 1.000 | S.F. | .017 | .13 | .73 | .86 |
| TOTAL | | S.F. | .057 | 2.35 | 2.72 | 5.07 |
| **RESQUARED & REBUTTED PERFECTIONS, 5-1/2″ EXPOSURE** | | | | | | |
| Resquared & rebutted perfections, 5-1/2″ exposure | 1.000 | S.F. | .027 | 2.59 | 1.31 | 3.90 |
| Building wrap, spunbonded polypropylene | 1.100 | S.F. | .002 | .15 | .11 | .26 |
| Trim, cedar | .125 | S.F. | .005 | .16 | .25 | .41 |
| Stain, sealer & 1 coat | 1.000 | S.F. | .017 | .13 | .73 | .86 |
| TOTAL | | S.F. | .051 | 3.03 | 2.40 | 5.43 |
| **HAND-SPLIT SHAKES, 8-1/2″ EXPOSURE** | | | | | | |
| Hand-split red cedar shakes, 18″ long, 8-1/2″ exposure | 1.000 | S.F. | .040 | 1.61 | 1.96 | 3.57 |
| Building wrap, spunbonded polypropylene | 1.100 | S.F. | .002 | .15 | .11 | .26 |
| Trim, cedar | .125 | S.F. | .005 | .16 | .25 | .41 |
| Stain, sealer & 1 coat | 1.000 | S.F. | .017 | .13 | .73 | .86 |
| TOTAL | | S.F. | .064 | 2.05 | 3.05 | 5.10 |

The costs in this system are based on a square foot of wall area.
Do not subtract area for door or window openings.

| Description | QUAN. | UNIT | LABOR HOURS | COST PER S.F. | | |
|---|---|---|---|---|---|---|
| | | | | MAT. | INST. | TOTAL |
| | | | | | | |
| | | | | | | |
| | | | | | | |
| | | | | | | |
| | | | | | | |
| | | | | | | |
| | | | | | | |

| Shingle Siding Price Sheet | QUAN. | UNIT | LABOR HOURS | COST PER S.F. | | |
|---|---|---|---|---|---|---|
| | | | | MAT. | INST. | TOTAL |
| Shingles wood, white cedar 16" long, "A" grade, 5" exposure | 1.000 | S.F. | .033 | 1.91 | 1.63 | 3.54 |
| 7" exposure | 1.000 | S.F. | .030 | 1.72 | 1.47 | 3.19 |
| 8-1/2" exposure | 1.000 | S.F. | .032 | 1.10 | 1.57 | 2.67 |
| 10" exposure | 1.000 | S.F. | .028 | .96 | 1.37 | 2.33 |
| "B" grade, 5" exposure | 1.000 | S.F. | .040 | 1.65 | 1.96 | 3.61 |
| 7" exposure | 1.000 | S.F. | .028 | 1.16 | 1.37 | 2.53 |
| 8-1/2" exposure | 1.000 | S.F. | .024 | .99 | 1.18 | 2.17 |
| 10" exposure | 1.000 | S.F. | .020 | .83 | .98 | 1.81 |
| Fire retardant, "A" grade, 5" exposure | 1.000 | S.F. | .033 | 2.52 | 1.63 | 4.15 |
| 7" exposure | 1.000 | S.F. | .028 | 1.58 | 1.37 | 2.95 |
| 8-1/2" exposure | 1.000 | S.F. | .032 | 1.93 | 1.57 | 3.50 |
| 10" exposure | 1.000 | S.F. | .025 | 1.50 | 1.22 | 2.72 |
| Fire retardant, 5" exposure | 1.000 | S.F. | .029 | 3.53 | 1.42 | 4.95 |
| 7" exposure | 1.000 | S.F. | .036 | 2.75 | 1.74 | 4.49 |
| 8-1/2" exposure | 1.000 | S.F. | .032 | 2.47 | 1.57 | 4.04 |
| 10" exposure | 1.000 | S.F. | .025 | 1.92 | 1.22 | 3.14 |
| Resquared & rebutted, 5-1/2" exposure | 1.000 | S.F. | .027 | 2.59 | 1.31 | 3.90 |
| 7" exposure | 1.000 | S.F. | .024 | 2.33 | 1.18 | 3.51 |
| 8-1/2" exposure | 1.000 | S.F. | .021 | 2.07 | 1.05 | 3.12 |
| 10" exposure | 1.000 | S.F. | .019 | 1.81 | .92 | 2.73 |
| Fire retardant, 5" exposure | 1.000 | S.F. | .027 | 3.20 | 1.31 | 4.51 |
| 7" exposure | 1.000 | S.F. | .024 | 2.87 | 1.18 | 4.05 |
| 8-1/2" exposure | 1.000 | S.F. | .021 | 2.55 | 1.05 | 3.60 |
| 10" exposure | 1.000 | S.F. | .023 | 1.75 | 1.12 | 2.87 |
| Hand-split, red cedar, 24" long, 7" exposure | 1.000 | S.F. | .045 | 2.55 | 2.20 | 4.75 |
| 8-1/2" exposure | 1.000 | S.F. | .038 | 2.18 | 1.88 | 4.06 |
| 10" exposure | 1.000 | S.F. | .032 | 1.82 | 1.57 | 3.39 |
| 12" exposure | 1.000 | S.F. | .026 | 1.46 | 1.26 | 2.72 |
| Fire retardant, 7" exposure | 1.000 | S.F. | .045 | 3.40 | 2.20 | 5.60 |
| 8-1/2" exposure | 1.000 | S.F. | .038 | 2.91 | 1.88 | 4.79 |
| 10" exposure | 1.000 | S.F. | .032 | 2.43 | 1.57 | 4 |
| 12" exposure | 1.000 | S.F. | .026 | 1.94 | 1.26 | 3.20 |
| 18" long, 5" exposure | 1.000 | S.F. | .068 | 2.74 | 3.33 | 6.07 |
| 7" exposure | 1.000 | S.F. | .048 | 1.93 | 2.35 | 4.28 |
| 8-1/2" exposure | 1.000 | S.F. | .040 | 1.61 | 1.96 | 3.57 |
| 10" exposure | 1.000 | S.F. | .036 | 1.45 | 1.76 | 3.21 |
| Fire retardant, 5" exposure | 1.000 | S.F. | .068 | 3.77 | 3.33 | 7.10 |
| 7" exposure | 1.000 | S.F. | .048 | 2.66 | 2.35 | 5.01 |
| 8-1/2" exposure | 1.000 | S.F. | .040 | 2.22 | 1.96 | 4.18 |
| 10" exposure | 1.000 | S.F. | .036 | 1.99 | 1.76 | 3.75 |
| Paper, #15 asphalt felt | 1.100 | S.F. | .002 | .06 | .11 | .17 |
| Trim, cedar | .125 | S.F. | .005 | .16 | .25 | .41 |
| Fir | .125 | S.F. | .005 | .11 | .25 | .36 |
| Redwood | .125 | S.F. | .005 | .16 | .25 | .41 |
| White pine | .125 | S.F. | .005 | .11 | .25 | .36 |
| Painting, primer, & 1 coat | 1.000 | S.F. | .013 | .12 | .56 | .68 |
| 2 coats | 1.000 | S.F. | .017 | .18 | .72 | .90 |
| Staining, sealer, & 1 coat | 1.000 | S.F. | .017 | .13 | .73 | .86 |
| 2 coats | 1.000 | S.F. | .019 | .21 | .79 | 1 |

Aluminum Trim

Building Paper

Alum. Horizontal Siding

Backer Insulation Board

| System Description | QUAN. | UNIT | LABOR HOURS | COST PER S.F. | | |
|---|---|---|---|---|---|---|
| | | | | MAT. | INST. | TOTAL |
| **ALUMINUM CLAPBOARD SIDING, 8″ WIDE, WHITE** | | | | | | |
| Aluminum horizontal siding, 8″ clapboard | 1.000 | S.F. | .031 | 1.90 | 1.52 | 3.42 |
| Backer, insulation board | 1.000 | S.F. | .008 | .70 | .39 | 1.09 |
| Trim, aluminum | .600 | L.F. | .016 | .92 | .77 | 1.69 |
| Building wrap, spunbonded polypropylene | 1.100 | S.F. | .002 | .15 | .11 | .26 |
| TOTAL | | S.F. | .057 | 3.67 | 2.79 | 6.46 |
| **ALUMINUM VERTICAL BOARD & BATTEN, WHITE** | | | | | | |
| Aluminum vertical board & batten | 1.000 | S.F. | .027 | 2.16 | 1.33 | 3.49 |
| Backer insulation board | 1.000 | S.F. | .008 | .70 | .39 | 1.09 |
| Trim, aluminum | .600 | L.F. | .016 | .92 | .77 | 1.69 |
| Building wrap, spunbonded polypropylene | 1.100 | S.F. | .002 | .15 | .11 | .26 |
| TOTAL | | S.F. | .053 | 3.93 | 2.60 | 6.53 |
| **VINYL CLAPBOARD SIDING, 8″ WIDE, WHITE** | | | | | | |
| Vinyl siding, clabboard profile, smooth texture, .042 thick, single 8 | 1.000 | S.F. | .032 | 1.06 | 1.58 | 2.64 |
| Backer, insulation board | 1.000 | S.F. | .008 | .70 | .39 | 1.09 |
| Vinyl siding, access., outside corner, woodgrain, 4″ face, 3/4″ pocket | 1.000 | L.F. | .023 | 1.93 | 1.12 | 3.05 |
| Building wrap, spunbonded polypropylene | 1.100 | S.F. | .002 | .15 | .11 | .26 |
| TOTAL | | S.F. | .065 | 3.84 | 3.20 | 7.04 |
| **VINYL VERTICAL BOARD & BATTEN, WHITE** | | | | | | |
| Vinyl siding, vertical pattern, .046 thick, double 5 | 1.000 | S.F. | .029 | 1.34 | 1.42 | 2.76 |
| Backer, insulation board | 1.000 | S.F. | .008 | .70 | .39 | 1.09 |
| Vinyl siding, access., outside corner, woodgrain, 4″ face, 3/4″ pocket | .600 | L.F. | .014 | 1.16 | .67 | 1.83 |
| Building wrap, spunbonded polypropylene | 1.100 | S.F. | .002 | .15 | .11 | .26 |
| TOTAL | | S.F. | .053 | 3.35 | 2.59 | 5.94 |

The costs in this system are on a square foot of wall basis.
Subtract openings from wall area.

| Description | QUAN. | UNIT | LABOR HOURS | COST PER S.F. | | |
|---|---|---|---|---|---|---|
| | | | | MAT. | INST. | TOTAL |
| | | | | | | |
| | | | | | | |
| | | | | | | |

| Metal & Plastic Siding Price Sheet | QUAN. | UNIT | LABOR HOURS | COST PER S.F. | | |
|---|---|---|---|---|---|---|
| | | | | MAT. | INST. | TOTAL |
| Siding, aluminum, .024" thick, smooth, 8" wide, white | 1.000 | S.F. | .031 | 1.90 | 1.52 | 3.42 |
| Color | 1.000 | S.F. | .031 | 2.03 | 1.52 | 3.55 |
| Double 4" pattern, 8" wide, white | 1.000 | S.F. | .031 | 2.24 | 1.52 | 3.76 |
| Color | 1.000 | S.F. | .031 | 2.37 | 1.52 | 3.89 |
| Double 5" pattern, 10" wide, white | 1.000 | S.F. | .029 | 2.31 | 1.42 | 3.73 |
| Color | 1.000 | S.F. | .029 | 2.44 | 1.42 | 3.86 |
| Embossed, single, 8" wide, white | 1.000 | S.F. | .031 | 1.90 | 1.52 | 3.42 |
| Color | 1.000 | S.F. | .031 | 2.03 | 1.52 | 3.55 |
| Double 4" pattern, 8" wide, white | 1.000 | S.F. | .031 | 2.37 | 1.52 | 3.89 |
| Color | 1.000 | S.F. | .031 | 2.50 | 1.52 | 4.02 |
| Double 5" pattern, 10" wide, white | 1.000 | S.F. | .029 | 2.34 | 1.42 | 3.76 |
| Color | 1.000 | S.F. | .029 | 2.47 | 1.42 | 3.89 |
| Alum siding with insulation board, smooth, 8" wide, white | 1.000 | S.F. | .031 | 2.08 | 1.52 | 3.60 |
| Color | 1.000 | S.F. | .031 | 2.21 | 1.52 | 3.73 |
| Double 4" pattern, 8" wide, white | 1.000 | S.F. | .031 | 2.06 | 1.52 | 3.58 |
| Color | 1.000 | S.F. | .031 | 2.19 | 1.52 | 3.71 |
| Double 5" pattern, 10" wide, white | 1.000 | S.F. | .029 | 2.06 | 1.42 | 3.48 |
| Color | 1.000 | S.F. | .029 | 2.19 | 1.42 | 3.61 |
| Embossed, single, 8" wide, white | 1.000 | S.F. | .031 | 2.40 | 1.52 | 3.92 |
| Color | 1.000 | S.F. | .031 | 2.53 | 1.52 | 4.05 |
| Double 4" pattern, 8" wide, white | 1.000 | S.F. | .031 | 2.43 | 1.52 | 3.95 |
| Color | 1.000 | S.F. | .031 | 2.56 | 1.52 | 4.08 |
| Double 5" pattern, 10" wide, white | 1.000 | S.F. | .029 | 2.43 | 1.42 | 3.85 |
| Color | 1.000 | S.F. | .029 | 2.56 | 1.42 | 3.98 |
| Aluminum, shake finish, 10" wide, white | 1.000 | S.F. | .029 | 2.59 | 1.42 | 4.01 |
| Color | 1.000 | S.F. | .029 | 2.72 | 1.42 | 4.14 |
| Aluminum, vertical, 12" wide, white | 1.000 | S.F. | .027 | 2.16 | 1.33 | 3.49 |
| Color | 1.000 | S.F. | .027 | 2.29 | 1.33 | 3.62 |
| Vinyl siding, 8" wide, smooth, white | 1.000 | S.F. | .032 | 1.06 | 1.58 | 2.64 |
| Color | 1.000 | S.F. | .032 | 1.24 | 1.58 | 2.82 |
| 10" wide, Dutch lap, smooth, white | 1.000 | S.F. | .029 | 1.01 | 1.42 | 2.43 |
| Color | 1.000 | S.F. | .029 | 1.19 | 1.42 | 2.61 |
| Double 4" pattern, 8" wide, white | 1.000 | S.F. | .032 | .83 | 1.58 | 2.41 |
| Color | 1.000 | S.F. | .032 | 1.01 | 1.58 | 2.59 |
| Double 5" pattern, 10" wide, white | 1.000 | S.F. | .029 | .83 | 1.42 | 2.25 |
| Color | 1.000 | S.F. | .029 | 1.01 | 1.42 | 2.43 |
| Embossed, single, 8" wide, white | 1.000 | S.F. | .032 | 1.06 | 1.58 | 2.64 |
| Color | 1.000 | S.F. | .032 | 1.24 | 1.58 | 2.82 |
| 10" wide, white | 1.000 | S.F. | .029 | 1.27 | 1.42 | 2.69 |
| Color | 1.000 | S.F. | .029 | 1.45 | 1.42 | 2.87 |
| Double 4" pattern, 8" wide, white | 1.000 | S.F. | .032 | 1.01 | 1.58 | 2.59 |
| Color | 1.000 | S.F. | .032 | 1.19 | 1.58 | 2.77 |
| Double 5" pattern, 10" wide, white | 1.000 | S.F. | .029 | 1.01 | 1.42 | 2.43 |
| Color | 1.000 | S.F. | .029 | 1.19 | 1.42 | 2.61 |
| Vinyl, shake finish, 10" wide, white | 1.000 | S.F. | .029 | 2.41 | 1.96 | 4.37 |
| Color | 1.000 | S.F. | .029 | 2.59 | 1.96 | 4.55 |
| Vinyl, vertical, double 5" pattern, 10" wide, white | 1.000 | S.F. | .029 | 1.34 | 1.42 | 2.76 |
| Color | 1.000 | S.F. | .029 | 1.52 | 1.42 | 2.94 |
| Backer board, installed in siding panels 8" or 10" wide | 1.000 | S.F. | .008 | .70 | .39 | 1.09 |
| 4' x 8' sheets, polystyrene, 3/4" thick | 1.000 | S.F. | .010 | .56 | .49 | 1.05 |
| 4' x 8' fiberboard, plain | 1.000 | S.F. | .008 | .70 | .39 | 1.09 |
| Trim, aluminum, white | .600 | L.F. | .016 | .92 | .77 | 1.69 |
| Color | .600 | L.F. | .016 | .99 | .77 | 1.76 |
| Vinyl, white | .600 | L.F. | .014 | 1.16 | .67 | 1.83 |
| Color | .600 | L.F. | .014 | 1.37 | .67 | 2.04 |
| Paper, #15 asphalt felt | 1.100 | S.F. | .002 | .07 | .12 | .19 |
| Kraft paper, plain | 1.100 | S.F. | .002 | .11 | .12 | .23 |
| Foil backed | 1.100 | S.F. | .002 | .11 | .12 | .23 |

167

| Description | QUAN. | UNIT | LABOR HOURS | COST PER S.F. | | |
|---|---|---|---|---|---|---|
| | | | | MAT. | INST. | TOTAL |
| Poured insulation, cellulose fiber, R3.8 per inch (1" thick) | 1.000 | S.F. | .003 | .05 | .16 | .21 |
| Fiberglass , R4.0 per inch (1" thick) | 1.000 | S.F. | .003 | .04 | .16 | .20 |
| Mineral wool, R3.0 per inch (1" thick) | 1.000 | S.F. | .003 | .04 | .16 | .20 |
| Polystyrene, R4.0 per inch (1" thick) | 1.000 | S.F. | .003 | .28 | .16 | .44 |
| Vermiculite, R2.7 per inch (1" thick) | 1.000 | S.F. | .003 | .16 | .16 | .32 |
| Perlite, R2.7 per inch (1" thick) | 1.000 | S.F. | .003 | .16 | .16 | .32 |
| Reflective insulation, aluminum foil reinforced with scrim | 1.000 | S.F. | .004 | .16 | .21 | .37 |
| Reinforced with woven polyolefin | 1.000 | S.F. | .004 | .19 | .21 | .40 |
| With single bubble air space, R8.8 | 1.000 | S.F. | .005 | .28 | .26 | .54 |
| With double bubble air space, R9.8 | 1.000 | S.F. | .005 | .29 | .26 | .55 |
| Rigid insulation, fiberglass, unfaced, | | | | | | |
| 1-1/2" thick, R6.2 | 1.000 | S.F. | .008 | .70 | .39 | 1.09 |
| 2" thick, R8.3 | 1.000 | S.F. | .008 | .76 | .39 | 1.15 |
| 2-1/2" thick, R10.3 | 1.000 | S.F. | .010 | .88 | .49 | 1.37 |
| 3" thick, R12.4 | 1.000 | S.F. | .010 | .88 | .49 | 1.37 |
| Foil faced, 1" thick, R4.3 | 1.000 | S.F. | .008 | 1.01 | .39 | 1.40 |
| 1-1/2" thick, R6.2 | 1.000 | S.F. | .008 | 1.50 | .39 | 1.89 |
| 2" thick, R8.7 | 1.000 | S.F. | .009 | 1.88 | .44 | 2.32 |
| 2-1/2" thick, R10.9 | 1.000 | S.F. | .010 | 2.22 | .49 | 2.71 |
| 3" thick, R13.0 | 1.000 | S.F. | .010 | 2.41 | .49 | 2.90 |
| Foam glass, 1-1/2" thick R2.64 | 1.000 | S.F. | .010 | 1.54 | .49 | 2.03 |
| 2" thick R5.26 | 1.000 | S.F. | .011 | 3.80 | .54 | 4.34 |
| Perlite, 1" thick R2.77 | 1.000 | S.F. | .010 | .33 | .49 | .82 |
| 2" thick R5.55 | 1.000 | S.F. | .011 | .66 | .54 | 1.20 |
| Polystyrene, extruded, blue, 2.2#/C.F., 3/4" thick R4 | 1.000 | S.F. | .010 | .56 | .49 | 1.05 |
| 1-1/2" thick R8.1 | 1.000 | S.F. | .011 | 1.14 | .54 | 1.68 |
| 2" thick R10.8 | 1.000 | S.F. | .011 | 1.54 | .54 | 2.08 |
| Molded bead board, white, 1" thick R3.85 | 1.000 | S.F. | .010 | .40 | .49 | .89 |
| 1-1/2" thick, R5.6 | 1.000 | S.F. | .011 | .79 | .54 | 1.33 |
| 2" thick, R7.7 | 1.000 | S.F. | .011 | 1.19 | .54 | 1.73 |
| Non-rigid insulation, batts | | | | | | |
| Fiberglass, kraft faced, 3-1/2" thick, R13, 11" wide | 1.000 | S.F. | .005 | .36 | .29 | .65 |
| 15" wide | 1.000 | S.F. | .005 | .36 | .29 | .65 |
| 23" wide | 1.000 | S.F. | .005 | .36 | .29 | .65 |
| 6" thick, R19, 11" wide | 1.000 | S.F. | .006 | .47 | .29 | .76 |
| 15" wide | 1.000 | S.F. | .006 | .47 | .29 | .76 |
| 23" wide | 1.000 | S.F. | .006 | .47 | .29 | .76 |
| 9" thick, R30, 15" wide | 1.000 | S.F. | .006 | .77 | .29 | 1.06 |
| 23" wide | 1.000 | S.F. | .006 | .77 | .29 | 1.06 |
| 12" thick, R38, 15" wide | 1.000 | S.F. | .006 | 1.10 | .29 | 1.39 |
| 23" wide | 1.000 | S.F. | .006 | 1.10 | .29 | 1.39 |
| Fiberglass, foil faced, 3-1/2" thick, R13, 15" wide | 1.000 | S.F. | .005 | .59 | .29 | .88 |
| 23" wide | 1.000 | S.F. | .005 | .59 | .29 | .88 |
| 6" thick, R19, 15" thick | 1.000 | S.F. | .005 | .85 | .24 | 1.09 |
| 23" wide | 1.000 | S.F. | .005 | .85 | .24 | 1.09 |
| 9" thick, R30, 15" wide | 1.000 | S.F. | .006 | .98 | .29 | 1.27 |
| 23" wide | 1.000 | S.F. | .006 | .98 | .29 | 1.27 |

| Insulation Systems | QUAN. | UNIT | LABOR HOURS | COST PER S.F. | | |
|---|---|---|---|---|---|---|
| | | | | MAT. | INST. | TOTAL |
| Non-rigid insulation batts | | | | | | |
|   Fiberglass unfaced, 3-1/2″ thick, R13, 15″ wide | 1.000 | S.F. | .005 | .33 | .24 | .57 |
|     23″ wide | 1.000 | S.F. | .005 | .33 | .24 | .57 |
|   6″ thick, R19, 15″ wide | 1.000 | S.F. | .006 | .50 | .29 | .79 |
|     23″ wide | 1.000 | S.F. | .006 | .50 | .29 | .79 |
|   9″ thick, R19, 15″ wide | 1.000 | S.F. | .007 | .70 | .34 | 1.04 |
|     23″ wide | 1.000 | S.F. | .007 | .70 | .34 | 1.04 |
|   12″ thick, R38, 15″ wide | 1.000 | S.F. | .007 | .89 | .34 | 1.23 |
|     23″ wide | 1.000 | S.F. | .007 | .89 | .34 | 1.23 |
| | | | | | | |
|   Mineral fiber batts, 3″ thick, R11 | 1.000 | S.F. | .005 | .42 | .24 | .66 |
|     3-1/2″ thick, R13 | 1.000 | S.F. | .005 | .42 | .24 | .66 |
|     6″ thick, R19 | 1.000 | S.F. | .005 | .53 | .24 | .77 |
|     6-1/2″ thick, R22 | 1.000 | S.F. | .005 | .53 | .24 | .77 |
|     10″ thick, R30 | 1.000 | S.F. | .006 | .80 | .29 | 1.09 |

Drip Cap — Snap-in Grille

Caulking

Interior Trim

Window

| System Description | QUAN. | UNIT | LABOR HOURS | COST EACH | | |
|---|---|---|---|---|---|---|
| | | | | MAT. | INST. | TOTAL |
| **BUILDER'S QUALITY WOOD WINDOW 2′ X 3′, DOUBLE HUNG** | | | | | | |
| Window, primed, builder's quality, 2′ x 3′, insulating glass | 1.000 | Ea. | .800 | 229 | 39 | 268 |
| Trim, interior casing | 11.000 | L.F. | .367 | 16.06 | 17.93 | 33.99 |
| Paint, interior & exterior, primer & 2 coats | 2.000 | Face | 1.778 | 2.14 | 75 | 77.14 |
| Caulking | 10.000 | L.F. | .278 | 1.70 | 13.40 | 15.10 |
| Snap-in grille | 1.000 | Set | .333 | 53 | 16.30 | 69.30 |
| Drip cap, metal | 2.000 | L.F. | .040 | .84 | 1.96 | 2.80 |
| TOTAL | | Ea. | 3.596 | 302.74 | 163.59 | 466.33 |
| **PLASTIC CLAD WOOD WINDOW 3′ X 4′, DOUBLE HUNG** | | | | | | |
| Window, plastic clad, premium, 3′ x 4′, insulating glass | 1.000 | Ea. | .889 | 405 | 43.50 | 448.50 |
| Trim, interior casing | 15.000 | L.F. | .500 | 21.90 | 24.45 | 46.35 |
| Paint, interior, primer & 2 coats | 1.000 | Face | .889 | 1.07 | 37.50 | 38.57 |
| Caulking | 14.000 | L.F. | .389 | 2.38 | 18.76 | 21.14 |
| Snap-in grille | 1.000 | Set | .333 | 53 | 16.30 | 69.30 |
| TOTAL | | Ea. | 3.000 | 483.35 | 140.51 | 623.86 |
| **METAL CLAD WOOD WINDOW, 3′ X 5′, DOUBLE HUNG** | | | | | | |
| Window, metal clad, deluxe, 3′ x 5′, insulating glass | 1.000 | Ea. | 1.000 | 400 | 49 | 449 |
| Trim, interior casing | 17.000 | L.F. | .567 | 24.82 | 27.71 | 52.53 |
| Paint, interior, primer & 2 coats | 1.000 | Face | .889 | 1.07 | 37.50 | 38.57 |
| Caulking | 16.000 | L.F. | .444 | 2.72 | 21.44 | 24.16 |
| Snap-in grille | 1.000 | Set | .235 | 141 | 11.50 | 152.50 |
| Drip cap, metal | 3.000 | L.F. | .060 | 1.26 | 2.94 | 4.20 |
| TOTAL | | Ea. | 3.195 | 570.87 | 150.09 | 720.96 |

The cost of this system is on a cost per each window basis.

| Description | QUAN. | UNIT | LABOR HOURS | COST EACH | | |
|---|---|---|---|---|---|---|
| | | | | MAT. | INST. | TOTAL |
| | | | | | | |
| | | | | | | |
| | | | | | | |
| | | | | | | |
| | | | | | | |

| Double Hung Window Price Sheet | QUAN. | UNIT | LABOR HOURS | COST EACH | | |
|---|---|---|---|---|---|---|
| | | | | MAT. | INST. | TOTAL |
| Windows, double-hung, builder's quality, 2' x 3', single glass | 1.000 | Ea. | .800 | 202 | 39 | 241 |
| Insulating glass | 1.000 | Ea. | .800 | 229 | 39 | 268 |
| 3' x 4', single glass | 1.000 | Ea. | .889 | 283 | 43.50 | 326.50 |
| Insulating glass | 1.000 | Ea. | .889 | 305 | 43.50 | 348.50 |
| 4' x 4'-6", single glass | 1.000 | Ea. | 1.000 | 345 | 49 | 394 |
| Insulating glass | 1.000 | Ea. | 1.000 | 375 | 49 | 424 |
| Plastic clad premium insulating glass, 2'-6" x 3' | 1.000 | Ea. | .800 | 248 | 39 | 287 |
| 3' x 3'-6" | 1.000 | Ea. | .800 | 287 | 39 | 326 |
| 3' x 4' | 1.000 | Ea. | .889 | 405 | 43.50 | 448.50 |
| 3' x 4'-6" | 1.000 | Ea. | .889 | 370 | 43.50 | 413.50 |
| 3' x 5' | 1.000 | Ea. | 1.000 | 345 | 49 | 394 |
| 3'-6" x 6' | 1.000 | Ea. | 1.000 | 405 | 49 | 454 |
| Metal clad deluxe insulating glass, 2'-6" x 3' | 1.000 | Ea. | .800 | 292 | 39 | 331 |
| 3' x 3'-6" | 1.000 | Ea. | .800 | 335 | 39 | 374 |
| 3' x 4' | 1.000 | Ea. | .889 | 350 | 43.50 | 393.50 |
| 3' x 4'-6" | 1.000 | Ea. | .889 | 370 | 43.50 | 413.50 |
| 3' x 5' | 1.000 | Ea. | 1.000 | 400 | 49 | 449 |
| 3'-6" x 6' | 1.000 | Ea. | 1.000 | 480 | 49 | 529 |
| Trim, interior casing, window 2' x 3' | 11.000 | L.F. | .367 | 16.05 | 17.95 | 34 |
| 2'-6" x 3' | 12.000 | L.F. | .400 | 17.50 | 19.55 | 37.05 |
| 3' x 3'-6" | 14.000 | L.F. | .467 | 20.50 | 23 | 43.50 |
| 3' x 4' | 15.000 | L.F. | .500 | 22 | 24.50 | 46.50 |
| 3' x 4'-6" | 16.000 | L.F. | .533 | 23.50 | 26 | 49.50 |
| 3' x 5' | 17.000 | L.F. | .567 | 25 | 27.50 | 52.50 |
| 3'-6" x 6' | 20.000 | L.F. | .667 | 29 | 32.50 | 61.50 |
| 4' x 4'-6" | 18.000 | L.F. | .600 | 26.50 | 29.50 | 56 |
| Paint or stain, interior or exterior, 2' x 3' window, 1 coat | 1.000 | Face | .444 | .35 | 18.65 | 19 |
| 2 coats | 1.000 | Face | .727 | .70 | 30.50 | 31.20 |
| Primer & 1 coat | 1.000 | Face | .727 | .73 | 30.50 | 31.23 |
| Primer & 2 coats | 1.000 | Face | .889 | 1.07 | 37.50 | 38.57 |
| 3' x 4' window, 1 coat | 1.000 | Face | .667 | 1.18 | 28 | 29.18 |
| 2 coats | 1.000 | Face | .667 | 1.75 | 28 | 29.75 |
| Primer & 1 coat | 1.000 | Face | .727 | 1.09 | 30.50 | 31.59 |
| Primer & 2 coats | 1.000 | Face | .889 | 1.07 | 37.50 | 38.57 |
| 4' x 4'-6" window, 1 coat | 1.000 | Face | .667 | 1.18 | 28 | 29.18 |
| 2 coats | 1.000 | Face | .667 | 1.75 | 28 | 29.75 |
| Primer & 1 coat | 1.000 | Face | .727 | 1.09 | 30.50 | 31.59 |
| Primer & 2 coats | 1.000 | Face | .889 | 1.07 | 37.50 | 38.57 |
| Caulking, window, 2' x 3' | 10.000 | L.F. | .323 | 1.70 | 13.40 | 15.10 |
| 2'-6" x 3' | 11.000 | L.F. | .355 | 1.87 | 14.75 | 16.62 |
| 3' x 3'-6" | 13.000 | L.F. | .419 | 2.21 | 17.40 | 19.61 |
| 3' x 4' | 14.000 | L.F. | .452 | 2.38 | 18.75 | 21.13 |
| 3' x 4'-6" | 15.000 | L.F. | .484 | 2.55 | 20 | 22.55 |
| 3' x 5' | 16.000 | L.F. | .516 | 2.72 | 21.50 | 24.22 |
| 3'-6" x 6' | 19.000 | L.F. | .613 | 3.23 | 25.50 | 28.73 |
| 4' x 4'-6" | 17.000 | L.F. | .548 | 2.89 | 23 | 25.89 |
| Grilles, glass size to, 16" x 24" per sash | 1.000 | Set | .333 | 53 | 16.30 | 69.30 |
| 32" x 32" per sash | 1.000 | Set | .235 | 141 | 11.50 | 152.50 |
| Drip cap, aluminum, 2' long | 2.000 | L.F. | .040 | .84 | 1.96 | 2.80 |
| 3' long | 3.000 | L.F. | .060 | 1.26 | 2.94 | 4.20 |
| 4' long | 4.000 | L.F. | .080 | 1.68 | 3.92 | 5.60 |
| Wood, 2' long | 2.000 | L.F. | .067 | 2.92 | 3.26 | 6.18 |
| 3' long | 3.000 | L.F. | .100 | 4.38 | 4.89 | 9.27 |
| 4' long | 4.000 | L.F. | .133 | 5.85 | 6.50 | 12.35 |
| | | | | | | |
| | | | | | | |
| | | | | | | |
| | | | | | | |

| System Description | QUAN. | UNIT | LABOR HOURS | COST EACH | | |
|---|---|---|---|---|---|---|
| | | | | MAT. | INST. | TOTAL |
| **BUILDER'S QUALITY WINDOW, WOOD, 2′ BY 3′, CASEMENT** | | | | | | |
| Window, primed, builder's quality, 2′ x 3′, insulating glass | 1.000 | Ea. | .800 | 248 | 39 | 287 |
| Trim, interior casing | 11.000 | L.F. | .367 | 16.06 | 17.93 | 33.99 |
| Paint, interior & exterior, primer & 2 coats | 2.000 | Face | 1.778 | 2.14 | 75 | 77.14 |
| Caulking | 10.000 | L.F. | .278 | 1.70 | 13.40 | 15.10 |
| Snap-in grille | 1.000 | Ea. | .267 | 31.50 | 13.05 | 44.55 |
| Drip cap, metal | 2.000 | L.F. | .040 | .84 | 1.96 | 2.80 |
| TOTAL | | Ea. | 3.530 | 300.24 | 160.34 | 460.58 |
| **PLASTIC CLAD WOOD WINDOW, 2′ X 4′, CASEMENT** | | | | | | |
| Window, plastic clad, premium, 2′ x 4′, insulating glass | 1.000 | Ea. | .889 | 340 | 43.50 | 383.50 |
| Trim, interior casing | 13.000 | L.F. | .433 | 18.98 | 21.19 | 40.17 |
| Paint, interior, primer & 2 coats | 1.000 | Ea. | .889 | 1.07 | 37.50 | 38.57 |
| Caulking | 12.000 | L.F. | .333 | 2.04 | 16.08 | 18.12 |
| Snap-in grille | 1.000 | Ea. | .267 | 31.50 | 13.05 | 44.55 |
| TOTAL | | Ea. | 2.811 | 393.59 | 131.32 | 524.91 |
| **METAL CLAD WOOD WINDOW, 2′ X 5′, CASEMENT** | | | | | | |
| Window, metal clad, deluxe, 2′ x 5′, insulating glass | 1.000 | Ea. | 1.000 | 350 | 49 | 399 |
| Trim, interior casing | 15.000 | L.F. | .500 | 21.90 | 24.45 | 46.35 |
| Paint, interior, primer & 2 coats | 1.000 | Ea. | .889 | 1.07 | 37.50 | 38.57 |
| Caulking | 14.000 | L.F. | .389 | 2.38 | 18.76 | 21.14 |
| Snap-in grille | 1.000 | Ea. | .250 | 44 | 12.25 | 56.25 |
| Drip cap, metal | 12.000 | L.F. | .040 | .84 | 1.96 | 2.80 |
| TOTAL | | Ea. | 3.068 | 420.19 | 143.92 | 564.11 |

The cost of this system is on a cost per each window basis.

| Description | QUAN. | UNIT | LABOR HOURS | COST EACH | | |
|---|---|---|---|---|---|---|
| | | | | MAT. | INST. | TOTAL |
| | | | | | | |
| | | | | | | |
| | | | | | | |
| | | | | | | |
| | | | | | | |

| Casement Window Price Sheet | QUAN. | UNIT | LABOR HOURS | COST EACH | | |
|---|---|---|---|---|---|---|
| | | | | MAT. | INST. | TOTAL |
| Window, casement, builders quality, 2' x 3', single glass | 1.000 | Ea. | .800 | 305 | 39 | 344 |
| Insulating glass | 1.000 | Ea. | .800 | 248 | 39 | 287 |
| 2' x 4'-6", single glass | 1.000 | Ea. | .727 | 940 | 35.50 | 975.50 |
| Insulating glass | 1.000 | Ea. | .727 | 515 | 35.50 | 550.50 |
| 2' x 6', single glass | 1.000 | Ea. | .889 | 390 | 49 | 439 |
| Insulating glass | 1.000 | Ea. | .889 | 1,200 | 43.50 | 1,243.50 |
| Plastic clad premium insulating glass, 2' x 3' | 1.000 | Ea. | .800 | 277 | 39 | 316 |
| 2' x 4' | 1.000 | Ea. | .889 | 430 | 43.50 | 473.50 |
| 2' x 5' | 1.000 | Ea. | 1.000 | 580 | 49 | 629 |
| 2' x 6' | 1.000 | Ea. | 1.000 | 390 | 49 | 439 |
| Metal clad deluxe insulating glass, 2' x 3' | 1.000 | Ea. | .800 | 299 | 39 | 338 |
| 2' x 4' | 1.000 | Ea. | .889 | 299 | 43.50 | 342.50 |
| 2' x 5' | 1.000 | Ea. | 1.000 | 340 | 49 | 389 |
| 2' x 6' | 1.000 | Ea. | 1.000 | 390 | 49 | 439 |
| Trim, interior casing, window 2' x 3' | 11.000 | L.F. | .367 | 16.05 | 17.95 | 34 |
| 2' x 4' | 13.000 | L.F. | .433 | 19 | 21 | 40 |
| 2' x 4'-6" | 14.000 | L.F. | .467 | 20.50 | 23 | 43.50 |
| 2' x 5' | 15.000 | L.F. | .500 | 22 | 24.50 | 46.50 |
| 2' x 6' | 17.000 | L.F. | .567 | 25 | 27.50 | 52.50 |
| | | | | | | |
| Paint or stain, interior or exterior, 2' x 3' window, 1 coat | 1.000 | Face | .444 | .35 | 18.65 | 19 |
| 2 coats | 1.000 | Face | .727 | .70 | 30.50 | 31.20 |
| Primer & 1 coat | 1.000 | Face | .727 | .73 | 30.50 | 31.23 |
| Primer & 2 coats | 1.000 | Face | .889 | 1.07 | 37.50 | 38.57 |
| 2' x 4' window, 1 coat | 1.000 | Face | .444 | .35 | 18.65 | 19 |
| 2 coats | 1.000 | Face | .727 | .70 | 30.50 | 31.20 |
| Primer & 1 coat | 1.000 | Face | .727 | .73 | 30.50 | 31.23 |
| Primer & 2 coats | 1.000 | Face | .889 | 1.07 | 37.50 | 38.57 |
| 2' x 6' window, 1 coat | 1.000 | Face | .667 | 1.18 | 28 | 29.18 |
| 2 coats | 1.000 | Face | .667 | 1.75 | 28 | 29.75 |
| Primer & 1 coat | 1.000 | Face | .727 | 1.09 | 30.50 | 31.59 |
| Primer & 2 coats | 1.000 | Face | .889 | 1.07 | 37.50 | 38.57 |
| Caulking, window, 2' x 3' | 10.000 | L.F. | .323 | 1.70 | 13.40 | 15.10 |
| 2' x 4' | 12.000 | L.F. | .387 | 2.04 | 16.10 | 18.14 |
| 2' x 4'-6" | 13.000 | L.F. | .419 | 2.21 | 17.40 | 19.61 |
| 2' x 5' | 14.000 | L.F. | .452 | 2.38 | 18.75 | 21.13 |
| 2' x 6' | 16.000 | L.F. | .516 | 2.72 | 21.50 | 24.22 |
| | | | | | | |
| Grilles, glass size, to 20" x 36" | 1.000 | Ea. | .267 | 31.50 | 13.05 | 44.55 |
| To 20" x 56" | 1.000 | Ea. | .250 | 44 | 12.25 | 56.25 |
| Drip cap, metal, 2' long | 2.000 | L.F. | .040 | .84 | 1.96 | 2.80 |
| Wood, 2' long | 2.000 | L.F. | .067 | 2.92 | 3.26 | 6.18 |
| | | | | | | |
| | | | | | | |
| | | | | | | |
| | | | | | | |
| | | | | | | |
| | | | | | | |
| | | | | | | |
| | | | | | | |
| | | | | | | |

| System Description | QUAN. | UNIT | LABOR HOURS | COST EACH | | |
|---|---|---|---|---|---|---|
| | | | | MAT. | INST. | TOTAL |
| **BUILDER'S QUALITY WINDOW, WOOD, 34" X 22", AWNING** | | | | | | |
| Window, builder quality, 34" x 22", insulating glass | 1.000 | Ea. | .800 | 282 | 39 | 321 |
| Trim, interior casing | 10.500 | L.F. | .350 | 15.33 | 17.12 | 32.45 |
| Paint, interior & exterior, primer & 2 coats | 2.000 | Face | 1.778 | 2.14 | 75 | 77.14 |
| Caulking | 9.500 | L.F. | .264 | 1.62 | 12.73 | 14.35 |
| Snap-in grille | 1.000 | Ea. | .267 | 26.50 | 13.05 | 39.55 |
| Drip cap, metal | 3.000 | L.F. | .060 | 1.26 | 2.94 | 4.20 |
| | | | | | | |
| TOTAL | | Ea. | 3.519 | 328.85 | 159.84 | 488.69 |
| **PLASTIC CLAD WOOD WINDOW, 40" X 28", AWNING** | | | | | | |
| Window, plastic clad, premium, 40" x 28", insulating glass | 1.000 | Ea. | .889 | 370 | 43.50 | 413.50 |
| Trim interior casing | 13.500 | L.F. | .450 | 19.71 | 22.01 | 41.72 |
| Paint, interior, primer & 2 coats | 1.000 | Face | .889 | 1.07 | 37.50 | 38.57 |
| Caulking | 12.500 | L.F. | .347 | 2.13 | 16.75 | 18.88 |
| Snap-in grille | 1.000 | Ea. | .267 | 26.50 | 13.05 | 39.55 |
| | | | | | | |
| TOTAL | | Ea. | 2.842 | 419.41 | 132.81 | 552.22 |
| **METAL CLAD WOOD WINDOW, 48" X 36", AWNING** | | | | | | |
| Window, metal clad, deluxe, 48" x 36", insulating glass | 1.000 | Ea. | 1.000 | 405 | 49 | 454 |
| Trim, interior casing | 15.000 | L.F. | .500 | 21.90 | 24.45 | 46.35 |
| Paint, interior, primer & 2 coats | 1.000 | Face | .889 | 1.07 | 37.50 | 38.57 |
| Caulking | 14.000 | L.F. | .389 | 2.38 | 18.76 | 21.14 |
| Snap-in grille | 1.000 | Ea. | .250 | 39.50 | 12.25 | 51.75 |
| Drip cap, metal | 4.000 | L.F. | .080 | 1.68 | 3.92 | 5.60 |
| | | | | | | |
| TOTAL | | Ea. | 3.108 | 471.53 | 145.88 | 617.41 |

The cost of this system is on a cost per each window basis.

| Description | QUAN. | UNIT | LABOR HOURS | COST EACH | | |
|---|---|---|---|---|---|---|
| | | | | MAT. | INST. | TOTAL |
| | | | | | | |
| | | | | | | |
| | | | | | | |
| | | | | | | |
| | | | | | | |

| Awning Window Price Sheet | QUAN. | UNIT | LABOR HOURS | COST EACH | | |
|---|---|---|---|---|---|---|
| | | | | MAT. | INST. | TOTAL |
| Windows, awning, builder's quality, 34″ x 22″, insulated glass | 1.000 | Ea. | .800 | 278 | 39 | 317 |
| Low E glass | 1.000 | Ea. | .800 | 282 | 39 | 321 |
| 40″ x 28″, insulated glass | 1.000 | Ea. | .889 | 340 | 43.50 | 383.50 |
| Low E glass | 1.000 | Ea. | .889 | 365 | 43.50 | 408.50 |
| 48″ x 36″, insulated glass | 1.000 | Ea. | 1.000 | 495 | 49 | 544 |
| Low E glass | 1.000 | Ea. | 1.000 | 520 | 49 | 569 |
| Plastic clad premium insulating glass, 34″ x 22″ | 1.000 | Ea. | .800 | 285 | 39 | 324 |
| 40″ x 22″ | 1.000 | Ea. | .800 | 310 | 39 | 349 |
| 36″ x 28″ | 1.000 | Ea. | .889 | 330 | 43.50 | 373.50 |
| 36″ x 36″ | 1.000 | Ea. | .889 | 370 | 43.50 | 413.50 |
| 48″ x 28″ | 1.000 | Ea. | 1.000 | 400 | 49 | 449 |
| 60″ x 36″ | 1.000 | Ea. | 1.000 | 555 | 49 | 604 |
| Metal clad deluxe insulating glass, 34″ x 22″ | 1.000 | Ea. | .800 | 266 | 39 | 305 |
| 40″ x 22″ | 1.000 | Ea. | .800 | 315 | 39 | 354 |
| 36″ x 25″ | 1.000 | Ea. | .889 | 296 | 43.50 | 339.50 |
| 40″ x 30″ | 1.000 | Ea. | .889 | 370 | 43.50 | 413.50 |
| 48″ x 28″ | 1.000 | Ea. | 1.000 | 380 | 49 | 429 |
| 60″ x 36″ | 1.000 | Ea. | 1.000 | 405 | 49 | 454 |
| Trim, interior casing window, 34″ x 22″ | 10.500 | L.F. | .350 | 15.35 | 17.10 | 32.45 |
| 40″ x 22″ | 11.500 | L.F. | .383 | 16.80 | 18.75 | 35.55 |
| 36″ x 28″ | 12.500 | L.F. | .417 | 18.25 | 20.50 | 38.75 |
| 40″ x 28″ | 13.500 | L.F. | .450 | 19.70 | 22 | 41.70 |
| 48″ x 28″ | 14.500 | L.F. | .483 | 21 | 23.50 | 44.50 |
| 48″ x 36″ | 15.000 | L.F. | .500 | 22 | 24.50 | 46.50 |
| Paint or stain, interior or exterior, 34″ x 22″, 1 coat | 1.000 | Face | .444 | .35 | 18.65 | 19 |
| 2 coats | 1.000 | Face | .727 | .70 | 30.50 | 31.20 |
| Primer & 1 coat | 1.000 | Face | .727 | .73 | 30.50 | 31.23 |
| Primer & 2 coats | 1.000 | Face | .889 | 1.07 | 37.50 | 38.57 |
| 36″ x 28″, 1 coat | 1.000 | Face | .444 | .35 | 18.65 | 19 |
| 2 coats | 1.000 | Face | .727 | .70 | 30.50 | 31.20 |
| Primer & 1 coat | 1.000 | Face | .727 | .73 | 30.50 | 31.23 |
| Primer & 2 coats | 1.000 | Face | .889 | 1.07 | 37.50 | 38.57 |
| 48″ x 36″, 1 coat | 1.000 | Face | .667 | 1.18 | 28 | 29.18 |
| 2 coats | 1.000 | Face | .667 | 1.75 | 28 | 29.75 |
| Primer & 1 coat | 1.000 | Face | .727 | 1.09 | 30.50 | 31.59 |
| Primer & 2 coats | 1.000 | Face | .889 | 1.07 | 37.50 | 38.57 |
| Caulking, window, 34″ x 22″ | 9.500 | L.F. | .306 | 1.62 | 12.75 | 14.37 |
| 40″ x 22″ | 10.500 | L.F. | .339 | 1.79 | 14.05 | 15.84 |
| 36″ x 28″ | 11.500 | L.F. | .371 | 1.96 | 15.40 | 17.36 |
| 40″ x 28″ | 12.500 | L.F. | .403 | 2.13 | 16.75 | 18.88 |
| 48″ x 28″ | 13.500 | L.F. | .436 | 2.30 | 18.10 | 20.40 |
| 48″ x 36″ | 14.000 | L.F. | .452 | 2.38 | 18.75 | 21.13 |
| Grilles, glass size, to 28″ by 16″ | 1.000 | Ea. | .267 | 26.50 | 13.05 | 39.55 |
| To 44″ by 24″ | 1.000 | Ea. | .250 | 39.50 | 12.25 | 51.75 |
| Drip cap, aluminum, 3′ long | 3.000 | L.F. | .060 | 1.26 | 2.94 | 4.20 |
| 3′-6″ long | 3.500 | L.F. | .070 | 1.47 | 3.43 | 4.90 |
| 4′ long | 4.000 | L.F. | .080 | 1.68 | 3.92 | 5.60 |
| Wood, 3′ long | 3.000 | L.F. | .100 | 4.38 | 4.89 | 9.27 |
| 3′-6″ long | 3.500 | L.F. | .117 | 5.10 | 5.70 | 10.80 |
| 4′ long | 4.000 | L.F. | .133 | 5.85 | 6.50 | 12.35 |
| | | | | | | |
| | | | | | | |
| | | | | | | |
| | | | | | | |
| | | | | | | |

| System Description | QUAN. | UNIT | LABOR HOURS | COST EACH | | |
|---|---|---|---|---|---|---|
| | | | | MAT. | INST. | TOTAL |
| **BUILDER'S QUALITY WOOD WINDOW, 3′ X 2′, SLIDING** | | | | | | |
| Window, primed, builder's quality, 3′ x 3′, insul. glass | 1.000 | Ea. | .800 | 320 | 39 | 359 |
| Trim, interior casing | 11.000 | L.F. | .367 | 16.06 | 17.93 | 33.99 |
| Paint, interior & exterior, primer & 2 coats | 2.000 | Face | 1.778 | 2.14 | 75 | 77.14 |
| Caulking | 10.000 | L.F. | .278 | 1.70 | 13.40 | 15.10 |
| Snap-in grille | 1.000 | Set | .333 | 29 | 16.30 | 45.30 |
| Drip cap, metal | 3.000 | L.F. | .060 | 1.26 | 2.94 | 4.20 |
| TOTAL | | Ea. | 3.616 | 370.16 | 164.57 | 534.73 |
| **PLASTIC CLAD WOOD WINDOW, 4′ X 3′-6″, SLIDING** | | | | | | |
| Window, plastic clad, premium, 4′ x 3′-6″, insulating glass | 1.000 | Ea. | .889 | 735 | 43.50 | 778.50 |
| Trim, interior casing | 16.000 | L.F. | .533 | 23.36 | 26.08 | 49.44 |
| Paint, interior, primer & 2 coats | 1.000 | Face | .889 | 1.07 | 37.50 | 38.57 |
| Caulking | 17.000 | L.F. | .472 | 2.89 | 22.78 | 25.67 |
| Snap-in grille | 1.000 | Set | .333 | 29 | 16.30 | 45.30 |
| TOTAL | | Ea. | 3.116 | 791.32 | 146.16 | 937.48 |
| **METAL CLAD WOOD WINDOW, 6′ X 5′, SLIDING** | | | | | | |
| Window, metal clad, deluxe, 6′ x 5′, insulating glass | 1.000 | Ea. | 1.000 | 775 | 49 | 824 |
| Trim, interior casing | 23.000 | L.F. | .767 | 33.58 | 37.49 | 71.07 |
| Paint, interior, primer & 2 coats | 1.000 | Face | .889 | 1.07 | 37.50 | 38.57 |
| Caulking | 22.000 | L.F. | .611 | 3.74 | 29.48 | 33.22 |
| Snap-in grille | 1.000 | Set | .364 | 43 | 17.80 | 60.80 |
| Drip cap, metal | 6.000 | L.F. | .120 | 2.52 | 5.88 | 8.40 |
| TOTAL | | Ea. | 3.751 | 858.91 | 177.15 | 1,036.06 |

The cost of this system is on a cost per each window basis.

| Description | QUAN. | UNIT | LABOR HOURS | COST EACH | | |
|---|---|---|---|---|---|---|
| | | | | MAT. | INST. | TOTAL |
| | | | | | | |
| | | | | | | |
| | | | | | | |
| | | | | | | |
| | | | | | | |

| Sliding Window Price Sheet | QUAN. | UNIT | LABOR HOURS | COST EACH | | |
|---|---|---|---|---|---|---|
| | | | | MAT. | INST. | TOTAL |
| Windows, sliding, builder's quality, 3' x 3', single glass | 1.000 | Ea. | .800 | 299 | 39 | 338 |
| Insulating glass | 1.000 | Ea. | .800 | 320 | 39 | 359 |
| 4' x 3'-6", single glass | 1.000 | Ea. | .889 | 360 | 43.50 | 403.50 |
| Insulating glass | 1.000 | Ea. | .889 | 385 | 43.50 | 428.50 |
| 6' x 5', single glass | 1.000 | Ea. | 1.000 | 510 | 49 | 559 |
| Insulating glass | 1.000 | Ea. | 1.000 | 550 | 49 | 599 |
| Plastic clad premium insulating glass, 3' x 3' | 1.000 | Ea. | .800 | 630 | 39 | 669 |
| 4' x 3'-6" | 1.000 | Ea. | .889 | 735 | 43.50 | 778.50 |
| 5' x 4' | 1.000 | Ea. | .889 | 945 | 43.50 | 988.50 |
| 6' x 5' | 1.000 | Ea. | 1.000 | 1,200 | 49 | 1,249 |
| Metal clad deluxe insulating glass, 3' x 3' | 1.000 | Ea. | .800 | 360 | 39 | 399 |
| 4' x 3'-6" | 1.000 | Ea. | .889 | 440 | 43.50 | 483.50 |
| 5' x 4' | 1.000 | Ea. | .889 | 525 | 43.50 | 568.50 |
| 6' x 5' | 1.000 | Ea. | 1.000 | 775 | 49 | 824 |
| Trim, interior casing, window 3' x 2' | 11.000 | L.F. | .367 | 16.05 | 17.95 | 34 |
| 3' x 3' | 13.000 | L.F. | .433 | 19 | 21 | 40 |
| 4' x 3'-6" | 16.000 | L.F. | .533 | 23.50 | 26 | 49.50 |
| 5' x 4' | 19.000 | L.F. | .633 | 27.50 | 31 | 58.50 |
| 6' x 5' | 23.000 | L.F. | .767 | 33.50 | 37.50 | 71 |
| | | | | | | |
| Paint or stain, interior or exterior, 3' x 2' window, 1 coat | 1.000 | Face | .444 | .35 | 18.65 | 19 |
| 2 coats | 1.000 | Face | .727 | .70 | 30.50 | 31.20 |
| Primer & 1 coat | 1.000 | Face | .727 | .73 | 30.50 | 31.23 |
| Primer & 2 coats | 1.000 | Face | .889 | 1.07 | 37.50 | 38.57 |
| 4' x 3'-6" window, 1 coat | 1.000 | Face | .667 | 1.18 | 28 | 29.18 |
| 2 coats | 1.000 | Face | .667 | 1.75 | 28 | 29.75 |
| Primer & 1 coat | 1.000 | Face | .727 | 1.09 | 30.50 | 31.59 |
| Primer & 2 coats | 1.000 | Face | .889 | 1.07 | 37.50 | 38.57 |
| 6' x 5' window, 1 coat | 1.000 | Face | .889 | 1.99 | 37.50 | 39.49 |
| 2 coats | 1.000 | Face | 1.333 | 3.63 | 56 | 59.63 |
| Primer & 1 coat | 1.000 | Face | 1.333 | 3.88 | 56 | 59.88 |
| Primer & 2 coats | 1.000 | Face | 1.600 | 5.70 | 67 | 72.70 |
| Caulking, window, 3' x 2' | 10.000 | L.F. | .323 | 1.70 | 13.40 | 15.10 |
| 3' x 3' | 12.000 | L.F. | .387 | 2.04 | 16.10 | 18.14 |
| 4' x 3'-6" | 15.000 | L.F. | .484 | 2.55 | 20 | 22.55 |
| 5' x 4' | 18.000 | L.F. | .581 | 3.06 | 24 | 27.06 |
| 6' x 5' | 22.000 | L.F. | .710 | 3.74 | 29.50 | 33.24 |
| | | | | | | |
| Grilles, glass size, to 14" x 36" | 1.000 | Set | .333 | 29 | 16.30 | 45.30 |
| To 36" x 36" | 1.000 | Set | .364 | 43 | 17.80 | 60.80 |
| Drip cap, aluminum, 3' long | 3.000 | L.F. | .060 | 1.26 | 2.94 | 4.20 |
| 4' long | 4.000 | L.F. | .080 | 1.68 | 3.92 | 5.60 |
| 5' long | 5.000 | L.F. | .100 | 2.10 | 4.90 | 7 |
| 6' long | 6.000 | L.F. | .120 | 2.52 | 5.90 | 8.42 |
| Wood, 3' long | 3.000 | L.F. | .100 | 4.38 | 4.89 | 9.27 |
| 4' long | 4.000 | L.F. | .133 | 5.85 | 6.50 | 12.35 |
| 5' long | 5.000 | L.F. | .167 | 7.30 | 8.15 | 15.45 |
| 6' long | 6.000 | L.F. | .200 | 8.75 | 9.80 | 18.55 |
| | | | | | | |
| | | | | | | |
| | | | | | | |
| | | | | | | |
| | | | | | | |
| | | | | | | |

| System Description | QUAN. | UNIT | LABOR HOURS | COST EACH | | |
|---|---|---|---|---|---|---|
| | | | | MAT. | INST. | TOTAL |
| **AWNING TYPE BOW WINDOW, BUILDER'S QUALITY, 8′ X 5′** | | | | | | |
| Window, primed, builder's quality, 8′ x 5′, insulating glass | 1.000 | Ea. | 1.600 | 1,450 | 78.50 | 1,528.50 |
| Trim, interior casing | 27.000 | L.F. | .900 | 39.42 | 44.01 | 83.43 |
| Paint, interior & exterior, primer & 1 coat | 2.000 | Face | 3.200 | 11.40 | 134 | 145.40 |
| Drip cap, vinyl | 1.000 | Ea. | .533 | 110 | 26 | 136 |
| Caulking | 26.000 | L.F. | .722 | 4.42 | 34.84 | 39.26 |
| Snap-in grilles | 1.000 | Set | 1.067 | 126 | 52.20 | 178.20 |
| | | | | | | |
| TOTAL | | Ea. | 8.022 | 1,741.24 | 369.55 | 2,110.79 |
| **CASEMENT TYPE BOW WINDOW, PLASTIC CLAD, 10′ X 6′** | | | | | | |
| Window, plastic clad, premium, 10′ x 6′, insulating glass | 1.000 | Ea. | 2.286 | 2,775 | 112 | 2,887 |
| Trim, interior casing | 33.000 | L.F. | 1.100 | 48.18 | 53.79 | 101.97 |
| Paint, interior, primer & 1 coat | 1.000 | Face | 1.778 | 2.14 | 75 | 77.14 |
| Drip cap, vinyl | 1.000 | Ea. | .615 | 121 | 30 | 151 |
| Caulking | 32.000 | L.F. | .889 | 5.44 | 42.88 | 48.32 |
| Snap-in grilles | 1.000 | Set | 1.333 | 157.50 | 65.25 | 222.75 |
| | | | | | | |
| TOTAL | | Ea. | 8.001 | 3,109.26 | 378.92 | 3,488.18 |
| **DOUBLE HUNG TYPE, METAL CLAD, 9′ X 5′** | | | | | | |
| Window, metal clad, deluxe, 9′ x 5′, insulating glass | 1.000 | Ea. | 2.667 | 1,550 | 131 | 1,681 |
| Trim, interior casing | 29.000 | L.F. | .967 | 42.34 | 47.27 | 89.61 |
| Paint, interior, primer & 1 coat | 1.000 | Face | 1.778 | 2.14 | 75 | 77.14 |
| Drip cap, vinyl | 1.000 | Set | .615 | 121 | 30 | 151 |
| Caulking | 28.000 | L.F. | .778 | 4.76 | 37.52 | 42.28 |
| Snap-in grilles | 1.000 | Set | 1.067 | 126 | 52.20 | 178.20 |
| | | | | | | |
| TOTAL | | Ea. | 7.872 | 1,846.24 | 372.99 | 2,219.23 |

The cost of this system is on a cost per each window basis.

| Description | QUAN. | UNIT | LABOR HOURS | COST EACH | | |
|---|---|---|---|---|---|---|
| | | | | MAT. | INST. | TOTAL |
| | | | | | | |
| | | | | | | |
| | | | | | | |
| | | | | | | |
| | | | | | | |

| Bow/Bay Window Price Sheet | QUAN. | UNIT | LABOR HOURS | COST EACH | | |
|---|---|---|---|---|---|---|
| | | | | MAT. | INST. | TOTAL |
| Windows, bow awning type, builder's quality, 8' x 5', insulating glass | 1.000 | Ea. | 1.600 | 1,650 | 78.50 | 1,728.50 |
| Low E glass | 1.000 | Ea. | 1.600 | 1,450 | 78.50 | 1,528.50 |
| 12' x 6', insulating glass | 1.000 | Ea. | 2.667 | 1,500 | 131 | 1,631 |
| Low E glass | 1.000 | Ea. | 2.667 | 1,600 | 131 | 1,731 |
| Plastic clad premium insulating glass, 6' x 4' | 1.000 | Ea. | 1.600 | 1,125 | 78.50 | 1,203.50 |
| 9' x 4' | 1.000 | Ea. | 2.000 | 1,500 | 98 | 1,598 |
| 10' x 5' | 1.000 | Ea. | 2.286 | 2,475 | 112 | 2,587 |
| 12' x 6' | 1.000 | Ea. | 2.667 | 3,225 | 131 | 3,356 |
| Metal clad deluxe insulating glass, 6' x 4' | 1.000 | Ea. | 1.600 | 1,000 | 78.50 | 1,078.50 |
| 9' x 4' | 1.000 | Ea. | 2.000 | 1,375 | 98 | 1,473 |
| 10' x 5' | 1.000 | Ea. | 2.286 | 1,900 | 112 | 2,012 |
| 12' x 6' | 1.000 | Ea. | 2.667 | 2,650 | 131 | 2,781 |
| Bow casement type, builder's quality, 8' x 5', single glass | 1.000 | Ea. | 1.600 | 2,025 | 78.50 | 2,103.50 |
| Insulating glass | 1.000 | Ea. | 1.600 | 2,450 | 78.50 | 2,528.50 |
| 12' x 6', single glass | 1.000 | Ea. | 2.667 | 2,525 | 131 | 2,656 |
| Insulating glass | 1.000 | Ea. | 2.667 | 2,600 | 131 | 2,731 |
| Plastic clad premium insulating glass, 8' x 5' | 1.000 | Ea. | 1.600 | 1,925 | 78.50 | 2,003.50 |
| 10' x 5' | 1.000 | Ea. | 2.000 | 2,500 | 98 | 2,598 |
| 10' x 6' | 1.000 | Ea. | 2.286 | 2,775 | 112 | 2,887 |
| 12' x 6' | 1.000 | Ea. | 2.667 | 3,525 | 131 | 3,656 |
| Metal clad deluxe insulating glass, 8' x 5' | 1.000 | Ea. | 1.600 | 1,775 | 78.50 | 1,853.50 |
| 10' x 5' | 1.000 | Ea. | 2.000 | 1,925 | 98 | 2,023 |
| 10' x 6' | 1.000 | Ea. | 2.286 | 2,275 | 112 | 2,387 |
| 12' x 6' | 1.000 | Ea. | 2.667 | 3,150 | 131 | 3,281 |
| Bow, double hung type, builder's quality, 8' x 4', single glass | 1.000 | Ea. | 1.600 | 1,425 | 78.50 | 1,503.50 |
| Insulating glass | 1.000 | Ea. | 1.600 | 1,525 | 78.50 | 1,603.50 |
| 9' x 5', single glass | 1.000 | Ea. | 2.667 | 1,525 | 131 | 1,656 |
| Insulating glass | 1.000 | Ea. | 2.667 | 1,625 | 131 | 1,756 |
| Plastic clad premium insulating glass, 7' x 4' | 1.000 | Ea. | 1.600 | 1,475 | 78.50 | 1,553.50 |
| 8' x 4' | 1.000 | Ea. | 2.000 | 1,500 | 98 | 1,598 |
| 8' x 5' | 1.000 | Ea. | 2.286 | 1,575 | 112 | 1,687 |
| 9' x 5' | 1.000 | Ea. | 2.667 | 1,625 | 131 | 1,756 |
| Metal clad deluxe insulating glass, 7' x 4' | 1.000 | Ea. | 1.600 | 1,350 | 78.50 | 1,428.50 |
| 8' x 4' | 1.000 | Ea. | 2.000 | 1,400 | 98 | 1,498 |
| 8' x 5' | 1.000 | Ea. | 2.286 | 1,450 | 112 | 1,562 |
| 9' x 5' | 1.000 | Ea. | 2.667 | 1,550 | 131 | 1,681 |
| Trim, interior casing, window 7' x 4' | 1.000 | Ea. | .767 | 33.50 | 37.50 | 71 |
| 8' x 5' | 1.000 | Ea. | .900 | 39.50 | 44 | 83.50 |
| 10' x 6' | 1.000 | Ea. | 1.100 | 48 | 54 | 102 |
| 12' x 6' | 1.000 | Ea. | 1.233 | 54 | 60.50 | 114.50 |
| Paint or stain, interior, or exterior, 7' x 4' window, 1 coat | 1.000 | Face | .889 | 1.99 | 37.50 | 39.49 |
| Primer & 1 coat | 1.000 | Face | 1.333 | 3.88 | 56 | 59.88 |
| 8' x 5' window, 1 coat | 1.000 | Face | .889 | 1.99 | 37.50 | 39.49 |
| Primer & 1 coat | 1.000 | Face | 1.333 | 3.88 | 56 | 59.88 |
| 10' x 6' window, 1 coat | 1.000 | Face | 1.333 | 2.36 | 56 | 58.36 |
| Primer & 1 coat | 1.000 | Face | 1.778 | 2.14 | 75 | 77.14 |
| 12' x 6' window, 1 coat | 1.000 | Face | 1.778 | 3.98 | 75 | 78.98 |
| Primer & 1 coat | 1.000 | Face | 2.667 | 7.75 | 112 | 119.75 |
| Drip cap, vinyl moulded window, 7' long | 1.000 | Ea. | .533 | 96.50 | 23 | 119.50 |
| 8' long | 1.000 | Ea. | .533 | 110 | 26 | 136 |
| Caulking, window, 7' x 4' | 1.000 | Ea. | .710 | 3.74 | 29.50 | 33.24 |
| 8' x 5' | 1.000 | Ea. | .839 | 4.42 | 35 | 39.42 |
| 10' x 6' | 1.000 | Ea. | 1.032 | 5.45 | 43 | 48.45 |
| 12' x 6' | 1.000 | Ea. | 1.161 | 6.10 | 48 | 54.10 |
| Grilles, window, 7' x 4' | 1.000 | Set | .800 | 94.50 | 39 | 133.50 |
| 8' x 5' | 1.000 | Set | 1.067 | 126 | 52 | 178 |
| 10' x 6' | 1.000 | Set | 1.333 | 158 | 65.50 | 223.50 |
| 12' x 6' | 1.000 | Set | 1.600 | 189 | 78.50 | 267.50 |

Drip Cap

Interior Trim

Caulking

Snap-in Grille

Window

| System Description | QUAN. | UNIT | LABOR HOURS | COST EACH | | |
|---|---|---|---|---|---|---|
| | | | | MAT. | INST. | TOTAL |
| **BUILDER'S QUALITY PICTURE WINDOW, 4' X 4'** | | | | | | |
| Window, primed, builder's quality, 3'-0" x 4', insulating glass | 1.000 | Ea. | 1.333 | 450 | 65.50 | 515.50 |
| Trim, interior casing | 17.000 | L.F. | .567 | 24.82 | 27.71 | 52.53 |
| Paint, interior & exterior, primer & 2 coats | 2.000 | Face | 1.778 | 2.14 | 75 | 77.14 |
| Caulking | 16.000 | L.F. | .444 | 2.72 | 21.44 | 24.16 |
| Snap-in grille | 1.000 | Ea. | .267 | 125 | 13.05 | 138.05 |
| Drip cap, metal | 4.000 | L.F. | .080 | 1.68 | 3.92 | 5.60 |
| TOTAL | | Ea. | 4.469 | 606.36 | 206.62 | 812.98 |
| **PLASTIC CLAD WOOD WINDOW, 4'-6" X 6'-6"** | | | | | | |
| Window, plastic clad, prem., 4'-6" x 6'-6", insul. glass | 1.000 | Ea. | 1.455 | 1,000 | 71 | 1,071 |
| Trim, interior casing | 23.000 | L.F. | .767 | 33.58 | 37.49 | 71.07 |
| Paint, interior, primer & 2 coats | 1.000 | Face | .889 | 1.07 | 37.50 | 38.57 |
| Caulking | 22.000 | L.F. | .611 | 3.74 | 29.48 | 33.22 |
| Snap-in grille | 1.000 | Ea. | .267 | 125 | 13.05 | 138.05 |
| TOTAL | | Ea. | 3.989 | 1,163.39 | 188.52 | 1,351.91 |
| **METAL CLAD WOOD WINDOW, 6'-6" X 6'-6"** | | | | | | |
| Window, metal clad, deluxe, 6'-0" x 6'-0", insulating glass | 1.000 | Ea. | 1.600 | 750 | 78.50 | 828.50 |
| Trim interior casing | 27.000 | L.F. | .900 | 39.42 | 44.01 | 83.43 |
| Paint, interior, primer & 2 coats | 1.000 | Face | 1.600 | 5.70 | 67 | 72.70 |
| Caulking | 26.000 | L.F. | .722 | 4.42 | 34.84 | 39.26 |
| Snap-in grille | 1.000 | Ea. | .267 | 125 | 13.05 | 138.05 |
| Drip cap, metal | 6.500 | L.F. | .130 | 2.73 | 6.37 | 9.10 |
| TOTAL | | Ea. | 5.219 | 927.27 | 243.77 | 1,171.04 |

The cost of this system is on a cost per each window basis.

| Description | QUAN. | UNIT | LABOR HOURS | COST EACH | | |
|---|---|---|---|---|---|---|
| | | | | MAT. | INST. | TOTAL |
| | | | | | | |
| | | | | | | |
| | | | | | | |
| | | | | | | |
| | | | | | | |

| Fixed Window Price Sheet | QUAN. | UNIT | LABOR HOURS | COST EACH | | |
|---|---|---|---|---|---|---|
| | | | | MAT. | INST. | TOTAL |
| Window-picture, builder's quality, 4' x 4', single glass | 1.000 | Ea. | 1.333 | 380 | 65.50 | 445.50 |
| Insulating glass | 1.000 | Ea. | 1.333 | 450 | 65.50 | 515.50 |
| 4' x 4'-6", single glass | 1.000 | Ea. | 1.455 | 540 | 71 | 611 |
| Insulating glass | 1.000 | Ea. | 1.455 | 570 | 71 | 641 |
| 5' x 4', single glass | 1.000 | Ea. | 1.455 | 625 | 71 | 696 |
| Insulating glass | 1.000 | Ea. | 1.455 | 650 | 71 | 721 |
| 6' x 4'-6", single glass | 1.000 | Ea. | 1.600 | 675 | 78.50 | 753.50 |
| Insulating glass | 1.000 | Ea. | 1.600 | 685 | 78.50 | 763.50 |
| Plastic clad premium insulating glass, 4' x 4' | 1.000 | Ea. | 1.333 | 545 | 65.50 | 610.50 |
| 4'-6" x 6'-6" | 1.000 | Ea. | 1.455 | 1,000 | 71 | 1,071 |
| 5'-6" x 6'-6" | 1.000 | Ea. | 1.600 | 1,125 | 78.50 | 1,203.50 |
| 6'-6" x 6'-6" | 1.000 | Ea. | 1.600 | 1,125 | 78.50 | 1,203.50 |
| Metal clad deluxe insulating glass, 4' x 4' | 1.000 | Ea. | 1.333 | 405 | 65.50 | 470.50 |
| 4'-6" x 6'-6" | 1.000 | Ea. | 1.455 | 590 | 71 | 661 |
| 5'-6" x 6'-6" | 1.000 | Ea. | 1.600 | 655 | 78.50 | 733.50 |
| 6'-6" x 6'-6" | 1.000 | Ea. | 1.600 | 750 | 78.50 | 828.50 |
| Trim, interior casing, window 4' x 4' | 17.000 | L.F. | .567 | 25 | 27.50 | 52.50 |
| 4'-6" x 4'-6" | 19.000 | L.F. | .633 | 27.50 | 31 | 58.50 |
| 5'-0" x 4'-0" | 19.000 | L.F. | .633 | 27.50 | 31 | 58.50 |
| 4'-6" x 6'-6" | 23.000 | L.F. | .767 | 33.50 | 37.50 | 71 |
| 5'-6" x 6'-6" | 25.000 | L.F. | .833 | 36.50 | 41 | 77.50 |
| 6'-6" x 6'-6" | 27.000 | L.F. | .900 | 39.50 | 44 | 83.50 |
| Paint or stain, interior or exterior, 4' x 4' window, 1 coat | 1.000 | Face | .667 | 1.18 | 28 | 29.18 |
| 2 coats | 1.000 | Face | .667 | 1.75 | 28 | 29.75 |
| Primer & 1 coat | 1.000 | Face | .727 | 1.09 | 30.50 | 31.59 |
| Primer & 2 coats | 1.000 | Face | .889 | 1.07 | 37.50 | 38.57 |
| 4'-6" x 6'-6" window, 1 coat | 1.000 | Face | .667 | 1.18 | 28 | 29.18 |
| 2 coats | 1.000 | Face | .667 | 1.75 | 28 | 29.75 |
| Primer & 1 coat | 1.000 | Face | .727 | 1.09 | 30.50 | 31.59 |
| Primer & 2 coats | 1.000 | Face | .889 | 1.07 | 37.50 | 38.57 |
| 6'-6" x 6'-6" window, 1 coat | 1.000 | Face | .889 | 1.99 | 37.50 | 39.49 |
| 2 coats | 1.000 | Face | 1.333 | 3.63 | 56 | 59.63 |
| Primer & 1 coat | 1.000 | Face | 1.333 | 3.88 | 56 | 59.88 |
| Primer & 2 coats | 1.000 | Face | 1.600 | 5.70 | 67 | 72.70 |
| Caulking, window, 4' x 4' | 1.000 | Ea. | .516 | 2.72 | 21.50 | 24.22 |
| 4'-6" x 4'-6" | 1.000 | Ea. | .581 | 3.06 | 24 | 27.06 |
| 5'-0" x 4'-0" | 1.000 | Ea. | .581 | 3.06 | 24 | 27.06 |
| 4'-6" x 6'-6" | 1.000 | Ea. | .710 | 3.74 | 29.50 | 33.24 |
| 5'-6" x 6'-6" | 1.000 | Ea. | .774 | 4.08 | 32 | 36.08 |
| 6'-6" x 6'-6" | 1.000 | Ea. | .839 | 4.42 | 35 | 39.42 |
| Grilles, glass size, to 48" x 48" | 1.000 | Ea. | .267 | 125 | 13.05 | 138.05 |
| To 60" x 68" | 1.000 | Ea. | .286 | 176 | 14 | 190 |
| Drip cap, aluminum, 4' long | 4.000 | L.F. | .080 | 1.68 | 3.92 | 5.60 |
| 4'-6" long | 4.500 | L.F. | .090 | 1.89 | 4.41 | 6.30 |
| 5' long | 5.000 | L.F. | .100 | 2.10 | 4.90 | 7 |
| 6' long | 6.000 | L.F. | .120 | 2.52 | 5.90 | 8.42 |
| Wood, 4' long | 4.000 | L.F. | .133 | 5.85 | 6.50 | 12.35 |
| 4'-6" long | 4.500 | L.F. | .150 | 6.55 | 7.35 | 13.90 |
| 5' long | 5.000 | L.F. | .167 | 7.30 | 8.15 | 15.45 |
| 6' long | 6.000 | L.F. | .200 | 8.75 | 9.80 | 18.55 |
| | | | | | | |
| | | | | | | |
| | | | | | | |
| | | | | | | |

| System Description | QUAN. | UNIT | LABOR HOURS | COST EACH | | |
|---|---|---|---|---|---|---|
| | | | | MAT. | INST. | TOTAL |
| **COLONIAL, 6 PANEL, 3′ X 6′-8″, WOOD** | | | | | | |
| Door, 3′ x 6′-8″ x 1-3/4″ thick, pine, 6 panel colonial | 1.000 | Ea. | 1.067 | 475 | 52 | 527 |
| Frame, 5-13/16″ deep, incl. exterior casing & drip cap | 17.000 | L.F. | .725 | 212.50 | 35.53 | 248.03 |
| Interior casing, 2-1/2″ wide | 18.000 | L.F. | .600 | 26.28 | 29.34 | 55.62 |
| Sill, 8/4 x 8″ deep | 3.000 | L.F. | .480 | 56.40 | 23.55 | 79.95 |
| Butt hinges, brass, 4-1/2″ x 4-1/2″ | 1.500 | Pr. | | 26.55 | | 26.55 |
| Lockset | 1.000 | Ea. | .571 | 44 | 28 | 72 |
| Weatherstripping, metal, spring type, bronze | 1.000 | Set | 1.053 | 24 | 51.50 | 75.50 |
| Paint, interior & exterior, primer & 2 coats | 2.000 | Face | 1.778 | 11.30 | 75 | 86.30 |
| TOTAL | | Ea. | 6.274 | 876.03 | 294.92 | 1,170.95 |
| **SOLID CORE BIRCH, FLUSH, 3′ X 6′-8″** | | | | | | |
| Door, 3′ x 6′-8″, 1-3/4″ thick, birch, flush solid core | 1.000 | Ea. | 1.067 | 125 | 52 | 177 |
| Frame, 5-13/16″ deep, incl. exterior casing & drip cap | 17.000 | L.F. | .725 | 212.50 | 35.53 | 248.03 |
| Interior casing, 2-1/2″ wide | 18.000 | L.F. | .600 | 26.28 | 29.34 | 55.62 |
| Sill, 8/4 x 8″ deep | 3.000 | L.F. | .480 | 56.40 | 23.55 | 79.95 |
| Butt hinges, brass, 4-1/2″ x 4-1/2″ | 1.500 | Pr. | | 26.55 | | 26.55 |
| Lockset | 1.000 | Ea. | .571 | 44 | 28 | 72 |
| Weatherstripping, metal, spring type, bronze | 1.000 | Set | 1.053 | 24 | 51.50 | 75.50 |
| Paint, Interior & exterior, primer & 2 coats | 2.000 | Face | 1.778 | 10.60 | 75 | 85.60 |
| TOTAL | | Ea. | 6.274 | 525.33 | 294.92 | 820.25 |

These systems are on a cost per each door basis.

| Description | QUAN. | UNIT | LABOR HOURS | COST EACH | | |
|---|---|---|---|---|---|---|
| | | | | MAT. | INST. | TOTAL |
| | | | | | | |
| | | | | | | |
| | | | | | | |
| | | | | | | |
| | | | | | | |

| Entrance Door Price Sheet | QUAN. | UNIT | LABOR HOURS | COST EACH MAT. | COST EACH INST. | COST EACH TOTAL |
|---|---|---|---|---|---|---|
| Door exterior wood 1-3/4" thick, pine, dutch door, 2'-8" x 6'-8" minimum | 1.000 | Ea. | 1.333 | 745 | 65.50 | 810.50 |
| Maximum | 1.000 | Ea. | 1.600 | 910 | 78.50 | 988.50 |
| 3'-0" x 6'-8", minimum | 1.000 | Ea. | 1.333 | 755 | 65.50 | 820.50 |
| Maximum | 1.000 | Ea. | 1.600 | 990 | 78.50 | 1,068.50 |
| Colonial, 6 panel, 2'-8" x 6'-8" | 1.000 | Ea. | 1.000 | 505 | 49 | 554 |
| 3'-0" x 6'-8" | 1.000 | Ea. | 1.067 | 475 | 52 | 527 |
| 8 panel, 2'-6" x 6'-8" | 1.000 | Ea. | 1.000 | 630 | 49 | 679 |
| 3'-0" x 6'-8" | 1.000 | Ea. | 1.067 | 610 | 52 | 662 |
| Flush, birch, solid core, 2'-8" x 6'-8" | 1.000 | Ea. | 1.000 | 114 | 49 | 163 |
| 3'-0" x 6'-8" | 1.000 | Ea. | 1.067 | 125 | 52 | 177 |
| Porch door, 2'-8" x 6'-8" | 1.000 | Ea. | 1.000 | 615 | 49 | 664 |
| 3'-0" x 6'-8" | 1.000 | Ea. | 1.067 | 645 | 52 | 697 |
| Hand carved mahogany, 2'-8" x 6'-8" | 1.000 | Ea. | 1.067 | 715 | 52 | 767 |
| 3'-0" x 6'-8" | 1.000 | Ea. | 1.067 | 735 | 52 | 787 |
| Rosewood, 2'-8" x 6'-8" | 1.000 | Ea. | 1.067 | 890 | 52 | 942 |
| 3'-0" x 6-8" | 1.000 | Ea. | 1.067 | 915 | 52 | 967 |
| Door, metal clad wood 1-3/8" thick raised panel, 2'-8" x 6'-8" | 1.000 | Ea. | 1.067 | 320 | 46 | 366 |
| 3'-0" x 6'-8" | 1.000 | Ea. | 1.067 | 299 | 52 | 351 |
| Deluxe metal door, 3'-0" x 6'-8" | 1.000 | Ea. | 1.231 | 299 | 52 | 351 |
| 3'-0" x 6'-8" | 1.000 | Ea. | 1.231 | 299 | 52 | 351 |
| Frame, pine, including exterior trim & drip cap, 5/4, x 4-9/16" deep | 17.000 | L.F. | .725 | 104 | 35.50 | 139.50 |
| 5-13/16" deep | 17.000 | L.F. | .725 | 213 | 35.50 | 248.50 |
| 6-9/16" deep | 17.000 | L.F. | .725 | 159 | 35.50 | 194.50 |
| Safety glass lites, add | 1.000 | Ea. | | 82 | | 82 |
| Interior casing, 2'-8" x 6'-8" door | 18.000 | L.F. | .600 | 26.50 | 29.50 | 56 |
| 3'-0" x 6'-8" door | 19.000 | L.F. | .633 | 27.50 | 31 | 58.50 |
| Sill, oak, 8/4 x 8" deep | 3.000 | L.F. | .480 | 56.50 | 23.50 | 80 |
| 8/4 x 10" deep | 3.000 | L.F. | .533 | 70.50 | 26 | 96.50 |
| Butt hinges, steel plated, 4-1/2" x 4-1/2", plain | 1.500 | Pr. | | 26.50 | | 26.50 |
| Ball bearing | 1.500 | Pr. | | 52.50 | | 52.50 |
| Bronze, 4-1/2" x 4-1/2", plain | 1.500 | Pr. | | 37.50 | | 37.50 |
| Ball bearing | 1.500 | Pr. | | 55.50 | | 55.50 |
| Lockset, minimum | 1.000 | Ea. | .571 | 44 | 28 | 72 |
| Maximum | 1.000 | Ea. | 1.000 | 176 | 49 | 225 |
| Weatherstripping, metal, interlocking, zinc | 1.000 | Set | 2.667 | 17.25 | 131 | 148.25 |
| Bronze | 1.000 | Set | 2.667 | 27.50 | 131 | 158.50 |
| Spring type, bronze | 1.000 | Set | 1.053 | 24 | 51.50 | 75.50 |
| Rubber, minimum | 1.000 | Set | 1.053 | 5.90 | 51.50 | 57.40 |
| Maximum | 1.000 | Set | 1.143 | 6.45 | 56 | 62.45 |
| Felt minimum | 1.000 | Set | .571 | 2.74 | 28 | 30.74 |
| Maximum | 1.000 | Set | .615 | 3.14 | 30 | 33.14 |
| Paint or stain, flush door, interior or exterior, 1 coat | 2.000 | Face | .941 | 3.76 | 39.50 | 43.26 |
| 2 coats | 2.000 | Face | 1.455 | 7.50 | 61 | 68.50 |
| Primer & 1 coat | 2.000 | Face | 1.455 | 7.05 | 61 | 68.05 |
| Primer & 2 coats | 2.000 | Face | 1.778 | 10.60 | 75 | 85.60 |
| Paneled door, interior & exterior, 1 coat | 2.000 | Face | 1.143 | 4.02 | 48 | 52.02 |
| 2 coats | 2.000 | Face | 2.000 | 8.05 | 84 | 92.05 |
| Primer & 1 coat | 2.000 | Face | 1.455 | 7.50 | 61 | 68.50 |
| Primer & 2 coats | 2.000 | Face | 1.778 | 11.30 | 75 | 86.30 |
| | | | | | | |
| | | | | | | |
| | | | | | | |
| | | | | | | |
| | | | | | | |

183

Drip Cap

Frame & Exterior Casing

Interior Casing

Door

Sill

| System Description | QUAN. | UNIT | LABOR HOURS | COST EACH | | |
|---|---|---|---|---|---|---|
| | | | | MAT. | INST. | TOTAL |
| **WOOD SLIDING DOOR, 8′ WIDE, PREMIUM** | | | | | | |
| Wood, 5/8″ thick tempered insul. glass, 8′ wide, premium | 1.000 | Ea. | 5.333 | 1,950 | 261 | 2,211 |
| Interior casing | 22.000 | L.F. | .733 | 32.12 | 35.86 | 67.98 |
| Exterior casing | 22.000 | L.F. | .733 | 32.12 | 35.86 | 67.98 |
| Sill, oak, 8/4 x 8″ deep | 8.000 | L.F. | 1.280 | 150.40 | 62.80 | 213.20 |
| Drip cap | 8.000 | L.F. | .160 | 3.36 | 7.84 | 11.20 |
| Paint, interior & exterior, primer & 2 coats | 2.000 | Face | 2.816 | 15.84 | 117.92 | 133.76 |
| TOTAL | | Ea. | 11.055 | 2,183.84 | 521.28 | 2,705.12 |
| **ALUMINUM SLIDING DOOR, 8′ WIDE, PREMIUM** | | | | | | |
| Aluminum, 5/8″ tempered insul. glass, 8′ wide, premium | 1.000 | Ea. | 5.333 | 1,775 | 261 | 2,036 |
| Interior casing | 22.000 | L.F. | .733 | 32.12 | 35.86 | 67.98 |
| Exterior casing | 22.000 | L.F. | .733 | 32.12 | 35.86 | 67.98 |
| Sill, oak, 8/4 x 8″ deep | 8.000 | L.F. | 1.280 | 150.40 | 62.80 | 213.20 |
| Drip cap | 8.000 | L.F. | .160 | 3.36 | 7.84 | 11.20 |
| Paint, interior & exterior, primer & 2 coats | 2.000 | Face | 2.816 | 15.84 | 117.92 | 133.76 |
| TOTAL | | Ea. | 11.055 | 2,008.84 | 521.28 | 2,530.12 |

The cost of this system is on a cost per each door basis.

| Description | QUAN. | UNIT | LABOR HOURS | COST EACH | | |
|---|---|---|---|---|---|---|
| | | | | MAT. | INST. | TOTAL |
| | | | | | | |
| | | | | | | |
| | | | | | | |
| | | | | | | |
| | | | | | | |
| | | | | | | |
| | | | | | | |

| Sliding Door Price Sheet | QUAN. | UNIT | LABOR HOURS | COST PER UNIT | | |
|---|---|---|---|---|---|---|
| | | | | MAT. | INST. | TOTAL |
| Sliding door, wood, 5/8" thick, tempered insul. glass, 6' wide, premium | 1.000 | Ea. | 4.000 | 1,525 | 196 | 1,721 |
| Economy | 1.000 | Ea. | 4.000 | 1,225 | 196 | 1,421 |
| 8'wide, wood premium | 1.000 | Ea. | 5.333 | 1,950 | 261 | 2,211 |
| Economy | 1.000 | Ea. | 5.333 | 1,625 | 261 | 1,886 |
| 12' wide, wood premium | 1.000 | Ea. | 6.400 | 3,225 | 315 | 3,540 |
| Economy | 1.000 | Ea. | 6.400 | 2,650 | 315 | 2,965 |
| Aluminum, 5/8" thick, tempered insul. glass, 6'wide, premium | 1.000 | Ea. | 4.000 | 1,725 | 196 | 1,921 |
| Economy | 1.000 | Ea. | 4.000 | 960 | 196 | 1,156 |
| 8'wide, premium | 1.000 | Ea. | 5.333 | 1,775 | 261 | 2,036 |
| Economy | 1.000 | Ea. | 5.333 | 1,525 | 261 | 1,786 |
| 12' wide, premium | 1.000 | Ea. | 6.400 | 3,250 | 315 | 3,565 |
| Economy | 1.000 | Ea. | 6.400 | 1,650 | 315 | 1,965 |
| Interior casing, 6' wide door | 20.000 | L.F. | .667 | 29 | 32.50 | 61.50 |
| 8' wide door | 22.000 | L.F. | .733 | 32 | 36 | 68 |
| 12' wide door | 26.000 | L.F. | .867 | 38 | 42.50 | 80.50 |
| Exterior casing, 6' wide door | 20.000 | L.F. | .667 | 29 | 32.50 | 61.50 |
| 8' wide door | 22.000 | L.F. | .733 | 32 | 36 | 68 |
| 12' wide door | 26.000 | L.F. | .867 | 38 | 42.50 | 80.50 |
| Sill, oak, 8/4 x 8" deep, 6' wide door | 6.000 | L.F. | .960 | 113 | 47 | 160 |
| 8' wide door | 8.000 | L.F. | 1.280 | 150 | 63 | 213 |
| 12' wide door | 12.000 | L.F. | 1.920 | 226 | 94 | 320 |
| 8/4 x 10" deep, 6' wide door | 6.000 | L.F. | 1.067 | 141 | 52 | 193 |
| 8' wide door | 8.000 | L.F. | 1.422 | 188 | 69.50 | 257.50 |
| 12' wide door | 12.000 | L.F. | 2.133 | 282 | 104 | 386 |
| Drip cap, 6' wide door | 6.000 | L.F. | .120 | 2.52 | 5.90 | 8.42 |
| 8' wide door | 8.000 | L.F. | .160 | 3.36 | 7.85 | 11.21 |
| 12' wide door | 12.000 | L.F. | .240 | 5.05 | 11.75 | 16.80 |
| Paint or stain, interior & exterior, 6' wide door, 1 coat | 2.000 | Face | 1.600 | 4.80 | 67 | 71.80 |
| 2 coats | 2.000 | Face | 1.600 | 4.80 | 67 | 71.80 |
| Primer & 1 coat | 2.000 | Face | 1.778 | 10.40 | 74.50 | 84.90 |
| Primer & 2 coats | 2.000 | Face | 2.560 | 14.40 | 107 | 121.40 |
| 8' wide door, 1 coat | 2.000 | Face | 1.760 | 5.30 | 74 | 79.30 |
| 2 coats | 2.000 | Face | 1.760 | 5.30 | 74 | 79.30 |
| Primer & 1 coat | 2.000 | Face | 1.955 | 11.45 | 82 | 93.45 |
| Primer & 2 coats | 2.000 | Face | 2.816 | 15.85 | 118 | 133.85 |
| 12' wide door, 1 coat | 2.000 | Face | 2.080 | 6.25 | 87.50 | 93.75 |
| 2 coats | 2.000 | Face | 2.080 | 6.25 | 87.50 | 93.75 |
| Primer & 1 coat | 2.000 | Face | 2.311 | 13.50 | 96.50 | 110 |
| Primer & 2 coats | 2.000 | Face | 3.328 | 18.70 | 139 | 157.70 |
| Aluminum door, trim only, interior & exterior, 6' door, 1 coat | 2.000 | Face | .800 | 2.40 | 33.50 | 35.90 |
| 2 coats | 2.000 | Face | .800 | 2.40 | 33.50 | 35.90 |
| Primer & 1 coat | 2.000 | Face | .889 | 5.20 | 37 | 42.20 |
| Primer & 2 coats | 2.000 | Face | 1.280 | 7.20 | 53.50 | 60.70 |
| 8' wide door, 1 coat | 2.000 | Face | .880 | 2.64 | 37 | 39.64 |
| 2 coats | 2.000 | Face | .880 | 2.64 | 37 | 39.64 |
| Primer & 1 coat | 2.000 | Face | .978 | 5.70 | 41 | 46.70 |
| Primer & 2 coats | 2.000 | Face | 1.408 | 7.90 | 59 | 66.90 |
| 12' wide door, 1 coat | 2.000 | Face | 1.040 | 3.12 | 43.50 | 46.62 |
| 2 coats | 2.000 | Face | 1.040 | 3.12 | 43.50 | 46.62 |
| Primer & 1 coat | 2.000 | Face | 1.155 | 6.75 | 48.50 | 55.25 |
| Primer & 2 coats | 2.000 | Face | 1.664 | 9.35 | 69.50 | 78.85 |

Exterior Trim — Drip Cap

Door

Jamb — Weatherstripping

| System Description | QUAN. | UNIT | LABOR HOURS | COST EACH | | |
|---|---|---|---|---|---|---|
| | | | | MAT. | INST. | TOTAL |
| **OVERHEAD, SECTIONAL GARAGE DOOR, 9′ X 7′** | | | | | | |
| Wood, overhead sectional door, std., incl. hardware, 9′ x 7′ | 1.000 | Ea. | 2.000 | 790 | 98 | 888 |
| Jamb & header blocking, 2″ x 6″ | 25.000 | L.F. | .901 | 10.25 | 44 | 54.25 |
| Exterior trim | 25.000 | L.F. | .833 | 36.50 | 40.75 | 77.25 |
| Paint, interior & exterior, primer & 2 coats | 2.000 | Face | 3.556 | 22.60 | 150 | 172.60 |
| Weatherstripping, molding type | 1.000 | Set | .767 | 33.58 | 37.49 | 71.07 |
| Drip cap | 9.000 | L.F. | .180 | 3.78 | 8.82 | 12.60 |
| TOTAL | | Ea. | 8.237 | 896.71 | 379.06 | 1,275.77 |
| **OVERHEAD, SECTIONAL GARAGE DOOR, 16′ X 7′** | | | | | | |
| Wood, overhead sectional, std., incl. hardware, 16′ x 7′ | 1.000 | Ea. | 2.667 | 1,575 | 131 | 1,706 |
| Jamb & header blocking, 2″ x 6″ | 30.000 | L.F. | 1.081 | 12.30 | 52.80 | 65.10 |
| Exterior trim | 30.000 | L.F. | 1.000 | 43.80 | 48.90 | 92.70 |
| Paint, interior & exterior, primer & 2 coats | 2.000 | Face | 5.333 | 33.90 | 225 | 258.90 |
| Weatherstripping, molding type | 1.000 | Set | 1.000 | 43.80 | 48.90 | 92.70 |
| Drip cap | 16.000 | L.F. | .320 | 6.72 | 15.68 | 22.40 |
| TOTAL | | Ea. | 11.401 | 1,715.52 | 522.28 | 2,237.80 |
| **OVERHEAD, SWING-UP TYPE, GARAGE DOOR, 16′ X 7′** | | | | | | |
| Wood, overhead, swing-up, std., incl. hardware, 16′ x 7′ | 1.000 | Ea. | 2.667 | 800 | 131 | 931 |
| Jamb & header blocking, 2″ x 6″ | 30.000 | L.F. | 1.081 | 12.30 | 52.80 | 65.10 |
| Exterior trim | 30.000 | L.F. | 1.000 | 43.80 | 48.90 | 92.70 |
| Paint, interior & exterior, primer & 2 coats | 2.000 | Face | 5.333 | 33.90 | 225 | 258.90 |
| Weatherstripping, molding type | 1.000 | Set | 1.000 | 43.80 | 48.90 | 92.70 |
| Drip cap | 16.000 | L.F. | .320 | 6.72 | 15.68 | 22.40 |
| TOTAL | | Ea. | 11.401 | 940.52 | 522.28 | 1,462.80 |

This system is on a cost per each door basis.

| Description | QUAN. | UNIT | LABOR HOURS | COST EACH | | |
|---|---|---|---|---|---|---|
| | | | | MAT. | INST. | TOTAL |
| | | | | | | |
| | | | | | | |
| | | | | | | |
| | | | | | | |
| | | | | | | |

| Resi Garage Door Price Sheet | QUAN. | UNIT | LABOR HOURS | COST EACH | | |
|---|---|---|---|---|---|---|
| | | | | MAT. | INST. | TOTAL |
| Overhead, sectional, including hardware, fiberglass, 9' x 7', standard | 1.000 | Ea. | 3.030 | 805 | 148 | 953 |
| Deluxe | 1.000 | Ea. | 3.030 | 1,025 | 148 | 1,173 |
| 16' x 7', standard | 1.000 | Ea. | 2.667 | 1,700 | 131 | 1,831 |
| Deluxe | 1.000 | Ea. | 2.667 | 2,175 | 131 | 2,306 |
| Hardboard, 9' x 7', standard | 1.000 | Ea. | 2.000 | 605 | 98 | 703 |
| Deluxe | 1.000 | Ea. | 2.000 | 855 | 98 | 953 |
| 16' x 7', standard | 1.000 | Ea. | 2.667 | 1,250 | 131 | 1,381 |
| Deluxe | 1.000 | Ea. | 2.667 | 1,475 | 131 | 1,606 |
| Metal, 9' x 7', standard | 1.000 | Ea. | 3.030 | 640 | 148 | 788 |
| Deluxe | 1.000 | Ea. | 2.000 | 940 | 98 | 1,038 |
| 16' x 7', standard | 1.000 | Ea. | 5.333 | 800 | 261 | 1,061 |
| Deluxe | 1.000 | Ea. | 2.667 | 1,500 | 131 | 1,631 |
| Wood, 9' x 7', standard | 1.000 | Ea. | 2.000 | 790 | 98 | 888 |
| Deluxe | 1.000 | Ea. | 2.000 | 2,250 | 98 | 2,348 |
| 16' x 7', standard | 1.000 | Ea. | 2.667 | 1,575 | 131 | 1,706 |
| Deluxe | 1.000 | Ea. | 2.667 | 3,275 | 131 | 3,406 |
| Overhead swing-up type including hardware, fiberglass, 9' x 7', standard | 1.000 | Ea. | 2.000 | 1,075 | 98 | 1,173 |
| Deluxe | 1.000 | Ea. | 2.000 | 870 | 98 | 968 |
| 16' x 7', standard | 1.000 | Ea. | 2.667 | 1,350 | 131 | 1,481 |
| Deluxe | 1.000 | Ea. | 2.667 | 1,075 | 131 | 1,206 |
| Hardboard, 9' x 7', standard | 1.000 | Ea. | 2.000 | 380 | 98 | 478 |
| Deluxe | 1.000 | Ea. | 2.000 | 505 | 98 | 603 |
| 16' x 7', standard | 1.000 | Ea. | 2.667 | 530 | 131 | 661 |
| Deluxe | 1.000 | Ea. | 2.667 | 785 | 131 | 916 |
| Metal, 9' x 7', standard | 1.000 | Ea. | 2.000 | 420 | 98 | 518 |
| Deluxe | 1.000 | Ea. | 2.000 | 915 | 98 | 1,013 |
| 16' x 7', standard | 1.000 | Ea. | 2.667 | 660 | 131 | 791 |
| Deluxe | 1.000 | Ea. | 2.667 | 1,050 | 131 | 1,181 |
| Wood, 9' x 7', standard | 1.000 | Ea. | 2.000 | 495 | 98 | 593 |
| Deluxe | 1.000 | Ea. | 2.000 | 1,025 | 98 | 1,123 |
| 16' x 7', standard | 1.000 | Ea. | 2.667 | 800 | 131 | 931 |
| Deluxe | 1.000 | Ea. | 2.667 | 1,125 | 131 | 1,256 |
| Jamb & header blocking, 2" x 6", 9' x 7' door | 25.000 | L.F. | .901 | 10.25 | 44 | 54.25 |
| 16' x 7' door | 30.000 | L.F. | 1.081 | 12.30 | 53 | 65.30 |
| 2" x 8", 9' x 7' door | 25.000 | L.F. | 1.000 | 15.25 | 49 | 64.25 |
| 16' x 7' door | 30.000 | L.F. | 1.200 | 18.30 | 59 | 77.30 |
| Exterior trim, 9' x 7' door | 25.000 | L.F. | .833 | 36.50 | 41 | 77.50 |
| 16' x 7' door | 30.000 | L.F. | 1.000 | 44 | 49 | 93 |
| Paint or stain, interior & exterior, 9' x 7' door, 1 coat | 1.000 | Face | 2.286 | 8.05 | 96 | 104.05 |
| 2 coats | 1.000 | Face | 4.000 | 16.10 | 168 | 184.10 |
| Primer & 1 coat | 1.000 | Face | 2.909 | 15.05 | 122 | 137.05 |
| Primer & 2 coats | 1.000 | Face | 3.556 | 22.50 | 150 | 172.50 |
| 16' x 7' door, 1 coat | 1.000 | Face | 3.429 | 12.05 | 144 | 156.05 |
| 2 coats | 1.000 | Face | 6.000 | 24 | 252 | 276 |
| Primer & 1 coat | 1.000 | Face | 4.364 | 22.50 | 183 | 205.50 |
| Primer & 2 coats | 1.000 | Face | 5.333 | 34 | 225 | 259 |
| Weatherstripping, molding type, 9' x 7' door | 1.000 | Set | .767 | 33.50 | 37.50 | 71 |
| 16' x 7' door | 1.000 | Set | 1.000 | 44 | 49 | 93 |
| Drip cap, 9' door | 9.000 | L.F. | .180 | 3.78 | 8.80 | 12.58 |
| 16' door | 16.000 | L.F. | .320 | 6.70 | 15.70 | 22.40 |
| Garage door opener, economy | 1.000 | Ea. | 1.000 | 450 | 49 | 499 |
| Deluxe, including remote control | 1.000 | Ea. | 1.000 | 660 | 49 | 709 |
| | | | | | | |
| | | | | | | |
| | | | | | | |
| | | | | | | |

Drywall →    ← Finish Drywall

← Window

Corner Bead →

← Sill

| System Description | QUAN. | UNIT | LABOR HOURS | COST EACH | | |
|---|---|---|---|---|---|---|
| | | | | MAT. | INST. | TOTAL |
| **SINGLE HUNG, 2′ X 3′ OPENING** | | | | | | |
| Window, 2′ x 3′ opening, enameled, insulating glass | 1.000 | Ea. | 1.600 | 264 | 95.50 | 359.50 |
| Blocking, 1″ x 3″ furring strip nailers | 10.000 | L.F. | .146 | 3.80 | 7.10 | 10.90 |
| Drywall, 1/2″ thick, standard | 5.000 | S.F. | .040 | 1.30 | 1.95 | 3.25 |
| Corner bead, 1″ x 1″, galvanized steel | 8.000 | L.F. | .160 | 1.28 | 7.84 | 9.12 |
| Finish drywall, tape and finish corners inside and outside | 16.000 | L.F. | .269 | 1.60 | 13.12 | 14.72 |
| Sill, slate | 2.000 | L.F. | .400 | 25.30 | 17.40 | 42.70 |
| TOTAL | | Ea. | 2.615 | 297.28 | 142.91 | 440.19 |
| **SLIDING, 3′ X 2′ OPENING** | | | | | | |
| Window, 3′ x 2′ opening, enameled, insulating glass | 1.000 | Ea. | 1.600 | 246 | 95.50 | 341.50 |
| Blocking, 1″ x 3″ furring strip nailers | 10.000 | L.F. | .146 | 3.80 | 7.10 | 10.90 |
| Drywall, 1/2″ thick, standard | 5.000 | S.F. | .040 | 1.30 | 1.95 | 3.25 |
| Corner bead, 1″ x 1″, galvanized steel | 7.000 | L.F. | .140 | 1.12 | 6.86 | 7.98 |
| Finish drywall, tape and finish corners inside and outside | 14.000 | L.F. | .236 | 1.40 | 11.48 | 12.88 |
| Sill, slate | 3.000 | L.F. | .600 | 37.95 | 26.10 | 64.05 |
| TOTAL | | Ea. | 2.762 | 291.57 | 148.99 | 440.56 |
| **AWNING, 3′-1″ X 3′-2″** | | | | | | |
| Window, 3′-1″ x 3′-2″ opening, enameled, insul. glass | 1.000 | Ea. | 1.600 | 320 | 95.50 | 415.50 |
| Blocking, 1″ x 3″ furring strip, nailers | 12.500 | L.F. | .182 | 4.75 | 8.88 | 13.63 |
| Drywall, 1/2″ thick, standard | 4.500 | S.F. | .036 | 1.17 | 1.76 | 2.93 |
| Corner bead, 1″ x 1″, galvanized steel | 9.250 | L.F. | .185 | 1.48 | 9.07 | 10.55 |
| Finish drywall, tape and finish corners, inside and outside | 18.500 | L.F. | .312 | 1.85 | 15.17 | 17.02 |
| Sill, slate | 3.250 | L.F. | .650 | 41.11 | 28.28 | 69.39 |
| TOTAL | | Ea. | 2.965 | 370.36 | 158.66 | 529.02 |

| Description | QUAN. | UNIT | LABOR HOURS | COST PER S.F. | | |
|---|---|---|---|---|---|---|
| | | | | MAT. | INST. | TOTAL |
| | | | | | | |
| | | | | | | |
| | | | | | | |
| | | | | | | |

| Aluminum Window Price Sheet | QUAN. | UNIT | LABOR HOURS | COST EACH | | |
|---|---|---|---|---|---|---|
| | | | | MAT. | INST. | TOTAL |
| Window, aluminum, awning, 3'-1" x 3'-2", standard glass | 1.000 | Ea. | 1.600 | 370 | 95.50 | 465.50 |
| Insulating glass | 1.000 | Ea. | 1.600 | 320 | 95.50 | 415.50 |
| 4'-5" x 5'-3", standard glass | 1.000 | Ea. | 2.000 | 420 | 119 | 539 |
| Insulating glass | 1.000 | Ea. | 2.000 | 445 | 119 | 564 |
| Casement, 3'-1" x 3'-2", standard glass | 1.000 | Ea. | 1.600 | 390 | 95.50 | 485.50 |
| Insulating glass | 1.000 | Ea. | 1.600 | 505 | 95.50 | 600.50 |
| Single hung, 2' x 3', standard glass | 1.000 | Ea. | 1.600 | 218 | 95.50 | 313.50 |
| Insulating glass | 1.000 | Ea. | 1.600 | 264 | 95.50 | 359.50 |
| 2'-8" x 6'-8", standard glass | 1.000 | Ea. | 2.000 | 385 | 119 | 504 |
| Insulating glass | 1.000 | Ea. | 2.000 | 495 | 119 | 614 |
| 3'-4" x 5'-0", standard glass | 1.000 | Ea. | 1.778 | 315 | 106 | 421 |
| Insulating glass | 1.000 | Ea. | 1.778 | 350 | 106 | 456 |
| Sliding, 3' x 2', standard glass | 1.000 | Ea. | 1.600 | 230 | 95.50 | 325.50 |
| Insulating glass | 1.000 | Ea. | 1.600 | 246 | 95.50 | 341.50 |
| 5' x 3', standard glass | 1.000 | Ea. | 1.778 | 350 | 106 | 456 |
| Insulating glass | 1.000 | Ea. | 1.778 | 410 | 106 | 516 |
| 8' x 4', standard glass | 1.000 | Ea. | 2.667 | 370 | 159 | 529 |
| Insulating glass | 1.000 | Ea. | 2.667 | 595 | 159 | 754 |
| Blocking, 1" x 3" furring, opening 3' x 2' | 10.000 | L.F. | .146 | 3.80 | 7.10 | 10.90 |
| 3' x 3' | 12.500 | L.F. | .182 | 4.75 | 8.90 | 13.65 |
| 3' x 5' | 16.000 | L.F. | .233 | 6.10 | 11.35 | 17.45 |
| 4' x 4' | 16.000 | L.F. | .233 | 6.10 | 11.35 | 17.45 |
| 4' x 5' | 18.000 | L.F. | .262 | 6.85 | 12.80 | 19.65 |
| 4' x 6' | 20.000 | L.F. | .291 | 7.60 | 14.20 | 21.80 |
| 4' x 8' | 24.000 | L.F. | .349 | 9.10 | 17.05 | 26.15 |
| 6'-8" x 2'-8" | 19.000 | L.F. | .276 | 7.20 | 13.50 | 20.70 |
| Drywall, 1/2" thick, standard, opening 3' x 2' | 5.000 | S.F. | .040 | 1.30 | 1.95 | 3.25 |
| 3' x 3' | 6.000 | S.F. | .048 | 1.56 | 2.34 | 3.90 |
| 3' x 5' | 8.000 | S.F. | .064 | 2.08 | 3.12 | 5.20 |
| 4' x 4' | 8.000 | S.F. | .064 | 2.08 | 3.12 | 5.20 |
| 4' x 5' | 9.000 | S.F. | .072 | 2.34 | 3.51 | 5.85 |
| 4' x 6' | 10.000 | S.F. | .080 | 2.60 | 3.90 | 6.50 |
| 4' x 8' | 12.000 | S.F. | .096 | 3.12 | 4.68 | 7.80 |
| 6'-8" x 2' | 9.500 | S.F. | .076 | 2.47 | 3.71 | 6.18 |
| Corner bead, 1" x 1", galvanized steel, opening 3' x 2' | 7.000 | L.F. | .140 | 1.12 | 6.85 | 7.97 |
| 3' x 3' | 9.000 | L.F. | .180 | 1.44 | 8.80 | 10.24 |
| 3' x 5' | 11.000 | L.F. | .220 | 1.76 | 10.80 | 12.56 |
| 4' x 4' | 12.000 | L.F. | .240 | 1.92 | 11.75 | 13.67 |
| 4' x 5' | 13.000 | L.F. | .260 | 2.08 | 12.75 | 14.83 |
| 4' x 6' | 14.000 | L.F. | .280 | 2.24 | 13.70 | 15.94 |
| 4' x 8' | 16.000 | L.F. | .320 | 2.56 | 15.70 | 18.26 |
| 6'-8" x 2' | 15.000 | L.F. | .300 | 2.40 | 14.70 | 17.10 |
| Tape and finish corners, inside and outside, opening 3' x 2' | 14.000 | L.F. | .204 | 1.40 | 11.50 | 12.90 |
| 3' x 3' | 18.000 | L.F. | .262 | 1.80 | 14.75 | 16.55 |
| 3' x 5' | 22.000 | L.F. | .320 | 2.20 | 18.05 | 20.25 |
| 4' x 4' | 24.000 | L.F. | .349 | 2.40 | 19.70 | 22.10 |
| 4' x 5' | 26.000 | L.F. | .378 | 2.60 | 21.50 | 24.10 |
| 4' x 6' | 28.000 | L.F. | .407 | 2.80 | 23 | 25.80 |
| 4' x 8' | 32.000 | L.F. | .466 | 3.20 | 26 | 29.20 |
| 6'-8" x 2' | 30.000 | L.F. | .437 | 3 | 24.50 | 27.50 |
| Sill, slate, 2' long | 2.000 | L.F. | .400 | 25.50 | 17.40 | 42.90 |
| 3' long | 3.000 | L.F. | .600 | 38 | 26 | 64 |
| 4' long | 4.000 | L.F. | .800 | 50.50 | 35 | 85.50 |
| Wood, 1-5/8" x 6-1/4", 2' long | 2.000 | L.F. | .128 | 14.90 | 6.25 | 21.15 |
| 3' long | 3.000 | L.F. | .192 | 22.50 | 9.40 | 31.90 |
| 4' long | 4.000 | L.F. | .256 | 30 | 12.50 | 42.50 |
| | | | | | | |
| | | | | | | |

Aluminum Window → ← Aluminum Door

| System Description | QUAN. | UNIT | LABOR HOURS | COST EACH | | |
|---|---|---|---|---|---|---|
| | | | | MAT. | INST. | TOTAL |
| Storm door, aluminum, combination, storm & screen, anodized, 2'-6" x 6'-8" | 1.000 | Ea. | 1.067 | 189 | 52 | 241 |
| 2'-8" x 6'-8" | 1.000 | Ea. | 1.143 | 171 | 56 | 227 |
| 3'-0" x 6'-8" | 1.000 | Ea. | 1.143 | 171 | 56 | 227 |
| Mill finish, 2'-6" x 6'-8" | 1.000 | Ea. | 1.067 | 248 | 52 | 300 |
| 2'-8" x 6'-8" | 1.000 | Ea. | 1.143 | 248 | 56 | 304 |
| 3'-0" x 6'-8" | 1.000 | Ea. | 1.143 | 271 | 56 | 327 |
| Painted, 2'-6" x 6'-8" | 1.000 | Ea. | 1.067 | 310 | 52 | 362 |
| 2'-8" x 6'-8" | 1.000 | Ea. | 1.143 | 305 | 56 | 361 |
| 3'-0" x 6'-8" | 1.000 | Ea. | 1.143 | 320 | 56 | 376 |
| Wood, combination, storm & screen, crossbuck, 2'-6" x 6'-9" | 1.000 | Ea. | 1.455 | 360 | 71 | 431 |
| 2'-8" x 6'-9" | 1.000 | Ea. | 1.600 | 315 | 78.50 | 393.50 |
| 3'-0" x 6'-9" | 1.000 | Ea. | 1.778 | 325 | 87 | 412 |
| Full lite, 2'-6" x 6'-9" | 1.000 | Ea. | 1.455 | 325 | 71 | 396 |
| 2'-8" x 6'-9" | 1.000 | Ea. | 1.600 | 325 | 78.50 | 403.50 |
| 3'-0" x 6'-9" | 1.000 | Ea. | 1.778 | 330 | 87 | 417 |
| | | | | | | |
| Windows, aluminum, combination storm & screen, basement, 1'-10" x 1'-0" | 1.000 | Ea. | .533 | 38.50 | 26 | 64.50 |
| 2'-9" x 1'-6" | 1.000 | Ea. | .533 | 42 | 26 | 68 |
| 3'-4" x 2'-0" | 1.000 | Ea. | .533 | 48.50 | 26 | 74.50 |
| Double hung, anodized, 2'-0" x 3'-5" | 1.000 | Ea. | .533 | 99 | 26 | 125 |
| 2'-6" x 5'-0" | 1.000 | Ea. | .571 | 121 | 28 | 149 |
| 4'-0" x 6'-0" | 1.000 | Ea. | .640 | 249 | 31.50 | 280.50 |
| Painted, 2'-0" x 3'-5" | 1.000 | Ea. | .533 | 110 | 26 | 136 |
| 2'-6" x 5'-0" | 1.000 | Ea. | .571 | 176 | 28 | 204 |
| 4'-0" x 6'-0" | 1.000 | Ea. | .640 | 300 | 31.50 | 331.50 |
| | | | | | | |
| Fixed window, anodized, 4'-6" x 4'-6" | 1.000 | Ea. | .640 | 132 | 31.50 | 163.50 |
| 5'-8" x 4'-6" | 1.000 | Ea. | .800 | 158 | 39 | 197 |
| Painted, 4'-6" x 4'-6" | 1.000 | Ea. | .640 | 139 | 31.50 | 170.50 |
| 5'-8" x 4'-6" | 1.000 | Ea. | .800 | 158 | 39 | 197 |

Aluminum Louvered

Raised Panel

Wood Louvered

| System Description | QUAN. | UNIT | LABOR HOURS | COST PER PAIR | | |
|---|---|---|---|---|---|---|
| | | | | MAT. | INST. | TOTAL |
| Shutters, exterior blinds, aluminum, louvered, 1'-4" wide, 3"-0" long | 1.000 | Set | .800 | 66.50 | 39 | 105.50 |
| 4'-0" long | 1.000 | Set | .800 | 79.50 | 39 | 118.50 |
| 5'-4" long | 1.000 | Set | .800 | 105 | 39 | 144 |
| 6'-8" long | 1.000 | Set | .889 | 134 | 43.50 | 177.50 |
| Wood, louvered, 1'-2" wide, 3'-3" long | 1.000 | Set | .800 | 116 | 39 | 155 |
| 4'-7" long | 1.000 | Set | .800 | 156 | 39 | 195 |
| 5'-3" long | 1.000 | Set | .800 | 177 | 39 | 216 |
| 1'-6" wide, 3'-3" long | 1.000 | Set | .800 | 123 | 39 | 162 |
| 4'-7" long | 1.000 | Set | .800 | 173 | 39 | 212 |
| Polystyrene, louvered, 1'-2" wide, 3'-3" long | 1.000 | Set | .800 | 30.50 | 39 | 69.50 |
| 4'-7" long | 1.000 | Set | .800 | 37.50 | 39 | 76.50 |
| 5'-3" long | 1.000 | Set | .800 | 43 | 39 | 82 |
| 6'-8" long | 1.000 | Set | .889 | 51 | 43.50 | 94.50 |
| Vinyl, louvered, 1'-2" wide, 4'-7" long | 1.000 | Set | .720 | 34 | 35 | 69 |
| 1'-4" x 6'-8" long | 1.000 | Set | .889 | 52.50 | 43.50 | 96 |
| | | | | | | |
| | | | | | | |
| | | | | | | |
| | | | | | | |
| | | | | | | |
| | | | | | | |
| | | | | | | |
| | | | | | | |
| | | | | | | |
| | | | | | | |
| | | | | | | |

| System Description | QUAN. | UNIT | LABOR HOURS | COST PER S.F. | | |
|---|---|---|---|---|---|---|
| | | | | MAT. | INST. | TOTAL |
| **ASPHALT, ROOF SHINGLES, CLASS A** | | | | | | |
| Shingles, inorganic class A, 210-235 lb./sq., 4/12 pitch | 1.160 | S.F. | .017 | .97 | .77 | 1.74 |
| Drip edge, metal, 5″ wide | .150 | L.F. | .003 | .08 | .15 | .23 |
| Building paper, #15 felt | 1.300 | S.F. | .002 | .08 | .08 | .16 |
| Ridge shingles, asphalt | .042 | L.F. | .001 | .09 | .04 | .13 |
| Soffit & fascia, white painted aluminum, 1′ overhang | .083 | L.F. | .012 | .28 | .59 | .87 |
| Rake trim, 1″ x 6″ | .040 | L.F. | .002 | .05 | .08 | .13 |
| Rake trim, prime and paint | .040 | L.F. | .002 | .01 | .07 | .08 |
| Gutter, seamless, aluminum painted | .083 | L.F. | .006 | .22 | .30 | .52 |
| Downspouts, aluminum painted | .035 | L.F. | .002 | .07 | .08 | .15 |
| TOTAL | | S.F. | .047 | 1.85 | 2.16 | 4.01 |
| **WOOD, CEDAR SHINGLES NO. 1 PERFECTIONS, 18″ LONG** | | | | | | |
| Shingles, wood, cedar, No. 1 perfections, 4/12 pitch | 1.160 | S.F. | .035 | 3.50 | 1.70 | 5.20 |
| Drip edge, metal, 5″ wide | .150 | L.F. | .003 | .08 | .15 | .23 |
| Building paper, #15 felt | 1.300 | S.F. | .002 | .08 | .08 | .16 |
| Ridge shingles, cedar | .042 | L.F. | .001 | .17 | .06 | .23 |
| Soffit & fascia, white painted aluminum, 1′ overhang | .083 | L.F. | .012 | .28 | .59 | .87 |
| Rake trim, 1″ x 6″ | .040 | L.F. | .002 | .05 | .08 | .13 |
| Rake trim, prime and paint | .040 | L.F. | .002 | .01 | .07 | .08 |
| Gutter, seamless, aluminum, painted | .083 | L.F. | .006 | .22 | .30 | .52 |
| Downspouts, aluminum, painted | .035 | L.F. | .002 | .07 | .08 | .15 |
| TOTAL | | S.F. | .065 | 4.46 | 3.11 | 7.57 |

The prices in these systems are based on a square foot of plan area.
All quantities have been adjusted accordingly.

| Description | QUAN. | UNIT | LABOR HOURS | COST PER S.F. | | |
|---|---|---|---|---|---|---|
| | | | | MAT. | INST. | TOTAL |
| | | | | | | |
| | | | | | | |
| | | | | | | |
| | | | | | | |

| Gable End Roofing Price Sheet | QUAN. | UNIT | LABOR HOURS | COST PER S.F. | | |
|---|---|---|---|---|---|---|
| | | | | MAT. | INST. | TOTAL |
| Shingles, asphalt, inorganic, class A, 210-235 lb./sq., 4/12 pitch | 1.160 | S.F. | .017 | .97 | .77 | 1.74 |
| 8/12 pitch | 1.330 | S.F. | .019 | 1.05 | .83 | 1.88 |
| Laminated, multi-layered, 240-260 lb./sq., 4/12 pitch | 1.160 | S.F. | .021 | 1.15 | .94 | 2.09 |
| 8/12 pitch | 1.330 | S.F. | .023 | 1.24 | 1.02 | 2.26 |
| Premium laminated, multi-layered, 260-300 lb./sq., 4/12 pitch | 1.160 | S.F. | .027 | 1.32 | 1.21 | 2.53 |
| 8/12 pitch | 1.330 | S.F. | .030 | 1.43 | 1.31 | 2.74 |
| Clay tile, Spanish tile, red, 4/12 pitch | 1.160 | S.F. | .053 | 4.26 | 2.36 | 6.62 |
| 8/12 pitch | 1.330 | S.F. | .058 | 4.62 | 2.56 | 7.18 |
| Mission tile, red, 4/12 pitch | 1.160 | S.F. | .083 | 9.80 | 3.72 | 13.52 |
| 8/12 pitch | 1.330 | S.F. | .090 | 10.60 | 4.03 | 14.63 |
| French tile, red, 4/12 pitch | 1.160 | S.F. | .071 | 8.90 | 3.14 | 12.04 |
| 8/12 pitch | 1.330 | S.F. | .077 | 9.60 | 3.41 | 13.01 |
| Slate, Buckingham, Virginia, black, 4/12 pitch | 1.160 | S.F. | .055 | 6.30 | 2.42 | 8.72 |
| 8/12 pitch | 1.330 | S.F. | .059 | 6.85 | 2.63 | 9.48 |
| Vermont, black or grey, 4/12 pitch | 1.160 | S.F. | .055 | 6.05 | 2.42 | 8.47 |
| 8/12 pitch | 1.330 | S.F. | .059 | 6.55 | 2.63 | 9.18 |
| Wood, No. 1 red cedar, 5X, 16″ long, 5″ exposure, 4/12 pitch | 1.160 | S.F. | .038 | 4.08 | 1.88 | 5.96 |
| 8/12 pitch | 1.330 | S.F. | .042 | 4.42 | 2.04 | 6.46 |
| Fire retardant, 4/12 pitch | 1.160 | S.F. | .038 | 4.81 | 1.88 | 6.69 |
| 8/12 pitch | 1.330 | S.F. | .042 | 5.20 | 2.04 | 7.24 |
| 18″ long, No.1 perfections, 5″ exposure, 4/12 pitch | 1.160 | S.F. | .035 | 3.50 | 1.70 | 5.20 |
| 8/12 pitch | 1.330 | S.F. | .038 | 3.80 | 1.85 | 5.65 |
| Fire retardant, 4/12 pitch | 1.160 | S.F. | .035 | 4.23 | 1.70 | 5.93 |
| 8/12 pitch | 1.330 | S.F. | .038 | 4.59 | 1.85 | 6.44 |
| Resquared & rebutted, 18″ long, 6″ exposure, 4/12 pitch | 1.160 | S.F. | .032 | 3.11 | 1.57 | 4.68 |
| 8/12 pitch | 1.330 | S.F. | .035 | 3.37 | 1.70 | 5.07 |
| Fire retardant, 4/12 pitch | 1.160 | S.F. | .032 | 3.84 | 1.57 | 5.41 |
| 8/12 pitch | 1.330 | S.F. | .035 | 4.16 | 1.70 | 5.86 |
| Wood shakes hand split, 24″ long, 10″ exposure, 4/12 pitch | 1.160 | S.F. | .038 | 2.18 | 1.88 | 4.06 |
| 8/12 pitch | 1.330 | S.F. | .042 | 2.37 | 2.04 | 4.41 |
| Fire retardant, 4/12 pitch | 1.160 | S.F. | .038 | 2.91 | 1.88 | 4.79 |
| 8/12 pitch | 1.330 | S.F. | .042 | 3.16 | 2.04 | 5.20 |
| 18″ long, 8″ exposure, 4/12 pitch | 1.160 | S.F. | .048 | 1.93 | 2.35 | 4.28 |
| 8/12 pitch | 1.330 | S.F. | .052 | 2.09 | 2.55 | 4.64 |
| Fire retardant, 4/12 pitch | 1.160 | S.F. | .048 | 2.66 | 2.35 | 5.01 |
| 8/12 pitch | 1.330 | S.F. | .052 | 2.88 | 2.55 | 5.43 |
| Drip edge, metal, 5″ wide | .150 | L.F. | .003 | .08 | .15 | .23 |
| 8″ wide | .150 | L.F. | .003 | .11 | .15 | .26 |
| Building paper, #15 asphalt felt | 1.300 | S.F. | .002 | .08 | .08 | .16 |
| Ridge shingles, asphalt | .042 | L.F. | .001 | .09 | .04 | .13 |
| Clay | .042 | L.F. | .002 | .50 | .07 | .57 |
| Slate | .042 | L.F. | .002 | .43 | .07 | .50 |
| Wood, shingles | .042 | L.F. | .001 | .17 | .06 | .23 |
| Shakes | .042 | L.F. | .001 | .17 | .06 | .23 |
| Soffit & fascia, aluminum, vented, 1′ overhang | .083 | L.F. | .012 | .28 | .59 | .87 |
| 2′ overhang | .083 | L.F. | .013 | .46 | .65 | 1.11 |
| Vinyl, vented, 1′ overhang | .083 | L.F. | .011 | .31 | .54 | .85 |
| 2′ overhang | .083 | L.F. | .012 | .42 | .65 | 1.07 |
| Wood, board fascia, plywood soffit, 1′ overhang | .083 | L.F. | .004 | .02 | .15 | .17 |
| 2′ overhang | .083 | L.F. | .006 | .03 | .23 | .26 |
| Rake trim, painted, 1″ x 6″ | .040 | L.F. | .004 | .06 | .15 | .21 |
| 1″ x 8″ | .040 | L.F. | .004 | .10 | .16 | .26 |
| Gutter, 5″ box, aluminum, seamless, painted | .083 | L.F. | .006 | .22 | .30 | .52 |
| Vinyl | .083 | L.F. | .006 | .13 | .30 | .43 |
| Downspout, 2″ x 3″, aluminum, one story house | .035 | L.F. | .001 | .06 | .08 | .14 |
| Two story house | .060 | L.F. | .003 | .11 | .14 | .25 |
| Vinyl, one story house | .035 | L.F. | .002 | .07 | .08 | .15 |
| Two story house | .060 | L.F. | .003 | .11 | .14 | .25 |

195

Ridge Shingles

Building Paper

Drip Edge

Shingles

Soffit & Fascia

Gutter

Downspouts

| System Description | QUAN. | UNIT | LABOR HOURS | COST PER S.F. | | |
|---|---|---|---|---|---|---|
| | | | | MAT. | INST. | TOTAL |
| **ASPHALT, ROOF SHINGLES, CLASS A** | | | | | | |
| Shingles, inorganic, class A, 210-235 lb./sq. 4/12 pitch | 1.570 | S.F. | .023 | 1.29 | 1.02 | 2.31 |
| Drip edge, metal, 5″ wide | .122 | L.F. | .002 | .06 | .12 | .18 |
| Building paper, #15 asphalt felt | 1.800 | S.F. | .002 | .12 | .11 | .23 |
| Ridge shingles, asphalt | .075 | L.F. | .002 | .16 | .08 | .24 |
| Soffit & fascia, white painted aluminum, 1′ overhang | .120 | L.F. | .017 | .40 | .85 | 1.25 |
| Gutter, seamless, aluminum, painted | .120 | L.F. | .008 | .32 | .43 | .75 |
| Downspouts, aluminum, painted | .035 | L.F. | .002 | .07 | .08 | .15 |
| | | | | | | |
| TOTAL | | S.F. | .056 | 2.42 | 2.69 | 5.11 |
| **WOOD, CEDAR SHINGLES, NO. 1 PERFECTIONS, 18″ LONG** | | | | | | |
| Shingles, red cedar, No. 1 perfections, 5″ exp., 4/12 pitch | 1.570 | S.F. | .047 | 4.67 | 2.27 | 6.94 |
| Drip edge, metal, 5″ wide | .122 | L.F. | .002 | .06 | .12 | .18 |
| Building paper, #15 asphalt felt | 1.800 | S.F. | .002 | .12 | .11 | .23 |
| Ridge shingles, wood, cedar | .075 | L.F. | .002 | .30 | .11 | .41 |
| Soffit & fascia, white painted aluminum, 1′ overhang | .120 | L.F. | .017 | .40 | .85 | 1.25 |
| Gutter, seamless, aluminum, painted | .120 | L.F. | .008 | .32 | .43 | .75 |
| Downspouts, aluminum, painted | .035 | L.F. | .002 | .07 | .08 | .15 |
| | | | | | | |
| TOTAL | | S.F. | .080 | 5.94 | 3.97 | 9.91 |

The prices in these systems are based on a square foot of plan area.
All quantities have been adjusted accordingly.

| Description | QUAN. | UNIT | LABOR HOURS | COST PER S.F. | | |
|---|---|---|---|---|---|---|
| | | | | MAT. | INST. | TOTAL |
| | | | | | | |
| | | | | | | |
| | | | | | | |
| | | | | | | |
| | | | | | | |

| Hip Roof - Roofing Price Sheet | QUAN. | UNIT | LABOR HOURS | COST PER S.F. | | |
|---|---|---|---|---|---|---|
| | | | | MAT. | INST. | TOTAL |
| Shingles, asphalt, inorganic, class A, 210-235 lb./sq., 4/12 pitch | 1.570 | S.F. | .023 | 1.29 | 1.02 | 2.31 |
| 8/12 pitch | 1.850 | S.F. | .028 | 1.53 | 1.22 | 2.75 |
| Laminated, multi-layered, 240-260 lb./sq., 4/12 pitch | 1.570 | S.F. | .028 | 1.53 | 1.26 | 2.79 |
| 8/12 pitch | 1.850 | S.F. | .034 | 1.81 | 1.49 | 3.30 |
| Prem. laminated, multi-layered, 260-300 lb./sq., 4/12 pitch | 1.570 | S.F. | .037 | 1.76 | 1.62 | 3.38 |
| 8/12 pitch | 1.850 | S.F. | .043 | 2.09 | 1.92 | 4.01 |
| Clay tile, Spanish tile, red, 4/12 pitch | 1.570 | S.F. | .071 | 5.70 | 3.15 | 8.85 |
| 8/12 pitch | 1.850 | S.F. | .084 | 6.75 | 3.74 | 10.49 |
| Mission tile, red, 4/12 pitch | 1.570 | S.F. | .111 | 13.05 | 4.96 | 18.01 |
| 8/12 pitch | 1.850 | S.F. | .132 | 15.50 | 5.90 | 21.40 |
| French tile, red, 4/12 pitch | 1.570 | S.F. | .095 | 11.85 | 4.19 | 16.04 |
| 8/12 pitch | 1.850 | S.F. | .113 | 14.05 | 4.98 | 19.03 |
| Slate, Buckingham, Virginia, black, 4/12 pitch | 1.570 | S.F. | .073 | 8.40 | 3.23 | 11.63 |
| 8/12 pitch | 1.850 | S.F. | .087 | 10 | 3.84 | 13.84 |
| Vermont, black or grey, 4/12 pitch | 1.570 | S.F. | .073 | 8.10 | 3.23 | 11.33 |
| 8/12 pitch | 1.850 | S.F. | .087 | 9.60 | 3.84 | 13.44 |
| Wood, red cedar, No.1 5X, 16″ long, 5″ exposure, 4/12 pitch | 1.570 | S.F. | .051 | 5.45 | 2.51 | 7.96 |
| 8/12 pitch | 1.850 | S.F. | .061 | 6.45 | 2.98 | 9.43 |
| Fire retardant, 4/12 pitch | 1.570 | S.F. | .051 | 6.40 | 2.51 | 8.91 |
| 8/12 pitch | 1.850 | S.F. | .061 | 7.60 | 2.98 | 10.58 |
| 18″ long, No.1 perfections, 5″ exposure, 4/12 pitch | 1.570 | S.F. | .047 | 4.67 | 2.27 | 6.94 |
| 8/12 pitch | 1.850 | S.F. | .055 | 5.55 | 2.70 | 8.25 |
| Fire retardant, 4/12 pitch | 1.570 | S.F. | .047 | 5.65 | 2.27 | 7.92 |
| 8/12 pitch | 1.850 | S.F. | .055 | 6.70 | 2.70 | 9.40 |
| Resquared & rebutted, 18″ long, 6″ exposure, 4/12 pitch | 1.570 | S.F. | .043 | 4.14 | 2.10 | 6.24 |
| 8/12 pitch | 1.850 | S.F. | .051 | 4.92 | 2.49 | 7.41 |
| Fire retardant, 4/12 pitch | 1.570 | S.F. | .043 | 5.10 | 2.10 | 7.20 |
| 8/12 pitch | 1.850 | S.F. | .051 | 6.05 | 2.49 | 8.54 |
| Wood shakes hand split, 24″ long, 10″ exposure, 4/12 pitch | 1.570 | S.F. | .051 | 2.91 | 2.51 | 5.42 |
| 8/12 pitch | 1.850 | S.F. | .061 | 3.46 | 2.98 | 6.44 |
| Fire retardant, 4/12 pitch | 1.570 | S.F. | .051 | 3.88 | 2.51 | 6.39 |
| 8/12 pitch | 1.850 | S.F. | .061 | 4.61 | 2.98 | 7.59 |
| 18″ long, 8″ exposure, 4/12 pitch | 1.570 | S.F. | .064 | 2.58 | 3.14 | 5.72 |
| 8/12 pitch | 1.850 | S.F. | .076 | 3.06 | 3.72 | 6.78 |
| Fire retardant, 4/12 pitch | 1.570 | S.F. | .064 | 3.55 | 3.14 | 6.69 |
| 8/12 pitch | 1.850 | S.F. | .076 | 4.21 | 3.72 | 7.93 |
| Drip edge, metal, 5″ wide | .122 | L.F. | .002 | .06 | .12 | .18 |
| 8″ wide | .122 | L.F. | .002 | .09 | .12 | .21 |
| Building paper, #15 asphalt felt | 1.800 | S.F. | .002 | .12 | .11 | .23 |
| Ridge shingles, asphalt | .075 | L.F. | .002 | .16 | .08 | .24 |
| Clay | .075 | L.F. | .003 | .89 | .13 | 1.02 |
| Slate | .075 | L.F. | .003 | .77 | .13 | .90 |
| Wood, shingles | .075 | L.F. | .002 | .30 | .11 | .41 |
| Shakes | .075 | L.F. | .002 | .30 | .11 | .41 |
| Soffit & fascia, aluminum, vented, 1′ overhang | .120 | L.F. | .017 | .40 | .85 | 1.25 |
| 2′ overhang | .120 | L.F. | .019 | .66 | .94 | 1.60 |
| Vinyl, vented, 1′ overhang | .120 | L.F. | .016 | .44 | .79 | 1.23 |
| 2′ overhang | .120 | L.F. | .017 | .61 | .94 | 1.55 |
| Wood, board fascia, plywood soffit, 1′ overhang | .120 | L.F. | .004 | .02 | .15 | .17 |
| 2′ overhang | .120 | L.F. | .006 | .03 | .23 | .26 |
| Gutter, 5″ box, aluminum, seamless, painted | .120 | L.F. | .008 | .32 | .43 | .75 |
| Vinyl | .120 | L.F. | .009 | .18 | .43 | .61 |
| Downspout, 2″ x 3″, aluminum, one story house | .035 | L.F. | .002 | .07 | .08 | .15 |
| Two story house | .060 | L.F. | .003 | .11 | .14 | .25 |
| Vinyl, one story house | .035 | L.F. | .001 | .06 | .08 | .14 |
| Two story house | .060 | L.F. | .003 | .11 | .14 | .25 |

| System Description | QUAN. | UNIT | LABOR HOURS | COST PER S.F. | | |
|---|---|---|---|---|---|---|
| | | | | MAT. | INST. | TOTAL |
| **ASPHALT, ROOF SHINGLES, CLASS A** | | | | | | |
| Shingles, asphalt, inorganic, class A, 210-235 lb./sq. | 1.450 | S.F. | .022 | 1.21 | .96 | 2.17 |
| Drip edge, metal, 5" wide | .146 | L.F. | .003 | .08 | .14 | .22 |
| Building paper, #15 asphalt felt | 1.500 | S.F. | .002 | .10 | .09 | .19 |
| Ridge shingles, asphalt | .042 | L.F. | .001 | .09 | .04 | .13 |
| Soffit & fascia, painted aluminum, 1' overhang | .083 | L.F. | .012 | .28 | .59 | .87 |
| Rake trim, 1" x 6" | .063 | L.F. | .003 | .07 | .12 | .19 |
| Rake trim, prime and paint | .063 | L.F. | .003 | .02 | .12 | .14 |
| Gutter, seamless, aluminum, painted | .083 | L.F. | .006 | .22 | .30 | .52 |
| Downspouts, aluminum, painted | .042 | L.F. | .002 | .08 | .10 | .18 |
| TOTAL | | S.F. | .054 | 2.15 | 2.46 | 4.61 |
| **WOOD, CEDAR SHINGLES, NO. 1 PERFECTIONS, 18" LONG** | | | | | | |
| Shingles, wood, red cedar, No. 1 perfections, 5" exposure | 1.450 | S.F. | .044 | 4.38 | 2.13 | 6.51 |
| Drip edge, metal, 5" wide | .146 | L.F. | .003 | .08 | .14 | .22 |
| Building paper, #15 asphalt felt | 1.500 | S.F. | .002 | .10 | .09 | .19 |
| Ridge shingles, wood | .042 | L.F. | .001 | .17 | .06 | .23 |
| Soffit & fascia, white painted aluminum, 1' overhang | .083 | L.F. | .012 | .28 | .59 | .87 |
| Rake trim, 1" x 6" | .063 | L.F. | .003 | .07 | .12 | .19 |
| Rake trim, prime and paint | .063 | L.F. | .001 | .01 | .05 | .06 |
| Gutter, seamless, aluminum, painted | .083 | L.F. | .006 | .22 | .30 | .52 |
| Downspouts, aluminum, painted | .042 | L.F. | .002 | .08 | .10 | .18 |
| TOTAL | | S.F. | .074 | 5.39 | 3.58 | 8.97 |

The prices in this system are based on a square foot of plan area.
All quantities have been adjusted accordingly.

| Description | QUAN. | UNIT | LABOR HOURS | COST PER S.F. | | |
|---|---|---|---|---|---|---|
| | | | | MAT. | INST. | TOTAL |
| | | | | | | |
| | | | | | | |
| | | | | | | |
| | | | | | | |

| Gambrel Roofing Price Sheet | QUAN. | UNIT | LABOR HOURS | COST PER S.F. | | |
|---|---|---|---|---|---|---|
| | | | | MAT. | INST. | TOTAL |
| Shingles, asphalt, standard, inorganic, class A, 210-235 lb./sq. | 1.450 | S.F. | .022 | 1.21 | .96 | 2.17 |
| Laminated, multi-layered, 240-260 lb./sq. | 1.450 | S.F. | .027 | 1.43 | 1.18 | 2.61 |
| Premium laminated, multi-layered, 260-300 lb./sq. | 1.450 | S.F. | .034 | 1.65 | 1.52 | 3.17 |
| | | | | | | |
| Slate, Buckingham, Virginia, black | 1.450 | S.F. | .069 | 7.90 | 3.03 | 10.93 |
| Vermont, black or grey | 1.450 | S.F. | .069 | 7.60 | 3.03 | 10.63 |
| Wood, red cedar, No.1 5X, 16″ long, 5″ exposure, plain | 1.450 | S.F. | .048 | 5.10 | 2.36 | 7.46 |
| Fire retardant | 1.450 | S.F. | .048 | 6 | 2.36 | 8.36 |
| 18″ long, No.1 perfections, 6″ exposure, plain | 1.450 | S.F. | .044 | 4.38 | 2.13 | 6.51 |
| Fire retardant | 1.450 | S.F. | .044 | 5.30 | 2.13 | 7.43 |
| Resquared & rebutted, 18″ long, 6″ exposure, plain | 1.450 | S.F. | .040 | 3.89 | 1.97 | 5.86 |
| Fire retardant | 1.450 | S.F. | .040 | 4.80 | 1.97 | 6.77 |
| Shakes, hand split, 24″ long, 10″ exposure, plain | 1.450 | S.F. | .048 | 2.73 | 2.36 | 5.09 |
| Fire retardant | 1.450 | S.F. | .048 | 3.64 | 2.36 | 6 |
| 18″ long, 8″ exposure, plain | 1.450 | S.F. | .060 | 2.42 | 2.94 | 5.36 |
| Fire retardant | 1.450 | S.F. | .060 | 3.33 | 2.94 | 6.27 |
| Drip edge, metal, 5″ wide | .146 | L.F. | .003 | .08 | .14 | .22 |
| 8″ wide | .146 | L.F. | .003 | .11 | .14 | .25 |
| Building paper, #15 asphalt felt | 1.500 | S.F. | .002 | .10 | .09 | .19 |
| | | | | | | |
| Ridge shingles, asphalt | .042 | L.F. | .001 | .09 | .04 | .13 |
| Slate | .042 | L.F. | .002 | .43 | .07 | .50 |
| Wood, shingles | .042 | L.F. | .001 | .17 | .06 | .23 |
| Shakes | .042 | L.F. | .001 | .17 | .06 | .23 |
| Soffit & fascia, aluminum, vented, 1′ overhang | .083 | L.F. | .012 | .28 | .59 | .87 |
| 2′ overhang | .083 | L.F. | .013 | .46 | .65 | 1.11 |
| Vinyl vented, 1′ overhang | .083 | L.F. | .011 | .31 | .54 | .85 |
| 2′ overhang | .083 | L.F. | .012 | .42 | .65 | 1.07 |
| Wood board fascia, plywood soffit, 1′ overhang | .083 | L.F. | .004 | .02 | .15 | .17 |
| 2′ overhang | .083 | L.F. | .006 | .03 | .23 | .26 |
| Rake trim, painted, 1″ x 6″ | .063 | L.F. | .006 | .09 | .24 | .33 |
| 1″ x 8″ | .063 | L.F. | .007 | .12 | .31 | .43 |
| Gutter, 5″ box, aluminum, seamless, painted | .083 | L.F. | .006 | .22 | .30 | .52 |
| Vinyl | .083 | L.F. | .006 | .13 | .30 | .43 |
| Downspout 2″ x 3″, aluminum, one story house | .042 | L.F. | .002 | .07 | .09 | .16 |
| Two story house | .070 | L.F. | .003 | .12 | .16 | .28 |
| Vinyl, one story house | .042 | L.F. | .002 | .07 | .09 | .16 |
| Two story house | .070 | L.F. | .003 | .12 | .16 | .28 |
| | | | | | | |
| | | | | | | |
| | | | | | | |
| | | | | | | |
| | | | | | | |
| | | | | | | |
| | | | | | | |
| | | | | | | |
| | | | | | | |
| | | | | | | |
| | | | | | | |

| System Description | QUAN. | UNIT | LABOR HOURS | COST PER S.F. | | |
|---|---|---|---|---|---|---|
| | | | | MAT. | INST. | TOTAL |
| **ASPHALT, ROOF SHINGLES, CLASS A** | | | | | | |
| Shingles, standard inorganic class A 210-235 lb./sq. | 2.210 | S.F. | .032 | 1.77 | 1.41 | 3.18 |
| Drip edge, metal, 5" wide | .122 | L.F. | .002 | .06 | .12 | .18 |
| Building paper, #15 asphalt felt | 2.300 | S.F. | .003 | .15 | .14 | .29 |
| Ridge shingles, asphalt | .090 | L.F. | .002 | .19 | .10 | .29 |
| Soffit & fascia, white painted aluminum, 1' overhang | .122 | L.F. | .018 | .41 | .87 | 1.28 |
| Gutter, seamless, aluminum, painted | .122 | L.F. | .008 | .33 | .44 | .77 |
| Downspouts, aluminum, painted | .042 | L.F. | .002 | .08 | .10 | .18 |
| TOTAL | | S.F. | .067 | 2.99 | 3.18 | 6.17 |
| **WOOD, CEDAR SHINGLES, NO. 1 PERFECTIONS, 18" LONG** | | | | | | |
| Shingles, wood, red cedar, No. 1 perfections, 5" exposure | 2.210 | S.F. | .064 | 6.42 | 3.12 | 9.54 |
| Drip edge, metal, 5" wide | .122 | L.F. | .002 | .06 | .12 | .18 |
| Building paper, #15 asphalt felt | 2.300 | S.F. | .003 | .15 | .14 | .29 |
| Ridge shingles, wood | .090 | L.F. | .003 | .36 | .13 | .49 |
| Soffit & fascia, white painted aluminum, 1' overhang | .122 | L.F. | .018 | .41 | .87 | 1.28 |
| Gutter, seamless, aluminum, painted | .122 | L.F. | .008 | .33 | .44 | .77 |
| Downspouts, aluminum, painted | .042 | L.F. | .002 | .08 | .10 | .18 |
| TOTAL | | S.F. | .100 | 7.81 | 4.92 | 12.73 |

The prices in these systems are based on a square foot of plan area.
All quantities have been adjusted accordingly.

| Description | QUAN. | UNIT | LABOR HOURS | COST PER S.F. | | |
|---|---|---|---|---|---|---|
| | | | | MAT. | INST. | TOTAL |
| | | | | | | |
| | | | | | | |
| | | | | | | |
| | | | | | | |
| | | | | | | |

| Mansard Roofing Price Sheet | QUAN. | UNIT | LABOR HOURS | COST PER S.F. | | |
|---|---|---|---|---|---|---|
| | | | | MAT. | INST. | TOTAL |
| Shingles, asphalt, standard, inorganic, class A, 210-235 lb./sq. | 2.210 | S.F. | .032 | 1.77 | 1.41 | 3.18 |
| Laminated, multi-layered, 240-260 lb./sq. | 2.210 | S.F. | .039 | 2.10 | 1.73 | 3.83 |
| Premium laminated, multi-layered, 260-300 lb./sq. | 2.210 | S.F. | .050 | 2.42 | 2.22 | 4.64 |
| | | | | | | |
| Slate Buckingham, Virginia, black | 2.210 | S.F. | .101 | 11.55 | 4.44 | 15.99 |
| Vermont, black or grey | 2.210 | S.F. | .101 | 11.10 | 4.44 | 15.54 |
| Wood, red cedar, No.1 5X, 16" long, 5" exposure, plain | 2.210 | S.F. | .070 | 7.50 | 3.45 | 10.95 |
| Fire retardant | 2.210 | S.F. | .070 | 8.80 | 3.45 | 12.25 |
| 18" long, No.1 perfections 6" exposure, plain | 2.210 | S.F. | .064 | 6.40 | 3.12 | 9.52 |
| Fire retardant | 2.210 | S.F. | .064 | 7.75 | 3.12 | 10.87 |
| Fire retardant | 2.210 | S.F. | .059 | 7.05 | 2.88 | 9.93 |
| Shakes, hand split, 24" long 10" exposure, plain | 2.210 | S.F. | .070 | 4 | 3.45 | 7.45 |
| Fire retardant | 2.210 | S.F. | .070 | 5.35 | 3.45 | 8.80 |
| 18" long, 8" exposure, plain | 2.210 | S.F. | .088 | 3.54 | 4.31 | 7.85 |
| Fire retardant | 2.210 | S.F. | .088 | 4.87 | 4.31 | 9.18 |
| Drip edge, metal, 5" wide | .122 | S.F. | .002 | .06 | .12 | .18 |
| 8" wide | .122 | S.F. | .002 | .09 | .12 | .21 |
| Building paper, #15 asphalt felt | 2.300 | S.F. | .003 | .15 | .14 | .29 |
| | | | | | | |
| Ridge shingles, asphalt | .090 | L.F. | .002 | .19 | .10 | .29 |
| Slate | .090 | L.F. | .004 | .92 | .16 | 1.08 |
| Wood, shingles | .090 | L.F. | .003 | .36 | .13 | .49 |
| Shakes | .090 | L.F. | .003 | .36 | .13 | .49 |
| Soffit & fascia, aluminum vented, 1' overhang | .122 | L.F. | .018 | .41 | .87 | 1.28 |
| 2' overhang | .122 | L.F. | .020 | .67 | .96 | 1.63 |
| Vinyl vented, 1' overhang | .122 | L.F. | .016 | .45 | .80 | 1.25 |
| 2' overhang | .122 | L.F. | .018 | .62 | .96 | 1.58 |
| Wood board fascia, plywood soffit, 1' overhang | .122 | L.F. | .013 | .30 | .59 | .89 |
| 2' overhang | .122 | L.F. | .019 | .40 | .90 | 1.30 |
| Gutter, 5" box, aluminum, seamless, painted | .122 | L.F. | .008 | .33 | .44 | .77 |
| Vinyl | .122 | L.F. | .009 | .19 | .43 | .62 |
| Downspout 2" x 3", aluminum, one story house | .042 | L.F. | .002 | .07 | .09 | .16 |
| Two story house | .070 | L.F. | .003 | .12 | .16 | .28 |
| Vinyl, one story house | .042 | L.F. | .002 | .07 | .09 | .16 |
| Two story house | .070 | L.F. | .003 | .12 | .16 | .28 |

| System Description | QUAN. | UNIT | LABOR HOURS | COST PER S.F. | | |
|---|---|---|---|---|---|---|
| | | | | MAT. | INST. | TOTAL |
| **ASPHALT, ROOF SHINGLES, CLASS A** | | | | | | |
| Shingles, inorganic class A 210-235 lb./sq. 4/12 pitch | 1.230 | S.F. | .019 | 1.05 | .83 | 1.88 |
| Drip edge, metal, 5″ wide | .100 | L.F. | .002 | .05 | .10 | .15 |
| Building paper, #15 asphalt felt | 1.300 | S.F. | .002 | .08 | .08 | .16 |
| Soffit & fascia, white painted aluminum, 1′ overhang | .080 | L.F. | .012 | .27 | .57 | .84 |
| Rake trim, 1″ x 6″ | .043 | L.F. | .002 | .05 | .08 | .13 |
| Rake trim, prime and paint | .043 | L.F. | .002 | .01 | .08 | .09 |
| Gutter, seamless, aluminum, painted | .040 | L.F. | .003 | .11 | .14 | .25 |
| Downspouts, painted aluminum | .020 | L.F. | .001 | .04 | .05 | .09 |
| | | | | | | |
| TOTAL | | S.F. | .043 | 1.66 | 1.93 | 3.59 |
| **WOOD, CEDAR SHINGLES, NO. 1 PERFECTIONS, 18″ LONG** | | | | | | |
| Shingles, red cedar, No. 1 perfections, 5″ exp., 4/12 pitch | 1.230 | S.F. | .035 | 3.50 | 1.70 | 5.20 |
| Drip edge, metal, 5″ wide | .100 | L.F. | .002 | .05 | .10 | .15 |
| Building paper, #15 asphalt felt | 1.300 | S.F. | .002 | .08 | .08 | .16 |
| Soffit & fascia, white painted aluminum, 1′ overhang | .080 | L.F. | .012 | .27 | .57 | .84 |
| Rake trim, 1″ x 6″ | .043 | L.F. | .002 | .05 | .08 | .13 |
| Rake trim, prime and paint | .043 | L.F. | .001 | .01 | .04 | .05 |
| Gutter, seamless, aluminum, painted | .040 | L.F. | .003 | .11 | .14 | .25 |
| Downspouts, painted aluminum | .020 | L.F. | .001 | .04 | .05 | .09 |
| | | | | | | |
| TOTAL | | S.F. | .058 | 4.11 | 2.76 | 6.87 |

The prices in these systems are based on a square foot of plan area.
All quantities have been adjusted accordingly.

| Description | QUAN. | UNIT | LABOR HOURS | COST PER S.F. | | |
|---|---|---|---|---|---|---|
| | | | | MAT. | INST. | TOTAL |
| | | | | | | |
| | | | | | | |
| | | | | | | |
| | | | | | | |

| Shed Roofing Price Sheet | QUAN. | UNIT | LABOR HOURS | COST PER S.F. | | |
|---|---|---|---|---|---|---|
| | | | | MAT. | INST. | TOTAL |
| Shingles, asphalt, inorganic, class A, 210-235 lb./sq., 4/12 pitch | 1.230 | S.F. | .017 | .97 | .77 | 1.74 |
| 8/12 pitch | 1.330 | S.F. | .019 | 1.05 | .83 | 1.88 |
| Laminated, multi-layered, 240-260 lb./sq. 4/12 pitch | 1.230 | S.F. | .021 | 1.15 | .94 | 2.09 |
| 8/12 pitch | 1.330 | S.F. | .023 | 1.24 | 1.02 | 2.26 |
| Premium laminated, multi-layered, 260-300 lb./sq. 4/12 pitch | 1.230 | S.F. | .027 | 1.32 | 1.21 | 2.53 |
| 8/12 pitch | 1.330 | S.F. | .030 | 1.43 | 1.31 | 2.74 |
| Clay tile, Spanish tile, red, 4/12 pitch | 1.230 | S.F. | .053 | 4.26 | 2.36 | 6.62 |
| 8/12 pitch | 1.330 | S.F. | .058 | 4.62 | 2.56 | 7.18 |
| Mission tile, red, 4/12 pitch | 1.230 | S.F. | .083 | 9.80 | 3.72 | 13.52 |
| 8/12 pitch | 1.330 | S.F. | .090 | 10.60 | 4.03 | 14.63 |
| French tile, red, 4/12 pitch | 1.230 | S.F. | .071 | 8.90 | 3.14 | 12.04 |
| 8/12 pitch | 1.330 | S.F. | .077 | 9.60 | 3.41 | 13.01 |
| Slate, Buckingham, Virginia, black, 4/12 pitch | 1.230 | S.F. | .055 | 6.30 | 2.42 | 8.72 |
| 8/12 pitch | 1.330 | S.F. | .059 | 6.85 | 2.63 | 9.48 |
| Vermont, black or grey, 4/12 pitch | 1.230 | S.F. | .055 | 6.05 | 2.42 | 8.47 |
| 8/12 pitch | 1.330 | S.F. | .059 | 6.55 | 2.63 | 9.18 |
| Wood, red cedar, No.1 5X, 16" long, 5" exposure, 4/12 pitch | 1.230 | S.F. | .038 | 4.08 | 1.88 | 5.96 |
| 8/12 pitch | 1.330 | S.F. | .042 | 4.42 | 2.04 | 6.46 |
| Fire retardant, 4/12 pitch | 1.230 | S.F. | .038 | 4.81 | 1.88 | 6.69 |
| 8/12 pitch | 1.330 | S.F. | .042 | 5.20 | 2.04 | 7.24 |
| 18" long, 6" exposure, 4/12 pitch | 1.230 | S.F. | .035 | 3.50 | 1.70 | 5.20 |
| 8/12 pitch | 1.330 | S.F. | .038 | 3.80 | 1.85 | 5.65 |
| Fire retardant, 4/12 pitch | 1.230 | S.F. | .035 | 4.23 | 1.70 | 5.93 |
| 8/12 pitch | 1.330 | S.F. | .038 | 4.59 | 1.85 | 6.44 |
| Resquared & rebutted, 18" long, 6" exposure, 4/12 pitch | 1.230 | S.F. | .032 | 3.11 | 1.57 | 4.68 |
| 8/12 pitch | 1.330 | S.F. | .035 | 3.37 | 1.70 | 5.07 |
| Fire retardant, 4/12 pitch | 1.230 | S.F. | .032 | 3.84 | 1.57 | 5.41 |
| 8/12 pitch | 1.330 | S.F. | .035 | 4.16 | 1.70 | 5.86 |
| Wood shakes, hand split, 24" long, 10" exposure, 4/12 pitch | 1.230 | S.F. | .038 | 2.18 | 1.88 | 4.06 |
| 8/12 pitch | 1.330 | S.F. | .042 | 2.37 | 2.04 | 4.41 |
| Fire retardant, 4/12 pitch | 1.230 | S.F. | .038 | 2.91 | 1.88 | 4.79 |
| 8/12 pitch | 1.330 | S.F. | .042 | 3.16 | 2.04 | 5.20 |
| 18" long, 8" exposure, 4/12 pitch | 1.230 | S.F. | .048 | 1.93 | 2.35 | 4.28 |
| 8/12 pitch | 1.330 | S.F. | .052 | 2.09 | 2.55 | 4.64 |
| Fire retardant, 4/12 pitch | 1.230 | S.F. | .048 | 2.66 | 2.35 | 5.01 |
| 8/12 pitch | 1.330 | S.F. | .052 | 2.88 | 2.55 | 5.43 |
| Drip edge, metal, 5" wide | .100 | L.F. | .002 | .05 | .10 | .15 |
| 8" wide | .100 | L.F. | .002 | .08 | .10 | .18 |
| Building paper, #15 asphalt felt | 1.300 | S.F. | .002 | .08 | .08 | .16 |
| Soffit & fascia, aluminum vented, 1' overhang | .080 | L.F. | .012 | .27 | .57 | .84 |
| 2' overhang | .080 | L.F. | .013 | .44 | .63 | 1.07 |
| Vinyl vented, 1' overhang | .080 | L.F. | .011 | .30 | .52 | .82 |
| 2' overhang | .080 | L.F. | .012 | .40 | .63 | 1.03 |
| Wood board fascia, plywood soffit, 1' overhang | .080 | L.F. | .010 | .21 | .44 | .65 |
| 2' overhang | .080 | L.F. | .014 | .28 | .66 | .94 |
| Rake, trim, painted, 1" x 6" | .043 | L.F. | .004 | .06 | .16 | .22 |
| 1" x 8" | .043 | L.F. | .004 | .06 | .16 | .22 |
| Gutter, 5" box, aluminum, seamless, painted | .040 | L.F. | .003 | .11 | .14 | .25 |
| Vinyl | .040 | L.F. | .003 | .06 | .14 | .20 |
| Downspout 2" x 3", aluminum, one story house | .020 | L.F. | .001 | .04 | .05 | .09 |
| Two story house | .020 | L.F. | .001 | .06 | .07 | .13 |
| Vinyl, one story house | .020 | L.F. | .001 | .04 | .05 | .09 |
| Two story house | .020 | L.F. | .001 | .06 | .07 | .13 |
| | | | | | | |
| | | | | | | |
| | | | | | | |

Ridge Shingles — Building Paper — Rake Boards — Drip Edge — Soffit & Fascia — Shingles — Flashing

| System Description | QUAN. | UNIT | LABOR HOURS | COST PER S.F. | | |
|---|---|---|---|---|---|---|
| | | | | MAT. | INST. | TOTAL |
| **ASPHALT, ROOF SHINGLES, CLASS A** | | | | | | |
| Shingles, standard inorganic class A 210-235 lb./sq | 1.400 | S.F. | .020 | 1.13 | .90 | 2.03 |
| Drip edge, metal, 5" wide | .220 | L.F. | .004 | .12 | .22 | .34 |
| Building paper, #15 asphalt felt | 1.500 | S.F. | .002 | .10 | .09 | .19 |
| Ridge shingles, asphalt | .280 | L.F. | .007 | .59 | .30 | .89 |
| Soffit & fascia, aluminum, vented | .220 | L.F. | .032 | .74 | 1.56 | 2.30 |
| Flashing, aluminum, mill finish, .013" thick | 1.500 | S.F. | .083 | 1.11 | 3.65 | 4.76 |
| TOTAL | | S.F. | .148 | 3.79 | 6.72 | 10.51 |
| **WOOD, CEDAR, NO. 1 PERFECTIONS** | | | | | | |
| Shingles, red cedar, No.1 perfections, 18" long, 5" exp. | 1.400 | S.F. | .041 | 4.09 | 1.99 | 6.08 |
| Drip edge, metal, 5" wide | .220 | L.F. | .004 | .12 | .22 | .34 |
| Building paper, #15 asphalt felt | 1.500 | S.F. | .002 | .10 | .09 | .19 |
| Ridge shingles, wood | .280 | L.F. | .008 | 1.11 | .39 | 1.50 |
| Soffit & fascia, aluminum, vented | .220 | L.F. | .032 | .74 | 1.56 | 2.30 |
| Flashing, aluminum, mill finish, .013" thick | 1.500 | S.F. | .083 | 1.11 | 3.65 | 4.76 |
| TOTAL | | S.F. | .170 | 7.27 | 7.90 | 15.17 |
| **SLATE, BUCKINGHAM, BLACK** | | | | | | |
| Shingles, Buckingham, Virginia, black | 1.400 | S.F. | .064 | 7.35 | 2.83 | 10.18 |
| Drip edge, metal, 5" wide | .220 | L.F. | .004 | .12 | .22 | .34 |
| Building paper, #15 asphalt felt | 1.500 | S.F. | .002 | .10 | .09 | .19 |
| Ridge shingles, slate | .280 | L.F. | .011 | 2.86 | .50 | 3.36 |
| Soffit & fascia, aluminum, vented | .220 | L.F. | .032 | .74 | 1.56 | 2.30 |
| Flashing, copper, 16 oz. | 1.500 | S.F. | .104 | 12.45 | 4.59 | 17.04 |
| TOTAL | | S.F. | .217 | 23.62 | 9.79 | 33.41 |

The prices in these systems are based on a square foot of plan area under the dormer roof.

| Description | QUAN. | UNIT | LABOR HOURS | COST PER S.F. | | |
|---|---|---|---|---|---|---|
| | | | | MAT. | INST. | TOTAL |
| | | | | | | |
| | | | | | | |
| | | | | | | |
| | | | | | | |
| | | | | | | |

# Gable Dormer Roofing Price Sheet

| | QUAN. | UNIT | LABOR HOURS | COST PER S.F. | | |
|---|---|---|---|---|---|---|
| | | | | MAT. | INST. | TOTAL |
| Shingles, asphalt, standard, inorganic, class A, 210-235 lb./sq. | 1.400 | S.F. | .020 | 1.13 | .90 | 2.03 |
| Laminated, multi-layered, 240-260 lb./sq. | 1.400 | S.F. | .025 | 1.34 | 1.10 | 2.44 |
| Premium laminated, multi-layered, 260-300 lb./sq. | 1.400 | S.F. | .032 | 1.54 | 1.41 | 2.95 |
| | | | | | | |
| Clay tile, Spanish tile, red | 1.400 | S.F. | .062 | 4.97 | 2.76 | 7.73 |
| Mission tile, red | 1.400 | S.F. | .097 | 11.40 | 4.34 | 15.74 |
| French tile, red | 1.400 | S.F. | .083 | 10.35 | 3.67 | 14.02 |
| | | | | | | |
| Slate Buckingham, Virginia, black | 1.400 | S.F. | .064 | 7.35 | 2.83 | 10.18 |
| Vermont, black or grey | 1.400 | S.F. | .064 | 7.05 | 2.83 | 9.88 |
| Wood, red cedar, No.1 5X, 16" long, 5" exposure | 1.400 | S.F. | .045 | 4.76 | 2.20 | 6.96 |
| Fire retardant | 1.400 | S.F. | .045 | 5.60 | 2.20 | 7.80 |
| 18" long, No.1 perfections, 5" exposure | 1.400 | S.F. | .041 | 4.09 | 1.99 | 6.08 |
| Fire retardant | 1.400 | S.F. | .041 | 4.94 | 1.99 | 6.93 |
| Resquared & rebutted, 18" long, 5" exposure | 1.400 | S.F. | .037 | 3.63 | 1.83 | 5.46 |
| Fire retardant | 1.400 | S.F. | .037 | 4.48 | 1.83 | 6.31 |
| Shakes hand split, 24" long, 10" exposure | 1.400 | S.F. | .045 | 2.55 | 2.20 | 4.75 |
| Fire retardant | 1.400 | S.F. | .045 | 3.40 | 2.20 | 5.60 |
| 18" long, 8" exposure | 1.400 | S.F. | .056 | 2.25 | 2.74 | 4.99 |
| Fire retardant | 1.400 | S.F. | .056 | 3.10 | 2.74 | 5.84 |
| Drip edge, metal, 5" wide | .220 | L.F. | .004 | .12 | .22 | .34 |
| 8" wide | .220 | L.F. | .004 | .17 | .22 | .39 |
| Building paper, #15 asphalt felt | 1.500 | S.F. | .002 | .10 | .09 | .19 |
| | | | | | | |
| Ridge shingles, asphalt | .280 | L.F. | .007 | .59 | .30 | .89 |
| Clay | .280 | L.F. | .011 | 3.30 | .50 | 3.80 |
| Slate | .280 | L.F. | .011 | 2.86 | .50 | 3.36 |
| Wood | .280 | L.F. | .008 | 1.11 | .39 | 1.50 |
| Soffit & fascia, aluminum, vented | .220 | L.F. | .032 | .74 | 1.56 | 2.30 |
| Vinyl, vented | .220 | L.F. | .029 | .81 | 1.44 | 2.25 |
| Wood, board fascia, plywood soffit | .220 | L.F. | .026 | .58 | 1.20 | 1.78 |
| | | | | | | |
| Flashing, aluminum, .013" thick | 1.500 | S.F. | .083 | 1.11 | 3.65 | 4.76 |
| .032" thick | 1.500 | S.F. | .083 | 2.45 | 3.65 | 6.10 |
| .040" thick | 1.500 | S.F. | .083 | 3.65 | 3.65 | 7.30 |
| .050" thick | 1.500 | S.F. | .083 | 4.16 | 3.65 | 7.81 |
| Copper, 16 oz. | 1.500 | S.F. | .104 | 12.45 | 4.59 | 17.04 |
| 20 oz. | 1.500 | S.F. | .109 | 14.95 | 4.80 | 19.75 |
| 24 oz. | 1.500 | S.F. | .114 | 18.70 | 5.05 | 23.75 |
| 32 oz. | 1.500 | S.F. | .120 | 23.50 | 5.30 | 28.80 |
| | | | | | | |
| | | | | | | |
| | | | | | | |
| | | | | | | |
| | | | | | | |
| | | | | | | |
| | | | | | | |
| | | | | | | |
| | | | | | | |

Building Paper — Shingles

Drip Edge

Rake Boards

Soffit & Fascia

Flashing

| System Description | QUAN. | UNIT | LABOR HOURS | COST PER S.F. | | |
|---|---|---|---|---|---|---|
| | | | | MAT. | INST. | TOTAL |
| **ASPHALT, ROOF SHINGLES, CLASS A** | | | | | | |
| Shingles, standard inorganic class A 210-235 lb./sq. | 1.100 | S.F. | .016 | .89 | .70 | 1.59 |
| Drip edge, aluminum, 5" wide | .250 | L.F. | .005 | .11 | .25 | .36 |
| Building paper, #15 asphalt felt | 1.200 | S.F. | .002 | .08 | .07 | .15 |
| Soffit & fascia, aluminum, vented, 1' overhang | .250 | L.F. | .036 | .84 | 1.78 | 2.62 |
| Flashing, aluminum, mill finish, 0.013" thick | .800 | L.F. | .044 | .59 | 1.94 | 2.53 |
| TOTAL | | S.F. | .103 | 2.51 | 4.74 | 7.25 |
| **WOOD, CEDAR, NO. 1 PERFECTIONS, 18" LONG** | | | | | | |
| Shingles, wood, red cedar, #1 perfections, 5" exposure | 1.100 | S.F. | .032 | 3.21 | 1.56 | 4.77 |
| Drip edge, aluminum, 5" wide | .250 | L.F. | .005 | .11 | .25 | .36 |
| Building paper, #15 asphalt felt | 1.200 | S.F. | .002 | .08 | .07 | .15 |
| Soffit & fascia, aluminum, vented, 1' overhang | .250 | L.F. | .036 | .84 | 1.78 | 2.62 |
| Flashing, aluminum, mill finish, 0.013" thick | .800 | L.F. | .044 | .59 | 1.94 | 2.53 |
| TOTAL | | S.F. | .119 | 4.83 | 5.60 | 10.43 |
| **SLATE, BUCKINGHAM, BLACK** | | | | | | |
| Shingles, slate, Buckingham, black | 1.100 | S.F. | .050 | 5.78 | 2.22 | 8 |
| Drip edge, aluminum, 5" wide | .250 | L.F. | .005 | .11 | .25 | .36 |
| Building paper, #15 asphalt felt | 1.200 | S.F. | .002 | .08 | .07 | .15 |
| Soffit & fascia, aluminum, vented, 1' overhang | .250 | L.F. | .036 | .84 | 1.78 | 2.62 |
| Flashing, copper, 16 oz. | .800 | L.F. | .056 | 6.64 | 2.45 | 9.09 |
| TOTAL | | S.F. | .149 | 13.45 | 6.77 | 20.22 |

The prices in this system are based on a square foot of plan area under the dormer roof.

| Description | QUAN. | UNIT | LABOR HOURS | COST PER S.F. | | |
|---|---|---|---|---|---|---|
| | | | | MAT. | INST. | TOTAL |
| | | | | | | |
| | | | | | | |
| | | | | | | |
| | | | | | | |
| | | | | | | |

| Shed Dormer Roofing Price Sheet | QUAN. | UNIT | LABOR HOURS | COST PER S.F. | | |
|---|---|---|---|---|---|---|
| | | | | MAT. | INST. | TOTAL |
| Shingles, asphalt, standard, inorganic, class A, 210-235 lb./sq. | 1.100 | S.F. | .016 | .89 | .70 | 1.59 |
| Laminated, multi-layered, 240-260 lb./sq. | 1.100 | S.F. | .020 | 1.05 | .86 | 1.91 |
| Premium laminated, multi-layered, 260-300 lb./sq. | 1.100 | S.F. | .025 | 1.21 | 1.11 | 2.32 |
| | | | | | | |
| Clay tile, Spanish tile, red | 1.100 | S.F. | .049 | 3.91 | 2.17 | 6.08 |
| Mission tile, red | 1.100 | S.F. | .077 | 8.95 | 3.41 | 12.36 |
| French tile, red | 1.100 | S.F. | .065 | 8.15 | 2.88 | 11.03 |
| | | | | | | |
| Slate Buckingham, Virginia, black | 1.100 | S.F. | .050 | 5.80 | 2.22 | 8.02 |
| Vermont, black or grey | 1.100 | S.F. | .050 | 5.55 | 2.22 | 7.77 |
| Wood, red cedar, No. 1 5X, 16" long, 5" exposure | 1.100 | S.F. | .035 | 3.74 | 1.73 | 5.47 |
| Fire retardant | 1.100 | S.F. | .035 | 4.41 | 1.73 | 6.14 |
| 18" long, No.1 perfections, 5" exposure | 1.100 | S.F. | .032 | 3.21 | 1.56 | 4.77 |
| Fire retardant | 1.100 | S.F. | .032 | 3.88 | 1.56 | 5.44 |
| Resquared & rebutted, 18" long, 5" exposure | 1.100 | S.F. | .029 | 2.85 | 1.44 | 4.29 |
| Fire retardant | 1.100 | S.F. | .029 | 3.52 | 1.44 | 4.96 |
| Shakes hand split, 24" long, 10" exposure | 1.100 | S.F. | .035 | 2 | 1.73 | 3.73 |
| Fire retardant | 1.100 | S.F. | .035 | 2.67 | 1.73 | 4.40 |
| 18" long, 8" exposure | 1.100 | S.F. | .044 | 1.77 | 2.16 | 3.93 |
| Fire retardant | 1.100 | S.F. | .044 | 2.44 | 2.16 | 4.60 |
| Drip edge, metal, 5" wide | .250 | L.F. | .005 | .11 | .25 | .36 |
| 8" wide | .250 | L.F. | .005 | .19 | .25 | .44 |
| Building paper, #15 asphalt felt | 1.200 | S.F. | .002 | .08 | .07 | .15 |
| | | | | | | |
| Soffit & fascia, aluminum, vented | .250 | L.F. | .036 | .84 | 1.78 | 2.62 |
| Vinyl, vented | .250 | L.F. | .033 | .93 | 1.64 | 2.57 |
| Wood, board fascia, plywood soffit | .250 | L.F. | .030 | .65 | 1.38 | 2.03 |
| | | | | | | |
| Flashing, aluminum, .013" thick | .800 | L.F. | .044 | .59 | 1.94 | 2.53 |
| .032" thick | .800 | L.F. | .044 | 1.30 | 1.94 | 3.24 |
| .040" thick | .800 | L.F. | .044 | 1.94 | 1.94 | 3.88 |
| .050" thick | .800 | L.F. | .044 | 2.22 | 1.94 | 4.16 |
| Copper, 16 oz. | .800 | L.F. | .056 | 6.65 | 2.45 | 9.10 |
| 20 oz. | .800 | L.F. | .058 | 7.95 | 2.56 | 10.51 |
| 24 oz. | .800 | L.F. | .061 | 9.95 | 2.69 | 12.64 |
| 32 oz. | .800 | L.F. | .064 | 12.40 | 2.82 | 15.22 |
| | | | | | | |
| | | | | | | |
| | | | | | | |
| | | | | | | |
| | | | | | | |
| | | | | | | |
| | | | | | | |
| | | | | | | |
| | | | | | | |
| | | | | | | |
| | | | | | | |
| | | | | | | |

| System Description | QUAN. | UNIT | LABOR HOURS | COST EACH | | |
|---|---|---|---|---|---|---|
| | | | | MAT. | INST. | TOTAL |
| **SKYLIGHT, FIXED, 32″ X 32″** | | | | | | |
| Skylight, fixed bubble, insulating, 32″ x 32″ | 1.000 | Ea. | 1.422 | 192 | 64 | 256 |
| Trimmer rafters, 2″ x 6″ | 28.000 | L.F. | .448 | 11.48 | 21.84 | 33.32 |
| Headers, 2″ x 6″ | 6.000 | L.F. | .267 | 2.46 | 13.08 | 15.54 |
| Curb, 2″ x 4″ | 12.000 | L.F. | .154 | 3.24 | 7.56 | 10.80 |
| Flashing, aluminum, .013″ thick | 13.500 | S.F. | .745 | 9.99 | 32.81 | 42.80 |
| Trim, stock pine, 11/16″ x 2-1/2″ | 12.000 | L.F. | .400 | 17.52 | 19.56 | 37.08 |
| Trim primer coat, oil base, brushwork | 12.000 | L.F. | .148 | .48 | 6.24 | 6.72 |
| Trim paint, 1 coat, brushwork | 12.000 | L.F. | .148 | .72 | 6.24 | 6.96 |
| TOTAL | | Ea. | 3.732 | 237.89 | 171.33 | 409.22 |
| **SKYLIGHT, FIXED, 48″ X 48″** | | | | | | |
| Skylight, fixed bubble, insulating, 48″ x 48″ | 1.000 | Ea. | 1.296 | 416 | 58.24 | 474.24 |
| Trimmer rafters, 2″ x 6″ | 28.000 | L.F. | .448 | 11.48 | 21.84 | 33.32 |
| Headers, 2″ x 6″ | 8.000 | L.F. | .356 | 3.28 | 17.44 | 20.72 |
| Curb, 2″ x 4″ | 16.000 | L.F. | .205 | 4.32 | 10.08 | 14.40 |
| Flashing, aluminum, .013″ thick | 16.000 | S.F. | .883 | 11.84 | 38.88 | 50.72 |
| Trim, stock pine, 11/16″ x 2-1/2″ | 16.000 | L.F. | .533 | 23.36 | 26.08 | 49.44 |
| Trim primer coat, oil base, brushwork | 16.000 | L.F. | .197 | .64 | 8.32 | 8.96 |
| Trim paint, 1 coat, brushwork | 16.000 | L.F. | .197 | .96 | 8.32 | 9.28 |
| TOTAL | | Ea. | 4.115 | 471.88 | 189.20 | 661.08 |
| **SKYWINDOW, OPERATING, 24″ X 48″** | | | | | | |
| Skywindow, operating, thermopane glass, 24″ x 48″ | 1.000 | Ea. | 3.200 | 620 | 144 | 764 |
| Trimmer rafters, 2″ x 6″ | 28.000 | L.F. | .448 | 11.48 | 21.84 | 33.32 |
| Headers, 2″ x 6″ | 8.000 | L.F. | .267 | 2.46 | 13.08 | 15.54 |
| Curb, 2″ x 4″ | 14.000 | L.F. | .179 | 3.78 | 8.82 | 12.60 |
| Flashing, aluminum, .013″ thick | 14.000 | S.F. | .772 | 10.36 | 34.02 | 44.38 |
| Trim, stock pine, 11/16″ x 2-1/2″ | 14.000 | L.F. | .467 | 20.44 | 22.82 | 43.26 |
| Trim primer coat, oil base, brushwork | 14.000 | L.F. | .172 | .56 | 7.28 | 7.84 |
| Trim paint, 1 coat, brushwork | 14.000 | L.F. | .172 | .84 | 7.28 | 8.12 |
| TOTAL | | Ea. | 5.677 | 669.92 | 259.14 | 929.06 |

The prices in these systems are on a cost each basis.

| Description | QUAN. | UNIT | LABOR HOURS | COST EACH | | |
|---|---|---|---|---|---|---|
| | | | | MAT. | INST. | TOTAL |
| | | | | | | |

| Skylight/Skywindow Price Sheet | QUAN. | UNIT | LABOR HOURS | COST EACH | | |
|---|---|---|---|---|---|---|
| | | | | MAT. | INST. | TOTAL |
| Skylight, fixed bubble insulating, 24″ x 24″ | 1.000 | Ea. | .800 | 108 | 36 | 144 |
| 32″ x 32″ | 1.000 | Ea. | 1.422 | 192 | 64 | 256 |
| 32″ x 48″ | 1.000 | Ea. | .864 | 277 | 39 | 316 |
| 48″ x 48″ | 1.000 | Ea. | 1.296 | 415 | 58 | 473 |
| Ventilating bubble insulating, 36″ x 36″ | 1.000 | Ea. | 2.667 | 505 | 120 | 625 |
| 52″ x 52″ | 1.000 | Ea. | 2.667 | 705 | 120 | 825 |
| 28″ x 52″ | 1.000 | Ea. | 3.200 | 515 | 144 | 659 |
| 36″ x 52″ | 1.000 | Ea. | 3.200 | 570 | 144 | 714 |
| Skywindow, operating, thermopane glass, 24″ x 48″ | 1.000 | Ea. | 3.200 | 620 | 144 | 764 |
| 32″ x 48″ | 1.000 | Ea. | 3.556 | 645 | 160 | 805 |
| Trimmer rafters, 2″ x 6″ | 28.000 | L.F. | .448 | 11.50 | 22 | 33.50 |
| 2″ x 8″ | 28.000 | L.F. | .472 | 17.10 | 23 | 40.10 |
| 2″ x 10″ | 28.000 | L.F. | .711 | 22.50 | 34.50 | 57 |
| Headers, 24″ window, 2″ x 6″ | 4.000 | L.F. | .178 | 1.64 | 8.70 | 10.34 |
| 2″ x 8″ | 4.000 | L.F. | .188 | 2.44 | 9.20 | 11.64 |
| 2″ x 10″ | 4.000 | L.F. | .200 | 3.20 | 9.80 | 13 |
| 32″ window, 2″ x 6″ | 6.000 | L.F. | .267 | 2.46 | 13.10 | 15.56 |
| 2″ x 8″ | 6.000 | L.F. | .282 | 3.66 | 13.80 | 17.46 |
| 2″ x 10″ | 6.000 | L.F. | .300 | 4.80 | 14.70 | 19.50 |
| 48″ window, 2″ x 6″ | 8.000 | L.F. | .356 | 3.28 | 17.45 | 20.73 |
| 2″ x 8″ | 8.000 | L.F. | .376 | 4.88 | 18.40 | 23.28 |
| 2″ x 10″ | 8.000 | L.F. | .400 | 6.40 | 19.60 | 26 |
| Curb, 2″ x 4″, skylight, 24″ x 24″ | 8.000 | L.F. | .102 | 2.16 | 5.05 | 7.21 |
| 32″ x 32″ | 12.000 | L.F. | .154 | 3.24 | 7.55 | 10.79 |
| 32″ x 48″ | 14.000 | L.F. | .179 | 3.78 | 8.80 | 12.58 |
| 48″ x 48″ | 16.000 | L.F. | .205 | 4.32 | 10.10 | 14.42 |
| Flashing, aluminum .013″ thick, skylight, 24″ x 24″ | 9.000 | S.F. | .497 | 6.65 | 22 | 28.65 |
| 32″ x 32″ | 13.500 | S.F. | .745 | 10 | 33 | 43 |
| 32″ x 48″ | 14.000 | S.F. | .772 | 10.35 | 34 | 44.35 |
| 48″ x 48″ | 16.000 | S.F. | .883 | 11.85 | 39 | 50.85 |
| Copper 16 oz., skylight, 24″ x 24″ | 9.000 | S.F. | .626 | 74.50 | 27.50 | 102 |
| 32″ x 32″ | 13.500 | S.F. | .939 | 112 | 41.50 | 153.50 |
| 32″ x 48″ | 14.000 | S.F. | .974 | 116 | 43 | 159 |
| 48″ x 48″ | 16.000 | S.F. | 1.113 | 133 | 49 | 182 |
| Trim, interior casing painted, 24″ x 24″ | 8.000 | L.F. | .347 | 12.55 | 16.40 | 28.95 |
| 32″ x 32″ | 12.000 | L.F. | .520 | 18.85 | 24.50 | 43.35 |
| 32″ x 48″ | 14.000 | L.F. | .607 | 22 | 28.50 | 50.50 |
| 48″ x 48″ | 16.000 | L.F. | .693 | 25 | 33 | 58 |

| System Description | QUAN. | UNIT | LABOR HOURS | COST PER S.F. | | |
|---|---|---|---|---|---|---|
| | | | | MAT. | INST. | TOTAL |
| **ASPHALT, ORGANIC, 4-PLY, INSULATED DECK** | | | | | | |
| Membrane, asphalt, 4-plies #15 felt, gravel surfacing | 1.000 | S.F. | .025 | 1.33 | 1.29 | 2.62 |
| Insulation board, 2-layers of 1-1/16" glass fiber | 2.000 | S.F. | .016 | 2.04 | .70 | 2.74 |
| Wood blocking, 2" x 6" | .040 | L.F. | .004 | .05 | .21 | .26 |
| Treated 4" x 4" cant strip | .040 | L.F. | .001 | .07 | .05 | .12 |
| Flashing, aluminum, 0.040" thick | .050 | S.F. | .003 | .12 | .12 | .24 |
| TOTAL | | S.F. | .049 | 3.61 | 2.37 | 5.98 |
| **ASPHALT, INORGANIC, 3-PLY, INSULATED DECK** | | | | | | |
| Membrane, asphalt, 3-plies type IV glass felt, gravel surfacing | 1.000 | S.F. | .028 | 1.21 | 1.42 | 2.63 |
| Insulation board, 2-layers of 1-1/16" glass fiber | 2.000 | S.F. | .016 | 2.04 | .70 | 2.74 |
| Wood blocking, 2" x 6" | .040 | L.F. | .004 | .05 | .21 | .26 |
| Treated 4" x 4" cant strip | .040 | L.F. | .001 | .07 | .05 | .12 |
| Flashing, aluminum, 0.040" thick | .050 | S.F. | .003 | .12 | .12 | .24 |
| TOTAL | | S.F. | .052 | 3.49 | 2.50 | 5.99 |
| **COAL TAR, ORGANIC, 4-PLY, INSULATED DECK** | | | | | | |
| Membrane, coal tar, 4-plies #15 felt, gravel surfacing | 1.000 | S.F. | .027 | 2.01 | 1.35 | 3.36 |
| Insulation board, 2-layers of 1-1/16" glass fiber | 2.000 | S.F. | .016 | 2.04 | .70 | 2.74 |
| Wood blocking, 2" x 6" | .040 | L.F. | .004 | .05 | .21 | .26 |
| Treated 4" x 4" cant strip | .040 | L.F. | .001 | .07 | .05 | .12 |
| Flashing, aluminum, 0.040" thick | .050 | S.F. | .003 | .12 | .12 | .24 |
| TOTAL | | S.F. | .051 | 4.29 | 2.43 | 6.72 |
| **COAL TAR, INORGANIC, 3-PLY, INSULATED DECK** | | | | | | |
| Membrane, coal tar, 3-plies type IV glass felt, gravel surfacing | 1.000 | S.F. | .029 | 1.65 | 1.50 | 3.15 |
| Insulation board, 2-layers of 1-1/16" glass fiber | 2.000 | S.F. | .016 | 2.04 | .70 | 2.74 |
| Wood blocking, 2" x 6" | .040 | L.F. | .004 | .05 | .21 | .26 |
| Treated 4" x 4" cant strip | .040 | L.F. | .001 | .07 | .05 | .12 |
| Flashing, aluminum, 0.040" thick | .050 | S.F. | .003 | .12 | .12 | .24 |
| TOTAL | | S.F. | .053 | 3.93 | 2.58 | 6.51 |

| Built-Up Roofing Price Sheet | QUAN. | UNIT | LABOR HOURS | COST PER S.F. | | |
|---|---|---|---|---|---|---|
| | | | | MAT. | INST. | TOTAL |
| Membrane, asphalt, 4-plies #15 organic felt, gravel surfacing | 1.000 | S.F. | .025 | 1.33 | 1.29 | 2.62 |
| Asphalt base sheet & 3-plies #15 asphalt felt | 1.000 | S.F. | .025 | 1.03 | 1.29 | 2.32 |
| 3-plies type IV glass fiber felt | 1.000 | S.F. | .028 | 1.21 | 1.42 | 2.63 |
| 4-plies type IV glass fiber felt | 1.000 | S.F. | .028 | 1.48 | 1.42 | 2.90 |
| Coal tar, 4-plies #15 organic felt, gravel surfacing | 1.000 | S.F. | .027 | | | |
| 4-plies tarred felt | 1.000 | S.F. | .027 | 2.01 | 1.35 | 3.36 |
| 3-plies type IV glass fiber felt | 1.000 | S.F. | .029 | 1.65 | 1.50 | 3.15 |
| 4-plies type IV glass fiber felt | 1.000 | S.F. | .027 | 2.26 | 1.35 | 3.61 |
| Roll, asphalt, 1-ply #15 organic felt, 2-plies mineral surfaced | 1.000 | S.F. | .021 | .70 | 1.05 | 1.75 |
| 3-plies type IV glass fiber, 1-ply mineral surfaced | 1.000 | S.F. | .022 | 1.14 | 1.14 | 2.28 |
| Insulation boards, glass fiber, 1-1/16" thick | 1.000 | S.F. | .008 | 1.02 | .35 | 1.37 |
| 2-1/16" thick | 1.000 | S.F. | .010 | 1.49 | .44 | 1.93 |
| 2-7/16" thick | 1.000 | S.F. | .010 | 1.71 | .44 | 2.15 |
| Expanded perlite, 1" thick | 1.000 | S.F. | .010 | .51 | .44 | .95 |
| 1-1/2" thick | 1.000 | S.F. | .010 | .53 | .44 | .97 |
| 2" thick | 1.000 | S.F. | .011 | .88 | .50 | 1.38 |
| Fiberboard, 1" thick | 1.000 | S.F. | .010 | .46 | .44 | .90 |
| 1-1/2" thick | 1.000 | S.F. | .010 | .70 | .44 | 1.14 |
| 2" thick | 1.000 | S.F. | .010 | .94 | .44 | 1.38 |
| Extruded polystyrene, 15 PSI compressive strength, 2" thick R10 | 1.000 | S.F. | .006 | .68 | .28 | .96 |
| 3" thick R15 | 1.000 | S.F. | .008 | 1.40 | .35 | 1.75 |
| 4" thick R20 | 1.000 | S.F. | .008 | 1.80 | .35 | 2.15 |
| Tapered for drainage | 1.000 | S.F. | .005 | .58 | .23 | .81 |
| 40 PSI compressive strength, 1" thick R5 | 1.000 | S.F. | .005 | .56 | .23 | .79 |
| 2" thick R10 | 1.000 | S.F. | .006 | 1.06 | .28 | 1.34 |
| 3" thick R15 | 1.000 | S.F. | .008 | 1.54 | .35 | 1.89 |
| 4" thick R20 | 1.000 | S.F. | .008 | 2.07 | .35 | 2.42 |
| Fiberboard high density, 1/2" thick R1.3 | 1.000 | S.F. | .008 | .24 | .35 | .59 |
| 1" thick R2.5 | 1.000 | S.F. | .010 | .48 | .44 | .92 |
| 1 1/2" thick R3.8 | 1.000 | S.F. | .010 | .73 | .44 | 1.17 |
| Polyisocyanurate, 1 1/2" thick | 1.000 | S.F. | .006 | .68 | .28 | .96 |
| 2" thick | 1.000 | S.F. | .007 | .95 | .32 | 1.27 |
| 3 1/2" thick | 1.000 | S.F. | .008 | 2.15 | .35 | 2.50 |
| Tapered for drainage | 1.000 | S.F. | .006 | 2.15 | .25 | 2.40 |
| Expanded polystyrene, 1" thick | 1.000 | S.F. | .005 | .40 | .23 | .63 |
| 2" thick R10 | 1.000 | S.F. | .006 | .79 | .28 | 1.07 |
| 3" thick | 1.000 | S.F. | .006 | 1.19 | .28 | 1.47 |
| Wood blocking, treated, 6" x 2" & 4" x 4" cant | .040 | L.F. | .002 | .11 | .12 | .23 |
| 6" x 4-1/2" & 4" x 4" cant | .040 | L.F. | .005 | .15 | .26 | .41 |
| 6" x 5" & 4" x 4" cant | .040 | L.F. | .007 | .17 | .33 | .50 |
| Flashing, aluminum, 0.019" thick | .050 | S.F. | .003 | .06 | .12 | .18 |
| 0.032" thick | .050 | S.F. | .003 | .08 | .12 | .20 |
| 0.040" thick | .050 | S.F. | .003 | .12 | .12 | .24 |
| Copper sheets, 16 oz., under 500 lbs. | .050 | S.F. | .003 | .42 | .15 | .57 |
| Over 500 lbs. | .050 | S.F. | .003 | .37 | .11 | .48 |
| 20 oz., under 500 lbs. | .050 | S.F. | .004 | .50 | .16 | .66 |
| Over 500 lbs. | .050 | S.F. | .003 | .45 | .12 | .57 |
| Stainless steel, 32 gauge | .050 | S.F. | .003 | .21 | .11 | .32 |
| 28 gauge | .050 | S.F. | .003 | .26 | .11 | .37 |
| 26 gauge | .050 | S.F. | .003 | .31 | .11 | .42 |
| 24 gauge | .050 | S.F. | .003 | .41 | .11 | .52 |

| System Description | QUAN. | UNIT | LABOR HOURS | COST PER S.F. | | |
|---|---|---|---|---|---|---|
| | | | | MAT. | INST. | TOTAL |
| **1/2″ DRYWALL, TAPED & FINISHED** | | | | | | |
| Gypsum wallboard, 1/2″ thick, standard | 1.000 | S.F. | .008 | .26 | .39 | .65 |
| Finish, taped & finished joints | 1.000 | S.F. | .008 | .05 | .39 | .44 |
| Corners, taped & finished, 32 L.F. per 12′ x 12′ room | .083 | L.F. | .002 | .01 | .07 | .08 |
| Painting, primer & 2 coats | 1.000 | S.F. | .011 | .17 | .44 | .61 |
| Paint trim, to 6″ wide, primer + 1 coat enamel | .125 | L.F. | .001 | .01 | .05 | .06 |
| Trim, baseboard | .125 | L.F. | .005 | .34 | .25 | .59 |
| TOTAL | | S.F. | .035 | .84 | 1.59 | 2.43 |
| **THINCOAT, SKIM-COAT, ON 1/2″ BACKER DRYWALL** | | | | | | |
| Gypsum wallboard, 1/2″ thick, thincoat backer | 1.000 | S.F. | .008 | .26 | .39 | .65 |
| Thincoat plaster | 1.000 | S.F. | .011 | .09 | .50 | .59 |
| Corners, taped & finished, 32 L.F. per 12′ x 12′ room | .083 | L.F. | .002 | .01 | .07 | .08 |
| Painting, primer & 2 coats | 1.000 | S.F. | .011 | .17 | .44 | .61 |
| Paint trim, to 6″ wide, primer + 1 coat enamel | .125 | L.F. | .001 | .01 | .05 | .06 |
| Trim, baseboard | .125 | L.F. | .005 | .34 | .25 | .59 |
| TOTAL | | S.F. | .038 | .88 | 1.70 | 2.58 |
| **5/8″ DRYWALL, TAPED & FINISHED** | | | | | | |
| Gypsum wallboard, 5/8″ thick, standard | 1.000 | S.F. | .008 | .31 | .39 | .70 |
| Finish, taped & finished joints | 1.000 | S.F. | .008 | .05 | .39 | .44 |
| Corners, taped & finished, 32 L.F. per 12′ x 12′ room | .083 | L.F. | .002 | .01 | .07 | .08 |
| Painting, primer & 2 coats | 1.000 | S.F. | .011 | .17 | .44 | .61 |
| Trim, baseboard | .125 | L.F. | .005 | .34 | .25 | .59 |
| Paint trim, to 6″ wide, primer + 1 coat enamel | .125 | L.F. | .001 | .01 | .05 | .06 |
| TOTAL | | S.F. | .035 | .89 | 1.59 | 2.48 |

The costs in this system are based on a square foot of wall.
Do not deduct for openings.

| Description | QUAN. | UNIT | LABOR HOURS | COST PER S.F. | | |
|---|---|---|---|---|---|---|
| | | | | MAT. | INST. | TOTAL |
| | | | | | | |
| | | | | | | |
| | | | | | | |

| Drywall & Thincoat Wall Price Sheet | QUAN. | UNIT | LABOR HOURS | COST PER S.F. | | |
|---|---|---|---|---|---|---|
| | | | | MAT. | INST. | TOTAL |
| Gypsum wallboard, 1/2" thick, standard | 1.000 | S.F. | .008 | .26 | .39 | .65 |
| Fire resistant | 1.000 | S.F. | .008 | .31 | .39 | .70 |
| Water resistant | 1.000 | S.F. | .008 | .39 | .39 | .78 |
| 5/8" thick, standard | 1.000 | S.F. | .008 | .31 | .39 | .70 |
| Fire resistant | 1.000 | S.F. | .008 | .30 | .39 | .69 |
| Water resistant | 1.000 | S.F. | .008 | .47 | .39 | .86 |
| Gypsum wallboard backer for thincoat system, 1/2" thick | 1.000 | S.F. | .008 | .26 | .39 | .65 |
| 5/8" thick | 1.000 | S.F. | .008 | .31 | .39 | .70 |
| Gypsum wallboard, taped & finished | 1.000 | S.F. | .008 | .05 | .39 | .44 |
| Texture spray | 1.000 | S.F. | .010 | .06 | .42 | .48 |
| Thincoat plaster, including tape | 1.000 | S.F. | .011 | .09 | .50 | .59 |
| Gypsum wallboard corners, taped & finished, 32 L.F. per 4' x 4' room | .250 | L.F. | .004 | .03 | .21 | .24 |
| 6' x 6' room | .110 | L.F. | .002 | .01 | .09 | .10 |
| 10' x 10' room | .100 | L.F. | .001 | .01 | .08 | .09 |
| 12' x 12' room | .083 | L.F. | .001 | .01 | .07 | .08 |
| 16' x 16' room | .063 | L.F. | .001 | .01 | .05 | .06 |
| Thincoat system, 32 L.F. per 4' x 4' room | .250 | L.F. | .003 | .02 | .13 | .15 |
| 6' x 6' room | .110 | L.F. | .001 | .01 | .05 | .06 |
| 10' x 10' room | .100 | L.F. | .001 | .01 | .05 | .06 |
| 12' x 12' room | .083 | L.F. | .001 | .01 | .04 | .05 |
| 16' x 16' room | .063 | L.F. | .001 | .01 | .03 | .04 |
| Painting, primer, & 1 coat | 1.000 | S.F. | .008 | .11 | .34 | .45 |
| & 2 coats | 1.000 | S.F. | .011 | .17 | .44 | .61 |
| Wallpaper, $7/double roll | 1.000 | S.F. | .013 | .41 | .53 | .94 |
| $17/double roll | 1.000 | S.F. | .015 | .78 | .63 | 1.41 |
| $40/double roll | 1.000 | S.F. | .018 | 2.72 | .78 | 3.50 |
| Wallcovering, medium weight vinyl | | S.F. | .017 | .90 | .70 | 1.60 |
| Tile, ceramic adhesive thin set, 4 1/4" x 4 1/4" tiles | 1.000 | S.F. | .084 | 2.58 | 3.33 | 5.91 |
| 6" x 6" tiles | 1.000 | S.F. | .080 | 3.35 | 3.16 | 6.51 |
| Pregrouted sheets | 1.000 | S.F. | .067 | 5.20 | 2.64 | 7.84 |
| Trim, painted or stained, baseboard | .125 | L.F. | .006 | .35 | .30 | .65 |
| Base shoe | .125 | L.F. | .005 | .17 | .25 | .42 |
| Chair rail | .125 | L.F. | .005 | .21 | .23 | .44 |
| Cornice molding | .125 | L.F. | .004 | .15 | .20 | .35 |
| Cove base, vinyl | .125 | L.F. | .003 | .11 | .14 | .25 |
| Paneling, not including furring or trim | | | | | | |
| Plywood, prefinished, 1/4" thick, 4' x 8' sheets, vert. grooves | | | | | | |
| Birch faced, minimum | 1.000 | S.F. | .032 | .98 | 1.57 | 2.55 |
| Average | 1.000 | S.F. | .038 | 1.49 | 1.87 | 3.36 |
| Maximum | 1.000 | S.F. | .046 | 2.17 | 2.24 | 4.41 |
| Mahogany, African | 1.000 | S.F. | .040 | 2.76 | 1.96 | 4.72 |
| Philippine (lauan) | 1.000 | S.F. | .032 | 1.19 | 1.57 | 2.76 |
| Oak or cherry, minimum | 1.000 | S.F. | .032 | 2.31 | 1.57 | 3.88 |
| Maximum | 1.000 | S.F. | .040 | 3.54 | 1.96 | 5.50 |
| Rosewood | 1.000 | S.F. | .050 | 5.05 | 2.45 | 7.50 |
| Teak | 1.000 | S.F. | .040 | 3.54 | 1.96 | 5.50 |
| Chestnut | 1.000 | S.F. | .043 | 5.25 | 2.09 | 7.34 |
| Pecan | 1.000 | S.F. | .040 | 2.27 | 1.96 | 4.23 |
| Walnut, minimum | 1.000 | S.F. | .032 | 3.03 | 1.57 | 4.60 |
| Maximum | 1.000 | S.F. | .040 | 5.75 | 1.96 | 7.71 |

215

| System Description | QUAN. | UNIT | LABOR HOURS | COST PER S.F. | | |
|---|---|---|---|---|---|---|
| | | | | MAT. | INST. | TOTAL |
| **1/2″ SHEETROCK, TAPED & FINISHED** | | | | | | |
| Gypsum wallboard, 1/2″ thick, standard | 1.000 | S.F. | .008 | .26 | .39 | .65 |
| Finish, taped & finished | 1.000 | S.F. | .008 | .05 | .39 | .44 |
| Corners, taped & finished, 12′ x 12′ room | .333 | L.F. | .006 | .03 | .27 | .30 |
| Paint, primer & 2 coats | 1.000 | S.F. | .011 | .17 | .44 | .61 |
| TOTAL | | S.F. | .033 | .51 | 1.49 | 2 |
| **THINCOAT, SKIM COAT ON 1/2″ GYPSUM WALLBOARD** | | | | | | |
| Gypsum wallboard, 1/2″ thick, thincoat backer | 1.000 | S.F. | .008 | .26 | .39 | .65 |
| Thincoat plaster | 1.000 | S.F. | .011 | .09 | .50 | .59 |
| Corners, taped & finished, 12′ x 12′ room | .333 | L.F. | .006 | .03 | .27 | .30 |
| Paint, primer & 2 coats | 1.000 | S.F. | .011 | .17 | .44 | .61 |
| TOTAL | | S.F. | .036 | .55 | 1.60 | 2.15 |
| **WATER-RESISTANT GYPSUM WALLBOARD, 1/2″ THICK, TAPED & FINISHED** | | | | | | |
| Gypsum wallboard, 1/2″ thick, water-resistant | 1.000 | S.F. | .008 | .39 | .39 | .78 |
| Finish, taped & finished | 1.000 | S.F. | .008 | .05 | .39 | .44 |
| Corners, taped & finished, 12′ x 12′ room | .333 | L.F. | .006 | .03 | .27 | .30 |
| Paint, primer & 2 coats | 1.000 | S.F. | .011 | .17 | .44 | .61 |
| TOTAL | | S.F. | .033 | .64 | 1.49 | 2.13 |
| **5/8″ GYPSUM WALLBOARD, TAPED & FINISHED** | | | | | | |
| Gypsum wallboard, 5/8″ thick, standard | 1.000 | S.F. | .008 | .31 | .39 | .70 |
| Finish, taped & finished | 1.000 | S.F. | .008 | .05 | .39 | .44 |
| Corners, taped & finished, 12′ x 12′ room | .333 | L.F. | .006 | .03 | .27 | .30 |
| Paint, primer & 2 coats | 1.000 | S.F. | .011 | .17 | .44 | .61 |
| TOTAL | | S.F. | .033 | .56 | 1.49 | 2.05 |

The costs in this system are based on a square foot of ceiling.

| Description | QUAN. | UNIT | LABOR HOURS | COST PER S.F. | | |
|---|---|---|---|---|---|---|
| | | | | MAT. | INST. | TOTAL |
| | | | | | | |
| | | | | | | |
| | | | | | | |

| Drywall & Thincoat Ceilings | QUAN. | UNIT | LABOR HOURS | COST PER S.F. | | |
|---|---|---|---|---|---|---|
| | | | | MAT. | INST. | TOTAL |
| Gypsum wallboard ceilings, 1/2" thick, standard | 1.000 | S.F. | .008 | .26 | .39 | .65 |
| Fire resistant | 1.000 | S.F. | .008 | .31 | .39 | .70 |
| Water resistant | 1.000 | S.F. | .008 | .39 | .39 | .78 |
| 5/8" thick, standard | 1.000 | S.F. | .008 | .31 | .39 | .70 |
| Fire resistant | 1.000 | S.F. | .008 | .30 | .39 | .69 |
| Water resistant | 1.000 | S.F. | .008 | .47 | .39 | .86 |
| Gypsum wallboard backer for thincoat ceiling system, 1/2" thick | 1.000 | S.F. | .016 | .57 | .78 | 1.35 |
| 5/8" thick | 1.000 | S.F. | .016 | .62 | .78 | 1.40 |
| Gypsum wallboard ceilings, taped & finished | 1.000 | S.F. | .008 | .05 | .39 | .44 |
| Texture spray | 1.000 | S.F. | .010 | .06 | .42 | .48 |
| Thincoat plaster | 1.000 | S.F. | .011 | .09 | .50 | .59 |
| Corners taped & finished, 4' x 4' room | 1.000 | L.F. | .015 | .10 | .82 | .92 |
| 6' x 6' room | .667 | L.F. | .010 | .07 | .55 | .62 |
| 10' x 10' room | .400 | L.F. | .006 | .04 | .33 | .37 |
| 12' x 12' room | .333 | L.F. | .005 | .03 | .27 | .30 |
| 16' x 16' room | .250 | L.F. | .003 | .02 | .15 | .17 |
| Thincoat system, 4' x 4' room | 1.000 | L.F. | .011 | .09 | .50 | .59 |
| 6' x 6' room | .667 | L.F. | .007 | .06 | .34 | .40 |
| 10' x 10' room | .400 | L.F. | .004 | .04 | .20 | .24 |
| 12' x 12' room | .333 | L.F. | .004 | .03 | .16 | .19 |
| 16' x 16' room | .250 | L.F. | .002 | .02 | .10 | .12 |
| Painting, primer & 1 coat | 1.000 | S.F. | .008 | .11 | .34 | .45 |
| & 2 coats | 1.000 | S.F. | .011 | .17 | .44 | .61 |
| Wallpaper, double roll, solid pattern, avg. workmanship | 1.000 | S.F. | .013 | .41 | .53 | .94 |
| Basic pattern, avg. workmanship | 1.000 | S.F. | .015 | .78 | .63 | 1.41 |
| Basic pattern, quality workmanship | 1.000 | S.F. | .018 | 2.72 | .78 | 3.50 |
| Tile, ceramic adhesive thin set, 4 1/4" x 4 1/4" tiles | 1.000 | S.F. | .084 | 2.58 | 3.33 | 5.91 |
| 6" x 6" tiles | 1.000 | S.F. | .080 | 3.35 | 3.16 | 6.51 |
| Pregrouted sheets | 1.000 | S.F. | .067 | 5.20 | 2.64 | 7.84 |
| | | | | | | |
| | | | | | | |
| | | | | | | |
| | | | | | | |
| | | | | | | |
| | | | | | | |
| | | | | | | |
| | | | | | | |
| | | | | | | |
| | | | | | | |
| | | | | | | |
| | | | | | | |

| System Description | QUAN. | UNIT | LABOR HOURS | COST PER S.F. | | |
|---|---|---|---|---|---|---|
| | | | | MAT. | INST. | TOTAL |
| **PLASTER ON GYPSUM LATH** | | | | | | |
| Plaster, gypsum or perlite, 2 coats | 1.000 | S.F. | .053 | .46 | 2.39 | 2.85 |
| Lath, 3/8" gypsum | 1.000 | S.F. | .010 | .62 | .44 | 1.06 |
| Corners, expanded metal, 32 L.F. per 12' x 12' room | .083 | L.F. | .002 | .01 | .08 | .09 |
| Painting, primer & 2 coats | 1.000 | S.F. | .011 | .17 | .44 | .61 |
| Paint trim, to 6" wide, primer + 1 coat enamel | .125 | L.F. | .001 | .01 | .05 | .06 |
| Trim, baseboard | .125 | L.F. | .005 | .34 | .25 | .59 |
| | | | | | | |
| TOTAL | | S.F. | .082 | 1.61 | 3.65 | 5.26 |
| **PLASTER ON METAL LATH** | | | | | | |
| Plaster, gypsum or perlite, 2 coats | 1.000 | S.F. | .053 | .46 | 2.39 | 2.85 |
| Lath, 2.5 Lb. diamond, metal | 1.000 | S.F. | .010 | .50 | .44 | .94 |
| Corners, expanded metal, 32 L.F. per 12' x 12' room | .083 | L.F. | .002 | .01 | .08 | .09 |
| Painting, primer & 2 coats | 1.000 | S.F. | .011 | .17 | .44 | .61 |
| Paint trim, to 6" wide, primer + 1 coat enamel | .125 | L.F. | .001 | .01 | .05 | .06 |
| Trim, baseboard | .125 | L.F. | .005 | .34 | .25 | .59 |
| | | | | | | |
| TOTAL | | S.F. | .082 | 1.49 | 3.65 | 5.14 |
| **STUCCO ON METAL LATH** | | | | | | |
| Stucco, 2 coats | 1.000 | S.F. | .041 | .26 | 1.83 | 2.09 |
| Lath, 2.5 Lb. diamond, metal | 1.000 | S.F. | .010 | .50 | .44 | .94 |
| Corners, expanded metal, 32 L.F. per 12' x 12' room | .083 | L.F. | .002 | .01 | .08 | .09 |
| Painting, primer & 2 coats | 1.000 | S.F. | .011 | .17 | .44 | .61 |
| Paint trim, to 6" wide, primer + 1 coat enamel | .125 | L.F. | .001 | .01 | .05 | .06 |
| Trim, baseboard | .125 | L.F. | .005 | .34 | .25 | .59 |
| | | | | | | |
| TOTAL | | S.F. | .070 | 1.29 | 3.09 | 4.38 |

The costs in these systems are based on a per square foot of wall area.
Do not deduct for openings.

| Description | QUAN. | UNIT | LABOR HOURS | COST PER S.F. | | |
|---|---|---|---|---|---|---|
| | | | | MAT. | INST. | TOTAL |
| | | | | | | |
| | | | | | | |
| | | | | | | |

| Plaster & Stucco Wall Price Sheet | QUAN. | UNIT | LABOR HOURS | COST PER S.F. | | |
|---|---|---|---|---|---|---|
| | | | | MAT. | INST. | TOTAL |
| Plaster, gypsum or perlite, 2 coats | 1.000 | S.F. | .053 | .46 | 2.39 | 2.85 |
| 3 coats | 1.000 | S.F. | .065 | .66 | 2.89 | 3.55 |
| Lath, gypsum, standard, 3/8" thick | 1.000 | S.F. | .010 | .62 | .44 | 1.06 |
| Fire resistant, 3/8" thick | 1.000 | S.F. | .013 | .30 | .53 | .83 |
| 1/2" thick | 1.000 | S.F. | .014 | .30 | .57 | .87 |
| Metal, diamond, 2.5 Lb. | 1.000 | S.F. | .010 | .50 | .44 | .94 |
| 3.4 Lb. | 1.000 | S.F. | .012 | .52 | .49 | 1.01 |
| Rib, 2.75 Lb. | 1.000 | S.F. | .012 | .41 | .49 | .90 |
| 3.4 Lb. | 1.000 | S.F. | .013 | .63 | .53 | 1.16 |
| Corners, expanded metal, 32 L.F. per 4' x 4' room | .250 | L.F. | .005 | .04 | .25 | .29 |
| 6' x 6' room | .110 | L.F. | .002 | .02 | .11 | .13 |
| 10' x 10' room | .100 | L.F. | .002 | .02 | .10 | .12 |
| 12' x 12' room | .083 | L.F. | .002 | .01 | .08 | .09 |
| 16' x 16' room | .063 | L.F. | .001 | .01 | .06 | .07 |
| | | | | | | |
| Painting, primer & 1 coats | 1.000 | S.F. | .008 | .11 | .34 | .45 |
| Primer & 2 coats | 1.000 | S.F. | .011 | .17 | .44 | .61 |
| Wallpaper, low price double roll | 1.000 | S.F. | .013 | .41 | .53 | .94 |
| Medium price double roll | 1.000 | S.F. | .015 | .78 | .63 | 1.41 |
| High price double roll | 1.000 | S.F. | .018 | 2.72 | .78 | 3.50 |
| | | | | | | |
| Tile, ceramic thin set, 4-1/4" x 4-1/4" tiles | 1.000 | S.F. | .084 | 2.58 | 3.33 | 5.91 |
| 6" x 6" tiles | 1.000 | S.F. | .080 | 3.35 | 3.16 | 6.51 |
| Pregrouted sheets | 1.000 | S.F. | .067 | 5.20 | 2.64 | 7.84 |
| | | | | | | |
| Trim, painted or stained, baseboard | .125 | L.F. | .006 | .35 | .30 | .65 |
| Base shoe | .125 | L.F. | .005 | .17 | .25 | .42 |
| Chair rail | .125 | L.F. | .005 | .21 | .23 | .44 |
| Cornice molding | .125 | L.F. | .004 | .15 | .20 | .35 |
| Cove base, vinyl | .125 | L.F. | .003 | .11 | .14 | .25 |
| | | | | | | |
| Paneling not including furring or trim | | | | | | |
| Plywood, prefinished, 1/4" thick, 4' x 8' sheets, vert. grooves | | | | | | |
| Birch faced, minimum | 1.000 | S.F. | .032 | .98 | 1.57 | 2.55 |
| Average | 1.000 | S.F. | .038 | 1.49 | 1.87 | 3.36 |
| Maximum | 1.000 | S.F. | .046 | 2.17 | 2.24 | 4.41 |
| Mahogany, African | 1.000 | S.F. | .040 | 2.76 | 1.96 | 4.72 |
| Philippine (lauan) | 1.000 | S.F. | .032 | 1.19 | 1.57 | 2.76 |
| Oak or cherry, minimum | 1.000 | S.F. | .032 | 2.31 | 1.57 | 3.88 |
| Maximum | 1.000 | S.F. | .040 | 3.54 | 1.96 | 5.50 |
| Rosewood | 1.000 | S.F. | .050 | 5.05 | 2.45 | 7.50 |
| Teak | 1.000 | S.F. | .040 | 3.54 | 1.96 | 5.50 |
| Chestnut | 1.000 | S.F. | .043 | 5.25 | 2.09 | 7.34 |
| Pecan | 1.000 | S.F. | .040 | 2.27 | 1.96 | 4.23 |
| Walnut, minimum | 1.000 | S.F. | .032 | 3.03 | 1.57 | 4.60 |
| Maximum | 1.000 | S.F. | .040 | 5.75 | 1.96 | 7.71 |
| | | | | | | |
| | | | | | | |
| | | | | | | |
| | | | | | | |
| | | | | | | |
| | | | | | | |

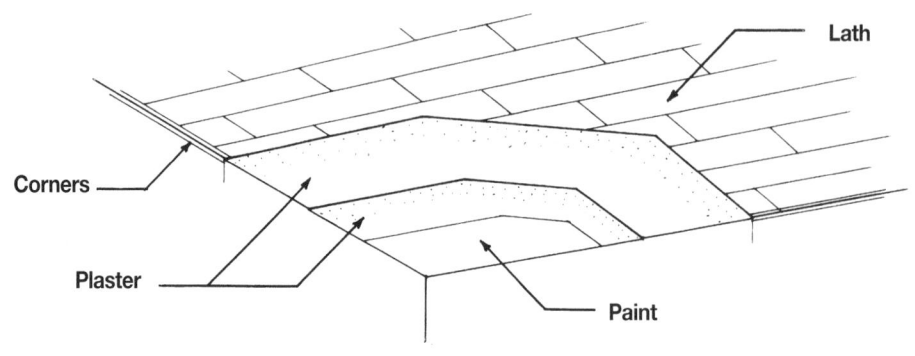

| System Description | QUAN. | UNIT | LABOR HOURS | COST PER S.F. | | |
|---|---|---|---|---|---|---|
| | | | | MAT. | INST. | TOTAL |
| **PLASTER ON GYPSUM LATH** | | | | | | |
| Plaster, gypsum or perlite, 2 coats | 1.000 | S.F. | .061 | .46 | 2.72 | 3.18 |
| Gypsum lath, plain or perforated, nailed, 3/8" thick | 1.000 | S.F. | .010 | .62 | .44 | 1.06 |
| Gypsum lath, ceiling installation adder | 1.000 | S.F. | .004 | | .17 | .17 |
| Corners, expanded metal, 12' x 12' room | .330 | L.F. | .007 | .05 | .32 | .37 |
| Painting, primer & 2 coats | 1.000 | S.F. | .011 | .17 | .44 | .61 |
| TOTAL | | S.F. | .093 | 1.30 | 4.09 | 5.39 |
| **PLASTER ON METAL LATH** | | | | | | |
| Plaster, gypsum or perlite, 2 coats | 1.000 | S.F. | .061 | .46 | 2.72 | 3.18 |
| Lath, 2.5 Lb. diamond, metal | 1.000 | S.F. | .012 | .50 | .49 | .99 |
| Corners, expanded metal, 12' x 12' room | .330 | L.F. | .007 | .05 | .32 | .37 |
| Painting, primer & 2 coats | 1.000 | S.F. | .011 | .17 | .44 | .61 |
| TOTAL | | S.F. | .091 | 1.18 | 3.97 | 5.15 |
| **STUCCO ON GYPSUM LATH** | | | | | | |
| Stucco, 2 coats | 1.000 | S.F. | .041 | .26 | 1.83 | 2.09 |
| Gypsum lath, plain or perforated, nailed, 3/8" thick | 1.000 | S.F. | .010 | .62 | .44 | 1.06 |
| Gypsum lath, ceiling installation adder | 1.000 | S.F. | .004 | | .17 | .17 |
| Corners, expanded metal, 12' x 12' room | .330 | L.F. | .007 | .05 | .32 | .37 |
| Painting, primer & 2 coats | 1.000 | S.F. | .011 | .17 | .44 | .61 |
| TOTAL | | S.F. | .073 | 1.10 | 3.20 | 4.30 |
| **STUCCO ON METAL LATH** | | | | | | |
| Stucco, 2 coats | 1.000 | S.F. | .041 | .26 | 1.83 | 2.09 |
| Lath, 2.5 Lb. diamond, metal | 1.000 | S.F. | .012 | .50 | .49 | .99 |
| Corners, expanded metal, 12' x 12' room | .330 | L.F. | .007 | .05 | .32 | .37 |
| Painting, primer & 2 coats | 1.000 | S.F. | .011 | .17 | .44 | .61 |
| TOTAL | | S.F. | .071 | .98 | 3.08 | 4.06 |

The costs in these systems are based on a square foot of ceiling area.

| Description | QUAN. | UNIT | LABOR HOURS | COST PER S.F. | | |
|---|---|---|---|---|---|---|
| | | | | MAT. | INST. | TOTAL |
| | | | | | | |
| | | | | | | |

| Plaster & Stucco Ceiling Price Sheet | QUAN. | UNIT | LABOR HOURS | COST PER S.F. | | |
|---|---|---|---|---|---|---|
| | | | | MAT. | INST. | TOTAL |
| Plaster, gypsum or perlite, 2 coats | 1.000 | S.F. | .061 | .46 | 2.72 | 3.18 |
| 3 coats | 1.000 | S.F. | .065 | .66 | 2.89 | 3.55 |
| Lath, gypsum, standard, 3/8″ thick | 1.000 | S.F. | .014 | .62 | .61 | 1.23 |
| 1/2″ thick | 1.000 | S.F. | .015 | .61 | .63 | 1.24 |
| Fire resistant, 3/8″ thick | 1.000 | S.F. | .017 | .30 | .70 | 1 |
| 1/2″ thick | 1.000 | S.F. | .018 | .30 | .74 | 1.04 |
| Metal, diamond, 2.5 Lb. | 1.000 | S.F. | .012 | .50 | .49 | .99 |
| 3.4 Lb. | 1.000 | S.F. | .015 | .52 | .62 | 1.14 |
| Rib, 2.75 Lb. | 1.000 | S.F. | .012 | .41 | .49 | .90 |
| 3.4 Lb. | 1.000 | S.F. | .013 | .63 | .53 | 1.16 |
| Corners expanded metal, 4′ x 4′ room | 1.000 | L.F. | .020 | .16 | .98 | 1.14 |
| 6′ x 6′ room | .667 | L.F. | .013 | .11 | .66 | .77 |
| 10′ x 10′ room | .400 | L.F. | .008 | .06 | .39 | .45 |
| 12′ x 12′ room | .333 | L.F. | .007 | .05 | .32 | .37 |
| 16′ x 16′ room | .250 | L.F. | .004 | .03 | .18 | .21 |
| | | | | | | |
| Painting, primer & 1 coat | 1.000 | S.F. | .008 | .11 | .34 | .45 |
| Primer & 2 coats | 1.000 | S.F. | .011 | .17 | .44 | .61 |

| System Description | QUAN. | UNIT | LABOR HOURS | COST PER S.F. | | |
|---|---|---|---|---|---|---|
| | | | | MAT. | INST. | TOTAL |
| **2' X 2' GRID, FILM FACED FIBERGLASS, 5/8" THICK** | | | | | | |
| Suspension system, 2' x 2' grid, T bar | 1.000 | S.F. | .012 | .93 | .60 | 1.53 |
| Ceiling board, film faced fiberglass, 5/8" thick | 1.000 | S.F. | .013 | .77 | .63 | 1.40 |
| Carrier channels, 1-1/2" x 3/4" | 1.000 | S.F. | .017 | .12 | .83 | .95 |
| Hangers, #12 wire | 1.000 | S.F. | .002 | .09 | .08 | .17 |
| TOTAL | | S.F. | .044 | 1.91 | 2.14 | 4.05 |
| **2' X 4' GRID, FILM FACED FIBERGLASS, 5/8" THICK** | | | | | | |
| Suspension system, 2' x 4' grid, T bar | 1.000 | S.F. | .010 | .75 | .49 | 1.24 |
| Ceiling board, film faced fiberglass, 5/8" thick | 1.000 | S.F. | .013 | .77 | .63 | 1.40 |
| Carrier channels, 1-1/2" x 3/4" | 1.000 | S.F. | .017 | .12 | .83 | .95 |
| Hangers, #12 wire | 1.000 | S.F. | .002 | .09 | .08 | .17 |
| TOTAL | | S.F. | .042 | 1.73 | 2.03 | 3.76 |
| **2' X 2' GRID, MINERAL FIBER, REVEAL EDGE, 1" THICK** | | | | | | |
| Suspension system, 2' x 2' grid, T bar | 1.000 | S.F. | .012 | .93 | .60 | 1.53 |
| Ceiling board, mineral fiber, reveal edge, 1" thick | 1.000 | S.F. | .013 | 1.69 | .65 | 2.34 |
| Carrier channels, 1-1/2" x 3/4" | 1.000 | S.F. | .017 | .12 | .83 | .95 |
| Hangers, #12 wire | 1.000 | S.F. | .002 | .09 | .08 | .17 |
| TOTAL | | S.F. | .044 | 2.83 | 2.16 | 4.99 |
| **2' X 4' GRID, MINERAL FIBER, REVEAL EDGE, 1" THICK** | | | | | | |
| Suspension system, 2' x 4' grid, T bar | 1.000 | S.F. | .010 | .75 | .49 | 1.24 |
| Ceiling board, mineral fiber, reveal edge, 1" thick | 1.000 | S.F. | .013 | 1.69 | .65 | 2.34 |
| Carrier channels, 1-1/2" x 3/4" | 1.000 | S.F. | .017 | .12 | .83 | .95 |
| Hangers, #12 wire | 1.000 | S.F. | .002 | .09 | .08 | .17 |
| TOTAL | | S.F. | .042 | 2.65 | 2.05 | 4.70 |

| Description | QUAN. | UNIT | LABOR HOURS | COST PER S.F. | | |
|---|---|---|---|---|---|---|
| | | | | MAT. | INST. | TOTAL |
| | | | | | | |
| | | | | | | |
| | | | | | | |

| Suspended Ceiling Price Sheet | QUAN. | UNIT | LABOR HOURS | COST PER S.F. | | |
|---|---|---|---|---|---|---|
| | | | | MAT. | INST. | TOTAL |
| Suspension systems, T bar, 2' x 2' grid | 1.000 | S.F. | .012 | .93 | .60 | 1.53 |
| 2' x 4' grid | 1.000 | S.F. | .010 | .75 | .49 | 1.24 |
| Concealed Z bar, 12" module | 1.000 | S.F. | .015 | .76 | .75 | 1.51 |
| | | | | | | |
| Ceiling boards, fiberglass, film faced, 2' x 2' or 2' x 4', 5/8" thick | 1.000 | S.F. | .013 | .77 | .63 | 1.40 |
| 3/4" thick | 1.000 | S.F. | .013 | 1.77 | .65 | 2.42 |
| 3" thick thermal R11 | 1.000 | S.F. | .018 | 1.68 | .87 | 2.55 |
| Glass cloth faced, 3/4" thick | 1.000 | S.F. | .016 | 3.16 | .78 | 3.94 |
| 1" thick | 1.000 | S.F. | .016 | 2.40 | .81 | 3.21 |
| 1-1/2" thick, nubby face | 1.000 | S.F. | .017 | 2.93 | .82 | 3.75 |
| Mineral fiber boards, 5/8" thick, aluminum face 2' x 2' | 1.000 | S.F. | .013 | 2 | .65 | 2.65 |
| 2' x 4' | 1.000 | S.F. | .012 | 1.62 | .60 | 2.22 |
| Standard faced, 2' x 2' or 2' x 4' | 1.000 | S.F. | .012 | .86 | .58 | 1.44 |
| Plastic coated face, 2' x 2' or 2' x 4' | 1.000 | S.F. | .020 | 1.35 | .98 | 2.33 |
| Fire rated, 2 hour rating, 5/8" thick | 1.000 | S.F. | .012 | 1.29 | .58 | 1.87 |
| | | | | | | |
| Tegular edge, 2' x 2' or 2' x 4', 5/8" thick, fine textured | 1.000 | S.F. | .013 | 1.60 | .83 | 2.43 |
| Rough textured | 1.000 | S.F. | .015 | 2.09 | .83 | 2.92 |
| 3/4" thick, fine textured | 1.000 | S.F. | .016 | 2.29 | .87 | 3.16 |
| Rough textured | 1.000 | S.F. | .018 | 2.59 | .87 | 3.46 |
| Luminous panels, prismatic, acrylic | 1.000 | S.F. | .020 | 2.44 | .98 | 3.42 |
| Polystyrene | 1.000 | S.F. | .020 | 1.25 | .98 | 2.23 |
| Flat or ribbed, acrylic | 1.000 | S.F. | .020 | 4.25 | .98 | 5.23 |
| Polystyrene | 1.000 | S.F. | .020 | 2.92 | .98 | 3.90 |
| Drop pan, white, acrylic | 1.000 | S.F. | .020 | 6.25 | .98 | 7.23 |
| Polystyrene | 1.000 | S.F. | .020 | 5.20 | .98 | 6.18 |
| Carrier channels, 4'-0" on center, 3/4" x 1-1/2" | 1.000 | S.F. | .017 | .12 | .83 | .95 |
| 1-1/2" x 3-1/2" | 1.000 | S.F. | .017 | .30 | .83 | 1.13 |
| Hangers, #12 wire | 1.000 | S.F. | .002 | .09 | .08 | .17 |
| | | | | | | |
| | | | | | | |
| | | | | | | |
| | | | | | | |
| | | | | | | |
| | | | | | | |
| | | | | | | |
| | | | | | | |
| | | | | | | |
| | | | | | | |
| | | | | | | |
| | | | | | | |
| | | | | | | |
| | | | | | | |
| | | | | | | |
| | | | | | | |

| System Description | QUAN. | UNIT | LABOR HOURS | COST EACH | | |
|---|---|---|---|---|---|---|
| | | | | MAT. | INST. | TOTAL |
| **LAUAN, FLUSH DOOR, HOLLOW CORE** | | | | | | |
| Door, flush, lauan, hollow core, 2'-8" wide x 6'-8" high | 1.000 | Ea. | .889 | 39.50 | 43.50 | 83 |
| Frame, pine, 4-5/8" jamb | 17.000 | L.F. | .725 | 121.55 | 35.53 | 157.08 |
| Trim, stock pine, 11/16" x 2-1/2" | 34.000 | L.F. | 1.133 | 49.64 | 55.42 | 105.06 |
| Paint trim, to 6" wide, primer + 1 coat enamel | 34.000 | L.F. | .340 | 3.74 | 14.28 | 18.02 |
| Butt hinges, chrome, 3-1/2" x 3-1/2" | 1.500 | Pr. | | 42.75 | | 42.75 |
| Lockset, passage | 1.000 | Ea. | .500 | 24 | 24.50 | 48.50 |
| Prime door & frame, oil, brushwork | 2.000 | Face | 1.600 | 6.38 | 67 | 73.38 |
| Paint door and frame, oil, 2 coats | 2.000 | Face | 2.667 | 11.30 | 112 | 123.30 |
| TOTAL | | Ea. | 7.854 | 298.86 | 352.23 | 651.09 |
| **BIRCH, FLUSH DOOR, HOLLOW CORE** | | | | | | |
| Door, flush, birch, hollow core, 2'-8" wide x 6'-8" high | 1.000 | Ea. | .889 | 54.50 | 43.50 | 98 |
| Frame, pine, 4-5/8" jamb | 17.000 | L.F. | .725 | 121.55 | 35.53 | 157.08 |
| Trim, stock pine, 11/16" x 2-1/2" | 34.000 | L.F. | 1.133 | 49.64 | 55.42 | 105.06 |
| Butt hinges, chrome, 3-1/2" x 3-1/2" | 1.500 | Pr. | | 42.75 | | 42.75 |
| Lockset, passage | 1.000 | Ea. | .500 | 24 | 24.50 | 48.50 |
| Prime door & frame, oil, brushwork | 2.000 | Face | 1.600 | 6.38 | 67 | 73.38 |
| Paint door and frame, oil, 2 coats | 2.000 | Face | 2.667 | 11.30 | 112 | 123.30 |
| TOTAL | | Ea. | 7.514 | 310.12 | 337.95 | 648.07 |
| **RAISED PANEL, SOLID, PINE DOOR** | | | | | | |
| Door, pine, raised panel, 2'-8" wide x 6'-8" high | 1.000 | Ea. | .889 | 177 | 43.50 | 220.50 |
| Frame, pine, 4-5/8" jamb | 17.000 | L.F. | .725 | 121.55 | 35.53 | 157.08 |
| Trim, stock pine, 11/16" x 2-1/2" | 34.000 | L.F. | 1.133 | 49.64 | 55.42 | 105.06 |
| Butt hinges, bronze, 3-1/2" x 3-1/2" | 1.500 | Pr. | | 52.50 | | 52.50 |
| Lockset, passage | 1.000 | Ea. | .500 | 24 | 24.50 | 48.50 |
| Prime door & frame, oil, brushwork | 2.000 | | 1.600 | 6.38 | 67 | 73.38 |
| Paint door and frame, oil, 2 coats | 2.000 | | 2.667 | 11.30 | 112 | 123.30 |
| TOTAL | | Ea. | 7.514 | 442.37 | 337.95 | 780.32 |

The costs in these systems are based on a cost per each door.

| Description | QUAN. | UNIT | LABOR HOURS | COST EACH | | |
|---|---|---|---|---|---|---|
| | | | | MAT. | INST. | TOTAL |
| | | | | | | |
| | | | | | | |
| | | | | | | |

| Interior Door Price Sheet | QUAN. | UNIT | LABOR HOURS | COST EACH | | |
|---|---|---|---|---|---|---|
| | | | | MAT. | INST. | TOTAL |
| Door, hollow core, lauan 1-3/8″ thick, 6′-8″ high x 1′-6″ wide | 1.000 | Ea. | .889 | 34 | 43.50 | 77.50 |
| 2′-0″ wide | 1.000 | Ea. | .889 | 34 | 43.50 | 77.50 |
| 2′-6″ wide | 1.000 | Ea. | .889 | 38 | 43.50 | 81.50 |
| 2′-8″ wide | 1.000 | Ea. | .889 | 39.50 | 43.50 | 83 |
| 3′-0″ wide | 1.000 | Ea. | .941 | 40.50 | 46 | 86.50 |
| Birch 1-3/8″ thick, 6′-8″ high x 1′-6″ wide | 1.000 | Ea. | .889 | 42 | 43.50 | 85.50 |
| 2′-0″ wide | 1.000 | Ea. | .889 | 45 | 43.50 | 88.50 |
| 2′-6″ wide | 1.000 | Ea. | .889 | 53.50 | 43.50 | 97 |
| 2′-8″ wide | 1.000 | Ea. | .889 | 54.50 | 43.50 | 98 |
| 3′-0″ wide | 1.000 | Ea. | .941 | 56 | 46 | 102 |
| Louvered pine 1-3/8″ thick, 6′-8″ high x 1′-6″ wide | 1.000 | Ea. | .842 | 111 | 41 | 152 |
| 2′-0″ wide | 1.000 | Ea. | .889 | 140 | 43.50 | 183.50 |
| 2′-6″ wide | 1.000 | Ea. | .889 | 153 | 43.50 | 196.50 |
| 2′-8″ wide | 1.000 | Ea. | .889 | 161 | 43.50 | 204.50 |
| 3′-0″ wide | 1.000 | Ea. | .941 | 183 | 46 | 229 |
| Paneled pine 1-3/8″ thick, 6′-8″ high x 1′-6″ wide | 1.000 | Ea. | .842 | 122 | 41 | 163 |
| 2′-0″ wide | 1.000 | Ea. | .889 | 143 | 43.50 | 186.50 |
| 2′-6″ wide | 1.000 | Ea. | .889 | 173 | 43.50 | 216.50 |
| 2′-8″ wide | 1.000 | Ea. | .889 | 177 | 43.50 | 220.50 |
| 3′-0″ wide | 1.000 | Ea. | .941 | 183 | 46 | 229 |
| Frame, pine, 1′-6″ thru 2′-0″ wide door, 3-5/8″ deep | 16.000 | L.F. | .683 | 97.50 | 33.50 | 131 |
| 4-5/8″ deep | 16.000 | L.F. | .683 | 114 | 33.50 | 147.50 |
| 5-5/8″ deep | 16.000 | L.F. | .683 | 75.50 | 33.50 | 109 |
| 2′-6″ thru 3′0″ wide door, 3-5/8″ deep | 17.000 | L.F. | .725 | 104 | 35.50 | 139.50 |
| 4-5/8″ deep | 17.000 | L.F. | .725 | 122 | 35.50 | 157.50 |
| 5-5/8″ deep | 17.000 | L.F. | .725 | 80 | 35.50 | 115.50 |
| Trim, casing, painted, both sides, 1′-6″ thru 2′-6″ wide door | 32.000 | L.F. | 1.855 | 50 | 85.50 | 135.50 |
| 2′-6″ thru 3′-0″ wide door | 34.000 | L.F. | 1.971 | 53 | 91 | 144 |
| Butt hinges 3-1/2″ x 3-1/2″, steel plated, chrome | 1.500 | Pr. | | 43 | | 43 |
| Bronze | 1.500 | Pr. | | 52.50 | | 52.50 |
| Locksets, passage, minimum | 1.000 | Ea. | .500 | 24 | 24.50 | 48.50 |
| Maximum | 1.000 | Ea. | .575 | 27.50 | 28 | 55.50 |
| Privacy, minimum | 1.000 | Ea. | .625 | 30 | 30.50 | 60.50 |
| Maximum | 1.000 | Ea. | .675 | 32.50 | 33 | 65.50 |
| Paint 2 sides, primer & 2 cts., flush door, 1′-6″ to 2′-0″ wide | 2.000 | Face | 5.547 | 24 | 233 | 257 |
| 2′-6″ thru 3′-0″ wide | 2.000 | Face | 6.933 | 30 | 291 | 321 |
| Louvered door, 1′-6″ thru 2′-0″ wide | 2.000 | Face | 6.400 | 23.50 | 269 | 292.50 |
| 2′-6″ thru 3′-0″ wide | 2.000 | Face | 8.000 | 29.50 | 335 | 364.50 |
| Paneled door, 1′-6″ thru 2′-0″ wide | 2.000 | Face | 6.400 | 23.50 | 269 | 292.50 |
| 2′-6″ thru 3′-0″ wide | 2.000 | Face | 8.000 | 29.50 | 335 | 364.50 |

| System Description | QUAN. | UNIT | LABOR HOURS | COST EACH | | |
|---|---|---|---|---|---|---|
| | | | | MAT. | INST. | TOTAL |
| **BI-PASSING, FLUSH, LAUAN, HOLLOW CORE, 4'-0" X 6'-8"** | | | | | | |
| Door, flush, lauan, hollow core, 4'-0" x 6'-8" opening | 1.000 | Ea. | 1.333 | 185 | 65.50 | 250.50 |
| Frame, pine, 4-5/8" jamb | 18.000 | L.F. | .768 | 128.70 | 37.62 | 166.32 |
| Trim, stock pine, 11/16" x 2-1/2" | 36.000 | L.F. | 1.200 | 52.56 | 58.68 | 111.24 |
| Prime door & frame, oil, brushwork | 2.000 | Face | 1.600 | 6.38 | 67 | 73.38 |
| Paint door and frame, oil, 2 coats | 2.000 | Face | 2.667 | 11.30 | 112 | 123.30 |
| TOTAL | | Ea. | 7.568 | 383.94 | 340.80 | 724.74 |
| **BI-PASSING, FLUSH, BIRCH, HOLLOW CORE, 6'-0" X 6'-8"** | | | | | | |
| Door, flush, birch, hollow core, 6'-0" x 6'-8" opening | 1.000 | Ea. | 1.600 | 279 | 78.50 | 357.50 |
| Frame, pine, 4-5/8" jamb | 19.000 | L.F. | .811 | 135.85 | 39.71 | 175.56 |
| Trim, stock pine, 11/16" x 2-1/2" | 38.000 | L.F. | 1.267 | 55.48 | 61.94 | 117.42 |
| Prime door & frame, oil, brushwork | 2.000 | Face | 2.000 | 7.98 | 83.75 | 91.73 |
| Paint door and frame, oil, 2 coats | 2.000 | Face | 3.333 | 14.13 | 140 | 154.13 |
| TOTAL | | Ea. | 9.011 | 492.44 | 403.90 | 896.34 |
| **BI-FOLD, PINE, PANELED, 3'-0" X 6'-8"** | | | | | | |
| Door, pine, paneled, 3'-0" x 6'-8" opening | 1.000 | Ea. | 1.231 | 217 | 60.50 | 277.50 |
| Frame, pine, 4-5/8" jamb | 17.000 | L.F. | .725 | 121.55 | 35.53 | 157.08 |
| Trim, stock pine, 11/16" x 2-1/2" | 34.000 | L.F. | 1.133 | 49.64 | 55.42 | 105.06 |
| Prime door & frame, oil, brushwork | 2.000 | Face | 1.600 | 6.38 | 67 | 73.38 |
| Paint door and frame, oil, 2 coats | 2.000 | Face | 2.667 | 11.30 | 112 | 123.30 |
| TOTAL | | Ea. | 7.356 | 405.87 | 330.45 | 736.32 |
| **BI-FOLD, PINE, LOUVERED, 6'-0" X 6'-8"** | | | | | | |
| Door, pine, louvered, 6'-0" x 6'-8" opening | 1.000 | Ea. | 1.600 | 305 | 78.50 | 383.50 |
| Frame, pine, 4-5/8" jamb | 19.000 | L.F. | .811 | 135.85 | 39.71 | 175.56 |
| Trim, stock pine, 11/16" x 2-1/2" | 38.000 | L.F. | 1.267 | 55.48 | 61.94 | 117.42 |
| Prime door & frame, oil, brushwork | 2.500 | Face | 2.000 | 7.98 | 83.75 | 91.73 |
| Paint door and frame, oil, 2 coats | 2.500 | Face | 3.333 | 14.13 | 140 | 154.13 |
| TOTAL | | Ea. | 9.011 | 518.44 | 403.90 | 922.34 |

The costs in this system are based on a cost per each door.

| Description | QUAN. | UNIT | LABOR HOURS | COST EACH | | |
|---|---|---|---|---|---|---|
| | | | | MAT. | INST. | TOTAL |
| | | | | | | |

# Closet Door Price Sheet

| | QUAN. | UNIT | LABOR HOURS | COST EACH MAT. | COST EACH INST. | COST EACH TOTAL |
|---|---|---|---|---|---|---|
| Doors, bi-passing, pine, louvered, 4'-0" x 6'-8" opening | 1.000 | Ea. | 1.333 | 440 | 65.50 | 505.50 |
| 6'-0" x 6'-8" opening | 1.000 | Ea. | 1.600 | 570 | 78.50 | 648.50 |
| Paneled, 4'-0" x 6'-8" opening | 1.000 | Ea. | 1.333 | 550 | 65.50 | 615.50 |
| 6'-0" x 6'-8" opening | 1.000 | Ea. | 1.600 | 655 | 78.50 | 733.50 |
| Flush, birch, hollow core, 4'-0" x 6'-8" opening | 1.000 | Ea. | 1.333 | 239 | 65.50 | 304.50 |
| 6'-0" x 6'-8" opening | 1.000 | Ea. | 1.600 | 279 | 78.50 | 357.50 |
| Flush, lauan, hollow core, 4'-0" x 6'-8" opening | 1.000 | Ea. | 1.333 | 185 | 65.50 | 250.50 |
| 6'-0" x 6'-8" opening | 1.000 | Ea. | 1.600 | 218 | 78.50 | 296.50 |
| Bi-fold, pine, louvered, 3'-0" x 6'-8" opening | 1.000 | Ea. | 1.231 | 217 | 60.50 | 277.50 |
| 6'-0" x 6'-8" opening | 1.000 | Ea. | 1.600 | 305 | 78.50 | 383.50 |
| Paneled, 3'-0" x 6'-8" opening | 1.000 | Ea. | 1.231 | 217 | 60.50 | 277.50 |
| 6'-0" x 6'-8" opening | 1.000 | Ea. | 1.600 | 305 | 78.50 | 383.50 |
| Flush, birch, hollow core, 3'-0" x 6'-8" opening | 1.000 | Ea. | 1.231 | 60 | 60.50 | 120.50 |
| 6'-0" x 6'-8" opening | 1.000 | Ea. | 1.600 | 139 | 78.50 | 217.50 |
| Flush, lauan, hollow core, 3'-0" x 6'8" opening | 1.000 | Ea. | 1.231 | 300 | 60.50 | 360.50 |
| 6'-0" x 6'-8" opening | 1.000 | Ea. | 1.600 | 440 | 78.50 | 518.50 |
| Frame pine, 3'-0" door, 3-5/8" deep | 17.000 | L.F. | .725 | 104 | 35.50 | 139.50 |
| 4-5/8" deep | 17.000 | L.F. | .725 | 122 | 35.50 | 157.50 |
| 5-5/8" deep | 17.000 | L.F. | .725 | 80 | 35.50 | 115.50 |
| 4'-0" door, 3-5/8" deep | 18.000 | L.F. | .768 | 110 | 37.50 | 147.50 |
| 4-5/8" deep | 18.000 | L.F. | .768 | 129 | 37.50 | 166.50 |
| 5-5/8" deep | 18.000 | L.F. | .768 | 85 | 37.50 | 122.50 |
| 6'-0" door, 3-5/8" deep | 19.000 | L.F. | .811 | 116 | 39.50 | 155.50 |
| 4-5/8" deep | 19.000 | L.F. | .811 | 136 | 39.50 | 175.50 |
| 5-5/8" deep | 19.000 | L.F. | .811 | 89.50 | 39.50 | 129 |
| Trim both sides, painted 3'-0" x 6'-8" door | 34.000 | L.F. | 1.971 | 53 | 91 | 144 |
| 4'-0" x 6'-8" door | 36.000 | L.F. | 2.086 | 56 | 96 | 152 |
| 6'-0" x 6'-8" door | 38.000 | L.F. | 2.203 | 59.50 | 101 | 160.50 |
| Paint 2 sides, primer & 2 cts., flush door & frame, 3' x 6'-8" opng | 2.000 | Face | 2.914 | 13.25 | 134 | 147.25 |
| 4'-0" x 6'-8" opening | 2.000 | Face | 3.886 | 17.70 | 179 | 196.70 |
| 6'-0" x 6'-8" opening | 2.000 | Face | 4.857 | 22 | 224 | 246 |
| Paneled door & frame, 3'-0" x 6'-8" opening | 2.000 | Face | 6.000 | 22.50 | 252 | 274.50 |
| 4'-0" x 6'-8" opening | 2.000 | Face | 8.000 | 29.50 | 335 | 364.50 |
| 6'-0" x 6'-8" opening | 2.000 | Face | 10.000 | 37 | 420 | 457 |
| Louvered door & frame, 3'-0" x 6'-8" opening | 2.000 | Face | 6.000 | 22.50 | 252 | 274.50 |
| 4'-0" x 6'-8" opening | 2.000 | Face | 8.000 | 29.50 | 335 | 364.50 |
| 6'-0" x 6'-8" opening | 2.000 | Face | 10.000 | 37 | 420 | 457 |
| | | | | | | |
| | | | | | | |
| | | | | | | |
| | | | | | | |
| | | | | | | |
| | | | | | | |
| | | | | | | |
| | | | | | | |
| | | | | | | |
| | | | | | | |

| System Description | QUAN. | UNIT | LABOR HOURS | COST PER S.F. | | |
|---|---|---|---|---|---|---|
| | | | | MAT. | INST. | TOTAL |
| Carpet, direct glue-down, nylon, level loop, 26 oz. | 1.000 | S.F. | .018 | 3.27 | .79 | 4.06 |
| 32 oz. | 1.000 | S.F. | .018 | 4.06 | .79 | 4.85 |
| 40 oz. | 1.000 | S.F. | .018 | 6.05 | .79 | 6.84 |
| Nylon, plush, 20 oz. | 1.000 | S.F. | .018 | 2.11 | .79 | 2.90 |
| 24 oz. | 1.000 | S.F. | .018 | 2.11 | .79 | 2.90 |
| 30 oz. | 1.000 | S.F. | .018 | 3.12 | .79 | 3.91 |
| 42 oz. | 1.000 | S.F. | .022 | 4.64 | .95 | 5.59 |
| 48 oz. | 1.000 | S.F. | .022 | 5.45 | .95 | 6.40 |
| 54 oz. | 1.000 | S.F. | .022 | 5.95 | .95 | 6.90 |
| Olefin, 15 oz. | 1.000 | S.F. | .018 | 1.10 | .79 | 1.89 |
| 22 oz. | 1.000 | S.F. | .018 | 1.33 | .79 | 2.12 |
| Tile, foam backed, needle punch | 1.000 | S.F. | .014 | 4.32 | .62 | 4.94 |
| Tufted loop or shag | 1.000 | S.F. | .014 | 2.86 | .62 | 3.48 |
| Wool, 36 oz., level loop | 1.000 | S.F. | .018 | 14.20 | .79 | 14.99 |
| 32 oz., patterned | 1.000 | S.F. | .020 | 14.05 | .88 | 14.93 |
| 48 oz., patterned | 1.000 | S.F. | .020 | 14.40 | .88 | 15.28 |
| | | | | | | |
| Padding, sponge rubber cushion, minimum | 1.000 | S.F. | .006 | .49 | .26 | .75 |
| Maximum | 1.000 | S.F. | .006 | 1.22 | .26 | 1.48 |
| Felt, 32 oz. to 56 oz., minimum | 1.000 | S.F. | .006 | .51 | .26 | .77 |
| Maximum | 1.000 | S.F. | .006 | .86 | .26 | 1.12 |
| Bonded urethane, 3/8" thick, minimum | 1.000 | S.F. | .006 | .56 | .26 | .82 |
| Maximum | 1.000 | S.F. | .006 | .95 | .26 | 1.21 |
| Prime urethane, 1/4" thick, minimum | 1.000 | S.F. | .006 | .32 | .26 | .58 |
| Maximum | 1.000 | S.F. | .006 | .59 | .26 | .85 |
| Stairs, for stairs, add to above carpet prices | 1.000 | Riser | .267 | | 11.75 | 11.75 |
| | | | | | | |
| Underlayment plywood, 3/8" thick | 1.000 | S.F. | .011 | .85 | .52 | 1.37 |
| 1/2" thick | 1.000 | S.F. | .011 | .88 | .54 | 1.42 |
| 5/8" thick | 1.000 | S.F. | .011 | 1.29 | .56 | 1.85 |
| 3/4" thick | 1.000 | S.F. | .012 | 1.35 | .60 | 1.95 |
| Particle board, 3/8" thick | 1.000 | S.F. | .011 | .40 | .52 | .92 |
| 1/2" thick | 1.000 | S.F. | .011 | .43 | .54 | .97 |
| 5/8" thick | 1.000 | S.F. | .011 | .55 | .56 | 1.11 |
| 3/4" thick | 1.000 | S.F. | .012 | .72 | .60 | 1.32 |
| Hardboard, 4' x 4', 0.215" thick | 1.000 | S.F. | .011 | .63 | .52 | 1.15 |
| | | | | | | |
| | | | | | | |
| | | | | | | |
| | | | | | | |
| | | | | | | |
| | | | | | | |

| System Description | QUAN. | UNIT | LABOR HOURS | COST PER S.F. | | |
|---|---|---|---|---|---|---|
| | | | | MAT. | INST. | TOTAL |
| Resilient flooring, asphalt tile on concrete, 1/8" thick | | | | | | |
| Color group B | 1.000 | S.F. | .020 | 1.31 | .88 | 2.19 |
| Color group C & D | 1.000 | S.F. | .020 | 1.43 | .88 | 2.31 |
| | | | | | | |
| Asphalt tile on wood subfloor, 1/8" thick | | | | | | |
| Color group B | 1.000 | S.F. | .020 | 1.53 | .88 | 2.41 |
| Color group C & D | 1.000 | S.F. | .020 | 1.65 | .88 | 2.53 |
| | | | | | | |
| Vinyl composition tile, 12" x 12", 1/16" thick | 1.000 | S.F. | .016 | 1.01 | .71 | 1.72 |
| Embossed | 1.000 | S.F. | .016 | 2.39 | .71 | 3.10 |
| Marbleized | 1.000 | S.F. | .016 | 2.39 | .71 | 3.10 |
| Plain | 1.000 | S.F. | .016 | 3.07 | .71 | 3.78 |
| .080" thick, embossed | 1.000 | S.F. | .016 | 1.52 | .71 | 2.23 |
| Marbleized | 1.000 | S.F. | .016 | 2.74 | .71 | 3.45 |
| Plain | 1.000 | S.F. | .016 | 2.54 | .71 | 3.25 |
| | | | | | | |
| 1/8" thick, marbleized | 1.000 | S.F. | .016 | 1.80 | .71 | 2.51 |
| Plain | 1.000 | S.F. | .016 | 1.98 | .71 | 2.69 |
| Vinyl tile, 12" x 12", .050" thick, minimum | 1.000 | S.F. | .016 | 3.30 | .71 | 4.01 |
| Maximum | 1.000 | S.F. | .016 | 6.60 | .71 | 7.31 |
| 1/8" thick, minimum | 1.000 | S.F. | .016 | 4.79 | .71 | 5.50 |
| Maximum | 1.000 | S.F. | .016 | 5.45 | .71 | 6.16 |
| 1/8" thick, solid colors | 1.000 | S.F. | .016 | 6.20 | .71 | 6.91 |
| Florentine pattern | 1.000 | S.F. | .016 | 6.60 | .71 | 7.31 |
| Marbleized or travertine pattern | 1.000 | S.F. | .016 | 13.95 | .71 | 14.66 |
| | | | | | | |
| Vinyl sheet goods, backed, .070" thick, minimum | 1.000 | S.F. | .032 | 3.85 | 1.41 | 5.26 |
| Maximum | 1.000 | S.F. | .040 | 3.97 | 1.76 | 5.73 |
| .093" thick, minimum | 1.000 | S.F. | .035 | 3.96 | 1.53 | 5.49 |
| Maximum | 1.000 | S.F. | .040 | 5.60 | 1.76 | 7.36 |
| .125" thick, minimum | 1.000 | S.F. | .035 | 4.51 | 1.53 | 6.04 |
| Maximum | 1.000 | S.F. | .040 | 6.70 | 1.76 | 8.46 |
| Wood, oak, finished in place, 25/32" x 2-1/2" clear | 1.000 | S.F. | .074 | 3.50 | 3.28 | 6.78 |
| Select | 1.000 | S.F. | .074 | 4.09 | 3.28 | 7.37 |
| No. 1 common | 1.000 | S.F. | .074 | 5.05 | 3.28 | 8.33 |
| Prefinished, oak, 2-1/2" wide | 1.000 | S.F. | .047 | 5.25 | 2.30 | 7.55 |
| 3-1/4" wide | 1.000 | S.F. | .043 | 6.75 | 2.12 | 8.87 |
| Ranch plank, oak, random width | 1.000 | S.F. | .055 | 7.40 | 2.70 | 10.10 |
| Parquet, 5/16" thick, finished in place, oak, minimum | 1.000 | S.F. | .077 | 5.70 | 3.43 | 9.13 |
| Maximum | 1.000 | S.F. | .107 | 6.30 | 4.90 | 11.20 |
| Teak, minimum | 1.000 | S.F. | .077 | 6.10 | 3.43 | 9.53 |
| Maximum | 1.000 | S.F. | .107 | 10.05 | 4.90 | 14.95 |
| Sleepers, treated, 16" O.C., 1" x 2" | 1.000 | S.F. | .007 | .36 | .33 | .69 |
| 1" x 3" | 1.000 | S.F. | .008 | .58 | .39 | .97 |
| 2" x 4" | 1.000 | S.F. | .011 | .38 | .52 | .90 |
| 2" x 6" | 1.000 | S.F. | .012 | .61 | .60 | 1.21 |
| Subfloor, plywood, 1/2" thick | 1.000 | S.F. | .011 | .46 | .52 | .98 |
| 5/8" thick | 1.000 | S.F. | .012 | .56 | .58 | 1.14 |
| 3/4" thick | 1.000 | S.F. | .013 | .64 | .63 | 1.27 |
| Ceramic tile, color group 2, 1" x 1" | 1.000 | S.F. | .087 | 5.20 | 3.46 | 8.66 |
| 2" x 2" or 2" x 1" | 1.000 | S.F. | .084 | 5.50 | 3.33 | 8.83 |
| Color group 1, 8" x 8" | | S.F. | .064 | 3.94 | 2.53 | 6.47 |
| 12" x 12" | | S.F. | .049 | 4.92 | 1.95 | 6.87 |
| 16" x 16" | | S.F. | .029 | 6.75 | 1.15 | 7.90 |
| | | | | | | |

| System Description | QUAN. | UNIT | LABOR HOURS | COST EACH MAT. | COST EACH INST. | COST EACH TOTAL |
|---|---|---|---|---|---|---|
| **7 RISERS, OAK TREADS, BOX STAIRS** | | | | | | |
| Treads, oak, 1-1/4" x 10" wide, 3' long | 6.000 | Ea. | 2.667 | 495 | 132 | 627 |
| Risers, 3/4" thick, beech | 7.000 | Ea. | 2.625 | 145.95 | 128.10 | 274.05 |
| 30" primed pine balusters | 12.000 | Ea. | 1.000 | 37.68 | 48.96 | 86.64 |
| Newels, 3" wide | 2.000 | Ea. | 2.286 | 92 | 112 | 204 |
| Handrails, oak laminated | 7.000 | L.F. | .933 | 266 | 45.85 | 311.85 |
| Stringers, 2" x 10", 3 each | 21.000 | L.F. | .306 | 5.67 | 14.91 | 20.58 |
| TOTAL | | Ea. | 9.817 | 1,042.30 | 481.82 | 1,524.12 |
| **14 RISERS, OAK TREADS, BOX STAIRS** | | | | | | |
| Treads, oak, 1-1/4" x 10" wide, 3' long | 13.000 | Ea. | 5.778 | 1,072.50 | 286 | 1,358.50 |
| Risers, 3/4" thick, beech | 14.000 | Ea. | 5.250 | 291.90 | 256.20 | 548.10 |
| 30" primed pine balusters | 26.000 | Ea. | 2.167 | 81.64 | 106.08 | 187.72 |
| Newels, 3" wide | 2.000 | Ea. | 2.286 | 92 | 112 | 204 |
| Handrails, oak, laminated | 14.000 | L.F. | 1.867 | 532 | 91.70 | 623.70 |
| Stringers, 2" x 10", 3 each | 42.000 | L.F. | 5.169 | 33.60 | 252 | 285.60 |
| TOTAL | | Ea. | 22.517 | 2,103.64 | 1,103.98 | 3,207.62 |
| **14 RISERS, PINE TREADS, BOX STAIRS** | | | | | | |
| Treads, pine, 9-1/2" x 3/4" thick | 13.000 | Ea. | 5.778 | 188.50 | 286 | 474.50 |
| Risers, 3/4" thick, pine | 14.000 | Ea. | 5.091 | 143.22 | 249.90 | 393.12 |
| 30" primed pine balusters | 26.000 | Ea. | 2.167 | 81.64 | 106.08 | 187.72 |
| Newels, 3" wide | 2.000 | Ea. | 2.286 | 92 | 112 | 204 |
| Handrails, oak, laminated | 14.000 | L.F. | 1.867 | 532 | 91.70 | 623.70 |
| Stringers, 2" x 10", 3 each | 42.000 | L.F. | 5.169 | 33.60 | 252 | 285.60 |
| TOTAL | | Ea. | 22.358 | 1,070.96 | 1,097.68 | 2,168.64 |

| Description | QUAN. | UNIT | LABOR HOURS | COST EACH MAT. | COST EACH INST. | COST EACH TOTAL |
|---|---|---|---|---|---|---|
| | | | | | | |
| | | | | | | |
| | | | | | | |
| | | | | | | |
| | | | | | | |

| Stairway Price Sheet | QUAN. | UNIT | LABOR HOURS | COST EACH | | |
|---|---|---|---|---|---|---|
| | | | | MAT. | INST. | TOTAL |
| Treads, oak, 1-1/16" x 9-1/2", 3' long, 7 riser stair | 6.000 | Ea. | 2.667 | 495 | 132 | 627 |
| 14 riser stair | 13.000 | Ea. | 5.778 | 1,075 | 286 | 1,361 |
| 1-1/16" x 11-1/2", 3' long, 7 riser stair | 6.000 | Ea. | 2.667 | 535 | 132 | 667 |
| 14 riser stair | 13.000 | Ea. | 5.778 | 1,150 | 286 | 1,436 |
| Pine, 3/4" x 9-1/2", 3' long, 7 riser stair | 6.000 | Ea. | 2.667 | 87 | 132 | 219 |
| 14 riser stair | 13.000 | Ea. | 5.778 | 189 | 286 | 475 |
| 3/4" x 11-1/4", 3' long, 7 riser stair | 6.000 | Ea. | 2.667 | 132 | 132 | 264 |
| 14 riser stair | 13.000 | Ea. | 5.778 | 286 | 286 | 572 |
| Risers, oak, 3/4" x 7-1/2" high, 7 riser stair | 7.000 | Ea. | 2.625 | 125 | 128 | 253 |
| 14 riser stair | 14.000 | Ea. | 5.250 | 250 | 256 | 506 |
| Beech, 3/4" x 7-1/2" high, 7 riser stair | 7.000 | Ea. | 2.625 | 146 | 128 | 274 |
| 14 riser stair | 14.000 | Ea. | 5.250 | 292 | 256 | 548 |
| Baluster, turned, 30" high, primed pine, 7 riser stair | 12.000 | Ea. | 3.429 | 37.50 | 49 | 86.50 |
| 14 riser stair | 26.000 | Ea. | 7.428 | 81.50 | 106 | 187.50 |
| 30" birch, 7 riser stair | 12.000 | Ea. | 3.429 | 34.50 | 44.50 | 79 |
| 14 riser stair | 26.000 | Ea. | 7.428 | 74 | 96.50 | 170.50 |
| 42" pine, 7 riser stair | 12.000 | Ea. | 3.556 | 58.50 | 49 | 107.50 |
| 14 riser stair | 26.000 | Ea. | 7.704 | 126 | 106 | 232 |
| 42" birch, 7 riser stair | 12.000 | Ea. | 3.556 | 58.50 | 49 | 107.50 |
| 14 riser stair | 26.000 | Ea. | 7.704 | 126 | 106 | 232 |
| Newels, 3-1/4" wide, starting, 7 riser stair | 2.000 | Ea. | 2.286 | 92 | 112 | 204 |
| 14 riser stair | 2.000 | Ea. | 2.286 | 92 | 112 | 204 |
| Landing, 7 riser stair | 2.000 | Ea. | 3.200 | 250 | 157 | 407 |
| 14 riser stair | 2.000 | Ea. | 3.200 | 250 | 157 | 407 |
| Handrails, oak, laminated, 7 riser stair | 7.000 | L.F. | .933 | 266 | 46 | 312 |
| 14 riser stair | 14.000 | L.F. | 1.867 | 530 | 91.50 | 621.50 |
| Stringers, fir, 2" x 10" 7 riser stair | 21.000 | L.F. | 2.585 | 16.80 | 126 | 142.80 |
| 14 riser stair | 42.000 | L.F. | 5.169 | 33.50 | 252 | 285.50 |
| 2" x 12", 7 riser stair | 21.000 | L.F. | 2.585 | 24.50 | 126 | 150.50 |
| 14 riser stair | 42.000 | L.F. | 5.169 | 49 | 252 | 301 |

| Special Stairways | QUAN. | UNIT | LABOR HOURS | COST EACH | | |
|---|---|---|---|---|---|---|
| | | | | MAT. | INST. | TOTAL |
| Basement stairs, open risers | 1.000 | Flight | 4.000 | 785 | 196 | 981 |
| Spiral stairs, oak, 4'-6" diameter, prefabricated, 9' high | 1.000 | Flight | 10.667 | 3,975 | 520 | 4,495 |
| Aluminum, 5'-0" diameter stock unit | 1.000 | Flight | 9.956 | 7,700 | 650 | 8,350 |
| Custom unit | 1.000 | Flight | 9.956 | 14,700 | 650 | 15,350 |
| Cast iron, 4'-0" diameter, minimum | 1.000 | Flight | 9.956 | 6,850 | 650 | 7,500 |
| Maximum | 1.000 | Flight | 17.920 | 9,375 | 1,175 | 10,550 |
| Steel, industrial, pre-erected, 3'-6" wide, bar rail | 1.000 | Flight | 7.724 | 7,000 | 740 | 7,740 |
| Picket rail | 1.000 | Flight | 7.724 | 7,850 | 740 | 8,590 |

Soffit Drywall — Soffit Framing
Top Cabinets
Counter Top — Bottom Cabinets

| System Description | QUAN. | UNIT | LABOR HOURS | COST PER L.F. | | |
|---|---|---|---|---|---|---|
| | | | | MAT. | INST. | TOTAL |
| **KITCHEN, ECONOMY GRADE** | | | | | | |
| Top cabinets, economy grade | 1.000 | L.F. | .171 | 51.52 | 8.32 | 59.84 |
| Bottom cabinets, economy grade | 1.000 | L.F. | .256 | 77.28 | 12.48 | 89.76 |
| Square edge, plastic face countertop | 1.000 | L.F. | .267 | 29 | 13.05 | 42.05 |
| Blocking, wood, 2″ x 4″ | 1.000 | L.F. | .032 | .27 | 1.57 | 1.84 |
| Soffit, framing, wood, 2″ x 4″ | 4.000 | L.F. | .071 | 1.08 | 3.48 | 4.56 |
| Soffit drywall | 2.000 | S.F. | .047 | .70 | 2.32 | 3.02 |
| Drywall painting | 2.000 | S.F. | .013 | .10 | .66 | .76 |
| TOTAL | | L.F. | .857 | 159.95 | 41.88 | 201.83 |
| **AVERAGE GRADE** | | | | | | |
| Top cabinets, average grade | 1.000 | L.F. | .213 | 64.40 | 10.40 | 74.80 |
| Bottom cabinets, average grade | 1.000 | L.F. | .320 | 96.60 | 15.60 | 112.20 |
| Solid surface countertop, solid color | 1.000 | L.F. | .800 | 66 | 39 | 105 |
| Blocking, wood, 2″ x 4″ | 1.000 | L.F. | .032 | .27 | 1.57 | 1.84 |
| Soffit framing, wood, 2″ x 4″ | 4.000 | L.F. | .071 | 1.08 | 3.48 | 4.56 |
| Soffit drywall | 2.000 | S.F. | .047 | .70 | 2.32 | 3.02 |
| Drywall painting | 2.000 | S.F. | .013 | .10 | .66 | .76 |
| TOTAL | | L.F. | 1.496 | 229.15 | 73.03 | 302.18 |
| **CUSTOM GRADE** | | | | | | |
| Top cabinets, custom grade | 1.000 | L.F. | .256 | 138 | 12.60 | 150.60 |
| Bottom cabinets, custom grade | 1.000 | L.F. | .384 | 207 | 18.90 | 225.90 |
| Solid surface countertop, premium patterned color | 1.000 | L.F. | 1.067 | 115 | 52 | 167 |
| Blocking, wood, 2″ x 4″ | 1.000 | L.F. | .032 | .27 | 1.57 | 1.84 |
| Soffit framing, wood, 2″ x 4″ | 4.000 | L.F. | .071 | 1.08 | 3.48 | 4.56 |
| Soffit drywall | 2.000 | S.F. | .047 | .70 | 2.32 | 3.02 |
| Drywall painting | 2.000 | S.F. | .013 | .10 | .66 | .76 |
| TOTAL | | L.F. | 1.870 | 462.15 | 91.53 | 553.68 |

| Description | QUAN. | UNIT | LABOR HOURS | COST PER L.F. | | |
|---|---|---|---|---|---|---|
| | | | | MAT. | INST. | TOTAL |
| | | | | | | |
| | | | | | | |
| | | | | | | |

| Kitchen Price Sheet | QUAN. | UNIT | LABOR HOURS | COST PER L.F. | | |
|---|---|---|---|---|---|---|
| | | | | MAT. | INST. | TOTAL |
| Top cabinets, economy grade | 1.000 | L.F. | .171 | 51.50 | 8.30 | 59.80 |
| Average grade | 1.000 | L.F. | .213 | 64.50 | 10.40 | 74.90 |
| Custom grade | 1.000 | L.F. | .256 | 138 | 12.60 | 150.60 |
| | | | | | | |
| Bottom cabinets, economy grade | 1.000 | L.F. | .256 | 77.50 | 12.50 | 90 |
| Average grade | 1.000 | L.F. | .320 | 96.50 | 15.60 | 112.10 |
| Custom grade | 1.000 | L.F. | .384 | 207 | 18.90 | 225.90 |
| | | | | | | |
| Counter top, laminated plastic, 7/8″ thick, no splash | 1.000 | L.F. | .267 | 23 | 13.05 | 36.05 |
| With backsplash | 1.000 | L.F. | .267 | 30 | 13.05 | 43.05 |
| 1-1/4″ thick, no splash | 1.000 | L.F. | .286 | 34 | 14 | 48 |
| With backsplash | 1.000 | L.F. | .286 | 33 | 14 | 47 |
| Post formed, laminated plastic | 1.000 | L.F. | .267 | 11.80 | 13.05 | 24.85 |
| Ceramic tile, with backsplash | | L.F. | .427 | 17.05 | 7.85 | 24.90 |
| Marble, with backsplash, minimum | 1.000 | L.F. | .471 | 42 | 22.50 | 64.50 |
| Maximum | 1.000 | L.F. | .615 | 105 | 29.50 | 134.50 |
| Maple, solid laminated, no backsplash | 1.000 | L.F. | .286 | 68.50 | 14 | 82.50 |
| With backsplash | 1.000 | L.F. | .286 | 81.50 | 14 | 95.50 |
| Solid Surface, with backsplash, minimum | | L.F. | .842 | 72.50 | 41 | 113.50 |
| Maximum | | L.F. | 1.067 | 115 | 52 | 167 |
| Blocking, wood, 2″ x 4″ | 1.000 | L.F. | .032 | .27 | 1.57 | 1.84 |
| 2″ x 6″ | 1.000 | L.F. | .036 | .41 | 1.76 | 2.17 |
| 2″ x 8″ | 1.000 | L.F. | .040 | .61 | 1.96 | 2.57 |
| | | | | | | |
| Soffit framing, wood, 2″ x 3″ | 4.000 | L.F. | .064 | 1.16 | 3.12 | 4.28 |
| 2″ x 4″ | 4.000 | L.F. | .071 | 1.08 | 3.48 | 4.56 |
| Soffit, drywall, painted | 2.000 | S.F. | .060 | .80 | 2.98 | 3.78 |
| | | | | | | |
| Paneling, standard | 2.000 | S.F. | .064 | 1.96 | 3.14 | 5.10 |
| Deluxe | 2.000 | S.F. | .091 | 4.34 | 4.48 | 8.82 |
| Sinks, porcelain on cast iron, single bowl, 21″ x 24″ | 1.000 | Ea. | 10.334 | 580 | 525 | 1,105 |
| 21″ x 30″ | 1.000 | Ea. | 10.334 | 630 | 525 | 1,155 |
| Double bowl, 20″ x 32″ | 1.000 | Ea. | 10.810 | 725 | 550 | 1,275 |
| | | | | | | |
| Stainless steel, single bowl, 16″ x 20″ | 1.000 | Ea. | 10.334 | 910 | 525 | 1,435 |
| 22″ x 25″ | 1.000 | Ea. | 10.334 | 980 | 525 | 1,505 |
| Double bowl, 20″ x 32″ | 1.000 | Ea. | 10.810 | 525 | 550 | 1,075 |

| Kitchen Price Sheet | QUAN. | UNIT | LABOR HOURS | COST PER L.F. | | |
|---|---|---|---|---|---|---|
| | | | | MAT. | INST. | TOTAL |
| Range, free standing, minimum | 1.000 | Ea. | 3.600 | 470 | 165 | 635 |
| Maximum | 1.000 | Ea. | 6.000 | 2,200 | 252 | 2,452 |
| Built-in, minimum | 1.000 | Ea. | 3.333 | 840 | 179 | 1,019 |
| Maximum | 1.000 | Ea. | 10.000 | 1,750 | 495 | 2,245 |
| Counter top range, 4-burner, minimum | 1.000 | Ea. | 3.333 | 420 | 179 | 599 |
| Maximum | 1.000 | Ea. | 4.667 | 750 | 250 | 1,000 |
| Compactor, built-in, minimum | 1.000 | Ea. | 2.215 | 605 | 112 | 717 |
| Maximum | 1.000 | Ea. | 3.282 | 930 | 164 | 1,094 |
| Dishwasher, built-in, minimum | 1.000 | Ea. | 6.735 | 465 | 375 | 840 |
| Maximum | 1.000 | Ea. | 9.235 | 580 | 515 | 1,095 |
| Garbage disposer, minimum | 1.000 | Ea. | 2.810 | 184 | 158 | 342 |
| Maximum | 1.000 | Ea. | 2.810 | 315 | 158 | 473 |
| Microwave oven, minimum | 1.000 | Ea. | 2.615 | 143 | 140 | 283 |
| Maximum | 1.000 | Ea. | 4.615 | 480 | 247 | 727 |
| Range hood, ducted, minimum | 1.000 | Ea. | 4.658 | 91.50 | 235 | 326.50 |
| Maximum | 1.000 | Ea. | 5.991 | 930 | 300 | 1,230 |
| Ductless, minimum | 1.000 | Ea. | 2.615 | 100 | 133 | 233 |
| Maximum | 1.000 | Ea. | 3.948 | 940 | 199 | 1,139 |
| Refrigerator, 16 cu.ft., minimum | 1.000 | Ea. | 2.000 | 615 | 72.50 | 687.50 |
| Maximum | 1.000 | Ea. | 3.200 | 980 | 116 | 1,096 |
| 16 cu.ft. with icemaker, minimum | 1.000 | Ea. | 4.210 | 840 | 189 | 1,029 |
| Maximum | 1.000 | Ea. | 5.410 | 1,200 | 233 | 1,433 |
| 19 cu.ft., minimum | 1.000 | Ea. | 2.667 | 495 | 96.50 | 591.50 |
| Maximum | 1.000 | Ea. | 4.667 | 865 | 169 | 1,034 |
| 19 cu.ft. with icemaker, minimum | 1.000 | Ea. | 5.143 | 725 | 223 | 948 |
| Maximum | 1.000 | Ea. | 7.143 | 1,100 | 295 | 1,395 |
| Sinks, porcelain on cast iron single bowl, 21" x 24" | 1.000 | Ea. | 10.334 | 580 | 525 | 1,105 |
| 21" x 30" | 1.000 | Ea. | 10.334 | 630 | 525 | 1,155 |
| Double bowl, 20" x 32" | 1.000 | Ea. | 10.810 | 725 | 550 | 1,275 |
| Stainless steel, single bowl 16" x 20" | 1.000 | Ea. | 10.334 | 910 | 525 | 1,435 |
| 22" x 25" | 1.000 | Ea. | 10.334 | 980 | 525 | 1,505 |
| Double bowl, 20" x 32" | 1.000 | Ea. | 10.810 | 525 | 550 | 1,075 |
| Water heater, electric, 30 gallon | 1.000 | Ea. | 3.636 | 635 | 205 | 840 |
| 40 gallon | 1.000 | Ea. | 4.000 | 675 | 225 | 900 |
| Gas, 30 gallon | 1.000 | Ea. | 4.000 | 985 | 225 | 1,210 |
| 75 gallon | 1.000 | Ea. | 5.333 | 1,350 | 300 | 1,650 |
| Wall, packaged terminal heater/air conditioner cabinet, wall sleeve, louver, electric heat, thermostat, manual changeover, 208V | | Ea. | | | | |
| 6000 BTUH cooling, 8800 BTU heating | 1.000 | Ea. | 2.667 | 750 | 135 | 885 |
| 9000 BTUH cooling, 13,900 BTU heating | 1.000 | Ea. | 3.200 | 865 | 162 | 1,027 |
| 12,000 BTUH cooling, 13,900 BTU heating | 1.000 | Ea. | 4.000 | 935 | 202 | 1,137 |
| 15,000 BTUH cooling, 13,900 BTU heating | 1.000 | Ea. | 5.333 | 1,000 | 269 | 1,269 |

| System Description | QUAN. | UNIT | LABOR HOURS | COST EACH | | |
|---|---|---|---|---|---|---|
| | | | | MAT. | INST. | TOTAL |
| Curtain rods, stainless, 1" diameter, 3' long | 1.000 | Ea. | .615 | 38 | 30 | 68 |
| 5' long | 1.000 | Ea. | .615 | 38 | 30 | 68 |
| Grab bar, 1" diameter, 12" long | 1.000 | Ea. | .283 | 28.50 | 13.85 | 42.35 |
| 36" long | 1.000 | Ea. | .340 | 32.50 | 16.65 | 49.15 |
| 1-1/4" diameter, 12" long | 1.000 | Ea. | .333 | 33.50 | 16.30 | 49.80 |
| 36" long | 1.000 | Ea. | .400 | 38 | 19.60 | 57.60 |
| 1-1/2" diameter, 12" long | 1.000 | Ea. | .383 | 38.50 | 18.75 | 57.25 |
| 36" long | 1.000 | Ea. | .460 | 43.50 | 22.50 | 66 |
| Mirror, 18" x 24" | 1.000 | Ea. | .400 | 62.50 | 19.60 | 82.10 |
| 72" x 24" | 1.000 | Ea. | 1.333 | 231 | 65.50 | 296.50 |
| Medicine chest with mirror, 18" x 24" | 1.000 | Ea. | .400 | 208 | 19.60 | 227.60 |
| 36" x 24" | 1.000 | Ea. | .600 | 310 | 29.50 | 339.50 |
| Toilet tissue dispenser, surface mounted, minimum | 1.000 | Ea. | .267 | 19.15 | 13.05 | 32.20 |
| Maximum | 1.000 | Ea. | .400 | 28.50 | 19.60 | 48.10 |
| Flush mounted, minimum | 1.000 | Ea. | .293 | 21 | 14.35 | 35.35 |
| Maximum | 1.000 | Ea. | .427 | 30.50 | 21 | 51.50 |
| Towel bar, 18" long, minimum | 1.000 | Ea. | .278 | 35 | 13.65 | 48.65 |
| Maximum | 1.000 | Ea. | .348 | 43.50 | 17.05 | 60.55 |
| 24" long, minimum | 1.000 | Ea. | .313 | 39 | 15.35 | 54.35 |
| Maximum | 1.000 | Ea. | .383 | 48 | 18.75 | 66.75 |
| 36" long, minimum | 1.000 | Ea. | .381 | 123 | 18.65 | 141.65 |
| Maximum | 1.000 | Ea. | .419 | 135 | 20.50 | 155.50 |
| | | | | | | |
| | | | | | | |
| | | | | | | |
| | | | | | | |
| | | | | | | |
| | | | | | | |
| | | | | | | |
| | | | | | | |
| | | | | | | |
| | | | | | | |
| | | | | | | |
| | | | | | | |
| | | | | | | |
| | | | | | | |
| | | | | | | |
| | | | | | | |
| | | | | | | |

Chimney

Mantle

Facing Brick

Damper

Firebox

Hearth

Foundation

Footing

Cleanout

| System Description | QUAN. | UNIT | LABOR HOURS | COST EACH | | |
|---|---|---|---|---|---|---|
| | | | | MAT. | INST. | TOTAL |
| **MASONRY FIREPLACE** | | | | | | |
| Footing, 8" thick, concrete, 4' x 7' | .700 | C.Y. | 2.800 | 115.50 | 129.64 | 245.14 |
| Foundation, concrete block, 32" x 60" x 4' deep | 1.000 | Ea. | 5.275 | 172.20 | 234.60 | 406.80 |
| Fireplace, brick firebox, 30" x 29" opening | 1.000 | Ea. | 40.000 | 590 | 1,750 | 2,340 |
| Damper, cast iron, 30" opening | 1.000 | Ea. | 1.333 | 97.50 | 64.50 | 162 |
| Facing brick, standard size brick, 6' x 5' | 30.000 | S.F. | 5.217 | 119.10 | 232.50 | 351.60 |
| Hearth, standard size brick, 3' x 6' | 1.000 | Ea. | 8.000 | 217 | 350 | 567 |
| Chimney, standard size brick, 8" x 12" flue, one story house | 12.000 | V.L.F. | 12.000 | 444 | 522 | 966 |
| Mantle, 4" x 8", wood | 6.000 | L.F. | 1.333 | 45.60 | 65.40 | 111 |
| Cleanout, cast iron, 8" x 8" | 1.000 | Ea. | .667 | 41 | 32 | 73 |
| | | | | | | |
| TOTAL | | Ea. | 76.625 | 1,841.90 | 3,380.64 | 5,222.54 |

The costs in this system are on a cost each basis.

| Description | QUAN. | UNIT | LABOR HOURS | COST EACH | | |
|---|---|---|---|---|---|---|
| | | | | MAT. | INST. | TOTAL |
| | | | | | | |
| | | | | | | |
| | | | | | | |
| | | | | | | |
| | | | | | | |
| | | | | | | |
| | | | | | | |
| | | | | | | |
| | | | | | | |

| Masonry Fireplace Price Sheet | QUAN. | UNIT | LABOR HOURS | COST EACH | | |
|---|---|---|---|---|---|---|
| | | | | MAT. | INST. | TOTAL |
| Footing 8" thick, 3' x 6' | .440 | C.Y. | 1.326 | 72.50 | 81.50 | 154 |
| 4' x 7' | .700 | C.Y. | 2.110 | 116 | 130 | 246 |
| 5' x 8' | 1.000 | C.Y. | 3.014 | 165 | 185 | 350 |
| 1' thick, 3' x 6' | .670 | C.Y. | 2.020 | 111 | 124 | 235 |
| 4' x 7' | 1.030 | C.Y. | 3.105 | 170 | 191 | 361 |
| 5' x 8' | 1.480 | C.Y. | 4.461 | 244 | 274 | 518 |
| Foundation-concrete block, 24" x 48", 4' deep | 1.000 | Ea. | 4.267 | 138 | 188 | 326 |
| 8' deep | 1.000 | Ea. | 8.533 | 276 | 375 | 651 |
| 24" x 60", 4' deep | 1.000 | Ea. | 4.978 | 161 | 219 | 380 |
| 8' deep | 1.000 | Ea. | 9.956 | 320 | 440 | 760 |
| 32" x 48", 4' deep | 1.000 | Ea. | 4.711 | 152 | 207 | 359 |
| 8' deep | 1.000 | Ea. | 9.422 | 305 | 415 | 720 |
| 32" x 60", 4' deep | 1.000 | Ea. | 5.333 | 172 | 235 | 407 |
| 8' deep | 1.000 | Ea. | 10.845 | 350 | 475 | 825 |
| 32" x 72", 4' deep | 1.000 | Ea. | 6.133 | 198 | 270 | 468 |
| 8' deep | 1.000 | Ea. | 12.267 | 395 | 540 | 935 |
| Fireplace, brick firebox 30" x 29" opening | 1.000 | Ea. | 40.000 | 590 | 1,750 | 2,340 |
| 48" x 30" opening | 1.000 | Ea. | 60.000 | 885 | 2,625 | 3,510 |
| Steel fire box with registers, 25" opening | 1.000 | Ea. | 26.667 | 1,075 | 1,175 | 2,250 |
| 48" opening | 1.000 | Ea. | 44.000 | 1,800 | 1,950 | 3,750 |
| Damper, cast iron, 30" opening | 1.000 | Ea. | 1.333 | 97.50 | 64.50 | 162 |
| 36" opening | 1.000 | Ea. | 1.556 | 114 | 75.50 | 189.50 |
| Steel, 30" opening | 1.000 | Ea. | 1.333 | 87.50 | 64.50 | 152 |
| 36" opening | 1.000 | Ea. | 1.556 | 102 | 75.50 | 177.50 |
| Facing for fireplace, standard size brick, 6' x 5' | 30.000 | S.F. | 5.217 | 119 | 233 | 352 |
| 7' x 5' | 35.000 | S.F. | 6.087 | 139 | 271 | 410 |
| 8' x 6' | 48.000 | S.F. | 8.348 | 191 | 370 | 561 |
| Fieldstone, 6' x 5' | 30.000 | S.F. | 5.217 | 585 | 233 | 818 |
| 7' x 5' | 35.000 | S.F. | 6.087 | 680 | 271 | 951 |
| 8' x 6' | 48.000 | S.F. | 8.348 | 935 | 370 | 1,305 |
| Sheetrock on metal, studs, 6' x 5' | 30.000 | S.F. | .980 | 21.50 | 48 | 69.50 |
| 7' x 5' | 35.000 | S.F. | 1.143 | 25 | 56 | 81 |
| 8' x 6' | 48.000 | S.F. | 1.568 | 34.50 | 77 | 111.50 |
| Hearth, standard size brick, 3' x 6' | 1.000 | Ea. | 8.000 | 217 | 350 | 567 |
| 3' x 7' | 1.000 | Ea. | 9.280 | 252 | 405 | 657 |
| 3' x 8' | 1.000 | Ea. | 10.640 | 289 | 465 | 754 |
| Stone, 3' x 6' | 1.000 | Ea. | 8.000 | 234 | 350 | 584 |
| 3' x 7' | 1.000 | Ea. | 9.280 | 272 | 405 | 677 |
| 3' x 8' | 1.000 | Ea. | 10.640 | 310 | 465 | 775 |
| Chimney, standard size brick, 8" x 12" flue, one story house | 12.000 | V.L.F. | 12.000 | 445 | 520 | 965 |
| Two story house | 20.000 | V.L.F. | 20.000 | 740 | 870 | 1,610 |
| Mantle wood, beams, 4" x 8" | 6.000 | L.F. | 1.333 | 45.50 | 65.50 | 111 |
| 4" x 10" | 6.000 | L.F. | 1.371 | 84.50 | 67 | 151.50 |
| Ornate, prefabricated, 6' x 3'-6" opening, minimum | 1.000 | Ea. | 1.600 | 251 | 78.50 | 329.50 |
| Maximum | 1.000 | Ea. | 1.600 | 455 | 78.50 | 533.50 |
| Cleanout, door and frame, cast iron, 8" x 8" | 1.000 | Ea. | .667 | 41 | 32 | 73 |
| 12" x 12" | 1.000 | Ea. | .800 | 50 | 38.50 | 88.50 |

Chimney, Flue, Fittings & Framing

Framing

Mantle

Facing Brick

Prefabricated Fireplace

Hearth

| System Description | QUAN. | UNIT | LABOR HOURS | COST EACH | | |
|---|---|---|---|---|---|---|
| | | | | MAT. | INST. | TOTAL |
| **PREFABRICATED FIREPLACE** | | | | | | |
| Prefabricated fireplace, metal, minimum | 1.000 | Ea. | 6.154 | 1,325 | 300 | 1,625 |
| Framing, 2" x 4" studs, 6' x 5' | 35.000 | L.F. | .509 | 9.45 | 24.85 | 34.30 |
| Fire resistant gypsum drywall, unfinished | 40.000 | S.F. | .320 | 12.40 | 15.60 | 28 |
| Drywall finishing adder | 40.000 | S.F. | .320 | 2 | 15.60 | 17.60 |
| Facing, brick, standard size brick, 6' x 5' | 30.000 | S.F. | 5.217 | 119.10 | 232.50 | 351.60 |
| Hearth, standard size brick, 3' x 6' | 1.000 | Ea. | 8.000 | 217 | 350 | 567 |
| Chimney, one story house, framing, 2" x 4" studs | 80.000 | L.F. | 1.164 | 21.60 | 56.80 | 78.40 |
| Sheathing, plywood, 5/8" thick | 32.000 | S.F. | .758 | 85.44 | 37.12 | 122.56 |
| Flue, 10" metal, insulated pipe | 12.000 | V.L.F. | 4.000 | 444 | 193.20 | 637.20 |
| Fittings, ceiling support | 1.000 | Ea. | .667 | 165 | 32 | 197 |
| Fittings, joist shield | 1.000 | Ea. | .667 | 94.50 | 32 | 126.50 |
| Fittings, roof flashing | 1.000 | Ea. | .667 | 198 | 32 | 230 |
| Mantle beam, wood, 4" x 8" | 6.000 | L.F. | 1.333 | 45.60 | 65.40 | 111 |
| | | | | | | |
| TOTAL | | Ea. | 29.776 | 2,739.09 | 1,387.07 | 4,126.16 |

The costs in this system are on a cost each basis.

| Description | QUAN. | UNIT | LABOR HOURS | COST EACH | | |
|---|---|---|---|---|---|---|
| | | | | MAT. | INST. | TOTAL |
| | | | | | | |
| | | | | | | |
| | | | | | | |
| | | | | | | |
| | | | | | | |
| | | | | | | |
| | | | | | | |
| | | | | | | |

# Prefabricated Fireplace Price Sheet

| | QUAN. | UNIT | LABOR HOURS | COST EACH MAT. | INST. | TOTAL |
|---|---|---|---|---|---|---|
| Prefabricated fireplace, minimum | 1.000 | Ea. | 6.154 | 1,325 | 300 | 1,625 |
| Average | 1.000 | Ea. | 8.000 | 1,850 | 390 | 2,240 |
| Maximum | 1.000 | Ea. | 8.889 | 3,700 | 435 | 4,135 |
| Framing, 2" x 4" studs, fireplace, 6' x 5' | 35.000 | L.F. | .509 | 9.45 | 25 | 34.45 |
| 7' x 5' | 40.000 | L.F. | .582 | 10.80 | 28.50 | 39.30 |
| 8' x 6' | 45.000 | L.F. | .655 | 12.15 | 32 | 44.15 |
| Sheetrock, 1/2" thick, fireplace, 6' x 5' | 40.000 | S.F. | .640 | 14.40 | 31 | 45.40 |
| 7' x 5' | 45.000 | S.F. | .720 | 16.20 | 35 | 51.20 |
| 8' x 6' | 50.000 | S.F. | .800 | 18 | 39 | 57 |
| Facing for fireplace, brick, 6' x 5' | 30.000 | S.F. | 5.217 | 119 | 233 | 352 |
| 7' x 5' | 35.000 | S.F. | 6.087 | 139 | 271 | 410 |
| 8' x 6' | 48.000 | S.F. | 8.348 | 191 | 370 | 561 |
| Fieldstone, 6' x 5' | 30.000 | S.F. | 5.217 | 630 | 233 | 863 |
| 7' x 5' | 35.000 | S.F. | 6.087 | 735 | 271 | 1,006 |
| 8' x 6' | 48.000 | S.F. | 8.348 | 1,000 | 370 | 1,370 |
| Hearth, standard size brick, 3' x 6' | 1.000 | Ea. | 8.000 | 217 | 350 | 567 |
| 3' x 7' | 1.000 | Ea. | 9.280 | 252 | 405 | 657 |
| 3' x 8' | 1.000 | Ea. | 10.640 | 289 | 465 | 754 |
| Stone, 3' x 6' | 1.000 | Ea. | 8.000 | 234 | 350 | 584 |
| 3' x 7' | 1.000 | Ea. | 9.280 | 272 | 405 | 677 |
| 3' x 8' | 1.000 | Ea. | 10.640 | 310 | 465 | 775 |
| Chimney, framing, 2" x 4", one story house | 80.000 | L.F. | 1.164 | 21.50 | 57 | 78.50 |
| Two story house | 120.000 | L.F. | 1.746 | 32.50 | 85 | 117.50 |
| Sheathing, plywood, 5/8" thick | 32.000 | S.F. | .758 | 85.50 | 37 | 122.50 |
| Stucco on plywood | 32.000 | S.F. | 1.125 | 46 | 53 | 99 |
| Flue, 10" metal pipe, insulated, one story house | 12.000 | V.L.F. | 4.000 | 445 | 193 | 638 |
| Two story house | 20.000 | V.L.F. | 6.667 | 740 | 320 | 1,060 |
| Fittings, ceiling support | 1.000 | Ea. | .667 | 165 | 32 | 197 |
| Fittings joist sheild, one story house | 1.000 | Ea. | .667 | 94.50 | 32 | 126.50 |
| Two story house | 2.000 | Ea. | 1.333 | 189 | 64 | 253 |
| Fittings roof flashing | 1.000 | Ea. | .667 | 198 | 32 | 230 |
| Mantle, wood beam, 4" x 8" | 6.000 | L.F. | 1.333 | 45.50 | 65.50 | 111 |
| 4" x 10" | 6.000 | L.F. | 1.371 | 84.50 | 67 | 151.50 |
| Ornate prefabricated, 6' x 3'-6" opening, minimum | 1.000 | Ea. | 1.600 | 251 | 78.50 | 329.50 |
| Maximum | 1.000 | Ea. | 1.600 | 455 | 78.50 | 533.50 |

| System Description | QUAN. | UNIT | LABOR HOURS | COST EACH | | |
|---|---|---|---|---|---|---|
| | | | | MAT. | INST. | TOTAL |
| Economy, lean to, shell only, not including 2' stub wall, fndtn, flrs, heat | | | | | | |
| 4' x 16' | 1.000 | Ea. | 26.212 | 2,050 | 1,275 | 3,325 |
| 4' x 24' | 1.000 | Ea. | 30.259 | 2,375 | 1,475 | 3,850 |
| 6' x 10' | 1.000 | Ea. | 16.552 | 2,525 | 810 | 3,335 |
| 6' x 16' | 1.000 | Ea. | 23.034 | 3,500 | 1,125 | 4,625 |
| 6' x 24' | 1.000 | Ea. | 29.793 | 4,525 | 1,450 | 5,975 |
| 8' x 10' | 1.000 | Ea. | 22.069 | 3,350 | 1,075 | 4,425 |
| 8' x 16' | 1.000 | Ea. | 38.400 | 5,850 | 1,875 | 7,725 |
| 8' x 24' | 1.000 | Ea. | 49.655 | 7,550 | 2,425 | 9,975 |
| Free standing, 8' x 8' | 1.000 | Ea. | 17.356 | 2,650 | 850 | 3,500 |
| 8' x 16' | 1.000 | Ea. | 30.211 | 4,625 | 1,475 | 6,100 |
| 8' x 24' | 1.000 | Ea. | 39.051 | 5,975 | 1,900 | 7,875 |
| 10' x 10' | 1.000 | Ea. | 18.824 | 2,950 | 920 | 3,870 |
| 10' x 16' | 1.000 | Ea. | 24.095 | 3,775 | 1,175 | 4,950 |
| 10' x 24' | 1.000 | Ea. | 31.624 | 4,950 | 1,550 | 6,500 |
| 14' x 10' | 1.000 | Ea. | 20.741 | 3,575 | 1,025 | 4,600 |
| 14' x 16' | 1.000 | Ea. | 24.889 | 4,275 | 1,225 | 5,500 |
| 14' x 24' | 1.000 | Ea. | 33.349 | 5,750 | 1,625 | 7,375 |
| Standard, lean to, shell only, not incl. 2' stub wall, fndtn, flrs, heat 4' x 10' | 1.000 | Ea. | 28.235 | 2,225 | 1,375 | 3,600 |
| 4' x 16' | 1.000 | Ea. | 39.341 | 3,100 | 1,925 | 5,025 |
| 4' x 24' | 1.000 | Ea. | 45.412 | 3,575 | 2,225 | 5,800 |
| 6' x 10' | 1.000 | Ea. | 24.827 | 3,775 | 1,225 | 5,000 |
| 6' x 16' | 1.000 | Ea. | 34.538 | 5,250 | 1,700 | 6,950 |
| 6' x 24' | 1.000 | Ea. | 44.689 | 6,800 | 2,175 | 8,975 |
| 8' x 10' | 1.000 | Ea. | 33.103 | 5,050 | 1,625 | 6,675 |
| 8' x 16' | 1.000 | Ea. | 57.600 | 8,775 | 2,825 | 11,600 |
| 8' x 24' | 1.000 | Ea. | 74.482 | 11,300 | 3,650 | 14,950 |
| Free standing, 8' x 8' | 1.000 | Ea. | 26.034 | 3,975 | 1,275 | 5,250 |
| 8' x 16' | 1.000 | Ea. | 45.316 | 6,925 | 2,225 | 9,150 |
| 8' x 24' | 1.000 | Ea. | 58.577 | 8,975 | 2,850 | 11,825 |
| 10' x 10' | 1.000 | Ea. | 28.236 | 4,425 | 1,375 | 5,800 |
| 10' x 16' | 1.000 | Ea. | 36.142 | 5,675 | 1,775 | 7,450 |
| 10' x 24' | 1.000 | Ea. | 47.436 | 7,425 | 2,325 | 9,750 |
| 14' x 10' | 1.000 | Ea. | 31.112 | 5,350 | 1,525 | 6,875 |
| 14' x 16' | 1.000 | Ea. | 37.334 | 6,425 | 1,825 | 8,250 |
| 14' x 24' | 1.000 | Ea. | 50.030 | 8,600 | 2,450 | 11,050 |
| Deluxe, lean to, shell only, not incl. 2' stub wall, fndtn, flrs or heat, 4' x 10' | 1.000 | Ea. | 20.645 | 3,400 | 1,025 | 4,425 |
| 4' x 16' | 1.000 | Ea. | 33.032 | 5,450 | 1,625 | 7,075 |
| 4' x 24' | 1.000 | Ea. | 49.548 | 8,150 | 2,450 | 10,600 |
| 6' x 10' | 1.000 | Ea. | 30.968 | 5,100 | 1,525 | 6,625 |
| 6' x 16' | 1.000 | Ea. | 49.548 | 8,150 | 2,450 | 10,600 |
| 6' x 24' | 1.000 | Ea. | 74.323 | 12,200 | 3,675 | 15,875 |
| 8' x 10' | 1.000 | Ea. | 41.290 | 6,800 | 2,050 | 8,850 |
| 8' x 16' | 1.000 | Ea. | 66.065 | 10,900 | 3,275 | 14,175 |
| 8' x 24' | 1.000 | Ea. | 99.097 | 16,300 | 4,900 | 21,200 |
| Freestanding, 8' x 8' | 1.000 | Ea. | 18.618 | 5,600 | 910 | 6,510 |
| 8' x 16' | 1.000 | Ea. | 37.236 | 11,200 | 1,825 | 13,025 |
| 8' x 24' | 1.000 | Ea. | 55.855 | 16,800 | 2,725 | 19,525 |
| 10' x 10' | 1.000 | Ea. | 29.091 | 8,750 | 1,425 | 10,175 |
| 10' x 16' | 1.000 | Ea. | 46.546 | 14,000 | 2,275 | 16,275 |
| 10' x 24' | 1.000 | Ea. | 69.818 | 21,000 | 3,425 | 24,425 |
| 14' x 10' | 1.000 | Ea. | 40.727 | 12,300 | 2,000 | 14,300 |
| 14' x 16' | 1.000 | Ea. | 65.164 | 19,600 | 3,200 | 22,800 |
| 14' x 24' | 1.000 | Ea. | 97.746 | 29,400 | 4,800 | 34,200 |

| System Description | QUAN. | UNIT | LABOR HOURS | COST EACH | | |
|---|---|---|---|---|---|---|
| | | | | MAT. | INST. | TOTAL |
| Swimming pools, vinyl lined, metal sides, sand bottom, 12' x 28' | 1.000 | Ea. | 50.177 | 4,100 | 2,575 | 6,675 |
| 12' x 32' | 1.000 | Ea. | 55.366 | 4,525 | 2,825 | 7,350 |
| 12' x 36' | 1.000 | Ea. | 60.061 | 4,900 | 3,075 | 7,975 |
| 16' x 32' | 1.000 | Ea. | 66.798 | 5,450 | 3,425 | 8,875 |
| 16' x 36' | 1.000 | Ea. | 71.190 | 5,825 | 3,650 | 9,475 |
| 16' x 40' | 1.000 | Ea. | 74.703 | 6,100 | 3,850 | 9,950 |
| 20' x 36' | 1.000 | Ea. | 77.860 | 6,350 | 4,000 | 10,350 |
| 20' x 40' | 1.000 | Ea. | 82.135 | 6,700 | 4,225 | 10,925 |
| 20' x 44' | 1.000 | Ea. | 90.348 | 7,375 | 4,625 | 12,000 |
| 24' x 40' | 1.000 | Ea. | 98.562 | 8,050 | 5,075 | 13,125 |
| 24' x 44' | 1.000 | Ea. | 108.418 | 8,850 | 5,575 | 14,425 |
| 24' x 48' | 1.000 | Ea. | 118.274 | 9,650 | 6,075 | 15,725 |
| Vinyl lined, concrete sides, 12' x 28' | 1.000 | Ea. | 79.447 | 6,500 | 4,075 | 10,575 |
| 12' x 32' | 1.000 | Ea. | 88.818 | 7,250 | 4,575 | 11,825 |
| 12' x 36' | 1.000 | Ea. | 97.656 | 7,975 | 5,000 | 12,975 |
| 16' x 32' | 1.000 | Ea. | 111.393 | 9,100 | 5,700 | 14,800 |
| 16' x 36' | 1.000 | Ea. | 121.354 | 9,925 | 6,225 | 16,150 |
| 16' x 40' | 1.000 | Ea. | 130.445 | 10,700 | 6,675 | 17,375 |
| 28' x 36' | 1.000 | Ea. | 140.585 | 11,500 | 7,225 | 18,725 |
| 20' x 40' | 1.000 | Ea. | 149.336 | 12,200 | 7,650 | 19,850 |
| 20' x 44' | 1.000 | Ea. | 164.270 | 13,400 | 8,450 | 21,850 |
| 24' x 40' | 1.000 | Ea. | 179.203 | 14,600 | 9,200 | 23,800 |
| 24' x 44' | 1.000 | Ea. | 197.124 | 16,100 | 10,100 | 26,200 |
| 24' x 48' | 1.000 | Ea. | 215.044 | 17,600 | 11,000 | 28,600 |
| Gunite, bottom and sides, 12' x 28' | 1.000 | Ea. | 129.767 | 9,575 | 6,650 | 16,225 |
| 12' x 32' | 1.000 | Ea. | 142.164 | 10,500 | 7,275 | 17,775 |
| 12' x 36' | 1.000 | Ea. | 153.028 | 11,300 | 7,850 | 19,150 |
| 16' x 32' | 1.000 | Ea. | 167.743 | 12,400 | 8,600 | 21,000 |
| 16' x 36' | 1.000 | Ea. | 176.421 | 13,000 | 9,050 | 22,050 |
| 16' x 40' | 1.000 | Ea. | 182.368 | 13,500 | 9,350 | 22,850 |
| 20' x 36' | 1.000 | Ea. | 187.949 | 13,900 | 9,650 | 23,550 |
| 20' x 40' | 1.000 | Ea. | 179.200 | 18,400 | 9,175 | 27,575 |
| 20' x 44' | 1.000 | Ea. | 197.120 | 20,200 | 10,100 | 30,300 |
| 24' x 40' | 1.000 | Ea. | 215.040 | 22,100 | 11,000 | 33,100 |
| 24' x 44' | 1.000 | Ea. | 273.244 | 20,200 | 14,000 | 34,200 |
| 24' x 48' | 1.000 | Ea. | 298.077 | 22,000 | 15,300 | 37,300 |
| | | | | | | |
| | | | | | | |
| | | | | | | |
| | | | | | | |
| | | | | | | |
| | | | | | | |
| | | | | | | |
| | | | | | | |
| | | | | | | |
| | | | | | | |
| | | | | | | |

| System Description | QUAN. | UNIT | LABOR HOURS | COST PER S.F. | | |
|---|---|---|---|---|---|---|
| | | | | MAT. | INST. | TOTAL |
| **8' X 12' DECK, PRESSURE TREATED LUMBER, JOISTS 16" O.C.** | | | | | | |
| Decking, 2" x 6" lumber | 2.080 | L.F. | .027 | .85 | 1.31 | 2.16 |
| Lumber preservative | 2.080 | L.F. | | .35 | | .35 |
| Joists, 2" x 8", 16" O.C. | 1.000 | L.F. | .015 | .61 | .71 | 1.32 |
| Lumber preservative | 1.000 | L.F. | | .23 | | .23 |
| Girder, 2" x 10" | .125 | L.F. | .002 | .10 | .11 | .21 |
| Lumber preservative | .125 | L.F. | | .04 | | .04 |
| Hand excavation for footings | .250 | L.F. | .006 | | .22 | .22 |
| Concrete footings | .250 | L.F. | .008 | .33 | .37 | .70 |
| 4" x 4" Posts | .250 | L.F. | .010 | .43 | .50 | .93 |
| Lumber preservative | .250 | L.F. | | .06 | | .06 |
| Framing, pressure treated wood stairs, 3' wide, 8 closed risers | 1.000 | Set | .080 | 1.51 | 3.90 | 5.41 |
| Railings, 2" x 4" | 1.000 | L.F. | .026 | .27 | 1.26 | 1.53 |
| Lumber preservative | 1.000 | L.F. | | .11 | | .11 |
| TOTAL | | S.F. | .174 | 4.89 | 8.38 | 13.27 |
| **12' X 16' DECK, PRESSURE TREATED LUMBER, JOISTS 24" O.C.** | | | | | | |
| Decking, 2" x 6" | 2.080 | L.F. | .027 | .85 | 1.31 | 2.16 |
| Lumber preservative | 2.080 | L.F. | | .35 | | .35 |
| Joists, 2" x 10", 24" O.C. | .800 | L.F. | .014 | .64 | .70 | 1.34 |
| Lumber preservative | .800 | L.F. | | .23 | | .23 |
| Girder, 2" x 10" | .083 | L.F. | .001 | .07 | .07 | .14 |
| Lumber preservative | .083 | L.F. | | .02 | | .02 |
| Hand excavation for footings | .122 | L.F. | .006 | | .22 | .22 |
| Concrete footings | .122 | L.F. | .008 | .33 | .37 | .70 |
| 4" x 4" Posts | .122 | L.F. | .005 | .21 | .25 | .46 |
| Lumber preservative | .122 | L.F. | | .03 | | .03 |
| Framing, pressure treated wood stairs, 3' wide, 8 closed risers | 1.000 | Set | .040 | .76 | 1.95 | 2.71 |
| Railings, 2" x 4" | .670 | L.F. | .017 | .18 | .84 | 1.02 |
| Lumber preservative | .670 | L.F. | | .07 | | .07 |
| TOTAL | | S.F. | .118 | 3.74 | 5.71 | 9.45 |
| **12' X 24' DECK, REDWOOD OR CEDAR, JOISTS 16" O.C.** | | | | | | |
| Decking, 2" x 6" redwood | 2.080 | L.F. | .027 | 7.78 | 1.31 | 9.09 |
| Joists, 2" x 10", 16" O.C. | 1.000 | L.F. | .018 | 8.30 | .87 | 9.17 |
| Girder, 2" x 10" | .083 | L.F. | .001 | .69 | .07 | .76 |
| Hand excavation for footings | .111 | L.F. | .006 | | .22 | .22 |
| Concrete footings | .111 | L.F. | .008 | .33 | .37 | .70 |
| Lumber preservative | .111 | L.F. | | .03 | | .03 |
| Post, 4" x 4", including concrete footing | .111 | L.F. | .009 | 7.33 | .44 | 7.77 |
| Framing, redwood or cedar stairs, 3' wide, 8 closed risers | 1.000 | Set | .028 | 1.37 | 1.37 | 2.74 |
| Railings, 2" x 4" | .540 | L.F. | .005 | 1.35 | .23 | 1.58 |
| TOTAL | | S.F. | .102 | 27.18 | 4.88 | 32.06 |

The costs in this system are on a square foot basis.

| Wood Deck Price Sheet | QUAN. | UNIT | LABOR HOURS | COST PER S.F. | | |
|---|---|---|---|---|---|---|
| | | | | MAT. | INST. | TOTAL |
| Decking, treated lumber, 1" x 4" | 3.430 | L.F. | .031 | 2.84 | 1.54 | 4.38 |
| 1" x 6" | 2.180 | L.F. | .033 | 2.98 | 1.62 | 4.60 |
| 2" x 4" | 3.200 | L.F. | .041 | 1.23 | 2.02 | 3.25 |
| 2" x 6" | 2.080 | L.F. | .027 | 1.20 | 1.31 | 2.51 |
| Redwood or cedar,, 1" x 4" | 3.430 | L.F. | .035 | 3.31 | 1.69 | 5 |
| 1" x 6" | 2.180 | L.F. | .036 | 3.46 | 1.77 | 5.23 |
| 2" x 4" | 3.200 | L.F. | .028 | 8.25 | 1.39 | 9.64 |
| 2" x 6" | 2.080 | L.F. | .027 | 7.80 | 1.31 | 9.11 |
| Joists for deck, treated lumber, 2" x 8", 16" O.C. | 1.000 | L.F. | .015 | .84 | .71 | 1.55 |
| 24" O.C. | .800 | L.F. | .012 | .67 | .57 | 1.24 |
| 2" x 10", 16" O.C. | 1.000 | L.F. | .018 | 1.08 | .87 | 1.95 |
| 24" O.C. | .800 | L.F. | .014 | .87 | .70 | 1.57 |
| Redwood or cedar, 2" x 8", 16" O.C. | 1.000 | L.F. | .015 | 4.98 | .71 | 5.69 |
| 24" O.C. | .800 | L.F. | .012 | 3.98 | .57 | 4.55 |
| 2" x 10", 16" O.C. | 1.000 | L.F. | .018 | 8.30 | .87 | 9.17 |
| 24" O.C. | .800 | L.F. | .014 | 6.65 | .70 | 7.35 |
| Girder for joists, treated lumber, 2" x 10", 8' x 12' deck | .125 | L.F. | .002 | .14 | .11 | .25 |
| 12' x 16' deck | .083 | L.F. | .001 | .09 | .07 | .16 |
| 12' x 24' deck | .083 | L.F. | .001 | .09 | .07 | .16 |
| Redwood or cedar, 2" x 10", 8' x 12' deck | .125 | L.F. | .002 | 1.04 | .11 | 1.15 |
| 12' x 16' deck | .083 | L.F. | .001 | .69 | .07 | .76 |
| 12' x 24' deck | .083 | L.F. | .001 | .69 | .07 | .76 |
| Posts, 4" x 4", including concrete footing, 8' x 12' deck | .250 | S.F. | .022 | .82 | 1.09 | 1.91 |
| 12' x 16' deck | .122 | L.F. | .017 | .57 | .84 | 1.41 |
| 12' x 24' deck | .111 | L.F. | .017 | .55 | .81 | 1.36 |
| Stairs 2" x 10" stringers, treated lumber, 8' x 12' deck | 1.000 | Set | .020 | 1.51 | 3.90 | 5.41 |
| 12' x 16' deck | 1.000 | Set | .012 | .76 | 1.95 | 2.71 |
| 12' x 24' deck | 1.000 | Set | .008 | .53 | 1.37 | 1.90 |
| Redwood or cedar, 8' x 12' deck | 1.000 | Set | .040 | 3.90 | 3.90 | 7.80 |
| 12' x 16' deck | 1.000 | Set | .020 | 1.95 | 1.95 | 3.90 |
| 12' x 24' deck | 1.000 | Set | .012 | 1.37 | 1.37 | 2.74 |
| Railings 2" x 4", treated lumber, 8' x 12' deck | 1.000 | L.F. | .026 | .38 | 1.26 | 1.64 |
| 12' x 16' deck | .670 | L.F. | .017 | .25 | .84 | 1.09 |
| 12' x 24' deck | .540 | L.F. | .014 | .21 | .68 | .89 |
| Redwood or cedar, 8' x 12' deck | 1.000 | L.F. | .009 | 2.51 | .42 | 2.93 |
| 12' x 16' deck | .670 | L.F. | .006 | 1.65 | .28 | 1.93 |
| 12' x 24' deck | .540 | L.F. | .005 | 1.35 | .23 | 1.58 |

| System Description | QUAN. | UNIT | LABOR HOURS | COST EACH | | |
|---|---|---|---|---|---|---|
| | | | | MAT. | INST. | TOTAL |
| **LAVATORY INSTALLED WITH VANITY, PLUMBING IN 2 WALLS** | | | | | | |
| Water closet, floor mounted, 2 piece, close coupled, white | 1.000 | Ea. | 3.019 | 284 | 153 | 437 |
| Rough-in, vent, 2″ diameter DWV piping | 1.000 | Ea. | .955 | 32.40 | 48.40 | 80.80 |
| Waste, 4″ diameter DWV piping | 1.000 | Ea. | .828 | 43.65 | 42 | 85.65 |
| Supply, 1/2″ diameter type "L" copper supply piping | 1.000 | Ea. | .593 | 16.44 | 33.30 | 49.74 |
| Lavatory, 20″ x 18″, P.E. cast iron white | 1.000 | Ea. | 2.500 | 286 | 127 | 413 |
| Rough-in, vent, 1-1/2″ diameter DWV piping | 1.000 | Ea. | .901 | 31 | 45.60 | 76.60 |
| Waste, 2″ diameter DWV piping | 1.000 | Ea. | .955 | 32.40 | 48.40 | 80.80 |
| Supply, 1/2″ diameter type "L" copper supply piping | 1.000 | Ea. | .988 | 27.40 | 55.50 | 82.90 |
| Piping, supply, 1/2″ diameter type "L" copper supply piping | 10.000 | L.F. | .988 | 27.40 | 55.50 | 82.90 |
| Waste, 4″ diameter DWV piping | 7.000 | L.F. | 1.931 | 101.85 | 98 | 199.85 |
| Vent, 2″ diameter DWV piping | 12.000 | L.F. | 2.866 | 97.20 | 145.20 | 242.40 |
| Vanity base cabinet, 2 door, 30″ wide | 1.000 | Ea. | 1.000 | 288 | 49 | 337 |
| Vanity top, plastic & laminated, square edge | 2.670 | L.F. | .712 | 97.46 | 34.84 | 132.30 |
| TOTAL | | Ea. | 18.236 | 1,365.20 | 935.74 | 2,300.94 |
| **LAVATORY WITH WALL-HUNG LAVATORY, PLUMBING IN 2 WALLS** | | | | | | |
| Water closet, floor mounted, 2 piece close coupled, white | 1.000 | Ea. | 3.019 | 284 | 153 | 437 |
| Rough-in, vent, 2″ diameter DWV piping | 1.000 | Ea. | .955 | 32.40 | 48.40 | 80.80 |
| Waste, 4″ diameter DWV piping | 1.000 | Ea. | .828 | 43.65 | 42 | 85.65 |
| Supply, 1/2″ diameter type "L" copper supply piping | 1.000 | Ea. | .593 | 16.44 | 33.30 | 49.74 |
| Lavatory, 20″ x 18″, P.E. cast iron, wall hung, white | 1.000 | Ea. | 2.000 | 390 | 101 | 491 |
| Rough-in, vent, 1-1/2″ diameter DWV piping | 1.000 | Ea. | .901 | 31 | 45.60 | 76.60 |
| Waste, 2″ diameter DWV piping | 1.000 | Ea. | .955 | 32.40 | 48.40 | 80.80 |
| Supply, 1/2″ diameter type "L" copper supply piping | 1.000 | Ea. | .988 | 27.40 | 55.50 | 82.90 |
| Piping, supply, 1/2″ diameter type "L" copper supply piping | 10.000 | L.F. | .988 | 27.40 | 55.50 | 82.90 |
| Waste, 4″ diameter DWV piping | 7.000 | L.F. | 1.931 | 101.85 | 98 | 199.85 |
| Vent, 2″ diameter DWV piping | 12.000 | L.F. | 2.866 | 97.20 | 145.20 | 242.40 |
| Carrier, steel for studs, no arms | 1.000 | Ea. | 1.143 | 78 | 64.50 | 142.50 |
| TOTAL | | Ea. | 17.167 | 1,161.74 | 890.40 | 2,052.14 |

| Description | QUAN. | UNIT | LABOR HOURS | COST EACH | | |
|---|---|---|---|---|---|---|
| | | | | MAT. | INST. | TOTAL |
| | | | | | | |
| | | | | | | |

| Two Fixture Lavatory Price Sheet | QUAN. | UNIT | LABOR HOURS | COST EACH MAT. | COST EACH INST. | COST EACH TOTAL |
|---|---|---|---|---|---|---|
| Water closet, close coupled standard 2 piece, white | 1.000 | Ea. | 3.019 | 284 | 153 | 437 |
| Color | 1.000 | Ea. | 3.019 | 380 | 153 | 533 |
| One piece elongated bowl, white | 1.000 | Ea. | 3.019 | 590 | 153 | 743 |
| Color | 1.000 | Ea. | 3.019 | 850 | 153 | 1,003 |
| Low profile, one piece elongated bowl, white | 1.000 | Ea. | 3.019 | 1,025 | 153 | 1,178 |
| Color | 1.000 | Ea. | 3.019 | 1,350 | 153 | 1,503 |
| Rough-in for water closet | | | | | | |
| 1/2" copper supply, 4" cast iron waste, 2" cast iron vent | 1.000 | Ea. | 2.376 | 92.50 | 124 | 216.50 |
| 4" PVC waste, 2" PVC vent | 1.000 | Ea. | 2.678 | 47.50 | 139 | 186.50 |
| 4" copper waste , 2" copper vent | 1.000 | Ea. | 2.520 | 210 | 136 | 346 |
| 3" cast iron waste, 1-1/2" cast iron vent | 1.000 | Ea. | 2.244 | 81 | 117 | 198 |
| 3" PVC waste, 1-1/2" PVC vent | 1.000 | Ea. | 2.388 | 40 | 129 | 169 |
| 3" copper waste, 1-1/2" copper vent | 1.000 | Ea. | 2.524 | 198 | 131 | 329 |
| 1/2" PVC supply, 4" PVC waste, 2" PVC vent | 1.000 | Ea. | 2.974 | 52.50 | 156. | 208.50 |
| 3" PVC waste, 1-1/2" PVC vent | 1.000 | Ea. | 2.684 | 45.50 | 146 | 191.50 |
| 1/2" steel supply, 4" cast iron waste, 2" cast iron vent | 1.000 | Ea. | 2.545 | 110 | 133 | 243 |
| 4" cast iron waste, 2" steel vent | 1.000 | Ea. | 2.590 | 154 | 136 | 290 |
| 4" PVC waste, 2" PVC vent | 1.000 | Ea. | 2.847 | 65 | 149 | 214 |
| Lavatory, vanity top mounted, P.E. on cast iron 20" x 18" white | 1.000 | Ea. | 2.500 | 286 | 127 | 413 |
| Color | 1.000 | Ea. | 2.500 | 286 | 127 | 413 |
| Steel, enameled 10" x 17" white | 1.000 | Ea. | 2.759 | 203 | 140 | 343 |
| Color | 1.000 | Ea. | 2.500 | 211 | 127 | 338 |
| Vitreous china 20" x 16", white | 1.000 | Ea. | 2.963 | 305 | 150 | 455 |
| Color | 1.000 | Ea. | 2.963 | 305 | 150 | 455 |
| Wall hung, P.E. on cast iron, 20" x 18", white | 1.000 | Ea. | 2.000 | 390 | 101 | 491 |
| Color | 1.000 | Ea. | 2.000 | 385 | 101 | 486 |
| Vitreous china 19" x 17", white | 1.000 | Ea. | 2.286 | 217 | 116 | 333 |
| Color | 1.000 | Ea. | 2.286 | 241 | 116 | 357 |
| Rough-in supply waste and vent for lavatory | | | | | | |
| 1/2" copper supply, 2" cast iron waste, 1-1/2" cast iron vent | 1.000 | Ea. | 2.844 | 91 | 150 | 241 |
| 2" PVC waste, 1-1/2" PVC vent | 1.000 | Ea. | 2.962 | 47 | 161 | 208 |
| 2" copper waste, 1-1/2" copper vent | 1.000 | Ea. | 2.308 | 123 | 130 | 253 |
| 1-1/2" PVC waste, 1-1/4" PVC vent | 1.000 | Ea. | 2.639 | 45 | 148 | 193 |
| 1-1/2" copper waste, 1-1/4" copper vent | 1.000 | Ea. | 2.114 | 111 | 119 | 230 |
| 1/2" PVC supply, 2" PVC waste, 1-1/2" PVC vent | 1.000 | Ea. | 3.456 | 55.50 | 189 | 244.50 |
| 1-1/2" PVC waste, 1-1/4" PVC vent | 1.000 | Ea. | 3.133 | 53.50 | 176 | 229.50 |
| 1/2" steel supply, 2" cast iron waste, 1-1/2" cast iron vent | 1.000 | Ea. | 3.126 | 120 | 166 | 286 |
| 2" cast iron waste, 2" steel vent | 1.000 | Ea. | 3.225 | 165 | 171 | 336 |
| 2" PVC waste, 1-1/2" PVC vent | 1.000 | Ea. | 3.244 | 76 | 177 | 253 |
| 1-1/2" PVC waste, 1-1/4" PVC vent | 1.000 | Ea. | 2.921 | 74 | 164 | 238 |
| Piping, supply, 1/2" copper, type "L" | 10.000 | L.F. | .988 | 27.50 | 55.50 | 83 |
| 1/2" steel | 10.000 | L.F. | 1.270 | 56.50 | 71.50 | 128 |
| 1/2" PVC | 10.000 | L.F. | 1.482 | 36 | 83.50 | 119.50 |
| Waste, 4" cast iron | 7.000 | L.F. | 1.931 | 102 | 98 | 200 |
| 4" copper | 7.000 | L.F. | 2.800 | 320 | 144 | 464 |
| 4" PVC | 7.000 | L.F. | 2.333 | 47.50 | 118 | 165.50 |
| Vent, 2" cast iron | 12.000 | L.F. | 2.866 | 97 | 145 | 242 |
| 2" copper | 12.000 | L.F. | 2.182 | 166 | 123 | 289 |
| 2" PVC | 12.000 | L.F. | 3.254 | 32 | 165 | 197 |
| 2" steel | 12.000 | Ea. | 3.000 | 228 | 152 | 380 |
| Vanity base cabinet, 2 door, 24" x 30" | 1.000 | Ea. | 1.000 | 288 | 49 | 337 |
| 24" x 36" | 1.000 | Ea. | 1.200 | 385 | 59 | 444 |
| Vanity top, laminated plastic, square edge 25" x 32" | 2.670 | L.F. | .712 | 97.50 | 35 | 132.50 |
| 25" x 38" | 3.170 | L.F. | .845 | 116 | 41.50 | 157.50 |
| Post formed, laminated plastic, 25" x 32" | 2.670 | L.F. | .712 | 31.50 | 35 | 66.50 |
| 25" x 38" | 3.170 | L.F. | .845 | 37.50 | 41.50 | 79 |
| Cultured marble, 25" x 32" with bowl | 1.000 | Ea. | 2.500 | 262 | 127 | 389 |
| 25" x 38" with bowl | 1.000 | Ea. | 2.500 | 283 | 127 | 410 |
| Carrier for lavatory, steel for studs | 1.000 | Ea. | 1.143 | 78 | 64.50 | 142.50 |
| Wood 2" x 8" blocking | 1.330 | L.F. | .053 | .81 | 2.61 | 3.42 |

| System Description | QUAN. | UNIT | LABOR HOURS | COST EACH | | |
|---|---|---|---|---|---|---|
| | | | | MAT. | INST. | TOTAL |
| **BATHROOM INSTALLED WITH VANITY** | | | | | | |
| Water closet, floor mounted, 2 piece, close coupled, white | 1.000 | Ea. | 3.019 | 284 | 153 | 437 |
| Rough-in, waste, 4" diameter DWV piping | 1.000 | Ea. | .828 | 43.65 | 42 | 85.65 |
| Vent, 2" diameter DWV piping | 1.000 | Ea. | .955 | 32.40 | 48.40 | 80.80 |
| Supply, 1/2" diameter type "L" copper supply piping | 1.000 | Ea. | .593 | 16.44 | 33.30 | 49.74 |
| Lavatory, 20" x 18", P.E. cast iron with accessories, white | 1.000 | Ea. | 2.500 | 286 | 127 | 413 |
| Rough-in, supply, 1/2" diameter type "L" copper supply piping | 1.000 | Ea. | .988 | 27.40 | 55.50 | 82.90 |
| Waste, 1-1/2" diameter DWV piping | 1.000 | Ea. | 1.803 | 62 | 91.20 | 153.20 |
| Bathtub, P.E. cast iron, 5' long with accessories, white | 1.000 | Ea. | 3.636 | 1,050 | 184 | 1,234 |
| Rough-in, waste, 4" diameter DWV piping | 1.000 | Ea. | .828 | 43.65 | 42 | 85.65 |
| Vent, 1-1/2" diameter DWV piping | 1.000 | Ea. | .593 | 40.80 | 33.40 | 74.20 |
| Supply, 1/2" diameter type "L" copper supply piping | 1.000 | Ea. | .988 | 27.40 | 55.50 | 82.90 |
| Piping, supply, 1/2" diameter type "L" copper supply piping | 20.000 | L.F. | 1.975 | 54.80 | 111 | 165.80 |
| Waste, 4" diameter DWV piping | 9.000 | L.F. | 2.483 | 130.95 | 126 | 256.95 |
| Vent, 2" diameter DWV piping | 6.000 | L.F. | 1.500 | 114 | 75.90 | 189.90 |
| Vanity base cabinet, 2 door, 30" wide | 1.000 | Ea. | 1.000 | 288 | 49 | 337 |
| Vanity top, plastic laminated square edge | 2.670 | L.F. | .712 | 77.43 | 34.84 | 112.27 |
| **TOTAL** | | Ea. | 24.401 | 2,578.92 | 1,262.04 | 3,840.96 |
| **BATHROOM WITH WALL HUNG LAVATORY** | | | | | | |
| Water closet, floor mounted, 2 piece, close coupled, white | 1.000 | Ea. | 3.019 | 284 | 153 | 437 |
| Rough-in, vent, 2" diameter DWV piping | 1.000 | Ea. | .955 | 32.40 | 48.40 | 80.80 |
| Waste, 4" diameter DWV piping | 1.000 | Ea. | .828 | 43.65 | 42 | 85.65 |
| Supply, 1/2" diameter type "L" copper supply piping | 1.000 | Ea. | .593 | 16.44 | 33.30 | 49.74 |
| Lavatory, 20" x 18" P.E. cast iron, wall hung, white | 1.000 | Ea. | 2.000 | 390 | 101 | 491 |
| Rough-in, waste, 1-1/2" diameter DWV piping | 1.000 | Ea. | 1.803 | 62 | 91.20 | 153.20 |
| Supply, 1/2" diameter type "L" copper supply piping | 1.000 | Ea. | .988 | 27.40 | 55.50 | 82.90 |
| Bathtub, P.E. cast iron, 5' long with accessories, white | 1.000 | Ea. | 3.636 | 1,050 | 184 | 1,234 |
| Rough-in, waste, 4" diameter DWV piping | 1.000 | Ea. | .828 | 43.65 | 42 | 85.65 |
| Supply, 1/2" diameter type "L" copper supply piping | 1.000 | Ea. | .988 | 27.40 | 55.50 | 82.90 |
| Vent, 1-1/2" diameter DWV piping | 1.000 | Ea. | 1.482 | 102 | 83.50 | 185.50 |
| Piping, supply, 1/2" diameter type "L" copper supply piping | 20.000 | L.F. | 1.975 | 54.80 | 111 | 165.80 |
| Waste, 4" diameter DWV piping | 9.000 | L.F. | 2.483 | 130.95 | 126 | 256.95 |
| Vent, 2" diameter DWV piping | 6.000 | L.F. | 1.500 | 114 | 75.90 | 189.90 |
| Carrier, steel, for studs, no arms | 1.000 | Ea. | 1.143 | 78 | 64.50 | 142.50 |
| **TOTAL** | | Ea. | 24.221 | 2,456.69 | 1,266.80 | 3,723.49 |

The costs in this system are a cost each basis, all necessary piping is included.

## Three Fixture Bathroom Price Sheet

| Three Fixture Bathroom Price Sheet | QUAN. | UNIT | LABOR HOURS | COST EACH | | |
|---|---|---|---|---|---|---|
| | | | | MAT. | INST. | TOTAL |
| Water closet, close coupled standard 2 piece, white | 1.000 | Ea. | 3.019 | 284 | 153 | 437 |
| Color | 1.000 | Ea. | 3.019 | 380 | 153 | 533 |
| One piece, elongated bowl, white | 1.000 | Ea. | 3.019 | 590 | 153 | 743 |
| Color | 1.000 | Ea. | 3.019 | 850 | 153 | 1,003 |
| Low profile, one piece elongated bowl, white | 1.000 | Ea. | 3.019 | 1,025 | 153 | 1,178 |
| Color | 1.000 | Ea. | 3.019 | 1,350 | 153 | 1,503 |
| Rough-in, for water closet | | | | | | |
| 1/2" copper supply, 4" cast iron waste, 2" cast iron vent | 1.000 | Ea. | 2.376 | 92.50 | 124 | 216.50 |
| 4" PVC/DWV waste, 2" PVC vent | 1.000 | Ea. | 2.678 | 47.50 | 139 | 186.50 |
| 4" copper waste, 2" copper vent | 1.000 | Ea. | 2.520 | 210 | 136 | 346 |
| 3" cast iron waste, 1-1/2" cast iron vent | 1.000 | Ea. | 2.244 | 81 | 117 | 198 |
| 3" PVC waste, 1-1/2" PVC vent | 1.000 | Ea. | 2.388 | 40 | 129 | 169 |
| 3" copper waste, 1-1/2" copper vent | 1.000 | Ea. | 2.014 | 135 | 109 | 244 |
| 1/2" PVC supply, 4" PVC waste, 2" PVC vent | 1.000 | Ea. | 2.974 | 52.50 | 156 | 208.50 |
| 3" PVC waste, 1-1/2" PVC supply | 1.000 | Ea. | 2.684 | 45.50 | 146 | 191.50 |
| 1/2" steel supply, 4" cast iron waste, 2" cast iron vent | 1.000 | Ea. | 2.545 | 110 | 133 | 243 |
| 4" cast iron waste, 2" steel vent | 1.000 | Ea. | 2.590 | 154 | 136 | 290 |
| 4" PVC waste, 2" PVC vent | 1.000 | Ea. | 2.847 | 65 | 149 | 214 |
| Lavatory, wall hung, P.E. cast iron 20" x 18", white | 1.000 | Ea. | 2.000 | 390 | 101 | 491 |
| Color | 1.000 | Ea. | 2.000 | 385 | 101 | 486 |
| Vitreous china 19" x 17", white | 1.000 | Ea. | 2.286 | 217 | 116 | 333 |
| Color | 1.000 | Ea. | 2.286 | 241 | 116 | 357 |
| Lavatory, for vanity top, P.E. cast iron 20" x 18"", white | 1.000 | Ea. | 2.500 | 286 | 127 | 413 |
| Color | 1.000 | Ea. | 2.500 | 286 | 127 | 413 |
| Steel, enameled 20" x 17", white | 1.000 | Ea. | 2.759 | 203 | 140 | 343 |
| Color | 1.000 | Ea. | 2.500 | 211 | 127 | 338 |
| Vitreous china 20" x 16", white | 1.000 | Ea. | 2.963 | 305 | 150 | 455 |
| Color | 1.000 | Ea. | 2.963 | 305 | 150 | 455 |
| Rough-in, for lavatory | | | | | | |
| 1/2" copper supply, 1-1/2" C.I. waste, 1-1/2" C.I. vent | 1.000 | Ea. | 2.791 | 89.50 | 147 | 236.50 |
| 1-1/2" PVC waste, 1-1/4" PVC vent | 1.000 | Ea. | 2.639 | 45 | 148 | 193 |
| 1/2" steel supply, 1-1/4" cast iron waste, 1-1/4" steel vent | 1.000 | Ea. | 2.890 | 136 | 154 | 290 |
| 1-1/4" PVC@ waste, 1-1/4" PVC vent | 1.000 | Ea. | 2.794 | 74 | 157 | 231 |
| 1/2" PVC supply, 1-1/2" PVC waste, 1-1/2" PVC vent | 1.000 | Ea. | 3.260 | 53.50 | 184 | 237.50 |
| Bathtub, P.E. cast iron, 5' long corner with fittings, white | 1.000 | Ea. | 3.636 | 1,050 | 184 | 1,234 |
| Color | 1.000 | Ea. | 3.636 | 1,300 | 184 | 1,484 |
| Rough-in, for bathtub | | | | | | |
| 1/2" copper supply, 4" cast iron waste, 1-1/2" copper vent | 1.000 | Ea. | 2.409 | 112 | 131 | 243 |
| 4" PVC waste, 1-1/2" PVC vent | 1.000 | Ea. | 2.877 | 56.50 | 156 | 212.50 |
| 1/2" steel supply, 4" cast iron waste, 1-1/2" steel vent | 1.000 | Ea. | 2.898 | 157 | 154 | 311 |
| 4" PVC waste, 1-1/2" PVC vent | 1.000 | Ea. | 3.159 | 85.50 | 172 | 257.50 |
| 1/2" PVC supply, 4" PVC waste, 1-1/2" PVC vent | 1.000 | Ea. | 3.371 | 65 | 184 | 249 |
| Piping, supply 1/2" copper | 20.000 | L.F. | 1.975 | 55 | 111 | 166 |
| 1/2" steel | 20.000 | L.F. | 2.540 | 113 | 143 | 256 |
| 1/2" PVC | 20.000 | L.F. | 2.963 | 72 | 167 | 239 |
| Piping, waste, 4" cast iron no hub | 9.000 | L.F. | 2.483 | 131 | 126 | 257 |
| 4" PVC/DWV | 9.000 | L.F. | 3.000 | 61 | 152 | 213 |
| 4" copper/DWV | 9.000 | L.F. | 3.600 | 415 | 185 | 600 |
| Piping, vent 2" cast iron no hub | 6.000 | L.F. | 1.433 | 48.50 | 72.50 | 121 |
| 2" copper/DWV | 6.000 | L.F. | 1.091 | 83 | 61.50 | 144.50 |
| 2" PVC/DWV | 6.000 | L.F. | 1.627 | 15.90 | 82.50 | 98.40 |
| 2" steel, galvanized | 6.000 | L.F. | 1.500 | 114 | 76 | 190 |
| Vanity base cabinet, 2 door, 24" x 30" | 1.000 | Ea. | 1.000 | 288 | 49 | 337 |
| 24" x 36" | 1.000 | Ea. | 1.200 | 385 | 59 | 444 |
| Vanity top, laminated plastic square edge 25" x 32" | 2.670 | L.F. | .712 | 77.50 | 35 | 112.50 |
| 25" x 38" | 3.160 | L.F. | .843 | 91.50 | 41 | 132.50 |
| Cultured marble, 25" x 32", with bowl | 1.000 | Ea. | 2.500 | 262 | 127 | 389 |
| 25" x 38", with bowl | 1.000 | Ea. | 2.500 | 283 | 127 | 410 |
| Carrier, for lavatory, steel for studs, no arms | 1.000 | Ea. | 1.143 | 78 | 64.50 | 142.50 |
| Wood, 2" x 8" blocking | 1.300 | L.F. | .052 | .79 | 2.55 | 3.34 |

| System Description | QUAN. | UNIT | LABOR HOURS | COST EACH | | |
|---|---|---|---|---|---|---|
| | | | | MAT. | INST. | TOTAL |
| **BATHROOM WITH LAVATORY INSTALLED IN VANITY** | | | | | | |
| Water closet, floor mounted, 2 piece, close coupled, white | 1.000 | Ea. | 3.019 | 284 | 153 | 437 |
| Rough-in, waste, 4″ diameter DWV piping | 1.000 | Ea. | .828 | 43.65 | 42 | 85.65 |
| Vent, 2″ diameter DWV piping | 1.000 | Ea. | .955 | 32.40 | 48.40 | 80.80 |
| Supply, 1/2″ diameter type "L" copper supply piping | 1.000 | Ea. | .593 | 16.44 | 33.30 | 49.74 |
| Lavatory, 20″ x 18″, P.E. cast iron with accessories, white | 1.000 | Ea. | 2.500 | 286 | 127 | 413 |
| Rough-in, waste, 1-1/2″ diameter DWV piping | 1.000 | Ea. | 1.803 | 62 | 91.20 | 153.20 |
| Supply, 1/2″ diameter type "L" copper supply piping | 1.000 | Ea. | .988 | 27.40 | 55.50 | 82.90 |
| Bathtub, P.E. cast iron 5′ long with accessories, white | 1.000 | Ea. | 3.636 | 1,050 | 184 | 1,234 |
| Rough-in, waste, 4″ diameter DWV piping | 1.000 | Ea. | .828 | 43.65 | 42 | 85.65 |
| Vent, 1-1/2″ diameter DWV piping | 1.000 | Ea. | .593 | 40.80 | 33.40 | 74.20 |
| Supply, 1/2″ diameter type "L" copper supply piping | 1.000 | Ea. | .988 | 27.40 | 55.50 | 82.90 |
| Piping, supply, 1/2″ diameter type "L" copper supply piping | 10.000 | L.F. | .988 | 27.40 | 55.50 | 82.90 |
| Waste, 4″ diameter DWV piping | 6.000 | L.F. | 1.655 | 87.30 | 84 | 171.30 |
| Vent, 2″ diameter DWV piping | 6.000 | L.F. | 1.500 | 114 | 75.90 | 189.90 |
| Vanity base cabinet, 2 door, 30″ wide | 1.000 | Ea. | 1.000 | 288 | 49 | 337 |
| Vanity top, plastic laminated square edge | 2.670 | L.F. | .712 | 77.43 | 34.84 | 112.27 |
| TOTAL | | Ea. | 22.586 | 2,507.87 | 1,164.54 | 3,672.41 |
| **BATHROOM WITH WALL HUNG LAVATORY** | | | | | | |
| Water closet, floor mounted, 2 piece, close coupled, white | 1.000 | Ea. | 3.019 | 284 | 153 | 437 |
| Rough-in, vent, 2″ diameter DWV piping | 1.000 | Ea. | .955 | 32.40 | 48.40 | 80.80 |
| Waste, 4″ diameter DWV piping | 1.000 | Ea. | .828 | 43.65 | 42 | 85.65 |
| Supply, 1/2″ diameter type "L" copper supply piping | 1.000 | Ea. | .593 | 16.44 | 33.30 | 49.74 |
| Lavatory, 20″ x 18″ P.E. cast iron, wall hung, white | 1.000 | Ea. | 2.000 | 390 | 101 | 491 |
| Rough-in, waste, 1-1/2″ diameter DWV piping | 1.000 | Ea. | 1.803 | 62 | 91.20 | 153.20 |
| Supply, 1/2″ diameter type "L" copper supply piping | 1.000 | Ea. | .988 | 27.40 | 55.50 | 82.90 |
| Bathtub, P.E. cast iron, 5′ long with accessories, white | 1.000 | Ea. | 3.636 | 1,050 | 184 | 1,234 |
| Rough-in, waste, 4″ diameter DWV piping | 1.000 | Ea. | .828 | 43.65 | 42 | 85.65 |
| Supply, 1/2″ diameter type "L" copper supply piping | 1.000 | Ea. | .988 | 27.40 | 55.50 | 82.90 |
| Vent, 1-1/2″ diameter DWV piping | 1.000 | Ea. | .593 | 40.80 | 33.40 | 74.20 |
| Piping, supply, 1/2″ diameter type "L" copper supply piping | 10.000 | L.F. | .988 | 27.40 | 55.50 | 82.90 |
| Waste, 4″ diameter DWV piping | 6.000 | L.F. | 1.655 | 87.30 | 84 | 171.30 |
| Vent, 2″ diameter DWV piping | 6.000 | L.F. | 1.500 | 114 | 75.90 | 189.90 |
| Carrier, steel, for studs, no arms | 1.000 | Ea. | 1.143 | 78 | 64.50 | 142.50 |
| TOTAL | | Ea. | 21.517 | 2,324.44 | 1,119.20 | 3,443.64 |

The costs in this system are on a cost each basis. All necessary piping is included.

## Three Fixture Bathroom Price Sheet

| Three Fixture Bathroom Price Sheet | QUAN. | UNIT | LABOR HOURS | COST EACH | | |
|---|---|---|---|---|---|---|
| | | | | MAT. | INST. | TOTAL |
| Water closet, close coupled standard 2 piece, white | 1.000 | Ea. | 3.019 | 284 | 153 | 437 |
| Color | 1.000 | Ea. | 3.019 | 380 | 153 | 533 |
| One piece elongated bowl, white | 1.000 | Ea. | 3.019 | 590 | 153 | 743 |
| Color | 1.000 | Ea. | 3.019 | 850 | 153 | 1,003 |
| Low profile, one piece elongated bowl, white | 1.000 | Ea. | 3.019 | 1,025 | 153 | 1,178 |
| Color | 1.000 | Ea. | 3.019 | 1,350 | 153 | 1,503 |
| Rough-in for water closet | | | | | | |
| 1/2" copper supply, 4" cast iron waste, 2" cast iron vent | 1.000 | Ea. | 2.376 | 92.50 | 124 | 216.50 |
| 4" PVC/DWV waste, 2" PVC vent | 1.000 | Ea. | 2.678 | 47.50 | 139 | 186.50 |
| 4" carrier waste, 2" copper vent | 1.000 | Ea. | 2.520 | 210 | 136 | 346 |
| 3" cast iron waste, 1-1/2" cast iron vent | 1.000 | Ea. | 2.244 | 81 | 117 | 198 |
| 3" PVC waste, 1-1/2" PVC vent | 1.000 | Ea. | 2.388 | 40 | 129 | 169 |
| 3" copper waste, 1-1/2" copper vent | 1.000 | Ea. | 2.014 | 135 | 109 | 244 |
| 1/2" PVC supply, 4" PVC waste, 2" PVC vent | 1.000 | Ea. | 2.974 | 52.50 | 156 | 208.50 |
| 3" PVC waste, 1-1/2" PVC supply | 1.000 | Ea. | 2.684 | 45.50 | 146 | 191.50 |
| 1/2" steel supply, 4" cast iron waste, 2" cast iron vent | 1.000 | Ea. | 2.545 | 110 | 133 | 243 |
| 4" cast iron waste, 2" steel vent | 1.000 | Ea. | 2.590 | 154 | 136 | 290 |
| 4" PVC waste, 2" PVC vent | 1.000 | Ea. | 2.847 | 65 | 149 | 214 |
| Lavatory, wall hung, PE cast iron 20" x 18", white | 1.000 | Ea. | 2.000 | 390 | 101 | 491 |
| Color | 1.000 | Ea. | 2.000 | 385 | 101 | 486 |
| Vitreous china 19" x 17", white | 1.000 | Ea. | 2.286 | 217 | 116 | 333 |
| Color | 1.000 | Ea. | 2.286 | 241 | 116 | 357 |
| Lavatory, for vanity top, PE cast iron 20" x 18", white | 1.000 | Ea. | 2.500 | 286 | 127 | 413 |
| Color | 1.000 | Ea. | 2.500 | 286 | 127 | 413 |
| Steel enameled 20" x 17", white | 1.000 | Ea. | 2.759 | 203 | 140 | 343 |
| Color | 1.000 | Ea. | 2.500 | 211 | 127 | 338 |
| Vitreous china 20" x 16", white | 1.000 | Ea. | 2.963 | 305 | 150 | 455 |
| Color | 1.000 | Ea. | 2.963 | 305 | 150 | 455 |
| Rough-in for lavatory | | | | | | |
| 1/2" copper supply, 1-1/2" cast iron waste, 1-1/2" cast iron vent | 1.000 | Ea. | 2.791 | 89.50 | 147 | 236.50 |
| 1-1/2" PVC waste, 1-1/4" PVC vent | 1.000 | Ea. | 2.639 | 45 | 148 | 193 |
| 1/2" steel supply, 1-1/4" cast iron waste, 1-1/4" steel vent | 1.000 | Ea. | 2.890 | 136 | 154 | 290 |
| 1-1/4" PVC waste, 1-1/4" PVC vent | 1.000 | Ea. | 2.794 | 74 | 157 | 231 |
| 1/2" PVC supply, 1-1/2" PVC waste, 1-1/2" PVC vent | 1.000 | Ea. | 3.260 | 53.50 | 184 | 237.50 |
| Bathtub, PE cast iron, 5' long corner with fittings, white | 1.000 | Ea. | 3.636 | 1,050 | 184 | 1,234 |
| Color | 1.000 | Ea. | 3.636 | 1,300 | 184 | 1,484 |
| Rough-in for bathtub | | | | | | |
| 1/2" copper supply, 4" cast iron waste, 1-1/2" copper vent | 1.000 | Ea. | 2.409 | 112 | 131 | 243 |
| 4" PVC waste, 1/2" PVC vent | 1.000 | Ea. | 2.877 | 56.50 | 156 | 212.50 |
| 1/2" steel supply, 4" cast iron waste, 1-1/2" steel vent | 1.000 | Ea. | 2.898 | 157 | 154 | 311 |
| 4" PVC waste, 1-1/2" PVC vent | 1.000 | Ea. | 3.159 | 85.50 | 172 | 257.50 |
| 1/2" PVC supply, 4" PVC waste, 1-1/2" PVC vent | 1.000 | Ea. | 3.371 | 65 | 184 | 249 |
| Piping supply, 1/2" copper | 10.000 | L.F. | .988 | 27.50 | 55.50 | 83 |
| 1/2" steel | 10.000 | L.F. | 1.270 | 56.50 | 71.50 | 128 |
| 1/2" PVC | 10.000 | L.F. | 1.482 | 36 | 83.50 | 119.50 |
| Piping waste, 4" cast iron no hub | 6.000 | L.F. | 1.655 | 87.50 | 84 | 171.50 |
| 4" PVC/DWV | 6.000 | L.F. | 2.000 | 40.50 | 101 | 141.50 |
| 4" copper/DWV | 6.000 | L.F. | 2.400 | 276 | 123 | 399 |
| Piping vent 2" cast iron no hub | 6.000 | L.F. | 1.433 | 48.50 | 72.50 | 121 |
| 2" copper/DWV | 6.000 | L.F. | 1.091 | 83 | 61.50 | 144.50 |
| 2" PVC/DWV | 6.000 | L.F. | 1.627 | 15.90 | 82.50 | 98.40 |
| 2" steel, galvanized | 6.000 | L.F. | 1.500 | 114 | 76 | 190 |
| Vanity base cabinet, 2 door, 24" x 30" | 1.000 | Ea. | 1.000 | 288 | 49 | 337 |
| 24" x 36" | 1.000 | Ea. | 1.200 | 385 | 59 | 444 |
| Vanity top, laminated plastic square edge 25" x 32" | 2.670 | L.F. | .712 | 77.50 | 35 | 112.50 |
| 25" x 38" | 3.160 | L.F. | .843 | 91.50 | 41 | 132.50 |
| Cultured marble, 25" x 32", with bowl | 1.000 | Ea. | 2.500 | 262 | 127 | 389 |
| 25" x 38", with bowl | 1.000 | Ea. | 2.500 | 283 | 127 | 410 |
| Carrier, for lavatory, steel for studs, no arms | 1.000 | Ea. | 1.143 | 78 | 64.50 | 142.50 |
| Wood, 2" x 8" blocking | 1.300 | L.F. | .052 | .79 | 2.55 | 3.34 |

Bathtub

Water Closet

Lavatory

Vanity Top

Vanity Base Cabinet

| System Description | QUAN. | UNIT | LABOR HOURS | COST EACH | | |
|---|---|---|---|---|---|---|
| | | | | MAT. | INST. | TOTAL |
| **BATHROOM WITH LAVATORY INSTALLED IN VANITY** | | | | | | |
| Water closet, floor mounted, 2 piece, close coupled, white | 1.000 | Ea. | 3.019 | 284 | 153 | 437 |
| Rough-in, vent, 2" diameter DWV piping | 1.000 | Ea. | .955 | 32.40 | 48.40 | 80.80 |
| Waste, 4" diameter DWV piping | 1.000 | Ea. | .828 | 43.65 | 42 | 85.65 |
| Supply, 1/2" diameter type "L" copper supply piping | 1.000 | Ea. | .593 | 16.44 | 33.30 | 49.74 |
| Lavatory, 20" x 18", PE cast iron with accessories, white | 1.000 | Ea. | 2.500 | 286 | 127 | 413 |
| Rough-in, vent, 1-1/2" diameter DWV piping | 1.000 | Ea. | 1.803 | 62 | 91.20 | 153.20 |
| Supply, 1/2" diameter type "L" copper supply piping | 1.000 | Ea. | .988 | 27.40 | 55.50 | 82.90 |
| Bathtub, P.E. cast iron, 5' long with accessories, white | 1.000 | Ea. | 3.636 | 1,050 | 184 | 1,234 |
| Rough-in, waste, 4" diameter DWV piping | 1.000 | Ea. | .828 | 43.65 | 42 | 85.65 |
| Supply, 1/2" diameter type "L" copper supply piping | 1.000 | Ea. | .988 | 27.40 | 55.50 | 82.90 |
| Vent, 1-1/2" diameter DWV piping | 1.000 | Ea. | .593 | 40.80 | 33.40 | 74.20 |
| Piping, supply, 1/2" diameter type "L" copper supply piping | 32.000 | L.F. | 3.161 | 87.68 | 177.60 | 265.28 |
| Waste, 4" diameter DWV piping | 12.000 | L.F. | 3.310 | 174.60 | 168 | 342.60 |
| Vent, 2" diameter DWV piping | 6.000 | L.F. | 1.500 | 114 | 75.90 | 189.90 |
| Vanity base cabinet, 2 door, 30" wide | 1.000 | Ea. | 1.000 | 288 | 49 | 337 |
| Vanity top, plastic laminated square edge | 2.670 | L.F. | .712 | 77.43 | 34.84 | 112.27 |
| TOTAL | | Ea. | 26.414 | 2,655.45 | 1,370.64 | 4,026.09 |
| **BATHROOM WITH WALL HUNG LAVATORY** | | | | | | |
| Water closet, floor mounted, 2 piece, close coupled, white | 1.000 | Ea. | 3.019 | 284 | 153 | 437 |
| Rough-in, vent, 2" diameter DWV piping | 1.000 | Ea. | .955 | 32.40 | 48.40 | 80.80 |
| Waste, 4" diameter DWV piping | 1.000 | Ea. | .828 | 43.65 | 42 | 85.65 |
| Supply, 1/2" diameter type "L" copper supply piping | 1.000 | Ea. | .593 | 16.44 | 33.30 | 49.74 |
| Lavatory, 20" x 18" P.E. cast iron, wall hung, white | 1.000 | Ea. | 2.000 | 390 | 101 | 491 |
| Rough-in, waste, 1-1/2" diameter DWV piping | 1.000 | Ea. | 1.803 | 62 | 91.20 | 153.20 |
| Supply, 1/2" diameter type "L" copper supply piping | 1.000 | Ea. | .988 | 27.40 | 55.50 | 82.90 |
| Bathtub, P.E. cast iron, 5' long with accessories, white | 1.000 | Ea. | 3.636 | 1,050 | 184 | 1,234 |
| Rough-in, waste, 4" diameter DWV piping | 1.000 | Ea. | .828 | 43.65 | 42 | 85.65 |
| Supply, 1/2" diameter type "L" copper supply piping | 1.000 | Ea. | .988 | 27.40 | 55.50 | 82.90 |
| Vent, 1-1/2" diameter DWV piping | 1.000 | Ea. | .593 | 40.80 | 33.40 | 74.20 |
| Piping, supply, 1/2" diameter type "L" copper supply piping | 32.000 | L.F. | 3.161 | 87.68 | 177.60 | 265.28 |
| Waste, 4" diameter DWV piping | 12.000 | L.F. | 3.310 | 174.60 | 168 | 342.60 |
| Vent, 2" diameter DWV piping | 6.000 | L.F. | 1.500 | 114 | 75.90 | 189.90 |
| Carrier steel, for studs, no arms | 1.000 | Ea. | 1.143 | 78 | 64.50 | 142.50 |
| TOTAL | | Ea. | 25.345 | 2,472.02 | 1,325.30 | 3,797.32 |

The costs in this system are on a cost each basis. All necessary piping is included.

# Three Fixture Bathroom Price Sheet

| | QUAN. | UNIT | LABOR HOURS | COST EACH MAT. | COST EACH INST. | COST EACH TOTAL |
|---|---|---|---|---|---|---|
| Water closet, close coupled, standard 2 piece, white | 1.000 | Ea. | 3.019 | 284 | 153 | 437 |
| Color | 1.000 | Ea. | 3.019 | 380 | 153 | 533 |
| One piece, elongated bowl, white | 1.000 | Ea. | 3.019 | 590 | 153 | 743 |
| Color | 1.000 | Ea. | 3.019 | 850 | 153 | 1,003 |
| Low profile, one piece, elongated bowl, white | 1.000 | Ea. | 3.019 | 1,025 | 153 | 1,178 |
| Color | 1.000 | Ea. | 3.019 | 1,350 | 153 | 1,503 |
| Rough-in, for water closet | | | | | | |
| 1/2″ copper supply, 4″ cast iron waste, 2″ cast iron vent | 1.000 | Ea. | 2.376 | 92.50 | 124 | 216.50 |
| 4″ PVC/DWV waste, 2″ PVC vent | 1.000 | Ea. | 2.678 | 47.50 | 139 | 186.50 |
| 4″ copper waste, 2″ copper vent | 1.000 | Ea. | 2.520 | 210 | 136 | 346 |
| 3″ cast iron waste, 1-1/2″ cast iron vent | 1.000 | Ea. | 2.244 | 81 | 117 | 198 |
| 3″ PVC waste, 1-1/2″ PVC vent | 1.000 | Ea. | 2.388 | 40 | 129 | 169 |
| 3″ copper waste, 1-1/2″ copper vent | 1.000 | Ea. | 2.014 | 135 | 109 | 244 |
| 1/2″ PVC supply, 4″ PVC waste, 2″ PVC vent | 1.000 | Ea. | 2.974 | 52.50 | 156 | 208.50 |
| 3″ PVC waste, 1-1/2″ PVC supply | 1.000 | Ea. | 2.684 | 45.50 | 146 | 191.50 |
| 1/2″ steel supply, 4″ cast iron waste, 2″ cast iron vent | 1.000 | Ea. | 2.545 | 110 | 133 | 243 |
| 4″ cast iron waste, 2″ steel vent | 1.000 | Ea. | 2.590 | 154 | 136 | 290 |
| 4″ PVC waste, 2″ PVC vent | 1.000 | Ea. | 2.847 | 65 | 149 | 214 |
| Lavatory wall hung, P.E. cast iron, 20″ x 18″, white | 1.000 | Ea. | 2.000 | 390 | 101 | 491 |
| Color | 1.000 | Ea. | 2.000 | 385 | 101 | 486 |
| Vitreous china, 19″ x 17″, white | 1.000 | Ea. | 2.286 | 217 | 116 | 333 |
| Color | 1.000 | Ea. | 2.286 | 241 | 116 | 357 |
| Lavatory, for vanity top, P.E., cast iron, 20″ x 18″, white | 1.000 | Ea. | 2.500 | 286 | 127 | 413 |
| Color | 1.000 | Ea. | 2.500 | 286 | 127 | 413 |
| Steel, enameled, 20″ x 17″, white | 1.000 | Ea. | 2.759 | 203 | 140 | 343 |
| Color | 1.000 | Ea. | 2.500 | 211 | 127 | 338 |
| Vitreous china, 20″ x 16″, white | 1.000 | Ea. | 2.963 | 305 | 150 | 455 |
| Color | 1.000 | Ea. | 2.963 | 305 | 150 | 455 |
| Rough-in, for lavatory | | | | | | |
| 1/2″ copper supply, 1-1/2″ C.I. waste, 1-1/2″ C.I. vent | 1.000 | Ea. | 2.791 | 89.50 | 147 | 236.50 |
| 1-1/2″ PVC waste, 1-1/4″ PVC vent | 1.000 | Ea. | 2.639 | 45 | 148 | 193 |
| 1/2″ steel supply, 1-1/4″ cast iron waste, 1-1/4″ steel vent | 1.000 | Ea. | 2.890 | 136 | 154 | 290 |
| 1-1/4″ PVC waste, 1-1/4″ PVC vent | 1.000 | Ea. | 2.794 | 74 | 157 | 231 |
| 1/2″ PVC supply, 1-1/2″ PVC waste, 1-1/2″ PVC vent | 1.000 | Ea. | 3.260 | 53.50 | 184 | 237.50 |
| Bathtub, P.E. cast iron, 5′ long corner with fittings, white | 1.000 | Ea. | 3.636 | 1,050 | 184 | 1,234 |
| Color | 1.000 | Ea. | 3.636 | 1,300 | 184 | 1,484 |
| Rough-in, for bathtub | | | | | | |
| 1/2″ copper supply, 4″ cast iron waste, 1-1/2″ copper vent | 1.000 | Ea. | 2.409 | 112 | 131 | 243 |
| 4″ PVC waste, 1/2″ PVC vent | 1.000 | Ea. | 2.877 | 56.50 | 156 | 212.50 |
| 1/2″ steel supply, 4″ cast iron waste, 1-1/2″ steel vent | 1.000 | Ea. | 2.898 | 157 | 154 | 311 |
| 4″ PVC waste, 1-1/2″ PVC vent | 1.000 | Ea. | 3.159 | 85.50 | 172 | 257.50 |
| 1/2″ PVC supply, 4″ PVC waste, 1-1/2″ PVC vent | 1.000 | Ea. | 3.371 | 65 | 184 | 249 |
| Piping, supply, 1/2″ copper | 32.000 | L.F. | 3.161 | 87.50 | 178 | 265.50 |
| 1/2″ steel | 32.000 | L.F. | 4.063 | 181 | 229 | 410 |
| 1/2″ PVC | 32.000 | L.F. | 4.741 | 115 | 267 | 382 |
| Piping, waste, 4″ cast iron no hub | 12.000 | L.F. | 3.310 | 175 | 168 | 343 |
| 4″ PVC/DWV | 12.000 | L.F. | 4.000 | 81 | 203 | 284 |
| 4″ copper/DWV | 12.000 | L.F. | 4.800 | 550 | 246 | 796 |
| Piping, vent, 2″ cast iron no hub | 6.000 | L.F. | 1.433 | 48.50 | 72.50 | 121 |
| 2″ copper/DWV | 6.000 | L.F. | 1.091 | 83 | 61.50 | 144.50 |
| 2″ PVC/DWV | 6.000 | L.F. | 1.627 | 15.90 | 82.50 | 98.40 |
| 2″ steel, galvanized | 6.000 | L.F. | 1.500 | 114 | 76 | 190 |
| Vanity base cabinet, 2 door, 24″ x 30″ | 1.000 | Ea. | 1.000 | 288 | 49 | 337 |
| 24″ x 36″ | 1.000 | Ea. | 1.200 | 385 | 59 | 444 |
| Vanity top, laminated plastic square edge, 25″ x 32″ | 2.670 | L.F. | .712 | 77.50 | 35 | 112.50 |
| 25″ x 38″ | 3.160 | L.F. | .843 | 91.50 | 41 | 132.50 |
| Cultured marble, 25″ x 32″, with bowl | 1.000 | Ea. | 2.500 | 262 | 127 | 389 |
| 25″ x 38″, with bowl | 1.000 | Ea. | 2.500 | 283 | 127 | 410 |
| Carrier, for lavatory, steel for studs, no arms | 1.000 | Ea. | 1.143 | 78 | 64.50 | 142.50 |
| Wood, 2″ x 8″ blocking | 1.300 | L.F. | .052 | .79 | 2.55 | 3.34 |

Corner Bathtub

Water Closet

Lavatory

Vanity Top

Vanity Base Cabinet

| System Description | QUAN. | UNIT | LABOR HOURS | COST EACH | | |
|---|---|---|---|---|---|---|
| | | | | MAT. | INST. | TOTAL |
| **BATHROOM WITH LAVATORY INSTALLED IN VANITY** | | | | | | |
| Water closet, floor mounted, 2 piece, close coupled, white | 1.000 | Ea. | 3.019 | 284 | 153 | 437 |
| Rough-in, vent, 2" diameter DWV piping | 1.000 | Ea. | .955 | 32.40 | 48.40 | 80.80 |
| Waste, 4" diameter DWV piping | 1.000 | Ea. | .828 | 43.65 | 42 | 85.65 |
| Supply, 1/2" diameter type "L" copper supply piping | 1.000 | Ea. | .593 | 16.44 | 33.30 | 49.74 |
| Lavatory, 20" x 18", P.E. cast iron with fittings, white | 1.000 | Ea. | 2.500 | 286 | 127 | 413 |
| Rough-in, waste, 1-1/2" diameter DWV piping | 1.000 | Ea. | 1.803 | 62 | 91.20 | 153.20 |
| Supply, 1/2" diameter type "L" copper supply piping | 1.000 | Ea. | .988 | 27.40 | 55.50 | 82.90 |
| Bathtub, P.E. cast iron, corner with fittings, white | 1.000 | Ea. | 3.636 | 2,375 | 184 | 2,559 |
| Rough-in, waste, 4" diameter DWV piping | 1.000 | Ea. | .828 | 43.65 | 42 | 85.65 |
| Supply, 1/2" diameter type "L" copper supply piping | 1.000 | Ea. | .988 | 27.40 | 55.50 | 82.90 |
| Vent, 1-1/2" diameter DWV piping | 1.000 | Ea. | .593 | 40.80 | 33.40 | 74.20 |
| Piping, supply, 1/2" diameter type "L" copper supply piping | 32.000 | L.F. | 3.161 | 87.68 | 177.60 | 265.28 |
| Waste, 4" diameter DWV piping | 12.000 | L.F. | 3.310 | 174.60 | 168 | 342.60 |
| Vent, 2" diameter DWV piping | 6.000 | L.F. | 1.500 | 114 | 75.90 | 189.90 |
| Vanity base cabinet, 2 door, 30" wide | 1.000 | Ea. | 1.000 | 288 | 49 | 337 |
| Vanity top, plastic laminated, square edge | 2.670 | L.F. | .712 | 97.46 | 34.84 | 132.30 |
| TOTAL | | Ea. | 26.414 | 4,000.48 | 1,370.64 | 5,371.12 |
| **BATHROOM WITH WALL HUNG LAVATORY** | | | | | | |
| Water closet, floor mounted, 2 piece, close coupled, white | 1.000 | Ea. | 3.019 | 284 | 153 | 437 |
| Rough-in, vent, 2" diameter DWV piping | 1.000 | Ea. | .955 | 32.40 | 48.40 | 80.80 |
| Waste, 4" diameter DWV piping | 1.000 | Ea. | .828 | 43.65 | 42 | 85.65 |
| Supply, 1/2" diameter type "L" copper supply piping | 1.000 | Ea. | .593 | 16.44 | 33.30 | 49.74 |
| Lavatory, 20" x 18", P.E. cast iron, with fittings, white | 1.000 | Ea. | 2.000 | 390 | 101 | 491 |
| Rough-in, waste, 1-1/2" diameter DWV piping | 1.000 | Ea. | 1.803 | 62 | 91.20 | 153.20 |
| Supply, 1/2" diameter type "L" copper supply piping | 1.000 | Ea. | .988 | 27.40 | 55.50 | 82.90 |
| Bathtub, P.E. cast iron, corner, with fittings, white | 1.000 | Ea. | 3.636 | 2,375 | 184 | 2,559 |
| Rough-in, waste, 4" diameter DWV piping | 1.000 | Ea. | .828 | 43.65 | 42 | 85.65 |
| Supply, 1/2" diameter type "L" copper supply piping | 1.000 | Ea. | .988 | 27.40 | 55.50 | 82.90 |
| Vent, 1-1/2" diameter DWV piping | 1.000 | Ea. | .593 | 40.80 | 33.40 | 74.20 |
| Piping, supply, 1/2" diameter type "L" copper supply piping | 32.000 | L.F. | 3.161 | 87.68 | 177.60 | 265.28 |
| Waste, 4" diameter DWV piping | 12.000 | L.F. | 3.310 | 174.60 | 168 | 342.60 |
| Vent, 2" diameter DWV piping | 6.000 | L.F. | 1.500 | 114 | 75.90 | 189.90 |
| Carrier, steel, for studs, no arms | 1.000 | Ea. | 1.143 | 78 | 64.50 | 142.50 |
| TOTAL | | Ea. | 25.345 | 3,797.02 | 1,325.30 | 5,122.32 |

The costs in this system are on a cost each basis. All necessary piping is included.

| Three Fixture Bathroom Price Sheet | QUAN. | UNIT | LABOR HOURS | COST EACH | | |
|---|---|---|---|---|---|---|
| | | | | MAT. | INST. | TOTAL |
| Water closet, close coupled, standard 2 piece, white | 1.000 | Ea. | 3.019 | 284 | 153 | 437 |
| Color | 1.000 | Ea. | 3.019 | 380 | 153 | 533 |
| One piece elongated bowl, white | 1.000 | Ea. | 3.019 | 590 | 153 | 743 |
| Color | 1.000 | Ea. | 3.019 | 850 | 153 | 1,003 |
| Low profile, one piece elongated bowl, white | 1.000 | Ea. | 3.019 | 1,025 | 153 | 1,178 |
| Color | 1.000 | Ea. | 3.019 | 1,350 | 153 | 1,503 |
| Rough-in, for water closet | | | | | | |
| 1/2" copper supply, 4" cast iron waste, 2" cast iron vent | 1.000 | Ea. | 2.376 | 92.50 | 124 | 216.50 |
| 4" PVC/DWV waste, 2" PVC vent | 1.000 | Ea. | 2.678 | 47.50 | 139 | 186.50 |
| 4" copper waste, 2" copper vent | 1.000 | Ea. | 2.520 | 210 | 136 | 346 |
| 3" cast iron waste, 1-1/2" cast iron vent | 1.000 | Ea. | 2.244 | 81 | 117 | 198 |
| 3" PVC waste, 1-1/2" PVC vent | 1.000 | Ea. | 2.388 | 40 | 129 | 169 |
| 3" copper waste, 1-1/2" copper vent | 1.000 | Ea. | 2.014 | 135 | 109 | 244 |
| 1/2" PVC supply, 4" PVC waste, 2" PVC vent | 1.000 | Ea. | 2.974 | 52.50 | 156 | 208.50 |
| 3" PVC waste, 1-1/2" PVC supply | 1.000 | Ea. | 2.684 | 45.50 | 146 | 191.50 |
| 1/2" steel supply, 4" cast iron waste, 2" cast iron vent | 1.000 | Ea. | 2.545 | 110 | 133 | 243 |
| 4" cast iron waste, 2" steel vent | 1.000 | Ea. | 2.590 | 154 | 136 | 290 |
| 4" PVC waste, 2" PVC vent | 1.000 | Ea. | 2.847 | 65 | 149 | 214 |
| Lavatory, wall hung P.E. cast iron 20" x 18", white | 1.000 | Ea. | 2.000 | 390 | 101 | 491 |
| Color | 1.000 | Ea. | 2.000 | 385 | 101 | 486 |
| Vitreous china 19" x 17", white | 1.000 | Ea. | 2.286 | 217 | 116 | 333 |
| Color | 1.000 | Ea. | 2.286 | 241 | 116 | 357 |
| Lavatory, for vanity top, P.E., cast iron, 20" x 18", white | 1.000 | Ea. | 2.500 | 286 | 127 | 413 |
| Color | 1.000 | Ea. | 2.500 | 286 | 127 | 413 |
| Steel enameled 20" x 17", white | 1.000 | Ea. | 2.759 | 203 | 140 | 343 |
| Color | 1.000 | Ea. | 2.500 | 211 | 127 | 338 |
| Vitreous china 20" x 16", white | 1.000 | Ea. | 2.963 | 305 | 150 | 455 |
| Color | 1.000 | Ea. | 2.963 | 305 | 150 | 455 |
| Rough-in, for lavatory | | | | | | |
| 1/2" copper supply, 1-1/2" cast iron waste, 1-1/2" cast iron vent | 1.000 | Ea. | 2.791 | 89.50 | 147 | 236.50 |
| 1-1/2" PVC waste, 1-1/4" PVC vent | 1.000 | Ea. | 2.639 | 45 | 148 | 193 |
| 1/2" steel supply, 1-1/4" cast iron waste, 1-1/4" steel vent | 1.000 | Ea. | 2.890 | 136 | 154 | 290 |
| 1-1/4" PVC waste, 1-1/4" PVC vent | 1.000 | Ea. | 2.794 | 74 | 157 | 231 |
| 1/2" PVC supply, 1-1/2" PVC waste, 1-1/2" PVC vent | 1.000 | Ea. | 3.260 | 53.50 | 184 | 237.50 |
| Bathtub, P.E. cast iron, corner with fittings, white | 1.000 | Ea. | 3.636 | 2,375 | 184 | 2,559 |
| Color | 1.000 | Ea. | 4.000 | 2,675 | 203 | 2,878 |
| Rough-in, for bathtub | | | | | | |
| 1/2" copper supply, 4" cast iron waste, 1-1/2" copper vent | 1.000 | Ea. | 2.409 | 112 | 131 | 243 |
| 4" PVC waste, 1-1/2" PVC vent | 1.000 | Ea. | 2.877 | 56.50 | 156 | 212.50 |
| 1/2" steel supply, 4" cast iron waste, 1-1/2" steel vent | 1.000 | Ea. | 2.898 | 157 | 154 | 311 |
| 4" PVC waste, 1-1/2" PVC vent | 1.000 | Ea. | 3.159 | 85.50 | 172 | 257.50 |
| 1/2" PVC supply, 4" PVC waste, 1-1/2" PVC vent | 1.000 | Ea. | 3.371 | 65 | 184 | 249 |
| Piping, supply, 1/2" copper | 32.000 | L.F. | 3.161 | 87.50 | 178 | 265.50 |
| 1/2" steel | 32.000 | L.F. | 4.063 | 181 | 229 | 410 |
| 1/2" PVC | 32.000 | L.F. | 4.741 | 115 | 267 | 382 |
| Piping, waste, 4" cast iron, no hub | 12.000 | L.F. | 3.310 | 175 | 168 | 343 |
| 4" PVC/DWV | 12.000 | L.F. | 4.000 | 81 | 203 | 284 |
| 4" copper/DWV | 12.000 | L.F. | 4.800 | 550 | 246 | 796 |
| Piping, vent 2" cast iron, no hub | 6.000 | L.F. | 1.433 | 48.50 | 72.50 | 121 |
| 2" copper/DWV | 6.000 | L.F. | 1.091 | 83 | 61.50 | 144.50 |
| 2" PVC/DWV | 6.000 | L.F. | 1.627 | 15.90 | 82.50 | 98.40 |
| 2" steel, galvanized | 6.000 | L.F. | 1.500 | 114 | 76 | 190 |
| Vanity base cabinet, 2 door, 24" x 30" | 1.000 | Ea. | 1.000 | 288 | 49 | 337 |
| 24" x 36" | 1.000 | Ea. | 1.200 | 385 | 59 | 444 |
| Vanity top, laminated plastic square edge 25" x 32" | 2.670 | L.F. | .712 | 97.50 | 35 | 132.50 |
| 25" x 38" | 3.160 | L.F. | .843 | 115 | 41 | 156 |
| Cultured marble, 25" x 32", with bowl | 1.000 | Ea. | 2.500 | 262 | 127 | 389 |
| 25" x 38", with bowl | 1.000 | Ea. | 2.500 | 283 | 127 | 410 |
| Carrier, for lavatory, steel for studs, no arms | 1.000 | Ea. | 1.143 | 78 | 64.50 | 142.50 |
| Wood, 2" x 8" blocking | 1.300 | L.F. | .053 | .81 | 2.61 | 3.42 |

| System Description | QUAN. | UNIT | LABOR HOURS | COST EACH | | |
|---|---|---|---|---|---|---|
| | | | | MAT. | INST. | TOTAL |
| **BATHROOM WITH SHOWER, LAVATORY INSTALLED IN VANITY** | | | | | | |
| Water closet, floor mounted, 2 piece, close coupled, white | 1.000 | Ea. | 3.019 | 284 | 153 | 437 |
| Rough-in, vent, 2" diameter DWV piping | 1.000 | Ea. | .955 | 32.40 | 48.40 | 80.80 |
| Waste, 4" diameter DWV piping | 1.000 | Ea. | .828 | 43.65 | 42 | 85.65 |
| Supply, 1/2" diameter type "L" copper supply piping | 1.000 | Ea. | .593 | 16.44 | 33.30 | 49.74 |
| Lavatory, 20" x 18" P.E. cast iron with fittings, white | 1.000 | Ea. | 2.500 | 286 | 127 | 413 |
| Rough-in, waste, 1-1/2" diameter DWV piping | 1.000 | Ea. | 1.803 | 62 | 91.20 | 153.20 |
| Supply, 1/2" diameter type "L" copper supply piping | 1.000 | Ea. | .988 | 27.40 | 55.50 | 82.90 |
| Shower, steel enameled, stone base, corner, white | 1.000 | Ea. | 3.200 | 975 | 162 | 1,137 |
| Shower mixing valve | 1.000 | Ea. | 1.333 | 156 | 75 | 231 |
| Shower door | 1.000 | Ea. | 1.000 | 259 | 53.50 | 312.50 |
| Rough-in, vent, 1-1/2" diameter DWV piping | 1.000 | Ea. | .225 | 7.75 | 11.40 | 19.15 |
| Waste, 2" diameter DWV piping | 1.000 | Ea. | 1.433 | 48.60 | 72.60 | 121.20 |
| Supply, 1/2" diameter type "L" copper supply piping | 1.000 | Ea. | 1.580 | 43.84 | 88.80 | 132.64 |
| Piping, supply, 1/2" diameter type "L" copper supply piping | 36.000 | L.F. | 4.148 | 115.08 | 233.10 | 348.18 |
| Waste, 4" diameter DWV piping | 7.000 | L.F. | 2.759 | 145.50 | 140 | 285.50 |
| Vent, 2" diameter DWV piping | 6.000 | L.F. | 2.250 | 171 | 113.85 | 284.85 |
| Vanity base 2 door, 30" wide | 1.000 | Ea. | 1.000 | 288 | 49 | 337 |
| Vanity top, plastic laminated, square edge | 2.170 | L.F. | .712 | 80.10 | 34.84 | 114.94 |
| TOTAL | | Ea. | 30.326 | 3,041.76 | 1,584.49 | 4,626.25 |
| | | | | | | |
| **BATHROOM WITH SHOWER, WALL HUNG LAVATORY** | | | | | | |
| Water closet, floor mounted, close coupled | 1.000 | Ea. | 3.019 | 284 | 153 | 437 |
| Rough-in, vent, 2" diameter DWV piping | 1.000 | Ea. | .955 | 32.40 | 48.40 | 80.80 |
| Waste, 4" diameter DWV piping | 1.000 | Ea. | .828 | 43.65 | 42 | 85.65 |
| Supply, 1/2" diameter type "L" copper supply piping | 1.000 | Ea. | .593 | 16.44 | 33.30 | 49.74 |
| Lavatory, 20" x 18" P.E. cast iron with fittings, white | 1.000 | Ea. | 2.000 | 390 | 101 | 491 |
| Rough-in, waste, 1-1/2" diameter DWV piping | 1.000 | Ea. | 1.803 | 62 | 91.20 | 153.20 |
| Supply, 1/2" diameter type "L" copper supply piping | 1.000 | Ea. | .988 | 27.40 | 55.50 | 82.90 |
| Shower, steel enameled, stone base, white | 1.000 | Ea. | 3.200 | 975 | 162 | 1,137 |
| Mixing valve | 1.000 | Ea. | 1.333 | 156 | 75 | 231 |
| Shower door | 1.000 | Ea. | 1.000 | 259 | 53.50 | 312.50 |
| Rough-in, vent, 1-1/2" diameter DWV piping | 1.000 | Ea. | .225 | 7.75 | 11.40 | 19.15 |
| Waste, 2" diameter DWV piping | 1.000 | Ea. | 1.433 | 48.60 | 72.60 | 121.20 |
| Supply, 1/2" diameter type "L" copper supply piping | 1.000 | Ea. | 1.580 | 43.84 | 88.80 | 132.64 |
| Piping, supply, 1/2" diameter type "L" copper supply piping | 36.000 | L.F. | 4.148 | 115.08 | 233.10 | 348.18 |
| Waste, 4" diameter DWV piping | 7.000 | L.F. | 2.759 | 145.50 | 140 | 285.50 |
| Vent, 2" diameter DWV piping | 6.000 | L.F. | 2.250 | 171 | 113.85 | 284.85 |
| Carrier, steel, for studs, no arms | 1.000 | Ea. | 1.143 | 78 | 64.50 | 142.50 |
| TOTAL | | Ea. | 29.257 | 2,855.66 | 1,539.15 | 4,394.81 |

The costs in this system are on a cost each basis. All necessary piping is included.

| Three Fixture Bathroom Price Sheet | QUAN. | UNIT | LABOR HOURS | COST EACH | | |
|---|---|---|---|---|---|---|
| | | | | MAT. | INST. | TOTAL |
| Water closet, close coupled, standard 2 piece, white | 1.000 | Ea. | 3.019 | 284 | 153 | 437 |
| Color | 1.000 | Ea. | 3.019 | 380 | 153 | 533 |
| One piece elongated bowl, white | 1.000 | Ea. | 3.019 | 590 | 153 | 743 |
| Color | 1.000 | Ea. | 3.019 | 850 | 153 | 1,003 |
| Low profile, one piece elongated bowl, white | 1.000 | Ea. | 3.019 | 1,025 | 153 | 1,178 |
| Color | 1.000 | Ea. | 3.019 | 1,350 | 153 | 1,503 |
| Rough-in, for water closet | | | | | | |
| 1/2" copper supply, 4" cast iron waste, 2" cast iron vent | 1.000 | Ea. | 2.376 | 92.50 | 124 | 216.50 |
| 4" PVC/DWV waste, 2" PVC vent | 1.000 | Ea. | 2.678 | 47.50 | 139 | 186.50 |
| 4" copper waste, 2" copper vent | 1.000 | Ea. | 2.520 | 210 | 136 | 346 |
| 3" cast iron waste, 1-1/2" cast iron vent | 1.000 | Ea. | 2.244 | 81 | 117 | 198 |
| 3" PVC waste, 1-1/2" PVC vent | 1.000 | Ea. | 2.388 | 40 | 129 | 169 |
| 3" copper waste, 1-1/2" copper vent | 1.000 | Ea. | 2.014 | 135 | 109 | 244 |
| 1/2" PVC supply, 4" PVC waste, 2" PVC vent | 1.000 | Ea. | 2.974 | 52.50 | 156 | 208.50 |
| 3" PVC waste, 1-1/2" PVC supply | 1.000 | Ea. | 2.684 | 45.50 | 146 | 191.50 |
| 1/2" steel supply, 4" cast iron waste, 2" cast iron vent | 1.000 | Ea. | 2.545 | 110 | 133 | 243 |
| 4" cast iron waste, 2" steel vent | 1.000 | Ea. | 2.590 | 154 | 136 | 290 |
| 4" PVC waste, 2" PVC vent | 1.000 | Ea. | 2.847 | 65 | 149 | 214 |
| Lavatory, wall hung, P.E. cast iron 20" x 18", white | 1.000 | Ea. | 2.000 | 390 | 101 | 491 |
| Color | 1.000 | Ea. | 2.000 | 385 | 101 | 486 |
| Vitreous china 19" x 17", white | 1.000 | Ea. | 2.286 | 217 | 116 | 333 |
| Color | 1.000 | Ea. | 2.286 | 241 | 116 | 357 |
| Lavatory, for vanity top, P.E. cast iron 20" x 18", white | 1.000 | Ea. | 2.500 | 286 | 127 | 413 |
| Color | 1.000 | Ea. | 2.500 | 286 | 127 | 413 |
| Steel enameled 20" x 17", white | 1.000 | Ea. | 2.759 | 203 | 140 | 343 |
| Color | 1.000 | Ea. | 2.500 | 211 | 127 | 338 |
| Vitreous china 20" x 16", white | 1.000 | Ea. | 2.963 | 305 | 150 | 455 |
| Color | 1.000 | Ea. | 2.963 | 305 | 150 | 455 |
| Rough-in, for lavatory | | | | | | |
| 1/2" copper supply, 1-1/2" cast iron waste, 1-1/2" cast iron vent | 1.000 | Ea. | 2.791 | 89.50 | 147 | 236.50 |
| 1-1/2" PVC waste, 1-1/2" PVC vent | 1.000 | Ea. | 2.639 | 45 | 148 | 193 |
| 1/2" steel supply, 1-1/4" cast iron waste, 1-1/4" steel vent | 1.000 | Ea. | 2.890 | 136 | 154 | 290 |
| 1-1/4" PVC waste, 1-1/4" PVC vent | 1.000 | Ea. | 2.921 | 74 | 164 | 238 |
| 1/2" PVC supply, 1-1/2" PVC waste, 1-1/2" PVC vent | 1.000 | Ea. | 3.260 | 53.50 | 184 | 237.50 |
| Shower, steel enameled stone base, 32" x 32", white | 1.000 | Ea. | 8.000 | 975 | 162 | 1,137 |
| Color | 1.000 | Ea. | 7.822 | 1,425 | 149 | 1,574 |
| 36" x 36" white | 1.000 | Ea. | 8.889 | 1,575 | 169 | 1,744 |
| Color | 1.000 | Ea. | 8.889 | 1,625 | 169 | 1,794 |
| Rough-in, for shower | | | | | | |
| 1/2" copper supply, 4" cast iron waste, 1-1/2" copper vent | 1.000 | Ea. | 3.238 | 100 | 173 | 273 |
| 4" PVC waste, 1-1/2" PVC vent | 1.000 | Ea. | 3.429 | 62 | 184 | 246 |
| 1/2" steel supply, 4" cast iron waste, 1-1/2" steel vent | 1.000 | Ea. | 3.665 | 153 | 197 | 350 |
| 4" PVC waste, 1-1/2" PVC vent | 1.000 | Ea. | 3.881 | 109 | 209 | 318 |
| 1/2" PVC supply, 4" PVC waste, 1-1/2" PVC vent | 1.000 | Ea. | 4.219 | 75.50 | 229 | 304.50 |
| Piping, supply, 1/2" copper | 36.000 | L.F. | 4.148 | 115 | 233 | 348 |
| 1/2" steel | 36.000 | L.F. | 5.333 | 237 | 300 | 537 |
| 1/2" PVC | 36.000 | L.F. | 6.222 | 151 | 350 | 501 |
| Piping, waste, 4" cast iron no hub | 7.000 | L.F. | 2.759 | 146 | 140 | 286 |
| 4" PVC/DWV | 7.000 | L.F. | 3.333 | 67.50 | 169 | 236.50 |
| 4" copper/DWV | 7.000 | L.F. | 4.000 | 460 | 205 | 665 |
| Piping, vent, 2" cast iron no hub | 6.000 | L.F. | 2.149 | 73 | 109 | 182 |
| 2" copper/DWV | 6.000 | L.F. | 1.636 | 124 | 92.50 | 216.50 |
| 2" PVC/DWV | 6.000 | L.F. | 2.441 | 24 | 124 | 148 |
| 2" steel, galvanized | 6.000 | L.F. | 2.250 | 171 | 114 | 285 |
| Vanity base cabinet, 2 door, 24" x 30" | 1.000 | Ea. | 1.000 | 288 | 49 | 337 |
| 24" x 36" | 1.000 | Ea. | 1.200 | 385 | 59 | 444 |
| Vanity top, laminated plastic square edge, 25" x 32" | 2.170 | L.F. | .712 | 80 | 35 | 115 |
| 25" x 38" | 2.670 | L.F. | .845 | 95 | 41.50 | 136.50 |
| Carrier, for lavatory, steel for studs, no arms | 1.000 | Ea. | 1.143 | 78 | 64.50 | 142.50 |
| Wood, 2" x 8" blocking | 1.300 | L.F. | .052 | .79 | 2.55 | 3.34 |

259

**Shower**

**Lavatory**

**Vanity Top**

**Water Closet**

**Vanity Base Cabinet**

| System Description | QUAN. | UNIT | LABOR HOURS | COST EACH | | |
|---|---|---|---|---|---|---|
| | | | | MAT. | INST. | TOTAL |
| **BATHROOM WITH LAVATORY INSTALLED IN VANITY** | | | | | | |
| Water closet, floor mounted, 2 piece, close coupled, white | 1.000 | Ea. | 3.019 | 284 | 153 | 437 |
| Rough-in, vent, 2" diameter DWV piping | 1.000 | Ea. | .955 | 32.40 | 48.40 | 80.80 |
| Waste, 4" diameter DWV piping | 1.000 | Ea. | .828 | 43.65 | 42 | 85.65 |
| Supply, 1/2" diameter type "L" copper supply piping | 1.000 | Ea. | .593 | 16.44 | 33.30 | 49.74 |
| Lavatory, 20" x 18", P.E. cast iron with fittings, white | 1.000 | Ea. | 2.500 | 286 | 127 | 413 |
| Rough-in, waste, 1-1/2" diameter DWV piping | 1.000 | Ea. | 1.803 | 62 | 91.20 | 153.20 |
| Supply, 1/2" diameter type "L" copper supply piping | 1.000 | Ea. | .988 | 27.40 | 55.50 | 82.90 |
| Shower, steel enameled, stone base, corner, white | 1.000 | Ea. | 3.200 | 975 | 162 | 1,137 |
| Mixing valve | 1.000 | Ea. | 1.333 | 156 | 75 | 231 |
| Shower door | 1.000 | Ea. | 1.000 | 259 | 53.50 | 312.50 |
| Rough-in, vent, 1-1/2" diameter DWV piping | 1.000 | Ea. | .225 | 7.75 | 11.40 | 19.15 |
| Waste, 2" diameter DWV piping | 1.000 | Ea. | 1.433 | 48.60 | 72.60 | 121.20 |
| Supply, 1/2" diameter type "L" copper supply piping | 1.000 | Ea. | 1.580 | 43.84 | 88.80 | 132.64 |
| Piping, supply, 1/2" diameter type "L" copper supply piping | 36.000 | L.F. | 3.556 | 98.64 | 199.80 | 298.44 |
| Waste, 4" diameter DWV piping | 7.000 | L.F. | 1.931 | 101.85 | 98 | 199.85 |
| Vent, 2" diameter DWV piping | 6.000 | L.F. | 1.500 | 114 | 75.90 | 189.90 |
| Vanity base, 2 door, 30" wide | 1.000 | Ea. | 1.000 | 288 | 49 | 337 |
| Vanity top, plastic laminated, square edge | 2.670 | L.F. | .712 | 77.43 | 34.84 | 112.27 |
| TOTAL | | Ea. | 28.156 | 2,922 | 1,471.24 | 4,393.24 |
| **BATHROOM, WITH WALL HUNG LAVATORY** | | | | | | |
| Water closet, floor mounted, 2 piece, close coupled, white | 1.000 | Ea. | 3.019 | 284 | 153 | 437 |
| Rough-in, vent, 2" diameter DWV piping | 1.000 | Ea. | .955 | 32.40 | 48.40 | 80.80 |
| Waste, 4" diameter DWV piping | 1.000 | Ea. | .828 | 43.65 | 42 | 85.65 |
| Supply, 1/2" diameter type "L" copper supply piping | 1.000 | Ea. | .593 | 16.44 | 33.30 | 49.74 |
| Lavatory, wall hung, 20" x 18" P.E. cast iron with fittings, white | 1.000 | Ea. | 2.000 | 390 | 101 | 491 |
| Rough-in, waste, 1-1/2" diameter DWV piping | 1.000 | Ea. | 1.803 | 62 | 91.20 | 153.20 |
| Supply, 1/2" diameter type "L" copper supply piping | 1.000 | Ea. | .988 | 27.40 | 55.50 | 82.90 |
| Shower, steel enameled, stone base, corner, white | 1.000 | Ea. | 3.200 | 975 | 162 | 1,137 |
| Mixing valve | 1.000 | Ea. | 1.333 | 156 | 75 | 231 |
| Shower door | 1.000 | Ea. | 1.000 | 259 | 53.50 | 312.50 |
| Rough-in, waste, 1-1/2" diameter DWV piping | 1.000 | Ea. | .225 | 7.75 | 11.40 | 19.15 |
| Waste, 2" diameter DWV piping | 1.000 | Ea. | 1.433 | 48.60 | 72.60 | 121.20 |
| Supply, 1/2" diameter type "L" copper supply piping | 1.000 | Ea. | 1.580 | 43.84 | 88.80 | 132.64 |
| Piping, supply, 1/2" diameter type "L" copper supply piping | 36.000 | L.F. | 3.556 | 98.64 | 199.80 | 298.44 |
| Waste, 4" diameter DWV piping | 7.000 | L.F. | 1.931 | 101.85 | 98 | 199.85 |
| Vent, 2" diameter DWV piping | 6.000 | L.F. | 1.500 | 114 | 75.90 | 189.90 |
| Carrier, steel, for studs, no arms | 1.000 | Ea. | 1.143 | 78 | 64.50 | 142.50 |
| TOTAL | | Ea. | 27.087 | 2,738.57 | 1,425.90 | 4,164.47 |

The costs in this system are on a cost each basis. All necessary piping is included.

| Three Fixture Bathroom Price Sheet | QUAN. | UNIT | LABOR HOURS | COST EACH MAT. | COST EACH INST. | COST EACH TOTAL |
|---|---|---|---|---|---|---|
| Water closet, close coupled, standard 2 piece, white | 1.000 | Ea. | 3.019 | 284 | 153 | 437 |
| Color | 1.000 | Ea. | 3.019 | 380 | 153 | 533 |
| One piece elongated bowl, white | 1.000 | Ea. | 3.019 | 590 | 153 | 743 |
| Color | 1.000 | Ea. | 3.019 | 850 | 153 | 1,003 |
| Low profile one piece elongated bowl, white | 1.000 | Ea. | 3.019 | 1,025 | 153 | 1,178 |
| Color | 1.000 | Ea. | 3.623 | 1,350 | 153 | 1,503 |
| Rough-in, for water closet | | | | | | |
| 1/2" copper supply, 4" cast iron waste, 2" cast iron vent | 1.000 | Ea. | 2.376 | 92.50 | 124 | 216.50 |
| 4" P.V.C./DWV waste, 2" PVC vent | 1.000 | Ea. | 2.678 | 47.50 | 139 | 186.50 |
| 4" copper waste, 2" copper vent | 1.000 | Ea. | 2.520 | 210 | 136 | 346 |
| 3" cast iron waste, 1-1/2" cast iron vent | 1.000 | Ea. | 2.244 | 81 | 117 | 198 |
| 3" PVC waste, 1-1/2" PVC vent | 1.000 | Ea. | 2.388 | 40 | 129 | 169 |
| 3" copper waste, 1-1/2" copper vent | 1.000 | Ea. | 2.014 | 135 | 109 | 244 |
| 1/2" P.V.C. supply, 4" P.V.C. waste, 2" P.V.C. vent | 1.000 | Ea. | 2.974 | 52.50 | 156 | 208.50 |
| 3" P.V.C. waste, 1-1/2" P.V.C. vent | 1.000 | Ea. | 2.684 | 45.50 | 146 | 191.50 |
| 1/2" steel supply, 4" cast iron waste, 2" cast iron vent | 1.000 | Ea. | 2.545 | 110 | 133 | 243 |
| 4" cast iron waste, 2" steel vent | 1.000 | Ea. | 2.590 | 154 | 136 | 290 |
| 4" P.V.C. waste, 2" P.V.C. vent | 1.000 | Ea. | 2.847 | 65 | 149 | 214 |
| Lavatory, wall hung P.E. cast iron 20" x 18", white | 1.000 | Ea. | 2.000 | 390 | 101 | 491 |
| Color | 1.000 | Ea. | 2.000 | 385 | 101 | 486 |
| Vitreous china 19" x 17", white | 1.000 | Ea. | 2.286 | 217 | 116 | 333 |
| Color | 1.000 | Ea. | 2.286 | 241 | 116 | 357 |
| Lavatory, for vanity top P.E. cast iron 20" x 18", white | 1.000 | Ea. | 2.500 | 286 | 127 | 413 |
| Color | 1.000 | Ea. | 2.500 | 286 | 127 | 413 |
| Steel enameled 20" x 17", white | 1.000 | Ea. | 2.759 | 203 | 140 | 343 |
| Color | 1.000 | Ea. | 2.500 | 211 | 127 | 338 |
| Vitreous china 20" x 16", white | 1.000 | Ea. | 2.963 | 305 | 150 | 455 |
| Color | 1.000 | Ea. | 2.963 | 305 | 150 | 455 |
| Rough-in, for lavatory | | | | | | |
| 1/2" copper supply, 1-1/2" cast iron waste, 1-1/2" cast iron vent | 1.000 | Ea. | 2.791 | 89.50 | 147 | 236.50 |
| 1-1/2" P.V.C. waste, 1-1/2" P.V.C. vent | 1.000 | Ea. | 2.639 | 45 | 148 | 193 |
| 1/2" steel supply, 1-1/2" cast iron waste, 1-1/4" steel vent | 1.000 | Ea. | 2.890 | 136 | 154 | 290 |
| 1-1/2" P.V.C. waste, 1-1/4" P.V.C. vent | 1.000 | Ea. | 2.921 | 74 | 164 | 238 |
| 1/2" P.V.C. supply, 1-1/2" P.V.C. waste, 1-1/2" P.V.C. vent | 1.000 | Ea. | 3.260 | 53.50 | 184 | 237.50 |
| Shower, steel enameled stone base, 32" x 32", white | 1.000 | Ea. | 8.000 | 975 | 162 | 1,137 |
| Color | 1.000 | Ea. | 7.822 | 1,425 | 149 | 1,574 |
| 36" x 36", white | 1.000 | Ea. | 8.889 | 1,575 | 169 | 1,744 |
| Color | 1.000 | Ea. | 8.889 | 1,625 | 169 | 1,794 |
| Rough-in, for shower | | | | | | |
| 1/2" copper supply, 2" cast iron waste, 1-1/2" copper vent | 1.000 | Ea. | 3.161 | 103 | 170 | 273 |
| 2" P.V.C. waste, 1-1/2" P.V.C. vent | 1.000 | Ea. | 3.429 | 62 | 184 | 246 |
| 1/2" steel supply, 2" cast iron waste, 1-1/2" steel vent | 1.000 | Ea. | 3.887 | 192 | 209 | 401 |
| 2" P.V.C. waste, 1-1/2" P.V.C. vent | 1.000 | Ea. | 3.881 | 109 | 209 | 318 |
| 1/2" P.V.C. supply, 2" P.V.C. waste, 1-1/2" P.V.C. vent | 1.000 | Ea. | 4.219 | 75.50 | 229 | 304.50 |
| Piping, supply, 1/2" copper | 36.000 | L.F. | 3.556 | 98.50 | 200 | 298.50 |
| 1/2" steel | 36.000 | L.F. | 4.571 | 203 | 257 | 460 |
| 1/2" P.V.C. | 36.000 | L.F. | 5.333 | 130 | 300 | 430 |
| Waste, 4" cast iron, no hub | 7.000 | L.F. | 1.931 | 102 | 98 | 200 |
| 4" P.V.C./DWV | 7.000 | L.F. | 2.333 | 47.50 | 118 | 165.50 |
| 4" copper/DWV | 7.000 | L.F. | 2.800 | 320 | 144 | 464 |
| Vent, 2" cast iron, no hub | 6.000 | L.F. | 1.091 | 83 | 61.50 | 144.50 |
| 2" copper/DWV | 6.000 | L.F. | 1.091 | 83 | 61.50 | 144.50 |
| 2" P.V.C./DWV | 6.000 | L.F. | 1.627 | 15.90 | 82.50 | 98.40 |
| 2" steel, galvanized | 6.000 | L.F. | 1.500 | 114 | 76 | 190 |
| Vanity base cabinet, 2 door, 24" x 30" | 1.000 | Ea. | 1.000 | 288 | 49 | 337 |
| 24" x 36" | 1.000 | Ea. | 1.200 | 385 | 59 | 444 |
| Vanity top, laminated plastic square edge, 25" x 32" | 2.670 | L.F. | .712 | 77.50 | 35 | 112.50 |
| 25" x 38" | 3.170 | L.F. | .845 | 92 | 41.50 | 133.50 |
| Carrier, for lavatory, steel, for studs, no arms | 1.000 | Ea. | 1.143 | 78 | 64.50 | 142.50 |
| Wood, 2" x 8" blocking | 1.300 | L.F. | .052 | .79 | 2.55 | 3.34 |

261

Shower — Bathtub — Lavatory — Vanity Top — Vanity Base — Water Closet

| System Description | QUAN. | UNIT | LABOR HOURS | COST EACH | | |
|---|---|---|---|---|---|---|
| | | | | MAT. | INST. | TOTAL |
| **BATHROOM WITH LAVATORY INSTALLED IN VANITY** | | | | | | |
| Water closet, floor mounted, 2 piece, close coupled, white | 1.000 | Ea. | 3.019 | 284 | 153 | 437 |
| Rough-in, vent, 2″ diameter DWV piping | 1.000 | Ea. | .955 | 32.40 | 48.40 | 80.80 |
| Waste, 4″ diameter DWV piping | 1.000 | Ea. | .828 | 43.65 | 42 | 85.65 |
| Supply, 1/2″ diameter type "L" copper supply piping | 1.000 | Ea. | .593 | 16.44 | 33.30 | 49.74 |
| Lavatory, 20″ x 18″ P.E. cast iron with fittings, white | 1.000 | Ea. | 2.500 | 286 | 127 | 413 |
| Shower, steel, enameled, stone base, corner, white | 1.000 | Ea. | 3.333 | 1,825 | 169 | 1,994 |
| Mixing valve | 1.000 | Ea. | 1.333 | 156 | 75 | 231 |
| Shower door | 1.000 | Ea. | 1.000 | 259 | 53.50 | 312.50 |
| Rough-in, waste, 1-1/2″ diameter DWV piping | 2.000 | Ea. | 4.507 | 155 | 228 | 383 |
| Supply, 1/2″ diameter type "L" copper supply piping | 2.000 | Ea. | 3.161 | 87.68 | 177.60 | 265.28 |
| Bathtub, P.E. cast iron, 5′ long with fittings, white | 1.000 | Ea. | 3.636 | 1,050 | 184 | 1,234 |
| Rough-in, waste, 4″ diameter DWV piping | 1.000 | Ea. | .828 | 43.65 | 42 | 85.65 |
| Supply, 1/2″ diameter type "L" copper supply piping | 1.000 | Ea. | .988 | 27.40 | 55.50 | 82.90 |
| Vent, 1-1/2″ diameter DWV piping | 1.000 | Ea. | .593 | 40.80 | 33.40 | 74.20 |
| Piping, supply, 1/2″ diameter type "L" copper supply piping | 42.000 | L.F. | 4.148 | 115.08 | 233.10 | 348.18 |
| Waste, 4″ diameter DWV piping | 10.000 | L.F. | 2.759 | 145.50 | 140 | 285.50 |
| Vent, 2″ diameter DWV piping | 13.000 | L.F. | 3.250 | 247 | 164.45 | 411.45 |
| Vanity base, 2 doors, 30″ wide | 1.000 | Ea. | 1.000 | 288 | 49 | 337 |
| Vanity top, plastic laminated, square edge | 2.670 | L.F. | .712 | 77.43 | 34.84 | 112.27 |
| TOTAL | | Ea. | 39.143 | 5,180.03 | 2,043.09 | 7,223.12 |
| **BATHROOM WITH WALL HUNG LAVATORY** | | | | | | |
| Water closet, floor mounted, 2 piece, close coupled, white | 1.000 | Ea. | 3.019 | 284 | 153 | 437 |
| Rough-in, vent, 2″ diameter DWV piping | 1.000 | Ea. | .955 | 32.40 | 48.40 | 80.80 |
| Waste, 4″ diameter DWV piping | 1.000 | Ea. | .828 | 43.65 | 42 | 85.65 |
| Supply, 1/2″ diameter type "L" copper supply piping | 1.000 | Ea. | .593 | 16.44 | 33.30 | 49.74 |
| Lavatory, 20″ x 18″ P.E. cast iron with fittings, white | 1.000 | Ea. | 2.000 | 390 | 101 | 491 |
| Shower, steel enameled, stone base, corner , white | 1.000 | Ea. | 3.333 | 1,825 | 169 | 1,994 |
| Mixing valve | 1.000 | Ea. | 1.333 | 156 | 75 | 231 |
| Shower door | 1.000 | Ea. | 1.000 | 259 | 53.50 | 312.50 |
| Rough-in, waste, 1-1/2″ diameter DWV piping | 2.000 | Ea. | 4.507 | 155 | 228 | 383 |
| Supply, 1/2″ diameter type "L" copper supply piping | 2.000 | Ea. | 3.161 | 87.68 | 177.60 | 265.28 |
| Bathtub, P.E. cast iron, 5′ long with fittings, white | 1.000 | Ea. | 3.636 | 1,050 | 184 | 1,234 |
| Rough-in, waste, 4″ diameter DWV piping | 1.000 | Ea. | .828 | 43.65 | 42 | 85.65 |
| Supply, 1/2″ diameter type "L" copper supply piping | 1.000 | Ea. | .988 | 27.40 | 55.50 | 82.90 |
| Vent, 1-1/2″ diameter copper DWV piping | 1.000 | Ea. | .593 | 40.80 | 33.40 | 74.20 |
| Piping, supply, 1/2″ diameter type "L" copper supply piping | 42.000 | L.F. | 4.148 | 115.08 | 233.10 | 348.18 |
| Waste, 4″ diameter DWV piping | 10.000 | L.F. | 2.759 | 145.50 | 140 | 285.50 |
| Vent, 2″ diameter DWV piping | 13.000 | L.F. | 3.250 | 247 | 164.45 | 411.45 |
| Carrier, steel, for studs, no arms | 1.000 | Ea. | 1.143 | 78 | 64.50 | 142.50 |
| TOTAL | | Ea. | 38.074 | 4,996.60 | 1,997.75 | 6,994.35 |

The costs in this system are on a cost each basis. All necessary piping is included.

| Four Fixture Bathroom Price Sheet | QUAN. | UNIT | LABOR HOURS | COST EACH | | |
|---|---|---|---|---|---|---|
| | | | | MAT. | INST. | TOTAL |
| Water closet, close coupled, standard 2 piece, white | 1.000 | Ea. | 3.019 | 284 | 153 | 437 |
| Color | 1.000 | Ea. | 3.019 | 380 | 153 | 533 |
| One piece elongated bowl, white | 1.000 | Ea. | 3.019 | 590 | 153 | 743 |
| Color | 1.000 | Ea. | 3.019 | 850 | 153 | 1,003 |
| Low profile, one piece elongated bowl, white | 1.000 | Ea. | 3.019 | 1,025 | 153 | 1,178 |
| Color | 1.000 | Ea. | 3.019 | 1,350 | 153 | 1,503 |
| 1/2" copper supply, 4" cast iron waste, 2" cast iron vent | 1.000 | Ea. | 2.376 | 92.50 | 124 | 216.50 |
| 4" PVC/DWV waste, 2" PVC vent | 1.000 | Ea. | 2.678 | 47.50 | 139 | 186.50 |
| 4" copper waste, 2" copper vent | 1.000 | Ea. | 2.520 | 210 | 136 | 346 |
| 3" cast iron waste, 1-1/2" cast iron vent | 1.000 | Ea. | 2.244 | 81 | 117 | 198 |
| 3" P.V.C. waste, 1-1/2" P.V.C. vent | 1.000 | Ea. | 2.388 | 40 | 129 | 169 |
| 3" copper waste, 1-1/2" copper vent | 1.000 | Ea. | 2.014 | 135 | 109 | 244 |
| 1/2" P.V.C. supply, 4" P.V.C. waste, 2" P.V.C. vent | 1.000 | Ea. | 2.974 | 52.50 | 156 | 208.50 |
| 3" P.V.C. waste, 1-1/2" P.V.C. vent | 1.000 | Ea. | 2.684 | 45.50 | 146 | 191.50 |
| 1/2" steel supply, 4" cast iron waste, 2" cast iron vent | 1.000 | Ea. | 2.545 | 110 | 133 | 243 |
| 4" cast iron waste, 2" steel vent | 1.000 | Ea. | 2.590 | 154 | 136 | 290 |
| 4" PVC waste, 2" P.V.C. vent | 1.000 | Ea. | 2.847 | 65 | 149 | 214 |
| Lavatory, wall hung P.E. cast iron 20" x 18", white | 1.000 | Ea. | 2.000 | 390 | 101 | 491 |
| Color | 1.000 | Ea. | 2.000 | 385 | 101 | 486 |
| Vitreous china 19" x 17", white | 1.000 | Ea. | 2.286 | 217 | 116 | 333 |
| Color | 1.000 | Ea. | 2.286 | 241 | 116 | 357 |
| Lavatory for vanity top, P.E. cast iron 20" x 18", white | 1.000 | Ea. | 2.500 | 286 | 127 | 413 |
| Color | 1.000 | Ea. | 2.500 | 286 | 127 | 413 |
| Steel enameled, 20" x 17", white | 1.000 | Ea. | 2.759 | 203 | 140 | 343 |
| Color | 1.000 | Ea. | 2.500 | 211 | 127 | 338 |
| Vitreous china 20" x 16", white | 1.000 | Ea. | 2.963 | 305 | 150 | 455 |
| Color | 1.000 | Ea. | 2.963 | 305 | 150 | 455 |
| Shower, steel enameled stone base, 36" square, white | 1.000 | Ea. | 8.889 | 1,825 | 169 | 1,994 |
| Color | 1.000 | Ea. | 8.889 | 1,900 | 169 | 2,069 |
| Rough-in, for lavatory or shower | | | | | | |
| 1/2" copper supply, 1-1/2" cast iron waste, 1-1/2" cast iron vent | 1.000 | Ea. | 3.834 | 121 | 203 | 324 |
| 1-1/2" PVC waste, 1-1/4" P.V.C. vent | 1.000 | Ea. | 3.675 | 66 | 207 | 273 |
| 1/2" steel supply, 1-1/4" cast iron waste, 1-1/4" steel vent | 1.000 | Ea. | 4.103 | 185 | 219 | 404 |
| 1-1/4" PVC waste, 1-1/4" P.V.C. vent | 1.000 | Ea. | 3.937 | 112 | 221 | 333 |
| 1/2" P.V.C. supply, 1-1/2" P.V.C. waste, 1-1/2" P.V.C. vent | 1.000 | Ea. | 4.592 | 79.50 | 259 | 338.50 |
| Bathtub, P.E. cast iron, 5' long with fittings, white | 1.000 | Ea. | 3.636 | 1,050 | 184 | 1,234 |
| Color | 1.000 | Ea. | 3.636 | 1,300 | 184 | 1,484 |
| Steel, enameled 5' long with fittings, white | 1.000 | Ea. | 2.909 | 460 | 147 | 607 |
| Color | 1.000 | Ea. | 2.909 | 460 | 147 | 607 |
| Rough-in, for bathtub | | | | | | |
| 1/2" copper supply, 4" cast iron waste, 1-1/2" copper vent | 1.000 | Ea. | 2.409 | 112 | 131 | 243 |
| 4" P.V.C. waste, 1-1/2" P.V.C. vent | 1.000 | Ea. | 2.877 | 56.50 | 156 | 212.50 |
| 1/2" steel supply, 4" cast iron waste, 1-1/2" steel vent | 1.000 | Ea. | 2.898 | 157 | 154 | 311 |
| 4" P.V.C. waste, 1-1/2" P.V.C. vent | 1.000 | Ea. | 3.159 | 85.50 | 172 | 257.50 |
| 1/2" P.V.C. supply, 4" P.V.C. waste, 1-1/2" P.V.C. vent | 1.000 | Ea. | 3.371 | 65 | 184 | 249 |
| Piping, supply, 1/2" copper | 42.000 | L.F. | 4.148 | 115 | 233 | 348 |
| 1/2" steel | 42.000 | L.F. | 5.333 | 237 | 300 | 537 |
| 1/2" P.V.C. | 42.000 | L.F. | 6.222 | 151 | 350 | 501 |
| Waste, 4" cast iron, no hub | 10.000 | L.F. | 2.759 | 146 | 140 | 286 |
| 4" P.V.C./DWV | 10.000 | L.F. | 3.333 | 67.50 | 169 | 236.50 |
| 4" copper/DWV | 10.000 | Ea. | 4.000 | 460 | 205 | 665 |
| Vent 2" cast iron, no hub | 13.000 | L.F. | 3.105 | 105 | 157 | 262 |
| 2" copper/DWV | 13.000 | L.F. | 2.364 | 179 | 133 | 312 |
| 2" P.V.C./DWV | 13.000 | L.F. | 3.525 | 34.50 | 179 | 213.50 |
| 2" steel, galvanized | 13.000 | L.F. | 3.250 | 247 | 164 | 411 |
| Vanity base cabinet, 2 doors, 30" wide | 1.000 | Ea. | 1.000 | 288 | 49 | 337 |
| Vanity top, plastic laminated, square edge | 2.670 | L.F. | .712 | 77.50 | 35 | 112.50 |
| Carrier, steel for studs, no arms | 1.000 | Ea. | 1.143 | 78 | 64.50 | 142.50 |
| Wood, 2" x 8" blocking | 1.300 | L.F. | .052 | .79 | 2.55 | 3.34 |

| System Description | QUAN. | UNIT | LABOR HOURS | COST EACH | | |
|---|---|---|---|---|---|---|
| | | | | MAT. | INST. | TOTAL |
| **BATHROOM WITH LAVATORY INSTALLED IN VANITY** | | | | | | |
| Water closet, floor mounted, 2 piece, close coupled, white | 1.000 | Ea. | 3.019 | 284 | 153 | 437 |
| Rough-in, vent, 2" diameter DWV piping | 1.000 | Ea. | .955 | 32.40 | 48.40 | 80.80 |
| Waste, 4" diameter DWV piping | 1.000 | Ea. | .828 | 43.65 | 42 | 85.65 |
| Supply, 1/2" diameter type "L" copper supply piping | 1.000 | Ea. | .593 | 16.44 | 33.30 | 49.74 |
| Lavatory, 20" x 18" P.E. cast iron with fittings, white | 1.000 | Ea. | 2.500 | 286 | 127 | 413 |
| Shower, steel, enameled, stone base, corner, white | 1.000 | Ea. | 3.333 | 1,825 | 169 | 1,994 |
| Mixing valve | 1.000 | Ea. | 1.333 | 156 | 75 | 231 |
| Shower door | 1.000 | Ea. | 1.000 | 259 | 53.50 | 312.50 |
| Rough-in, waste, 1-1/2" diameter DWV piping | 2.000 | Ea. | 4.507 | 155 | 228 | 383 |
| Supply, 1/2" diameter type "L" copper supply piping | 2.000 | Ea. | 3.161 | 87.68 | 177.60 | 265.28 |
| Bathtub, P.E. cast iron, 5' long with fittings, white | 1.000 | Ea. | 3.636 | 1,050 | 184 | 1,234 |
| Rough-in, waste, 4" diameter DWV piping | 1.000 | Ea. | .828 | 43.65 | 42 | 85.65 |
| Supply, 1/2" diameter type "L" copper supply piping | 1.000 | Ea. | .988 | 27.40 | 55.50 | 82.90 |
| Vent, 1-1/2" diameter DWV piping | 1.000 | Ea. | .593 | 40.80 | 33.40 | 74.20 |
| Piping, supply, 1/2" diameter type "L" copper supply piping | 42.000 | L.F. | 4.939 | 137 | 277.50 | 414.50 |
| Waste, 4" diameter DWV piping | 10.000 | L.F. | 4.138 | 218.25 | 210 | 428.25 |
| Vent, 2" diameter DWV piping | 13.000 | L.F. | 4.500 | 342 | 227.70 | 569.70 |
| Vanity base, 2 doors, 30" wide | 1.000 | Ea. | 1.000 | 288 | 49 | 337 |
| Vanity top, plastic laminated, square edge | 2.670 | L.F. | .712 | 80.10 | 34.84 | 114.94 |
| TOTAL | | Ea. | 42.563 | 5,372.37 | 2,220.74 | 7,593.11 |
| **BATHROOM WITH WALL HUNG LAVATORY** | | | | | | |
| Water closet, floor mounted, 2 piece, close coupled, white | 1.000 | Ea. | 3.019 | 284 | 153 | 437 |
| Rough-in, vent, 2" diameter DWV piping | 1.000 | Ea. | .955 | 32.40 | 48.40 | 80.80 |
| Waste, 4" diameter DWV piping | 1.000 | Ea. | .828 | 43.65 | 42 | 85.65 |
| Supply, 1/2" diameter type "L" copper supply piping | 1.000 | Ea. | .593 | 16.44 | 33.30 | 49.74 |
| Lavatory, 20" x 18" P.E. cast iron with fittings, white | 1.000 | Ea. | 2.000 | 390 | 101 | 491 |
| Shower, steel enameled, stone base, corner, white | 1.000 | Ea. | 3.333 | 1,825 | 169 | 1,994 |
| Mixing valve | 1.000 | Ea. | 1.333 | 156 | 75 | 231 |
| Shower door | 1.000 | Ea. | 1.000 | 259 | 53.50 | 312.50 |
| Rough-in, waste, 1-1/2" diameter DWV piping | 2.000 | Ea. | 4.507 | 155 | 228 | 383 |
| Supply, 1/2" diameter type "L" copper supply piping | 2.000 | Ea. | 3.161 | 87.68 | 177.60 | 265.28 |
| Bathtub, P.E. cast iron, 5" long with fittings, white | 1.000 | Ea. | 3.636 | 1,050 | 184 | 1,234 |
| Rough-in, waste, 4" diameter DWV piping | 1.000 | Ea. | .828 | 43.65 | 42 | 85.65 |
| Supply, 1/2" diameter type "L" copper supply piping | 1.000 | Ea. | .988 | 27.40 | 55.50 | 82.90 |
| Vent, 1-1/2" diameter DWV piping | 1.000 | Ea. | .593 | 40.80 | 33.40 | 74.20 |
| Piping, supply, 1/2" diameter type "L" copper supply piping | 42.000 | L.F. | 4.939 | 137 | 277.50 | 414.50 |
| Waste, 4" diameter DWV piping | 10.000 | L.F. | 4.138 | 218.25 | 210 | 428.25 |
| Vent, 2" diameter DWV piping | 13.000 | L.F. | 4.500 | 342 | 227.70 | 569.70 |
| Carrier, steel for studs, no arms | 1.000 | Ea. | 1.143 | 78 | 64.50 | 142.50 |
| TOTAL | | Ea. | 41.494 | 5,186.27 | 2,175.40 | 7,361.67 |

The costs in this system are on a cost each basis. All necessary piping is included.

| Four Fixture Bathroom Price Sheet | QUAN. | UNIT | LABOR HOURS | COST EACH | | |
|---|---|---|---|---|---|---|
| | | | | MAT. | INST. | TOTAL |
| Water closet, close coupled, standard 2 piece, white | 1.000 | Ea. | 3.019 | 284 | 153 | 437 |
| Color | 1.000 | Ea. | 3.019 | 380 | 153 | 533 |
| One piece, elongated bowl, white | 1.000 | Ea. | 3.019 | 590 | 153 | 743 |
| Color | 1.000 | Ea. | 3.019 | 850 | 153 | 1,003 |
| Low profile, one piece elongated bowl, white | 1.000 | Ea. | 3.019 | 1,025 | 153 | 1,178 |
| Color | 1.000 | Ea. | 3.019 | 1,350 | 153 | 1,503 |
| Rough-in, for water closet | | | | | | |
| 1/2" copper supply, 4" cast iron waste, 2" cast iron vent | 1.000 | Ea. | 2.376 | 92.50 | 124 | 216.50 |
| 4" PVC/DWV waste, 2" PVC vent | 1.000 | Ea. | 2.678 | 47.50 | 139 | 186.50 |
| 4" copper waste, 2" copper vent | 1.000 | Ea. | 2.520 | 210 | 136 | 346 |
| 3" cast iron waste, 1-1/2" cast iron vent | 1.000 | Ea. | 2.244 | 81 | 117 | 198 |
| 3" PVC waste, 1-1/2" PVC vent | 1.000 | Ea. | 2.388 | 40 | 129 | 169 |
| 3" PVC waste, 1-1/2" PVC vent | 1.000 | Ea. | 2.014 | 135 | 109 | 244 |
| 1/2" PVC supply, 4" PVC waste, 2" PVC vent | 1.000 | Ea. | 2.974 | 52.50 | 156 | 208.50 |
| 3" PVC waste, 1-1/2" PVC vent | 1.000 | Ea. | 2.684 | 45.50 | 146 | 191.50 |
| 1/2" steel supply, 4" cast iron waste, 2" cast iron vent | 1.000 | Ea. | 2.545 | 110 | 133 | 243 |
| 4" cast iron waste, 2" steel vent | 1.000 | Ea. | 2.590 | 154 | 136 | 290 |
| 4" PVC waste, 2" PVC vent | 1.000 | Ea. | 2.847 | 65 | 149 | 214 |
| Lavatory wall hung, P.E. cast iron 20" x 18", white | 1.000 | Ea. | 2.000 | 390 | 101 | 491 |
| Color | 1.000 | Ea. | 2.000 | 385 | 101 | 486 |
| Vitreous china 19" x 17", white | 1.000 | Ea. | 2.286 | 217 | 116 | 333 |
| Color | 1.000 | Ea. | 2.286 | 241 | 116 | 357 |
| Lavatory for vanity top, P.E. cast iron, 20" x 18", white | 1.000 | Ea. | 2.500 | 286 | 127 | 413 |
| Color | 1.000 | Ea. | 2.500 | 286 | 127 | 413 |
| Steel, enameled 20" x 17", white | 1.000 | Ea. | 2.759 | 203 | 140 | 343 |
| Color | 1.000 | Ea. | 2.500 | 211 | 127 | 338 |
| Vitreous china 20" x 16", white | 1.000 | Ea. | 2.963 | 305 | 150 | 455 |
| Color | 1.000 | Ea. | 2.963 | 305 | 150 | 455 |
| Shower, steel enameled, stone base 36" square, white | 1.000 | Ea. | 8.889 | 1,825 | 169 | 1,994 |
| Color | 1.000 | Ea. | 8.889 | 1,900 | 169 | 2,069 |
| Rough-in, for lavatory and shower | | | | | | |
| 1/2" copper supply, 1-1/2" cast iron waste, 1-1/2" cast iron vent | 1.000 | Ea. | 7.668 | 243 | 405 | 648 |
| 1-1/2" PVC waste, 1-1/4" PVC vent | 1.000 | Ea. | 7.352 | 132 | 415 | 547 |
| 1/2" steel supply, 1-1/4" cast iron waste, 1-1/4" steel vent | 1.000 | Ea. | 8.205 | 370 | 440 | 810 |
| 1-1/4" PVC waste, 1-1/4" PVC vent | 1.000 | Ea. | 7.873 | 225 | 445 | 670 |
| 1/2" PVC supply, 1-1/2" PVC waste, 1-1/2" PVC vent | 1.000 | Ea. | 9.185 | 159 | 515 | 674 |
| Bathtub, P.E. cast iron, 5' long with fittings, white | 1.000 | Ea. | 3.636 | 1,050 | 184 | 1,234 |
| Color | 1.000 | Ea. | 3.636 | 1,300 | 184 | 1,484 |
| Steel enameled, 5' long with fittings, white | 1.000 | Ea. | 2.909 | 460 | 147 | 607 |
| Color | 1.000 | Ea. | 2.909 | 460 | 147 | 607 |
| Rough-in, for bathtub | | | | | | |
| 1/2" copper supply, 4" cast iron waste, 1-1/2" copper vent | 1.000 | Ea. | 2.409 | 112 | 131 | 243 |
| 4" PVC waste, 1-1/2" PVC vent | 1.000 | Ea. | 2.877 | 56.50 | 156 | 212.50 |
| 1/2" steel supply, 4" cast iron waste, 1-1/2" steel vent | 1.000 | Ea. | 2.898 | 157 | 154 | 311 |
| 4" PVC waste, 1-1/2" PVC vent | 1.000 | Ea. | 3.159 | 85.50 | 172 | 257.50 |
| 1/2" PVC supply, 4" PVC waste, 1-1/2" PVC vent | 1.000 | Ea. | 3.371 | 65 | 184 | 249 |
| Piping supply, 1/2" copper | 42.000 | L.F. | 4.148 | 115 | 233 | 348 |
| 1/2" steel | 42.000 | L.F. | 5.333 | 237 | 300 | 537 |
| 1/2" PVC | 42.000 | L.F. | 6.222 | 151 | 350 | 501 |
| Piping, waste, 4" cast iron, no hub | 10.000 | L.F. | 3.586 | 189 | 182 | 371 |
| 4" PVC/DWV | 10.000 | L.F. | 4.333 | 88 | 220 | 308 |
| 4" copper/DWV | 10.000 | L.F. | 5.200 | 600 | 267 | 867 |
| Piping, vent, 2" cast iron, no hub | 13.000 | L.F. | 3.105 | 105 | 157 | 262 |
| 2" copper/DWV | 13.000 | L.F. | 2.364 | 179 | 133 | 312 |
| 2" PVC/DWV | 13.000 | L.F. | 3.525 | 34.50 | 179 | 213.50 |
| 2" steel, galvanized | 13.000 | L.F. | 3.250 | 247 | 164 | 411 |
| Vanity base cabinet, 2 doors, 30" wide | 1.000 | Ea. | 1.000 | 288 | 49 | 337 |
| Vanity top, plastic laminated, square edge | 3.160 | L.F. | .843 | 91.50 | 41 | 132.50 |
| Carrier, steel, for studs, no arms | 1.000 | Ea. | 1.143 | 78 | 64.50 | 142.50 |
| Wood, 2" x 8" blocking | 1.300 | L.F. | .052 | .79 | 2.55 | 3.34 |

Shower — Vanity Top — Water Closet — Bathtub — Cabinet

| System Description | QUAN. | UNIT | LABOR HOURS | COST EACH MAT. | COST EACH INST. | COST EACH TOTAL |
|---|---|---|---|---|---|---|
| **BATHROOM WITH SHOWER, BATHTUB, LAVATORIES IN VANITY** | | | | | | |
| Water closet, floor mounted, 1 piece, white | 1.000 | Ea. | 3.019 | 1,025 | 153 | 1,178 |
| Rough-in, vent, 2" diameter DWV piping | 1.000 | Ea. | .955 | 32.40 | 48.40 | 80.80 |
| Waste, 4" diameter DWV piping | 1.000 | Ea. | .828 | 43.65 | 42 | 85.65 |
| Supply, 1/2" diameter type "L" copper supply piping | 1.000 | Ea. | .593 | 16.44 | 33.30 | 49.74 |
| Lavatory, 20" x 16", vitreous china oval, with fittings, white | 2.000 | Ea. | 5.926 | 610 | 300 | 910 |
| Shower, steel enameled, stone base, corner, white | 1.000 | Ea. | 3.333 | 1,825 | 169 | 1,994 |
| Mixing valve | 1.000 | Ea. | 1.333 | 156 | 75 | 231 |
| Shower door | 1.000 | Ea. | 1.000 | 259 | 53.50 | 312.50 |
| Rough-in, waste, 1-1/2" diameter DWV piping | 3.000 | Ea. | 5.408 | 186 | 273.60 | 459.60 |
| Supply, 1/2" diameter type "L" copper supply piping | 3.000 | Ea. | 2.963 | 82.20 | 166.50 | 248.70 |
| Bathtub, P.E. cast iron, 5' long with fittings, white | 1.000 | Ea. | 3.636 | 1,050 | 184 | 1,234 |
| Rough-in, waste, 4" diameter DWV piping | 1.000 | Ea. | 1.103 | 58.20 | 56 | 114.20 |
| Supply, 1/2" diameter type "L" copper supply piping | 1.000 | Ea. | .988 | 27.40 | 55.50 | 82.90 |
| Vent, 1-1/2" diameter copper DWV piping | 1.000 | Ea. | .593 | 40.80 | 33.40 | 74.20 |
| Piping, supply, 1/2" diameter type "L" copper supply piping | 42.000 | L.F. | 4.148 | 115.08 | 233.10 | 348.18 |
| Waste, 4" diameter DWV piping | 10.000 | L.F. | 2.759 | 145.50 | 140 | 285.50 |
| Vent, 2" diameter DWV piping | 13.000 | L.F. | 3.250 | 247 | 164.45 | 411.45 |
| Vanity base, 2 door, 24" x 48" | 1.000 | Ea. | 1.400 | 460 | 68.50 | 528.50 |
| Vanity top, plastic laminated, square edge | 4.170 | L.F. | 1.112 | 120.93 | 54.42 | 175.35 |
| TOTAL | | Ea. | 44.347 | 6,500.60 | 2,303.67 | 8,804.27 |

The costs in this system are on a cost each basis. All necessary piping is included.

| Description | QUAN. | UNIT | LABOR HOURS | COST EACH MAT. | COST EACH INST. | COST EACH TOTAL |
|---|---|---|---|---|---|---|
| | | | | | | |
| | | | | | | |

| Five Fixture Bathroom Price Sheet | QUAN. | UNIT | LABOR HOURS | COST EACH | | |
|---|---|---|---|---|---|---|
| | | | | MAT. | INST. | TOTAL |
| Water closet, close coupled, standard 2 piece, white | 1.000 | Ea. | 3.019 | 284 | 153 | 437 |
| Color | 1.000 | Ea. | 3.019 | 380 | 153 | 533 |
| One piece elongated bowl, white | 1.000 | Ea. | 3.019 | 590 | 153 | 743 |
| Color | 1.000 | Ea. | 3.019 | 850 | 153 | 1,003 |
| Low profile, one piece elongated bowl, white | 1.000 | Ea. | 3.019 | 1,025 | 153 | 1,178 |
| Color | 1.000 | Ea. | 3.019 | 1,350 | 153 | 1,503 |
| Rough-in, supply, waste and vent for water closet | | | | | | |
| 1/2" copper supply, 4" cast iron waste, 2" cast iron vent | 1.000 | Ea. | 2.376 | 92.50 | 124 | 216.50 |
| 4" P.V.C./DWV waste, 2" P.V.C. vent | 1.000 | Ea. | 2.678 | 47.50 | 139 | 186.50 |
| 4" copper waste, 2" copper vent | 1.000 | Ea. | 2.520 | 210 | 136 | 346 |
| 3" cast iron waste, 1-1/2" cast iron vent | 1.000 | Ea. | 2.244 | 81 | 117 | 198 |
| 3" P.V.C. waste, 1-1/2" P.V.C. vent | 1.000 | Ea. | 2.388 | 40 | 129 | 169 |
| 3" copper waste, 1-1/2" copper vent | 1.000 | Ea. | 2.014 | 135 | 109 | 244 |
| 1/2" P.V.C. supply, 4" P.V.C. waste, 2" P.V.C. vent | 1.000 | Ea. | 2.974 | 52.50 | 156 | 208.50 |
| 3" P.V.C. waste, 1-1/2" P.V.C. supply | 1.000 | Ea. | 2.684 | 45.50 | 146 | 191.50 |
| 1/2" steel supply, 4" cast iron waste, 2" cast iron vent | 1.000 | Ea. | 2.545 | 110 | 133 | 243 |
| 4" cast iron waste, 2" steel vent | 1.000 | Ea. | 2.590 | 154 | 136 | 290 |
| 4" P.V.C. waste, 2" P.V.C. vent | 1.000 | Ea. | 2.847 | 65 | 149 | 214 |
| Lavatory, wall hung, P.E. cast iron 20" x 18", white | 2.000 | Ea. | 4.000 | 780 | 202 | 982 |
| Color | 2.000 | Ea. | 4.000 | 770 | 202 | 972 |
| Vitreous china, 19" x 17", white | 2.000 | Ea. | 4.571 | 435 | 232 | 667 |
| Color | 2.000 | Ea. | 4.571 | 480 | 232 | 712 |
| Lavatory, for vanity top, P.E. cast iron, 20" x 18", white | 2.000 | Ea. | 5.000 | 570 | 254 | 824 |
| Color | 2.000 | Ea. | 5.000 | 570 | 254 | 824 |
| Steel enameled 20" x 17", white | 2.000 | Ea. | 5.517 | 405 | 280 | 685 |
| Color | 2.000 | Ea. | 5.000 | 420 | 254 | 674 |
| Vitreous china 20" x 16", white | 2.000 | Ea. | 5.926 | 610 | 300 | 910 |
| Color | 2.000 | Ea. | 5.926 | 610 | 300 | 910 |
| Shower, steel enameled, stone base 36" square, white | 1.000 | Ea. | 8.889 | 1,825 | 169 | 1,994 |
| Color | 1.000 | Ea. | 8.889 | 1,900 | 169 | 2,069 |
| Rough-in, for lavatory or shower | | | | | | |
| 1/2" copper supply, 1-1/2" cast iron waste, 1-1/2" cast iron vent | 3.000 | Ea. | 8.371 | 268 | 440 | 708 |
| 1-1/2" P.V.C. waste, 1-1/4" P.V.C. vent | 3.000 | Ea. | 7.916 | 135 | 445 | 580 |
| 1/2" steel supply, 1-1/4" cast iron waste, 1-1/4" steel vent | 3.000 | Ea. | 8.670 | 405 | 460 | 865 |
| 1-1/4" P.V.C. waste, 1-1/4" P.V.C. vent | 3.000 | Ea. | 8.381 | 222 | 470 | 692 |
| 1/2" P.V.C. supply, 1-1/2" P.V.C. waste, 1-1/2" P.V.C. vent | 3.000 | Ea. | 9.778 | 161 | 550 | 711 |
| Bathtub, P.E. cast iron 5' long with fittings, white | 1.000 | Ea. | 3.636 | 1,050 | 184 | 1,234 |
| Color | 1.000 | Ea. | 3.636 | 1,300 | 184 | 1,484 |
| Steel, enameled 5' long with fittings, white | 1.000 | Ea. | 2.909 | 460 | 147 | 607 |
| Color | 1.000 | Ea. | 2.909 | 460 | 147 | 607 |
| Rough-in, for bathtub | | | | | | |
| 1/2" copper supply, 4" cast iron waste, 1-1/2" copper vent | 1.000 | Ea. | 2.684 | 126 | 145 | 271 |
| 4" P.V.C. waste, 1-1/2" P.V.C. vent | 1.000 | Ea. | 3.210 | 63 | 173 | 236 |
| 1/2" steel supply, 4" cast iron waste, 1-1/2" steel vent | 1.000 | Ea. | 3.173 | 172 | 168 | 340 |
| 4" P.V.C. waste, 1-1/2" P.V.C. vent | 1.000 | Ea. | 3.492 | 92.50 | 189 | 281.50 |
| 1/2" P.V.C. supply, 4" P.V.C. waste, 1-1/2" P.V.C. vent | 1.000 | Ea. | 3.704 | 72 | 201 | 273 |
| Piping, supply, 1/2" copper | 42.000 | L.F. | 4.148 | 115 | 233 | 348 |
| 1/2" steel | 42.000 | L.F. | 5.333 | 237 | 300 | 537 |
| 1/2" P.V.C. | 42.000 | L.F. | 6.222 | 151 | 350 | 501 |
| Piping, waste, 4" cast iron, no hub | 10.000 | L.F. | 2.759 | 146 | 140 | 286 |
| 4" P.V.C./DWV | 10.000 | L.F. | 3.333 | 67.50 | 169 | 236.50 |
| 4" copper/DWV | 10.000 | L.F. | 4.000 | 460 | 205 | 665 |
| Piping, vent, 2" cast iron, no hub | 13.000 | L.F. | 3.105 | 105 | 157 | 262 |
| 2" copper/DWV | 13.000 | L.F. | 2.364 | 179 | 133 | 312 |
| 2" P.V.C./DWV | 13.000 | L.F. | 3.525 | 34.50 | 179 | 213.50 |
| 2" steel, galvanized | 13.000 | L.F. | 3.250 | 247 | 164 | 411 |
| Vanity base cabinet, 2 doors, 24" x 48" | 1.000 | Ea. | 1.400 | 460 | 68.50 | 528.50 |
| Vanity top, plastic laminated, square edge | 4.170 | L.F. | 1.112 | 121 | 54.50 | 175.50 |
| Carrier, steel, for studs, no arms | 1.000 | Ea. | 1.143 | 78 | 64.50 | 142.50 |
| Wood, 2" x 8" blocking | 1.300 | L.F. | .052 | .79 | 2.55 | 3.34 |

| System Description | QUAN. | UNIT | LABOR HOURS | COST PER SYSTEM | | |
|---|---|---|---|---|---|---|
| | | | | MAT. | INST. | TOTAL |
| **HEATING ONLY, GAS FIRED HOT AIR, ONE ZONE, 1200 S.F. BUILDING** | | | | | | |
| Furnace, gas, up flow | 1.000 | Ea. | 5.000 | 765 | 241 | 1,006 |
| Intermittent pilot | 1.000 | Ea. | | 165 | | 165 |
| Supply duct, rigid fiberglass | 176.000 | S.F. | 12.068 | 149.60 | 603.68 | 753.28 |
| Return duct, sheet metal, galvanized | 158.000 | Lb. | 16.137 | 82.16 | 805.80 | 887.96 |
| Lateral ducts, 6″ flexible fiberglass | 144.000 | L.F. | 8.862 | 377.28 | 427.68 | 804.96 |
| Register, elbows | 12.000 | Ea. | 3.200 | 354 | 154.20 | 508.20 |
| Floor registers, enameled steel | 12.000 | Ea. | 3.000 | 342 | 160.80 | 502.80 |
| Floor grille, return air | 2.000 | Ea. | .727 | 52 | 39 | 91 |
| Thermostat | 1.000 | Ea. | 1.000 | 48 | 53.50 | 101.50 |
| Plenum | 1.000 | Ea. | 1.000 | 88 | 48 | 136 |
| TOTAL | | System | 50.994 | 2,423.04 | 2,533.66 | 4,956.70 |
| **HEATING/COOLING, GAS FIRED FORCED AIR, ONE ZONE, 1200 S.F. BUILDING** | | | | | | |
| Furnace, including plenum, compressor, coil | 1.000 | Ea. | 14.720 | 5,037 | 708.40 | 5,745.40 |
| Intermittent pilot | 1.000 | Ea. | | 165 | | 165 |
| Supply duct, rigid fiberglass | 176.000 | S.F. | 12.068 | 149.60 | 603.68 | 753.28 |
| Return duct, sheet metal, galvanized | 158.000 | Lb. | 16.137 | 82.16 | 805.80 | 887.96 |
| Lateral duct, 6″ flexible fiberglass | 144.000 | L.F. | 8.862 | 377.28 | 427.68 | 804.96 |
| Register elbows | 12.000 | Ea. | 3.200 | 354 | 154.20 | 508.20 |
| Floor registers, enameled steel | 12.000 | Ea. | 3.000 | 342 | 160.80 | 502.80 |
| Floor grille return air | 2.000 | Ea. | .727 | 52 | 39 | 91 |
| Thermostat | 1.000 | Ea. | 1.000 | 48 | 53.50 | 101.50 |
| Refrigeration piping, 25 ft. (pre-charged) | 1.000 | Ea. | | 259 | | 259 |
| TOTAL | | System | 59.714 | 6,866.04 | 2,953.06 | 9,819.10 |

The costs in these systems are based on complete system basis. For larger buildings use the price sheet on the opposite page.

| Description | QUAN. | UNIT | LABOR HOURS | COST PER SYSTEM | | |
|---|---|---|---|---|---|---|
| | | | | MAT. | INST. | TOTAL |
| | | | | | | |
| | | | | | | |
| | | | | | | |
| | | | | | | |
| | | | | | | |

| Gas Heating/Cooling Price Sheet | QUAN. | UNIT | LABOR HOURS | COST EACH MAT. | COST EACH INST. | COST EACH TOTAL |
|---|---|---|---|---|---|---|
| Furnace, heating only, 100 MBH, area to 1200 S.F. | 1.000 | Ea. | 5.000 | 765 | 241 | 1,006 |
| 120 MBH, area to 1500 S.F. | 1.000 | Ea. | 5.000 | 765 | 241 | 1,006 |
| 160 MBH, area to 2000 S.F. | 1.000 | Ea. | 5.714 | 775 | 276 | 1,051 |
| 200 MBH, area to 2400 S.F. | 1.000 | Ea. | 6.154 | 2,650 | 297 | 2,947 |
| Heating/cooling, 100 MBH heat, 36 MBH cool, to 1200 S.F. | 1.000 | Ea. | 16.000 | 5,475 | 770 | 6,245 |
| 120 MBH heat, 42 MBH cool, to 1500 S.F. | 1.000 | Ea. | 18.462 | 5,850 | 925 | 6,775 |
| 144 MBH heat, 47 MBH cool, to 2000 S.F. | 1.000 | Ea. | 20.000 | 6,750 | 1,000 | 7,750 |
| 200 MBH heat, 60 MBH cool, to 2400 S.F. | 1.000 | Ea. | 34.286 | 7,100 | 1,725 | 8,825 |
| Intermittent pilot, 100 MBH furnace | 1.000 | Ea. | | 165 | | 165 |
| 200 MBH furnace | 1.000 | Ea. | | 165 | | 165 |
| Supply duct, rectangular, area to 1200 S.F., rigid fiberglass | 176.000 | S.F. | 12.068 | 150 | 605 | 755 |
| Sheet metal insulated | 228.000 | Lb. | 31.331 | 251 | 1,525 | 1,776 |
| Area to 1500 S.F., rigid fiberglass | 176.000 | S.F. | 12.068 | 150 | 605 | 755 |
| Sheet metal insulated | 228.000 | Lb. | 31.331 | 251 | 1,525 | 1,776 |
| Area to 2400 S.F., rigid fiberglass | 205.000 | S.F. | 14.057 | 174 | 705 | 879 |
| Sheet metal insulated | 271.000 | Lb. | 37.048 | 295 | 1,800 | 2,095 |
| Round flexible, insulated 6" diameter, to 1200 S.F. | 156.000 | L.F. | 9.600 | 410 | 465 | 875 |
| To 1500 S.F. | 184.000 | L.F. | 11.323 | 480 | 545 | 1,025 |
| 8" diameter, to 2000 S.F. | 269.000 | L.F. | 23.911 | 890 | 1,150 | 2,040 |
| To 2400 S.F. | 248.000 | L.F. | 22.045 | 820 | 1,075 | 1,895 |
| Return duct, sheet metal galvanized, to 1500 S.F. | 158.000 | Lb. | 16.137 | 82 | 805 | 887 |
| To 2400 S.F. | 191.000 | Lb. | 19.507 | 99.50 | 975 | 1,074.50 |
| Lateral ducts, flexible round 6" insulated, to 1200 S.F. | 144.000 | L.F. | 8.862 | 375 | 430 | 805 |
| To 1500 S.F. | 172.000 | L.F. | 10.585 | 450 | 510 | 960 |
| To 2000 S.F. | 261.000 | L.F. | 16.062 | 685 | 775 | 1,460 |
| To 2400 S.F. | 300.000 | L.F. | 18.462 | 785 | 890 | 1,675 |
| Spiral steel insulated, to 1200 S.F. | 144.000 | L.F. | 20.067 | 450 | 940 | 1,390 |
| To 1500 S.F. | 172.000 | L.F. | 23.952 | 535 | 1,125 | 1,660 |
| To 2000 S.F. | 261.000 | L.F. | 36.352 | 815 | 1,700 | 2,515 |
| To 2400 S.F. | 300.000 | L.F. | 41.825 | 935 | 1,950 | 2,885 |
| Rectangular sheet metal galvanized insulated, to 1200 S.F. | 228.000 | Lb. | 39.056 | 375 | 1,875 | 2,250 |
| To 1500 S.F. | 344.000 | Lb. | 53.966 | 490 | 2,625 | 3,115 |
| To 2000 S.F. | 522.000 | Lb. | 81.926 | 740 | 3,975 | 4,715 |
| To 2400 S.F. | 600.000 | Lb. | 94.189 | 850 | 4,575 | 5,425 |
| Register elbows, to 1500 S.F. | 12.000 | Ea. | 3.200 | 355 | 154 | 509 |
| To 2400 S.F. | 14.000 | Ea. | 3.733 | 415 | 180 | 595 |
| Floor registers, enameled steel w/damper, to 1500 S.F. | 12.000 | Ea. | 3.000 | 340 | 161 | 501 |
| To 2400 S.F. | 14.000 | Ea. | 4.308 | 460 | 231 | 691 |
| Return air grille, area to 1500 S.F. 12" x 12" | 2.000 | Ea. | .727 | 52 | 39 | 91 |
| Area to 2400 S.F. 8" x 16" | 2.000 | Ea. | .444 | 36 | 24 | 60 |
| Area to 2400 S.F. 8" x 16" | 2.000 | Ea. | .727 | 49 | 39 | 88 |
| 16" x 16" | 1.000 | Ea. | .364 | 35 | 19.50 | 54.50 |
| Thermostat, manual, 1 set back | 1.000 | Ea. | 1.000 | 48 | 53.50 | 101.50 |
| Electric, timed, 1 set back | 1.000 | Ea. | 1.000 | 36.50 | 53.50 | 90 |
| 2 set back | 1.000 | Ea. | 1.000 | 157 | 53.50 | 210.50 |
| Plenum, heating only, 100 M.B.H. | 1.000 | Ea. | 1.000 | 88 | 48 | 136 |
| 120 MBH | 1.000 | Ea. | 1.000 | 88 | 48 | 136 |
| 160 MBH | 1.000 | Ea. | 1.000 | 88 | 48 | 136 |
| 200 MBH | 1.000 | Ea. | 1.000 | 88 | 48 | 136 |
| Refrigeration piping, 3/8" | 25.000 | L.F. | | 27.50 | | 27.50 |
| 3/4" | 25.000 | L.F. | | 63 | | 63 |
| 7/8" | 25.000 | L.F. | | 73.50 | | 73.50 |
| Refrigerant piping, 25 ft. (precharged) | 1.000 | Ea. | | 259 | | 259 |
| Diffusers, ceiling, 6" diameter, to 1500 S.F. | 10.000 | Ea. | 4.444 | 255 | 240 | 495 |
| To 2400 S.F. | 12.000 | Ea. | 6.000 | 330 | 325 | 655 |
| Floor, aluminum, adjustable, 2-1/4" x 12" to 1500 S.F. | 12.000 | Ea. | 3.000 | 246 | 161 | 407 |
| To 2400 S.F. | 14.000 | Ea. | 3.500 | 287 | 188 | 475 |
| Side wall, aluminum, adjustable, 8" x 4", to 1500 S.F. | 12.000 | Ea. | 3.000 | 565 | 161 | 726 |
| 5" x 10" to 2400 S.F. | 12.000 | Ea. | 3.692 | 760 | 198 | 958 |

| System Description | QUAN. | UNIT | LABOR HOURS | COST PER SYSTEM | | |
|---|---|---|---|---|---|---|
| | | | | MAT. | INST. | TOTAL |
| **HEATING ONLY, OIL FIRED HOT AIR, ONE ZONE, 1200 S.F. BUILDING** | | | | | | |
| Furnace, oil fired, atomizing gun type burner | 1.000 | Ea. | 4.571 | 2,050 | 220 | 2,270 |
| 3/8" diameter copper supply pipe | 1.000 | Ea. | 2.759 | 62.10 | 156 | 218.10 |
| Shut off valve | 1.000 | Ea. | .333 | 11.85 | 18.75 | 30.60 |
| Oil tank, 275 gallon, on legs | 1.000 | Ea. | 3.200 | 410 | 162 | 572 |
| Supply duct, rigid fiberglass | 176.000 | S.F. | 12.068 | 149.60 | 603.68 | 753.28 |
| Return duct, sheet metal, galvanized | 158.000 | Lb. | 16.137 | 82.16 | 805.80 | 887.96 |
| Lateral ducts, 6" flexible fiberglass | 144.000 | L.F. | 8.862 | 377.28 | 427.68 | 804.96 |
| Register elbows | 12.000 | Ea. | 3.200 | 354 | 154.20 | 508.20 |
| Floor register, enameled steel | 12.000 | Ea. | 3.000 | 342 | 160.80 | 502.80 |
| Floor grille, return air | 2.000 | Ea. | .727 | 52 | 39 | 91 |
| Thermostat | 1.000 | Ea. | 1.000 | 48 | 53.50 | 101.50 |
| TOTAL | | System | 55.857 | 3,938.99 | 2,801.41 | 6,740.40 |
| **HEATING/COOLING, OIL FIRED, FORCED AIR, ONE ZONE, 1200 S.F. BUILDING** | | | | | | |
| Furnace, including plenum, compressor, coil | 1.000 | Ea. | 16.000 | 5,850 | 770 | 6,620 |
| 3/8" diameter copper supply pipe | 1.000 | Ea. | 2.759 | 62.10 | 156 | 218.10 |
| Shut off valve | 1.000 | Ea. | .333 | 11.85 | 18.75 | 30.60 |
| Oil tank, 275 gallon on legs | 1.000 | Ea. | 3.200 | 410 | 162 | 572 |
| Supply duct, rigid fiberglass | 176.000 | S.F. | 12.068 | 149.60 | 603.68 | 753.28 |
| Return duct, sheet metal, galvanized | 158.000 | Lb. | 16.137 | 82.16 | 805.80 | 887.96 |
| Lateral ducts, 6" flexible fiberglass | 144.000 | L.F. | 8.862 | 377.28 | 427.68 | 804.96 |
| Register elbows | 12.000 | Ea. | 3.200 | 354 | 154.20 | 508.20 |
| Floor registers, enameled steel | 12.000 | Ea. | 3.000 | 342 | 160.80 | 502.80 |
| Floor grille, return air | 2.000 | Ea. | .727 | 52 | 39 | 91 |
| Refrigeration piping (precharged) | 25.000 | L.F. | | 259 | | 259 |
| TOTAL | | System | 66.286 | 7,949.99 | 3,297.91 | 11,247.90 |

| Description | QUAN. | UNIT | LABOR HOURS | COST EACH | | |
|---|---|---|---|---|---|---|
| | | | | MAT. | INST. | TOTAL |
| | | | | | | |
| | | | | | | |
| | | | | | | |
| | | | | | | |
| | | | | | | |

| Oil Fired Heating/Cooling | QUAN. | UNIT | LABOR HOURS | COST EACH MAT. | COST EACH INST. | COST EACH TOTAL |
|---|---|---|---|---|---|---|
| Furnace, heating, 95.2 MBH, area to 1200 S.F. | 1.000 | Ea. | 4.706 | 2,075 | 227 | 2,302 |
| 123.2 MBH, area to 1500 S.F. | 1.000 | Ea. | 5.000 | 2,150 | 241 | 2,391 |
| 151.2 MBH, area to 2000 S.F. | 1.000 | Ea. | 5.333 | 2,500 | 257 | 2,757 |
| 200 MBH, area to 2400 S.F. | 1.000 | Ea. | 6.154 | 2,550 | 297 | 2,847 |
| Heating/cooling, 95.2 MBH heat, 36 MBH cool, to 1200 S.F. | 1.000 | Ea. | 16.000 | 5,850 | 770 | 6,620 |
| 112 MBH heat, 42 MBH cool, to 1500 S.F. | 1.000 | Ea. | 24.000 | 8,775 | 1,150 | 9,925 |
| 151 MBH heat, 47 MBH cool, to 2000 S.F. | 1.000 | Ea. | 20.800 | 7,600 | 1,000 | 8,600 |
| 184.8 MBH heat, 60 MBH cool, to 2400 S.F. | 1.000 | Ea. | 24.000 | 2,700 | 1,200 | 3,900 |
| Oil piping to furnace, 3/8" dia., copper | 1.000 | Ea. | 3.412 | 191 | 190 | 381 |
| Oil tank, on legs above ground, 275 gallons | 1.000 | Ea. | 3.200 | 410 | 162 | 572 |
| 550 gallons | 1.000 | Ea. | 5.926 | 2,475 | 299 | 2,774 |
| Below ground, 275 gallons | 1.000 | Ea. | 3.200 | 410 | 162 | 572 |
| 550 gallons | 1.000 | Ea. | 5.926 | 2,475 | 299 | 2,774 |
| 1000 gallons | 1.000 | Ea. | 6.400 | 3,125 | 325 | 3,450 |
| Supply duct, rectangular, area to 1200 S.F., rigid fiberglass | 176.000 | S.F. | 12.068 | 150 | 605 | 755 |
| Sheet metal, insulated | 228.000 | Lb. | 31.331 | 251 | 1,525 | 1,776 |
| Area to 1500 S.F., rigid fiberglass | 176.000 | S.F. | 12.068 | 150 | 605 | 755 |
| Sheet metal, insulated | 228.000 | Lb. | 31.331 | 251 | 1,525 | 1,776 |
| Area to 2400 S.F., rigid fiberglass | 205.000 | S.F. | 14.057 | 174 | 705 | 879 |
| Sheet metal, insulated | 271.000 | Lb. | 37.048 | 295 | 1,800 | 2,095 |
| Round flexible, insulated, 6" diameter to 1200 S.F. | 156.000 | L.F. | 9.600 | 410 | 465 | 875 |
| To 1500 S.F. | 184.000 | L.F. | 11.323 | 480 | 545 | 1,025 |
| 8" diameter to 2000 S.F. | 269.000 | L.F. | 23.911 | 890 | 1,150 | 2,040 |
| To 2400 S.F. | 269.000 | L.F. | 22.045 | 820 | 1,075 | 1,895 |
| Return duct, sheet metal galvanized, to 1500 S.F. | 158.000 | Lb. | 16.137 | 82 | 805 | 887 |
| To 2400 S.F. | 191.000 | Lb. | 19.507 | 99.50 | 975 | 1,074.50 |
| Lateral ducts, flexible round, 6", insulated to 1200 S.F. | 144.000 | L.F. | 8.862 | 375 | 430 | 805 |
| To 1500 S.F. | 172.000 | L.F. | 10.585 | 450 | 510 | 960 |
| To 2000 S.F. | 261.000 | L.F. | 16.062 | 685 | 775 | 1,460 |
| To 2400 S.F. | 300.000 | L.F. | 18.462 | 785 | 890 | 1,675 |
| Spiral steel, insulated to 1200 S.F. | 144.000 | L.F. | 20.067 | 450 | 940 | 1,390 |
| To 1500 S.F. | 172.000 | L.F. | 23.952 | 535 | 1,125 | 1,660 |
| To 2000 S.F. | 261.000 | L.F. | 36.352 | 815 | 1,700 | 2,515 |
| To 2400 S.F. | 300.000 | L.F. | 41.825 | 935 | 1,950 | 2,885 |
| Rectangular sheet metal galvanized insulated, to 1200 S.F. | 288.000 | Lb. | 45.183 | 410 | 2,200 | 2,610 |
| To 1500 S.F. | 344.000 | Lb. | 53.966 | 490 | 2,625 | 3,115 |
| To 2000 S.F. | 522.000 | Lb. | 81.926 | 740 | 3,975 | 4,715 |
| To 2400 S.F. | 600.000 | Lb. | 94.189 | 850 | 4,575 | 5,425 |
| Register elbows, to 1500 S.F. | 12.000 | Ea. | 3.200 | 355 | 154 | 509 |
| To 2400 S.F. | 14.000 | Ea. | 3.733 | 415 | 180 | 595 |
| Floor registers, enameled steel w/damper, to 1500 S.F. | 12.000 | Ea. | 3.000 | 340 | 161 | 501 |
| To 2400 S.F. | 14.000 | Ea. | 4.308 | 460 | 231 | 691 |
| Return air grille, area to 1500 S.F., 12" x 12" | 2.000 | Ea. | .727 | 52 | 39 | 91 |
| 12" x 24" | 1.000 | Ea. | .444 | 36 | 24 | 60 |
| Area to 2400 S.F., 8" x 16" | 2.000 | Ea. | .727 | 49 | 39 | 88 |
| 16" x 16" | 1.000 | Ea. | .364 | 35 | 19.50 | 54.50 |
| Thermostat, manual, 1 set back | 1.000 | Ea. | 1.000 | 48 | 53.50 | 101.50 |
| Electric, timed, 1 set back | 1.000 | Ea. | 1.000 | 36.50 | 53.50 | 90 |
| 2 set back | 1.000 | Ea. | 1.000 | 157 | 53.50 | 210.50 |
| Refrigeration piping, 3/8" | 25.000 | L.F. | | 27.50 | | 27.50 |
| 3/4" | 25.000 | L.F. | | 63 | | 63 |
| Diffusers, ceiling, 6" diameter, to 1500 S.F. | 10.000 | Ea. | 4.444 | 255 | 240 | 495 |
| To 2400 S.F. | 12.000 | Ea. | 6.000 | 330 | 325 | 655 |
| Floor, aluminum, adjustable, 2-1/4" x 12" to 1500 S.F. | 12.000 | Ea. | 3.000 | 246 | 161 | 407 |
| To 2400 S.F. | 14.000 | Ea. | 3.500 | 287 | 188 | 475 |
| Side wall, aluminum, adjustable, 8" x 4", to 1500 S.F. | 12.000 | Ea. | 3.000 | 565 | 161 | 726 |
| 5" x 10" to 2400 S.F. | 12.000 | Ea. | 3.692 | 760 | 198 | 958 |

| System Description | QUAN. | UNIT | LABOR HOURS | COST EACH | | |
|---|---|---|---|---|---|---|
| | | | | MAT. | INST. | TOTAL |
| **OIL FIRED HOT WATER HEATING SYSTEM, AREA TO 1200 S.F.** | | | | | | |
| Boiler package, oil fired, 97 MBH, area to 1200 S.F. building | 1.000 | Ea. | 15.000 | 1,900 | 730 | 2,630 |
| 3/8" diameter copper supply pipe | 1.000 | Ea. | 2.759 | 62.10 | 156 | 218.10 |
| Shut off valve | 1.000 | Ea. | .333 | 11.85 | 18.75 | 30.60 |
| Oil tank, 275 gallon, with black iron filler pipe | 1.000 | Ea. | 3.200 | 410 | 162 | 572 |
| Supply piping, 3/4" copper tubing | 176.000 | L.F. | 18.526 | 740.96 | 1,047.20 | 1,788.16 |
| Supply fittings, copper 3/4" | 36.000 | Ea. | 15.158 | 129.60 | 846 | 975.60 |
| Supply valves, 3/4" | 2.000 | Ea. | .800 | 204 | 45 | 249 |
| Baseboard radiation, 3/4" | 106.000 | L.F. | 35.333 | 526.82 | 1,786.10 | 2,312.92 |
| Zone valve | 1.000 | Ea. | .400 | 172 | 22.50 | 194.50 |
| TOTAL | | Ea. | 91.509 | 4,157.33 | 4,813.55 | 8,970.88 |
| **OIL FIRED HOT WATER HEATING SYSTEM, AREA TO 2400 S.F.** | | | | | | |
| Boiler package, oil fired, 225 MBH, area to 2400 S.F. building | 1.000 | Ea. | 25.105 | 6,100 | 1,225 | 7,325 |
| 3/8" diameter copper supply pipe | 1.000 | Ea. | 2.759 | 62.10 | 156 | 218.10 |
| Shut off valve | 1.000 | Ea. | .333 | 11.85 | 18.75 | 30.60 |
| Oil tank, 550 gallon, with black iron pipe filler pipe | 1.000 | Ea. | 5.926 | 2,475 | 299 | 2,774 |
| Supply piping, 3/4" copper tubing | 228.000 | L.F. | 23.999 | 959.88 | 1,356.60 | 2,316.48 |
| Supply fittings, copper | 46.000 | Ea. | 19.368 | 165.60 | 1,081 | 1,246.60 |
| Supply valves | 2.000 | Ea. | .800 | 204 | 45 | 249 |
| Baseboard radiation | 212.000 | L.F. | 70.666 | 1,053.64 | 3,572.20 | 4,625.84 |
| Zone valve | 1.000 | Ea. | .400 | 172 | 22.50 | 194.50 |
| TOTAL | | Ea. | 149.356 | 11,204.07 | 7,776.05 | 18,980.12 |

The costs in this system are on a cost each basis. The costs represent total cost for the system based on a gross square foot of plan area.

| Description | QUAN. | UNIT | LABOR HOURS | COST EACH | | |
|---|---|---|---|---|---|---|
| | | | | MAT. | INST. | TOTAL |
| | | | | | | |
| | | | | | | |
| | | | | | | |
| | | | | | | |

## Hot Water Heating Price Sheet

| | QUAN. | UNIT | LABOR HOURS | COST EACH MAT. | COST EACH INST. | COST EACH TOTAL |
|---|---|---|---|---|---|---|
| Boiler, oil fired, 97 MBH, area to 1200 S.F. | 1.000 | Ea. | 15.000 | 1,900 | 730 | 2,630 |
| 118 MBH, area to 1500 S.F. | 1.000 | Ea. | 16.506 | 2,000 | 805 | 2,805 |
| 161 MBH, area to 2000 S.F. | 1.000 | Ea. | 18.405 | 2,225 | 895 | 3,120 |
| 215 MBH, area to 2400 S.F. | 1.000 | Ea. | 19.704 | 3,525 | 1,900 | 5,425 |
| Oil piping, (valve & filter), 3/8" copper | 1.000 | Ea. | 3.289 | 74 | 175 | 249 |
| 1/4" copper | 1.000 | Ea. | 3.242 | 93 | 182 | 275 |
| Oil tank, filler pipe and cap on legs, 275 gallon | 1.000 | Ea. | 3.200 | 410 | 162 | 572 |
| 550 gallon | 1.000 | Ea. | 5.926 | 2,475 | 299 | 2,774 |
| Buried underground, 275 gallon | 1.000 | Ea. | 3.200 | 410 | 162 | 572 |
| 550 gallon | 1.000 | Ea. | 5.926 | 2,475 | 299 | 2,774 |
| 1000 gallon | 1.000 | Ea. | 6.400 | 3,125 | 325 | 3,450 |
| | | | | | | |
| Supply piping copper, area to 1200 S.F., 1/2" tubing | 176.000 | L.F. | 17.384 | 480 | 975 | 1,455 |
| 3/4" tubing | 176.000 | L.F. | 18.526 | 740 | 1,050 | 1,790 |
| Area to 1500 S.F., 1/2" tubing | 186.000 | L.F. | 18.371 | 510 | 1,025 | 1,535 |
| 3/4" tubing | 186.000 | L.F. | 19.578 | 785 | 1,100 | 1,885 |
| Area to 2000 S.F., 1/2" tubing | 204.000 | L.F. | 20.149 | 560 | 1,125 | 1,685 |
| 3/4" tubing | 204.000 | L.F. | 21.473 | 860 | 1,225 | 2,085 |
| Area to 2400 S.F., 1/2" tubing | 228.000 | L.F. | 22.520 | 625 | 1,275 | 1,900 |
| 3/4" tubing | 228.000 | L.F. | 23.999 | 960 | 1,350 | 2,310 |
| Supply pipe fittings copper, area to 1200 S.F., 1/2" | 36.000 | Ea. | 14.400 | 57.50 | 810 | 867.50 |
| 3/4" | 36.000 | Ea. | 15.158 | 130 | 845 | 975 |
| Area to 1500 S.F., 1/2" | 40.000 | Ea. | 16.000 | 64 | 900 | 964 |
| 3/4" | 40.000 | Ea. | 16.842 | 144 | 940 | 1,084 |
| Area to 2000 S.F., 1/2" | 44.000 | Ea. | 17.600 | 70.50 | 990 | 1,060.50 |
| 3/4" | 44.000 | Ea. | 18.526 | 158 | 1,025 | 1,183 |
| Area to 2400, S.F., 1/2" | 46.000 | Ea. | 18.400 | 73.50 | 1,025 | 1,098.50 |
| 3/4" | 46.000 | Ea. | 19.368 | 166 | 1,075 | 1,241 |
| Supply valves, 1/2" pipe size | 2.000 | Ea. | .667 | 151 | 37.50 | 188.50 |
| 3/4" | 2.000 | Ea. | .800 | 204 | 45 | 249 |
| Baseboard radiation, area to 1200 S.F., 1/2" tubing | 106.000 | L.F. | 28.267 | 880 | 1,425 | 2,305 |
| 3/4" tubing | 106.000 | L.F. | 35.333 | 525 | 1,775 | 2,300 |
| Area to 1500 S.F., 1/2" tubing | 134.000 | L.F. | 35.734 | 1,100 | 1,800 | 2,900 |
| 3/4" tubing | 134.000 | L.F. | 44.666 | 665 | 2,250 | 2,915 |
| Area to 2000 S.F., 1/2" tubing | 178.000 | L.F. | 47.467 | 1,475 | 2,400 | 3,875 |
| 3/4" tubing | 178.000 | L.F. | 59.333 | 885 | 3,000 | 3,885 |
| Area to 2400 S.F., 1/2" tubing | 212.000 | L.F. | 56.534 | 1,750 | 2,850 | 4,600 |
| 3/4" tubing | 212.000 | L.F. | 70.666 | 1,050 | 3,575 | 4,625 |
| Zone valves, 1/2" tubing | 1.000 | Ea. | .400 | 172 | 22.50 | 194.50 |
| 3/4" tubing | 1.000 | Ea. | .400 | 173 | 22.50 | 195.50 |

273

| System Description | QUAN. | UNIT | LABOR HOURS | COST EACH | | |
|---|---|---|---|---|---|---|
| | | | | MAT. | INST. | TOTAL |
| **ROOFTOP HEATING/COOLING UNIT, AREA TO 2000 S.F.** | | | | | | |
| Rooftop unit, single zone, electric cool, gas heat, to 2000 S.F. | 1.000 | Ea. | 28.521 | 5,350 | 1,450 | 6,800 |
| Gas piping | 34.500 | L.F. | 5.207 | 238.05 | 293.25 | 531.30 |
| Duct, supply and return, galvanized steel | 38.000 | Lb. | 3.881 | 19.76 | 193.80 | 213.56 |
| Insulation, ductwork | 33.000 | S.F. | 1.508 | 24.75 | 68.97 | 93.72 |
| Lateral duct, flexible duct 12" diameter, insulated | 72.000 | L.F. | 11.520 | 345.60 | 554.40 | 900 |
| Diffusers | 4.000 | Ea. | 4.571 | 1,160 | 246 | 1,406 |
| Return registers | 1.000 | Ea. | .727 | 101 | 39 | 140 |
| TOTAL | | Ea. | 55.935 | 7,239.16 | 2,845.42 | 10,084.58 |
| **ROOFTOP HEATING/COOLING UNIT, AREA TO 5000 S.F.** | | | | | | |
| Rooftop unit, single zone, electric cool, gas heat, to 5000 S.F. | 1.000 | Ea. | 42.032 | 16,500 | 2,050 | 18,550 |
| Gas piping | 86.250 | L.F. | 13.019 | 595.13 | 733.13 | 1,328.26 |
| Duct supply and return, galvanized steel | 95.000 | Lb. | 9.702 | 49.40 | 484.50 | 533.90 |
| Insulation, ductwork | 82.000 | S.F. | 3.748 | 61.50 | 171.38 | 232.88 |
| Lateral duct, flexible duct, 12" diameter, insulated | 180.000 | L.F. | 28.800 | 864 | 1,386 | 2,250 |
| Diffusers | 10.000 | Ea. | 11.429 | 2,900 | 615 | 3,515 |
| Return registers | 3.000 | Ea. | 2.182 | 303 | 117 | 420 |
| TOTAL | | Ea. | 110.912 | 21,273.03 | 5,557.01 | 26,830.04 |

| Description | QUAN. | UNIT | LABOR HOURS | COST EACH | | |
|---|---|---|---|---|---|---|
| | | | | MAT. | INST. | TOTAL |
| | | | | | | |
| | | | | | | |
| | | | | | | |
| | | | | | | |
| | | | | | | |
| | | | | | | |
| | | | | | | |

| Rooftop Price Sheet | QUAN. | UNIT | LABOR HOURS | COST EACH | | |
|---|---|---|---|---|---|---|
| | | | | MAT. | INST. | TOTAL |
| Rooftop unit, single zone, electric cool, gas heat to 2000 S.F. | 1.000 | Ea. | 28.521 | 5,350 | 1,450 | 6,800 |
| Area to 3000 S.F. | 1.000 | Ea. | 35.982 | 11,600 | 1,750 | 13,350 |
| Area to 5000 S.F. | 1.000 | Ea. | 42.032 | 16,500 | 2,050 | 18,550 |
| Area to 10000 S.F. | 1.000 | Ea. | 68.376 | 28,100 | 3,450 | 31,550 |
| Gas piping, area 2000 through 4000 S.F. | 34.500 | L.F. | 5.207 | 238 | 293 | 531 |
| Area 5000 to 10000 S.F. | 86.250 | L.F. | 13.019 | 595 | 735 | 1,330 |
| Duct, supply and return, galvanized steel, to 2000 S.F. | 38.000 | Lb. | 3.881 | 19.75 | 194 | 213.75 |
| Area to 3000 S.F. | 57.000 | Lb. | 5.821 | 29.50 | 291 | 320.50 |
| Area to 5000 S.F. | 95.000 | Lb. | 9.702 | 49.50 | 485 | 534.50 |
| Area to 10000 S.F. | 190.000 | Lb. | 19.405 | 99 | 970 | 1,069 |
| Rigid fiberglass, area to 2000 S.F. | 33.000 | S.F. | 2.263 | 28 | 113 | 141 |
| Area to 3000 S.F. | 49.000 | S.F. | 3.360 | 41.50 | 168 | 209.50 |
| Area to 5000 S.F. | 82.000 | S.F. | 5.623 | 69.50 | 281 | 350.50 |
| Area to 10000 S.F. | 164.000 | S.F. | 11.245 | 139 | 565 | 704 |
| Insulation, supply and return, blanket type, area to 2000 S.F. | 33.000 | S.F. | 1.508 | 25 | 69 | 94 |
| Area to 3000 S.F. | 49.000 | S.F. | 2.240 | 37 | 102 | 139 |
| Area to 5000 S.F. | 82.000 | S.F. | 3.748 | 61.50 | 171 | 232.50 |
| Area to 10000 S.F. | 164.000 | S.F. | 7.496 | 123 | 345 | 468 |
| Lateral ducts, flexible round, 12" insulated, to 2000 S.F. | 72.000 | L.F. | 11.520 | 345 | 555 | 900 |
| Area to 3000 S.F. | 108.000 | L.F. | 17.280 | 520 | 830 | 1,350 |
| Area to 5000 S.F. | 180.000 | L.F. | 28.800 | 865 | 1,375 | 2,240 |
| Area to 10000 S.F. | 360.000 | L.F. | 57.600 | 1,725 | 2,775 | 4,500 |
| Rectangular, galvanized steel, to 2000 S.F. | 239.000 | Lb. | 24.409 | 124 | 1,225 | 1,349 |
| Area to 3000 S.F. | 360.000 | Lb. | 36.767 | 187 | 1,825 | 2,012 |
| Area to 5000 S.F. | 599.000 | Lb. | 61.176 | 310 | 3,050 | 3,360 |
| Area to 10000 S.F. | 998.000 | Lb. | 101.926 | 520 | 5,100 | 5,620 |
| Diffusers, ceiling, 1 to 4 way blow, 24" x 24", to 2000 S.F. | 4.000 | Ea. | 4.571 | 1,150 | 246 | 1,396 |
| Area to 3000 S.F. | 6.000 | Ea. | 6.857 | 1,750 | 370 | 2,120 |
| Area to 5000 S.F. | 10.000 | Ea. | 11.429 | 2,900 | 615 | 3,515 |
| Area to 10000 S.F. | 20.000 | Ea. | 22.857 | 5,800 | 1,225 | 7,025 |
| Return grilles, 24" x 24", to 2000 S.F. | 1.000 | Ea. | .727 | 101 | 39 | 140 |
| Area to 3000 S.F. | 2.000 | Ea. | 1.455 | 202 | 78 | 280 |
| Area to 5000 S.F. | 3.000 | Ea. | 2.182 | 305 | 117 | 422 |
| Area to 10000 S.F. | 5.000 | Ea. | 3.636 | 505 | 195 | 700 |
| | | | | | | |
| | | | | | | |
| | | | | | | |
| | | | | | | |
| | | | | | | |
| | | | | | | |
| | | | | | | |
| | | | | | | |
| | | | | | | |
| | | | | | | |
| | | | | | | |
| | | | | | | |

| System Description | QUAN. | UNIT | LABOR HOURS | COST EACH | | |
|---|---|---|---|---|---|---|
| | | | | MAT. | INST. | TOTAL |
| **100 AMP SERVICE** | | | | | | |
| Weather cap | 1.000 | Ea. | .667 | 14.30 | 35.50 | 49.80 |
| Service entrance cable | 10.000 | L.F. | .762 | 39.70 | 40.70 | 80.40 |
| Meter socket | 1.000 | Ea. | 2.500 | 48.50 | 134 | 182.50 |
| Ground rod with clamp | 1.000 | Ea. | 1.455 | 18.40 | 78 | 96.40 |
| Ground cable | 5.000 | L.F. | .250 | 10.65 | 13.35 | 24 |
| Panel board, 12 circuit | 1.000 | Ea. | 6.667 | 277 | 355 | 632 |
| | | | | | | |
| TOTAL | | Ea. | 12.301 | 408.55 | 656.55 | 1,065.10 |
| **200 AMP SERVICE** | | | | | | |
| Weather cap | 1.000 | Ea. | 1.000 | 39.50 | 53.50 | 93 |
| Service entrance cable | 10.000 | L.F. | 1.143 | 62.50 | 61 | 123.50 |
| Meter socket | 1.000 | Ea. | 4.211 | 81.50 | 225 | 306.50 |
| Ground rod with clamp | 1.000 | Ea. | 1.818 | 40 | 97 | 137 |
| Ground cable | 10.000 | L.F. | .500 | 21.30 | 26.70 | 48 |
| 3/4" EMT | 5.000 | L.F. | .308 | 5.30 | 16.45 | 21.75 |
| Panel board, 24 circuit | 1.000 | Ea. | 12.308 | 630 | 555 | 1,185 |
| | | | | | | |
| TOTAL | | Ea. | 21.288 | 880.10 | 1,034.65 | 1,914.75 |
| **400 AMP SERVICE** | | | | | | |
| Weather cap | 1.000 | Ea. | 2.963 | 490 | 158 | 648 |
| Service entrance cable | 180.000 | L.F. | 5.760 | 658.80 | 307.80 | 966.60 |
| Meter socket | 1.000 | Ea. | 4.211 | 81.50 | 225 | 306.50 |
| Ground rod with clamp | 1.000 | Ea. | 2.000 | 101 | 107 | 208 |
| Ground cable | 20.000 | L.F. | .485 | 46.40 | 26 | 72.40 |
| 3/4" greenfield | 20.000 | L.F. | 1.000 | 17.20 | 53.40 | 70.60 |
| Current transformer cabinet | 1.000 | Ea. | 6.154 | 231 | 330 | 561 |
| Panel board, 42 circuit | 1.000 | Ea. | 33.333 | 3,275 | 1,775 | 5,050 |
| | | | | | | |
| TOTAL | | Ea. | 55.906 | 4,900.90 | 2,982.20 | 7,883.10 |

Thermostat →

Electric Baseboard →

| System Description | QUAN. | UNIT | LABOR HOURS | COST EACH | | |
|---|---|---|---|---|---|---|
| | | | | MAT. | INST. | TOTAL |
| **4' BASEBOARD HEATER** | | | | | | |
| Electric baseboard heater, 4' long | 1.000 | Ea. | 1.194 | 59.50 | 64 | 123.50 |
| Thermostat, integral | 1.000 | Ea. | .500 | 33 | 26.50 | 59.50 |
| Romex, 12-3 with ground | 40.000 | L.F. | 1.600 | 21.20 | 85.60 | 106.80 |
| Panel board breaker, 20 Amp | 1.000 | Ea. | .300 | 11.55 | 16.05 | 27.60 |
| TOTAL | | Ea. | 3.594 | 125.25 | 192.15 | 317.40 |
| **6' BASEBOARD HEATER** | | | | | | |
| Electric baseboard heater, 6' long | 1.000 | Ea. | 1.600 | 81.50 | 85.50 | 167 |
| Thermostat, integral | 1.000 | Ea. | .500 | 33 | 26.50 | 59.50 |
| Romex, 12-3 with ground | 40.000 | L.F. | 1.600 | 21.20 | 85.60 | 106.80 |
| Panel board breaker, 20 Amp | 1.000 | Ea. | .400 | 15.40 | 21.40 | 36.80 |
| TOTAL | | Ea. | 4.100 | 151.10 | 219 | 370.10 |
| **8' BASEBOARD HEATER** | | | | | | |
| Electric baseboard heater, 8' long | 1.000 | Ea. | 2.000 | 101 | 107 | 208 |
| Thermostat, integral | 1.000 | Ea. | .500 | 33 | 26.50 | 59.50 |
| Romex, 12-3 with ground | 40.000 | L.F. | 1.600 | 21.20 | 85.60 | 106.80 |
| Panel board breaker, 20 Amp | 1.000 | Ea. | .500 | 19.25 | 26.75 | 46 |
| TOTAL | | Ea. | 4.600 | 174.45 | 245.85 | 420.30 |
| **10' BASEBOARD HEATER** | | | | | | |
| Electric baseboard heater, 10' long | 1.000 | Ea. | 2.424 | 212 | 130 | 342 |
| Thermostat, integral | 1.000 | Ea. | .500 | 33 | 26.50 | 59.50 |
| Romex, 12-3 with ground | 40.000 | L.F. | 1.600 | 21.20 | 85.60 | 106.80 |
| Panel board breaker, 20 Amp | 1.000 | Ea. | .750 | 28.88 | 40.13 | 69.01 |
| TOTAL | | Ea. | 5.274 | 295.08 | 282.23 | 577.31 |

The costs in this system are on a cost each basis and include all necessary conduit fittings.

| Description | QUAN. | UNIT | LABOR HOURS | COST EACH | | |
|---|---|---|---|---|---|---|
| | | | | MAT. | INST. | TOTAL |
| | | | | | | |
| | | | | | | |

| System Description | QUAN. | UNIT | LABOR HOURS | COST EACH | | |
|---|---|---|---|---|---|---|
| | | | | MAT. | INST. | TOTAL |
| Air conditioning receptacles | | | | | | |
| Using non-metallic sheathed cable | 1.000 | Ea. | .800 | 22 | 43 | 65 |
| Using BX cable | 1.000 | Ea. | .964 | 39 | 51.50 | 90.50 |
| Using EMT conduit | 1.000 | Ea. | 1.194 | 48 | 64 | 112 |
| Disposal wiring | | | | | | |
| Using non-metallic sheathed cable | 1.000 | Ea. | .889 | 16.20 | 47.50 | 63.70 |
| Using BX cable | 1.000 | Ea. | 1.067 | 32.50 | 57 | 89.50 |
| Using EMT conduit | 1.000 | Ea. | 1.333 | 43.50 | 71.50 | 115 |
| Dryer circuit | | | | | | |
| Using non-metallic sheathed cable | 1.000 | Ea. | 1.455 | 42 | 78 | 120 |
| Using BX cable | 1.000 | Ea. | 1.739 | 57.50 | 93 | 150.50 |
| Using EMT conduit | 1.000 | Ea. | 2.162 | 58 | 116 | 174 |
| Duplex receptacles | | | | | | |
| Using non-metallic sheathed cable | 1.000 | Ea. | .615 | 22 | 33 | 55 |
| Using BX cable | 1.000 | Ea. | .741 | 39 | 39.50 | 78.50 |
| Using EMT conduit | 1.000 | Ea. | .920 | 48 | 49 | 97 |
| Exhaust fan wiring | | | | | | |
| Using non-metallic sheathed cable | 1.000 | Ea. | .800 | 18.50 | 43 | 61.50 |
| Using BX cable | 1.000 | Ea. | .964 | 35.50 | 51.50 | 87 |
| Using EMT conduit | 1.000 | Ea. | 1.194 | 45 | 64 | 109 |
| Furnace circuit & switch | | | | | | |
| Using non-metallic sheathed cable | 1.000 | Ea. | 1.333 | 25.50 | 71.50 | 97 |
| Using BX cable | 1.000 | Ea. | 1.600 | 45 | 85.50 | 130.50 |
| Using EMT conduit | 1.000 | Ea. | 2.000 | 51 | 107 | 158 |
| Ground fault | | | | | | |
| Using non-metallic sheathed cable | 1.000 | Ea. | 1.000 | 55.50 | 53.50 | 109 |
| Using BX cable | 1.000 | Ea. | 1.212 | 71 | 65 | 136 |
| Using EMT conduit | 1.000 | Ea. | 1.481 | 90 | 79 | 169 |
| Heater circuits | | | | | | |
| Using non-metallic sheathed cable | 1.000 | Ea. | 1.000 | 28 | 53.50 | 81.50 |
| Using BX cable | 1.000 | Ea. | 1.212 | 37.50 | 65 | 102.50 |
| Using EMT conduit | 1.000 | Ea. | 1.481 | 46.50 | 79 | 125.50 |
| Lighting wiring | | | | | | |
| Using non-metallic sheathed cable | 1.000 | Ea. | .500 | 29 | 26.50 | 55.50 |
| Using BX cable | 1.000 | Ea. | .602 | 38.50 | 32 | 70.50 |
| Using EMT conduit | 1.000 | Ea. | .748 | 44 | 40 | 84 |
| Range circuits | | | | | | |
| Using non-metallic sheathed cable | 1.000 | Ea. | 2.000 | 89 | 107 | 196 |
| Using BX cable | 1.000 | Ea. | 2.424 | 143 | 130 | 273 |
| Using EMT conduit | 1.000 | Ea. | 2.963 | 103 | 158 | 261 |
| Switches, single pole | | | | | | |
| Using non-metallic sheathed cable | 1.000 | Ea. | .500 | 18.50 | 26.50 | 45 |
| Using BX cable | 1.000 | Ea. | .602 | 35.50 | 32 | 67.50 |
| Using EMT conduit | 1.000 | Ea. | .748 | 45 | 40 | 85 |
| Switches, 3-way | | | | | | |
| Using non-metallic sheathed cable | 1.000 | Ea. | .667 | 23.50 | 35.50 | 59 |
| Using BX cable | 1.000 | Ea. | .800 | 37.50 | 43 | 80.50 |
| Using EMT conduit | 1.000 | Ea. | 1.333 | 64.50 | 71.50 | 136 |
| Water heater | | | | | | |
| Using non-metallic sheathed cable | 1.000 | Ea. | 1.600 | 30.50 | 85.50 | 116 |
| Using BX cable | 1.000 | Ea. | 1.905 | 56 | 102 | 158 |
| Using EMT conduit | 1.000 | Ea. | 2.353 | 52.50 | 126 | 178.50 |
| Weatherproof receptacle | | | | | | |
| Using non-metallic sheathed cable | 1.000 | Ea. | 1.333 | 156 | 71.50 | 227.50 |
| Using BX cable | 1.000 | Ea. | 1.600 | 166 | 85.50 | 251.50 |
| Using EMT conduit | 1.000 | Ea. | 2.000 | 175 | 107 | 282 |

| DESCRIPTION | QUAN. | UNIT | LABOR HOURS | COST EACH | | |
|---|---|---|---|---|---|---|
| | | | | MAT. | INST. | TOTAL |
| Fluorescent strip, 4' long, 1 light, average | 1.000 | Ea. | .941 | 34.50 | 50.50 | 85 |
| Deluxe | 1.000 | Ea. | 1.129 | 41.50 | 60.50 | 102 |
| 2 lights, average | 1.000 | Ea. | 1.000 | 38 | 53.50 | 91.50 |
| Deluxe | 1.000 | Ea. | 1.200 | 45.50 | 64 | 109.50 |
| 8' long, 1 light, average | 1.000 | Ea. | 1.194 | 52 | 64 | 116 |
| Deluxe | 1.000 | Ea. | 1.433 | 62.50 | 77 | 139.50 |
| 2 lights, average | 1.000 | Ea. | 1.290 | 62.50 | 69 | 131.50 |
| Deluxe | 1.000 | Ea. | 1.548 | 75 | 83 | 158 |
| Surface mounted, 4' x 1', economy | 1.000 | Ea. | .914 | 65 | 49 | 114 |
| Average | 1.000 | Ea. | 1.143 | 81.50 | 61 | 142.50 |
| Deluxe | 1.000 | Ea. | 1.371 | 98 | 73 | 171 |
| 4' x 2', economy | 1.000 | Ea. | 1.208 | 83 | 64.50 | 147.50 |
| Average | 1.000 | Ea. | 1.509 | 104 | 80.50 | 184.50 |
| Deluxe | 1.000 | Ea. | 1.811 | 125 | 96.50 | 221.50 |
| Recessed, 4' x 1', 2 lamps, economy | 1.000 | Ea. | 1.123 | 47 | 60 | 107 |
| Average | 1.000 | Ea. | 1.404 | 59 | 75 | 134 |
| Deluxe | 1.000 | Ea. | 1.684 | 71 | 90 | 161 |
| 4' x 2', 4' lamps, economy | 1.000 | Ea. | 1.362 | 57.50 | 73 | 130.50 |
| Average | 1.000 | Ea. | 1.702 | 72 | 91 | 163 |
| Deluxe | 1.000 | Ea. | 2.043 | 86.50 | 109 | 195.50 |
| Incandescent, exterior, 150W, single spot | 1.000 | Ea. | .500 | 33.50 | 26.50 | 60 |
| Double spot | 1.000 | Ea. | 1.167 | 104 | 62 | 166 |
| Recessed, 100W, economy | 1.000 | Ea. | .800 | 61.50 | 43 | 104.50 |
| Average | 1.000 | Ea. | 1.000 | 77 | 53.50 | 130.50 |
| Deluxe | 1.000 | Ea. | 1.200 | 92.50 | 64 | 156.50 |
| 150W, economy | 1.000 | Ea. | .800 | 89.50 | 43 | 132.50 |
| Average | 1.000 | Ea. | 1.000 | 112 | 53.50 | 165.50 |
| Deluxe | 1.000 | Ea. | 1.200 | 134 | 64 | 198 |
| Surface mounted, 60W, economy | 1.000 | Ea. | .800 | 48 | 43 | 91 |
| Average | 1.000 | Ea. | 1.000 | 54 | 53.50 | 107.50 |
| Deluxe | 1.000 | Ea. | 1.194 | 76 | 64 | 140 |
| Metal halide, recessed 2' x 2' 250W | 1.000 | Ea. | 2.500 | 340 | 134 | 474 |
| 2' x 2', 400W | 1.000 | Ea. | 2.759 | 395 | 147 | 542 |
| Surface mounted, 2' x 2', 250W | 1.000 | Ea. | 2.963 | 370 | 158 | 528 |
| 2' x 2', 400W | 1.000 | Ea. | 3.333 | 435 | 178 | 613 |
| High bay, single, unit, 400W | 1.000 | Ea. | 3.478 | 445 | 186 | 631 |
| Twin unit, 400W | 1.000 | Ea. | 5.000 | 885 | 267 | 1,152 |
| Low bay, 250W | 1.000 | Ea. | 2.500 | 390 | 134 | 524 |
| | | | | | | |
| | | | | | | |
| | | | | | | |
| | | | | | | |

# Unit Price Section

## Table of Contents

# Table of Contents (cont.)

# How to Use the Unit Price Pages

*The following is a detailed explanation of a sample entry in the Unit Price Section. Next to each bold number below is the described item with the appropriate component of the sample entry following in parentheses. Some prices are listed as bare costs; others as costs that include overhead and profit of the installing contractor. In most cases, if the work is to be subcontracted, the general contractor will need to add an additional markup (RSMeans suggests using 10%) to the figures in the column "Total Incl. O&P."*

## 1 Division Number/Title
### (03 30/Cast-In-Place Concrete)

Use the Unit Price Section Table of Contents to locate specific items. The sections are classified according to the CSI MasterFormat 2004 system.

## 2 Line Numbers
### (03 30 53.40 3920)

Each unit price line item has been assigned a unique 12-digit code based on the CSI MasterFormat classification.

MasterFormat Division (03)

MasterFormat Level 2 (03 30 00)

MasterFormat Level 3

**03  30  53.40   3920**

MasterFormat Level 4

RSMeans 12-Digit Line Number

## 3 Description
### (Concrete In Place, etc.)

Each line item is described in detail. Sub-items and additional sizes are indented beneath the appropriate line items. The first line or two after the main item (in boldface) may contain descriptive information that pertains to all line items beneath this boldface listing.

## 4 Reference Number
### Information

| R033053 -50 |
| --- |

You'll see reference numbers shown in shaded boxes at the beginning of some sections. These refer to related items in the Reference Section, visually identified by a vertical gray bar on the page edges.

The relation may be an estimating procedure that should be read before estimating, or technical information.

The "R" designates the Reference Section. The numbers refer to the MasterFormat 2004 classification system.

**It is strongly recommended that you review all reference numbers that appear within the section in which you are working.**

## 03 30 Cast-In-Place Concrete

### 03 30 53 – Miscellaneous Cast-In-Place Concrete

| 03 30 53.40 Concrete In Place | | Crew | Daily Output | Labor-Hours | Unit | Material | 2010 Bare Costs Labor | Equipment | Total | Total Incl O&P |
|---|---|---|---|---|---|---|---|---|---|---|
| 0510 | Maximum | " | 23.71 | 4.724 | " | 162 | 129 | 1.28 | 292.28 | 395 |
| 3540 | Equipment pad (3000 psi), 3' x 3' x 6" thick | C-14H | 45 | 1.067 | Ea. | 42.50 | 30 | .67 | 73.17 | 99 |
| 3550 | 4' x 4' x 6" thick | | 30 | 1.600 | | 62.50 | 45.50 | 1.01 | 109.01 | 146 |
| 3560 | 5' x 5' x 8" thick | | 18 | 2.667 | | 108 | 75.50 | 1.68 | 185.18 | 248 |
| 3570 | 6' x 6' x 8" thick | | 14 | 3.429 | | 146 | 97 | 2.16 | 245.16 | 325 |
| 3580 | 8' x 8' x 10" thick | | 8 | 6 | | 310 | 170 | 3.78 | 483.78 | 630 |
| 3590 | 10' x 10' x 12" thick | | 5 | 9.600 | | 530 | 272 | 6.05 | 808.05 | 1,050 |
| 3800 | Footings (3000 psi), spread under 1 C.Y. | C-14C | 28 | 4 | C.Y. | 150 | 109 | 1.08 | 260.08 | 350 |
| 3825 | 1 C.Y. to 5 C.Y. | | 43 | 2.605 | | 173 | 71 | .70 | 244.70 | 310 |
| 3850 | Over 5 C.Y. | | 75 | 1.493 | | 158 | 41 | .40 | 199.40 | 243 |
| 3900 | Footings, strip (3000 psi), 18" x 9", unreinforced | C-14L | 40 | 2.400 | | 112 | 64 | .77 | 176.77 | 231 |
| 3920 | 18" x 9", reinforced | C-14C | 35 | 3.200 | | 131 | 87.50 | .86 | 219.36 | 292 |
| 3925 | 20" x 10", unreinforced | C-14L | 45 | 2.133 | | 110 | 57 | .68 | 167.68 | 217 |
| 3930 | 20" x 10", reinforced | C-14C | 40 | 2.800 | | 126 | 76.50 | .76 | 203.26 | 268 |

286

## Crew (C-14C)

The "Crew" column designates the typical trade or crew used to install the item. If an installation can be accomplished by one trade and requires no power equipment, that trade and the number of workers are listed (for example, "2 Carpenters"). If an installation requires a composite crew, a crew code designation is listed (for example, "C-14C"). You'll find full details on all composite crews in the Crew Listings.

- For a complete list of all trades utilized in this book and their abbreviations, see the inside back cover.

### Crews

| Crew No. | Bare Costs | | Incl. Subs O&P | | Cost Per Labor-Hour | |
|---|---|---|---|---|---|---|
| Crew C-14C | Hr. | Daily | Hr. | Daily | Bare Costs | Incl. O&P |
| 1 Carpenter Foreman (out) | $31.10 | $248.80 | $52.30 | $418.40 | $27.30 | $46.06 |
| 6 Carpenters | 29.10 | 1396.80 | 48.95 | 2349.60 | | |
| 2 Rodmen (reinf.) | 31.35 | 501.60 | 54.90 | 878.40 | | |
| 4 Laborers | 21.50 | 688.00 | 36.15 | 1156.80 | | |
| 1 Cement Finisher | 27.80 | 222.40 | 44.50 | 356.00 | | |
| 1 Gas Engine Vibrator | | 30.40 | | 33.44 | 0.27 | 0.30 |
| 112 L.H., Daily Totals | | $3088.00 | | $5192.64 | $27.57 | $46.36 |

## Productivity: Daily Output (35.0)/ Labor-Hours (3.20)

The "Daily Output" represents the typical number of units the designated crew will install in a normal 8-hour day. To find out the number of days the given crew would require to complete the installation, divide your quantity by the daily output. For example:

| Quantity | ÷ | Daily Output | = | Duration |
|---|---|---|---|---|
| 100 C.Y. | ÷ | 35.0/ Crew Day | = | 2.86 Crew Days |

The "Labor-Hours" figure represents the number of labor-hours required to install one unit of work. To find out the number of labor-hours required for your particular task, multiply the quantity of the item times the number of labor-hours shown. For example:

| Quantity | x | Productivity Rate | = | Duration |
|---|---|---|---|---|
| 100 C.Y. | x | 3.20 Labor-Hours/ C.Y. | = | 320 Labor-Hours |

## Unit (C.Y.)

The abbreviated designation indicates the unit of measure upon which the price, production, and crew are based (C.Y. = Cubic Yard). For a complete listing of abbreviations, refer to the Abbreviations Listing in the Reference Section of this book.

## Bare Costs:
### Mat. (Bare Material Cost) (131)

The unit material cost is the "bare" material cost with no overhead or profit included. Costs shown reflect national average material prices for January of the current year and include delivery to the job site. No sales taxes are included.

### Labor (87.50)

The unit labor cost is derived by multiplying bare labor-hour costs for Crew C-14C by labor-hour units. The bare labor-hour cost is found in the Crew Section under C-14C. (If a trade is listed, the hourly labor cost—the wage rate—is found on the inside back cover.)

| Labor-Hour Cost Crew C-14C | x | Labor-Hour Units | = | Labor |
|---|---|---|---|---|
| $27.30 | x | 3.20 | = | $87.50 |

### Equip. (Equipment) (.86)

Equipment costs for each crew are listed in the description of each crew. Tools or equipment whose value justifies purchase or ownership by a contractor are considered overhead as shown on the inside back cover. The unit equipment cost is derived by multiplying the bare equipment hourly cost by the labor-hour units.

| Equipment Cost Crew C-14C | x | Labor-Hour Units | = | Equip. |
|---|---|---|---|---|
| $.27 | x | 3.20 | = | $.86 |

### Total (219.36)

The total of the bare costs is the arithmetic total of the three previous columns: mat., labor, and equip.

| Material | + | Labor | + | Equip. | = | Total |
|---|---|---|---|---|---|---|
| $131 | + | $87.50 | + | $.86 | = | $219.36 |

## Total Costs Including O&P

This figure is the sum of the bare material cost plus 10% for profit; the bare labor cost plus total overhead and profit (per the inside back cover or, if a crew is listed, from the crew listings); and the bare equipment cost plus 10% for profit.

| | | |
|---|---|---|
| Material is Bare Material Cost + 10% = 131 + 13.10 | = | $144.10 |
| Labor for Crew C-14C = Labor-Hour Cost (46.06) x Labor-Hour Units (3.20) | = | $147.39 |
| Equip. is Bare Equip. Cost + 10% = .86 + .09 | = | $ .95 |
| Total (Rounded) | = | $ 292 |

# Estimating Tips

## 01 20 00 Price and Payment Procedures

- Allowances that should be added to estimates to cover contingencies and job conditions that are not included in the national average material and labor costs are shown in section 01 21.

- When estimating historic preservation projects (depending on the condition of the existing structure and the owner's requirements), a 15%–20% contingency or allowance is recommended, regardless of the stage of the drawings.

## 01 30 00 Administrative Requirements

- Before determining a final cost estimate, it is a good practice to review all the items listed in Subdivisions 01 31 and 01 32 to make final adjustments for items that may need customizing to specific job conditions.

- Requirements for initial and periodic submittals can represent a significant cost to the General Requirements of a job. Thoroughly check the submittal specifications when estimating a project to determine any costs that should be included.

## 01 40 00 Quality Requirements

- All projects will require some degree of Quality Control. This cost is not included in the unit cost of construction listed in each division. Depending upon the terms of the contract, the various costs of inspection and testing can be the responsibility of either the owner or the contractor. Be sure to include the required costs in your estimate.

## 01 50 00 Temporary Facilities and Controls

- Barricades, access roads, safety nets, scaffolding, security, and many more requirements for the execution of a safe project are elements of direct cost. These costs can easily be overlooked when preparing an estimate. When looking through the major classifications of this subdivision, determine which items apply to each division in your estimate.

- Construction Equipment Rental Costs can be found in the Reference Section in section 01 54 33. Operators' wages are not included in equipment rental costs.

- Equipment mobilization and demobilization costs are not included in equipment rental costs and must be considered separately in section 01 54 36.50.

- The cost of small tools provided by the installing contractor for his workers is covered in the "Overhead" column on the "Installing Contractor's Overhead and Profit" table that lists labor trades, base rates and markups and, therefore, is included in the "Total Incl. O&P" cost of any Unit Price line item. For those users who are constrained by contract terms to use only bare costs, there are two line items in section 01 54 39.70 for small tools as a percentage of bare labor cost. If some of those users are further constrained by contract terms to refrain from using line items from Division 1, you are advised to cover the cost of small tools within your coefficient or multiplier.

## 01 70 00 Execution and Closeout Requirements

- When preparing an estimate, thoroughly read the specifications to determine the requirements for Contract Closeout. Final cleaning, record documentation, operation and maintenance data, warranties and bonds, and spare parts and maintenance materials can all be elements of cost for the completion of a contract. Do not overlook these in your estimate.

## Reference Numbers

Reference numbers are shown in shaded boxes at the beginning of some major classifications. These numbers refer to related items in the Reference Section. The reference information may be an estimating procedure, an alternate pricing method, or technical information.

*Note:* Not all subdivisions listed here necessarily appear in this publication.

# 01 11 Summary of Work

## 01 11 31 – Professional Consultants

| 01 11 31.10 Architectural Fees | | Crew | Daily Output | Labor-Hours | Unit | Material | 2010 Bare Costs Labor | Equipment | Total | Total Incl O&P |
|---|---|---|---|---|---|---|---|---|---|---|
| 0010 | **ARCHITECTURAL FEES** | R011110-10 | | | | | | | | |
| 0020 | For new construction | | | | | | | | | |
| 0060 | Minimum | | | | Project | | | | | 4.90% |
| 0090 | Maximum | | | | | | | | | 16% |
| 0100 | For alteration work, to $500,000, add to new construction fee | | | | | | | | | 50% |
| 0150 | Over $500,000, add to new construction fee | | | | | | | | | 25% |

### 01 11 31.20 Construction Management Fees

| | | | | | | | | | | |
|---|---|---|---|---|---|---|---|---|---|---|
| 0010 | **CONSTRUCTION MANAGEMENT FEES** | | | | | | | | | |
| 0060 | For work to $100,000 | | | | Project | | | | | 10% |
| 0070 | To $250,000 | | | | | | | | | 9% |
| 0090 | To $1,000,000 | | | | | | | | | 6% |

### 01 11 31.75 Renderings

| | | | | | | | | | | |
|---|---|---|---|---|---|---|---|---|---|---|
| 0010 | **RENDERINGS** Color, matted, 20" x 30", eye level, | | | | | | | | | |
| 0050 | Average | | | | Ea. | 2,775 | | | 2,775 | 3,075 |

# 01 21 Allowances

## 01 21 16 – Contingency Allowances

### 01 21 16.50 Contingencies

| | | | | | | | | | | |
|---|---|---|---|---|---|---|---|---|---|---|
| 0010 | **CONTINGENCIES**, Add to estimate | | | | | | | | | |
| 0020 | Conceptual stage | | | | Project | | | | | 20% |
| 0150 | Final working drawing stage | | | | " | | | | | 3% |

## 01 21 63 – Taxes

### 01 21 63.10 Taxes

| | | | | | | | | | | |
|---|---|---|---|---|---|---|---|---|---|---|
| 0010 | **TAXES** | R012909-80 | | | | | | | | |
| 0020 | Sales tax, State, average | | | | % | 5.01% | | | | |
| 0050 | Maximum | R012909-85 | | | | 8.25% | | | | |
| 0200 | Social Security, on first $106,800 of wages | | | | | | 7.65% | | | |
| 0300 | Unemployment, combined Federal and State, minimum | | | | | | .80% | | | |
| 0350 | Average | | | | | | 6.20% | | | |
| 0400 | Maximum | | | | | | 10.96% | | | |

# 01 31 Project Management and Coordination

## 01 31 13 – Project Coordination

### 01 31 13.30 Insurance

| | | | | | | | | | | |
|---|---|---|---|---|---|---|---|---|---|---|
| 0010 | **INSURANCE** | R013113-40 | | | | | | | | |
| 0020 | Builders risk, standard, minimum | | | | Job | | | | | .24% |
| 0050 | Maximum | R013113-60 | | | | | | | | .64% |
| 0200 | All-risk type, minimum | | | | | | | | | .25% |
| 0250 | Maximum | | | | | | | | | .62% |
| 0400 | Contractor's equipment floater, minimum | | | | Value | | | | | .50% |
| 0450 | Maximum | | | | " | | | | | 1.50% |
| 0600 | Public liability, average | | | | Job | | | | | 2.02% |
| 0800 | Workers' compensation & employer's liability, average | | | | | | | | | |
| 0850 | by trade, carpentry, general | | | | Payroll | | 16.88% | | | |
| 0900 | Clerical | | | | | | .52% | | | |
| 0950 | Concrete | | | | | | 13.72% | | | |
| 1000 | Electrical | | | | | | 6.38% | | | |
| 1050 | Excavation | | | | | | 9.42% | | | |

# 01 31 Project Management and Coordination

## 01 31 13 – Project Coordination

| 01 31 13.30 Insurance | | Crew | Daily Output | Labor-Hours | Unit | Material | 2010 Bare Costs Labor | Equipment | Total | Total Incl O&P |
|---|---|---|---|---|---|---|---|---|---|---|
| 1100 | Glazing | | | | Payroll | | 13.27% | | | |
| 1150 | Insulation | | | | | | 13.11% | | | |
| 1200 | Lathing | | | | | | 9.79% | | | |
| 1250 | Masonry | | | | | | 13.47% | | | |
| 1300 | Painting & decorating | | | | | | 11.46% | | | |
| 1350 | Pile driving | | | | | | 18.54% | | | |
| 1400 | Plastering | | | | | | 11.92% | | | |
| 1450 | Plumbing | | | | | | 7.62% | | | |
| 1500 | Roofing | | | | | | 28.89% | | | |
| 1550 | Sheet metal work (HVAC) | | | | | | 9.14% | | | |
| 1600 | Steel erection, structural | | | | | | 35.99% | | | |
| 1650 | Tile work, interior ceramic | | | | | | 8.78% | | | |
| 1700 | Waterproofing, brush or hand caulking | | | | | | 6.48% | | | |
| 1800 | Wrecking | | | | | | 30.31% | | | |
| 2000 | Range of 35 trades in 50 states, excl. wrecking, min. | | | | | | 2.39% | | | |
| 2100 | Average | | | | | | 14.40% | | | |
| 2200 | Maximum | | | | | | 170.80% | | | |

# 01 41 Regulatory Requirements

## 01 41 26 – Permits

### 01 41 26.50 Permits

| | | Crew | Daily Output | Labor-Hours | Unit | Material | 2010 Bare Costs Labor | Equipment | Total | Total Incl O&P |
|---|---|---|---|---|---|---|---|---|---|---|
| 0010 | **PERMITS** | | | | | | | | | |
| 0020 | Rule of thumb, most cities, minimum | | | | Job | | | | | .50% |
| 0100 | Maximum | | | | " | | | | | 2% |

# 01 54 Construction Aids

## 01 54 16 – Temporary Hoists

### 01 54 16.50 Weekly Forklift Crew

| | | Crew | Daily Output | Labor-Hours | Unit | Material | 2010 Bare Costs Labor | Equipment | Total | Total Incl O&P |
|---|---|---|---|---|---|---|---|---|---|---|
| 0010 | **WEEKLY FORKLIFT CREW** | | | | | | | | | |
| 0100 | All-terrain forklift, 45' lift, 35' reach, 9000 lb. capacity | A-3P | .20 | 40 | Week | | 1,150 | 2,400 | 3,550 | 4,500 |

## 01 54 19 – Temporary Cranes

### 01 54 19.50 Daily Crane Crews

| | | Crew | Daily Output | Labor-Hours | Unit | Material | 2010 Bare Costs Labor | Equipment | Total | Total Incl O&P |
|---|---|---|---|---|---|---|---|---|---|---|
| 0010 | **DAILY CRANE CREWS** for small jobs, portal to portal | | | | | | | | | |
| 0100 | 12-ton truck-mounted hydraulic crane | A-3H | 1 | 8 | Day | | 245 | 870 | 1,115 | 1,350 |

## 01 54 23 – Temporary Scaffolding and Platforms

### 01 54 23.60 Pump Staging

| | | | Crew | Daily Output | Labor-Hours | Unit | Material | 2010 Bare Costs Labor | Equipment | Total | Total Incl O&P |
|---|---|---|---|---|---|---|---|---|---|---|---|
| 0010 | **PUMP STAGING**, Aluminum | | | | | | | | | | |
| 1300 | System in place, 50' working height, per use based on 50 uses | | 2 Carp | 84.80 | .189 | C.S.F. | 6.40 | 5.50 | | 11.90 | 16.30 |
| 1400 | 100 uses | R015423-20 | | 84.80 | .189 | | 3.21 | 5.50 | | 8.71 | 12.80 |
| 1500 | 150 uses | | | 84.80 | .189 | | 2.15 | 5.50 | | 7.65 | 11.60 |

### 01 54 23.70 Scaffolding

| | | | Crew | Daily Output | Labor-Hours | Unit | Material | 2010 Bare Costs Labor | Equipment | Total | Total Incl O&P |
|---|---|---|---|---|---|---|---|---|---|---|---|
| 0010 | **SCAFFOLDING** | R015423-10 | | | | | | | | | |
| 0015 | Steel tube, regular, no plank, labor only to erect & dismantle | | | | | | | | | | |
| 0091 | Building exterior, wall face, 1 to 5 stories, 6'-4" x 5' frames | | 3 Clab | 8 | 3 | C.S.F. | | 64.50 | | 64.50 | 108 |
| 0201 | 6 to 12 stories | | 4 Clab | 8 | 4 | | | 86 | | 86 | 145 |
| 0310 | 13 to 20 stories | | 5 Carp | 8 | 5 | | | 146 | | 146 | 245 |
| 0461 | Building interior, walls face area, up to 16' high | | 3 Clab | 12 | 2 | | | 43 | | 43 | 72.50 |
| 0561 | 16' to 40' high | | | 10 | 2.400 | | | 51.50 | | 51.50 | 87 |

# 01 54 Construction Aids

## 01 54 23 – Temporary Scaffolding and Platforms

| 01 54 23.70 Scaffolding | Crew | Daily Output | Labor-Hours | Unit | Material | 2010 Bare Costs Labor | Equipment | Total | Total Incl O&P |
|---|---|---|---|---|---|---|---|---|---|
| 0801 | Building interior floor area, up to 30' high | 3 Clab | 150 | .160 | C.C.F. | | 3.44 | | 3.44 | 5.80 |
| 0901 | Over 30' high | 4 Clab | 160 | .200 | " | | 4.30 | | 4.30 | 7.25 |
| 0906 | Complete system for face of walls, no plank, material only rent/mo | | | | C.S.F. | 36 | | | 36 | 39.50 |
| 0908 | Interior spaces, no plank, material only rent/mo | | | | C.C.F. | 3.42 | | | 3.42 | 3.76 |
| 0910 | Steel tubular, heavy duty shoring, buy | | | | | | | | | |
| 0920 | Frames 5' high 2' wide | | | | Ea. | 93 | | | 93 | 102 |
| 0925 | 5' high 4' wide | | | | | 105 | | | 105 | 116 |
| 0930 | 6' high 2' wide | | | | | 106 | | | 106 | 117 |
| 0935 | 6' high 4' wide | | | | | 124 | | | 124 | 136 |
| 0940 | Accessories | | | | | | | | | |
| 0945 | Cross braces | | | | Ea. | 18 | | | 18 | 19.80 |
| 0950 | U-head, 8" x 8" | | | | | 21.50 | | | 21.50 | 24 |
| 0955 | J-head, 4" x 8" | | | | | 15.80 | | | 15.80 | 17.40 |
| 0960 | Base plate, 8" x 8" | | | | | 17.60 | | | 17.60 | 19.35 |
| 0965 | Leveling jack | | | | | 38 | | | 38 | 41.50 |
| 1000 | Steel tubular, regular, buy | | | | | | | | | |
| 1100 | Frames 3' high 5' wide | | | | Ea. | 71 | | | 71 | 78 |
| 1150 | 5' high 5' wide | | | | | 83 | | | 83 | 91.50 |
| 1200 | 6'-4" high 5' wide | | | | | 104 | | | 104 | 114 |
| 1350 | 7'-6" high 6' wide | | | | | 179 | | | 179 | 197 |
| 1500 | Accessories cross braces | | | | | 20.50 | | | 20.50 | 22.50 |
| 1550 | Guardrail post | | | | | 18.60 | | | 18.60 | 20.50 |
| 1600 | Guardrail 7' section | | | | | 9.90 | | | 9.90 | 10.90 |
| 1650 | Screw jacks & plates | | | | | 27 | | | 27 | 29.50 |
| 1700 | Sidearm brackets | | | | | 43 | | | 43 | 47.50 |
| 1750 | 8" casters | | | | | 35.50 | | | 35.50 | 39 |
| 1800 | Plank 2" x 10" x 16'-0" | | | | | 51 | | | 51 | 56 |
| 1900 | Stairway section | | | | | 325 | | | 325 | 360 |
| 1910 | Stairway starter bar | | | | | 36.50 | | | 36.50 | 40 |
| 1920 | Stairway inside handrail | | | | | 66 | | | 66 | 72.50 |
| 1930 | Stairway outside handrail | | | | | 98 | | | 98 | 108 |
| 1940 | Walk-thru frame guardrail | | | | | 47 | | | 47 | 51.50 |
| 2000 | Steel tubular, regular, rent/mo. | | | | | | | | | |
| 2100 | Frames 3' high 5' wide | | | | Ea. | 5 | | | 5 | 5.50 |
| 2150 | 5' high 5' wide | | | | | 5 | | | 5 | 5.50 |
| 2200 | 6'-4" high 5' wide | | | | | 5.15 | | | 5.15 | 5.65 |
| 2250 | 7'-6" high 6' wide | | | | | 7 | | | 7 | 7.70 |
| 2500 | Accessories, cross braces | | | | | 1 | | | 1 | 1.10 |
| 2550 | Guardrail post | | | | | 1 | | | 1 | 1.10 |
| 2600 | Guardrail 7' section | | | | | 1 | | | 1 | 1.10 |
| 2650 | Screw jacks & plates | | | | | 2 | | | 2 | 2.20 |
| 2700 | Sidearm brackets | | | | | 2 | | | 2 | 2.20 |
| 2750 | 8" casters | | | | | 8 | | | 8 | 8.80 |
| 2800 | Outrigger for rolling tower | | | | | 3 | | | 3 | 3.30 |
| 2850 | Plank 2" x 10" x 16'-0" | | | | | 6 | | | 6 | 6.60 |
| 2900 | Stairway section | | | | | 40 | | | 40 | 44 |
| 2940 | Walk-thru frame guardrail | | | | | 2.50 | | | 2.50 | 2.75 |
| 3000 | Steel tubular, heavy duty shoring, rent/mo. | | | | | | | | | |
| 3250 | 5' high 2' & 4' wide | | | | Ea. | 5 | | | 5 | 5.50 |
| 3300 | 6' high 2' & 4' wide | | | | | 5 | | | 5 | 5.50 |
| 3500 | Accessories, cross braces | | | | | 1 | | | 1 | 1.10 |
| 3600 | U - head, 8" x 8" | | | | | 1 | | | 1 | 1.10 |
| 3650 | J - head, 4" x 8" | | | | | 1 | | | 1 | 1.10 |

# 01 54 Construction Aids

## 01 54 23 – Temporary Scaffolding and Platforms

### 01 54 23.70 Scaffolding

| | | Crew | Daily Output | Labor-Hours | Unit | Material | 2010 Bare Costs Labor | 2010 Bare Costs Equipment | Total | Total Incl O&P |
|---|---|---|---|---|---|---|---|---|---|---|
| 3700 | Base plate, 8" x 8" | | | | Ea. | 1 | | | 1 | 1.10 |
| 3750 | Leveling jack | | | | | 2 | | | 2 | 2.20 |
| 5700 | Planks, 2" x 10" x 16'-0", labor only to erect & remove to 50' H | 3 Carp | 72 | .333 | | | 9.70 | | 9.70 | 16.30 |
| 5800 | Over 50' high | 4 Carp | 80 | .400 | | | 11.65 | | 11.65 | 19.60 |

### 01 54 23.80 Staging Aids

| | | Crew | Daily Output | Labor-Hours | Unit | Material | 2010 Bare Costs Labor | 2010 Bare Costs Equipment | Total | Total Incl O&P |
|---|---|---|---|---|---|---|---|---|---|---|
| 0010 | **STAGING AIDS** and fall protection equipment | | | | | | | | | |
| 0100 | Sidewall staging bracket, tubular, buy | | | | Ea. | 46 | | | 46 | 50.50 |
| 0110 | Cost each per day, based on 250 days use | | | | Day | .18 | | | .18 | .20 |
| 0200 | Guard post, buy | | | | Ea. | 22.50 | | | 22.50 | 25 |
| 0210 | Cost each per day, based on 250 days use | | | | Day | .09 | | | .09 | .10 |
| 0300 | End guard chains, buy per pair | | | | Pair | 31 | | | 31 | 34 |
| 0310 | Cost per set per day, based on 250 days use | | | | Day | .18 | | | .18 | .20 |
| 1010 | Cost each per day, based on 250 days use | | | | " | .04 | | | .04 | .04 |
| 1100 | Wood bracket, buy | | | | Ea. | 16.60 | | | 16.60 | 18.25 |
| 1110 | Cost each per day, based on 250 days use | | | | Day | .07 | | | .07 | .07 |
| 2010 | Cost per pair per day, based on 250 days use | | | | " | .43 | | | .43 | .48 |
| 2100 | Steel siderail jack, buy per pair | | | | Pair | 122 | | | 122 | 134 |
| 2110 | Cost per pair per day, based on 250 days use | | | | Day | .49 | | | .49 | .54 |
| 3010 | Cost each per day, based on 250 days use | | | | " | .20 | | | .20 | .22 |
| 3100 | Aluminum scaffolding plank, 20" wide x 24' long, buy | | | | Ea. | 890 | | | 890 | 975 |
| 3110 | Cost each per day, based on 250 days use | | | | Day | 3.55 | | | 3.55 | 3.91 |
| 4010 | Cost each per day, based on 250 days use | | | | " | .86 | | | .86 | .95 |
| 4100 | Rope for safety line, 5/8" x 100' nylon, buy | | | | Ea. | 70 | | | 70 | 77 |
| 4110 | Cost each per day, based on 250 days use | | | | Day | .28 | | | .28 | .31 |
| 4200 | Permanent U-Bolt roof anchor, buy | | | | Ea. | 35 | | | 35 | 38.50 |
| 4300 | Temporary (one use) roof ridge anchor, buy | | | | " | 28.50 | | | 28.50 | 31 |
| 5000 | Installation (setup and removal) of staging aids | | | | | | | | | |
| 5010 | Sidewall staging bracket | 2 Carp | 64 | .250 | Ea. | | 7.30 | | 7.30 | 12.25 |
| 5020 | Guard post with 2 wood rails | " | 64 | .250 | | | 7.30 | | 7.30 | 12.25 |
| 5030 | End guard chains, set | 1 Carp | 64 | .125 | | | 3.64 | | 3.64 | 6.10 |
| 5100 | Roof shingling bracket | | 96 | .083 | | | 2.42 | | 2.42 | 4.08 |
| 5200 | Ladder jack | | 64 | .125 | | | 3.64 | | 3.64 | 6.10 |
| 5300 | Wood plank, 2" x 10" x 16' | 2 Carp | 80 | .200 | | | 5.80 | | 5.80 | 9.80 |
| 5310 | Aluminum scaffold plank, 20" x 24' | " | 40 | .400 | | | 11.65 | | 11.65 | 19.60 |
| 5410 | Safety rope | 1 Carp | 40 | .200 | | | 5.80 | | 5.80 | 9.80 |
| 5420 | Permanent U-Bolt roof anchor (install only) | 2 Carp | 40 | .400 | | | 11.65 | | 11.65 | 19.60 |
| 5430 | Temporary roof ridge anchor (install only) | 1 Carp | 64 | .125 | | | 3.64 | | 3.64 | 6.10 |

## 01 54 36 – Equipment Mobilization

### 01 54 36.50 Mobilization

| | | Crew | Daily Output | Labor-Hours | Unit | Material | 2010 Bare Costs Labor | 2010 Bare Costs Equipment | Total | Total Incl O&P |
|---|---|---|---|---|---|---|---|---|---|---|
| 0010 | **MOBILIZATION** (Use line item again for demobilization) | | | | | | | | | |
| 0015 | Up to 25 mi haul dist (50 mi RT for mob/demob crew) | | | | | | | | | |
| 0020 | Dozer, loader, backhoe, excav., grader, paver, roller, 70 to 150 H.P. | B-34N | 4 | 2 | Ea. | | 47 | 136 | 183 | 229 |
| 0900 | Shovel or dragline, 3/4 C.Y. | B-34K | 3.60 | 2.222 | | | 52.50 | 256 | 308.50 | 370 |
| 1100 | Small equipment, placed in rear of, or towed by pickup truck | A-3A | 8 | 1 | | | 23 | 18.90 | 41.90 | 59 |
| 1150 | Equip up to 70 HP, on flatbed trailer behind pickup truck | A-3D | 4 | 2 | | | 46 | 64 | 110 | 147 |
| 2000 | Crane, truck-mounted, up to 75 ton, (driver only, one-way) | 1 Eqhv | 7.20 | 1.111 | | | 34 | | 34 | 55.50 |
| 2200 | Crawler-mounted, up to 75 ton | A-3F | 2 | 8 | | | 217 | 475 | 692 | 875 |
| 2500 | For each additional 5 miles haul distance, add | | | | | | 10% | 10% | | |
| 3000 | For large pieces of equipment, allow for assembly/knockdown | | | | | | | | | |
| 3100 | For mob/demob of micro-tunneling equip, see Div. 33 05 23.19 | | | | | | | | | |

# 01 54 Construction Aids

## 01 54 39 – Construction Equipment

| 01 54 39.70 Small Tools | Crew | Daily Output | Labor-Hours | Unit | Material | 2010 Bare Costs Labor | Equipment | Total | Total Incl O&P |
|---|---|---|---|---|---|---|---|---|---|
| 0010 **SMALL TOOLS** | | | | | | | | | |
| 0020   As % of contractor's bare labor cost for project, minimum | | | | Total | | | | | .50% |
| 0100     Maximum | | | | " | | | | | 2% |

# 01 56 Temporary Barriers and Enclosures

## 01 56 13 – Temporary Air Barriers

### 01 56 13.60 Tarpaulins

| | | Crew | Daily Output | Labor-Hours | Unit | Material | 2010 Bare Costs Labor | Equipment | Total | Total Incl O&P |
|---|---|---|---|---|---|---|---|---|---|---|
| 0010 | **TARPAULINS** | | | | | | | | | |
| 0020 | Cotton duck, 10 oz. to 13.13 oz. per S.Y., minimum | | | | S.F. | .59 | | | .59 | .65 |
| 0050 |   Maximum | | | | | .53 | | | .53 | .58 |
| 0200 | Reinforced polyethylene 3 mils thick, white | | | | | .15 | | | .15 | .17 |
| 0300 |   4 mils thick, white, clear or black | | | | | .20 | | | .20 | .22 |
| 0730 | Polyester reinforced w/integral fastening system 11 mils thick | | | | | 1.07 | | | 1.07 | 1.18 |

# 01 71 Examination and Preparation

## 01 71 23 – Field Engineering

### 01 71 23.13 Construction Layout

| | | Crew | Daily Output | Labor-Hours | Unit | Material | 2010 Bare Costs Labor | Equipment | Total | Total Incl O&P |
|---|---|---|---|---|---|---|---|---|---|---|
| 0010 | **CONSTRUCTION LAYOUT** | | | | | | | | | |
| 1100 | Crew for layout of building, trenching or pipe laying, 2 person crew | A-6 | 1 | 16 | Day | | 460 | 70 | 530 | 845 |
| 1200 |   3 person crew | A-7 | 1 | 24 | " | | 740 | 70 | 810 | 1,300 |

# 01 74 Cleaning and Waste Management

## 01 74 13 – Progress Cleaning

### 01 74 13.20 Cleaning Up

| | | Crew | Daily Output | Labor-Hours | Unit | Material | 2010 Bare Costs Labor | Equipment | Total | Total Incl O&P |
|---|---|---|---|---|---|---|---|---|---|---|
| 0010 | **CLEANING UP** | | | | | | | | | |
| 0020 | After job completion, allow, minimum | | | | Job | | | | | .30% |
| 0040 |   Maximum | | | | " | | | | | 1% |

# Estimating Tips

## 02 30 00 Subsurface Investigation

In preparing estimates on structures involving earthwork or foundations, all information concerning soil characteristics should be obtained. Look particularly for hazardous waste, evidence of prior dumping of debris, and previous stream beds.

## 02 41 00 Demolition and Structure Moving

The costs shown for selective demolition do not include rubbish handling or disposal. These items should be estimated separately using RSMeans data or other sources.

- Historic preservation often requires that the contractor remove materials from the existing structure, rehab them, and replace them. The estimator must be aware of any related measures and precautions that must be taken when doing selective demolition and cutting and patching. Requirements may include special handling and storage, as well as security.

- In addition to Subdivision 02 41 00, you can find selective demolition items in each division. Example: Roofing demolition is in Division 7.

## 02 42 10 Building Deconstruction

This is a new section on the careful demantling and recycling of most of low-rise building materials.

## 02 56 13 Containment of Hazardous Waste

This is a new section for disposal of hazardous waste on site.

## 02 80 00 Hazardous Material Disposal/ Remediation

This subdivision includes information on hazardous waste handling, asbestos remediation, lead remediation, and mold remediation. See reference R028213-20 and R028319-60 for further guidance in using these unit price lines.

## 02 91 10 Monitoring Chemical Sampling, Testing Analysis

This is a new section for on-site sampling and testing hazardous waste.

## Reference Numbers

Reference numbers are shown in shaded boxes at the beginning of some major classifications. These numbers refer to related items in the Reference Section. The reference information may be an estimating procedure, an alternate pricing method, or technical information.

*Note:* Not all subdivisions listed here necessarily appear in this publication.

# 02 21 Surveys

## 02 21 13 – Site Surveys

| 02 21 13.09 Topographical Surveys | Crew | Daily Output | Labor-Hours | Unit | Material | 2010 Bare Costs Labor | Equipment | Total | Total Incl O&P |
|---|---|---|---|---|---|---|---|---|---|
| **0010 TOPOGRAPHICAL SURVEYS** | | | | | | | | | |
| 0020 Topographical surveying, conventional, minimum | A-7 | 3.30 | 7.273 | Acre | 18 | 224 | 21 | 263 | 420 |
| 0100 Maximum | A-8 | .60 | 53.333 | " | 55 | 1,600 | 116 | 1,771 | 2,875 |

### 02 21 13.13 Boundary and Survey Markers

| | Crew | Daily Output | Labor-Hours | Unit | Material | Labor | Equipment | Total | Total Incl O&P |
|---|---|---|---|---|---|---|---|---|---|
| **0010 BOUNDARY AND SURVEY MARKERS** | | | | | | | | | |
| 0300 Lot location and lines, large quantities, minimum | A-7 | 2 | 12 | Acre | 32 | 370 | 35 | 437 | 690 |
| 0320 Average | " | 1.25 | 19.200 | | 51 | 590 | 56 | 697 | 1,100 |
| 0400 Small quantities, maximum | A-8 | 1 | 32 | ↓ | 68 | 965 | 70 | 1,103 | 1,750 |
| 0600 Monuments, 3' long | A-7 | 10 | 2.400 | Ea. | 30 | 74 | 7 | 111 | 164 |
| 0800 Property lines, perimeter, cleared land | " | 1000 | .024 | L.F. | .03 | .74 | .07 | .84 | 1.34 |
| 0900 Wooded land | A-8 | 875 | .037 | " | .05 | 1.10 | .08 | 1.23 | 1.98 |

# 02 32 Geotechnical Investigations

## 02 32 13 – Subsurface Drilling and Sampling

### 02 32 13.10 Boring and Exploratory Drilling

| | Crew | Daily Output | Labor-Hours | Unit | Material | Labor | Equipment | Total | Total Incl O&P |
|---|---|---|---|---|---|---|---|---|---|
| **0010 BORING AND EXPLORATORY DRILLING** | | | | | | | | | |
| 0020 Borings, initial field stake out & determination of elevations | A-6 | 1 | 16 | Day | | 460 | 70 | 530 | 845 |
| 0100 Drawings showing boring details | | | | Total | | 185 | | 185 | 270 |
| 0200 Report and recommendations from P.E. | | | | | | 415 | | 415 | 595 |
| 0300 Mobilization and demobilization, minimum | B-55 | 4 | 4 | ↓ | | 89 | 261 | 350 | 435 |
| 0350 For over 100 miles, per added mile | | 450 | .036 | Mile | | .79 | 2.32 | 3.11 | 3.88 |
| 0600 Auger holes in earth, no samples, 2-1/2" diameter | | 78.60 | .204 | L.F. | | 4.52 | 13.30 | 17.82 | 22 |
| 0800 Cased borings in earth, with samples, 2-1/2" diameter | | 55.50 | .288 | " | 20.50 | 6.40 | 18.85 | 45.75 | 53.50 |
| 1400 Borings, earth, drill rig and crew with truck mounted auger | ↓ | 1 | 16 | Day | | 355 | 1,050 | 1,405 | 1,750 |
| 1500 For inner city borings add, minimum | | | | | | | | | 10% |
| 1510 Maximum | | | | | | | | | 20% |

# 02 41 Demolition

## 02 41 13 – Selective Site Demolition

### 02 41 13.17 Demolish, Remove Pavement and Curb

| | Crew | Daily Output | Labor-Hours | Unit | Material | Labor | Equipment | Total | Total Incl O&P |
|---|---|---|---|---|---|---|---|---|---|
| **0010 DEMOLISH, REMOVE PAVEMENT AND CURB** R024119-10 | | | | | | | | | |
| 5010 Pavement removal, bituminous roads, 3" thick | B-38 | 690 | .035 | S.Y. | | .83 | .71 | 1.54 | 2.16 |
| 5050 4" to 6" thick | | 420 | .057 | | | 1.36 | 1.17 | 2.53 | 3.56 |
| 5100 Bituminous driveways | | 640 | .038 | | | .89 | .77 | 1.66 | 2.34 |
| 5200 Concrete to 6" thick, hydraulic hammer, mesh reinforced | | 255 | .094 | | | 2.24 | 1.93 | 4.17 | 5.85 |
| 5300 Rod reinforced | | 200 | .120 | ↓ | | 2.86 | 2.46 | 5.32 | 7.45 |
| 5600 With hand held air equipment, bituminous, to 6" thick | B-39 | 1900 | .025 | S.F. | | .55 | .12 | .67 | 1.06 |
| 5700 Concrete to 6" thick, no reinforcing | | 1600 | .030 | | | .65 | .14 | .79 | 1.25 |
| 5800 Mesh reinforced | | 1400 | .034 | | | .75 | .16 | .91 | 1.44 |
| 5900 Rod reinforced | ↓ | 765 | .063 | ↓ | | 1.37 | .29 | 1.66 | 2.62 |
| 6000 Curbs, concrete, plain | B-6 | 360 | .067 | L.F. | | 1.59 | .94 | 2.53 | 3.67 |
| 6100 Reinforced | | 275 | .087 | | | 2.08 | 1.23 | 3.31 | 4.81 |
| 6200 Granite | | 360 | .067 | | | 1.59 | .94 | 2.53 | 3.67 |
| 6300 Bituminous | ↓ | 528 | .045 | ↓ | | 1.08 | .64 | 1.72 | 2.50 |

### 02 41 13.33 Minor Site Demolition

| | Crew | Daily Output | Labor-Hours | Unit | Material | Labor | Equipment | Total | Total Incl O&P |
|---|---|---|---|---|---|---|---|---|---|
| **0010 MINOR SITE DEMOLITION** R024119-10 | | | | | | | | | |
| 0015 No hauling, abandon catch basin or manhole | B-6 | 7 | 3.429 | Ea. | | 81.50 | 48.50 | 130 | 189 |
| 0020 Remove existing catch basin or manhole, masonry | | 4 | 6 | | | 143 | 84.50 | 227.50 | 330 |
| 0030 Catch basin or manhole frames and covers, stored | | 13 | 1.846 | ↓ | | 44 | 26 | 70 | 102 |

# 02 41 Demolition

## 02 41 13 – Selective Site Demolition

### 02 41 13.33 Minor Site Demolition

| | | Crew | Daily Output | Labor-Hours | Unit | Material | 2010 Bare Costs Labor | 2010 Bare Costs Equipment | Total | Total Incl O&P |
|---|---|---|---|---|---|---|---|---|---|---|
| 0040 | Remove and reset | B-6 | 7 | 3.429 | Ea. | | 81.50 | 48.50 | 130 | 189 |
| 1000 | Masonry walls, block, solid | B-5 | 1800 | .022 | C.F. | | .52 | .72 | 1.24 | 1.67 |
| 1200 | Brick, solid | | 900 | .044 | | | 1.05 | 1.45 | 2.50 | 3.34 |
| 1400 | Stone, with mortar | | 900 | .044 | | | 1.05 | 1.45 | 2.50 | 3.34 |
| 1500 | Dry set | ↓ | 1500 | .027 | ↓ | | .63 | .87 | 1.50 | 2 |
| 2900 | Pipe removal, sewer/water, no excavation, 12" diameter | B-6 | 175 | .137 | L.F. | | 3.27 | 1.93 | 5.20 | 7.55 |
| 2960 | 21"-24" diameter | | 120 | .200 | " | | 4.77 | 2.82 | 7.59 | 11.05 |
| 4000 | Sidewalk removal, bituminous, 2-1/2" thick | | 325 | .074 | S.Y. | | 1.76 | 1.04 | 2.80 | 4.07 |
| 4050 | Brick, set in mortar | | 185 | .130 | | | 3.09 | 1.83 | 4.92 | 7.15 |
| 4100 | Concrete, plain, 4" | | 160 | .150 | | | 3.57 | 2.11 | 5.68 | 8.25 |
| 4200 | Mesh reinforced | ↓ | 150 | .160 | ↓ | | 3.81 | 2.25 | 6.06 | 8.85 |
| 4300 | Slab on grade removal, plain | B-5 | 45 | .889 | C.Y. | | 21 | 29 | 50 | 67 |
| 4310 | Mesh reinforced | | 33 | 1.212 | | | 28.50 | 39.50 | 68 | 91 |
| 4320 | Rod reinforced | ↓ | 25 | 1.600 | | | 37.50 | 52 | 89.50 | 121 |
| 4400 | For congested sites or small quantities, add up to | | | | | | | | 200% | 200% |
| 4450 | For disposal on site, add | B-11A | 232 | .069 | | | 1.76 | 5.15 | 6.91 | 8.55 |
| 4500 | To 5 miles, add | B-34D | 76 | .105 | ↓ | | 2.48 | 9.55 | 12.03 | 14.65 |

### 02 41 13.60 Selective Demolition Fencing

| | | Crew | Daily Output | Labor-Hours | Unit | Material | 2010 Bare Costs Labor | 2010 Bare Costs Equipment | Total | Total Incl O&P |
|---|---|---|---|---|---|---|---|---|---|---|
| 0010 | **SELECTIVE DEMOLITION FENCING** | R024119-10 | | | | | | | | |
| 1600 | Fencing, barbed wire, 3 strand | 2 Clab | 430 | .037 | L.F. | | .80 | | .80 | 1.35 |
| 1650 | 5 strand | " | 280 | .057 | | | 1.23 | | 1.23 | 2.07 |
| 1700 | Chain link, posts & fabric, 8' to 10' high, remove only | B-6 | 445 | .054 | | | 1.29 | .76 | 2.05 | 2.97 |
| 1750 | Remove and reset | " | 70 | .343 | ↓ | | 8.15 | 4.83 | 12.98 | 18.90 |

## 02 41 16 – Structure Demolition

### 02 41 16.13 Building Demolition

| | | Crew | Daily Output | Labor-Hours | Unit | Material | 2010 Bare Costs Labor | 2010 Bare Costs Equipment | Total | Total Incl O&P |
|---|---|---|---|---|---|---|---|---|---|---|
| 0010 | **BUILDING DEMOLITION** Large urban projects, incl. 20 mi. haul | R024119-10 | | | | | | | | |
| 0500 | Small bldgs, or single bldgs, no salvage included, steel | B-3 | 14800 | .003 | C.F. | | .08 | .16 | .24 | .31 |
| 0600 | Concrete | " | 11300 | .004 | " | | .10 | .21 | .31 | .41 |
| 0605 | Concrete, plain | B-5 | 33 | 1.212 | C.Y. | | 28.50 | 39.50 | 68 | 91 |
| 0610 | Reinforced | | 25 | 1.600 | | | 37.50 | 52 | 89.50 | 121 |
| 0615 | Concrete walls | | 34 | 1.176 | | | 27.50 | 38.50 | 66 | 88.50 |
| 0620 | Elevated slabs | ↓ | 26 | 1.538 | ↓ | | 36 | 50 | 86 | 116 |
| 0650 | Masonry | B-3 | 14800 | .003 | C.F. | | .08 | .16 | .24 | .31 |
| 0700 | Wood | " | 14800 | .003 | " | | .08 | .16 | .24 | .31 |
| 1000 | Single family, one story house, wood, minimum | | | | Ea. | | | | 2,525 | 2,975 |
| 1020 | Maximum | | | | | | | | 4,400 | 5,275 |
| 1200 | Two family, two story house, wood, minimum | | | | | | | | 3,300 | 3,950 |
| 1220 | Maximum | | | | | | | | 6,375 | 7,700 |
| 1300 | Three family, three story house, wood, minimum | | | | | | | | 4,400 | 5,275 |
| 1320 | Maximum | | | | ↓ | | | | 7,700 | 9,250 |

### 02 41 16.17 Building Demolition Footings and Foundations

| | | Crew | Daily Output | Labor-Hours | Unit | Material | 2010 Bare Costs Labor | 2010 Bare Costs Equipment | Total | Total Incl O&P |
|---|---|---|---|---|---|---|---|---|---|---|
| 0010 | **BUILDING DEMOLITION FOOTINGS AND FOUNDATIONS** | R024119-10 | | | | | | | | |
| 0200 | Floors, concrete slab on grade, | | | | | | | | | |
| 0240 | 4" thick, plain concrete | B-9 | 500 | .080 | S.F. | | 1.75 | .45 | 2.20 | 3.44 |
| 0280 | Reinforced, wire mesh | | 470 | .085 | | | 1.86 | .48 | 2.34 | 3.66 |
| 0300 | Rods | | 400 | .100 | | | 2.19 | .56 | 2.75 | 4.30 |
| 0400 | 6" thick, plain concrete | | 375 | .107 | | | 2.34 | .60 | 2.94 | 4.59 |
| 0420 | Reinforced, wire mesh | | 340 | .118 | | | 2.58 | .66 | 3.24 | 5.05 |
| 0440 | Rods | ↓ | 300 | .133 | ↓ | | 2.92 | .75 | 3.67 | 5.75 |
| 1000 | Footings, concrete, 1' thick, 2' wide | B-5 | 300 | .133 | L.F. | | 3.14 | 4.34 | 7.48 | 10 |
| 1080 | 1'-6" thick, 2' wide | | 250 | .160 | | | 3.76 | 5.20 | 8.96 | 12.05 |
| 1120 | 3' wide | ↓ | 200 | .200 | ↓ | | 4.71 | 6.50 | 11.21 | 15 |

# 02 41 Demolition

## 02 41 16 – Structure Demolition

| 02 41 16.17 Building Demolition Footings and Foundations | Crew | Daily Output | Labor-Hours | Unit | Material | 2010 Bare Costs Labor | Equipment | Total | Total Incl O&P |
|---|---|---|---|---|---|---|---|---|---|
| 1200      Average reinforcing, add | | | | L.F. | | | | 10% | 10% |
| 2000   Walls, block, 4" thick | 1 Clab | 180 | .044 | S.F. | | .96 | | .96 | 1.61 |
| 2040        6" thick | | 170 | .047 | | | 1.01 | | 1.01 | 1.70 |
| 2080        8" thick | | 150 | .053 | | | 1.15 | | 1.15 | 1.93 |
| 2100        12" thick | | 150 | .053 | | | 1.15 | | 1.15 | 1.93 |
| 2400     Concrete, plain concrete, 6" thick | B-9 | 160 | .250 | | | 5.50 | 1.41 | 6.91 | 10.75 |
| 2420        8" thick | | 140 | .286 | | | 6.25 | 1.61 | 7.86 | 12.25 |
| 2440        10" thick | | 120 | .333 | | | 7.30 | 1.87 | 9.17 | 14.35 |
| 2500        12" thick | | 100 | .400 | | | 8.75 | 2.25 | 11 | 17.20 |
| 2600      For average reinforcing, add | | | | | | | | 10% | 10% |
| 4000   For congested sites or small quantities, add up to | | | | | | | | 200% | 200% |
| 4200   Add for disposal, on site | B-11A | 232 | .069 | C.Y. | | 1.76 | 5.15 | 6.91 | 8.55 |
| 4250      To five miles | B-30 | 220 | .109 | " | | 2.79 | 10.70 | 13.49 | 16.35 |

## 02 41 19 – Selective Structure Demolition

### 02 41 19.13 Selective Building Demolition

| | | | | | | | | | |
|---|---|---|---|---|---|---|---|---|---|
| 0010   **SELECTIVE BUILDING DEMOLITION** | | | | | | | | | |
| 0020     Costs related to selective demolition of specific building components | | | | | | | | | |
| 0025       are included under Common Work Results (XX 05 00) | | | | | | | | | |
| 0030       in the component's appropriate division. | | | | | | | | | |

### 02 41 19.16 Selective Demolition, Cutout

| | Crew | Daily Output | Labor-Hours | Unit | Material | Labor | Equipment | Total | Total Incl O&P |
|---|---|---|---|---|---|---|---|---|---|
| 0010   **SELECTIVE DEMOLITION, CUTOUT**    R024119-10 | | | | | | | | | |
| 0020     Concrete, elev. slab, light reinforcement, under 6 C.F. | B-9 | 65 | .615 | C.F. | | 13.50 | 3.46 | 16.96 | 26.50 |
| 0050       Light reinforcing, over 6 C.F. | | 75 | .533 | " | | 11.70 | 3 | 14.70 | 23 |
| 0200      Slab on grade to 6" thick, not reinforced, under 8 S.F. | | 85 | .471 | S.F. | | 10.30 | 2.64 | 12.94 | 20.50 |
| 0250        8 – 16 S.F. | | 175 | .229 | " | | 5 | 1.28 | 6.28 | 9.80 |
| 0255         For over 16 S.F. see Div. 02 41 16.17 0400 | | | | | | | | | |
| 0600     Walls, not reinforced, under 6 C.F. | B-9 | 60 | .667 | C.F. | | 14.60 | 3.75 | 18.35 | 28.50 |
| 0650        6 – 12 C.F. | " | 80 | .500 | " | | 10.95 | 2.81 | 13.76 | 21.50 |
| 0655         For over 12 C.F. see Div. 02 41 16.17 2500 | | | | | | | | | |
| 1000     Concrete, elevated slab, bar reinforced, under 6 C.F. | B-9 | 45 | .889 | C.F. | | 19.45 | 5 | 24.45 | 38 |
| 1050       Bar reinforced, over 6 C.F. | | 50 | .800 | " | | 17.50 | 4.50 | 22 | 34.50 |
| 1200      Slab on grade to 6" thick, bar reinforced, under 8 S.F. | | 75 | .533 | S.F. | | 11.70 | 3 | 14.70 | 23 |
| 1250        8 – 16 S.F. | | 150 | .267 | " | | 5.85 | 1.50 | 7.35 | 11.45 |
| 1255         For over 16 S.F. see Div. 02 41 16.17 0440 | | | | | | | | | |
| 1400     Walls, bar reinforced, under 6 C.F. | B-9 | 50 | .800 | C.F. | | 17.50 | 4.50 | 22 | 34.50 |
| 1450        6 – 12 C.F. | " | 70 | .571 | " | | 12.50 | 3.21 | 15.71 | 24.50 |
| 1455         For over 12 C.F. see Div. 02 41 16.17 2500 and 2600 | | | | | | | | | |
| 2000     Brick, to 4 S.F. opening, not including toothing | | | | | | | | | |
| 2040        4" thick | B-9 | 30 | 1.333 | Ea. | | 29 | 7.50 | 36.50 | 57.50 |
| 2060        8" thick | | 18 | 2.222 | | | 48.50 | 12.50 | 61 | 96 |
| 2080        12" thick | | 10 | 4 | | | 87.50 | 22.50 | 110 | 172 |
| 2400     Concrete block, to 4 S.F. opening, 2" thick | | 35 | 1.143 | | | 25 | 6.40 | 31.40 | 49 |
| 2420        4" thick | | 30 | 1.333 | | | 29 | 7.50 | 36.50 | 57.50 |
| 2440        8" thick | | 27 | 1.481 | | | 32.50 | 8.35 | 40.85 | 63.50 |
| 2460        12" thick | | 24 | 1.667 | | | 36.50 | 9.35 | 45.85 | 72 |
| 2600     Gypsum block, to 4 S.F. opening, 2" thick | | 80 | .500 | | | 10.95 | 2.81 | 13.76 | 21.50 |
| 2620        4" thick | | 70 | .571 | | | 12.50 | 3.21 | 15.71 | 24.50 |
| 2640        8" thick | | 55 | .727 | | | 15.95 | 4.09 | 20.04 | 31.50 |
| 2800     Terra cotta, to 4 S.F. opening, 4" thick | | 70 | .571 | | | 12.50 | 3.21 | 15.71 | 24.50 |
| 2840        8" thick | | 65 | .615 | | | 13.50 | 3.46 | 16.96 | 26.50 |
| 2880        12" thick | | 50 | .800 | | | 17.50 | 4.50 | 22 | 34.50 |
| 3000     Toothing masonry cutouts, brick, soft old mortar | 1 Brhe | 40 | .200 | V.L.F. | | 4.71 | | 4.71 | 7.75 |

# 02 41 Demolition

## 02 41 19 – Selective Structure Demolition

| 02 41 19.16 Selective Demolition, Cutout | | Crew | Daily Output | Labor-Hours | Unit | Material | 2010 Bare Costs Labor | Equipment | Total | Total Incl O&P |
|---|---|---|---|---|---|---|---|---|---|---|
| 3100 | Hard mortar | 1 Brhe | 30 | .267 | V.L.F. | | 6.30 | | 6.30 | 10.35 |
| 3200 | Block, soft old mortar | | 70 | .114 | | | 2.69 | | 2.69 | 4.43 |
| 3400 | Hard mortar | | 50 | .160 | | | 3.77 | | 3.77 | 6.20 |
| 6000 | Walls, interior, not including re-framing, | | | | | | | | | |
| 6010 | openings to 5 S.F. | | | | | | | | | |
| 6100 | Drywall to 5/8" thick | 1 Clab | 24 | .333 | Ea. | | 7.15 | | 7.15 | 12.05 |
| 6200 | Paneling to 3/4" thick | | 20 | .400 | | | 8.60 | | 8.60 | 14.45 |
| 6300 | Plaster, on gypsum lath | | 20 | .400 | | | 8.60 | | 8.60 | 14.45 |
| 6340 | On wire lath | | 14 | .571 | | | 12.30 | | 12.30 | 20.50 |
| 7000 | Wood frame, not including re-framing, openings to 5 S.F. | | | | | | | | | |
| 7200 | Floors, sheathing and flooring to 2" thick | 1 Clab | 5 | 1.600 | Ea. | | 34.50 | | 34.50 | 58 |
| 7310 | Roofs, sheathing to 1" thick, not including roofing | | 6 | 1.333 | | | 28.50 | | 28.50 | 48 |
| 7410 | Walls, sheathing to 1" thick, not including siding | | 7 | 1.143 | | | 24.50 | | 24.50 | 41.50 |

## 02 41 19.19 Selective Demolition, Dump Charges

| 02 41 19.19 Selective Demolition, Dump Charges | | Crew | Daily Output | Labor-Hours | Unit | Material | 2010 Bare Costs Labor | Equipment | Total | Total Incl O&P |
|---|---|---|---|---|---|---|---|---|---|---|
| 0010 | **SELECTIVE DEMOLITION, DUMP CHARGES** | R024119-10 | | | | | | | | |
| 0020 | Dump charges, typical urban city, tipping fees only | | | | | | | | | |
| 0100 | Building construction materials | | | | Ton | | | | | 70 |
| 0200 | Trees, brush, lumber | | | | | | | | | 50 |
| 0300 | Rubbish only | | | | | | | | | 60 |
| 0500 | Reclamation station, usual charge | | | | | 95 | | | 95 | 104.50 |

## 02 41 19.21 Selective Demolition, Gutting

| 02 41 19.21 Selective Demolition, Gutting | | Crew | Daily Output | Labor-Hours | Unit | Material | 2010 Bare Costs Labor | Equipment | Total | Total Incl O&P |
|---|---|---|---|---|---|---|---|---|---|---|
| 0010 | **SELECTIVE DEMOLITION, GUTTING** | R024119-10 | | | | | | | | |
| 0020 | Building interior, including disposal, dumpster fees not included | | | | | | | | | |
| 0500 | Residential building | | | | | | | | | |
| 0560 | Minimum | B-16 | 400 | .080 | SF Flr. | | 1.80 | 1.67 | 3.47 | 4.86 |
| 0580 | Maximum | " | 360 | .089 | " | | 2 | 1.86 | 3.86 | 5.40 |
| 0900 | Commercial building | | | | | | | | | |
| 1000 | Minimum | B-16 | 350 | .091 | SF Flr. | | 2.06 | 1.91 | 3.97 | 5.55 |
| 1020 | Maximum | " | 250 | .128 | " | | 2.88 | 2.67 | 5.55 | 7.75 |

## 02 41 19.23 Selective Demolition, Rubbish Handling

| 02 41 19.23 Selective Demolition, Rubbish Handling | | Crew | Daily Output | Labor-Hours | Unit | Material | 2010 Bare Costs Labor | Equipment | Total | Total Incl O&P |
|---|---|---|---|---|---|---|---|---|---|---|
| 0010 | **SELECTIVE DEMOLITION, RUBBISH HANDLING** | R024119-10 | | | | | | | | |
| 0020 | The following are to be added to the demolition prices | | | | | | | | | |
| 0400 | Chute, circular, prefabricated steel, 18" diameter | B-1 | 40 | .600 | L.F. | 48.50 | 13.30 | | 61.80 | 76 |
| 0440 | 30" diameter | " | 30 | .800 | " | 50 | 17.75 | | 67.75 | 85 |
| 0600 | Dumpster, weekly rental, 1 dump/week, 6 C.Y. capacity (2 Tons) | | | | Week | | | | | 315 |
| 0700 | 10 C.Y. capacity (4 Tons) | | | | | | | | | 375 |
| 0725 | 20 C.Y. capacity (8 Tons) | R024119-20 | | | | | | | | 440 |
| 0800 | 30 C.Y. capacity (10 Tons) | | | | | | | | | 665 |
| 0840 | 40 C.Y. capacity (13 Tons) | | | | | | | | | 805 |
| 1000 | Dust partition, 6 mil polyethylene, 1" x 3" frame | 2 Carp | 2000 | .008 | S.F. | .45 | .23 | | .68 | .88 |
| 1080 | 2" x 4" frame | " | 2000 | .008 | " | .24 | .23 | | .47 | .65 |
| 2000 | Load, haul, dump and return, 50' haul, hand carried | 2 Clab | 24 | .667 | C.Y. | | 14.35 | | 14.35 | 24 |
| 2005 | Wheeled | | 37 | .432 | | | 9.30 | | 9.30 | 15.65 |
| 2040 | 100' haul, hand carried | | 16.50 | .970 | | | 21 | | 21 | 35 |
| 2045 | Wheeled | | 25 | .640 | | | 13.75 | | 13.75 | 23 |
| 2080 | Over 100' haul, add per 100 L.F., hand carried | | 35.50 | .451 | | | 9.70 | | 9.70 | 16.30 |
| 2085 | Wheeled | | 54 | .296 | | | 6.35 | | 6.35 | 10.70 |
| 2120 | In elevators, per 10 floors, add | | 140 | .114 | | | 2.46 | | 2.46 | 4.13 |
| 2130 | Load, haul, dump and return, 50' haul, incl. 5 riser stair, hand carried | | 23 | .696 | | | 14.95 | | 14.95 | 25 |
| 2135 | Wheeled | | 35 | .457 | | | 9.85 | | 9.85 | 16.55 |
| 2140 | 6 – 10 riser stairs, hand carried | | 22 | .727 | | | 15.65 | | 15.65 | 26.50 |
| 2145 | Wheeled | | 34 | .471 | | | 10.10 | | 10.10 | 17 |

# 02 41 Demolition

## 02 41 19 – Selective Structure Demolition

### 02 41 19.23 Selective Demolition, Rubbish Handling

| | | Crew | Daily Output | Labor-Hours | Unit | Material | 2010 Bare Costs Labor | Equipment | Total | Total Incl O&P |
|---|---|---|---|---|---|---|---|---|---|---|
| 2150 | 11 – 20 riser stairs, hand carried | 2 Clab | 20 | .800 | C.Y. | | 17.20 | | 17.20 | 29 |
| 2155 | Wheeled | | 31 | .516 | | | 11.10 | | 11.10 | 18.65 |
| 2160 | 21 – 40 riser stairs, hand carried | | 16 | 1 | | | 21.50 | | 21.50 | 36 |
| 2165 | Wheeled | | 24 | .667 | | | 14.35 | | 14.35 | 24 |
| 2170 | 100' haul, incl. 5 riser stair, hand carried | | 15 | 1.067 | | | 23 | | 23 | 38.50 |
| 2175 | Wheeled | | 23 | .696 | | | 14.95 | | 14.95 | 25 |
| 2180 | 6 – 10 riser stair, hand carried | | 14 | 1.143 | | | 24.50 | | 24.50 | 41.50 |
| 2185 | Wheeled | | 21 | .762 | | | 16.40 | | 16.40 | 27.50 |
| 2190 | 11 – 20 riser stair, hand carried | | 12 | 1.333 | | | 28.50 | | 28.50 | 48 |
| 2195 | Wheeled | | 18 | .889 | | | 19.10 | | 19.10 | 32 |
| 2200 | 21 – 40 riser stair, hand carried | | 8 | 2 | | | 43 | | 43 | 72.50 |
| 2205 | Wheeled | | 12 | 1.333 | | | 28.50 | | 28.50 | 48 |
| 2210 | Over 100' haul, add per 100 L.F., hand carried | | 35.50 | .451 | | | 9.70 | | 9.70 | 16.30 |
| 2215 | Wheeled | | 54 | .296 | | | 6.35 | | 6.35 | 10.70 |
| 2220 | For each additional flight of stairs, 5 risers | | 550 | .029 | Flight | | .63 | | .63 | 1.05 |
| 2225 | 6 – 10 risers | | 275 | .058 | | | 1.25 | | 1.25 | 2.10 |
| 2230 | 11-20 risers | | 138 | .116 | | | 2.49 | | 2.49 | 4.19 |
| 2235 | 21 – 40 risers | | 69 | .232 | | | 4.99 | | 4.99 | 8.40 |
| 3000 | Loading & trucking, including 2 mile haul, chute loaded | B-16 | 45 | .711 | C.Y. | | 16 | 14.85 | 30.85 | 43.50 |
| 3040 | Hand loading truck, 50' haul | " | 48 | .667 | | | 15 | 13.90 | 28.90 | 40.50 |
| 3080 | Machine loading truck | B-17 | 120 | .267 | | | 6.35 | 6.15 | 12.50 | 17.35 |
| 5000 | Haul, per mile, up to 8 C.Y. truck | B-34B | 1165 | .007 | | | .16 | .57 | .73 | .90 |
| 5100 | Over 8 C.Y. truck | " | 1550 | .005 | | | .12 | .43 | .55 | .67 |

# 02 83 Lead Remediation

## 02 83 19 – Lead-Based Paint Remediation

### 02 83 19.23 Encapsulation of Lead-Based Paint

| | | Crew | Daily Output | Labor-Hours | Unit | Material | 2010 Bare Costs Labor | Equipment | Total | Total Incl O&P |
|---|---|---|---|---|---|---|---|---|---|---|
| 0010 | **ENCAPSULATION OF LEAD-BASED PAINT** | | | | | | | | | |
| 0020 | Interior, brushwork, trim, under 6" | 1 Pord | 240 | .033 | L.F. | 2.46 | .86 | | 3.32 | 4.11 |
| 0030 | 6" to 12" wide | | 180 | .044 | | 3.28 | 1.15 | | 4.43 | 5.50 |
| 0040 | Balustrades | | 300 | .027 | | 1.98 | .69 | | 2.67 | 3.30 |
| 0050 | Pipe to 4" diameter | | 500 | .016 | | 1.19 | .41 | | 1.60 | 1.98 |
| 0060 | To 8" diameter | | 375 | .021 | | 1.57 | .55 | | 2.12 | 2.63 |
| 0070 | To 12" diameter | | 250 | .032 | | 2.36 | .83 | | 3.19 | 3.94 |
| 0080 | To 16" diameter | | 170 | .047 | | 3.47 | 1.21 | | 4.68 | 5.80 |
| 0090 | Cabinets, ornate design | | 200 | .040 | S.F. | 2.97 | 1.03 | | 4 | 4.95 |
| 0100 | Simple design | | 250 | .032 | " | 2.36 | .83 | | 3.19 | 3.94 |
| 0110 | Doors, 3' x 7', both sides, incl. frame & trim | | | | | | | | | |
| 0120 | Flush | 1 Pord | 6 | 1.333 | Ea. | 30.50 | 34.50 | | 65 | 89.50 |
| 0130 | French, 10 – 15 lite | | 3 | 2.667 | | 6.05 | 69 | | 75.05 | 119 |
| 0140 | Panel | | 4 | 2 | | 36.50 | 51.50 | | 88 | 124 |
| 0150 | Louvered | | 2.75 | 2.909 | | 33.50 | 75 | | 108.50 | 159 |
| 0160 | Windows, per interior side, per 15 S.F. | | | | | | | | | |
| 0170 | 1 to 6 lite | 1 Pord | 14 | .571 | Ea. | 21 | 14.75 | | 35.75 | 47 |
| 0180 | 7 to 10 lite | | 7.50 | 1.067 | | 23 | 27.50 | | 50.50 | 70.50 |
| 0190 | 12 lite | | 5.75 | 1.391 | | 31 | 36 | | 67 | 92.50 |
| 0200 | Radiators | | 8 | 1 | | 73.50 | 26 | | 99.50 | 123 |
| 0210 | Grilles, vents | | 275 | .029 | S.F. | 2.15 | .75 | | 2.90 | 3.59 |
| 0220 | Walls, roller, drywall or plaster | | 1000 | .008 | | .59 | .21 | | .80 | .99 |
| 0230 | With spunbonded reinforcing fabric | | 720 | .011 | | .68 | .29 | | .97 | 1.22 |
| 0240 | Wood | | 800 | .010 | | .74 | .26 | | 1 | 1.23 |

# 02 83 Lead Remediation

## 02 83 19 – Lead-Based Paint Remediation

### 02 83 19.23 Encapsulation of Lead-Based Paint

| | | Crew | Daily Output | Labor-Hours | Unit | Material | 2010 Bare Costs Labor | Equipment | Total | Total Incl O&P |
|---|---|---|---|---|---|---|---|---|---|---|
| 0250 | Ceilings, roller, drywall or plaster | 1 Pord | 900 | .009 | S.F. | .68 | .23 | | .91 | 1.12 |
| 0260 | Wood | | 700 | .011 | ↓ | .84 | .29 | | 1.13 | 1.40 |
| 0270 | Exterior, brushwork, gutters and downspouts | | 300 | .027 | L.F. | 1.98 | .69 | | 2.67 | 3.30 |
| 0280 | Columns | | 400 | .020 | S.F. | 1.47 | .52 | | 1.99 | 2.46 |
| 0290 | Spray, siding | ↓ | 600 | .013 | " | .99 | .34 | | 1.33 | 1.65 |
| 0300 | Miscellaneous | | | | | | | | | |
| 0310 | Electrical conduit, brushwork, to 2" diameter | 1 Pord | 500 | .016 | L.F. | 1.19 | .41 | | 1.60 | 1.98 |
| 0320 | Brick, block or concrete, spray | | 500 | .016 | S.F. | 1.19 | .41 | | 1.60 | 1.98 |
| 0330 | Steel, flat surfaces and tanks to 12" | | 500 | .016 | | 1.19 | .41 | | 1.60 | 1.98 |
| 0340 | Beams, brushwork | | 400 | .020 | | 1.47 | .52 | | 1.99 | 2.46 |
| 0350 | Trusses | ↓ | 400 | .020 | ↓ | 1.47 | .52 | | 1.99 | 2.46 |

### 02 83 19.26 Removal of Lead-Based Paint

| | | Crew | Daily Output | Labor-Hours | Unit | Material | 2010 Bare Costs Labor | Equipment | Total | Total Incl O&P |
|---|---|---|---|---|---|---|---|---|---|---|
| 0010 | **REMOVAL OF LEAD-BASED PAINT** | | | | | | | | | |
| 0011 | By chemicals, per application | | | | | | | | | |
| 0050 | Baseboard, to 6" wide | 1 Pord | 64 | .125 | L.F. | .66 | 3.23 | | 3.89 | 6 |
| 0070 | To 12" wide | | 32 | .250 | " | 1.32 | 6.45 | | 7.77 | 11.95 |
| 0200 | Balustrades, one side | | 28 | .286 | S.F. | 1.32 | 7.35 | | 8.67 | 13.45 |
| 1400 | Cabinets, simple design | | 32 | .250 | | 1.32 | 6.45 | | 7.77 | 11.95 |
| 1420 | Ornate design | | 25 | .320 | | 1.32 | 8.25 | | 9.57 | 14.90 |
| 1600 | Cornice, simple design | | 60 | .133 | | 1.32 | 3.44 | | 4.76 | 7.05 |
| 1620 | Ornate design | | 20 | .400 | | 5.05 | 10.30 | | 15.35 | 22.50 |
| 2800 | Doors, one side, flush | | 84 | .095 | | 1 | 2.46 | | 3.46 | 5.10 |
| 2820 | Two panel | | 80 | .100 | | 1.32 | 2.58 | | 3.90 | 5.65 |
| 2840 | Four panel | | 45 | .178 | ↓ | 1.32 | 4.59 | | 5.91 | 8.90 |
| 2880 | For trim, one side, add | | 64 | .125 | L.F. | .66 | 3.23 | | 3.89 | 6 |
| 3000 | Fence, picket, one side | | 30 | .267 | S.F. | 1.32 | 6.90 | | 8.22 | 12.65 |
| 3200 | Grilles, one side, simple design | | 30 | .267 | | 1.32 | 6.90 | | 8.22 | 12.65 |
| 3220 | Ornate design | | 25 | .320 | ↓ | 1.32 | 8.25 | | 9.57 | 14.90 |
| 4400 | Pipes, to 4" diameter | | 90 | .089 | L.F. | 1 | 2.29 | | 3.29 | 4.83 |
| 4420 | To 8" diameter | | 50 | .160 | | 2 | 4.13 | | 6.13 | 8.90 |
| 4440 | To 12" diameter | | 36 | .222 | | 3 | 5.75 | | 8.75 | 12.65 |
| 4460 | To 16" diameter | | 20 | .400 | ↓ | 4 | 10.30 | | 14.30 | 21 |
| 4500 | For hangers, add | | 40 | .200 | Ea. | 2.54 | 5.15 | | 7.69 | 11.20 |
| 4800 | Siding | | 90 | .089 | S.F. | 1.17 | 2.29 | | 3.46 | 5 |
| 5000 | Trusses, open | | 55 | .145 | SF Face | 1.85 | 3.75 | | 5.60 | 8.15 |
| 6200 | Windows, one side only, double hung, 1/1 light, 24" x 48" high | | 4 | 2 | Ea. | 25.50 | 51.50 | | 77 | 112 |
| 6220 | 30" x 60" high | | 3 | 2.667 | | 34 | 69 | | 103 | 150 |
| 6240 | 36" x 72" high | | 2.50 | 3.200 | | 41 | 82.50 | | 123.50 | 179 |
| 6280 | 40" x 80" high | | 2 | 4 | | 51 | 103 | | 154 | 224 |
| 6400 | Colonial window, 6/6 light, 24" x 48" high | | 2 | 4 | | 51 | 103 | | 154 | 225 |
| 6420 | 30" x 60" high | | 1.50 | 5.333 | | 68 | 138 | | 206 | 299 |
| 6440 | 36" x 72" high | | 1 | 8 | | 102 | 206 | | 308 | 445 |
| 6480 | 40" x 80" high | | 1 | 8 | | 102 | 206 | | 308 | 445 |
| 6600 | 8/8 light, 24" x 48" high | | 2 | 4 | | 51 | 103 | | 154 | 225 |
| 6620 | 40" x 80" high | | 1 | 8 | | 102 | 206 | | 308 | 445 |
| 6800 | 12/12 light, 24" x 48" high | | 1 | 8 | | 102 | 206 | | 308 | 445 |
| 6820 | 40" x 80" high | ↓ | .75 | 10.667 | ↓ | 136 | 275 | | 411 | 600 |
| 6840 | Window frame & trim items, included in pricing above | | | | | | | | | |

# Division Notes

| | CREW | DAILY OUTPUT | LABOR-HOURS | UNIT | 2010 BARE COSTS | | | | TOTAL INCL O&P |
|---|---|---|---|---|---|---|---|---|---|
| | | | | | MAT. | LABOR | EQUIP. | TOTAL | |
| | | | | | | | | | |
| | | | | | | | | | |
| | | | | | | | | | |
| | | | | | | | | | |
| | | | | | | | | | |
| | | | | | | | | | |
| | | | | | | | | | |
| | | | | | | | | | |
| | | | | | | | | | |
| | | | | | | | | | |
| | | | | | | | | | |
| | | | | | | | | | |
| | | | | | | | | | |
| | | | | | | | | | |
| | | | | | | | | | |
| | | | | | | | | | |
| | | | | | | | | | |
| | | | | | | | | | |
| | | | | | | | | | |
| | | | | | | | | | |
| | | | | | | | | | |

# Estimating Tips

## General

- Carefully check all the plans and specifications. Concrete often appears on drawings other than structural drawings, including mechanical and electrical drawings for equipment pads. The cost of cutting and patching is often difficult to estimate. See Subdivision 03 81 for Concrete Cutting, Subdivision 02 41 19.16 for Cutout Demolition, Subdivision 03 05 05.10 for Concrete Demolition, and Subdivision 02 41 19.23 for Rubbish Handling (handling, loading and hauling of debris).
- Always obtain concrete prices from suppliers near the job site. A volume discount can often be negotiated, depending upon competition in the area. Remember to add for waste, particularly for slabs and footings on grade.

## 03 10 00 Concrete Forming and Accessories

- A primary cost for concrete construction is forming. Most jobs today are constructed with prefabricated forms. The selection of the forms best suited for the job and the total square feet of forms required for efficient concrete forming and placing are key elements in estimating concrete construction. Enough forms must be available for erection to make efficient use of the concrete placing equipment and crew.

- Concrete accessories for forming and placing depend upon the systems used. Study the plans and specifications to ensure that all special accessory requirements have been included in the cost estimate, such as anchor bolts, inserts, and hangers.
- Included within costs for forms-in-place are all necessary bracing and shoring.

## 03 20 00 Concrete Reinforcing

- Ascertain that the reinforcing steel supplier has included all accessories, cutting, bending, and an allowance for lapping, splicing, and waste. A good rule of thumb is 10% for lapping, splicing, and waste. Also, 10% waste should be allowed for welded wire fabric.
- The unit price items in the subdivision for Reinforcing In Place include the labor to install accessories such as beam and slab bolsters, high chairs, and bar ties and tie wire. The material cost for these accessories is not included; they may be obtained from the Accessories Division.

## 03 30 00 Cast-In-Place Concrete

- When estimating structural concrete, pay particular attention to requirements for concrete additives, curing methods, and surface treatments. Special consideration for climate, hot or cold, must be included in your estimate. Be sure to include requirements for concrete placing equipment, and concrete finishing.

- For accurate concrete estimating, the estimator must consider each of the following major components individually: forms, reinforcing steel, ready-mix concrete, placement of the concrete, and finishing of the top surface. For faster estimating, Subdivision 03 30 53.40 for Concrete-In-Place can be used; here, various items of concrete work are presented that include the costs of all five major components (unless specifically stated otherwise).

## 03 40 00 Precast Concrete
## 03 50 00 Cast Decks and Underlayment

- The cost of hauling precast concrete structural members is often an important factor. For this reason, it is important to get a quote from the nearest supplier. It may become economically feasible to set up precasting beds on the site if the hauling costs are prohibitive.

## Reference Numbers

Reference numbers are shown in shaded boxes at the beginning of some major classifications. These numbers refer to related items in the Reference Section. The reference information may be an estimating procedure, an alternate pricing method, or technical information.

*Note:* Not all subdivisions listed here necessarily appear in this publication.

## Division 3 - Concrete

# 03 01 Maintenance of Concrete

## 03 01 30 – Maintenance of Cast-In-Place Concrete

| 03 01 30.64 Floor Patching | | Crew | Daily Output | Labor-Hours | Unit | Material | 2010 Bare Costs Labor | Equipment | Total | Total Incl O&P |
|---|---|---|---|---|---|---|---|---|---|---|
| 0010 | **FLOOR PATCHING** | | | | | | | | | |
| 0012 | Floor patching, 1/4" thick, small areas, regular | 1 Cefi | 170 | .047 | S.F. | 2.50 | 1.31 | | 3.81 | 4.84 |
| 0100 | Epoxy | " | 100 | .080 | " | 5.70 | 2.22 | | 7.92 | 9.85 |

# 03 05 Common Work Results for Concrete

## 03 05 13 – Basic Concrete Materials

### 03 05 13.85 Winter Protection

| | | Crew | Daily Output | Labor-Hours | Unit | Material | 2010 Bare Costs Labor | Equipment | Total | Total Incl O&P |
|---|---|---|---|---|---|---|---|---|---|---|
| 0010 | **WINTER PROTECTION** | | | | | | | | | |
| 0012 | For heated ready mix, add, minimum | | | | C.Y. | 4.25 | | | 4.25 | 4.68 |
| 0050 | Maximum | | | | " | 5.30 | | | 5.30 | 5.85 |
| 0100 | Temporary heat to protect concrete, 24 hours, minimum | 2 Clab | 50 | .320 | M.S.F. | 520 | 6.90 | | 526.90 | 585 |
| 0200 | Temporary shelter for slab on grade, wood frame/polyethylene sheeting | | | | | | | | | |
| 0201 | Build or remove, minimum | 2 Carp | 10 | 1.600 | M.S.F. | 215 | 46.50 | | 261.50 | 315 |
| 0210 | Maximum | " | 3 | 5.333 | " | 261 | 155 | | 416 | 550 |
| 0710 | Electrically, heated pads, 15 watts/S.F., 20 uses, minimum | | | | S.F. | .24 | | | .24 | .26 |
| 0800 | Maximum | | | | " | .39 | | | .39 | .43 |

# 03 11 Concrete Forming

## 03 11 13 – Structural Cast-In-Place Concrete Forming

### 03 11 13.25 Forms In Place, Columns

| | | | Crew | Daily Output | Labor-Hours | Unit | Material | 2010 Bare Costs Labor | Equipment | Total | Total Incl O&P |
|---|---|---|---|---|---|---|---|---|---|---|---|
| 0010 | **FORMS IN PLACE, COLUMNS** | | | | | | | | | | |
| 1500 | Round fiber tube, recycled paper, 1 use, 8" diameter | G | C-1 | 155 | .206 | L.F. | 1.44 | 5.25 | | 6.69 | 10.40 |
| 1550 | 10" diameter | G | | 155 | .206 | | 1.99 | 5.25 | | 7.24 | 11 |
| 1600 | 12" diameter | G | | 150 | .213 | | 2.33 | 5.40 | | 7.73 | 11.65 |
| 1700 | 16" diameter | G | | 140 | .229 | | 3.99 | 5.80 | | 9.79 | 14.15 |
| 1720 | 18" diameter | G | | 140 | .229 | | 4.67 | 5.80 | | 10.47 | 14.90 |
| 5000 | Job-built plywood, 8" x 8" columns, 1 use | | | 165 | .194 | SFCA | 2.27 | 4.92 | | 7.19 | 10.75 |
| 5500 | 12" x 12" columns, 1 use | | | 180 | .178 | " | 2.11 | 4.51 | | 6.62 | 9.90 |
| 7400 | Steel framed plywood, based on 50 uses of purchased | | | | | | | | | | |
| 7420 | forms, and 4 uses of bracing lumber | | | | | | | | | | |
| 7500 | 8" x 8" column | | C-1 | 340 | .094 | SFCA | 4.51 | 2.39 | | 6.90 | 8.95 |
| 7550 | 10" x 10" | | | 350 | .091 | | 3.97 | 2.32 | | 6.29 | 8.25 |
| 7600 | 12" x 12" | | | 370 | .086 | | 3.36 | 2.19 | | 5.55 | 7.40 |

### 03 11 13.45 Forms In Place, Footings

| | | Crew | Daily Output | Labor-Hours | Unit | Material | 2010 Bare Costs Labor | Equipment | Total | Total Incl O&P |
|---|---|---|---|---|---|---|---|---|---|---|---|
| 0010 | **FORMS IN PLACE, FOOTINGS** | | | | | | | | | |
| 0020 | Continuous wall, plywood, 1 use | C-1 | 375 | .085 | SFCA | 5.25 | 2.16 | | 7.41 | 9.40 |
| 0150 | 4 use | " | 485 | .066 | " | 1.70 | 1.67 | | 3.37 | 4.69 |
| 1500 | Keyway, 4 use, tapered wood, 2" x 4" | 1 Carp | 530 | .015 | L.F. | .13 | .44 | | .57 | .89 |
| 1550 | 2" x 6" | " | 500 | .016 | " | .19 | .47 | | .66 | .99 |
| 5000 | Spread footings, job-built lumber, 1 use | C-1 | 305 | .105 | SFCA | 1.54 | 2.66 | | 4.20 | 6.15 |
| 5150 | 4 use | " | 414 | .077 | " | .50 | 1.96 | | 2.46 | 3.84 |

### 03 11 13.50 Forms In Place, Grade Beam

| | | Crew | Daily Output | Labor-Hours | Unit | Material | 2010 Bare Costs Labor | Equipment | Total | Total Incl O&P |
|---|---|---|---|---|---|---|---|---|---|---|---|
| 0010 | **FORMS IN PLACE, GRADE BEAM** | | | | | | | | | |
| 0020 | Job-built plywood, 1 use | C-2 | 530 | .091 | SFCA | 2.30 | 2.33 | | 4.63 | 6.45 |
| 0150 | 4 use | " | 605 | .079 | " | .75 | 2.04 | | 2.79 | 4.25 |

### 03 11 13.65 Forms In Place, Slab On Grade

| | | Crew | Daily Output | Labor-Hours | Unit | Material | 2010 Bare Costs Labor | Equipment | Total | Total Incl O&P |
|---|---|---|---|---|---|---|---|---|---|---|---|
| 0010 | **FORMS IN PLACE, SLAB ON GRADE** | | | | | | | | | |
| 1000 | Bulkhead forms w/keyway, wood, 6" high, 1 use | C-1 | 510 | .063 | L.F. | .64 | 1.59 | | 2.23 | 3.38 |

# 03 11 Concrete Forming

## 03 11 13 – Structural Cast-In-Place Concrete Forming

### 03 11 13.65 Forms In Place, Slab On Grade

| | | Crew | Daily Output | Labor-Hours | Unit | Material | 2010 Bare Costs Labor | Equipment | Total | Total Incl O&P |
|---|---|---|---|---|---|---|---|---|---|---|
| 1400 | Bulkhead form for slab, 4-1/2" high, exp metal, incl keyway & stakes [G] | C-1 | 1200 | .027 | L.F. | 1.94 | .68 | | 2.62 | 3.27 |
| 1410 | 5-1/2" high [G] | | 1100 | .029 | | 2.27 | .74 | | 3.01 | 3.74 |
| 1420 | 7-1/2" high [G] | | 960 | .033 | | 2.99 | .85 | | 3.84 | 4.71 |
| 1430 | 9-1/2" high [G] | | 840 | .038 | | 3.39 | .97 | | 4.36 | 5.35 |
| 2000 | Curb forms, wood, 6" to 12" high, on grade, 1 use | | 215 | .149 | SFCA | 2.21 | 3.77 | | 5.98 | 8.80 |
| 2150 | 4 use | | 275 | .116 | " | .72 | 2.95 | | 3.67 | 5.75 |
| 3000 | Edge forms, wood, 4 use, on grade, to 6" high | | 600 | .053 | L.F. | .27 | 1.35 | | 1.62 | 2.57 |
| 3050 | 7" to 12" high | | 435 | .074 | SFCA | .59 | 1.87 | | 2.46 | 3.78 |
| 4000 | For slab blockouts, to 12" high, 1 use | | 200 | .160 | L.F. | .49 | 4.06 | | 4.55 | 7.35 |
| 4100 | Plastic (extruded), to 6" high, multiple use, on grade | | 800 | .040 | " | 7.90 | 1.01 | | 8.91 | 10.40 |
| 8760 | Void form, corrugated fiberboard, 6" x 12", 10' long [G] | | 240 | .133 | S.F. | .95 | 3.38 | | 4.33 | 6.75 |

### 03 11 13.85 Forms In Place, Walls

| | | Crew | Daily Output | Labor-Hours | Unit | Material | 2010 Bare Costs Labor | Equipment | Total | Total Incl O&P |
|---|---|---|---|---|---|---|---|---|---|---|
| 0010 | **FORMS IN PLACE, WALLS** | | | | | | | | | |
| 0100 | Box out for wall openings, to 16" thick, to 10 S.F. | C-2 | 24 | 2 | Ea. | 16.85 | 51.50 | | 68.35 | 105 |
| 0150 | Over 10 S.F. (use perimeter) | " | 280 | .171 | L.F. | 1.44 | 4.41 | | 5.85 | 9 |
| 0250 | Brick shelf, 4" w, add to wall forms, use wall area abv shelf | | | | | | | | | |
| 0260 | 1 use | C-2 | 240 | .200 | SFCA | 1.53 | 5.15 | | 6.68 | 10.35 |
| 0350 | 4 use | | 300 | .160 | " | .61 | 4.12 | | 4.73 | 7.55 |
| 0500 | Bulkhead, wood with keyway, 1 use, 2 piece | | 265 | .181 | L.F. | 1.31 | 4.66 | | 5.97 | 9.25 |
| 0600 | Bulkhead forms with keyway, 1 piece expanded metal, 8" wall [G] | C-1 | 1000 | .032 | | 2.99 | .81 | | 3.80 | 4.65 |
| 0610 | 10" wall [G] | " | 800 | .040 | | 3.39 | 1.01 | | 4.40 | 5.45 |
| 2000 | Wall, job-built plywood, to 8' high, 1 use | C-2 | 370 | .130 | SFCA | 2.24 | 3.34 | | 5.58 | 8.05 |
| 2050 | 2 use | | 435 | .110 | | 1.38 | 2.84 | | 4.22 | 6.30 |
| 2100 | 3 use | | 495 | .097 | | 1 | 2.49 | | 3.49 | 5.30 |
| 2150 | 4 use | | 505 | .095 | | .81 | 2.44 | | 3.25 | 5 |
| 2400 | Over 8' to 16' high, 1 use | | 280 | .171 | | 2.51 | 4.41 | | 6.92 | 10.15 |
| 2450 | 2 use | | 345 | .139 | | 1 | 3.58 | | 4.58 | 7.10 |
| 2500 | 3 use | | 375 | .128 | | .72 | 3.29 | | 4.01 | 6.35 |
| 2550 | 4 use | | 395 | .122 | | .59 | 3.13 | | 3.72 | 5.90 |
| 3000 | For architectural finish, add | | 1820 | .026 | | 5.45 | .68 | | 6.13 | 7.15 |
| 7800 | Modular prefabricated plywood, based on 20 uses of purchased | | | | | | | | | |
| 7820 | forms, and 4 uses of bracing lumber | | | | | | | | | |
| 7860 | To 8' high | C-2 | 800 | .060 | SFCA | 1.44 | 1.54 | | 2.98 | 4.18 |
| 8060 | Over 8' to 16' high | " | 600 | .080 | " | 1.47 | 2.06 | | 3.53 | 5.10 |

## 03 11 19 – Insulating Concrete Forming

### 03 11 19.10 Insulating Forms, Left In Place

| | | Crew | Daily Output | Labor-Hours | Unit | Material | 2010 Bare Costs Labor | Equipment | Total | Total Incl O&P |
|---|---|---|---|---|---|---|---|---|---|---|
| 0010 | **INSULATING FORMS, LEFT IN PLACE** | | | | | | | | | |
| 0020 | S.F. is for exterior face, but includes forms for both faces (total R22) | | | | | | | | | |
| 2000 | 4" wall, straight block, 16" x 48" (5.33 SF) [G] | 2 Carp | 90 | .178 | Ea. | 15.60 | 5.15 | | 20.75 | 26 |
| 2010 | 90 corner block, exterior 16" x 38" x 22" (6.67 SF) [G] | | 75 | .213 | | 17.60 | 6.20 | | 23.80 | 30 |
| 2020 | 45 corner block, exterior 16" x 34" x 18" (5.78 SF) [G] | | 75 | .213 | | 17 | 6.20 | | 23.20 | 29 |
| 2100 | 6" wall, straight block, 16" x 48" (5.33 SF) [G] | | 90 | .178 | | 15.75 | 5.15 | | 20.90 | 26 |
| 2110 | 90 corner block, exterior 16" x 32" x 24" (6.22 SF) [G] | | 75 | .213 | | 18.05 | 6.20 | | 24.25 | 30.50 |
| 2120 | 45 corner block, exterior 16" x 26" x 18" (4.89 SF) [G] | | 75 | .213 | | 16.75 | 6.20 | | 22.95 | 29 |
| 2130 | Brick ledge block, 16" x 48" (5.33 SF) [G] | | 80 | .200 | | 19.45 | 5.80 | | 25.25 | 31.50 |
| 2140 | Taper top block, 16" x 48" (5.33 SF) [G] | | 80 | .200 | | 17.35 | 5.80 | | 23.15 | 29 |
| 2200 | 8" wall, straight block, 16" x 48" (5.33 SF) [G] | | 90 | .178 | | 16.55 | 5.15 | | 21.70 | 27 |
| 2210 | 90 corner block, exterior 16" x 34" x 26" (6.67 SF) [G] | | 75 | .213 | | 19.50 | 6.20 | | 25.70 | 32 |
| 2220 | 45 corner block, exterior 16" x 28" x 20" (5.33 SF) [G] | | 75 | .213 | | 17.55 | 6.20 | | 23.75 | 30 |
| 2230 | Brick ledge block, 16" x 48" (5.33 SF) [G] | | 80 | .200 | | 20 | 5.80 | | 25.80 | 32 |
| 2240 | Taper top block, 16" x 48" (5.33 SF) [G] | | 80 | .200 | | 18.10 | 5.80 | | 23.90 | 29.50 |

# 03 11 Concrete Forming

## 03 11 23 – Permanent Stair Forming

### 03 11 23.75 Forms In Place, Stairs

| | | Crew | Daily Output | Labor-Hours | Unit | Material | 2010 Bare Costs Labor | Equipment | Total | Total Incl O&P |
|---|---|---|---|---|---|---|---|---|---|---|
| 0010 | **FORMS IN PLACE, STAIRS** | | | | | | | | | |
| 0015 | (Slant length x width), 1 use | C-2 | 165 | .291 | S.F. | 4.23 | 7.50 | | 11.73 | 17.20 |
| 0150 | 4 use | | 190 | .253 | | 1.83 | 6.50 | | 8.33 | 12.90 |
| 2000 | Stairs, cast on sloping ground (length x width), 1 use | | 220 | .218 | | 1.43 | 5.60 | | 7.03 | 10.95 |
| 2025 | 2 use | | 232 | .207 | | .79 | 5.30 | | 6.09 | 9.80 |
| 2050 | 3 use | | 244 | .197 | | .57 | 5.05 | | 5.62 | 9.15 |
| 2100 | 4 use | | 256 | .188 | | .46 | 4.82 | | 5.28 | 8.60 |

# 03 15 Concrete Accessories

## 03 15 05 – Concrete Forming Accessories

### 03 15 05.02 Anchor Bolts

| | | | Crew | Daily Output | Labor-Hours | Unit | Material | 2010 Bare Costs Labor | Equipment | Total | Total Incl O&P |
|---|---|---|---|---|---|---|---|---|---|---|---|
| 0010 | **ANCHOR BOLTS** | | | | | | | | | | |
| 0015 | J-type, plain, incl. nut and washer | | | | | | | | | | |
| 0020 | 1/2" diameter, 6" long | G | 1 Carp | 90 | .089 | Ea. | 1.22 | 2.59 | | 3.81 | 5.70 |
| 0050 | 10" long | G | | 85 | .094 | | 1.39 | 2.74 | | 4.13 | 6.15 |
| 0100 | 12" long | G | | 85 | .094 | | 1.53 | 2.74 | | 4.27 | 6.30 |
| 0200 | 5/8" diameter, 12" long | G | | 80 | .100 | | 2.72 | 2.91 | | 5.63 | 7.90 |
| 0250 | 18" long | G | | 70 | .114 | | 3.20 | 3.33 | | 6.53 | 9.10 |
| 0300 | 24" long | G | | 60 | .133 | | 3.68 | 3.88 | | 7.56 | 10.60 |
| 0350 | 3/4" diameter, 8" long | G | | 80 | .100 | | 3.20 | 2.91 | | 6.11 | 8.40 |
| 0400 | 12" long | G | | 70 | .114 | | 4 | 3.33 | | 7.33 | 10 |
| 0450 | 18" long | G | | 60 | .133 | | 5.20 | 3.88 | | 9.08 | 12.25 |
| 0500 | 24" long | G | | 50 | .160 | | 6.80 | 4.66 | | 11.46 | 15.35 |

### 03 15 05.12 Chamfer Strips

| | | Crew | Daily Output | Labor-Hours | Unit | Material | 2010 Bare Costs Labor | Equipment | Total | Total Incl O&P |
|---|---|---|---|---|---|---|---|---|---|---|
| 0010 | **CHAMFER STRIPS** | | | | | | | | | |
| 5000 | Wood, 1/2" wide | 1 Carp | 535 | .015 | L.F. | .22 | .44 | | .66 | .97 |
| 5200 | 3/4" wide | | 525 | .015 | | .20 | .44 | | .64 | .97 |
| 5400 | 1" wide | | 515 | .016 | | .34 | .45 | | .79 | 1.13 |

### 03 15 05.15 Column Form Accessories

| | | | Crew | Daily Output | Labor-Hours | Unit | Material | 2010 Bare Costs Labor | Equipment | Total | Total Incl O&P |
|---|---|---|---|---|---|---|---|---|---|---|---|
| 0010 | **COLUMN FORM ACCESSORIES** | | | | | | | | | | |
| 1000 | Column clamps, adjustable to 24" x 24", buy | G | | | | Set | 126 | | | 126 | 138 |
| 1400 | Rent per month | G | | | | " | 14 | | | 14 | 15.40 |

### 03 15 05.25 Expansion Joints

| | | | Crew | Daily Output | Labor-Hours | Unit | Material | 2010 Bare Costs Labor | Equipment | Total | Total Incl O&P |
|---|---|---|---|---|---|---|---|---|---|---|---|
| 0010 | **EXPANSION JOINTS** | | | | | | | | | | |
| 0020 | Keyed, cold, 24 ga., incl. stakes, 3-1/2" high | G | 1 Carp | 200 | .040 | L.F. | 1.71 | 1.16 | | 2.87 | 3.84 |
| 0050 | 4-1/2" high | G | | 200 | .040 | | 1.94 | 1.16 | | 3.10 | 4.09 |
| 0100 | 5-1/2" high | G | | 195 | .041 | | 2.27 | 1.19 | | 3.46 | 4.51 |
| 2000 | Premolded, bituminous fiber, 1/2" x 6" | | | 375 | .021 | | .41 | .62 | | 1.03 | 1.49 |
| 2050 | 1" x 12" | | | 300 | .027 | | 1.91 | .78 | | 2.69 | 3.41 |
| 2140 | Concrete expansion joint, recycled paper and fiber, 1/2" x 6" | G | | 390 | .021 | | .36 | .60 | | .96 | 1.40 |
| 2150 | 1/2" x 12" | G | | 360 | .022 | | .72 | .65 | | 1.37 | 1.89 |
| 2500 | Neoprene sponge, closed cell, 1/2" x 6" | | | 375 | .021 | | 1.93 | .62 | | 2.55 | 3.16 |
| 2550 | 1" x 12" | | | 300 | .027 | | 7.10 | .78 | | 7.88 | 9.10 |
| 5000 | For installation in walls, add | | | | | | | 75% | | | |
| 5250 | For installation in boxouts, add | | | | | | | 25% | | | |

### 03 15 05.35 Inserts

| | | | Crew | Daily Output | Labor-Hours | Unit | Material | 2010 Bare Costs Labor | Equipment | Total | Total Incl O&P |
|---|---|---|---|---|---|---|---|---|---|---|---|
| 0010 | **INSERTS** | | | | | | | | | | |
| 1000 | Inserts, slotted nut type for 3/4" bolts, 4" long | G | 1 Carp | 84 | .095 | Ea. | 17.60 | 2.77 | | 20.37 | 24 |
| 2100 | 6" long | G | | 84 | .095 | | 19.65 | 2.77 | | 22.42 | 26 |

# 03 15 Concrete Accessories

## 03 15 05 – Concrete Forming Accessories

### 03 15 05.35 Inserts

| | | | Crew | Daily Output | Labor-Hours | Unit | Material | 2010 Bare Costs Labor | Equipment | Total | Total Incl O&P |
|---|---|---|---|---|---|---|---|---|---|---|---|
| 2150 | 8" long | G | 1 Carp | 84 | .095 | Ea. | 24.50 | 2.77 | | 27.27 | 31.50 |
| 2200 | Slotted, strap type, 4" long | G | | 84 | .095 | | 17.10 | 2.77 | | 19.87 | 23.50 |
| 2300 | 8" long | G | ↓ | 84 | .095 | ↓ | 24.50 | 2.77 | | 27.27 | 31.50 |

### 03 15 05.75 Sleeves and Chases

| | | | Crew | Daily Output | Labor-Hours | Unit | Material | 2010 Bare Costs Labor | Equipment | Total | Total Incl O&P |
|---|---|---|---|---|---|---|---|---|---|---|---|
| 0010 | **SLEEVES AND CHASES** | | | | | | | | | | |
| 0100 | Plastic, 1 use, 9" long, 2" diameter | | 1 Carp | 100 | .080 | Ea. | 1.36 | 2.33 | | 3.69 | 5.40 |
| 0150 | 4" diameter | | | 90 | .089 | | 4.01 | 2.59 | | 6.60 | 8.75 |
| 0200 | 6" diameter | | ↓ | 75 | .107 | ↓ | 7.05 | 3.10 | | 10.15 | 13 |

### 03 15 05.80 Snap Ties

| | | | Crew | Daily Output | Labor-Hours | Unit | Material | 2010 Bare Costs Labor | Equipment | Total | Total Incl O&P |
|---|---|---|---|---|---|---|---|---|---|---|---|
| 0010 | **SNAP TIES**, 8-1/4" L&W (Lumber and wedge) | | | | | | | | | | |
| 0100 | 2250 lb., w/flat washer, 8" wall | G | | | | C | 178 | | | 178 | 195 |
| 0250 | 16" wall | G | | | | | 211 | | | 211 | 232 |
| 0300 | 18" wall | G | | | | | 222 | | | 222 | 244 |
| 0500 | With plastic cone, 8" wall | G | | | | | 191 | | | 191 | 210 |
| 0600 | 12" wall | G | | | | | 207 | | | 207 | 228 |
| 0650 | 16" wall | G | | | | | 227 | | | 227 | 249 |
| 0700 | 18" wall | G | | | | ↓ | 237 | | | 237 | 261 |

### 03 15 05.95 Wall and Foundation Form Accessories

| | | | Crew | Daily Output | Labor-Hours | Unit | Material | 2010 Bare Costs Labor | Equipment | Total | Total Incl O&P |
|---|---|---|---|---|---|---|---|---|---|---|---|
| 0010 | **WALL AND FOUNDATION FORM ACCESSORIES** | | | | | | | | | | |
| 0020 | Coil tie system | | | | | | | | | | |
| 0700 | 1-1/4", 36,000 lb., to 8" | G | | | | C | 1,525 | | | 1,525 | 1,675 |
| 1200 | 1-1/4" diameter x 3" long | G | | | | " | 2,625 | | | 2,625 | 2,900 |
| 4200 | 30" long | G | | | | Ea. | 5.50 | | | 5.50 | 6.05 |
| 4250 | 36" long | G | | | | " | 6.15 | | | 6.15 | 6.80 |

## 03 15 13 – Waterstops

### 03 15 13.50 Waterstops

| | | | Crew | Daily Output | Labor-Hours | Unit | Material | 2010 Bare Costs Labor | Equipment | Total | Total Incl O&P |
|---|---|---|---|---|---|---|---|---|---|---|---|
| 0010 | **WATERSTOPS**, PVC and Rubber | | | | | | | | | | |
| 0020 | PVC, ribbed 3/16" thick, 4" wide | | 1 Carp | 155 | .052 | L.F. | 1.08 | 1.50 | | 2.58 | 3.72 |
| 0050 | 6" wide | | | 145 | .055 | | 1.98 | 1.61 | | 3.59 | 4.88 |
| 0500 | With center bulb, 6" wide, 3/16" thick | | | 135 | .059 | | 1.75 | 1.72 | | 3.47 | 4.83 |
| 0550 | 3/8" thick | | | 130 | .062 | | 3.16 | 1.79 | | 4.95 | 6.50 |
| 0600 | 9" wide x 3/8" thick | | ↓ | 125 | .064 | ↓ | 4.84 | 1.86 | | 6.70 | 8.45 |

# 03 21 Reinforcing Steel

## 03 21 10 – Uncoated Reinforcing Steel

### 03 21 10.60 Reinforcing In Place

| | | | Crew | Daily Output | Labor-Hours | Unit | Material | 2010 Bare Costs Labor | Equipment | Total | Total Incl O&P |
|---|---|---|---|---|---|---|---|---|---|---|---|
| 0015 | **REINFORCING IN PLACE**, 50-60 ton lots, A615 Grade 60 | | | | | | | | | | |
| 0020 | Includes labor, but not material cost, to install accessories | | | | | | | | | | |
| 0030 | Made from recycled materials | G | | | | | | | | | |
| 0502 | Footings, #4 to #7 | G | 4 Rodm | 4200 | .008 | Lb. | .42 | .24 | | .66 | .88 |
| 0550 | #8 to #18 | G | | 3.60 | 8.889 | Ton | 720 | 279 | | 999 | 1,275 |
| 0702 | Walls, #3 to #7 | G | | 6000 | .005 | Lb. | .42 | .17 | | .59 | .75 |
| 0750 | #8 to #18 | G | ↓ | 4 | 8 | Ton | 760 | 251 | | 1,011 | 1,275 |
| 0900 | For other than 50-60 ton lots | | | | | | | | | | |
| 1000 | Under 10 ton job, #3 to #7, add | | | | | Ton | 25% | 10% | | | |
| 1010 | #8 to #18, add | | | | | | 20% | 10% | | | |
| 1050 | 10 – 50 ton job, #3 to #7, add | | | | | | 10% | | | | |
| 1060 | #8 to #18, add | | | | | | 5% | | | | |
| 1100 | 60 – 100 ton job, #3 - #7, deduct | | | | | | 5% | | | | |
| 1110 | #8 to #18, deduct | | | | | ↓ | 10% | | | | |

# 03 21 Reinforcing Steel

## 03 21 10 – Uncoated Reinforcing Steel

| 03 21 10.60 Reinforcing In Place | | Crew | Daily Output | Labor-Hours | Unit | Material | 2010 Bare Costs Labor | Equipment | Total | Total Incl O&P |
|---|---|---|---|---|---|---|---|---|---|---|
| 1150 | Over 100 ton job, #3 - #7, deduct | | | | Ton | 10% | | | | |
| 1160 | #8 - #18, deduct | | | | ↓ | 15% | | | | |
| 2400 | Dowels, 2 feet long, deformed, #3 | G 2 Rodm | 520 | .031 | Ea. | .33 | .96 | | 1.29 | 2.05 |
| 2410 | #4 | G | 480 | .033 | | .59 | 1.04 | | 1.63 | 2.48 |
| 2420 | #5 | G | 435 | .037 | | .92 | 1.15 | | 2.07 | 3.03 |
| 2430 | #6 | G ↓ | 360 | .044 | ↓ | 1.32 | 1.39 | | 2.71 | 3.89 |
| 2600 | Dowel sleeves for CIP concrete, 2-part system | | | | | | | | | |
| 2610 | Sleeve base, plastic, for 5/8" smooth dowel sleeve, fasten to edge form | 1 Rodm | 200 | .040 | Ea. | .49 | 1.25 | | 1.74 | 2.74 |
| 2615 | Sleeve, plastic, 12" long, for 5/8" smooth dowel, snap onto base | | 400 | .020 | | 1.06 | .63 | | 1.69 | 2.27 |
| 2620 | Sleeve base, for 3/4" smooth dowel sleeve | | 175 | .046 | | .52 | 1.43 | | 1.95 | 3.08 |
| 2625 | Sleeve, 12" long, for 3/4" smooth dowel | | 350 | .023 | | 1.59 | .72 | | 2.31 | 3.01 |
| 2630 | Sleeve base, for 1" smooth dowel sleeve | | 150 | .053 | | .63 | 1.67 | | 2.30 | 3.62 |
| 2635 | Sleeve, 12" long, for 1" smooth dowel | ↓ | 300 | .027 | | 2.26 | .84 | | 3.10 | 3.95 |
| 2700 | Dowel caps, visual warning only, plastic, #3 to #8 | 2 Rodm | 800 | .020 | | .42 | .63 | | 1.05 | 1.56 |
| 2720 | #8 to #18 | | 750 | .021 | | 1.05 | .67 | | 1.72 | 2.33 |
| 2750 | Impalement protective, plastic, #4 to #9 | ↓ | 800 | .020 | ↓ | 1.62 | .63 | | 2.25 | 2.88 |

# 03 22 Welded Wire Fabric Reinforcing

## 03 22 05 – Uncoated Welded Wire Fabric

### 03 22 05.50 Welded Wire Fabric

| | | Crew | Daily Output | Labor-Hours | Unit | Material | Labor | Equipment | Total | Total Incl O&P |
|---|---|---|---|---|---|---|---|---|---|---|
| 0011 | **WELDED WIRE FABRIC**, 6 x 6 - W1.4 x W1.4 (10 x 10) | G 2 Rodm | 3500 | .005 | S.F. | .12 | .14 | | .26 | .38 |
| 0301 | 6 x 6 - W2.9 x W2.9 (6 x 6) 42 lb. per C.S.F. | G | 2900 | .006 | | .24 | .17 | | .41 | .56 |
| 0501 | 4 x 4 - W1.4 x W1.4 (10 x 10) 31 lb. per C.S.F. | G ↓ | 3100 | .005 | ↓ | .18 | .16 | | .34 | .48 |
| 0750 | Rolls | | | | | | | | | |
| 0901 | 2 x 2 - #12 galv. for gunite reinforcing | G 2 Rodm | 650 | .025 | S.F. | .35 | .77 | | 1.12 | 1.74 |

# 03 23 Stressing Tendons

## 03 23 05 – Prestressing Tendons

### 03 23 05.50 Prestressing Steel

| | | Crew | Daily Output | Labor-Hours | Unit | Material | Labor | Equipment | Total | Total Incl O&P |
|---|---|---|---|---|---|---|---|---|---|---|
| 0010 | **PRESTRESSING STEEL** | | | | | | | | | |
| 3000 | Slabs on grade, 0.5-inch diam. non-bonded strands, HDPE sheathed, | | | | | | | | | |
| 3050 | attached dead-end anchors, loose stressing-end anchors | | | | | | | | | |
| 3100 | 25' x 30' slab, strands @ 36" O.C., placing | 2 Rodm | 2940 | .005 | S.F. | .51 | .17 | | .68 | .86 |
| 3105 | Stressing | C-4A | 3750 | .004 | | | .13 | .01 | .14 | .24 |
| 3110 | 42" O.C., placing | 2 Rodm | 3200 | .005 | | .45 | .16 | | .61 | .77 |
| 3115 | Stressing | C-4A | 4040 | .004 | | | .12 | .01 | .13 | .23 |
| 3120 | 48" O.C., placing | 2 Rodm | 3510 | .005 | | .39 | .14 | | .53 | .68 |
| 3125 | Stressing | C-4A | 4390 | .004 | | | .11 | .01 | .12 | .21 |
| 3150 | 25' x 40' slab, strands @ 36" O.C., placing | 2 Rodm | 3370 | .005 | | .50 | .15 | | .65 | .81 |
| 3155 | Stressing | C-4A | 4360 | .004 | | | .12 | .01 | .13 | .21 |
| 3160 | 42" O.C., placing | 2 Rodm | 3760 | .004 | | .43 | .13 | | .56 | .71 |
| 3165 | Stressing | C-4A | 4820 | .003 | | | .10 | .01 | .11 | .19 |
| 3170 | 48" O.C., placing | 2 Rodm | 4090 | .004 | | .38 | .12 | | .50 | .63 |
| 3175 | Stressing | C-4A | 5190 | .003 | | | .10 | .01 | .11 | .18 |
| 3200 | 30' x 30' slab, strands @ 36" O.C., placing | 2 Rodm | 3260 | .005 | | .50 | .15 | | .65 | .82 |
| 3205 | Stressing | C-4A | 4190 | .004 | | | .12 | .01 | .13 | .22 |
| 3210 | 42" O.C., placing | 2 Rodm | 3530 | .005 | | .45 | .14 | | .59 | .74 |
| 3215 | Stressing | C-4A | 4500 | .004 | | | .11 | .01 | .12 | .21 |
| 3220 | 48" O.C., placing | 2 Rodm | 3840 | .004 | | .40 | .13 | | .53 | .67 |

# 03 23 Stressing Tendons

## 03 23 05 – Prestressing Tendons

### 03 23 05.50 Prestressing Steel

| | | Crew | Daily Output | Labor-Hours | Unit | Material | 2010 Bare Costs Labor | Equipment | Total | Total Incl O&P |
|---|---|---|---|---|---|---|---|---|---|---|
| 3225 | Stressing | C-4A | 4850 | .003 | S.F. | | .10 | .01 | .11 | .19 |
| 3230 | 30' x 40' slab, strands @ 36" O.C., placing | 2 Rodm | 3780 | .004 | | .49 | .13 | | .62 | .77 |
| 3235 | Stressing | C-4A | 4920 | .003 | | | .10 | .01 | .11 | .19 |
| 3240 | 42" O.C., placing | 2 Rodm | 4190 | .004 | | .43 | .12 | | .55 | .68 |
| 3245 | Stressing | C-4A | 5410 | .003 | | | .09 | .01 | .10 | .17 |
| 3250 | 48" O.C., placing | 2 Rodm | 4520 | .004 | | .39 | .11 | | .50 | .62 |
| 3255 | Stressing | C-4A | 5790 | .003 | | | .09 | .01 | .10 | .16 |
| 3260 | 30' x 50' slab, strands @ 36" O.C., placing | 2 Rodm | 4300 | .004 | | .47 | .12 | | .59 | .72 |
| 3265 | Stressing | C-4A | 5650 | .003 | | | .09 | .01 | .10 | .17 |
| 3270 | 42" O.C., placing | 2 Rodm | 4720 | .003 | | .42 | .11 | | .53 | .65 |
| 3275 | Stressing | C-4A | 6150 | .003 | | | .08 | .01 | .09 | .15 |
| 3280 | 48" O.C., placing | 2 Rodm | 5240 | .003 | | .37 | .10 | | .47 | .57 |
| 3285 | Stressing | C-4A | 6760 | .002 | | | .07 | .01 | .08 | .14 |

# 03 24 Fibrous Reinforcing

## 03 24 05 – Reinforcing Fibers

### 03 24 05.30 Synthetic Fibers

| | | | | | Unit | Material | Labor | Equipment | Total | Total Incl O&P |
|---|---|---|---|---|---|---|---|---|---|---|
| 0010 | **SYNTHETIC FIBERS** | | | | | | | | | |
| 0100 | Synthetic fibers, add to concrete | | | | Lb. | 4.72 | | | 4.72 | 5.20 |
| 0110 | 1-1/2 lb. per C.Y. | | | | C.Y. | 7.30 | | | 7.30 | 8 |

### 03 24 05.70 Steel Fibers

| | | | | | | Unit | Material | Labor | Equipment | Total | Total Incl O&P |
|---|---|---|---|---|---|---|---|---|---|---|---|
| 0010 | **STEEL FIBERS** | | | | | | | | | | |
| 0150 | Steel fibers, add to concrete | G | | | | Lb. | .77 | | | .77 | .85 |
| 0155 | 25 lb. per C.Y. | G | | | | C.Y. | 19.25 | | | 19.25 | 21 |
| 0160 | 50 lb. per C.Y. | G | | | | | 38.50 | | | 38.50 | 42.50 |
| 0170 | 75 lb. per C.Y. | G | | | | | 59.50 | | | 59.50 | 65 |
| 0180 | 100 lb. per C.Y. | G | | | | | 77 | | | 77 | 84.50 |

# 03 30 Cast-In-Place Concrete

## 03 30 53 – Miscellaneous Cast-In-Place Concrete

### 03 30 53.40 Concrete In Place

| | | Crew | Daily Output | Labor-Hours | Unit | Material | Labor | Equipment | Total | Total Incl O&P |
|---|---|---|---|---|---|---|---|---|---|---|
| 0010 | **CONCRETE IN PLACE** | | | | | | | | | |
| 0020 | Including forms (4 uses), reinforcing steel, concrete, placement, | | | | | | | | | |
| 0050 | and finishing unless otherwise indicated | | | | | | | | | |
| 0500 | Chimney foundations (5000 psi), industrial, minimum | C-14C | 32.22 | 3.476 | C.Y. | 140 | 95 | .94 | 235.94 | 315 |
| 0510 | Maximum | " | 23.71 | 4.724 | " | 162 | 129 | 1.28 | 292.28 | 395 |
| 3540 | Equipment pad (3000 psi), 3' x 3' x 6" thick | C-14H | 45 | 1.067 | Ea. | 42.50 | 30 | .67 | 73.17 | 99 |
| 3550 | 4' x 4' x 6" thick | | 30 | 1.600 | | 62.50 | 45.50 | 1.01 | 109.01 | 146 |
| 3560 | 5' x 5' x 8" thick | | 18 | 2.667 | | 108 | 75.50 | 1.68 | 185.18 | 248 |
| 3570 | 6' x 6' x 8" thick | | 14 | 3.429 | | 146 | 97 | 2.16 | 245.16 | 325 |
| 3580 | 8' x 8' x 10" thick | | 8 | 6 | | 310 | 170 | 3.78 | 483.78 | 630 |
| 3590 | 10' x 10' x 12" thick | | 5 | 9.600 | | 530 | 272 | 6.05 | 808.05 | 1,050 |
| 3800 | Footings (3000 psi), spread under 1 C.Y. | C-14C | 28 | 4 | C.Y. | 150 | 109 | 1.08 | 260.08 | 350 |
| 3825 | 1 C.Y to 5 C.Y. | | 43 | 2.605 | | 173 | 71 | .70 | 244.70 | 310 |
| 3850 | Over 5 C.Y. | | 75 | 1.493 | | 158 | 41 | .40 | 199.40 | 243 |
| 3900 | Footings, strip (3000 psi), 18" x 9", unreinforced | C-14L | 40 | 2.400 | | 112 | 64 | .77 | 176.77 | 231 |
| 3920 | 18" x 9", reinforced | C-14C | 35 | 3.200 | | 131 | 87.50 | .86 | 219.36 | 292 |
| 3925 | 20" x 10", unreinforced | C-14L | 45 | 2.133 | | 110 | 57 | .68 | 167.68 | 217 |
| 3930 | 20" x 10", reinforced | C-14C | 40 | 2.800 | | 126 | 76.50 | .76 | 203.26 | 268 |

# 03 30 Cast-In-Place Concrete

## 03 30 53 – Miscellaneous Cast-In-Place Concrete

### 03 30 53.40 Concrete In Place

| | | Crew | Daily Output | Labor-Hours | Unit | Material | 2010 Bare Costs Labor | 2010 Bare Costs Equipment | Total | Total Incl O&P |
|---|---|---|---|---|---|---|---|---|---|---|
| 3935 | 24" x 12", unreinforced | C-14L | 55 | 1.745 | C.Y. | 110 | 46.50 | .56 | 157.06 | 200 |
| 3940 | 24" x 12", reinforced | C-14C | 48 | 2.333 | | 126 | 63.50 | .63 | 190.13 | 246 |
| 3945 | 36" x 12", unreinforced | C-14L | 70 | 1.371 | | 107 | 36.50 | .44 | 143.94 | 179 |
| 3950 | 36" x 12", reinforced | C-14C | 60 | 1.867 | | 122 | 51 | .50 | 173.50 | 221 |
| 4000 | Foundation mat (3000 psi), under 10 C.Y. | | 38.67 | 2.896 | | 180 | 79 | .78 | 259.78 | 330 |
| 4050 | Over 20 C.Y. | | 56.40 | 1.986 | | 159 | 54 | .54 | 213.54 | 267 |
| 4520 | Handicap access ramp (4000 psi), railing both sides, 3' wide | C-14H | 14.58 | 3.292 | L.F. | 273 | 93.50 | 2.07 | 368.57 | 460 |
| 4525 | 5' wide | | 12.22 | 3.928 | | 283 | 111 | 2.47 | 396.47 | 500 |
| 4530 | With 6" curb and rails both sides, 3' wide | | 8.55 | 5.614 | | 282 | 159 | 3.54 | 444.54 | 580 |
| 4535 | 5' wide | | 7.31 | 6.566 | | 287 | 186 | 4.14 | 477.14 | 635 |
| 4650 | Slab on grade (3500 psi), not including finish, 4" thick | C-14E | 60.75 | 1.449 | C.Y. | 117 | 40.50 | .51 | 158.01 | 198 |
| 4700 | 6" thick | " | 92 | .957 | " | 113 | 26.50 | .33 | 139.83 | 170 |
| 4701 | Thickened slab edge (3500 psi), for slab on grade poured | | | | | | | | | |
| 4702 | monolithically with slab; depth is in addition to slab thickness; | | | | | | | | | |
| 4703 | formed vertical outside edge, earthen bottom and inside slope | | | | | | | | | |
| 4705 | 8" deep x 8" wide bottom, unreinforced | C-14L | 2190 | .044 | L.F. | 3.07 | 1.17 | .01 | 4.25 | 5.35 |
| 4710 | 8" x 8", reinforced | C-14C | 1670 | .067 | | 4.95 | 1.83 | .02 | 6.80 | 8.55 |
| 4715 | 12" deep x 12" wide bottom, unreinforced | C-14L | 1800 | .053 | | 6.40 | 1.42 | .02 | 7.84 | 9.45 |
| 4720 | 12" x 12", reinforced | C-14C | 1310 | .086 | | 9.80 | 2.33 | .02 | 12.15 | 14.75 |
| 4725 | 16" deep x 16" wide bottom, unreinforced | C-14L | 1440 | .067 | | 10.90 | 1.78 | .02 | 12.70 | 15 |
| 4730 | 16" x 16", reinforced | C-14C | 1120 | .100 | | 15 | 2.73 | .03 | 17.76 | 21 |
| 4735 | 20" deep x 20" wide bottom, unreinforced | C-14L | 1150 | .083 | | 16.65 | 2.22 | .03 | 18.90 | 22 |
| 4740 | 20" x 20", reinforced | C-14C | 920 | .122 | | 22 | 3.32 | .03 | 25.35 | 29.50 |
| 4745 | 24" deep x 24" wide bottom, unreinforced | C-14L | 930 | .103 | | 23.50 | 2.75 | .03 | 26.28 | 30.50 |
| 4750 | 24" x 24", reinforced | C-14C | 740 | .151 | | 30.50 | 4.13 | .04 | 34.67 | 40.50 |
| 4751 | Slab on grade (3500 psi), incl. troweled finish, not incl. forms | | | | | | | | | |
| 4760 | or reinforcing, over 10,000 S.F., 4" thick | C-14F | 3425 | .021 | S.F. | 1.29 | .54 | .01 | 1.84 | 2.31 |
| 4820 | 6" thick | " | 3350 | .021 | " | 1.89 | .56 | .01 | 2.46 | 2.99 |
| 5000 | Slab on grade (3000 psi), incl. textured finish, not incl. forms | | | | | | | | | |
| 5001 | or reinforcing, 4" thick | C-14G | 2873 | .019 | S.F. | 1.26 | .49 | .01 | 1.76 | 2.21 |
| 5010 | 6" thick | | 2590 | .022 | | 1.97 | .55 | .01 | 2.53 | 3.08 |
| 5020 | 8" thick | | 2320 | .024 | | 2.57 | .61 | .01 | 3.19 | 3.84 |
| 6800 | Stairs (3500 psi), not including safety treads, free standing, 3'-6" wide | C-14H | 83 | .578 | LF Nose | 5.10 | 16.40 | .36 | 21.86 | 33.50 |
| 6850 | Cast on ground | | 125 | .384 | " | 4.03 | 10.90 | .24 | 15.17 | 23 |
| 7000 | Stair landings, free standing | | 200 | .240 | S.F. | 4.20 | 6.80 | .15 | 11.15 | 16.25 |
| 7050 | Cast on ground | | 475 | .101 | " | 3.13 | 2.86 | .06 | 6.05 | 8.30 |

# 03 31 Structural Concrete

## 03 31 05 – Normal Weight Structural Concrete

### 03 31 05.35 Normal Weight Concrete, Ready Mix

| | | Crew | Daily Output | Labor-Hours | Unit | Material | 2010 Bare Costs Labor | 2010 Bare Costs Equipment | Total | Total Incl O&P |
|---|---|---|---|---|---|---|---|---|---|---|
| 0010 | **NORMAL WEIGHT CONCRETE, READY MIX**, delivered | | | | | | | | | |
| 0012 | Includes local aggregate, sand, Portland cement, and water | | | | | | | | | |
| 0015 | Excludes all additives and treatments | | | | | | | | | |
| 0020 | 2000 psi | | | | C.Y. | 91.50 | | | 91.50 | 101 |
| 0100 | 2500 psi | | | | | 94 | | | 94 | 103 |
| 0150 | 3000 psi | | | | | 97 | | | 97 | 107 |
| 0200 | 3500 psi | | | | | 99.50 | | | 99.50 | 110 |
| 0300 | 4000 psi | | | | | 103 | | | 103 | 113 |
| 0350 | 4500 psi | | | | | 106 | | | 106 | 116 |
| 0400 | 5000 psi | | | | | 109 | | | 109 | 120 |
| 0411 | 6000 psi | | | | | 124 | | | 124 | 137 |

## 03 31 05 – Normal Weight Structural Concrete

| 03 31 05.35 Normal Weight Concrete, Ready Mix | Crew | Daily Output | Labor-Hours | Unit | Material | 2010 Bare Costs Labor | Equipment | Total | Total Incl O&P |
|---|---|---|---|---|---|---|---|---|---|
| 0412 | 8000 psi | | | | C.Y. | 203 | | | 203 | 223 |
| 0413 | 10,000 psi | | | | | 288 | | | 288 | 315 |
| 0414 | 12,000 psi | | | | | 350 | | | 350 | 380 |
| 1000 | For high early strength cement, add | | | | | 10% | | | | |
| 1300 | For winter concrete (hot water), add | | | | | 4.25 | | | 4.25 | 4.68 |
| 1400 | For hot weather concrete (ice), add | | | | | 9.10 | | | 9.10 | 10 |
| 1410 | For mid-range water reducer, add | | | | | 4.13 | | | 4.13 | 4.54 |
| 1420 | For high-range water reducer/superplasticizer, add | | | | | 6.35 | | | 6.35 | 6.95 |
| 1430 | For retarder, add | | | | | 2.71 | | | 2.71 | 2.98 |
| 1440 | For non-Chloride accelerator, add | | | | | 4.83 | | | 4.83 | 5.30 |
| 1450 | For Chloride accelerator, per 1%, add | | | | | 3.28 | | | 3.28 | 3.61 |
| 1460 | For fiber reinforcing, synthetic (1 Lb./C.Y.), add | | | | | 6.65 | | | 6.65 | 7.30 |
| 1500 | For Saturday delivery, add | | | | | 8.85 | | | 8.85 | 9.70 |
| 1510 | For truck holding/waiting time past 1st hour per load, add | | | | Hr. | 87.50 | | | 87.50 | 96.50 |
| 1520 | For short load (less than 4 C.Y.), add per load | | | | Ea. | 112 | | | 112 | 124 |
| 2000 | For all lightweight aggregate, add | | | | C.Y. | 45% | | | | |

### 03 31 05.70 Placing Concrete

| | | Crew | Daily Output | Labor-Hours | Unit | Material | 2010 Bare Costs Labor | Equipment | Total | Total Incl O&P |
|---|---|---|---|---|---|---|---|---|---|---|
| 0010 | **PLACING CONCRETE** | | | | | | | | | |
| 0020 | Includes labor and equipment to place, strike off and consolidate | | | | | | | | | |
| 1900 | Footings, continuous, shallow, direct chute | C-6 | 120 | .400 | C.Y. | | 9.15 | .51 | 9.66 | 15.80 |
| 1950 | Pumped | C-20 | 150 | .427 | | | 10.05 | 5.35 | 15.40 | 22.50 |
| 2000 | With crane and bucket | C-7 | 90 | .800 | | | 19.10 | 14.35 | 33.45 | 47.50 |
| 2400 | Footings, spread, under 1 C.Y., direct chute | C-6 | 55 | .873 | | | 19.95 | 1.11 | 21.06 | 34.50 |
| 2600 | Over 5 C.Y., direct chute | | 120 | .400 | | | 9.15 | .51 | 9.66 | 15.80 |
| 2900 | Foundation mats, over 20 C.Y., direct chute | | 350 | .137 | | | 3.14 | .17 | 3.31 | 5.45 |
| 4300 | Slab on grade, up to 6" thick, direct chute | | 110 | .436 | | | 10 | .55 | 10.55 | 17.25 |
| 4350 | Pumped | C-20 | 130 | .492 | | | 11.60 | 6.15 | 17.75 | 26 |
| 4400 | With crane and bucket | C-7 | 110 | .655 | | | 15.65 | 11.75 | 27.40 | 39 |
| 4900 | Walls, 8" thick, direct chute | C-6 | 90 | .533 | | | 12.20 | .68 | 12.88 | 21 |
| 4950 | Pumped | C-20 | 100 | .640 | | | 15.10 | 8 | 23.10 | 34 |
| 5000 | With crane and bucket | C-7 | 80 | .900 | | | 21.50 | 16.15 | 37.65 | 53.50 |
| 5050 | 12" thick, direct chute | C-6 | 100 | .480 | | | 11 | .61 | 11.61 | 18.95 |
| 5100 | Pumped | C-20 | 110 | .582 | | | 13.70 | 7.25 | 20.95 | 31 |
| 5200 | With crane and bucket | C-7 | 90 | .800 | | | 19.10 | 14.35 | 33.45 | 47.50 |
| 5600 | Wheeled concrete dumping, add to placing costs above | | | | | | | | | |
| 5610 | Walking cart, 50' haul, add | C-18 | 32 | .281 | C.Y. | | 6.10 | 1.83 | 7.93 | 12.25 |
| 5620 | 150' haul, add | | 24 | .375 | | | 8.15 | 2.43 | 10.58 | 16.40 |
| 5700 | 250' haul, add | | 18 | .500 | | | 10.85 | 3.25 | 14.10 | 22 |
| 5800 | Riding cart, 50' haul, add | C-19 | 80 | .113 | | | 2.44 | 1.17 | 3.61 | 5.40 |
| 5810 | 150' haul, add | | 60 | .150 | | | 3.26 | 1.57 | 4.83 | 7.20 |
| 5900 | 250' haul, add | | 45 | .200 | | | 4.34 | 2.09 | 6.43 | 9.60 |

# 03 35 Concrete Finishing

## 03 35 29 – Tooled Concrete Finishing

### 03 35 29.30 Finishing Floors

| 03 35 29.30 | Finishing Floors | Crew | Daily Output | Labor-Hours | Unit | Material | 2010 Bare Costs Labor | 2010 Bare Costs Equipment | Total | Total Incl O&P |
|---|---|---|---|---|---|---|---|---|---|---|
| 0010 | **FINISHING FLOORS** | | | | | | | | | |
| 0012 | Finishing requires that concrete first be placed, struck off & consolidated | | | | | | | | | |
| 0015 | Basic finishing for various unspecified flatwork | | | | | | | | | |
| 0100 | Bull float only | C-10 | 4000 | .006 | S.F. | | .15 | | .15 | .25 |
| 0125 | Bull float & manual float | | 2000 | .012 | | | .31 | | .31 | .50 |
| 0150 | Bull float, manual float, & broom finish, w/edging & joints | | 1850 | .013 | | | .33 | | .33 | .54 |
| 0200 | Bull float, manual float & manual steel trowel | | 1265 | .019 | | | .49 | | .49 | .79 |
| 0210 | For specified Random Access Floors in ACI Classes 1, 2, 3 and 4 to achieve | | | | | | | | | |
| 0215 | Composite Overall Floor Flatness and Levelness values up to F35/F25 | | | | | | | | | |
| 0250 | Bull float, machine float & machine trowel (walk-behind) | C-10C | 1715 | .014 | S.F. | | .36 | .03 | .39 | .61 |
| 0300 | Power screed, bull float, machine float & trowel (walk-behind) | C-10D | 2400 | .010 | | | .26 | .05 | .31 | .47 |
| 0350 | Power screed, bull float, machine float & trowel (ride-on) | C-10E | 4000 | .006 | | | .15 | .06 | .21 | .32 |
| 1600 | Exposed local aggregate finish, minimum | 1 Cefi | 625 | .013 | | .23 | .36 | | .59 | .82 |
| 1650 | Maximum | " | 465 | .017 | | .70 | .48 | | 1.18 | 1.54 |

### 03 35 29.35 Control Joints, Saw Cut

| 03 35 29.35 | Control Joints, Saw Cut | Crew | Daily Output | Labor-Hours | Unit | Material | Labor | Equipment | Total | Total Incl O&P |
|---|---|---|---|---|---|---|---|---|---|---|
| 0010 | **CONTROL JOINTS, SAW CUT** | | | | | | | | | |
| 0100 | Sawcut in green concrete | | | | | | | | | |
| 0120 | 1" depth | C-27 | 2000 | .008 | L.F. | .06 | .22 | .08 | .36 | .52 |
| 0140 | 1-1/2" depth | | 1800 | .009 | | .09 | .25 | .09 | .43 | .60 |
| 0160 | 2" depth | | 1600 | .010 | | .12 | .28 | .10 | .50 | .69 |
| 0200 | Blow construction debris out of control joint | C-28 | 6000 | .001 | | | .04 | | .04 | .06 |
| 0300 | Joint sealant | | | | | | | | | |
| 0320 | Backer rod, polyethylene, 1/4" diameter | 1 Cefi | 460 | .017 | L.F. | .03 | .48 | | .51 | .80 |
| 0340 | Sealant, polyurethane | | | | | | | | | |
| 0360 | 1/4" x 1/4" (308 LF/Gal) | 1 Cefi | 270 | .030 | L.F. | .16 | .82 | | .98 | 1.50 |
| 0380 | 1/4" x 1/2" (154 LF/Gal) | " | 255 | .031 | " | .32 | .87 | | 1.19 | 1.76 |

### 03 35 29.60 Finishing Walls

| 03 35 29.60 | Finishing Walls | Crew | Daily Output | Labor-Hours | Unit | Material | Labor | Equipment | Total | Total Incl O&P |
|---|---|---|---|---|---|---|---|---|---|---|
| 0010 | **FINISHING WALLS** | | | | | | | | | |
| 0020 | Break ties and patch voids | 1 Cefi | 540 | .015 | S.F. | .03 | .41 | | .44 | .70 |
| 0050 | Burlap rub with grout | " | 450 | .018 | | .03 | .49 | | .52 | .83 |
| 0300 | Bush hammer, green concrete | B-39 | 1000 | .048 | | | 1.05 | .22 | 1.27 | 2.01 |
| 0350 | Cured concrete | " | 650 | .074 | | | 1.61 | .35 | 1.96 | 3.09 |

## 03 35 33 – Stamped Concrete Finishing

### 03 35 33.50 Slab Texture Stamping

| 03 35 33.50 | Slab Texture Stamping | Crew | Daily Output | Labor-Hours | Unit | Material | Labor | Equipment | Total | Total Incl O&P |
|---|---|---|---|---|---|---|---|---|---|---|
| 0010 | **SLAB TEXTURE STAMPING** | | | | | | | | | |
| 0050 | Stamping requires that concrete first be placed, struck off, consolidated, | | | | | | | | | |
| 0060 | bull floated and free of bleed water. Decorative stamping tasks include: | | | | | | | | | |
| 0100 | Step 1 - first application of dry shake colored hardener | 1 Cefi | 6400 | .001 | S.F. | .38 | .03 | | .41 | .48 |
| 0110 | Step 2 - bull float | | 6400 | .001 | | | .03 | | .03 | .06 |
| 0130 | Step 3 - second application of dry shake colored hardener | | 6400 | .001 | | .19 | .03 | | .22 | .27 |
| 0140 | Step 4 - bull float, manual float & steel trowel | 3 Cefi | 1280 | .019 | | | .52 | | .52 | .83 |
| 0150 | Step 5 - application of dry shake colored release agent | 1 Cefi | 6400 | .001 | | .09 | .03 | | .12 | .15 |
| 0160 | Step 6 - place, tamp & remove mats | 3 Cefi | 2400 | .010 | | 1.41 | .28 | | 1.69 | 2 |
| 0170 | Step 7 - touch up edges, mat joints & simulated grout lines | 1 Cefi | 1280 | .006 | | | .17 | | .17 | .28 |
| 0300 | Alternate stamping estimating method includes all tasks above | 4 Cefi | 800 | .040 | | 2.07 | 1.11 | | 3.18 | 4.06 |
| 0400 | Step 8 - pressure wash @ 3000 psi after 24 hours | 1 Cefi | 1600 | .005 | | | .14 | | .14 | .22 |
| 0500 | Step 9 - roll 2 coats cure/seal compound when dry | " | 800 | .010 | | .49 | .28 | | .77 | .99 |

# 03 39 Concrete Curing

## 03 39 13 – Water Concrete Curing

### 03 39 13.50 Water Curing

| | | Crew | Daily Output | Labor-Hours | Unit | Material | 2010 Bare Costs Labor | Equipment | Total | Total Incl O&P |
|---|---|---|---|---|---|---|---|---|---|---|
| 0011 | **WATER CURING** | | | | | | | | | |
| 0020 | With burlap, 4 uses assumed, 7.5 oz. | 2 Clab | 5500 | .003 | S.F. | .09 | .06 | | .15 | .21 |
| 0101 | 10 oz. | " | 5500 | .003 | " | .16 | .06 | | .22 | .28 |

## 03 39 23 – Membrane Concrete Curing

### 03 39 23.13 Chemical Compound Membrane Concrete Curing

| | | Crew | Daily Output | Labor-Hours | Unit | Material | Labor | Equipment | Total | Total Incl O&P |
|---|---|---|---|---|---|---|---|---|---|---|
| 0010 | **CHEMICAL COMPOUND MEMBRANE CONCRETE CURING** | | | | | | | | | |
| 0301 | Sprayed membrane curing compound | 2 Clab | 9500 | .002 | S.F. | .06 | .04 | | .10 | .13 |

### 03 39 23.23 Sheet Membrane Concrete Curing

| | | Crew | Daily Output | Labor-Hours | Unit | Material | Labor | Equipment | Total | Total Incl O&P |
|---|---|---|---|---|---|---|---|---|---|---|
| 0010 | **SHEET MEMBRANE CONCRETE CURING** | | | | | | | | | |
| 0201 | Curing blanket, burlap/poly, 2-ply | 2 Clab | 7000 | .002 | S.F. | .16 | .05 | | .21 | .26 |

# 03 41 Precast Structural Concrete

## 03 41 23 – Precast Concrete Stairs

### 03 41 23.50 Precast Stairs

| | | Crew | Daily Output | Labor-Hours | Unit | Material | 2010 Bare Costs Labor | Equipment | Total | Total Incl O&P |
|---|---|---|---|---|---|---|---|---|---|---|
| 0010 | **PRECAST STAIRS** | | | | | | | | | |
| 0020 | Precast concrete treads on steel stringers, 3' wide | C-12 | 75 | .640 | Riser | 105 | 18.20 | 8.75 | 131.95 | 156 |
| 0300 | Front entrance, 5' wide with 48" platform, 2 risers | | 16 | 3 | Flight | 460 | 85.50 | 41 | 586.50 | 695 |
| 0350 | 5 risers | | 12 | 4 | | 715 | 114 | 54.50 | 883.50 | 1,025 |
| 0500 | 6' wide, 2 risers | | 15 | 3.200 | | 510 | 91 | 43.50 | 644.50 | 760 |
| 0550 | 5 risers | | 11 | 4.364 | | 790 | 124 | 59.50 | 973.50 | 1,150 |
| 0700 | 7' wide, 2 risers | | 14 | 3.429 | | 620 | 97.50 | 47 | 764.50 | 895 |
| 1200 | Basement entrance stairs, steel bulkhead doors, minimum | B-51 | 22 | 2.182 | | 1,350 | 48 | 10.90 | 1,408.90 | 1,575 |
| 1250 | Maximum | " | 11 | 4.364 | | 2,225 | 96.50 | 22 | 2,343.50 | 2,625 |

# 03 48 Precast Concrete Specialties

## 03 48 43 – Precast Concrete Trim

### 03 48 43.40 Precast Lintels

| | | Crew | Daily Output | Labor-Hours | Unit | Material | Labor | Equipment | Total | Total Incl O&P |
|---|---|---|---|---|---|---|---|---|---|---|
| 0010 | **PRECAST LINTELS**, smooth gray, prestressed, stock units only | | | | | | | | | |
| 0800 | 4" wide, 8" high, x 4' long | D-10 | 28 | 1.143 | Ea. | 21 | 33 | 23.50 | 77.50 | 103 |
| 0850 | 8' long | | 24 | 1.333 | | 56.50 | 38 | 27.50 | 122 | 155 |
| 1000 | 6" wide, 8" high, x 4' long | | 26 | 1.231 | | 31 | 35.50 | 25 | 91.50 | 120 |
| 1050 | 10' long | | 22 | 1.455 | | 83 | 41.50 | 30 | 154.50 | 193 |

### 03 48 43.90 Precast Window Sills

| | | Crew | Daily Output | Labor-Hours | Unit | Material | Labor | Equipment | Total | Total Incl O&P |
|---|---|---|---|---|---|---|---|---|---|---|
| 0010 | **PRECAST WINDOW SILLS** | | | | | | | | | |
| 0600 | Precast concrete, 4" tapers to 3", 9" wide | D-1 | 70 | .229 | L.F. | 12.25 | 6.05 | | 18.30 | 23.50 |
| 0650 | 11" wide | | 60 | .267 | | 16 | 7.05 | | 23.05 | 29 |
| 0700 | 13" wide, 3 1/2" tapers to 2 1/2", 12" wall | | 50 | .320 | | 16 | 8.45 | | 24.45 | 31.50 |

# 03 63 Epoxy Grouting

## 03 63 05 – Grouting of Dowels and Fasteners

### 03 63 05.10 Epoxy Only

| | Crew | Daily Output | Labor-Hours | Unit | Material | 2010 Bare Costs Labor | Equipment | Total | Total Incl O&P |
|---|---|---|---|---|---|---|---|---|---|
| 0010 **EPOXY ONLY** | | | | | | | | | |
| 1500 Chemical anchoring, epoxy cartridge, excludes layout, drilling, fastener | | | | | | | | | |
| 1530 For fastener 3/4" diam. x 6" embedment | 2 Skwk | 72 | .222 | Ea. | 4.57 | 6.50 | | 11.07 | 15.95 |
| 1535 1" diam. x 8" embedment | | 66 | .242 | | 6.85 | 7.10 | | 13.95 | 19.45 |
| 1540 1-1/4" diam. x 10" embedment | | 60 | .267 | | 13.70 | 7.80 | | 21.50 | 28 |
| 1545 1-3/4" diam. x 12" embedment | | 54 | .296 | | 23 | 8.65 | | 31.65 | 39.50 |
| 1550 14" embedment | | 48 | .333 | | 27.50 | 9.75 | | 37.25 | 46.50 |
| 1555 2" diam. x 12" embedment | | 42 | .381 | | 36.50 | 11.15 | | 47.65 | 58.50 |
| 1560 18" embedment | | 32 | .500 | | 45.50 | 14.65 | | 60.15 | 75 |

# 03 82 Concrete Boring

## 03 82 16 – Concrete Drilling

### 03 82 16.10 Concrete Impact Drilling

| | Crew | Daily Output | Labor-Hours | Unit | Material | 2010 Bare Costs Labor | Equipment | Total | Total Incl O&P |
|---|---|---|---|---|---|---|---|---|---|
| 0010 **CONCRETE IMPACT DRILLING** | | | | | | | | | |
| 0050 Up to 4" deep in conc/brick floor/wall, incl. bit & layout, no anchor | | | | | | | | | |
| 0100 Holes, 1/4" diameter | 1 Carp | 75 | .107 | Ea. | .07 | 3.10 | | 3.17 | 5.25 |
| 0150 For each additional inch of depth, add | | 430 | .019 | | .02 | .54 | | .56 | .93 |
| 0200 3/8" diameter | | 63 | .127 | | .06 | 3.70 | | 3.76 | 6.25 |
| 0250 For each additional inch of depth, add | | 340 | .024 | | .02 | .68 | | .70 | 1.17 |
| 0300 1/2" diameter | | 50 | .160 | | .06 | 4.66 | | 4.72 | 7.90 |
| 0350 For each additional inch of depth, add | | 250 | .032 | | .02 | .93 | | .95 | 1.59 |
| 0400 5/8" diameter | | 48 | .167 | | .09 | 4.85 | | 4.94 | 8.25 |
| 0450 For each additional inch of depth, add | | 240 | .033 | | .02 | .97 | | .99 | 1.66 |
| 0500 3/4" diameter | | 45 | .178 | | .11 | 5.15 | | 5.26 | 8.80 |
| 0550 For each additional inch of depth, add | | 220 | .036 | | .03 | 1.06 | | 1.09 | 1.81 |
| 0600 7/8" diameter | | 43 | .186 | | .13 | 5.40 | | 5.53 | 9.25 |
| 0650 For each additional inch of depth, add | | 210 | .038 | | .03 | 1.11 | | 1.14 | 1.91 |
| 0700 1" diameter | | 40 | .200 | | .15 | 5.80 | | 5.95 | 9.95 |
| 0750 For each additional inch of depth, add | | 190 | .042 | | .04 | 1.23 | | 1.27 | 2.10 |
| 0800 1-1/4" diameter | | 38 | .211 | | .22 | 6.15 | | 6.37 | 10.55 |
| 0850 For each additional inch of depth, add | | 180 | .044 | | .06 | 1.29 | | 1.35 | 2.24 |
| 0900 1-1/2" diameter | | 35 | .229 | | .32 | 6.65 | | 6.97 | 11.55 |
| 0950 For each additional inch of depth, add | | 165 | .048 | | .08 | 1.41 | | 1.49 | 2.46 |
| 1000 For ceiling installations, add | | | | | | 40% | | | |

# Estimating Tips

## 04 05 00 Common Work Results for Masonry

- The terms *mortar* and *grout* are often used interchangeably, and incorrectly. Mortar is used to bed masonry units, seal the entry of air and moisture, provide architectural appearance, and allow for size variations in the units. Grout is used primarily in reinforced masonry construction and is used to bond the masonry to the reinforcing steel. Common mortar types are M(2500 psi), S(1800 psi), N(750 psi), and O(350 psi), and conform to ASTM C270. Grout is either fine or coarse and conforms to ASTM C476, and in-place strengths generally exceed 2500 psi. Mortar and grout are different components of masonry construction and are placed by entirely different methods. An estimator should be aware of their unique uses and costs.

- Waste, specifically the loss/droppings of mortar and the breakage of brick and block, is included in all masonry assemblies in this division. A factor of 25% is added for mortar and 3% for brick and concrete masonry units.

- Scaffolding or staging is not included in any of the Division 4 costs. Refer to Subdivision 01 54 23 for scaffolding and staging costs.

## 04 20 00 Unit Masonry

- The most common types of unit masonry are brick and concrete masonry. The major classifications of brick are building brick (ASTM C62), facing brick (ASTM C216), glazed brick, fire brick, and pavers. Many varieties of texture and appearance can exist within these classifications, and the estimator would be wise to check local custom and availability within the project area. For repair and remodeling jobs, matching the existing brick may be the most important criteria.

- Brick and concrete block are priced by the piece and then converted into a price per square foot of wall. Openings less than two square feet are generally ignored by the estimator because any savings in units used is offset by the cutting and trimming required.

- It is often difficult and expensive to find and purchase small lots of historic brick. Costs can vary widely. Many design issues affect costs, selection of mortar mix, and repairs or replacement of masonry materials. Cleaning techniques must be reflected in the estimate.

- All masonry walls, whether interior or exterior, require bracing. The cost of bracing walls during construction should be included by the estimator, and this bracing must remain in place until permanent bracing is complete. Permanent bracing of masonry walls is accomplished by masonry itself, in the form of pilasters or abutting wall corners, or by anchoring the walls to the structural frame. Accessories in the form of anchors, anchor slots, and ties are used, but their supply and installation can be by different trades. For instance, anchor slots on spandrel beams and columns are supplied and welded in place by the steel fabricator, but the ties from the slots into the masonry are installed by the bricklayer. Regardless of the installation method, the estimator must be certain that these accessories are accounted for in pricing.

# Reference Numbers

Reference numbers are shown in shaded boxes at the beginning of some major classifications. These numbers refer to related items in the Reference Section. The reference information may be an estimating procedure, an alternate pricing method, or technical information.

*Note:* Not all subdivisions listed here necessarily appear in this publication.

# 04 01 Maintenance of Masonry

## 04 01 20 – Maintenance of Unit Masonry

### 04 01 20.20 Pointing Masonry

| | | Crew | Daily Output | Labor-Hours | Unit | Material | 2010 Bare Costs Labor | Equipment | Total | Total Incl O&P |
|---|---|---|---|---|---|---|---|---|---|---|
| 0010 | **POINTING MASONRY** | | | | | | | | | |
| 0300 | Cut and repoint brick, hard mortar, running bond | 1 Bric | 80 | .100 | S.F. | .53 | 2.93 | | 3.46 | 5.40 |
| 0320 | Common bond | | 77 | .104 | | .53 | 3.04 | | 3.57 | 5.60 |
| 0360 | Flemish bond | | 70 | .114 | | .56 | 3.34 | | 3.90 | 6.10 |
| 0400 | English bond | | 65 | .123 | | .56 | 3.60 | | 4.16 | 6.55 |
| 0600 | Soft old mortar, running bond | | 100 | .080 | | .53 | 2.34 | | 2.87 | 4.44 |
| 0620 | Common bond | | 96 | .083 | | .53 | 2.44 | | 2.97 | 4.60 |
| 0640 | Flemish bond | | 90 | .089 | | .56 | 2.60 | | 3.16 | 4.89 |
| 0680 | English bond | | 82 | .098 | ▼ | .56 | 2.85 | | 3.41 | 5.30 |
| 0700 | Stonework, hard mortar | | 140 | .057 | L.F. | .70 | 1.67 | | 2.37 | 3.52 |
| 0720 | Soft old mortar | | 160 | .050 | " | .70 | 1.46 | | 2.16 | 3.18 |
| 1000 | Repoint, mask and grout method, running bond | | 95 | .084 | S.F. | .70 | 2.46 | | 3.16 | 4.83 |
| 1020 | Common bond | | 90 | .089 | | .70 | 2.60 | | 3.30 | 5.05 |
| 1040 | Flemish bond | | 86 | .093 | | .74 | 2.72 | | 3.46 | 5.30 |
| 1060 | English bond | | 77 | .104 | | .74 | 3.04 | | 3.78 | 5.80 |
| 2000 | Scrub coat, sand grout on walls, minimum | | 120 | .067 | | 2.91 | 1.95 | | 4.86 | 6.40 |
| 2020 | Maximum | ▼ | 98 | .082 | ▼ | 4.04 | 2.39 | | 6.43 | 8.40 |

### 04 01 20.30 Pointing CMU

| | | Crew | Daily Output | Labor-Hours | Unit | Material | 2010 Bare Costs Labor | Equipment | Total | Total Incl O&P |
|---|---|---|---|---|---|---|---|---|---|---|
| 0010 | **POINTING CMU** | | | | | | | | | |
| 0300 | Cut and repoint block, hard mortar, running bond | 1 Bric | 190 | .042 | S.F. | .22 | 1.23 | | 1.45 | 2.27 |
| 0310 | Stacked bond | | 200 | .040 | | .22 | 1.17 | | 1.39 | 2.17 |
| 0600 | Soft old mortar, running bond | | 230 | .035 | | .22 | 1.02 | | 1.24 | 1.92 |
| 0610 | Stacked bond | ▼ | 245 | .033 | ▼ | .22 | .96 | | 1.18 | 1.81 |

## 04 01 30 – Unit Masonry Cleaning

### 04 01 30.60 Brick Washing

| | | | Crew | Daily Output | Labor-Hours | Unit | Material | 2010 Bare Costs Labor | Equipment | Total | Total Incl O&P |
|---|---|---|---|---|---|---|---|---|---|---|---|
| 0010 | **BRICK WASHING** | R040130-10 | | | | | | | | | |
| 0012 | Acid cleanser, smooth brick surface | | 1 Bric | 560 | .014 | S.F. | .04 | .42 | | .46 | .73 |
| 0050 | Rough brick | | | 400 | .020 | | .05 | .59 | | .64 | 1.02 |
| 0060 | Stone, acid wash | | ▼ | 600 | .013 | ▼ | .06 | .39 | | .45 | .71 |
| 1000 | Muriatic acid, price per gallon in 5 gallon lots | | | | | Gal. | 7.55 | | | 7.55 | 8.30 |

# 04 05 Common Work Results for Masonry

## 04 05 05 – Selective Masonry Demolition

### 04 05 05.10 Selective Demolition

| | | | Crew | Daily Output | Labor-Hours | Unit | Material | 2010 Bare Costs Labor | Equipment | Total | Total Incl O&P |
|---|---|---|---|---|---|---|---|---|---|---|---|
| 0010 | **SELECTIVE DEMOLITION** | R024119-10 | | | | | | | | | |
| 0200 | Bond beams, 8" block with #4 bar | | 2 Clab | 32 | .500 | L.F. | | 10.75 | | 10.75 | 18.10 |
| 0300 | Concrete block walls, unreinforced, 2" thick | | | 1200 | .013 | S.F. | | .29 | | .29 | .48 |
| 0310 | 4" thick | | | 1150 | .014 | | | .30 | | .30 | .50 |
| 0320 | 6" thick | | | 1100 | .015 | | | .31 | | .31 | .53 |
| 0330 | 8" thick | | | 1050 | .015 | | | .33 | | .33 | .55 |
| 0340 | 10" thick | | | 1000 | .016 | | | .34 | | .34 | .58 |
| 0360 | 12" thick | | | 950 | .017 | | | .36 | | .36 | .61 |
| 0380 | Reinforced alternate courses, 2" thick | | | 1130 | .014 | | | .30 | | .30 | .51 |
| 0390 | 4" thick | | | 1080 | .015 | | | .32 | | .32 | .54 |
| 0400 | 6" thick | | | 1035 | .015 | | | .33 | | .33 | .56 |
| 0410 | 8" thick | | | 990 | .016 | | | .35 | | .35 | .58 |
| 0420 | 10" thick | | | 940 | .017 | | | .37 | | .37 | .62 |
| 0430 | 12" thick | | | 890 | .018 | | | .39 | | .39 | .65 |
| 0440 | Reinforced alternate courses & vertically 48" OC, 4" thick | | | 900 | .018 | | | .38 | | .38 | .64 |
| 0450 | 6" thick | | ▼ | 850 | .019 | ▼ | | .40 | | .40 | .68 |

## 04 05 05 – Selective Masonry Demolition

| 04 05 05.10 Selective Demolition | | Crew | Daily Output | Labor- Hours | Unit | Material | 2010 Bare Costs Labor | 2010 Bare Costs Equipment | Total | Total Incl O&P |
|---|---|---|---|---|---|---|---|---|---|---|
| 0460 | 8" thick | 2 Clab | 800 | .020 | S.F. | | .43 | | .43 | .72 |
| 0480 | 10" thick | | 750 | .021 | | | .46 | | .46 | .77 |
| 0490 | 12" thick | ↓ | 700 | .023 | ↓ | | .49 | | .49 | .83 |
| 1000 | Chimney, 16" x 16", soft old mortar | 1 Clab | 55 | .145 | C.F. | | 3.13 | | 3.13 | 5.25 |
| 1020 | Hard mortar | | 40 | .200 | | | 4.30 | | 4.30 | 7.25 |
| 1030 | 16" x 20", soft old mortar | | 55 | .145 | | | 3.13 | | 3.13 | 5.25 |
| 1040 | Hard mortar | | 40 | .200 | | | 4.30 | | 4.30 | 7.25 |
| 1050 | 16" x 24", soft old mortar | | 55 | .145 | | | 3.13 | | 3.13 | 5.25 |
| 1060 | Hard mortar | | 40 | .200 | | | 4.30 | | 4.30 | 7.25 |
| 1080 | 20" x 20", soft old mortar | | 55 | .145 | | | 3.13 | | 3.13 | 5.25 |
| 1100 | Hard mortar | | 40 | .200 | | | 4.30 | | 4.30 | 7.25 |
| 1110 | 20" x 24", soft old mortar | | 55 | .145 | | | 3.13 | | 3.13 | 5.25 |
| 1120 | Hard mortar | | 40 | .200 | | | 4.30 | | 4.30 | 7.25 |
| 1140 | 20" x 32", soft old mortar | | 55 | .145 | | | 3.13 | | 3.13 | 5.25 |
| 1160 | Hard mortar | | 40 | .200 | | | 4.30 | | 4.30 | 7.25 |
| 1200 | 48" x 48", soft old mortar | | 55 | .145 | | | 3.13 | | 3.13 | 5.25 |
| 1220 | Hard mortar | ↓ | 40 | .200 | ↓ | | 4.30 | | 4.30 | 7.25 |
| 1250 | Metal, high temp steel jacket, 24" diameter | E-2 | 130 | .369 | V.L.F. | | 11.65 | 12.35 | 24 | 35 |
| 1260 | 60" diameter | " | 60 | .800 | | | 25.50 | 27 | 52.50 | 76.50 |
| 1280 | Flue lining, up to 12" x 12" | 1 Clab | 200 | .040 | | | .86 | | .86 | 1.45 |
| 1282 | Up to 24" x 24" | | 150 | .053 | | | 1.15 | | 1.15 | 1.93 |
| 2000 | Columns, 8" x 8", soft old mortar | | 48 | .167 | | | 3.58 | | 3.58 | 6.05 |
| 2020 | Hard mortar | | 40 | .200 | | | 4.30 | | 4.30 | 7.25 |
| 2060 | 16" x 16", soft old mortar | | 16 | .500 | | | 10.75 | | 10.75 | 18.10 |
| 2100 | Hard mortar | | 14 | .571 | | | 12.30 | | 12.30 | 20.50 |
| 2140 | 24" x 24", soft old mortar | | 8 | 1 | | | 21.50 | | 21.50 | 36 |
| 2160 | Hard mortar | | 6 | 1.333 | | | 28.50 | | 28.50 | 48 |
| 2200 | 36" x 36", soft old mortar | | 4 | 2 | | | 43 | | 43 | 72.50 |
| 2220 | Hard mortar | | 3 | 2.667 | ↓ | | 57.50 | | 57.50 | 96.50 |
| 2230 | Alternate pricing method, soft old mortar | | 30 | .267 | C.F. | | 5.75 | | 5.75 | 9.65 |
| 2240 | Hard mortar | ↓ | 23 | .348 | " | | 7.50 | | 7.50 | 12.55 |
| 3000 | Copings, precast or masonry, to 8" wide | | | | | | | | | |
| 3020 | Soft old mortar | 1 Clab | 180 | .044 | L.F. | | .96 | | .96 | 1.61 |
| 3040 | Hard mortar | " | 160 | .050 | " | | 1.08 | | 1.08 | 1.81 |
| 3100 | To 12" wide | | | | | | | | | |
| 3120 | Soft old mortar | 1 Clab | 160 | .050 | L.F. | | 1.08 | | 1.08 | 1.81 |
| 3140 | Hard mortar | " | 140 | .057 | " | | 1.23 | | 1.23 | 2.07 |
| 4000 | Fireplace, brick, 30" x 24" opening | | | | | | | | | |
| 4020 | Soft old mortar | 1 Clab | 2 | 4 | Ea. | | 86 | | 86 | 145 |
| 4040 | Hard mortar | | 1.25 | 6.400 | | | 138 | | 138 | 231 |
| 4100 | Stone, soft old mortar | | 1.50 | 5.333 | | | 115 | | 115 | 193 |
| 4120 | Hard mortar | | 1 | 8 | ↓ | | 172 | | 172 | 289 |
| 5000 | Veneers, brick, soft old mortar | | 140 | .057 | S.F. | | 1.23 | | 1.23 | 2.07 |
| 5020 | Hard mortar | | 125 | .064 | | | 1.38 | | 1.38 | 2.31 |
| 5100 | Granite and marble, 2" thick | | 180 | .044 | | | .96 | | .96 | 1.61 |
| 5120 | 4" thick | | 170 | .047 | | | 1.01 | | 1.01 | 1.70 |
| 5140 | Stone, 4" thick | | 180 | .044 | | | .96 | | .96 | 1.61 |
| 5160 | 8" thick | | 175 | .046 | ↓ | | .98 | | .98 | 1.65 |
| 5400 | Alternate pricing method, stone, 4" thick | | 60 | .133 | C.F. | | 2.87 | | 2.87 | 4.82 |
| 5420 | 8" thick | ↓ | 85 | .094 | " | | 2.02 | | 2.02 | 3.40 |

# 04 05 Common Work Results for Masonry

## 04 05 13 – Masonry Mortaring

### 04 05 13.10 Cement

| | | Crew | Daily Output | Labor-Hours | Unit | Material | 2010 Bare Costs Labor | Equipment | Total | Total Incl O&P |
|---|---|---|---|---|---|---|---|---|---|---|
| 0010 | **CEMENT**        R040513-10 | | | | | | | | | |
| 0100 | Masonry, 70 lb. bag, T.L. lots | | | | Bag | 8.80 | | | 8.80 | 9.70 |
| 0150 | L.T.L. lots | | | | | 9.35 | | | 9.35 | 10.30 |
| 0200 | White, 70 lb. bag, T.L. lots | | | | | 14.85 | | | 14.85 | 16.35 |
| 0250 | L.T.L. lots | | | | | 16.70 | | | 16.70 | 18.35 |

## 04 05 16 – Masonry Grouting

### 04 05 16.30 Grouting

| | | Crew | Daily Output | Labor-Hours | Unit | Material | Labor | Equipment | Total | Total Incl O&P |
|---|---|---|---|---|---|---|---|---|---|---|
| 0010 | **GROUTING** | | | | | | | | | |
| 0200 | Concrete block cores, solid, 4" thk., by hand, 0.067 C.F./S.F. of wall | D-8 | 1100 | .036 | S.F. | .28 | .98 | | 1.26 | 1.93 |
| 0210 | 6" thick, pumped, 0.175 C.F. per S.F. | D-4 | 720 | .056 | | .74 | 1.35 | .18 | 2.27 | 3.25 |
| 0250 | 8" thick, pumped, 0.258 C.F. per S.F. | | 680 | .059 | | 1.10 | 1.43 | .20 | 2.73 | 3.78 |
| 0300 | 10" thick, pumped, 0.340 C.F. per S.F. | | 660 | .061 | | 1.45 | 1.47 | .20 | 3.12 | 4.24 |
| 0350 | 12" thick, pumped, 0.422 C.F. per S.F. | | 640 | .063 | | 1.79 | 1.52 | .21 | 3.52 | 4.71 |

## 04 05 19 – Masonry Anchorage and Reinforcing

### 04 05 19.05 Anchor Bolts

| | | Crew | Daily Output | Labor-Hours | Unit | Material | Labor | Equipment | Total | Total Incl O&P |
|---|---|---|---|---|---|---|---|---|---|---|
| 0010 | **ANCHOR BOLTS** | | | | | | | | | |
| 0020 | Hooked, with nut and washer, 1/2" diam., 8" long | 1 Bric | 200 | .040 | Ea. | .80 | 1.17 | | 1.97 | 2.81 |
| 0030 | 12" long | | 190 | .042 | | 1.53 | 1.23 | | 2.76 | 3.71 |
| 0060 | 3/4" diameter, 8" long | | 160 | .050 | | 3.20 | 1.46 | | 4.66 | 5.95 |
| 0070 | 12" long | | 150 | .053 | | 4 | 1.56 | | 5.56 | 6.95 |

### 04 05 19.16 Masonry Anchors

| | | Crew | Daily Output | Labor-Hours | Unit | Material | Labor | Equipment | Total | Total Incl O&P |
|---|---|---|---|---|---|---|---|---|---|---|
| 0010 | **MASONRY ANCHORS** | | | | | | | | | |
| 0020 | For brick veneer, galv., corrugated, 7/8" x 7", 22 Ga. | 1 Bric | 10.50 | .762 | C | 9.60 | 22.50 | | 32.10 | 47 |
| 0100 | 24 Ga. | | 10.50 | .762 | | 9 | 22.50 | | 31.50 | 46.50 |
| 0150 | 16 Ga. | | 10.50 | .762 | | 23.50 | 22.50 | | 46 | 62.50 |
| 0200 | Buck anchors, galv., corrugated, 16 gauge, 2" bend, 8" x 2" | | 10.50 | .762 | | 148 | 22.50 | | 170.50 | 200 |
| 0250 | 8" x 3" | | 10.50 | .762 | | 138 | 22.50 | | 160.50 | 189 |
| 0660 | Cavity wall, Z-type, galvanized, 6" long, 1/8" diam. | | 10.50 | .762 | | 23 | 22.50 | | 45.50 | 61.50 |
| 0670 | 3/16" diameter | | 10.50 | .762 | | 20 | 22.50 | | 42.50 | 59 |
| 0680 | 1/4" diameter | | 10.50 | .762 | | 38 | 22.50 | | 60.50 | 78.50 |
| 0850 | 8" long, 3/16" diameter | | 10.50 | .762 | | 23 | 22.50 | | 45.50 | 62 |
| 0855 | 1/4" diameter | | 10.50 | .762 | | 45 | 22.50 | | 67.50 | 86 |
| 1000 | Rectangular type, galvanized, 1/4" diameter, 2" x 6" | | 10.50 | .762 | | 65.50 | 22.50 | | 88 | 109 |
| 1050 | 4" x 6" | | 10.50 | .762 | | 81.50 | 22.50 | | 104 | 127 |
| 1100 | 3/16" diameter, 2" x 6" | | 10.50 | .762 | | 35.50 | 22.50 | | 58 | 76 |
| 1150 | 4" x 6" | | 10.50 | .762 | | 39 | 22.50 | | 61.50 | 79.50 |
| 1500 | Rigid partition anchors, plain, 8" long, 1" x 1/8" | | 10.50 | .762 | | 91 | 22.50 | | 113.50 | 137 |
| 1550 | 1" x 1/4" | | 10.50 | .762 | | 150 | 22.50 | | 172.50 | 202 |
| 1580 | 1-1/2" x 1/8" | | 10.50 | .762 | | 121 | 22.50 | | 143.50 | 170 |
| 1600 | 1-1/2" x 1/4" | | 10.50 | .762 | | 246 | 22.50 | | 268.50 | 310 |
| 1650 | 2" x 1/8" | | 10.50 | .762 | | 157 | 22.50 | | 179.50 | 209 |
| 1700 | 2" x 1/4" | | 10.50 | .762 | | 288 | 22.50 | | 310.50 | 350 |

### 04 05 19.26 Masonry Reinforcing Bars

| | | Crew | Daily Output | Labor-Hours | Unit | Material | Labor | Equipment | Total | Total Incl O&P |
|---|---|---|---|---|---|---|---|---|---|---|
| 0010 | **MASONRY REINFORCING BARS**        R040519-50 | | | | | | | | | |
| 0015 | Steel bars A615, placed horiz., #3 & #4 bars | 1 Bric | 450 | .018 | Lb. | .40 | .52 | | .92 | 1.30 |
| 0050 | Placed vertical, #3 & #4 bars | | 350 | .023 | | .40 | .67 | | 1.07 | 1.54 |
| 0060 | #5 & #6 bars | | 650 | .012 | | .40 | .36 | | .76 | 1.03 |
| 0200 | Joint reinforcing, regular truss, to 6" wide, mill std galvanized | | 30 | .267 | C.L.F. | 15.20 | 7.80 | | 23 | 29.50 |
| 0250 | 12" wide | | 20 | .400 | | 16.95 | 11.70 | | 28.65 | 38 |
| 0400 | Cavity truss with drip section, to 6" wide | | 30 | .267 | | 13.45 | 7.80 | | 21.25 | 27.50 |

# 04 05 Common Work Results for Masonry

## 04 05 19 – Masonry Anchorage and Reinforcing

| 04 05 19.26 Masonry Reinforcing Bars | | Crew | Daily Output | Labor-Hours | Unit | Material | 2010 Bare Costs Labor | Equipment | Total | Total Incl O&P |
|---|---|---|---|---|---|---|---|---|---|---|
| 0450 | 12" wide | 1 Bric | 20 | .400 | C.L.F. | 13.80 | 11.70 | | 25.50 | 34.50 |

# 04 21 Clay Unit Masonry

## 04 21 13 – Brick Masonry

### 04 21 13.13 Brick Veneer Masonry

| | | | Crew | Daily Output | Labor-Hours | Unit | Material | 2010 Bare Costs Labor | Equipment | Total | Total Incl O&P |
|---|---|---|---|---|---|---|---|---|---|---|---|
| 0010 | **BRICK VENEER MASONRY**, T.L. lots, excl. scaff., grout & reinforcing | | | | | | | | | | |
| 0015 | Material costs incl. 3% brick and 25% mortar waste | R042110-10 | | | | | | | | | |
| 2000 | Standard, sel. common, 4" x 2-2/3" x 8", (6.75/S.F.) | R042110-20 | D-8 | 230 | .174 | S.F. | 3.61 | 4.69 | | 8.30 | 11.70 |
| 2020 | Standard, red, 4" x 2-2/3" x 8", running bond (6.75/SF) | | | 220 | .182 | | 4.67 | 4.90 | | 9.57 | 13.25 |
| 2050 | Full header every 6th course (7.88/S.F.) | R042110-50 | | 185 | .216 | | 5.45 | 5.85 | | 11.30 | 15.60 |
| 2100 | English, full header every 2nd course (10.13/S.F.) | | | 140 | .286 | | 6.95 | 7.70 | | 14.65 | 20.50 |
| 2150 | Flemish, alternate header every course (9.00/S.F.) | | | 150 | .267 | | 6.20 | 7.20 | | 13.40 | 18.65 |
| 2200 | Flemish, alt. header every 6th course (7.13/S.F.) | | | 205 | .195 | | 4.93 | 5.25 | | 10.18 | 14.05 |
| 2250 | Full headers throughout (13.50/S.F.) | | | 105 | .381 | | 9.25 | 10.25 | | 19.50 | 27 |
| 2300 | Rowlock course (13.50/S.F.) | | | 100 | .400 | | 9.25 | 10.80 | | 20.05 | 28 |
| 2350 | Rowlock stretcher (4.50/S.F.) | | | 310 | .129 | | 3.13 | 3.48 | | 6.61 | 9.20 |
| 2400 | Soldier course (6.75/S.F.) | | | 200 | .200 | | 4.67 | 5.40 | | 10.07 | 14.05 |
| 2450 | Sailor course (4.50/S.F.) | | | 290 | .138 | | 3.13 | 3.72 | | 6.85 | 9.60 |
| 2600 | Buff or gray face, running bond, (6.75/S.F.) | | | 220 | .182 | | 4.94 | 4.90 | | 9.84 | 13.55 |
| 2700 | Glazed face brick, running bond | | | 210 | .190 | | 11.95 | 5.15 | | 17.10 | 21.50 |
| 2750 | Full header every 6th course (7.88/S.F.) | | | 170 | .235 | | 13.95 | 6.35 | | 20.30 | 26 |
| 3000 | Jumbo, 6" x 4" x 12" running bond (3.00/S.F.) | | | 435 | .092 | | 4.87 | 2.48 | | 7.35 | 9.45 |
| 3050 | Norman, 4" x 2-2/3" x 12" running bond, (4.5/S.F.) | | | 320 | .125 | | 5.70 | 3.37 | | 9.07 | 11.80 |
| 3100 | Norwegian, 4" x 3-1/5" x 12" (3.75/S.F.) | | | 375 | .107 | | 4.15 | 2.88 | | 7.03 | 9.30 |
| 3150 | Economy, 4" x 4" x 8" (4.50/S.F.) | | | 310 | .129 | | 4.19 | 3.48 | | 7.67 | 10.35 |
| 3200 | Engineer, 4" x 3-1/5" x 8" (5.63/S.F.) | | | 260 | .154 | | 3.44 | 4.15 | | 7.59 | 10.65 |
| 3250 | Roman, 4" x 2" x 12" (6.00/S.F.) | | | 250 | .160 | | 5.75 | 4.32 | | 10.07 | 13.45 |
| 3300 | SCR, 6" x 2-2/3" x 12" (4.50/S.F.) | | | 310 | .129 | | 5.25 | 3.48 | | 8.73 | 11.50 |
| 3350 | Utility, 4" x 4" x 12" (3.00/S.F.) | | | 450 | .089 | | 4.50 | 2.40 | | 6.90 | 8.90 |
| 3400 | For cavity wall construction, add | | | | | | | 15% | | | |
| 3450 | For stacked bond, add | | | | | | | 10% | | | |
| 3500 | For interior veneer construction, add | | | | | | | 15% | | | |
| 3550 | For curved walls, add | | | | | | | 30% | | | |

### 04 21 13.14 Thin Brick Veneer

| | | | Crew | Daily Output | Labor-Hours | Unit | Material | 2010 Bare Costs Labor | Equipment | Total | Total Incl O&P |
|---|---|---|---|---|---|---|---|---|---|---|---|
| 0010 | **THIN BRICK VENEER** | | | | | | | | | | |
| 0015 | Material costs incl. 3% brick and 25% mortar waste | | | | | | | | | | |
| 0020 | On & incl. metal panel support sys, modular, 2-2/3" x 5/8" x 8", red | | D-7 | 92 | .174 | S.F. | 8.75 | 4.30 | | 13.05 | 16.55 |
| 0100 | Closure, 4" x 5/8" x 8" | | | 110 | .145 | | 8.75 | 3.59 | | 12.34 | 15.40 |
| 0110 | Norman, 2-2/3" x 5/8" x 12" | | | 110 | .145 | | 8.95 | 3.59 | | 12.54 | 15.60 |
| 0120 | Utility, 4" x 5/8" x 12" | | | 125 | .128 | | 8.95 | 3.16 | | 12.11 | 14.90 |
| 0130 | Emperor, 4" x 3/4" x 16" | | | 175 | .091 | | 10.15 | 2.26 | | 12.41 | 14.80 |
| 0140 | Super emperor, 8" x 3/4" x 16" | | | 195 | .082 | | 10.15 | 2.03 | | 12.18 | 14.45 |
| 0150 | For L shaped corners with 4" return, add | | | | | L.F. | 9.25 | | | 9.25 | 10.20 |
| 0200 | On masonry/plaster back-up, modular, 2-2/3" x 5/8" x 8", red | | D-7 | 137 | .117 | S.F. | 3.95 | 2.88 | | 6.83 | 8.95 |
| 0210 | Closure, 4" x 5/8" x 8" | | | 165 | .097 | | 3.95 | 2.40 | | 6.35 | 8.20 |
| 0220 | Norman, 2-2/3" x 5/8" x 12" | | | 165 | .097 | | 4.15 | 2.40 | | 6.55 | 8.40 |
| 0230 | Utility, 4" x 5/8" x 12" | | | 185 | .086 | | 4.15 | 2.14 | | 6.29 | 8 |
| 0240 | Emperor, 4" x 3/4" x 16" | | | 260 | .062 | | 5.35 | 1.52 | | 6.87 | 8.35 |
| 0250 | Super emperor, 8" x 3/4" x 16" | | | 285 | .056 | | 5.35 | 1.39 | | 6.74 | 8.10 |
| 0260 | For L shaped corners with 4" return, add | | | | | L.F. | 9.25 | | | 9.25 | 10.20 |
| 0270 | For embedment into pre-cast concrete panels, add | | | | | S.F. | 14.40 | | | 14.40 | 15.85 |

# 04 21 Clay Unit Masonry

## 04 21 13 – Brick Masonry

### 04 21 13.15 Chimney

| | | Crew | Daily Output | Labor-Hours | Unit | Material | 2010 Bare Costs Labor | Equipment | Total | Total Incl O&P |
|---|---|---|---|---|---|---|---|---|---|---|
| 0010 | **CHIMNEY**, excludes foundation, scaffolding, grout and reinforcing | | | | | | | | | |
| 0100 | Brick, 16" x 16", 8" flue | D-1 | 18.20 | .879 | V.L.F. | 21 | 23 | | 44 | 61.50 |
| 0150 | 16" x 20" with one 8" x 12" flue | | 16 | 1 | | 33.50 | 26.50 | | 60 | 80.50 |
| 0200 | 16" x 24" with two 8" x 8" flues | | 14 | 1.143 | | 49 | 30 | | 79 | 104 |
| 0250 | 20" x 20" with one 12" x 12" flue | | 13.70 | 1.168 | | 38.50 | 31 | | 69.50 | 93.50 |
| 0300 | 20" x 24" with two 8" x 12" flues | | 12 | 1.333 | | 55.50 | 35 | | 90.50 | 119 |
| 0350 | 20" x 32" with two 12" x 12" flues | | 10 | 1.600 | | 68 | 42 | | 110 | 145 |

### 04 21 13.18 Columns

| | | Crew | Daily Output | Labor-Hours | Unit | Material | 2010 Bare Costs Labor | Equipment | Total | Total Incl O&P |
|---|---|---|---|---|---|---|---|---|---|---|
| 0010 | **COLUMNS**, solid, excludes scaffolding, grout and reinforcing | | | | | | | | | |
| 0050 | Brick, 8" x 8", 9 brick per VLF | D-1 | 56 | .286 | V.L.F. | 6.05 | 7.55 | | 13.60 | 19.15 |
| 0100 | 12" x 8", 13.5 brick per VLF | | 37 | .432 | | 9.10 | 11.40 | | 20.50 | 29 |
| 0200 | 12" x 12", 20 brick per VLF | | 25 | .640 | | 13.50 | 16.90 | | 30.40 | 43 |
| 0300 | 16" x 12", 27 brick per VLF | | 19 | .842 | | 18.20 | 22 | | 40.20 | 56.50 |
| 0400 | 16" x 16", 36 brick per VLF | | 14 | 1.143 | | 24.50 | 30 | | 54.50 | 76 |
| 0500 | 20" x 16", 45 brick per VLF | | 11 | 1.455 | | 30.50 | 38.50 | | 69 | 97 |
| 0600 | 20" x 20", 56 brick per VLF | | 9 | 1.778 | | 38 | 47 | | 85 | 119 |

### 04 21 13.30 Oversized Brick

| | | Crew | Daily Output | Labor-Hours | Unit | Material | 2010 Bare Costs Labor | Equipment | Total | Total Incl O&P |
|---|---|---|---|---|---|---|---|---|---|---|
| 0010 | **OVERSIZED BRICK**, excludes scaffolding, grout and reinforcing | | | | | | | | | |
| 0100 | Veneer, 4" x 2.25" x 16" | D-8 | 387 | .103 | S.F. | 6.40 | 2.79 | | 9.19 | 11.65 |
| 0105 | 4" x 2.75" x 16" | | 412 | .097 | | 5.80 | 2.62 | | 8.42 | 10.65 |
| 0110 | 4" x 4" x 16" | | 460 | .087 | | 5.30 | 2.35 | | 7.65 | 9.70 |
| 0120 | 4" x 8" x 16" | | 533 | .075 | | 6.10 | 2.02 | | 8.12 | 10.05 |
| 0125 | Loadbearing, 6" x 4" x 16", grouted and reinforced | | 387 | .103 | | 8.95 | 2.79 | | 11.74 | 14.45 |
| 0130 | 8" x 4" x 16", grouted and reinforced | | 327 | .122 | | 9.45 | 3.30 | | 12.75 | 15.85 |
| 0135 | 6" x 8" x 16", grouted and reinforced | | 440 | .091 | | 8.70 | 2.45 | | 11.15 | 13.60 |
| 0140 | 8" x 8" x 16", grouted and reinforced | | 400 | .100 | | 9.55 | 2.70 | | 12.25 | 15 |
| 0145 | Curtainwall/reinforced veneer, 6" x 4" x 16" | | 387 | .103 | | 13.25 | 2.79 | | 16.04 | 19.15 |
| 0150 | 8" x 4" x 16" | | 327 | .122 | | 15.75 | 3.30 | | 19.05 | 23 |
| 0155 | 6" x 8" x 16" | | 440 | .091 | | 13.35 | 2.45 | | 15.80 | 18.75 |
| 0160 | 8" x 8" x 16" | | 400 | .100 | | 15.85 | 2.70 | | 18.55 | 22 |
| 0200 | For 1 to 3 slots in face, add | | | | | 15% | | | | |
| 0210 | For 4 to 7 slots in face, add | | | | | 25% | | | | |
| 0220 | For bond beams, add | | | | | 20% | | | | |
| 0230 | For bullnose shapes, add | | | | | 20% | | | | |
| 0240 | For open end knockout, add | | | | | 10% | | | | |
| 0250 | For white or gray color group, add | | | | | 10% | | | | |
| 0260 | For 135 degree corner, add | | | | | 250% | | | | |

### 04 21 13.35 Common Building Brick

| | | | | | Unit | Material | Labor | Equipment | Total | Total Incl O&P |
|---|---|---|---|---|---|---|---|---|---|---|
| 0010 | **COMMON BUILDING BRICK**, C62, TL lots, material only | R042110-20 | | | | | | | | |
| 0020 | Standard, minimum | | | | | M | 400 | | | 400 | 440 |
| 0050 | Average (select) | | | | | " | 430 | | | 430 | 475 |

### 04 21 13.45 Face Brick

| | | | | | Unit | Material | Labor | Equipment | Total | Total Incl O&P |
|---|---|---|---|---|---|---|---|---|---|---|
| 0010 | **FACE BRICK** Material Only, C216, TL lots | R042110-20 | | | | | | | | |
| 0300 | Standard modular, 4" x 2-2/3" x 8", minimum | | | | | M | 585 | | | 585 | 640 |
| 0350 | Maximum | | | | | | 700 | | | 700 | 770 |
| 2170 | For less than truck load lots, add | | | | | | 15 | | | 15 | 16.50 |
| 2180 | For buff or gray brick, add | | | | | | 16 | | | 16 | 17.60 |

# 04 22 Concrete Unit Masonry

## 04 22 10 – Concrete Masonry Units

| 04 22 10.11 Autoclave Aerated Concrete Block | | Crew | Daily Output | Labor-Hours | Unit | Material | 2010 Bare Costs Labor | Equipment | Total | Total Incl O&P |
|---|---|---|---|---|---|---|---|---|---|---|
| 0010 | **AUTOCLAVE AERATED CONCRETE BLOCK**, excl. scaffolding, grout & reinforcing | | | | | | | | | |
| 0050 | Solid, 4" x 12" x 24", incl mortar [G] | D-8 | 600 | .067 | S.F. | 1.36 | 1.80 | | 3.16 | 4.45 |
| 0060 | 6" x 12" x 24" [G] | | 600 | .067 | | 2.03 | 1.80 | | 3.83 | 5.20 |
| 0070 | 8" x 8" x 24" [G] | | 575 | .070 | | 2.72 | 1.88 | | 4.60 | 6.10 |
| 0080 | 10" x 12" x 24" [G] | | 575 | .070 | | 3.32 | 1.88 | | 5.20 | 6.75 |
| 0090 | 12" x 12" x 24" [G] | | 550 | .073 | | 4.07 | 1.96 | | 6.03 | 7.70 |

| 04 22 10.14 Concrete Block, Back-Up | | Crew | Daily Output | Labor-Hours | Unit | Material | 2010 Bare Costs Labor | Equipment | Total | Total Incl O&P |
|---|---|---|---|---|---|---|---|---|---|---|
| 0010 | **CONCRETE BLOCK, BACK-UP**, C90, 2000 psi    R042210-20 | | | | | | | | | |
| 0020 | Normal weight, 8" x 16" units, tooled joint 1 side | | | | | | | | | |
| 0050 | Not-reinforced, 2000 psi, 2" thick | D-8 | 475 | .084 | S.F. | 1.39 | 2.27 | | 3.66 | 5.25 |
| 0200 | 4" thick | | 460 | .087 | | 1.56 | 2.35 | | 3.91 | 5.55 |
| 0300 | 6" thick | | 440 | .091 | | 2.17 | 2.45 | | 4.62 | 6.45 |
| 0350 | 8" thick | | 400 | .100 | | 2.45 | 2.70 | | 5.15 | 7.15 |
| 0400 | 10" thick | | 330 | .121 | | 3.09 | 3.27 | | 6.36 | 8.80 |
| 0450 | 12" thick | D-9 | 310 | .155 | | 3.51 | 4.09 | | 7.60 | 10.60 |
| 1000 | Reinforced, alternate courses, 4" thick | D-8 | 450 | .089 | | 1.67 | 2.40 | | 4.07 | 5.80 |
| 1100 | 6" thick | | 430 | .093 | | 2.30 | 2.51 | | 4.81 | 6.65 |
| 1150 | 8" thick | | 395 | .101 | | 2.58 | 2.73 | | 5.31 | 7.35 |
| 1200 | 10" thick | | 320 | .125 | | 3.23 | 3.37 | | 6.60 | 9.10 |
| 1250 | 12" thick | D-9 | 300 | .160 | | 3.66 | 4.22 | | 7.88 | 10.95 |

| 04 22 10.16 Concrete Block, Bond Beam | | Crew | Daily Output | Labor-Hours | Unit | Material | 2010 Bare Costs Labor | Equipment | Total | Total Incl O&P |
|---|---|---|---|---|---|---|---|---|---|---|
| 0010 | **CONCRETE BLOCK, BOND BEAM**, C90, 2000 psi | | | | | | | | | |
| 0020 | Not including grout or reinforcing | | | | | | | | | |
| 0125 | Regular block, 6" thick | D-8 | 584 | .068 | L.F. | 2.32 | 1.85 | | 4.17 | 5.60 |
| 0130 | 8" high, 8" thick | " | 565 | .071 | | 2.50 | 1.91 | | 4.41 | 5.90 |
| 0150 | 12" thick | D-9 | 510 | .094 | | 3.50 | 2.48 | | 5.98 | 7.95 |
| 0525 | Lightweight, 6" thick | D-8 | 592 | .068 | | 2.55 | 1.82 | | 4.37 | 5.80 |

| 04 22 10.19 Concrete Block, Insulation Inserts | | Crew | Daily Output | Labor-Hours | Unit | Material | 2010 Bare Costs Labor | Equipment | Total | Total Incl O&P |
|---|---|---|---|---|---|---|---|---|---|---|
| 0010 | **CONCRETE BLOCK, INSULATION INSERTS** | | | | | | | | | |
| 0100 | Styrofoam, plant installed, add to block prices | | | | | | | | | |
| 0200 | 8" x 16" units, 6" thick | | | | S.F. | 1.81 | | | 1.81 | 1.99 |
| 0250 | 8" thick | | | | | 1.81 | | | 1.81 | 1.99 |
| 0300 | 10" thick | | | | | 2.13 | | | 2.13 | 2.34 |
| 0350 | 12" thick | | | | | 2.24 | | | 2.24 | 2.46 |

| 04 22 10.23 Concrete Block, Decorative | | Crew | Daily Output | Labor-Hours | Unit | Material | 2010 Bare Costs Labor | Equipment | Total | Total Incl O&P |
|---|---|---|---|---|---|---|---|---|---|---|
| 0010 | **CONCRETE BLOCK, DECORATIVE**, C90, 2000 psi | | | | | | | | | |
| 5000 | Split rib profile units, 1" deep ribs, 8 ribs | | | | | | | | | |
| 5100 | 8" x 16" x 4" thick | D-8 | 345 | .116 | S.F. | 3.16 | 3.13 | | 6.29 | 8.65 |
| 5150 | 6" thick | | 325 | .123 | | 3.64 | 3.32 | | 6.96 | 9.45 |
| 5200 | 8" thick | | 300 | .133 | | 4.17 | 3.60 | | 7.77 | 10.55 |
| 5250 | 12" thick | D-9 | 275 | .175 | | 4.94 | 4.61 | | 9.55 | 13.05 |
| 5400 | For special deeper colors, 4" thick, add | | | | | 1.15 | | | 1.15 | 1.27 |
| 5450 | 12" thick, add | | | | | 1.19 | | | 1.19 | 1.31 |
| 5600 | For white, 4" thick, add | | | | | 1.15 | | | 1.15 | 1.27 |
| 5650 | 6" thick, add | | | | | 1.14 | | | 1.14 | 1.26 |
| 5700 | 8" thick, add | | | | | 1.20 | | | 1.20 | 1.32 |
| 5750 | 12" thick, add | | | | | 1.23 | | | 1.23 | 1.35 |

| 04 22 10.24 Concrete Block, Exterior | | Crew | Daily Output | Labor-Hours | Unit | Material | 2010 Bare Costs Labor | Equipment | Total | Total Incl O&P |
|---|---|---|---|---|---|---|---|---|---|---|
| 0010 | **CONCRETE BLOCK, EXTERIOR**, C90, 2000 psi | | | | | | | | | |
| 0020 | Reinforced alt courses, tooled joints 2 sides | | | | | | | | | |
| 0100 | Normal weight, 8" x 16" x 6" thick | D-8 | 395 | .101 | S.F. | 2.55 | 2.73 | | 5.28 | 7.30 |

# 04 22 Concrete Unit Masonry

## 04 22 10 - Concrete Masonry Units

| 04 22 10.24 Concrete Block, Exterior | | Crew | Daily Output | Labor-Hours | Unit | Material | 2010 Bare Costs Labor | Equipment | Total | Total Incl O&P |
|---|---|---|---|---|---|---|---|---|---|---|
| 0200 | 8" thick | D-8 | 360 | .111 | S.F. | 3.67 | 3 | | 6.67 | 8.95 |
| 0250 | 10" thick | ↓ | 290 | .138 | | 4.29 | 3.72 | | 8.01 | 10.85 |
| 0300 | 12" thick | D-9 | 250 | .192 | ↓ | 4.53 | 5.05 | | 9.58 | 13.35 |

### 04 22 10.26 Concrete Block Foundation Wall

| | | Crew | Daily Output | Labor-Hours | Unit | Material | Labor | Equipment | Total | Total Incl O&P |
|---|---|---|---|---|---|---|---|---|---|---|
| 0010 | **CONCRETE BLOCK FOUNDATION WALL**, C90/C145 | | | | | | | | | |
| 0050 | Normal-weight, cut joints, horiz joint reinf, no vert reinf | | | | | | | | | |
| 0200 | Hollow, 8" x 16" x 6" thick | D-8 | 455 | .088 | S.F. | 2.61 | 2.37 | | 4.98 | 6.80 |
| 0250 | 8" thick | | 425 | .094 | | 2.90 | 2.54 | | 5.44 | 7.35 |
| 0300 | 10" thick | ↓ | 350 | .114 | | 3.55 | 3.08 | | 6.63 | 9 |
| 0350 | 12" thick | D-9 | 300 | .160 | | 3.98 | 4.22 | | 8.20 | 11.35 |
| 0500 | Solid, 8" x 16" block, 6" thick | D-8 | 440 | .091 | | 2.68 | 2.45 | | 5.13 | 7 |
| 0550 | 8" thick | " | 415 | .096 | | 3.78 | 2.60 | | 6.38 | 8.45 |
| 0600 | 12" thick | D-9 | 350 | .137 | ↓ | 5.45 | 3.62 | | 9.07 | 11.95 |

### 04 22 10.32 Concrete Block, Lintels

| | | Crew | Daily Output | Labor-Hours | Unit | Material | Labor | Equipment | Total | Total Incl O&P |
|---|---|---|---|---|---|---|---|---|---|---|
| 0010 | **CONCRETE BLOCK, LINTELS**, C90, normal weight | | | | | | | | | |
| 0100 | Including grout and horizontal reinforcing | | | | | | | | | |
| 0200 | 8" x 8" x 8", 1 #4 bar | D-4 | 300 | .133 | L.F. | 4.83 | 3.24 | .44 | 8.51 | 11.15 |
| 0250 | 2 #4 bars | ↓ | 295 | .136 | | 5 | 3.29 | .45 | 8.74 | 11.45 |
| 1000 | 12" x 8" x 8", 1 #4 bar | | 275 | .145 | | 6.80 | 3.53 | .48 | 10.81 | 13.85 |
| 1150 | 2 #5 bars | ↓ | 270 | .148 | ↓ | 7.15 | 3.60 | .49 | 11.24 | 14.40 |

### 04 22 10.34 Concrete Block, Partitions

| | | Crew | Daily Output | Labor-Hours | Unit | Material | Labor | Equipment | Total | Total Incl O&P |
|---|---|---|---|---|---|---|---|---|---|---|
| 0010 | **CONCRETE BLOCK, PARTITIONS**, excludes scaffolding | | | | | | | | | |
| 1000 | Lightweight block, tooled joints, 2 sides, hollow | | | | | | | | | |
| 1100 | Not reinforced, 8" x 16" x 4" thick | D-8 | 440 | .091 | S.F. | 1.65 | 2.45 | | 4.10 | 5.85 |
| 1150 | 6" thick | | 410 | .098 | | 2.37 | 2.63 | | 5 | 6.95 |
| 1200 | 8" thick | | 385 | .104 | | 2.88 | 2.80 | | 5.68 | 7.80 |
| 1250 | 10" thick | ↓ | 370 | .108 | | 3.49 | 2.92 | | 6.41 | 8.65 |
| 1300 | 12" thick | D-9 | 350 | .137 | | 4.34 | 3.62 | | 7.96 | 10.70 |
| 4000 | Regular block, tooled joints, 2 sides, hollow | | | | | | | | | |
| 4100 | Not reinforced, 8" x 16" x 4" thick | D-8 | 430 | .093 | S.F. | 1.47 | 2.51 | | 3.98 | 5.75 |
| 4150 | 6" thick | | 400 | .100 | | 2.08 | 2.70 | | 4.78 | 6.75 |
| 4200 | 8" thick | | 375 | .107 | | 2.36 | 2.88 | | 5.24 | 7.35 |
| 4250 | 10" thick | ↓ | 360 | .111 | | 3 | 3 | | 6 | 8.25 |
| 4300 | 12" thick | D-9 | 340 | .141 | ↓ | 3.42 | 3.73 | | 7.15 | 9.90 |

# 04 23 Glass Unit Masonry

## 04 23 13 - Vertical Glass Unit Masonry

| 04 23 13.10 Glass Block | | Crew | Daily Output | Labor-Hours | Unit | Material | Labor | Equipment | Total | Total Incl O&P |
|---|---|---|---|---|---|---|---|---|---|---|
| 0010 | **GLASS BLOCK** | | | | | | | | | |
| 0150 | 8" x 8" | D-8 | 160 | .250 | S.F. | 15.55 | 6.75 | | 22.30 | 28 |
| 0160 | end block | | 160 | .250 | | 47 | 6.75 | | 53.75 | 62.50 |
| 0170 | 90 deg corner | | 160 | .250 | | 46 | 6.75 | | 52.75 | 61.50 |
| 0180 | 45 deg corner | | 160 | .250 | | 33.50 | 6.75 | | 40.25 | 48 |
| 0200 | 12" x 12" | | 175 | .229 | | 20 | 6.15 | | 26.15 | 32 |
| 0210 | 4" x 8" | | 160 | .250 | | 15.20 | 6.75 | | 21.95 | 28 |
| 0220 | 6" x 8" | ↓ | 160 | .250 | | 14.60 | 6.75 | | 21.35 | 27 |
| 0700 | For solar reflective blocks, add | | | | | 100% | | | | |
| 1000 | Thinline, plain, 3-1/8" thick, under 1,000 S.F., 6" x 6" | D-8 | 115 | .348 | S.F. | 17.35 | 9.40 | | 26.75 | 34.50 |
| 1050 | 8" x 8" | | 160 | .250 | | 9.70 | 6.75 | | 16.45 | 22 |
| 1400 | For cleaning block after installation (both sides), add | ↓ | 1000 | .040 | ↓ | .11 | 1.08 | | 1.19 | 1.90 |

# 04 24 Adobe Unit Masonry

## 04 24 16 – Manufactured Adobe Unit Masonry

| 04 24 16.06  Adobe Brick | | Crew | Daily Output | Labor-Hours | Unit | Material | 2010 Bare Costs Labor | Equipment | Total | Total Incl O&P |
|---|---|---|---|---|---|---|---|---|---|---|
| 0010 | **ADOBE BRICK**, Semi-stabilized, with cement mortar | | | | | | | | | |
| 0060 | Brick, 10" x 4" x 14", 2.6/S.F. | G | D-8 | 560 | .071 | S.F. | 3.45 | 1.93 | | 5.38 | 6.95 |
| 0080 | 12" x 4" x 16", 2.3/S.F. | G | | 580 | .069 | | 4.61 | 1.86 | | 6.47 | 8.10 |
| 0100 | 10" x 4" x 16", 2.3/S.F. | G | | 590 | .068 | | 4.37 | 1.83 | | 6.20 | 7.80 |
| 0120 | 8" x 4" x 16", 2.3/S.F. | G | | 560 | .071 | | 3.36 | 1.93 | | 5.29 | 6.85 |
| 0140 | 4" x 4" x 16", 2.3/S.F. | G | | 540 | .074 | | 2.56 | 2 | | 4.56 | 6.10 |
| 0160 | 6" x 4" x 16", 2.3/S.F. | G | | 540 | .074 | | 2.59 | 2 | | 4.59 | 6.15 |
| 0180 | 4" x 4" x 12", 3.0/S.F. | G | | 520 | .077 | | 2.45 | 2.07 | | 4.52 | 6.10 |
| 0200 | 8" x 4" x 12", 3.0/S.F. | G | | 520 | .077 | | 3.16 | 2.07 | | 5.23 | 6.90 |

# 04 27 Multiple-Wythe Unit Masonry

## 04 27 10 – Multiple-Wythe Masonry

### 04 27 10.10  Cornices

| | | Crew | Daily Output | Labor-Hours | Unit | Material | Labor | Equipment | Total | Total Incl O&P |
|---|---|---|---|---|---|---|---|---|---|---|
| 0010 | **CORNICES** | | | | | | | | | |
| 0110 | Face bricks, 12 brick/S.F., minimum | D-1 | 30 | .533 | SF Face | 5.95 | 14.10 | | 20.05 | 29.50 |
| 0150 | 15 brick/S.F., maximum | " | 23 | .696 | " | 7.15 | 18.35 | | 25.50 | 38.50 |

### 04 27 10.30  Brick Walls

| | | Crew | Daily Output | Labor-Hours | Unit | Material | Labor | Equipment | Total | Total Incl O&P |
|---|---|---|---|---|---|---|---|---|---|---|
| 0010 | **BRICK WALLS**, including mortar, excludes scaffolding | | | | | | | | | |
| 0800 | Face brick, 4" thick wall, 6.75 brick/S.F. | D-8 | 215 | .186 | S.F. | 4.61 | 5 | | 9.61 | 13.30 |
| 0850 | Common brick, 4" thick wall, 6.75 brick/S.F. | | 240 | .167 | | 3.33 | 4.50 | | 7.83 | 11.05 |
| 0900 | 8" thick, 13.50 bricks per S.F. | | 135 | .296 | | 6.90 | 8 | | 14.90 | 21 |
| 1000 | 12" thick, 20.25 bricks per S.F. | | 95 | .421 | | 10.40 | 11.35 | | 21.75 | 30 |
| 1050 | 16" thick, 27.00 bricks per S.F. | | 75 | .533 | | 14.05 | 14.40 | | 28.45 | 39 |
| 1200 | Reinforced, face brick, 4" thick wall, 6.75 brick/S.F. | | 210 | .190 | | 4.74 | 5.15 | | 9.89 | 13.65 |
| 1220 | Common brick, 4" thick wall, 6.75 brick/S.F. | | 235 | .170 | | 3.46 | 4.59 | | 8.05 | 11.35 |
| 1250 | 8" thick, 13.50 bricks per S.F. | | 130 | .308 | | 7.15 | 8.30 | | 15.45 | 21.50 |
| 1300 | 12" thick, 20.25 bricks per S.F. | | 90 | .444 | | 10.80 | 12 | | 22.80 | 31.50 |
| 1350 | 16" thick, 27.00 bricks per S.F. | | 70 | .571 | | 14.60 | 15.40 | | 30 | 41.50 |

# 04 41 Dry-Placed Stone

## 04 41 10 – Dry Placed Stone

### 04 41 10.10  Rough Stone Wall

| | | | Crew | Daily Output | Labor-Hours | Unit | Material | Labor | Equipment | Total | Total Incl O&P |
|---|---|---|---|---|---|---|---|---|---|---|---|
| 0011 | **ROUGH STONE WALL**, Dry | | | | | | | | | | |
| 0012 | Dry laid (no mortar), under 18" thick | | D-1 | 60 | .267 | C.F. | 8.80 | 7.05 | | 15.85 | 21.50 |
| 0100 | Random fieldstone, under 18" thick | G | D-12 | 60 | .533 | | 8.80 | 14.10 | | 22.90 | 32.50 |
| 0150 | Over 18" thick | G | " | 63 | .508 | | 10.55 | 13.40 | | 23.95 | 33.50 |
| 0500 | Field stone veneer | G | D-8 | 120 | .333 | S.F. | 9.95 | 9 | | 18.95 | 26 |
| 0510 | Valley stone veneer | G | | 120 | .333 | | 9.95 | 9 | | 18.95 | 26 |
| 0520 | River stone veneer | G | | 120 | .333 | | 9.95 | 9 | | 18.95 | 26 |
| 0600 | Rubble stone walls, in mortar bed, up to 18" thick | G | D-11 | 75 | .320 | C.F. | 10.65 | 8.75 | | 19.40 | 26 |

323

# 04 43 Stone Masonry

## 04 43 10 - Masonry with Natural and Processed Stone

### 04 43 10.45 Granite

| | | Crew | Daily Output | Labor-Hours | Unit | Material | 2010 Bare Costs Labor | 2010 Bare Costs Equipment | Total | Total Incl O&P |
|---|---|---|---|---|---|---|---|---|---|---|
| 0010 | **GRANITE**, cut to size | | | | | | | | | |
| 2450 | For radius under 5', add | | | | L.F. | 100% | | | | |
| 2500 | Steps, copings, etc., finished on more than one surface | | | | | | | | | |
| 2550 | Minimum | D-10 | 50 | .640 | C.F. | 91 | 18.35 | 13.10 | 122.45 | 144 |
| 2600 | Maximum | " | 50 | .640 | " | 146 | 18.35 | 13.10 | 177.45 | 204 |
| 2800 | Pavers, 4" x 4" x 4" blocks, split face and joints | | | | | | | | | |
| 2850 | Minimum | D-11 | 80 | .300 | S.F. | 12.75 | 8.20 | | 20.95 | 27.50 |
| 2900 | Maximum | " | 80 | .300 | " | 28.50 | 8.20 | | 36.70 | 44.50 |

### 04 43 10.55 Limestone

| | | Crew | Daily Output | Labor-Hours | Unit | Material | 2010 Bare Costs Labor | 2010 Bare Costs Equipment | Total | Total Incl O&P |
|---|---|---|---|---|---|---|---|---|---|---|
| 0010 | **LIMESTONE**, cut to size | | | | | | | | | |
| 0020 | Veneer facing panels | | | | | | | | | |
| 0500 | Texture finish, light stick, 4-1/2" thick, 5' x 12' | D-4 | 300 | .133 | S.F. | 48 | 3.24 | .44 | 51.68 | 59 |
| 0750 | 5" thick, 5' x 14' panels | D-10 | 275 | .116 | | 52.50 | 3.34 | 2.38 | 58.22 | 65.50 |
| 1000 | Sugarcube finish, 2" Thick, 3' x 5' panels | | 275 | .116 | | 35 | 3.34 | 2.38 | 40.72 | 46.50 |
| 1050 | 3" Thick, 4' x 9' panels | | 275 | .116 | | 38 | 3.34 | 2.38 | 43.72 | 50 |
| 1200 | 4" Thick, 5' x 11' panels | | 275 | .116 | | 41 | 3.34 | 2.38 | 46.72 | 53 |
| 1400 | Sugarcube, textured finish, 4-1/2" thick, 5' x 12' | | 275 | .116 | | 45 | 3.34 | 2.38 | 50.72 | 57.50 |
| 1450 | 5" thick, 5' x 14' panels | | 275 | .116 | | 53.50 | 3.34 | 2.38 | 59.22 | 66.50 |
| 2000 | Coping, sugarcube finish, top & 2 sides | | 30 | 1.067 | C.F. | 68 | 30.50 | 22 | 120.50 | 150 |
| 2100 | Sills, lintels, jambs, trim, stops, sugarcube finish, average | | 20 | 1.600 | | 68 | 46 | 33 | 147 | 187 |
| 2150 | Detailed | | 20 | 1.600 | | 68 | 46 | 33 | 147 | 187 |
| 2300 | Steps, extra hard, 14" wide, 6" rise | | 50 | .640 | L.F. | 41.50 | 18.35 | 13.10 | 72.95 | 90.50 |
| 3000 | Quoins, plain finish, 6" x 12" x 12" | D-12 | 25 | 1.280 | Ea. | 38 | 34 | | 72 | 97.50 |
| 3050 | 6" x 16" x 24" | " | 25 | 1.280 | " | 50.50 | 34 | | 84.50 | 111 |

### 04 43 10.60 Marble

| | | Crew | Daily Output | Labor-Hours | Unit | Material | 2010 Bare Costs Labor | 2010 Bare Costs Equipment | Total | Total Incl O&P |
|---|---|---|---|---|---|---|---|---|---|---|
| 0011 | **MARBLE**, ashlar, split face, 4" + or - thick, random | | | | | | | | | |
| 0040 | Lengths 1' to 4' & heights 2" to 7-1/2", average | D-8 | 175 | .229 | S.F. | 17.75 | 6.15 | | 23.90 | 29.50 |
| 0100 | Base, polished, 3/4" or 7/8" thick, polished, 6" high | D-10 | 65 | .492 | L.F. | 16.15 | 14.10 | 10.10 | 40.35 | 52 |
| 1000 | Facing, polished finish, cut to size, 3/4" to 7/8" thick | | | | | | | | | |
| 1050 | Average | D-10 | 130 | .246 | S.F. | 23.50 | 7.05 | 5.05 | 35.60 | 43 |
| 1100 | Maximum | " | 130 | .246 | " | 55 | 7.05 | 5.05 | 67.10 | 77.50 |
| 2200 | Window sills, 6" x 3/4" thick | D-1 | 85 | .188 | L.F. | 8.95 | 4.97 | | 13.92 | 18 |
| 2500 | Flooring, polished tiles, 12" x 12" x 3/8" thick | | | | | | | | | |
| 2510 | Thin set, average | D-11 | 90 | .267 | S.F. | 11.90 | 7.30 | | 19.20 | 25 |
| 2600 | Maximum | | 90 | .267 | | 183 | 7.30 | | 190.30 | 213 |
| 2700 | Mortar bed, average | | 65 | .369 | | 10.65 | 10.10 | | 20.75 | 28.50 |
| 2740 | Maximum | | 65 | .369 | | 183 | 10.10 | | 193.10 | 218 |
| 2780 | Travertine, 3/8" thick, average | D-10 | 130 | .246 | | 15.15 | 7.05 | 5.05 | 27.25 | 34 |
| 2790 | Maximum | " | 130 | .246 | | 37 | 7.05 | 5.05 | 49.10 | 58 |
| 3500 | Thresholds, 3' long, 7/8" thick, 4" to 5" wide, plain | D-12 | 24 | 1.333 | Ea. | 17.15 | 35 | | 52.15 | 77 |
| 3550 | Beveled | | 24 | 1.333 | " | 19.90 | 35 | | 54.90 | 80 |
| 3700 | Window stools, polished, 7/8" thick, 5" wide | | 85 | .376 | L.F. | 15.95 | 9.95 | | 25.90 | 34 |

### 04 43 10.75 Sandstone or Brownstone

| | | Crew | Daily Output | Labor-Hours | Unit | Material | 2010 Bare Costs Labor | 2010 Bare Costs Equipment | Total | Total Incl O&P |
|---|---|---|---|---|---|---|---|---|---|---|
| 0011 | **SANDSTONE OR BROWNSTONE** | | | | | | | | | |
| 0100 | Sawed face veneer, 2-1/2" thick, to 2' x 4' panels | D-10 | 130 | .246 | S.F. | 20 | 7.05 | 5.05 | 32.10 | 39.50 |
| 0150 | 4" thick, to 3'-6" x 8' panels | | 100 | .320 | | 20 | 9.20 | 6.55 | 35.75 | 45 |
| 0300 | Split face, random sizes | | 100 | .320 | | 13.55 | 9.20 | 6.55 | 29.30 | 37.50 |
| 0350 | Cut stone trim (limestone) | | | | | | | | | |
| 0360 | Ribbon stone, 4" thick, 5' pieces | D-8 | 120 | .333 | Ea. | 167 | 9 | | 176 | 199 |
| 0370 | Cove stone, 4" thick, 5' pieces | | 105 | .381 | | 168 | 10.25 | | 178.25 | 202 |
| 0380 | Cornice stone, 10" to 12" wide | | 90 | .444 | | 207 | 12 | | 219 | 248 |
| 0390 | Band stone, 4" thick, 5' pieces | | 145 | .276 | | 107 | 7.45 | | 114.45 | 130 |

# 04 43 Stone Masonry

## 04 43 10 – Masonry with Natural and Processed Stone

| 04 43 10.75 Sandstone or Brownstone | | Crew | Daily Output | Labor-Hours | Unit | Material | 2010 Bare Costs | | Total | Total Incl O&P |
|---|---|---|---|---|---|---|---|---|---|---|
| | | | | | | | Labor | Equipment | | |
| 0410 | Window and door trim, 3" to 4" wide | D-8 | 160 | .250 | Ea. | 91 | 6.75 | | 97.75 | 111 |
| 0420 | Key stone, 18" long | ↓ | 60 | .667 | ↓ | 95.50 | 18 | | 113.50 | 135 |

### 04 43 10.80 Slate

| 0010 | **SLATE** | | | | | | | | | |
|---|---|---|---|---|---|---|---|---|---|---|
| 3500 | Stair treads, sand finish, 1" thick x 12" wide | | | | | | | | | |
| 3600 | 3 L.F. to 6 L.F. | D-10 | 120 | .267 | L.F. | 24 | 7.65 | 5.45 | 37.10 | 44.50 |
| 3700 | Ribbon, sand finish, 1" thick x 12" wide | | | | | | | | | |
| 3750 | To 6 L.F. | D-10 | 120 | .267 | L.F. | 20 | 7.65 | 5.45 | 33.10 | 40.50 |

### 04 43 10.85 Window Sill

| 0010 | **WINDOW SILL** | | | | | | | | | |
|---|---|---|---|---|---|---|---|---|---|---|
| 0020 | Bluestone, thermal top, 10" wide, 1-1/2" thick | D-1 | 85 | .188 | S.F. | 16.05 | 4.97 | | 21.02 | 26 |
| 0050 | 2" thick | | 75 | .213 | " | 18.75 | 5.65 | | 24.40 | 30 |
| 0100 | Cut stone, 5" x 8" plain | | 48 | .333 | L.F. | 11.90 | 8.80 | | 20.70 | 27.50 |
| 0200 | Face brick on edge, brick, 8" wide | | 80 | .200 | | 2.53 | 5.30 | | 7.83 | 11.50 |
| 0400 | Marble, 9" wide, 1" thick | | 85 | .188 | | 8.50 | 4.97 | | 13.47 | 17.55 |
| 0900 | Slate, colored, unfading, honed, 12" wide, 1" thick | | 85 | .188 | | 17.10 | 4.97 | | 22.07 | 27 |
| 0950 | 2" thick | ↓ | 70 | .229 | ↓ | 24 | 6.05 | | 30.05 | 36 |

# 04 51 Flue Liner Masonry

## 04 51 10 – Clay Flue Lining

### 04 51 10.10 Flue Lining

| 0010 | **FLUE LINING**, including mortar | | | | | | | | | |
|---|---|---|---|---|---|---|---|---|---|---|
| 0020 | Clay, 8" x 8" | D-1 | 125 | .128 | V.L.F. | 4.67 | 3.38 | | 8.05 | 10.70 |
| 0100 | 8" x 12" | | 103 | .155 | | 7.20 | 4.10 | | 11.30 | 14.65 |
| 0200 | 12" x 12" | | 93 | .172 | | 9.45 | 4.54 | | 13.99 | 17.90 |
| 0300 | 12" x 18" | | 84 | .190 | | 17.70 | 5.05 | | 22.75 | 28 |
| 0400 | 18" x 18" | | 75 | .213 | | 22 | 5.65 | | 27.65 | 33.50 |
| 0500 | 20" x 20" | | 66 | .242 | | 34 | 6.40 | | 40.40 | 48 |
| 0600 | 24" x 24" | | 56 | .286 | | 43.50 | 7.55 | | 51.05 | 60.50 |
| 1000 | Round, 18" diameter | | 66 | .242 | | 30 | 6.40 | | 36.40 | 43.50 |
| 1100 | 24" diameter | ↓ | 47 | .340 | ↓ | 62.50 | 9 | | 71.50 | 84 |

# 04 57 Masonry Fireplaces

## 04 57 10 – Brick or Stone Fireplaces

### 04 57 10.10 Fireplace

| 0010 | **FIREPLACE** | | | | | | | | | |
|---|---|---|---|---|---|---|---|---|---|---|
| 0100 | Brick fireplace, not incl. foundations or chimneys | | | | | | | | | |
| 0110 | 30" x 29" opening, incl. chamber, plain brickwork | D-1 | .40 | 40 | Ea. | 535 | 1,050 | | 1,585 | 2,350 |
| 0200 | Fireplace box only (110 brick) | " | 2 | 8 | " | 176 | 211 | | 387 | 545 |
| 0300 | For elaborate brickwork and details, add | | | | | 35% | 35% | | | |
| 0400 | For hearth, brick & stone, add | D-1 | 2 | 8 | Ea. | 197 | 211 | | 408 | 565 |
| 0410 | For steel angle, damper, cleanouts, add | | 4 | 4 | | 138 | 106 | | 244 | 325 |
| 0600 | Plain brickwork, incl. metal circulator | | .50 | 32 | ↓ | 1,025 | 845 | | 1,870 | 2,525 |
| 0800 | Face brick only, standard size, 8" x 2-2/3" x 4" | ↓ | .30 | 53.333 | M | 535 | 1,400 | | 1,935 | 2,925 |
| 0900 | Stone fireplace, fieldstone, add | | | | SF Face | 14.05 | | | 14.05 | 15.50 |
| 1000 | Cut stone, add | | | | " | 15.50 | | | 15.50 | 17.05 |

# 04 72 Cast Stone Masonry

## 04 72 10 – Cast Stone Masonry Features

### 04 72 10.10 Coping

| | | Crew | Daily Output | Labor-Hours | Unit | Material | 2010 Bare Costs Labor | 2010 Bare Costs Equipment | Total | Total Incl O&P |
|---|---|---|---|---|---|---|---|---|---|---|
| 0010 | **COPING**, stock units | | | | | | | | | |
| 0050 | Precast concrete, 10" wide, 4" tapers to 3-1/2", 8" wall | D-1 | 75 | .213 | L.F. | 17.55 | 5.65 | | 23.20 | 28.50 |
| 0100 | 12" wide, 3-1/2" tapers to 3", 10" wall | | 70 | .229 | | 17.55 | 6.05 | | 23.60 | 29.50 |
| 0150 | 16" wide, 4" tapers to 3-1/2", 14" wall | | 60 | .267 | | 17.10 | 7.05 | | 24.15 | 30.50 |
| 0300 | Limestone for 12" wall, 4" thick | | 90 | .178 | | 15.35 | 4.69 | | 20.04 | 24.50 |
| 0350 | 6" thick | | 80 | .200 | | 23 | 5.30 | | 28.30 | 34 |
| 0500 | Marble, to 4" thick, no wash, 9" wide | | 90 | .178 | | 23 | 4.69 | | 27.69 | 33.50 |
| 0550 | 12" wide | | 80 | .200 | | 35 | 5.30 | | 40.30 | 47 |
| 0700 | Terra cotta, 9" wide | | 90 | .178 | | 5.60 | 4.69 | | 10.29 | 13.90 |
| 0800 | Aluminum, for 12" wall | | 80 | .200 | | 13.30 | 5.30 | | 18.60 | 23.50 |

## 04 72 20 – Cultured Stone Veneer

### 04 72 20.10 Cultured Stone Veneer Components

| | | Crew | Daily Output | Labor-Hours | Unit | Material | 2010 Bare Costs Labor | 2010 Bare Costs Equipment | Total | Total Incl O&P |
|---|---|---|---|---|---|---|---|---|---|---|
| 0010 | **CULTURED STONE VENEER COMPONENTS** | | | | | | | | | |
| 0110 | On wood frame and sheathing substrate, random sized cobbles, corner stones | D-8 | 70 | .571 | V.L.F. | 12.15 | 15.40 | | 27.55 | 39 |
| 0120 | Field stones | | 140 | .286 | S.F. | 8.80 | 7.70 | | 16.50 | 22.50 |
| 0130 | Random sized flats, corner stones | | 70 | .571 | V.L.F. | 11.95 | 15.40 | | 27.35 | 38.50 |
| 0140 | Field stones | | 140 | .286 | S.F. | 10.10 | 7.70 | | 17.80 | 24 |
| 0150 | Horizontal lined ledgestones, corner stones | | 75 | .533 | V.L.F. | 12.15 | 14.40 | | 26.55 | 37 |
| 0160 | Field stones | | 150 | .267 | S.F. | 8.80 | 7.20 | | 16 | 21.50 |
| 0170 | Random shaped flats, corner stones | | 65 | .615 | V.L.F. | 12.15 | 16.60 | | 28.75 | 41 |
| 0180 | Field stones | | 150 | .267 | S.F. | 8.80 | 7.20 | | 16 | 21.50 |
| 0190 | Random shaped/textured face, corner stones | | 65 | .615 | V.L.F. | 12.15 | 16.60 | | 28.75 | 41 |
| 0200 | Field stones | | 130 | .308 | S.F. | 8.80 | 8.30 | | 17.10 | 23.50 |
| 0210 | Random shaped river rock, corner stones | | 65 | .615 | V.L.F. | 12.15 | 16.60 | | 28.75 | 41 |
| 0220 | Field stones | | 130 | .308 | S.F. | 8.80 | 8.30 | | 17.10 | 23.50 |
| 0240 | On concrete or CMU substrate, random sized cobbles, corner stones | | 70 | .571 | V.L.F. | 11.50 | 15.40 | | 26.90 | 38 |
| 0250 | Field stones | | 140 | .286 | S.F. | 8.50 | 7.70 | | 16.20 | 22 |
| 0260 | Random sized flats, corner stones | | 70 | .571 | V.L.F. | 11.30 | 15.40 | | 26.70 | 38 |
| 0270 | Field stones | | 140 | .286 | S.F. | 9.75 | 7.70 | | 17.45 | 23.50 |
| 0280 | Horizontal lined ledgestones, corner stones | | 75 | .533 | V.L.F. | 11.50 | 14.40 | | 25.90 | 36 |
| 0290 | Field stones | | 150 | .267 | S.F. | 8.50 | 7.20 | | 15.70 | 21 |
| 0300 | Random shaped flats, corner stones | | 70 | .571 | V.L.F. | 11.50 | 15.40 | | 26.90 | 38 |
| 0310 | Field stones | | 140 | .286 | S.F. | 8.50 | 7.70 | | 16.20 | 22 |
| 0320 | Random shaped/textured face, corner stones | | 65 | .615 | V.L.F. | 11.50 | 16.60 | | 28.10 | 40 |
| 0330 | Field stones | | 130 | .308 | S.F. | 8.50 | 8.30 | | 16.80 | 23 |
| 0340 | Random shaped river rock, corner stones | | 65 | .615 | V.L.F. | 11.50 | 16.60 | | 28.10 | 40 |
| 0350 | Field stones | | 130 | .308 | S.F. | 8.50 | 8.30 | | 16.80 | 23 |
| 0360 | Cultured stone veneer, #15 felt weather resistant barrier | 1 Clab | 3700 | .002 | Sq. | 5.90 | .05 | | 5.95 | 6.55 |
| 0390 | Water table or window sill, 18" long | 1 Bric | 80 | .100 | Ea. | 11.85 | 2.93 | | 14.78 | 17.85 |

# Estimating Tips

## 05 05 00 Common Work Results for Metals

- Nuts, bolts, washers, connection angles, and plates can add a significant amount to both the tonnage of a structural steel job and the estimated cost. As a rule of thumb, add 10% to the total weight to account for these accessories.

- Type 2 steel construction, commonly referred to as "simple construction," consists generally of field-bolted connections with lateral bracing supplied by other elements of the building, such as masonry walls or x-bracing. The estimator should be aware, however, that shop connections may be accomplished by welding or bolting. The method may be particular to the fabrication shop and may have an impact on the estimated cost.

## 05 12 23 Structural Steel

- Steel items can be obtained from two sources: a fabrication shop or a metals service center. Fabrication shops can fabricate items under more controlled conditions than can crews in the field. They are also more efficient and can produce items more economically. Metal service centers serve as a source of long mill shapes to both fabrication shops and contractors.

- Most line items in this structural steel subdivision, and most items in 05 50 00 Metal Fabrications, are indicated as being shop fabricated. The bare material cost for these shop fabricated items is the "Invoice Cost" from the shop and includes the mill base price of steel plus mill extras, transportation to the shop, shop drawings and detailing where warranted, shop fabrication and handling, sandblasting and a shop coat of primer paint, all necessary structural bolts, and delivery to the job site. The bare labor cost and bare equipment cost for these shop fabricated items is for field installation or erection.

- Line items in Subdivision 05 12 23.40 Lightweight Framing, and other items scattered in Division 5, are indicated as being field fabricated. The bare material cost for these field fabricated items is the "Invoice Cost" from the metals service center and includes the mill base price of steel plus mill extras, transportation to the metals service center, material handling, and delivery of long lengths of mill shapes to the job site. Material costs for structural bolts and welding rods should be added to the estimate. The bare labor cost and bare equipment cost for these items is for both field fabrication and field installation or erection, and include time for cutting, welding and drilling in the fabricated metal items. Drilling into concrete and fasteners to fasten field fabricated items to other work are not included and should be added to the estimate.

## 05 20 00 Steel Joist Framing

- In any given project the total weight of open web steel joists is determined by the loads to be supported and the design. However, economies can be realized in minimizing the amount of labor used to place the joists. This is done by maximizing the joist spacing, and therefore minimizing the number of joists required to be installed on the job. Certain spacings and locations may be required by the design, but in other cases maximizing the spacing and keeping it as uniform as possible will keep the costs down.

## 05 30 00 Steel Decking

- The takeoff and estimating of metal deck involves more than simply the area of the floor or roof and the type of deck specified or shown on the drawings. Many different sizes and types of openings may exist. Small openings for individual pipes or conduits may be drilled after the floor/roof is installed, but larger openings may require special deck lengths as well as reinforcing or structural support. The estimator should determine who will be supplying this reinforcing. Additionally, some deck terminations are part of the deck package, such as screed angles and pour stops, and others will be part of the steel contract, such as angles attached to structural members and cast-in-place angles and plates. The estimator must ensure that all pieces are accounted for in the complete estimate.

## 05 50 00 Metal Fabrications

- The most economical steel stairs are those that use common materials, standard details, and most importantly, a uniform and relatively simple method of field assembly. Commonly available A36 channels and plates are very good choices for the main stringers of the stairs, as are angles and tees for the carrier members. Risers and treads are usually made by specialty shops, and it is most economical to use a typical detail in as many places as possible. The stairs should be pre-assembled and shipped directly to the site. The field connections should be simple and straightforward to be accomplished efficiently, and with minimum equipment and labor.

# Reference Numbers

Reference numbers are shown in shaded boxes at the beginning of some major classifications. These numbers refer to related items in the Reference Section. The reference information may be an estimating procedure, an alternate pricing method, or technical information. *Note:* Not all subdivisions listed here necessarily appear in this publication.

# 05 05 Common Work Results for Metals

## 05 05 21 – Fastening Methods for Metal

### 05 05 21.15 Drilling Steel

| | | Crew | Daily Output | Labor-Hours | Unit | Material | 2010 Bare Costs Labor | 2010 Bare Costs Equipment | Total | Total Incl O&P |
|---|---|---|---|---|---|---|---|---|---|---|
| 0010 | **DRILLING STEEL** | | | | | | | | | |
| 1910 | Drilling & layout for steel, up to 1/4" deep, no anchor | | | | | | | | | |
| 1920 | Holes, 1/4" diameter | 1 Sswk | 112 | .071 | Ea. | .09 | 2.24 | | 2.33 | 4.36 |
| 1925 | For each additional 1/4" depth, add | | 336 | .024 | | .09 | .75 | | .84 | 1.52 |
| 1930 | 3/8" diameter | | 104 | .077 | | .10 | 2.42 | | 2.52 | 4.69 |
| 1935 | For each additional 1/4" depth, add | | 312 | .026 | | .10 | .81 | | .91 | 1.64 |
| 1940 | 1/2" diameter | | 96 | .083 | | .11 | 2.62 | | 2.73 | 5.10 |
| 1945 | For each additional 1/4" depth, add | | 288 | .028 | | .11 | .87 | | .98 | 1.78 |
| 1950 | 5/8" diameter | | 88 | .091 | | .15 | 2.85 | | 3 | 5.55 |
| 1955 | For each additional 1/4" depth, add | | 264 | .030 | | .15 | .95 | | 1.10 | 1.97 |
| 1960 | 3/4" diameter | | 80 | .100 | | .17 | 3.14 | | 3.31 | 6.15 |
| 1965 | For each additional 1/4" depth, add | | 240 | .033 | | .17 | 1.05 | | 1.22 | 2.17 |
| 1970 | 7/8" diameter | | 72 | .111 | | .20 | 3.49 | | 3.69 | 6.80 |
| 1975 | For each additional 1/4" depth, add | | 216 | .037 | | .20 | 1.16 | | 1.36 | 2.42 |
| 1980 | 1" diameter | | 64 | .125 | | .22 | 3.93 | | 4.15 | 7.70 |
| 1985 | For each additional 1/4" depth, add | | 192 | .042 | | .22 | 1.31 | | 1.53 | 2.73 |
| 1990 | For drilling up, add | | | | | | 40% | | | |

## 05 05 23 – Metal Fastenings

### 05 05 23.10 Bolts and Hex Nuts

| | | | Crew | Daily Output | Labor-Hours | Unit | Material | 2010 Bare Costs Labor | 2010 Bare Costs Equipment | Total | Total Incl O&P |
|---|---|---|---|---|---|---|---|---|---|---|---|
| 0010 | **BOLTS & HEX NUTS**, Steel, A307 | | | | | | | | | | |
| 0100 | 1/4" diameter, 1/2" long | G | 1 Sswk | 140 | .057 | Ea. | .10 | 1.79 | | 1.89 | 3.52 |
| 0200 | 1" long | G | | 140 | .057 | | .12 | 1.79 | | 1.91 | 3.54 |
| 0300 | 2" long | G | | 130 | .062 | | .15 | 1.93 | | 2.08 | 3.84 |
| 0400 | 3" long | G | | 130 | .062 | | .22 | 1.93 | | 2.15 | 3.91 |
| 0500 | 4" long | G | | 120 | .067 | | .24 | 2.09 | | 2.33 | 4.23 |
| 0600 | 3/8" diameter, 1" long | G | | 130 | .062 | | .22 | 1.93 | | 2.15 | 3.91 |
| 0700 | 2" long | G | | 130 | .062 | | .27 | 1.93 | | 2.20 | 3.97 |
| 0800 | 3" long | G | | 120 | .067 | | .36 | 2.09 | | 2.45 | 4.37 |
| 0900 | 4" long | G | | 120 | .067 | | .45 | 2.09 | | 2.54 | 4.47 |
| 1000 | 5" long | G | | 115 | .070 | | .56 | 2.18 | | 2.74 | 4.76 |
| 1100 | 1/2" diameter, 1-1/2" long | G | | 120 | .067 | | .50 | 2.09 | | 2.59 | 4.52 |
| 1200 | 2" long | G | | 120 | .067 | | .57 | 2.09 | | 2.66 | 4.59 |
| 1300 | 4" long | G | | 115 | .070 | | .86 | 2.18 | | 3.04 | 5.10 |
| 1400 | 6" long | G | | 110 | .073 | | 1.17 | 2.28 | | 3.45 | 5.60 |
| 1500 | 8" long | G | | 105 | .076 | | 1.51 | 2.39 | | 3.90 | 6.20 |
| 1600 | 5/8" diameter, 1-1/2" long | G | | 120 | .067 | | 1.15 | 2.09 | | 3.24 | 5.25 |
| 1700 | 2" long | G | | 120 | .067 | | 1.26 | 2.09 | | 3.35 | 5.35 |
| 1800 | 4" long | G | | 115 | .070 | | 1.75 | 2.18 | | 3.93 | 6.05 |
| 1900 | 6" long | G | | 110 | .073 | | 2.20 | 2.28 | | 4.48 | 6.75 |
| 2000 | 8" long | G | | 105 | .076 | | 3.20 | 2.39 | | 5.59 | 8.05 |
| 2100 | 10" long | G | | 100 | .080 | | 3.99 | 2.51 | | 6.50 | 9.15 |
| 2200 | 3/4" diameter, 2" long | G | | 120 | .067 | | 1.63 | 2.09 | | 3.72 | 5.75 |
| 2300 | 4" long | G | | 110 | .073 | | 2.30 | 2.28 | | 4.58 | 6.85 |
| 2400 | 6" long | G | | 105 | .076 | | 2.94 | 2.39 | | 5.33 | 7.75 |
| 2500 | 8" long | G | | 95 | .084 | | 4.39 | 2.64 | | 7.03 | 9.85 |
| 2600 | 10" long | G | | 85 | .094 | | 5.75 | 2.96 | | 8.71 | 11.90 |
| 2700 | 12" long | G | | 80 | .100 | | 6.70 | 3.14 | | 9.84 | 13.30 |
| 2800 | 1" diameter, 3" long | G | | 105 | .076 | | 4.94 | 2.39 | | 7.33 | 10 |
| 2900 | 6" long | G | | 90 | .089 | | 7.75 | 2.79 | | 10.54 | 13.80 |
| 3000 | 12" long | G | | 75 | .107 | | 14.85 | 3.35 | | 18.20 | 22.50 |
| 3100 | For galvanized, add | | | | | | 75% | | | | |
| 3200 | For stainless, add | | | | | | 350% | | | | |

# 05 05 Common Work Results for Metals

## 05 05 23 - Metal Fastenings

| 05 05 23.15 Chemical Anchors | | Crew | Daily Output | Labor-Hours | Unit | Material | 2010 Bare Costs Labor | Equipment | Total | Total Incl O&P |
|---|---|---|---|---|---|---|---|---|---|---|
| 0010 | **CHEMICAL ANCHORS** | | | | | | | | | |
| 0020 | Includes layout & drilling | | | | | | | | | |
| 1430 | Chemical anchor, w/rod & epoxy cartridge, 3/4" diam. x 9-1/2" long | B-89A | 27 | .593 | Ea. | 9.45 | 15.05 | 4.21 | 28.71 | 40 |
| 1435 | 1" diameter x 11-3/4" long | | 24 | .667 | | 16.55 | 16.90 | 4.74 | 38.19 | 52 |
| 1440 | 1-1/4" diameter x 14" long | | 21 | .762 | | 29 | 19.35 | 5.40 | 53.75 | 70 |
| 1445 | 1-3/4" diameter x 15" long | | 20 | .800 | | 50.50 | 20.50 | 5.70 | 76.70 | 96 |
| 1450 | 18" long | | 17 | .941 | | 60.50 | 24 | 6.70 | 91.20 | 114 |
| 1455 | 2" diameter x 18" long | | 16 | 1 | | 82.50 | 25.50 | 7.10 | 115.10 | 141 |
| 1460 | 24" long | | 15 | 1.067 | | 107 | 27 | 7.60 | 141.60 | 171 |

| 05 05 23.20 Expansion Anchors | | | Crew | Daily Output | Labor-Hours | Unit | Material | 2010 Bare Costs Labor | Equipment | Total | Total Incl O&P |
|---|---|---|---|---|---|---|---|---|---|---|---|
| 0010 | **EXPANSION ANCHORS** | | | | | | | | | | |
| 0100 | Anchors for concrete, brick or stone, no layout and drilling | | | | | | | | | | |
| 0200 | Expansion shields, zinc, 1/4" diameter, 1-5/16" long, single | G | 1 Carp | 90 | .089 | Ea. | .34 | 2.59 | | 2.93 | 4.72 |
| 0300 | 1-3/8" long, double | G | | 85 | .094 | | .47 | 2.74 | | 3.21 | 5.15 |
| 0500 | 2" long, double | G | | 80 | .100 | | 1.17 | 2.91 | | 4.08 | 6.20 |
| 0700 | 2-1/2" long, double | G | | 75 | .107 | | 1.63 | 3.10 | | 4.73 | 7 |
| 0900 | 2-3/4" long, double | G | | 70 | .114 | | 2.33 | 3.33 | | 5.66 | 8.15 |
| 1100 | 3-15/16" long, double | G | | 65 | .123 | | 4.51 | 3.58 | | 8.09 | 10.95 |
| 2100 | Hollow wall anchors for gypsum wall board, plaster or tile | | | | | | | | | | |
| 2500 | 3/16" diameter, short | G | 1 Carp | 150 | .053 | Ea. | .32 | 1.55 | | 1.87 | 2.96 |
| 3000 | Toggle bolts, bright steel, 1/8" diameter, 2" long | G | | 85 | .094 | | .18 | 2.74 | | 2.92 | 4.81 |
| 3100 | 4" long | G | | 80 | .100 | | .23 | 2.91 | | 3.14 | 5.15 |
| 3200 | 3/16" diameter, 3" long | G | | 80 | .100 | | .22 | 2.91 | | 3.13 | 5.15 |
| 3300 | 6" long | G | | 75 | .107 | | .31 | 3.10 | | 3.41 | 5.55 |
| 3400 | 1/4" diameter, 3" long | G | | 75 | .107 | | .29 | 3.10 | | 3.39 | 5.50 |
| 3500 | 6" long | G | | 70 | .114 | | .46 | 3.33 | | 3.79 | 6.10 |
| 3600 | 3/8" diameter, 3" long | G | | 70 | .114 | | .70 | 3.33 | | 4.03 | 6.35 |
| 3700 | 6" long | G | | 60 | .133 | | 1.20 | 3.88 | | 5.08 | 7.85 |
| 3800 | 1/2" diameter, 4" long | G | | 60 | .133 | | 1.69 | 3.88 | | 5.57 | 8.40 |
| 3900 | 6" long | G | | 50 | .160 | | 2.02 | 4.66 | | 6.68 | 10.05 |
| 4000 | Nailing anchors | | | | | | | | | | |
| 4100 | Nylon nailing anchor, 1/4" diameter, 1" long | | 1 Carp | 3.20 | 2.500 | C | 11.30 | 73 | | 84.30 | 134 |
| 4200 | 1-1/2" long | | | 2.80 | 2.857 | | 12.45 | 83 | | 95.45 | 154 |
| 4300 | 2" long | | | 2.40 | 3.333 | | 17.50 | 97 | | 114.50 | 182 |
| 4400 | Metal nailing anchor, 1/4" diameter, 1" long | G | | 3.20 | 2.500 | | 16.65 | 73 | | 89.65 | 140 |
| 4500 | 1-1/2" long | G | | 2.80 | 2.857 | | 22.50 | 83 | | 105.50 | 165 |
| 4600 | 2" long | G | | 2.40 | 3.333 | | 26 | 97 | | 123 | 192 |
| 5000 | Screw anchors for concrete, masonry, | | | | | | | | | | |
| 5100 | stone & tile, no layout or drilling included | | | | | | | | | | |
| 5700 | Lag screw shields, 1/4" diameter, short | G | 1 Carp | 90 | .089 | Ea. | .29 | 2.59 | | 2.88 | 4.67 |
| 5800 | Long | G | | 85 | .094 | | .35 | 2.74 | | 3.09 | 5 |
| 5900 | 3/8" diameter, short | G | | 85 | .094 | | .59 | 2.74 | | 3.33 | 5.25 |
| 6000 | Long | G | | 80 | .100 | | .72 | 2.91 | | 3.63 | 5.70 |
| 6100 | 1/2" diameter, short | G | | 80 | .100 | | .92 | 2.91 | | 3.83 | 5.90 |
| 6200 | Long | G | | 75 | .107 | | 1.15 | 3.10 | | 4.25 | 6.45 |
| 6300 | 5/8" diameter, short | G | | 70 | .114 | | 1.45 | 3.33 | | 4.78 | 7.20 |
| 6400 | Long | G | | 65 | .123 | | 1.94 | 3.58 | | 5.52 | 8.15 |
| 6600 | Lead, #6 & #8, 3/4" long | G | | 260 | .031 | | .12 | .90 | | 1.02 | 1.64 |
| 6700 | #10 - #14, 1-1/2" long | G | | 200 | .040 | | .18 | 1.16 | | 1.34 | 2.16 |
| 6800 | #16 & #18, 1-1/2" long | G | | 160 | .050 | | .29 | 1.46 | | 1.75 | 2.77 |
| 6900 | Plastic, #6 & #8, 3/4" long | | | 260 | .031 | | .03 | .90 | | .93 | 1.54 |
| 7000 | #8 & #10, 7/8" long | | | 240 | .033 | | .02 | .97 | | .99 | 1.65 |

# 05 05 Common Work Results for Metals

## 05 05 23 – Metal Fastenings

### 05 05 23.20 Expansion Anchors

| | | Crew | Daily Output | Labor-Hours | Unit | Material | 2010 Bare Costs Labor | Equipment | Total | Total Incl O&P |
|---|---|---|---|---|---|---|---|---|---|---|
| 7100 | #10 & #12, 1" long | 1 Carp | 220 | .036 | Ea. | .03 | 1.06 | | 1.09 | 1.81 |
| 7200 | #14 & #16, 1-1/2" long | | 160 | .050 | | .05 | 1.46 | | 1.51 | 2.51 |
| 8950 | Self-drilling concrete screw, hex washer head, 3/16" diam. x 1-3/4" long G | | 300 | .027 | | .19 | .78 | | .97 | 1.52 |
| 8960 | 2-1/4" long G | | 250 | .032 | | .20 | .93 | | 1.13 | 1.79 |
| 8970 | Phillips flat head, 3/16" diam. x 1-3/4" long G | | 300 | .027 | | .17 | .78 | | .95 | 1.50 |
| 8980 | 2-1/4" long G | | 250 | .032 | | .20 | .93 | | 1.13 | 1.79 |

### 05 05 23.30 Lag Screws

| | | Crew | Daily Output | Labor-Hours | Unit | Material | 2010 Bare Costs Labor | Equipment | Total | Total Incl O&P |
|---|---|---|---|---|---|---|---|---|---|---|
| 0010 | **LAG SCREWS** | | | | | | | | | |
| 0020 | Steel, 1/4" diameter, 2" long G | 1 Carp | 200 | .040 | Ea. | .09 | 1.16 | | 1.25 | 2.06 |
| 0100 | 3/8" diameter, 3" long G | | 150 | .053 | | .26 | 1.55 | | 1.81 | 2.90 |
| 0200 | 1/2" diameter, 3" long G | | 130 | .062 | | .48 | 1.79 | | 2.27 | 3.54 |
| 0300 | 5/8" diameter, 3" long G | | 120 | .067 | | 1.11 | 1.94 | | 3.05 | 4.48 |

### 05 05 23.50 Powder Actuated Tools and Fasteners

| | | Crew | Daily Output | Labor-Hours | Unit | Material | 2010 Bare Costs Labor | Equipment | Total | Total Incl O&P |
|---|---|---|---|---|---|---|---|---|---|---|
| 0010 | **POWDER ACTUATED TOOLS & FASTENERS** | | | | | | | | | |
| 0020 | Stud driver, .22 caliber, buy, minimum | | | | Ea. | 219 | | | 219 | 241 |
| 0100 | Maximum | | | | " | 370 | | | 370 | 405 |
| 0300 | Powder charges for above, low velocity | | | | C | 4.99 | | | 4.99 | 5.50 |
| 0400 | Standard velocity | | | | | 5.95 | | | 5.95 | 6.55 |
| 0600 | Drive pins & studs, 1/4" & 3/8" diam., to 3" long, minimum G | 1 Carp | 4.80 | 1.667 | | 4.38 | 48.50 | | 52.88 | 86.50 |
| 0700 | Maximum G | " | 4 | 2 | | 9.40 | 58 | | 67.40 | 108 |

### 05 05 23.55 Rivets

| | | Crew | Daily Output | Labor-Hours | Unit | Material | 2010 Bare Costs Labor | Equipment | Total | Total Incl O&P |
|---|---|---|---|---|---|---|---|---|---|---|
| 0010 | **RIVETS** | | | | | | | | | |
| 0100 | Aluminum rivet & mandrel, 1/2" grip length x 1/8" diameter G | 1 Carp | 4.80 | 1.667 | C | 6.35 | 48.50 | | 54.85 | 88.50 |
| 0200 | 3/16" diameter G | | 4 | 2 | | 11.15 | 58 | | 69.15 | 110 |
| 0300 | Aluminum rivet, steel mandrel, 1/8" diameter G | | 4.80 | 1.667 | | 6.65 | 48.50 | | 55.15 | 89 |
| 0400 | 3/16" diameter G | | 4 | 2 | | 10.55 | 58 | | 68.55 | 110 |
| 0500 | Copper rivet, steel mandrel, 1/8" diameter G | | 4.80 | 1.667 | | 7.75 | 48.50 | | 56.25 | 90 |
| 0800 | Stainless rivet & mandrel, 1/8" diameter G | | 4.80 | 1.667 | | 23.50 | 48.50 | | 72 | 108 |
| 0900 | 3/16" diameter G | | 4 | 2 | | 38.50 | 58 | | 96.50 | 141 |
| 1000 | Stainless rivet, steel mandrel, 1/8" diameter G | | 4.80 | 1.667 | | 19.65 | 48.50 | | 68.15 | 103 |
| 1100 | 3/16" diameter G | | 4 | 2 | | 27.50 | 58 | | 85.50 | 128 |
| 1200 | Steel rivet and mandrel, 1/8" diameter G | | 4.80 | 1.667 | | 6.50 | 48.50 | | 55 | 88.50 |
| 1300 | 3/16" diameter G | | 4 | 2 | | 10.65 | 58 | | 68.65 | 110 |
| 1400 | Hand riveting tool, minimum | | | | Ea. | 40 | | | 40 | 44 |
| 1500 | Maximum | | | | | 227 | | | 227 | 250 |
| 1600 | Power riveting tool, minimum | | | | | 450 | | | 450 | 495 |
| 1700 | Maximum | | | | | 2,275 | | | 2,275 | 2,525 |

# 05 12 Structural Steel Framing

## 05 12 23 – Structural Steel for Buildings

### 05 12 23.10 Ceiling Supports

| | | Crew | Daily Output | Labor-Hours | Unit | Material | 2010 Bare Costs Labor | Equipment | Total | Total Incl O&P |
|---|---|---|---|---|---|---|---|---|---|---|
| 0010 | **CEILING SUPPORTS** | | | | | | | | | |
| 1000 | Entrance door/folding partition supports, shop fabricated G | E-4 | 60 | .533 | L.F. | 22 | 17 | 2.43 | 41.43 | 59 |
| 1100 | Linear accelerator door supports G | | 14 | 2.286 | | 100 | 73 | 10.40 | 183.40 | 259 |
| 1200 | Lintels or shelf angles, hung, exterior hot dipped galv. G | | 267 | .120 | | 15 | 3.82 | .55 | 19.37 | 24.50 |
| 1250 | Two coats primer paint instead of galv. G | | 267 | .120 | | 13 | 3.82 | .55 | 17.37 | 22 |
| 1400 | Monitor support, ceiling hung, expansion bolted G | | 4 | 8 | Ea. | 350 | 255 | 36.50 | 641.50 | 910 |
| 1450 | Hung from pre-set inserts G | | 6 | 5.333 | | 375 | 170 | 24.50 | 569.50 | 765 |
| 1600 | Motor supports for overhead doors G | | 4 | 8 | | 177 | 255 | 36.50 | 468.50 | 720 |
| 1700 | Partition support for heavy folding partitions, without pocket G | | 24 | 1.333 | L.F. | 50 | 42.50 | 6.10 | 98.60 | 142 |

# 05 12 Structural Steel Framing

## 05 12 23 – Structural Steel for Buildings

### 05 12 23.10 Ceiling Supports

| | | Crew | Daily Output | Labor-Hours | Unit | Material | 2010 Bare Costs Labor | Equipment | Total | Total Incl O&P |
|---|---|---|---|---|---|---|---|---|---|---|
| 1750 | Supports at pocket only | E-4 | 12 | 2.667 | L.F. | 100 | 85 | 12.15 | 197.15 | 284 |
| 2000 | Rolling grilles & fire door supports | | 34 | .941 | ↓ | 43 | 30 | 4.29 | 77.29 | 109 |
| 2100 | Spider-leg light supports, expansion bolted to ceiling slab | | 8 | 4 | Ea. | 143 | 128 | 18.25 | 289.25 | 420 |
| 2150 | Hung from pre-set inserts | | 12 | 2.667 | " | 154 | 85 | 12.15 | 251.15 | 345 |
| 2400 | Toilet partition support | | 36 | .889 | L.F. | 50 | 28.50 | 4.05 | 82.55 | 113 |
| 2500 | X-ray travel gantry support | | 12 | 2.667 | " | 172 | 85 | 12.15 | 269.15 | 365 |

### 05 12 23.15 Columns, Lightweight

| | | Crew | Daily Output | Labor-Hours | Unit | Material | 2010 Bare Costs Labor | Equipment | Total | Total Incl O&P |
|---|---|---|---|---|---|---|---|---|---|---|
| 0010 | **COLUMNS, LIGHTWEIGHT** | | | | | | | | | |
| 1000 | Lightweight units (lally), 3-1/2" diameter | E-2 | 780 | .062 | L.F. | 6.60 | 1.95 | 2.06 | 10.61 | 13.15 |
| 1050 | 4" diameter | " | 900 | .053 | " | 7.65 | 1.69 | 1.79 | 11.13 | 13.50 |
| 8000 | Lally columns, to 8', 3-1/2" diameter | 2 Carp | 24 | .667 | Ea. | 52.50 | 19.40 | | 71.90 | 90.50 |
| 8080 | 4" diameter | " | 20 | .800 | " | 61 | 23.50 | | 84.50 | 106 |

### 05 12 23.17 Columns, Structural

| | | Crew | Daily Output | Labor-Hours | Unit | Material | 2010 Bare Costs Labor | Equipment | Total | Total Incl O&P |
|---|---|---|---|---|---|---|---|---|---|---|
| 0010 | **COLUMNS, STRUCTURAL** | | | | | | | | | |
| 0015 | Made from recycled materials | G | | | | | | | | |
| 0020 | Shop fab'd for 100-ton, 1-2 story project, bolted connections | | | | | | | | | |
| 0800 | Steel, concrete filled, extra strong pipe, 3-1/2" diameter | E-2 | 660 | .073 | L.F. | 36.50 | 2.30 | 2.44 | 41.24 | 47 |
| 0830 | 4" diameter | | 780 | .062 | | 40.50 | 1.95 | 2.06 | 44.51 | 50.50 |
| 0890 | 5" diameter | | 1020 | .047 | | 48 | 1.49 | 1.58 | 51.07 | 57.50 |
| 0930 | 6" diameter | | 1200 | .040 | | 64 | 1.26 | 1.34 | 66.60 | 74 |
| 0940 | 8" diameter | | 1100 | .044 | ↓ | 64 | 1.38 | 1.46 | 66.84 | 74 |
| 1100 | For galvanizing, add | | | | Lb. | .21 | | | .21 | .23 |
| 1300 | For web ties, angles, etc., add per added lb. | 1 Sswk | 945 | .008 | | 1.10 | .27 | | 1.37 | 1.71 |
| 1500 | Steel pipe, extra strong, no concrete, 3" to 5" diameter | G E-2 | 16000 | .003 | | 1.10 | .09 | .10 | 1.29 | 1.50 |
| 1600 | 6" to 12" diameter | G | 14000 | .003 | | 1.10 | .11 | .11 | 1.32 | 1.54 |
| 2700 | 12" x 8" x 1/2" thk wall | G | 24000 | .002 | | 1.10 | .06 | .07 | 1.23 | 1.40 |
| 2800 | Heavy section | G | 32000 | .002 | | 1.10 | .05 | .05 | 1.20 | 1.36 |
| 5100 | Structural tubing, rect, 5" to 6" wide, light section | G | 8000 | .006 | ↓ | 1.10 | .19 | .20 | 1.49 | 1.78 |
| 8090 | For projects 75 to 99 tons, add | | | | All | 10% | | | | |
| 8092 | 50 to 74 tons, add | | | | | 20% | | | | |
| 8094 | 25 to 49 tons, add | | | | | 30% | 10% | | | |
| 8096 | 10 to 24 tons, add | | | | | 50% | 25% | | | |
| 8098 | 2 to 9 tons, add | | | | | 75% | 50% | | | |
| 8099 | Less than 2 tons, add | | | | | 100% | 100% | | | |

### 05 12 23.45 Lintels

| | | Crew | Daily Output | Labor-Hours | Unit | Material | 2010 Bare Costs Labor | Equipment | Total | Total Incl O&P |
|---|---|---|---|---|---|---|---|---|---|---|
| 0010 | **LINTELS** | | | | | | | | | |
| 0015 | Made from recycled materials | G | | | | | | | | |
| 0020 | Plain steel angles, shop fabricated, under 500 lb. | G 1 Bric | 550 | .015 | Lb. | .85 | .43 | | 1.28 | 1.63 |
| 0100 | 500 to 1000 lb. | G | 640 | .013 | " | .83 | .37 | | 1.20 | 1.51 |
| 2000 | Steel angles, 3-1/2" x 3", 1/4" thick, 2'-6" long | G | 47 | .170 | Ea. | 11.90 | 4.98 | | 16.88 | 21.50 |
| 2100 | 4'-6" long | G | 26 | .308 | | 21.50 | 9 | | 30.50 | 38.50 |
| 2600 | 4" x 3-1/2", 1/4" thick, 5'-0" long | G | 21 | .381 | | 27.50 | 11.15 | | 38.65 | 48.50 |
| 2700 | 9'-0" long | G | 12 | .667 | ↓ | 49 | 19.50 | | 68.50 | 86 |

### 05 12 23.65 Plates

| | | Crew | Daily Output | Labor-Hours | Unit | Material | 2010 Bare Costs Labor | Equipment | Total | Total Incl O&P |
|---|---|---|---|---|---|---|---|---|---|---|
| 0010 | **PLATES** | | | | | | | | | |
| 0015 | Made from recycled materials | G | | | | | | | | |
| 0020 | For connections & stiffener plates, shop fabricated | | | | | | | | | |
| 0050 | 1/8" thick (5.1 Lb./S.F.) | G | | | S.F. | 5.60 | | | 5.60 | 6.15 |
| 0100 | 1/4" thick (10.2 Lb./S.F.) | G | | | | 11.20 | | | 11.20 | 12.35 |
| 0300 | 3/8" thick (15.3 Lb./S.F.) | G | | | | 16.85 | | | 16.85 | 18.50 |
| 0400 | 1/2" thick (20.4 Lb./S.F.) | G | | | | 22.50 | | | 22.50 | 24.50 |
| 0450 | 3/4" thick (30.6 Lb./S.F.) | G | | | | 33.50 | | | 33.50 | 37 |

# 05 12 Structural Steel Framing

## 05 12 23 – Structural Steel for Buildings

### 05 12 23.65 Plates

| 05 12 23.65 Plates | | Crew | Daily Output | Labor-Hours | Unit | Material | 2010 Bare Costs Labor | Equipment | Total | Total Incl O&P |
|---|---|---|---|---|---|---|---|---|---|---|
| 0500 | 1" thick (40.8 Lb.S.F.) | G | | | | S.F. | 45 | | | 45 | 49.50 |
| 2000 | Steel plate, warehouse prices, no shop fabrication | | | | | | | | | | |
| 2100 | 1/4" thick (10.2 Lb./S.F.) | G | | | | S.F. | 8.40 | | | 8.40 | 9.25 |

### 05 12 23.79 Structural Steel

| 05 12 23.79 Structural Steel | | Crew | Daily Output | Labor-Hours | Unit | Material | 2010 Bare Costs Labor | Equipment | Total | Total Incl O&P |
|---|---|---|---|---|---|---|---|---|---|---|
| 0010 | **STRUCTURAL STEEL** | | | | | | | | | | |
| 0020 | Shop fab'd for 100-ton, 1-2 story project, bolted conn's. | | | | | | | | | | |
| 0050 | Beams, W 6 x 9 | G | E-2 | 720 | .067 | L.F. | 11.90 | 2.11 | 2.23 | 16.24 | 19.40 |
| 0100 | W 8 x 10 | G | | 720 | .067 | | 13.20 | 2.11 | 2.23 | 17.54 | 21 |
| 0200 | Columns, W 6 x 15 | G | | 540 | .089 | | 21.50 | 2.81 | 2.98 | 27.29 | 32 |
| 0250 | W 8 x 31 | G | | 540 | .089 | | 44.50 | 2.81 | 2.98 | 50.29 | 57.50 |
| 7990 | For projects 75 to 99 tons, add | | | | | All | 10% | | | | |
| 7992 | 50 to 75 tons, add | | | | | | 20% | | | | |
| 7994 | 25 to 49 tons, add | | | | | | 30% | 10% | | | |
| 7996 | 10 to 24 tons, add | | | | | | 50% | 25% | | | |
| 7998 | 2 to 9 tons, add | | | | | | 75% | 50% | | | |
| 7999 | Less than 2 tons, add | | | | | | 100% | 100% | | | |

# 05 31 Steel Decking

## 05 31 23 – Steel Roof Decking

### 05 31 23.50 Roof Decking

| 05 31 23.50 Roof Decking | | Crew | Daily Output | Labor-Hours | Unit | Material | 2010 Bare Costs Labor | Equipment | Total | Total Incl O&P |
|---|---|---|---|---|---|---|---|---|---|---|
| 0010 | **ROOF DECKING** | | | | | | | | | | |
| 0015 | Made from recycled materials | G | | | | | | | | | |
| 2100 | Open type B wide rib, galvanized, 1-1/2" deep, 22 gauge, under 50 sq | G | E-4 | 4500 | .007 | S.F. | 1.29 | .23 | .03 | 1.55 | 1.89 |
| 2600 | 20 gauge, under 50 squares | G | | 3865 | .008 | | 1.52 | .26 | .04 | 1.82 | 2.21 |
| 2900 | 18 gauge, under 50 squares | G | | 3800 | .008 | | 1.96 | .27 | .04 | 2.27 | 2.70 |
| 3050 | 16 gauge, under 50 squares | G | | 3700 | .009 | | 2.64 | .28 | .04 | 2.96 | 3.46 |

## 05 31 33 – Steel Form Decking

### 05 31 33.50 Form Decking

| 05 31 33.50 Form Decking | | Crew | Daily Output | Labor-Hours | Unit | Material | 2010 Bare Costs Labor | Equipment | Total | Total Incl O&P |
|---|---|---|---|---|---|---|---|---|---|---|
| 0010 | **FORM DECKING** | | | | | | | | | | |
| 0015 | Made from recycled materials | G | | | | | | | | | |
| 6100 | Slab form, steel, 28 gauge, 9/16" deep, uncoated | G | E-4 | 4000 | .008 | S.F. | .98 | .26 | .04 | 1.28 | 1.60 |
| 6200 | Galvanized | G | | 4000 | .008 | | .87 | .26 | .04 | 1.17 | 1.48 |
| 6220 | 24 gauge, 1" deep, uncoated | G | | 3900 | .008 | | .94 | .26 | .04 | 1.24 | 1.58 |
| 6240 | Galvanized | G | | 3900 | .008 | | 1.11 | .26 | .04 | 1.41 | 1.76 |
| 6300 | 24 gauge, 1-5/16" deep, uncoated | G | | 3800 | .008 | | 1 | .27 | .04 | 1.31 | 1.65 |
| 6400 | Galvanized | G | | 3800 | .008 | | 1.18 | .27 | .04 | 1.49 | 1.85 |
| 6500 | 22 gauge, 1-5/16" deep, uncoated | G | | 3700 | .009 | | 1.25 | .28 | .04 | 1.57 | 1.94 |
| 6600 | Galvanized | G | | 3700 | .009 | | 1.28 | .28 | .04 | 1.60 | 1.97 |
| 6700 | 22 gauge, 2" deep uncoated | G | | 3600 | .009 | | 1.65 | .28 | .04 | 1.97 | 2.40 |
| 6800 | Galvanized | G | | 3600 | .009 | | 1.62 | .28 | .04 | 1.94 | 2.36 |

# 05 41 Structural Metal Stud Framing

## 05 41 13 – Load-Bearing Metal Stud Framing

### 05 41 13.05 Bracing

| | | Crew | Daily Output | Labor-Hours | Unit | Material | 2010 Bare Costs Labor | 2010 Bare Costs Equipment | Total | Total Incl O&P |
|---|---|---|---|---|---|---|---|---|---|---|
| 0010 | **BRACING**, shear wall X-bracing, per 10' x 10' bay, one face | | | | | | | | | |
| 0015 | Made of recycled materials | G | | | | | | | | |
| 0120 | Metal strap, 20 ga x 4" wide | G | 2 Carp | 18 | .889 | Ea. | 19.35 | 26 | | 45.35 | 65 |
| 0130 | 6" wide | G | | 18 | .889 | | 30 | 26 | | 56 | 76.50 |
| 0160 | 18 ga x 4" wide | G | | 16 | 1 | | 28 | 29 | | 57 | 79.50 |
| 0170 | 6" wide | G | | 16 | 1 | | 41 | 29 | | 70 | 94 |
| 0410 | Continuous strap bracing, per horizontal row on both faces | | | | | | | | | |
| 0420 | Metal strap, 20 ga x 2" wide, studs 12" O.C. | G | 1 Carp | 7 | 1.143 | C.L.F. | 48.50 | 33.50 | | 82 | 109 |
| 0430 | 16" O.C. | G | | 8 | 1 | | 48.50 | 29 | | 77.50 | 102 |
| 0440 | 24" O.C. | G | | 10 | .800 | | 48.50 | 23.50 | | 72 | 92 |
| 0450 | 18 ga x 2" wide, studs 12" O.C. | G | | 6 | 1.333 | | 68 | 39 | | 107 | 141 |
| 0460 | 16" O.C. | G | | 7 | 1.143 | | 68 | 33.50 | | 101.50 | 131 |
| 0470 | 24" O.C. | G | | 8 | 1 | | 68 | 29 | | 97 | 124 |

### 05 41 13.10 Bridging

| | | Crew | Daily Output | Labor-Hours | Unit | Material | 2010 Bare Costs Labor | 2010 Bare Costs Equipment | Total | Total Incl O&P |
|---|---|---|---|---|---|---|---|---|---|---|
| 0010 | **BRIDGING**, solid between studs w/1-1/4" leg track, per stud bay | | | | | | | | | |
| 0015 | Made from recycled materials | G | | | | | | | | |
| 0200 | Studs 12" O.C., 18 ga x 2-1/2" wide | G | 1 Carp | 125 | .064 | Ea. | .82 | 1.86 | | 2.68 | 4.04 |
| 0210 | 3-5/8" wide | G | | 120 | .067 | | 1 | 1.94 | | 2.94 | 4.36 |
| 0220 | 4" wide | G | | 120 | .067 | | 1.07 | 1.94 | | 3.01 | 4.44 |
| 0230 | 6" wide | G | | 115 | .070 | | 1.38 | 2.02 | | 3.40 | 4.92 |
| 0240 | 8" wide | G | | 110 | .073 | | 1.75 | 2.12 | | 3.87 | 5.50 |
| 0300 | 16 ga x 2-1/2" wide | G | | 115 | .070 | | 1.03 | 2.02 | | 3.05 | 4.54 |
| 0310 | 3-5/8" wide | G | | 110 | .073 | | 1.26 | 2.12 | | 3.38 | 4.95 |
| 0320 | 4" wide | G | | 110 | .073 | | 1.34 | 2.12 | | 3.46 | 5.05 |
| 0330 | 6" wide | G | | 105 | .076 | | 1.72 | 2.22 | | 3.94 | 5.65 |
| 0340 | 8" wide | G | | 100 | .080 | | 2.20 | 2.33 | | 4.53 | 6.35 |
| 1200 | Studs 16" O.C., 18 ga x 2-1/2" wide | G | | 125 | .064 | | 1.06 | 1.86 | | 2.92 | 4.29 |
| 1210 | 3-5/8" wide | G | | 120 | .067 | | 1.29 | 1.94 | | 3.23 | 4.68 |
| 1220 | 4" wide | G | | 120 | .067 | | 1.37 | 1.94 | | 3.31 | 4.77 |
| 1230 | 6" wide | G | | 115 | .070 | | 1.77 | 2.02 | | 3.79 | 5.35 |
| 1240 | 8" wide | G | | 110 | .073 | | 2.24 | 2.12 | | 4.36 | 6.05 |
| 1300 | 16 ga x 2-1/2" wide | G | | 115 | .070 | | 1.32 | 2.02 | | 3.34 | 4.86 |
| 1310 | 3-5/8" wide | G | | 110 | .073 | | 1.62 | 2.12 | | 3.74 | 5.35 |
| 1320 | 4" wide | G | | 110 | .073 | | 1.72 | 2.12 | | 3.84 | 5.45 |
| 1330 | 6" wide | G | | 105 | .076 | | 2.21 | 2.22 | | 4.43 | 6.15 |
| 1340 | 8" wide | G | | 100 | .080 | | 2.82 | 2.33 | | 5.15 | 7 |
| 2200 | Studs 24" O.C., 18 ga x 2-1/2" wide | G | | 125 | .064 | | 1.53 | 1.86 | | 3.39 | 4.81 |
| 2210 | 3-5/8" wide | G | | 120 | .067 | | 1.86 | 1.94 | | 3.80 | 5.30 |
| 2220 | 4" wide | G | | 120 | .067 | | 1.98 | 1.94 | | 3.92 | 5.45 |
| 2230 | 6" wide | G | | 115 | .070 | | 2.55 | 2.02 | | 4.57 | 6.20 |
| 2240 | 8" wide | G | | 110 | .073 | | 3.25 | 2.12 | | 5.37 | 7.15 |
| 2300 | 16 ga x 2-1/2" wide | G | | 115 | .070 | | 1.91 | 2.02 | | 3.93 | 5.50 |
| 2310 | 3-5/8" wide | G | | 110 | .073 | | 2.34 | 2.12 | | 4.46 | 6.15 |
| 2320 | 4" wide | G | | 110 | .073 | | 2.48 | 2.12 | | 4.60 | 6.30 |
| 2330 | 6" wide | G | | 105 | .076 | | 3.20 | 2.22 | | 5.42 | 7.25 |
| 2340 | 8" wide | G | | 100 | .080 | | 4.08 | 2.33 | | 6.41 | 8.40 |
| 3000 | Continuous bridging, per row | | | | | | | | | |
| 3100 | 16 ga x 1-1/2" channel thru studs 12" O.C. | G | 1 Carp | 6 | 1.333 | C.L.F. | 45.50 | 39 | | 84.50 | 116 |
| 3110 | 16" O.C. | G | | 7 | 1.143 | | 45.50 | 33.50 | | 79 | 106 |
| 3120 | 24" O.C. | G | | 8.80 | .909 | | 45.50 | 26.50 | | 72 | 94.50 |
| 4100 | 2" x 2" angle x 18 ga, studs 12" O.C. | G | | 7 | 1.143 | | 68 | 33.50 | | 101.50 | 131 |
| 4110 | 16" O.C. | G | | 9 | .889 | | 68 | 26 | | 94 | 119 |

333

# 05 41 Structural Metal Stud Framing

## 05 41 13 – Load-Bearing Metal Stud Framing

### 05 41 13.10 Bridging

| | | Crew | Daily Output | Labor-Hours | Unit | Material | 2010 Bare Costs Labor | Equipment | Total | Total Incl O&P |
|---|---|---|---|---|---|---|---|---|---|---|
| 4120 | 24" O.C. | G 1 Carp | 12 | .667 | C.L.F. | 68 | 19.40 | | 87.40 | 108 |
| 4200 | 16 ga, studs 12" O.C. | G | 5 | 1.600 | | 86 | 46.50 | | 132.50 | 173 |
| 4210 | 16" O.C. | G | 7 | 1.143 | | 86 | 33.50 | | 119.50 | 151 |
| 4220 | 24" O.C. | G | 10 | .800 | | 86 | 23.50 | | 109.50 | 134 |

### 05 41 13.25 Framing, Boxed Headers/Beams

| | | Crew | Daily Output | Labor-Hours | Unit | Material | 2010 Bare Costs Labor | Equipment | Total | Total Incl O&P |
|---|---|---|---|---|---|---|---|---|---|---|
| 0010 | **FRAMING, BOXED HEADERS/BEAMS** | | | | | | | | | |
| 0015 | Made from recycled materials | G | | | | | | | | |
| 0200 | Double, 18 ga x 6" deep | G 2 Carp | 220 | .073 | L.F. | 4.81 | 2.12 | | 6.93 | 8.85 |
| 0210 | 8" deep | G | 210 | .076 | | 5.35 | 2.22 | | 7.57 | 9.65 |
| 0220 | 10" deep | G | 200 | .080 | | 6.45 | 2.33 | | 8.78 | 11 |
| 0230 | 12 " deep | G | 190 | .084 | | 7.10 | 2.45 | | 9.55 | 11.90 |
| 0300 | 16 ga x 8" deep | G | 180 | .089 | | 6.15 | 2.59 | | 8.74 | 11.10 |
| 0310 | 10" deep | G | 170 | .094 | | 7.35 | 2.74 | | 10.09 | 12.65 |
| 0320 | 12 " deep | G | 160 | .100 | | 8 | 2.91 | | 10.91 | 13.70 |
| 0400 | 14 ga x 10" deep | G | 140 | .114 | | 8.55 | 3.33 | | 11.88 | 15 |
| 0410 | 12 " deep | G | 130 | .123 | | 9.40 | 3.58 | | 12.98 | 16.30 |
| 1210 | Triple, 18 ga x 8" deep | G | 170 | .094 | | 7.70 | 2.74 | | 10.44 | 13.10 |
| 1220 | 10" deep | G | 165 | .097 | | 9.25 | 2.82 | | 12.07 | 14.95 |
| 1230 | 12 " deep | G | 160 | .100 | | 10.20 | 2.91 | | 13.11 | 16.15 |
| 1300 | 16 ga x 8" deep | G | 145 | .110 | | 8.90 | 3.21 | | 12.11 | 15.20 |
| 1310 | 10" deep | G | 140 | .114 | | 10.60 | 3.33 | | 13.93 | 17.25 |
| 1320 | 12 " deep | G | 135 | .119 | | 11.60 | 3.45 | | 15.05 | 18.55 |
| 1400 | 14 ga x 10" deep | G | 115 | .139 | | 11.65 | 4.05 | | 15.70 | 19.65 |
| 1410 | 12 " deep | G | 110 | .145 | | 12.90 | 4.23 | | 17.13 | 21.50 |

### 05 41 13.30 Framing, Stud Walls

| | | Crew | Daily Output | Labor-Hours | Unit | Material | 2010 Bare Costs Labor | Equipment | Total | Total Incl O&P |
|---|---|---|---|---|---|---|---|---|---|---|
| 0010 | **FRAMING, STUD WALLS** w/top & bottom track, no openings, | | | | | | | | | |
| 0020 | Headers, beams, bridging or bracing | | | | | | | | | |
| 0025 | Made from recycled materials | G | | | | | | | | |
| 4100 | 8' high walls, 18 ga x 2-1/2" wide, studs 12" O.C. | G 2 Carp | 54 | .296 | L.F. | 8.05 | 8.60 | | 16.65 | 23.50 |
| 4110 | 16" O.C. | G | 77 | .208 | | 6.45 | 6.05 | | 12.50 | 17.20 |
| 4120 | 24" O.C. | G | 107 | .150 | | 4.81 | 4.35 | | 9.16 | 12.60 |
| 4130 | 3-5/8" wide, studs 12" O.C. | G | 53 | .302 | | 9.60 | 8.80 | | 18.40 | 25.50 |
| 4140 | 16" O.C. | G | 76 | .211 | | 7.65 | 6.15 | | 13.80 | 18.75 |
| 4150 | 24" O.C. | G | 105 | .152 | | 5.75 | 4.43 | | 10.18 | 13.80 |
| 4160 | 4" wide, studs 12" O.C. | G | 52 | .308 | | 10.05 | 8.95 | | 19 | 26 |
| 4170 | 16" O.C. | G | 74 | .216 | | 8.05 | 6.30 | | 14.35 | 19.45 |
| 4180 | 24" O.C. | G | 103 | .155 | | 6.05 | 4.52 | | 10.57 | 14.25 |
| 4190 | 6" wide, studs 12" O.C. | G | 51 | .314 | | 12.70 | 9.15 | | 21.85 | 29.50 |
| 4200 | 16" O.C. | G | 73 | .219 | | 10.20 | 6.40 | | 16.60 | 22 |
| 4210 | 24" O.C. | G | 101 | .158 | | 7.65 | 4.61 | | 12.26 | 16.20 |
| 4220 | 8" wide, studs 12" O.C. | G | 50 | .320 | | 15.55 | 9.30 | | 24.85 | 33 |
| 4230 | 16" O.C. | G | 72 | .222 | | 12.50 | 6.45 | | 18.95 | 24.50 |
| 4240 | 24" O.C. | G | 100 | .160 | | 9.45 | 4.66 | | 14.11 | 18.25 |
| 4300 | 16 ga x 2-1/2" wide, studs 12" O.C. | G | 47 | .340 | | 9.50 | 9.90 | | 19.40 | 27 |
| 4310 | 16" O.C. | G | 68 | .235 | | 7.50 | 6.85 | | 14.35 | 19.75 |
| 4320 | 24" O.C. | G | 94 | .170 | | 5.55 | 4.95 | | 10.50 | 14.45 |
| 4330 | 3-5/8" wide, studs 12" O.C. | G | 46 | .348 | | 11.35 | 10.10 | | 21.45 | 29.50 |
| 4340 | 16" O.C. | G | 66 | .242 | | 9 | 7.05 | | 16.05 | 22 |
| 4350 | 24" O.C. | G | 92 | .174 | | 6.65 | 5.05 | | 11.70 | 15.80 |
| 4360 | 4" wide, studs 12" O.C. | G | 45 | .356 | | 11.95 | 10.35 | | 22.30 | 30.50 |
| 4370 | 16" O.C. | G | 65 | .246 | | 9.45 | 7.15 | | 16.60 | 22.50 |
| 4380 | 24" O.C. | G | 90 | .178 | | 7 | 5.15 | | 12.15 | 16.40 |

# 05 41 Structural Metal Stud Framing

## 05 41 13 – Load-Bearing Metal Stud Framing

| 05 41 13.30 Framing, Stud Walls | | Crew | Daily Output | Labor-Hours | Unit | Material | 2010 Bare Costs Labor | Equipment | Total | Total Incl O&P |
|---|---|---|---|---|---|---|---|---|---|---|
| 4390 | 6" wide, studs 12" O.C. | G | 2 Carp | 44 | .364 | L.F. | 15 | 10.60 | | 25.60 | 34.50 |
| 4400 | 16" O.C. | G | | 64 | .250 | | 11.90 | 7.30 | | 19.20 | 25.50 |
| 4410 | 24" O.C. | G | | 88 | .182 | | 8.80 | 5.30 | | 14.10 | 18.60 |
| 4420 | 8" wide, studs 12" O.C. | G | | 43 | .372 | | 18.55 | 10.85 | | 29.40 | 38.50 |
| 4430 | 16" O.C. | G | | 63 | .254 | | 14.75 | 7.40 | | 22.15 | 28.50 |
| 4440 | 24" O.C. | G | | 86 | .186 | | 10.95 | 5.40 | | 16.35 | 21 |
| 5100 | 10' high walls, 18 ga x 2-1/2" wide, studs 12" O.C. | G | | 54 | .296 | | 9.65 | 8.60 | | 18.25 | 25 |
| 5110 | 16" O.C. | G | | 77 | .208 | | 7.65 | 6.05 | | 13.70 | 18.55 |
| 5120 | 24" O.C. | G | | 107 | .150 | | 5.60 | 4.35 | | 9.95 | 13.50 |
| 5130 | 3-5/8" wide, studs 12" O.C. | G | | 53 | .302 | | 11.50 | 8.80 | | 20.30 | 27.50 |
| 5140 | 16" O.C. | G | | 76 | .211 | | 9.10 | 6.15 | | 15.25 | 20.50 |
| 5150 | 24" O.C. | G | | 105 | .152 | | 6.70 | 4.43 | | 11.13 | 14.85 |
| 5160 | 4" wide, studs 12" O.C. | G | | 52 | .308 | | 12.05 | 8.95 | | 21 | 28.50 |
| 5170 | 16" O.C. | G | | 74 | .216 | | 9.55 | 6.30 | | 15.85 | 21 |
| 5180 | 24" O.C. | G | | 103 | .155 | | 7.05 | 4.52 | | 11.57 | 15.35 |
| 5190 | 6" wide, studs 12" O.C. | G | | 51 | .314 | | 15.20 | 9.15 | | 24.35 | 32 |
| 5200 | 16" O.C. | G | | 73 | .219 | | 12.05 | 6.40 | | 18.45 | 24 |
| 5210 | 24" O.C. | G | | 101 | .158 | | 8.90 | 4.61 | | 13.51 | 17.55 |
| 5220 | 8" wide, studs 12" O.C. | G | | 50 | .320 | | 18.65 | 9.30 | | 27.95 | 36 |
| 5230 | 16" O.C. | G | | 72 | .222 | | 14.80 | 6.45 | | 21.25 | 27 |
| 5240 | 24" O.C. | G | | 100 | .160 | | 11 | 4.66 | | 15.66 | 19.95 |
| 5300 | 16 ga x 2-1/2" wide, studs 12" O.C. | G | | 47 | .340 | | 11.45 | 9.90 | | 21.35 | 29.50 |
| 5310 | 16" O.C. | G | | 68 | .235 | | 9 | 6.85 | | 15.85 | 21.50 |
| 5320 | 24" O.C. | G | | 94 | .170 | | 6.50 | 4.95 | | 11.45 | 15.50 |
| 5330 | 3-5/8" wide, studs 12" O.C. | G | | 46 | .348 | | 13.70 | 10.10 | | 23.80 | 32 |
| 5340 | 16" O.C. | G | | 66 | .242 | | 10.75 | 7.05 | | 17.80 | 23.50 |
| 5350 | 24" O.C. | G | | 92 | .174 | | 7.80 | 5.05 | | 12.85 | 17.10 |
| 5360 | 4" wide, studs 12" O.C. | G | | 45 | .356 | | 14.45 | 10.35 | | 24.80 | 33.50 |
| 5370 | 16" O.C. | G | | 65 | .246 | | 11.35 | 7.15 | | 18.50 | 24.50 |
| 5380 | 24" O.C. | G | | 90 | .178 | | 8.25 | 5.15 | | 13.40 | 17.75 |
| 5390 | 6" wide, studs 12" O.C. | G | | 44 | .364 | | 18.10 | 10.60 | | 28.70 | 38 |
| 5400 | 16" O.C. | G | | 64 | .250 | | 14.25 | 7.30 | | 21.55 | 28 |
| 5410 | 24" O.C. | G | | 88 | .182 | | 10.35 | 5.30 | | 15.65 | 20.50 |
| 5420 | 8" wide, studs 12" O.C. | G | | 43 | .372 | | 22.50 | 10.85 | | 33.35 | 42.50 |
| 5430 | 16" O.C. | G | | 63 | .254 | | 17.60 | 7.40 | | 25 | 32 |
| 5440 | 24" O.C. | G | | 86 | .186 | | 12.85 | 5.40 | | 18.25 | 23 |
| 6190 | 12' high walls, 18 ga x 6" wide, studs 12" O.C. | G | | 41 | .390 | | 17.75 | 11.35 | | 29.10 | 38.50 |
| 6200 | 16" O.C. | G | | 58 | .276 | | 13.95 | 8.05 | | 22 | 29 |
| 6210 | 24" O.C. | G | | 81 | .198 | | 10.20 | 5.75 | | 15.95 | 21 |
| 6220 | 8" wide, studs 12" O.C. | G | | 40 | .400 | | 21.50 | 11.65 | | 33.15 | 43.50 |
| 6230 | 16" O.C. | G | | 57 | .281 | | 17.10 | 8.15 | | 25.25 | 32.50 |
| 6240 | 24" O.C. | G | | 80 | .200 | | 12.50 | 5.80 | | 18.30 | 23.50 |
| 6390 | 16 ga x 6" wide, studs 12" O.C. | G | | 35 | .457 | | 21 | 13.30 | | 34.30 | 46 |
| 6400 | 16" O.C. | G | | 51 | .314 | | 16.55 | 9.15 | | 25.70 | 33.50 |
| 6410 | 24" O.C. | G | | 70 | .229 | | 11.90 | 6.65 | | 18.55 | 24.50 |
| 6420 | 8" wide, studs 12" O.C. | G | | 34 | .471 | | 26 | 13.70 | | 39.70 | 52 |
| 6430 | 16" O.C. | G | | 50 | .320 | | 20.50 | 9.30 | | 29.80 | 38 |
| 6440 | 24" O.C. | G | | 69 | .232 | | 14.75 | 6.75 | | 21.50 | 27.50 |
| 6530 | 14 ga x 3-5/8" wide, studs 12" O.C. | G | | 34 | .471 | | 20 | 13.70 | | 33.70 | 45 |
| 6540 | 16" O.C. | G | | 48 | .333 | | 15.70 | 9.70 | | 25.40 | 33.50 |
| 6550 | 24" O.C. | G | | 65 | .246 | | 11.30 | 7.15 | | 18.45 | 24.50 |
| 6560 | 4" wide, studs 12" O.C. | G | | 33 | .485 | | 21.50 | 14.10 | | 35.60 | 47 |
| 6570 | 16" O.C. | G | | 47 | .340 | | 16.60 | 9.90 | | 26.50 | 35 |

## 05 41 13 – Load-Bearing Metal Stud Framing

| 05 41 13.30 Framing, Stud Walls | | Crew | Daily Output | Labor-Hours | Unit | Material | 2010 Bare Costs Labor | Equipment | Total | Total Incl O&P |
|---|---|---|---|---|---|---|---|---|---|---|
| 6580 | 24" O.C. | G 2 Carp | 64 | .250 | L.F. | 11.90 | 7.30 | | 19.20 | 25.50 |
| 6730 | 12 ga x 3-5/8" wide, studs 12" O.C. | G | 31 | .516 | | 28 | 15 | | 43 | 56 |
| 6740 | 16" O.C. | G | 43 | .372 | | 21.50 | 10.85 | | 32.35 | 41.50 |
| 6750 | 24" O.C. | G | 59 | .271 | | 15.10 | 7.90 | | 23 | 30 |
| 6760 | 4" wide, studs 12" O.C. | G | 30 | .533 | | 30 | 15.50 | | 45.50 | 59 |
| 6770 | 16" O.C. | G | 42 | .381 | | 23 | 11.10 | | 34.10 | 44 |
| 6780 | 24" O.C. | G | 58 | .276 | | 16.25 | 8.05 | | 24.30 | 31.50 |
| 7390 | 16' high walls, 16 ga x 6" wide, studs 12" O.C. | G | 33 | .485 | | 27.50 | 14.10 | | 41.60 | 53.50 |
| 7400 | 16" O.C. | G | 48 | .333 | | 21 | 9.70 | | 30.70 | 40 |
| 7410 | 24" O.C. | G | 67 | .239 | | 15 | 6.95 | | 21.95 | 28 |
| 7420 | 8" wide, studs 12" O.C. | G | 32 | .500 | | 33.50 | 14.55 | | 48.05 | 61.50 |
| 7430 | 16" O.C. | G | 47 | .340 | | 26 | 9.90 | | 35.90 | 45.50 |
| 7440 | 24" O.C. | G | 66 | .242 | | 18.55 | 7.05 | | 25.60 | 32.50 |
| 7560 | 14 ga x 4" wide, studs 12" O.C. | G | 31 | .516 | | 27.50 | 15 | | 42.50 | 56 |
| 7570 | 16" O.C. | G | 45 | .356 | | 21.50 | 10.35 | | 31.85 | 41 |
| 7580 | 24" O.C. | G | 61 | .262 | | 15.05 | 7.65 | | 22.70 | 29.50 |
| 7590 | 6" wide, studs 12" O.C. | G | 30 | .533 | | 34.50 | 15.50 | | 50 | 64 |
| 7600 | 16" O.C. | G | 44 | .364 | | 27 | 10.60 | | 37.60 | 47.50 |
| 7610 | 24" O.C. | G | 60 | .267 | | 18.95 | 7.75 | | 26.70 | 34 |
| 7760 | 12 ga x 4" wide, studs 12" O.C. | G | 29 | .552 | | 39 | 16.05 | | 55.05 | 70 |
| 7770 | 16" O.C. | G | 40 | .400 | | 30 | 11.65 | | 41.65 | 52.50 |
| 7780 | 24" O.C. | G | 55 | .291 | | 21 | 8.45 | | 29.45 | 37.50 |
| 7790 | 6" wide, studs 12" O.C. | G | 28 | .571 | | 49 | 16.65 | | 65.65 | 82 |
| 7800 | 16" O.C. | G | 39 | .410 | | 37.50 | 11.95 | | 49.45 | 61.50 |
| 7810 | 24" O.C. | G | 54 | .296 | | 26 | 8.60 | | 34.60 | 43.50 |
| 8590 | 20' high walls, 14 ga x 6" wide, studs 12" O.C. | G | 29 | .552 | | 42.50 | 16.05 | | 58.55 | 73.50 |
| 8600 | 16" O.C. | G | 42 | .381 | | 32.50 | 11.10 | | 43.60 | 54.50 |
| 8610 | 24" O.C. | G | 57 | .281 | | 23 | 8.15 | | 31.15 | 39 |
| 8620 | 8" wide, studs 12" O.C. | G | 28 | .571 | | 52 | 16.65 | | 68.65 | 85 |
| 8630 | 16" O.C. | G | 41 | .390 | | 40 | 11.35 | | 51.35 | 63 |
| 8640 | 24" O.C. | G | 56 | .286 | | 28 | 8.30 | | 36.30 | 45 |
| 8790 | 12 ga x 6" wide, studs 12" O.C. | G | 27 | .593 | | 60.50 | 17.25 | | 77.75 | 96 |
| 8800 | 16" O.C. | G | 37 | .432 | | 46.50 | 12.60 | | 59.10 | 72 |
| 8810 | 24" O.C. | G | 51 | .314 | | 32 | 9.15 | | 41.15 | 50.50 |
| 8820 | 8" wide, studs 12" O.C. | G | 26 | .615 | | 74 | 17.90 | | 91.90 | 112 |
| 8830 | 16" O.C. | G | 36 | .444 | | 56.50 | 12.95 | | 69.45 | 84 |
| 8840 | 24" O.C. | G | 50 | .320 | | 39 | 9.30 | | 48.30 | 58.50 |

## 05 42 13 – Cold-Formed Metal Floor Joist Framing

### 05 42 13.05 Bracing

| | | Crew | Daily Output | Labor-Hours | Unit | Material | 2010 Bare Costs Labor | Equipment | Total | Total Incl O&P |
|---|---|---|---|---|---|---|---|---|---|---|
| 0010 | **BRACING**, continuous, per row, top & bottom | | | | | | | | | |
| 0015 | Made from recycled materials | G | | | | | | | | |
| 0120 | Flat strap, 20 ga x 2" wide, joists at 12" O.C. | G 1 Carp | 4.67 | 1.713 | C.L.F. | 50.50 | 50 | | 100.50 | 140 |
| 0130 | 16" O.C. | G | 5.33 | 1.501 | | 49 | 43.50 | | 92.50 | 127 |
| 0140 | 24" O.C. | G | 6.66 | 1.201 | | 47 | 35 | | 82 | 111 |
| 0150 | 18 ga x 2" wide, joists at 12" O.C. | G | 4 | 2 | | 67.50 | 58 | | 125.50 | 173 |
| 0160 | 16" O.C. | G | 4.67 | 1.713 | | 66.50 | 50 | | 116.50 | 157 |
| 0170 | 24" O.C. | G | 5.33 | 1.501 | | 65 | 43.50 | | 108.50 | 145 |

## 05 42 13 – Cold-Formed Metal Floor Joist Framing

### 05 42 13.10 Bridging

| | | Crew | Daily Output | Labor-Hours | Unit | Material | 2010 Bare Costs Labor | Equipment | Total | Total Incl O&P |
|---|---|---|---|---|---|---|---|---|---|---|
| 0010 | **BRIDGING**, solid between joists w/1-1/4" leg track, per joist bay | | | | | | | | | |
| 0015 | Made from recycled materials | G | | | | | | | | |
| 0230 | Joists 12" O.C., 18 ga track x 6" wide | G | 1 Carp | 80 | .100 | Ea. | 1.38 | 2.91 | 4.29 | 6.40 |
| 0240 | 8" wide | G | | 75 | .107 | | 1.75 | 3.10 | 4.85 | 7.15 |
| 0250 | 10" wide | G | | 70 | .114 | | 2.16 | 3.33 | 5.49 | 8 |
| 0260 | 12" wide | G | | 65 | .123 | | 2.50 | 3.58 | 6.08 | 8.75 |
| 0330 | 16 ga track x 6" wide | G | | 70 | .114 | | 1.72 | 3.33 | 5.05 | 7.50 |
| 0340 | 8" wide | G | | 65 | .123 | | 2.20 | 3.58 | 5.78 | 8.40 |
| 0350 | 10" wide | G | | 60 | .133 | | 2.70 | 3.88 | 6.58 | 9.50 |
| 0360 | 12" wide | G | | 55 | .145 | | 3.11 | 4.23 | 7.34 | 10.55 |
| 0440 | 14 ga track x 8" wide | G | | 60 | .133 | | 2.78 | 3.88 | 6.66 | 9.60 |
| 0450 | 10" wide | G | | 55 | .145 | | 3.41 | 4.23 | 7.64 | 10.85 |
| 0460 | 12" wide | G | | 50 | .160 | | 3.94 | 4.66 | 8.60 | 12.20 |
| 0550 | 12 ga track x 10" wide | G | | 45 | .178 | | 5 | 5.15 | 10.15 | 14.20 |
| 0560 | 12" wide | G | | 40 | .200 | | 5.65 | 5.80 | 11.45 | 16.05 |
| 1230 | 16" O.C., 18 ga track x 6" wide | G | | 80 | .100 | | 1.77 | 2.91 | 4.68 | 6.85 |
| 1240 | 8" wide | G | | 75 | .107 | | 2.24 | 3.10 | 5.34 | 7.65 |
| 1250 | 10" wide | G | | 70 | .114 | | 2.77 | 3.33 | 6.10 | 8.65 |
| 1260 | 12" wide | G | | 65 | .123 | | 3.20 | 3.58 | 6.78 | 9.50 |
| 1330 | 16 ga track x 6" wide | G | | 70 | .114 | | 2.21 | 3.33 | 5.54 | 8.05 |
| 1340 | 8" wide | G | | 65 | .123 | | 2.82 | 3.58 | 6.40 | 9.10 |
| 1350 | 10" wide | G | | 60 | .133 | | 3.47 | 3.88 | 7.35 | 10.35 |
| 1360 | 12" wide | G | | 55 | .145 | | 3.99 | 4.23 | 8.22 | 11.50 |
| 1440 | 14 ga track x 8" wide | G | | 60 | .133 | | 3.56 | 3.88 | 7.44 | 10.45 |
| 1450 | 10" wide | G | | 55 | .145 | | 4.37 | 4.23 | 8.60 | 11.90 |
| 1460 | 12" wide | G | | 50 | .160 | | 5.05 | 4.66 | 9.71 | 13.40 |
| 1550 | 12 ga track x 10" wide | G | | 45 | .178 | | 6.40 | 5.15 | 11.55 | 15.75 |
| 1560 | 12" wide | G | | 40 | .200 | | 7.25 | 5.80 | 13.05 | 17.80 |
| 2230 | 24" O.C., 18 ga track x 6" wide | G | | 80 | .100 | | 2.55 | 2.91 | 5.46 | 7.70 |
| 2240 | 8" wide | G | | 75 | .107 | | 3.25 | 3.10 | 6.35 | 8.75 |
| 2250 | 10" wide | G | | 70 | .114 | | 4.01 | 3.33 | 7.34 | 10 |
| 2260 | 12" wide | G | | 65 | .123 | | 4.63 | 3.58 | 8.21 | 11.10 |
| 2330 | 16 ga track x 6" wide | G | | 70 | .114 | | 3.20 | 3.33 | 6.53 | 9.10 |
| 2340 | 8" wide | G | | 65 | .123 | | 4.08 | 3.58 | 7.66 | 10.50 |
| 2350 | 10" wide | G | | 60 | .133 | | 5 | 3.88 | 8.88 | 12.05 |
| 2360 | 12" wide | G | | 55 | .145 | | 5.80 | 4.23 | 10.03 | 13.45 |
| 2440 | 14 ga track x 8" wide | G | | 60 | .133 | | 5.15 | 3.88 | 9.03 | 12.20 |
| 2450 | 10" wide | G | | 55 | .145 | | 6.35 | 4.23 | 10.58 | 14.05 |
| 2460 | 12" wide | G | | 50 | .160 | | 7.30 | 4.66 | 11.96 | 15.90 |
| 2550 | 12 ga track x 10" wide | G | | 45 | .178 | | 9.30 | 5.15 | 14.45 | 18.90 |
| 2560 | 12" wide | G | | 40 | .200 | | 10.50 | 5.80 | 16.30 | 21.50 |

### 05 42 13.25 Framing, Band Joist

| | | Crew | Daily Output | Labor-Hours | Unit | Material | 2010 Bare Costs Labor | Equipment | Total | Total Incl O&P |
|---|---|---|---|---|---|---|---|---|---|---|
| 0010 | **FRAMING, BAND JOIST** (track) fastened to bearing wall | | | | | | | | | |
| 0015 | Made from recycled materials | G | | | | | | | | |
| 0220 | 18 ga track x 6" deep | G | 2 Carp | 1000 | .016 | L.F. | 1.12 | .47 | 1.59 | 2.02 |
| 0230 | 8" deep | G | | 920 | .017 | | 1.43 | .51 | 1.94 | 2.42 |
| 0240 | 10" deep | G | | 860 | .019 | | 1.76 | .54 | 2.30 | 2.85 |
| 0320 | 16 ga track x 6" deep | G | | 900 | .018 | | 1.41 | .52 | 1.93 | 2.42 |
| 0330 | 8" deep | G | | 840 | .019 | | 1.80 | .55 | 2.35 | 2.91 |
| 0340 | 10" deep | G | | 780 | .021 | | 2.21 | .60 | 2.81 | 3.43 |
| 0350 | 12" deep | G | | 740 | .022 | | 2.54 | .63 | 3.17 | 3.86 |
| 0430 | 14 ga track x 8" deep | G | | 750 | .021 | | 2.27 | .62 | 2.89 | 3.53 |

# 05 42 Cold-Formed Metal Joist Framing

## 05 42 13 – Cold-Formed Metal Floor Joist Framing

### 05 42 13.25 Framing, Band Joist

| | | | Crew | Daily Output | Labor-Hours | Unit | Material | 2010 Bare Costs Labor | Equipment | Total | Total Incl O&P |
|---|---|---|---|---|---|---|---|---|---|---|---|
| 0440 | 10" deep | G | 2 Carp | 720 | .022 | L.F. | 2.78 | .65 | | 3.43 | 4.15 |
| 0450 | 12" deep | G | | 700 | .023 | | 3.21 | .67 | | 3.88 | 4.65 |
| 0540 | 12 ga track x 10" deep | G | | 670 | .024 | | 4.08 | .69 | | 4.77 | 5.65 |
| 0550 | 12" deep | G | | 650 | .025 | | 4.62 | .72 | | 5.34 | 6.30 |

### 05 42 13.30 Framing, Boxed Headers/Beams

| | | | Crew | Daily Output | Labor-Hours | Unit | Material | 2010 Bare Costs Labor | Equipment | Total | Total Incl O&P |
|---|---|---|---|---|---|---|---|---|---|---|---|
| 0010 | **FRAMING, BOXED HEADERS/BEAMS** | | | | | | | | | | |
| 0015 | Made from recycled materials | G | | | | | | | | | |
| 0200 | Double, 18 ga x 6" deep | G | 2 Carp | 220 | .073 | L.F. | 4.81 | 2.12 | | 6.93 | 8.85 |
| 0210 | 8" deep | G | | 210 | .076 | | 5.35 | 2.22 | | 7.57 | 9.65 |
| 0220 | 10" deep | G | | 200 | .080 | | 6.45 | 2.33 | | 8.78 | 11 |
| 0230 | 12" deep | G | | 190 | .084 | | 7.10 | 2.45 | | 9.55 | 11.90 |
| 0300 | 16 ga x 8" deep | G | | 180 | .089 | | 6.15 | 2.59 | | 8.74 | 11.10 |
| 0310 | 10" deep | G | | 170 | .094 | | 7.35 | 2.74 | | 10.09 | 12.65 |
| 0320 | 12" deep | G | | 160 | .100 | | 8 | 2.91 | | 10.91 | 13.70 |
| 0400 | 14 ga x 10" deep | G | | 140 | .114 | | 8.55 | 3.33 | | 11.88 | 15 |
| 0410 | 12" deep | G | | 130 | .123 | | 9.40 | 3.58 | | 12.98 | 16.30 |
| 0500 | 12 ga x 10" deep | G | | 110 | .145 | | 11.30 | 4.23 | | 15.53 | 19.55 |
| 0510 | 12" deep | G | | 100 | .160 | | 12.50 | 4.66 | | 17.16 | 21.50 |
| 1210 | Triple, 18 ga x 8" deep | G | | 170 | .094 | | 7.70 | 2.74 | | 10.44 | 13.10 |
| 1220 | 10" deep | G | | 165 | .097 | | 9.25 | 2.82 | | 12.07 | 14.95 |
| 1230 | 12" deep | G | | 160 | .100 | | 10.20 | 2.91 | | 13.11 | 16.15 |
| 1300 | 16 ga x 8" deep | G | | 145 | .110 | | 8.90 | 3.21 | | 12.11 | 15.20 |
| 1310 | 10" deep | G | | 140 | .114 | | 10.60 | 3.33 | | 13.93 | 17.25 |
| 1320 | 12" deep | G | | 135 | .119 | | 11.60 | 3.45 | | 15.05 | 18.55 |
| 1400 | 14 ga x 10" deep | G | | 115 | .139 | | 12.40 | 4.05 | | 16.45 | 20.50 |
| 1410 | 12" deep | G | | 110 | .145 | | 13.65 | 4.23 | | 17.88 | 22 |
| 1500 | 12 ga x 10" deep | G | | 90 | .178 | | 16.55 | 5.15 | | 21.70 | 27 |
| 1510 | 12" deep | G | | 85 | .188 | | 18.40 | 5.50 | | 23.90 | 29 |

### 05 42 13.40 Framing, Joists

| | | | Crew | Daily Output | Labor-Hours | Unit | Material | 2010 Bare Costs Labor | Equipment | Total | Total Incl O&P |
|---|---|---|---|---|---|---|---|---|---|---|---|
| 0010 | **FRAMING, JOISTS**, no band joists (track), web stiffeners, headers, | | | | | | | | | | |
| 0020 | Beams, bridging or bracing | | | | | | | | | | |
| 0025 | Made from recycled materials | G | | | | | | | | | |
| 0030 | Joists (2" flange) and fasteners, materials only | | | | | | | | | | |
| 0220 | 18 ga x 6" deep | G | | | | L.F. | 1.48 | | | 1.48 | 1.63 |
| 0230 | 8" deep | G | | | | | 1.76 | | | 1.76 | 1.94 |
| 0240 | 10" deep | G | | | | | 2.07 | | | 2.07 | 2.28 |
| 0320 | 16 ga x 6" deep | G | | | | | 1.82 | | | 1.82 | 2 |
| 0330 | 8" deep | G | | | | | 2.18 | | | 2.18 | 2.40 |
| 0340 | 10" deep | G | | | | | 2.54 | | | 2.54 | 2.80 |
| 0350 | 12" deep | G | | | | | 2.89 | | | 2.89 | 3.18 |
| 0430 | 14 ga x 8" deep | G | | | | | 2.75 | | | 2.75 | 3.03 |
| 0440 | 10" deep | G | | | | | 3.17 | | | 3.17 | 3.49 |
| 0450 | 12" deep | G | | | | | 3.61 | | | 3.61 | 3.97 |
| 0540 | 12 ga x 10" deep | G | | | | | 4.62 | | | 4.62 | 5.10 |
| 0550 | 12" deep | G | | | | | 5.25 | | | 5.25 | 5.80 |
| 1010 | Installation of joists to band joists, beams & headers, labor only | | | | | | | | | | |
| 1220 | 18 ga x 6" deep | | 2 Carp | 110 | .145 | Ea. | | 4.23 | | 4.23 | 7.10 |
| 1230 | 8" deep | | | 90 | .178 | | | 5.15 | | 5.15 | 8.70 |
| 1240 | 10" deep | | | 80 | .200 | | | 5.80 | | 5.80 | 9.80 |
| 1320 | 16 ga x 6" deep | | | 95 | .168 | | | 4.90 | | 4.90 | 8.25 |
| 1330 | 8" deep | | | 70 | .229 | | | 6.65 | | 6.65 | 11.20 |
| 1340 | 10" deep | | | 60 | .267 | | | 7.75 | | 7.75 | 13.05 |

# 05 42 Cold-Formed Metal Joist Framing

## 05 42 13 – Cold-Formed Metal Floor Joist Framing

### 05 42 13.40 Framing, Joists

| | | Crew | Daily Output | Labor-Hours | Unit | Material | 2010 Bare Costs Labor | Equipment | Total | Total Incl O&P |
|---|---|---|---|---|---|---|---|---|---|---|
| 1350 | 12" deep | 2 Carp | 55 | .291 | Ea. | | 8.45 | | 8.45 | 14.25 |
| 1430 | 14 ga x 8" deep | | 65 | .246 | | | 7.15 | | 7.15 | 12.05 |
| 1440 | 10" deep | | 45 | .356 | | | 10.35 | | 10.35 | 17.40 |
| 1450 | 12" deep | | 35 | .457 | | | 13.30 | | 13.30 | 22.50 |
| 1540 | 12 ga x 10" deep | | 40 | .400 | | | 11.65 | | 11.65 | 19.60 |
| 1550 | 12" deep | | 30 | .533 | | | 15.50 | | 15.50 | 26 |

### 05 42 13.45 Framing, Web Stiffeners

| | | | Crew | Daily Output | Labor-Hours | Unit | Material | 2010 Bare Costs Labor | Equipment | Total | Total Incl O&P |
|---|---|---|---|---|---|---|---|---|---|---|---|
| 0010 | **FRAMING, WEB STIFFENERS** at joist bearing, fabricated from | | | | | | | | | | |
| 0020 | Stud piece (1-5/8" flange) to stiffen joist (2" flange) | | | | | | | | | | |
| 0025 | Made from recycled materials | G | | | | | | | | | |
| 2120 | For 6" deep joist, with 18 ga x 2-1/2" stud | G | 1 Carp | 120 | .067 | Ea. | 1.78 | 1.94 | | 3.72 | 5.20 |
| 2130 | 3-5/8" stud | G | | 110 | .073 | | 1.97 | 2.12 | | 4.09 | 5.70 |
| 2140 | 4" stud | G | | 105 | .076 | | 1.90 | 2.22 | | 4.12 | 5.80 |
| 2150 | 6" stud | G | | 100 | .080 | | 2.08 | 2.33 | | 4.41 | 6.20 |
| 2160 | 8" stud | G | | 95 | .084 | | 2.14 | 2.45 | | 4.59 | 6.50 |
| 2220 | 8" deep joist, with 2-1/2" stud | G | | 120 | .067 | | 1.95 | 1.94 | | 3.89 | 5.40 |
| 2230 | 3-5/8" stud | G | | 110 | .073 | | 2.12 | 2.12 | | 4.24 | 5.90 |
| 2240 | 4" stud | G | | 105 | .076 | | 2.08 | 2.22 | | 4.30 | 6 |
| 2250 | 6" stud | G | | 100 | .080 | | 2.28 | 2.33 | | 4.61 | 6.45 |
| 2260 | 8" stud | G | | 95 | .084 | | 2.46 | 2.45 | | 4.91 | 6.85 |
| 2320 | 10" deep joist, with 2-1/2" stud | G | | 110 | .073 | | 2.76 | 2.12 | | 4.88 | 6.60 |
| 2330 | 3-5/8" stud | G | | 100 | .080 | | 3.03 | 2.33 | | 5.36 | 7.25 |
| 2340 | 4" stud | G | | 95 | .084 | | 2.99 | 2.45 | | 5.44 | 7.40 |
| 2350 | 6" stud | G | | 90 | .089 | | 3.24 | 2.59 | | 5.83 | 7.90 |
| 2360 | 8" stud | G | | 85 | .094 | | 3.30 | 2.74 | | 6.04 | 8.25 |
| 2420 | 12" deep joist, with 2-1/2" stud | G | | 110 | .073 | | 2.92 | 2.12 | | 5.04 | 6.75 |
| 2430 | 3-5/8" stud | G | | 100 | .080 | | 3.17 | 2.33 | | 5.50 | 7.40 |
| 2440 | 4" stud | G | | 95 | .084 | | 3.10 | 2.45 | | 5.55 | 7.55 |
| 2450 | 6" stud | G | | 90 | .089 | | 3.40 | 2.59 | | 5.99 | 8.10 |
| 2460 | 8" stud | G | | 85 | .094 | | 3.67 | 2.74 | | 6.41 | 8.65 |
| 3130 | For 6" deep joist, with 16 ga x 3-5/8" stud | G | | 100 | .080 | | 2.07 | 2.33 | | 4.40 | 6.20 |
| 3140 | 4" stud | G | | 95 | .084 | | 2.05 | 2.45 | | 4.50 | 6.35 |
| 3150 | 6" stud | G | | 90 | .089 | | 2.25 | 2.59 | | 4.84 | 6.80 |
| 3160 | 8" stud | G | | 85 | .094 | | 2.38 | 2.74 | | 5.12 | 7.20 |
| 3230 | 8" deep joist, with 3-5/8" stud | G | | 100 | .080 | | 2.29 | 2.33 | | 4.62 | 6.45 |
| 3240 | 4" stud | G | | 95 | .084 | | 2.24 | 2.45 | | 4.69 | 6.60 |
| 3250 | 6" stud | G | | 90 | .089 | | 2.49 | 2.59 | | 5.08 | 7.10 |
| 3260 | 8" stud | G | | 85 | .094 | | 2.67 | 2.74 | | 5.41 | 7.55 |
| 3330 | 10" deep joist, with 3-5/8" stud | G | | 85 | .094 | | 3.13 | 2.74 | | 5.87 | 8.05 |
| 3340 | 4" stud | G | | 80 | .100 | | 3.19 | 2.91 | | 6.10 | 8.40 |
| 3350 | 6" stud | G | | 75 | .107 | | 3.47 | 3.10 | | 6.57 | 9 |
| 3360 | 8" stud | G | | 70 | .114 | | 3.63 | 3.33 | | 6.96 | 9.60 |
| 3430 | 12" deep joist, with 3-5/8" stud | G | | 85 | .094 | | 3.42 | 2.74 | | 6.16 | 8.35 |
| 3440 | 4" stud | G | | 80 | .100 | | 3.35 | 2.91 | | 6.26 | 8.60 |
| 3450 | 6" stud | G | | 75 | .107 | | 3.72 | 3.10 | | 6.82 | 9.30 |
| 3460 | 8" stud | G | | 70 | .114 | | 3.99 | 3.33 | | 7.32 | 10 |
| 4230 | For 8" deep joist, with 14 ga x 3-5/8" stud | G | | 90 | .089 | | 2.97 | 2.59 | | 5.56 | 7.60 |
| 4240 | 4" stud | G | | 85 | .094 | | 3.03 | 2.74 | | 5.77 | 7.95 |
| 4250 | 6" stud | G | | 80 | .100 | | 3.28 | 2.91 | | 6.19 | 8.50 |
| 4260 | 8" stud | G | | 75 | .107 | | 3.52 | 3.10 | | 6.62 | 9.10 |
| 4330 | 10" deep joist, with 3-5/8" stud | G | | 75 | .107 | | 4.18 | 3.10 | | 7.28 | 9.80 |
| 4340 | 4" stud | G | | 70 | .114 | | 4.14 | 3.33 | | 7.47 | 10.15 |

# 05 42 Cold-Formed Metal Joist Framing

## 05 42 13 – Cold-Formed Metal Floor Joist Framing

### 05 42 13.45 Framing, Web Stiffeners

| | | Crew | Daily Output | Labor-Hours | Unit | Material | 2010 Bare Costs Labor | Equipment | Total | Total Incl O&P |
|---|---|---|---|---|---|---|---|---|---|---|
| 4350 | 6" stud | 1 Carp G | 65 | .123 | Ea. | 4.56 | 3.58 | | 8.14 | 11 |
| 4360 | 8" stud | G | 60 | .133 | | 4.76 | 3.88 | | 8.64 | 11.80 |
| 4430 | 12" deep joist, with 3-5/8" stud | G | 75 | .107 | | 4.44 | 3.10 | | 7.54 | 10.10 |
| 4440 | 4" stud | G | 70 | .114 | | 4.52 | 3.33 | | 7.85 | 10.60 |
| 4450 | 6" stud | G | 65 | .123 | | 4.90 | 3.58 | | 8.48 | 11.40 |
| 4460 | 8" stud | G | 60 | .133 | | 5.25 | 3.88 | | 9.13 | 12.35 |
| 5330 | For 10" deep joist, with 12 ga x 3-5/8" stud | G | 65 | .123 | | 4.40 | 3.58 | | 7.98 | 10.85 |
| 5340 | 4" stud | G | 60 | .133 | | 4.54 | 3.88 | | 8.42 | 11.55 |
| 5350 | 6" stud | G | 55 | .145 | | 5 | 4.23 | | 9.23 | 12.60 |
| 5360 | 8" stud | G | 50 | .160 | | 5.50 | 4.66 | | 10.16 | 13.90 |
| 5430 | 12" deep joist, with 3-5/8" stud | G | 65 | .123 | | 4.88 | 3.58 | | 8.46 | 11.35 |
| 5440 | 4" stud | G | 60 | .133 | | 4.79 | 3.88 | | 8.67 | 11.80 |
| 5450 | 6" stud | G | 55 | .145 | | 5.45 | 4.23 | | 9.68 | 13.10 |
| 5460 | 8" stud | G | 50 | .160 | | 6.30 | 4.66 | | 10.96 | 14.75 |

## 05 42 23 – Cold-Formed Metal Roof Joist Framing

### 05 42 23.05 Framing, Bracing

| | | Crew | Daily Output | Labor-Hours | Unit | Material | 2010 Bare Costs Labor | Equipment | Total | Total Incl O&P |
|---|---|---|---|---|---|---|---|---|---|---|
| 0010 | **FRAMING, BRACING** | | | | | | | | | |
| 0015 | Made from recycled materials | G | | | | | | | | |
| 0020 | Continuous bracing, per row | | | | | | | | | |
| 0100 | 16 ga x 1-1/2" channel thru rafters/trusses @ 16" O.C. | 1 Carp G | 4.50 | 1.778 | C.L.F. | 45.50 | 51.50 | | 97 | 137 |
| 0120 | 24" O.C. | G | 6 | 1.333 | | 45.50 | 39 | | 84.50 | 116 |
| 0300 | 2" x 2" angle x 18 ga, rafters/trusses @ 16" O.C. | G | 6 | 1.333 | | 68 | 39 | | 107 | 141 |
| 0320 | 24" O.C. | G | 8 | 1 | | 68 | 29 | | 97 | 124 |
| 0400 | 16 ga, rafters/trusses @ 16" O.C. | G | 4.50 | 1.778 | | 86 | 51.50 | | 137.50 | 182 |
| 0420 | 24" O.C. | G | 6.50 | 1.231 | | 86 | 36 | | 122 | 155 |

### 05 42 23.10 Framing, Bridging

| | | Crew | Daily Output | Labor-Hours | Unit | Material | 2010 Bare Costs Labor | Equipment | Total | Total Incl O&P |
|---|---|---|---|---|---|---|---|---|---|---|
| 0010 | **FRAMING, BRIDGING** | | | | | | | | | |
| 0015 | Made from recycled materials | G | | | | | | | | |
| 0020 | Solid, between rafters w/1-1/4" leg track, per rafter bay | | | | | | | | | |
| 1200 | Rafters 16" O.C., 18 ga x 4" deep | 1 Carp G | 60 | .133 | Ea. | 1.37 | 3.88 | | 5.25 | 8.05 |
| 1210 | 6" deep | G | 57 | .140 | | 1.77 | 4.08 | | 5.85 | 8.80 |
| 1220 | 8" deep | G | 55 | .145 | | 2.24 | 4.23 | | 6.47 | 9.55 |
| 1230 | 10" deep | G | 52 | .154 | | 2.77 | 4.48 | | 7.25 | 10.60 |
| 1240 | 12" deep | G | 50 | .160 | | 3.20 | 4.66 | | 7.86 | 11.35 |
| 2200 | 24" O.C., 18 ga x 4" deep | G | 60 | .133 | | 1.98 | 3.88 | | 5.86 | 8.75 |
| 2210 | 6" deep | G | 57 | .140 | | 2.55 | 4.08 | | 6.63 | 9.65 |
| 2220 | 8" deep | G | 55 | .145 | | 3.25 | 4.23 | | 7.48 | 10.65 |
| 2230 | 10" deep | G | 52 | .154 | | 4.01 | 4.48 | | 8.49 | 11.95 |
| 2240 | 12" deep | G | 50 | .160 | | 4.63 | 4.66 | | 9.29 | 12.95 |

### 05 42 23.50 Framing, Parapets

| | | Crew | Daily Output | Labor-Hours | Unit | Material | 2010 Bare Costs Labor | Equipment | Total | Total Incl O&P |
|---|---|---|---|---|---|---|---|---|---|---|
| 0010 | **FRAMING, PARAPETS** | | | | | | | | | |
| 0015 | Made from recycled materials | G | | | | | | | | |
| 0100 | 3' high installed on 1st story, 18 ga x 4" wide studs, 12" O.C. | 2 Carp G | 100 | .160 | L.F. | 5.05 | 4.66 | | 9.71 | 13.40 |
| 0110 | 16" O.C. | G | 150 | .107 | | 4.28 | 3.10 | | 7.38 | 9.90 |
| 0120 | 24" O.C. | G | 200 | .080 | | 3.53 | 2.33 | | 5.86 | 7.80 |
| 0200 | 6" wide studs, 12" O.C. | G | 100 | .160 | | 6.40 | 4.66 | | 11.06 | 14.90 |
| 0210 | 16" O.C. | G | 150 | .107 | | 5.45 | 3.10 | | 8.55 | 11.20 |
| 0220 | 24" O.C. | G | 200 | .080 | | 4.51 | 2.33 | | 6.84 | 8.90 |
| 1100 | Installed on 2nd story, 18 ga x 4" wide studs, 12" O.C. | G | 95 | .168 | | 5.05 | 4.90 | | 9.95 | 13.80 |
| 1110 | 16" O.C. | G | 145 | .110 | | 4.28 | 3.21 | | 7.49 | 10.10 |
| 1120 | 24" O.C. | G | 190 | .084 | | 3.53 | 2.45 | | 5.98 | 8 |
| 1200 | 6" wide studs, 12" O.C. | G | 95 | .168 | | 6.40 | 4.90 | | 11.30 | 15.30 |

# 05 42 Cold-Formed Metal Joist Framing

## 05 42 23 – Cold-Formed Metal Roof Joist Framing

### 05 42 23.50 Framing, Parapets

| | | Crew | Daily Output | Labor-Hours | Unit | Material | 2010 Bare Costs Labor | Equipment | Total | Total Incl O&P |
|---|---|---|---|---|---|---|---|---|---|---|
| 1210 | 16" O.C. | 2 Carp | 145 | .110 | L.F. | 5.45 | 3.21 | | 8.66 | 11.40 |
| 1220 | 24" O.C. | | 190 | .084 | | 4.51 | 2.45 | | 6.96 | 9.10 |
| 2100 | Installed on gable, 18 ga x 4" wide studs, 12" O.C. | | 85 | .188 | | 5.05 | 5.50 | | 10.55 | 14.75 |
| 2110 | 16" O.C. | | 130 | .123 | | 4.28 | 3.58 | | 7.86 | 10.70 |
| 2120 | 24" O.C. | | 170 | .094 | | 3.53 | 2.74 | | 6.27 | 8.50 |
| 2200 | 6" wide studs, 12" O.C. | | 85 | .188 | | 6.40 | 5.50 | | 11.90 | 16.25 |
| 2210 | 16" O.C. | | 130 | .123 | | 5.45 | 3.58 | | 9.03 | 12 |
| 2220 | 24" O.C. | | 170 | .094 | | 4.51 | 2.74 | | 7.25 | 9.55 |

### 05 42 23.60 Framing, Roof Rafters

| | | Crew | Daily Output | Labor-Hours | Unit | Material | 2010 Bare Costs Labor | Equipment | Total | Total Incl O&P |
|---|---|---|---|---|---|---|---|---|---|---|
| 0010 | **FRAMING, ROOF RAFTERS** | | | | | | | | | |
| 0015 | Made from recycled materials | | | | | | | | | |
| 0100 | Boxed ridge beam, double, 18 ga x 6" deep | 2 Carp | 160 | .100 | L.F. | 4.81 | 2.91 | | 7.72 | 10.20 |
| 0110 | 8" deep | | 150 | .107 | | 5.35 | 3.10 | | 8.45 | 11.10 |
| 0120 | 10" deep | | 140 | .114 | | 6.45 | 3.33 | | 9.78 | 12.70 |
| 0130 | 12" deep | | 130 | .123 | | 7.10 | 3.58 | | 10.68 | 13.80 |
| 0200 | 16 ga x 6" deep | | 150 | .107 | | 5.45 | 3.10 | | 8.55 | 11.20 |
| 0210 | 8" deep | | 140 | .114 | | 6.15 | 3.33 | | 9.48 | 12.35 |
| 0220 | 10" deep | | 130 | .123 | | 7.35 | 3.58 | | 10.93 | 14.05 |
| 0230 | 12" deep | | 120 | .133 | | 8 | 3.88 | | 11.88 | 15.35 |
| 1100 | Rafters, 2" flange, material only, 18 ga x 6" deep | | | | | 1.48 | | | 1.48 | 1.63 |
| 1110 | 8" deep | | | | | 1.76 | | | 1.76 | 1.94 |
| 1120 | 10" deep | | | | | 2.07 | | | 2.07 | 2.28 |
| 1130 | 12" deep | | | | | 2.40 | | | 2.40 | 2.64 |
| 1200 | 16 ga x 6" deep | | | | | 1.82 | | | 1.82 | 2 |
| 1210 | 8" deep | | | | | 2.18 | | | 2.18 | 2.40 |
| 1220 | 10" deep | | | | | 2.54 | | | 2.54 | 2.80 |
| 1230 | 12" deep | | | | | 2.89 | | | 2.89 | 3.18 |
| 2100 | Installation only, ordinary rafter to 4:12 pitch, 18 ga x 6" deep | 2 Carp | 35 | .457 | Ea. | | 13.30 | | 13.30 | 22.50 |
| 2110 | 8" deep | | 30 | .533 | | | 15.50 | | 15.50 | 26 |
| 2120 | 10" deep | | 25 | .640 | | | 18.60 | | 18.60 | 31.50 |
| 2130 | 12" deep | | 20 | .800 | | | 23.50 | | 23.50 | 39 |
| 2200 | 16 ga x 6" deep | | 30 | .533 | | | 15.50 | | 15.50 | 26 |
| 2210 | 8" deep | | 25 | .640 | | | 18.60 | | 18.60 | 31.50 |
| 2220 | 10" deep | | 20 | .800 | | | 23.50 | | 23.50 | 39 |
| 2230 | 12" deep | | 15 | 1.067 | | | 31 | | 31 | 52 |
| 8100 | Add to labor, ordinary rafters on steep roofs | | | | | | 25% | | | |
| 8110 | Dormers & complex roofs | | | | | | 50% | | | |
| 8200 | Hip & valley rafters to 4:12 pitch | | | | | | 25% | | | |
| 8210 | Steep roofs | | | | | | 50% | | | |
| 8220 | Dormers & complex roofs | | | | | | 75% | | | |
| 8300 | Hip & valley jack rafters to 4:12 pitch | | | | | | 50% | | | |
| 8310 | Steep roofs | | | | | | 75% | | | |
| 8320 | Dormers & complex roofs | | | | | | 100% | | | |

### 05 42 23.70 Framing, Soffits and Canopies

| | | Crew | Daily Output | Labor-Hours | Unit | Material | 2010 Bare Costs Labor | Equipment | Total | Total Incl O&P |
|---|---|---|---|---|---|---|---|---|---|---|
| 0010 | **FRAMING, SOFFITS & CANOPIES** | | | | | | | | | |
| 0015 | Made from recycled materials | | | | | | | | | |
| 0130 | Continuous ledger track @ wall, studs @ 16" O.C., 18 ga x 4" wide | 2 Carp | 535 | .030 | L.F. | .91 | .87 | | 1.78 | 2.46 |
| 0140 | 6" wide | | 500 | .032 | | 1.18 | .93 | | 2.11 | 2.86 |
| 0150 | 8" wide | | 465 | .034 | | 1.50 | 1 | | 2.50 | 3.33 |
| 0160 | 10" wide | | 430 | .037 | | 1.85 | 1.08 | | 2.93 | 3.85 |
| 0230 | Studs @ 24" O.C., 18 ga x 4" wide | | 800 | .020 | | .87 | .58 | | 1.45 | 1.94 |
| 0240 | 6" wide | | 750 | .021 | | 1.12 | .62 | | 1.74 | 2.28 |

341

# 05 42 Cold-Formed Metal Joist Framing

## 05 42 23 – Cold-Formed Metal Roof Joist Framing

### 05 42 23.70 Framing, Soffits and Canopies

| | | | Crew | Daily Output | Labor-Hours | Unit | Material | 2010 Bare Costs Labor | Equipment | Total | Total Incl O&P |
|---|---|---|---|---|---|---|---|---|---|---|---|
| 0250 | 8" wide | G | 2 Carp | 700 | .023 | L.F. | 1.43 | .67 | | 2.10 | 2.69 |
| 0260 | 10" wide | | ↓ | 650 | .025 | ↓ | 1.76 | .72 | | 2.48 | 3.15 |
| 1000 | Horizontal soffit and canopy members, material only | | | | | | | | | | |
| 1030 | 1-5/8" flange studs, 18 ga x 4" deep | G | | | | L.F. | 1.20 | | | 1.20 | 1.32 |
| 1040 | 6" deep | G | | | | | 1.51 | | | 1.51 | 1.66 |
| 1050 | 8" deep | G | | | | | 1.84 | | | 1.84 | 2.02 |
| 1140 | 2" flange joists, 18 ga x 6" deep | G | | | | | 1.69 | | | 1.69 | 1.86 |
| 1150 | 8" deep | G | | | | | 2.02 | | | 2.02 | 2.22 |
| 1160 | 10" deep | G | | | | ↓ | 2.36 | | | 2.36 | 2.60 |
| 4030 | Installation only, 18 ga, 1-5/8" flange x 4" deep | | 2 Carp | 130 | .123 | Ea. | | 3.58 | | 3.58 | 6 |
| 4040 | 6" deep | | | 110 | .145 | | | 4.23 | | 4.23 | 7.10 |
| 4050 | 8" deep | | | 90 | .178 | | | 5.15 | | 5.15 | 8.70 |
| 4140 | 2" flange, 18 ga x 6" deep | | | 110 | .145 | | | 4.23 | | 4.23 | 7.10 |
| 4150 | 8" deep | | | 90 | .178 | | | 5.15 | | 5.15 | 8.70 |
| 4160 | 10" deep | | ↓ | 80 | .200 | | | 5.80 | | 5.80 | 9.80 |
| 6010 | Clips to attach facia to rafter tails, 2" x 2" x 18 ga angle | G | 1 Carp | 120 | .067 | | .81 | 1.94 | | 2.75 | 4.15 |
| 6020 | 16 ga angle | G | " | 100 | .080 | ↓ | 1.01 | 2.33 | | 3.34 | 5.05 |

# 05 44 Cold-Formed Metal Trusses

## 05 44 13 – Cold-Formed Metal Roof Trusses

### 05 44 13.60 Framing, Roof Trusses

| | | | Crew | Daily Output | Labor-Hours | Unit | Material | 2010 Bare Costs Labor | Equipment | Total | Total Incl O&P |
|---|---|---|---|---|---|---|---|---|---|---|---|
| 0010 | **FRAMING, ROOF TRUSSES** | | | | | | | | | | |
| 0015 | Made from recycled materials | G | | | | | | | | | |
| 0020 | Fabrication of trusses on ground, Fink (W) or King Post, to 4:12 pitch | | | | | | | | | | |
| 0120 | 18 ga x 4" chords, 16' span | G | 2 Carp | 12 | 1.333 | Ea. | 56 | 39 | | 95 | 127 |
| 0130 | 20' span | G | | 11 | 1.455 | | 70 | 42.50 | | 112.50 | 148 |
| 0140 | 24' span | G | | 11 | 1.455 | | 84 | 42.50 | | 126.50 | 164 |
| 0150 | 28' span | G | | 10 | 1.600 | | 98 | 46.50 | | 144.50 | 187 |
| 0160 | 32' span | G | | 10 | 1.600 | | 112 | 46.50 | | 158.50 | 202 |
| 0250 | 6" chords, 28' span | G | | 9 | 1.778 | | 123 | 51.50 | | 174.50 | 223 |
| 0260 | 32' span | G | | 9 | 1.778 | | 141 | 51.50 | | 192.50 | 242 |
| 0270 | 36' span | G | | 8 | 2 | | 159 | 58 | | 217 | 273 |
| 0280 | 40' span | G | | 8 | 2 | | 176 | 58 | | 234 | 292 |
| 1120 | 5:12 to 8:12 pitch, 18 ga x 4" chords, 16' span | G | | 10 | 1.600 | | 64 | 46.50 | | 110.50 | 149 |
| 1130 | 20' span | G | | 9 | 1.778 | | 80 | 51.50 | | 131.50 | 175 |
| 1140 | 24' span | G | | 9 | 1.778 | | 96 | 51.50 | | 147.50 | 193 |
| 1150 | 28' span | G | | 8 | 2 | | 112 | 58 | | 170 | 221 |
| 1160 | 32' span | G | | 8 | 2 | | 128 | 58 | | 186 | 239 |
| 1250 | 6" chords, 28' span | G | | 7 | 2.286 | | 141 | 66.50 | | 207.50 | 267 |
| 1260 | 32' span | G | | 7 | 2.286 | | 161 | 66.50 | | 227.50 | 289 |
| 1270 | 36' span | G | | 6 | 2.667 | | 181 | 77.50 | | 258.50 | 330 |
| 1280 | 40' span | G | | 6 | 2.667 | | 202 | 77.50 | | 279.50 | 355 |
| 2120 | 9:12 to 12:12 pitch, 18 ga x 4" chords, 16' span | G | | 8 | 2 | | 80 | 58 | | 138 | 186 |
| 2130 | 20' span | G | | 7 | 2.286 | | 100 | 66.50 | | 166.50 | 222 |
| 2140 | 24' span | G | | 7 | 2.286 | | 120 | 66.50 | | 186.50 | 244 |
| 2150 | 28' span | G | | 6 | 2.667 | | 140 | 77.50 | | 217.50 | 285 |
| 2160 | 32' span | G | | 6 | 2.667 | | 160 | 77.50 | | 237.50 | 305 |
| 2250 | 6" chords, 28' span | G | | 5 | 3.200 | | 176 | 93 | | 269 | 350 |
| 2260 | 32' span | G | | 5 | 3.200 | | 202 | 93 | | 295 | 380 |
| 2270 | 36' span | G | | 4 | 4 | | 227 | 116 | | 343 | 445 |
| 2280 | 40' span | G | | 4 | 4 | | 252 | 116 | | 368 | 475 |

# 05 44 Cold-Formed Metal Trusses

## 05 44 13 – Cold-Formed Metal Roof Trusses

### 05 44 13.60 Framing, Roof Trusses

| | | Crew | Daily Output | Labor-Hours | Unit | Material | 2010 Bare Costs Labor | 2010 Bare Costs Equipment | Total | Total Incl O&P |
|---|---|---|---|---|---|---|---|---|---|---|
| 5120 | Erection only of roof trusses, to 4:12 pitch, 16' span | F-6 | 48 | .833 | Ea. | | 22 | 13.65 | 35.65 | 51.50 |
| 5130 | 20' span | | 46 | .870 | | | 23 | 14.25 | 37.25 | 54 |
| 5140 | 24' span | | 44 | .909 | | | 24 | 14.90 | 38.90 | 56.50 |
| 5150 | 28' span | | 42 | .952 | | | 25 | 15.60 | 40.60 | 59 |
| 5160 | 32' span | | 40 | 1 | | | 26.50 | 16.40 | 42.90 | 62 |
| 5170 | 36' span | | 38 | 1.053 | | | 28 | 17.25 | 45.25 | 65.50 |
| 5180 | 40' span | | 36 | 1.111 | | | 29.50 | 18.20 | 47.70 | 69 |
| 5220 | 5:12 to 8:12 pitch, 16' span | | 42 | .952 | | | 25 | 15.60 | 40.60 | 59 |
| 5230 | 20' span | | 40 | 1 | | | 26.50 | 16.40 | 42.90 | 62 |
| 5240 | 24' span | | 38 | 1.053 | | | 28 | 17.25 | 45.25 | 65.50 |
| 5250 | 28' span | | 36 | 1.111 | | | 29.50 | 18.20 | 47.70 | 69 |
| 5260 | 32' span | | 34 | 1.176 | | | 31 | 19.30 | 50.30 | 73 |
| 5270 | 36' span | | 32 | 1.250 | | | 33 | 20.50 | 53.50 | 77.50 |
| 5280 | 40' span | | 30 | 1.333 | | | 35 | 22 | 57 | 83 |
| 5320 | 9:12 to 12:12 pitch, 16' span | | 36 | 1.111 | | | 29.50 | 18.20 | 47.70 | 69 |
| 5330 | 20' span | | 34 | 1.176 | | | 31 | 19.30 | 50.30 | 73 |
| 5340 | 24' span | | 32 | 1.250 | | | 33 | 20.50 | 53.50 | 77.50 |
| 5350 | 28' span | | 30 | 1.333 | | | 35 | 22 | 57 | 83 |
| 5360 | 32' span | | 28 | 1.429 | | | 37.50 | 23.50 | 61 | 89 |
| 5370 | 36' span | | 26 | 1.538 | | | 40.50 | 25 | 65.50 | 95.50 |
| 5380 | 40' span | | 24 | 1.667 | | | 44 | 27.50 | 71.50 | 104 |

# 05 51 Metal Stairs

## 05 51 13 – Metal Pan Stairs

### 05 51 13.50 Pan Stairs

| | | | Crew | Daily Output | Labor-Hours | Unit | Material | Labor | Equipment | Total | Total Incl O&P |
|---|---|---|---|---|---|---|---|---|---|---|---|
| 0010 | **PAN STAIRS**, shop fabricated, steel stringers | | | | | | | | | | |
| 0015 | Made from recycled materials | G | | | | | | | | | |
| 1700 | Pre-erected, steel pan tread, 3'-6" wide, 2 line pipe rail | G | E-2 | 87 | .552 | Riser | 455 | 17.45 | 18.45 | 490.90 | 555 |
| 1800 | With flat bar picket rail | G | " | 87 | .552 | " | 510 | 17.45 | 18.45 | 545.90 | 615 |

## 05 51 23 – Metal Fire Escapes

### 05 51 23.50 Fire Escape Stairs

| | | | Crew | Daily Output | Labor-Hours | Unit | Material | Labor | Equipment | Total | Total Incl O&P |
|---|---|---|---|---|---|---|---|---|---|---|---|
| 0010 | **FIRE ESCAPE STAIRS**, shop fabricated | | | | | | | | | | |
| 0020 | One story, disappearing, stainless steel | G | 2 Sswk | 20 | .800 | V.L.F. | 212 | 25 | | 237 | 281 |
| 0100 | Portable ladder | | | | | Ea. | 99 | | | 99 | 109 |
| 1100 | Fire escape, galvanized steel, 8'-0" to 10'-4" ceiling | G | 2 Carp | 1 | 16 | | 1,525 | 465 | | 1,990 | 2,450 |
| 1110 | 10'-6" to 13'-6" ceiling | G | " | 1 | 16 | | 2,000 | 465 | | 2,465 | 2,975 |

# 05 52 Metal Railings

## 05 52 13 – Pipe and Tube Railings

### 05 52 13.50 Railings, Pipe

| | | | Crew | Daily Output | Labor-Hours | Unit | Material | Labor | Equipment | Total | Total Incl O&P |
|---|---|---|---|---|---|---|---|---|---|---|---|
| 0010 | **RAILINGS, PIPE**, shop fab'd, 3'-6" high, posts @ 5' O.C. | | | | | | | | | | |
| 0015 | Made from recycled materials | G | | | | | | | | | |
| 0020 | Aluminum, 2 rail, satin finish, 1-1/4" diameter | G | E-4 | 160 | .200 | L.F. | 31.50 | 6.40 | .91 | 38.81 | 47.50 |
| 0030 | Clear anodized | G | | 160 | .200 | | 39 | 6.40 | .91 | 46.31 | 55.50 |
| 0040 | Dark anodized | G | | 160 | .200 | | 44 | 6.40 | .91 | 51.31 | 61 |
| 0080 | 1-1/2" diameter, satin finish | G | | 160 | .200 | | 37.50 | 6.40 | .91 | 44.81 | 54.50 |
| 0090 | Clear anodized | G | | 160 | .200 | | 42 | 6.40 | .91 | 49.31 | 59 |
| 0100 | Dark anodized | G | | 160 | .200 | | 46.50 | 6.40 | .91 | 53.81 | 64 |
| 0140 | Aluminum, 3 rail, 1-1/4" diam., satin finish | G | | 137 | .234 | | 48 | 7.45 | 1.07 | 56.52 | 68.50 |

343

## 05 52 13 – Pipe and Tube Railings

| 05 52 13.50 Railings, Pipe | | Crew | Daily Output | Labor-Hours | Unit | Material | 2010 Bare Costs Labor | Equipment | Total | Total Incl O&P |
|---|---|---|---|---|---|---|---|---|---|---|
| 0150 | Clear anodized | G | E-4 | 137 | .234 | L.F. | 60 | 7.45 | 1.07 | 68.52 | 81.50 |
| 0160 | Dark anodized | G | | 137 | .234 | | 66.50 | 7.45 | 1.07 | 75.02 | 88.50 |
| 0200 | 1-1/2" diameter, satin finish | G | | 137 | .234 | | 57.50 | 7.45 | 1.07 | 66.02 | 79 |
| 0210 | Clear anodized | G | | 137 | .234 | | 65.50 | 7.45 | 1.07 | 74.02 | 87.50 |
| 0220 | Dark anodized | G | | 137 | .234 | | 71.50 | 7.45 | 1.07 | 80.02 | 94.50 |
| 0500 | Steel, 2 rail, on stairs, primed, 1-1/4" diameter | G | | 160 | .200 | | 20.50 | 6.40 | .91 | 27.81 | 35.50 |
| 0520 | 1-1/2" diameter | G | | 160 | .200 | | 22.50 | 6.40 | .91 | 29.81 | 38 |
| 0540 | Galvanized, 1-1/4" diameter | G | | 160 | .200 | | 28.50 | 6.40 | .91 | 35.81 | 44.50 |
| 0560 | 1-1/2" diameter | G | | 160 | .200 | | 32 | 6.40 | .91 | 39.31 | 48 |
| 0580 | Steel, 3 rail, primed, 1-1/4" diameter | G | | 137 | .234 | | 30.50 | 7.45 | 1.07 | 39.02 | 49.50 |
| 0600 | 1-1/2" diameter | G | | 137 | .234 | | 32.50 | 7.45 | 1.07 | 41.02 | 51.50 |
| 0620 | Galvanized, 1-1/4" diameter | G | | 137 | .234 | | 43 | 7.45 | 1.07 | 51.52 | 63 |
| 0640 | 1-1/2" diameter | G | | 137 | .234 | | 50.50 | 7.45 | 1.07 | 59.02 | 71.50 |
| 0700 | Stainless steel, 2 rail, 1-1/4" diam. #4 finish | G | | 137 | .234 | | 90.50 | 7.45 | 1.07 | 99.02 | 115 |
| 0720 | High polish | G | | 137 | .234 | | 146 | 7.45 | 1.07 | 154.52 | 176 |
| 0740 | Mirror polish | G | | 137 | .234 | | 183 | 7.45 | 1.07 | 191.52 | 216 |
| 0760 | Stainless steel, 3 rail, 1-1/2" diam., #4 finish | G | | 120 | .267 | | 137 | 8.50 | 1.22 | 146.72 | 168 |
| 0770 | High polish | G | | 120 | .267 | | 226 | 8.50 | 1.22 | 235.72 | 266 |
| 0780 | Mirror finish | G | | 120 | .267 | | 275 | 8.50 | 1.22 | 284.72 | 320 |
| 0900 | Wall rail, alum. pipe, 1-1/4" diam., satin finish | G | | 213 | .150 | | 17.95 | 4.79 | .69 | 23.43 | 29.50 |
| 0905 | Clear anodized | G | | 213 | .150 | | 22 | 4.79 | .69 | 27.48 | 34 |
| 0910 | Dark anodized | G | | 213 | .150 | | 26.50 | 4.79 | .69 | 31.98 | 39 |
| 0915 | 1-1/2" diameter, satin finish | G | | 213 | .150 | | 19.85 | 4.79 | .69 | 25.33 | 32 |
| 0920 | Clear anodized | G | | 213 | .150 | | 25 | 4.79 | .69 | 30.48 | 37.50 |
| 0925 | Dark anodized | G | | 213 | .150 | | 31 | 4.79 | .69 | 36.48 | 44 |
| 0930 | Steel pipe, 1-1/4" diameter, primed | G | | 213 | .150 | | 12.45 | 4.79 | .69 | 17.93 | 23.50 |
| 0935 | Galvanized | G | | 213 | .150 | | 18.05 | 4.79 | .69 | 23.53 | 30 |
| 0940 | 1-1/2" diameter | G | | 176 | .182 | | 12.85 | 5.80 | .83 | 19.48 | 26 |
| 0945 | Galvanized | G | | 213 | .150 | | 18.15 | 4.79 | .69 | 23.63 | 30 |
| 0955 | Stainless steel pipe, 1-1/2" diam., #4 finish | G | | 107 | .299 | | 72.50 | 9.55 | 1.36 | 83.41 | 99 |
| 0960 | High polish | G | | 107 | .299 | | 148 | 9.55 | 1.36 | 158.91 | 182 |
| 0965 | Mirror polish | G | ▼ | 107 | .299 | ▼ | 174 | 9.55 | 1.36 | 184.91 | 211 |
| 2000 | Aluminum pipe & picket railing, double top rail, pickets @ 4-1/2" OC | | | | | | | | | | |
| 2010 | 36" high, straight & level | G | 2 Sswk | 80 | .200 | L.F. | 81 | 6.30 | | 87.30 | 101 |
| 2020 | Curved & level | G | | 60 | .267 | | 111 | 8.35 | | 119.35 | 138 |
| 2030 | Straight & sloped | G | ▼ | 40 | .400 | ▼ | 93 | 12.55 | | 105.55 | 126 |

# 05 58 Formed Metal Fabrications

## 05 58 25 – Formed Lamp Posts

| 05 58 25.40 Lamp Posts | | Crew | Daily Output | Labor-Hours | Unit | Material | 2010 Bare Costs Labor | Equipment | Total | Total Incl O&P |
|---|---|---|---|---|---|---|---|---|---|---|
| 0010 | **LAMP POSTS** | | | | | | | | | | |
| 0020 | Aluminum, 7' high, stock units, post only | G | 1 Carp | 16 | .500 | Ea. | 31.50 | 14.55 | | 46.05 | 59 |
| 0100 | Mild steel, plain | G | " | 16 | .500 | " | 28 | 14.55 | | 42.55 | 55.50 |

| 05 71 13.50 Spiral Stairs | | Crew | Daily Output | Labor-Hours | Unit | Material | 2010 Bare Costs Labor | Equipment | Total | Total Incl O&P |
|---|---|---|---|---|---|---|---|---|---|---|
| 0010 | **SPIRAL STAIRS**, shop fabricated | | | | | | | | | |
| 1810 | Spiral aluminum, 5'-0" diameter, stock units | G | E-4 | 45 | .711 | Riser | 500 | 22.50 | 3.24 | 525.74 | 595 |
| 1820 | Custom units | G | | 45 | .711 | | 945 | 22.50 | 3.24 | 970.74 | 1,100 |
| 1900 | Spiral, cast iron, 4'-0" diameter, ornamental, minimum | G | | 45 | .711 | | 445 | 22.50 | 3.24 | 470.74 | 535 |
| 1920 | Maximum | G | | 25 | 1.280 | | 605 | 41 | 5.85 | 651.85 | 755 |

# Division Notes

| | CREW | DAILY OUTPUT | LABOR-HOURS | UNIT | 2010 BARE COSTS | | | | TOTAL INCL O&P |
|---|---|---|---|---|---|---|---|---|---|
| | | | | | MAT. | LABOR | EQUIP. | TOTAL | |
| | | | | | | | | | |
| | | | | | | | | | |
| | | | | | | | | | |
| | | | | | | | | | |
| | | | | | | | | | |
| | | | | | | | | | |
| | | | | | | | | | |
| | | | | | | | | | |
| | | | | | | | | | |
| | | | | | | | | | |
| | | | | | | | | | |
| | | | | | | | | | |
| | | | | | | | | | |
| | | | | | | | | | |
| | | | | | | | | | |
| | | | | | | | | | |
| | | | | | | | | | |
| | | | | | | | | | |
| | | | | | | | | | |
| | | | | | | | | | |

# Estimating Tips

## 06 05 00 Common Work Results for Wood, Plastics, and Composites

• Common to any wood-framed structure are the accessory connector items such as screws, nails, adhesives, hangers, connector plates, straps, angles, and hold-downs. For typical wood-framed buildings, such as residential projects, the aggregate total for these items can be significant, especially in areas where seismic loading is a concern. For floor and wall framing, the material cost is based on 10 to 25 lbs. per MBF. Hold-downs, hangers, and other connectors should be taken off by the piece.

## 06 10 00 Carpentry

• Lumber is a traded commodity and therefore sensitive to supply and demand in the marketplace. Even in "budgetary" estimating of wood-framed projects, it is advisable to call local suppliers for the latest market pricing.

• Common quantity units for wood-framed projects are "thousand board feet" (MBF). A board foot is a volume of wood, 1" x 1' x 1', or 144 cubic inches. Board-foot quantities are generally calculated using nominal material dimensions—dressed sizes are ignored. Board foot per lineal foot of any stick of lumber can be calculated by dividing the nominal cross-sectional area by 12. As an example, 2,000 lineal feet of 2 x 12 equates to 4 MBF by dividing the nominal area, 2 x 12, by 12, which equals 2, and multiplying by 2,000 to give 4,000 board feet. This simple rule applies to all nominal dimensioned lumber.

• Waste is an issue of concern at the quantity takeoff for any area of construction. Framing lumber is sold in even foot lengths, i.e., 10', 12', 14', 16', and depending on spans, wall heights, and the grade of lumber, waste is inevitable. A rule of thumb for lumber waste is 5%–10% depending on material quality and the complexity of the framing.

• Wood in various forms and shapes is used in many projects, even where the main structural framing is steel, concrete, or masonry. Plywood as a back-up partition material and 2x boards used as blocking and cant strips around roof edges are two common examples. The estimator should ensure that the costs of all wood materials are included in the final estimate.

## 06 20 00 Finish Carpentry

• It is necessary to consider the grade of workmanship when estimating labor costs for erecting millwork and interior finish. In practice, there are three grades: premium, custom, and economy. The RSMeans daily output for base and case moldings is in the range of 200 to 250 L.F. per carpenter per day. This is appropriate for most average custom-grade projects. For premium projects, an adjustment to productivity of 25%–50% should be made, depending on the complexity of the job.

## Reference Numbers

Reference numbers are shown in shaded boxes at the beginning of some major classifications. These numbers refer to related items in the Reference Section. The reference information may be an estimating procedure, an alternate pricing method, or technical information.

*Note:* Not all subdivisions listed here necessarily appear in this publication.

## 06 05 05 – Selective Wood and Plastics Demolition

| 06 05 05.10 Selective Demolition Wood Framing | Crew | Daily Output | Labor-Hours | Unit | Material | 2010 Bare Costs Labor | Equipment | Total | Total Incl O&P |
|---|---|---|---|---|---|---|---|---|---|
| 0010 **SELECTIVE DEMOLITION WOOD FRAMING** R024119-10 | | | | | | | | | |
| 0100 Timber connector, nailed, small | 1 Clab | 96 | .083 | Ea. | | 1.79 | | 1.79 | 3.01 |
| 0110 Medium | | 60 | .133 | | | 2.87 | | 2.87 | 4.82 |
| 0120 Large | | 48 | .167 | | | 3.58 | | 3.58 | 6.05 |
| 0130 Bolted, small | | 48 | .167 | | | 3.58 | | 3.58 | 6.05 |
| 0140 Medium | | 32 | .250 | | | 5.40 | | 5.40 | 9.05 |
| 0150 Large | | 24 | .333 | | | 7.15 | | 7.15 | 12.05 |
| 2958 Beams, 2" x 6" | 2 Clab | 1100 | .015 | L.F. | | .31 | | .31 | .53 |
| 2960 2" x 8" | | 825 | .019 | | | .42 | | .42 | .70 |
| 2965 2" x 10" | | 665 | .024 | | | .52 | | .52 | .87 |
| 2970 2" x 12" | | 550 | .029 | | | .63 | | .63 | 1.05 |
| 2972 2" x 14" | | 470 | .034 | | | .73 | | .73 | 1.23 |
| 2975 4" x 8" | B-1 | 413 | .058 | | | 1.29 | | 1.29 | 2.17 |
| 2980 4" x 10" | | 330 | .073 | | | 1.61 | | 1.61 | 2.71 |
| 2985 4" x 12" | | 275 | .087 | | | 1.93 | | 1.93 | 3.25 |
| 3000 6" x 8" | | 275 | .087 | | | 1.93 | | 1.93 | 3.25 |
| 3040 6" x 10" | | 220 | .109 | | | 2.42 | | 2.42 | 4.07 |
| 3080 6" x 12" | | 185 | .130 | | | 2.88 | | 2.88 | 4.84 |
| 3120 8" x 12" | | 140 | .171 | | | 3.80 | | 3.80 | 6.40 |
| 3160 10" x 12" | | 110 | .218 | | | 4.84 | | 4.84 | 8.15 |
| 3162 Alternate pricing method | | 1.10 | 21.818 | M.B.F. | | 485 | | 485 | 815 |
| 3170 Blocking, in 16" OC wall framing, 2" x 4" | 1 Clab | 600 | .013 | L.F. | | .29 | | .29 | .48 |
| 3172 2" x 6" | | 400 | .020 | | | .43 | | .43 | .72 |
| 3174 In 24" OC wall framing, 2" x 4" | | 600 | .013 | | | .29 | | .29 | .48 |
| 3176 2" x 6" | | 400 | .020 | | | .43 | | .43 | .72 |
| 3178 Alt method, wood blocking removal from wood framing | | .40 | 20 | M.B.F. | | 430 | | 430 | 725 |
| 3179 Wood blocking removal from steel framing | | .36 | 22.222 | " | | 480 | | 480 | 805 |
| 3180 Bracing, let in, 1" x 3", studs 16" OC | | 1050 | .008 | L.F. | | .16 | | .16 | .28 |
| 3181 Studs 24" OC | | 1080 | .007 | | | .16 | | .16 | .27 |
| 3182 1" x 4", studs 16" OC | | 1050 | .008 | | | .16 | | .16 | .28 |
| 3183 Studs 24" OC | | 1080 | .007 | | | .16 | | .16 | .27 |
| 3184 1" x 6", studs 16" OC | | 1050 | .008 | | | .16 | | .16 | .28 |
| 3185 Studs 24" OC | | 1080 | .007 | | | .16 | | .16 | .27 |
| 3186 2" x 3", studs 16" OC | | 800 | .010 | | | .22 | | .22 | .36 |
| 3187 Studs 24" OC | | 830 | .010 | | | .21 | | .21 | .35 |
| 3188 2" x 4", studs 16" OC | | 800 | .010 | | | .22 | | .22 | .36 |
| 3189 Studs 24" OC | | 830 | .010 | | | .21 | | .21 | .35 |
| 3190 2" x 6", studs 16" OC | | 800 | .010 | | | .22 | | .22 | .36 |
| 3191 Studs 24" OC | | 830 | .010 | | | .21 | | .21 | .35 |
| 3192 2" x 8", studs 16" OC | | 800 | .010 | | | .22 | | .22 | .36 |
| 3193 Studs 24" OC | | 830 | .010 | | | .21 | | .21 | .35 |
| 3194 "T" shaped metal bracing, studs at 16" OC | | 1060 | .008 | | | .16 | | .16 | .27 |
| 3195 Studs at 24" OC | | 1200 | .007 | | | .14 | | .14 | .24 |
| 3196 Metal straps, studs at 16" OC | | 1200 | .007 | | | .14 | | .14 | .24 |
| 3197 Studs at 24" OC | | 1240 | .006 | | | .14 | | .14 | .23 |
| 3200 Columns, round, 8' to 14' tall | | 40 | .200 | Ea. | | 4.30 | | 4.30 | 7.25 |
| 3202 Dimensional lumber sizes | 2 Clab | 1.10 | 14.545 | M.B.F. | | 315 | | 315 | 525 |
| 3250 Blocking, between joists | 1 Clab | 320 | .025 | Ea. | | .54 | | .54 | .90 |
| 3252 Bridging, metal strap, between joists | | 320 | .025 | Pr. | | .54 | | .54 | .90 |
| 3254 Wood, between joists | | 320 | .025 | " | | .54 | | .54 | .90 |
| 3260 Door buck, studs, header & access., 8' high 2" x 4" wall, 3' wide | | 32 | .250 | Ea. | | 5.40 | | 5.40 | 9.05 |
| 3261 4' wide | | 32 | .250 | | | 5.40 | | 5.40 | 9.05 |
| 3262 5' wide | | 32 | .250 | | | 5.40 | | 5.40 | 9.05 |

## 06 05 05 – Selective Wood and Plastics Demolition

| 06 05 05.10 Selective Demolition Wood Framing | Crew | Daily Output | Labor-Hours | Unit | Material | 2010 Bare Costs Labor | Equipment | Total | Total Incl O&P |
|---|---|---|---|---|---|---|---|---|---|
| 3263 | 6' wide | 1 Clab | 32 | .250 | Ea. | | 5.40 | | 5.40 | 9.05 |
| 3264 | 8' wide | | 30 | .267 | | | 5.75 | | 5.75 | 9.65 |
| 3265 | 10' wide | | 30 | .267 | | | 5.75 | | 5.75 | 9.65 |
| 3266 | 12' wide | | 30 | .267 | | | 5.75 | | 5.75 | 9.65 |
| 3267 | 2" x 6" wall, 3' wide | | 32 | .250 | | | 5.40 | | 5.40 | 9.05 |
| 3268 | 4' wide | | 32 | .250 | | | 5.40 | | 5.40 | 9.05 |
| 3269 | 5' wide | | 32 | .250 | | | 5.40 | | 5.40 | 9.05 |
| 3270 | 6' wide | | 32 | .250 | | | 5.40 | | 5.40 | 9.05 |
| 3271 | 8' wide | | 30 | .267 | | | 5.75 | | 5.75 | 9.65 |
| 3272 | 10' wide | | 30 | .267 | | | 5.75 | | 5.75 | 9.65 |
| 3273 | 12' wide | | 30 | .267 | | | 5.75 | | 5.75 | 9.65 |
| 3274 | Window buck, studs, header & access, 8' high 2" x 4" wall, 2' wide | | 24 | .333 | | | 7.15 | | 7.15 | 12.05 |
| 3275 | 3' wide | | 24 | .333 | | | 7.15 | | 7.15 | 12.05 |
| 3276 | 4' wide | | 24 | .333 | | | 7.15 | | 7.15 | 12.05 |
| 3277 | 5' wide | | 24 | .333 | | | 7.15 | | 7.15 | 12.05 |
| 3278 | 6' wide | | 24 | .333 | | | 7.15 | | 7.15 | 12.05 |
| 3279 | 7' wide | | 24 | .333 | | | 7.15 | | 7.15 | 12.05 |
| 3280 | 8' wide | | 22 | .364 | | | 7.80 | | 7.80 | 13.15 |
| 3281 | 10' wide | | 22 | .364 | | | 7.80 | | 7.80 | 13.15 |
| 3282 | 12' wide | | 22 | .364 | | | 7.80 | | 7.80 | 13.15 |
| 3283 | 2" x 6" wall, 2' wide | | 24 | .333 | | | 7.15 | | 7.15 | 12.05 |
| 3284 | 3' wide | | 24 | .333 | | | 7.15 | | 7.15 | 12.05 |
| 3285 | 4' wide | | 24 | .333 | | | 7.15 | | 7.15 | 12.05 |
| 3286 | 5' wide | | 24 | .333 | | | 7.15 | | 7.15 | 12.05 |
| 3287 | 6' wide | | 24 | .333 | | | 7.15 | | 7.15 | 12.05 |
| 3288 | 7' wide | | 24 | .333 | | | 7.15 | | 7.15 | 12.05 |
| 3289 | 8' wide | | 22 | .364 | | | 7.80 | | 7.80 | 13.15 |
| 3290 | 10' wide | | 22 | .364 | | | 7.80 | | 7.80 | 13.15 |
| 3291 | 12' wide | | 22 | .364 | | | 7.80 | | 7.80 | 13.15 |
| 3400 | Fascia boards, 1" x 6" | | 500 | .016 | L.F. | | .34 | | .34 | .58 |
| 3440 | 1" x 8" | | 450 | .018 | | | .38 | | .38 | .64 |
| 3480 | 1" x 10" | | 400 | .020 | | | .43 | | .43 | .72 |
| 3490 | 2" x 6" | | 450 | .018 | | | .38 | | .38 | .64 |
| 3500 | 2" x 8" | | 400 | .020 | | | .43 | | .43 | .72 |
| 3510 | 2" x 10" | | 350 | .023 | | | .49 | | .49 | .83 |
| 3610 | Furring, on wood walls or ceiling | | 4000 | .002 | S.F. | | .04 | | .04 | .07 |
| 3620 | On masonry or concrete walls or ceiling | | 1200 | .007 | " | | .14 | | .14 | .24 |
| 3800 | Headers over openings, 2 @ 2" x 6" | | 110 | .073 | L.F. | | 1.56 | | 1.56 | 2.63 |
| 3840 | 2 @ 2" x 8" | | 100 | .080 | | | 1.72 | | 1.72 | 2.89 |
| 3880 | 2 @ 2" x 10" | | 90 | .089 | | | 1.91 | | 1.91 | 3.21 |
| 3885 | Alternate pricing method | | .26 | 30.651 | M.B.F. | | 660 | | 660 | 1,100 |
| 3920 | Joists, 1" x 4" | | 1250 | .006 | L.F. | | .14 | | .14 | .23 |
| 3930 | 1" x 6" | | 1135 | .007 | | | .15 | | .15 | .25 |
| 3950 | 1" x 10" | | 895 | .009 | | | .19 | | .19 | .32 |
| 3960 | 1" x 12" | | 765 | .010 | | | .22 | | .22 | .38 |
| 4200 | 2" x 4" | 2 Clab | 1000 | .016 | | | .34 | | .34 | .58 |
| 4230 | 2" x 6" | | 970 | .016 | | | .35 | | .35 | .60 |
| 4240 | 2" x 8" | | 940 | .017 | | | .37 | | .37 | .62 |
| 4250 | 2" x 10" | | 910 | .018 | | | .38 | | .38 | .64 |
| 4280 | 2" x 12" | | 880 | .018 | | | .39 | | .39 | .66 |
| 4281 | 2" x 14" | | 850 | .019 | | | .40 | | .40 | .68 |
| 4282 | Composite joists, 9-1/2" | | 960 | .017 | | | .36 | | .36 | .60 |
| 4283 | 11-7/8" | | 930 | .017 | | | .37 | | .37 | .62 |

## 06 05 05 – Selective Wood and Plastics Demolition

| 06 05 05.10 Selective Demolition Wood Framing | Crew | Daily Output | Labor-Hours | Unit | Material | 2010 Bare Costs Labor | Equipment | Total | Total Incl O&P |
|---|---|---|---|---|---|---|---|---|---|
| 4284 | 14" | 2 Clab | 897 | .018 | L.F. | | .38 | | .38 | .64 |
| 4285 | 16" | | 865 | .019 | | | .40 | | .40 | .67 |
| 4290 | Wood joists, alternate pricing method | | 1.50 | 10.667 | M.B.F. | | 229 | | 229 | 385 |
| 4500 | Open web joist, 12" deep | | 500 | .032 | L.F. | | .69 | | .69 | 1.16 |
| 4505 | 14" deep | | 475 | .034 | | | .72 | | .72 | 1.22 |
| 4510 | 16" deep | | 450 | .036 | | | .76 | | .76 | 1.29 |
| 4520 | 18" deep | | 425 | .038 | | | .81 | | .81 | 1.36 |
| 4530 | 24" deep | | 400 | .040 | | | .86 | | .86 | 1.45 |
| 4550 | Ledger strips, 1" x 2" | 1 Clab | 1200 | .007 | | | .14 | | .14 | .24 |
| 4560 | 1" x 3" | | 1200 | .007 | | | .14 | | .14 | .24 |
| 4570 | 1" x 4" | | 1200 | .007 | | | .14 | | .14 | .24 |
| 4580 | 2" x 2" | | 1100 | .007 | | | .16 | | .16 | .26 |
| 4590 | 2" x 4" | | 1000 | .008 | | | .17 | | .17 | .29 |
| 4600 | 2" x 6" | | 1000 | .008 | | | .17 | | .17 | .29 |
| 4601 | 2" x 8" or 2" x 10" | | 800 | .010 | | | .22 | | .22 | .36 |
| 4602 | 4" x 6" | | 600 | .013 | | | .29 | | .29 | .48 |
| 4604 | 4" x 8" | | 450 | .018 | | | .38 | | .38 | .64 |
| 5400 | Posts, 4" x 4" | 2 Clab | 800 | .020 | | | .43 | | .43 | .72 |
| 5405 | 4" x 6" | | 550 | .029 | | | .63 | | .63 | 1.05 |
| 5410 | 4" x 8" | | 440 | .036 | | | .78 | | .78 | 1.31 |
| 5425 | 4" x 10" | | 390 | .041 | | | .88 | | .88 | 1.48 |
| 5430 | 4" x 12" | | 350 | .046 | | | .98 | | .98 | 1.65 |
| 5440 | 6" x 6" | | 400 | .040 | | | .86 | | .86 | 1.45 |
| 5445 | 6" x 8" | | 350 | .046 | | | .98 | | .98 | 1.65 |
| 5450 | 6" x 10" | | 320 | .050 | | | 1.08 | | 1.08 | 1.81 |
| 5455 | 6" x 12" | | 290 | .055 | | | 1.19 | | 1.19 | 1.99 |
| 5480 | 8" x 8" | | 300 | .053 | | | 1.15 | | 1.15 | 1.93 |
| 5500 | 10" x 10" | | 240 | .067 | | | 1.43 | | 1.43 | 2.41 |
| 5660 | Tongue and groove floor planks | | 2 | 8 | M.B.F. | | 172 | | 172 | 289 |
| 5750 | Rafters, ordinary, 16" OC, 2" x 4" | | 880 | .018 | S.F. | | .39 | | .39 | .66 |
| 5755 | 2" x 6" | | 840 | .019 | | | .41 | | .41 | .69 |
| 5760 | 2" x 8" | | 820 | .020 | | | .42 | | .42 | .71 |
| 5770 | 2" x 10" | | 820 | .020 | | | .42 | | .42 | .71 |
| 5780 | 2" x 12" | | 810 | .020 | | | .42 | | .42 | .71 |
| 5785 | 24" OC, 2" x 4" | | 1170 | .014 | | | .29 | | .29 | .49 |
| 5786 | 2" x 6" | | 1117 | .014 | | | .31 | | .31 | .52 |
| 5787 | 2" x 8" | | 1091 | .015 | | | .32 | | .32 | .53 |
| 5788 | 2" x 10" | | 1091 | .015 | | | .32 | | .32 | .53 |
| 5789 | 2" x 12" | | 1077 | .015 | | | .32 | | .32 | .54 |
| 5795 | Rafters, ordinary, 2" x 4" (alternate method) | | 862 | .019 | L.F. | | .40 | | .40 | .67 |
| 5800 | 2" x 6" (alternate method) | | 850 | .019 | | | .40 | | .40 | .68 |
| 5840 | 2" x 8" (alternate method) | | 837 | .019 | | | .41 | | .41 | .69 |
| 5855 | 2" x 10" (alternate method) | | 825 | .019 | | | .42 | | .42 | .70 |
| 5865 | 2" x 12" (alternate method) | | 812 | .020 | | | .42 | | .42 | .71 |
| 5870 | Sill plate, 2" x 4" | 1 Clab | 1170 | .007 | | | .15 | | .15 | .25 |
| 5871 | 2" x 6" | | 780 | .010 | | | .22 | | .22 | .37 |
| 5872 | 2" x 8" | | 586 | .014 | | | .29 | | .29 | .49 |
| 5873 | Alternate pricing method | | .78 | 10.256 | M.B.F. | | 221 | | 221 | 370 |
| 5885 | Ridge board, 1" x 4" | 2 Clab | 900 | .018 | L.F. | | .38 | | .38 | .64 |
| 5886 | 1" x 6" | | 875 | .018 | | | .39 | | .39 | .66 |
| 5887 | 1" x 8" | | 850 | .019 | | | .40 | | .40 | .68 |
| 5888 | 1" x 10" | | 825 | .019 | | | .42 | | .42 | .70 |
| 5889 | 1" x 12" | | 800 | .020 | | | .43 | | .43 | .72 |

| 06 05 05.10 Selective Demolition Wood Framing | Crew | Daily Output | Labor-Hours | Unit | Material | 2010 Bare Costs Labor | Equipment | Total | Total Incl O&P |
|---|---|---|---|---|---|---|---|---|---|
| 5890 | 2" x 4" | 2 Clab | 900 | .018 | L.F. | | .38 | | .38 | .64 |
| 5892 | 2" x 6" | | 875 | .018 | | | .39 | | .39 | .66 |
| 5894 | 2" x 8" | | 850 | .019 | | | .40 | | .40 | .68 |
| 5896 | 2" x 10" | | 825 | .019 | | | .42 | | .42 | .70 |
| 5898 | 2" x 12" | | 800 | .020 | | | .43 | | .43 | .72 |
| 6050 | Rafter tie, 1" x 4" | | 1250 | .013 | | | .28 | | .28 | .46 |
| 6052 | 1" x 6" | | 1135 | .014 | | | .30 | | .30 | .51 |
| 6054 | 2" x 4" | | 1000 | .016 | | | .34 | | .34 | .58 |
| 6056 | 2" x 6" | | 970 | .016 | | | .35 | | .35 | .60 |
| 6070 | Sleepers, on concrete, 1" x 2" | 1 Clab | 4700 | .002 | | | .04 | | .04 | .06 |
| 6075 | 1" x 3" | | 4000 | .002 | | | .04 | | .04 | .07 |
| 6080 | 2" x 4" | | 3000 | .003 | | | .06 | | .06 | .10 |
| 6085 | 2" x 6" | | 2600 | .003 | | | .07 | | .07 | .11 |
| 6086 | Sheathing from roof, 5/16" | 2 Clab | 1600 | .010 | S.F. | | .22 | | .22 | .36 |
| 6088 | 3/8" | | 1525 | .010 | | | .23 | | .23 | .38 |
| 6090 | 1/2" | | 1400 | .011 | | | .25 | | .25 | .41 |
| 6092 | 5/8" | | 1300 | .012 | | | .26 | | .26 | .45 |
| 6094 | 3/4" | | 1200 | .013 | | | .29 | | .29 | .48 |
| 6096 | Board sheathing from roof | | 1400 | .011 | | | .25 | | .25 | .41 |
| 6100 | Sheathing, from walls, 1/4" | | 1200 | .013 | | | .29 | | .29 | .48 |
| 6110 | 5/16" | | 1175 | .014 | | | .29 | | .29 | .49 |
| 6120 | 3/8" | | 1150 | .014 | | | .30 | | .30 | .50 |
| 6130 | 1/2" | | 1125 | .014 | | | .31 | | .31 | .51 |
| 6140 | 5/8" | | 1100 | .015 | | | .31 | | .31 | .53 |
| 6150 | 3/4" | | 1075 | .015 | | | .32 | | .32 | .54 |
| 6152 | Board sheathing from walls | | 1500 | .011 | | | .23 | | .23 | .39 |
| 6158 | Subfloor, with boards | | 1050 | .015 | | | .33 | | .33 | .55 |
| 6160 | Plywood, 1/2" thick | | 768 | .021 | | | .45 | | .45 | .75 |
| 6162 | 5/8" thick | | 760 | .021 | | | .45 | | .45 | .76 |
| 6164 | 3/4" thick | | 750 | .021 | | | .46 | | .46 | .77 |
| 6165 | 1-1/8" thick | | 720 | .022 | | | .48 | | .48 | .80 |
| 6166 | Underlayment, particle board, 3/8" thick | 1 Clab | 780 | .010 | | | .22 | | .22 | .37 |
| 6168 | 1/2" thick | | 768 | .010 | | | .22 | | .22 | .38 |
| 6170 | 5/8" thick | | 760 | .011 | | | .23 | | .23 | .38 |
| 6172 | 3/4" thick | | 750 | .011 | | | .23 | | .23 | .39 |
| 6200 | Stairs and stringers, minimum | 2 Clab | 40 | .400 | Riser | | 8.60 | | 8.60 | 14.45 |
| 6240 | Maximum | " | 26 | .615 | " | | 13.25 | | 13.25 | 22.50 |
| 6300 | Components, tread | 1 Clab | 110 | .073 | Ea. | | 1.56 | | 1.56 | 2.63 |
| 6320 | Riser | | 80 | .100 | " | | 2.15 | | 2.15 | 3.62 |
| 6390 | Stringer, 2" x 10" | | 260 | .031 | L.F. | | .66 | | .66 | 1.11 |
| 6400 | 2" x 12" | | 260 | .031 | | | .66 | | .66 | 1.11 |
| 6410 | 3" x 10" | | 250 | .032 | | | .69 | | .69 | 1.16 |
| 6420 | 3" x 12" | | 250 | .032 | | | .69 | | .69 | 1.16 |
| 6590 | Wood studs, 2" x 3" | 2 Clab | 3076 | .005 | | | .11 | | .11 | .19 |
| 6600 | 2" x 4" | | 2000 | .008 | | | .17 | | .17 | .29 |
| 6640 | 2" x 6" | | 1600 | .010 | | | .22 | | .22 | .36 |
| 6720 | Wall framing, including studs, plates and blocking, 2" x 4" | 1 Clab | 600 | .013 | S.F. | | .29 | | .29 | .48 |
| 6740 | 2" x 6" | | 480 | .017 | " | | .36 | | .36 | .60 |
| 6750 | Headers, 2" x 4" | | 1125 | .007 | L.F. | | .15 | | .15 | .26 |
| 6755 | 2" x 6" | | 1125 | .007 | | | .15 | | .15 | .26 |
| 6760 | 2" x 8" | | 1050 | .008 | | | .16 | | .16 | .28 |
| 6765 | 2" x 10" | | 1050 | .008 | | | .16 | | .16 | .28 |
| 6770 | 2" x 12" | | 1000 | .008 | | | .17 | | .17 | .29 |

## 06 05 05 – Selective Wood and Plastics Demolition

### 06 05 05.10 Selective Demolition Wood Framing

| | | Crew | Daily Output | Labor-Hours | Unit | Material | 2010 Bare Costs Labor | Equipment | Total | Total Incl O&P |
|---|---|---|---|---|---|---|---|---|---|---|
| 6780 | 4" x 10" | 1 Clab | 525 | .015 | L.F. | | .33 | | .33 | .55 |
| 6785 | 4" x 12" | | 500 | .016 | | | .34 | | .34 | .58 |
| 6790 | 6" x 8" | | 560 | .014 | | | .31 | | .31 | .52 |
| 6795 | 6" x 10" | | 525 | .015 | | | .33 | | .33 | .55 |
| 6797 | 6" x 12" | | 500 | .016 | | | .34 | | .34 | .58 |
| 7000 | Trusses | | | | | | | | | |
| 7050 | 12' span | 2 Clab | 74 | .216 | Ea. | | 4.65 | | 4.65 | 7.80 |
| 7150 | 24' span | F-3 | 66 | .606 | | | 16.05 | 9.95 | 26 | 38 |
| 7200 | 26' span | | 64 | .625 | | | 16.55 | 10.25 | 26.80 | 39 |
| 7250 | 28' span | | 62 | .645 | | | 17.10 | 10.55 | 27.65 | 40 |
| 7300 | 30' span | | 58 | .690 | | | 18.25 | 11.30 | 29.55 | 43 |
| 7350 | 32' span | | 56 | .714 | | | 18.90 | 11.70 | 30.60 | 44.50 |
| 7400 | 34' span | | 54 | .741 | | | 19.60 | 12.15 | 31.75 | 46 |
| 7450 | 36' span | | 52 | .769 | | | 20.50 | 12.60 | 33.10 | 48 |
| 8000 | Soffit, T & G wood | 1 Clab | 520 | .015 | S.F. | | .33 | | .33 | .56 |
| 8010 | Hardboard, vinyl or aluminum | " | 640 | .013 | | | .27 | | .27 | .45 |
| 8030 | Plywood | 2 Carp | 315 | .051 | | | 1.48 | | 1.48 | 2.49 |

### 06 05 05.20 Selective Demolition Millwork and Trim

| | | Crew | Daily Output | Labor-Hours | Unit | Material | 2010 Bare Costs Labor | Equipment | Total | Total Incl O&P |
|---|---|---|---|---|---|---|---|---|---|---|
| 0010 | **SELECTIVE DEMOLITION MILLWORK AND TRIM**  R024119-10 | | | | | | | | | |
| 1000 | Cabinets, wood, base cabinets, per L.F. | 2 Clab | 80 | .200 | L.F. | | 4.30 | | 4.30 | 7.25 |
| 1020 | Wall cabinets, per L.F. | | 80 | .200 | | | 4.30 | | 4.30 | 7.25 |
| 1100 | Steel, painted, base cabinets | | 60 | .267 | | | 5.75 | | 5.75 | 9.65 |
| 1500 | Counter top, minimum | | 200 | .080 | | | 1.72 | | 1.72 | 2.89 |
| 1510 | Maximum | | 120 | .133 | | | 2.87 | | 2.87 | 4.82 |
| 2000 | Paneling, 4' x 8' sheets | | 2000 | .008 | S.F. | | .17 | | .17 | .29 |
| 2100 | Boards, 1" x 4" | | 700 | .023 | | | .49 | | .49 | .83 |
| 2120 | 1" x 6" | | 750 | .021 | | | .46 | | .46 | .77 |
| 2140 | 1" x 8" | | 800 | .020 | | | .43 | | .43 | .72 |
| 3000 | Trim, baseboard, to 6" wide | | 1200 | .013 | L.F. | | .29 | | .29 | .48 |
| 3040 | Greater than 6" and up to 12" wide | | 1000 | .016 | | | .34 | | .34 | .58 |
| 3100 | Ceiling trim | | 1000 | .016 | | | .34 | | .34 | .58 |
| 3120 | Chair rail | | 1200 | .013 | | | .29 | | .29 | .48 |
| 3140 | Railings with balusters | | 240 | .067 | | | 1.43 | | 1.43 | 2.41 |
| 3160 | Wainscoting | | 700 | .023 | S.F. | | .49 | | .49 | .83 |
| 4000 | Curtain rod | 1 Clab | 80 | .100 | L.F. | | 2.15 | | 2.15 | 3.62 |
| 9000 | Minimum labor/equipment charge | " | 4 | 2 | Job | | 43 | | 43 | 72.50 |

## 06 05 23 – Wood, Plastic, and Composite Fastenings

### 06 05 23.10 Nails

| | | Crew | Daily Output | Labor-Hours | Unit | Material | 2010 Bare Costs Labor | Equipment | Total | Total Incl O&P |
|---|---|---|---|---|---|---|---|---|---|---|
| 0010 | **NAILS**, material only, based upon 50# box purchase | | | | | | | | | |
| 0020 | Copper nails, plain | | | | Lb. | 10 | | | 10 | 11 |
| 0400 | Stainless steel, plain | | | | | 7.55 | | | 7.55 | 8.30 |
| 0500 | Box, 3d to 20d, bright | | | | | 1.26 | | | 1.26 | 1.39 |
| 0520 | Galvanized | | | | | 1.77 | | | 1.77 | 1.95 |
| 0600 | Common, 3d to 60d, plain | | | | | 1.30 | | | 1.30 | 1.43 |
| 0700 | Galvanized | | | | | 1.56 | | | 1.56 | 1.72 |
| 0800 | Aluminum | | | | | 4.55 | | | 4.55 | 5 |
| 1000 | Annular or spiral thread, 4d to 60d, plain | | | | | 1.80 | | | 1.80 | 1.98 |
| 1200 | Galvanized | | | | | 3 | | | 3 | 3.30 |
| 1400 | Drywall nails, plain | | | | | .85 | | | .85 | .94 |
| 1600 | Galvanized | | | | | 1.75 | | | 1.75 | 1.93 |
| 1800 | Finish nails, 4d to 10d, plain | | | | | 1.40 | | | 1.40 | 1.54 |
| 2000 | Galvanized | | | | | 1.79 | | | 1.79 | 1.97 |

# 06 05 Common Work Results for Wood, Plastics, and Composites

## 06 05 23 – Wood, Plastic, and Composite Fastenings

### 06 05 23.10 Nails

| | | Crew | Daily Output | Labor-Hours | Unit | Material | 2010 Bare Costs Labor | Equipment | Total | Total Incl O&P |
|---|---|---|---|---|---|---|---|---|---|---|
| 2100 | Aluminum | | | | Lb. | 4.10 | | | 4.10 | 4.51 |
| 2300 | Flooring nails, hardened steel, 2d to 10d, plain | | | | | 2.55 | | | 2.55 | 2.81 |
| 2400 | Galvanized | | | | | 3.88 | | | 3.88 | 4.27 |
| 2500 | Gypsum lath nails, 1-1/8", 13 ga. flathead, blued | | | | | 2.68 | | | 2.68 | 2.95 |
| 2600 | Masonry nails, hardened steel, 3/4" to 3" long, plain | | | | | 2.45 | | | 2.45 | 2.70 |
| 2700 | Galvanized | | | | | 3.72 | | | 3.72 | 4.09 |
| 2900 | Roofing nails, threaded, galvanized | | | | | 1.63 | | | 1.63 | 1.79 |
| 3100 | Aluminum | | | | | 4.80 | | | 4.80 | 5.30 |
| 3300 | Compressed lead head, threaded, galvanized | | | | | 2.47 | | | 2.47 | 2.72 |
| 3600 | Siding nails, plain shank, galvanized | | | | | 2 | | | 2 | 2.20 |
| 3800 | Aluminum | | | | | 4.11 | | | 4.11 | 4.52 |
| 5000 | Add to prices above for cement coating | | | | | .11 | | | .11 | .12 |
| 5200 | Zinc or tin plating | | | | | .14 | | | .14 | .15 |
| 5500 | Vinyl coated sinkers, 8d to 16d | | | | | .62 | | | .62 | .68 |

### 06 05 23.40 Sheet Metal Screws

| | | Crew | Daily Output | Labor-Hours | Unit | Material | 2010 Bare Costs Labor | Equipment | Total | Total Incl O&P |
|---|---|---|---|---|---|---|---|---|---|---|
| 0010 | **SHEET METAL SCREWS** | | | | | | | | | |
| 0020 | Steel, standard, #8 x 3/4", plain | | | | C | 3.42 | | | 3.42 | 3.76 |
| 0100 | Galvanized | | | | | 3.42 | | | 3.42 | 3.76 |
| 0300 | #10 x 1", plain | | | | | 4.70 | | | 4.70 | 5.15 |
| 0400 | Galvanized | | | | | 4.70 | | | 4.70 | 5.15 |
| 1500 | Self-drilling, with washers, (pinch point) #8 x 3/4", plain | | | | | 12.25 | | | 12.25 | 13.45 |
| 1600 | Galvanized | | | | | 12.25 | | | 12.25 | 13.45 |
| 1800 | #10 x 3/4", plain | | | | | 14.50 | | | 14.50 | 15.95 |
| 1900 | Galvanized | | | | | 14.50 | | | 14.50 | 15.95 |
| 3000 | Stainless steel w/aluminum or neoprene washers, #14 x 1", plain | | | | | 35 | | | 35 | 38.50 |
| 3100 | #14 x 2", plain | | | | | 44 | | | 44 | 48.50 |

### 06 05 23.50 Wood Screws

| | | Crew | Daily Output | Labor-Hours | Unit | Material | 2010 Bare Costs Labor | Equipment | Total | Total Incl O&P |
|---|---|---|---|---|---|---|---|---|---|---|
| 0010 | **WOOD SCREWS** | | | | | | | | | |
| 0020 | #8 x 1" long, steel | | | | C | 5.10 | | | 5.10 | 5.60 |
| 0100 | Brass | | | | | 10.30 | | | 10.30 | 11.35 |
| 0200 | #8, 2" long, steel | | | | | 5.10 | | | 5.10 | 5.60 |
| 0300 | Brass | | | | | 17.40 | | | 17.40 | 19.10 |
| 0400 | #10, 1" long, steel | | | | | 3.63 | | | 3.63 | 3.99 |
| 0500 | Brass | | | | | 15.80 | | | 15.80 | 17.40 |
| 0600 | #10, 2" long, steel | | | | | 6.15 | | | 6.15 | 6.80 |
| 0700 | Brass | | | | | 24 | | | 24 | 26.50 |
| 0800 | #10, 3" long, steel | | | | | 10.30 | | | 10.30 | 11.30 |
| 1000 | #12, 2" long, steel | | | | | 9.05 | | | 9.05 | 9.95 |
| 1100 | Brass | | | | | 31.50 | | | 31.50 | 34.50 |
| 1500 | #12, 3" long, steel | | | | | 12.10 | | | 12.10 | 13.30 |
| 2000 | #12, 4" long, steel | | | | | 18.15 | | | 18.15 | 19.95 |

### 06 05 23.60 Timber Connectors

| | | Crew | Daily Output | Labor-Hours | Unit | Material | 2010 Bare Costs Labor | Equipment | Total | Total Incl O&P |
|---|---|---|---|---|---|---|---|---|---|---|
| 0010 | **TIMBER CONNECTORS** | | | | | | | | | |
| 0020 | Add up cost of each part for total cost of connection | | | | | | | | | |
| 0100 | Connector plates, steel, with bolts, straight | 2 Carp | 75 | .213 | Ea. | 25.50 | 6.20 | | 31.70 | 38.50 |
| 0110 | Tee, 7 gauge | | 50 | .320 | | 29.50 | 9.30 | | 38.80 | 47.50 |
| 0120 | T- Strap, 14 gauge, 12" x 8" x 2" | | 50 | .320 | | 29.50 | 9.30 | | 38.80 | 47.50 |
| 0150 | Anchor plates, 7 ga, 9" x 7" | | 75 | .213 | | 25.50 | 6.20 | | 31.70 | 38.50 |
| 0200 | Bolts, machine, sq. hd. with nut & washer, 1/2" diameter, 4" long | 1 Carp | 140 | .057 | | .86 | 1.66 | | 2.52 | 3.75 |
| 0300 | 7-1/2" long | | 130 | .062 | | 1.50 | 1.79 | | 3.29 | 4.66 |
| 0500 | 3/4" diameter, 7-1/2" long | | 130 | .062 | | 4.39 | 1.79 | | 6.18 | 7.85 |
| 0610 | Machine bolts, w/nut, washer, 3/4" diam., 15" L, HD's & beam hangers | | 95 | .084 | | 8.10 | 2.45 | | 10.55 | 13.05 |

# 06 05 Common Work Results for Wood, Plastics, and Composites

## 06 05 23 – Wood, Plastic, and Composite Fastenings

| 06 05 23.60 Timber Connectors | | Crew | Daily Output | Labor-Hours | Unit | Material | 2010 Bare Costs Labor | Equipment | Total | Total Incl O&P |
|---|---|---|---|---|---|---|---|---|---|---|
| 0720 | Machine bolts, sq. hd. w/nut & wash | 1 Carp | 150 | .053 | Lb. | 2.90 | 1.55 | | 4.45 | 5.80 |
| 0800 | Drilling bolt holes in timber, 1/2" diameter | | 450 | .018 | Inch | | .52 | | .52 | .87 |
| 0900 | 1" diameter | | 350 | .023 | " | | .67 | | .67 | 1.12 |
| 1100 | Framing anchor, angle, 3" x 3" x 1-1/2", 12 ga | | 175 | .046 | Ea. | 2.20 | 1.33 | | 3.53 | 4.66 |
| 1150 | Framing anchors, 18 gauge, 4-1/2" x 2-3/4" | | 175 | .046 | | 2.20 | 1.33 | | 3.53 | 4.66 |
| 1160 | Framing anchors, 18 gauge, 4-1/2" x 3" | | 175 | .046 | | 2.20 | 1.33 | | 3.53 | 4.66 |
| 1170 | Clip anchors plates, 18 gauge, 12" x 1-1/8" | | 175 | .046 | | 2.20 | 1.33 | | 3.53 | 4.66 |
| 1250 | Holdowns, 3 gauge base, 10 gauge body | | 8 | 1 | | 21 | 29 | | 50 | 72 |
| 1260 | Holdowns, 7 gauge 11-1/16" x 3-1/4" | | 8 | 1 | | 21 | 29 | | 50 | 72 |
| 1270 | Holdowns, 7 gauge 14-3/8" x 3-1/8" | | 8 | 1 | | 21 | 29 | | 50 | 72 |
| 1275 | Holdowns, 12 gauge 8" x 2-1/2" | | 8 | 1 | | 21 | 29 | | 50 | 72 |
| 1300 | Joist and beam hangers, 18 ga. galv., for 2" x 4" joist | | 175 | .046 | | .61 | 1.33 | | 1.94 | 2.91 |
| 1400 | 2" x 6" to 2" x 10" joist | | 165 | .048 | | 1.17 | 1.41 | | 2.58 | 3.66 |
| 1600 | 16 ga. galv., 3" x 6" to 3" x 10" joist | | 160 | .050 | | 2.49 | 1.46 | | 3.95 | 5.20 |
| 1700 | 3" x 10" to 3" x 14" joist | | 160 | .050 | | 4.14 | 1.46 | | 5.60 | 7 |
| 1800 | 4" x 6" to 4" x 10" joist | | 155 | .052 | | 2.58 | 1.50 | | 4.08 | 5.35 |
| 1900 | 4" x 10" to 4" x 14" joist | | 155 | .052 | | 4.23 | 1.50 | | 5.73 | 7.20 |
| 2000 | Two-2" x 6" to two-2" x 10" joists | | 150 | .053 | | 3.52 | 1.55 | | 5.07 | 6.50 |
| 2100 | Two-2" x 10" to two-2" x 14" joists | | 150 | .053 | | 3.94 | 1.55 | | 5.49 | 6.95 |
| 2300 | 3/16" thick, 6" x 8" joist | | 145 | .055 | | 54.50 | 1.61 | | 56.11 | 62.50 |
| 2400 | 6" x 10" joist | | 140 | .057 | | 57 | 1.66 | | 58.66 | 65.50 |
| 2500 | 6" x 12" joist | | 135 | .059 | | 59.50 | 1.72 | | 61.22 | 68 |
| 2700 | 1/4" thick, 6" x 14" joist | | 130 | .062 | | 61.50 | 1.79 | | 63.29 | 71 |
| 2900 | Plywood clips, extruded aluminum H clip, for 3/4" panels | | | | | .20 | | | .20 | .22 |
| 3000 | Galvanized 18 ga. back-up clip | | | | | .16 | | | .16 | .18 |
| 3200 | Post framing, 16 ga. galv. for 4" x 4" base, 2 piece | 1 Carp | 130 | .062 | | 13.80 | 1.79 | | 15.59 | 18.15 |
| 3300 | Cap | | 130 | .062 | | 19.15 | 1.79 | | 20.94 | 24 |
| 3500 | Rafter anchors, 18 ga. galv., 1-1/2" wide, 5-1/4" long | | 145 | .055 | | .41 | 1.61 | | 2.02 | 3.15 |
| 3600 | 10-3/4" long | | 145 | .055 | | 1.23 | 1.61 | | 2.84 | 4.05 |
| 3800 | Shear plates, 2-5/8" diameter | | 120 | .067 | | 2 | 1.94 | | 3.94 | 5.45 |
| 3900 | 4" diameter | | 115 | .070 | | 4.75 | 2.02 | | 6.77 | 8.65 |
| 4000 | Sill anchors, embedded in concrete or block, 25-1/2" long | | 115 | .070 | | 10.70 | 2.02 | | 12.72 | 15.15 |
| 4100 | Spike grids, 3" x 6" | | 120 | .067 | | .81 | 1.94 | | 2.75 | 4.15 |
| 4400 | Split rings, 2-1/2" diameter | | 120 | .067 | | 1.65 | 1.94 | | 3.59 | 5.10 |
| 4500 | 4" diameter | | 110 | .073 | | 2.50 | 2.12 | | 4.62 | 6.30 |
| 4550 | Tie plate, 20 gauge, 7" x 3 1/8" | | 110 | .073 | | 2.50 | 2.12 | | 4.62 | 6.30 |
| 4560 | Tie plate, 20 gauge, 5" x 4 1/8" | | 110 | .073 | | 2.50 | 2.12 | | 4.62 | 6.30 |
| 4575 | Twist straps, 18 gauge, 12" x 1 1/4" | | 110 | .073 | | 2.50 | 2.12 | | 4.62 | 6.30 |
| 4580 | Twist straps, 18 gauge, 16" x 1 1/4" | | 110 | .073 | | 2.50 | 2.12 | | 4.62 | 6.30 |
| 4600 | Strap ties, 20 ga., 2-1/16" wide, 12 13/16" long | | 180 | .044 | | .80 | 1.29 | | 2.09 | 3.06 |
| 4700 | Strap ties, 16 ga., 1-3/8" wide, 12" long | | 180 | .044 | | .80 | 1.29 | | 2.09 | 3.06 |
| 4800 | 21-5/8" x 1-1/4" | | 160 | .050 | | 2.49 | 1.46 | | 3.95 | 5.20 |
| 5000 | Toothed rings, 2-5/8" or 4" diameter | | 90 | .089 | | 1.49 | 2.59 | | 4.08 | 6 |
| 5200 | Truss plates, nailed, 20 gauge, up to 32' span | | 17 | .471 | Truss Ea. | 10.85 | 13.70 | | 24.55 | 35 |
| 5400 | Washers, 2" x 2" x 1/8" | | | | Ea. | .34 | | | .34 | .37 |
| 5500 | 3" x 3" x 3/16" | | | | " | .89 | | | .89 | .98 |
| 6000 | Angles and gussets, painted | | | | | | | | | |
| 6012 | 7 ga., 3-1/4" x 3-1/4" x 2-1/2" long | 1 Carp | 1.90 | 4.211 | C | 930 | 123 | | 1,053 | 1,225 |
| 6014 | 3-1/4" x 3-1/4" x 5" long | | 1.90 | 4.211 | | 1,825 | 123 | | 1,948 | 2,200 |
| 6016 | 3-1/4" x 3-1/4" x 7-1/2" long | | 1.85 | 4.324 | | 3,425 | 126 | | 3,551 | 3,975 |
| 6018 | 5-3/4" x 5-3/4" x 2-1/2" long | | 1.85 | 4.324 | | 2,225 | 126 | | 2,351 | 2,625 |
| 6020 | 5-3/4" x 5-3/4" x 5" long | | 1.85 | 4.324 | | 3,525 | 126 | | 3,651 | 4,075 |
| 6022 | 5-3/4" x 5-3/4" x 7-1/2" long | | 1.80 | 4.444 | | 5,200 | 129 | | 5,329 | 5,950 |

354

## 06 05 23 – Wood, Plastic, and Composite Fastenings

| 06 05 23.60 Timber Connectors | | Crew | Daily Output | Labor-Hours | Unit | Material | 2010 Bare Costs | | Total | Total Incl O&P |
|---|---|---|---|---|---|---|---|---|---|---|
| | | | | | | | Labor | Equipment | | |
| 6024 | 3 ga., 4-1/4" x 4-1/4" x 3" long | 1 Carp | 1.85 | 4.324 | C | 2,350 | 126 | | 2,476 | 2,775 |
| 6026 | 4-1/4" x 4-1/4" x 6" long | | 1.85 | 4.324 | | 5,050 | 126 | | 5,176 | 5,750 |
| 6028 | 4-1/4" x 4-1/4" x 9" long | | 1.80 | 4.444 | | 5,675 | 129 | | 5,804 | 6,475 |
| 6030 | 7-1/4" x 7-1/4" x 3" long | | 1.80 | 4.444 | | 4,075 | 129 | | 4,204 | 4,700 |
| 6032 | 7-1/4" x 7-1/4" x 6" long | | 1.80 | 4.444 | | 5,475 | 129 | | 5,604 | 6,250 |
| 6034 | 7-1/4" x 7-1/4" x 9" long | ▼ | 1.75 | 4.571 | ▼ | 12,300 | 133 | | 12,433 | 13,700 |
| 6036 | Gussets | | | | | | | | | |
| 6038 | 7 ga., 8-1/8" x 8-1/8" x 2-3/4" long | 1 Carp | 1.80 | 4.444 | C | 3,875 | 129 | | 4,004 | 4,500 |
| 6040 | 3 ga., 9-3/4" x 9-3/4" x 3-1/4" long | " | 1.80 | 4.444 | " | 5,400 | 129 | | 5,529 | 6,150 |
| 6101 | Beam hangers, polymer painted | | | | | | | | | |
| 6102 | Bolted, 3 ga., (W x H x L) | | | | | | | | | |
| 6104 | 3-1/4" x 9" x 12" top flange | 1 Carp | 1 | 8 | C | 16,500 | 233 | | 16,733 | 18,600 |
| 6106 | 5-1/4" x 9" x 12" top flange | | 1 | 8 | | 17,200 | 233 | | 17,433 | 19,300 |
| 6108 | 5-1/4" x 11" x 11-3/4" top flange | | 1 | 8 | | 19,600 | 233 | | 19,833 | 21,900 |
| 6110 | 6-7/8" x 9" x 12" top flange | | 1 | 8 | | 17,800 | 233 | | 18,033 | 20,000 |
| 6112 | 6-7/8" x 11" x 13-1/2" top flange | | 1 | 8 | | 20,600 | 233 | | 20,833 | 23,000 |
| 6114 | 8-7/8" x 11" x 15-1/2" top flange | ▼ | 1 | 8 | ▼ | 22,000 | 233 | | 22,233 | 24,600 |
| 6116 | Nailed, 3 ga., (W x H x L) | | | | | | | | | |
| 6118 | 3-1/4" x 10-1/2" x 10" top flange | 1 Carp | 1.80 | 4.444 | C | 17,200 | 129 | | 17,329 | 19,100 |
| 6120 | 3-1/4" x 10-1/2" x 12" top flange | | 1.80 | 4.444 | | 17,200 | 129 | | 17,329 | 19,100 |
| 6122 | 5-1/4" x 9-1/2" x 10" top flange | | 1.80 | 4.444 | | 17,600 | 129 | | 17,729 | 19,500 |
| 6124 | 5-1/4" x 9-1/2" x 12" top flange | | 1.80 | 4.444 | | 17,600 | 129 | | 17,729 | 19,500 |
| 6128 | 6-7/8" x 8-1/2" x 12" top flange | ▼ | 1.80 | 4.444 | ▼ | 18,000 | 129 | | 18,129 | 20,000 |
| 6134 | Saddle hangers, glu-lam (W x H x L) | | | | | | | | | |
| 6136 | 3-1/4" x 10-1/2" x 5-1/4" x 6" saddle | 1 Carp | .50 | 16 | C | 12,900 | 465 | | 13,365 | 15,000 |
| 6138 | 3-1/4" x 10-1/2" x 6-7/8" x 6" saddle | | .50 | 16 | | 13,600 | 465 | | 14,065 | 15,700 |
| 6140 | 3-1/4" x 10-1/2" x 8-7/8" x 6" saddle | | .50 | 16 | | 14,200 | 465 | | 14,665 | 16,500 |
| 6142 | 3-1/4" x 19-1/2" x 5-1/4" x 10-1/8" saddle | | .40 | 20 | | 12,900 | 580 | | 13,480 | 15,200 |
| 6144 | 3-1/4" x 19-1/2" x 6-7/8" x 10-1/8" saddle | | .40 | 20 | | 13,600 | 580 | | 14,180 | 15,900 |
| 6146 | 3-1/4" x 19-1/2" x 8-7/8" x 10-1/8" saddle | | .40 | 20 | | 14,200 | 580 | | 14,780 | 16,700 |
| 6148 | 5-1/4" x 9-1/2" x 5-1/4" x 12" saddle | | .50 | 16 | | 15,400 | 465 | | 15,865 | 17,700 |
| 6150 | 5-1/4" x 9-1/2" x 6-7/8" x 9" saddle | | .50 | 16 | | 16,800 | 465 | | 17,265 | 19,300 |
| 6152 | 5-1/4" x 10-1/2" x spec x 12" saddle | | .50 | 16 | | 18,300 | 465 | | 18,765 | 20,900 |
| 6154 | 5-1/4" x 18" x 5-1/4" x 12-1/8" saddle | | .40 | 20 | | 15,400 | 580 | | 15,980 | 17,900 |
| 6156 | 5-1/4" x 18" x 6-7/8" x 12-1/8" saddle | | .40 | 20 | | 16,800 | 580 | | 17,380 | 19,500 |
| 6158 | 5-1/4" x 18" x spec x 12-1/8" saddle | | .40 | 20 | | 18,300 | 580 | | 18,880 | 21,100 |
| 6160 | 6-7/8" x 8-1/2" x 6-7/8" x 12" saddle | | .50 | 16 | | 18,400 | 465 | | 18,865 | 21,000 |
| 6162 | 6-7/8" x 8-1/2" x 8-7/8" x 12" saddle | | .50 | 16 | | 19,000 | 465 | | 19,465 | 21,700 |
| 6164 | 6-7/8" x 10-1/2" x spec x 12" saddle | | .50 | 16 | | 18,400 | 465 | | 18,865 | 21,000 |
| 6166 | 6-7/8" x 18" x 6-7/8" x 13-3/4" saddle | | .40 | 20 | | 18,400 | 580 | | 18,980 | 21,200 |
| 6168 | 6-7/8" x 18" x 8-7/8" x 13-3/4" saddle | | .40 | 20 | | 19,000 | 580 | | 19,580 | 21,900 |
| 6170 | 6-7/8" x 18" x spec x 13-3/4" saddle | | .40 | 20 | | 20,500 | 580 | | 21,080 | 23,500 |
| 6172 | 8-7/8" x 18" x spec x 15-3/4" saddle | ▼ | .40 | 20 | ▼ | 32,000 | 580 | | 32,580 | 36,200 |
| 6201 | Beam and purlin hangers, galvanized, 12 ga. | | | | | | | | | |
| 6202 | Purlin or joist size, 3" x 8" | 1 Carp | 1.70 | 4.706 | C | 1,700 | 137 | | 1,837 | 2,100 |
| 6204 | 3" x 10" | | 1.70 | 4.706 | | 1,850 | 137 | | 1,987 | 2,250 |
| 6206 | 3" x 12" | | 1.65 | 4.848 | | 2,100 | 141 | | 2,241 | 2,550 |
| 6208 | 3" x 14" | | 1.65 | 4.848 | | 2,250 | 141 | | 2,391 | 2,700 |
| 6210 | 3" x 16" | | 1.65 | 4.848 | | 2,375 | 141 | | 2,516 | 2,850 |
| 6212 | 4" x 8" | | 1.65 | 4.848 | | 1,725 | 141 | | 1,866 | 2,100 |
| 6214 | 4" x 10" | | 1.65 | 4.848 | | 1,850 | 141 | | 1,991 | 2,250 |
| 6216 | 4" x 12" | | 1.60 | 5 | | 2,200 | 146 | | 2,346 | 2,650 |
| 6218 | 4" x 14" | ▼ | 1.60 | 5 | ▼ | 2,325 | 146 | | 2,471 | 2,800 |

| 06 05 23.60 Timber Connectors | | Crew | Daily Output | Labor-Hours | Unit | Material | 2010 Bare Costs Labor | Equipment | Total | Total Incl O&P |
|---|---|---|---|---|---|---|---|---|---|---|
| 6220 | 4" x 16" | 1 Carp | 1.60 | 5 | C | 2,450 | 146 | | 2,596 | 2,950 |
| 6222 | 6" x 8" | | 1.60 | 5 | | 2,200 | 146 | | 2,346 | 2,675 |
| 6224 | 6" x 10" | | 1.55 | 5.161 | | 2,250 | 150 | | 2,400 | 2,725 |
| 6226 | 6" x 12" | | 1.55 | 5.161 | | 3,850 | 150 | | 4,000 | 4,500 |
| 6228 | 6" x 14" | | 1.50 | 5.333 | | 4,075 | 155 | | 4,230 | 4,750 |
| 6230 | 6" x 16" | | 1.50 | 5.333 | | 4,325 | 155 | | 4,480 | 5,000 |
| 6250 | Beam seats | | | | | | | | | |
| 6252 | Beam size, 5-1/4" wide | | | | | | | | | |
| 6254 | 5" x 7" x 1/4" | 1 Carp | 1.80 | 4.444 | C | 6,500 | 129 | | 6,629 | 7,375 |
| 6256 | 6" x 7" x 3/8" | | 1.80 | 4.444 | | 7,275 | 129 | | 7,404 | 8,225 |
| 6258 | 7" x 7" x 3/8" | | 1.80 | 4.444 | | 7,775 | 129 | | 7,904 | 8,775 |
| 6260 | 8" x 7" x 3/8" | | 1.80 | 4.444 | | 9,175 | 129 | | 9,304 | 10,300 |
| 6262 | Beam size, 6-7/8" wide | | | | | | | | | |
| 6264 | 5" x 9" x 1/4" | 1 Carp | 1.80 | 4.444 | C | 7,750 | 129 | | 7,879 | 8,750 |
| 6266 | 6" x 9" x 3/8" | | 1.80 | 4.444 | | 10,100 | 129 | | 10,229 | 11,300 |
| 6268 | 7" x 9" x 3/8" | | 1.80 | 4.444 | | 10,200 | 129 | | 10,329 | 11,500 |
| 6270 | 8" x 9" x 3/8" | | 1.80 | 4.444 | | 12,100 | 129 | | 12,229 | 13,500 |
| 6272 | Special beams, over 6-7/8" wide | | | | | | | | | |
| 6274 | 5" x 10" x 3/8" | 1 Carp | 1.80 | 4.444 | C | 10,500 | 129 | | 10,629 | 11,800 |
| 6276 | 6" x 10" x 3/8" | | 1.80 | 4.444 | | 12,200 | 129 | | 12,329 | 13,700 |
| 6278 | 7" x 10" x 3/8" | | 1.80 | 4.444 | | 12,800 | 129 | | 12,929 | 14,300 |
| 6280 | 8" x 10" x 3/8" | | 1.75 | 4.571 | | 13,700 | 133 | | 13,833 | 15,300 |
| 6282 | 5-1/4" x 12" x 5/16" | | 1.75 | 4.571 | | 10,600 | 133 | | 10,733 | 11,900 |
| 6284 | 6-1/2" x 12" x 3/8" | | 1.75 | 4.571 | | 17,600 | 133 | | 17,733 | 19,600 |
| 6286 | 5-1/4" x 16" x 5/16" | | 1.70 | 4.706 | | 15,600 | 137 | | 15,737 | 17,400 |
| 6288 | 6-1/2" x 16" x 3/8" | | 1.70 | 4.706 | | 20,400 | 137 | | 20,537 | 22,600 |
| 6290 | 5-1/4" x 20" x 5/16" | | 1.70 | 4.706 | | 18,400 | 137 | | 18,537 | 20,400 |
| 6292 | 6-1/2" x 20" x 3/8" | | 1.65 | 4.848 | | 24,000 | 141 | | 24,141 | 26,600 |
| 6300 | Column bases | | | | | | | | | |
| 6302 | 4 x 4, 16 ga. | 1 Carp | 1.80 | 4.444 | C | 655 | 129 | | 784 | 940 |
| 6306 | 7 ga. | | 1.80 | 4.444 | | 2,400 | 129 | | 2,529 | 2,875 |
| 6308 | 4 x 6, 16 ga. | | 1.80 | 4.444 | | 1,525 | 129 | | 1,654 | 1,900 |
| 6312 | 7 ga. | | 1.80 | 4.444 | | 2,500 | 129 | | 2,629 | 2,975 |
| 6314 | 6 x 6, 16 ga. | | 1.75 | 4.571 | | 1,725 | 133 | | 1,858 | 2,125 |
| 6318 | 7 ga. | | 1.75 | 4.571 | | 3,425 | 133 | | 3,558 | 3,975 |
| 6320 | 6 x 8, 7 ga. | | 1.70 | 4.706 | | 2,675 | 137 | | 2,812 | 3,150 |
| 6322 | 6 x 10, 7 ga. | | 1.70 | 4.706 | | 2,850 | 137 | | 2,987 | 3,375 |
| 6324 | 6 x 12, 7 ga. | | 1.70 | 4.706 | | 3,100 | 137 | | 3,237 | 3,625 |
| 6326 | 8 x 8, 7 ga. | | 1.65 | 4.848 | | 5,225 | 141 | | 5,366 | 5,975 |
| 6330 | 8 x 10, 7 ga. | | 1.65 | 4.848 | | 6,250 | 141 | | 6,391 | 7,100 |
| 6332 | 8 x 12, 7 ga. | | 1.60 | 5 | | 6,800 | 146 | | 6,946 | 7,725 |
| 6334 | 10 x 10, 3 ga. | | 1.60 | 5 | | 6,925 | 146 | | 7,071 | 7,875 |
| 6336 | 10 x 12, 3 ga. | | 1.60 | 5 | | 7,975 | 146 | | 8,121 | 9,000 |
| 6338 | 12 x 12, 3 ga. | | 1.55 | 5.161 | | 8,650 | 150 | | 8,800 | 9,750 |
| 6350 | Column caps, painted, 3 ga. | | | | | | | | | |
| 6352 | 3-1/4" x 3-5/8" | 1 Carp | 1.80 | 4.444 | C | 8,800 | 129 | | 8,929 | 9,900 |
| 6354 | 3-1/4" x 5-1/2" | | 1.80 | 4.444 | | 8,800 | 129 | | 8,929 | 9,900 |
| 6356 | 3-5/8" x 3-5/8" | | 1.80 | 4.444 | | 7,200 | 129 | | 7,329 | 8,125 |
| 6358 | 3-5/8" x 5-1/2" | | 1.80 | 4.444 | | 7,200 | 129 | | 7,329 | 8,125 |
| 6360 | 5-1/4" x 5-1/2" | | 1.75 | 4.571 | | 9,400 | 133 | | 9,533 | 10,500 |
| 6362 | 5-1/4" x 7-1/2" | | 1.75 | 4.571 | | 9,400 | 133 | | 9,533 | 10,500 |
| 6364 | 5-1/2" x 3-5/8" | | 1.75 | 4.571 | | 10,100 | 133 | | 10,233 | 11,400 |
| 6366 | 5-1/2" x 5-1/2" | | 1.75 | 4.571 | | 10,100 | 133 | | 10,233 | 11,400 |

| 06 05 23.60 Timber Connectors | | Crew | Daily Output | Labor-Hours | Unit | Material | 2010 Bare Costs Labor | Equipment | Total | Total Incl O&P |
|---|---|---|---|---|---|---|---|---|---|---|
| 6368 | 5-1/2" x 7-1/2" | 1 Carp | 1.70 | 4.706 | C | 10,100 | 137 | | 10,237 | 11,400 |
| 6370 | 6-7/8" x 5-1/2" | | 1.70 | 4.706 | | 10,600 | 137 | | 10,737 | 11,800 |
| 6372 | 6-7/8" x 6-7/8" | | 1.70 | 4.706 | | 10,600 | 137 | | 10,737 | 11,800 |
| 6374 | 6-7/8" x 7-1/2" | | 1.70 | 4.706 | | 10,600 | 137 | | 10,737 | 11,800 |
| 6376 | 7-1/2" x 5-1/2" | | 1.65 | 4.848 | | 11,100 | 141 | | 11,241 | 12,400 |
| 6378 | 7-1/2" x 7-1/2" | | 1.65 | 4.848 | | 11,100 | 141 | | 11,241 | 12,400 |
| 6380 | 8-7/8" x 5-1/2" | | 1.60 | 5 | | 11,700 | 146 | | 11,846 | 13,100 |
| 6382 | 8-7/8" x 7-1/2" | | 1.60 | 5 | | 11,700 | 146 | | 11,846 | 13,100 |
| 6384 | 9-1/2" x 5-1/2" | | 1.60 | 5 | | 15,800 | 146 | | 15,946 | 17,600 |
| 6400 | Floor tie anchors, polymer paint | | | | | | | | | |
| 6402 | 10 ga., 3" x 37-1/2" | 1 Carp | 1.80 | 4.444 | C | 4,200 | 129 | | 4,329 | 4,850 |
| 6404 | 3-1/2" x 45-1/2" | | 1.75 | 4.571 | | 4,400 | 133 | | 4,533 | 5,075 |
| 6406 | 3 ga., 3-1/2" x 56" | | 1.70 | 4.706 | | 7,775 | 137 | | 7,912 | 8,775 |
| 6410 | Girder hangers | | | | | | | | | |
| 6412 | 6" wall thickness, 4" x 6" | 1 Carp | 1.80 | 4.444 | C | 2,375 | 129 | | 2,504 | 2,825 |
| 6414 | 4" x 8" | | 1.80 | 4.444 | | 2,650 | 129 | | 2,779 | 3,125 |
| 6416 | 8" wall thickness, 4" x 6" | | 1.80 | 4.444 | | 2,725 | 129 | | 2,854 | 3,225 |
| 6418 | 4" x 8" | | 1.80 | 4.444 | | 2,725 | 129 | | 2,854 | 3,225 |
| 6420 | Hinge connections, polymer painted | | | | | | | | | |
| 6422 | 3/4" thick top plate | | | | | | | | | |
| 6424 | 5-1/4" x 12" w/5" x 5" top | 1 Carp | 1 | 8 | C | 30,200 | 233 | | 30,433 | 33,600 |
| 6426 | 5-1/4" x 15" w/6" x 6" top | | .80 | 10 | | 32,100 | 291 | | 32,391 | 35,800 |
| 6428 | 5-1/4" x 18" w/7" x 7" top | | .70 | 11.429 | | 33,700 | 335 | | 34,035 | 37,700 |
| 6430 | 5-1/4" x 26" w/9" x 9" top | | .60 | 13.333 | | 35,900 | 390 | | 36,290 | 40,200 |
| 6432 | 1" thick top plate | | | | | | | | | |
| 6434 | 6-7/8" x 14" w/5" x 5" top | 1 Carp | .80 | 10 | C | 36,800 | 291 | | 37,091 | 40,900 |
| 6436 | 6-7/8" x 17" w/6" x 6" top | | .80 | 10 | | 40,900 | 291 | | 41,191 | 45,500 |
| 6438 | 6-7/8" x 21" w/7" x 7" top | | .70 | 11.429 | | 44,600 | 335 | | 44,935 | 49,600 |
| 6440 | 6-7/8" x 31" w/9" x 9" top | | .60 | 13.333 | | 48,800 | 390 | | 49,190 | 54,000 |
| 6442 | 1-1/4" thick top plate | | | | | | | | | |
| 6444 | 8-7/8" x 16" w/5" x 5" top | 1 Carp | .60 | 13.333 | C | 45,800 | 390 | | 46,190 | 51,000 |
| 6446 | 8-7/8" x 21" w/6" x 6" top | | .50 | 16 | | 50,500 | 465 | | 50,965 | 56,500 |
| 6448 | 8-7/8" x 26" w/7" x 7" top | | .40 | 20 | | 57,000 | 580 | | 57,580 | 64,000 |
| 6450 | 8-7/8" x 39" w/9" x 9" top | | .30 | 26.667 | | 71,000 | 775 | | 71,775 | 80,000 |
| 6460 | Holddowns | | | | | | | | | |
| 6462 | Embedded along edge | | | | | | | | | |
| 6464 | 26" long, 12 ga. | 1 Carp | .90 | 8.889 | C | 1,150 | 259 | | 1,409 | 1,700 |
| 6466 | 35" long, 12 ga. | | .85 | 9.412 | | 1,525 | 274 | | 1,799 | 2,125 |
| 6468 | 35" long, 10 ga. | | .85 | 9.412 | | 1,200 | 274 | | 1,474 | 1,775 |
| 6470 | Embedded away from edge | | | | | | | | | |
| 6472 | Medium duty, 12 ga. | | | | | | | | | |
| 6474 | 18-1/2" long | 1 Carp | .95 | 8.421 | C | 695 | 245 | | 940 | 1,175 |
| 6476 | 23-3/4" long | | .90 | 8.889 | | 810 | 259 | | 1,069 | 1,325 |
| 6478 | 28" long | | .85 | 9.412 | | 825 | 274 | | 1,099 | 1,375 |
| 6480 | 35" long | | .85 | 9.412 | | 1,125 | 274 | | 1,399 | 1,700 |
| 6482 | Heavy duty, 10 ga. | | | | | | | | | |
| 6484 | 28" long | 1 Carp | .85 | 9.412 | C | 1,475 | 274 | | 1,749 | 2,075 |
| 6486 | 35" long | " | .85 | 9.412 | " | 1,625 | 274 | | 1,899 | 2,225 |
| 6490 | Surface mounted (W x H) | | | | | | | | | |
| 6492 | 2-1/2" x 5-3/4", 7 ga. | 1 Carp | 1 | 8 | C | 1,675 | 233 | | 1,908 | 2,250 |
| 6494 | 2-1/2" x 8", 12 ga. | | 1 | 8 | | 1,025 | 233 | | 1,258 | 1,550 |
| 6496 | 2-7/8" x 6-3/8", 7 ga. | | 1 | 8 | | 3,725 | 233 | | 3,958 | 4,500 |
| 6498 | 2-7/8" x 12-1/2", 3 ga. | | 1 | 8 | | 3,825 | 233 | | 4,058 | 4,625 |

| 06 05 23.60 Timber Connectors | | Crew | Daily Output | Labor-Hours | Unit | Material | 2010 Bare Costs Labor | Equipment | Total | Total Incl O&P |
|---|---|---|---|---|---|---|---|---|---|---|
| 6500 | 3-3/16" x 9-3/8", 10 ga. | 1 Carp | 1 | 8 | C | 2,550 | 233 | | 2,783 | 3,200 |
| 6502 | 3-1/2" x 11-5/8", 3 ga. | | 1 | 8 | | 4,650 | 233 | | 4,883 | 5,525 |
| 6504 | 3-1/2" x 14-3/4", 3 ga. | | 1 | 8 | | 3,100 | 233 | | 3,333 | 3,825 |
| 6506 | 3-1/2" x 16-1/2", 3 ga. | | 1 | 8 | | 7,125 | 233 | | 7,358 | 8,225 |
| 6508 | 3-1/2" x 20-1/2", 3 ga. | | .90 | 8.889 | | 7,275 | 259 | | 7,534 | 8,450 |
| 6510 | 3-1/2" x 24-1/2", 3 ga. | | .90 | 8.889 | | 9,200 | 259 | | 9,459 | 10,500 |
| 6512 | 4-1/4" x 20-3/4", 3 ga. | ↓ | .90 | 8.889 | ↓ | 6,275 | 259 | | 6,534 | 7,325 |
| 6520 | Joist hangers | | | | | | | | | |
| 6522 | Sloped, field adjustable, 18 ga. | | | | | | | | | |
| 6524 | 2" x 6" | 1 Carp | 1.65 | 4.848 | C | 460 | 141 | | 601 | 740 |
| 6526 | 2" x 8" | | 1.65 | 4.848 | | 825 | 141 | | 966 | 1,150 |
| 6528 | 2" x 10" and up | | 1.65 | 4.848 | | 1,375 | 141 | | 1,516 | 1,750 |
| 6530 | 3" x 10" and up | | 1.60 | 5 | | 1,025 | 146 | | 1,171 | 1,375 |
| 6532 | 4" x 10" and up | ↓ | 1.55 | 5.161 | ↓ | 1,250 | 150 | | 1,400 | 1,625 |
| 6536 | Skewed 45°, 16 ga. | | | | | | | | | |
| 6538 | 2" x 4" | 1 Carp | 1.75 | 4.571 | C | 735 | 133 | | 868 | 1,025 |
| 6540 | 2" x 6" or 2" x 8" | | 1.65 | 4.848 | | 745 | 141 | | 886 | 1,050 |
| 6542 | 2" x 10" or 2" x 12" | | 1.65 | 4.848 | | 855 | 141 | | 996 | 1,175 |
| 6544 | 2" x 14" or 2" x 16" | | 1.60 | 5 | | 1,525 | 146 | | 1,671 | 1,925 |
| 6546 | (2) 2" x 6" or (2) 2" x 8" | | 1.60 | 5 | | 1,375 | 146 | | 1,521 | 1,775 |
| 6548 | (2) 2" x 10" or (2) 2" x 12" | | 1.55 | 5.161 | | 1,475 | 150 | | 1,625 | 1,875 |
| 6550 | (2) 2" x 14" or (2) 2" x 16" | | 1.50 | 5.333 | | 2,325 | 155 | | 2,480 | 2,825 |
| 6552 | 4" x 6" or 4" x 8" | | 1.60 | 5 | | 1,150 | 146 | | 1,296 | 1,525 |
| 6554 | 4" x 10" or 4" x 12" | | 1.55 | 5.161 | | 1,350 | 150 | | 1,500 | 1,725 |
| 6556 | 4" x 14" or 4" x 16" | ↓ | 1.55 | 5.161 | ↓ | 2,100 | 150 | | 2,250 | 2,550 |
| 6560 | Skewed 45°, 14 ga. | | | | | | | | | |
| 6562 | (2) 2" x 6" or (2) 2" x 8" | 1 Carp | 1.60 | 5 | C | 1,600 | 146 | | 1,746 | 2,000 |
| 6564 | (2) 2" x 10" or (2) 2" x 12" | | 1.55 | 5.161 | | 2,200 | 150 | | 2,350 | 2,675 |
| 6566 | (2) 2" x 14" or (2) 2" x 16" | | 1.50 | 5.333 | | 3,225 | 155 | | 3,380 | 3,800 |
| 6568 | 4" x 6" or 4" x 8" | | 1.60 | 5 | | 1,900 | 146 | | 2,046 | 2,325 |
| 6570 | 4" x 10" or 4" x 12" | | 1.55 | 5.161 | | 2,000 | 150 | | 2,150 | 2,450 |
| 6572 | 4" x 14" or 4" x 16" | ↓ | 1.55 | 5.161 | ↓ | 2,675 | 150 | | 2,825 | 3,200 |
| 6590 | Joist hangers, heavy duty 12 ga., galvanized | | | | | | | | | |
| 6592 | 2" x 4" | 1 Carp | 1.75 | 4.571 | C | 1,075 | 133 | | 1,208 | 1,400 |
| 6594 | 2" x 6" | | 1.65 | 4.848 | | 1,175 | 141 | | 1,316 | 1,525 |
| 6595 | 2" x 6", 16 gauge | | 1.65 | 4.848 | | 1,175 | 141 | | 1,316 | 1,525 |
| 6596 | 2" x 8" | | 1.65 | 4.848 | | 1,775 | 141 | | 1,916 | 2,175 |
| 6597 | 2" x 8", 16 gauge | | 1.65 | 4.848 | | 1,775 | 141 | | 1,916 | 2,175 |
| 6598 | 2" x 10" | | 1.65 | 4.848 | | 1,825 | 141 | | 1,966 | 2,225 |
| 6600 | 2" x 12" | | 1.65 | 4.848 | | 2,250 | 141 | | 2,391 | 2,700 |
| 6602 | 2" x 14" | | 1.65 | 4.848 | | 2,350 | 141 | | 2,491 | 2,800 |
| 6604 | 2" x 16" | | 1.65 | 4.848 | | 2,475 | 141 | | 2,616 | 2,950 |
| 6606 | 3" x 4" | | 1.65 | 4.848 | | 1,475 | 141 | | 1,616 | 1,850 |
| 6608 | 3" x 6" | | 1.65 | 4.848 | | 2,000 | 141 | | 2,141 | 2,425 |
| 6610 | 3" x 8" | | 1.65 | 4.848 | | 2,025 | 141 | | 2,166 | 2,450 |
| 6612 | 3" x 10" | | 1.60 | 5 | | 2,350 | 146 | | 2,496 | 2,825 |
| 6614 | 3" x 12" | | 1.60 | 5 | | 2,800 | 146 | | 2,946 | 3,350 |
| 6616 | 3" x 14" | | 1.60 | 5 | | 3,300 | 146 | | 3,446 | 3,875 |
| 6618 | 3" x 16" | | 1.60 | 5 | | 3,625 | 146 | | 3,771 | 4,250 |
| 6620 | (2) 2" x 4" | | 1.75 | 4.571 | | 1,750 | 133 | | 1,883 | 2,150 |
| 6622 | (2) 2" x 6" | | 1.60 | 5 | | 2,100 | 146 | | 2,246 | 2,550 |
| 6624 | (2) 2" x 8" | | 1.60 | 5 | | 2,150 | 146 | | 2,296 | 2,600 |
| 6626 | (2) 2" x 10" | | 1.55 | 5.161 | | 2,325 | 150 | | 2,475 | 2,800 |

## 06 05 23 – Wood, Plastic, and Composite Fastenings

| 06 05 23.60 Timber Connectors | Crew | Daily Output | Labor-Hours | Unit | Material | 2010 Bare Costs Labor | Equipment | Total | Total Incl O&P |
|---|---|---|---|---|---|---|---|---|---|
| 6628 | (2) 2" x 12" | 1 Carp | 1.55 | 5.161 | C | 2,975 | 150 | | 3,125 | 3,525 |
| 6630 | (2) 2" x 14" | | 1.50 | 5.333 | | 3,000 | 155 | | 3,155 | 3,550 |
| 6632 | (2) 2" x 16" | | 1.50 | 5.333 | | 3,025 | 155 | | 3,180 | 3,575 |
| 6634 | 4" x 4" | | 1.65 | 4.848 | | 1,275 | 141 | | 1,416 | 1,625 |
| 6636 | 4" x 6" | | 1.60 | 5 | | 1,375 | 146 | | 1,521 | 1,775 |
| 6638 | 4" x 8" | | 1.60 | 5 | | 1,600 | 146 | | 1,746 | 2,025 |
| 6640 | 4" x 10" | | 1.55 | 5.161 | | 1,975 | 150 | | 2,125 | 2,425 |
| 6642 | 4" x 12" | | 1.55 | 5.161 | | 2,100 | 150 | | 2,250 | 2,550 |
| 6644 | 4" x 14" | | 1.55 | 5.161 | | 2,500 | 150 | | 2,650 | 3,000 |
| 6646 | 4" x 16" | | 1.55 | 5.161 | | 2,750 | 150 | | 2,900 | 3,275 |
| 6648 | (3) 2" x 10" | | 1.50 | 5.333 | | 3,050 | 155 | | 3,205 | 3,600 |
| 6650 | (3) 2" x 12" | | 1.50 | 5.333 | | 3,400 | 155 | | 3,555 | 3,975 |
| 6652 | (3) 2" x 14" | | 1.45 | 5.517 | | 3,650 | 161 | | 3,811 | 4,275 |
| 6654 | (3) 2" x 16" | | 1.45 | 5.517 | | 3,700 | 161 | | 3,861 | 4,350 |
| 6656 | 6" x 6" | | 1.60 | 5 | | 1,625 | 146 | | 1,771 | 2,050 |
| 6658 | 6" x 8" | | 1.60 | 5 | | 1,675 | 146 | | 1,821 | 2,100 |
| 6660 | 6" x 10" | | 1.55 | 5.161 | | 2,025 | 150 | | 2,175 | 2,475 |
| 6662 | 6" x 12" | | 1.55 | 5.161 | | 2,300 | 150 | | 2,450 | 2,775 |
| 6664 | 6" x 14" | | 1.50 | 5.333 | | 2,875 | 155 | | 3,030 | 3,425 |
| 6666 | 6" x 16" | | 1.50 | 5.333 | | 3,400 | 155 | | 3,555 | 3,975 |
| 6690 | Knee braces, galvanized, 12 ga. | | | | | | | | | |
| 6692 | Beam depth, 10" x 15" x 5' long | 1 Carp | 1.80 | 4.444 | C | 4,400 | 129 | | 4,529 | 5,075 |
| 6694 | 15" x 22-1/2" x 7' long | | 1.70 | 4.706 | | 5,050 | 137 | | 5,187 | 5,775 |
| 6696 | 22-1/2" x 28-1/2" x 8' long | | 1.60 | 5 | | 5,425 | 146 | | 5,571 | 6,225 |
| 6698 | 28-1/2" x 36" x 10' long | | 1.55 | 5.161 | | 5,650 | 150 | | 5,800 | 6,475 |
| 6700 | 36" x 42" x 12' long | | 1.50 | 5.333 | | 6,250 | 155 | | 6,405 | 7,125 |
| 6710 | Mudsill anchors | | | | | | | | | |
| 6714 | 2" x 4" or 3" x 4" | 1 Carp | 115 | .070 | C | 1,125 | 2.02 | | 1,127.02 | 1,250 |
| 6716 | 2" x 6" or 3" x 6" | | 115 | .070 | | 1,125 | 2.02 | | 1,127.02 | 1,250 |
| 6718 | Block wall, 13-1/4" long | | 115 | .070 | | 780 | 2.02 | | 782.02 | 865 |
| 6720 | 21-1/4" long | | 115 | .070 | | 116 | 2.02 | | 118.02 | 131 |
| 6730 | Post bases, 12 ga. galvanized | | | | | | | | | |
| 6732 | Adjustable, 3-9/16" x 3-9/16" | 1 Carp | 1.30 | 6.154 | C | 900 | 179 | | 1,079 | 1,300 |
| 6734 | 3-9/16" x 5-1/2" | | 1.30 | 6.154 | | 1,175 | 179 | | 1,354 | 1,575 |
| 6736 | 4" x 4" | | 1.30 | 6.154 | | 655 | 179 | | 834 | 1,025 |
| 6738 | 4" x 6" | | 1.30 | 6.154 | | 1,525 | 179 | | 1,704 | 1,975 |
| 6740 | 5-1/2" x 5-1/2" | | 1.30 | 6.154 | | 2,250 | 179 | | 2,429 | 2,800 |
| 6742 | 6" x 6" | | 1.30 | 6.154 | | 1,725 | 179 | | 1,904 | 2,200 |
| 6744 | Elevated, 3-9/16" x 3-1/4" | | 1.30 | 6.154 | | 975 | 179 | | 1,154 | 1,375 |
| 6746 | 5-1/2" x 3-5/16" | | 1.30 | 6.154 | | 1,375 | 179 | | 1,554 | 1,825 |
| 6748 | 5-1/2" x 5" | | 1.30 | 6.154 | | 2,075 | 179 | | 2,254 | 2,575 |
| 6750 | Regular, 3-9/16" x 3-3/8" | | 1.30 | 6.154 | | 745 | 179 | | 924 | 1,125 |
| 6752 | 4" x 3-3/8" | | 1.30 | 6.154 | | 1,050 | 179 | | 1,229 | 1,450 |
| 6754 | 18 gauge, 5-1/4" x 3-1/8" | | 1.30 | 6.154 | | 1,100 | 179 | | 1,279 | 1,500 |
| 6755 | 5-1/2" x 3-3/8" | | 1.30 | 6.154 | | 1,100 | 179 | | 1,279 | 1,500 |
| 6756 | 5-1/2" x 5-3/8" | | 1.30 | 6.154 | | 1,575 | 179 | | 1,754 | 2,025 |
| 6758 | 6" x 3-3/8" | | 1.30 | 6.154 | | 1,900 | 179 | | 2,079 | 2,400 |
| 6760 | 6" x 5-3/8" | | 1.30 | 6.154 | | 2,125 | 179 | | 2,304 | 2,625 |
| 6762 | Post combination cap/bases | | | | | | | | | |
| 6764 | 3-9/16" x 3-9/16" | 1 Carp | 1.20 | 6.667 | C | 425 | 194 | | 619 | 795 |
| 6766 | 3-9/16" x 5-1/2" | | 1.20 | 6.667 | | 965 | 194 | | 1,159 | 1,375 |
| 6768 | 4" x 4" | | 1.20 | 6.667 | | 1,925 | 194 | | 2,119 | 2,425 |
| 6770 | 5-1/2" x 5-1/2" | | 1.20 | 6.667 | | 1,075 | 194 | | 1,269 | 1,500 |

| 06 05 23.60 Timber Connectors | | Crew | Daily Output | Labor-Hours | Unit | Material | 2010 Bare Costs Labor | Equipment | Total | Total Incl O&P |
|---|---|---|---|---|---|---|---|---|---|---|
| 6772 | 6" x 6" | 1 Carp | 1.20 | 6.667 | C | 3,500 | 194 | | 3,694 | 4,175 |
| 6774 | 7-1/2" x 7-1/2" | | 1.20 | 6.667 | | 3,850 | 194 | | 4,044 | 4,550 |
| 6776 | 8" x 8" | ↓ | 1.20 | 6.667 | ↓ | 3,975 | 194 | | 4,169 | 4,700 |
| 6790 | Post-beam connection caps | | | | | | | | | |
| 6792 | Beam size 3-9/16" | | | | | | | | | |
| 6794 | 12 ga. post, 4" x 4" | 1 Carp | 1 | 8 | C | 2,425 | 233 | | 2,658 | 3,075 |
| 6796 | 4" x 6" | | 1 | 8 | | 3,250 | 233 | | 3,483 | 3,975 |
| 6798 | 4" x 8" | | 1 | 8 | | 4,800 | 233 | | 5,033 | 5,675 |
| 6800 | 16 ga. post, 4" x 4" | | 1 | 8 | | 1,100 | 233 | | 1,333 | 1,600 |
| 6802 | 4" x 6" | | 1 | 8 | | 1,825 | 233 | | 2,058 | 2,425 |
| 6804 | 4" x 8" | | 1 | 8 | | 3,100 | 233 | | 3,333 | 3,800 |
| 6805 | 18 ga. post, 2-7/8" x 3" | ↓ | 1 | 8 | ↓ | 3,100 | 233 | | 3,333 | 3,800 |
| 6806 | Beam size 5-1/2" | | | | | | | | | |
| 6808 | 12 ga. post, 6" x 4" | 1 Carp | 1 | 8 | C | 3,175 | 233 | | 3,408 | 3,900 |
| 6810 | 6" x 6" | | 1 | 8 | | 5,000 | 233 | | 5,233 | 5,900 |
| 6812 | 6" x 8" | | 1 | 8 | | 3,450 | 233 | | 3,683 | 4,200 |
| 6816 | 16 ga. post, 6" x 4" | | 1 | 8 | | 1,725 | 233 | | 1,958 | 2,300 |
| 6818 | 6" x 6" | ↓ | 1 | 8 | ↓ | 1,825 | 233 | | 2,058 | 2,425 |
| 6820 | Beam size 7-1/2" | | | | | | | | | |
| 6822 | 12 ga. post, 8" x 4" | 1 Carp | 1 | 8 | C | 4,400 | 233 | | 4,633 | 5,250 |
| 6824 | 8" x 6" | | 1 | 8 | | 4,600 | 233 | | 4,833 | 5,475 |
| 6826 | 8" x 8" | ↓ | 1 | 8 | ↓ | 6,950 | 233 | | 7,183 | 8,025 |
| 6840 | Purlin anchors, embedded | | | | | | | | | |
| 6842 | Heavy duty, 10 ga. | | | | | | | | | |
| 6844 | Straight, 28" long | 1 Carp | 1.60 | 5 | C | 1,200 | 146 | | 1,346 | 1,575 |
| 6846 | 35" long | | 1.50 | 5.333 | | 1,500 | 155 | | 1,655 | 1,900 |
| 6848 | Twisted, 28" long | | 1.60 | 5 | | 1,200 | 146 | | 1,346 | 1,575 |
| 6850 | 35" long | ↓ | 1.50 | 5.333 | ↓ | 1,500 | 155 | | 1,655 | 1,900 |
| 6852 | Regular duty, 12 ga. | | | | | | | | | |
| 6854 | Straight, 18-1/2" long | 1 Carp | 1.80 | 4.444 | C | 695 | 129 | | 824 | 980 |
| 6856 | 23-3/4" long | | 1.70 | 4.706 | | 870 | 137 | | 1,007 | 1,175 |
| 6858 | 29" long | | 1.60 | 5 | | 890 | 146 | | 1,036 | 1,225 |
| 6860 | 35" long | | 1.50 | 5.333 | | 1,225 | 155 | | 1,380 | 1,600 |
| 6862 | Twisted, 18" long | | 1.80 | 4.444 | | 695 | 129 | | 824 | 980 |
| 6866 | 28" long | | 1.60 | 5 | | 825 | 146 | | 971 | 1,150 |
| 6868 | 35" long | ↓ | 1.50 | 5.333 | ↓ | 1,225 | 155 | | 1,380 | 1,600 |
| 6870 | Straight, plastic coated | | | | | | | | | |
| 6872 | 23-1/2" long | 1 Carp | 1.60 | 5 | C | 1,700 | 146 | | 1,846 | 2,125 |
| 6874 | 26-7/8" long | | 1.60 | 5 | | 2,000 | 146 | | 2,146 | 2,450 |
| 6876 | 32-1/2" long | | 1.50 | 5.333 | | 2,125 | 155 | | 2,280 | 2,600 |
| 6878 | 35-7/8" long | ↓ | 1.50 | 5.333 | ↓ | 2,225 | 155 | | 2,380 | 2,675 |
| 6890 | Purlin hangers, painted | | | | | | | | | |
| 6892 | 12 ga., 2" x 6" | 1 Carp | 1.80 | 4.444 | C | 1,575 | 129 | | 1,704 | 1,950 |
| 6894 | 2" x 8" | | 1.80 | 4.444 | | 1,700 | 129 | | 1,829 | 2,100 |
| 6896 | 2" x 10" | | 1.80 | 4.444 | | 1,825 | 129 | | 1,954 | 2,250 |
| 6898 | 2" x 12" | | 1.75 | 4.571 | | 1,975 | 133 | | 2,108 | 2,400 |
| 6900 | 2" x 14" | | 1.75 | 4.571 | | 2,100 | 133 | | 2,233 | 2,525 |
| 6902 | 2" x 16" | | 1.75 | 4.571 | | 2,225 | 133 | | 2,358 | 2,675 |
| 6904 | 3" x 6" | | 1.70 | 4.706 | | 1,575 | 137 | | 1,712 | 1,950 |
| 6906 | 3" x 8" | | 1.70 | 4.706 | | 1,700 | 137 | | 1,837 | 2,100 |
| 6908 | 3" x 10" | | 1.70 | 4.706 | | 1,850 | 137 | | 1,987 | 2,250 |
| 6910 | 3" x 12" | | 1.65 | 4.848 | | 2,100 | 141 | | 2,241 | 2,550 |
| 6912 | 3" x 14" | ↓ | 1.65 | 4.848 | ↓ | 2,250 | 141 | | 2,391 | 2,700 |

## 06 05 23 – Wood, Plastic, and Composite Fastenings

| 06 05 23.60 Timber Connectors | | Crew | Daily Output | Labor-Hours | Unit | Material | 2010 Bare Costs Labor | Equipment | Total | Total Incl O&P |
|---|---|---|---|---|---|---|---|---|---|---|
| 6914 | 3" x 16" | 1 Carp | 1.65 | 4.848 | C | 2,375 | 141 | | 2,516 | 2,850 |
| 6916 | 4" x 6" | | 1.65 | 4.848 | | 1,575 | 141 | | 1,716 | 1,950 |
| 6918 | 4" x 8" | | 1.65 | 4.848 | | 1,725 | 141 | | 1,866 | 2,100 |
| 6920 | 4" x 10" | | 1.65 | 4.848 | | 1,850 | 141 | | 1,991 | 2,250 |
| 6922 | 4" x 12" | | 1.60 | 5 | | 2,200 | 146 | | 2,346 | 2,650 |
| 6924 | 4" x 14" | | 1.60 | 5 | | 2,325 | 146 | | 2,471 | 2,800 |
| 6926 | 4" x 16" | | 1.60 | 5 | | 2,450 | 146 | | 2,596 | 2,950 |
| 6928 | 6" x 6" | | 1.60 | 5 | | 2,075 | 146 | | 2,221 | 2,550 |
| 6930 | 6" x 8" | | 1.60 | 5 | | 2,200 | 146 | | 2,346 | 2,675 |
| 6932 | 6" x 10" | | 1.55 | 5.161 | | 2,250 | 150 | | 2,400 | 2,725 |
| 6934 | double 2" x 6" | | 1.70 | 4.706 | | 1,700 | 137 | | 1,837 | 2,100 |
| 6936 | double 2" x 8" | | 1.70 | 4.706 | | 1,850 | 137 | | 1,987 | 2,250 |
| 6938 | double 2" x 10" | | 1.70 | 4.706 | | 1,975 | 137 | | 2,112 | 2,400 |
| 6940 | double 2" x 12" | | 1.65 | 4.848 | | 2,100 | 141 | | 2,241 | 2,550 |
| 6942 | double 2" x 14" | | 1.65 | 4.848 | | 2,250 | 141 | | 2,391 | 2,700 |
| 6944 | double 2" x 16" | | 1.65 | 4.848 | | 2,375 | 141 | | 2,516 | 2,850 |
| 6960 | 11 ga., 4" x 6" | | 1.65 | 4.848 | | 3,125 | 141 | | 3,266 | 3,650 |
| 6962 | 4" x 8" | | 1.65 | 4.848 | | 3,350 | 141 | | 3,491 | 3,925 |
| 6964 | 4" x 10" | | 1.65 | 4.848 | | 3,575 | 141 | | 3,716 | 4,175 |
| 6966 | 6" x 6" | | 1.60 | 5 | | 3,150 | 146 | | 3,296 | 3,725 |
| 6968 | 6" x 8" | | 1.60 | 5 | | 3,400 | 146 | | 3,546 | 3,975 |
| 6970 | 6" x 10" | | 1.55 | 5.161 | | 3,625 | 150 | | 3,775 | 4,225 |
| 6972 | 6" x 12" | | 1.55 | 5.161 | | 3,850 | 150 | | 4,000 | 4,500 |
| 6974 | 6" x 14" | | 1.55 | 5.161 | | 4,075 | 150 | | 4,225 | 4,750 |
| 6976 | 6" x 16" | | 1.50 | 5.333 | | 4,325 | 155 | | 4,480 | 5,000 |
| 6978 | 7 ga., 8" x 6" | | 1.60 | 5 | | 3,425 | 146 | | 3,571 | 4,025 |
| 6980 | 8" x 8" | | 1.60 | 5 | | 3,650 | 146 | | 3,796 | 4,275 |
| 6982 | 8" x 10" | | 1.55 | 5.161 | | 3,900 | 150 | | 4,050 | 4,525 |
| 6984 | 8" x 12" | | 1.55 | 5.161 | | 4,125 | 150 | | 4,275 | 4,775 |
| 6986 | 8" x 14" | | 1.50 | 5.333 | | 4,350 | 155 | | 4,505 | 5,050 |
| 6988 | 8" x 16" | | 1.50 | 5.333 | | 4,575 | 155 | | 4,730 | 5,300 |
| 7000 | Strap connectors, galvanized | | | | | | | | | |
| 7002 | 12 ga., 2-1/16" x 36" | 1 Carp | 1.55 | 5.161 | C | 995 | 150 | | 1,145 | 1,350 |
| 7004 | 2-1/16" x 47" | | 1.50 | 5.333 | | 1,375 | 155 | | 1,530 | 1,775 |
| 7005 | 10 ga., 2-1/16" x 72" | | 1.50 | 5.333 | | 1,375 | 155 | | 1,530 | 1,775 |
| 7006 | 7 ga., 2-1/16" x 34" | | 1.55 | 5.161 | | 2,475 | 150 | | 2,625 | 2,975 |
| 7008 | 2-1/16" x 45" | | 1.50 | 5.333 | | 3,200 | 155 | | 3,355 | 3,775 |
| 7010 | 3 ga., 3" x 32" | | 1.55 | 5.161 | | 4,150 | 150 | | 4,300 | 4,825 |
| 7012 | 3" x 41" | | 1.55 | 5.161 | | 4,325 | 150 | | 4,475 | 5,000 |
| 7014 | 3" x 50" | | 1.50 | 5.333 | | 6,575 | 155 | | 6,730 | 7,475 |
| 7016 | 3" x 59" | | 1.50 | 5.333 | | 8,000 | 155 | | 8,155 | 9,050 |
| 7018 | 3-1/2" x 68" | | 1.45 | 5.517 | | 8,125 | 161 | | 8,286 | 9,225 |
| 7030 | Tension ties | | | | | | | | | |
| 7032 | 19-1/8" long, 16 ga., 3/4" anchor bolt | 1 Carp | 1.80 | 4.444 | C | 1,150 | 129 | | 1,279 | 1,475 |
| 7034 | 20" long, 12 ga., 1/2" anchor bolt | | 1.80 | 4.444 | | 1,475 | 129 | | 1,604 | 1,850 |
| 7036 | 20" long, 12 ga., 3/4" anchor bolt | | 1.80 | 4.444 | | 1,475 | 129 | | 1,604 | 1,850 |
| 7038 | 27-3/4" long, 12 ga., 3/4" anchor bolt | | 1.75 | 4.571 | | 2,625 | 133 | | 2,758 | 3,100 |
| 7050 | Truss connectors, galvanized | | | | | | | | | |
| 7052 | Adjustable hanger | | | | | | | | | |
| 7054 | 18 ga., 2" x 6" | 1 Carp | 1.65 | 4.848 | C | 445 | 141 | | 586 | 725 |
| 7056 | 4" x 6" | | 1.65 | 4.848 | | 585 | 141 | | 726 | 880 |
| 7058 | 16 ga., 4" x 10" | | 1.60 | 5 | | 860 | 146 | | 1,006 | 1,200 |
| 7060 | (2) 2" x 10" | | 1.60 | 5 | | 860 | 146 | | 1,006 | 1,200 |

# 06 05 Common Work Results for Wood, Plastics, and Composites

## 06 05 23 – Wood, Plastic, and Composite Fastenings

| 06 05 23.60  Timber Connectors | Crew | Daily Output | Labor-Hours | Unit | Material | 2010 Bare Costs Labor | Equipment | Total | Total Incl O&P |
|---|---|---|---|---|---|---|---|---|---|
| 7062  Connectors to plate | | | | | | | | | |
| 7064  16 ga., 2" x 4" plate | 1 Carp | 1.80 | 4.444 | C | 440 | 129 | | 569 | 705 |
| 7066  2" x 6" plate | " | 1.80 | 4.444 | " | 570 | 129 | | 699 | 845 |
| 7068  Hip jack connector | | | | | | | | | |
| 7070  14 ga. | 1 Carp | 1.50 | 5.333 | C | 2,325 | 155 | | 2,480 | 2,800 |

| 06 05 23.70  Rough Hardware | | | | | | | | | |
|---|---|---|---|---|---|---|---|---|---|
| 0010  **ROUGH HARDWARE**, average percent of carpentry material | | | | | | | | | |
| 0020  Minimum | | | | Job | .50% | | | | |
| 0200  Maximum | | | | | 1.50% | | | | |
| 0210  In seismic or hurricane areas, up to | | | | | 10% | | | | |

| 06 05 23.80  Metal Bracing | | | | | | | | | |
|---|---|---|---|---|---|---|---|---|---|
| 0010  **METAL BRACING** | | | | | | | | | |
| 0302  Let-in, "T" shaped, 22 ga. galv. steel, studs at 16" O.C. | 1 Carp | 580 | .014 | L.F. | .75 | .40 | | 1.15 | 1.51 |
| 0402  Studs at 24" O.C. | | 600 | .013 | | .75 | .39 | | 1.14 | 1.48 |
| 0502  16 ga. galv. steel straps, studs at 16" O.C. | | 600 | .013 | | .97 | .39 | | 1.36 | 1.72 |
| 0602  Studs at 24" O.C. | | 620 | .013 | | .97 | .38 | | 1.35 | 1.70 |

# 06 11 Wood Framing

## 06 11 10 – Framing with Dimensional, Engineered or Composite Lumber

### 06 11 10.02  Blocking

| | Crew | Daily Output | Labor-Hours | Unit | Material | Labor | Equipment | Total | Total Incl O&P |
|---|---|---|---|---|---|---|---|---|---|
| 0010  **BLOCKING** | | | | | | | | | |
| 1950  Miscellaneous, to wood construction | | | | | | | | | |
| 2000  2" x 4" | 1 Carp | 250 | .032 | L.F. | .25 | .93 | | 1.18 | 1.84 |
| 2005  Pneumatic nailed | | 305 | .026 | | .25 | .76 | | 1.01 | 1.55 |
| 2050  2" x 6" | | 222 | .036 | | .38 | 1.05 | | 1.43 | 2.17 |
| 2055  Pneumatic nailed | | 271 | .030 | | .38 | .86 | | 1.24 | 1.86 |
| 2100  2" x 8" | | 200 | .040 | | .56 | 1.16 | | 1.72 | 2.57 |
| 2105  Pneumatic nailed | | 244 | .033 | | .56 | .95 | | 1.51 | 2.22 |
| 2150  2" x 10" | | 178 | .045 | | .72 | 1.31 | | 2.03 | 3 |
| 2155  Pneumatic nailed | | 217 | .037 | | .72 | 1.07 | | 1.79 | 2.60 |
| 2200  2" x 12" | | 151 | .053 | | 1.06 | 1.54 | | 2.60 | 3.76 |
| 2205  Pneumatic nailed | | 185 | .043 | | 1.06 | 1.26 | | 2.32 | 3.29 |
| 2300  To steel construction | | | | | | | | | |
| 2320  2" x 4" | 1 Carp | 208 | .038 | L.F. | .25 | 1.12 | | 1.37 | 2.15 |
| 2340  2" x 6" | | 180 | .044 | | .38 | 1.29 | | 1.67 | 2.59 |
| 2360  2" x 8" | | 158 | .051 | | .56 | 1.47 | | 2.03 | 3.09 |
| 2380  2" x 10" | | 136 | .059 | | .72 | 1.71 | | 2.43 | 3.68 |
| 2400  2" x 12" | | 109 | .073 | | 1.06 | 2.14 | | 3.20 | 4.76 |

### 06 11 10.04  Bracing

| | Crew | Daily Output | Labor-Hours | Unit | Material | Labor | Equipment | Total | Total Incl O&P |
|---|---|---|---|---|---|---|---|---|---|
| 0012  **BRACING** Let-in, with 1" x 6" boards, studs @ 16" O.C. | 1 Carp | 150 | .053 | L.F. | .64 | 1.55 | | 2.19 | 3.31 |
| 0202  Studs @ 24" O.C. | " | 230 | .035 | " | .64 | 1.01 | | 1.65 | 2.40 |

### 06 11 10.06  Bridging

| | Crew | Daily Output | Labor-Hours | Unit | Material | Labor | Equipment | Total | Total Incl O&P |
|---|---|---|---|---|---|---|---|---|---|
| 0012  **BRIDGING** Wood, for joists 16" O.C., 1" x 3" | 1 Carp | 130 | .062 | Pr. | .51 | 1.79 | | 2.30 | 3.57 |
| 0017  Pneumatic nailed | | 170 | .047 | | .51 | 1.37 | | 1.88 | 2.86 |
| 0102  2" x 3" bridging | | 130 | .062 | | .40 | 1.79 | | 2.19 | 3.45 |
| 0107  Pneumatic nailed | | 170 | .047 | | .40 | 1.37 | | 1.77 | 2.74 |
| 0302  Steel, galvanized, 18 ga., for 2" x 10" joists at 12" O.C. | | 130 | .062 | | 1.58 | 1.79 | | 3.37 | 4.75 |
| 0402  24" O.C. | | 140 | .057 | | 1.69 | 1.66 | | 3.35 | 4.66 |
| 0602  For 2" x 14" joists at 16" O.C. | | 130 | .062 | | 1.70 | 1.79 | | 3.49 | 4.88 |
| 0902  Compression type, 16" O.C., 2" x 8" joists | | 200 | .040 | | 1.64 | 1.16 | | 2.80 | 3.76 |

# 06 11 Wood Framing

## 06 11 10 – Framing with Dimensional, Engineered or Composite Lumber

| 06 11 10.06 Bridging | | Crew | Daily Output | Labor-Hours | Unit | Material | 2010 Bare Costs Labor | Equipment | Total | Total Incl O&P |
|---|---|---|---|---|---|---|---|---|---|---|
| 1002 | 2" x 12" joists | 1 Carp | 200 | .040 | Pr. | 1.64 | 1.16 | | 2.80 | 3.76 |

### 06 11 10.10 Beam and Girder Framing

| 0010 | **BEAM AND GIRDER FRAMING** | R061110-30 | | | | | | | | |
|---|---|---|---|---|---|---|---|---|---|---|
| 1000 | Single, 2" x 6" | 2 Carp | 700 | .023 | L.F. | .38 | .67 | | 1.05 | 1.53 |
| 1005 | Pneumatic nailed | | 812 | .020 | | .38 | .57 | | .95 | 1.37 |
| 1020 | 2" x 8" | | 650 | .025 | | .56 | .72 | | 1.28 | 1.82 |
| 1025 | Pneumatic nailed | | 754 | .021 | | .56 | .62 | | 1.18 | 1.65 |
| 1040 | 2" x 10" | | 600 | .027 | | .72 | .78 | | 1.50 | 2.11 |
| 1045 | Pneumatic nailed | | 696 | .023 | | .72 | .67 | | 1.39 | 1.93 |
| 1060 | 2" x 12" | | 550 | .029 | | 1.06 | .85 | | 1.91 | 2.59 |
| 1065 | Pneumatic nailed | | 638 | .025 | | 1.06 | .73 | | 1.79 | 2.40 |
| 1080 | 2" x 14" | | 500 | .032 | | 2 | .93 | | 2.93 | 3.77 |
| 1085 | Pneumatic nailed | | 580 | .028 | | 2 | .80 | | 2.80 | 3.55 |
| 1100 | 3" x 8" | | 550 | .029 | | 2.08 | .85 | | 2.93 | 3.71 |
| 1120 | 3" x 10" | | 500 | .032 | | 2.77 | .93 | | 3.70 | 4.62 |
| 1140 | 3" x 12" | | 450 | .036 | | 3.54 | 1.03 | | 4.57 | 5.65 |
| 1160 | 3" x 14" | | 400 | .040 | | 4.48 | 1.16 | | 5.64 | 6.90 |
| 1170 | 4" x 6" | F-3 | 1100 | .036 | | 2.39 | .96 | .60 | 3.95 | 4.90 |
| 1180 | 4" x 8" | | 1000 | .040 | | 2.88 | 1.06 | .66 | 4.60 | 5.65 |
| 1200 | 4" x 10" | | 950 | .042 | | 3.64 | 1.11 | .69 | 5.44 | 6.65 |
| 1220 | 4" x 12" | | 900 | .044 | | 6.10 | 1.18 | .73 | 8.01 | 9.45 |
| 1240 | 4" x 14" | | 850 | .047 | | 7.15 | 1.25 | .77 | 9.17 | 10.80 |
| 2000 | Double, 2" x 6" | 2 Carp | 625 | .026 | | .75 | .75 | | 1.50 | 2.08 |
| 2005 | Pneumatic nailed | | 725 | .022 | | .75 | .64 | | 1.39 | 1.91 |
| 2020 | 2" x 8" | | 575 | .028 | | 1.12 | .81 | | 1.93 | 2.59 |
| 2025 | Pneumatic nailed | | 667 | .024 | | 1.12 | .70 | | 1.82 | 2.40 |
| 2040 | 2" x 10" | | 550 | .029 | | 1.45 | .85 | | 2.30 | 3.01 |
| 2045 | Pneumatic nailed | | 638 | .025 | | 1.45 | .73 | | 2.18 | 2.82 |
| 2060 | 2" x 12" | | 525 | .030 | | 2.12 | .89 | | 3.01 | 3.82 |
| 2065 | Pneumatic nailed | | 610 | .026 | | 2.12 | .76 | | 2.88 | 3.61 |
| 2080 | 2" x 14" | | 475 | .034 | | 4 | .98 | | 4.98 | 6.05 |
| 2085 | Pneumatic nailed | | 551 | .029 | | 4 | .85 | | 4.85 | 5.80 |
| 3000 | Triple, 2" x 6" | | 550 | .029 | | 1.13 | .85 | | 1.98 | 2.66 |
| 3005 | Pneumatic nailed | | 638 | .025 | | 1.13 | .73 | | 1.86 | 2.47 |
| 3020 | 2" x 8" | | 525 | .030 | | 1.67 | .89 | | 2.56 | 3.33 |
| 3025 | Pneumatic nailed | | 609 | .026 | | 1.67 | .76 | | 2.43 | 3.13 |
| 3040 | 2" x 10" | | 500 | .032 | | 2.17 | .93 | | 3.10 | 3.96 |
| 3045 | Pneumatic nailed | | 580 | .028 | | 2.17 | .80 | | 2.97 | 3.74 |
| 3060 | 2" x 12" | | 475 | .034 | | 3.18 | .98 | | 4.16 | 5.15 |
| 3065 | Pneumatic nailed | | 551 | .029 | | 3.18 | .85 | | 4.03 | 4.92 |
| 3080 | 2" x 14" | | 450 | .036 | | 6 | 1.03 | | 7.03 | 8.35 |
| 3085 | Pneumatic nailed | | 522 | .031 | | 6 | .89 | | 6.89 | 8.10 |

### 06 11 10.12 Ceiling Framing

| 0010 | **CEILING FRAMING** | | | | | | | | | |
|---|---|---|---|---|---|---|---|---|---|---|
| 6000 | Suspended, 2" x 3" | 2 Carp | 1000 | .016 | L.F. | .27 | .47 | | .74 | 1.07 |
| 6050 | 2" x 4" | | 900 | .018 | | .25 | .52 | | .77 | 1.14 |
| 6100 | 2" x 6" | | 800 | .020 | | .38 | .58 | | .96 | 1.39 |
| 6150 | 2" x 8" | | 650 | .025 | | .56 | .72 | | 1.28 | 1.82 |

### 06 11 10.14 Posts and Columns

| 0010 | **POSTS AND COLUMNS** | | | | | | | | | |
|---|---|---|---|---|---|---|---|---|---|---|
| 0101 | 4" x 4" | 2 Carp | 390 | .041 | L.F. | 1.55 | 1.19 | | 2.74 | 3.71 |
| 0151 | 4" x 6" | | 275 | .058 | | 2.39 | 1.69 | | 4.08 | 5.50 |

# 06 11 Wood Framing

## 06 11 10 – Framing with Dimensional, Engineered or Composite Lumber

### 06 11 10.14 Posts and Columns

| | | Crew | Daily Output | Labor-Hours | Unit | Material | 2010 Bare Costs Labor | Equipment | Total | Total Incl O&P |
|---|---|---|---|---|---|---|---|---|---|---|
| 0201 | 4" x 8" | 2 Carp | 220 | .073 | L.F. | 2.88 | 2.12 | | 5 | 6.75 |
| 0251 | 6" x 6" | | 215 | .074 | | 3.19 | 2.17 | | 5.36 | 7.15 |
| 0301 | 6" x 8" | | 175 | .091 | | 4.28 | 2.66 | | 6.94 | 9.20 |
| 0351 | 6" x 10" | | 150 | .107 | | 6.60 | 3.10 | | 9.70 | 12.50 |

### 06 11 10.18 Joist Framing

| | | Crew | Daily Output | Labor-Hours | Unit | Material | 2010 Bare Costs Labor | Equipment | Total | Total Incl O&P |
|---|---|---|---|---|---|---|---|---|---|---|
| 0010 | **JOIST FRAMING** | | | | | | | | | |
| 2002 | Joists, 2" x 4" | 2 Carp | 1250 | .013 | L.F. | .25 | .37 | | .62 | .90 |
| 2007 | Pneumatic nailed | | 1438 | .011 | | .25 | .32 | | .57 | .81 |
| 2100 | 2" x 6" | | 1250 | .013 | | .38 | .37 | | .75 | 1.04 |
| 2105 | Pneumatic nailed | | 1438 | .011 | | .38 | .32 | | .70 | .95 |
| 2152 | 2" x 8" | | 1100 | .015 | | .56 | .42 | | .98 | 1.32 |
| 2157 | Pneumatic nailed | | 1265 | .013 | | .56 | .37 | | .93 | 1.23 |
| 2202 | 2" x 10" | | 900 | .018 | | .72 | .52 | | 1.24 | 1.67 |
| 2207 | Pneumatic nailed | | 1035 | .015 | | .72 | .45 | | 1.17 | 1.56 |
| 2252 | 2" x 12" | | 875 | .018 | | 1.06 | .53 | | 1.59 | 2.07 |
| 2257 | Pneumatic nailed | | 1006 | .016 | | 1.06 | .46 | | 1.52 | 1.95 |
| 2302 | 2" x 14" | | 770 | .021 | | 2 | .60 | | 2.60 | 3.22 |
| 2307 | Pneumatic nailed | | 886 | .018 | | 2 | .53 | | 2.53 | 3.08 |
| 2352 | 3" x 6" | | 925 | .017 | | 1.39 | .50 | | 1.89 | 2.38 |
| 2402 | 3" x 10" | | 780 | .021 | | 2.77 | .60 | | 3.37 | 4.05 |
| 2452 | 3" x 12" | | 600 | .027 | | 3.54 | .78 | | 4.32 | 5.20 |
| 2502 | 4" x 6" | | 800 | .020 | | 2.39 | .58 | | 2.97 | 3.61 |
| 2552 | 4" x 10" | | 600 | .027 | | 3.64 | .78 | | 4.42 | 5.30 |
| 2602 | 4" x 12" | | 450 | .036 | | 6.10 | 1.03 | | 7.13 | 8.45 |
| 2607 | Sister joist, 2" x 6" | | 800 | .020 | | .38 | .58 | | .96 | 1.39 |
| 2608 | Pneumatic nailed | | 960 | .017 | | .38 | .49 | | .87 | 1.23 |
| 3000 | Composite wood joist 9-1/2" deep | | .90 | 17.778 | M.L.F. | 1,575 | 515 | | 2,090 | 2,600 |
| 3010 | 11-1/2" deep | | .88 | 18.182 | | 1,700 | 530 | | 2,230 | 2,750 |
| 3020 | 14" deep | | .82 | 19.512 | | 2,325 | 570 | | 2,895 | 3,525 |
| 3030 | 16" deep | | .78 | 20.513 | | 3,075 | 595 | | 3,670 | 4,375 |
| 4000 | Open web joist 12" deep | | .88 | 18.182 | | 2,775 | 530 | | 3,305 | 3,950 |
| 4010 | 14" deep | | .82 | 19.512 | | 2,975 | 570 | | 3,545 | 4,225 |
| 4020 | 16" deep | | .78 | 20.513 | | 2,950 | 595 | | 3,545 | 4,250 |
| 4030 | 18" deep | | .74 | 21.622 | | 3,175 | 630 | | 3,805 | 4,550 |
| 6000 | Composite rim joist, 1-1/4" x 9-1/2" | | .90 | 17.778 | | 1,700 | 515 | | 2,215 | 2,750 |
| 6010 | 1-1/4" x 11-1/2" | | .88 | 18.182 | | 2,125 | 530 | | 2,655 | 3,225 |
| 6020 | 1-1/4" x 14-1/2" | | .82 | 19.512 | | 2,425 | 570 | | 2,995 | 3,625 |
| 6030 | 1-1/4" x 16-1/2" | | .78 | 20.513 | | 3,100 | 595 | | 3,695 | 4,425 |

### 06 11 10.24 Miscellaneous Framing

| | | Crew | Daily Output | Labor-Hours | Unit | Material | 2010 Bare Costs Labor | Equipment | Total | Total Incl O&P |
|---|---|---|---|---|---|---|---|---|---|---|
| 0010 | **MISCELLANEOUS FRAMING** | | | | | | | | | |
| 2002 | Firestops, 2" x 4" | 2 Carp | 780 | .021 | L.F. | .25 | .60 | | .85 | 1.27 |
| 2007 | Pneumatic nailed | | 952 | .017 | | .25 | .49 | | .74 | 1.09 |
| 2102 | 2" x 6" | | 600 | .027 | | .38 | .78 | | 1.16 | 1.72 |
| 2107 | Pneumatic nailed | | 732 | .022 | | .38 | .64 | | 1.02 | 1.48 |
| 5002 | Nailers, treated, wood construction, 2" x 4" | | 800 | .020 | | .35 | .58 | | .93 | 1.36 |
| 5007 | Pneumatic nailed | | 960 | .017 | | .35 | .49 | | .84 | 1.20 |
| 5102 | 2" x 6" | | 750 | .021 | | .56 | .62 | | 1.18 | 1.65 |
| 5107 | Pneumatic nailed | | 900 | .018 | | .56 | .52 | | 1.08 | 1.48 |
| 5122 | 2" x 8" | | 700 | .023 | | 1.03 | .67 | | 1.70 | 2.26 |
| 5127 | Pneumatic nailed | | 840 | .019 | | 1.03 | .55 | | 1.58 | 2.07 |
| 5202 | Steel construction, 2" x 4" | | 750 | .021 | | .35 | .62 | | .97 | 1.42 |
| 5222 | 2" x 6" | | 700 | .023 | | .56 | .67 | | 1.23 | 1.73 |

# 06 11 Wood Framing

## 06 11 10 – Framing with Dimensional, Engineered or Composite Lumber

| 06 11 10.24 Miscellaneous Framing | | Crew | Daily Output | Labor-Hours | Unit | Material | 2010 Bare Costs Labor | Equipment | Total | Total Incl O&P |
|---|---|---|---|---|---|---|---|---|---|---|
| 5242 | 2" x 8" | 2 Carp | 650 | .025 | L.F. | 1.03 | .72 | | 1.75 | 2.35 |
| 7002 | Rough bucks, treated, for doors or windows, 2" x 6" | | 400 | .040 | | .56 | 1.16 | | 1.72 | 2.57 |
| 7007 | Pneumatic nailed | | 480 | .033 | | .56 | .97 | | 1.53 | 2.24 |
| 7102 | 2" x 8" | | 380 | .042 | | 1.03 | 1.23 | | 2.26 | 3.20 |
| 7107 | Pneumatic nailed | | 456 | .035 | | 1.03 | 1.02 | | 2.05 | 2.86 |
| 8001 | Stair stringers, 2" x 10" | | 130 | .123 | | .72 | 3.58 | | 4.30 | 6.80 |
| 8101 | 2" x 12" | | 130 | .123 | | 1.06 | 3.58 | | 4.64 | 7.15 |
| 8151 | 3" x 10" | | 125 | .128 | | 2.77 | 3.72 | | 6.49 | 9.30 |
| 8201 | 3" x 12" | | 125 | .128 | | 3.54 | 3.72 | | 7.26 | 10.15 |
| 8870 | Laminated structural lumber, 1-1/4" x 11-1/2" | | 130 | .123 | | 2.11 | 3.58 | | 5.69 | 8.30 |
| 8880 | 1-1/4" x 14-1/2" | | 130 | .123 | | 2.43 | 3.58 | | 6.01 | 8.70 |

## 06 11 10.26 Partitions

| | | Crew | Daily Output | Labor-Hours | Unit | Material | 2010 Bare Costs Labor | Equipment | Total | Total Incl O&P |
|---|---|---|---|---|---|---|---|---|---|---|
| 0010 | **PARTITIONS** | | | | | | | | | |
| 0020 | Single bottom and double top plate, no waste, std. & better lumber | | | | | | | | | |
| 0182 | 2" x 4" studs, 8' high, studs 12" O.C. | 2 Carp | 80 | .200 | L.F. | 3.01 | 5.80 | | 8.81 | 13.10 |
| 0187 | 12" O.C., pneumatic nailed | | 96 | .167 | | 3.01 | 4.85 | | 7.86 | 11.45 |
| 0202 | 16" O.C. | | 100 | .160 | | 2.46 | 4.66 | | 7.12 | 10.55 |
| 0207 | 16" O.C., pneumatic nailed | | 120 | .133 | | 2.46 | 3.88 | | 6.34 | 9.25 |
| 0302 | 24" O.C. | | 125 | .128 | | 1.91 | 3.72 | | 5.63 | 8.35 |
| 0307 | 24" O.C., pneumatic nailed | | 150 | .107 | | 1.91 | 3.10 | | 5.01 | 7.30 |
| 0382 | 10' high, studs 12" O.C. | | 80 | .200 | | 3.56 | 5.80 | | 9.36 | 13.70 |
| 0387 | 12" O.C., pneumatic nailed | | 96 | .167 | | 3.56 | 4.85 | | 8.41 | 12.05 |
| 0402 | 16" O.C. | | 100 | .160 | | 2.87 | 4.66 | | 7.53 | 11 |
| 0407 | 16" O.C., pneumatic nailed | | 120 | .133 | | 2.87 | 3.88 | | 6.75 | 9.70 |
| 0502 | 24" O.C. | | 125 | .128 | | 2.19 | 3.72 | | 5.91 | 8.65 |
| 0507 | 24" O.C., pneumatic nailed | | 150 | .107 | | 2.19 | 3.10 | | 5.29 | 7.60 |
| 0582 | 12' high, studs 12" O.C. | | 65 | .246 | | 4.10 | 7.15 | | 11.25 | 16.55 |
| 0587 | 12" O.C., pneumatic nailed | | 78 | .205 | | 4.10 | 5.95 | | 10.05 | 14.55 |
| 0602 | 16" O.C. | | 80 | .200 | | 3.28 | 5.80 | | 9.08 | 13.40 |
| 0607 | 16" O.C., pneumatic nailed | | 96 | .167 | | 3.28 | 4.85 | | 8.13 | 11.75 |
| 0700 | 24" O.C. | | 100 | .160 | | 2.24 | 4.66 | | 6.90 | 10.30 |
| 0705 | 24" O.C., pneumatic nailed | | 120 | .133 | | 2.24 | 3.88 | | 6.12 | 9 |
| 0782 | 2" x 6" studs, 8' high, studs 12" O.C. | | 70 | .229 | | 4.56 | 6.65 | | 11.21 | 16.20 |
| 0787 | 12" O.C., pneumatic nailed | | 84 | .190 | | 4.56 | 5.55 | | 10.11 | 14.30 |
| 0802 | 16" O.C. | | 90 | .178 | | 3.73 | 5.15 | | 8.88 | 12.80 |
| 0807 | 16" O.C., pneumatic nailed | | 108 | .148 | | 3.73 | 4.31 | | 8.04 | 11.35 |
| 0902 | 24" O.C. | | 115 | .139 | | 2.90 | 4.05 | | 6.95 | 10 |
| 0907 | 24" O.C., pneumatic nailed | | 138 | .116 | | 2.90 | 3.37 | | 6.27 | 8.90 |
| 0982 | 10' high, studs 12" O.C. | | 70 | .229 | | 5.40 | 6.65 | | 12.05 | 17.15 |
| 0987 | 12" O.C., pneumatic nailed | | 84 | .190 | | 5.40 | 5.55 | | 10.95 | 15.25 |
| 1002 | 16" O.C. | | 90 | .178 | | 4.35 | 5.15 | | 9.50 | 13.50 |
| 1007 | 16" O.C., pneumatic nailed | | 108 | .148 | | 4.35 | 4.31 | | 8.66 | 12.05 |
| 1102 | 24" O.C. | | 115 | .139 | | 3.32 | 4.05 | | 7.37 | 10.45 |
| 1107 | 24" O.C., pneumatic nailed | | 138 | .116 | | 3.32 | 3.37 | | 6.69 | 9.35 |
| 1182 | 12' high, studs 12" O.C. | | 55 | .291 | | 6.20 | 8.45 | | 14.65 | 21 |
| 1187 | 12" O.C., pneumatic nailed | | 66 | .242 | | 6.20 | 7.05 | | 13.25 | 18.70 |
| 1202 | 16" O.C. | | 70 | .229 | | 4.98 | 6.65 | | 11.63 | 16.65 |
| 1207 | 16" O.C., pneumatic nailed | | 84 | .190 | | 4.98 | 5.55 | | 10.53 | 14.75 |
| 1302 | 24" O.C. | | 90 | .178 | | 3.73 | 5.15 | | 8.88 | 12.80 |
| 1307 | 24" O.C., pneumatic nailed | | 108 | .148 | | 3.73 | 4.31 | | 8.04 | 11.35 |
| 1402 | For horizontal blocking, 2" x 4", add | | 600 | .027 | | .27 | .78 | | 1.05 | 1.61 |
| 1502 | 2" x 6", add | | 600 | .027 | | .41 | .78 | | 1.19 | 1.77 |

# 06 11 Wood Framing

## 06 11 10 – Framing with Dimensional, Engineered or Composite Lumber

| 06 11 10.26 Partitions | Crew | Daily Output | Labor-Hours | Unit | Material | 2010 Bare Costs Labor | Equipment | Total | Total Incl O&P |
|---|---|---|---|---|---|---|---|---|---|
| 1600 | For openings, add | 2 Carp | 250 | .064 | L.F. | | 1.86 | | 1.86 | 3.13 |
| 1702 | Headers for above openings, material only, add | | | | B.F. | .46 | | | .46 | .51 |

## 06 11 10.28 Porch or Deck Framing

| | | Crew | Daily Output | Labor-Hours | Unit | Material | 2010 Bare Costs Labor | Equipment | Total | Total Incl O&P |
|---|---|---|---|---|---|---|---|---|---|---|
| 0010 | **PORCH OR DECK FRAMING** | | | | | | | | | |
| 0100 | Treated lumber, posts or columns, 4" x 4" | 2 Carp | 390 | .041 | L.F. | 1.56 | 1.19 | | 2.75 | 3.72 |
| 0110 | 4" x 6" | | 275 | .058 | | 2.30 | 1.69 | | 3.99 | 5.40 |
| 0120 | 4" x 8" | | 220 | .073 | | 4.74 | 2.12 | | 6.86 | 8.75 |
| 0130 | Girder, single, 4" x 4" | | 675 | .024 | | 1.56 | .69 | | 2.25 | 2.87 |
| 0140 | 4" x 6" | | 600 | .027 | | 2.30 | .78 | | 3.08 | 3.84 |
| 0150 | 4" x 8" | | 525 | .030 | | 4.74 | .89 | | 5.63 | 6.70 |
| 0160 | Double, 2" x 4" | | 625 | .026 | | .72 | .75 | | 1.47 | 2.05 |
| 0170 | 2" x 6" | | 600 | .027 | | 1.16 | .78 | | 1.94 | 2.59 |
| 0180 | 2" x 8" | | 575 | .028 | | 2.13 | .81 | | 2.94 | 3.70 |
| 0190 | 2" x 10" | | 550 | .029 | | 2.78 | .85 | | 3.63 | 4.48 |
| 0200 | 2" x 12" | | 525 | .030 | | 3.69 | .89 | | 4.58 | 5.55 |
| 0210 | Triple, 2" x 4" | | 575 | .028 | | 1.09 | .81 | | 1.90 | 2.55 |
| 0220 | 2" x 6" | | 550 | .029 | | 1.74 | .85 | | 2.59 | 3.34 |
| 0230 | 2" x 8" | | 525 | .030 | | 3.19 | .89 | | 4.08 | 5 |
| 0240 | 2" x 10" | | 500 | .032 | | 4.17 | .93 | | 5.10 | 6.15 |
| 0250 | 2" x 12" | | 475 | .034 | | 5.55 | .98 | | 6.53 | 7.75 |
| 0260 | Ledger, bolted 4' O.C., 2" x 4" | | 400 | .040 | | .47 | 1.16 | | 1.63 | 2.47 |
| 0270 | 2" x 6" | | 395 | .041 | | .68 | 1.18 | | 1.86 | 2.72 |
| 0280 | 2" x 8" | | 390 | .041 | | 1.15 | 1.19 | | 2.34 | 3.28 |
| 0300 | 2" x 12" | | 380 | .042 | | 1.92 | 1.23 | | 3.15 | 4.17 |
| 0310 | Joists, 2" x 4" | | 1250 | .013 | | .36 | .37 | | .73 | 1.03 |
| 0320 | 2" x 6" | | 1250 | .013 | | .58 | .37 | | .95 | 1.27 |
| 0330 | 2" x 8" | | 1100 | .015 | | 1.07 | .42 | | 1.49 | 1.89 |
| 0340 | 2" x 10" | | 900 | .018 | | 1.40 | .52 | | 1.92 | 2.41 |
| 0350 | 2" x 12" | | 875 | .018 | | 1.68 | .53 | | 2.21 | 2.74 |
| 0360 | Railings and trim , 1" x 4" | 1 Carp | 300 | .027 | | .44 | .78 | | 1.22 | 1.79 |
| 0370 | 2" x 2" | | 300 | .027 | | .32 | .78 | | 1.10 | 1.66 |
| 0380 | 2" x 4" | | 300 | .027 | | .35 | .78 | | 1.13 | 1.69 |
| 0390 | 2" x 6" | | 300 | .027 | | .56 | .78 | | 1.34 | 1.92 |
| 0400 | Decking, 1" x 4" | | 275 | .029 | S.F. | 1.55 | .85 | | 2.40 | 3.13 |
| 0410 | 2" x 4" | | 300 | .027 | | 1.19 | .78 | | 1.97 | 2.61 |
| 0420 | 2" x 6" | | 320 | .025 | | 1.21 | .73 | | 1.94 | 2.56 |
| 0430 | 5/4" x 6" | | 320 | .025 | | 2.35 | .73 | | 3.08 | 3.81 |
| 0440 | Balusters, square, 2" x 2" | 2 Carp | 660 | .024 | L.F. | .33 | .71 | | 1.04 | 1.55 |
| 0450 | Turned, 2" x 2" | | 420 | .038 | | .44 | 1.11 | | 1.55 | 2.35 |
| 0460 | Stair stringer, 2" x 10" | | 130 | .123 | | 1.40 | 3.58 | | 4.98 | 7.55 |
| 0470 | 2" x 12" | | 130 | .123 | | 1.68 | 3.58 | | 5.26 | 7.85 |
| 0480 | Stair treads, 1" x 4" | | 140 | .114 | | 4.66 | 3.33 | | 7.99 | 10.70 |
| 0490 | 2" x 4" | | 140 | .114 | | .36 | 3.33 | | 3.69 | 6 |
| 0500 | 2" x 6" | | 160 | .100 | | .55 | 2.91 | | 3.46 | 5.50 |
| 0510 | 5/4" x 6" | | 160 | .100 | | 1.10 | 2.91 | | 4.01 | 6.10 |
| 0520 | Turned handrail post, 4" x 4" | | 64 | .250 | Ea. | 32 | 7.30 | | 39.30 | 47.50 |
| 0530 | Lattice panel, 4' x 8', 1/2" | | 1600 | .010 | S.F. | .68 | .29 | | .97 | 1.24 |
| 0535 | 3/4" | | 1600 | .010 | " | 1.02 | .29 | | 1.31 | 1.61 |
| 0540 | Cedar, posts or columns, 4" x 4" | | 390 | .041 | L.F. | 3.01 | 1.19 | | 4.20 | 5.30 |
| 0550 | 4" x 6" | | 275 | .058 | | 5.75 | 1.69 | | 7.44 | 9.15 |
| 0560 | 4" x 8" | | 220 | .073 | | 9.70 | 2.12 | | 11.82 | 14.25 |
| 0800 | Decking, 1" x 4" | | 550 | .029 | | 1.65 | .85 | | 2.50 | 3.23 |

# 06 11 Wood Framing

## 06 11 10 – Framing with Dimensional, Engineered or Composite Lumber

### 06 11 10.28 Porch or Deck Framing

| | | Crew | Daily Output | Labor-Hours | Unit | Material | 2010 Bare Costs Labor | Equipment | Total | Total Incl O&P |
|---|---|---|---|---|---|---|---|---|---|---|
| 0810 | 2" x 4" | 2 Carp | 600 | .027 | L.F. | 3.40 | .78 | | 4.18 | 5.05 |
| 0820 | 2" x 6" | | 640 | .025 | | 5.55 | .73 | | 6.28 | 7.30 |
| 0830 | 5/4" x 6" | | 640 | .025 | | 3.73 | .73 | | 4.46 | 5.35 |
| 0840 | Railings and trim, 1" x 4" | | 600 | .027 | | 1.65 | .78 | | 2.43 | 3.12 |
| 0860 | 2" x 4" | | 600 | .027 | | 3.40 | .78 | | 4.18 | 5.05 |
| 0870 | 2" x 6" | | 600 | .027 | | 5.55 | .78 | | 6.33 | 7.40 |
| 0920 | Stair treads, 1" x 4" | | 140 | .114 | | 1.65 | 3.33 | | 4.98 | 7.40 |
| 0930 | 2" x 4" | | 140 | .114 | | 3.40 | 3.33 | | 6.73 | 9.35 |
| 0940 | 2" x 6" | | 160 | .100 | | 5.55 | 2.91 | | 8.46 | 11 |
| 0950 | 5/4" x 6" | | 160 | .100 | | 3.73 | 2.91 | | 6.64 | 9 |
| 0980 | Redwood, posts or columns, 4" x 4" | | 390 | .041 | | 6.40 | 1.19 | | 7.59 | 9.05 |
| 0990 | 4" x 6" | | 275 | .058 | | 11.20 | 1.69 | | 12.89 | 15.15 |
| 1000 | 4" x 8" | ▼ | 220 | .073 | ▼ | 20.50 | 2.12 | | 22.62 | 26 |
| 1240 | Redwood decking, 1" x 4" | 1 Carp | 275 | .029 | S.F. | 3.97 | .85 | | 4.82 | 5.80 |
| 1260 | 2" x 6" | | 340 | .024 | | 7.50 | .68 | | 8.18 | 9.40 |
| 1270 | 5/4" x 6" | ▼ | 320 | .025 | ▼ | 4.74 | .73 | | 5.47 | 6.40 |
| 1280 | Railings and trim, 1" x 4" | 2 Carp | 600 | .027 | L.F. | 1.17 | .78 | | 1.95 | 2.59 |
| 1310 | 2" x 6" | | 600 | .027 | | 7.50 | .78 | | 8.28 | 9.55 |
| 1420 | Alternative decking, wood/plastic composite, 5/4" x 6" [G] | | 640 | .025 | | 3.01 | .73 | | 3.74 | 4.54 |
| 1430 | Vinyl, 1-1/2" x 5-1/2" | | 640 | .025 | | 4.15 | .73 | | 4.88 | 5.80 |
| 1440 | 1" x 4" square edge fir | | 550 | .029 | | 1.57 | .85 | | 2.42 | 3.14 |
| 1450 | 1" x 4" tongue and groove fir | | 450 | .036 | | 1.41 | 1.03 | | 2.44 | 3.29 |
| 1460 | 1" x 4" mahogany | | 550 | .029 | | 2.51 | .85 | | 3.36 | 4.18 |
| 1462 | 5/4" x 6" PVC | ▼ | 550 | .029 | ▼ | 2.72 | .85 | | 3.57 | 4.41 |
| 1470 | Accessories, joist hangers, 2" x 4" | 1 Carp | 160 | .050 | Ea. | .61 | 1.46 | | 2.07 | 3.12 |
| 1480 | 2" x 6" through 2" x 12" | " | 150 | .053 | | 1.17 | 1.55 | | 2.72 | 3.90 |
| 1530 | Post footing, incl excav, backfill, tube form & concrete, 4' deep, 8" dia | F-7 | 12 | 2.667 | | 10.60 | 67.50 | | 78.10 | 125 |
| 1540 | 10" diameter | | 11 | 2.909 | | 15.70 | 73.50 | | 89.20 | 141 |
| 1550 | 12" diameter | ▼ | 10 | 3.200 | ▼ | 21 | 81 | | 102 | 159 |

### 06 11 10.30 Roof Framing

| | | Crew | Daily Output | Labor-Hours | Unit | Material | 2010 Bare Costs Labor | Equipment | Total | Total Incl O&P |
|---|---|---|---|---|---|---|---|---|---|---|
| 0010 | **ROOF FRAMING** | | | | | | | | | |
| 2001 | Fascia boards, 2" x 8" | 2 Carp | 225 | .071 | L.F. | .56 | 2.07 | | 2.63 | 4.09 |
| 2101 | 2" x 10" | | 180 | .089 | | .72 | 2.59 | | 3.31 | 5.15 |
| 5002 | Rafters, to 4 in 12 pitch, 2" x 6", ordinary | | 1000 | .016 | | .38 | .47 | | .85 | 1.19 |
| 5021 | On steep roofs | | 800 | .020 | | .38 | .58 | | .96 | 1.39 |
| 5041 | On dormers or complex roofs | | 590 | .027 | | .38 | .79 | | 1.17 | 1.74 |
| 5062 | 2" x 8", ordinary | | 950 | .017 | | .56 | .49 | | 1.05 | 1.43 |
| 5081 | On steep roofs | | 750 | .021 | | .56 | .62 | | 1.18 | 1.65 |
| 5101 | On dormers or complex roofs | | 540 | .030 | | .56 | .86 | | 1.42 | 2.06 |
| 5122 | 2" x 10", ordinary | | 630 | .025 | | .72 | .74 | | 1.46 | 2.04 |
| 5141 | On steep roofs | | 495 | .032 | | .72 | .94 | | 1.66 | 2.38 |
| 5161 | On dormers or complex roofs | | 425 | .038 | | .72 | 1.10 | | 1.82 | 2.64 |
| 5182 | 2" x 12", ordinary | | 575 | .028 | | 1.06 | .81 | | 1.87 | 2.53 |
| 5201 | On steep roofs | | 455 | .035 | | 1.06 | 1.02 | | 2.08 | 2.89 |
| 5221 | On dormers or complex roofs | | 395 | .041 | | 1.06 | 1.18 | | 2.24 | 3.15 |
| 5250 | Composite rafter, 9-1/2" deep | | 575 | .028 | | 1.56 | .81 | | 2.37 | 3.08 |
| 5260 | 11-1/2" deep | | 575 | .028 | | 1.69 | .81 | | 2.50 | 3.22 |
| 5301 | Hip and valley rafters, 2" x 6", ordinary | | 760 | .021 | | .38 | .61 | | .99 | 1.44 |
| 5321 | On steep roofs | | 585 | .027 | | .38 | .80 | | 1.18 | 1.75 |
| 5341 | On dormers or complex roofs | | 510 | .031 | | .38 | .91 | | 1.29 | 1.95 |
| 5361 | 2" x 8", ordinary | | 720 | .022 | | .56 | .65 | | 1.21 | 1.70 |
| 5381 | On steep roofs | ▼ | 545 | .029 | ▼ | .56 | .85 | | 1.41 | 2.05 |

# 06 11 Wood Framing

## 06 11 10 – Framing with Dimensional, Engineered or Composite Lumber

### 06 11 10.30 Roof Framing

| | | Crew | Daily Output | Labor-Hours | Unit | Material | 2010 Bare Costs Labor | Equipment | Total | Total Incl O&P |
|---|---|---|---|---|---|---|---|---|---|---|
| 5401 | On dormers or complex roofs | 2 Carp | 470 | .034 | L.F. | .56 | .99 | | 1.55 | 2.28 |
| 5421 | 2" x 10", ordinary | | 570 | .028 | | .72 | .82 | | 1.54 | 2.17 |
| 5441 | On steep roofs | | 440 | .036 | | .72 | 1.06 | | 1.78 | 2.58 |
| 5461 | On dormers or complex roofs | | 380 | .042 | | .72 | 1.23 | | 1.95 | 2.86 |
| 5470 | | | | | | | | | | |
| 5481 | Hip and valley rafters, 2" x 12", ordinary | 2 Carp | 525 | .030 | L.F. | 1.06 | .89 | | 1.95 | 2.66 |
| 5501 | On steep roofs | | 410 | .039 | | 1.06 | 1.14 | | 2.20 | 3.08 |
| 5521 | On dormers or complex roofs | | 355 | .045 | | 1.06 | 1.31 | | 2.37 | 3.38 |
| 5541 | Hip and valley jacks, 2" x 6", ordinary | | 600 | .027 | | .38 | .78 | | 1.16 | 1.72 |
| 5561 | On steep roofs | | 475 | .034 | | .38 | .98 | | 1.36 | 2.06 |
| 5581 | On dormers or complex roofs | | 410 | .039 | | .38 | 1.14 | | 1.52 | 2.32 |
| 5601 | 2" x 8", ordinary | | 490 | .033 | | .56 | .95 | | 1.51 | 2.21 |
| 5621 | On steep roofs | | 385 | .042 | | .56 | 1.21 | | 1.77 | 2.64 |
| 5641 | On dormers or complex roofs | | 335 | .048 | | .56 | 1.39 | | 1.95 | 2.95 |
| 5661 | 2" x 10", ordinary | | 450 | .036 | | .72 | 1.03 | | 1.75 | 2.54 |
| 5681 | On steep roofs | | 350 | .046 | | .72 | 1.33 | | 2.05 | 3.04 |
| 5701 | On dormers or complex roofs | | 305 | .052 | | .72 | 1.53 | | 2.25 | 3.37 |
| 5721 | 2" x 12", ordinary | | 375 | .043 | | 1.06 | 1.24 | | 2.30 | 3.26 |
| 5741 | On steep roofs | | 295 | .054 | | 1.06 | 1.58 | | 2.64 | 3.83 |
| 5762 | On dormers or complex roofs | | 255 | .063 | | 1.06 | 1.83 | | 2.89 | 4.24 |
| 5781 | Rafter tie, 1" x 4", #3 | | 800 | .020 | | .44 | .58 | | 1.02 | 1.46 |
| 5791 | 2" x 4", #3 | | 800 | .020 | | .25 | .58 | | .83 | 1.25 |
| 5801 | Ridge board, #2 or better, 1" x 6" | | 600 | .027 | | .64 | .78 | | 1.42 | 2.01 |
| 5821 | 1" x 8" | | 550 | .029 | | .84 | .85 | | 1.69 | 2.34 |
| 5841 | 1" x 10" | | 500 | .032 | | 1.17 | .93 | | 2.10 | 2.85 |
| 5861 | 2" x 6" | | 500 | .032 | | .38 | .93 | | 1.31 | 1.98 |
| 5881 | 2" x 8" | | 450 | .036 | | .56 | 1.03 | | 1.59 | 2.35 |
| 5901 | 2" x 10" | | 400 | .040 | | .72 | 1.16 | | 1.88 | 2.76 |
| 5921 | Roof cants, split, 4" x 4" | | 650 | .025 | | 1.55 | .72 | | 2.27 | 2.91 |
| 5941 | 6" x 6" | | 600 | .027 | | 3.19 | .78 | | 3.97 | 4.82 |
| 5961 | Roof curbs, untreated, 2" x 6" | | 520 | .031 | | .38 | .90 | | 1.28 | 1.92 |
| 5981 | 2" x 12" | | 400 | .040 | | 1.06 | 1.16 | | 2.22 | 3.13 |
| 6001 | Sister rafters, 2" x 6" | | 800 | .020 | | .38 | .58 | | .96 | 1.39 |
| 6021 | 2" x 8" | | 640 | .025 | | .56 | .73 | | 1.29 | 1.83 |
| 6041 | 2" x 10" | | 535 | .030 | | .72 | .87 | | 1.59 | 2.26 |
| 6061 | 2" x 12" | | 455 | .035 | | 1.06 | 1.02 | | 2.08 | 2.89 |

### 06 11 10.32 Sill and Ledger Framing

| | | Crew | Daily Output | Labor-Hours | Unit | Material | 2010 Bare Costs Labor | Equipment | Total | Total Incl O&P |
|---|---|---|---|---|---|---|---|---|---|---|
| 0010 | **SILL AND LEDGER FRAMING** | | | | | | | | | |
| 2002 | Ledgers, nailed, 2" x 4" | 2 Carp | 755 | .021 | L.F. | .25 | .62 | | .87 | 1.31 |
| 2052 | 2" x 6" | | 600 | .027 | | .38 | .78 | | 1.16 | 1.72 |
| 2102 | Bolted, not including bolts, 3" x 6" | | 325 | .049 | | 1.39 | 1.43 | | 2.82 | 3.94 |
| 2152 | 3" x 12" | | 233 | .069 | | 3.54 | 2 | | 5.54 | 7.25 |
| 2602 | Mud sills, redwood, construction grade, 2" x 4" | | 895 | .018 | | 2.26 | .52 | | 2.78 | 3.37 |
| 2622 | 2" x 6" | | 780 | .021 | | 3.40 | .60 | | 4 | 4.74 |
| 4002 | Sills, 2" x 4" | | 600 | .027 | | .25 | .78 | | 1.03 | 1.58 |
| 4052 | 2" x 6" | | 550 | .029 | | .38 | .85 | | 1.23 | 1.83 |
| 4082 | 2" x 8" | | 500 | .032 | | .56 | .93 | | 1.49 | 2.18 |
| 4101 | 2" x 10" | | 450 | .036 | | .72 | 1.03 | | 1.75 | 2.54 |
| 4121 | 2" x 12" | | 400 | .040 | | 1.06 | 1.16 | | 2.22 | 3.13 |
| 4202 | Treated, 2" x 4" | | 550 | .029 | | .35 | .85 | | 1.20 | 1.80 |
| 4222 | 2" x 6" | | 500 | .032 | | .56 | .93 | | 1.49 | 2.18 |
| 4242 | 2" x 8" | | 450 | .036 | | 1.03 | 1.03 | | 2.06 | 2.88 |

# 06 11 Wood Framing

## 06 11 10 – Framing with Dimensional, Engineered or Composite Lumber

| 06 11 10.32 Sill and Ledger Framing | | Crew | Daily Output | Labor-Hours | Unit | 2010 Bare Costs | | | Total | Total Incl O&P |
|---|---|---|---|---|---|---|---|---|---|---|
| | | | | | | Material | Labor | Equipment | | |
| 4261 | 2" x 10" | 2 Carp | 400 | .040 | L.F. | 1.35 | 1.16 | | 2.51 | 3.45 |
| 4281 | 2" x 12" | | 350 | .046 | | 1.80 | 1.33 | | 3.13 | 4.22 |
| 4402 | 4" x 4" | | 450 | .036 | | 1.52 | 1.03 | | 2.55 | 3.42 |
| 4422 | 4" x 6" | | 350 | .046 | | 2.25 | 1.33 | | 3.58 | 4.72 |
| 4462 | 4" x 8" | | 300 | .053 | | 4.68 | 1.55 | | 6.23 | 7.75 |
| 4480 | 4" x 10" | ▼ | 260 | .062 | ▼ | 5.85 | 1.79 | | 7.64 | 9.45 |

| 06 11 10.34 Sleepers | | Crew | Daily Output | Labor-Hours | Unit | Material | Labor | Equipment | Total | Total Incl O&P |
|---|---|---|---|---|---|---|---|---|---|---|
| 0010 | **SLEEPERS** | | | | | | | | | |
| 0100 | On concrete, treated, 1" x 2" | 2 Carp | 2350 | .007 | L.F. | .33 | .20 | | .53 | .69 |
| 0150 | 1" x 3" | | 2000 | .008 | | .53 | .23 | | .76 | .97 |
| 0200 | 2" x 4" | | 1500 | .011 | | .35 | .31 | | .66 | .90 |
| 0250 | 2" x 6" | ▼ | 1300 | .012 | ▼ | .56 | .36 | | .92 | 1.21 |

| 06 11 10.36 Soffit and Canopy Framing | | Crew | Daily Output | Labor-Hours | Unit | Material | Labor | Equipment | Total | Total Incl O&P |
|---|---|---|---|---|---|---|---|---|---|---|
| 0010 | **SOFFIT AND CANOPY FRAMING** | | | | | | | | | |
| 1002 | Canopy or soffit framing , 1" x 4" | 2 Carp | 900 | .018 | L.F. | .44 | .52 | | .96 | 1.35 |
| 1021 | 1" x 6" | | 850 | .019 | | .64 | .55 | | 1.19 | 1.62 |
| 1042 | 1" x 8" | | 750 | .021 | | .84 | .62 | | 1.46 | 1.96 |
| 1102 | 2" x 4" | | 620 | .026 | | .25 | .75 | | 1 | 1.53 |
| 1121 | 2" x 6" | | 560 | .029 | | .38 | .83 | | 1.21 | 1.81 |
| 1142 | 2" x 8" | | 500 | .032 | | .56 | .93 | | 1.49 | 2.18 |
| 1202 | 3" x 4" | | 500 | .032 | | .83 | .93 | | 1.76 | 2.48 |
| 1221 | 3" x 6" | | 400 | .040 | | 1.39 | 1.16 | | 2.55 | 3.49 |
| 1242 | 3" x 10" | ▼ | 300 | .053 | ▼ | 2.77 | 1.55 | | 4.32 | 5.65 |
| 1250 | | | | | | | | | | |

| 06 11 10.38 Treated Lumber Framing Material | | Crew | Daily Output | Labor-Hours | Unit | Material | Labor | Equipment | Total | Total Incl O&P |
|---|---|---|---|---|---|---|---|---|---|---|
| 0010 | **TREATED LUMBER FRAMING MATERIAL** | | | | | | | | | |
| 0100 | 2" x 4" | | | | M.B.F. | 520 | | | 520 | 570 |
| 0110 | 2" x 6" | | | | | 555 | | | 555 | 615 |
| 0120 | 2" x 8" | | | | | 775 | | | 775 | 855 |
| 0130 | 2" x 10" | | | | | 810 | | | 810 | 890 |
| 0140 | 2" x 12" | | | | | 900 | | | 900 | 990 |
| 0200 | 4" x 4" | | | | | 1,150 | | | 1,150 | 1,250 |
| 0210 | 4" x 6" | | | | | 1,125 | | | 1,125 | 1,250 |
| 0220 | 4" x 8" | | | | ▼ | 1,750 | | | 1,750 | 1,925 |

| 06 11 10.40 Wall Framing | | Crew | Daily Output | Labor-Hours | Unit | Material | Labor | Equipment | Total | Total Incl O&P |
|---|---|---|---|---|---|---|---|---|---|---|
| 0010 | **WALL FRAMING** R061110-30 | | | | | | | | | |
| 0100 | Door buck, studs, header, access, 8' H, 2" x 4" wall, 3' W | 1 Carp | 32 | .250 | Ea. | 10.40 | 7.30 | | 17.70 | 23.50 |
| 0110 | 4' wide | | 32 | .250 | | 11.15 | 7.30 | | 18.45 | 24.50 |
| 0120 | 5' wide | | 32 | .250 | | 13.80 | 7.30 | | 21.10 | 27.50 |
| 0130 | 6' wide | | 32 | .250 | | 14.95 | 7.30 | | 22.25 | 28.50 |
| 0140 | 8' wide | | 30 | .267 | | 19.90 | 7.75 | | 27.65 | 35 |
| 0150 | 10' wide | | 30 | .267 | | 29.50 | 7.75 | | 37.25 | 45.50 |
| 0160 | 12' wide | | 30 | .267 | | 57 | 7.75 | | 64.75 | 75.50 |
| 0170 | 2" x 6" wall, 3' wide | | 32 | .250 | | 14.50 | 7.30 | | 21.80 | 28 |
| 0180 | 4' wide | | 32 | .250 | | 15.25 | 7.30 | | 22.55 | 29 |
| 0190 | 5' wide | | 32 | .250 | | 17.90 | 7.30 | | 25.20 | 32 |
| 0200 | 6' wide | | 32 | .250 | | 19.05 | 7.30 | | 26.35 | 33.50 |
| 0210 | 8' wide | | 30 | .267 | | 24 | 7.75 | | 31.75 | 39.50 |
| 0220 | 10' wide | | 30 | .267 | | 34 | 7.75 | | 41.75 | 50 |
| 0230 | 12' wide | | 30 | .267 | | 61 | 7.75 | | 68.75 | 80 |
| 0240 | Window buck, studs, header & access, 8' high 2" x 4" wall, 2' wide | | 24 | .333 | | 11.05 | 9.70 | | 20.75 | 28.50 |
| 0250 | 3' wide | ▼ | 24 | .333 | ▼ | 12.90 | 9.70 | | 22.60 | 30.50 |

# 06 11 Wood Framing

## 06 11 10 – Framing with Dimensional, Engineered or Composite Lumber

| 06 11 10.40 Wall Framing | | Crew | Daily Output | Labor-Hours | Unit | Material | 2010 Bare Costs Labor | Equipment | Total | Total Incl O&P |
|---|---|---|---|---|---|---|---|---|---|---|
| 0260 | 4' wide | 1 Carp | 24 | .333 | Ea. | 14.15 | 9.70 | | 23.85 | 32 |
| 0270 | 5' wide | | 24 | .333 | | 16.80 | 9.70 | | 26.50 | 35 |
| 0280 | 6' wide | | 24 | .333 | | 18.65 | 9.70 | | 28.35 | 37 |
| 0300 | 8' wide | | 22 | .364 | | 25 | 10.60 | | 35.60 | 45.50 |
| 0310 | 10' wide | | 22 | .364 | | 35.50 | 10.60 | | 46.10 | 57 |
| 0320 | 12' wide | | 22 | .364 | | 64.50 | 10.60 | | 75.10 | 89 |
| 0330 | 2" x 6" wall, 2' wide | | 24 | .333 | | 16.20 | 9.70 | | 25.90 | 34 |
| 0340 | 3' wide | | 24 | .333 | | 18.30 | 9.70 | | 28 | 36.50 |
| 0350 | 4' wide | | 24 | .333 | | 19.60 | 9.70 | | 29.30 | 38 |
| 0360 | 5' wide | | 24 | .333 | | 22.50 | 9.70 | | 32.20 | 41 |
| 0370 | 6' wide | | 24 | .333 | | 24.50 | 9.70 | | 34.20 | 43.50 |
| 0380 | 7' wide | | 24 | .333 | | 29.50 | 9.70 | | 39.20 | 49 |
| 0390 | 8' wide | | 22 | .364 | | 32 | 10.60 | | 42.60 | 53 |
| 0400 | 10' wide | | 22 | .364 | | 43 | 10.60 | | 53.60 | 65 |
| 0410 | 12' wide | | 22 | .364 | | 72.50 | 10.60 | | 83.10 | 97.50 |
| 2002 | Headers over openings, 2" x 6" | 2 Carp | 360 | .044 | L.F. | .38 | 1.29 | | 1.67 | 2.59 |
| 2007 | 2" x 6", pneumatic nailed | | 432 | .037 | | .38 | 1.08 | | 1.46 | 2.22 |
| 2052 | 2" x 8" | | 340 | .047 | | .56 | 1.37 | | 1.93 | 2.91 |
| 2057 | 2" x 8", pneumatic nailed | | 408 | .039 | | .56 | 1.14 | | 1.70 | 2.53 |
| 2101 | 2" x 10" | | 320 | .050 | | .72 | 1.46 | | 2.18 | 3.25 |
| 2106 | 2" x 10", pneumatic nailed | | 384 | .042 | | .72 | 1.21 | | 1.93 | 2.84 |
| 2152 | 2" x 12" | | 300 | .053 | | 1.06 | 1.55 | | 2.61 | 3.78 |
| 2157 | 2" x 12", pneumatic nailed | | 360 | .044 | | 1.06 | 1.29 | | 2.35 | 3.35 |
| 2191 | 4" x 10" | | 240 | .067 | | 3.64 | 1.94 | | 5.58 | 7.25 |
| 2196 | 4" x 10", pneumatic nailed | | 288 | .056 | | 3.64 | 1.62 | | 5.26 | 6.75 |
| 2202 | 4" x 12" | | 190 | .084 | | 6.10 | 2.45 | | 8.55 | 10.80 |
| 2207 | 4" x 12", pneumatic nailed | | 228 | .070 | | 6.10 | 2.04 | | 8.14 | 10.15 |
| 2241 | 6" x 10" | | 165 | .097 | | 6.60 | 2.82 | | 9.42 | 12.05 |
| 2246 | 6" x 10", pneumatic nailed | | 198 | .081 | | 6.60 | 2.35 | | 8.95 | 11.25 |
| 2251 | 6" x 12" | | 140 | .114 | | 10.15 | 3.33 | | 13.48 | 16.80 |
| 2256 | 6" x 12", pneumatic nailed | | 168 | .095 | | 10.15 | 2.77 | | 12.92 | 15.85 |
| 5002 | Plates, untreated, 2" x 3" | | 850 | .019 | | .27 | .55 | | .82 | 1.21 |
| 5007 | 2" x 3", pneumatic nailed | | 1020 | .016 | | .27 | .46 | | .73 | 1.06 |
| 5022 | 2" x 4" | | 800 | .020 | | .25 | .58 | | .83 | 1.25 |
| 5027 | 2" x 4", pneumatic nailed | | 960 | .017 | | .25 | .49 | | .74 | 1.09 |
| 5040 | 2" x 6" | | 750 | .021 | | .38 | .62 | | 1 | 1.45 |
| 5045 | 2" x 6", pneumatic nailed | | 900 | .018 | | .38 | .52 | | .90 | 1.28 |
| 5061 | Treated, 2" x 3" | | 850 | .019 | | .52 | .55 | | 1.07 | 1.49 |
| 5066 | 2" x 3", treated, pneumatic nailed | | 1020 | .016 | | .52 | .46 | | .98 | 1.34 |
| 5081 | 2" x 4" | | 800 | .020 | | .35 | .58 | | .93 | 1.36 |
| 5086 | 2" x 4", treated, pneumatic nailed | | 960 | .017 | | .35 | .49 | | .84 | 1.20 |
| 5101 | 2" x 6" | | 750 | .021 | | .56 | .62 | | 1.18 | 1.65 |
| 5106 | 2" x 6", treated, pneumatic nailed | | 900 | .018 | | .56 | .52 | | 1.08 | 1.48 |
| 5122 | Studs, 8' high wall, 2" x 3" | | 1200 | .013 | | .27 | .39 | | .66 | .94 |
| 5127 | 2" x 3", pneumatic nailed | | 1440 | .011 | | .27 | .32 | | .59 | .83 |
| 5142 | 2" x 4" | | 1100 | .015 | | .25 | .42 | | .67 | .98 |
| 5147 | 2" x 4", pneumatic nailed | | 1320 | .012 | | .25 | .35 | | .60 | .86 |
| 5162 | 2" x 6" | | 1000 | .016 | | .38 | .47 | | .85 | 1.19 |
| 5167 | 2" x 6", pneumatic nailed | | 1200 | .013 | | .38 | .39 | | .77 | 1.06 |
| 5182 | 3" x 4" | | 800 | .020 | | .83 | .58 | | 1.41 | 1.89 |
| 5187 | 3" x 4", pneumatic nailed | | 960 | .017 | | .83 | .49 | | 1.32 | 1.73 |
| 5201 | Installed on second story, 2" x 3" | | 1170 | .014 | | .27 | .40 | | .67 | .96 |
| 5206 | 2" x 3", pneumatic nailed | | 1200 | .013 | | .27 | .39 | | .66 | .94 |

| 06 11 10.40 Wall Framing | Crew | Daily Output | Labor-Hours | Unit | Material | 2010 Bare Costs Labor | Equipment | Total | Total Incl O&P |
|---|---|---|---|---|---|---|---|---|---|
| 5221 | 2" x 4" | 2 Carp | 1015 | .016 | L.F. | .25 | .46 | | .71 | 1.04 |
| 5226 | 2" x 4", pneumatic nailed | | 1080 | .015 | | .25 | .43 | | .68 | .99 |
| 5241 | 2" x 6" | | 890 | .018 | | .38 | .52 | | .90 | 1.29 |
| 5246 | 2" x 6", pneumatic nailed | | 1020 | .016 | | .38 | .46 | | .84 | 1.18 |
| 5261 | 3" x 4" | | 800 | .020 | | .83 | .58 | | 1.41 | 1.89 |
| 5266 | 3" x 4", pneumatic nailed | | 960 | .017 | | .83 | .49 | | 1.32 | 1.73 |
| 5281 | Installed on dormer or gable, 2" x 3" | | 1045 | .015 | | .27 | .45 | | .72 | 1.04 |
| 5286 | 2" x 3", pneumatic nailed | | 1254 | .013 | | .27 | .37 | | .64 | .91 |
| 5301 | 2" x 4" | | 905 | .018 | | .25 | .51 | | .76 | 1.14 |
| 5306 | 2" x 4", pneumatic nailed | | 1086 | .015 | | .25 | .43 | | .68 | .99 |
| 5321 | 2" x 6" | | 800 | .020 | | .38 | .58 | | .96 | 1.39 |
| 5326 | 2" x 6", pneumatic nailed | | 960 | .017 | | .38 | .49 | | .87 | 1.23 |
| 5341 | 3" x 4" | | 700 | .023 | | .83 | .67 | | 1.50 | 2.03 |
| 5346 | 3" x 4", pneumatic nailed | | 840 | .019 | | .83 | .55 | | 1.38 | 1.84 |
| 5361 | 6' high wall, 2" x 3" | | 970 | .016 | | .27 | .48 | | .75 | 1.10 |
| 5366 | 2" x 3", pneumatic nailed | | 1164 | .014 | | .27 | .40 | | .67 | .96 |
| 5381 | 2" x 4" | | 850 | .019 | | .25 | .55 | | .80 | 1.19 |
| 5386 | 2" x 4", pneumatic nailed | | 1020 | .016 | | .25 | .46 | | .71 | 1.04 |
| 5401 | 2" x 6" | | 740 | .022 | | .38 | .63 | | 1.01 | 1.47 |
| 5406 | 2" x 6", pneumatic nailed | | 888 | .018 | | .38 | .52 | | .90 | 1.29 |
| 5421 | 3" x 4" | | 600 | .027 | | .83 | .78 | | 1.61 | 2.22 |
| 5426 | 3" x 4", pneumatic nailed | | 720 | .022 | | .83 | .65 | | 1.48 | 2 |
| 5441 | Installed on second story, 2" x 3" | | 950 | .017 | | .27 | .49 | | .76 | 1.11 |
| 5446 | 2" x 3", pneumatic nailed | | 1140 | .014 | | .27 | .41 | | .68 | .98 |
| 5461 | 2" x 4" | | 810 | .020 | | .25 | .57 | | .82 | 1.24 |
| 5466 | 2" x 4", pneumatic nailed | | 972 | .016 | | .25 | .48 | | .73 | 1.08 |
| 5481 | 2" x 6" | | 700 | .023 | | .38 | .67 | | 1.05 | 1.53 |
| 5486 | 2" x 6", pneumatic nailed | | 840 | .019 | | .38 | .55 | | .93 | 1.34 |
| 5501 | 3" x 4" | | 550 | .029 | | .83 | .85 | | 1.68 | 2.33 |
| 5506 | 3" x 4", pneumatic nailed | | 660 | .024 | | .83 | .71 | | 1.54 | 2.10 |
| 5521 | Installed on dormer or gable, 2" x 3" | | 850 | .019 | | .27 | .55 | | .82 | 1.21 |
| 5526 | 2" x 3", pneumatic nailed | | 1020 | .016 | | .27 | .46 | | .73 | 1.06 |
| 5541 | 2" x 4" | | 720 | .022 | | .25 | .65 | | .90 | 1.36 |
| 5546 | 2" x 4", pneumatic nailed | | 864 | .019 | | .25 | .54 | | .79 | 1.18 |
| 5561 | 2" x 6" | | 620 | .026 | | .38 | .75 | | 1.13 | 1.67 |
| 5566 | 2" x 6", pneumatic nailed | | 744 | .022 | | .38 | .63 | | 1.01 | 1.46 |
| 5581 | 3" x 4" | | 480 | .033 | | .83 | .97 | | 1.80 | 2.54 |
| 5586 | 3" x 4", pneumatic nailed | | 576 | .028 | | .83 | .81 | | 1.64 | 2.27 |
| 5601 | 3' high wall, 2" x 3" | | 740 | .022 | | .27 | .63 | | .90 | 1.35 |
| 5606 | 2" x 3", pneumatic nailed | | 888 | .018 | | .27 | .52 | | .79 | 1.17 |
| 5621 | 2" x 4" | | 640 | .025 | | .25 | .73 | | .98 | 1.49 |
| 5626 | 2" x 4", pneumatic nailed | | 768 | .021 | | .25 | .61 | | .86 | 1.29 |
| 5641 | 2" x 6" | | 550 | .029 | | .38 | .85 | | 1.23 | 1.83 |
| 5646 | 2" x 6", pneumatic nailed | | 660 | .024 | | .38 | .71 | | 1.09 | 1.60 |
| 5661 | 3" x 4" | | 440 | .036 | | .83 | 1.06 | | 1.89 | 2.69 |
| 5666 | 3" x 4", pneumatic nailed | | 528 | .030 | | .83 | .88 | | 1.71 | 2.39 |
| 5681 | Installed on second story, 2" x 3" | | 700 | .023 | | .27 | .67 | | .94 | 1.41 |
| 5686 | 2" x 3", pneumatic nailed | | 840 | .019 | | .27 | .55 | | .82 | 1.22 |
| 5701 | 2" x 4" | | 610 | .026 | | .25 | .76 | | 1.01 | 1.55 |
| 5706 | 2" x 4", pneumatic nailed | | 732 | .022 | | .25 | .64 | | .89 | 1.34 |
| 5721 | 2" x 6" | | 520 | .031 | | .38 | .90 | | 1.28 | 1.92 |
| 5726 | 2" x 6", pneumatic nailed | | 624 | .026 | | .38 | .75 | | 1.13 | 1.67 |
| 5741 | 3" x 4" | | 430 | .037 | | .83 | 1.08 | | 1.91 | 2.73 |

# 06 11 Wood Framing

## 06 11 10 – Framing with Dimensional, Engineered or Composite Lumber

### 06 11 10.40 Wall Framing

| | | Crew | Daily Output | Labor-Hours | Unit | Material | 2010 Bare Costs Labor | Equipment | Total | Total Incl O&P |
|---|---|---|---|---|---|---|---|---|---|---|
| 5746 | 3" x 4", pneumatic nailed | 2 Carp | 516 | .031 | L.F. | .83 | .90 | | 1.73 | 2.43 |
| 5761 | Installed on dormer or gable, 2" x 3" | | 625 | .026 | | .27 | .75 | | 1.02 | 1.54 |
| 5766 | 2" x 3", pneumatic nailed | | 750 | .021 | | .27 | .62 | | .89 | 1.33 |
| 5781 | 2" x 4" | | 545 | .029 | | .25 | .85 | | 1.10 | 1.71 |
| 5786 | 2" x 4", pneumatic nailed | | 654 | .024 | | .25 | .71 | | .96 | 1.47 |
| 5801 | 2" x 6" | | 465 | .034 | | .38 | 1 | | 1.38 | 2.09 |
| 5806 | 2" x 6", pneumatic nailed | | 558 | .029 | | .38 | .83 | | 1.21 | 1.81 |
| 5821 | 3" x 4" | | 380 | .042 | | .83 | 1.23 | | 2.06 | 2.97 |
| 5826 | 3" x 4", pneumatic nailed | ↓ | 456 | .035 | ↓ | .83 | 1.02 | | 1.85 | 2.63 |
| 8250 | For second story & above, add | | | | | | 5% | | | |
| 8300 | For dormer & gable, add | | | | | | 15% | | | |

### 06 11 10.42 Furring

| | | Crew | Daily Output | Labor-Hours | Unit | Material | 2010 Bare Costs Labor | Equipment | Total | Total Incl O&P |
|---|---|---|---|---|---|---|---|---|---|---|
| 0010 | **FURRING** | | | | | | | | | |
| 0012 | Wood strips, 1" x 2", on walls, on wood | 1 Carp | 550 | .015 | L.F. | .25 | .42 | | .67 | .98 |
| 0017 | Pneumatic nailed | | 710 | .011 | | .25 | .33 | | .58 | .82 |
| 0300 | On masonry | | 495 | .016 | | .25 | .47 | | .72 | 1.06 |
| 0400 | On concrete | | 260 | .031 | | .25 | .90 | | 1.15 | 1.78 |
| 0600 | 1" x 3", on walls, on wood | | 550 | .015 | | .34 | .42 | | .76 | 1.09 |
| 0607 | Pneumatic nailed | | 710 | .011 | | .34 | .33 | | .67 | .93 |
| 0700 | On masonry | | 495 | .016 | | .34 | .47 | | .81 | 1.17 |
| 0800 | On concrete | | 260 | .031 | | .34 | .90 | | 1.24 | 1.89 |
| 0850 | On ceilings, on wood | | 350 | .023 | | .34 | .67 | | 1.01 | 1.50 |
| 0857 | Pneumatic nailed | | 450 | .018 | | .34 | .52 | | .86 | 1.25 |
| 0900 | On masonry | | 320 | .025 | | .34 | .73 | | 1.07 | 1.60 |
| 0950 | On concrete | ↓ | 210 | .038 | ↓ | .34 | 1.11 | | 1.45 | 2.25 |

### 06 11 10.44 Grounds

| | | Crew | Daily Output | Labor-Hours | Unit | Material | 2010 Bare Costs Labor | Equipment | Total | Total Incl O&P |
|---|---|---|---|---|---|---|---|---|---|---|
| 0010 | **GROUNDS** | | | | | | | | | |
| 0020 | For casework, 1" x 2" wood strips, on wood | 1 Carp | 330 | .024 | L.F. | .25 | .71 | | .96 | 1.46 |
| 0100 | On masonry | | 285 | .028 | | .25 | .82 | | 1.07 | 1.64 |
| 0200 | On concrete | | 250 | .032 | | .25 | .93 | | 1.18 | 1.84 |
| 0400 | For plaster, 3/4" deep, on wood | | 450 | .018 | | .25 | .52 | | .77 | 1.14 |
| 0500 | On masonry | | 225 | .036 | | .25 | 1.03 | | 1.28 | 2.01 |
| 0600 | On concrete | | 175 | .046 | | .25 | 1.33 | | 1.58 | 2.51 |
| 0700 | On metal lath | ↓ | 200 | .040 | ↓ | .25 | 1.16 | | 1.41 | 2.23 |

# 06 12 Structural Panels

## 06 12 10 – Structural Insulated Panels

### 06 12 10.10 OSB Faced Panels

| | | | Crew | Daily Output | Labor-Hours | Unit | Material | 2010 Bare Costs Labor | Equipment | Total | Total Incl O&P |
|---|---|---|---|---|---|---|---|---|---|---|---|
| 0010 | **OSB FACED PANELS** | | | | | | | | | | |
| 0100 | Structural insul. panels, 7/16" OSB both faces, EPS insul, 3-5/8" T | G | F-3 | 2075 | .019 | S.F. | 2.91 | .51 | .32 | 3.74 | 4.40 |
| 0110 | 5-5/8" thick | G | | 1725 | .023 | | 3.33 | .61 | .38 | 4.32 | 5.10 |
| 0120 | 7-3/8" thick | G | | 1425 | .028 | | 3.69 | .74 | .46 | 4.89 | 5.80 |
| 0130 | 9-3/8" thick | G | | 1125 | .036 | | 4.13 | .94 | .58 | 5.65 | 6.75 |
| 0140 | 7/16" OSB one face, EPS insul, 3-5/8" thick | G | | 2175 | .018 | | 2.77 | .49 | .30 | 3.56 | 4.19 |
| 0150 | 5-5/8" thick | G | | 1825 | .022 | | 3.05 | .58 | .36 | 3.99 | 4.73 |
| 0160 | 7-3/8" thick | G | | 1525 | .026 | | 3.33 | .69 | .43 | 4.45 | 5.30 |
| 0170 | 9-3/8" thick | G | | 1225 | .033 | | 3.64 | .86 | .54 | 5.04 | 6.05 |
| 0190 | 7/16" OSB - 1/2" GWB faces, EPS insul, 3-5/8" T | G | | 2075 | .019 | | 2.87 | .51 | .32 | 3.70 | 4.36 |
| 0200 | 5-5/8" thick | G | | 1725 | .023 | | 3.29 | .61 | .38 | 4.28 | 5.05 |
| 0210 | 7-3/8" thick | G | ↓ | 1425 | .028 | ↓ | 3.45 | .74 | .46 | 4.65 | 5.55 |

# 06 12 Structural Panels

## 06 12 10 – Structural Insulated Panels

### 06 12 10.10 OSB Faced Panels

| | | | Crew | Daily Output | Labor-Hours | Unit | Material | 2010 Bare Costs Labor | Equipment | Total | Total Incl O&P |
|---|---|---|---|---|---|---|---|---|---|---|---|
| 0220 | 9-3/8" thick | G | F-3 | 1125 | .036 | S.F. | 3.87 | .94 | .58 | 5.39 | 6.45 |
| 0240 | 7/16" OSB - 1/2" MRGWB faces , EPS insul, 3-5/8" T | G | | 2075 | .019 | | 2.87 | .51 | .32 | 3.70 | 4.36 |
| 0250 | 5-5/8" thick | G | | 1725 | .023 | | 3.29 | .61 | .38 | 4.28 | 5.05 |
| 0260 | 7-3/8" thick | G | | 1425 | .028 | | 3.45 | .74 | .46 | 4.65 | 5.55 |
| 0270 | 9-3/8" thick | G | ▼ | 1125 | .036 | | 3.87 | .94 | .58 | 5.39 | 6.45 |
| 0300 | For 1/2" GWB added to OSB skin, add | G | | | | | .60 | | | .60 | .66 |
| 0310 | For 1/2" MRGWB added to OSB skin, add | G | | | | | .75 | | | .75 | .83 |
| 0320 | For one T1-11 skin, add to OSB-OSB | G | | | | | .74 | | | .74 | .81 |
| 0330 | For one 19/32" CDX skin, add to OSB-OSB | G | | | | ▼ | .69 | | | .69 | .76 |
| 0500 | Structural insulated panel, 7/16" OSB both sides, straw core | | | | | | | | | | |
| 0510 | 4-3/8" T, walls (w/sill, splines, plates) | G | F-6 | 2400 | .017 | S.F. | 7.60 | .44 | .27 | 8.31 | 9.40 |
| 0520 | Floors (w/splines) | G | | 2400 | .017 | | 7.60 | .44 | .27 | 8.31 | 9.40 |
| 0530 | Roof (w/splines) | G | | 2400 | .017 | | 7.60 | .44 | .27 | 8.31 | 9.40 |
| 0550 | 7-7/8" T, walls (w/sill, splines, plates) | G | | 2400 | .017 | | 10.95 | .44 | .27 | 11.66 | 13.10 |
| 0560 | Floors (w/splines) | G | | 2400 | .017 | | 10.95 | .44 | .27 | 11.66 | 13.10 |
| 0570 | Roof (w/splines) | G | ▼ | 2400 | .017 | ▼ | 10.95 | .44 | .27 | 11.66 | 13.10 |

# 06 13 Heavy Timber

## 06 13 13 – Log Construction

### 06 13 13.10 Log Structures

| | | Crew | Daily Output | Labor-Hours | Unit | Material | 2010 Bare Costs Labor | Equipment | Total | Total Incl O&P |
|---|---|---|---|---|---|---|---|---|---|---|
| 0010 | **LOG STRUCTURES** | | | | | | | | | |
| 0020 | Exterior walls, pine, D logs, with double T & G, 6" x 6" | 2 Carp | 500 | .032 | L.F. | 4 | .93 | | 4.93 | 5.95 |
| 0030 | 6" x 8" | | 375 | .043 | | 4.80 | 1.24 | | 6.04 | 7.40 |
| 0040 | 8" x 6" | | 375 | .043 | | 4 | 1.24 | | 5.24 | 6.50 |
| 0050 | 8" x 7" | | 322 | .050 | | 4 | 1.45 | | 5.45 | 6.85 |
| 0060 | Square/rectangular logs, with double T & G, 6" x 6" | | 500 | .032 | | 4 | .93 | | 4.93 | 5.95 |
| 0160 | Upper floor framing, pine, posts/columns, 4" x 6" | | 750 | .021 | | 2.39 | .62 | | 3.01 | 3.67 |
| 0180 | 4" x 8" | | 562 | .028 | | 2.88 | .83 | | 3.71 | 4.56 |
| 0190 | 6" x 6" | | 500 | .032 | | 3.19 | .93 | | 4.12 | 5.10 |
| 0200 | 6" x 8" | | 375 | .043 | | 4.28 | 1.24 | | 5.52 | 6.80 |
| 0210 | 8" x 8" | | 281 | .057 | | 7.95 | 1.66 | | 9.61 | 11.55 |
| 0220 | 8" x 10" | | 225 | .071 | | 9.95 | 2.07 | | 12.02 | 14.45 |
| 0230 | Beams, 4" x 8" | | 562 | .028 | | 2.88 | .83 | | 3.71 | 4.56 |
| 0240 | 4" x 10" | | 449 | .036 | | 3.64 | 1.04 | | 4.68 | 5.75 |
| 0250 | 4" x 12" | | 375 | .043 | | 6.10 | 1.24 | | 7.34 | 8.80 |
| 0260 | 6" x 8" | | 375 | .043 | | 4.28 | 1.24 | | 5.52 | 6.80 |
| 0270 | 6" x 10" | | 300 | .053 | | 6.60 | 1.55 | | 8.15 | 9.90 |
| 0280 | 6" x 12" | | 250 | .064 | | 10.15 | 1.86 | | 12.01 | 14.35 |
| 0290 | 8" x 10" | | 225 | .071 | | 9.95 | 2.07 | | 12.02 | 14.45 |
| 0300 | 8" x 12" | | 188 | .085 | | 11.95 | 2.48 | | 14.43 | 17.30 |
| 0310 | Joists, 4" x 8" | | 562 | .028 | | 2.88 | .83 | | 3.71 | 4.56 |
| 0320 | 4" x 10" | | 449 | .036 | | 3.64 | 1.04 | | 4.68 | 5.75 |
| 0330 | 4" x 12" | | 375 | .043 | | 6.10 | 1.24 | | 7.34 | 8.80 |
| 0340 | 6" x 8" | | 375 | .043 | | 4.28 | 1.24 | | 5.52 | 6.80 |
| 0350 | 6" x 10" | | 300 | .053 | ▼ | 6.60 | 1.55 | | 8.15 | 9.90 |
| 0390 | Decking, 1" x 6" T & G | | 964 | .017 | S.F. | 1.64 | .48 | | 2.12 | 2.61 |
| 0400 | 1" x 8" T & G | | 700 | .023 | " | 1.43 | .67 | | 2.10 | 2.69 |
| 0420 | Gable end roof framing, rafters, 4" x 8" | ▼ | 562 | .028 | L.F. | 2.88 | .83 | | 3.71 | 4.56 |

# 06 13 Heavy Timber

## 06 13 23 – Heavy Timber Construction

### 06 13 23.10 Heavy Framing

| | | Crew | Daily Output | Labor-Hours | Unit | Material | 2010 Bare Costs Labor | 2010 Bare Costs Equipment | Total | Total Incl O&P |
|---|---|---|---|---|---|---|---|---|---|---|
| 0010 | **HEAVY FRAMING** | | | | | | | | | |
| 0020 | Beams, single 6" x 10" | 2 Carp | 1.10 | 14.545 | M.B.F. | 1,600 | 425 | | 2,025 | 2,450 |
| 0100 | Single 8" x 16" | | 1.20 | 13.333 | " | 1,975 | 390 | | 2,365 | 2,825 |
| 0202 | Built from 2" lumber, multiple 2" x 14" | | 900 | .018 | B.F. | .86 | .52 | | 1.38 | 1.81 |
| 0212 | Built from 3" lumber, multiple 3" x 6" | | 700 | .023 | | .93 | .67 | | 1.60 | 2.14 |
| 0222 | Multiple 3" x 8" | | 800 | .020 | | 1.04 | .58 | | 1.62 | 2.13 |
| 0232 | Multiple 3" x 10" | | 900 | .018 | | 1.11 | .52 | | 1.63 | 2.09 |
| 0242 | Multiple 3" x 12" | | 1000 | .016 | | 1.18 | .47 | | 1.65 | 2.08 |
| 0252 | Built from 4" lumber, multiple 4" x 6" | | 800 | .020 | | 1.19 | .58 | | 1.77 | 2.29 |
| 0262 | Multiple 4" x 8" | | 900 | .018 | | 1.08 | .52 | | 1.60 | 2.06 |
| 0272 | Multiple 4" x 10" | | 1000 | .016 | | 1.09 | .47 | | 1.56 | 1.98 |
| 0282 | Multiple 4" x 12" | | 1100 | .015 | | 1.53 | .42 | | 1.95 | 2.39 |
| 0292 | Columns, structural grade, 1500f, 4" x 4" | | 450 | .036 | L.F. | 1.70 | 1.03 | | 2.73 | 3.61 |
| 0302 | 6" x 6" | | 225 | .071 | | 3.95 | 2.07 | | 6.02 | 7.80 |
| 0402 | 8" x 8" | | 240 | .067 | | 7.20 | 1.94 | | 9.14 | 11.15 |
| 0502 | 10" x 10" | | 90 | .178 | | 12.10 | 5.15 | | 17.25 | 22 |
| 0602 | 12" x 12" | | 70 | .229 | | 18.35 | 6.65 | | 25 | 31 |
| 0802 | Floor planks, 2" thick, T & G, 2" x 6" | | 1050 | .015 | B.F. | 1.05 | .44 | | 1.49 | 1.91 |
| 0902 | 2" x 10" | | 1100 | .015 | | 1.05 | .42 | | 1.47 | 1.87 |
| 1102 | 3" thick, 3" x 6" | | 1050 | .015 | | 1.25 | .44 | | 1.69 | 2.13 |
| 1202 | 3" x 10" | | 1100 | .015 | | 1.25 | .42 | | 1.67 | 2.09 |
| 1402 | Girders, structural grade, 12" x 12" | | 800 | .020 | | 1.53 | .58 | | 2.11 | 2.66 |
| 1502 | 10" x 16" | | 1000 | .016 | | 2.43 | .47 | | 2.90 | 3.45 |
| 2302 | Roof purlins, 4" thick, structural grade | | 1050 | .015 | | 1.33 | .44 | | 1.77 | 2.21 |
| 2502 | Roof trusses, add timber connectors, Division 06 05 23.60 | | 450 | .036 | | 1.22 | 1.03 | | 2.25 | 3.08 |

# 06 15 Wood Decking

## 06 15 16 – Wood Roof Decking

### 06 15 16.10 Solid Wood Roof Decking

| | | Crew | Daily Output | Labor-Hours | Unit | Material | 2010 Bare Costs Labor | 2010 Bare Costs Equipment | Total | Total Incl O&P |
|---|---|---|---|---|---|---|---|---|---|---|
| 0010 | **SOLID WOOD ROOF DECKING** | | | | | | | | | |
| 0400 | Cedar planks, 3" thick | 2 Carp | 320 | .050 | S.F. | 7.70 | 1.46 | | 9.16 | 10.95 |
| 0500 | 4" thick | | 250 | .064 | | 10.30 | 1.86 | | 12.16 | 14.50 |
| 0702 | Douglas fir, 3" thick | | 320 | .050 | | 3.28 | 1.46 | | 4.74 | 6.05 |
| 0802 | 4" thick | | 250 | .064 | | 4.36 | 1.86 | | 6.22 | 7.95 |
| 1002 | Hemlock, 3" thick | | 320 | .050 | | 3.28 | 1.46 | | 4.74 | 6.05 |
| 1102 | 4" thick | | 250 | .064 | | 4.36 | 1.86 | | 6.22 | 7.95 |
| 1302 | Western white spruce, 3" thick | | 320 | .050 | | 3.28 | 1.46 | | 4.74 | 6.05 |
| 1402 | 4" thick | | 250 | .064 | | 4.36 | 1.86 | | 6.22 | 7.95 |

## 06 15 23 – Laminated Wood Decking

### 06 15 23.10 Laminated Roof Deck

| | | Crew | Daily Output | Labor-Hours | Unit | Material | 2010 Bare Costs Labor | 2010 Bare Costs Equipment | Total | Total Incl O&P |
|---|---|---|---|---|---|---|---|---|---|---|
| 0010 | **LAMINATED ROOF DECK** | | | | | | | | | |
| 0020 | Pine or hemlock, 3" thick | 2 Carp | 425 | .038 | S.F. | 3.36 | 1.10 | | 4.46 | 5.55 |
| 0100 | 4" thick | | 325 | .049 | | 4.47 | 1.43 | | 5.90 | 7.35 |
| 0300 | Cedar, 3" thick | | 425 | .038 | | 4.11 | 1.10 | | 5.21 | 6.35 |
| 0400 | 4" thick | | 325 | .049 | | 5.25 | 1.43 | | 6.68 | 8.15 |
| 0600 | Fir, 3" thick | | 425 | .038 | | 3.43 | 1.10 | | 4.53 | 5.60 |
| 0700 | 4" thick | | 325 | .049 | | 4.29 | 1.43 | | 5.72 | 7.15 |

# Reed Construction Data
# The leader in construction information and BIM solutions

**Reed Construction Data, Inc.** is a leading provider of construction information and building information modeling (BIM) solutions. The company's portfolio of information products and services is designed specifically to help construction industry professionals advance their business with timely and accurate project, product, and cost data. Reed Construction Data is a division of Reed Business Information, a member of the Reed Elsevier PLC group of companies.

## Cost Information

RSMeans, the undisputed market leader in construction costs, provides current cost and estimating information through its innovative MeansCostworks.com® web-based solution. In addition, RSMeans publishes annual cost books, estimating software, and a rich library of reference books. RSMeans also conducts a series of professional seminars and provides construction cost consulting for owners, manufacturers, designers, and contractors to sharpen personal skills and maximize the effective use of cost estimating and management tools.

## Project Data

Reed Construction Data assembles one of the largest databases of public and private project data for use by contractors, distributors, and building product manufacturers in the U.S. and Canadian markets. In addition, Reed Construction Data is the North American construction community's premier resource for project leads and bid documents. Reed Bulletin and Reed CONNECT™ provide project leads and project data through all stages of construction for many of the country's largest public sector, commercial, industrial, and multi-family residential projects.

## Research and Analytics

Reed Construction Data's forecasting tools cover most aspects of the construction business in the U.S. and Canada. With a vast network of resources, Reed Construction Data is uniquely qualified to give you the information you need to keep your business profitable.

## SmartBIM Solutions

Reed Construction Data has emerged as the leader in the field of building information modeling (BIM) with products and services that have helped to advance the evolution of BIM. Through an in-depth SmartBIM Object Creation Program, BPMs can rely on Reed to create high-quality, real world objects embedded with superior cost data (RSMeans). In addition, Reed has made it easy for architects to manage these manufacturer-specific objects as well as generic objects in Revit with the SmartBIM Library.

## SmartBuilding Index

The leading industry source for product research, product documentation, BIM objects, design ideas, and source locations. Search, select, and specify available building products with our online directories of manufacturer profiles, MANU-SPEC, SPEC-DATA, guide specs, manufacturer catalogs, building codes, historical project data, and BIM objects.

## SmartBuilding Studio

A vibrant online resource library which brings together a comprehensive catalog of commercial interior finishes and products under a single standard for high-definition imagery, product data, and searchable attributes.

## Associated Construction Publications (ACP)

Reed Construction Data's regional construction magazines cover the nation through a network of 14 regional magazines. Serving the construction market for more than 100 years, our magazines are a trusted source of news and information in the local and national construction communities.

For more information, please visit our website at www.reedconstructiondata.com

The leader in construction information and BIM solutions.

Reed Construction Data®

# 06 16 Sheathing

## 06 16 23 – Subflooring

### 06 16 23.10 Subfloor

| | | Crew | Daily Output | Labor-Hours | Unit | Material | 2010 Bare Costs Labor | Equipment | Total | Total Incl O&P |
|---|---|---|---|---|---|---|---|---|---|---|
| 0010 | **SUBFLOOR** | | | | | | | | | |
| 0011 | Plywood, CDX, 1/2" thick | 2 Carp | 1500 | .011 | SF Flr. | .42 | .31 | | .73 | .98 |
| 0015 | Pneumatic nailed | | 1860 | .009 | | .42 | .25 | | .67 | .88 |
| 0017 | Pneumatic nailed | | 1860 | .009 | | .42 | .25 | | .67 | .88 |
| 0102 | 5/8" thick | | 1350 | .012 | | .51 | .34 | | .85 | 1.14 |
| 0107 | Pneumatic nailed | | 1674 | .010 | | .51 | .28 | | .79 | 1.03 |
| 0202 | 3/4" thick | | 1250 | .013 | | .58 | .37 | | .95 | 1.27 |
| 0207 | Pneumatic nailed | | 1550 | .010 | | .58 | .30 | | .88 | 1.15 |
| 0302 | 1-1/8" thick, 2-4-1 including underlayment | | 1050 | .015 | | 1.50 | .44 | | 1.94 | 2.40 |
| 0440 | With boards, 1" x 6", S4S, laid regular | | 900 | .018 | | 1.40 | .52 | | 1.92 | 2.40 |
| 0452 | 1" x 8", laid regular | | 1000 | .016 | | 1.34 | .47 | | 1.81 | 2.25 |
| 0462 | Laid diagonal | | 850 | .019 | | 1.34 | .55 | | 1.89 | 2.39 |
| 0502 | 1" x 10", laid regular | | 1100 | .015 | | 1.47 | .42 | | 1.89 | 2.33 |
| 0602 | Laid diagonal | | 900 | .018 | ▼ | 1.47 | .52 | | 1.99 | 2.49 |
| 1500 | OSB, 5/8" thick | | 1330 | .012 | S.F. | .50 | .35 | | .85 | 1.14 |
| 1600 | 3/4" thick | ▼ | 1230 | .013 | " | .65 | .38 | | 1.03 | 1.36 |
| 8990 | Subfloor adhesive, 3/8" bead | 1 Carp | 2300 | .003 | L.F. | .09 | .10 | | .19 | .27 |

## 06 16 26 – Underlayment

### 06 16 26.10 Wood Product Underlayment

| | | Crew | Daily Output | Labor-Hours | Unit | Material | 2010 Bare Costs Labor | Equipment | Total | Total Incl O&P |
|---|---|---|---|---|---|---|---|---|---|---|
| 0010 | **WOOD PRODUCT UNDERLAYMENT** | | | | | | | | | |
| 0030 | Plywood, underlayment grade, 3/8" thick | 2 Carp | 1500 | .011 | SF Flr. | .77 | .31 | | 1.08 | 1.37 |
| 0080 | Pneumatic nailed | | 1860 | .009 | | .77 | .25 | | 1.02 | 1.27 |
| 0102 | 1/2" thick | | 1450 | .011 | | .80 | .32 | | 1.12 | 1.42 |
| 0107 | Pneumatic nailed | | 1798 | .009 | | .80 | .26 | | 1.06 | 1.32 |
| 0202 | 5/8" thick | | 1400 | .011 | | 1.17 | .33 | | 1.50 | 1.85 |
| 0207 | Pneumatic nailed | | 1736 | .009 | | 1.17 | .27 | | 1.44 | 1.74 |
| 0302 | 3/4" thick | | 1300 | .012 | | 1.23 | .36 | | 1.59 | 1.95 |
| 0306 | Pneumatic nailed | | 1612 | .010 | | 1.23 | .29 | | 1.52 | 1.84 |
| 0502 | Particle board, 3/8" thick | | 1500 | .011 | | .36 | .31 | | .67 | .92 |
| 0507 | Pneumatic nailed | | 1860 | .009 | | .36 | .25 | | .61 | .82 |
| 0602 | 1/2" thick | | 1450 | .011 | | .39 | .32 | | .71 | .97 |
| 0607 | Pneumatic nailed | | 1798 | .009 | | .39 | .26 | | .65 | .87 |
| 0802 | 5/8" thick | | 1400 | .011 | | .50 | .33 | | .83 | 1.11 |
| 0807 | Pneumatic nailed | | 1736 | .009 | | .50 | .27 | | .77 | 1 |
| 0902 | 3/4" thick | | 1300 | .012 | | .65 | .36 | | 1.01 | 1.32 |
| 0907 | Pneumatic nailed | | 1612 | .010 | ▼ | .65 | .29 | | .94 | 1.21 |
| 0955 | Particleboard, 100% recycled straw/wheat, 4' x 8' x 1/4" [G] | | 1450 | .011 | S.F. | .26 | .32 | | .58 | .83 |
| 0960 | 4' x 8' x 3/8" [G] | | 1450 | .011 | | .39 | .32 | | .71 | .97 |
| 0965 | 4' x 8' x 1/2" [G] | | 1350 | .012 | | .53 | .34 | | .87 | 1.16 |
| 0970 | 4' x 8' x 5/8" [G] | | 1300 | .012 | | .63 | .36 | | .99 | 1.29 |
| 0975 | 4' x 8' x 3/4" [G] | | 1250 | .013 | | .73 | .37 | | 1.10 | 1.43 |
| 0980 | 4' x 8' x 1" [G] | | 1150 | .014 | | .98 | .40 | | 1.38 | 1.76 |
| 0985 | 4' x 8' x 1-1/4" [G] | | 1100 | .015 | ▼ | 1.15 | .42 | | 1.57 | 1.98 |
| 1102 | Hardboard, underlayment grade, 4' x 4', .215" thick | ▼ | 1500 | .011 | SF Flr. | .57 | .31 | | .88 | 1.15 |

## 06 16 36 – Wood Panel Product Sheathing

### 06 16 36.10 Sheathing

| | | | Crew | Daily Output | Labor-Hours | Unit | Material | 2010 Bare Costs Labor | Equipment | Total | Total Incl O&P |
|---|---|---|---|---|---|---|---|---|---|---|---|
| 0010 | **SHEATHING** | R061636-20 | | | | | | | | | |
| 0012 | Plywood on roofs, CDX | | | | | | | | | | |
| 0032 | 5/16" thick | | 2 Carp | 1600 | .010 | S.F. | .53 | .29 | | .82 | 1.07 |
| 0037 | Pneumatic nailed | | | 1952 | .008 | | .53 | .24 | | .77 | .98 |
| 0052 | 3/8" thick | | | 1525 | .010 | | .36 | .31 | | .67 | .91 |
| 0057 | Pneumatic nailed | | ▼ | 1860 | .009 | ▼ | .36 | .25 | | .61 | .82 |

## 06 16 36 – Wood Panel Product Sheathing

| 06 16 36.10 Sheathing | | Crew | Daily Output | Labor-Hours | Unit | Material | 2010 Bare Costs Labor | Equipment | Total | Total Incl O&P |
|---|---|---|---|---|---|---|---|---|---|---|
| 0102 | 1/2" thick | 2 Carp | 1400 | .011 | S.F. | .42 | .33 | | .75 | 1.02 |
| 0103 | Pneumatic nailed | | 1708 | .009 | | .42 | .27 | | .69 | .92 |
| 0202 | 5/8" thick | | 1300 | .012 | | .51 | .36 | | .87 | 1.16 |
| 0207 | Pneumatic nailed | | 1586 | .010 | | .51 | .29 | | .80 | 1.05 |
| 0302 | 3/4" thick | | 1200 | .013 | | .58 | .39 | | .97 | 1.29 |
| 0307 | Pneumatic nailed | | 1464 | .011 | | .58 | .32 | | .90 | 1.18 |
| 0502 | Plywood on walls with exterior CDX, 3/8" thick | | 1200 | .013 | | .36 | .39 | | .75 | 1.05 |
| 0507 | Pneumatic nailed | | 1488 | .011 | | .36 | .31 | | .67 | .93 |
| 0603 | 1/2" thick | | 1125 | .014 | | .42 | .41 | | .83 | 1.16 |
| 0608 | Pneumatic nailed | | 1395 | .011 | | .42 | .33 | | .75 | 1.02 |
| 0702 | 5/8" thick | | 1050 | .015 | | .51 | .44 | | .95 | 1.31 |
| 0707 | Pneumatic nailed | | 1302 | .012 | | .51 | .36 | | .87 | 1.16 |
| 0803 | 3/4" thick | | 975 | .016 | | .58 | .48 | | 1.06 | 1.44 |
| 0808 | Pneumatic nailed | | 1209 | .013 | | .58 | .39 | | .97 | 1.29 |
| 0840 | Oriented strand board, 7/16" thick | G | 1400 | .011 | | .22 | .33 | | .55 | .80 |
| 0845 | Pneumatic nailed | G | 1736 | .009 | | .22 | .27 | | .49 | .69 |
| 0846 | 1/2" thick | G | 1325 | .012 | | .22 | .35 | | .57 | .83 |
| 0847 | Pneumatic nailed | G | 1643 | .010 | | .22 | .28 | | .50 | .72 |
| 0852 | 5/8" thick | G | 1250 | .013 | | .34 | .37 | | .71 | 1 |
| 0857 | Pneumatic nailed | G | 1550 | .010 | | .34 | .30 | | .64 | .88 |
| 1000 | For shear wall construction, add | | | | | | 20% | | | |
| 1200 | For structural 1 exterior plywood, add | | | | S.F. | 10% | | | | |
| 1402 | With boards, on roof 1" x 6" boards, laid horizontal | 2 Carp | 725 | .022 | | 1.40 | .64 | | 2.04 | 2.61 |
| 1502 | Laid diagonal | | 650 | .025 | | 1.40 | .72 | | 2.12 | 2.74 |
| 1702 | 1" x 8" boards, laid horizontal | | 875 | .018 | | 1.34 | .53 | | 1.87 | 2.37 |
| 1802 | Laid diagonal | | 725 | .022 | | 1.34 | .64 | | 1.98 | 2.55 |
| 2000 | For steep roofs, add | | | | | | 40% | | | |
| 2200 | For dormers, hips and valleys, add | | | | | 5% | 50% | | | |
| 2402 | Boards on walls, 1" x 6" boards, laid regular | 2 Carp | 650 | .025 | | 1.40 | .72 | | 2.12 | 2.74 |
| 2502 | Laid diagonal | | 585 | .027 | | 1.40 | .80 | | 2.20 | 2.87 |
| 2702 | 1" x 8" boards, laid regular | | 765 | .021 | | 1.34 | .61 | | 1.95 | 2.49 |
| 2802 | Laid diagonal | | 650 | .025 | | 1.34 | .72 | | 2.06 | 2.68 |
| 2852 | Gypsum, weatherproof, 1/2" thick | | 1050 | .015 | | .38 | .44 | | .82 | 1.17 |
| 2900 | With embedded glass mats | | 1100 | .015 | | .49 | .42 | | .91 | 1.25 |
| 3000 | Wood fiber, regular, no vapor barrier, 1/2" thick | | 1200 | .013 | | .56 | .39 | | .95 | 1.27 |
| 3100 | 5/8" thick | | 1200 | .013 | | .71 | .39 | | 1.10 | 1.43 |
| 3300 | No vapor barrier, in colors, 1/2" thick | | 1200 | .013 | | .75 | .39 | | 1.14 | 1.48 |
| 3400 | 5/8" thick | | 1200 | .013 | | .80 | .39 | | 1.19 | 1.53 |
| 3600 | With vapor barrier one side, white, 1/2" thick | | 1200 | .013 | | .55 | .39 | | .94 | 1.26 |
| 3700 | Vapor barrier 2 sides, 1/2" thick | | 1200 | .013 | | .77 | .39 | | 1.16 | 1.50 |
| 3800 | Asphalt impregnated, 25/32" thick | | 1200 | .013 | | .28 | .39 | | .67 | .96 |
| 3850 | Intermediate, 1/2" thick | | 1200 | .013 | | .20 | .39 | | .59 | .87 |
| 4000 | OSB on roof, 1/2" thick | G | 1455 | .011 | | .22 | .32 | | .54 | .78 |
| 4100 | 5/8" thick | G | 1330 | .012 | | .34 | .35 | | .69 | .96 |

# 06 17 Shop-Fabricated Structural Wood

## 06 17 33 – Wood I-Joists

| 06 17 33.10 Wood and Composite I-Joists | Crew | Daily Output | Labor-Hours | Unit | 2010 Bare Costs Material | Labor | Equipment | Total | Total Incl O&P |
|---|---|---|---|---|---|---|---|---|---|
| 0010 **WOOD AND COMPOSITE I-JOISTS** | | | | | | | | | |
| 0100 Plywood webs, incl. bridging & blocking, panels 24" O.C. | | | | | | | | | |
| 1200 15' to 24' span, 50 psf live load | F-5 | 2400 | .013 | SF Flr. | 1.78 | .34 | | 2.12 | 2.53 |
| 1300 55 psf live load | | 2250 | .014 | | 1.93 | .36 | | 2.29 | 2.73 |
| 1400 24' to 30' span, 45 psf live load | | 2600 | .012 | | 2.66 | .31 | | 2.97 | 3.45 |
| 1500 55 psf live load | | 2400 | .013 | | 3.50 | .34 | | 3.84 | 4.42 |
| 1600 Tubular steel open webs, 45 psf, 24" O.C., 40' span | F-3 | 6250 | .006 | | 2.24 | .17 | .10 | 2.51 | 2.86 |
| 1700 55' span | | 7750 | .005 | | 2.17 | .14 | .08 | 2.39 | 2.71 |
| 1800 70' span | | 9250 | .004 | | 2.82 | .11 | .07 | 3 | 3.37 |
| 1900 85 psf live load, 26' span | | 2300 | .017 | | 2.63 | .46 | .29 | 3.38 | 3.97 |

## 06 17 53 – Shop-Fabricated Wood Trusses

### 06 17 53.10 Roof Trusses

| 06 17 53.10 Roof Trusses | Crew | Daily Output | Labor-Hours | Unit | 2010 Bare Costs Material | Labor | Equipment | Total | Total Incl O&P |
|---|---|---|---|---|---|---|---|---|---|
| 0010 **ROOF TRUSSES** | | | | | | | | | |
| 5000 Common wood, 2" x 4" metal plate connected, 24" O.C., 4/12 slope | | | | | | | | | |
| 5010 1' overhang, 12' span | F-5 | 55 | .582 | Ea. | 46 | 14.80 | | 60.80 | 76 |
| 5050 20' span | F-6 | 62 | .645 | | 70 | 17 | 10.55 | 97.55 | 117 |
| 5100 24' span | | 60 | .667 | | 80.50 | 17.60 | 10.95 | 109.05 | 130 |
| 5150 26' span | | 57 | .702 | | 80 | 18.50 | 11.50 | 110 | 132 |
| 5200 28' span | | 53 | .755 | | 87.50 | 19.90 | 12.35 | 119.75 | 144 |
| 5240 30' span | | 51 | .784 | | 88.50 | 20.50 | 12.85 | 121.85 | 146 |
| 5250 32' span | | 50 | .800 | | 109 | 21 | 13.10 | 143.10 | 170 |
| 5280 34' span | | 48 | .833 | | 117 | 22 | 13.65 | 152.65 | 180 |
| 5350 8/12 pitch, 1' overhang, 20' span | | 57 | .702 | | 76.50 | 18.50 | 11.50 | 106.50 | 128 |
| 5400 24' span | | 55 | .727 | | 97 | 19.20 | 11.90 | 128.10 | 152 |
| 5450 26' span | | 52 | .769 | | 101 | 20.50 | 12.60 | 134.10 | 159 |
| 5500 28' span | | 49 | .816 | | 111 | 21.50 | 13.40 | 145.90 | 174 |
| 5550 32' span | | 45 | .889 | | 134 | 23.50 | 14.55 | 172.05 | 202 |
| 5600 36' span | | 41 | .976 | | 167 | 25.50 | 16 | 208.50 | 244 |
| 5650 38' span | | 40 | 1 | | 182 | 26.50 | 16.40 | 224.90 | 262 |
| 5700 40' span | | 40 | 1 | | 188 | 26.50 | 16.40 | 230.90 | 268 |

# 06 18 Glued-Laminated Construction

## 06 18 13 – Glued-Laminated Beams

### 06 18 13.10 Laminated Beams

| 06 18 13.10 Laminated Beams | Crew | Daily Output | Labor-Hours | Unit | 2010 Bare Costs Material | Labor | Equipment | Total | Total Incl O&P |
|---|---|---|---|---|---|---|---|---|---|
| 0010 **LAMINATED BEAMS** | | | | | | | | | |
| 0050 3-1/2" x 18" | F-3 | 480 | .083 | L.F. | 29 | 2.21 | 1.37 | 32.58 | 36.50 |
| 0100 5-1/4" x 11-7/8" | | 450 | .089 | | 28.50 | 2.35 | 1.46 | 32.31 | 37 |
| 0150 5-1/4" x 16" | | 360 | .111 | | 38.50 | 2.94 | 1.82 | 43.26 | 49 |
| 0200 5-1/4" x 18" | | 290 | .138 | | 43 | 3.65 | 2.26 | 48.91 | 56 |
| 0250 5-1/4" x 24" | | 220 | .182 | | 57.50 | 4.81 | 2.98 | 65.29 | 74.50 |
| 0300 7" x 11-7/8" | | 320 | .125 | | 38 | 3.31 | 2.05 | 43.36 | 49.50 |
| 0350 7" x 16" | | 260 | .154 | | 51 | 4.07 | 2.52 | 57.59 | 65.50 |
| 0400 7" x 18" | | 210 | .190 | | 57.50 | 5.05 | 3.12 | 65.67 | 75.50 |
| 0500 For premium appearance, add to S.F. prices | | | | | 5% | | | | |
| 0550 For industrial type, deduct | | | | | 15% | | | | |
| 0600 For stain and varnish, add | | | | | 5% | | | | |
| 0650 For 3/4" laminations, add | | | | | 25% | | | | |

### 06 18 13.20 Laminated Framing

| | | | | | | | | | |
|---|---|---|---|---|---|---|---|---|---|
| 0010 **LAMINATED FRAMING** | | | | | | | | | |
| 0020 30 lb., short term live load, 15 lb. dead load | | | | | | | | | |

# 06 18 Glued-Laminated Construction

## 06 18 13 – Glued-Laminated Beams

| 06 18 13.20 Laminated Framing | | Crew | Daily Output | Labor-Hours | Unit | Material | 2010 Bare Costs Labor | Equipment | Total | Total Incl O&P |
|---|---|---|---|---|---|---|---|---|---|---|
| 0200 | Straight roof beams, 20' clear span, beams 8' O.C. | F-3 | 2560 | .016 | SF Flr. | 1.76 | .41 | .26 | 2.43 | 2.91 |
| 0300 | Beams 16' O.C. | | 3200 | .013 | | 1.27 | .33 | .20 | 1.80 | 2.18 |
| 0500 | 40' clear span, beams 8' O.C. | | 3200 | .013 | | 3.36 | .33 | .20 | 3.89 | 4.48 |
| 0600 | Beams 16' O.C. | | 3840 | .010 | | 2.75 | .28 | .17 | 3.20 | 3.68 |
| 0800 | 60' clear span, beams 8' O.C. | F-4 | 2880 | .014 | | 5.80 | .37 | .42 | 6.59 | 7.40 |
| 0900 | Beams 16' O.C. | " | 3840 | .010 | | 4.31 | .28 | .32 | 4.91 | 5.55 |
| 1100 | Tudor arches, 30' to 40' clear span, frames 8' O.C. | F-3 | 1680 | .024 | | 7.55 | .63 | .39 | 8.57 | 9.80 |
| 1200 | Frames 16' O.C. | " | 2240 | .018 | | 5.90 | .47 | .29 | 6.66 | 7.60 |
| 1400 | 50' to 60' clear span, frames 8' O.C. | F-4 | 2200 | .018 | | 8.15 | .48 | .55 | 9.18 | 10.35 |
| 1500 | Frames 16' O.C. | | 2640 | .015 | | 6.90 | .40 | .46 | 7.76 | 8.75 |
| 1700 | Radial arches, 60' clear span, frames 8' O.C. | | 1920 | .021 | | 7.60 | .55 | .63 | 8.78 | 9.95 |
| 1800 | Frames 16' O.C. | | 2880 | .014 | | 5.85 | .37 | .42 | 6.64 | 7.50 |
| 2000 | 100' clear span, frames 8' O.C. | | 1600 | .025 | | 7.90 | .66 | .76 | 9.32 | 10.60 |
| 2100 | Frames 16' O.C. | | 2400 | .017 | | 6.90 | .44 | .50 | 7.84 | 8.90 |
| 2300 | 120' clear span, frames 8' O.C. | | 1440 | .028 | | 10.45 | .74 | .84 | 12.03 | 13.65 |
| 2400 | Frames 16' O.C. | | 1920 | .021 | | 9.55 | .55 | .63 | 10.73 | 12.10 |
| 2600 | Bowstring trusses, 20' O.C., 40' clear span | F-3 | 2400 | .017 | | 4.72 | .44 | .27 | 5.43 | 6.25 |
| 2700 | 60' clear span | F-4 | 3600 | .011 | | 4.24 | .29 | .34 | 4.87 | 5.50 |
| 2800 | 100' clear span | | 4000 | .010 | | 6 | .26 | .30 | 6.56 | 7.35 |
| 2900 | 120' clear span | | 3600 | .011 | | 6.45 | .29 | .34 | 7.08 | 7.90 |
| 3100 | For premium appearance, add to S.F. prices | | | | | 5% | | | | |
| 3300 | For industrial type, deduct | | | | | 15% | | | | |
| 3500 | For stain and varnish, add | | | | | 5% | | | | |
| 3900 | For 3/4" laminations, add to straight | | | | | 25% | | | | |
| 4100 | Add to curved | | | | | 15% | | | | |
| 4300 | Alternate pricing method: (use nominal footage of | | | | | | | | | |
| 4310 | components). Straight beams, camber less than 6" | F-3 | 3.50 | 11.429 | M.B.F. | 2,600 | 305 | 187 | 3,092 | 3,575 |
| 4400 | Columns, including hardware | | 2 | 20 | | 2,800 | 530 | 330 | 3,660 | 4,325 |
| 4600 | Curved members, radius over 32' | | 2.50 | 16 | | 2,875 | 425 | 262 | 3,562 | 4,150 |
| 4700 | Radius 10' to 32' | | 3 | 13.333 | | 2,850 | 355 | 219 | 3,424 | 3,950 |
| 4900 | For complicated shapes, add maximum | | | | | 100% | | | | |
| 5100 | For pressure treating, add to straight | | | | | 35% | | | | |
| 5200 | Add to curved | | | | | 45% | | | | |
| 6000 | Laminated veneer members, southern pine or western species | | | | | | | | | |
| 6050 | 1-3/4" wide x 5-1/2" deep | 2 Carp | 480 | .033 | L.F. | 2.39 | .97 | | 3.36 | 4.26 |
| 6100 | 9-1/2" deep | | 480 | .033 | | 3.64 | .97 | | 4.61 | 5.65 |
| 6150 | 14" deep | | 450 | .036 | | 5.60 | 1.03 | | 6.63 | 7.90 |
| 6200 | 18" deep | | 450 | .036 | | 7.25 | 1.03 | | 8.28 | 9.75 |
| 6300 | Parallel strand members, southern pine or western species | | | | | | | | | |
| 6350 | 1-3/4" wide x 9-1/4" deep | 2 Carp | 480 | .033 | L.F. | 4.50 | .97 | | 5.47 | 6.60 |
| 6400 | 11-1/4" deep | | 450 | .036 | | 5.60 | 1.03 | | 6.63 | 7.95 |
| 6450 | 14" deep | | 400 | .040 | | 6.65 | 1.16 | | 7.81 | 9.25 |
| 6500 | 3-1/2" wide x 9-1/4" deep | | 480 | .033 | | 15.15 | .97 | | 16.12 | 18.35 |
| 6550 | 11-1/4" deep | | 450 | .036 | | 18.10 | 1.03 | | 19.13 | 21.50 |
| 6600 | 14" deep | | 400 | .040 | | 22.50 | 1.16 | | 23.66 | 26.50 |
| 6650 | 7" wide x 9-1/4" deep | | 450 | .036 | | 30.50 | 1.03 | | 31.53 | 35 |
| 6700 | 11-1/4" deep | | 420 | .038 | | 38 | 1.11 | | 39.11 | 43.50 |
| 6750 | 14" deep | | 400 | .040 | | 44.50 | 1.16 | | 45.66 | 51 |
| 8000 | Straight beams | | | | | | | | | |
| 8102 | 20' span | | | | | | | | | |
| 8104 | 3-1/8" x 9" | F-3 | 30 | 1.333 | Ea. | 122 | 35.50 | 22 | 179.50 | 218 |
| 8106 | X 10-1/2" | | 30 | 1.333 | | 143 | 35.50 | 22 | 200.50 | 240 |
| 8108 | X 12" | | 30 | 1.333 | | 163 | 35.50 | 22 | 220.50 | 262 |

## 06 18 13 — Glued-Laminated Beams

| 06 18 13.20 Laminated Framing | | Crew | Daily Output | Labor-Hours | Unit | Material | 2010 Bare Costs Labor | Equipment | Total | Total Incl O&P |
|---|---|---|---|---|---|---|---|---|---|---|
| 8110 | X 13-1/2" | F-3 | 30 | 1.333 | Ea. | 184 | 35.50 | 22 | 241.50 | 285 |
| 8112 | X 15" | | 29 | 1.379 | | 204 | 36.50 | 22.50 | 263 | 310 |
| 8114 | 5-1/8" x 10-1/2" | | 30 | 1.333 | | 234 | 35.50 | 22 | 291.50 | 340 |
| 8116 | X 12" | | 30 | 1.333 | | 268 | 35.50 | 22 | 325.50 | 375 |
| 8118 | X 13-1/2" | | 30 | 1.333 | | 300 | 35.50 | 22 | 357.50 | 415 |
| 8120 | X 15" | | 29 | 1.379 | | 335 | 36.50 | 22.50 | 394 | 455 |
| 8122 | X 16-1/2" | | 29 | 1.379 | | 370 | 36.50 | 22.50 | 429 | 490 |
| 8124 | X 18" | | 29 | 1.379 | | 400 | 36.50 | 22.50 | 459 | 525 |
| 8126 | X 19-1/2" | | 29 | 1.379 | | 435 | 36.50 | 22.50 | 494 | 565 |
| 8128 | X 21" | | 28 | 1.429 | | 470 | 38 | 23.50 | 531.50 | 605 |
| 8130 | X 22-1/2" | | 28 | 1.429 | | 500 | 38 | 23.50 | 561.50 | 640 |
| 8132 | X 24" | | 28 | 1.429 | | 535 | 38 | 23.50 | 596.50 | 680 |
| 8134 | 6-3/4" x 12" | | 29 | 1.379 | | 350 | 36.50 | 22.50 | 409 | 475 |
| 8136 | X 13-1/2" | | 29 | 1.379 | | 395 | 36.50 | 22.50 | 454 | 520 |
| 8138 | X 15" | | 29 | 1.379 | | 440 | 36.50 | 22.50 | 499 | 570 |
| 8140 | X 16-1/2" | | 28 | 1.429 | | 485 | 38 | 23.50 | 546.50 | 625 |
| 8142 | X 18" | | 28 | 1.429 | | 530 | 38 | 23.50 | 591.50 | 670 |
| 8144 | X 19-1/2" | | 28 | 1.429 | | 575 | 38 | 23.50 | 636.50 | 720 |
| 8146 | X 21" | | 27 | 1.481 | | 615 | 39 | 24.50 | 678.50 | 770 |
| 8148 | X 22-1/2" | | 27 | 1.481 | | 660 | 39 | 24.50 | 723.50 | 815 |
| 8150 | X 24" | | 27 | 1.481 | | 705 | 39 | 24.50 | 768.50 | 865 |
| 8152 | X 25-1/2" | | 27 | 1.481 | | 750 | 39 | 24.50 | 813.50 | 915 |
| 8154 | X 27" | | 26 | 1.538 | | 795 | 40.50 | 25 | 860.50 | 965 |
| 8156 | X 28-1/2" | | 26 | 1.538 | | 835 | 40.50 | 25 | 900.50 | 1,025 |
| 8158 | X 30" | | 26 | 1.538 | | 880 | 40.50 | 25 | 945.50 | 1,075 |
| 8200 | 30' span | | | | | | | | | |
| 8250 | 3-1/8" x 9" | F-3 | 30 | 1.333 | Ea. | 184 | 35.50 | 22 | 241.50 | 285 |
| 8252 | X 10-1/2" | | 30 | 1.333 | | 214 | 35.50 | 22 | 271.50 | 320 |
| 8254 | X 12" | | 30 | 1.333 | | 245 | 35.50 | 22 | 302.50 | 350 |
| 8256 | X 13-1/2" | | 30 | 1.333 | | 275 | 35.50 | 22 | 332.50 | 390 |
| 8258 | X 15" | | 29 | 1.379 | | 305 | 36.50 | 22.50 | 364 | 420 |
| 8260 | 5-1/8" x 10-1/2" | | 30 | 1.333 | | 350 | 35.50 | 22 | 407.50 | 470 |
| 8262 | X 12" | | 30 | 1.333 | | 400 | 35.50 | 22 | 457.50 | 525 |
| 8264 | X 13-1/2" | | 30 | 1.333 | | 450 | 35.50 | 22 | 507.50 | 580 |
| 8266 | X 15" | | 29 | 1.379 | | 500 | 36.50 | 22.50 | 559 | 635 |
| 8268 | X 16-1/2" | | 29 | 1.379 | | 550 | 36.50 | 22.50 | 609 | 690 |
| 8270 | X 18" | | 29 | 1.379 | | 600 | 36.50 | 22.50 | 659 | 745 |
| 8272 | X 19-1/2" | | 29 | 1.379 | | 650 | 36.50 | 22.50 | 709 | 805 |
| 8274 | X 21" | | 28 | 1.429 | | 700 | 38 | 23.50 | 761.50 | 865 |
| 8276 | X 22-1/2" | | 28 | 1.429 | | 755 | 38 | 23.50 | 816.50 | 920 |
| 8278 | X 24" | | 28 | 1.429 | | 805 | 38 | 23.50 | 866.50 | 975 |
| 8280 | 6-3/4" x 12" | | 29 | 1.379 | | 530 | 36.50 | 22.50 | 589 | 665 |
| 8282 | X 13-1/2" | | 29 | 1.379 | | 595 | 36.50 | 22.50 | 654 | 740 |
| 8284 | X 15" | | 29 | 1.379 | | 660 | 36.50 | 22.50 | 719 | 810 |
| 8286 | X 16-1/2" | | 28 | 1.429 | | 725 | 38 | 23.50 | 786.50 | 890 |
| 8288 | X 18" | | 28 | 1.429 | | 795 | 38 | 23.50 | 856.50 | 960 |
| 8290 | X 19-1/2" | | 28 | 1.429 | | 860 | 38 | 23.50 | 921.50 | 1,025 |
| 8292 | X 21" | | 27 | 1.481 | | 925 | 39 | 24.50 | 988.50 | 1,125 |
| 8294 | X 22-1/2" | | 27 | 1.481 | | 990 | 39 | 24.50 | 1,053.50 | 1,200 |
| 8296 | X 24" | | 27 | 1.481 | | 1,050 | 39 | 24.50 | 1,113.50 | 1,275 |
| 8298 | X 25-1/2" | | 27 | 1.481 | | 1,125 | 39 | 24.50 | 1,188.50 | 1,325 |
| 8300 | X 27" | | 26 | 1.538 | | 1,200 | 40.50 | 25 | 1,265.50 | 1,400 |
| 8302 | X 28-1/2" | | 26 | 1.538 | | 1,250 | 40.50 | 25 | 1,315.50 | 1,475 |

# 06 18 Glued-Laminated Construction

## 06 18 13 – Glued-Laminated Beams

| 06 18 13.20 Laminated Framing | | Crew | Daily Output | Labor-Hours | Unit | Material | 2010 Bare Costs Labor | Equipment | Total | Total Incl O&P |
|---|---|---|---|---|---|---|---|---|---|---|
| 8304 | X 30" | F-3 | 26 | 1.538 | Ea. | 1,325 | 40.50 | 25 | 1,390.50 | 1,550 |
| 8400 | 40' span | | | | | | | | | |
| 8402 | 3-1/8" x 9" | F-3 | 30 | 1.333 | Ea. | 245 | 35.50 | 22 | 302.50 | 350 |
| 8404 | X 10-1/2" | | 30 | 1.333 | | 286 | 35.50 | 22 | 343.50 | 400 |
| 8406 | X 12" | | 30 | 1.333 | | 325 | 35.50 | 22 | 382.50 | 445 |
| 8408 | X 13-1/2" | | 30 | 1.333 | | 365 | 35.50 | 22 | 422.50 | 490 |
| 8410 | X 15" | | 29 | 1.379 | | 410 | 36.50 | 22.50 | 469 | 535 |
| 8412 | 5-1/8" x 10-1/2" | | 30 | 1.333 | | 470 | 35.50 | 22 | 527.50 | 600 |
| 8414 | X 12" | | 30 | 1.333 | | 535 | 35.50 | 22 | 592.50 | 675 |
| 8416 | X 13-1/2" | | 30 | 1.333 | | 600 | 35.50 | 22 | 657.50 | 745 |
| 8418 | X 15" | | 29 | 1.379 | | 670 | 36.50 | 22.50 | 729 | 820 |
| 8420 | X 16-1/2" | | 29 | 1.379 | | 735 | 36.50 | 22.50 | 794 | 895 |
| 8422 | X 18" | | 29 | 1.379 | | 805 | 36.50 | 22.50 | 864 | 970 |
| 8424 | X 19-1/2" | | 29 | 1.379 | | 870 | 36.50 | 22.50 | 929 | 1,050 |
| 8426 | X 21" | | 28 | 1.429 | | 935 | 38 | 23.50 | 996.50 | 1,125 |
| 8428 | X 22-1/2" | | 28 | 1.429 | | 1,000 | 38 | 23.50 | 1,061.50 | 1,200 |
| 8430 | X 24" | | 28 | 1.429 | | 1,075 | 38 | 23.50 | 1,136.50 | 1,275 |
| 8432 | 6-3/4" x 12" | | 29 | 1.379 | | 705 | 36.50 | 22.50 | 764 | 860 |
| 8434 | X 13-1/2" | | 29 | 1.379 | | 795 | 36.50 | 22.50 | 854 | 955 |
| 8436 | X 15" | | 29 | 1.379 | | 880 | 36.50 | 22.50 | 939 | 1,050 |
| 8438 | X 16-1/2" | | 28 | 1.429 | | 970 | 38 | 23.50 | 1,031.50 | 1,175 |
| 8440 | X 18" | | 28 | 1.429 | | 1,050 | 38 | 23.50 | 1,111.50 | 1,275 |
| 8442 | X 19-1/2" | | 28 | 1.429 | | 1,150 | 38 | 23.50 | 1,211.50 | 1,350 |
| 8444 | X 21" | | 27 | 1.481 | | 1,225 | 39 | 24.50 | 1,288.50 | 1,450 |
| 8446 | X 22-1/2" | | 27 | 1.481 | | 1,325 | 39 | 24.50 | 1,388.50 | 1,550 |
| 8448 | X 24" | | 27 | 1.481 | | 1,400 | 39 | 24.50 | 1,463.50 | 1,650 |
| 8450 | X 25-1/2" | | 27 | 1.481 | | 1,500 | 39 | 24.50 | 1,563.50 | 1,750 |
| 8452 | X 27" | | 26 | 1.538 | | 1,575 | 40.50 | 25 | 1,640.50 | 1,850 |
| 8454 | X 28-1/2" | | 26 | 1.538 | | 1,675 | 40.50 | 25 | 1,740.50 | 1,950 |
| 8456 | X 30" | | 26 | 1.538 | | 1,750 | 40.50 | 25 | 1,815.50 | 2,050 |

# 06 22 Millwork

## 06 22 13 – Standard Pattern Wood Trim

### 06 22 13.10 Millwork

| | | Crew | Daily Output | Labor-Hours | Unit | Material | Labor | Equipment | Total | Total Incl O&P |
|---|---|---|---|---|---|---|---|---|---|---|
| 0010 | **MILLWORK** | | | | | | | | | |
| 1020 | 1" x 12", custom birch | | | | L.F. | 5.40 | | | 5.40 | 5.95 |
| 1040 | Cedar | | | | | 3.90 | | | 3.90 | 4.29 |
| 1060 | Oak | | | | | 4.35 | | | 4.35 | 4.79 |
| 1080 | Redwood | | | | | 4.68 | | | 4.68 | 5.15 |
| 1100 | Southern yellow pine | | | | | 3.35 | | | 3.35 | 3.69 |
| 1120 | Sugar pine | | | | | 3.50 | | | 3.50 | 3.85 |
| 1140 | Teak | | | | | 19.15 | | | 19.15 | 21 |
| 1160 | Walnut | | | | | 6.95 | | | 6.95 | 7.65 |
| 1180 | White pine | | | | | 4.19 | | | 4.19 | 4.61 |

### 06 22 13.15 Moldings, Base

| | | Crew | Daily Output | Labor-Hours | Unit | Material | Labor | Equipment | Total | Total Incl O&P |
|---|---|---|---|---|---|---|---|---|---|---|
| 0010 | **MOLDINGS, BASE** | | | | | | | | | |
| 0500 | Base, stock pine, 9/16" x 3-1/2" | 1 Carp | 240 | .033 | L.F. | 2.22 | .97 | | 3.19 | 4.07 |
| 0501 | Oak or birch, 9/16" x 3-1/2" | | 240 | .033 | | 3.38 | .97 | | 4.35 | 5.35 |
| 0550 | 9/16" x 4-1/2" | | 200 | .040 | | 2.46 | 1.16 | | 3.62 | 4.67 |
| 0561 | Base shoe, oak, 3/4" x 1" | | 240 | .033 | | 1.13 | .97 | | 2.10 | 2.87 |
| 0570 | Base, prefinished, 2-1/2" x 9/16" | | 242 | .033 | | .95 | .96 | | 1.91 | 2.67 |

## 06 22 13 – Standard Pattern Wood Trim

| 06 22 13.15 Moldings, Base | Crew | Daily Output | Labor-Hours | Unit | Material | 2010 Bare Costs Labor | Equipment | Total | Total Incl O&P |
|---|---|---|---|---|---|---|---|---|---|
| 0580 | Shoe, prefinished, 3/8" x 5/8" | 1 Carp | 266 | .030 | L.F. | .45 | .88 | | 1.33 | 1.97 |
| 0585 | Flooring cant strip, 3/4" x 1/2" | | 500 | .016 | | .52 | .47 | | .99 | 1.35 |

### 06 22 13.30 Moldings, Casings

| | | Crew | Daily Output | Labor-Hours | Unit | Material | Labor | Equipment | Total | Total Incl O&P |
|---|---|---|---|---|---|---|---|---|---|---|
| 0010 | **MOLDINGS, CASINGS** | | | | | | | | | |
| 0090 | Apron, stock pine, 5/8" x 2" | 1 Carp | 250 | .032 | L.F. | 1.22 | .93 | | 2.15 | 2.91 |
| 0110 | 5/8" x 3-1/2" | | 220 | .036 | | 1.62 | 1.06 | | 2.68 | 3.56 |
| 0300 | Band, stock pine, 11/16" x 1-1/8" | | 270 | .030 | | .82 | .86 | | 1.68 | 2.35 |
| 0350 | 11/16" x 1-3/4" | | 250 | .032 | | 1.06 | .93 | | 1.99 | 2.74 |
| 0700 | Casing, stock pine, 11/16" x 2-1/2" | | 240 | .033 | | 1.33 | .97 | | 2.30 | 3.09 |
| 0701 | Oak or birch | | 240 | .033 | | 2.58 | .97 | | 3.55 | 4.47 |
| 0750 | 11/16" x 3-1/2" | | 215 | .037 | | 1.62 | 1.08 | | 2.70 | 3.60 |
| 0760 | Door & window casing, exterior, 1-1/4" x 2" | | 200 | .040 | | 2.14 | 1.16 | | 3.30 | 4.31 |
| 0770 | Finger jointed, 1-1/4" x 2" | | 200 | .040 | | .99 | 1.16 | | 2.15 | 3.05 |
| 4600 | Mullion casing, stock pine, 5/16" x 2" | | 200 | .040 | | .84 | 1.16 | | 2 | 2.88 |
| 4601 | Oak or birch, 9/16" x 2-1/2" | | 200 | .040 | | 2.79 | 1.16 | | 3.95 | 5.05 |
| 4700 | Teak, custom, nominal 1" x 1" | | 215 | .037 | | 2 | 1.08 | | 3.08 | 4.02 |
| 4800 | Nominal 1" x 3" | | 200 | .040 | | 5.70 | 1.16 | | 6.86 | 8.20 |

### 06 22 13.35 Moldings, Ceilings

| | | Crew | Daily Output | Labor-Hours | Unit | Material | Labor | Equipment | Total | Total Incl O&P |
|---|---|---|---|---|---|---|---|---|---|---|
| 0010 | **MOLDINGS, CEILINGS** | | | | | | | | | |
| 0600 | Bed, stock pine, 9/16" x 1-3/4" | 1 Carp | 270 | .030 | L.F. | 1.02 | .86 | | 1.88 | 2.57 |
| 0650 | 9/16" x 2" | | 240 | .033 | | 1.22 | .97 | | 2.19 | 2.97 |
| 1200 | Cornice molding, stock pine, 9/16" x 1-3/4" | | 330 | .024 | | 1.02 | .71 | | 1.73 | 2.31 |
| 1300 | 9/16" x 2-1/4" | | 300 | .027 | | 1.24 | .78 | | 2.02 | 2.67 |
| 2400 | Cove scotia, stock pine, 9/16" x 1-3/4" | | 270 | .030 | | .67 | .86 | | 1.53 | 2.19 |
| 2401 | Oak or birch, 9/16" x 1-3/4" | | 270 | .030 | | .89 | .86 | | 1.75 | 2.43 |
| 2500 | 11/16" x 2-3/4" | | 255 | .031 | | 1.86 | .91 | | 2.77 | 3.59 |
| 2600 | Crown, stock pine, 9/16" x 3-5/8" | | 250 | .032 | | 2.30 | .93 | | 3.23 | 4.10 |
| 2700 | 11/16" x 4-5/8" | | 220 | .036 | | 3.87 | 1.06 | | 4.93 | 6.05 |

### 06 22 13.40 Moldings, Exterior

| | | Crew | Daily Output | Labor-Hours | Unit | Material | Labor | Equipment | Total | Total Incl O&P |
|---|---|---|---|---|---|---|---|---|---|---|
| 0010 | **MOLDINGS, EXTERIOR** | | | | | | | | | |
| 1500 | Cornice, boards, pine, 1" x 2" | 1 Carp | 330 | .024 | L.F. | .25 | .71 | | .96 | 1.46 |
| 1600 | 1" x 4" | | 250 | .032 | | .44 | .93 | | 1.37 | 2.05 |
| 1700 | 1" x 6" | | 250 | .032 | | .64 | .93 | | 1.57 | 2.27 |
| 1800 | 1" x 8" | | 200 | .040 | | .84 | 1.16 | | 2 | 2.88 |
| 1900 | 1" x 10" | | 180 | .044 | | 1.17 | 1.29 | | 2.46 | 3.46 |
| 2000 | 1" x 12" | | 180 | .044 | | 1.42 | 1.29 | | 2.71 | 3.74 |
| 2200 | Three piece, built-up, pine, minimum | | 80 | .100 | | 1.33 | 2.91 | | 4.24 | 6.35 |
| 2300 | Maximum | | 65 | .123 | | 3.42 | 3.58 | | 7 | 9.75 |
| 3000 | Corner board, sterling pine, 1" x 4" | | 200 | .040 | | .79 | 1.16 | | 1.95 | 2.83 |
| 3100 | 1" x 6" | | 200 | .040 | | 1.05 | 1.16 | | 2.21 | 3.12 |
| 3350 | Fascia, sterling pine, 1" x 6" | | 250 | .032 | | 1.05 | .93 | | 1.98 | 2.73 |
| 3370 | 1" x 8" | | 225 | .036 | | 1.43 | 1.03 | | 2.46 | 3.31 |
| 3376 | 1" x 10" | | 180 | .044 | | 1.20 | 1.29 | | 2.49 | 3.50 |
| 3395 | Grounds, 1" x 1" redwood | | 300 | .027 | | .25 | .78 | | 1.03 | 1.58 |
| 3400 | Trim, back band, 11/16" x 1-1/16" | | 250 | .032 | | .83 | .93 | | 1.76 | 2.48 |
| 3500 | Casing, 11/16" x 4-1/4" | | 250 | .032 | | 2.74 | .93 | | 3.67 | 4.58 |
| 3600 | Crown, 11/16" x 4-1/4" | | 250 | .032 | | 3.85 | .93 | | 4.78 | 5.80 |
| 3700 | 1" x 4" and 1" x 6" railing w/balusters 4" O.C. | | 22 | .364 | | 22.50 | 10.60 | | 33.10 | 42.50 |
| 3800 | Insect screen framing stock, 1-1/16" x 1-3/4" | | 395 | .020 | | 2.03 | .59 | | 2.62 | 3.22 |
| 4100 | Verge board, sterling pine, 1" x 4" | | 200 | .040 | | .79 | 1.16 | | 1.95 | 2.83 |
| 4200 | 1" x 6" | | 200 | .040 | | 1.05 | 1.16 | | 2.21 | 3.12 |
| 4300 | 2" x 6" | | 165 | .048 | | 2.10 | 1.41 | | 3.51 | 4.68 |

# 06 22 Millwork

## 06 22 13 – Standard Pattern Wood Trim

### 06 22 13.40 Moldings, Exterior

| | | Crew | Daily Output | Labor-Hours | Unit | Material | 2010 Bare Costs Labor | 2010 Bare Costs Equipment | Total | Total Incl O&P |
|---|---|---|---|---|---|---|---|---|---|---|
| 4400 | 2" x 8" | 1 Carp | 165 | .048 | L.F. | 2.86 | 1.41 | | 4.27 | 5.50 |
| 4700 | For redwood trim, add | | | | | 200% | | | | |
| 5000 | Casing/fascia, rough-sawn cedar | | | | | | | | | |
| 5100 | 1" x 2" | 1 Carp | 275 | .029 | L.F. | .42 | .85 | | 1.27 | 1.88 |
| 5200 | 1" x 6" | | 250 | .032 | | 1.27 | .93 | | 2.20 | 2.97 |
| 5300 | 1" x 8" | | 230 | .035 | | 2 | 1.01 | | 3.01 | 3.90 |
| 5400 | 2" x 4" | | 220 | .036 | | 1.57 | 1.06 | | 2.63 | 3.51 |
| 5500 | 2" x 6" | | 220 | .036 | | 2.56 | 1.06 | | 3.62 | 4.60 |
| 5600 | 2" x 8" | | 200 | .040 | | 3.89 | 1.16 | | 5.05 | 6.25 |
| 5700 | 2" x 10" | | 180 | .044 | | 4.35 | 1.29 | | 5.64 | 6.95 |
| 5800 | 2" x 12" | | 170 | .047 | | 5.60 | 1.37 | | 6.97 | 8.50 |

### 06 22 13.45 Moldings, Trim

| | | Crew | Daily Output | Labor-Hours | Unit | Material | 2010 Bare Costs Labor | 2010 Bare Costs Equipment | Total | Total Incl O&P |
|---|---|---|---|---|---|---|---|---|---|---|
| 0010 | **MOLDINGS, TRIM** | | | | | | | | | |
| 0200 | Astragal, stock pine, 11/16" x 1-3/4" | 1 Carp | 255 | .031 | L.F. | 1.22 | .91 | | 2.13 | 2.88 |
| 0250 | 1-5/16" x 2-3/16" | | 240 | .033 | | 2.57 | .97 | | 3.54 | 4.46 |
| 0800 | Chair rail, stock pine, 5/8" x 2-1/2" | | 270 | .030 | | 1.43 | .86 | | 2.29 | 3.02 |
| 0900 | 5/8" x 3-1/2" | | 240 | .033 | | 2.26 | .97 | | 3.23 | 4.12 |
| 1000 | Closet pole, stock pine, 1-1/8" diameter | | 200 | .040 | | 1.05 | 1.16 | | 2.21 | 3.12 |
| 1100 | Fir, 1-5/8" diameter | | 200 | .040 | | 1.93 | 1.16 | | 3.09 | 4.08 |
| 1150 | Corner, inside, 5/16" x 1" | | 225 | .036 | | .34 | 1.03 | | 1.37 | 2.11 |
| 1160 | Outside, 1-1/16" x 1-1/16" | | 240 | .033 | | 1.32 | .97 | | 2.29 | 3.08 |
| 1161 | 1-5/16" x 1-5/16" | | 240 | .033 | | 1.73 | .97 | | 2.70 | 3.53 |
| 3300 | Half round, stock pine, 1/4" x 1/2" | | 270 | .030 | | .24 | .86 | | 1.10 | 1.71 |
| 3350 | 1/2" x 1" | | 255 | .031 | | .62 | .91 | | 1.53 | 2.22 |
| 3400 | Handrail, fir, single piece, stock, hardware not included | | | | | | | | | |
| 3450 | 1-1/2" x 1-3/4" | 1 Carp | 80 | .100 | L.F. | 2.03 | 2.91 | | 4.94 | 7.15 |
| 3470 | Pine, 1-1/2" x 1-3/4" | | 80 | .100 | | 2.03 | 2.91 | | 4.94 | 7.15 |
| 3500 | 1-1/2" x 2-1/2" | | 76 | .105 | | 3.04 | 3.06 | | 6.10 | 8.50 |
| 3600 | Lattice, stock pine, 1/4" x 1-1/8" | | 270 | .030 | | .42 | .86 | | 1.28 | 1.91 |
| 3700 | 1/4" x 1-3/4" | | 250 | .032 | | .65 | .93 | | 1.58 | 2.29 |
| 3800 | Miscellaneous, custom, pine, 1" x 1" | | 270 | .030 | | .35 | .86 | | 1.21 | 1.83 |
| 3900 | 1" x 3" | | 240 | .033 | | 1.05 | .97 | | 2.02 | 2.78 |
| 4100 | Birch or oak, nominal 1" x 1" | | 240 | .033 | | .45 | .97 | | 1.42 | 2.12 |
| 4200 | Nominal 1" x 3" | | 215 | .037 | | 1.35 | 1.08 | | 2.43 | 3.30 |
| 4400 | Walnut, nominal 1" x 1" | | 215 | .037 | | .58 | 1.08 | | 1.66 | 2.46 |
| 4500 | Nominal 1" x 3" | | 200 | .040 | | 1.74 | 1.16 | | 2.90 | 3.87 |
| 4700 | Teak, nominal 1" x 1" | | 215 | .037 | | 1.60 | 1.08 | | 2.68 | 3.58 |
| 4800 | Nominal 1" x 3" | | 200 | .040 | | 4.79 | 1.16 | | 5.95 | 7.20 |
| 4900 | Quarter round, stock pine, 1/4" x 1/4" | | 275 | .029 | | .22 | .85 | | 1.07 | 1.66 |
| 4950 | 3/4" x 3/4" | | 255 | .031 | | .60 | .91 | | 1.51 | 2.20 |
| 5600 | Wainscot moldings, 1-1/8" x 9/16", 2' high, minimum | | 76 | .105 | S.F. | 11.15 | 3.06 | | 14.21 | 17.45 |
| 5700 | Maximum | | 65 | .123 | " | 20 | 3.58 | | 23.58 | 28.50 |

### 06 22 13.50 Moldings, Window and Door

| | | Crew | Daily Output | Labor-Hours | Unit | Material | 2010 Bare Costs Labor | 2010 Bare Costs Equipment | Total | Total Incl O&P |
|---|---|---|---|---|---|---|---|---|---|---|
| 0010 | **MOLDINGS, WINDOW AND DOOR** | | | | | | | | | |
| 2800 | Door moldings, stock, decorative, 1-1/8" wide, plain | 1 Carp | 17 | .471 | Set | 45 | 13.70 | | 58.70 | 72.50 |
| 2900 | Detailed | | 17 | .471 | " | 87.50 | 13.70 | | 101.20 | 120 |
| 2960 | Clear pine door jamb, no stops, 11/16" x 4-9/16" | | 240 | .033 | L.F. | 5.15 | .97 | | 6.12 | 7.30 |
| 3150 | Door trim set, 1 head and 2 sides, pine, 2-1/2 wide | | 12 | .667 | Opng. | 22.50 | 19.40 | | 41.90 | 57.50 |
| 3170 | 3-1/2" wide | | 11 | .727 | " | 27.50 | 21 | | 48.50 | 66 |
| 3250 | Glass beads, stock pine, 3/8" x 1/2" | | 275 | .029 | L.F. | .31 | .85 | | 1.16 | 1.76 |
| 3270 | 3/8" x 7/8" | | 270 | .030 | | .41 | .86 | | 1.27 | 1.90 |
| 4850 | Parting bead, stock pine, 3/8" x 3/4" | | 275 | .029 | | .36 | .85 | | 1.21 | 1.82 |

# 06 22 Millwork

## 06 22 13 – Standard Pattern Wood Trim

### 06 22 13.50 Moldings, Window and Door

| | 06 22 13.50 Moldings, Window and Door | Crew | Daily Output | Labor-Hours | Unit | Material | 2010 Bare Costs Labor | 2010 Bare Costs Equipment | Total | Total Incl O&P |
|---|---|---|---|---|---|---|---|---|---|---|
| 4870 | 1/2" x 3/4" | 1 Carp | 255 | .031 | L.F. | .45 | .91 | | 1.36 | 2.04 |
| 5000 | Stool caps, stock pine, 11/16" x 3-1/2" | | 200 | .040 | | 2.27 | 1.16 | | 3.43 | 4.46 |
| 5100 | 1-1/16" x 3-1/4" | | 150 | .053 | | 3.56 | 1.55 | | 5.11 | 6.55 |
| 5300 | Threshold, oak, 3' long, inside, 5/8" x 3-5/8" | | 32 | .250 | Ea. | 9 | 7.30 | | 16.30 | 22 |
| 5400 | Outside, 1-1/2" x 7-5/8" | | 16 | .500 | " | 38 | 14.55 | | 52.55 | 66.50 |
| 5900 | Window trim sets, including casings, header, stops, | | | | | | | | | |
| 5910 | stool and apron, 2-1/2" wide, minimum | 1 Carp | 13 | .615 | Opng. | 32.50 | 17.90 | | 50.40 | 65.50 |
| 5950 | Average | | 10 | .800 | | 38 | 23.50 | | 61.50 | 81 |
| 6000 | Maximum | | 6 | 1.333 | | 62.50 | 39 | | 101.50 | 134 |

### 06 22 13.60 Moldings, Soffits

| | 06 22 13.60 Moldings, Soffits | Crew | Daily Output | Labor-Hours | Unit | Material | 2010 Bare Costs Labor | 2010 Bare Costs Equipment | Total | Total Incl O&P |
|---|---|---|---|---|---|---|---|---|---|---|
| 0010 | **MOLDINGS, SOFFITS** | | | | | | | | | |
| 0200 | Soffits, pine, 1" x 4" | 2 Carp | 420 | .038 | L.F. | .44 | 1.11 | | 1.55 | 2.35 |
| 0210 | 1" x 6" | | 420 | .038 | | .64 | 1.11 | | 1.75 | 2.57 |
| 0220 | 1" x 8" | | 420 | .038 | | .84 | 1.11 | | 1.95 | 2.79 |
| 0230 | 1" x 10" | | 400 | .040 | | 1.17 | 1.16 | | 2.33 | 3.24 |
| 0240 | 1" x 12" | | 400 | .040 | | 1.42 | 1.16 | | 2.58 | 3.52 |
| 0250 | STK cedar, 1" x 4" | | 420 | .038 | | .52 | 1.11 | | 1.63 | 2.44 |
| 0260 | 1" x 6" | | 420 | .038 | | .84 | 1.11 | | 1.95 | 2.79 |
| 0270 | 1" x 8" | | 420 | .038 | | 1.31 | 1.11 | | 2.42 | 3.31 |
| 0280 | 1" x 10" | | 400 | .040 | | 1.89 | 1.16 | | 3.05 | 4.04 |
| 0290 | 1" x 12" | | 400 | .040 | | 2.63 | 1.16 | | 3.79 | 4.85 |
| 1000 | Exterior AC plywood, 1/4" thick | | 420 | .038 | S.F. | .68 | 1.11 | | 1.79 | 2.62 |
| 1050 | 3/8" thick | | 420 | .038 | | .77 | 1.11 | | 1.88 | 2.72 |
| 1100 | 1/2" thick | | 420 | .038 | | .80 | 1.11 | | 1.91 | 2.75 |
| 1150 | Polyvinyl chloride, white, solid | 1 Carp | 230 | .035 | | 1.09 | 1.01 | | 2.10 | 2.90 |
| 1160 | Perforated | " | 230 | .035 | | 1.09 | 1.01 | | 2.10 | 2.90 |
| 1170 | Accessories, "J" channel 5/8" | 2 Carp | 700 | .023 | L.F. | .42 | .67 | | 1.09 | 1.58 |

# 06 25 Prefinished Paneling

## 06 25 13 – Prefinished Hardboard Paneling

### 06 25 13.10 Paneling, Hardboard

| | 06 25 13.10 Paneling, Hardboard | | Crew | Daily Output | Labor-Hours | Unit | Material | 2010 Bare Costs Labor | 2010 Bare Costs Equipment | Total | Total Incl O&P |
|---|---|---|---|---|---|---|---|---|---|---|---|
| 0010 | **PANELING, HARDBOARD** | | | | | | | | | | |
| 0050 | Not incl. furring or trim, hardboard, tempered, 1/8" thick | G | 2 Carp | 500 | .032 | S.F. | .39 | .93 | | 1.32 | 2 |
| 0100 | 1/4" thick | G | | 500 | .032 | | .53 | .93 | | 1.46 | 2.15 |
| 0300 | Tempered pegboard, 1/8" thick | G | | 500 | .032 | | .44 | .93 | | 1.37 | 2.05 |
| 0400 | 1/4" thick | G | | 500 | .032 | | .67 | .93 | | 1.60 | 2.31 |
| 0600 | Untempered hardboard, natural finish, 1/8" thick | G | | 500 | .032 | | .38 | .93 | | 1.31 | 1.99 |
| 0700 | 1/4" thick | G | | 500 | .032 | | .46 | .93 | | 1.39 | 2.08 |
| 0900 | Untempered pegboard, 1/8" thick | G | | 500 | .032 | | .38 | .93 | | 1.31 | 1.99 |
| 1000 | 1/4" thick | G | | 500 | .032 | | .42 | .93 | | 1.35 | 2.03 |
| 1200 | Plastic faced hardboard, 1/8" thick | G | | 500 | .032 | | .67 | .93 | | 1.60 | 2.31 |
| 1300 | 1/4" thick | G | | 500 | .032 | | .85 | .93 | | 1.78 | 2.51 |
| 1500 | Plastic faced pegboard, 1/8" thick | G | | 500 | .032 | | .61 | .93 | | 1.54 | 2.24 |
| 1600 | 1/4" thick | G | | 500 | .032 | | .75 | .93 | | 1.68 | 2.40 |
| 1800 | Wood grained, plain or grooved, 1/4" thick, minimum | G | | 500 | .032 | | .57 | .93 | | 1.50 | 2.20 |
| 1900 | Maximum | | | 425 | .038 | | 1.19 | 1.10 | | 2.29 | 3.15 |
| 2100 | Moldings for hardboard, wood or aluminum, minimum | | | 500 | .032 | L.F. | .38 | .93 | | 1.31 | 1.99 |
| 2200 | Maximum | | | 425 | .038 | " | 1.08 | 1.10 | | 2.18 | 3.03 |

# 06 25 Prefinished Paneling

## 06 25 16 – Prefinished Plywood Paneling

### 06 25 16.10 Paneling, Plywood

| | Crew | Daily Output | Labor-Hours | Unit | Material | 2010 Bare Costs Labor | Equipment | Total | Total Incl O&P |
|---|---|---|---|---|---|---|---|---|---|
| 0010 **PANELING, PLYWOOD** | | | | | | | | | |
| 2400 Plywood, prefinished, 1/4" thick, 4' x 8' sheets | | | | | | | | | |
| 2410     with vertical grooves. Birch faced, minimum | 2 Carp | 500 | .032 | S.F. | .89 | .93 | | 1.82 | 2.55 |
| 2420         Average | | 420 | .038 | | 1.35 | 1.11 | | 2.46 | 3.36 |
| 2430         Maximum | | 350 | .046 | | 1.97 | 1.33 | | 3.30 | 4.41 |
| 2600     Mahogany, African | | 400 | .040 | | 2.51 | 1.16 | | 3.67 | 4.72 |
| 2700       Philippine (Lauan) | | 500 | .032 | | 1.08 | .93 | | 2.01 | 2.76 |
| 2900     Oak or Cherry, minimum | | 500 | .032 | | 2.10 | .93 | | 3.03 | 3.88 |
| 3000       Maximum | | 400 | .040 | | 3.22 | 1.16 | | 4.38 | 5.50 |
| 3200     Rosewood | | 320 | .050 | | 4.58 | 1.46 | | 6.04 | 7.50 |
| 3400     Teak | | 400 | .040 | | 3.22 | 1.16 | | 4.38 | 5.50 |
| 3600     Chestnut | | 375 | .043 | | 4.77 | 1.24 | | 6.01 | 7.35 |
| 3800     Pecan | | 400 | .040 | | 2.06 | 1.16 | | 3.22 | 4.23 |
| 3900     Walnut, minimum | | 500 | .032 | | 2.75 | .93 | | 3.68 | 4.60 |
| 3950       Maximum | | 400 | .040 | | 5.20 | 1.16 | | 6.36 | 7.70 |
| 4000 Plywood, prefinished, 3/4" thick, stock grades, minimum | | 320 | .050 | | 1.24 | 1.46 | | 2.70 | 3.81 |
| 4100       Maximum | | 224 | .071 | | 5.40 | 2.08 | | 7.48 | 9.40 |
| 4300       Architectural grade, minimum | | 224 | .071 | | 3.98 | 2.08 | | 6.06 | 7.90 |
| 4400         Maximum | | 160 | .100 | | 6.10 | 2.91 | | 9.01 | 11.60 |
| 4600 Plywood, "A" face, birch, V.C., 1/2" thick, natural | | 450 | .036 | | 1.89 | 1.03 | | 2.92 | 3.82 |
| 4700       Select | | 450 | .036 | | 2.06 | 1.03 | | 3.09 | 4.01 |
| 4900     Veneer core, 3/4" thick, natural | | 320 | .050 | | 1.99 | 1.46 | | 3.45 | 4.64 |
| 5000       Select | | 320 | .050 | | 2.23 | 1.46 | | 3.69 | 4.90 |
| 5200     Lumber core, 3/4" thick, natural | | 320 | .050 | | 2.99 | 1.46 | | 4.45 | 5.75 |
| 5500 Plywood, knotty pine, 1/4" thick, A2 grade | | 450 | .036 | | 1.63 | 1.03 | | 2.66 | 3.53 |
| 5600     A3 grade | | 450 | .036 | | 2.06 | 1.03 | | 3.09 | 4.01 |
| 5800     3/4" thick, veneer core, A2 grade | | 320 | .050 | | 2.11 | 1.46 | | 3.57 | 4.77 |
| 5900     A3 grade | | 320 | .050 | | 2.38 | 1.46 | | 3.84 | 5.05 |
| 6100     Aromatic cedar, 1/4" thick, plywood | | 400 | .040 | | 2.08 | 1.16 | | 3.24 | 4.25 |
| 6200     1/4" thick, particle board | | 400 | .040 | | 1.01 | 1.16 | | 2.17 | 3.07 |

## 06 25 26 – Panel System

### 06 25 26.10 Panel Systems

| | Crew | Daily Output | Labor-Hours | Unit | Material | 2010 Bare Costs Labor | Equipment | Total | Total Incl O&P |
|---|---|---|---|---|---|---|---|---|---|
| 0010 **PANEL SYSTEMS** | | | | | | | | | |
| 0100 Raised panel, eng. wood core w/wood veneer, std., paint grade | 2 Carp | 300 | .053 | S.F. | 11.90 | 1.55 | | 13.45 | 15.70 |
| 0110       Oak veneer | | 300 | .053 | | 19.70 | 1.55 | | 21.25 | 24 |
| 0120       Maple veneer | | 300 | .053 | | 25 | 1.55 | | 26.55 | 30 |
| 0130       Cherry veneer | | 300 | .053 | | 32 | 1.55 | | 33.55 | 37.50 |
| 0300     Class I fire rated, paint grade | | 300 | .053 | | 14.25 | 1.55 | | 15.80 | 18.25 |
| 0310       Oak veneer | | 300 | .053 | | 23.50 | 1.55 | | 25.05 | 28.50 |
| 0320       Maple veneer | | 300 | .053 | | 30 | 1.55 | | 31.55 | 35.50 |
| 0330       Cherry veneer | | 300 | .053 | | 38.50 | 1.55 | | 40.05 | 44.50 |
| 0510 Beadboard, 5/8" MDF, standard, primed | | 300 | .053 | | 8.40 | 1.55 | | 9.95 | 11.85 |
| 0520       Oak veneer, unfinished | | 300 | .053 | | 14.60 | 1.55 | | 16.15 | 18.65 |
| 0530       Maple veneer, unfinished | | 300 | .053 | | 17.25 | 1.55 | | 18.80 | 21.50 |
| 0610 Rustic paneling, 5/8" MDF, standard, maple veneer, unfinished | | 300 | .053 | | 22 | 1.55 | | 23.55 | 27 |

# 06 26 Board Paneling

## 06 26 13 – Profile Board Paneling

| 06 26 13.10 Paneling, Boards | Crew | Daily Output | Labor-Hours | Unit | Material | 2010 Bare Costs Labor | Equipment | Total | Total Incl O&P |
|---|---|---|---|---|---|---|---|---|---|
| 0010 **PANELING, BOARDS** | | | | | | | | | |
| 6400 Wood board paneling, 3/4" thick, knotty pine | 2 Carp | 300 | .053 | S.F. | 1.44 | 1.55 | | 2.99 | 4.19 |
| 6500 Rough sawn cedar | | 300 | .053 | | 1.85 | 1.55 | | 3.40 | 4.65 |
| 6700 Redwood, clear, 1" x 4" boards | | 300 | .053 | | 4.96 | 1.55 | | 6.51 | 8.05 |
| 6900 Aromatic cedar, closet lining, boards | ↓ | 275 | .058 | ↓ | 3.32 | 1.69 | | 5.01 | 6.50 |

# 06 43 Wood Stairs and Railings

## 06 43 13 – Wood Stairs

### 06 43 13.20 Prefabricated Wood Stairs

| | Crew | Daily Output | Labor-Hours | Unit | Material | 2010 Bare Costs Labor | Equipment | Total | Total Incl O&P |
|---|---|---|---|---|---|---|---|---|---|
| 0010 **PREFABRICATED WOOD STAIRS** | | | | | | | | | |
| 0100 Box stairs, prefabricated, 3'-0" wide | | | | | | | | | |
| 0110 Oak treads, up to 14 risers | 2 Carp | 39 | .410 | Riser | 85 | 11.95 | | 96.95 | 114 |
| 0600 With pine treads for carpet, up to 14 risers | " | 39 | .410 | " | 55 | 11.95 | | 66.95 | 80.50 |
| 1100 For 4' wide stairs, add | | | | Flight | 25% | | | | |
| 1550 Stairs, prefabricated stair handrail with balusters | 1 Carp | 30 | .267 | L.F. | 75 | 7.75 | | 82.75 | 95 |
| 1700 Basement stairs, prefabricated, pine treads | | | | | | | | | |
| 1710 Pine risers, 3' wide, up to 14 risers | 2 Carp | 52 | .308 | Riser | 55 | 8.95 | | 63.95 | 75.50 |
| 4000 Residential, wood, oak treads, prefabricated | | 1.50 | 10.667 | Flight | 1,100 | 310 | | 1,410 | 1,725 |
| 4200 Built in place | ↓ | .44 | 36.364 | " | 1,750 | 1,050 | | 2,800 | 3,700 |
| 4400 Spiral, oak, 4'-6" diameter, unfinished, prefabricated, | | | | | | | | | |
| 4500 incl. railing, 9' high | 2 Carp | 1.50 | 10.667 | Flight | 3,625 | 310 | | 3,935 | 4,500 |

### 06 43 13.40 Wood Stair Parts

| | Crew | Daily Output | Labor-Hours | Unit | Material | 2010 Bare Costs Labor | Equipment | Total | Total Incl O&P |
|---|---|---|---|---|---|---|---|---|---|
| 0010 **WOOD STAIR PARTS** | | | | | | | | | |
| 0020 Pin top balusters, 1-1/4", oak, 34" | 1 Carp | 96 | .083 | Ea. | 7.80 | 2.42 | | 10.22 | 12.70 |
| 0030 38" | | 96 | .083 | | 9.85 | 2.42 | | 12.27 | 14.95 |
| 0040 42" | | 96 | .083 | | 12.10 | 2.42 | | 14.52 | 17.40 |
| 0050 Poplar, 34" | | 96 | .083 | | 3.05 | 2.42 | | 5.47 | 7.45 |
| 0060 38" | | 96 | .083 | | 3.62 | 2.42 | | 6.04 | 8.05 |
| 0070 42" | | 96 | .083 | | 8.55 | 2.42 | | 10.97 | 13.55 |
| 0080 Maple, 34" | | 96 | .083 | | 4.90 | 2.42 | | 7.32 | 9.50 |
| 0090 38" | | 96 | .083 | | 6.20 | 2.42 | | 8.62 | 10.90 |
| 0100 42" | | 96 | .083 | | 7.60 | 2.42 | | 10.02 | 12.45 |
| 0130 Primed, 34" | | 96 | .083 | | 2.85 | 2.42 | | 5.27 | 7.20 |
| 0140 38" | | 96 | .083 | | 3.62 | 2.42 | | 6.04 | 8.05 |
| 0150 42" | | 96 | .083 | | 4.42 | 2.42 | | 6.84 | 8.95 |
| 0180 Box top balusters, 1-1/4", oak, 34" | | 60 | .133 | | 10.85 | 3.88 | | 14.73 | 18.50 |
| 0190 38" | | 60 | .133 | | 12.50 | 3.88 | | 16.38 | 20.50 |
| 0200 42" | | 60 | .133 | | 12.95 | 3.88 | | 16.83 | 21 |
| 0210 Poplar, 34" | | 60 | .133 | | 8.65 | 3.88 | | 12.53 | 16.05 |
| 0220 38" | | 60 | .133 | | 9.50 | 3.88 | | 13.38 | 17 |
| 0230 42" | | 60 | .133 | | 10 | 3.88 | | 13.88 | 17.55 |
| 0240 Maple, 34" | | 60 | .133 | | 11.90 | 3.88 | | 15.78 | 19.65 |
| 0250 38" | | 60 | .133 | | 13.80 | 3.88 | | 17.68 | 22 |
| 0260 42" | | 60 | .133 | | 14.20 | 3.88 | | 18.08 | 22 |
| 0290 Primed, 34" | | 60 | .133 | | 6.95 | 3.88 | | 10.83 | 14.20 |
| 0300 38" | | 60 | .133 | | 8 | 3.88 | | 11.88 | 15.35 |
| 0310 42" | | 60 | .133 | ↓ | 8.35 | 3.88 | | 12.23 | 15.75 |
| 0340 Square balusters, cut from lineal stock, pine, 1-1/16" x 1-1/16" | | 180 | .044 | L.F. | 1.32 | 1.29 | | 2.61 | 3.63 |
| 0350 1-5/16" x 1-5/16" | | 180 | .044 | | 1.70 | 1.29 | | 2.99 | 4.05 |
| 0360 1-5/8" x 1-5/8" | | 180 | .044 | ↓ | 2.82 | 1.29 | | 4.11 | 5.30 |
| 0370 Turned newel, oak, 3-1/2" square, 48" high | | 8 | 1 | Ea. | 94 | 29 | | 123 | 152 |

385

| 06 43 13.40 Wood Stair Parts | | Crew | Daily Output | Labor-Hours | Unit | Material | 2010 Bare Costs Labor | 2010 Bare Costs Equipment | Total | Total Incl O&P |
|---|---|---|---|---|---|---|---|---|---|---|
| 0380 | 62" high | 1 Carp | 8 | 1 | Ea. | 138 | 29 | | 167 | 201 |
| 0390 | Poplar, 3-1/2" square, 48" high | | 8 | 1 | | 52 | 29 | | 81 | 106 |
| 0400 | 62" high | | 8 | 1 | | 75 | 29 | | 104 | 132 |
| 0410 | Maple, 3-1/2" square, 48" high | | 8 | 1 | | 66 | 29 | | 95 | 122 |
| 0420 | 62" high | | 8 | 1 | | 93 | 29 | | 122 | 151 |
| 0430 | Square newel, oak, 3-1/2" square, 48" high | | 8 | 1 | | 74 | 29 | | 103 | 131 |
| 0440 | 58" high | | 8 | 1 | | 78 | 29 | | 107 | 135 |
| 0450 | Poplar, 3-1/2" square, 48" high | | 8 | 1 | | 49 | 29 | | 78 | 103 |
| 0460 | 58" high | | 8 | 1 | | 54 | 29 | | 83 | 109 |
| 0470 | Maple, 3" square, 48" high | | 8 | 1 | | 66 | 29 | | 95 | 122 |
| 0480 | 58" high | | 8 | 1 | | 70 | 29 | | 99 | 126 |
| 0490 | Railings, oak, minimum | | 96 | .083 | L.F. | 11 | 2.42 | | 13.42 | 16.20 |
| 0500 | Average | | 96 | .083 | | 14 | 2.42 | | 16.42 | 19.50 |
| 0510 | Maximum | | 96 | .083 | | 14.50 | 2.42 | | 16.92 | 20 |
| 0520 | Maple, minimum | | 96 | .083 | | 15 | 2.42 | | 17.42 | 20.50 |
| 0530 | Average | | 96 | .083 | | 15.25 | 2.42 | | 17.67 | 21 |
| 0540 | Maximum | | 96 | .083 | | 15.50 | 2.42 | | 17.92 | 21 |
| 0550 | Oak, for bending rail, minimum | | 48 | .167 | | 21 | 4.85 | | 25.85 | 31 |
| 0560 | Average | | 48 | .167 | | 22 | 4.85 | | 26.85 | 32 |
| 0570 | Maximum | | 48 | .167 | | 23 | 4.85 | | 27.85 | 33.50 |
| 0580 | Maple, for bending rail, minimum | | 48 | .167 | | 23 | 4.85 | | 27.85 | 33 |
| 0590 | Average | | 48 | .167 | | 25 | 4.85 | | 29.85 | 35 |
| 0600 | Maximum | | 48 | .167 | | 27 | 4.85 | | 31.85 | 37.50 |
| 0610 | Risers, oak, 3/4" x 8", 36" long | | 80 | .100 | Ea. | 18 | 2.91 | | 20.91 | 24.50 |
| 0620 | 42" long | | 80 | .100 | | 21 | 2.91 | | 23.91 | 28 |
| 0630 | 48" long | | 80 | .100 | | 24 | 2.91 | | 26.91 | 31.50 |
| 0640 | 54" long | | 80 | .100 | | 27 | 2.91 | | 29.91 | 34.50 |
| 0650 | 60" long | | 80 | .100 | | 30 | 2.91 | | 32.91 | 38 |
| 0660 | 72" long | | 80 | .100 | | 36 | 2.91 | | 38.91 | 44.50 |
| 0670 | Poplar, 3/4" x 8", 36" long | | 80 | .100 | | 11.10 | 2.91 | | 14.01 | 17.10 |
| 0680 | 42" long | | 80 | .100 | | 12.95 | 2.91 | | 15.86 | 19.15 |
| 0690 | 48" long | | 80 | .100 | | 14.80 | 2.91 | | 17.71 | 21 |
| 0700 | 54" long | | 80 | .100 | | 16.65 | 2.91 | | 19.56 | 23 |
| 0710 | 60" long | | 80 | .100 | | 18.50 | 2.91 | | 21.41 | 25.50 |
| 0720 | 72" long | | 80 | .100 | | 22 | 2.91 | | 24.91 | 29.50 |
| 0730 | Pine, 1" x 8", 36" long | | 80 | .100 | | 2.51 | 2.91 | | 5.42 | 7.65 |
| 0740 | 42" long | | 80 | .100 | | 2.93 | 2.91 | | 5.84 | 8.10 |
| 0750 | 48" long | | 80 | .100 | | 3.34 | 2.91 | | 6.25 | 8.60 |
| 0760 | 54" long | | 80 | .100 | | 3.76 | 2.91 | | 6.67 | 9.05 |
| 0770 | 60" long | | 80 | .100 | | 4.18 | 2.91 | | 7.09 | 9.50 |
| 0780 | 72" long | | 80 | .100 | | 5 | 2.91 | | 7.91 | 10.40 |
| 0790 | Treads, oak, no returns, 1-1/32" x 11-1/2" x 36" long | | 32 | .250 | | 32 | 7.30 | | 39.30 | 47.50 |
| 0800 | 42" long | | 32 | .250 | | 37.50 | 7.30 | | 44.80 | 53.50 |
| 0810 | 48" long | | 32 | .250 | | 42.50 | 7.30 | | 49.80 | 59.50 |
| 0820 | 54" long | | 32 | .250 | | 48 | 7.30 | | 55.30 | 65.50 |
| 0830 | 60" long | | 32 | .250 | | 53.50 | 7.30 | | 60.80 | 71 |
| 0840 | 72" long | | 32 | .250 | | 64 | 7.30 | | 71.30 | 83 |
| 0850 | Mitred return one end, 1-1/32" x 11-1/2" x 36" long | | 24 | .333 | | 45 | 9.70 | | 54.70 | 66 |
| 0860 | 42" long | | 24 | .333 | | 52.50 | 9.70 | | 62.20 | 74.50 |
| 0870 | 48" long | | 24 | .333 | | 60 | 9.70 | | 69.70 | 82.50 |
| 0880 | 54" long | | 24 | .333 | | 67.50 | 9.70 | | 77.20 | 91 |
| 0890 | 60" long | | 24 | .333 | | 75 | 9.70 | | 84.70 | 99 |
| 0900 | 72" long | | 24 | .333 | | 90 | 9.70 | | 99.70 | 115 |

# 06 43 Wood Stairs and Railings

## 06 43 13 – Wood Stairs

| 06 43 13.40 Wood Stair Parts | | Crew | Daily Output | Labor-Hours | Unit | Material | 2010 Bare Costs Labor | Equipment | Total | Total Incl O&P |
|---|---|---|---|---|---|---|---|---|---|---|
| 0910 | Mitred return two ends, 1-1/32" x 11-1/2" x 36" long | 1 Carp | 12 | .667 | Ea. | 49 | 19.40 | | 68.40 | 86.50 |
| 0920 | 42" long | | 12 | .667 | | 57 | 19.40 | | 76.40 | 95.50 |
| 0930 | 48" long | | 12 | .667 | | 65.50 | 19.40 | | 84.90 | 105 |
| 0940 | 54" long | | 12 | .667 | | 73.50 | 19.40 | | 92.90 | 114 |
| 0950 | 60" long | | 12 | .667 | | 81.50 | 19.40 | | 100.90 | 123 |
| 0960 | 72" long | | 12 | .667 | | 98 | 19.40 | | 117.40 | 141 |
| 0970 | Starting step, oak, 48", bullnose | | 8 | 1 | | 176 | 29 | | 205 | 243 |
| 0980 | Double end bullnose | | 8 | 1 | | 275 | 29 | | 304 | 355 |
| 1030 | Skirt board, pine, 1" x 10" | | 55 | .145 | L.F. | 1.17 | 4.23 | | 5.40 | 8.40 |
| 1040 | 1" x 12" | | 52 | .154 | " | 1.42 | 4.48 | | 5.90 | 9.10 |
| 1050 | Oak landing tread, 1-1/16" thick | | 54 | .148 | S.F. | 8.25 | 4.31 | | 12.56 | 16.35 |
| 1060 | Oak cove molding | | 96 | .083 | L.F. | 1.45 | 2.42 | | 3.87 | 5.70 |
| 1070 | Oak stringer molding | | 96 | .083 | " | 2.75 | 2.42 | | 5.17 | 7.10 |
| 1090 | Rail bolt, 5/16" x 3-1/2" | | 48 | .167 | Ea. | 2.75 | 4.85 | | 7.60 | 11.20 |
| 1100 | 5/16" x 4-1/2" | | 48 | .167 | | 2.75 | 4.85 | | 7.60 | 11.20 |
| 1120 | Newel post anchor | | 16 | .500 | | 13.50 | 14.55 | | 28.05 | 39.50 |
| 1130 | Tapered plug, 1/2" | | 240 | .033 | | .30 | .97 | | 1.27 | 1.96 |
| 1140 | 1" | | 240 | .033 | | .40 | .97 | | 1.37 | 2.07 |

## 06 43 16 – Wood Railings

### 06 43 16.10 Wood Handrails and Railings

| | | Crew | Daily Output | Labor-Hours | Unit | Material | 2010 Bare Costs Labor | Equipment | Total | Total Incl O&P |
|---|---|---|---|---|---|---|---|---|---|---|
| 0010 | **WOOD HANDRAILS AND RAILINGS** | | | | | | | | | |
| 0020 | Custom design, architectural grade, hardwood, minimum | 1 Carp | 38 | .211 | L.F. | 9.50 | 6.15 | | 15.65 | 21 |
| 0100 | Maximum | | 30 | .267 | | 50 | 7.75 | | 57.75 | 68 |
| 0300 | Stock interior railing with spindles 4" O.C., 4' long | | 40 | .200 | | 37 | 5.80 | | 42.80 | 50.50 |
| 0400 | 8' long | | 48 | .167 | | 37 | 4.85 | | 41.85 | 48.50 |

# 06 44 Ornamental Woodwork

## 06 44 19 – Wood Grilles

### 06 44 19.10 Grilles

| | | Crew | Daily Output | Labor-Hours | Unit | Material | 2010 Bare Costs Labor | Equipment | Total | Total Incl O&P |
|---|---|---|---|---|---|---|---|---|---|---|
| 0010 | **GRILLES** and panels, hardwood, sanded | | | | | | | | | |
| 0020 | 2' x 4' to 4' x 8', custom designs, unfinished, minimum | 1 Carp | 38 | .211 | S.F. | 54 | 6.15 | | 60.15 | 70 |
| 0050 | Average | | 30 | .267 | | 62.50 | 7.75 | | 70.25 | 82 |
| 0100 | Maximum | | 19 | .421 | | 71 | 12.25 | | 83.25 | 98.50 |

## 06 44 33 – Wood Mantels

### 06 44 33.10 Fireplace Mantels

| | | Crew | Daily Output | Labor-Hours | Unit | Material | 2010 Bare Costs Labor | Equipment | Total | Total Incl O&P |
|---|---|---|---|---|---|---|---|---|---|---|
| 0010 | **FIREPLACE MANTELS** | | | | | | | | | |
| 0015 | 6" molding, 6' x 3'-6" opening, minimum | 1 Carp | 5 | 1.600 | Opng. | 228 | 46.50 | | 274.50 | 330 |
| 0100 | Maximum | | 5 | 1.600 | | 410 | 46.50 | | 456.50 | 535 |
| 0300 | Prefabricated pine, colonial type, stock, deluxe | | 2 | 4 | | 1,250 | 116 | | 1,366 | 1,600 |
| 0400 | Economy | | 3 | 2.667 | | 530 | 77.50 | | 607.50 | 715 |

### 06 44 33.20 Fireplace Mantel Beam

| | | Crew | Daily Output | Labor-Hours | Unit | Material | 2010 Bare Costs Labor | Equipment | Total | Total Incl O&P |
|---|---|---|---|---|---|---|---|---|---|---|
| 0010 | **FIREPLACE MANTEL BEAM** | | | | | | | | | |
| 0020 | Rough texture wood, 4" x 8" | 1 Carp | 36 | .222 | L.F. | 6.90 | 6.45 | | 13.35 | 18.50 |
| 0100 | 4" x 10" | | 35 | .229 | " | 12.80 | 6.65 | | 19.45 | 25.50 |
| 0300 | Laminated hardwood, 2-1/4" x 10-1/2" wide, 6' long | | 5 | 1.600 | Ea. | 110 | 46.50 | | 156.50 | 200 |
| 0400 | 8' long | | 5 | 1.600 | " | 150 | 46.50 | | 196.50 | 244 |
| 0600 | Brackets for above, rough sawn | | 12 | .667 | Pr. | 10 | 19.40 | | 29.40 | 43.50 |
| 0700 | Laminated | | 12 | .667 | " | 15 | 19.40 | | 34.40 | 49 |

387

# 06 44 Ornamental Woodwork

## 06 44 39 – Wood Posts and Columns

### 06 44 39.10 Decorative Beams

| | 06 44 39.10 Decorative Beams | Crew | Daily Output | Labor-Hours | Unit | Material | 2010 Bare Costs Labor | Equipment | Total | Total Incl O&P |
|---|---|---|---|---|---|---|---|---|---|---|
| 0010 | **DECORATIVE BEAMS** | | | | | | | | | |
| 0020 | Rough sawn cedar, non-load bearing, 4" x 4" | 2 Carp | 180 | .089 | L.F. | 1 | 2.59 | | 3.59 | 5.45 |
| 0100 | 4" x 6" | | 170 | .094 | | 1.42 | 2.74 | | 4.16 | 6.15 |
| 0200 | 4" x 8" | | 160 | .100 | | 1.89 | 2.91 | | 4.80 | 7 |
| 0300 | 4" x 10" | | 150 | .107 | | 2.37 | 3.10 | | 5.47 | 7.80 |
| 0400 | 4" x 12" | | 140 | .114 | | 2.84 | 3.33 | | 6.17 | 8.70 |
| 0500 | 8" x 8" | | 130 | .123 | | 4.96 | 3.58 | | 8.54 | 11.45 |
| 0600 | Plastic beam, "hewn finish", 6" x 2" | | 240 | .067 | | 3.10 | 1.94 | | 5.04 | 6.65 |
| 0601 | 6" x 4" | | 220 | .073 | | 3.50 | 2.12 | | 5.62 | 7.40 |

### 06 44 39.20 Columns

| | 06 44 39.20 Columns | Crew | Daily Output | Labor-Hours | Unit | Material | 2010 Bare Costs Labor | Equipment | Total | Total Incl O&P |
|---|---|---|---|---|---|---|---|---|---|---|
| 0010 | **COLUMNS** | | | | | | | | | |
| 0050 | Aluminum, round colonial, 6" diameter | 2 Carp | 80 | .200 | V.L.F. | 16 | 5.80 | | 21.80 | 27.50 |
| 0100 | 8" diameter | | 62.25 | .257 | | 19.30 | 7.50 | | 26.80 | 33.50 |
| 0200 | 10" diameter | | 55 | .291 | | 23.50 | 8.45 | | 31.95 | 40.50 |
| 0250 | Fir, stock units, hollow round, 6" diameter | | 80 | .200 | | 26.50 | 5.80 | | 32.30 | 39 |
| 0300 | 8" diameter | | 80 | .200 | | 31 | 5.80 | | 36.80 | 44.50 |
| 0350 | 10" diameter | | 70 | .229 | | 39.50 | 6.65 | | 46.15 | 54.50 |
| 0400 | Solid turned, to 8' high, 3-1/2" diameter | | 80 | .200 | | 9 | 5.80 | | 14.80 | 19.70 |
| 0500 | 4-1/2" diameter | | 75 | .213 | | 14 | 6.20 | | 20.20 | 26 |
| 0600 | 5-1/2" diameter | | 70 | .229 | | 18.40 | 6.65 | | 25.05 | 31 |
| 0800 | Square columns, built-up, 5" x 5" | | 65 | .246 | | 15.50 | 7.15 | | 22.65 | 29 |
| 0900 | Solid, 3-1/2" x 3-1/2" | | 130 | .123 | | 9 | 3.58 | | 12.58 | 15.90 |
| 1600 | Hemlock, tapered, T & G, 12" diam, 10' high | | 100 | .160 | | 53 | 4.66 | | 57.66 | 66 |
| 1700 | 16' high | | 65 | .246 | | 79.50 | 7.15 | | 86.65 | 99 |
| 1900 | 10' high, 14" diameter | | 100 | .160 | | 121 | 4.66 | | 125.66 | 141 |
| 2000 | 18' high | | 65 | .246 | | 107 | 7.15 | | 114.15 | 130 |
| 2200 | 18" diameter, 12' high | | 65 | .246 | | 153 | 7.15 | | 160.15 | 181 |
| 2300 | 20' high | | 50 | .320 | | 148 | 9.30 | | 157.30 | 179 |
| 2500 | 20" diameter, 14' high | | 40 | .400 | | 159 | 11.65 | | 170.65 | 195 |
| 2600 | 20' high | | 35 | .457 | | 149 | 13.30 | | 162.30 | 186 |
| 2800 | For flat pilasters, deduct | | | | | 33% | | | | |
| 3000 | For splitting into halves, add | | | | Ea. | 116 | | | 116 | 128 |
| 4000 | Rough sawn cedar posts, 4" x 4" | 2 Carp | 250 | .064 | V.L.F. | 6.30 | 1.86 | | 8.16 | 10.10 |
| 4100 | 4" x 6" | | 235 | .068 | | 15 | 1.98 | | 16.98 | 19.85 |
| 4200 | 6" x 6" | | 220 | .073 | | 26.50 | 2.12 | | 28.62 | 32.50 |
| 4300 | 8" x 8" | | 200 | .080 | | 60 | 2.33 | | 62.33 | 70 |

# 06 48 Wood Frames

## 06 48 13 – Exterior Wood Door Frames

### 06 48 13.10 Exterior Wood Door Frames and Accessories

| | 06 48 13.10 Exterior Wood Door Frames and Accessories | Crew | Daily Output | Labor-Hours | Unit | Material | 2010 Bare Costs Labor | Equipment | Total | Total Incl O&P |
|---|---|---|---|---|---|---|---|---|---|---|
| 0010 | **EXTERIOR WOOD DOOR FRAMES AND ACCESSORIES** | | | | | | | | | |
| 0400 | Exterior frame, incl. ext. trim, pine, 5/4 x 4-9/16" deep | 2 Carp | 375 | .043 | L.F. | 5.55 | 1.24 | | 6.79 | 8.20 |
| 0420 | 5-3/16" deep | | 375 | .043 | | 11.35 | 1.24 | | 12.59 | 14.60 |
| 0440 | 6-9/16" deep | | 375 | .043 | | 8.50 | 1.24 | | 9.74 | 11.45 |
| 0600 | Oak, 5/4 x 4-9/16" deep | | 350 | .046 | | 10.70 | 1.33 | | 12.03 | 14.05 |
| 0620 | 5-3/16" deep | | 350 | .046 | | 11.80 | 1.33 | | 13.13 | 15.20 |
| 0640 | 6-9/16" deep | | 350 | .046 | | 14.50 | 1.33 | | 15.83 | 18.20 |
| 1000 | Sills, 8/4 x 8" deep, oak, no horns | | 100 | .160 | | 17 | 4.66 | | 21.66 | 26.50 |
| 1020 | 2" horns | | 100 | .160 | | 17.10 | 4.66 | | 21.76 | 26.50 |
| 1040 | 3" horns | | 100 | .160 | | 17.10 | 4.66 | | 21.76 | 26.50 |

# 06 48 Wood Frames

## 06 48 13 - Exterior Wood Door Frames

| 06 48 13.10 Exterior Wood Door Frames and Accessories | | Crew | Daily Output | Labor-Hours | Unit | Material | 2010 Bare Costs Labor | Equipment | Total | Total Incl O&P |
|---|---|---|---|---|---|---|---|---|---|---|
| 1100 | 8/4 x 10" deep, oak, no horns | 2 Carp | 90 | .178 | L.F. | 20.50 | 5.15 | | 25.65 | 31 |
| 1120 | 2" horns | | 90 | .178 | | 21 | 5.15 | | 26.15 | 32 |
| 1140 | 3" horns | | 90 | .178 | | 21 | 5.15 | | 26.15 | 32 |
| 2000 | Exterior, colonial, frame & trim, 3' opng., in-swing, minimum | | 22 | .727 | Ea. | 315 | 21 | | 336 | 385 |
| 2010 | Average | | 21 | .762 | | 470 | 22 | | 492 | 555 |
| 2020 | Maximum | | 20 | .800 | | 1,075 | 23.50 | | 1,098.50 | 1,225 |
| 2100 | 5'-4" opening, in-swing, minimum | | 17 | .941 | | 360 | 27.50 | | 387.50 | 440 |
| 2120 | Maximum | | 15 | 1.067 | | 1,075 | 31 | | 1,106 | 1,225 |
| 2140 | Out-swing, minimum | | 17 | .941 | | 370 | 27.50 | | 397.50 | 450 |
| 2160 | Maximum | | 15 | 1.067 | | 1,100 | 31 | | 1,131 | 1,275 |
| 2400 | 6'-0" opening, in-swing, minimum | | 16 | 1 | | 345 | 29 | | 374 | 430 |
| 2420 | Maximum | | 10 | 1.600 | | 1,100 | 46.50 | | 1,146.50 | 1,300 |
| 2460 | Out-swing, minimum | | 16 | 1 | | 375 | 29 | | 404 | 465 |
| 2480 | Maximum | | 10 | 1.600 | | 1,300 | 46.50 | | 1,346.50 | 1,500 |
| 2600 | For two sidelights, add, minimum | | 30 | .533 | Opng. | 355 | 15.50 | | 370.50 | 415 |
| 2620 | Maximum | | 20 | .800 | " | 1,125 | 23.50 | | 1,148.50 | 1,300 |
| 2700 | Custom birch frame, 3'-0" opening | | 16 | 1 | Ea. | 205 | 29 | | 234 | 275 |
| 2750 | 6'-0" opening | | 16 | 1 | | 305 | 29 | | 334 | 385 |
| 2900 | Exterior, modern, plain trim, 3' opng., in-swing, minimum | | 26 | .615 | | 35.50 | 17.90 | | 53.40 | 69 |
| 2920 | Average | | 24 | .667 | | 42 | 19.40 | | 61.40 | 78.50 |
| 2940 | Maximum | | 22 | .727 | | 50.50 | 21 | | 71.50 | 91 |

## 06 48 16 - Interior Wood Door Frames

### 06 48 16.10 Interior Wood Door Jamb and Frames

| | | Crew | Daily Output | Labor-Hours | Unit | Material | Labor | Equipment | Total | Total Incl O&P |
|---|---|---|---|---|---|---|---|---|---|---|
| 0010 | **INTERIOR WOOD DOOR JAMB AND FRAMES** | | | | | | | | | |
| 3000 | Interior frame, pine, 11/16" x 3-5/8" deep | 2 Carp | 375 | .043 | L.F. | 5.55 | 1.24 | | 6.79 | 8.20 |
| 3020 | 4-9/16" deep | | 375 | .043 | | 6.50 | 1.24 | | 7.74 | 9.25 |
| 3040 | 5-3/16" deep | | 375 | .043 | | 4.28 | 1.24 | | 5.52 | 6.80 |
| 3200 | Oak, 11/16" x 3-5/8" deep | | 350 | .046 | | 4.35 | 1.33 | | 5.68 | 7.05 |
| 3220 | 4-9/16" deep | | 350 | .046 | | 4.50 | 1.33 | | 5.83 | 7.20 |
| 3240 | 5-3/16" deep | | 350 | .046 | | 4.58 | 1.33 | | 5.91 | 7.30 |
| 3400 | Walnut, 11/16" x 3-5/8" deep | | 350 | .046 | | 7.30 | 1.33 | | 8.63 | 10.30 |
| 3420 | 4-9/16" deep | | 350 | .046 | | 7.50 | 1.33 | | 8.83 | 10.50 |
| 3440 | 5-3/16" deep | | 350 | .046 | | 7.90 | 1.33 | | 9.23 | 10.90 |
| 3800 | Threshold, oak, 5/8" x 3-5/8" deep | | 200 | .080 | | 3.83 | 2.33 | | 6.16 | 8.15 |
| 3820 | 4-5/8" deep | | 190 | .084 | | 4.58 | 2.45 | | 7.03 | 9.15 |
| 3840 | 5-5/8" deep | | 180 | .089 | | 7.15 | 2.59 | | 9.74 | 12.20 |

# 06 49 Wood Screens and Exterior Wood Shutters

## 06 49 19 - Exterior Wood Shutters

### 06 49 19.10 Shutters, Exterior

| | | Crew | Daily Output | Labor-Hours | Unit | Material | Labor | Equipment | Total | Total Incl O&P |
|---|---|---|---|---|---|---|---|---|---|---|
| 0010 | **SHUTTERS, EXTERIOR** | | | | | | | | | |
| 0012 | Aluminum, louvered, 1'-4" wide, 3'-0" long | 1 Carp | 10 | .800 | Pr. | 60.50 | 23.50 | | 84 | 106 |
| 0200 | 4'-0" long | | 10 | .800 | | 72.50 | 23.50 | | 96 | 119 |
| 0300 | 5'-4" long | | 10 | .800 | | 95.50 | 23.50 | | 119 | 144 |
| 0400 | 6'-8" long | | 9 | .889 | | 122 | 26 | | 148 | 178 |
| 1000 | Pine, louvered, primed, each 1'-2" wide, 3'-3" long | | 10 | .800 | | 105 | 23.50 | | 128.50 | 155 |
| 1100 | 4'-7" long | | 10 | .800 | | 142 | 23.50 | | 165.50 | 195 |
| 1250 | Each 1'-4" wide, 3'-0" long | | 10 | .800 | | 107 | 23.50 | | 130.50 | 157 |
| 1350 | 5'-3" long | | 10 | .800 | | 161 | 23.50 | | 184.50 | 216 |
| 1500 | Each 1'-6" wide, 3'-3" long | | 10 | .800 | | 112 | 23.50 | | 135.50 | 162 |

# 06 49 Wood Screens and Exterior Wood Shutters

## 06 49 19 – Exterior Wood Shutters

| | 06 49 19.10 Shutters, Exterior | Crew | Daily Output | Labor-Hours | Unit | Material | 2010 Bare Costs Labor | Equipment | Total | Total Incl O&P |
|---|---|---|---|---|---|---|---|---|---|---|
| 1600 | 4'-7" long | 1 Carp | 10 | .800 | Pr. | 157 | 23.50 | | 180.50 | 212 |
| 1620 | Hemlock, louvered, 1'-2" wide, 5'-7" long | | 10 | .800 | | 172 | 23.50 | | 195.50 | 228 |
| 1630 | Each 1'-4" wide, 2'-2" long | | 10 | .800 | | 107 | 23.50 | | 130.50 | 157 |
| 1640 | 3'-0" long | | 10 | .800 | | 107 | 23.50 | | 130.50 | 157 |
| 1650 | 3'-3" long | | 10 | .800 | | 116 | 23.50 | | 139.50 | 166 |
| 1660 | 3'-11" long | | 10 | .800 | | 132 | 23.50 | | 155.50 | 184 |
| 1670 | 4'-3" long | | 10 | .800 | | 128 | 23.50 | | 151.50 | 180 |
| 1680 | 5'-3" long | | 10 | .800 | | 160 | 23.50 | | 183.50 | 215 |
| 1690 | 5'-11" long | | 10 | .800 | | 181 | 23.50 | | 204.50 | 238 |
| 1700 | Door blinds, 6'-9" long, each 1'-3" wide | | 9 | .889 | | 182 | 26 | | 208 | 244 |
| 1710 | 1'-6" wide | | 9 | .889 | | 196 | 26 | | 222 | 259 |
| 1720 | Hemlock, solid raised panel, each 1'-4" wide, 3'-3" long | | 10 | .800 | | 174 | 23.50 | | 197.50 | 230 |
| 1730 | 3'-11" long | | 10 | .800 | | 203 | 23.50 | | 226.50 | 262 |
| 1740 | 4'-3" long | | 10 | .800 | | 220 | 23.50 | | 243.50 | 281 |
| 1750 | 4'-7" long | | 10 | .800 | | 237 | 23.50 | | 260.50 | 300 |
| 1760 | 4'-11" long | | 10 | .800 | | 258 | 23.50 | | 281.50 | 325 |
| 1770 | 5'-11" long | | 10 | .800 | | 294 | 23.50 | | 317.50 | 365 |
| 1800 | Door blinds, 6'-9" long, each 1'-3" wide | | 9 | .889 | | 330 | 26 | | 356 | 410 |
| 1900 | 1'-6" wide | | 9 | .889 | | 360 | 26 | | 386 | 440 |
| 2500 | Polystyrene, solid raised panel, each 1'-4" wide, 3'-3" long | | 10 | .800 | | 40.50 | 23.50 | | 64 | 83.50 |
| 2600 | 3'-11" long | | 10 | .800 | | 46.50 | 23.50 | | 70 | 90.50 |
| 2700 | 4'-7" long | | 10 | .800 | | 51 | 23.50 | | 74.50 | 95 |
| 2800 | 5'-3" long | | 10 | .800 | | 55 | 23.50 | | 78.50 | 99.50 |
| 2900 | 6'-8" long | | 9 | .889 | | 66 | 26 | | 92 | 116 |
| 4500 | Polystyrene, louvered, each 1'-2" wide, 3'-3" long | | 10 | .800 | | 27.50 | 23.50 | | 51 | 69.50 |
| 4600 | 4'-7" long | | 10 | .800 | | 34 | 23.50 | | 57.50 | 76.50 |
| 4750 | 5'-3" long | | 10 | .800 | | 39 | 23.50 | | 62.50 | 82 |
| 4850 | 6'-8" long | | 9 | .889 | | 46.50 | 26 | | 72.50 | 94.50 |
| 6000 | Vinyl, louvered, each 1'-2" x 4'-7" long | | 10 | .800 | | 34 | 23.50 | | 57.50 | 76.50 |
| 6200 | Each 1'-4" x 6'-8" long | | 9 | .889 | | 47.50 | 26 | | 73.50 | 96 |
| 8000 | PVC exterior rolling shutters | | | | | | | | | |
| 8100 | including crank control | 1 Carp | 8 | 1 | Ea. | 480 | 29 | | 509 | 580 |
| 8500 | Insulative - 6' x 6'8" stock unit | " | 8 | 1 | " | 685 | 29 | | 714 | 805 |

# 06 51 Structural Plastic Shapes and Plates

## 06 51 13 – Plastic Lumber

### 06 51 13.10 Recycled Plastic Lumber

| | | | Crew | Daily Output | Labor-Hours | Unit | Material | 2010 Bare Costs Labor | Equipment | Total | Total Incl O&P |
|---|---|---|---|---|---|---|---|---|---|---|---|
| 0010 | **RECYCLED PLASTIC LUMBER** | | | | | | | | | | |
| 4000 | Sheeting, recycled plastic, black or white, 4' x 8' x 1/8" | G | 2 Carp | 1100 | .015 | S.F. | 1.56 | .42 | | 1.98 | 2.43 |
| 4010 | 4' x 8' x 3/16" | G | | 1100 | .015 | | 2.33 | .42 | | 2.75 | 3.27 |
| 4020 | 4' x 8' x 1/4" | G | | 950 | .017 | | 3.11 | .49 | | 3.60 | 4.24 |
| 4030 | 4' x 8' x 3/8" | G | | 950 | .017 | | 4.67 | .49 | | 5.16 | 5.95 |
| 4040 | 4' x 8' x 1/2" | G | | 900 | .018 | | 6.20 | .52 | | 6.72 | 7.70 |
| 4050 | 4' x 8' x 5/8" | G | | 900 | .018 | | 7.70 | .52 | | 8.22 | 9.30 |
| 4060 | 4' x 8' x 3/4" | G | | 850 | .019 | | 9.15 | .55 | | 9.70 | 11 |
| 4070 | Add for colors | G | | | | Ea. | 5% | | | 5% | 6% |
| 8500 | 100% recycled plastic, var colors, NLB, 2" x 2" | G | | | | L.F. | 1.41 | | | 1.41 | 1.55 |
| 8510 | 2" x 4" | G | | | | | 2.95 | | | 2.95 | 3.25 |
| 8520 | 2" x 6" | G | | | | | 4.63 | | | 4.63 | 5.10 |
| 8530 | 2" x 8" | G | | | | | 6.35 | | | 6.35 | 6.95 |
| 8540 | 2" x 10" | G | | | | | 9.25 | | | 9.25 | 10.15 |

# 06 51 Structural Plastic Shapes and Plates

## 06 51 13 – Plastic Lumber

| 06 51 13.10 Recycled Plastic Lumber | | Crew | Daily Output | Labor-Hours | Unit | Material | 2010 Bare Costs Labor | Equipment | Total | Total Incl O&P |
|---|---|---|---|---|---|---|---|---|---|---|
| 8550 | 5/4" x 4" | G | | | L.F. | 3.02 | | | 3.02 | 3.32 |
| 8560 | 5/4" x 6" | G | | | | 3 | | | 3 | 3.30 |
| 8570 | 1" x 6" | G | | | | 2.28 | | | 2.28 | 2.51 |
| 8580 | 1/2" x 8" | G | | | | 2.46 | | | 2.46 | 2.71 |
| 8590 | 2" x 10" T & G | G | | | | 8.60 | | | 8.60 | 9.45 |
| 8600 | 3" x 10" T & G | G | | | | 14.25 | | | 14.25 | 15.70 |
| 8610 | Add for premium colors | G | | | | 20% | | | 20% | 22% |

# 06 63 Plastic Railings

## 06 63 10 – Plastic (PVC) Railings

### 06 63 10.10 Plastic Railings

| | | Crew | Daily Output | Labor-Hours | Unit | Material | 2010 Bare Costs Labor | Equipment | Total | Total Incl O&P |
|---|---|---|---|---|---|---|---|---|---|---|
| 0010 | **PLASTIC RAILINGS** | | | | | | | | | |
| 0100 | Horizontal PVC handrail with balusters, 3-1/2" wide, 36" high | 1 Carp | 96 | .083 | L.F. | 24 | 2.42 | | 26.42 | 30.50 |
| 0150 | 42" high | | 96 | .083 | | 27 | 2.42 | | 29.42 | 33.50 |
| 0200 | Angled PVC handrail with balusters, 3-1/2" wide, 36" high | | 72 | .111 | | 28 | 3.23 | | 31.23 | 36 |
| 0250 | 42" high | | 72 | .111 | | 30.50 | 3.23 | | 33.73 | 39 |
| 0300 | Post sleeve for 4 x 4 post | | 96 | .083 | | 12 | 2.42 | | 14.42 | 17.30 |
| 0400 | Post cap for 4 x 4 post, flat profile | | 48 | .167 | Ea. | 11.40 | 4.85 | | 16.25 | 20.50 |
| 0450 | Newel post style profile | | 48 | .167 | | 21 | 4.85 | | 25.85 | 31 |
| 0500 | Raised corbeled profile | | 48 | .167 | | 23 | 4.85 | | 27.85 | 33 |
| 0550 | Post base trim for 4 x 4 post | | 96 | .083 | | 12.80 | 2.42 | | 15.22 | 18.20 |

# 06 65 Plastic Simulated Wood Trim

## 06 65 10 – PVC Trim

### 06 65 10.10 PVC Trim, Exterior

| | | Crew | Daily Output | Labor-Hours | Unit | Material | 2010 Bare Costs Labor | Equipment | Total | Total Incl O&P |
|---|---|---|---|---|---|---|---|---|---|---|
| 0010 | **PVC TRIM, EXTERIOR** | | | | | | | | | |
| 0100 | Cornerboards, 5/4" x 6" x 6" | 1 Carp | 240 | .033 | L.F. | 5.70 | .97 | | 6.67 | 7.95 |
| 0110 | Door/window casing, 1" x 4" | | 200 | .040 | | 1.30 | 1.16 | | 2.46 | 3.39 |
| 0120 | 1" x 6" | | 200 | .040 | | 2.05 | 1.16 | | 3.21 | 4.22 |
| 0130 | 1" x 8" | | 195 | .041 | | 2.70 | 1.19 | | 3.89 | 4.98 |
| 0140 | 1" x 10" | | 195 | .041 | | 3.42 | 1.19 | | 4.61 | 5.75 |
| 0150 | 1" x 12" | | 190 | .042 | | 4.19 | 1.23 | | 5.42 | 6.65 |
| 0160 | 5/4" x 4" | | 195 | .041 | | 1.73 | 1.19 | | 2.92 | 3.91 |
| 0170 | 5/4" x 6" | | 195 | .041 | | 2.70 | 1.19 | | 3.89 | 4.98 |
| 0180 | 5/4" x 8" | | 190 | .042 | | 3.55 | 1.23 | | 4.78 | 5.95 |
| 0190 | 5/4" x 10" | | 190 | .042 | | 4.53 | 1.23 | | 5.76 | 7.05 |
| 0200 | 5/4" x 12" | | 185 | .043 | | 5.50 | 1.26 | | 6.76 | 8.15 |
| 0210 | Fascia, 1" x 4" | | 250 | .032 | | 1.30 | .93 | | 2.23 | 3 |
| 0220 | 1" x 6" | | 250 | .032 | | 2.05 | .93 | | 2.98 | 3.83 |
| 0230 | 1" x 8" | | 225 | .036 | | 2.70 | 1.03 | | 3.73 | 4.71 |
| 0240 | 1" x 10" | | 225 | .036 | | 3.42 | 1.03 | | 4.45 | 5.50 |
| 0250 | 1" x 12" | | 200 | .040 | | 4.19 | 1.16 | | 5.35 | 6.55 |
| 0260 | 5/4" x 4" | | 240 | .033 | | 1.73 | .97 | | 2.70 | 3.53 |
| 0270 | 5/4" x 6" | | 240 | .033 | | 2.70 | .97 | | 3.67 | 4.60 |
| 0280 | 5/4" x 8" | | 215 | .037 | | 3.55 | 1.08 | | 4.63 | 5.75 |
| 0290 | 5/4" x 10" | | 215 | .037 | | 4.53 | 1.08 | | 5.61 | 6.80 |
| 0300 | 5/4" x 12" | | 190 | .042 | | 5.50 | 1.23 | | 6.73 | 8.10 |
| 0310 | Frieze, 1" x 4" | | 250 | .032 | | 1.30 | .93 | | 2.23 | 3 |
| 0320 | 1" x 6" | | 250 | .032 | | 2.05 | .93 | | 2.98 | 3.83 |

# 06 65 Plastic Simulated Wood Trim

## 06 65 10 – PVC Trim

| 06 65 10.10 PVC Trim, Exterior | | Crew | Daily Output | Labor-Hours | Unit | Material | 2010 Bare Costs Labor | Equipment | Total | Total Incl O&P |
|---|---|---|---|---|---|---|---|---|---|---|
| 0330 | 1" x 8" | 1 Carp | 225 | .036 | L.F. | 2.70 | 1.03 | | 3.73 | 4.71 |
| 0340 | 1" x 10" | | 225 | .036 | | 3.42 | 1.03 | | 4.45 | 5.50 |
| 0350 | 1" x 12" | | 200 | .040 | | 4.19 | 1.16 | | 5.35 | 6.55 |
| 0360 | 5/4" x 4" | | 240 | .033 | | 1.73 | .97 | | 2.70 | 3.53 |
| 0370 | 5/4" x 6" | | 240 | .033 | | 2.70 | .97 | | 3.67 | 4.60 |
| 0380 | 5/4" x 8" | | 215 | .037 | | 3.55 | 1.08 | | 4.63 | 5.75 |
| 0390 | 5/4" x 10" | | 215 | .037 | | 4.53 | 1.08 | | 5.61 | 6.80 |
| 0400 | 5/4" x 12" | | 190 | .042 | | 5.50 | 1.23 | | 6.73 | 8.10 |
| 0410 | Rake, 1" x 4" | | 200 | .040 | | 1.30 | 1.16 | | 2.46 | 3.39 |
| 0420 | 1" x 6" | | 200 | .040 | | 2.05 | 1.16 | | 3.21 | 4.22 |
| 0430 | 1" x 8" | | 190 | .042 | | 2.70 | 1.23 | | 3.93 | 5.05 |
| 0440 | 1" x 10" | | 190 | .042 | | 3.42 | 1.23 | | 4.65 | 5.80 |
| 0450 | 1" x 12" | | 180 | .044 | | 4.19 | 1.29 | | 5.48 | 6.80 |
| 0460 | 5/4" x 4" | | 195 | .041 | | 1.73 | 1.19 | | 2.92 | 3.91 |
| 0470 | 5/4" x 6" | | 195 | .041 | | 2.70 | 1.19 | | 3.89 | 4.98 |
| 0480 | 5/4" x 8" | | 185 | .043 | | 3.55 | 1.26 | | 4.81 | 6.05 |
| 0490 | 5/4" x 10" | | 185 | .043 | | 4.53 | 1.26 | | 5.79 | 7.10 |
| 0500 | 5/4" x 12" | | 175 | .046 | | 5.50 | 1.33 | | 6.83 | 8.30 |
| 0510 | Rake trim, 1" x 4" | | 225 | .036 | | 1.30 | 1.03 | | 2.33 | 3.17 |
| 0520 | 1" x 6" | | 225 | .036 | | 2.05 | 1.03 | | 3.08 | 4 |
| 0560 | 5/4" x 4" | | 220 | .036 | | 1.73 | 1.06 | | 2.79 | 3.68 |
| 0570 | 5/4" x 6" | | 220 | .036 | | 2.70 | 1.06 | | 3.76 | 4.75 |
| 0610 | Soffit, 1" x 4" | 2 Carp | 420 | .038 | | 1.30 | 1.11 | | 2.41 | 3.30 |
| 0620 | 1" x 6" | | 420 | .038 | | 2.05 | 1.11 | | 3.16 | 4.13 |
| 0630 | 1" x 8" | | 420 | .038 | | 2.70 | 1.11 | | 3.81 | 4.84 |
| 0640 | 1" x 10" | | 400 | .040 | | 3.42 | 1.16 | | 4.58 | 5.70 |
| 0650 | 1" x 12" | | 400 | .040 | | 4.19 | 1.16 | | 5.35 | 6.55 |
| 0660 | 5/4" x 4" | | 410 | .039 | | 1.73 | 1.14 | | 2.87 | 3.81 |
| 0670 | 5/4" x 6" | | 410 | .039 | | 2.70 | 1.14 | | 3.84 | 4.88 |
| 0680 | 5/4" x 8" | | 410 | .039 | | 3.55 | 1.14 | | 4.69 | 5.80 |
| 0690 | 5/4" x 10" | | 390 | .041 | | 4.53 | 1.19 | | 5.72 | 7 |
| 0700 | 5/4" x 12" | | 390 | .041 | | 5.50 | 1.19 | | 6.69 | 8.05 |

# Estimating Tips

## 07 10 00 Dampproofing and Waterproofing

- Be sure of the job specifications before pricing this subdivision. The difference in cost between waterproofing and dampproofing can be great. Waterproofing will hold back standing water. Dampproofing prevents the transmission of water vapor. Also included in this section are vapor retarding membranes.

## 07 20 00 Thermal Protection

- Insulation and fireproofing products are measured by area, thickness, volume or R-value. Specifications may give only what the specific R-value should be in a certain situation. The estimator may need to choose the type of insulation to meet that R-value.

## 07 30 00 Steep Slope Roofing
## 07 40 00 Roofing and Siding Panels

- Many roofing and siding products are bought and sold by the square. One square is equal to an area that measures 100 square feet.

This simple change in unit of measure could create a large error if the estimator is not observant. Accessories necessary for a complete installation must be figured into any calculations for both material and labor.

## 07 50 00 Membrane Roofing
## 07 60 00 Flashing and Sheet Metal
## 07 70 00 Roofing and Wall Specialties and Accessories

- The items in these subdivisions compose a roofing system. No one component completes the installation, and all must be estimated. Built-up or single-ply membrane roofing systems are made up of many products and installation trades. Wood blocking at roof perimeters or penetrations, parapet coverings, reglets, roof drains, gutters, downspouts, sheet metal flashing, skylights, smoke vents, and roof hatches all need to be considered along with the roofing material. Several different installation trades will need to work together on the roofing system. Inherent difficulties in the scheduling and coordination of various trades must be accounted for when estimating labor costs.

## 07 90 00 Joint Protection

- To complete the weather-tight shell, the sealants and caulkings must be estimated. Where different materials meet—at expansion joints, at flashing penetrations, and at hundreds of other locations throughout a construction project—they provide another line of defense against water penetration. Often, an entire system is based on the proper location and placement of caulking or sealants. The detailed drawings that are included as part of a set of architectural plans show typical locations for these materials. When caulking or sealants are shown at typical locations, this means the estimator must include them for all the locations where this detail is applicable. Be careful to keep different types of sealants separate, and remember to consider backer rods and primers if necessary.

## Reference Numbers

Reference numbers are shown in shaded boxes at the beginning of some major classifications. These numbers refer to related items in the Reference Section. The reference information may be an estimating procedure, an alternate pricing method, or technical information.

*Note:* Not all subdivisions listed here necessarily appear in this publication.

# 07 01 Operation and Maint. of Thermal and Moisture Protection

## 07 01 50 – Maintenance of Membrane Roofing

| 07 01 50.10 Roof Coatings | Crew | Daily Output | Labor-Hours | Unit | Material | 2010 Bare Costs Labor | Equipment | Total | Total Incl O&P |
|---|---|---|---|---|---|---|---|---|---|
| 0010 **ROOF COATINGS** | | | | | | | | | |
| 0012 Asphalt, brush grade, material only | | | | Gal. | 8.05 | | | 8.05 | 8.85 |
| 0800 Glass fibered roof & patching cement, 5 gallon | | | | | 8 | | | 8 | 8.80 |
| 1100 Roof patch & flashing cement, 5 gallon | | | | ↓ | 9.70 | | | 9.70 | 10.65 |

# 07 05 Common Work Results for Thermal and Moisture Protection

## 07 05 05 – Selective Demolition

### 07 05 05.10 Selective Demo., Thermal and Moist. Protection

| | | Crew | Daily Output | Labor-Hours | Unit | Material | Labor | Equipment | Total | Total Incl O&P |
|---|---|---|---|---|---|---|---|---|---|---|
| 0010 | **SELECTIVE DEMOLITION, THERMAL AND MOISTURE PROTECTION** | | | | | | | | | |
| 0020 | Caulking/sealant, to 1" x 1" joint  R024119-10 | 1 Clab | 600 | .013 | L.F. | | .29 | | .29 | .48 |
| 0120 | Downspouts, including hangers | | 350 | .023 | " | | .49 | | .49 | .83 |
| 0220 | Flashing, sheet metal | | 290 | .028 | S.F. | | .59 | | .59 | 1 |
| 0420 | Gutters, aluminum or wood, edge hung | | 240 | .033 | L.F. | | .72 | | .72 | 1.20 |
| 0520 | Built-in | | 100 | .080 | " | | 1.72 | | 1.72 | 2.89 |
| 0620 | Insulation, air/vapor barrier | | 3500 | .002 | S.F. | | .05 | | .05 | .08 |
| 0670 | Batts or blankets | ↓ | 1400 | .006 | C.F. | | .12 | | .12 | .21 |
| 0720 | Foamed or sprayed in place | 2 Clab | 1000 | .016 | B.F. | | .34 | | .34 | .58 |
| 0770 | Loose fitting | 1 Clab | 3000 | .003 | C.F. | | .06 | | .06 | .10 |
| 0870 | Rigid board | | 3450 | .002 | B.F. | | .05 | | .05 | .08 |
| 1120 | Roll roofing, cold adhesive | | 12 | .667 | Sq. | | 14.35 | | 14.35 | 24 |
| 1170 | Roof accessories, adjustable metal chimney flashing | | 9 | .889 | Ea. | | 19.10 | | 19.10 | 32 |
| 1325 | Plumbing vent flashing | | 32 | .250 | " | | 5.40 | | 5.40 | 9.05 |
| 1375 | Ridge vent strip, aluminum | | 310 | .026 | L.F. | | .55 | | .55 | .93 |
| 1620 | Skylight to 10 S.F. | | 8 | 1 | Ea. | | 21.50 | | 21.50 | 36 |
| 2120 | Roof edge, aluminum soffit and fascia | ↓ | 570 | .014 | L.F. | | .30 | | .30 | .51 |
| 2170 | Concrete coping, up to 12" wide | 2 Clab | 160 | .100 | | | 2.15 | | 2.15 | 3.62 |
| 2220 | Drip edge | 1 Clab | 1650 | .005 | | | .10 | | .10 | .18 |
| 2270 | Gravel stop | | 1650 | .005 | | | .10 | | .10 | .18 |
| 2370 | Sheet metal coping, up to 12" wide | ↓ | 240 | .033 | ↓ | | .72 | | .72 | 1.20 |
| 2470 | Roof insulation board, over 2" thick | B-2 | 7800 | .005 | B.F. | | .11 | | .11 | .19 |
| 2520 | Up to 2" thick | " | 3900 | .010 | S.F. | | .22 | | .22 | .38 |
| 2620 | Roof ventilation, louvered gable vent | 1 Clab | 16 | .500 | Ea. | | 10.75 | | 10.75 | 18.10 |
| 2670 | Remove, roof hatch | G-3 | 15 | 2.133 | | | 57.50 | | 57.50 | 95.50 |
| 2675 | Rafter vents | 1 Clab | 960 | .008 | ↓ | | .18 | | .18 | .30 |
| 2720 | Soffit vent and/or fascia vent | | 575 | .014 | L.F. | | .30 | | .30 | .50 |
| 2775 | Soffit vent strip, aluminum, 3" to 4" wide | | 160 | .050 | | | 1.08 | | 1.08 | 1.81 |
| 2820 | Roofing accessories, shingle moulding, to 1" x 4" | ↓ | 1600 | .005 | | | .11 | | .11 | .18 |
| 2870 | Cant strip | B-2 | 2000 | .020 | | | .44 | | .44 | .74 |
| 2920 | Concrete block walkway | 1 Clab | 230 | .035 | ↓ | | .75 | | .75 | 1.26 |
| 3070 | Roofing, felt paper, 15# | | 70 | .114 | Sq. | | 2.46 | | 2.46 | 4.13 |
| 3125 | #30 felt | ↓ | 30 | .267 | " | | 5.75 | | 5.75 | 9.65 |
| 3170 | Asphalt shingles, 1 layer | B-2 | 3500 | .011 | S.F. | | .25 | | .25 | .42 |
| 3180 | 2 layers | | 1750 | .023 | " | | .50 | | .50 | .84 |
| 3370 | Modified bitumen | | 26 | 1.538 | Sq. | | 33.50 | | 33.50 | 56.50 |
| 3420 | Built-up, no gravel, 3 ply | | 25 | 1.600 | | | 35 | | 35 | 59 |
| 3470 | 4 ply | | 21 | 1.905 | ↓ | | 41.50 | | 41.50 | 70 |
| 3620 | 5 ply | | 1600 | .025 | S.F. | | .55 | | .55 | .92 |
| 3725 | Gravel removal, minimum | | 5000 | .008 | | | .18 | | .18 | .29 |
| 3730 | Maximum | | 2000 | .020 | | | .44 | | .44 | .74 |
| 3870 | Fiberglass sheet | | 1200 | .033 | | | .73 | | .73 | 1.23 |
| 4120 | Slate shingles | ↓ | 1900 | .021 | ↓ | | .46 | | .46 | .78 |

# 07 05 Common Work Results for Thermal and Moisture Protection

## 07 05 05 – Selective Demolition

### 07 05 05.10 Selective Demo., Thermal and Moist. Protection

| 07 05 05.10 Selective Demo., Thermal and Moist. Protection | Crew | Daily Output | Labor-Hours | Unit | Material | 2010 Bare Costs Labor | Equipment | Total | Total Incl O&P |
|---|---|---|---|---|---|---|---|---|---|
| 4170 | Ridge shingles, clay or slate | B-2 | 2000 | .020 | L.F. | | .44 | | .44 | .74 |
| 4320 | Single ply membrane, attached at seams | | 52 | .769 | Sq. | | 16.85 | | 16.85 | 28.50 |
| 4370 | Ballasted | | 75 | .533 | | | 11.70 | | 11.70 | 19.65 |
| 4420 | Fully adhered | | 39 | 1.026 | | | 22.50 | | 22.50 | 38 |
| 4550 | Roof hatch, 2'-6" x 3'-0" | 1 Clab | 10 | .800 | Ea. | | 17.20 | | 17.20 | 29 |
| 4670 | Wood shingles | B-2 | 2200 | .018 | S.F. | | .40 | | .40 | .67 |
| 4820 | Sheet metal roofing | " | 2150 | .019 | | | .41 | | .41 | .69 |
| 4970 | Siding, horizontal wood clapboards | 1 Clab | 380 | .021 | | | .45 | | .45 | .76 |
| 5025 | Exterior insulation finish system | " | 120 | .067 | | | 1.43 | | 1.43 | 2.41 |
| 5070 | Tempered hardboard, remove and reset | 1 Carp | 380 | .021 | | | .61 | | .61 | 1.03 |
| 5120 | Tempered hardboard sheet siding | " | 375 | .021 | | | .62 | | .62 | 1.04 |
| 5170 | Metal, corner strips | 1 Clab | 850 | .009 | L.F. | | .20 | | .20 | .34 |
| 5225 | Horizontal strips | | 444 | .018 | S.F. | | .39 | | .39 | .65 |
| 5320 | Vertical strips | | 400 | .020 | | | .43 | | .43 | .72 |
| 5520 | Wood shingles | | 350 | .023 | | | .49 | | .49 | .83 |
| 5620 | Stucco siding | | 360 | .022 | | | .48 | | .48 | .80 |
| 5670 | Textured plywood | | 725 | .011 | | | .24 | | .24 | .40 |
| 5720 | Vinyl siding | | 510 | .016 | | | .34 | | .34 | .57 |
| 5770 | Corner strips | | 900 | .009 | L.F. | | .19 | | .19 | .32 |
| 5870 | Wood, boards, vertical | | 400 | .020 | S.F. | | .43 | | .43 | .72 |
| 5920 | Waterproofing, protection/drain board | 2 Clab | 3900 | .004 | B.F. | | .09 | | .09 | .15 |
| 5970 | Over 1/2" thick | | 1750 | .009 | S.F. | | .20 | | .20 | .33 |
| 6020 | To 1/2" thick | | 2000 | .008 | " | | .17 | | .17 | .29 |

# 07 11 Dampproofing

## 07 11 13 – Bituminous Dampproofing

### 07 11 13.10 Bituminous Asphalt Coating

| 07 11 13.10 Bituminous Asphalt Coating | Crew | Daily Output | Labor-Hours | Unit | Material | 2010 Bare Costs Labor | Equipment | Total | Total Incl O&P |
|---|---|---|---|---|---|---|---|---|---|
| 0010 | **BITUMINOUS ASPHALT COATING** | | | | | | | | | |
| 0030 | Brushed on, below grade, 1 coat | 1 Rofc | 665 | .012 | S.F. | .20 | .29 | | .49 | .75 |
| 0100 | 2 coat | | 500 | .016 | | .40 | .39 | | .79 | 1.14 |
| 0300 | Sprayed on, below grade, 1 coat, 25.6 S.F./gal. | | 830 | .010 | | .20 | .24 | | .44 | .64 |
| 0400 | 2 coat, 20.5 S.F./gal. | | 500 | .016 | | .39 | .39 | | .78 | 1.13 |
| 0600 | Troweled on, asphalt with fibers, 1/16" thick | | 500 | .016 | | .42 | .39 | | .81 | 1.17 |
| 0700 | 1/8" thick | | 400 | .020 | | .75 | .49 | | 1.24 | 1.71 |
| 1000 | 1/2" thick | | 350 | .023 | | 2.44 | .56 | | 3 | 3.69 |

## 07 11 16 – Cementitious Dampproofing

### 07 11 16.20 Cementitious Parging

| 07 11 16.20 Cementitious Parging | Crew | Daily Output | Labor-Hours | Unit | Material | 2010 Bare Costs Labor | Equipment | Total | Total Incl O&P |
|---|---|---|---|---|---|---|---|---|---|
| 0010 | **CEMENTITIOUS PARGING** | | | | | | | | | |
| 0020 | Portland cement, 2 coats, 1/2" thick | D-1 | 250 | .064 | S.F. | .29 | 1.69 | | 1.98 | 3.10 |
| 0100 | Waterproofed Portland cement, 1/2" thick, 2 coats | " | 250 | .064 | " | 2.87 | 1.69 | | 4.56 | 5.95 |

# 07 19 Water Repellents

## 07 19 19 – Silicone Water Repellents

| 07 19 19.10 Silicone Based Water Repellents | | Crew | Daily Output | Labor-Hours | Unit | Material | 2010 Bare Costs Labor | Equipment | Total | Total Incl O&P |
|---|---|---|---|---|---|---|---|---|---|---|
| 0010 | **SILICONE BASED WATER REPELLENTS** | | | | | | | | | |
| 0020 | Water base liquid, roller applied | 2 Rofc | 7000 | .002 | S.F. | .65 | .06 | | .71 | .82 |
| 0200 | Silicone or stearate, sprayed on CMU, 1 coat | 1 Rofc | 4000 | .002 | | .36 | .05 | | .41 | .49 |
| 0300 | 2 coats | " | 3000 | .003 | | .73 | .07 | | .80 | .92 |

# 07 21 Thermal Insulation

## 07 21 13 – Board Insulation

### 07 21 13.10 Rigid Insulation

| 07 21 13.10 Rigid Insulation | | | Crew | Daily Output | Labor-Hours | Unit | Material | 2010 Bare Costs Labor | Equipment | Total | Total Incl O&P |
|---|---|---|---|---|---|---|---|---|---|---|---|
| 0010 | **RIGID INSULATION**, for walls | | | | | | | | | | |
| 0040 | Fiberglass, 1.5#/CF, unfaced, 1" thick, R4.1 | G | 1 Carp | 1000 | .008 | S.F. | .44 | .23 | | .67 | .87 |
| 0060 | 1-1/2" thick, R6.2 | G | | 1000 | .008 | | .64 | .23 | | .87 | 1.09 |
| 0080 | 2" thick, R8.3 | G | | 1000 | .008 | | .69 | .23 | | .92 | 1.15 |
| 0120 | 3" thick, R12.4 | G | | 800 | .010 | | .80 | .29 | | 1.09 | 1.37 |
| 0370 | 3#/CF, unfaced, 1" thick, R4.3 | G | | 1000 | .008 | | .49 | .23 | | .72 | .93 |
| 0390 | 1-1/2" thick, R6.5 | G | | 1000 | .008 | | .95 | .23 | | 1.18 | 1.44 |
| 0400 | 2" thick, R8.7 | G | | 890 | .009 | | 1.15 | .26 | | 1.41 | 1.71 |
| 0420 | 2-1/2" thick, R10.9 | G | | 800 | .010 | | 1.01 | .29 | | 1.30 | 1.60 |
| 0440 | 3" thick, R13 | G | | 800 | .010 | | 1.01 | .29 | | 1.30 | 1.60 |
| 0520 | Foil faced, 1" thick, R4.3 | G | | 1000 | .008 | | .92 | .23 | | 1.15 | 1.40 |
| 0540 | 1-1/2" thick, R6.5 | G | | 1000 | .008 | | 1.36 | .23 | | 1.59 | 1.89 |
| 0560 | 2" thick, R8.7 | G | | 890 | .009 | | 1.71 | .26 | | 1.97 | 2.32 |
| 0580 | 2-1/2" thick, R10.9 | G | | 800 | .010 | | 2.02 | .29 | | 2.31 | 2.71 |
| 0600 | 3" thick, R13 | G | | 800 | .010 | | 2.19 | .29 | | 2.48 | 2.90 |
| 1500 | Foamglass, 1-1/2" thick, R4.5 | G | | 800 | .010 | | 1.40 | .29 | | 1.69 | 2.03 |
| 1550 | 3" thick, R9 | G | | 730 | .011 | | 3.45 | .32 | | 3.77 | 4.34 |
| 1600 | Isocyanurate, 4' x 8' sheet, foil faced, both sides | | | | | | | | | | |
| 1610 | 1/2" thick | G | 1 Carp | 800 | .010 | S.F. | .31 | .29 | | .60 | .83 |
| 1620 | 5/8" thick | G | | 800 | .010 | | .34 | .29 | | .63 | .86 |
| 1630 | 3/4" thick | G | | 800 | .010 | | .36 | .29 | | .65 | .89 |
| 1640 | 1" thick | G | | 800 | .010 | | .55 | .29 | | .84 | 1.10 |
| 1650 | 1-1/2" thick | G | | 730 | .011 | | .67 | .32 | | .99 | 1.28 |
| 1660 | 2" thick | G | | 730 | .011 | | .84 | .32 | | 1.16 | 1.46 |
| 1670 | 3" thick | G | | 730 | .011 | | 1.90 | .32 | | 2.22 | 2.63 |
| 1680 | 4" thick | G | | 730 | .011 | | 2.14 | .32 | | 2.46 | 2.89 |
| 1700 | Perlite, 1" thick, R2.77 | G | | 800 | .010 | | .30 | .29 | | .59 | .82 |
| 1750 | 2" thick, R5.55 | G | | 730 | .011 | | .60 | .32 | | .92 | 1.20 |
| 1900 | Extruded polystyrene, 25 PSI compressive strength, 1" thick, R5 | G | | 800 | .010 | | .51 | .29 | | .80 | 1.05 |
| 1940 | 2" thick R10 | G | | 730 | .011 | | 1.04 | .32 | | 1.36 | 1.68 |
| 1960 | 3" thick, R15 | G | | 730 | .011 | | 1.40 | .32 | | 1.72 | 2.08 |
| 2100 | Expanded polystyrene, 1" thick, R3.85 | G | | 800 | .010 | | .36 | .29 | | .65 | .89 |
| 2120 | 2" thick, R7.69 | G | | 730 | .011 | | .72 | .32 | | 1.04 | 1.33 |
| 2140 | 3" thick, R11.49 | G | | 730 | .011 | | 1.08 | .32 | | 1.40 | 1.73 |

### 07 21 13.13 Foam Board Insulation

| 07 21 13.13 Foam Board Insulation | | | Crew | Daily Output | Labor-Hours | Unit | Material | 2010 Bare Costs Labor | Equipment | Total | Total Incl O&P |
|---|---|---|---|---|---|---|---|---|---|---|---|
| 0010 | **FOAM BOARD INSULATION** | | | | | | | | | | |
| 0600 | Polystyrene, expanded, 1" thick, R4 | G | 1 Carp | 680 | .012 | S.F. | .36 | .34 | | .70 | .98 |
| 0700 | 2" thick, R8 | G | " | 675 | .012 | " | .72 | .34 | | 1.06 | 1.37 |

## 07 21 16 – Blanket Insulation

### 07 21 16.10 Blanket Insulation for Floors/Ceilings

| 07 21 16.10 Blanket Insulation for Floors/Ceilings | | | | | | | | | | |
|---|---|---|---|---|---|---|---|---|---|---|
| 0010 | **BLANKET INSULATION FOR FLOORS/CEILINGS** | | | | | | | | | |
| 0020 | Including spring type wire fasteners | | | | | | | | | |

# 07 21 Thermal Insulation

## 07 21 16 – Blanket Insulation

### 07 21 16.10 Blanket Insulation for Floors/Ceilings

| | | Crew | Daily Output | Labor-Hours | Unit | Material | 2010 Bare Costs Labor | Equipment | Total | Total Incl O&P |
|---|---|---|---|---|---|---|---|---|---|---|
| 2000 | Fiberglass, blankets or batts, paper or foil backing | | | | | | | | | |
| 2100 | 3-1/2" thick, R13 | G 1 Carp | 700 | .011 | S.F. | .38 | .33 | | .71 | .98 |
| 2150 | 6-1/4" thick, R19 | G | 600 | .013 | | .48 | .39 | | .87 | 1.18 |
| 2210 | 9-1/2" thick, R 30 | G | 500 | .016 | | .69 | .47 | | 1.16 | 1.54 |
| 2220 | 12" thick, R 38 | G | 475 | .017 | | 1 | .49 | | 1.49 | 1.92 |
| 3000 | Unfaced, 3-1/2" thick, R 13 | G | 600 | .013 | | .30 | .39 | | .69 | .98 |
| 3010 | 6-1/4" thick, R 19 | G | 500 | .016 | | .45 | .47 | | .92 | 1.28 |
| 3020 | 9-1/2" thick, R30 | G | 450 | .018 | | .69 | .52 | | 1.21 | 1.63 |
| 3030 | 12" thick, R 38 | G | 425 | .019 | | .81 | .55 | | 1.36 | 1.81 |

### 07 21 16.20 Blanket Insulation for Walls

| | | Crew | Daily Output | Labor-Hours | Unit | Material | 2010 Bare Costs Labor | Equipment | Total | Total Incl O&P |
|---|---|---|---|---|---|---|---|---|---|---|
| 0010 | **BLANKET INSULATION FOR WALLS** | | | | | | | | | |
| 0020 | Kraft faced fiberglass, 3-1/2" thick, R11, 15" wide | G 1 Carp | 1350 | .006 | S.F. | .28 | .17 | | .45 | .60 |
| 0030 | 23" wide | G | 1600 | .005 | | .28 | .15 | | .43 | .55 |
| 0061 | 3-1/2" thick, R13, 11" wide | G | 1350 | .006 | | .33 | .17 | | .50 | .65 |
| 0080 | 15" wide | G | 1350 | .006 | | .33 | .17 | | .50 | .65 |
| 0110 | R-15, 11" wide | G | 1150 | .007 | | .45 | .20 | | .65 | .84 |
| 0120 | 15" wide | G | 1350 | .006 | | .45 | .17 | | .62 | .79 |
| 0141 | 6" thick, R19, 11" wide | G | 1350 | .006 | | .43 | .17 | | .60 | .76 |
| 0160 | 15" wide | G | 1350 | .006 | | .43 | .17 | | .60 | .76 |
| 0180 | 23" wide | G | 1600 | .005 | | .43 | .15 | | .58 | .71 |
| 0201 | 9" thick, R30, 15" wide | G | 1350 | .006 | | .70 | .17 | | .87 | 1.06 |
| 0241 | 12" thick, R38, 15" wide | G | 1350 | .006 | | 1 | .17 | | 1.17 | 1.39 |
| 0410 | Foil faced fiberglass, 3-1/2" thick, R13, 11" wide | G | 1150 | .007 | | .54 | .20 | | .74 | .93 |
| 0420 | 15" wide | G | 1350 | .006 | | .54 | .17 | | .71 | .88 |
| 0442 | R15, 11" wide | G | 1150 | .007 | | .56 | .20 | | .76 | .96 |
| 0444 | 15" wide | G | 1350 | .006 | | .56 | .17 | | .73 | .91 |
| 0461 | 6" thick, R19, 15" wide | G | 1600 | .005 | | .77 | .15 | | .92 | 1.09 |
| 0482 | R-21, 11" wide | G | 1150 | .007 | | .82 | .20 | | 1.02 | 1.24 |
| 0501 | 9" thick, R30, 15" wide | G | 1350 | .006 | | .89 | .17 | | 1.06 | 1.27 |
| 0620 | Unfaced fiberglass, 3-1/2" thick, R-13, 11" wide | G | 1150 | .007 | | .30 | .20 | | .50 | .67 |
| 0821 | 3-1/2" thick, R13, 15" wide | G | 1600 | .005 | | .30 | .15 | | .45 | .57 |
| 0832 | R15, 11" wide | G | 1150 | .007 | | .44 | .20 | | .64 | .82 |
| 0834 | 15" wide | G | 1350 | .006 | | .44 | .17 | | .61 | .77 |
| 0861 | 6" thick, R19, 15" wide | G | 1350 | .006 | | .45 | .17 | | .62 | .79 |
| 0901 | 9" thick, R30, 15" wide | G | 1150 | .007 | | .64 | .20 | | .84 | 1.04 |
| 0941 | 12" thick, R38, 15" wide | G | 1150 | .007 | | .81 | .20 | | 1.01 | 1.23 |
| 1300 | Mineral fiber batts, kraft faced | | | | | | | | | |
| 1320 | 3-1/2" thick, R12 | G 1 Carp | 1600 | .005 | S.F. | .38 | .15 | | .53 | .66 |
| 1340 | 6" thick, R19 | G | 1600 | .005 | | .48 | .15 | | .63 | .77 |
| 1380 | 10" thick, R30 | G | 1350 | .006 | | .73 | .17 | | .90 | 1.09 |
| 1850 | Friction fit wire insulation supports, 16" O.C. | | 960 | .008 | Ea. | .05 | .24 | | .29 | .47 |

## 07 21 23 – Loose-Fill Insulation

### 07 21 23.10 Poured Loose-Fill Insulation

| | | Crew | Daily Output | Labor-Hours | Unit | Material | 2010 Bare Costs Labor | Equipment | Total | Total Incl O&P |
|---|---|---|---|---|---|---|---|---|---|---|
| 0010 | **POURED LOOSE-FILL INSULATION** | | | | | | | | | |
| 0020 | Cellulose fiber, R3.8 per inch | G 1 Carp | 200 | .040 | C.F. | .60 | 1.16 | | 1.76 | 2.62 |
| 0080 | Fiberglass wool, R4 per inch | G | 200 | .040 | | .46 | 1.16 | | 1.62 | 2.47 |
| 0100 | Mineral wool, R3 per inch | G | 200 | .040 | | .39 | 1.16 | | 1.55 | 2.39 |
| 0300 | Polystyrene, R4 per inch | G | 200 | .040 | | 3.09 | 1.16 | | 4.25 | 5.35 |
| 0400 | Vermiculite or perlite, R2.7 per inch | G | 200 | .040 | | 1.75 | 1.16 | | 2.91 | 3.89 |

### 07 21 23.20 Masonry Loose-Fill Insulation

| | | Crew | Daily Output | Labor-Hours | Unit | Material | 2010 Bare Costs Labor | Equipment | Total | Total Incl O&P |
|---|---|---|---|---|---|---|---|---|---|---|
| 0010 | **MASONRY LOOSE-FILL INSULATION**, vermiculite or perlite | | | | | | | | | |
| 0100 | In cores of concrete block, 4" thick wall, .115 CF/SF | G D-1 | 4800 | .003 | S.F. | .20 | .09 | | .29 | .36 |

# 07 21 Thermal Insulation

## 07 21 23 – Loose-Fill Insulation

| 07 21 23.20 Masonry Loose-Fill Insulation | | Crew | Daily Output | Labor-Hours | Unit | Material | 2010 Bare Costs Labor | Equipment | Total | Total Incl O&P |
|---|---|---|---|---|---|---|---|---|---|---|
| 0700 | Foamed in place, urethane in 2-5/8" cavity | G | G-2A | 1035 | .023 | S.F. | .42 | .50 | .67 | 1.59 | 2.07 |
| 0800 | For each 1" added thickness, add | G | " | 2372 | .010 | | .12 | .22 | .29 | .63 | .83 |

## 07 21 26 – Blown Insulation

### 07 21 26.10 Blown Insulation

| | | | | | | | | | | |
|---|---|---|---|---|---|---|---|---|---|---|
| 0010 | **BLOWN INSULATION** Ceilings, with open access | | | | | | | | | | |
| 0020 | Cellulose, 3-1/2" thick, R13 | G | G-4 | 5000 | .005 | S.F. | .19 | .11 | .08 | .38 | .48 |
| 0030 | 5-3/16" thick, R19 | G | | 3800 | .006 | | .28 | .14 | .10 | .52 | .67 |
| 0050 | 6-1/2" thick, R22 | G | | 3000 | .008 | | .36 | .18 | .13 | .67 | .85 |
| 1000 | Fiberglass, 5.5" thick, R11 | G | | 3800 | .006 | | .19 | .14 | .10 | .43 | .57 |
| 1050 | 6" thick, R12 | G | | 3000 | .008 | | .23 | .18 | .13 | .54 | .70 |
| 1100 | 8.8" thick, R19 | G | | 2200 | .011 | | .33 | .24 | .18 | .75 | .97 |
| 1300 | 11.5" thick, R26 | G | | 1500 | .016 | | .46 | .35 | .27 | 1.08 | 1.40 |
| 1350 | 13" thick, R30 | G | | 1400 | .017 | | .50 | .38 | .28 | 1.16 | 1.50 |
| 1450 | 16" thick, R38 | G | | 1145 | .021 | | .61 | .46 | .35 | 1.42 | 1.83 |
| 1500 | 20" thick, R49 | G | | 920 | .026 | | .77 | .58 | .43 | 1.78 | 2.29 |
| 2000 | Mineral wool, 4" thick, R12 | G | | 3500 | .007 | | .23 | .15 | .11 | .49 | .64 |
| 2050 | 6" thick, R17 | G | | 2500 | .010 | | .26 | .21 | .16 | .63 | .83 |
| 2100 | 9" thick, R23 | G | | 1750 | .014 | | .34 | .30 | .23 | .87 | 1.13 |

## 07 21 27 – Reflective Insulation

### 07 21 27.10 Reflective Insulation Options

| | | | | | | | | | | |
|---|---|---|---|---|---|---|---|---|---|---|
| 0010 | **REFLECTIVE INSULATION OPTIONS** | | | | | | | | | | |
| 0020 | Aluminum foil on reinforced scrim | G | 1 Carp | 19 | .421 | C.S.F. | 14.20 | 12.25 | | 26.45 | 36 |
| 0100 | Reinforced with woven polyolefin | G | | 19 | .421 | | 17.20 | 12.25 | | 29.45 | 39.50 |
| 0500 | With single bubble air space, R8.8 | G | | 15 | .533 | | 25.50 | 15.50 | | 41 | 54 |
| 0600 | With double bubble air space, R9.8 | G | | 15 | .533 | | 26.50 | 15.50 | | 42 | 55 |

## 07 21 29 – Sprayed Insulation

### 07 21 29.10 Sprayed-On Insulation

| | | | | | | | | | | |
|---|---|---|---|---|---|---|---|---|---|---|
| 0010 | **SPRAYED-ON INSULATION** | | | | | | | | | | |
| 0300 | Closed cell, spray polyurethane foam, 2 pounds per cubic foot density | | | | | | | | | | |
| 0310 | 1" thick | G | G-2A | 6000 | .004 | S.F. | .41 | .09 | .12 | .62 | .73 |
| 0320 | 2" thick | G | | 3000 | .008 | | .82 | .17 | .23 | 1.22 | 1.45 |
| 0330 | 3" thick | G | | 2000 | .012 | | 1.23 | .26 | .35 | 1.84 | 2.19 |
| 0335 | 3-1/2" thick | G | | 1715 | .014 | | 1.44 | .30 | .40 | 2.14 | 2.55 |
| 0340 | 4" thick | G | | 1500 | .016 | | 1.64 | .34 | .46 | 2.44 | 2.92 |
| 0350 | 5" thick | G | | 1200 | .020 | | 2.05 | .43 | .58 | 3.06 | 3.64 |
| 0355 | 5-1/2" thick | G | | 1090 | .022 | | 2.26 | .47 | .63 | 3.36 | 4.01 |
| 0360 | 6" thick | G | | 1000 | .024 | | 2.46 | .51 | .69 | 3.66 | 4.37 |

# 07 22 Roof and Deck Insulation

## 07 22 16 – Roof Board Insulation

### 07 22 16.10 Roof Deck Insulation

| | | | | | | | | | | |
|---|---|---|---|---|---|---|---|---|---|---|
| 0010 | **ROOF DECK INSULATION** | | | | | | | | | | |
| 0020 | Fiberboard low density, 1/2" thick R1.39 | G | 1 Rofc | 1000 | .008 | S.F. | .24 | .20 | | .44 | .61 |
| 0030 | 1" thick R2.78 | G | | 800 | .010 | | .42 | .24 | | .66 | .90 |
| 0080 | 1 1/2" thick R4.17 | G | | 800 | .010 | | .64 | .24 | | .88 | 1.14 |
| 0100 | 2" thick R5.56 | G | | 800 | .010 | | .85 | .24 | | 1.09 | 1.38 |
| 0110 | Fiberboard high density, 1/2" thick R1.3 | G | | 1000 | .008 | | .22 | .20 | | .42 | .59 |
| 0120 | 1" thick R2.5 | G | | 800 | .010 | | .44 | .24 | | .68 | .92 |
| 0130 | 1-1/2" thick R3.8 | G | | 800 | .010 | | .66 | .24 | | .90 | 1.17 |

## 07 22 16 – Roof Board Insulation

| 07 22 16.10 Roof Deck Insulation | | Crew | Daily Output | Labor-Hours | Unit | Material | 2010 Bare Costs Labor | Equipment | Total | Total Incl O&P |
|---|---|---|---|---|---|---|---|---|---|---|
| 0200 | Fiberglass, 3/4" thick R2.78 | G | 1 Rofc | 1000 | .008 | S.F. | .56 | .20 | | .76 | .97 |
| 0400 | 15/16" thick R3.70 | G | | 1000 | .008 | | .74 | .20 | | .94 | 1.16 |
| 0460 | 1-1/16" thick R4.17 | G | | 1000 | .008 | | .93 | .20 | | 1.13 | 1.37 |
| 0600 | 1-5/16" thick R5.26 | G | | 1000 | .008 | | 1.26 | .20 | | 1.46 | 1.74 |
| 0650 | 2-1/16" thick R8.33 | G | | 800 | .010 | | 1.35 | .24 | | 1.59 | 1.93 |
| 0700 | 2-7/16" thick R10 | G | | 800 | .010 | | 1.55 | .24 | | 1.79 | 2.15 |
| 1650 | Perlite, 1/2" thick R1.32 | G | | 1050 | .008 | | .34 | .19 | | .53 | .71 |
| 1655 | 3/4" thick R2.08 | G | | 800 | .010 | | .37 | .24 | | .61 | .85 |
| 1660 | 1" thick R2.78 | G | | 800 | .010 | | .46 | .24 | | .70 | .95 |
| 1670 | 1-1/2" thick R4.17 | G | | 800 | .010 | | .48 | .24 | | .72 | .97 |
| 1680 | 2" thick R5.56 | G | | 700 | .011 | | .80 | .28 | | 1.08 | 1.38 |
| 1685 | 2-1/2" thick R6.67 | G | | 700 | .011 | | .95 | .28 | | 1.23 | 1.55 |
| 1700 | Polyisocyanurate, 2#/CF density, 3/4" thick | G | | 1500 | .005 | | .44 | .13 | | .57 | .71 |
| 1705 | 1" thick | G | | 1400 | .006 | | .51 | .14 | | .65 | .81 |
| 1715 | 1-1/2" thick | G | | 1250 | .006 | | .62 | .16 | | .78 | .96 |
| 1725 | 2" thick | G | | 1100 | .007 | | .86 | .18 | | 1.04 | 1.27 |
| 1735 | 2-1/2" thick | G | | 1050 | .008 | | 1.01 | .19 | | 1.20 | 1.45 |
| 1745 | 3" thick | G | | 1000 | .008 | | 1.24 | .20 | | 1.44 | 1.71 |
| 1755 | 3-1/2" thick | G | | 1000 | .008 | | 1.95 | .20 | | 2.15 | 2.50 |
| 1765 | Tapered for drainage | G | | 1400 | .006 | B.F. | 1.95 | .14 | | 2.09 | 2.40 |
| 1900 | Extruded Polystyrene | | | | | | | | | | |
| 1910 | 15 PSI compressive strength, 1" thick, R5 | G | 1 Rofc | 1500 | .005 | S.F. | .49 | .13 | | .62 | .77 |
| 1920 | 2" thick, R10 | G | | 1250 | .006 | | .62 | .16 | | .78 | .96 |
| 1930 | 3" thick R15 | G | | 1000 | .008 | | 1.27 | .20 | | 1.47 | 1.75 |
| 1932 | 4" thick R20 | G | | 1000 | .008 | | 1.64 | .20 | | 1.84 | 2.15 |
| 1934 | Tapered for drainage | G | | 1500 | .005 | B.F. | .53 | .13 | | .66 | .81 |
| 1940 | 25 PSI compressive strength, 1" thick R5 | G | | 1500 | .005 | S.F. | .67 | .13 | | .80 | .97 |
| 1942 | 2" thick R10 | G | | 1250 | .006 | | 1.27 | .16 | | 1.43 | 1.68 |
| 1944 | 3" thick R15 | G | | 1000 | .008 | | 1.93 | .20 | | 2.13 | 2.47 |
| 1946 | 4" thick R20 | G | | 1000 | .008 | | 2.72 | .20 | | 2.92 | 3.34 |
| 1948 | Tapered for drainage | G | | 1500 | .005 | B.F. | .56 | .13 | | .69 | .85 |
| 1950 | 40 psi compressive strength, 1" thick R5 | G | | 1500 | .005 | S.F. | .51 | .13 | | .64 | .79 |
| 1952 | 2" thick R10 | G | | 1250 | .006 | | .96 | .16 | | 1.12 | 1.34 |
| 1954 | 3" thick R15 | G | | 1000 | .008 | | 1.40 | .20 | | 1.60 | 1.89 |
| 1956 | 4" thick R20 | G | | 1000 | .008 | | 1.88 | .20 | | 2.08 | 2.42 |
| 1958 | Tapered for drainage | G | | 1400 | .006 | B.F. | .71 | .14 | | .85 | 1.03 |
| 1960 | 60 PSI compressive strength, 1" thick R5 | G | | 1450 | .006 | S.F. | .59 | .14 | | .73 | .89 |
| 1962 | 2" thick R10 | G | | 1200 | .007 | | 1.05 | .16 | | 1.21 | 1.45 |
| 1964 | 3" thick R15 | G | | 975 | .008 | | 1.55 | .20 | | 1.75 | 2.07 |
| 1966 | 4" thick R20 | G | | 950 | .008 | | 2.17 | .21 | | 2.38 | 2.76 |
| 1968 | Tapered for drainage | G | | 1400 | .006 | B.F. | .85 | .14 | | .99 | 1.19 |
| 2010 | Expanded polystyrene, 1#/CF density, 3/4" thick R2.89 | G | | 1500 | .005 | S.F. | .27 | .13 | | .40 | .53 |
| 2020 | 1" thick R3.85 | G | | 1500 | .005 | | .36 | .13 | | .49 | .63 |
| 2100 | 2" thick R7.69 | G | | 1250 | .006 | | .72 | .16 | | .88 | 1.07 |
| 2110 | 3" thick R11.49 | G | | 1250 | .006 | | 1.08 | .16 | | 1.24 | 1.47 |
| 2120 | 4" thick R15.38 | G | | 1200 | .007 | | 1.44 | .16 | | 1.60 | 1.87 |
| 2130 | 5" thick R19.23 | G | | 1150 | .007 | | 1.80 | .17 | | 1.97 | 2.29 |
| 2140 | 6" thick R23.26 | G | | 1150 | .007 | | 2.16 | .17 | | 2.33 | 2.69 |
| 2150 | Tapered for drainage | G | | 1500 | .005 | B.F. | .54 | .13 | | .67 | .82 |
| 2400 | Composites with 2" EPS | | | | | | | | | | |
| 2410 | 1" fiberboard | G | 1 Rofc | 950 | .008 | S.F. | 1.24 | .21 | | 1.45 | 1.73 |
| 2420 | 7/16" oriented strand board | G | | 800 | .010 | | .94 | .24 | | 1.18 | 1.47 |
| 2430 | 1/2" plywood | G | | 800 | .010 | | 1.14 | .24 | | 1.38 | 1.69 |

# 07 22 Roof and Deck Insulation

## 07 22 16 – Roof Board Insulation

| | 07 22 16.10 Roof Deck Insulation | | Crew | Daily Output | Labor-Hours | Unit | Material | 2010 Bare Costs Labor | Equipment | Total | Total Incl O&P |
|---|---|---|---|---|---|---|---|---|---|---|---|
| 2440 | 1" perlite | G | 1 Rofc | 800 | .010 | S.F. | 1.18 | .24 | | 1.42 | 1.74 |
| 2450 | Composites with 1-1/2" polyisocyanurate | | | | | | | | | | |
| 2460 | 1" fiberboard | G | 1 Rofc | 800 | .010 | S.F. | 1.14 | .24 | | 1.38 | 1.69 |
| 2470 | 1" perlite | G | | 850 | .009 | | 1.08 | .23 | | 1.31 | 1.60 |
| 2480 | 7/16" oriented strand board | G | | 800 | .010 | | .84 | .24 | | 1.08 | 1.36 |

# 07 24 Exterior Insulation and Finish Systems

## 07 24 13 – Polymer Based Exterior Insulation and Finish Systems

| | 07 24 13.10 Exterior Insulation and Finish Systems | | Crew | Daily Output | Labor-Hours | Unit | Material | 2010 Bare Costs Labor | Equipment | Total | Total Incl O&P |
|---|---|---|---|---|---|---|---|---|---|---|---|
| 0010 | **EXTERIOR INSULATION AND FINISH SYSTEMS** | | | | | | | | | | |
| 0095 | Field applied, 1" EPS insulation | G | J-1 | 390 | .103 | S.F. | 2.30 | 2.58 | .35 | 5.23 | 7.15 |
| 0100 | With 1/2" cement board sheathing | G | | 268 | .149 | | 2.95 | 3.76 | .51 | 7.22 | 9.95 |
| 0105 | 2" EPS insulation | G | | 390 | .103 | | 2.66 | 2.58 | .35 | 5.59 | 7.55 |
| 0110 | With 1/2" cement board sheathing | G | | 268 | .149 | | 3.31 | 3.76 | .51 | 7.58 | 10.35 |
| 0115 | 3" EPS insulation | G | | 390 | .103 | | 3.02 | 2.58 | .35 | 5.95 | 7.90 |
| 0120 | With 1/2" cement board sheathing | G | | 268 | .149 | | 3.67 | 3.76 | .51 | 7.94 | 10.75 |
| 0125 | 4" EPS insulation | G | | 390 | .103 | | 3.38 | 2.58 | .35 | 6.31 | 8.30 |
| 0130 | With 1/2" cement board sheathing | G | | 268 | .149 | | 4.67 | 3.76 | .51 | 8.94 | 11.85 |
| 0140 | Premium finish add | | | 1265 | .032 | | .31 | .80 | .11 | 1.22 | 1.76 |
| 0150 | Heavy duty reinforcement add | | | 914 | .044 | | 1.08 | 1.10 | .15 | 2.33 | 3.15 |
| 0160 | 2.5#/S.Y. metal lath substrate add | | 1 Lath | 75 | .107 | S.Y. | 2.37 | 2.76 | | 5.13 | 7.05 |
| 0170 | 3.4#/S.Y. metal lath substrate add | | " | 75 | .107 | " | 2.58 | 2.76 | | 5.34 | 7.30 |
| 0180 | Color or texture change, | | J-1 | 1265 | .032 | S.F. | .83 | .80 | .11 | 1.74 | 2.33 |
| 0190 | With substrate leveling base coat | | 1 Plas | 530 | .015 | | .83 | .39 | | 1.22 | 1.55 |
| 0210 | With substrate sealing base coat | | 1 Pord | 1224 | .007 | | .08 | .17 | | .25 | .36 |
| 0370 | V groove shape in panel face | | | | | L.F. | .60 | | | .60 | .66 |
| 0380 | U groove shape in panel face | | | | | " | .79 | | | .79 | .87 |

# 07 25 Weather Barriers

## 07 25 10 – Weather Barriers or Wraps

| | 07 25 10.10 Weather Barriers | | Crew | Daily Output | Labor-Hours | Unit | Material | 2010 Bare Costs Labor | Equipment | Total | Total Incl O&P |
|---|---|---|---|---|---|---|---|---|---|---|---|
| 0010 | **WEATHER BARRIERS** | | | | | | | | | | |
| 0400 | Asphalt felt paper, 15# | | 1 Carp | 37 | .216 | Sq. | 5.90 | 6.30 | | 12.20 | 17.05 |
| 0401 | Per square foot | | " | 3700 | .002 | S.F. | .06 | .06 | | .12 | .17 |
| 0450 | Housewrap, exterior, spun bonded polypropylene | | | | | | | | | | |
| 0470 | Small roll | | 1 Carp | 3800 | .002 | S.F. | .23 | .06 | | .29 | .35 |
| 0480 | Large roll | | " | 4000 | .002 | " | .13 | .06 | | .19 | .24 |
| 2100 | Asphalt felt roof deck vapor barrier, class 1 metal decks | | 1 Rofc | 37 | .216 | Sq. | 21.50 | 5.30 | | 26.80 | 33.50 |
| 2200 | For all other decks | | " | 37 | .216 | | 15.85 | 5.30 | | 21.15 | 27 |
| 2800 | Asphalt felt, 50% recycled content, 15 lb, 4 sq per roll | | 1 Carp | 36 | .222 | | 4.77 | 6.45 | | 11.22 | 16.15 |
| 2810 | 30 lb, 2 sq per roll | | " | 36 | .222 | | 9.55 | 6.45 | | 16 | 21.50 |
| 3000 | Building wrap, spunbonded polyethylene | | 2 Carp | 8000 | .002 | S.F. | .13 | .06 | | .19 | .24 |

# 07 26 Vapor Retarders

## 07 26 10 – Above-Grade Vapor Retarders

| 07 26 10.10 Building Paper | | Crew | Daily Output | Labor-Hours | Unit | Material | 2010 Bare Costs Labor | Equipment | Total | Total Incl O&P |
|---|---|---|---|---|---|---|---|---|---|---|
| 0011 | **BUILDING PAPER** Aluminum and kraft laminated, foil 1 side | 1 Carp | 3700 | .002 | S.F. | .09 | .06 | | .15 | .21 |
| 0101 | Foil 2 sides `G` | | 3700 | .002 | | .10 | .06 | | .16 | .21 |
| 0601 | Polyethylene vapor barrier, standard, .002" thick `G` | | 3700 | .002 | | .01 | .06 | | .07 | .12 |
| 0701 | .004" thick `G` | | 3700 | .002 | | .03 | .06 | | .09 | .15 |
| 0901 | .006" thick `G` | | 3700 | .002 | | .05 | .06 | | .11 | .17 |
| 1201 | .010" thick `G` | | 3700 | .002 | | .07 | .06 | | .13 | .18 |
| 1801 | Reinf. waterproof, .002" polyethylene backing, 1 side | | 3700 | .002 | | .06 | .06 | | .12 | .17 |
| 1901 | 2 sides | | 3700 | .002 | | .07 | .06 | | .13 | .19 |

# 07 31 Shingles and Shakes

## 07 31 13 – Asphalt Shingles

### 07 31 13.10 Asphalt Roof Shingles

| 07 31 13.10 Asphalt Roof Shingles | | Crew | Daily Output | Labor-Hours | Unit | Material | Labor | Equipment | Total | Total Incl O&P |
|---|---|---|---|---|---|---|---|---|---|---|
| 0010 | **ASPHALT ROOF SHINGLES** | | | | | | | | | |
| 0100 | Standard strip shingles | | | | | | | | | |
| 0150 | Inorganic, class A, 210-235 lb/sq | 1 Rofc | 5.50 | 1.455 | Sq. | 73.50 | 35.50 | | 109 | 145 |
| 0155 | Pneumatic nailed | | 7 | 1.143 | | 73.50 | 28 | | 101.50 | 131 |
| 0200 | Organic, class C, 235-240 lb/sq | | 5 | 1.600 | | 64 | 39 | | 103 | 141 |
| 0205 | Pneumatic nailed | | 6.25 | 1.280 | | 64 | 31.50 | | 95.50 | 127 |
| 0250 | Standard, laminated multi-layered shingles | | | | | | | | | |
| 0300 | Class A, 240-260 lb/sq | 1 Rofc | 4.50 | 1.778 | Sq. | 86.50 | 43.50 | | 130 | 174 |
| 0305 | Pneumatic nailed | | 5.63 | 1.422 | | 86.50 | 35 | | 121.50 | 158 |
| 0350 | Class C, 260-300 lb/square, 4 bundles/square | | 4 | 2 | | 84 | 49 | | 133 | 181 |
| 0355 | Pneumatic nailed | | 5 | 1.600 | | 84 | 39 | | 123 | 163 |
| 0400 | Premium, laminated multi-layered shingles | | | | | | | | | |
| 0450 | Class A, 260-300 lb, 4 bundles/sq | 1 Rofc | 3.50 | 2.286 | Sq. | 100 | 56 | | 156 | 211 |
| 0455 | Pneumatic nailed | | 4.37 | 1.831 | | 100 | 45 | | 145 | 191 |
| 0500 | Class C, 300-385 lb/square, 5 bundles/square | | 3 | 2.667 | | 132 | 65 | | 197 | 262 |
| 0505 | Pneumatic nailed | | 3.75 | 2.133 | | 132 | 52 | | 184 | 239 |
| 0800 | #15 felt underlayment | | 64 | .125 | | 5.90 | 3.06 | | 8.96 | 11.95 |
| 0825 | #30 felt underlayment | | 58 | .138 | | 11.95 | 3.37 | | 15.32 | 19.25 |
| 0850 | Self adhering polyethylene and rubberized asphalt underlayment | | 22 | .364 | | 60 | 8.90 | | 68.90 | 82 |
| 0900 | Ridge shingles | | 330 | .024 | L.F. | 1.90 | .59 | | 2.49 | 3.16 |
| 0905 | Pneumatic nailed | | 412.50 | .019 | " | 1.90 | .47 | | 2.37 | 2.94 |
| 1000 | For steep roofs (7 to 12 pitch or greater), add | | | | | | 50% | | | |

## 07 31 19 – Mineral-Fiber Cement Shingles

### 07 31 19.10 Fiber Cement Shingles

| 07 31 19.10 Fiber Cement Shingles | | Crew | Daily Output | Labor-Hours | Unit | Material | Labor | Equipment | Total | Total Incl O&P |
|---|---|---|---|---|---|---|---|---|---|---|
| 0010 | **FIBER CEMENT SHINGLES** | | | | | | | | | |
| 0012 | Field shingles, 16" x 9.35", 500 lb per square | 1 Rofc | 2.20 | 3.636 | Sq. | 335 | 89 | | 424 | 530 |
| 0200 | Shakes, 16" x 9.35", 550 lb per square | | 2.20 | 3.636 | " | 305 | 89 | | 394 | 495 |
| 0301 | Hip & ridge, 4.75 x 14" | | 100 | .080 | L.F. | 8.30 | 1.96 | | 10.26 | 12.65 |
| 0400 | Hexagonal, 16" x 16" | | 3 | 2.667 | Sq. | 230 | 65 | | 295 | 370 |
| 0500 | Square, 16" x 16" | | 3 | 2.667 | | 205 | 65 | | 270 | 345 |
| 2000 | For steep roofs (7/12 pitch or greater), add | | | | | | 50% | | | |

## 07 31 26 – Slate Shingles

### 07 31 26.10 Slate Roof Shingles

| 07 31 26.10 Slate Roof Shingles | | Crew | Daily Output | Labor-Hours | Unit | Material | Labor | Equipment | Total | Total Incl O&P |
|---|---|---|---|---|---|---|---|---|---|---|
| 0010 | **SLATE ROOF SHINGLES** R073126-20 | | | | | | | | | |
| 0100 | Buckingham Virginia black, 3/16" - 1/4" thick `G` | 1 Rots | 1.75 | 4.571 | Sq. | 475 | 112 | | 587 | 725 |
| 0200 | 1/4" thick `G` | | 1.75 | 4.571 | | 475 | 112 | | 587 | 725 |
| 0900 | Pennsylvania black, Bangor, #1 clear `G` | | 1.75 | 4.571 | | 490 | 112 | | 602 | 740 |
| 1200 | Vermont, unfading, green, mottled green `G` | | 1.75 | 4.571 | | 480 | 112 | | 592 | 725 |

# 07 31 Shingles and Shakes

## 07 31 26 – Slate Shingles

| | 07 31 26.10 Slate Roof Shingles | Crew | Daily Output | Labor-Hours | Unit | Material | 2010 Bare Costs Labor | Equipment | Total | Total Incl O&P |
|---|---|---|---|---|---|---|---|---|---|---|
| 1300 | Semi-weathering green & gray | G 1 Rots | 1.75 | 4.571 | Sq. | 350 | 112 | | 462 | 580 |
| 1400 | Purple | G | 1.75 | 4.571 | | 425 | 112 | | 537 | 665 |
| 1500 | Black or gray | G | 1.75 | 4.571 | | 460 | 112 | | 572 | 705 |
| 2700 | Ridge shingles, slate | | 200 | .040 | L.F. | 9.30 | .98 | | 10.28 | 11.95 |

## 07 31 29 – Wood Shingles and Shakes

### 07 31 29.13 Wood Shingles

| | | Crew | Daily Output | Labor-Hours | Unit | Material | 2010 Bare Costs Labor | Equipment | Total | Total Incl O&P |
|---|---|---|---|---|---|---|---|---|---|---|
| 0010 | **WOOD SHINGLES** | | | | | | | | | |
| 0012 | 16" No. 1 red cedar shingles, 5" exposure, on roof | 1 Carp | 2.50 | 3.200 | Sq. | 310 | 93 | | 403 | 495 |
| 0015 | Pneumatic nailed | | 3.25 | 2.462 | | 310 | 71.50 | | 381.50 | 460 |
| 0200 | 7-1/2" exposure, on walls | | 2.05 | 3.902 | | 207 | 114 | | 321 | 420 |
| 0205 | Pneumatic nailed | | 2.67 | 2.996 | | 207 | 87 | | 294 | 375 |
| 0300 | 18" No. 1 red cedar perfections, 5-1/2" exposure, on roof | | 2.75 | 2.909 | | 265 | 84.50 | | 349.50 | 435 |
| 0305 | Pneumatic nailed | | 3.57 | 2.241 | | 265 | 65 | | 330 | 400 |
| 0500 | 7-1/2" exposure, on walls | | 2.25 | 3.556 | | 195 | 103 | | 298 | 390 |
| 0505 | Pneumatic nailed | | 2.92 | 2.740 | | 195 | 79.50 | | 274.50 | 350 |
| 0600 | Resquared, and rebutted, 5-1/2" exposure, on roof | | 3 | 2.667 | | 236 | 77.50 | | 313.50 | 390 |
| 0605 | Pneumatic nailed | | 3.90 | 2.051 | | 236 | 59.50 | | 295.50 | 360 |
| 0900 | 7-1/2" exposure, on walls | | 2.45 | 3.265 | | 173 | 95 | | 268 | 350 |
| 0905 | Pneumatic nailed | | 3.18 | 2.516 | | 173 | 73 | | 246 | 315 |
| 1000 | Add to above for fire retardant shingles | | | | | 55 | | | 55 | 60.50 |
| 1050 | 18" long | | | | | 55 | | | 55 | 60.50 |
| 1060 | Preformed ridge shingles | 1 Carp | 400 | .020 | L.F. | 3.60 | .58 | | 4.18 | 4.94 |
| 2000 | White cedar shingles, 16" long, extras, 5" exposure, on roof | | 2.40 | 3.333 | Sq. | 174 | 97 | | 271 | 355 |
| 2005 | Pneumatic nailed | | 3.12 | 2.564 | | 174 | 74.50 | | 248.50 | 315 |
| 2050 | 5" exposure on walls | | 2 | 4 | | 174 | 116 | | 290 | 385 |
| 2055 | Pneumatic nailed | | 2.60 | 3.077 | | 174 | 89.50 | | 263.50 | 340 |
| 2100 | 7-1/2" exposure, on walls | | 2 | 4 | | 124 | 116 | | 240 | 335 |
| 2105 | Pneumatic nailed | | 2.60 | 3.077 | | 124 | 89.50 | | 213.50 | 288 |
| 2150 | "B" grade, 5" exposure on walls | | 2 | 4 | | 150 | 116 | | 266 | 360 |
| 2155 | Pneumatic nailed | | 2.60 | 3.077 | | 150 | 89.50 | | 239.50 | 315 |
| 2300 | For 15# organic felt underlayment on roof, 1 layer, add | | 64 | .125 | | 5.90 | 3.64 | | 9.54 | 12.55 |
| 2400 | 2 layers, add | | 32 | .250 | | 11.75 | 7.30 | | 19.05 | 25 |
| 2600 | For steep roofs (7/12 pitch or greater), add to above | | | | | | 50% | | | |
| 3000 | Ridge shakes or shingle wood | 1 Carp | 280 | .029 | L.F. | 3.60 | .83 | | 4.43 | 5.35 |

### 07 31 29.16 Wood Shakes

| | | Crew | Daily Output | Labor-Hours | Unit | Material | 2010 Bare Costs Labor | Equipment | Total | Total Incl O&P |
|---|---|---|---|---|---|---|---|---|---|---|
| 0010 | **WOOD SHAKES** | | | | | | | | | |
| 1100 | Hand-split red cedar shakes, 1/2" thick x 24" long, 10" exp. on roof | 1 Carp | 2.50 | 3.200 | Sq. | 165 | 93 | | 258 | 340 |
| 1105 | Pneumatic nailed | | 3.25 | 2.462 | | 165 | 71.50 | | 236.50 | 300 |
| 1110 | 3/4" thick x 24" long, 10" exp. on roof | | 2.25 | 3.556 | | 165 | 103 | | 268 | 355 |
| 1115 | Pneumatic nailed | | 2.92 | 2.740 | | 165 | 79.50 | | 244.50 | 315 |
| 1200 | 1/2" thick, 18" long, 8-1/2" exp. on roof | | 2 | 4 | | 146 | 116 | | 262 | 355 |
| 1205 | Pneumatic nailed | | 2.60 | 3.077 | | 146 | 89.50 | | 235.50 | 310 |
| 1210 | 3/4" thick x 18" long, 8 1/2" exp. on roof | | 1.80 | 4.444 | | 146 | 129 | | 275 | 380 |
| 1215 | Pneumatic nailed | | 2.34 | 3.419 | | 146 | 99.50 | | 245.50 | 330 |
| 1255 | 10" exp. on walls | | 2 | 4 | | 141 | 116 | | 257 | 350 |
| 1260 | 10" exposure on walls, pneumatic nailed | | 2.60 | 3.077 | | 141 | 89.50 | | 230.50 | 305 |
| 1700 | Add to above for fire retardant shakes, 24" long | | | | | 55 | | | 55 | 60.50 |
| 1800 | 18" long | | | | | 55 | | | 55 | 60.50 |
| 1810 | Ridge shakes | 1 Carp | 350 | .023 | L.F. | 3.60 | .67 | | 4.27 | 5.10 |

# 07 32 Roof Tiles

## 07 32 13 – Clay Roof Tiles

### 07 32 13.10 Clay Tiles

| 07 32 13.10 Clay Tiles | Crew | Daily Output | Labor-Hours | Unit | Material | 2010 Bare Costs Labor | Equipment | Total | Total Incl O&P |
|---|---|---|---|---|---|---|---|---|---|
| 0010 **CLAY TILES** | | | | | | | | | |
| 0200 Lanai tile or Classic tile, 158 pc per sq ⑥ | 1 Rots | 1.65 | 4.848 | Sq. | 500 | 119 | | 619 | 765 |
| 0300 Americana, 158 pc per sq, most colors ⑥ | | 1.65 | 4.848 | | 660 | 119 | | 779 | 945 |
| 0350 Green, gray or brown ⑥ | | 1.65 | 4.848 | | 625 | 119 | | 744 | 900 |
| 0400 Blue ⑥ | | 1.65 | 4.848 | | 625 | 119 | | 744 | 900 |
| 0600 Spanish tile, 171 pc per sq, red ⑥ | | 1.80 | 4.444 | | 325 | 109 | | 434 | 550 |
| 0800 Buff, green, gray, brown ⑥ | | 1.80 | 4.444 | | 600 | 109 | | 709 | 855 |
| 0900 Glazed white | | 1.80 | 4.444 | | 665 | 109 | | 774 | 925 |
| 1100 Mission tile, 192 pc per sq, machine scored finish, red ⑥ | | 1.15 | 6.957 | | 740 | 171 | | 911 | 1,125 |
| 1700 French tile, 133 pc per sq, smooth finish, red ⑥ | | 1.35 | 5.926 | | 675 | 145 | | 820 | 1,000 |
| 1750 Blue or green ⑥ | | 1.35 | 5.926 | | 870 | 145 | | 1,015 | 1,225 |
| 1800 Norman black 317 pc per sq ⑥ | | 1 | 8 | | 1,050 | 196 | | 1,246 | 1,500 |
| 2200 Williamsburg tile, 158 pc per sq, aged cedar ⑥ | | 1.35 | 5.926 | | 730 | 145 | | 875 | 1,050 |
| 2250 Gray or green ⑥ | | 1.35 | 5.926 | | 595 | 145 | | 740 | 915 |
| 2350 Ridge shingles, clay tile ⑥ | | 200 | .040 | L.F. | 10.70 | .98 | | 11.68 | 13.55 |
| 2510 One piece mission tile, natural red, 75 pc per square ⑥ | | 1.65 | 4.848 | Sq. | 231 | 119 | | 350 | 470 |
| 2530 Mission Tile, 134 pc per square ⑥ | | 1.15 | 6.957 | | 263 | 171 | | 434 | 600 |
| 3000 For steep roofs (7/12 pitch or greater), add to above | | | | | | 50% | | | |
| 3010 Clay tile, #15 felt underlayment | 1 Rofc | 64 | .125 | | 5.90 | 3.06 | | 8.96 | 11.95 |
| 3020 Clay tile, #30 felt underlayment | | 58 | .138 | | 11.95 | 3.37 | | 15.32 | 19.25 |
| 3040 Clay tile, polyethylene and rubberized asph. underlayment | | 22 | .364 | | 60 | 8.90 | | 68.90 | 82 |

## 07 32 16 – Concrete Roof Tiles

### 07 32 16.10 Concrete Tiles

| 07 32 16.10 Concrete Tiles | Crew | Daily Output | Labor-Hours | Unit | Material | 2010 Bare Costs Labor | Equipment | Total | Total Incl O&P |
|---|---|---|---|---|---|---|---|---|---|
| 0010 **CONCRETE TILES** | | | | | | | | | |
| 0020 Corrugated, 13" x 16-1/2", 90 per sq, 950 lb per sq | | | | | | | | | |
| 0050 Earthtone colors, nailed to wood deck | 1 Rots | 1.35 | 5.926 | Sq. | 103 | 145 | | 248 | 375 |
| 0150 Blues | | 1.35 | 5.926 | | 104 | 145 | | 249 | 375 |
| 0200 Greens | | 1.35 | 5.926 | | 104 | 145 | | 249 | 375 |
| 0250 Premium colors | | 1.35 | 5.926 | | 229 | 145 | | 374 | 515 |
| 0500 Shakes, 13" x 16-1/2", 90 per sq, 950 lb per sq | | | | | | | | | |
| 0600 All colors, nailed to wood deck | 1 Rots | 1.50 | 5.333 | Sq. | 270 | 131 | | 401 | 535 |
| 1500 Accessory pieces, ridge & hip, 10" x 16-1/2", 8 lbs. each | " | 120 | .067 | Ea. | 3.64 | 1.64 | | 5.28 | 6.95 |
| 1700 Rake, 6-1/2" x 16-3/4", 9 lbs. each | | | | | 3.64 | | | 3.64 | 4 |
| 1800 Mansard hip, 10" x 16-1/2", 9.2 lbs. each | | | | | 3.64 | | | 3.64 | 4 |
| 1900 Hip starter, 10" x 16-1/2", 10.5 lbs. each | | | | | 11.45 | | | 11.45 | 12.60 |
| 2000 3 or 4 way apex, 10" each side, 11.5 lbs. each | | | | | 13.25 | | | 13.25 | 14.55 |

# 07 33 Natural Roof Coverings

## 07 33 63 – Vegetated Roofing

### 07 33 63.10 Green Roof Systems

| 07 33 63.10 Green Roof Systems | Crew | Daily Output | Labor-Hours | Unit | Material | 2010 Bare Costs Labor | Equipment | Total | Total Incl O&P |
|---|---|---|---|---|---|---|---|---|---|
| 0010 **GREEN ROOF SYSTEMS** | | | | | | | | | |
| 0020 Soil mixture for green roof 30% sand, 55% gravel, 15% soil ⑥ | | | | | | | | | |
| 0100 Hoist and spread soil mixture 4 inch depth up to five stories tall roof ⑥ | B-13B | 4000 | .014 | S.F. | .22 | .33 | .30 | .85 | 1.13 |
| 0150 6 inch depth ⑥ | | 2667 | .021 | | .33 | .50 | .45 | 1.28 | 1.69 |
| 0200 8 inch depth ⑥ | | 2000 | .028 | | .44 | .67 | .60 | 1.71 | 2.26 |
| 0250 10 inch depth ⑥ | | 1600 | .035 | | .55 | .83 | .76 | 2.14 | 2.83 |
| 0300 12 inch depth ⑥ | | 1335 | .042 | | .66 | 1 | .91 | 2.57 | 3.39 |
| 0350 Mobilization 55 ton crane to site ⑥ | 1 Eqhv | 3.60 | 2.222 | Ea. | | 68 | | 68 | 111 |
| 0355 Hoisting cost to five stories per day (Avg. 28 picks per day) ⑥ | B-13B | 1 | 56 | Day | | 1,325 | 1,200 | 2,525 | 3,550 |
| 0360 Mobilization or demobilization, 100 ton crane to site driver & escort ⑥ | A-3E | 2.50 | 6.400 | Ea. | | 173 | 60.50 | 233.50 | 355 |

# 07 33 Natural Roof Coverings

## 07 33 63 – Vegetated Roofing

### 07 33 63.10 Green Roof Systems

| | | Crew | Daily Output | Labor-Hours | Unit | Material | 2010 Bare Costs Labor | Equipment | Total | Total Incl O&P |
|---|---|---|---|---|---|---|---|---|---|---|
| 0365 | Hoisting cost six to ten stories per day (Avg. 21 picks per day) G | B-13C | 1 | 56 | Day | | 1,325 | 1,725 | 3,050 | 4,125 |
| 0370 | Hoist and spread soil mixture 4 inch depth six to ten stories tall roof G | | 4000 | .014 | S.F. | .22 | .33 | .43 | .98 | 1.28 |
| 0375 | 6 inch depth G | | 2667 | .021 | | .33 | .50 | .65 | 1.48 | 1.90 |
| 0380 | 8 inch depth G | | 2000 | .028 | | .44 | .67 | .87 | 1.98 | 2.54 |
| 0385 | 10 inch depth G | | 1600 | .035 | | .55 | .83 | 1.08 | 2.46 | 3.19 |
| 0390 | 12 inch depth G | | 1335 | .042 | | .66 | 1 | 1.30 | 2.96 | 3.82 |
| 0400 | Green roof edging treated lumber 4" x4" no hoisting included G | 2 Carp | 400 | .040 | L.F. | 1.56 | 1.16 | | 2.72 | 3.67 |
| 0410 | 4" x 6" G | | 400 | .040 | | 2.30 | 1.16 | | 3.46 | 4.49 |
| 0420 | 4" x 8" G | | 360 | .044 | | 4.74 | 1.29 | | 6.03 | 7.40 |
| 0430 | 4" x 6" double stacked G | | 300 | .053 | | 4.60 | 1.55 | | 6.15 | 7.65 |
| 0500 | Green roof edging redwood lumber 4" x4" no hoisting included G | | 400 | .040 | | 6.40 | 1.16 | | 7.56 | 9 |
| 0510 | 4" x 6" G | | 400 | .040 | | 11.20 | 1.16 | | 12.36 | 14.25 |
| 0520 | 4" x 8" G | | 360 | .044 | | 20.50 | 1.29 | | 21.79 | 24.50 |
| 0530 | 4" x 6" double stacked G | | 300 | .053 | | 11.20 | 1.55 | | 12.75 | 14.95 |
| 0600 | Planting sedum, light soil, potted, 2-1/4" diameter, two per SF G | 1 Clab | 420 | .019 | S.F. | 4.98 | .41 | | 5.39 | 6.20 |
| 0610 | one per SF G | " | 840 | .010 | | 2.49 | .20 | | 2.69 | 3.08 |
| 0630 | Planting sedum mat per SF including shipping (4000 SF Minimum) G | 4 Clab | 4000 | .008 | | 6 | .17 | | 6.17 | 6.85 |
| 0640 | Installation sedum mat system (no soil required) per SF (4000 SF minimum) G | " | 4000 | .008 | | 8.30 | .17 | | 8.47 | 9.45 |
| 0645 | Note: pricing of sedum mats shipped in full truck loads (4000-5000 SF) G | | | | | | | | | |

# 07 41 Roof Panels

## 07 41 13 – Metal Roof Panels

### 07 41 13.10 Aluminum Roof Panels

| | | Crew | Daily Output | Labor-Hours | Unit | Material | Labor | Equipment | Total | Total Incl O&P |
|---|---|---|---|---|---|---|---|---|---|---|
| 0010 | **ALUMINUM ROOF PANELS** | | | | | | | | | |
| 0020 | Corrugated or ribbed, .0155" thick, natural | G-3 | 1200 | .027 | S.F. | .96 | .72 | | 1.68 | 2.26 |
| 0300 | Painted | " | 1200 | .027 | " | 1.40 | .72 | | 2.12 | 2.74 |

## 07 41 33 – Plastic Roof Panels

### 07 41 33.10 Fiberglass Panels

| | | Crew | Daily Output | Labor-Hours | Unit | Material | Labor | Equipment | Total | Total Incl O&P |
|---|---|---|---|---|---|---|---|---|---|---|
| 0010 | **FIBERGLASS PANELS** | | | | | | | | | |
| 0012 | Corrugated panels, roofing, 8 oz per S.F. | G-3 | 1000 | .032 | S.F. | 1.58 | .86 | | 2.44 | 3.18 |
| 0100 | 12 oz per S.F. | | 1000 | .032 | | 3.43 | .86 | | 4.29 | 5.20 |
| 0300 | Corrugated siding, 6 oz per S.F. | | 880 | .036 | | 1.58 | .98 | | 2.56 | 3.37 |
| 0400 | 8 oz per S.F. | | 880 | .036 | | 1.58 | .98 | | 2.56 | 3.37 |
| 0600 | 12 oz. siding, textured | | 880 | .036 | | 3.32 | .98 | | 4.30 | 5.30 |
| 0900 | Flat panels, 6 oz per S.F., clear or colors | | 880 | .036 | | 1.83 | .98 | | 2.81 | 3.64 |
| 1300 | 8 oz per S.F., clear or colors | | 880 | .036 | | 2.38 | .98 | | 3.36 | 4.25 |

# 07 42 Wall Panels

## 07 42 13 – Metal Wall Panels

### 07 42 13.20 Aluminum Siding

| | | Crew | Daily Output | Labor-Hours | Unit | Material | Labor | Equipment | Total | Total Incl O&P |
|---|---|---|---|---|---|---|---|---|---|---|
| 0011 | **ALUMINUM SIDING** | | | | | | | | | |
| 6040 | .024 thick smooth white single 8" wide | 2 Carp | 515 | .031 | S.F. | 1.73 | .90 | | 2.63 | 3.42 |
| 6060 | Double 4" pattern | | 515 | .031 | | 2.04 | .90 | | 2.94 | 3.76 |
| 6080 | Double 5" pattern | | 550 | .029 | | 2.10 | .85 | | 2.95 | 3.73 |
| 6120 | Embossed white, 8" wide | | 515 | .031 | | 1.73 | .90 | | 2.63 | 3.42 |
| 6140 | Double 4" pattern | | 515 | .031 | | 2.15 | .90 | | 3.05 | 3.89 |
| 6160 | Double 5" pattern | | 550 | .029 | | 2.13 | .85 | | 2.98 | 3.76 |
| 6170 | Vertical, embossed white, 12" wide | | 590 | .027 | | 2.13 | .79 | | 2.92 | 3.67 |
| 6320 | .019 thick, insulated, smooth white, 8" wide | | 515 | .031 | | 1.89 | .90 | | 2.79 | 3.60 |

## 07 42 13 – Metal Wall Panels

### 07 42 13.20 Aluminum Siding

| | | Crew | Daily Output | Labor-Hours | Unit | Material | 2010 Bare Costs Labor | Equipment | Total | Total Incl O&P |
|---|---|---|---|---|---|---|---|---|---|---|
| 6340 | Double 4" pattern | 2 Carp | 515 | .031 | S.F. | 1.87 | .90 | | 2.77 | 3.58 |
| 6360 | Double 5" pattern | | 550 | .029 | | 1.87 | .85 | | 2.72 | 3.48 |
| 6400 | Embossed white, 8" wide | | 515 | .031 | | 2.18 | .90 | | 3.08 | 3.92 |
| 6420 | Double 4" pattern | | 515 | .031 | | 2.21 | .90 | | 3.11 | 3.95 |
| 6440 | Double 5" pattern | | 550 | .029 | | 2.21 | .85 | | 3.06 | 3.85 |
| 6500 | Shake finish 10" wide white | | 550 | .029 | | 2.35 | .85 | | 3.20 | 4.01 |
| 6600 | Vertical pattern, 12" wide, white | | 590 | .027 | | 1.96 | .79 | | 2.75 | 3.49 |
| 6640 | For colors add | | | | | .12 | | | .12 | .13 |
| 6700 | Accessories, white | | | | | | | | | |
| 6720 | Starter strip 2-1/8" | 2 Carp | 610 | .026 | L.F. | .33 | .76 | | 1.09 | 1.64 |
| 6740 | Sill trim | | 450 | .036 | | .55 | 1.03 | | 1.58 | 2.35 |
| 6760 | Inside corner | | 610 | .026 | | 1.39 | .76 | | 2.15 | 2.81 |
| 6780 | Outside corner post | | 610 | .026 | | 3.06 | .76 | | 3.82 | 4.65 |
| 6800 | Door & window trim | | 440 | .036 | | .53 | 1.06 | | 1.59 | 2.36 |
| 6820 | For colors add | | | | | .10 | | | .10 | .11 |
| 6900 | Soffit & fascia 1' overhang solid | 2 Carp | 110 | .145 | | 3.06 | 4.23 | | 7.29 | 10.45 |
| 6920 | Vented | | 110 | .145 | | 3.06 | 4.23 | | 7.29 | 10.45 |
| 6940 | 2' overhang solid | | 100 | .160 | | 5 | 4.66 | | 9.66 | 13.35 |
| 6960 | Vented | | 100 | .160 | | 5 | 4.66 | | 9.66 | 13.35 |

### 07 42 13.30 Steel Siding

| | | Crew | Daily Output | Labor-Hours | Unit | Material | 2010 Bare Costs Labor | Equipment | Total | Total Incl O&P |
|---|---|---|---|---|---|---|---|---|---|---|
| 0010 | **STEEL SIDING** | | | | | | | | | |
| 0020 | Beveled, vinyl coated, 8" wide | 1 Carp | 265 | .030 | S.F. | 1.97 | .88 | | 2.85 | 3.65 |
| 0050 | 10" wide | " | 275 | .029 | | 2.11 | .85 | | 2.96 | 3.74 |
| 0081 | Galv., corrugated or ribbed, on steel frame, 30 gauge | G-3 | 775 | .041 | | 1.32 | 1.11 | | 2.43 | 3.30 |
| 0101 | 28 gauge | | 775 | .041 | | 1.38 | 1.11 | | 2.49 | 3.37 |
| 0301 | 26 gauge | | 775 | .041 | | 1.94 | 1.11 | | 3.05 | 3.98 |
| 0401 | 24 gauge | | 775 | .041 | | 1.95 | 1.11 | | 3.06 | 4 |
| 0601 | 22 gauge | | 775 | .041 | | 2.25 | 1.11 | | 3.36 | 4.33 |
| 0701 | Colored, corrugated/ribbed, on steel frame, 10 yr fnsh, 28 ga. | | 775 | .041 | | 2.05 | 1.11 | | 3.16 | 4.11 |
| 0901 | 26 gauge | | 775 | .041 | | 2.14 | 1.11 | | 3.25 | 4.20 |
| 1001 | 24 gauge | | 775 | .041 | | 2.49 | 1.11 | | 3.60 | 4.59 |

# 07 46 Siding

## 07 46 23 – Wood Siding

### 07 46 23.10 Wood Board Siding

| | | Crew | Daily Output | Labor-Hours | Unit | Material | 2010 Bare Costs Labor | Equipment | Total | Total Incl O&P |
|---|---|---|---|---|---|---|---|---|---|---|
| 0010 | **WOOD BOARD SIDING** | | | | | | | | | |
| 2000 | Board & batten, cedar, "B" grade, 1" x 10" | 1 Carp | 375 | .021 | S.F. | 2.69 | .62 | | 3.31 | 4 |
| 2200 | Redwood, clear, vertical grain, 1" x 10" | | 375 | .021 | | 5.30 | .62 | | 5.92 | 6.85 |
| 2400 | White pine, #2 & better, 1" x 10" | | 375 | .021 | | 1.65 | .62 | | 2.27 | 2.86 |
| 2410 | Board & batten siding, white pine #2, 1" x 12" | | 420 | .019 | | 1.65 | .55 | | 2.20 | 2.75 |
| 3200 | Wood, cedar bevel, A grade, 1/2" x 6" | | 295 | .027 | | 4.73 | .79 | | 5.52 | 6.55 |
| 3300 | 1/2" x 8" | | 330 | .024 | | 5.55 | .71 | | 6.26 | 7.30 |
| 3500 | 3/4" x 10", clear grade | | 375 | .021 | | 6.10 | .62 | | 6.72 | 7.75 |
| 3600 | "B" grade | | 375 | .021 | | 5.20 | .62 | | 5.82 | 6.75 |
| 3800 | Cedar, rough sawn, 1" x 4", A grade, natural | | 220 | .036 | | 3.77 | 1.06 | | 4.83 | 5.95 |
| 3900 | Stained | | 220 | .036 | | 4.17 | 1.06 | | 5.23 | 6.35 |
| 4100 | 1" x 12", board & batten, #3 & Btr., natural | | 420 | .019 | | 3.94 | .55 | | 4.49 | 5.25 |
| 4200 | Stained | | 420 | .019 | | 4.20 | .55 | | 4.75 | 5.55 |
| 4400 | 1" x 8" channel siding, #3 & Btr., natural | | 330 | .024 | | 2.34 | .71 | | 3.05 | 3.76 |
| 4500 | Stained | | 330 | .024 | | 2.50 | .71 | | 3.21 | 3.94 |
| 4700 | Redwood, clear, beveled, vertical grain, 1/2" x 4" | | 220 | .036 | | 3.10 | 1.06 | | 4.16 | 5.20 |

405

# 07 46 Siding

## 07 46 23 – Wood Siding

### 07 46 23.10 Wood Board Siding

| | 07 46 23.10 Wood Board Siding | Crew | Daily Output | Labor-Hours | Unit | Material | 2010 Bare Costs Labor | Equipment | Total | Total Incl O&P |
|---|---|---|---|---|---|---|---|---|---|---|
| 4750 | 1/2" x 6" | 1 Carp | 295 | .027 | S.F. | 3.10 | .79 | | 3.89 | 4.74 |
| 4800 | 1/2" x 8" | | 330 | .024 | | 3.24 | .71 | | 3.95 | 4.75 |
| 5000 | 3/4" x 10" | | 375 | .021 | | 3.32 | .62 | | 3.94 | 4.69 |
| 5200 | Channel siding, 1" x 10", B grade | | 375 | .021 | | 3.32 | .62 | | 3.94 | 4.69 |
| 5250 | Redwood, T&G boards, B grade, 1" x 4" | | 220 | .036 | | 3.10 | 1.06 | | 4.16 | 5.20 |
| 5270 | 1" x 8" | | 330 | .024 | | 3.24 | .71 | | 3.95 | 4.75 |
| 5400 | White pine, rough sawn, 1" x 8", natural | | 330 | .024 | | 2.20 | .71 | | 2.91 | 3.61 |
| 5500 | Stained | | 330 | .024 | | 2.60 | .71 | | 3.31 | 4.05 |
| 5600 | Tongue and groove, 1" x 8" | | 330 | .024 | | 2.20 | .71 | | 2.91 | 3.61 |

## 07 46 29 – Plywood Siding

### 07 46 29.10 Plywood Siding Options

| | 07 46 29.10 Plywood Siding Options | Crew | Daily Output | Labor-Hours | Unit | Material | 2010 Bare Costs Labor | Equipment | Total | Total Incl O&P |
|---|---|---|---|---|---|---|---|---|---|---|
| 0010 | **PLYWOOD SIDING OPTIONS** | | | | | | | | | |
| 0900 | Plywood, medium density overlaid, 3/8" thick | 2 Carp | 750 | .021 | S.F. | 1.14 | .62 | | 1.76 | 2.29 |
| 1000 | 1/2" thick | | 700 | .023 | | 1.22 | .67 | | 1.89 | 2.46 |
| 1100 | 3/4" thick | | 650 | .025 | | 1.55 | .72 | | 2.27 | 2.92 |
| 1600 | Texture 1-11, cedar, 5/8" thick, natural | | 675 | .024 | | 2.43 | .69 | | 3.12 | 3.83 |
| 1700 | Factory stained | | 675 | .024 | | 1.95 | .69 | | 2.64 | 3.31 |
| 1900 | Texture 1-11, fir, 5/8" thick, natural | | 675 | .024 | | 1.37 | .69 | | 2.06 | 2.67 |
| 2000 | Factory stained | | 675 | .024 | | 1.73 | .69 | | 2.42 | 3.06 |
| 2050 | Texture 1-11, S.Y.P., 5/8" thick, natural | | 675 | .024 | | 1.19 | .69 | | 1.88 | 2.47 |
| 2100 | Factory stained | | 675 | .024 | | 1.24 | .69 | | 1.93 | 2.52 |
| 2200 | Rough sawn cedar, 3/8" thick, natural | | 675 | .024 | | 1.20 | .69 | | 1.89 | 2.48 |
| 2300 | Factory stained | | 675 | .024 | | .96 | .69 | | 1.65 | 2.22 |
| 2500 | Rough sawn fir, 3/8" thick, natural | | 675 | .024 | | .76 | .69 | | 1.45 | 2 |
| 2600 | Factory stained | | 675 | .024 | | .96 | .69 | | 1.65 | 2.22 |
| 2800 | Redwood, textured siding, 5/8" thick | | 675 | .024 | | 1.92 | .69 | | 2.61 | 3.27 |

## 07 46 33 – Plastic Siding

### 07 46 33.10 Vinyl Siding

| | 07 46 33.10 Vinyl Siding | Crew | Daily Output | Labor-Hours | Unit | Material | 2010 Bare Costs Labor | Equipment | Total | Total Incl O&P |
|---|---|---|---|---|---|---|---|---|---|---|
| 0010 | **VINYL SIDING** | | | | | | | | | |
| 3995 | Clapboard profile, woodgrain texture, .048 thick, double 4 | 2 Carp | 495 | .032 | S.F. | .92 | .94 | | 1.86 | 2.59 |
| 4000 | Double 5 | | 550 | .029 | | .92 | .85 | | 1.77 | 2.43 |
| 4005 | Single 8 | | 495 | .032 | | .96 | .94 | | 1.90 | 2.64 |
| 4010 | Single 10 | | 550 | .029 | | 1.15 | .85 | | 2 | 2.69 |
| 4015 | .044 thick, double 4 | | 495 | .032 | | .84 | .94 | | 1.78 | 2.50 |
| 4020 | Double 5 | | 550 | .029 | | .84 | .85 | | 1.69 | 2.34 |
| 4025 | .042 thick, double 4 | | 495 | .032 | | .84 | .94 | | 1.78 | 2.50 |
| 4030 | Double 5 | | 550 | .029 | | .84 | .85 | | 1.69 | 2.34 |
| 4035 | Cross sawn texture, .040 thick, double 4 | | 495 | .032 | | .66 | .94 | | 1.60 | 2.31 |
| 4040 | Double 5 | | 550 | .029 | | .66 | .85 | | 1.51 | 2.15 |
| 4045 | Smooth texture, .042 thick, double 4 | | 495 | .032 | | .75 | .94 | | 1.69 | 2.41 |
| 4050 | Double 5 | | 550 | .029 | | .75 | .85 | | 1.60 | 2.25 |
| 4055 | Single 8 | | 495 | .032 | | .96 | .94 | | 1.90 | 2.64 |
| 4060 | Cedar texture, .044 thick, double 4 | | 495 | .032 | | .92 | .94 | | 1.86 | 2.59 |
| 4065 | Double 6 | | 600 | .027 | | .92 | .78 | | 1.70 | 2.32 |
| 4070 | Dutch lap profile, woodgrain texture, .048 thick, double 5 | | 550 | .029 | | .92 | .85 | | 1.77 | 2.43 |
| 4075 | .044 thick, double 4.5 | | 525 | .030 | | .92 | .89 | | 1.81 | 2.50 |
| 4080 | .042 thick, double 4.5 | | 525 | .030 | | .75 | .89 | | 1.64 | 2.32 |
| 4085 | .040 thick, double 4.5 | | 525 | .030 | | .66 | .89 | | 1.55 | 2.22 |
| 4090 | Shingle profile, random grooves, double 7 | | 400 | .040 | | 2.57 | 1.16 | | 3.73 | 4.79 |
| 4095 | Triple 5 | | 400 | .040 | | 2.57 | 1.16 | | 3.73 | 4.79 |
| 4100 | Shake profile, 10" wide | | 400 | .040 | | 2.19 | 1.16 | | 3.35 | 4.37 |
| 4105 | Vertical pattern, .046 thick, double 5 | | 550 | .029 | | 1.22 | .85 | | 2.07 | 2.76 |

# 07 46 Siding

## 07 46 33 – Plastic Siding

### 07 46 33.10 Vinyl Siding

| | | Crew | Daily Output | Labor-Hours | Unit | Material | 2010 Bare Costs Labor | Equipment | Total | Total Incl O&P |
|---|---|---|---|---|---|---|---|---|---|---|
| 4110 | .044 thick, triple 3 | 2 Carp | 550 | .029 | S.F. | 1.37 | .85 | | 2.22 | 2.93 |
| 4115 | .040 thick, triple 4 | | 550 | .029 | | 1.22 | .85 | | 2.07 | 2.76 |
| 4120 | .040 thick, triple 2.66 | | 550 | .029 | | 1.47 | .85 | | 2.32 | 3.04 |
| 4125 | Insulation, fan folded extruded polystyrene, 1/4" | | 2000 | .008 | | .25 | .23 | | .48 | .67 |
| 4130 | 3/8" | | 2000 | .008 | | .27 | .23 | | .50 | .69 |
| 4135 | Accessories, J channel, 5/8" pocket | | 700 | .023 | L.F. | .43 | .67 | | 1.10 | 1.59 |
| 4140 | 3/4" pocket | | 695 | .023 | | .48 | .67 | | 1.15 | 1.65 |
| 4145 | 1-1/4" pocket | | 680 | .024 | | .61 | .68 | | 1.29 | 1.82 |
| 4150 | Flexible, 3/4" pocket | | 600 | .027 | | 1.81 | .78 | | 2.59 | 3.30 |
| 4155 | Under sill finish trim | | 500 | .032 | | .45 | .93 | | 1.38 | 2.06 |
| 4160 | Vinyl starter strip | | 700 | .023 | | .36 | .67 | | 1.03 | 1.51 |
| 4165 | Aluminum starter strip | | 700 | .023 | | .27 | .67 | | .94 | 1.41 |
| 4170 | Window casing, 2-1/2" wide, 3/4" pocket | | 510 | .031 | | 1.14 | .91 | | 2.05 | 2.79 |
| 4175 | Outside corner, woodgrain finish, 4" face, 3/4" pocket | | 700 | .023 | | 1.75 | .67 | | 2.42 | 3.05 |
| 4180 | 5/8" pocket | | 700 | .023 | | 1.67 | .67 | | 2.34 | 2.96 |
| 4185 | Smooth finish, 4" face, 3/4" pocket | | 700 | .023 | | 1.84 | .67 | | 2.51 | 3.14 |
| 4190 | 7/8" pocket | | 690 | .023 | | 1.78 | .67 | | 2.45 | 3.10 |
| 4195 | 1-1/4" pocket | | 700 | .023 | | 1.23 | .67 | | 1.90 | 2.47 |
| 4200 | Soffit and fascia, 1' overhang, solid | | 120 | .133 | | 3.37 | 3.88 | | 7.25 | 10.25 |
| 4205 | Vented | | 120 | .133 | | 3.37 | 3.88 | | 7.25 | 10.25 |
| 4207 | 18" overhang, solid | | 110 | .145 | | 3.98 | 4.23 | | 8.21 | 11.45 |
| 4208 | Vented | | 110 | .145 | | 3.98 | 4.23 | | 8.21 | 11.45 |
| 4210 | 2' overhang, solid | | 100 | .160 | | 4.58 | 4.66 | | 9.24 | 12.90 |
| 4215 | Vented | | 100 | .160 | | 4.58 | 4.66 | | 9.24 | 12.90 |
| 4217 | 3' overhang, solid | | 100 | .160 | | 5.80 | 4.66 | | 10.46 | 14.20 |
| 4218 | Vented | | 100 | .160 | | 5.80 | 4.66 | | 10.46 | 14.20 |
| 4220 | Colors for siding and soffits, add | | | | S.F. | .16 | | | .16 | .18 |
| 4225 | Colors for accessories and trim, add | | | | L.F. | .32 | | | .32 | .35 |

## 07 46 46 – Mineral-Fiber Cement Siding

### 07 46 46.10 Fiber Cement Siding

| | | Crew | Daily Output | Labor-Hours | Unit | Material | 2010 Bare Costs Labor | Equipment | Total | Total Incl O&P |
|---|---|---|---|---|---|---|---|---|---|---|
| 0010 | **FIBER CEMENT SIDING** | | | | | | | | | |
| 0020 | Lap siding, 5/16" thick, 6" wide, 4-3/4" exposure, smooth texture | 2 Carp | 415 | .039 | S.F. | 1.29 | 1.12 | | 2.41 | 3.30 |
| 0025 | Woodgrain texture | | 415 | .039 | | 1.29 | 1.12 | | 2.41 | 3.30 |
| 0030 | 7-1/2" wide, 6-1/4" exposure, smooth texture | | 425 | .038 | | 1.36 | 1.10 | | 2.46 | 3.34 |
| 0035 | Woodgrain texture | | 425 | .038 | | 1.36 | 1.10 | | 2.46 | 3.34 |
| 0040 | 8" wide, 6-3/4" exposure, smooth texture | | 425 | .038 | | 1.51 | 1.10 | | 2.61 | 3.50 |
| 0045 | Roughsawn texture | | 425 | .038 | | 1.51 | 1.10 | | 2.61 | 3.50 |
| 0050 | 9-1/2" wide, 8-1/4" exposure, smooth texture | | 440 | .036 | | 1.45 | 1.06 | | 2.51 | 3.38 |
| 0055 | Woodgrain texture | | 440 | .036 | | 1.45 | 1.06 | | 2.51 | 3.38 |
| 0060 | 12" wide, 10-3/8" exposure, smooth texture | | 455 | .035 | | 1.34 | 1.02 | | 2.36 | 3.19 |
| 0065 | Woodgrain texture | | 455 | .035 | | 1.34 | 1.02 | | 2.36 | 3.19 |
| 0070 | Panel siding, 5/16" thick, smooth texture | | 750 | .021 | | 1.12 | .62 | | 1.74 | 2.28 |
| 0075 | Stucco texture | | 750 | .021 | | 1.12 | .62 | | 1.74 | 2.28 |
| 0080 | Grooved woodgrain texture | | 750 | .021 | | 1.12 | .62 | | 1.74 | 2.28 |
| 0085 | V - grooved woodgrain texture | | 750 | .021 | | 1.12 | .62 | | 1.74 | 2.28 |
| 0090 | Wood starter strip | | 400 | .040 | L.F. | .53 | 1.16 | | 1.69 | 2.54 |

## 07 46 73 – Soffit

### 07 46 73.10 Soffit Options

| | | Crew | Daily Output | Labor-Hours | Unit | Material | 2010 Bare Costs Labor | Equipment | Total | Total Incl O&P |
|---|---|---|---|---|---|---|---|---|---|---|
| 0010 | **SOFFIT OPTIONS** | | | | | | | | | |
| 0012 | Aluminum, residential, .020" thick | 1 Carp | 210 | .038 | S.F. | 1.62 | 1.11 | | 2.73 | 3.65 |
| 0100 | Baked enamel on steel, 16 or 18 gauge | | 105 | .076 | | 5.35 | 2.22 | | 7.57 | 9.65 |
| 0300 | Polyvinyl chloride, white, solid | | 230 | .035 | | 1.09 | 1.01 | | 2.10 | 2.90 |

# 07 46 Siding

## 07 46 73 – Soffit

| 07 46 73.10 Soffit Options | Crew | Daily Output | Labor-Hours | Unit | Material | 2010 Bare Costs Labor | Equipment | Total | Total Incl O&P |
|---|---|---|---|---|---|---|---|---|---|
| 0400 | Perforated | 1 Carp | 230 | .035 | S.F. | 1.09 | 1.01 | | 2.10 | 2.90 |
| 0500 | For colors, add | | | ↓ | | | .13 | | .13 | .14 |

# 07 51 Built-Up Bituminous Roofing

## 07 51 13 – Built-Up Asphalt Roofing

### 07 51 13.10 Built-Up Roofing Components

| | | Crew | Daily Output | Labor-Hours | Unit | Material | Labor | Equipment | Total | Total Incl O&P |
|---|---|---|---|---|---|---|---|---|---|---|
| 0010 | **BUILT-UP ROOFING COMPONENTS** | | | | | | | | | |
| 0012 | Asphalt saturated felt, #30, 2 square per roll | 1 Rofc | 58 | .138 | Sq. | 11.95 | 3.37 | | 15.32 | 19.25 |
| 0200 | #15, 4 sq per roll, plain or perforated, not mopped | | 58 | .138 | | 5.90 | 3.37 | | 9.27 | 12.55 |
| 0250 | Perforated | | 58 | .138 | | 5.90 | 3.37 | | 9.27 | 12.55 |
| 0300 | Roll roofing, smooth, #65 | | 15 | .533 | | 9.65 | 13.05 | | 22.70 | 34 |
| 0500 | #90 | | 15 | .533 | | 34.50 | 13.05 | | 47.55 | 61.50 |
| 0520 | Mineralized | | 15 | .533 | | 34.50 | 13.05 | | 47.55 | 61.50 |
| 0540 | D.C. (Double coverage), 19" selvage edge | ↓ | 10 | .800 | ↓ | 44 | 19.55 | | 63.55 | 83 |
| 0580 | Adhesive (lap cement) | | | | Gal. | 4.79 | | | 4.79 | 5.25 |

### 07 51 13.20 Built-Up Roofing Systems

| | | Crew | Daily Output | Labor-Hours | Unit | Material | Labor | Equipment | Total | Total Incl O&P |
|---|---|---|---|---|---|---|---|---|---|---|
| 0010 | **BUILT-UP ROOFING SYSTEMS** | | | | | | | | | |
| 0120 | Asphalt flood coat with gravel/slag surfacing, not including | | | | | | | | | |
| 0140 | Insulation, flashing or wood nailers | | | | | | | | | |
| 0200 | Asphalt base sheet, 3 plies #15 asphalt felt, mopped | G-1 | 22 | 2.545 | Sq. | 94 | 58.50 | 21.50 | 174 | 232 |
| 0350 | On nailable decks | | 21 | 2.667 | | 98 | 61 | 22.50 | 181.50 | 243 |
| 0500 | 4 plies #15 asphalt felt, mopped | | 20 | 2.800 | | 130 | 64 | 24 | 218 | 285 |
| 0550 | On nailable decks | ↓ | 19 | 2.947 | ↓ | 115 | 67.50 | 25 | 207.50 | 277 |
| 2000 | Asphalt flood coat, smooth surface | | | | | | | | | |
| 2200 | Asphalt base sheet & 3 plies #15 asphalt felt, mopped | G-1 | 24 | 2.333 | Sq. | 100 | 53.50 | 19.85 | 173.35 | 229 |
| 2400 | On nailable decks | | 23 | 2.435 | | 92.50 | 56 | 20.50 | 169 | 226 |
| 2600 | 4 plies #15 asphalt felt, mopped | | 24 | 2.333 | | 117 | 53.50 | 19.85 | 190.35 | 248 |
| 2700 | On nailable decks | ↓ | 23 | 2.435 | ↓ | 110 | 56 | 20.50 | 186.50 | 245 |
| 4500 | Coal tar pitch with gravel/slag surfacing | | | | | | | | | |
| 4600 | 4 plies #15 tarred felt, mopped | G-1 | 21 | 2.667 | Sq. | 183 | 61 | 22.50 | 266.50 | 335 |
| 4800 | 3 plies glass fiber felt (type IV), mopped | " | 19 | 2.947 | " | 150 | 67.50 | 25 | 242.50 | 315 |

### 07 51 13.30 Cants

| | | Crew | Daily Output | Labor-Hours | Unit | Material | Labor | Equipment | Total | Total Incl O&P |
|---|---|---|---|---|---|---|---|---|---|---|
| 0010 | **CANTS** | | | | | | | | | |
| 0012 | Lumber, treated, 4" x 4" cut diagonally | 1 Rofc | 325 | .025 | L.F. | 1.52 | .60 | | 2.12 | 2.75 |
| 0100 | Foamglass | | 325 | .025 | | 2.23 | .60 | | 2.83 | 3.53 |
| 0300 | Mineral or fiber, trapezoidal, 1" x 4" x 48" | | 325 | .025 | | .19 | .60 | | .79 | 1.29 |
| 0400 | 1-1/2" x 5-5/8" x 48" | ↓ | 325 | .025 | ↓ | .31 | .60 | | .91 | 1.42 |

# 07 52 Modified Bituminous Membrane Roofing

## 07 52 13 – Atactic-Polypropylene-Modified Bituminous Membrane Roofing

### 07 52 13.10 APP Modified Bituminous Membrane

| | | | Crew | Daily Output | Labor-Hours | Unit | Material | Labor | Equipment | Total | Total Incl O&P |
|---|---|---|---|---|---|---|---|---|---|---|---|
| 0010 | **APP MODIFIED BITUMINOUS MEMBRANE** | R075213-30 | | | | | | | | | |
| 0020 | Base sheet, #15 glass fiber felt, nailed to deck | | 1 Rofc | 58 | .138 | Sq. | 7.45 | 3.37 | | 10.82 | 14.30 |
| 0030 | Spot mopped to deck | | G-1 | 295 | .190 | | 11.55 | 4.35 | 1.61 | 17.51 | 22.50 |
| 0040 | Fully mopped to deck | | " | 192 | .292 | | 16.50 | 6.70 | 2.48 | 25.68 | 33 |
| 0050 | #15 organic felt, nailed to deck | | 1 Rofc | 58 | .138 | | 6.80 | 3.37 | | 10.17 | 13.60 |
| 0060 | Spot mopped to deck | | G-1 | 295 | .190 | | 10.85 | 4.35 | 1.61 | 16.81 | 21.50 |
| 0070 | Fully mopped to deck | | " | 192 | .292 | ↓ | 15.85 | 6.70 | 2.48 | 25.03 | 32 |
| 2100 | APP mod., smooth surf. cap sheet, poly. reinf., torched, 160 mils | | G-5 | 2100 | .019 | S.F. | .48 | .43 | .09 | 1 | 1.40 |

# 07 52 Modified Bituminous Membrane Roofing

## 07 52 13 – Atactic-Polypropylene-Modified Bituminous Membrane Roofing

| 07 52 13.10 APP Modified Bituminous Membrane | Crew | Daily Output | Labor-Hours | Unit | Material | 2010 Bare Costs Labor | Equipment | Total | Total Incl O&P |
|---|---|---|---|---|---|---|---|---|---|
| 2150 | 170 mils | G-5 | 2100 | .019 | S.F. | .55 | .43 | .09 | 1.07 | 1.48 |
| 2200 | Granule surface cap sheet, poly. reinf., torched, 180 mils | | 2000 | .020 | | .59 | .45 | .09 | 1.13 | 1.55 |
| 2250 | Smooth surface flashing, torched, 160 mils | | 1260 | .032 | | .48 | .71 | .15 | 1.34 | 1.97 |
| 2300 | 170 mils | | 1260 | .032 | | .55 | .71 | .15 | 1.41 | 2.05 |
| 2350 | Granule surface flashing, torched, 180 mils | | 1260 | .032 | | .59 | .71 | .15 | 1.45 | 2.09 |
| 2400 | Fibrated aluminum coating | 1 Rofc | 3800 | .002 | | .10 | .05 | | .15 | .20 |

## 07 52 16 – Styrene-Butadiene-Styrene Modified Bituminous Membrane Roofing

### 07 52 16.10 SBS Modified Bituminous Membrane

| | | Crew | Daily Output | Labor-Hours | Unit | Material | Labor | Equipment | Total | Total Incl O&P |
|---|---|---|---|---|---|---|---|---|---|---|
| 0010 | **SBS MODIFIED BITUMINOUS MEMBRANE** | | | | | | | | | |
| 0080 | SBS modified, granule surf cap sheet, polyester rein., mopped | | | | | | | | | |
| 1500 | Glass fiber reinforced, mopped, 160 mils | G-1 | 2000 | .028 | S.F. | .49 | .64 | .24 | 1.37 | 1.96 |
| 1600 | Smooth surface cap sheet, mopped, 145 mils | | 2100 | .027 | | .49 | .61 | .23 | 1.33 | 1.89 |
| 1700 | Smooth surface flashing, 145 mils | | 1260 | .044 | | .49 | 1.02 | .38 | 1.89 | 2.79 |
| 1800 | 150 mils | | 1260 | .044 | | .48 | 1.02 | .38 | 1.88 | 2.78 |
| 1900 | Granular surface flashing, 150 mils | | 1260 | .044 | | .58 | 1.02 | .38 | 1.98 | 2.89 |
| 2000 | 160 mils | | 1260 | .044 | | .77 | 1.02 | .38 | 2.17 | 3.10 |

# 07 57 Coated Foamed Roofing

## 07 57 13 – Sprayed Polyurethane Foam Roofing

### 07 57 13.10 Sprayed Polyurethane Foam Roofing (S.P.F.)

| | | Crew | Daily Output | Labor-Hours | Unit | Material | Labor | Equipment | Total | Total Incl O&P |
|---|---|---|---|---|---|---|---|---|---|---|
| 0010 | **SPRAYED POLYURETHANE FOAM ROOFING (S.P.F.)** | | | | | | | | | |
| 0100 | Primer for metal substrate (when required) | G-2A | 3000 | .008 | S.F. | .42 | .17 | .23 | .82 | 1.01 |
| 0200 | Primer for non-metal substrate (when required) | | 3000 | .008 | | .16 | .17 | .23 | .56 | .73 |
| 0300 | Closed cell spray, polyurethane foam, 3 lbs per CF density, 1", R6.7 | | 15000 | .002 | | .55 | .03 | .05 | .63 | .72 |
| 0400 | 2", R13.4 | | 13125 | .002 | | 1.10 | .04 | .05 | 1.19 | 1.34 |
| 0500 | 3", R18.6 | | 11485 | .002 | | 1.66 | .04 | .06 | 1.76 | 1.97 |
| 0550 | 4", R24.8 | | 10080 | .002 | | 2.21 | .05 | .07 | 2.33 | 2.60 |
| 0700 | Spray-on silicone coating | | 2500 | .010 | | .92 | .21 | .28 | 1.41 | 1.67 |
| 0800 | Warranty 5-20 year manufacturer's | | | | | | | | | .15 |
| 0900 | Warranty 20 year, no dollar limit | | | | | | | | | .20 |

# 07 58 Roll Roofing

## 07 58 10 – Asphalt Roll Roofing

### 07 58 10.10 Roll Roofing

| | | Crew | Daily Output | Labor-Hours | Unit | Material | Labor | Equipment | Total | Total Incl O&P |
|---|---|---|---|---|---|---|---|---|---|---|
| 0010 | **ROLL ROOFING** | | | | | | | | | |
| 0100 | Asphalt, mineral surface | | | | | | | | | |
| 0200 | 1 ply #15 organic felt, 1 ply mineral surfaced | | | | | | | | | |
| 0300 | Selvage roofing, lap 19", nailed & mopped | G-1 | 27 | 2.074 | Sq. | 64 | 47.50 | 17.65 | 129.15 | 175 |
| 0400 | 3 plies glass fiber felt (type IV), 1 ply mineral surfaced | | | | | | | | | |
| 0500 | Selvage roofing, lapped 19", mopped | G-1 | 25 | 2.240 | Sq. | 103 | 51.50 | 19.05 | 173.55 | 228 |
| 0600 | Coated glass fiber base sheet, 2 plies of glass fiber | | | | | | | | | |
| 0700 | Felt (type IV), 1 ply mineral surfaced selvage | | | | | | | | | |
| 0800 | Roofing, lapped 19", mopped | G-1 | 25 | 2.240 | Sq. | 111 | 51.50 | 19.05 | 181.55 | 236 |
| 0900 | On nailable decks | " | 24 | 2.333 | " | 101 | 53.50 | 19.85 | 174.35 | 230 |
| 1000 | 3 plies glass fiber felt (type III), 1 ply mineral surfaced | | | | | | | | | |
| 1100 | Selvage roofing, lapped 19", mopped | G-1 | 25 | 2.240 | Sq. | 103 | 51.50 | 19.05 | 173.55 | 228 |

# 07 61 Sheet Metal Roofing

## 07 61 13 – Standing Seam Sheet Metal Roofing

| 07 61 13.10 Standing Seam Sheet Metal Roofing, Field Fab. | Crew | Daily Output | Labor-Hours | Unit | Material | 2010 Bare Costs Labor | Equipment | Total | Total Incl O&P |
|---|---|---|---|---|---|---|---|---|---|
| 0010 **STANDING SEAM SHEET METAL ROOFING, FIELD FABRICATED** | | | | | | | | | |
| 0400 Copper standing seam roofing, over 10 squares, 16 oz, 125 lb per sq | 1 Shee | 1.30 | 6.154 | Sq. | 1,075 | 199 | | 1,274 | 1,525 |
| 0600 18 oz, 140 lb per sq | " | 1.20 | 6.667 | | 1,200 | 216 | | 1,416 | 1,650 |
| 1200 For abnormal conditions or small areas, add | | | | | 25% | 100% | | | |
| 1300 For lead-coated copper, add | | | | | 25% | | | | |

## 07 61 16 – Batten Seam Sheet Metal Roofing

### 07 61 16.10 Batten Seam Sheet Metal Roofing, Field Fabricated

| | Crew | Daily Output | Labor-Hours | Unit | Material | Labor | Equipment | Total | Total Incl O&P |
|---|---|---|---|---|---|---|---|---|---|
| 0009 **BATTEN SEAM SHEET METAL ROOFING, FIELD FABRICATED** | | | | | | | | | |
| 0012 Copper batten seam roofing, over 10 sq, 16 oz, 130 lb per sq | 1 Shee | 1.10 | 7.273 | Sq. | 1,075 | 236 | | 1,311 | 1,600 |
| 0100 Zinc/copper alloy batten seam roofing, .020 thick | | 1.20 | 6.667 | | 1,075 | 216 | | 1,291 | 1,550 |
| 0200 Copper roofing, batten seam, over 10 sq, 18 oz, 145 lb per sq | | 1 | 8 | | 1,200 | 259 | | 1,459 | 1,725 |
| 0800 Zinc, copper alloy roofing, batten seam, .027" thick | | 1.15 | 6.957 | | 1,550 | 225 | | 1,775 | 2,075 |
| 0900 .032" thick | | 1.10 | 7.273 | | 1,825 | 236 | | 2,061 | 2,400 |
| 1000 .040" thick | | 1.05 | 7.619 | | 2,200 | 247 | | 2,447 | 2,800 |

## 07 61 19 – Flat Seam Sheet Metal Roofing

### 07 61 19.10 Flat Seam Sheet Metal Roofing, Field Fabricated

| | Crew | Daily Output | Labor-Hours | Unit | Material | Labor | Equipment | Total | Total Incl O&P |
|---|---|---|---|---|---|---|---|---|---|
| 0010 **FLAT SEAM SHEET METAL ROOFING, FIELD FABRICATED** | | | | | | | | | |
| 0900 Copper flat seam roofing, over 10 squares, 16 oz, 115 lb per sq | 1 Shee | 1.20 | 6.667 | Sq. | 1,075 | 216 | | 1,291 | 1,550 |

# 07 62 Sheet Metal Flashing and Trim

## 07 62 10 – Sheet Metal Trim

### 07 62 10.10 Sheet Metal Cladding

| | Crew | Daily Output | Labor-Hours | Unit | Material | Labor | Equipment | Total | Total Incl O&P |
|---|---|---|---|---|---|---|---|---|---|
| 0010 **SHEET METAL CLADDING** | | | | | | | | | |
| 0100 Aluminum, up to 6 bends, .032" thick, window casing | 1 Carp | 180 | .044 | S.F. | .87 | 1.29 | | 2.16 | 3.14 |
| 0200 Window sill | | 72 | .111 | L.F. | .87 | 3.23 | | 4.10 | 6.40 |
| 0300 Door casing | | 180 | .044 | S.F. | .87 | 1.29 | | 2.16 | 3.14 |
| 0400 Fascia | | 250 | .032 | | .87 | .93 | | 1.80 | 2.53 |
| 0500 Rake trim | | 225 | .036 | | .87 | 1.03 | | 1.90 | 2.70 |
| 0700 .024" thick, window casing | | 180 | .044 | | 1.55 | 1.29 | | 2.84 | 3.89 |
| 0800 Window sill | | 72 | .111 | L.F. | 1.55 | 3.23 | | 4.78 | 7.15 |
| 0900 Door casing | | 180 | .044 | S.F. | 1.55 | 1.29 | | 2.84 | 3.89 |
| 1000 Fascia | | 250 | .032 | | 1.55 | .93 | | 2.48 | 3.28 |
| 1100 Rake trim | | 225 | .036 | | 1.55 | 1.03 | | 2.58 | 3.45 |
| 1200 Vinyl coated aluminum, up to 6 bends, window casing | | 180 | .044 | | 1.03 | 1.29 | | 2.32 | 3.31 |
| 1300 Window sill | | 72 | .111 | L.F. | 1.03 | 3.23 | | 4.26 | 6.60 |
| 1400 Door casing | | 180 | .044 | S.F. | 1.03 | 1.29 | | 2.32 | 3.31 |
| 1500 Fascia | | 250 | .032 | | 1.03 | .93 | | 1.96 | 2.70 |
| 1600 Rake trim | | 225 | .036 | | 1.03 | 1.03 | | 2.06 | 2.87 |

# 07 65 Flexible Flashing

## 07 65 10 – Sheet Metal Flashing

| 07 65 10.10 Sheet Metal Flashing and Counter Flashing | Crew | Daily Output | Labor-Hours | Unit | Material | 2010 Bare Costs Labor | Equipment | Total | Total Incl O&P |
|---|---|---|---|---|---|---|---|---|---|
| 0010 **SHEET METAL FLASHING AND COUNTER FLASHING** | | | | | | | | | |
| 0011 Including up to 4 bends | | | | | | | | | |
| 0020 Aluminum, mill finish, .013" thick | 1 Rofc | 145 | .055 | S.F. | .67 | 1.35 | | 2.02 | 3.17 |
| 0030 .016" thick | | 145 | .055 | | .79 | 1.35 | | 2.14 | 3.30 |
| 0060 .019" thick | | 145 | .055 | | 1.02 | 1.35 | | 2.37 | 3.55 |
| 0100 .032" thick | | 145 | .055 | | 1.48 | 1.35 | | 2.83 | 4.06 |
| 0200 .040" thick | | 145 | .055 | | 2.21 | 1.35 | | 3.56 | 4.86 |
| 0300 .050" thick | | 145 | .055 | | 2.52 | 1.35 | | 3.87 | 5.20 |
| 0325 Mill finish 5" x 7" step flashing, .016" thick | | 1920 | .004 | Ea. | .16 | .10 | | .26 | .36 |
| 0350 Mill finish 12" x 12" step flashing, .016" thick | | 1600 | .005 | " | .61 | .12 | | .73 | .89 |
| 0400 Painted finish, add | | | | S.F. | .37 | | | .37 | .41 |
| 1600 Copper, 16 oz, sheets, under 1000 lbs. | 1 Rofc | 115 | .070 | | 7.55 | 1.70 | | 9.25 | 11.35 |
| 1900 20 oz sheets, under 1000 lbs. | | 110 | .073 | | 9.05 | 1.78 | | 10.83 | 13.15 |
| 2200 24 oz sheets, under 1000 lbs. | | 105 | .076 | | 11.30 | 1.86 | | 13.16 | 15.80 |
| 2500 32 oz sheets, under 1000 lbs. | | 100 | .080 | | 14.10 | 1.96 | | 16.06 | 19 |
| 2700 W shape for valleys, 16 oz, 24" wide | | 100 | .080 | L.F. | 13.50 | 1.96 | | 15.46 | 18.35 |
| 5800 Lead, 2.5 lb. per SF, up to 12" wide | | 135 | .059 | S.F. | 4.55 | 1.45 | | 6 | 7.60 |
| 5900 Over 12" wide | | 135 | .059 | | 4.55 | 1.45 | | 6 | 7.60 |
| 8650 Copper, 16 oz | | 100 | .080 | | 6 | 1.96 | | 7.96 | 10.10 |
| 8900 Stainless steel sheets, 32 ga, .010" thick | | 155 | .052 | | 3.79 | 1.26 | | 5.05 | 6.45 |
| 9000 28 ga, .015" thick | | 155 | .052 | | 4.70 | 1.26 | | 5.96 | 7.40 |
| 9100 26 ga, .018" thick | | 155 | .052 | | 5.70 | 1.26 | | 6.96 | 8.50 |
| 9200 24 ga, .025" thick | | 155 | .052 | | 7.40 | 1.26 | | 8.66 | 10.40 |
| 9290 For mechanically keyed flashing, add | | | | | 40% | | | | |
| 9320 Steel sheets, galvanized, 20 gauge | 1 Rofc | 130 | .062 | S.F. | 1.19 | 1.50 | | 2.69 | 4.02 |
| 9340 30 gauge | | 160 | .050 | | .50 | 1.22 | | 1.72 | 2.75 |
| 9400 Terne coated stainless steel, .015" thick, 28 ga | | 155 | .052 | | 7.35 | 1.26 | | 8.61 | 10.35 |
| 9500 .018" thick, 26 ga | | 155 | .052 | | 8.30 | 1.26 | | 9.56 | 11.35 |
| 9600 Zinc and copper alloy (brass), .020" thick | | 155 | .052 | | 5.15 | 1.26 | | 6.41 | 7.90 |
| 9700 .027" thick | | 155 | .052 | | 6.90 | 1.26 | | 8.16 | 9.85 |
| 9800 .032" thick | | 155 | .052 | | 8.05 | 1.26 | | 9.31 | 11.10 |
| 9900 .040" thick | | 155 | .052 | | 9.85 | 1.26 | | 11.11 | 13.05 |

## 07 65 13 – Laminated Sheet Flashing

### 07 65 13.10 Laminated Sheet Flashing

| | Crew | Daily Output | Labor-Hours | Unit | Material | 2010 Bare Costs Labor | Equipment | Total | Total Incl O&P |
|---|---|---|---|---|---|---|---|---|---|
| 0010 **LAMINATED SHEET FLASHING**, Including up to 4 bends | | | | | | | | | |
| 2800 Copper, paperbacked 1 side, 2 oz | 1 Rofc | 330 | .024 | S.F. | 1.42 | .59 | | 2.01 | 2.63 |
| 2900 3 oz | | 330 | .024 | | 1.85 | .59 | | 2.44 | 3.11 |
| 3100 Paperbacked 2 sides, 2 oz | | 330 | .024 | | 1.43 | .59 | | 2.02 | 2.64 |
| 3150 3 oz | | 330 | .024 | | 1.84 | .59 | | 2.43 | 3.09 |
| 3200 5 oz | | 330 | .024 | | 2.76 | .59 | | 3.35 | 4.11 |
| 6100 Lead-coated copper, fabric-backed, 2 oz | | 330 | .024 | | 2.42 | .59 | | 3.01 | 3.73 |
| 6200 5 oz | | 330 | .024 | | 2.78 | .59 | | 3.37 | 4.13 |
| 6400 Mastic-backed 2 sides, 2 oz | | 330 | .024 | | 1.89 | .59 | | 2.48 | 3.15 |
| 6500 5 oz | | 330 | .024 | | 2.34 | .59 | | 2.93 | 3.64 |
| 6700 Paperbacked 1 side, 2 oz | | 330 | .024 | | 1.63 | .59 | | 2.22 | 2.86 |
| 6800 3 oz | | 330 | .024 | | 1.92 | .59 | | 2.51 | 3.18 |
| 7000 Paperbacked 2 sides, 2 oz | | 330 | .024 | | 1.69 | .59 | | 2.28 | 2.93 |
| 7100 5 oz | | 330 | .024 | | 2.75 | .59 | | 3.34 | 4.10 |
| 8550 3 ply copper and fabric, 3 oz | | 155 | .052 | | 2.31 | 1.26 | | 3.57 | 4.81 |
| 8600 7 oz | | 155 | .052 | | 3.25 | 1.26 | | 4.51 | 5.85 |
| 8700 Lead on copper and fabric, 5 oz | | 155 | .052 | | 2.78 | 1.26 | | 4.04 | 5.35 |
| 8800 7 oz | | 155 | .052 | | 5.25 | 1.26 | | 6.51 | 8.05 |

# 07 65 Flexible Flashing

## 07 65 13 – Laminated Sheet Flashing

| | 07 65 13.10 Laminated Sheet Flashing | Crew | Daily Output | Labor-Hours | Unit | Material | 2010 Bare Costs Labor | Equipment | Total | Total Incl O&P |
|---|---|---|---|---|---|---|---|---|---|---|
| 9300 | Stainless steel, paperbacked 2 sides, .005" thick | 1 Rofc | 330 | .024 | S.F. | 3.34 | .59 | | 3.93 | 4.74 |

# 07 71 Roof Specialties

## 07 71 19 – Manufactured Gravel Stops and Fascias

### 07 71 19.10 Gravel Stop

| | | Crew | Daily Output | Labor-Hours | Unit | Material | 2010 Bare Costs Labor | Equipment | Total | Total Incl O&P |
|---|---|---|---|---|---|---|---|---|---|---|
| 0010 | **GRAVEL STOP** | | | | | | | | | |
| 0020 | Aluminum, .050" thick, 4" face height, mill finish | 1 Shee | 145 | .055 | L.F. | 6.10 | 1.79 | | 7.89 | 9.70 |
| 0080 | Duranodic finish | | 145 | .055 | | 5.90 | 1.79 | | 7.69 | 9.45 |
| 0100 | Painted | | 145 | .055 | | 6.85 | 1.79 | | 8.64 | 10.45 |
| 1350 | Galv steel, 24 ga., 4" leg, plain, with continuous cleat, 4" face | | 145 | .055 | | 2.41 | 1.79 | | 4.20 | 5.60 |
| 1500 | Polyvinyl chloride, 6" face height | | 135 | .059 | | 4.45 | 1.92 | | 6.37 | 8.10 |
| 1800 | Stainless steel, 24 ga., 6" face height | | 135 | .059 | | 11.45 | 1.92 | | 13.37 | 15.80 |

### 07 71 19.30 Fascia

| | | Crew | Daily Output | Labor-Hours | Unit | Material | 2010 Bare Costs Labor | Equipment | Total | Total Incl O&P |
|---|---|---|---|---|---|---|---|---|---|---|
| 0010 | **FASCIA** | | | | | | | | | |
| 0100 | Aluminum, reverse board and batten, .032" thick, colored, no furring incl | 1 Shee | 145 | .055 | S.F. | 5.95 | 1.79 | | 7.74 | 9.50 |
| 0200 | Residential type, aluminum | 1 Carp | 200 | .040 | L.F. | 1.21 | 1.16 | | 2.37 | 3.29 |
| 0300 | Steel, galv and enameled, stock, no furring, long panels | 1 Shee | 145 | .055 | S.F. | 4 | 1.79 | | 5.79 | 7.35 |
| 0600 | Short panels | " | 115 | .070 | " | 5.45 | 2.25 | | 7.70 | 9.75 |

## 07 71 23 – Manufactured Gutters and Downspouts

### 07 71 23.10 Downspouts

| | | Crew | Daily Output | Labor-Hours | Unit | Material | 2010 Bare Costs Labor | Equipment | Total | Total Incl O&P |
|---|---|---|---|---|---|---|---|---|---|---|
| 0010 | **DOWNSPOUTS** | | | | | | | | | |
| 0020 | Aluminum 2" x 3", .020" thick, embossed | 1 Shee | 190 | .042 | L.F. | 1.04 | 1.36 | | 2.40 | 3.40 |
| 0100 | Enameled | | 190 | .042 | | 1.59 | 1.36 | | 2.95 | 4.01 |
| 0300 | Enameled, .024" thick, 2" x 3" | | 180 | .044 | | 1.84 | 1.44 | | 3.28 | 4.40 |
| 0400 | 3" x 4" | | 140 | .057 | | 2.16 | 1.85 | | 4.01 | 5.45 |
| 0600 | Round, corrugated aluminum, 3" diameter, .020" thick | | 190 | .042 | | 1.42 | 1.36 | | 2.78 | 3.82 |
| 0700 | 4" diameter, .025" thick | | 140 | .057 | | 2.39 | 1.85 | | 4.24 | 5.70 |
| 0900 | Wire strainer, round, 2" diameter | | 155 | .052 | Ea. | 3.32 | 1.67 | | 4.99 | 6.40 |
| 1000 | 4" diameter | | 155 | .052 | | 6.10 | 1.67 | | 7.77 | 9.50 |
| 1200 | Rectangular, perforated, 2" x 3" | | 145 | .055 | | 2.30 | 1.79 | | 4.09 | 5.50 |
| 1300 | 3" x 4" | | 145 | .055 | | 3.32 | 1.79 | | 5.11 | 6.60 |
| 1500 | Copper, round, 16 oz., stock, 2" diameter | | 190 | .042 | L.F. | 6.65 | 1.36 | | 8.01 | 9.60 |
| 1600 | 3" diameter | | 190 | .042 | | 6.25 | 1.36 | | 7.61 | 9.10 |
| 1800 | 4" diameter | | 145 | .055 | | 9 | 1.79 | | 10.79 | 12.85 |
| 1900 | 5" diameter | | 130 | .062 | | 14.20 | 1.99 | | 16.19 | 18.90 |
| 2100 | Rectangular, corrugated copper, stock, 2" x 3" | | 190 | .042 | | 7.35 | 1.36 | | 8.71 | 10.35 |
| 2200 | 3" x 4" | | 145 | .055 | | 8.60 | 1.79 | | 10.39 | 12.40 |
| 2400 | Rectangular, plain copper, stock, 2" x 3" | | 190 | .042 | | 7 | 1.36 | | 8.36 | 9.95 |
| 2500 | 3" x 4" | | 145 | .055 | | 9.10 | 1.79 | | 10.89 | 12.95 |
| 2700 | Wire strainers, rectangular, 2" x 3" | | 145 | .055 | Ea. | 5.50 | 1.79 | | 7.29 | 9 |
| 2800 | 3" x 4" | | 145 | .055 | | 6.60 | 1.79 | | 8.39 | 10.20 |
| 3000 | Round, 2" diameter | | 145 | .055 | | 6.90 | 1.79 | | 8.69 | 10.55 |
| 3100 | 3" diameter | | 145 | .055 | | 6.90 | 1.79 | | 8.69 | 10.55 |
| 3300 | 4" diameter | | 145 | .055 | | 12.70 | 1.79 | | 14.49 | 16.95 |
| 3400 | 5" diameter | | 115 | .070 | | 16.90 | 2.25 | | 19.15 | 22.50 |
| 3600 | Lead-coated copper, round, stock, 2" diameter | | 190 | .042 | L.F. | 22.50 | 1.36 | | 23.86 | 27 |
| 3700 | 3" diameter | | 190 | .042 | | 22 | 1.36 | | 23.36 | 26.50 |
| 3900 | 4" diameter | | 145 | .055 | | 23.50 | 1.79 | | 25.29 | 28.50 |
| 4300 | Rectangular, corrugated, stock, 2" x 3" | | 190 | .042 | | 12.70 | 1.36 | | 14.06 | 16.20 |
| 4500 | Plain, stock, 2" x 3" | | 190 | .042 | | 11 | 1.36 | | 12.36 | 14.35 |

# 07 71 Roof Specialties

## 07 71 23 - Manufactured Gutters and Downspouts

### 07 71 23.10 Downspouts

| | | Crew | Daily Output | Labor-Hours | Unit | Material | 2010 Bare Costs Labor | Equipment | Total | Total Incl O&P |
|---|---|---|---|---|---|---|---|---|---|---|
| 4600 | 3" x 4" | 1 Shee | 145 | .055 | L.F. | 12 | 1.79 | | 13.79 | 16.15 |
| 4800 | Steel, galvanized, round, corrugated, 2" or 3" diameter, 28 gauge | | 190 | .042 | | 2.24 | 1.36 | | 3.60 | 4.72 |
| 4900 | 4" diameter, 28 gauge | | 145 | .055 | | 2.73 | 1.79 | | 4.52 | 5.95 |
| 5700 | Rectangular, corrugated, 28 gauge, 2" x 3" | | 190 | .042 | | 1.28 | 1.36 | | 2.64 | 3.67 |
| 5800 | 3" x 4" | | 145 | .055 | | 2.16 | 1.79 | | 3.95 | 5.35 |
| 6000 | Rectangular, plain, 28 gauge, galvanized, 2" x 3" | | 190 | .042 | | 1.28 | 1.36 | | 2.64 | 3.67 |
| 6100 | 3" x 4" | | 145 | .055 | | 2.64 | 1.79 | | 4.43 | 5.85 |
| 6300 | Epoxy painted, 24 gauge, corrugated, 2" x 3" | | 190 | .042 | | 2 | 1.36 | | 3.36 | 4.46 |
| 6400 | 3" x 4" | | 145 | .055 | | 2.50 | 1.79 | | 4.29 | 5.70 |
| 6600 | Wire strainers, rectangular, 2" x 3" | | 145 | .055 | Ea. | 12 | 1.79 | | 13.79 | 16.15 |
| 6700 | 3" x 4" | | 145 | .055 | | 14 | 1.79 | | 15.79 | 18.35 |
| 6900 | Round strainers, 2" or 3" diameter | | 145 | .055 | | 3 | 1.79 | | 4.79 | 6.25 |
| 7000 | 4" diameter | | 145 | .055 | | 5.60 | 1.79 | | 7.39 | 9.10 |
| 8200 | Vinyl, rectangular, 2" x 3" | | 210 | .038 | L.F. | 1.29 | 1.23 | | 2.52 | 3.46 |
| 8300 | Round, 2-1/2" | | 220 | .036 | " | 1.28 | 1.18 | | 2.46 | 3.36 |

### 07 71 23.20 Downspout Elbows

| | | Crew | Daily Output | Labor-Hours | Unit | Material | 2010 Bare Costs Labor | Equipment | Total | Total Incl O&P |
|---|---|---|---|---|---|---|---|---|---|---|
| 0010 | **DOWNSPOUT ELBOWS** | | | | | | | | | |
| 0020 | Aluminum, 2" x 3", embossed | 1 Shee | 100 | .080 | Ea. | 1.31 | 2.59 | | 3.90 | 5.75 |
| 0100 | Enameled | | 100 | .080 | | 1.31 | 2.59 | | 3.90 | 5.75 |
| 0200 | 3" x 4", .025" thick, embossed | | 100 | .080 | | 3.99 | 2.59 | | 6.58 | 8.70 |
| 0300 | Enameled | | 100 | .080 | | 5.15 | 2.59 | | 7.74 | 9.95 |
| 0400 | Round corrugated, 3", embossed, .020" thick | | 100 | .080 | | 2.27 | 2.59 | | 4.86 | 6.80 |
| 0500 | 4", .025" thick | | 100 | .080 | | 6.50 | 2.59 | | 9.09 | 11.45 |
| 0600 | Copper, 16 oz. round, 2" diameter | | 100 | .080 | | 13.40 | 2.59 | | 15.99 | 19.05 |
| 0700 | 3" diameter | | 100 | .080 | | 11.60 | 2.59 | | 14.19 | 17.05 |
| 0800 | 4" diameter | | 100 | .080 | | 16.95 | 2.59 | | 19.54 | 23 |
| 1000 | 2" x 3" corrugated | | 100 | .080 | | 6.50 | 2.59 | | 9.09 | 11.45 |
| 1100 | 3" x 4" corrugated | | 100 | .080 | | 13.15 | 2.59 | | 15.74 | 18.75 |
| 1300 | Vinyl, 2-1/2" diameter, 45° or 75° | | 100 | .080 | | 3.88 | 2.59 | | 6.47 | 8.55 |
| 1400 | Tee Y junction | | 75 | .107 | | 12.90 | 3.46 | | 16.36 | 19.85 |

### 07 71 23.30 Gutters

| | | Crew | Daily Output | Labor-Hours | Unit | Material | 2010 Bare Costs Labor | Equipment | Total | Total Incl O&P |
|---|---|---|---|---|---|---|---|---|---|---|
| 0010 | **GUTTERS** | | | | | | | | | |
| 0012 | Aluminum, stock units, 5" K type, .027" thick, plain | 1 Shee | 120 | .067 | L.F. | 2.75 | 2.16 | | 4.91 | 6.60 |
| 0020 | Inside corner | | 25 | .320 | Ea. | 7.45 | 10.35 | | 17.80 | 25.50 |
| 0030 | Outside corner | | 25 | .320 | " | 7.45 | 10.35 | | 17.80 | 25.50 |
| 0100 | Enameled | | 120 | .067 | L.F. | 2.44 | 2.16 | | 4.60 | 6.25 |
| 0110 | Inside corner | | 25 | .320 | Ea. | 7.45 | 10.35 | | 17.80 | 25.50 |
| 0120 | Outside corner | | 25 | .320 | " | 7.45 | 10.35 | | 17.80 | 25.50 |
| 0300 | 5" K type type, .032" thick, plain | | 120 | .067 | L.F. | 2.74 | 2.16 | | 4.90 | 6.60 |
| 0310 | Inside corner | | 25 | .320 | Ea. | 7.45 | 10.35 | | 17.80 | 25.50 |
| 0320 | Outside corner | | 25 | .320 | " | 7.45 | 10.35 | | 17.80 | 25.50 |
| 0400 | Enameled | | 120 | .067 | L.F. | 2.90 | 2.16 | | 5.06 | 6.75 |
| 0410 | Inside corner | | 25 | .320 | Ea. | 7.45 | 10.35 | | 17.80 | 25.50 |
| 0420 | Outside corner | | 25 | .320 | " | 7.45 | 10.35 | | 17.80 | 25.50 |
| 0700 | Copper, half round, 16 oz, stock units, 4" wide | | 120 | .067 | L.F. | 6.95 | 2.16 | | 9.11 | 11.20 |
| 0900 | 5" wide | | 120 | .067 | | 7.35 | 2.16 | | 9.51 | 11.60 |
| 1000 | 6" wide | | 115 | .070 | | 9.95 | 2.25 | | 12.20 | 14.70 |
| 1200 | K type, 16 oz, stock, 4" wide | | 120 | .067 | | 6.80 | 2.16 | | 8.96 | 11.05 |
| 1300 | 5" wide | | 120 | .067 | | 8.20 | 2.16 | | 10.36 | 12.55 |
| 1500 | Lead coated copper, half round, stock, 4" wide | | 120 | .067 | | 9.45 | 2.16 | | 11.61 | 13.95 |
| 1600 | 6" wide | | 115 | .070 | | 15.60 | 2.25 | | 17.85 | 21 |
| 1800 | K type, stock, 4" wide | | 120 | .067 | | 11.35 | 2.16 | | 13.51 | 16.05 |

# 07 71 Roof Specialties

## 07 71 23 – Manufactured Gutters and Downspouts

### 07 71 23.30 Gutters

| | | Crew | Daily Output | Labor-Hours | Unit | Material | 2010 Bare Costs Labor | Equipment | Total | Total Incl O&P |
|---|---|---|---|---|---|---|---|---|---|---|
| 1900 | 5" wide | 1 Shee | 120 | .067 | L.F. | 16.35 | 2.16 | | 18.51 | 21.50 |
| 2100 | Stainless steel, half round or box, stock, 4" wide | | 120 | .067 | | 5.90 | 2.16 | | 8.06 | 10 |
| 2200 | 5" wide | | 120 | .067 | | 6.35 | 2.16 | | 8.51 | 10.50 |
| 2400 | Steel, galv, half round or box, 28 ga, 5" wide, plain | | 120 | .067 | | 1.46 | 2.16 | | 3.62 | 5.20 |
| 2500 | Enameled | | 120 | .067 | | 1.51 | 2.16 | | 3.67 | 5.25 |
| 2700 | 26 ga, stock, 5" wide | | 120 | .067 | | 1.59 | 2.16 | | 3.75 | 5.30 |
| 2800 | 6" wide | | 120 | .067 | | 2.99 | 2.16 | | 5.15 | 6.85 |
| 3000 | Vinyl, O.G., 4" wide | 1 Carp | 110 | .073 | | 1.08 | 2.12 | | 3.20 | 4.75 |
| 3100 | 5" wide | | 110 | .073 | | 1.38 | 2.12 | | 3.50 | 5.10 |
| 3200 | 4" half round, stock units | | 110 | .073 | | 1.08 | 2.12 | | 3.20 | 4.75 |
| 3250 | Joint connectors | | | | Ea. | 2.88 | | | 2.88 | 3.17 |
| 3300 | Wood, clear treated cedar, fir or hemlock, 3" x 4" | 1 Carp | 100 | .080 | L.F. | 7.95 | 2.33 | | 10.28 | 12.65 |
| 3400 | 4" x 5" | " | 100 | .080 | " | 9.45 | 2.33 | | 11.78 | 14.30 |

### 07 71 23.35 Gutter Guard

| | | Crew | Daily Output | Labor-Hours | Unit | Material | 2010 Bare Costs Labor | Equipment | Total | Total Incl O&P |
|---|---|---|---|---|---|---|---|---|---|---|
| 0010 | **GUTTER GUARD** | | | | | | | | | |
| 0020 | 6" wide strip, aluminum mesh | 1 Carp | 500 | .016 | L.F. | 2.18 | .47 | | 2.65 | 3.18 |
| 0100 | Vinyl mesh | " | 500 | .016 | " | 2.58 | .47 | | 3.05 | 3.62 |

## 07 71 43 – Drip Edge

### 07 71 43.10 Drip Edge, Rake Edge, Ice Belts

| | | Crew | Daily Output | Labor-Hours | Unit | Material | 2010 Bare Costs Labor | Equipment | Total | Total Incl O&P |
|---|---|---|---|---|---|---|---|---|---|---|
| 0010 | **DRIP EDGE, RAKE EDGE, ICE BELTS** | | | | | | | | | |
| 0020 | Aluminum, .016" thick, 5" wide, mill finish | 1 Carp | 400 | .020 | L.F. | .38 | .58 | | .96 | 1.40 |
| 0100 | White finish | | 400 | .020 | | .38 | .58 | | .96 | 1.40 |
| 0200 | 8" wide, mill finish | | 400 | .020 | | .46 | .58 | | 1.04 | 1.49 |
| 0300 | Ice belt, 28" wide, mill finish | | 100 | .080 | | 3.85 | 2.33 | | 6.18 | 8.15 |
| 0310 | Vented, mill finish | | 400 | .020 | | 2.76 | .58 | | 3.34 | 4.02 |
| 0320 | Painted finish | | 400 | .020 | | 2.86 | .58 | | 3.44 | 4.13 |
| 0400 | Galvanized, 5" wide | | 400 | .020 | | .48 | .58 | | 1.06 | 1.51 |
| 0500 | 8" wide, mill finish | | 400 | .020 | | .69 | .58 | | 1.27 | 1.74 |
| 0510 | Rake edge, aluminum, 1-1/2" x 1-1/2" | | 400 | .020 | | .26 | .58 | | .84 | 1.27 |
| 0520 | 3-1/2" x 1-1/2" | | 400 | .020 | | .43 | .58 | | 1.01 | 1.45 |

# 07 72 Roof Accessories

## 07 72 23 – Relief Vents

### 07 72 23.20 Vents

| | | Crew | Daily Output | Labor-Hours | Unit | Material | 2010 Bare Costs Labor | Equipment | Total | Total Incl O&P |
|---|---|---|---|---|---|---|---|---|---|---|
| 0010 | **VENTS** | | | | | | | | | |
| 0100 | Soffit or eave, aluminum, mill finish, strips, 2-1/2" wide | 1 Carp | 200 | .040 | L.F. | .40 | 1.16 | | 1.56 | 2.40 |
| 0200 | 3" wide | | 200 | .040 | | .44 | 1.16 | | 1.60 | 2.44 |
| 0300 | Enamel finish, 3" wide | | 200 | .040 | | .52 | 1.16 | | 1.68 | 2.53 |
| 0400 | Mill finish, rectangular, 4" x 16" | | 72 | .111 | Ea. | 1.43 | 3.23 | | 4.66 | 7 |
| 0500 | 8" x 16" | | 72 | .111 | | 2.15 | 3.23 | | 5.38 | 7.80 |
| 2420 | Roof ventilator | Q-9 | 16 | 1 | | 50.50 | 29 | | 79.50 | 104 |

## 07 72 26 – Ridge Vents

### 07 72 26.10 Ridge Vents and Accessories

| | | Crew | Daily Output | Labor-Hours | Unit | Material | 2010 Bare Costs Labor | Equipment | Total | Total Incl O&P |
|---|---|---|---|---|---|---|---|---|---|---|
| 0010 | **RIDGE VENTS AND ACCESSORIES** | | | | | | | | | |
| 0100 | Aluminum strips, mill finish | 1 Rofc | 160 | .050 | L.F. | 2.62 | 1.22 | | 3.84 | 5.10 |
| 0150 | Painted finish | | 160 | .050 | " | 3.74 | 1.22 | | 4.96 | 6.30 |
| 0200 | Connectors | | 48 | .167 | Ea. | 3.68 | 4.08 | | 7.76 | 11.40 |
| 0300 | End caps | | 48 | .167 | " | 1.37 | 4.08 | | 5.45 | 8.85 |
| 0400 | Galvanized strips | | 160 | .050 | L.F. | 2.26 | 1.22 | | 3.48 | 4.69 |
| 0430 | Molded polyethylene, shingles not included | | 160 | .050 | " | 3.05 | 1.22 | | 4.27 | 5.55 |

# 07 72 Roof Accessories

## 07 72 26 – Ridge Vents

| 07 72 26.10 Ridge Vents and Accessories | Crew | Daily Output | Labor-Hours | Unit | Material | 2010 Bare Costs Labor | Equipment | Total | Total Incl O&P |
|---|---|---|---|---|---|---|---|---|---|
| 0440 | End plugs | 1 Rofc | 48 | .167 | Ea. | 1.37 | 4.08 | | 5.45 | 8.85 |
| 0450 | Flexible roll, shingles not included | ↓ | 160 | .050 | L.F. | 2.25 | 1.22 | | 3.47 | 4.67 |
| 2300 | Ridge vent strip, mill finish | 1 Shee | 155 | .052 | " | 2.73 | 1.67 | | 4.40 | 5.75 |

## 07 72 53 – Snow Guards

### 07 72 53.10 Snow Guard Options

| | | Crew | Daily Output | Labor-Hours | Unit | Material | Labor | Equipment | Total | Total Incl O&P |
|---|---|---|---|---|---|---|---|---|---|---|
| 0010 | **SNOW GUARD OPTIONS** | | | | | | | | | |
| 0100 | Slate & asphalt shingle roofs, fastened with nails | 1 Rofc | 160 | .050 | Ea. | 9.40 | 1.22 | | 10.62 | 12.55 |
| 0200 | Standing seam metal roofs, fastened with set screws | | 48 | .167 | | 14.60 | 4.08 | | 18.68 | 23.50 |
| 0300 | Surface mount for metal roofs, fastened with solder | | 48 | .167 | ↓ | 7.70 | 4.08 | | 11.78 | 15.80 |
| 0400 | Double rail pipe type, including pipe | ↓ | 130 | .062 | L.F. | 22.50 | 1.50 | | 24 | 27.50 |

## 07 72 80 – Vents

### 07 72 80.30 Vent Options

| | | Crew | Daily Output | Labor-Hours | Unit | Material | Labor | Equipment | Total | Total Incl O&P |
|---|---|---|---|---|---|---|---|---|---|---|
| 0010 | **VENT OPTIONS** | | | | | | | | | |
| 0800 | Polystyrene baffles, 12" wide for 16" O.C. rafter spacing | 1 Carp | 90 | .089 | Ea. | .40 | 2.59 | | 2.99 | 4.79 |

# 07 91 Pre-formed Joint Seals

## 07 91 13 – Compression Seals

### 07 91 13.10 Compression Seals

| | | Crew | Daily Output | Labor-Hours | Unit | Material | Labor | Equipment | Total | Total Incl O&P |
|---|---|---|---|---|---|---|---|---|---|---|
| 0010 | **COMPRESSION SEALS** | | | | | | | | | |
| 4900 | Compression seals, O-ring type cord, 1/4" | 1 Bric | 472 | .017 | L.F. | .47 | .50 | | .97 | 1.34 |
| 4910 | 1/2" | | 440 | .018 | | 1.78 | .53 | | 2.31 | 2.84 |
| 4920 | 3/4" | | 424 | .019 | | 3.61 | .55 | | 4.16 | 4.88 |
| 4930 | 1" | | 408 | .020 | | 6.95 | .57 | | 7.52 | 8.60 |
| 4940 | 1-1/4" | | 384 | .021 | | 13.60 | .61 | | 14.21 | 15.95 |
| 4950 | 1-1/2" | | 368 | .022 | | 17.20 | .64 | | 17.84 | 20 |
| 4960 | 1-3/4" | | 352 | .023 | | 36 | .66 | | 36.66 | 40.50 |
| 4970 | 2" | ↓ | 344 | .023 | ↓ | 63.50 | .68 | | 64.18 | 71 |

## 07 91 16 – Joint Gaskets

### 07 91 16.10 Joint Gaskets

| | | Crew | Daily Output | Labor-Hours | Unit | Material | Labor | Equipment | Total | Total Incl O&P |
|---|---|---|---|---|---|---|---|---|---|---|
| 0010 | **JOINT GASKETS** | | | | | | | | | |
| 4400 | Joint gaskets, neoprene, closed cell w/adh, 1/8" x 3/8" | 1 Bric | 240 | .033 | L.F. | .26 | .97 | | 1.23 | 1.90 |
| 4500 | 1/4" x 3/4" | | 215 | .037 | | .58 | 1.09 | | 1.67 | 2.43 |
| 4700 | 1/2" x 1" | | 200 | .040 | | 1.30 | 1.17 | | 2.47 | 3.36 |
| 4800 | 3/4" x 1-1/2" | ↓ | 165 | .048 | ↓ | 1.44 | 1.42 | | 2.86 | 3.92 |

## 07 91 23 – Backer Rods

### 07 91 23.10 Backer Rods

| | | Crew | Daily Output | Labor-Hours | Unit | Material | Labor | Equipment | Total | Total Incl O&P |
|---|---|---|---|---|---|---|---|---|---|---|
| 0010 | **BACKER RODS** | | | | | | | | | |
| 0030 | Backer rod, polyethylene, 1/4" diameter | 1 Bric | 4.60 | 1.739 | C.L.F. | 2.82 | 51 | | 53.82 | 87 |
| 0050 | 1/2" diameter | | 4.60 | 1.739 | | 6.60 | 51 | | 57.60 | 91.50 |
| 0070 | 3/4" diameter | | 4.60 | 1.739 | | 10.10 | 51 | | 61.10 | 95 |
| 0090 | 1" diameter | ↓ | 4.60 | 1.739 | ↓ | 18.70 | 51 | | 69.70 | 105 |

## 07 91 26 – Joint Fillers

### 07 91 26.10 Joint Fillers

| | | Crew | Daily Output | Labor-Hours | Unit | Material | Labor | Equipment | Total | Total Incl O&P |
|---|---|---|---|---|---|---|---|---|---|---|
| 0010 | **JOINT FILLERS** | | | | | | | | | |
| 4360 | Butyl rubber filler, 1/4" x 1/4" | 1 Bric | 290 | .028 | L.F. | .14 | .81 | | .95 | 1.49 |
| 4365 | 1/2" x 1/2" | | 250 | .032 | | .57 | .94 | | 1.51 | 2.16 |
| 4370 | 1/2" x 3/4" | | 210 | .038 | | .85 | 1.11 | | 1.96 | 2.78 |
| 4375 | 3/4" x 3/4" | ↓ | 230 | .035 | | 1.28 | 1.02 | | 2.30 | 3.09 |

# 07 91 Pre-formed Joint Seals

## 07 91 26 – Joint Fillers

| 07 91 26.10 Joint Fillers | | Crew | Daily Output | Labor-Hours | Unit | Material | 2010 Bare Costs Labor | 2010 Bare Costs Equipment | Total | Total Incl O&P |
|---|---|---|---|---|---|---|---|---|---|---|
| 4380 | 1" x 1" | 1 Bric | 180 | .044 | L.F. | 1.71 | 1.30 | | 3.01 | 4.02 |
| 4390 | For coloring, add | | | | | 12% | | | | |
| 4980 | Polyethylene joint backing, 1/4" x 2" | 1 Bric | 2.08 | 3.846 | C.L.F. | 12 | 113 | | 125 | 198 |
| 4990 | 1/4" x 6" | | 1.28 | 6.250 | " | 36 | 183 | | 219 | 340 |
| 5600 | Silicone, room temp vulcanizing foam seal, 1/4" x 1/2" | | 1312 | .006 | L.F. | .29 | .18 | | .47 | .61 |
| 5610 | 1/2" x 1/2" | | 656 | .012 | | .57 | .36 | | .93 | 1.22 |
| 5620 | 1/2" x 3/4" | | 442 | .018 | | .86 | .53 | | 1.39 | 1.82 |
| 5630 | 3/4" x 3/4" | | 328 | .024 | | 1.29 | .71 | | 2 | 2.60 |
| 5640 | 1/8" x 1" | | 1312 | .006 | | .29 | .18 | | .47 | .61 |
| 5650 | 1/8" x 3" | | 442 | .018 | | .86 | .53 | | 1.39 | 1.82 |
| 5670 | 1/4" x 3" | | 295 | .027 | | 1.72 | .79 | | 2.51 | 3.20 |
| 5680 | 1/4" x 6" | | 148 | .054 | | 3.44 | 1.58 | | 5.02 | 6.40 |
| 5690 | 1/2" x 6" | | 82 | .098 | | 6.90 | 2.85 | | 9.75 | 12.25 |
| 5700 | 1/2" x 9" | | 52.50 | .152 | | 10.30 | 4.46 | | 14.76 | 18.70 |
| 5710 | 1/2" x 12" | | 33 | .242 | | 13.75 | 7.10 | | 20.85 | 27 |

# 07 92 Joint Sealants

## 07 92 13 – Elastomeric Joint Sealants

### 07 92 13.20 Caulking and Sealant Options

| 07 92 13.20 | | Crew | Daily Output | Labor-Hours | Unit | Material | 2010 Bare Costs Labor | 2010 Bare Costs Equipment | Total | Total Incl O&P |
|---|---|---|---|---|---|---|---|---|---|---|
| 0010 | **CAULKING AND SEALANT OPTIONS** | | | | | | | | | |
| 0050 | Latex acrylic based, bulk | | | | Gal. | 27 | | | 27 | 29.50 |
| 0055 | Bulk in place 1/4" x 1/4" bead | 1 Bric | 300 | .027 | L.F. | .09 | .78 | | .87 | 1.38 |
| 0060 | 1/4" x 3/8" | | 294 | .027 | | .14 | .80 | | .94 | 1.47 |
| 0065 | 1/4" x 1/2" | | 288 | .028 | | .19 | .81 | | 1 | 1.55 |
| 0075 | 3/8" x 3/8" | | 284 | .028 | | .21 | .82 | | 1.03 | 1.59 |
| 0080 | 3/8" x 1/2" | | 280 | .029 | | .28 | .84 | | 1.12 | 1.69 |
| 0085 | 3/8" x 5/8" | | 276 | .029 | | .35 | .85 | | 1.20 | 1.79 |
| 0095 | 3/8" x 3/4" | | 272 | .029 | | .42 | .86 | | 1.28 | 1.89 |
| 0100 | 1/2" x 1/2" | | 275 | .029 | | .38 | .85 | | 1.23 | 1.82 |
| 0105 | 1/2" x 5/8" | | 269 | .030 | | .47 | .87 | | 1.34 | 1.95 |
| 0110 | 1/2" x 3/4" | | 263 | .030 | | .57 | .89 | | 1.46 | 2.10 |
| 0115 | 1/2" x 7/8" | | 256 | .031 | | .66 | .91 | | 1.57 | 2.24 |
| 0120 | 1/2" x 1" | | 250 | .032 | | .76 | .94 | | 1.70 | 2.37 |
| 0125 | 3/4" x 3/4" | | 244 | .033 | | .85 | .96 | | 1.81 | 2.52 |
| 0130 | 3/4" x 1" | | 225 | .036 | | 1.14 | 1.04 | | 2.18 | 2.96 |
| 0135 | 1" x 1" | | 200 | .040 | | 1.52 | 1.17 | | 2.69 | 3.60 |
| 0190 | Cartridges | | | | Gal. | 22.50 | | | 22.50 | 24.50 |
| 0200 | 11 fl. oz cartridge | | | | Ea. | 1.93 | | | 1.93 | 2.12 |
| 0500 | 1/4" x 1/2" | 1 Bric | 288 | .028 | L.F. | .16 | .81 | | .97 | 1.51 |
| 0600 | 1/2" x 1/2" | | 275 | .029 | | .32 | .85 | | 1.17 | 1.75 |
| 0800 | 3/4" x 3/4" | | 244 | .033 | | .71 | .96 | | 1.67 | 2.36 |
| 0900 | 3/4" x 1" | | 225 | .036 | | .95 | 1.04 | | 1.99 | 2.75 |
| 1000 | 1" x 1" | | 200 | .040 | | 1.18 | 1.17 | | 2.35 | 3.23 |
| 1400 | Butyl based, bulk | | | | Gal. | 26 | | | 26 | 28.50 |
| 1500 | Cartridges | | | | " | 32 | | | 32 | 35 |
| 1700 | 1/4" x 1/2", 154 L.F./gal. | 1 Bric | 288 | .028 | L.F. | .17 | .81 | | .98 | 1.53 |
| 1800 | 1/2" x 1/2", 77 L.F./gal. | " | 275 | .029 | " | .34 | .85 | | 1.19 | 1.77 |
| 2300 | Polysulfide compounds, 1 component, bulk | | | | Gal. | 51 | | | 51 | 56 |
| 2400 | Cartridges | | | | " | 54.50 | | | 54.50 | 60 |
| 2600 | 1 or 2 component, in place, 1/4" x 1/4", 308 L.F./gal. | 1 Bric | 300 | .027 | L.F. | .17 | .78 | | .95 | 1.47 |
| 2700 | 1/2" x 1/4", 154 L.F./gal. | | 288 | .028 | | .33 | .81 | | 1.14 | 1.71 |

# 07 92 Joint Sealants

## 07 92 13 – Elastomeric Joint Sealants

### 07 92 13.20 Caulking and Sealant Options

| | | Crew | Daily Output | Labor-Hours | Unit | Material | 2010 Bare Costs Labor | Equipment | Total | Total Incl O&P |
|---|---|---|---|---|---|---|---|---|---|---|
| 2900 | 3/4" x 3/8", 68 L.F./gal. | 1 Bric | 272 | .029 | L.F. | .75 | .86 | | 1.61 | 2.25 |
| 3000 | 1" x 1/2", 38 L.F./gal. | ↓ | 250 | .032 | ↓ | 1.35 | .94 | | 2.29 | 3.02 |
| 3200 | Polyurethane, 1 or 2 component | | | | Gal. | 50 | | | 50 | 55 |
| 3300 | Cartridges | | | | " | 64 | | | 64 | 70.50 |
| 3500 | Bulk, in place, 1/4" x 1/4" | 1 Bric | 300 | .027 | L.F. | .16 | .78 | | .94 | 1.47 |
| 3655 | 1/2" x 1/4" | | 288 | .028 | | .32 | .81 | | 1.13 | 1.70 |
| 3800 | 3/4" x 3/8", 68 L.F./gal. | | 272 | .029 | | .74 | .86 | | 1.60 | 2.23 |
| 3900 | 1" x 1/2" | ↓ | 250 | .032 | ↓ | 1.30 | .94 | | 2.24 | 2.97 |
| 4100 | Silicone rubber, bulk | | | | Gal. | 41 | | | 41 | 45 |
| 4200 | Cartridges | | | | " | 41 | | | 41 | 45 |

## 07 92 19 – Acoustical Joint Sealants

### 07 92 19.10 Acoustical Sealant

| | | Crew | Daily Output | Labor-Hours | Unit | Material | 2010 Bare Costs Labor | Equipment | Total | Total Incl O&P |
|---|---|---|---|---|---|---|---|---|---|---|
| 0010 | **ACOUSTICAL SEALANT** | | | | | | | | | |
| 0020 | Acoustical sealant, elastomeric, cartridges | | | | Ea. | 2.25 | | | 2.25 | 2.48 |
| 0025 | In place, 1/4" x 1/4" | 1 Bric | 300 | .027 | L.F. | .09 | .78 | | .87 | 1.39 |
| 0030 | 1/4" x 1/2" | | 288 | .028 | | .18 | .81 | | .99 | 1.54 |
| 0035 | 1/2" x 1/2" | | 275 | .029 | | .37 | .85 | | 1.22 | 1.80 |
| 0040 | 1/2" x 3/4" | | 263 | .030 | | .55 | .89 | | 1.44 | 2.08 |
| 0045 | 3/4" x 3/4" | | 244 | .033 | | .83 | .96 | | 1.79 | 2.49 |
| 0050 | 1" x 1" | ↓ | 200 | .040 | ↓ | 1.47 | 1.17 | | 2.64 | 3.55 |

# Division Notes

| | CREW | DAILY OUTPUT | LABOR-HOURS | UNIT | 2010 BARE COSTS | | | | TOTAL INCL O&P |
| --- | --- | --- | --- | --- | --- | --- | --- | --- | --- |
| | | | | | MAT. | LABOR | EQUIP. | TOTAL | |
| | | | | | | | | | |
| | | | | | | | | | |
| | | | | | | | | | |
| | | | | | | | | | |
| | | | | | | | | | |
| | | | | | | | | | |
| | | | | | | | | | |
| | | | | | | | | | |
| | | | | | | | | | |
| | | | | | | | | | |
| | | | | | | | | | |
| | | | | | | | | | |
| | | | | | | | | | |
| | | | | | | | | | |
| | | | | | | | | | |
| | | | | | | | | | |
| | | | | | | | | | |
| | | | | | | | | | |
| | | | | | | | | | |
| | | | | | | | | | |

# Estimating Tips

## 08 10 00 Doors and Frames

All exterior doors should be addressed for their energy conservation.

- Most metal doors and frames look alike, but there may be significant differences among them. When estimating these items, be sure to choose the line item that most closely compares to the specification or door schedule requirements regarding:
  - type of metal
  - metal gauge
  - door core material
  - fire rating
  - finish
- Wood and plastic doors vary considerably in price. The primary determinant is the veneer material. Lauan, birch, and oak are the most common veneers. Other variables include the following:
  - hollow or solid core
  - fire rating
  - flush or raised panel
  - finish

## 08 30 00 Specialty Doors and Frames

- There are many varieties of special doors, and they are usually priced per each. Add frames, hardware, or operators required for a complete installation.

## 08 40 00 Entrances, Storefronts, and Curtain Walls

- Glazed curtain walls consist of the metal tube framing and the glazing material. The cost data in this subdivision is presented for the metal tube framing alone or the composite wall. If your estimate requires a detailed takeoff of the framing, be sure to add the glazing cost.

## 08 50 00 Windows

- Most metal windows are delivered preglazed. However, some metal windows are priced without glass. Refer to 08 80 00 Glazing for glass pricing. The grade C indicates commercial grade windows, usually ASTM C-35.
- All wood windows and vinyl are priced preglazed. The glazing is insulating glass. Some wood windows may have single pane float glass. Add the cost of screens and grills if required, and not already included.

## 08 70 00 Hardware

- Hardware costs add considerably to the cost of a door. The most efficient method to determine the hardware requirements for a project is to review the door schedule.

- Door hinges are priced by the pair, with most doors requiring 1-1/2 pairs per door. The hinge prices do not include installation labor because it is included in door installation. Hinges are classified according to the frequency of use.

## 08 80 00 Glazing

- Different openings require different types of glass. The three most common types are:
  - float
  - tempered
  - insulating
- Most exterior windows are glazed with insulating glass. Entrance doors and window walls, where the glass is less than 18" from the floor, are generally glazed with tempered glass. Interior windows and some residential windows are glazed with float glass.
- Coastal communities are starting to require the use of impact-resistant glass.
- The insulation or 'u' value is a strong consideration, along with solar heat gain.

# Reference Numbers

Reference numbers are shown in shaded boxes at the beginning of some major classifications. These numbers refer to related items in the Reference Section. The reference information may be an estimating procedure, an alternate pricing method, or technical information.

*Note:* Not all subdivisions listed here necessarily appear in this publication.

| 08 01 53.81 Solid Vinyl Replacement Windows | | Crew | Daily Output | Labor-Hours | Unit | Material | 2010 Bare Costs Labor | Equipment | Total | Total Incl O&P |
|---|---|---|---|---|---|---|---|---|---|---|
| 0010 | **SOLID VINYL REPLACEMENT WINDOWS** R085313-20 | | | | | | | | | |
| 0020 | Double hung, insulated glass, up to 83 united inches | G | 2 Carp | 8 | 2 | Ea. | 330 | 58 | | 388 | 460 |
| 0040 | 84 to 93 | G | | 8 | 2 | | 360 | 58 | | 418 | 495 |
| 0060 | 94 to 101 | G | | 6 | 2.667 | | 360 | 77.50 | | 437.50 | 525 |
| 0080 | 102 to 111 | G | | 6 | 2.667 | | 380 | 77.50 | | 457.50 | 545 |
| 0100 | 112 to 120 | G | | 6 | 2.667 | | 410 | 77.50 | | 487.50 | 585 |
| 0120 | For each united inch over 120 , add | G | | 800 | .020 | Inch | 5.20 | .58 | | 5.78 | 6.70 |
| 0140 | Casement windows, one operating sash , 42 to 60 united inches | G | | 8 | 2 | Ea. | 212 | 58 | | 270 | 330 |
| 0160 | 61 to 70 | G | | 8 | 2 | | 241 | 58 | | 299 | 365 |
| 0180 | 71 to 80 | G | | 8 | 2 | | 261 | 58 | | 319 | 385 |
| 0200 | 81 to 96 | G | | 8 | 2 | | 277 | 58 | | 335 | 405 |
| 0220 | Two operating sash, 58 to 78 united inches | G | | 8 | 2 | | 425 | 58 | | 483 | 565 |
| 0240 | 79 to 88 | G | | 8 | 2 | | 450 | 58 | | 508 | 595 |
| 0260 | 89 to 98 | G | | 8 | 2 | | 490 | 58 | | 548 | 640 |
| 0280 | 99 to 108 | G | | 6 | 2.667 | | 515 | 77.50 | | 592.50 | 695 |
| 0300 | 109 to 121 | G | | 6 | 2.667 | | 555 | 77.50 | | 632.50 | 740 |
| 0320 | Two operating.one fixed sash, 73 to 108 united inches | G | | 8 | 2 | | 670 | 58 | | 728 | 835 |
| 0340 | 109 to 118 | G | | 8 | 2 | | 705 | 58 | | 763 | 875 |
| 0360 | 119 to 128 | G | | 6 | 2.667 | | 725 | 77.50 | | 802.50 | 925 |
| 0380 | 129 to 138 | G | | 6 | 2.667 | | 775 | 77.50 | | 852.50 | 980 |
| 0400 | 139 to 156 | G | | 6 | 2.667 | | 815 | 77.50 | | 892.50 | 1,025 |
| 0420 | Four operating sash, 98 to 118 united inches | G | | 8 | 2 | | 960 | 58 | | 1,018 | 1,150 |
| 0440 | 119 to 128 | G | | 8 | 2 | | 1,025 | 58 | | 1,083 | 1,225 |
| 0460 | 129 to 138 | G | | 6 | 2.667 | | 1,100 | 77.50 | | 1,177.50 | 1,325 |
| 0480 | 139 to 148 | G | | 6 | 2.667 | | 1,150 | 77.50 | | 1,227.50 | 1,375 |
| 0500 | 149 to 168 | G | | 6 | 2.667 | | 1,225 | 77.50 | | 1,302.50 | 1,475 |
| 0520 | 169 to 178 | G | | 6 | 2.667 | | 1,325 | 77.50 | | 1,402.50 | 1,575 |
| 0560 | Fixed picture window, up to 63 united inches | G | | 8 | 2 | | 144 | 58 | | 202 | 256 |
| 0580 | 64 to 83 | G | | 8 | 2 | | 170 | 58 | | 228 | 285 |
| 0600 | 84 to 101 | G | | 8 | 2 | | 220 | 58 | | 278 | 340 |
| 0620 | For each united inch over 101, add | G | | 900 | .018 | Inch | 2.50 | .52 | | 3.02 | 3.62 |
| 0640 | Picture window opt., low E glazing, up to 101 united inches | G | | | | Ea. | 21 | | | 21 | 23 |
| 0660 | 102 to 124 | G | | | | | 26 | | | 26 | 28.50 |
| 0680 | 124 and over | G | | | | | 38 | | | 38 | 42 |
| 0700 | Options, low E glazing, up to w/gas 101 united inches | G | | | | | 32.50 | | | 32.50 | 36 |
| 0720 | 102 to 124 | G | | | | | 32.50 | | | 32.50 | 36 |
| 0740 | 124 and over | G | | | | | 32.50 | | | 32.50 | 36 |
| 0760 | Muntins, between glazing, square, per lite | | | | | | 4 | | | 4 | 4.40 |
| 0780 | Diamond shape, per full or partial diamond | | | | | | 5 | | | 5 | 5.50 |
| 0800 | Cellulose fiber insulation, poured into sash balance cavity | G | 1 Carp | 36 | .222 | C.F. | .60 | 6.45 | | 7.05 | 11.55 |
| 0820 | Silicone caulking at perimeter | G | " | 800 | .010 | L.F. | .13 | .29 | | .42 | .64 |

# 08 05 Common Work Results for Openings

## 08 05 05 – Selective Windows and Doors Demolition

### 08 05 05.10 Selective Demolition Doors

| | | Crew | Daily Output | Labor-Hours | Unit | Material | 2010 Bare Costs Labor | Equipment | Total | Total Incl O&P |
|---|---|---|---|---|---|---|---|---|---|---|
| 0010 | **SELECTIVE DEMOLITION DOORS** R024119-10 | | | | | | | | | |
| 0200 | Doors, exterior, 1-3/4" thick, single, 3' x 7' high | 1 Clab | 16 | .500 | Ea. | | 10.75 | | 10.75 | 18.10 |
| 0210 | Door demo, doors, exterior, 1-3/4" thick, single, 3'-0" x 8'-0" | | 10 | .800 | | | 17.20 | | 17.20 | 29 |
| 0215 | Door demo, doors, exterior, double 1-3/4" thick, 3'-0" x 8'-0" | | 6 | 1.333 | | | 28.50 | | 28.50 | 48 |
| 0220 | Double, 6' x 7' high | | 12 | .667 | | | 14.35 | | 14.35 | 24 |
| 0500 | Interior, 1-3/8" thick, single, 3' x 7' high | | 20 | .400 | | | 8.60 | | 8.60 | 14.45 |
| 0520 | Double, 6' x 7' high | | 16 | .500 | | | 10.75 | | 10.75 | 18.10 |
| 0700 | Bi-folding, 3' x 6'-8" high | | 20 | .400 | | | 8.60 | | 8.60 | 14.45 |
| 0720 | 6' x 6'-8" high | | 18 | .444 | | | 9.55 | | 9.55 | 16.05 |
| 0900 | Bi-passing, 3' x 6'-8" high | | 16 | .500 | | | 10.75 | | 10.75 | 18.10 |
| 0940 | 6' x 6'-8" high | ▼ | 14 | .571 | | | 12.30 | | 12.30 | 20.50 |
| 1500 | Remove and reset, minimum | 1 Carp | 8 | 1 | | | 29 | | 29 | 49 |
| 1520 | Maximum | | 6 | 1.333 | | | 39 | | 39 | 65.50 |
| 2000 | Frames, including trim, metal | ▼ | 8 | 1 | | | 29 | | 29 | 49 |
| 2200 | Wood | 2 Carp | 32 | .500 | ▼ | | 14.55 | | 14.55 | 24.50 |
| 2201 | Alternate pricing method | 1 Carp | 200 | .040 | L.F. | | 1.16 | | 1.16 | 1.96 |
| 3000 | Special doors, counter doors | 2 Carp | 6 | 2.667 | Ea. | | 77.50 | | 77.50 | 131 |
| 3300 | Glass, sliding, including frames | | 12 | 1.333 | | | 39 | | 39 | 65.50 |
| 3400 | Overhead, commercial, 12' x 12' high | | 4 | 4 | | | 116 | | 116 | 196 |
| 3500 | Residential, 9' x 7' high | | 8 | 2 | | | 58 | | 58 | 98 |
| 3540 | 16' x 7' high | | 7 | 2.286 | | | 66.50 | | 66.50 | 112 |
| 3600 | Remove and reset, minimum | | 4 | 4 | | | 116 | | 116 | 196 |
| 3620 | Maximum | ▼ | 2.50 | 6.400 | | | 186 | | 186 | 315 |
| 3660 | Remove and reset elec. garage door opener | 1 Carp | 8 | 1 | | | 29 | | 29 | 49 |
| 4000 | Residential lockset, exterior | | 28 | .286 | | | 8.30 | | 8.30 | 14 |
| 4010 | Residential lockset, exterior w/deadbolt | | 26 | .308 | | | 8.95 | | 8.95 | 15.05 |
| 4020 | Residential lockset, interior | | 30 | .267 | | | 7.75 | | 7.75 | 13.05 |
| 4200 | Deadbolt lock | | 32 | .250 | | | 7.30 | | 7.30 | 12.25 |
| 4224 | Pocket door | ▼ | 8 | 1 | | | 29 | | 29 | 49 |
| 5590 | Remove mail slot | 1 Clab | 45 | .178 | ▼ | | 3.82 | | 3.82 | 6.45 |
| 9000 | Minimum labor/equipment charge | 1 Carp | 4 | 2 | Job | | 58 | | 58 | 98 |

### 08 05 05.20 Selective Demolition of Windows

| | | Crew | Daily Output | Labor-Hours | Unit | Material | 2010 Bare Costs Labor | Equipment | Total | Total Incl O&P |
|---|---|---|---|---|---|---|---|---|---|---|
| 0010 | **SELECTIVE DEMOLITION OF WINDOWS** R024119-10 | | | | | | | | | |
| 0200 | Aluminum, including trim, to 12 S.F. | 1 Clab | 16 | .500 | Ea. | | 10.75 | | 10.75 | 18.10 |
| 0240 | To 25 S.F. | | 11 | .727 | | | 15.65 | | 15.65 | 26.50 |
| 0280 | To 50 S.F. | | 5 | 1.600 | | | 34.50 | | 34.50 | 58 |
| 0320 | Storm windows/screens, to 12 S.F. | | 27 | .296 | | | 6.35 | | 6.35 | 10.70 |
| 0360 | To 25 S.F. | | 21 | .381 | | | 8.20 | | 8.20 | 13.75 |
| 0400 | To 50 S.F. | | 16 | .500 | | | 10.75 | | 10.75 | 18.10 |
| 0500 | Screens, incl. aluminum frame, small | | 20 | .400 | | | 8.60 | | 8.60 | 14.45 |
| 0510 | Large | | 16 | .500 | ▼ | | 10.75 | | 10.75 | 18.10 |
| 0600 | Glass, minimum | | 200 | .040 | S.F. | | .86 | | .86 | 1.45 |
| 0620 | Maximum | | 150 | .053 | " | | 1.15 | | 1.15 | 1.93 |
| 2000 | Wood, including trim, to 12 S.F. | | 22 | .364 | Ea. | | 7.80 | | 7.80 | 13.15 |
| 2020 | To 25 S.F. | | 18 | .444 | | | 9.55 | | 9.55 | 16.05 |
| 2060 | To 50 S.F. | | 13 | .615 | | | 13.25 | | 13.25 | 22.50 |
| 2065 | To 180 S.F. | ▼ | 8 | 1 | | | 21.50 | | 21.50 | 36 |
| 4300 | Remove bay/bow window | 2 Carp | 6 | 2.667 | ▼ | | 77.50 | | 77.50 | 131 |
| 4410 | Remove skylight, plstc domes, flush/curb mtd | G-3 | 395 | .081 | S.F. | | 2.18 | | 2.18 | 3.64 |
| 5020 | Remove and reset window, minimum | 1 Carp | 6 | 1.333 | Ea. | | 39 | | 39 | 65.50 |
| 5040 | Average | | 4 | 2 | | | 58 | | 58 | 98 |
| 5080 | Maximum | ▼ | 2 | 4 | ▼ | | 116 | | 116 | 196 |

421

# 08 05 Common Work Results for Openings

## 08 05 05 – Selective Windows and Doors Demolition

| 08 05 05.20 Selective Demolition of Windows | Crew | Daily Output | Labor-Hours | Unit | Material | 2010 Bare Costs Labor | 2010 Bare Costs Equipment | Total | Total Incl O&P |
|---|---|---|---|---|---|---|---|---|---|
| 6000 Screening only | 1 Clab | 4000 | .002 | S.F. | | .04 | | .04 | .07 |
| 9100 Window awning, residential | " | 80 | .100 | L.F. | | 2.15 | | 2.15 | 3.62 |

# 08 11 Metal Doors and Frames

## 08 11 63 – Metal Screen and Storm Doors and Frames

### 08 11 63.23 Aluminum Screen and Storm Doors and Frames

| | | Crew | Daily Output | Labor-Hours | Unit | Material | 2010 Bare Costs Labor | 2010 Bare Costs Equipment | Total | Total Incl O&P |
|---|---|---|---|---|---|---|---|---|---|---|
| 0010 | **ALUMINUM SCREEN AND STORM DOORS AND FRAMES** | | | | | | | | | |
| 0020 | Combination storm and screen | | | | | | | | | |
| 0400 | Clear anodic coating, 6'-8" x 2'-6" wide | 2 Carp | 15 | 1.067 | Ea. | 172 | 31 | | 203 | 241 |
| 0420 | 2'-8" wide | | 14 | 1.143 | | 156 | 33.50 | | 189.50 | 227 |
| 0440 | 3'-0" wide | | 14 | 1.143 | | 156 | 33.50 | | 189.50 | 227 |
| 0500 | For 7' door height, add | | | | | 5% | | | | |
| 1000 | Mill finish, 6'-8" x 2'-6" wide | 2 Carp | 15 | 1.067 | Ea. | 225 | 31 | | 256 | 300 |
| 1020 | 2'-8" wide | | 14 | 1.143 | | 225 | 33.50 | | 258.50 | 305 |
| 1040 | 3'-0" wide | | 14 | 1.143 | | 246 | 33.50 | | 279.50 | 325 |
| 1100 | For 7'-0" door, add | | | | | 5% | | | | |
| 1500 | White painted, 6'-8" x 2'-6" wide | 2 Carp | 15 | 1.067 | | 282 | 31 | | 313 | 360 |
| 1520 | 2'-8" wide | | 14 | 1.143 | | 278 | 33.50 | | 311.50 | 360 |
| 1540 | 3'-0" wide | | 14 | 1.143 | | 292 | 33.50 | | 325.50 | 375 |
| 1541 | Storm door, painted, alum., insul., 6'-8" x 2'-6" wide | | 14 | 1.143 | | 262 | 33.50 | | 295.50 | 345 |
| 1545 | 2'-8" wide | | 14 | 1.143 | | 262 | 33.50 | | 295.50 | 345 |
| 1600 | For 7'-0" door, add | | | | | 5% | | | | |
| 1800 | Aluminum screen door, minimum, 6'-8" x 2'-8" wide | 2 Carp | 14 | 1.143 | | 120 | 33.50 | | 153.50 | 188 |
| 1810 | 3'-0" wide | | 14 | 1.143 | | 240 | 33.50 | | 273.50 | 320 |
| 1820 | Average, 6'-8" x 2'-8" wide | | 14 | 1.143 | | 170 | 33.50 | | 203.50 | 243 |
| 1830 | 3'-0" wide | | 14 | 1.143 | | 240 | 33.50 | | 273.50 | 320 |
| 1840 | Maximum, 6'-8" x 2'-8" wide | | 14 | 1.143 | | 325 | 33.50 | | 358.50 | 415 |
| 1850 | 3'-0" wide | | 14 | 1.143 | | 262 | 33.50 | | 295.50 | 345 |
| 2000 | Wood door & screen, see Div. 08 14 33.20 | | | | | | | | | |

# 08 12 Metal Frames

## 08 12 13 – Hollow Metal Frames

### 08 12 13.13 Standard Hollow Metal Frames

| | | Crew | Daily Output | Labor-Hours | Unit | Material | 2010 Bare Costs Labor | 2010 Bare Costs Equipment | Total | Total Incl O&P |
|---|---|---|---|---|---|---|---|---|---|---|
| 0010 | **STANDARD HOLLOW METAL FRAMES** | | | | | | | | | |
| 0020 | 16 ga., up to 5-3/4" jamb depth | | | | | | | | | |
| 0025 | 6'-8" high, 3'-0" wide, single | 2 Carp | 16 | 1 | Ea. | 136 | 29 | | 165 | 198 |
| 0028 | 3'-6" wide, single | | 16 | 1 | | 142 | 29 | | 171 | 206 |
| 0030 | 4'-0" wide, single | | 16 | 1 | | 142 | 29 | | 171 | 206 |
| 0040 | 6'-0" wide, double | | 14 | 1.143 | | 195 | 33.50 | | 228.50 | 270 |
| 0045 | 8'-0" wide, double | | 14 | 1.143 | | 203 | 33.50 | | 236.50 | 279 |
| 0100 | 7'-0" high, 3'-0" wide, single | | 16 | 1 | | 140 | 29 | | 169 | 203 |
| 0110 | 3'-6" wide, single | | 16 | 1 | | 147 | 29 | | 176 | 211 |
| 0112 | 4'-0" wide, single | | 16 | 1 | | 147 | 29 | | 176 | 211 |
| 0140 | 6'-0" wide, double | | 14 | 1.143 | | 185 | 33.50 | | 218.50 | 260 |
| 0145 | 8'-0" wide, double | | 14 | 1.143 | | 219 | 33.50 | | 252.50 | 297 |
| 0160 | 6'-0" wide, double | | 14 | 1.143 | | 185 | 33.50 | | 218.50 | 260 |
| 1000 | 16 ga., up to 4-7/8" deep, 7'-0" H, 3'-0" W, single | | 16 | 1 | | 154 | 29 | | 183 | 219 |
| 1140 | 6'-0" wide, double | | 14 | 1.143 | | 171 | 33.50 | | 204.50 | 244 |
| 1200 | 16 ga., 8-3/4" deep, 7'-0" H, 3'-0" W, single | | 16 | 1 | | 163 | 29 | | 192 | 228 |

# 08 12 Metal Frames

## 08 12 13 – Hollow Metal Frames

### 08 12 13.13 Standard Hollow Metal Frames

| | | Crew | Daily Output | Labor-Hours | Unit | Material | 2010 Bare Costs Labor | Equipment | Total | Total Incl O&P |
|---|---|---|---|---|---|---|---|---|---|---|
| 2800 | 14 ga., up to 3-7/8" deep, 7'-0" high, 3'-0" wide, single | 2 Carp | 16 | 1 | Ea. | 149 | 29 | | 178 | 212 |
| 2840 | 6'-0" wide, double | | 14 | 1.143 | | 174 | 33.50 | | 207.50 | 247 |
| 3000 | 14 ga., up to 5-3/4" deep, 6'-8" high, 3'-0" wide, single | | 16 | 1 | | 140 | 29 | | 169 | 203 |
| 3002 | 3'-6" wide, single | | 16 | 1 | | 183 | 29 | | 212 | 250 |
| 3005 | 4'-0" wide, single | | 16 | 1 | | 183 | 29 | | 212 | 250 |
| 3600 | up to 5-3/4" jamb depth, 7'-0" high, 4'-0" wide, single | | 15 | 1.067 | | 140 | 31 | | 171 | 206 |
| 3620 | 6'-0" wide, double | | 12 | 1.333 | | 182 | 39 | | 221 | 266 |
| 3640 | 8'-0" wide, double | | 12 | 1.333 | | 179 | 39 | | 218 | 263 |
| 3700 | 8'-0" high, 4'-0" wide, single | | 15 | 1.067 | | 169 | 31 | | 200 | 238 |
| 3740 | 8'-0" wide, double | | 12 | 1.333 | | 260 | 39 | | 299 | 350 |
| 4000 | 6-3/4" deep, 7'-0" high, 4'-0" wide, single | | 15 | 1.067 | | 198 | 31 | | 229 | 270 |
| 4020 | 6'-0" wide, double | | 12 | 1.333 | | 243 | 39 | | 282 | 335 |
| 4040 | 8'-0", wide double | | 12 | 1.333 | | 251 | 39 | | 290 | 340 |
| 4100 | 8'-0" high, 4'-0" wide, single | | 15 | 1.067 | | 208 | 31 | | 239 | 281 |
| 4140 | 8'-0" wide, double | | 12 | 1.333 | | 208 | 39 | | 247 | 295 |
| 4400 | 8-3/4" deep, 7'-0" high, 4'-0" wide, single | | 15 | 1.067 | | 176 | 31 | | 207 | 245 |
| 4440 | 8'-0" wide, double | | 12 | 1.333 | | 237 | 39 | | 276 | 325 |
| 4500 | 8'-0" high, 4'-0" wide, single | | 15 | 1.067 | | 177 | 31 | | 208 | 246 |
| 4540 | 8'-0" wide, double | ▼ | 12 | 1.333 | | 208 | 39 | | 247 | 295 |
| 4900 | For welded frames, add | | | | | 60 | | | 60 | 66 |
| 5400 | 14 ga., "B" label, up to 5-3/4" deep, 7'-0" high, 4'-0" wide, single | 2 Carp | 15 | 1.067 | | 194 | 31 | | 225 | 265 |
| 5440 | 8'-0" wide, double | | 12 | 1.333 | | 252 | 39 | | 291 | 345 |
| 5800 | 6-3/4" deep, 7'-0" high, 4'-0" wide, single | | 15 | 1.067 | | 208 | 31 | | 239 | 281 |
| 5840 | 8'-0" wide, double | | 12 | 1.333 | | 360 | 39 | | 399 | 460 |
| 6200 | 8-3/4" deep, 7'-0" high, 4'-0" wide, single | | 15 | 1.067 | | 289 | 31 | | 320 | 370 |
| 6240 | 8'-0" wide, double | ▼ | 12 | 1.333 | ▼ | 335 | 39 | | 374 | 435 |
| 6300 | For "A" label use same price as "B" label | | | | | | | | | |
| 6400 | For baked enamel finish, add | | | | | 30% | 15% | | | |
| 6500 | For galvanizing, add | | | | | 15% | | | | |
| 6600 | For hospital stop, add | | | | Ea. | 282 | | | 282 | 310 |
| 7900 | Transom lite frames, fixed, add | 2 Carp | 155 | .103 | S.F. | 52 | 3 | | 55 | 62 |
| 8000 | Movable, add | " | 130 | .123 | " | 65 | 3.58 | | 68.58 | 77.50 |

# 08 13 Metal Doors

## 08 13 13 – Hollow Metal Doors

### 08 13 13.15 Metal Fire Doors

| | | Crew | Daily Output | Labor-Hours | Unit | Material | 2010 Bare Costs Labor | Equipment | Total | Total Incl O&P |
|---|---|---|---|---|---|---|---|---|---|---|
| 0010 | **METAL FIRE DOORS** R081313-20 | | | | | | | | | |
| 0015 | Steel, flush, "B" label, 90 minute | | | | | | | | | |
| 0020 | Full panel, 20 ga., 2'-0" x 6'-8" | 2 Carp | 20 | .800 | Ea. | 340 | 23.50 | | 363.50 | 415 |
| 0040 | 2'-8" x 6'-8" | | 18 | .889 | | 345 | 26 | | 371 | 425 |
| 0060 | 3'-0" x 6'-8" | | 17 | .941 | | 345 | 27.50 | | 372.50 | 425 |
| 0080 | 3'-0" x 7'-0" | | 17 | .941 | | 360 | 27.50 | | 387.50 | 440 |
| 0140 | 18 ga., 3'-0" x 6'-8" | | 16 | 1 | | 395 | 29 | | 424 | 485 |
| 0160 | 2'-8" x 7'-0" | | 17 | .941 | | 415 | 27.50 | | 442.50 | 500 |
| 0180 | 3'-0" x 7'-0" | | 16 | 1 | | 395 | 29 | | 424 | 485 |
| 0200 | 4'-0" x 7'-0" | ▼ | 15 | 1.067 | ▼ | 520 | 31 | | 551 | 620 |
| 0220 | For "A" label, 3 hour, 18 ga., use same price as "B" label | | | | | | | | | |
| 0240 | For vision lite, add | | | | Ea. | 130 | | | 130 | 143 |
| 0520 | Flush, "B" label 90 min., composite, 20 ga., 2'-0" x 6'-8" | 2 Carp | 18 | .889 | | 430 | 26 | | 456 | 520 |
| 0540 | 2'-8" x 6'-8" | | 17 | .941 | | 435 | 27.50 | | 462.50 | 525 |
| 0560 | 3'-0" x 6'-8" | ▼ | 16 | 1 | | 440 | 29 | | 469 | 530 |

423

# 08 13 Metal Doors

## 08 13 13 – Hollow Metal Doors

| 08 13 13.15 Metal Fire Doors | | Crew | Daily Output | Labor-Hours | Unit | Material | 2010 Bare Costs Labor | Equipment | Total | Total Incl O&P |
|---|---|---|---|---|---|---|---|---|---|---|
| 0580 | 3'-0" x 7'-0" | 2 Carp | 16 | 1 | Ea. | 450 | 29 | | 479 | 545 |
| 0640 | Flush, "A" label 3 hour, composite, 18 ga., 3'-0" x 6'-8" | | 15 | 1.067 | | 495 | 31 | | 526 | 595 |
| 0660 | 2'-8" x 7'-0" | | 16 | 1 | | 515 | 29 | | 544 | 620 |
| 0680 | 3'-0" x 7'-0" | | 15 | 1.067 | | 505 | 31 | | 536 | 605 |
| 0700 | 4'-0" x 7'-0" | | 14 | 1.143 | | 630 | 33.50 | | 663.50 | 750 |

| 08 13 13.20 Residential Steel Doors | | | | | | | | | | |
|---|---|---|---|---|---|---|---|---|---|---|
| 0010 | **RESIDENTIAL STEEL DOORS** | | | | | | | | | |
| 0020 | Prehung, insulated, exterior | | | | | | | | | |
| 0030 | Embossed, full panel, 2'-8" x 6'-8"   G | 2 Carp | 17 | .941 | Ea. | 293 | 27.50 | | 320.50 | 365 |
| 0040 | 3'-0" x 6'-8"   G | | 15 | 1.067 | | 272 | 31 | | 303 | 350 |
| 0060 | 3'-0" x 7'-0"   G | | 15 | 1.067 | | 320 | 31 | | 351 | 400 |
| 0070 | 5'-4" x 6'-8", double   G | | 8 | 2 | | 575 | 58 | | 633 | 735 |
| 0220 | Half glass, 2'-8" x 6'-8" | | 17 | .941 | | 290 | 27.50 | | 317.50 | 365 |
| 0240 | 3'-0" x 6'-8" | | 16 | 1 | | 290 | 29 | | 319 | 370 |
| 0260 | 3'-0" x 7'-0" | | 16 | 1 | | 340 | 29 | | 369 | 425 |
| 0270 | 5'-4" x 6'-8", double | | 8 | 2 | | 585 | 58 | | 643 | 740 |
| 1320 | Flush face, full panel, 2'-8" x 6'-8" | | 16 | 1 | | 230 | 29 | | 259 | 300 |
| 1340 | 3'-0" x 6'-8" | | 15 | 1.067 | | 230 | 31 | | 261 | 305 |
| 1360 | 3'-0" x 7'-0" | | 15 | 1.067 | | 290 | 31 | | 321 | 370 |
| 1380 | 5'-4" x 6'-8", double | | 8 | 2 | | 470 | 58 | | 528 | 615 |
| 1420 | Half glass, 2'-8" x 6'-8" | | 17 | .941 | | 289 | 27.50 | | 316.50 | 365 |
| 1440 | 3'-0" x 6'-8" | | 16 | 1 | | 289 | 29 | | 318 | 370 |
| 1460 | 3'-0" x 7'-0" | | 16 | 1 | | 335 | 29 | | 364 | 420 |
| 1480 | 5'-4" x 6'-8", double | | 8 | 2 | | 555 | 58 | | 613 | 710 |
| 1500 | Sidelight, full lite, 1'-0" x 6'-8"with grille | | | | | 236 | | | 236 | 260 |
| 1510 | 1'-0" x 6'-8", low e | | | | | 257 | | | 257 | 282 |
| 1520 | 1'-0" x 6'-8", half lite | | | | | 254 | | | 254 | 280 |
| 1530 | 1'-0" x 6'-8", half lite, low e | | | | | 262 | | | 262 | 289 |
| 2300 | Interior, residential, closet, bi-fold, 6'-8" x 2'-0" wide | 2 Carp | 16 | 1 | | 158 | 29 | | 187 | 223 |
| 2330 | 3'-0" wide | | 16 | 1 | | 197 | 29 | | 226 | 266 |
| 2360 | 4'-0" wide | | 15 | 1.067 | | 255 | 31 | | 286 | 335 |
| 2400 | 5'-0" wide | | 14 | 1.143 | | 310 | 33.50 | | 343.50 | 395 |
| 2420 | 6'-0" wide | | 13 | 1.231 | | 330 | 36 | | 366 | 425 |
| 2510 | Bi-passing closet, incl. hardware, no frame or trim incl. | | | | | | | | | |
| 2511 | Mirrored, metal frame, 6'-8" x 4'-0" wide | 2 Carp | 10 | 1.600 | Opng. | 184 | 46.50 | | 230.50 | 282 |
| 2512 | 5'-0" wide | | 10 | 1.600 | | 214 | 46.50 | | 260.50 | 315 |
| 2513 | 6'-0" wide | | 10 | 1.600 | | 244 | 46.50 | | 290.50 | 345 |
| 2514 | 7'-0" wide | | 9 | 1.778 | | 264 | 51.50 | | 315.50 | 375 |
| 2515 | 8'-0" wide | | 9 | 1.778 | | 425 | 51.50 | | 476.50 | 555 |
| 2611 | Mirrored, metal, 8'-0" x 4'-0" wide | | 10 | 1.600 | | 310 | 46.50 | | 356.50 | 420 |
| 2612 | 5'-0" wide | | 10 | 1.600 | | 320 | 46.50 | | 366.50 | 435 |
| 2613 | 6'-0" wide | | 10 | 1.600 | | 350 | 46.50 | | 396.50 | 465 |
| 2614 | 7'-0" wide | | 9 | 1.778 | | 380 | 51.50 | | 431.50 | 505 |
| 2615 | 8'-0" wide | | 9 | 1.778 | | 430 | 51.50 | | 481.50 | 560 |

# 08 14 Wood Doors

## 08 14 13 - Carved Wood Doors

### 08 14 13.10 Types of Wood Doors, Carved

| 08 14 13.10 Types of Wood Doors, Carved | Crew | Daily Output | Labor-Hours | Unit | Material | 2010 Bare Costs Labor | Equipment | Total | Total Incl O&P |
|---|---|---|---|---|---|---|---|---|---|
| 0010 **TYPES OF WOOD DOORS, CARVED** | | | | | | | | | |
| 3000 Solid wood, 1-3/4" thick stile and rail | | | | | | | | | |
| 3020 Mahogany, 3'-0" x 7'-0", minimum | 2 Carp | 14 | 1.143 | Ea. | 945 | 33.50 | | 978.50 | 1,100 |
| 3030 Maximum | | 10 | 1.600 | | 1,500 | 46.50 | | 1,546.50 | 1,725 |
| 3040 3'-6" x 8'-0", minimum | | 10 | 1.600 | | 1,250 | 46.50 | | 1,296.50 | 1,450 |
| 3050 Maximum | | 8 | 2 | | 1,850 | 58 | | 1,908 | 2,150 |
| 3100 Pine, 3'-0" x 7'-0", minimum | | 14 | 1.143 | | 450 | 33.50 | | 483.50 | 550 |
| 3110 Maximum | | 10 | 1.600 | | 750 | 46.50 | | 796.50 | 905 |
| 3120 3'-6" x 8'-0", minimum | | 10 | 1.600 | | 885 | 46.50 | | 931.50 | 1,050 |
| 3130 Maximum | | 8 | 2 | | 1,800 | 58 | | 1,858 | 2,075 |
| 3200 Red oak, 3'-0" x 7'-0", minimum | | 14 | 1.143 | | 1,700 | 33.50 | | 1,733.50 | 1,925 |
| 3210 Maximum | | 10 | 1.600 | | 2,025 | 46.50 | | 2,071.50 | 2,300 |
| 3220 3'-6" x 8'-0", minimum | | 10 | 1.600 | | 2,200 | 46.50 | | 2,246.50 | 2,500 |
| 3230 Maximum | | 8 | 2 | | 3,200 | 58 | | 3,258 | 3,625 |
| 4000 Hand carved door, mahogany | | | | | | | | | |
| 4020 3'-0" x 7'-0", minimum | 2 Carp | 14 | 1.143 | Ea. | 1,600 | 33.50 | | 1,633.50 | 1,800 |
| 4030 Maximum | | 11 | 1.455 | | 3,600 | 42.50 | | 3,642.50 | 4,025 |
| 4040 3'-6" x 8'-0", minimum | | 10 | 1.600 | | 2,500 | 46.50 | | 2,546.50 | 2,825 |
| 4050 Maximum | | 8 | 2 | | 3,500 | 58 | | 3,558 | 3,950 |
| 4200 Rose wood, 3'-0" x 7'-0", minimum | | 14 | 1.143 | | 5,000 | 33.50 | | 5,033.50 | 5,550 |
| 4210 Maximum | | 11 | 1.455 | | 13,600 | 42.50 | | 13,642.50 | 15,100 |
| 4220 3'-6" x 8'-0", minimum | | 10 | 1.600 | | 5,700 | 46.50 | | 5,746.50 | 6,350 |
| 4280 For 6'-8" high door, deduct from 7'-0" door | | | | | 34 | | | 34 | 37.50 |
| 4400 For custom finish, add | | | | | 400 | | | 400 | 440 |
| 4600 Side light, mahogany, 7'-0" x 1'-6" wide, minimum | 2 Carp | 18 | .889 | | 900 | 26 | | 926 | 1,025 |
| 4610 Maximum | | 14 | 1.143 | | 2,625 | 33.50 | | 2,658.50 | 2,950 |
| 4620 8'-0" x 1'-6" wide, minimum | | 14 | 1.143 | | 1,700 | 33.50 | | 1,733.50 | 1,925 |
| 4630 Maximum | | 10 | 1.600 | | 1,950 | 46.50 | | 1,996.50 | 2,225 |
| 4640 Side light, oak, 7'-0" x 1'-6" wide, minimum | | 18 | .889 | | 1,100 | 26 | | 1,126 | 1,250 |
| 4650 Maximum | | 14 | 1.143 | | 1,900 | 33.50 | | 1,933.50 | 2,150 |
| 4660 8'-0" x 1'-6" wide, minimum | | 14 | 1.143 | | 1,000 | 33.50 | | 1,033.50 | 1,150 |
| 4670 Maximum | | 10 | 1.600 | | 1,900 | 46.50 | | 1,946.50 | 2,175 |

## 08 14 16 - Flush Wood Doors

### 08 14 16.09 Smooth Wood Doors

| | Crew | Daily Output | Labor-Hours | Unit | Material | 2010 Bare Costs Labor | Equipment | Total | Total Incl O&P |
|---|---|---|---|---|---|---|---|---|---|
| 0010 **SMOOTH WOOD DOORS** | | | | | | | | | |
| 4160 Walnut faced, 1-3/4" x 6'-8" x 3'-0" wide | 1 Carp | 17 | .471 | Ea. | 276 | 13.70 | | 289.70 | 330 |

## 08 14 33 - Stile and Rail Wood Doors

### 08 14 33.10 Wood Doors Paneled

| | Crew | Daily Output | Labor-Hours | Unit | Material | 2010 Bare Costs Labor | Equipment | Total | Total Incl O&P |
|---|---|---|---|---|---|---|---|---|---|
| 0010 **WOOD DOORS PANELED** | | | | | | | | | |
| 0020 Interior, six panel, hollow core, 1-3/8" thick | | | | | | | | | |
| 0040 Molded hardboard, 2'-0" x 6'-8" | 2 Carp | 17 | .941 | Ea. | 56 | 27.50 | | 83.50 | 108 |
| 0060 2'-6" x 6'-8" | | 17 | .941 | | 60 | 27.50 | | 87.50 | 112 |
| 0070 2'-8" x 6'-8" | | 17 | .941 | | 63 | 27.50 | | 90.50 | 116 |
| 0080 3'-0" x 6'-8" | | 17 | .941 | | 66 | 27.50 | | 93.50 | 119 |
| 0140 Embossed print, molded hardboard, 2'-0" x 6'-8" | | 17 | .941 | | 60 | 27.50 | | 87.50 | 112 |
| 0160 2'-6" x 6'-8" | | 17 | .941 | | 60 | 27.50 | | 87.50 | 112 |
| 0180 3'-0" x 6'-8" | | 17 | .941 | | 66 | 27.50 | | 93.50 | 119 |
| 0540 Six panel, solid, 1-3/8" thick, pine, 2'-0" x 6'-8" | | 15 | 1.067 | | 145 | 31 | | 176 | 212 |
| 0560 2'-6" x 6'-8" | | 14 | 1.143 | | 162 | 33.50 | | 195.50 | 234 |
| 0580 3'-0" x 6'-8" | | 13 | 1.231 | | 136 | 36 | | 172 | 211 |
| 1020 Two panel, bored rail, solid, 1-3/8" thick, pine, 1'-6" x 6'-8" | | 16 | 1 | | 263 | 29 | | 292 | 340 |
| 1040 2'-0" x 6'-8" | | 15 | 1.067 | | 345 | 31 | | 376 | 430 |

# 08 14 Wood Doors

## 08 14 33 – Stile and Rail Wood Doors

| 08 14 33.10 Wood Doors Paneled | Crew | Daily Output | Labor-Hours | Unit | Material | 2010 Bare Costs Labor | Equipment | Total | Total Incl O&P |
|---|---|---|---|---|---|---|---|---|---|
| 1060 | 2'-6" x 6'-8" | 2 Carp | 14 | 1.143 | Ea. | 395 | 33.50 | | 428.50 | 490 |
| 1340 | Two panel, solid, 1-3/8" thick, fir, 2'-0" x 6'-8" | | 15 | 1.067 | | 150 | 31 | | 181 | 217 |
| 1360 | 2'-6" x 6'-8" | | 14 | 1.143 | | 200 | 33.50 | | 233.50 | 276 |
| 1380 | 3'-0" x 6'-8" | | 13 | 1.231 | | 405 | 36 | | 441 | 505 |
| 1740 | Five panel, solid, 1-3/8" thick, fir, 2'-0" x 6'-8" | | 15 | 1.067 | | 270 | 31 | | 301 | 350 |
| 1760 | 2'-6" x 6'-8" | | 14 | 1.143 | | 415 | 33.50 | | 448.50 | 510 |
| 1780 | 3'-0" x 6'-8" | | 13 | 1.231 | | 415 | 36 | | 451 | 515 |

| 08 14 33.20 Wood Doors Residential | Crew | Daily Output | Labor-Hours | Unit | Material | 2010 Bare Costs Labor | Equipment | Total | Total Incl O&P |
|---|---|---|---|---|---|---|---|---|---|
| 0010 | **WOOD DOORS RESIDENTIAL** | | | | | | | | | |
| 0200 | Exterior, combination storm & screen, pine | | | | | | | | | |
| 0260 | 2'-8" wide | 2 Carp | 10 | 1.600 | Ea. | 286 | 46.50 | | 332.50 | 395 |
| 0280 | 3'-0" wide | | 9 | 1.778 | | 295 | 51.50 | | 346.50 | 410 |
| 0300 | 7'-1" x 3'-0" wide | | 9 | 1.778 | | 335 | 51.50 | | 386.50 | 455 |
| 0400 | Full lite, 6'-9" x 2'-6" wide | | 11 | 1.455 | | 296 | 42.50 | | 338.50 | 395 |
| 0420 | 2'-8" wide | | 10 | 1.600 | | 296 | 46.50 | | 342.50 | 405 |
| 0440 | 3'-0" wide | | 9 | 1.778 | | 300 | 51.50 | | 351.50 | 415 |
| 0500 | 7'-1" x 3'-0" wide | | 9 | 1.778 | | 325 | 51.50 | | 376.50 | 440 |
| 0604 | Door, screen, plain full | | 12 | 1.333 | | 218 | 39 | | 257 | 305 |
| 0614 | Divided | | 12 | 1.333 | | 241 | 39 | | 280 | 330 |
| 0634 | Decor full | | 12 | 1.333 | | 370 | 39 | | 409 | 475 |
| 0700 | Dutch door, pine, 1-3/4" x 6'-8" x 2'-8" wide, minimum | | 12 | 1.333 | | 675 | 39 | | 714 | 810 |
| 0720 | Maximum | | 10 | 1.600 | | 825 | 46.50 | | 871.50 | 990 |
| 0800 | 3'-0" wide, minimum | | 12 | 1.333 | | 690 | 39 | | 729 | 820 |
| 0820 | Maximum | | 10 | 1.600 | | 900 | 46.50 | | 946.50 | 1,075 |
| 1000 | Entrance door, colonial, 1-3/4" x 6'-8" x 2'-8" wide | | 16 | 1 | | 460 | 29 | | 489 | 555 |
| 1020 | 6 panel pine, 3'-0" wide | | 15 | 1.067 | | 430 | 31 | | 461 | 525 |
| 1100 | 8 panel pine, 2'-8" wide | | 16 | 1 | | 570 | 29 | | 599 | 680 |
| 1120 | 3'-0" wide | | 15 | 1.067 | | 555 | 31 | | 586 | 660 |
| 1200 | For tempered safety glass lites, (min of 2) add | | | | | 74.50 | | | 74.50 | 82 |
| 1300 | Flush, birch, solid core, 1-3/4" x 6'-8" x 2'-8" wide | 2 Carp | 16 | 1 | | 104 | 29 | | 133 | 163 |
| 1320 | 3'-0" wide | | 15 | 1.067 | | 114 | 31 | | 145 | 177 |
| 1350 | 7'-0" x 2'-8" wide | | 16 | 1 | | 113 | 29 | | 142 | 173 |
| 1360 | 3'-0" wide | | 15 | 1.067 | | 121 | 31 | | 152 | 185 |
| 1720 | Carved mahogany 3'-0" x 6'-8" | | 15 | 1.067 | | 670 | 31 | | 701 | 785 |
| 1760 | Mahogany 3'-0" x 6'-8" | | 15 | 1.067 | | 830 | 31 | | 861 | 965 |
| 2700 | Interior, closet, bi-fold, w/hardware, no frame or trim incl. | | | | | | | | | |
| 2720 | Flush, birch, 6'-6" or 6'-8" x 2'-6" wide | 2 Carp | 13 | 1.231 | Ea. | 51 | 36 | | 87 | 117 |
| 2740 | 3'-0" wide | | 13 | 1.231 | | 55 | 36 | | 91 | 121 |
| 2760 | 4'-0" wide | | 12 | 1.333 | | 97.50 | 39 | | 136.50 | 173 |
| 2780 | 5'-0" wide | | 11 | 1.455 | | 100 | 42.50 | | 142.50 | 181 |
| 2800 | 6'-0" wide | | 10 | 1.600 | | 126 | 46.50 | | 172.50 | 218 |
| 2920 | Hardboard, primed 7'-0" x 4'-0", wide | | 12 | 1.333 | | 170 | 39 | | 209 | 253 |
| 2930 | 6'-0" wide | | 10 | 1.600 | | 166 | 46.50 | | 212.50 | 262 |
| 3000 | Raised panel pine, 6'-6" or 6'-8" x 2'-6" wide | | 13 | 1.231 | | 178 | 36 | | 214 | 257 |
| 3020 | 3'-0" wide | | 13 | 1.231 | | 273 | 36 | | 309 | 360 |
| 3040 | 4'-0" wide | | 12 | 1.333 | | 305 | 39 | | 344 | 400 |
| 3060 | 5'-0" wide | | 11 | 1.455 | | 365 | 42.50 | | 407.50 | 470 |
| 3080 | 6'-0" wide | | 10 | 1.600 | | 400 | 46.50 | | 446.50 | 520 |
| 3200 | Louvered, pine 6'-6" or 6'-8" x 2'-6" wide | | 13 | 1.231 | | 137 | 36 | | 173 | 212 |
| 3220 | 3'-0" wide | | 13 | 1.231 | | 197 | 36 | | 233 | 278 |
| 3240 | 4'-0" wide | | 12 | 1.333 | | 222 | 39 | | 261 | 310 |
| 3260 | 5'-0" wide | | 11 | 1.455 | | 256 | 42.50 | | 298.50 | 355 |

## 08 14 33 – Stile and Rail Wood Doors

| 08 14 33.20 Wood Doors Residential | Crew | Daily Output | Labor-Hours | Unit | Material | 2010 Bare Costs Labor | Equipment | Total | Total Incl O&P |
|---|---|---|---|---|---|---|---|---|---|
| 3280      6'-0" wide | 2 Carp | 10 | 1.600 | Ea. | 280 | 46.50 | | 326.50 | 385 |
| 4400    Bi-passing closet, incl. hardware and frame, no trim incl. | | | | | | | | | |
| 4420      Flush, lauan, 6'-8" x 4'-0" wide | 2 Carp | 12 | 1.333 | Opng. | 169 | 39 | | 208 | 251 |
| 4440        5'-0" wide | | 11 | 1.455 | | 184 | 42.50 | | 226.50 | 273 |
| 4460        6'-0" wide | | 10 | 1.600 | | 198 | 46.50 | | 244.50 | 297 |
| 4600      Flush, birch, 6'-8" x 4'-0" wide | | 12 | 1.333 | | 217 | 39 | | 256 | 305 |
| 4620        5'-0" wide | | 11 | 1.455 | | 209 | 42.50 | | 251.50 | 300 |
| 4640        6'-0" wide | | 10 | 1.600 | | 254 | 46.50 | | 300.50 | 360 |
| 4800      Louvered, pine, 6'-8" x 4'-0" wide | | 12 | 1.333 | | 400 | 39 | | 439 | 505 |
| 4820        5'-0" wide | | 11 | 1.455 | | 390 | 42.50 | | 432.50 | 495 |
| 4840        6'-0" wide | | 10 | 1.600 | | 515 | 46.50 | | 561.50 | 650 |
| 4900      Mirrored, 6'-8" x 4'-0" wide | | 12 | 1.333 | Ea. | 300 | 39 | | 339 | 395 |
| 5000      Paneled, pine, 6'-8" x 4'-0" wide | | 12 | 1.333 | Opng. | 500 | 39 | | 539 | 615 |
| 5020        5'-0" wide | | 11 | 1.455 | | 405 | 42.50 | | 447.50 | 515 |
| 5040        6'-0" wide | | 10 | 1.600 | | 595 | 46.50 | | 641.50 | 735 |
| 5061      Hardboard, 6'-8" x 4'-0" wide | | 10 | 1.600 | | 188 | 46.50 | | 234.50 | 286 |
| 5062        5'-0" wide | | 10 | 1.600 | | 194 | 46.50 | | 240.50 | 293 |
| 5063        6'-0" wide | | 10 | 1.600 | | 215 | 46.50 | | 261.50 | 315 |
| 6100    Folding accordion, closet, including track and frame | | | | | | | | | |
| 6200      Rigid PVC | 2 Carp | 10 | 1.600 | Ea. | 33.50 | 46.50 | | 80 | 116 |
| 6220      For custom partition, add | | | | | 25% | 10% | | | |
| 7310    Passage doors, flush, no frame included | | | | | | | | | |
| 7320      Hardboard, hollow core, 1-3/8" x 6'-8" x 1'-6" wide | 2 Carp | 18 | .889 | Ea. | 42.50 | 26 | | 68.50 | 90 |
| 7330        2'-0" wide | | 18 | .889 | | 42 | 26 | | 68 | 89.50 |
| 7340        2'-6" wide | | 18 | .889 | | 46.50 | 26 | | 72.50 | 94.50 |
| 7350        2'-8" wide | | 18 | .889 | | 48 | 26 | | 74 | 96.50 |
| 7360        3'-0" wide | | 17 | .941 | | 51 | 27.50 | | 78.50 | 102 |
| 7420      Lauan, hollow core, 1-3/8" x 6'-8" x 1'-6" wide | | 18 | .889 | | 31 | 26 | | 57 | 77.50 |
| 7440        2'-0" wide | | 18 | .889 | | 31 | 26 | | 57 | 77.50 |
| 7450        2'-4" wide | | 18 | .889 | | 34.50 | 26 | | 60.50 | 81.50 |
| 7460        2'-6" wide | | 18 | .889 | | 34.50 | 26 | | 60.50 | 81.50 |
| 7480        2'-8" wide | | 18 | .889 | | 36 | 26 | | 62 | 83 |
| 7500        3'-0" wide | | 17 | .941 | | 37 | 27.50 | | 64.50 | 86.50 |
| 7700      Birch, hollow core, 1-3/8" x 6'-8" x 1'-6" wide | | 18 | .889 | | 38 | 26 | | 64 | 85.50 |
| 7720        2'-0" wide | | 18 | .889 | | 41 | 26 | | 67 | 88.50 |
| 7740        2'-6" wide | | 18 | .889 | | 49 | 26 | | 75 | 97 |
| 7760        2'-8" wide | | 18 | .889 | | 49.50 | 26 | | 75.50 | 98 |
| 7780        3'-0" wide | | 17 | .941 | | 51 | 27.50 | | 78.50 | 102 |
| 8000      Pine louvered, 1-3/8" x 6'-8" x 1'-6" wide | | 19 | .842 | | 101 | 24.50 | | 125.50 | 152 |
| 8020        2'-0" wide | | 18 | .889 | | 128 | 26 | | 154 | 184 |
| 8040        2'-6" wide | | 18 | .889 | | 139 | 26 | | 165 | 197 |
| 8060        2'-8" wide | | 18 | .889 | | 146 | 26 | | 172 | 205 |
| 8080        3'-0" wide | | 17 | .941 | | 167 | 27.50 | | 194.50 | 229 |
| 8300      Pine paneled, 1-3/8" x 6'-8" x 1'-6" wide | | 19 | .842 | | 111 | 24.50 | | 135.50 | 163 |
| 8320        2'-0" wide | | 18 | .889 | | 130 | 26 | | 156 | 187 |
| 8330        2'-4" wide | | 18 | .889 | | 150 | 26 | | 176 | 209 |
| 8340        2'-6" wide | | 18 | .889 | | 158 | 26 | | 184 | 217 |
| 8360        2'-8" wide | | 18 | .889 | | 161 | 26 | | 187 | 221 |
| 8380        3'-0" wide | | 17 | .941 | | 167 | 27.50 | | 194.50 | 229 |
| 8450      French door, pine, 15 lites, 1-3/8" x 6'-8" x 2'-6" wide | | 18 | .889 | | 178 | 26 | | 204 | 240 |
| 8470        2'-8" wide | | 18 | .889 | | 228 | 26 | | 254 | 295 |
| 8490        3'-0" wide | | 17 | .941 | | 252 | 27.50 | | 279.50 | 325 |
| 8804    Pocket door, 6 panel pine, 2'-6" x 6'-8" | | 10.50 | 1.524 | | 221 | 44.50 | | 265.50 | 320 |

# 08 14 Wood Doors

## 08 14 33 - Stile and Rail Wood Doors

| 08 14 33.20 Wood Doors Residential | | Crew | Daily Output | Labor-Hours | Unit | Material | 2010 Bare Costs Labor | Equipment | Total | Total Incl O&P |
|---|---|---|---|---|---|---|---|---|---|---|
| 8814 | 2'-8" x 6'-8" | 2 Carp | 10.50 | 1.524 | Ea. | 233 | 44.50 | | 277.50 | 330 |
| 8824 | 3'-0" x 6'-8" | | 10.50 | 1.524 | | 240 | 44.50 | | 284.50 | 340 |
| 9000 | Passage doors, flush, no frame, birch, solid core, 1-3/8" x 7'-0" x 2'-4" wide | | 16 | 1 | | 109 | 29 | | 138 | 169 |
| 9020 | 2'-8" wide | | 16 | 1 | | 116 | 29 | | 145 | 177 |
| 9040 | 3'-0" wide | | 16 | 1 | | 125 | 29 | | 154 | 187 |
| 9060 | 3'-4" wide | | 15 | 1.067 | ▼ | 144 | 31 | | 175 | 211 |
| 9080 | Pair of 3'-0" wide | | 9 | 1.778 | Pr. | 248 | 51.50 | | 299.50 | 360 |
| 9100 | Lauan, solid core, 1-3/8" x 7'-0" x 2'-4" wide | | 16 | 1 | Ea. | 101 | 29 | | 130 | 160 |
| 9120 | 2'-8" wide | | 16 | 1 | | 107 | 29 | | 136 | 167 |
| 9140 | 3'-0" wide | | 16 | 1 | | 114 | 29 | | 143 | 174 |
| 9160 | 3'-4" wide | | 15 | 1.067 | ▼ | 122 | 31 | | 153 | 186 |
| 9180 | Pair of 3'-0" wide | | 9 | 1.778 | Pr. | 207 | 51.50 | | 258.50 | 315 |
| 9200 | Hardboard, solid core, 1-3/8" x 7'-0" x 2'-4" wide | | 16 | 1 | Ea. | 124 | 29 | | 153 | 186 |
| 9220 | 2'-8" wide | | 16 | 1 | | 128 | 29 | | 157 | 190 |
| 9240 | 3'-0" wide | | 16 | 1 | | 133 | 29 | | 162 | 195 |
| 9260 | 3'-4" wide | ▼ | 15 | 1.067 | ▼ | 148 | 31 | | 179 | 215 |

## 08 14 40 - Interior Cafe Doors

### 08 14 40.10 Cafe Style Doors

| | | Crew | Daily Output | Labor-Hours | Unit | Material | Labor | Equipment | Total | Total Incl O&P |
|---|---|---|---|---|---|---|---|---|---|---|
| 0010 | **CAFE STYLE DOORS** | | | | | | | | | |
| 6520 | Interior cafe doors, 2'-6" opening, stock, panel pine | 2 Carp | 16 | 1 | Ea. | 188 | 29 | | 217 | 255 |
| 6540 | 3'-0" opening | " | 16 | 1 | " | 195 | 29 | | 224 | 264 |
| 6550 | Louvered pine | | | | | | | | | |
| 6560 | 2'-6" opening | 2 Carp | 16 | 1 | Ea. | 164 | 29 | | 193 | 229 |
| 8000 | 3'-0" opening | | 16 | 1 | | 175 | 29 | | 204 | 241 |
| 8010 | 2'-6" opening, hardwood | | 16 | 1 | | 238 | 29 | | 267 | 310 |
| 8020 | 3'-0" opening | ▼ | 16 | 1 | ▼ | 264 | 29 | | 293 | 340 |

# 08 16 Composite Doors

## 08 16 13 - Fiberglass Doors

### 08 16 13.10 Entrance Doors, Fiberous Glass

| | | | Crew | Daily Output | Labor-Hours | Unit | Material | Labor | Equipment | Total | Total Incl O&P |
|---|---|---|---|---|---|---|---|---|---|---|---|
| 0010 | **ENTRANCE DOORS, FIBEROUS GLASS** | | | | | | | | | | |
| 0020 | Exterior, fiberglass, door, 2'-8" wide x 6'-8" high | G | 2 Carp | 15 | 1.067 | Ea. | 252 | 31 | | 283 | 330 |
| 0040 | 3'-0" wide x 6'-8" high | G | | 15 | 1.067 | | 252 | 31 | | 283 | 330 |
| 0060 | 3'-0" wide x 7'-0" high | G | | 15 | 1.067 | | 450 | 31 | | 481 | 545 |
| 0080 | 3'-0" wide x 6'-8" high, with two lites | G | | 15 | 1.067 | | 294 | 31 | | 325 | 375 |
| 0100 | 3'-0" wide x 8'-0" high, with two lites | G | | 15 | 1.067 | | 490 | 31 | | 521 | 585 |
| 0110 | Half glass, 3'-0" wide x 6'-8" high | G | | 15 | 1.067 | | 294 | 31 | | 325 | 375 |
| 0120 | 3'-0" wide x 6'-8" high, low e | G | | 15 | 1.067 | | 325 | 31 | | 356 | 405 |
| 0130 | 3'-0" wide x 8'-0" high | G | | 15 | 1.067 | | 580 | 31 | | 611 | 685 |
| 0140 | 3'-0" wide x 8'-0" high, low e | G | ▼ | 15 | 1.067 | | 640 | 31 | | 671 | 750 |
| 0150 | Sidelights, 1'-0" wide x 6'-8" high, | G | | | | | 247 | | | 247 | 271 |
| 0160 | 1'-0" wide x 6'-8" high, low e | G | | | | | 256 | | | 256 | 281 |
| 0180 | 1'-0" wide x 6'-8" high, full glass | G | | | | | 275 | | | 275 | 305 |
| 0190 | 1'-0" wide x 6'-8" high, low e | G | | | | ▼ | 284 | | | 284 | 315 |

## 08 16 14 - French Doors

### 08 16 14.10 Exterior Doors With Glass Lites

| | | Crew | Daily Output | Labor-Hours | Unit | Material | Labor | Equipment | Total | Total Incl O&P |
|---|---|---|---|---|---|---|---|---|---|---|
| 0010 | **EXTERIOR DOORS WITH GLASS LITES** | | | | | | | | | |
| 0020 | French, Fir, 1-3/4", 3'-0"wide x 6'-8" high | 2 Carp | 12 | 1.333 | Ea. | 460 | 39 | | 499 | 570 |
| 0025 | double | | 12 | 1.333 | | 925 | 39 | | 964 | 1,100 |
| 0030 | Maple, 1-3/4", 3'-0"wide x 6'-8" high | ▼ | 12 | 1.333 | ▼ | 545 | 39 | | 584 | 665 |

# 08 16 Composite Doors

## 08 16 14 – French Doors

### 08 16 14.10 Exterior Doors With Glass Lites

| | | Crew | Daily Output | Labor-Hours | Unit | Material | 2010 Bare Costs Labor | 2010 Bare Costs Equipment | Total | Total Incl O&P |
|---|---|---|---|---|---|---|---|---|---|---|
| 0035 | double | 2 Carp | 12 | 1.333 | Ea. | 1,100 | 39 | | 1,139 | 1,275 |
| 0040 | Cherry, 1-3/4", 3'-0"wide x 6'-8" high | | 12 | 1.333 | | 625 | 39 | | 664 | 750 |
| 0045 | double | | 12 | 1.333 | | 1,250 | 39 | | 1,289 | 1,450 |
| 0100 | Mahogany, 1-3/4", 3'-0"wide x 8'-0" high | | 10 | 1.600 | | 510 | 46.50 | | 556.50 | 640 |
| 0105 | double | | 10 | 1.600 | | 1,025 | 46.50 | | 1,071.50 | 1,200 |
| 0110 | Fir, 1-3/4", 3'-0"wide x 8'-0" high | | 10 | 1.600 | | 870 | 46.50 | | 916.50 | 1,025 |
| 0115 | double | | 10 | 1.600 | | 1,750 | 46.50 | | 1,796.50 | 2,000 |
| 0120 | Oak, 1-3/4", 3'-0"wide x 8'-0" high | | 10 | 1.600 | | 1,800 | 46.50 | | 1,846.50 | 2,050 |
| 0125 | double | | 10 | 1.600 | | 3,600 | 46.50 | | 3,646.50 | 4,025 |

# 08 17 Integrated Door Opening Assemblies

## 08 17 23 – Integrated Wood Door Opening Assemblies

### 08 17 23.10 Pre-Hung Doors

| | | Crew | Daily Output | Labor-Hours | Unit | Material | 2010 Bare Costs Labor | 2010 Bare Costs Equipment | Total | Total Incl O&P |
|---|---|---|---|---|---|---|---|---|---|---|
| 0010 | **PRE-HUNG DOORS** | | | | | | | | | |
| 0300 | Exterior, wood, comb. storm & screen, 6'-9" x 2'-6" wide | 2 Carp | 15 | 1.067 | Ea. | 289 | 31 | | 320 | 370 |
| 0320 | 2'-8" wide | | 15 | 1.067 | | 289 | 31 | | 320 | 370 |
| 0340 | 3'-0" wide | | 15 | 1.067 | | 296 | 31 | | 327 | 375 |
| 0360 | For 7'-0" high door, add | | | | | 24 | | | 24 | 26.50 |
| 1600 | Entrance door, flush, birch, solid core | | | | | | | | | |
| 1620 | 4-5/8" solid jamb, 1-3/4" x 6'-8" x 2'-8" wide | 2 Carp | 16 | 1 | Ea. | 285 | 29 | | 314 | 365 |
| 1640 | 3'-0" wide | | 16 | 1 | | 350 | 29 | | 379 | 435 |
| 1642 | 5-5/8" jamb | | 16 | 1 | | 325 | 29 | | 354 | 405 |
| 1680 | For 7'-0" high door, add | | | | | 21 | | | 21 | 23 |
| 2000 | Entrance door, colonial, 6 panel pine | | | | | | | | | |
| 2020 | 4-5/8" solid jamb, 1-3/4" x 6'-8" x 2'-8" wide | 2 Carp | 16 | 1 | Ea. | 530 | 29 | | 559 | 630 |
| 2040 | 3'-0" wide | " | 16 | 1 | | 530 | 29 | | 559 | 630 |
| 2060 | For 7'-0" high door, add | | | | | 52.50 | | | 52.50 | 58 |
| 2200 | For 5-5/8" solid jamb, add | | | | | 40.50 | | | 40.50 | 44.50 |
| 2250 | French door, 6'-8" x 4'-0" wide, 1/2" insul. glass and grille | 2 Carp | 7 | 2.286 | Pr. | 1,100 | 66.50 | | 1,166.50 | 1,300 |
| 2260 | 5'-0" wide | | 7 | 2.286 | | 1,200 | 66.50 | | 1,266.50 | 1,425 |
| 2270 | Pine french door, Pair, 6'-8" x 5'-0" wide, including frame | | 7 | 2.286 | | 1,250 | 66.50 | | 1,316.50 | 1,475 |
| 2280 | French door, Two 6'-8" x 3'-0" wide, 15 lites | | 14 | 1.143 | Ea. | 1,200 | 33.50 | | 1,233.50 | 1,375 |
| 2500 | Exterior, metal face, insulated, incl. jamb, brickmold and | | | | | | | | | |
| 2520 | threshold, flush, 2'-8" x 6'-8" | 2 Carp | 16 | 1 | Ea. | 244 | 29 | | 273 | 320 |
| 2550 | 3'-0" x 6'-8" | | 16 | 1 | | 262 | 29 | | 291 | 335 |
| 3500 | Embossed, 6 panel, 2'-8" x 6'-8" | | 16 | 1 | | 250 | 29 | | 279 | 325 |
| 3550 | 3'-0" x 6'-8" | | 16 | 1 | | 251 | 29 | | 280 | 325 |
| 3600 | 2 narrow lites, 2'-8" x 6'-8" | | 16 | 1 | | 269 | 29 | | 298 | 345 |
| 3650 | 3'-0" x 6'-8" | | 16 | 1 | | 272 | 29 | | 301 | 350 |
| 3700 | Half glass, 2'-8" x 6'-8" | | 16 | 1 | | 294 | 29 | | 323 | 375 |
| 3750 | 3'-0" x 6'-8" | | 16 | 1 | | 300 | 29 | | 329 | 380 |
| 3800 | 2 top lites, 2'-8" x 6'-8" | | 16 | 1 | | 265 | 29 | | 294 | 340 |
| 3850 | 3'-0" x 6'-8" | | 16 | 1 | | 267 | 29 | | 296 | 340 |
| 4000 | Interior, passage door, 4-5/8" solid jamb | | | | | | | | | |
| 4400 | Lauan, flush, solid core, 1-3/8" x 6'-8" x 2'-6" wide | 2 Carp | 17 | .941 | Ea. | 182 | 27.50 | | 209.50 | 246 |
| 4420 | 2'-8" wide | | 17 | .941 | | 182 | 27.50 | | 209.50 | 246 |
| 4440 | 3'-0" wide | | 16 | 1 | | 195 | 29 | | 224 | 264 |
| 4600 | Hollow core, 1-3/8" x 6'-8" x 2'-6" wide | | 17 | .941 | | 120 | 27.50 | | 147.50 | 178 |
| 4620 | 2'-8" wide | | 17 | .941 | | 120 | 27.50 | | 147.50 | 178 |
| 4640 | 3'-0" wide | | 16 | 1 | | 135 | 29 | | 164 | 198 |
| 4700 | For 7'-0" high door, add | | | | | 25 | | | 25 | 27.50 |

# 08 17 Integrated Door Opening Assemblies

## 08 17 23 – Integrated Wood Door Opening Assemblies

### 08 17 23.10 Pre-Hung Doors

| | | Crew | Daily Output | Labor-Hours | Unit | Material | 2010 Bare Costs Labor | Equipment | Total | Total Incl O&P |
|---|---|---|---|---|---|---|---|---|---|---|
| 5000 | Birch, flush, solid core, 1-3/8" x 6'-8" x 2'-6" wide | 2 Carp | 17 | .941 | Ea. | 187 | 27.50 | | 214.50 | 252 |
| 5020 | 2'-8" wide | | 17 | .941 | | 195 | 27.50 | | 222.50 | 261 |
| 5040 | 3'-0" wide | | 16 | 1 | | 217 | 29 | | 246 | 288 |
| 5200 | Hollow core, 1-3/8" x 6'-8" x 2'-6" wide | | 17 | .941 | | 147 | 27.50 | | 174.50 | 208 |
| 5220 | 2'-8" wide | | 17 | .941 | | 153 | 27.50 | | 180.50 | 214 |
| 5240 | 3'-0" wide | | 16 | 1 | | 152 | 29 | | 181 | 217 |
| 5280 | For 7'-0" high door, add | | | | | 22 | | | 22 | 24 |
| 5500 | Hardboard paneled, 1-3/8" x 6'-8" x 2'-6" wide | 2 Carp | 17 | .941 | | 142 | 27.50 | | 169.50 | 202 |
| 5520 | 2'-8" wide | | 17 | .941 | | 150 | 27.50 | | 177.50 | 211 |
| 5540 | 3'-0" wide | | 16 | 1 | | 147 | 29 | | 176 | 211 |
| 6000 | Pine paneled, 1-3/8" x 6'-8" x 2'-6" wide | | 17 | .941 | | 245 | 27.50 | | 272.50 | 315 |
| 6020 | 2'-8" wide | | 17 | .941 | | 265 | 27.50 | | 292.50 | 340 |
| 6040 | 3'-0" wide | | 16 | 1 | | 270 | 29 | | 299 | 345 |
| 6500 | For 5-5/8" solid jamb, add | | | | | 19 | | | 19 | 21 |
| 6520 | For split jamb, deduct | | | | | 21 | | | 21 | 23 |
| 7600 | Oak, 6 panel, 1-3/4" x 6'-8" x 3'-0" | 1 Carp | 17 | .471 | | 860 | 13.70 | | 873.70 | 975 |
| 8500 | Pocket door frame with lauan, flush, hollow core , 1-3/8" x 3'-0" x 6'-8" | " | 17 | .471 | | 245 | 13.70 | | 258.70 | 293 |

# 08 31 Access Doors and Panels

## 08 31 13 – Access Doors and Frames

### 08 31 13.20 Bulkhead/Cellar Doors

| | | Crew | Daily Output | Labor-Hours | Unit | Material | 2010 Bare Costs Labor | Equipment | Total | Total Incl O&P |
|---|---|---|---|---|---|---|---|---|---|---|
| 0010 | **BULKHEAD/CELLAR DOORS** | | | | | | | | | |
| 0020 | Steel, not incl. sides, 44" x 62" | 1 Carp | 5.50 | 1.455 | Ea. | 490 | 42.50 | | 532.50 | 610 |
| 0100 | 52" x 73" | | 5.10 | 1.569 | | 660 | 45.50 | | 705.50 | 800 |
| 0500 | With sides and foundation plates, 57" x 45" x 24" | | 4.70 | 1.702 | | 700 | 49.50 | | 749.50 | 855 |
| 0600 | 42" x 49" x 51" | | 4.30 | 1.860 | | 790 | 54 | | 844 | 960 |

# 08 32 Sliding Glass Doors

## 08 32 13 – Sliding Aluminum-Framed Glass Doors

### 08 32 13.10 Sliding Aluminum Doors

| | | Crew | Daily Output | Labor-Hours | Unit | Material | 2010 Bare Costs Labor | Equipment | Total | Total Incl O&P |
|---|---|---|---|---|---|---|---|---|---|---|
| 0010 | **SLIDING ALUMINUM DOORS** | | | | | | | | | |
| 0350 | Aluminum, 5/8" tempered insulated glass, 6' wide | | | | | | | | | |
| 0400 | Premium | 2 Carp | 4 | 4 | Ea. | 1,550 | 116 | | 1,666 | 1,925 |
| 0450 | Economy | | 4 | 4 | | 870 | 116 | | 986 | 1,150 |
| 0500 | 8' wide, premium | | 3 | 5.333 | | 1,625 | 155 | | 1,780 | 2,025 |
| 0550 | Economy | | 3 | 5.333 | | 1,400 | 155 | | 1,555 | 1,775 |
| 0600 | 12' wide, premium | | 2.50 | 6.400 | | 2,950 | 186 | | 3,136 | 3,575 |
| 0650 | Economy | | 2.50 | 6.400 | | 1,500 | 186 | | 1,686 | 1,975 |
| 0700 | Non-insulated, 6' wide | | 4 | 4 | | 1,075 | 116 | | 1,191 | 1,375 |
| 4000 | Aluminum, baked on enamel, temp glass, 6'-8" x 10'-0" wide | | 4 | 4 | | 970 | 116 | | 1,086 | 1,275 |
| 4020 | Insulating glass, 6'-8" x 6'-0" wide | | 4 | 4 | | 860 | 116 | | 976 | 1,150 |
| 4040 | 8'-0" wide | | 3 | 5.333 | | 1,000 | 155 | | 1,155 | 1,350 |
| 4060 | 10'-0" wide | | 2 | 8 | | 1,275 | 233 | | 1,508 | 1,800 |
| 4080 | Anodized, temp glass, 6'-8" x 6'-0" wide | | 4 | 4 | | 440 | 116 | | 556 | 680 |
| 4100 | 8'-0" wide | | 3 | 5.333 | | 560 | 155 | | 715 | 875 |
| 4120 | 10'-0" wide | | 2 | 8 | | 630 | 233 | | 863 | 1,075 |
| 4200 | Vinyl clad, anodized, temp glass, 6'-8" x 6'-0" wide | | 4 | 4 | | 410 | 116 | | 526 | 645 |
| 4240 | 8'-0" wide | | 3 | 5.333 | | 570 | 155 | | 725 | 885 |
| 4260 | 10'-0" wide | | 2 | 8 | | 620 | 233 | | 853 | 1,075 |

# 08 32 Sliding Glass Doors

## 08 32 13 – Sliding Aluminum-Framed Glass Doors

| 08 32 13.10 Sliding Aluminum Doors | | Crew | Daily Output | Labor-Hours | Unit | Material | 2010 Bare Costs Labor | Equipment | Total | Total Incl O&P |
|---|---|---|---|---|---|---|---|---|---|---|
| 4280 | Insulating glass, 6'-8" x 6'-0' wide | 2 Carp | 4 | 4 | Ea. | 995 | 116 | | 1,111 | 1,300 |
| 4300 | 8'-0" wide | | 3 | 5.333 | | 920 | 155 | | 1,075 | 1,250 |
| 4320 | 10'-0" wide | | 4 | 4 | | 1,500 | 116 | | 1,616 | 1,850 |

## 08 32 19 – Sliding Wood-Framed Glass Doors

### 08 32 19.10 Sliding Wood Doors

| | | Crew | Daily Output | Labor-Hours | Unit | Material | Labor | Equipment | Total | Total Incl O&P |
|---|---|---|---|---|---|---|---|---|---|---|
| 0010 | **SLIDING WOOD DOORS** | | | | | | | | | |
| 0020 | Wood, 5/8" tempered insul. glass, 6' wide, premium | 2 Carp | 4 | 4 | Ea. | 1,400 | 116 | | 1,516 | 1,725 |
| 0100 | Economy | | 4 | 4 | | 1,100 | 116 | | 1,216 | 1,425 |
| 0150 | 8' wide, wood, premium | | 3 | 5.333 | | 1,775 | 155 | | 1,930 | 2,200 |
| 0200 | Economy | | 3 | 5.333 | | 1,475 | 155 | | 1,630 | 1,875 |
| 0250 | 12' wide, wood, vinyl clad | | 2.50 | 6.400 | | 2,925 | 186 | | 3,111 | 3,550 |
| 0300 | Economy | | 2.50 | 6.400 | | 2,400 | 186 | | 2,586 | 2,975 |

### 08 32 19.15 Sliding Glass Vinyl-Clad Wood Doors

| | | | Crew | Daily Output | Labor-Hours | Unit | Material | Labor | Equipment | Total | Total Incl O&P |
|---|---|---|---|---|---|---|---|---|---|---|---|
| 0010 | **SLIDING GLASS VINYL-CLAD WOOD DOORS** | | | | | | | | | | |
| 0012 | Vinyl clad, 1" insul. glass, 6'-0" x 6'-10" high | G | 2 Carp | 4 | 4 | Opng. | 1,575 | 116 | | 1,691 | 1,950 |
| 0020 | Glass, sliding vinyl clad, insul. glass, 6'-0" x 6'-8", | G | | 4 | 4 | Ea. | 1,525 | 116 | | 1,641 | 1,875 |
| 0030 | 6'-0" x 8'-0" high | G | | 4 | 4 | | 1,950 | 116 | | 2,066 | 2,350 |
| 0050 | 5'-0" x 6'-8" high | G | | 4 | 4 | | 1,475 | 116 | | 1,591 | 1,825 |
| 0100 | 8'-0" x 6'-10" high | G | | 4 | 4 | Opng. | 2,000 | 116 | | 2,116 | 2,400 |
| 0104 | 8'-0" x 6'-8" double | G | | 4 | 4 | Ea. | 1,875 | 116 | | 1,991 | 2,250 |
| 0150 | 8'-0" x 8'-0" high | G | | 4 | 4 | Opng. | 2,175 | 116 | | 2,291 | 2,600 |
| 0500 | 4 leaf, 9'-0" x 6'-10" high | G | | 3 | 5.333 | " | 3,175 | 155 | | 3,330 | 3,750 |
| 0550 | 9'-0" x 8'-0" high | G | | 3 | 5.333 | Ea. | 3,675 | 155 | | 3,830 | 4,300 |
| 0600 | 12'-0" x 6'-10" high | G | | 3 | 5.333 | Opng. | 3,800 | 155 | | 3,955 | 4,425 |

# 08 36 Panel Doors

## 08 36 13 – Sectional Doors

### 08 36 13.20 Residential Garage Doors

| | | Crew | Daily Output | Labor-Hours | Unit | Material | Labor | Equipment | Total | Total Incl O&P |
|---|---|---|---|---|---|---|---|---|---|---|---|
| 0010 | **RESIDENTIAL GARAGE DOORS** | | | | | | | | | |
| 0050 | Hinged, wood, custom, double door, 9' x 7' | 2 Carp | 4 | 4 | Ea. | 585 | 116 | | 701 | 840 |
| 0070 | 16' x 7' | | 3 | 5.333 | | 965 | 155 | | 1,120 | 1,300 |
| 0200 | Overhead, sectional, incl. hardware, fiberglass, 9' x 7', standard | | 5.28 | 3.030 | | 735 | 88 | | 823 | 955 |
| 0220 | Deluxe | | 5.28 | 3.030 | | 935 | 88 | | 1,023 | 1,175 |
| 0300 | 16' x 7', standard | | 6 | 2.667 | | 1,550 | 77.50 | | 1,627.50 | 1,825 |
| 0320 | Deluxe | | 6 | 2.667 | | 1,975 | 77.50 | | 2,052.50 | 2,300 |
| 0500 | Hardboard, 9' x 7', standard | | 8 | 2 | | 550 | 58 | | 608 | 705 |
| 0520 | Deluxe | | 8 | 2 | | 775 | 58 | | 833 | 955 |
| 0600 | 16' x 7', standard | | 6 | 2.667 | | 1,125 | 77.50 | | 1,202.50 | 1,375 |
| 0620 | Deluxe | | 6 | 2.667 | | 1,350 | 77.50 | | 1,427.50 | 1,600 |
| 0700 | Metal, 9' x 7', standard | | 5.28 | 3.030 | | 580 | 88 | | 668 | 790 |
| 0720 | Deluxe | | 8 | 2 | | 855 | 58 | | 913 | 1,050 |
| 0800 | 16' x 7', standard | | 3 | 5.333 | | 730 | 155 | | 885 | 1,050 |
| 0820 | Deluxe | | 6 | 2.667 | | 1,375 | 77.50 | | 1,452.50 | 1,625 |
| 0900 | Wood, 9' x 7', standard | | 8 | 2 | | 720 | 58 | | 778 | 890 |
| 0920 | Deluxe | | 8 | 2 | | 2,050 | 58 | | 2,108 | 2,350 |
| 1000 | 16' x 7', standard | | 6 | 2.667 | | 1,425 | 77.50 | | 1,502.50 | 1,700 |
| 1020 | Deluxe | | 6 | 2.667 | | 2,975 | 77.50 | | 3,052.50 | 3,400 |
| 1800 | Door hardware, sectional | 1 Carp | 4 | 2 | | 320 | 58 | | 378 | 450 |
| 1810 | Door tracks only | | 4 | 2 | | 138 | 58 | | 196 | 250 |
| 1820 | One side only | | 7 | 1.143 | | 110 | 33.50 | | 143.50 | 177 |

# 08 36 Panel Doors

## 08 36 13 – Sectional Doors

| 08 36 13.20 Residential Garage Doors | | Crew | Daily Output | Labor-Hours | Unit | Material | 2010 Bare Costs | | Total | Total Incl O&P |
|---|---|---|---|---|---|---|---|---|---|---|
| | | | | | | | Labor | Equipment | | |
| 3000 | Swing-up, including hardware, fiberglass, 9' x 7', standard | 2 Carp | 8 | 2 | Ea. | 980 | 58 | | 1,038 | 1,175 |
| 3020 | Deluxe | | 8 | 2 | | 790 | 58 | | 848 | 970 |
| 3100 | 16' x 7', standard | | 6 | 2.667 | | 1,225 | 77.50 | | 1,302.50 | 1,475 |
| 3120 | Deluxe | | 6 | 2.667 | | 980 | 77.50 | | 1,057.50 | 1,200 |
| 3200 | Hardboard, 9' x 7', standard | | 8 | 2 | | 345 | 58 | | 403 | 480 |
| 3220 | Deluxe | | 8 | 2 | | 455 | 58 | | 513 | 605 |
| 3300 | 16' x 7', standard | | 6 | 2.667 | | 480 | 77.50 | | 557.50 | 660 |
| 3320 | Deluxe | | 6 | 2.667 | | 715 | 77.50 | | 792.50 | 915 |
| 3400 | Metal, 9' x 7', standard | | 8 | 2 | | 380 | 58 | | 438 | 520 |
| 3420 | Deluxe | | 8 | 2 | | 835 | 58 | | 893 | 1,025 |
| 3500 | 16' x 7', standard | | 6 | 2.667 | | 600 | 77.50 | | 677.50 | 790 |
| 3520 | Deluxe | | 6 | 2.667 | | 960 | 77.50 | | 1,037.50 | 1,175 |
| 3600 | Wood, 9' x 7', standard | | 8 | 2 | | 450 | 58 | | 508 | 595 |
| 3620 | Deluxe | | 8 | 2 | | 935 | 58 | | 993 | 1,125 |
| 3700 | 16' x 7', standard | | 6 | 2.667 | | 725 | 77.50 | | 802.50 | 930 |
| 3720 | Deluxe | | 6 | 2.667 | | 1,025 | 77.50 | | 1,102.50 | 1,250 |
| 3900 | Door hardware only, swing up | 1 Carp | 4 | 2 | | 145 | 58 | | 203 | 258 |
| 3920 | One side only | | 7 | 1.143 | | 70 | 33.50 | | 103.50 | 133 |
| 4000 | For electric operator, economy, add | | 8 | 1 | | 410 | 29 | | 439 | 500 |
| 4100 | Deluxe, including remote control | | 8 | 1 | | 600 | 29 | | 629 | 710 |
| 4500 | For transmitter/receiver control , add to operator | | | | Total | 105 | | | 105 | 116 |
| 4600 | Transmitters, additional | | | | " | 50 | | | 50 | 55 |
| 6000 | Replace section, on sectional door, fiberglass, 9' x 7' | 1 Carp | 4 | 2 | Ea. | 445 | 58 | | 503 | 585 |
| 6020 | 16' x 7' | | 3.50 | 2.286 | | 525 | 66.50 | | 591.50 | 690 |
| 6200 | Hardboard, 9' x 7' | | 4 | 2 | | 113 | 58 | | 171 | 222 |
| 6220 | 16' x 7' | | 3.50 | 2.286 | | 214 | 66.50 | | 280.50 | 350 |
| 6300 | Metal, 9' x 7' | | 4 | 2 | | 181 | 58 | | 239 | 297 |
| 6320 | 16' x 7' | | 3.50 | 2.286 | | 295 | 66.50 | | 361.50 | 435 |
| 6500 | Wood, 9' x 7' | | 4 | 2 | | 114 | 58 | | 172 | 223 |
| 6520 | 16' x 7' | | 3.50 | 2.286 | | 221 | 66.50 | | 287.50 | 355 |

# 08 51 Metal Windows

## 08 51 13 – Aluminum Windows

### 08 51 13.20 Aluminum Windows

| | | Crew | Daily Output | Labor-Hours | Unit | Material | 2010 Bare Costs | | Total | Total Incl O&P |
|---|---|---|---|---|---|---|---|---|---|---|
| | | | | | | | Labor | Equipment | | |
| 0010 | **ALUMINUM WINDOWS**, incl. frame and glazing, commercial grade | | | | | | | | | |
| 1000 | Stock units, casement, 3'-1" x 3'-2" opening | 2 Sswk | 10 | 1.600 | Ea. | 355 | 50 | | 405 | 485 |
| 1040 | Insulating glass | " | 10 | 1.600 | | 460 | 50 | | 510 | 600 |
| 1050 | Add for storms | | | | | 115 | | | 115 | 126 |
| 1600 | Projected, with screen, 3'-1" x 3'-2" opening | 2 Sswk | 10 | 1.600 | | 335 | 50 | | 385 | 465 |
| 1650 | Insulating glass | " | 10 | 1.600 | | 290 | 50 | | 340 | 415 |
| 1700 | Add for storms | | | | | 112 | | | 112 | 123 |
| 2000 | 4'-5" x 5'-3" opening | 2 Sswk | 8 | 2 | | 380 | 63 | | 443 | 540 |
| 2050 | Insulating glass | " | 8 | 2 | | 405 | 63 | | 468 | 565 |
| 2100 | Add for storms | | | | | 120 | | | 120 | 132 |
| 2500 | Enamel finish windows, 3'-1" x 3'-2" | 2 Sswk | 10 | 1.600 | | 340 | 50 | | 390 | 470 |
| 2550 | Insulating glass | | 10 | 1.600 | | 255 | 50 | | 305 | 375 |
| 2600 | 4'-5" x 5'-3" | | 8 | 2 | | 385 | 63 | | 448 | 545 |
| 2700 | Insulating glass | | 8 | 2 | | 350 | 63 | | 413 | 500 |
| 3000 | Single hung, 2' x 3' opening, enameled, standard glazed | | 10 | 1.600 | | 198 | 50 | | 248 | 315 |
| 3100 | Insulating glass | | 10 | 1.600 | | 240 | 50 | | 290 | 360 |
| 3300 | 2'-8" x 6'-8" opening, standard glazed | | 8 | 2 | | 350 | 63 | | 413 | 505 |

# 08 51 Metal Windows

## 08 51 13 – Aluminum Windows

| 08 51 13.20 Aluminum Windows | Crew | Daily Output | Labor-Hours | Unit | Material | 2010 Bare Costs Labor | 2010 Bare Costs Equipment | Total | Total Incl O&P |
|---|---|---|---|---|---|---|---|---|---|
| 3400 | Insulating glass | 2 Sswk | 8 | 2 | Ea. | 450 | 63 | | 513 | 615 |
| 3700 | 3'-4" x 5'-0" opening, standard glazed | | 9 | 1.778 | | 286 | 56 | | 342 | 420 |
| 3800 | Insulating glass | | 9 | 1.778 | | 315 | 56 | | 371 | 455 |
| 4000 | Sliding aluminum, 3' x 2' opening, standard glazed | | 10 | 1.600 | | 209 | 50 | | 259 | 325 |
| 4100 | Insulating glass | | 10 | 1.600 | | 224 | 50 | | 274 | 340 |
| 4300 | 5' x 3' opening, standard glazed | | 9 | 1.778 | | 320 | 56 | | 376 | 455 |
| 4400 | Insulating glass | | 9 | 1.778 | | 370 | 56 | | 426 | 515 |
| 4600 | 8' x 4' opening, standard glazed | | 6 | 2.667 | | 335 | 83.50 | | 418.50 | 530 |
| 4700 | Insulating glass | | 6 | 2.667 | | 545 | 83.50 | | 628.50 | 755 |
| 5000 | 9' x 5' opening, standard glazed | | 4 | 4 | | 510 | 126 | | 636 | 800 |
| 5100 | Insulating glass | | 4 | 4 | | 820 | 126 | | 946 | 1,150 |
| 5500 | Sliding, with thermal barrier and screen, 6' x 4', 2 track | | 8 | 2 | | 695 | 63 | | 758 | 885 |
| 5700 | 4 track | | 8 | 2 | | 880 | 63 | | 943 | 1,100 |
| 6000 | For above units with bronze finish, add | | | | | 12% | | | | |
| 6200 | For installation in concrete openings, add | | | | | 5% | | | | |

## 08 51 23 – Steel Windows

### 08 51 23.10 Steel Sash

| | | Crew | Daily Output | Labor-Hours | Unit | Material | Labor | Equipment | Total | Total Incl O&P |
|---|---|---|---|---|---|---|---|---|---|---|
| 0010 | **STEEL SASH** Custom units, glazing and trim not included | | | | | | | | | |
| 1200 | Basement/utility window, 1'-11" x 2'-8" | 1 Carp | 14 | .571 | Ea. | 135 | 16.65 | | 151.65 | 177 |

### 08 51 23.40 Basement Utility Windows

| | | Crew | Daily Output | Labor-Hours | Unit | Material | Labor | Equipment | Total | Total Incl O&P |
|---|---|---|---|---|---|---|---|---|---|---|
| 0010 | **BASEMENT UTILITY WINDOWS** | | | | | | | | | |
| 0015 | 1'-3" x 2'-8" | 1 Carp | 16 | .500 | Ea. | 119 | 14.55 | | 133.55 | 156 |
| 1100 | 1'-7" x 2'-8" | " | 16 | .500 | " | 133 | 14.55 | | 147.55 | 171 |

## 08 51 66 – Metal Window Screens

### 08 51 66.10 Screens

| | | Crew | Daily Output | Labor-Hours | Unit | Material | Labor | Equipment | Total | Total Incl O&P |
|---|---|---|---|---|---|---|---|---|---|---|
| 0010 | **SCREENS** | | | | | | | | | |
| 0020 | For metal sash, aluminum or bronze mesh, flat screen | 2 Sswk | 1200 | .013 | S.F. | 4.10 | .42 | | 4.52 | 5.30 |
| 0500 | Wicket screen, inside window | " | 1000 | .016 | " | 6.30 | .50 | | 6.80 | 7.90 |
| 0600 | Residential, aluminum mesh and frame, 2' x 3' | 2 Carp | 32 | .500 | Ea. | 14 | 14.55 | | 28.55 | 40 |
| 0610 | Rescreen | | 50 | .320 | | 12 | 9.30 | | 21.30 | 29 |
| 0620 | 3' x 5' | | 32 | .500 | | 46 | 14.55 | | 60.55 | 75 |
| 0630 | Rescreen | | 45 | .356 | | 30 | 10.35 | | 40.35 | 50.50 |
| 0640 | 4' x 8' | | 25 | .640 | | 72.50 | 18.60 | | 91.10 | 112 |
| 0650 | Rescreen | | 40 | .400 | | 46 | 11.65 | | 57.65 | 70 |
| 0660 | Patio door | | 25 | .640 | | 135 | 18.60 | | 153.60 | 181 |
| 0680 | Rescreening | | 1600 | .010 | S.F. | 2 | .29 | | 2.29 | 2.69 |
| 1000 | For solar louvers, add | 2 Sswk | 160 | .100 | " | 23.50 | 3.14 | | 26.64 | 31.50 |

# 08 52 Wood Windows

## 08 52 10 – Plain Wood Windows

### 08 52 10.10 Wood Windows

| | | Crew | Daily Output | Labor-Hours | Unit | Material | Labor | Equipment | Total | Total Incl O&P |
|---|---|---|---|---|---|---|---|---|---|---|
| 0010 | **WOOD WINDOWS**, including frame, screens and grilles | | | | | | | | | |
| 0020 | Residential, stock units | | | | | | | | | |
| 0050 | Awning type, double insulated glass, 2'-10" x 1'-9" opening | 2 Carp | 12 | 1.333 | Opng. | 224 | 39 | | 263 | 315 |
| 0100 | 2'-10" x 6'-0" opening | 1 Carp | 8 | 1 | | 530 | 29 | | 559 | 635 |
| 0200 | 4'-0" x 3'-6" single pane | | 10 | .800 | | 360 | 23.50 | | 383.50 | 435 |
| 0300 | 6' x 5' single pane | | 8 | 1 | Ea. | 490 | 29 | | 519 | 585 |
| 1000 | Casement, 2'-0" x 3'-4" high | 2 Carp | 20 | .800 | | 258 | 23.50 | | 281.50 | 325 |
| 1020 | 2'-0" x 4'-0" | | 18 | .889 | | 276 | 26 | | 302 | 350 |
| 1040 | 2'-0" x 5'-0" | | 17 | .941 | | 305 | 27.50 | | 332.50 | 380 |

# 08 52 Wood Windows

## 08 52 10 – Plain Wood Windows

| 08 52 10.10 Wood Windows | Crew | Daily Output | Labor-Hours | Unit | Material | 2010 Bare Costs Labor | Equipment | Total | Total Incl O&P |
|---|---|---|---|---|---|---|---|---|---|
| 1060 | 2'-0" x 6'-0" | 2 Carp | 16 | 1 | Ea. | 300 | 29 | | 329 | 380 |
| 1080 | 4'-0" x 3'-4" | | 15 | 1.067 | | 575 | 31 | | 606 | 685 |
| 1100 | 4'-0" x 4'-0" | | 15 | 1.067 | | 645 | 31 | | 676 | 760 |
| 1120 | 4'-0" x 5'-0" | | 14 | 1.143 | | 730 | 33.50 | | 763.50 | 860 |
| 1140 | 4'-0" x 6'-0" | | 12 | 1.333 | | 825 | 39 | | 864 | 970 |
| 1600 | Casement units, 8' x 5', with screens, double insulated glass | | 2.50 | 6.400 | Opng. | 1,375 | 186 | | 1,561 | 1,850 |
| 1700 | Low E glass | | 2.50 | 6.400 | | 1,575 | 186 | | 1,761 | 2,050 |
| 2300 | Casements, including screens, 2'-0" x 3'-4", dbl insulated glass | | 11 | 1.455 | | 262 | 42.50 | | 304.50 | 360 |
| 2400 | Low E glass | | 11 | 1.455 | | 262 | 42.50 | | 304.50 | 360 |
| 2600 | 2 lite, 4'-0" x 4'-0", double insulated glass | | 9 | 1.778 | | 485 | 51.50 | | 536.50 | 615 |
| 2700 | Low E glass | | 9 | 1.778 | | 495 | 51.50 | | 546.50 | 625 |
| 2900 | 3 lite, 5'-2" x 5'-0", double insulated glass | | 7 | 2.286 | | 730 | 66.50 | | 796.50 | 915 |
| 3000 | Low E glass | | 7 | 2.286 | | 775 | 66.50 | | 841.50 | 965 |
| 3200 | 4 lite, 7'-0" x 5'-0", double insulated glass | | 6 | 2.667 | | 1,050 | 77.50 | | 1,127.50 | 1,275 |
| 3300 | Low E glass | | 6 | 2.667 | | 1,100 | 77.50 | | 1,177.50 | 1,350 |
| 3500 | 5 lite, 8'-6" x 5'-0", double insulated glass | | 5 | 3.200 | | 1,375 | 93 | | 1,468 | 1,675 |
| 3600 | Low E glass | | 5 | 3.200 | | 1,475 | 93 | | 1,568 | 1,750 |
| 3800 | For removable wood grilles, diamond pattern, add | | | | Leaf | 34 | | | 34 | 37.50 |
| 3900 | Rectangular pattern, add | | | | " | 34 | | | 34 | 37.50 |
| 4000 | Bow, fixed lites, 8' x 5', double insulated glass | 2 Carp | 3 | 5.333 | Opng. | 1,375 | 155 | | 1,530 | 1,775 |
| 4100 | Low E glass | " | 3 | 5.333 | " | 1,875 | 155 | | 2,030 | 2,325 |
| 4150 | 6'-0" x 5'-0" | 1 Carp | 8 | 1 | Ea. | 1,250 | 29 | | 1,279 | 1,425 |
| 4300 | Fixed lites, 9'-9" x 5'-0", double insulated glass | 2 Carp | 2 | 8 | Opng. | 950 | 233 | | 1,183 | 1,450 |
| 4400 | Low E glass | " | 2 | 8 | " | 1,050 | 233 | | 1,283 | 1,550 |
| 5000 | Bow, casement, 8'-1" x 4'-8" high | 3 Carp | 8 | 3 | Ea. | 1,550 | 87.50 | | 1,637.50 | 1,875 |
| 5020 | 9'-6" x 4'-8" | | 8 | 3 | | 1,650 | 87.50 | | 1,737.50 | 1,975 |
| 5040 | 8'-1" x 5'-1" | | 8 | 3 | | 1,875 | 87.50 | | 1,962.50 | 2,225 |
| 5060 | 9'-6" x 5'-1" | | 6 | 4 | | 1,900 | 116 | | 2,016 | 2,275 |
| 5080 | 8'-1" x 6'-0" | | 6 | 4 | | 1,875 | 116 | | 1,991 | 2,275 |
| 5100 | 9'-6" x 6'-0" | | 6 | 4 | | 1,975 | 116 | | 2,091 | 2,375 |
| 5800 | Skylights, hatches, vents, and sky roofs, see Div. 08 62 13.00 | | | | | | | | | |
| 9000 | Minimum labor/equipment charge | 2 Carp | 2 | 8 | Job | | 233 | | 233 | 390 |

## 08 52 10.20 Awning Window

| | | Crew | Daily Output | Labor-Hours | Unit | Material | 2010 Bare Costs Labor | Equipment | Total | Total Incl O&P |
|---|---|---|---|---|---|---|---|---|---|---|
| 0010 | **AWNING WINDOW**, Including frame, screens and grilles | | | | | | | | | |
| 0100 | Average quality, builders model, 34" x 22", double insulated glass | 1 Carp | 10 | .800 | Ea. | 253 | 23.50 | | 276.50 | 315 |
| 0200 | Low E glass | | 10 | .800 | | 257 | 23.50 | | 280.50 | 320 |
| 0300 | 40" x 28", double insulated glass | | 9 | .889 | | 310 | 26 | | 336 | 385 |
| 0400 | Low E Glass | | 9 | .889 | | 330 | 26 | | 356 | 410 |
| 0500 | 48" x 36", double insulated glass | | 8 | 1 | | 450 | 29 | | 479 | 545 |
| 0600 | Low E glass | | 8 | 1 | | 475 | 29 | | 504 | 570 |
| 0800 | Vinyl clad, premium, double insulated glass, 24" x 17" | | 12 | .667 | | 206 | 19.40 | | 225.40 | 260 |
| 0840 | 24" x 28" | | 11 | .727 | | 250 | 21 | | 271 | 310 |
| 0860 | 36" x 17" | | 11 | .727 | | 256 | 21 | | 277 | 315 |
| 0900 | 36" x 40" | | 10 | .800 | | 385 | 23.50 | | 408.50 | 465 |
| 1100 | 40" x 22" | | 10 | .800 | | 283 | 23.50 | | 306.50 | 350 |
| 1200 | 36" x 28" | | 9 | .889 | | 300 | 26 | | 326 | 375 |
| 1300 | 36" x 36" | | 9 | .889 | | 335 | 26 | | 361 | 415 |
| 1400 | 48" x 28" | | 8 | 1 | | 360 | 29 | | 389 | 450 |
| 1500 | 60" x 36" | | 8 | 1 | | 505 | 29 | | 534 | 605 |
| 2200 | Metal clad, 36" x 25" | | 9 | .889 | | 269 | 26 | | 295 | 340 |
| 2300 | 40" x 30" | | 9 | .889 | | 335 | 26 | | 361 | 415 |
| 2400 | 48" x 28" | | 8 | 1 | | 345 | 29 | | 374 | 430 |

# 08 52 Wood Windows

## 08 52 10 – Plain Wood Windows

### 08 52 10.20 Awning Window

| | | Crew | Daily Output | Labor-Hours | Unit | Material | 2010 Bare Costs Labor | 2010 Bare Costs Equipment | Total | Total Incl O&P |
|---|---|---|---|---|---|---|---|---|---|---|
| 2500 | 60" x 36" | 1 Carp | 8 | 1 | Ea. | 365 | 29 | | 394 | 455 |
| 4000 | Impact windows, minimum, add | | | | | 60% | | | | |
| 4010 | Impact windows, maximum, add | | | | | 160% | | | | |

### 08 52 10.30 Wood Windows

| | | Crew | Daily Output | Labor-Hours | Unit | Material | 2010 Bare Costs Labor | 2010 Bare Costs Equipment | Total | Total Incl O&P |
|---|---|---|---|---|---|---|---|---|---|---|
| 0010 | **WOOD WINDOWS**, double hung | | | | | | | | | |
| 0020 | Including frame, double insulated glass, screens and grilles | | | | | | | | | |
| 0040 | Double hung, 2'-2" x 3'-4" high | 2 Carp | 15 | 1.067 | Ea. | 206 | 31 | | 237 | 279 |
| 0060 | 2'-2" x 4'-4" | | 14 | 1.143 | | 223 | 33.50 | | 256.50 | 300 |
| 0080 | 2'-6" x 3'-4" | | 13 | 1.231 | | 214 | 36 | | 250 | 296 |
| 0100 | 2'-6" x 4'-0" | | 12 | 1.333 | | 226 | 39 | | 265 | 315 |
| 0120 | 2'-6" x 4'-8" | | 12 | 1.333 | | 244 | 39 | | 283 | 335 |
| 0140 | 2'-10" x 3'-4" | | 10 | 1.600 | | 219 | 46.50 | | 265.50 | 320 |
| 0160 | 2'-10" x 4'-0" | | 10 | 1.600 | | 242 | 46.50 | | 288.50 | 345 |
| 0180 | 3'-7" x 3'-4" | | 9 | 1.778 | | 248 | 51.50 | | 299.50 | 360 |
| 0200 | 3'-7" x 5'-4" | | 9 | 1.778 | | 320 | 51.50 | | 371.50 | 435 |
| 0220 | 3'-10" x 5'-4" | | 8 | 2 | | 495 | 58 | | 553 | 645 |
| 3200 | 20 S.F. and over | 1 Carp | 106 | .075 | S.F. | 16.85 | 2.20 | | 19.05 | 22 |
| 3800 | Triple glazing for above, add | | | | " | 8.35 | | | 8.35 | 9.15 |
| 4300 | Double hung, 2'-4" x 3'-2", double insulated glass | 2 Carp | 6.80 | 2.353 | Ea. | 177 | 68.50 | | 245.50 | 310 |
| 4400 | Low E glass | | 6.80 | 2.353 | | 192 | 68.50 | | 260.50 | 325 |
| 4600 | 3'-0" x 4'-6" opening, double insulated glass | | 6 | 2.667 | | 238 | 77.50 | | 315.50 | 395 |
| 4700 | Low E glass | | 6 | 2.667 | | 260 | 77.50 | | 337.50 | 415 |
| 5000 | Picture window, wood, double insulated glass, 4'-6" x 4'-6" | | 5 | 3.200 | | 460 | 93 | | 553 | 660 |
| 5100 | 5'-8" x 4'-6" | | 4.50 | 3.556 | | 515 | 103 | | 618 | 745 |
| 5300 | Add for snap-in muntins, 4'-6" x 4'-6" | | | | | 75 | | | 75 | 82.50 |
| 5400 | 5'-8" x 4'-6" | | | | | 64.50 | | | 64.50 | 71 |
| 6000 | Replacement sash, double hung, double glazing, to 12 S.F. | 1 Carp | 64 | .125 | S.F. | 25 | 3.64 | | 28.64 | 34 |
| 6100 | 12 S.F. to 20 S.F. | | 94 | .085 | " | 19.50 | 2.48 | | 21.98 | 25.50 |
| 7000 | Sash, single lite, 2'-0" x 2'-0" high | | 20 | .400 | Ea. | 49 | 11.65 | | 60.65 | 73 |
| 7050 | 2'-6" x 2'-0" high | | 19 | .421 | | 60 | 12.25 | | 72.25 | 86.50 |
| 7100 | 2'-6" x 2'-6" high | | 18 | .444 | | 67.50 | 12.95 | | 80.45 | 96.50 |
| 7150 | 3'-0" x 2'-0" high | | 17 | .471 | | 88 | 13.70 | | 101.70 | 120 |

### 08 52 10.40 Casement Window

| | | | Crew | Daily Output | Labor-Hours | Unit | Material | 2010 Bare Costs Labor | 2010 Bare Costs Equipment | Total | Total Incl O&P |
|---|---|---|---|---|---|---|---|---|---|---|---|
| 0010 | **CASEMENT WINDOW**, including frame, screen and grilles | R085216-10 | | | | | | | | | |
| 0100 | Avg. quality, bldrs. model, 2'-0" x 3'-0" H, dbl. insulated glass | G | 1 Carp | 10 | .800 | Ea. | 276 | 23.50 | | 299.50 | 345 |
| 0150 | Low E glass | G | | 10 | .800 | | 225 | 23.50 | | 248.50 | 287 |
| 0200 | 2'-0" x 4'-6" high, double insulated glass | G | | 9 | .889 | | 345 | 26 | | 371 | 425 |
| 0250 | Low E glass | G | | 9 | .889 | | 263 | 26 | | 289 | 335 |
| 0260 | Casement 4'-2" x 4'-2" double insulated glass | G | | 11 | .727 | | 855 | 21 | | 876 | 975 |
| 0270 | 4'-0" x 4'-0" Low E glass | G | | 11 | .727 | | 465 | 21 | | 486 | 550 |
| 0290 | 6'-4" x 5'-7" Low E glass | G | | 9 | .889 | | 1,100 | 26 | | 1,126 | 1,250 |
| 0300 | 2'-4" x 6'-0" high, double insulated glass | G | | 8 | 1 | | 400 | 29 | | 429 | 490 |
| 0350 | Low E glass | G | | 8 | 1 | | 465 | 29 | | 494 | 565 |
| 0522 | Vinyl clad, premium, double insulated glass, 2'-0" x 3'-0" | G | | 10 | .800 | | 266 | 23.50 | | 289.50 | 330 |
| 0524 | 2'-0" x 4'-0" | G | | 9 | .889 | | 310 | 26 | | 336 | 385 |
| 0525 | 2'-0" x 5'-0" | | | 8 | 1 | | 355 | 29 | | 384 | 440 |
| 0528 | 2'-0" x 6'-0" | G | | 8 | 1 | | 355 | 29 | | 384 | 440 |
| 0600 | 3'-0" x 5'-0" | | | 8 | 1 | | 650 | 29 | | 679 | 765 |
| 0700 | 4'-0" x 3'-0" | | | 8 | 1 | | 715 | 29 | | 744 | 840 |
| 0710 | 4'-0" x 4'-0" | G | | 8 | 1 | | 610 | 29 | | 639 | 725 |
| 0720 | 4'-8" x 4'-0" | | | 8 | 1 | | 675 | 29 | | 704 | 795 |
| 0730 | 4'-8" x 5'-0" | | | 6 | 1.333 | | 770 | 39 | | 809 | 915 |

| 08 52 10.40 Casement Window | | Crew | Daily Output | Labor-Hours | Unit | Material | 2010 Bare Costs Labor | 2010 Bare Costs Equipment | Total | Total Incl O&P |
|---|---|---|---|---|---|---|---|---|---|---|
| 0740 | 4'-8" x 6'-0" | 1 Carp | 6 | 1.333 | Ea. | 870 | 39 | | 909 | 1,025 |
| 0750 | 6'-0" x 4'-0" | | 6 | 1.333 | | 790 | 39 | | 829 | 930 |
| 0800 | 6'-0" x 5'-0" | | 6 | 1.333 | | 885 | 39 | | 924 | 1,025 |
| 0900 | 5'-6" x 5'-6" | G 2 Carp | 15 | 1.067 | | 1,400 | 31 | | 1,431 | 1,575 |
| 2000 | Bay, casement units, 8' x 5', w/screens, dbl insul. glass | | 2.50 | 6.400 | Opng. | 1,575 | 186 | | 1,761 | 2,050 |
| 2100 | Low E glass | | 2.50 | 6.400 | " | 1,650 | 186 | | 1,836 | 2,125 |
| 3020 | Vinyl clad, premium, double insulated glass, multiple leaf units | | | | | | | | | |
| 3080 | Single unit, 1'-6" x 5'-0" | G 2 Carp | 20 | .800 | Ea. | 310 | 23.50 | | 333.50 | 380 |
| 3100 | 2'-0" x 2'-0" | G | 20 | .800 | | 206 | 23.50 | | 229.50 | 266 |
| 3140 | 2'-0" x 2'-6" | G | 20 | .800 | | 266 | 23.50 | | 289.50 | 330 |
| 3220 | 2'-0" x 3'-6" | G | 20 | .800 | | 267 | 23.50 | | 290.50 | 335 |
| 3260 | 2'-0" x 4'-0" | G | 19 | .842 | | 310 | 24.50 | | 334.50 | 380 |
| 3300 | 2'-0" x 4'-6" | G | 19 | .842 | | 310 | 24.50 | | 334.50 | 380 |
| 3340 | 2'-0" x 5'-0" | G | 18 | .889 | | 355 | 26 | | 381 | 435 |
| 3460 | 2'-4" x 3'-0" | G | 20 | .800 | | 269 | 23.50 | | 292.50 | 335 |
| 3500 | 2'-4" x 4'-0" | G | 19 | .842 | | 335 | 24.50 | | 359.50 | 405 |
| 3540 | 2'-4" x 5'-0" | G | 18 | .889 | | 400 | 26 | | 426 | 480 |
| 3700 | Double unit, 2'-8" x 5'-0" | G | 18 | .889 | | 560 | 26 | | 586 | 660 |
| 3740 | 2'-8" x 6'-0" | G | 17 | .941 | | 650 | 27.50 | | 677.50 | 760 |
| 3840 | 3'-0" x 4'-6" | G | 18 | .889 | | 505 | 26 | | 531 | 600 |
| 3860 | 3'-0" x 5'-0" | G | 17 | .941 | | 650 | 27.50 | | 677.50 | 760 |
| 3880 | 3'-0" x 6'-0" | G | 17 | .941 | | 700 | 27.50 | | 727.50 | 815 |
| 3980 | 3'-4" x 2'-6" | G | 19 | .842 | | 430 | 24.50 | | 454.50 | 510 |
| 4000 | 3'-4" x 3'-0" | G | 12 | 1.333 | | 430 | 39 | | 469 | 535 |
| 4030 | 3'-4" x 4'-0" | G | 18 | .889 | | 520 | 26 | | 546 | 620 |
| 4050 | 3'-4" x 5'-0" | G | 12 | 1.333 | | 650 | 39 | | 689 | 780 |
| 4100 | 3'-4" x 6'-0" | G | 11 | 1.455 | | 700 | 42.50 | | 742.50 | 840 |
| 4200 | 3'-6" x 3'-0" | G | 18 | .889 | | 510 | 26 | | 536 | 605 |
| 4340 | 4'-0" x 3'-0" | G | 18 | .889 | | 480 | 26 | | 506 | 575 |
| 4380 | 4'-0" x 3'-6" | G | 17 | .941 | | 520 | 27.50 | | 547.50 | 615 |
| 4420 | 4'-0" x 4'-0" | G | 16 | 1 | | 610 | 29 | | 639 | 725 |
| 4460 | 4'-0" x 4'-4" | G | 16 | 1 | | 610 | 29 | | 639 | 720 |
| 4540 | 4'-0" x 5'-0" | G | 16 | 1 | | 665 | 29 | | 694 | 780 |
| 4580 | 4'-0" x 6'-0" | G | 15 | 1.067 | | 755 | 31 | | 786 | 880 |
| 4740 | 4'-8" x 3'-0" | G | 18 | .889 | | 545 | 26 | | 571 | 645 |
| 4780 | 4'-8" x 3'-6" | G | 17 | .941 | | 580 | 27.50 | | 607.50 | 685 |
| 4820 | 4'-8" x 4'-0" | G | 16 | 1 | | 675 | 29 | | 704 | 795 |
| 4860 | 4'-8" x 5'-0" | G | 15 | 1.067 | | 770 | 31 | | 801 | 900 |
| 4900 | 4'-8" x 6'-0" | G | 15 | 1.067 | | 870 | 31 | | 901 | 1,000 |
| 5060 | Triple unit, 5'-0" x 5'-0" | G | 15 | 1.067 | | 1,025 | 31 | | 1,056 | 1,175 |
| 5100 | 5'-6" x 3'-0" | G | 17 | .941 | | 700 | 27.50 | | 727.50 | 815 |
| 5140 | 5'-6" x 3'-6" | G | 16 | 1 | | 760 | 29 | | 789 | 885 |
| 5180 | 5'-6" x 4'-6" | G | 15 | 1.067 | | 855 | 31 | | 886 | 990 |
| 5220 | 5'-6" x 5'-6" | G | 15 | 1.067 | | 1,125 | 31 | | 1,156 | 1,275 |
| 5300 | 6'-0" x 4'-6" | G | 15 | 1.067 | | 835 | 31 | | 866 | 965 |
| 5850 | 5'-0" x 3'-0" | G | 12 | 1.333 | | 590 | 39 | | 629 | 715 |
| 5900 | 5'-0" x 4'-0" | G | 11 | 1.455 | | 895 | 42.50 | | 937.50 | 1,050 |
| 6100 | 5'-0" x 5'-6" | G | 10 | 1.600 | | 1,050 | 46.50 | | 1,096.50 | 1,225 |
| 6150 | 5'-0" x 6'-0" | G | 10 | 1.600 | | 1,150 | 46.50 | | 1,196.50 | 1,350 |
| 6200 | 6'-0" x 3'-0" | G | 12 | 1.333 | | 1,150 | 39 | | 1,189 | 1,350 |
| 6250 | 6'-0" x 3'-4" | G | 12 | 1.333 | | 740 | 39 | | 779 | 880 |
| 6300 | 6'-0" x 4'-0" | G | 11 | 1.455 | | 825 | 42.50 | | 867.50 | 980 |
| 6350 | 6'-0" x 5'-0" | G | 10 | 1.600 | | 900 | 46.50 | | 946.50 | 1,075 |

# 08 52 Wood Windows

## 08 52 10 – Plain Wood Windows

| 08 52 10.40 Casement Window | | Crew | Daily Output | Labor-Hours | Unit | Material | 2010 Bare Costs Labor | Equipment | Total | Total Incl O&P |
|---|---|---|---|---|---|---|---|---|---|---|
| 6400 | 6'-0" x 6'-0" G | 2 Carp | 10 | 1.600 | Ea. | 1,050 | 46.50 | | 1,096.50 | 1,250 |
| 6500 | Quadruple unit, 7'-0" x 4'-0" G | | 9 | 1.778 | | 1,075 | 51.50 | | 1,126.50 | 1,250 |
| 6700 | 8'-0" x 4'-6" G | | 9 | 1.778 | | 1,350 | 51.50 | | 1,401.50 | 1,575 |
| 6950 | 6'-8" x 4'-0" G | | 10 | 1.600 | | 1,050 | 46.50 | | 1,096.50 | 1,225 |
| 7000 | 6'-8" x 6'-0" G | | 10 | 1.600 | | 1,400 | 46.50 | | 1,446.50 | 1,625 |
| 8100 | Metal clad, deluxe, dbl. insul. glass, 2'-0" x 3'-0" high G | 1 Carp | 10 | .800 | | 272 | 23.50 | | 295.50 | 340 |
| 8120 | 2'-0" x 4'-0" high G | | 9 | .889 | | 305 | 26 | | 331 | 380 |
| 8140 | 2'-0" x 5'-0" high G | | 8 | 1 | | 320 | 29 | | 349 | 400 |
| 8160 | 2'-0" x 6'-0" high G | | 8 | 1 | | 355 | 29 | | 384 | 440 |
| 8161 | Casement window, metal clad, double insul. glass, 3'-6" x 3'-6" G | | 8.90 | .899 | | 470 | 26 | | 496 | 565 |
| 8190 | For installation, add per leaf | | | | | | 15% | | | |
| 8200 | For multiple leaf units, deduct for stationary sash | | | | | | | | | |
| 8220 | 2' high | | | | Ea. | 22.50 | | | 22.50 | 24.50 |
| 8240 | 4'-6" high | | | | | 25.50 | | | 25.50 | 28 |
| 8260 | 6' high | | | | | 33.50 | | | 33.50 | 37 |
| 8300 | Impact windows, minimum, add | | | | | 60% | | | | |
| 8310 | Impact windows, maximum, add | | | | | 160% | | | | |

## 08 52 10.50 Double Hung

| | | Crew | Daily Output | Labor-Hours | Unit | Material | 2010 Bare Costs Labor | Equipment | Total | Total Incl O&P |
|---|---|---|---|---|---|---|---|---|---|---|
| 0010 | **DOUBLE HUNG**, Including frame, screens and grilles | | | | | | | | | |
| 0100 | Avg. quality, bldrs. model, 2'-0" x 3'-0" high, dbl insul. glass G | 1 Carp | 10 | .800 | Ea. | 184 | 23.50 | | 207.50 | 241 |
| 0150 | Low E glass G | | 10 | .800 | | 208 | 23.50 | | 231.50 | 268 |
| 0200 | 3'-0" x 4'-0" high, double insulated glass G | | 9 | .889 | | 257 | 26 | | 283 | 325 |
| 0250 | Low E glass G | | 9 | .889 | | 278 | 26 | | 304 | 350 |
| 0300 | 4'-0" x 4'-6" high, double insulated glass G | | 8 | 1 | | 315 | 29 | | 344 | 395 |
| 0350 | Low E glass G | | 8 | 1 | | 340 | 29 | | 369 | 425 |
| 1000 | Vinyl clad, premium, double insulated glass, 2'-6" x 3'-0" G | | 10 | .800 | | 225 | 23.50 | | 248.50 | 287 |
| 1005 | 2'-6" x 4'-0" G | | 10 | .800 | | 276 | 23.50 | | 299.50 | 345 |
| 1100 | 3'-0" x 3'-6" G | | 10 | .800 | | 261 | 23.50 | | 284.50 | 325 |
| 1200 | 3'-0" x 4'-0" G | | 9 | .889 | | 370 | 26 | | 396 | 450 |
| 1300 | 3'-0" x 4'-6" G | | 9 | .889 | | 340 | 26 | | 366 | 415 |
| 1400 | 3'-0" x 5'-0" G | | 8 | 1 | | 315 | 29 | | 344 | 395 |
| 1490 | 3'-4" x 5'-0" G | | 8 | 1 | | 355 | 29 | | 384 | 440 |
| 1500 | 3'-6" x 6'-0" G | | 8 | 1 | | 370 | 29 | | 399 | 455 |
| 1520 | 4'-0" x 5'-0" G | | 7 | 1.143 | | 550 | 33.50 | | 583.50 | 660 |
| 1530 | 4'-0" x 6'-0" G | | 7 | 1.143 | | 685 | 33.50 | | 718.50 | 810 |
| 2000 | Metal clad, deluxe, dbl. insul. glass, 2'-6" x 3'-0" high G | | 10 | .800 | | 265 | 23.50 | | 288.50 | 330 |
| 2100 | 3'-0" x 3'-6" high G | | 10 | .800 | | 305 | 23.50 | | 328.50 | 375 |
| 2200 | 3'-0" x 4'-0" high G | | 9 | .889 | | 320 | 26 | | 346 | 395 |
| 2300 | 3'-0" x 4'-6" high G | | 9 | .889 | | 335 | 26 | | 361 | 415 |
| 2400 | 3'-0" x 5'-0" high G | | 8 | 1 | | 365 | 29 | | 394 | 450 |
| 2500 | 3'-6" x 6'-0" high G | | 8 | 1 | | 440 | 29 | | 469 | 530 |
| 8000 | Impact windows, minimum, add | | | | | 60% | | | | |
| 8010 | Impact windows, maximum, add | | | | | 160% | | | | |

## 08 52 10.55 Picture Window

| | | Crew | Daily Output | Labor-Hours | Unit | Material | 2010 Bare Costs Labor | Equipment | Total | Total Incl O&P |
|---|---|---|---|---|---|---|---|---|---|---|
| 0010 | **PICTURE WINDOW**, Including frame and grilles | | | | | | | | | |
| 0100 | Average quality, bldrs. model, 3'-6" x 4'-0" high, dbl insulated glass | 2 Carp | 12 | 1.333 | Ea. | 345 | 39 | | 384 | 445 |
| 0150 | Low E glass | | 12 | 1.333 | | 410 | 39 | | 449 | 515 |
| 0200 | 4'-0" x 4'-6" high, double insulated glass | | 11 | 1.455 | | 490 | 42.50 | | 532.50 | 610 |
| 0250 | Low E glass | | 11 | 1.455 | | 520 | 42.50 | | 562.50 | 640 |
| 0300 | 5'-0" x 4'-0" high, double insulated glass | | 11 | 1.455 | | 570 | 42.50 | | 612.50 | 695 |
| 0350 | Low E glass | | 11 | 1.455 | | 590 | 42.50 | | 632.50 | 720 |
| 0400 | 6'-0" x 4'-6" high, double insulated glass | | 10 | 1.600 | | 610 | 46.50 | | 656.50 | 755 |

# 08 52 Wood Windows

## 08 52 10 – Plain Wood Windows

### 08 52 10.55 Picture Window

| | | Crew | Daily Output | Labor-Hours | Unit | Material | 2010 Bare Costs Labor | 2010 Bare Costs Equipment | Total | Total Incl O&P |
|---|---|---|---|---|---|---|---|---|---|---|
| 0450 | Low E glass | 2 Carp | 10 | 1.600 | Ea. | 620 | 46.50 | | 666.50 | 765 |

### 08 52 10.65 Wood Sash

| | | Crew | Daily Output | Labor-Hours | Unit | Material | Labor | Equipment | Total | Total Incl O&P |
|---|---|---|---|---|---|---|---|---|---|---|
| 0010 | **WOOD SASH**, Including glazing but not trim | | | | | | | | | |
| 0050 | Custom, 5'-0" x 4'-0", 1" dbl. glazed, 3/16" thick lites | 2 Carp | 3.20 | 5 | Ea. | 167 | 146 | | 313 | 430 |
| 0100 | 1/4" thick lites | | | 5 | 3.200 | | 172 | 93 | | 265 | 345 |
| 0200 | 1" thick, triple glazed | | | 5 | 3.200 | | 395 | 93 | | 488 | 585 |
| 0300 | 7'-0" x 4'-6" high, 1" double glazed, 3/16" thick lites | | 4.30 | 3.721 | | 400 | 108 | | 508 | 620 |
| 0400 | 1/4" thick lites | | | 4.30 | 3.721 | | 450 | 108 | | 558 | 675 |
| 0500 | 1" thick, triple glazed | | | 4.30 | 3.721 | | 515 | 108 | | 623 | 745 |
| 0600 | 8'-6" x 5'-0" high, 1" double glazed, 3/16" thick lites | | 3.50 | 4.571 | | 540 | 133 | | 673 | 815 |
| 0700 | 1/4" thick lites | | | 3.50 | 4.571 | | 590 | 133 | | 723 | 875 |
| 0800 | 1" thick, triple glazed | | 3.50 | 4.571 | | 595 | 133 | | 728 | 880 |
| 0900 | Window frames only, based on perimeter length | | | | L.F. | 3.83 | | | 3.83 | 4.21 |

### 08 52 10.70 Sliding Windows

| | | | Crew | Daily Output | Labor-Hours | Unit | Material | Labor | Equipment | Total | Total Incl O&P |
|---|---|---|---|---|---|---|---|---|---|---|---|
| 0010 | **SLIDING WINDOWS** | | | | | | | | | | |
| 0100 | Average quality, bldrs. model, 3'-0" x 3'-0" high, double insulated | G | 1 Carp | 10 | .800 | Ea. | 272 | 23.50 | | 295.50 | 340 |
| 0120 | Low E glass | G | | 10 | .800 | | 293 | 23.50 | | 316.50 | 360 |
| 0200 | 4'-0" x 3'-6" high, double insulated | G | | 9 | .889 | | 325 | 26 | | 351 | 405 |
| 0220 | Low E glass | G | | 9 | .889 | | 350 | 26 | | 376 | 430 |
| 0300 | 6'-0" x 5'-0" high, double insulated | G | | 8 | 1 | | 460 | 29 | | 489 | 560 |
| 0320 | Low E glass | G | | 8 | 1 | | 500 | 29 | | 529 | 600 |
| 6000 | Sliding, insulating glass, including screens, | | | | | | | | | | |
| 6100 | 3'-0" x 3'-0" | | 2 Carp | 6.50 | 2.462 | Ea. | 320 | 71.50 | | 391.50 | 470 |
| 6200 | 4'-0" x 3'-6" | | | 6.30 | 2.540 | | 325 | 74 | | 399 | 480 |
| 6300 | 5'-0" x 4'-0" | | | 6 | 2.667 | | 400 | 77.50 | | 477.50 | 570 |

## 08 52 13 – Metal-Clad Wood Windows

### 08 52 13.10 Awning Windows, Metal-Clad

| | | Crew | Daily Output | Labor-Hours | Unit | Material | Labor | Equipment | Total | Total Incl O&P |
|---|---|---|---|---|---|---|---|---|---|---|
| 0010 | **AWNING WINDOWS, METAL-CLAD** | | | | | | | | | |
| 2000 | Metal clad, awning deluxe, double insulated glass, 34" x 22" | 1 Carp | 10 | .800 | Ea. | 242 | 23.50 | | 265.50 | 305 |
| 2100 | 40" x 22" | " | 10 | .800 | " | 285 | 23.50 | | 308.50 | 355 |

### 08 52 13.35 Picture and Sliding Windows Metal-Clad

| | | | Crew | Daily Output | Labor-Hours | Unit | Material | Labor | Equipment | Total | Total Incl O&P |
|---|---|---|---|---|---|---|---|---|---|---|---|
| 0010 | **PICTURE AND SLIDING WINDOWS METAL-CLAD** | | | | | | | | | | |
| 2000 | Metal clad, dlx picture, dbl. insul. glass, 4'-0" x 4'-0" high | | 2 Carp | 12 | 1.333 | Ea. | 365 | 39 | | 404 | 470 |
| 2100 | 4'-0" x 6'-0" high | | | 11 | 1.455 | | 535 | 42.50 | | 577.50 | 660 |
| 2200 | 5'-0" x 6'-0" high | | | 10 | 1.600 | | 595 | 46.50 | | 641.50 | 735 |
| 2300 | 6'-0" x 6'-0" high | | | 10 | 1.600 | | 680 | 46.50 | | 726.50 | 830 |
| 2400 | Metal clad, dlx sliding, double insulated glass, 3'-0" x 3'-0" high | G | 1 Carp | 10 | .800 | | 330 | 23.50 | | 353.50 | 400 |
| 2420 | 4'-0" x 3'-6" high | G | | 9 | .889 | | 400 | 26 | | 426 | 485 |
| 2440 | 5'-0" x 4'-0" high | G | | 9 | .889 | | 480 | 26 | | 506 | 570 |
| 2460 | 6'-0" x 5'-0" high | G | | 8 | 1 | | 705 | 29 | | 734 | 825 |

## 08 52 16 – Plastic-Clad Wood Windows

### 08 52 16.10 Bow Window

| | | Crew | Daily Output | Labor-Hours | Unit | Material | Labor | Equipment | Total | Total Incl O&P |
|---|---|---|---|---|---|---|---|---|---|---|
| 0010 | **BOW WINDOW** Including frames, screens, and grilles | | | | | | | | | |
| 0020 | End panels operable | | | | | | | | | |
| 1000 | Bow type, casement, wood, bldrs mdl, 8' x 5' dbl insltd glass, 4 panel | 2 Carp | 10 | 1.600 | Ea. | 1,500 | 46.50 | | 1,546.50 | 1,725 |
| 1050 | Low E glass | | 10 | 1.600 | | 1,325 | 46.50 | | 1,371.50 | 1,525 |
| 1100 | 10'-0" x 5'-0", double insulated glass, 6 panels | | 6 | 2.667 | | 1,350 | 77.50 | | 1,427.50 | 1,625 |
| 1200 | Low E glass, 6 panels | | 6 | 2.667 | | 1,450 | 77.50 | | 1,527.50 | 1,725 |
| 1300 | Vinyl clad, bldrs model, double insulated glass, 6'-0" x 4'-0", 3 panel | | 10 | 1.600 | | 1,025 | 46.50 | | 1,071.50 | 1,200 |
| 1340 | 9'-0" x 4'-0", 4 panel | | 8 | 2 | | 1,350 | 58 | | 1,408 | 1,600 |
| 1380 | 10'-0" x 6'-0", 5 panels | | 7 | 2.286 | | 2,250 | 66.50 | | 2,316.50 | 2,575 |

# 08 52 Wood Windows

## 08 52 16 – Plastic-Clad Wood Windows

### 08 52 16.10 Bow Window

| | | Crew | Daily Output | Labor-Hours | Unit | Material | 2010 Bare Costs Labor | Equipment | Total | Total Incl O&P |
|---|---|---|---|---|---|---|---|---|---|---|
| 1420 | 12'-0" x 6'-0", 6 panels | 2 Carp | 6 | 2.667 | Ea. | 2,925 | 77.50 | | 3,002.50 | 3,350 |
| 1600 | Metal clad, casement, bldrs mdl, 6'-0" x 4'-0", dbl insltd gls, 3 panels | | 10 | 1.600 | | 920 | 46.50 | | 966.50 | 1,075 |
| 1640 | 9'-0" x 4'-0", 4 panels | | 8 | 2 | | 1,250 | 58 | | 1,308 | 1,475 |
| 1680 | 10'-0" x 5'-0", 5 panels | | 7 | 2.286 | | 1,725 | 66.50 | | 1,791.50 | 2,000 |
| 1720 | 12'-0" x 6'-0", 6 panels | | 6 | 2.667 | | 2,400 | 77.50 | | 2,477.50 | 2,775 |
| 2000 | Bay window, builders model, 8' x 5' dbl insul glass, | | 10 | 1.600 | | 1,825 | 46.50 | | 1,871.50 | 2,100 |
| 2050 | Low E glass, | | 10 | 1.600 | | 2,225 | 46.50 | | 2,271.50 | 2,525 |
| 2100 | 12'-0" x 6'-0", double insulated glass, 6 panels | | 6 | 2.667 | | 2,300 | 77.50 | | 2,377.50 | 2,650 |
| 2200 | Low E glass | | 6 | 2.667 | | 2,350 | 77.50 | | 2,427.50 | 2,725 |
| 2280 | 6'-0" x 4'-0" | | 11 | 1.455 | | 1,225 | 42.50 | | 1,267.50 | 1,425 |
| 2300 | Vinyl clad, premium, double insulated glass, 8'-0" x 5'-0" | | 10 | 1.600 | | 1,750 | 46.50 | | 1,796.50 | 2,000 |
| 2340 | 10'-0" x 5'-0" | | 8 | 2 | | 2,275 | 58 | | 2,333 | 2,600 |
| 2380 | 10'-0" x 6'-0" | | 7 | 2.286 | | 2,525 | 66.50 | | 2,591.50 | 2,875 |
| 2420 | 12'-0" x 6'-0" | | 6 | 2.667 | | 3,200 | 77.50 | | 3,277.50 | 3,650 |
| 2430 | 14'-0" x 3'-0" | | 7 | 2.286 | | 2,950 | 66.50 | | 3,016.50 | 3,350 |
| 2440 | 14'-0" x 6'-0" | | 5 | 3.200 | | 4,950 | 93 | | 5,043 | 5,600 |
| 2600 | Metal clad, deluxe, dbl insul. glass, 8'-0" x 5'-0" high, 4 panels | | 10 | 1.600 | | 1,625 | 46.50 | | 1,671.50 | 1,850 |
| 2640 | 10'-0" x 5'-0" high, 5 panels | | 8 | 2 | | 1,750 | 58 | | 1,808 | 2,025 |
| 2680 | 10'-0" x 6'-0" high, 5 panels | | 7 | 2.286 | | 2,050 | 66.50 | | 2,116.50 | 2,375 |
| 2720 | 12'-0" x 6'-0" high, 6 panels | | 6 | 2.667 | | 2,850 | 77.50 | | 2,927.50 | 3,275 |
| 3000 | Double hung, bldrs. model, bay, 8' x 4' high, dbl insulated glass | | 10 | 1.600 | | 1,300 | 46.50 | | 1,346.50 | 1,500 |
| 3050 | Low E glass | | 10 | 1.600 | | 1,375 | 46.50 | | 1,421.50 | 1,600 |
| 3100 | 9'-0" x 5'-0" high, double insulated glass | | 6 | 2.667 | | 1,400 | 77.50 | | 1,477.50 | 1,650 |
| 3200 | Low E glass | | 6 | 2.667 | | 1,475 | 77.50 | | 1,552.50 | 1,750 |
| 3300 | Vinyl clad, premium, double insulated glass, 7'-0" x 4'-6" | | 10 | 1.600 | | 1,325 | 46.50 | | 1,371.50 | 1,550 |
| 3340 | 8'-0" x 4'-6" | | 8 | 2 | | 1,375 | 58 | | 1,433 | 1,600 |
| 3380 | 8'-0" x 5'-0" | | 7 | 2.286 | | 1,425 | 66.50 | | 1,491.50 | 1,675 |
| 3420 | 9'-0" x 5'-0" | | 6 | 2.667 | | 1,475 | 77.50 | | 1,552.50 | 1,750 |
| 3600 | Metal clad, deluxe, dbl insul. glass, 7'-0" x 4'-0" high | | 10 | 1.600 | | 1,225 | 46.50 | | 1,271.50 | 1,425 |
| 3640 | 8'-0" x 4'-0" high | | 8 | 2 | | 1,275 | 58 | | 1,333 | 1,500 |
| 3680 | 8'-0" x 5'-0" high | | 7 | 2.286 | | 1,325 | 66.50 | | 1,391.50 | 1,550 |
| 3720 | 9'-0" x 5'-0" high | | 6 | 2.667 | | 1,400 | 77.50 | | 1,477.50 | 1,675 |

### 08 52 16.20 Half Round, Vinyl Clad

| | | Crew | Daily Output | Labor-Hours | Unit | Material | 2010 Bare Costs Labor | Equipment | Total | Total Incl O&P |
|---|---|---|---|---|---|---|---|---|---|---|
| 0010 | **HALF ROUND, VINYL CLAD**, double insulated glass, incl. grille | | | | | | | | | |
| 0800 | 14" height x 24" base | 2 Carp | 9 | 1.778 | Ea. | 405 | 51.50 | | 456.50 | 530 |
| 1040 | 15" height x 25" base | | 8 | 2 | | 375 | 58 | | 433 | 515 |
| 1060 | 16" height x 28" base | | 7 | 2.286 | | 405 | 66.50 | | 471.50 | 555 |
| 1080 | 17" height x 29" base | | 7 | 2.286 | | 420 | 66.50 | | 486.50 | 570 |
| 2000 | 19" height x 33" base | 1 Carp | 6 | 1.333 | | 450 | 39 | | 489 | 560 |
| 2100 | 20" height x 35" base | | 6 | 1.333 | | 450 | 39 | | 489 | 560 |
| 2200 | 21" height x 37" base | | 6 | 1.333 | | 475 | 39 | | 514 | 590 |
| 2250 | 23" height x 41" base | 2 Carp | 6 | 2.667 | | 520 | 77.50 | | 597.50 | 700 |
| 2300 | 26" height x 48" base | | 6 | 2.667 | | 535 | 77.50 | | 612.50 | 715 |
| 2350 | 30" height x 56" base | | 6 | 2.667 | | 615 | 77.50 | | 692.50 | 805 |
| 3000 | 36" height x 67" base | 1 Carp | 4 | 2 | | 1,050 | 58 | | 1,108 | 1,250 |
| 3040 | 38" height x 71" base | 2 Carp | 5 | 3.200 | | 975 | 93 | | 1,068 | 1,225 |
| 3050 | 40" height x 75" base | " | 5 | 3.200 | | 1,275 | 93 | | 1,368 | 1,550 |
| 5000 | Elliptical, 71" x 16" | 1 Carp | 11 | .727 | | 975 | 21 | | 996 | 1,100 |
| 5100 | 95" x 21" | " | 10 | .800 | | 1,375 | 23.50 | | 1,398.50 | 1,575 |

### 08 52 16.30 Palladian Windows

| | | Crew | Daily Output | Labor-Hours | Unit | Material | 2010 Bare Costs Labor | Equipment | Total | Total Incl O&P |
|---|---|---|---|---|---|---|---|---|---|---|
| 0010 | **PALLADIAN WINDOWS** | | | | | | | | | |
| 0020 | Vinyl clad, double insulated glass, including frame and grilles | | | | | | | | | |

# 08 52 Wood Windows

## 08 52 16 – Plastic-Clad Wood Windows

| 08 52 16.30 Palladian Windows | | Crew | Daily Output | Labor-Hours | Unit | Material | 2010 Bare Costs Labor | Equipment | Total | Total Incl O&P |
|---|---|---|---|---|---|---|---|---|---|---|
| 0040 | 3'-2" x 2'-6" high | 2 Carp | 11 | 1.455 | Ea. | 1,250 | 42.50 | | 1,292.50 | 1,450 |
| 0060 | 3'-2" x 4'-10" | | 11 | 1.455 | | 1,750 | 42.50 | | 1,792.50 | 1,975 |
| 0080 | 3'-2" x 6'-4" | | 10 | 1.600 | | 1,700 | 46.50 | | 1,746.50 | 1,950 |
| 0100 | 4'-0" x 4'-0" | | 10 | 1.600 | | 1,525 | 46.50 | | 1,571.50 | 1,750 |
| 0120 | 4'-0" x 5'-4" | 3 Carp | 10 | 2.400 | | 1,875 | 70 | | 1,945 | 2,175 |
| 0140 | 4'-0" x 6'-0" | | 9 | 2.667 | | 1,950 | 77.50 | | 2,027.50 | 2,275 |
| 0160 | 4'-0" x 7'-4" | | 9 | 2.667 | | 2,125 | 77.50 | | 2,202.50 | 2,450 |
| 0180 | 5'-5" x 4'-10" | | 9 | 2.667 | | 2,275 | 77.50 | | 2,352.50 | 2,625 |
| 0200 | 5'-5" x 6'-10" | | 9 | 2.667 | | 2,575 | 77.50 | | 2,652.50 | 2,975 |
| 0220 | 5'-5" x 7'-9" | | 9 | 2.667 | | 2,800 | 77.50 | | 2,877.50 | 3,200 |
| 0240 | 6'-0" x 7'-11" | | 8 | 3 | | 3,475 | 87.50 | | 3,562.50 | 3,975 |
| 0260 | 8'-0" x 6'-0" | | 8 | 3 | | 3,075 | 87.50 | | 3,162.50 | 3,525 |

### 08 52 16.40 Transom Windows

| | | Crew | Daily Output | Labor-Hours | Unit | Material | Labor | Equipment | Total | Total Incl O&P |
|---|---|---|---|---|---|---|---|---|---|---|
| 0010 | **TRANSOM WINDOWS** | | | | | | | | | |
| 0050 | Vinyl clad, premium, double insulated glass, 32" x 8" | 1 Carp | 16 | .500 | Ea. | 176 | 14.55 | | 190.55 | 218 |
| 0100 | 36" x 8" | | 16 | .500 | | 186 | 14.55 | | 200.55 | 230 |
| 0110 | 36" x 12" | | 16 | .500 | | 199 | 14.55 | | 213.55 | 244 |
| 1000 | Vinyl clad, premium, dbl. insul. glass, 4'-0" x 4'-0" | 2 Carp | 12 | 1.333 | | 495 | 39 | | 534 | 610 |
| 1100 | 4'-0" x 6'-0" | | 11 | 1.455 | | 910 | 42.50 | | 952.50 | 1,075 |
| 1200 | 5'-0" x 6'-0" | | 10 | 1.600 | | 1,000 | 46.50 | | 1,046.50 | 1,200 |
| 1300 | 6'-0" x 6'-0" | | 10 | 1.600 | | 1,025 | 46.50 | | 1,071.50 | 1,200 |

### 08 52 16.45 Trapezoid Windows

| | | Crew | Daily Output | Labor-Hours | Unit | Material | Labor | Equipment | Total | Total Incl O&P |
|---|---|---|---|---|---|---|---|---|---|---|
| 0010 | **TRAPEZOID WINDOWS** | | | | | | | | | |
| 0100 | Vinyl clad, including frame and exterior trim | | | | | | | | | |
| 0900 | 20" base x 44" leg x 53" leg | 2 Carp | 13 | 1.231 | Ea. | 375 | 36 | | 411 | 475 |
| 1000 | 24" base x 90" leg x 102" leg | | 8 | 2 | | 640 | 58 | | 698 | 805 |
| 3000 | 36" base x 40" leg x 22" leg | | 12 | 1.333 | | 410 | 39 | | 449 | 515 |
| 3010 | 36" base x 44" leg x 25" leg | | 13 | 1.231 | | 430 | 36 | | 466 | 535 |
| 3050 | 36" base x 26" leg x 48" leg | | 9 | 1.778 | | 440 | 51.50 | | 491.50 | 570 |
| 3100 | 36" base x 42" legs, 50" peak | | 9 | 1.778 | | 520 | 51.50 | | 571.50 | 655 |
| 3200 | 36" base x 60" leg x 81" leg | | 11 | 1.455 | | 680 | 42.50 | | 722.50 | 820 |
| 4320 | 44" base x 23" leg x 56" leg | | 11 | 1.455 | | 535 | 42.50 | | 577.50 | 660 |
| 4350 | 44" base x 59" leg x 92" leg | | 10 | 1.600 | | 800 | 46.50 | | 846.50 | 960 |
| 4500 | 46" base x 15" leg x 46" leg | | 8 | 2 | | 405 | 58 | | 463 | 545 |
| 4550 | 46" base x 16" leg x 48" leg | | 8 | 2 | | 430 | 58 | | 488 | 575 |
| 4600 | 46" base x 50" leg x 80" leg | | 7 | 2.286 | | 650 | 66.50 | | 716.50 | 825 |
| 6600 | 66" base x 12" leg x 42" leg | | 8 | 2 | | 550 | 58 | | 608 | 705 |
| 6650 | 66" base x 12" legs, 28" peak | | 9 | 1.778 | | 440 | 51.50 | | 491.50 | 570 |
| 6700 | 68" base x 23" legs, 31" peak | | 8 | 2 | | 550 | 58 | | 608 | 705 |

### 08 52 16.70 Vinyl Clad, Premium, Dbl. Insulated Glass

| | | | Crew | Daily Output | Labor-Hours | Unit | Material | Labor | Equipment | Total | Total Incl O&P |
|---|---|---|---|---|---|---|---|---|---|---|---|
| 0010 | **VINYL CLAD, PREMIUM, DBL. INSULATED GLASS** | | | | | | | | | | |
| 1000 | Sliding, 3'-0" x 3'-0" | G | 1 Carp | 10 | .800 | Ea. | 575 | 23.50 | | 598.50 | 670 |
| 1020 | 4'-0" x 1'-11" | G | | 11 | .727 | | 555 | 21 | | 576 | 645 |
| 1040 | 4'-0" x 3'-0" | G | | 10 | .800 | | 665 | 23.50 | | 688.50 | 770 |
| 1050 | 4'-0" x 3'-6" | G | | 9 | .889 | | 670 | 26 | | 696 | 780 |
| 1090 | 4'-0" x 5'-0" | G | | 9 | .889 | | 870 | 26 | | 896 | 1,000 |
| 1100 | 5'-0" x 4'-0" | G | | 9 | .889 | | 860 | 26 | | 886 | 990 |
| 1120 | 5'-0" x 5'-0" | G | | 8 | 1 | | 960 | 29 | | 989 | 1,100 |
| 1140 | 6'-0" x 4'-0" | G | | 8 | 1 | | 970 | 29 | | 999 | 1,125 |
| 1150 | 6'-0" x 5'-0" | G | | 8 | 1 | | 1,075 | 29 | | 1,104 | 1,250 |

# 08 52 Wood Windows

## 08 52 50 – Window Accessories

| 08 52 50.10 Window Grille or Muntin | Crew | Daily Output | Labor-Hours | Unit | Material | 2010 Bare Costs Labor | Equipment | Total | Total Incl O&P |
|---|---|---|---|---|---|---|---|---|---|
| 0010 **WINDOW GRILLE OR MUNTIN**, snap in type | | | | | | | | | |
| 0020 Standard pattern interior grilles | | | | | | | | | |
| 2000 Wood, awning window, glass size 28" x 16" high | 1 Carp | 30 | .267 | Ea. | 24 | 7.75 | | 31.75 | 39.50 |
| 2060 44" x 24" high | | 32 | .250 | | 36 | 7.30 | | 43.30 | 52 |
| 2100 Casement, glass size, 20" x 36" high | | 30 | .267 | | 29 | 7.75 | | 36.75 | 44.50 |
| 2180 20" x 56" high | | 32 | .250 | | 40 | 7.30 | | 47.30 | 56.50 |
| 2200 Double hung, glass size, 16" x 24" high | | 24 | .333 | Set | 48 | 9.70 | | 57.70 | 69.50 |
| 2280 32" x 32" high | | 34 | .235 | " | 128 | 6.85 | | 134.85 | 153 |
| 2500 Picture, glass size, 48" x 48" high | | 30 | .267 | Ea. | 114 | 7.75 | | 121.75 | 138 |
| 2580 60" x 68" high | | 28 | .286 | " | 160 | 8.30 | | 168.30 | 190 |
| 2600 Sliding, glass size, 14" x 36" high | | 24 | .333 | Set | 26.50 | 9.70 | | 36.20 | 45.50 |
| 2680 36" x 36" high | | 22 | .364 | " | 39 | 10.60 | | 49.60 | 61 |

## 08 52 66 – Wood Window Screens

| 08 52 66.10 Wood Screens | Crew | Daily Output | Labor-Hours | Unit | Material | 2010 Bare Costs Labor | Equipment | Total | Total Incl O&P |
|---|---|---|---|---|---|---|---|---|---|
| 0010 **WOOD SCREENS** | | | | | | | | | |
| 0020 Over 3 S.F., 3/4" frames | 2 Carp | 375 | .043 | S.F. | 4.37 | 1.24 | | 5.61 | 6.90 |
| 0100 1-1/8" frames | " | 375 | .043 | " | 7.70 | 1.24 | | 8.94 | 10.60 |

## 08 52 69 – Wood Storm Windows

| 08 52 69.10 Storm Windows | Crew | Daily Output | Labor-Hours | Unit | Material | 2010 Bare Costs Labor | Equipment | Total | Total Incl O&P |
|---|---|---|---|---|---|---|---|---|---|
| 0010 **STORM WINDOWS**, aluminum residential | | | | | | | | | |
| 0300 Basement, mill finish, incl. fiberglass screen | | | | | | | | | |
| 0320 1'-10" x 1'-0" high | 2 Carp | 30 | .533 | Ea. | 35 | 15.50 | | 50.50 | 64.50 |
| 0340 2'-9" x 1'-6" high | | 30 | .533 | | 38 | 15.50 | | 53.50 | 68 |
| 0360 3'-4" x 2'-0" high | | 30 | .533 | | 44 | 15.50 | | 59.50 | 74.50 |
| 1600 Double-hung, combination, storm & screen | | | | | | | | | |
| 1700 Custom, clear anodic coating, 2'-0" x 3'-5" high | 2 Carp | 30 | .533 | Ea. | 90 | 15.50 | | 105.50 | 125 |
| 1720 2'-6" x 5'-0" high | | 28 | .571 | | 110 | 16.65 | | 126.65 | 149 |
| 1740 4'-0" x 6'-0" high | | 25 | .640 | | 226 | 18.60 | | 244.60 | 281 |
| 1800 White painted, 2'-0" x 3'-5" high | | 30 | .533 | | 100 | 15.50 | | 115.50 | 136 |
| 1820 2'-6" x 5'-0" high | | 28 | .571 | | 160 | 16.65 | | 176.65 | 204 |
| 1840 4'-0" x 6'-0" high | | 25 | .640 | | 273 | 18.60 | | 291.60 | 330 |
| 2000 Average quality, clear anodic coating, 2'-0" x 3'-5" high | | 30 | .533 | | 85 | 15.50 | | 100.50 | 120 |
| 2020 2'-6" x 5'-0" high | | 28 | .571 | | 107 | 16.65 | | 123.65 | 145 |
| 2040 4'-0" x 6'-0" high | | 25 | .640 | | 126 | 18.60 | | 144.60 | 171 |
| 2400 White painted, 2'-0" x 3'-5" high | | 30 | .533 | | 85 | 15.50 | | 100.50 | 120 |
| 2420 2'-6" x 5'-0" high | | 28 | .571 | | 90 | 16.65 | | 106.65 | 127 |
| 2440 4'-0" x 6'-0" high | | 25 | .640 | | 98 | 18.60 | | 116.60 | 140 |
| 2600 Mill finish, 2'-0" x 3'-5" high | | 30 | .533 | | 75 | 15.50 | | 90.50 | 109 |
| 2620 2'-6" x 5'-0" high | | 28 | .571 | | 85 | 16.65 | | 101.65 | 122 |
| 2640 4'-0" x 6'-8" high | | 25 | .640 | | 99 | 18.60 | | 117.60 | 141 |
| 4000 Picture window, storm, 1 lite, white or bronze finish | | | | | | | | | |
| 4020 4'-6" x 4'-6" high | 2 Carp | 25 | .640 | Ea. | 120 | 18.60 | | 138.60 | 164 |
| 4040 5'-8" x 4'-6" high | | 20 | .800 | | 144 | 23.50 | | 167.50 | 197 |
| 4400 Mill finish, 4'-6" x 4'-6" high | | 25 | .640 | | 126 | 18.60 | | 144.60 | 171 |
| 4420 5'-8" x 4'-6" high | | 20 | .800 | | 144 | 23.50 | | 167.50 | 197 |
| 4600 3 lite, white or bronze finish | | | | | | | | | |
| 4620 4'-6" x 4'-6" high | 2 Carp | 25 | .640 | Ea. | 152 | 18.60 | | 170.60 | 199 |
| 4640 5'-8" x 4'-6" high | | 20 | .800 | | 166 | 23.50 | | 189.50 | 222 |
| 4800 Mill finish, 4'-6" x 4'-6" high | | 25 | .640 | | 144 | 18.60 | | 162.60 | 190 |
| 4820 5'-8" x 4'-6" high | | 20 | .800 | | 152 | 23.50 | | 175.50 | 206 |
| 5000 Sliding glass door, storm 6' x 6'-8", standard | 1 Glaz | 2 | 4 | | 800 | 114 | | 914 | 1,075 |

# 08 52 Wood Windows

## 08 52 69 – Wood Storm Windows

| 08 52 69.10 Storm Windows | | Crew | Daily Output | Labor-Hours | Unit | Material | 2010 Bare Costs Labor | Equipment | Total | Total Incl O&P |
|---|---|---|---|---|---|---|---|---|---|---|
| 5100 | Economy | 1 Glaz | 2 | 4 | Ea. | 450 | 114 | | 564 | 685 |
| 6000 | Sliding window, storm, 2 lite, white or bronze finish | | | | | | | | | |
| 6020 | 3'-4" x 2'-7" high | 2 Carp | 28 | .571 | Ea. | 110 | 16.65 | | 126.65 | 149 |
| 6040 | 4'-4" x 3'-3" high | | 25 | .640 | | 150 | 18.60 | | 168.60 | 197 |
| 6060 | 5'-4" x 6'-0" high | ↓ | 20 | .800 | ↓ | 240 | 23.50 | | 263.50 | 305 |
| 9000 | Magnetic interior storm window | | | | | | | | | |
| 9100 | 3/16" plate glass | 1 Glaz | 107 | .075 | S.F. | 5.15 | 2.13 | | 7.28 | 9.15 |

# 08 53 Plastic Windows

## 08 53 13 – Vinyl Windows

### 08 53 13.10 Solid Vinyl Windows

| | | Crew | Daily Output | Labor-Hours | Unit | Material | Labor | Equipment | Total | Total Incl O&P |
|---|---|---|---|---|---|---|---|---|---|---|
| 0010 | **SOLID VINYL WINDOWS** | | | | | | | | | |
| 0020 | Double hung, including frame and screen, 2'-0" x 2'-6" | 2 Carp | 15 | 1.067 | Ea. | 182 | 31 | | 213 | 253 |
| 0040 | 2'-0" x 3'-6" | | 14 | 1.143 | | 188 | 33.50 | | 221.50 | 263 |
| 0060 | 2'-6" x 4'-6" | | 13 | 1.231 | | 226 | 36 | | 262 | 310 |
| 0080 | 3'-0" x 4'-0" | | 10 | 1.600 | | 193 | 46.50 | | 239.50 | 292 |
| 0100 | 3'-0" x 4'-6" | | 9 | 1.778 | | 254 | 51.50 | | 305.50 | 365 |
| 0120 | 3'-6" x 4'-6" | | 8 | 2 | | 268 | 58 | | 326 | 395 |
| 0140 | 3'-6" x 6'-0" | | 7 | 2.286 | ↓ | 315 | 66.50 | | 381.50 | 455 |
| 9100 | Minimum labor/equipment charge | ↓ | 2 | 8 | Job | | 233 | | 233 | 390 |

### 08 53 13.20 Vinyl Single Hung Windows

| | | | Crew | Daily Output | Labor-Hours | Unit | Material | Labor | Equipment | Total | Total Incl O&P |
|---|---|---|---|---|---|---|---|---|---|---|---|
| 0010 | **VINYL SINGLE HUNG WINDOWS** | | | | | | | | | | |
| 0100 | Grids, low E, J fin, ext. jambs, 21" x 53" | G | 2 Carp | 18 | .889 | Ea. | 162 | 26 | | 188 | 222 |
| 0110 | 21" x 57" | G | | 17 | .941 | | 166 | 27.50 | | 193.50 | 229 |
| 0120 | 21" x 65" | G | | 16 | 1 | | 173 | 29 | | 202 | 239 |
| 0130 | 25" x 41" | G | | 20 | .800 | | 157 | 23.50 | | 180.50 | 212 |
| 0140 | 25" x 49" | G | | 18 | .889 | | 169 | 26 | | 195 | 230 |
| 0150 | 25" x 57" | G | | 17 | .941 | | 173 | 27.50 | | 200.50 | 236 |
| 0160 | 25" x 65" | G | | 16 | 1 | | 180 | 29 | | 209 | 247 |
| 0170 | 29" x 41" | G | | 18 | .889 | | 163 | 26 | | 189 | 223 |
| 0180 | 29" x 53" | G | | 18 | .889 | | 175 | 26 | | 201 | 237 |
| 0190 | 29" x 57" | G | | 17 | .941 | | 179 | 27.50 | | 206.50 | 243 |
| 0200 | 29" x 65" | G | | 16 | 1 | | 185 | 29 | | 214 | 253 |
| 0210 | 33" x 41" | G | | 20 | .800 | | 169 | 23.50 | | 192.50 | 225 |
| 0220 | 33" x 53" | G | | 18 | .889 | | 182 | 26 | | 208 | 244 |
| 0230 | 33" x 57" | G | | 17 | .941 | | 185 | 27.50 | | 212.50 | 250 |
| 0240 | 33" x 65" | G | | 16 | 1 | | 196 | 29 | | 225 | 265 |
| 0250 | 37" x 41" | G | | 20 | .800 | | 178 | 23.50 | | 201.50 | 235 |
| 0260 | 37" x 53" | G | | 18 | .889 | | 191 | 26 | | 217 | 254 |
| 0270 | 37" x 57" | G | | 17 | .941 | | 195 | 27.50 | | 222.50 | 261 |
| 0280 | 37" x 65" | G | | 16 | 1 | | 203 | 29 | | 232 | 272 |
| 0500 | Vinyl clad, premium, double insulated glass, circle, 24" diameter | | 1 Carp | 6 | 1.333 | | 450 | 39 | | 489 | 560 |
| 1000 | 2'-4" diameter | | | 6 | 1.333 | | 525 | 39 | | 564 | 645 |
| 1500 | 2'-11" diameter | | ↓ | 6 | 1.333 | ↓ | 625 | 39 | | 664 | 750 |

### 08 53 13.30 Vinyl Double Hung Windows

| | | | Crew | Daily Output | Labor-Hours | Unit | Material | Labor | Equipment | Total | Total Incl O&P |
|---|---|---|---|---|---|---|---|---|---|---|---|
| 0010 | **VINYL DOUBLE HUNG WINDOWS** | | | | | | | | | | |
| 0100 | Grids, low E, J fin, ext. jambs, 21" x 53" | G | 2 Carp | 18 | .889 | Ea. | 186 | 26 | | 212 | 249 |
| 0102 | 21" x 37" | G | | 18 | .889 | | 165 | 26 | | 191 | 226 |
| 0104 | 21" x 41" | G | | 18 | .889 | | 170 | 26 | | 196 | 231 |
| 0106 | 21" x 49" | G | ↓ | 18 | .889 | ↓ | 178 | 26 | | 204 | 240 |

# 08 53 Plastic Windows

## 08 53 13 – Vinyl Windows

### 08 53 13.30 Vinyl Double Hung Windows

| | | Crew | Daily Output | Labor-Hours | Unit | Material | 2010 Bare Costs Labor | Equipment | Total | Total Incl O&P |
|---|---|---|---|---|---|---|---|---|---|---|
| 0110 | 21" x 57" | G 2 Carp | 17 | .941 | Ea. | 190 | 27.50 | | 217.50 | 255 |
| 0120 | 21" x 65" | G | 16 | 1 | | 198 | 29 | | 227 | 267 |
| 0128 | 25" x 37" | G | 20 | .800 | | 175 | 23.50 | | 198.50 | 232 |
| 0130 | 25" x 41" | G | 20 | .800 | | 179 | 23.50 | | 202.50 | 236 |
| 0140 | 25" x 49" | G | 18 | .889 | | 184 | 26 | | 210 | 246 |
| 0145 | 25" x 53" | G | 18 | .889 | | 192 | 26 | | 218 | 255 |
| 0150 | 25" x 57" | G | 17 | .941 | | 192 | 27.50 | | 219.50 | 257 |
| 0160 | 25" x 65" | G | 16 | 1 | | 204 | 29 | | 233 | 273 |
| 0162 | 25" x 69" | G | 16 | 1 | | 212 | 29 | | 241 | 282 |
| 0164 | 25" x 77" | G | 16 | 1 | | 225 | 29 | | 254 | 297 |
| 0168 | 29" x 37" | G | 18 | .889 | | 180 | 26 | | 206 | 242 |
| 0170 | 29" x 41" | G | 18 | .889 | | 184 | 26 | | 210 | 246 |
| 0172 | 29" x 49" | G | 18 | .889 | | 193 | 26 | | 219 | 256 |
| 0180 | 29" x 53" | G | 18 | .889 | | 197 | 26 | | 223 | 261 |
| 0190 | 29" x 57" | G | 17 | .941 | | 202 | 27.50 | | 229.50 | 268 |
| 0200 | 29" x 65" | G | 16 | 1 | | 217 | 29 | | 246 | 288 |
| 0202 | 29" x 69" | G | 16 | 1 | | 217 | 29 | | 246 | 288 |
| 0205 | 29" x 77" | G | 16 | 1 | | 230 | 29 | | 259 | 300 |
| 0208 | 33" x 37" | G | 20 | .800 | | 185 | 23.50 | | 208.50 | 243 |
| 0210 | 33" x 41" | G | 20 | .800 | | 189 | 23.50 | | 212.50 | 247 |
| 0215 | 33" x 49" | G | 20 | .800 | | 199 | 23.50 | | 222.50 | 258 |
| 0220 | 33" x 53" | G | 18 | .889 | | 204 | 26 | | 230 | 268 |
| 0230 | 33" x 57" | G | 17 | .941 | | 208 | 27.50 | | 235.50 | 275 |
| 0240 | 33" x 65" | G | 16 | 1 | | 214 | 29 | | 243 | 284 |
| 0242 | 33" x 69" | G | 16 | 1 | | 227 | 29 | | 256 | 299 |
| 0246 | 33" x 77" | G | 16 | 1 | | 238 | 29 | | 267 | 310 |
| 0250 | 37" x 41" | G | 20 | .800 | | 191 | 23.50 | | 214.50 | 249 |
| 0255 | 37" x 49" | G | 20 | .800 | | 204 | 23.50 | | 227.50 | 263 |
| 0260 | 37" x 53" | G | 18 | .889 | | 212 | 26 | | 238 | 277 |
| 0270 | 37" x 57" | G | 17 | .941 | | 217 | 27.50 | | 244.50 | 285 |
| 0280 | 37" x 65" | G | 16 | 1 | | 222 | 29 | | 251 | 293 |
| 0282 | 37" x 69" | G | 16 | 1 | | 227 | 29 | | 256 | 299 |
| 0286 | 37" x 77" | G | 16 | 1 | | 248 | 29 | | 277 | 320 |
| 0300 | Solid vinyl, average quality, double insulated glass, 2'-0" x 3'-0" | G 1 Carp | 10 | .800 | | 279 | 23.50 | | 302.50 | 345 |
| 0310 | 3'-0" x 4'-0" | G | 9 | .889 | | 195 | 26 | | 221 | 259 |
| 0320 | 4'-0" x 4'-6" | G | 8 | 1 | | 293 | 29 | | 322 | 370 |
| 0330 | Premium, double insulated glass, 2'-6" x 3'-0" | G | 10 | .800 | | 214 | 23.50 | | 237.50 | 275 |
| 0340 | 3'-0" x 3'-6" | G | 9 | .889 | | 245 | 26 | | 271 | 315 |
| 0350 | 3'-0" x 4"-0" | G | 9 | .889 | | 256 | 26 | | 282 | 325 |
| 0360 | 3'-0" x 4'-6" | G | 9 | .889 | | 248 | 26 | | 274 | 315 |
| 0370 | 3'-0" x 5'-0" | G | 8 | 1 | | 268 | 29 | | 297 | 345 |
| 0380 | 3'-6" x 6'-0" | G | 8 | 1 | | 300 | 29 | | 329 | 380 |

### 08 53 13.40 Vinyl Casement Windows

| | | Crew | Daily Output | Labor-Hours | Unit | Material | 2010 Bare Costs Labor | Equipment | Total | Total Incl O&P |
|---|---|---|---|---|---|---|---|---|---|---|
| 0010 | **VINYL CASEMENT WINDOWS** | | | | | | | | | |
| 0100 | Grids, low E, J fin, ext. jambs, 1 lt, 21" x 41" | G 2 Carp | 20 | .800 | Ea. | 242 | 23.50 | | 265.50 | 305 |
| 0110 | 21" x 47" | G | 20 | .800 | | 264 | 23.50 | | 287.50 | 330 |
| 0120 | 21" x 53" | G | 20 | .800 | | 286 | 23.50 | | 309.50 | 355 |
| 0128 | 24" x 35" | G | 19 | .842 | | 233 | 24.50 | | 257.50 | 297 |
| 0130 | 24" x 41" | G | 19 | .842 | | 253 | 24.50 | | 277.50 | 320 |
| 0140 | 24" x 47" | G | 19 | .842 | | 274 | 24.50 | | 298.50 | 340 |
| 0150 | 24" x 53" | G | 19 | .842 | | 296 | 24.50 | | 320.50 | 365 |
| 0158 | 28" x 35" | G | 19 | .842 | | 248 | 24.50 | | 272.50 | 315 |

# 08 53 Plastic Windows

## 08 53 13 – Vinyl Windows

### 08 53 13.40 Vinyl Casement Windows

| | | | Crew | Daily Output | Labor-Hours | Unit | Material | 2010 Bare Costs Labor | Equipment | Total | Total Incl O&P |
|---|---|---|---|---|---|---|---|---|---|---|---|
| 0160 | 28" x 41" | G | 2 Carp | 19 | .842 | Ea. | 268 | 24.50 | | 292.50 | 335 |
| 0170 | 28" x 47" | G | | 19 | .842 | | 290 | 24.50 | | 314.50 | 360 |
| 0180 | 28" x 53" | G | | 19 | .842 | | 320 | 24.50 | | 344.50 | 390 |
| 0184 | 28" x 59" | G | | 19 | .842 | | 325 | 24.50 | | 349.50 | 400 |
| 0188 | Two lites, 33" x 35" | G | | 18 | .889 | | 400 | 26 | | 426 | 485 |
| 0190 | 33" x 41" | G | | 18 | .889 | | 425 | 26 | | 451 | 515 |
| 0200 | 33" x 47" | G | | 18 | .889 | | 460 | 26 | | 486 | 550 |
| 0210 | 33" x 53" | G | | 18 | .889 | | 490 | 26 | | 516 | 585 |
| 0212 | 33" x 59" | G | | 18 | .889 | | 520 | 26 | | 546 | 615 |
| 0215 | 33" x 72" | G | | 18 | .889 | | 540 | 26 | | 566 | 640 |
| 0220 | 41" x 41" | G | | 18 | .889 | | 465 | 26 | | 491 | 560 |
| 0230 | 41" x 47" | G | | 18 | .889 | | 500 | 26 | | 526 | 595 |
| 0240 | 41" x 53" | G | | 17 | .941 | | 530 | 27.50 | | 557.50 | 625 |
| 0242 | 41" x 59" | G | | 17 | .941 | | 560 | 27.50 | | 587.50 | 660 |
| 0246 | 41" x 72" | G | | 17 | .941 | | 585 | 27.50 | | 612.50 | 685 |
| 0250 | 47" x 41" | G | | 17 | .941 | | 470 | 27.50 | | 497.50 | 565 |
| 0260 | 47" x 47" | G | | 17 | .941 | | 500 | 27.50 | | 527.50 | 595 |
| 0270 | 47" x 53" | G | | 17 | .941 | | 530 | 27.50 | | 557.50 | 630 |
| 0272 | 47" x 59" | G | | 17 | .941 | | 585 | 27.50 | | 612.50 | 685 |
| 0280 | 56" x 41" | G | | 15 | 1.067 | | 505 | 31 | | 536 | 605 |
| 0290 | 56" x 47" | G | | 15 | 1.067 | | 530 | 31 | | 561 | 635 |
| 0300 | 56" x 53" | G | | 15 | 1.067 | | 580 | 31 | | 611 | 690 |
| 0302 | 56" x 59" | G | | 15 | 1.067 | | 605 | 31 | | 636 | 720 |
| 0310 | 56" x 72" | G | | 15 | 1.067 | | 660 | 31 | | 691 | 775 |
| 0340 | Solid vinyl, premium, double insulated glass, 2'-0" x 3'-0" high | G | 1 Carp | 10 | .800 | | 252 | 23.50 | | 275.50 | 315 |
| 0360 | 2'-0" x 4'-0" high | G | | 9 | .889 | | 280 | 26 | | 306 | 355 |
| 0380 | 2'-0" x 5'-0" high | G | | 8 | 1 | | 291 | 29 | | 320 | 370 |

### 08 53 13.50 Vinyl Picture Windows

| | | | Crew | Daily Output | Labor-Hours | Unit | Material | 2010 Bare Costs Labor | Equipment | Total | Total Incl O&P |
|---|---|---|---|---|---|---|---|---|---|---|---|
| 0010 | **VINYL PICTURE WINDOWS** | | | | | | | | | | |
| 0100 | Grids, low E, J fin, ext. jambs, 33" x 47" | | 2 Carp | 12 | 1.333 | Ea. | 238 | 39 | | 277 | 330 |
| 0110 | 35" x 71" | | | 12 | 1.333 | | 310 | 39 | | 349 | 405 |
| 0120 | 41" x 47" | | | 12 | 1.333 | | 252 | 39 | | 291 | 345 |
| 0130 | 41" x 71" | | | 12 | 1.333 | | 320 | 39 | | 359 | 420 |
| 0140 | 47" x 47" | | | 12 | 1.333 | | 277 | 39 | | 316 | 370 |
| 0150 | 47" x 71" | | | 11 | 1.455 | | 350 | 42.50 | | 392.50 | 455 |
| 0160 | 53" x 47" | | | 11 | 1.455 | | 300 | 42.50 | | 342.50 | 400 |
| 0170 | 53" x 71" | | | 11 | 1.455 | | 315 | 42.50 | | 357.50 | 415 |
| 0180 | 59" x 47" | | | 11 | 1.455 | | 340 | 42.50 | | 382.50 | 445 |
| 0190 | 59" x 71" | | | 11 | 1.455 | | 365 | 42.50 | | 407.50 | 470 |
| 0200 | 71" x 47" | | | 10 | 1.600 | | 375 | 46.50 | | 421.50 | 495 |
| 0210 | 71" x 71" | | | 10 | 1.600 | | 395 | 46.50 | | 441.50 | 515 |

### 08 53 13.60 Vinyl Half Round Windows

| | | | Crew | Daily Output | Labor-Hours | Unit | Material | 2010 Bare Costs Labor | Equipment | Total | Total Incl O&P |
|---|---|---|---|---|---|---|---|---|---|---|---|
| 0010 | **VINYL HALF ROUND WINDOWS**, Including grille, j fin low E, ext. jambs | | | | | | | | | | |
| 0100 | 10" height x 20" base | | 2 Carp | 8 | 2 | Ea. | 475 | 58 | | 533 | 620 |
| 0110 | 15" height x 30" base | | | 8 | 2 | | 425 | 58 | | 483 | 570 |
| 0120 | 17" height x 34" base | | | 7 | 2.286 | | 287 | 66.50 | | 353.50 | 425 |
| 0130 | 19" height x 38" base | | | 7 | 2.286 | | 310 | 66.50 | | 376.50 | 450 |
| 0140 | 19" height x 33" base | | | 7 | 2.286 | | 555 | 66.50 | | 621.50 | 725 |
| 0150 | 24" height x 48" base | | 1 Carp | 6 | 1.333 | | 320 | 39 | | 359 | 420 |
| 0160 | 25" height x 50" base | " | | 6 | 1.333 | | 755 | 39 | | 794 | 895 |
| 0170 | 30" height x 60" base | | 2 Carp | 6 | 2.667 | | 635 | 77.50 | | 712.50 | 830 |

# 08 54 Composite Windows

## 08 54 13 – Fiberglass Windows

| 08 54 13.10 Fiberglass Single Hung Windows | | Crew | Daily Output | Labor-Hours | Unit | Material | 2010 Bare Costs Labor | Equipment | Total | Total Incl O&P |
|---|---|---|---|---|---|---|---|---|---|---|
| 0010 | **FIBERGLASS SINGLE HUNG WINDOWS** | | | | | | | | | |
| 0100 | Grids, low E, 18" x 24" | G | 2 Carp | 18 | .889 | Ea. | 335 | 26 | | 361 | 415 |
| 0110 | 18" x 40" | G | | 17 | .941 | | 300 | 27.50 | | 327.50 | 375 |
| 0130 | 24" x 40" | G | | 20 | .800 | | 330 | 23.50 | | 353.50 | 405 |
| 0230 | 36" x 36" | G | | 17 | .941 | | 370 | 27.50 | | 397.50 | 450 |
| 0250 | 36" x 48" | G | | 20 | .800 | | 405 | 23.50 | | 428.50 | 485 |
| 0260 | 36" x 60" | G | | 18 | .889 | | 445 | 26 | | 471 | 535 |
| 0280 | 36" x 72" | G | | 16 | 1 | | 470 | 29 | | 499 | 565 |
| 0290 | 48" x 40" | G | | 16 | 1 | | 470 | 29 | | 499 | 565 |

# 08 61 Roof Windows

## 08 61 13 – Metal Roof Windows

### 08 61 13.10 Roof Windows

| | | Crew | Daily Output | Labor-Hours | Unit | Material | 2010 Bare Costs Labor | Equipment | Total | Total Incl O&P |
|---|---|---|---|---|---|---|---|---|---|---|
| 0010 | **ROOF WINDOWS**, fixed high perf tmpd glazing, metallic framed | | | | | | | | | |
| 0020 | 46" x 21-1/2", Flashed for shingled roof | 1 Carp | 8 | 1 | Ea. | 245 | 29 | | 274 | 320 |
| 0100 | 46" x 28" | | 8 | 1 | | 272 | 29 | | 301 | 350 |
| 0125 | 57" x 44" | | 6 | 1.333 | | 335 | 39 | | 374 | 435 |
| 0130 | 72" x 28" | | 7 | 1.143 | | 335 | 33.50 | | 368.50 | 425 |
| 0150 | Fixed, laminated tempered glazing, 46" x 21-1/2" | | 8 | 1 | | 415 | 29 | | 444 | 505 |
| 0175 | 46" x 28" | | 8 | 1 | | 460 | 29 | | 489 | 555 |
| 0200 | 57" x 44" | | 6 | 1.333 | | 430 | 39 | | 469 | 540 |
| 0500 | Vented flashing set for shingled roof, 46" x 21-1/2" | | 7 | 1.143 | | 415 | 33.50 | | 448.50 | 510 |
| 0525 | 46" x 28" | | 6 | 1.333 | | 460 | 39 | | 499 | 570 |
| 0550 | 57" x 44" | | 5 | 1.600 | | 575 | 46.50 | | 621.50 | 715 |
| 0560 | 72" x 28" | | 5 | 1.600 | | 575 | 46.50 | | 621.50 | 715 |
| 0575 | Flashing set for low pitched roof, 46" x 21-1/2" | | 7 | 1.143 | | 475 | 33.50 | | 508.50 | 580 |
| 0600 | 46" x 28" | | 7 | 1.143 | | 525 | 33.50 | | 558.50 | 630 |
| 0625 | 57" x 44" | | 5 | 1.600 | | 650 | 46.50 | | 696.50 | 795 |
| 0650 | Flashing set for curb 46" x 21-1/2" | | 7 | 1.143 | | 550 | 33.50 | | 583.50 | 660 |
| 0675 | 46" x 28" | | 7 | 1.143 | | 600 | 33.50 | | 633.50 | 715 |
| 0700 | 57" x 44" | | 5 | 1.600 | | 740 | 46.50 | | 786.50 | 890 |

## 08 61 16 – Wood Roof Windows

### 08 61 16.16 Roof Windows, Wood Framed

| | | Crew | Daily Output | Labor-Hours | Unit | Material | 2010 Bare Costs Labor | Equipment | Total | Total Incl O&P |
|---|---|---|---|---|---|---|---|---|---|---|
| 0010 | **ROOF WINDOWS, WOOD FRAMED** | | | | | | | | | |
| 5600 | Roof window incl. frame, flashing, double insulated glass & screens, | | | | | | | | | |
| 5610 | complete unit, 22" x 38" | 2 Carp | 3 | 5.333 | Ea. | 251 | 155 | | 406 | 535 |
| 5650 | 2'-5" x 3'-8" | | 3.20 | 5 | | 293 | 146 | | 439 | 565 |
| 5700 | 3'-5" x 4'-9" | | 3.40 | 4.706 | | 375 | 137 | | 512 | 645 |

# 08 62 Unit Skylights

## 08 62 13 – Domed Unit Skylights

### 08 62 13.10 Domed Skylights

| | | Crew | Daily Output | Labor-Hours | Unit | Material | 2010 Bare Costs Labor | Equipment | Total | Total Incl O&P |
|---|---|---|---|---|---|---|---|---|---|---|
| 0010 | **DOMED SKYLIGHTS** | | | | | | | | | |
| 0020 | Skylight, fixed dome type, 22" x 22" | G | G-3 | 12 | 2.667 | Ea. | 200 | 72 | | 272 | 340 |
| 0030 | 22" x 46" | G | | 10 | 3.200 | | 229 | 86 | | 315 | 395 |
| 0040 | 30" x 30" | G | | 12 | 2.667 | | 230 | 72 | | 302 | 375 |
| 0050 | 30" x 46" | G | | 10 | 3.200 | | 290 | 86 | | 376 | 465 |
| 0110 | Fixed, double glazed, 22" x 27" | G | | 12 | 2.667 | | 213 | 72 | | 285 | 355 |
| 0120 | 22" x 46" | G | | 10 | 3.200 | | 269 | 86 | | 355 | 440 |
| 0130 | 44" x 46" | G | | 10 | 3.200 | | 400 | 86 | | 486 | 585 |
| 0210 | Operable, double glazed, 22" x 27" | G | | 12 | 2.667 | | 310 | 72 | | 382 | 460 |
| 0220 | 22" x 46" | G | | 10 | 3.200 | | 365 | 86 | | 451 | 545 |
| 0230 | 44" x 46" | G | | 10 | 3.200 | | 770 | 86 | | 856 | 990 |

### 08 62 13.20 Skylights

| | | Crew | Daily Output | Labor-Hours | Unit | Material | 2010 Bare Costs Labor | Equipment | Total | Total Incl O&P |
|---|---|---|---|---|---|---|---|---|---|---|
| 0010 | **SKYLIGHTS**, Plastic domes, flush or curb mounted ten or | | | | | | | | | |
| 0100 | more units | | | | | | | | | |
| 0300 | Nominal size under 10 S.F., double | G | G-3 | 130 | .246 | S.F. | 28 | 6.65 | | 34.65 | 42 |
| 0400 | Single | | | 160 | .200 | | 24.50 | 5.40 | | 29.90 | 36 |
| 0600 | 10 S.F. to 20 S.F., double | G | | 315 | .102 | | 24 | 2.74 | | 26.74 | 31 |
| 0700 | Single | | | 395 | .081 | | 24 | 2.18 | | 26.18 | 29.50 |
| 0900 | 20 S.F. to 30 S.F., double | G | | 395 | .081 | | 22 | 2.18 | | 24.18 | 28 |
| 1000 | Single | | | 465 | .069 | | 19.70 | 1.85 | | 21.55 | 24.50 |
| 1200 | 30 S.F. to 65 S.F., double | G | | 465 | .069 | | 22 | 1.85 | | 23.85 | 27.50 |
| 1300 | Single | | | 610 | .052 | | 17 | 1.41 | | 18.41 | 21 |
| 1500 | For insulated 4" curbs, double, add | | | | | | 25% | | | | |
| 1600 | Single, add | | | | | | 30% | | | | |
| 1800 | For integral insulated 9" curbs, double, add | | | | | | 30% | | | | |
| 1900 | Single, add | | | | | | 40% | | | | |
| 2120 | Ventilating insulated plexiglass dome with | | | | | | | | | | |
| 2130 | curb mounting, 36" x 36" | G | G-3 | 12 | 2.667 | Ea. | 460 | 72 | | 532 | 625 |
| 2150 | 52" x 52" | G | | 12 | 2.667 | | 640 | 72 | | 712 | 825 |
| 2160 | 28" x 52" | G | | 10 | 3.200 | | 470 | 86 | | 556 | 660 |
| 2170 | 36" x 52" | G | | 10 | 3.200 | | 520 | 86 | | 606 | 715 |
| 2180 | For electric opening system, add | G | | | | | 300 | | | 300 | 330 |
| 2210 | Operating skylight, with thermopane glass, 24" x 48" | G | G-3 | 10 | 3.200 | | 560 | 86 | | 646 | 765 |
| 2220 | 32" x 48" | G | " | 9 | 3.556 | | 590 | 96 | | 686 | 805 |
| 2310 | Non venting insulated plexiglass dome skylight with | | | | | | | | | | |
| 2320 | Flush mount 22" x 46" | G | G-3 | 15.23 | 2.101 | Ea. | 320 | 56.50 | | 376.50 | 445 |
| 2330 | 30" x 30" | G | | 16 | 2 | | 292 | 54 | | 346 | 410 |
| 2340 | 46" x 46" | G | | 13.91 | 2.301 | | 540 | 62 | | 602 | 700 |
| 2350 | Curb mount 22" x 46" | G | | 15.23 | 2.101 | | 350 | 56.50 | | 406.50 | 480 |
| 2360 | 30" x 30" | G | | 16 | 2 | | 390 | 54 | | 444 | 520 |
| 2370 | 46" x 46" | G | | 13.91 | 2.301 | | 600 | 62 | | 662 | 765 |
| 2381 | Non-insulated flush mount 22" x 46" | | | 15.23 | 2.101 | | 215 | 56.50 | | 271.50 | 330 |
| 2382 | 30" x 30" | | | 16 | 2 | | 194 | 54 | | 248 | 305 |
| 2383 | 46" x 46" | | | 13.91 | 2.301 | | 365 | 62 | | 427 | 505 |
| 2384 | Curb mount 22" x 46" | | | 15.23 | 2.101 | | 181 | 56.50 | | 237.50 | 294 |
| 2385 | 30" x 30" | | | 16 | 2 | | 180 | 54 | | 234 | 288 |
| 4000 | Skylight, solar tube kit, incl dome, flashing, diffuser, 1 pipe, 9" dia. | G | 1 Carp | 2 | 4 | | 220 | 116 | | 336 | 440 |
| 4010 | 13" dia. | G | | 2 | 4 | | 290 | 116 | | 406 | 515 |
| 4020 | 21" dia. | G | | 2 | 4 | | 490 | 116 | | 606 | 735 |
| 4030 | Accessories for, 1' long x 9" dia pipe | G | | 24 | .333 | | 30 | 9.70 | | 39.70 | 49.50 |
| 4040 | 2' long x 9" dia pipe | G | | 24 | .333 | | 44 | 9.70 | | 53.70 | 65 |
| 4050 | 4' long x 9" dia pipe | G | | 20 | .400 | | 72 | 11.65 | | 83.65 | 98.50 |

# 08 62 Unit Skylights

## 08 62 13 – Domed Unit Skylights

| 08 62 13.20 Skylights | | Crew | Daily Output | Labor-Hours | Unit | Material | 2010 Bare Costs Labor | Equipment | Total | Total Incl O&P |
|---|---|---|---|---|---|---|---|---|---|---|
| 4060 | 1' long x 13" dia pipe | G 1 Carp | 24 | .333 | Ea. | 44 | 9.70 | | 53.70 | 65 |
| 4070 | 2' long x 13" dia pipe | G | 24 | .333 | | 57 | 9.70 | | 66.70 | 79 |
| 4080 | 4' long x 13" dia pipe | G | 20 | .400 | | 99 | 11.65 | | 110.65 | 129 |
| 4090 | 2' long x 21" dia pipe | G | 16 | .500 | | 100 | 14.55 | | 114.55 | 135 |
| 4100 | 4' long x 21" dia pipe | G | 12 | .667 | | 162 | 19.40 | | 181.40 | 211 |
| 4110 | 45 degree elbow, 9" | G | 16 | .500 | | 90 | 14.55 | | 104.55 | 124 |
| 4120 | 13" | G | 16 | .500 | | 83 | 14.55 | | 97.55 | 116 |
| 4130 | Interior decorative ring, 9" | G | 20 | .400 | | 20 | 11.65 | | 31.65 | 41.50 |
| 4140 | 13" | G | 20 | .400 | | 22 | 11.65 | | 33.65 | 43.50 |

# 08 71 Door Hardware

## 08 71 20 – Hardware

### 08 71 20.15 Hardware

| | | Crew | Daily Output | Labor-Hours | Unit | Material | 2010 Bare Costs Labor | Equipment | Total | Total Incl O&P |
|---|---|---|---|---|---|---|---|---|---|---|
| 0009 | **HARDWARE** | | | | | | | | | |
| 0010 | Average percentage for hardware, total job cost | | | | | | | | | |
| 0025 | Minimum | | | | Job | | | | | .75% |
| 0050 | Maximum | | | | | | | | | 4% |
| 0500 | Total hardware for building, average distribution | | | | | 85% | 15% | | | |
| 1000 | Door hardware, apartment, interior | | | | Door | 490 | | | 490 | 540 |
| 1300 | Average, door hardware, motel/hotel interior | | | | " | 635 | | | 635 | 700 |
| 2100 | Pocket door | | | | Ea. | 134 | | | 134 | 147 |
| 4000 | Door knocker, bright brass | 1 Carp | 32 | .250 | | 49 | 7.30 | | 56.30 | 66.50 |
| 4100 | Mail slot, bright brass, 2" x 11" | " | 25 | .320 | | 62 | 9.30 | | 71.30 | 83.50 |
| 4200 | Peep hole, add to price of door | | | | | 10.50 | | | 10.50 | 11.55 |

### 08 71 20.40 Lockset

| | | Crew | Daily Output | Labor-Hours | Unit | Material | 2010 Bare Costs Labor | Equipment | Total | Total Incl O&P |
|---|---|---|---|---|---|---|---|---|---|---|
| 0010 | **LOCKSET**, Standard duty | | | | | | | | | |
| 0020 | Non-keyed, passage, w/sect.trim | 1 Carp | 12 | .667 | Ea. | 53.50 | 19.40 | | 72.90 | 91.50 |
| 0100 | Privacy | | 12 | .667 | | 62 | 19.40 | | 81.40 | 101 |
| 0400 | Keyed, single cylinder function | | 10 | .800 | | 86 | 23.50 | | 109.50 | 134 |
| 0500 | Lever handled, keyed, single cylinder function | | 10 | .800 | | 156 | 23.50 | | 179.50 | 211 |
| 1700 | Residential, interior door, minimum | | 16 | .500 | | 22 | 14.55 | | 36.55 | 48.50 |
| 1720 | Maximum | | 8 | 1 | | 55 | 29 | | 84 | 110 |
| 1800 | Exterior, minimum | | 14 | .571 | | 40 | 16.65 | | 56.65 | 72 |
| 1810 | Average | | 8 | 1 | | 72 | 29 | | 101 | 129 |
| 1820 | Maximum | | 8 | 1 | | 160 | 29 | | 189 | 225 |

### 08 71 20.50 Door Stops

| | | Crew | Daily Output | Labor-Hours | Unit | Material | 2010 Bare Costs Labor | Equipment | Total | Total Incl O&P |
|---|---|---|---|---|---|---|---|---|---|---|
| 0010 | **DOOR STOPS** | | | | | | | | | |
| 0020 | Holder & bumper, floor or wall | 1 Carp | 32 | .250 | Ea. | 34.50 | 7.30 | | 41.80 | 50.50 |
| 1300 | Wall bumper, 4" diameter, with rubber pad, aluminum | | 32 | .250 | | 10.95 | 7.30 | | 18.25 | 24.50 |
| 1600 | Door bumper, floor type, aluminum | | 32 | .250 | | 7 | 7.30 | | 14.30 | 19.95 |
| 1900 | Plunger type, door mounted | | 32 | .250 | | 28 | 7.30 | | 35.30 | 43 |

### 08 71 20.60 Entrance Locks

| | | Crew | Daily Output | Labor-Hours | Unit | Material | 2010 Bare Costs Labor | Equipment | Total | Total Incl O&P |
|---|---|---|---|---|---|---|---|---|---|---|
| 0010 | **ENTRANCE LOCKS** | | | | | | | | | |
| 0015 | Cylinder, grip handle deadlocking latch | 1 Carp | 9 | .889 | Ea. | 132 | 26 | | 158 | 189 |
| 0020 | Deadbolt | | 8 | 1 | | 160 | 29 | | 189 | 225 |
| 0100 | Push and pull plate, dead bolt | | 8 | 1 | | 150 | 29 | | 179 | 214 |
| 0900 | For handicapped lever, add | | | | | 170 | | | 170 | 187 |

### 08 71 20.65 Thresholds

| | | Crew | Daily Output | Labor-Hours | Unit | Material | 2010 Bare Costs Labor | Equipment | Total | Total Incl O&P |
|---|---|---|---|---|---|---|---|---|---|---|
| 0010 | **THRESHOLDS** | | | | | | | | | |
| 0011 | Threshold 3' long saddles aluminum | 1 Carp | 48 | .167 | L.F. | 4.16 | 4.85 | | 9.01 | 12.75 |

447

# 08 71 Door Hardware

## 08 71 20 – Hardware

### 08 71 20.65 Thresholds

| | | Crew | Daily Output | Labor-Hours | Unit | Material | 2010 Bare Costs Labor | Equipment | Total | Total Incl O&P |
|---|---|---|---|---|---|---|---|---|---|---|
| 0100 | Aluminum, 8" wide, 1/2" thick | 1 Carp | 12 | .667 | Ea. | 39 | 19.40 | | 58.40 | 75.50 |
| 0500 | Bronze | | 60 | .133 | L.F. | 40 | 3.88 | | 43.88 | 50.50 |
| 0600 | Bronze, panic threshold, 5" wide, 1/2" thick | | 12 | .667 | Ea. | 66 | 19.40 | | 85.40 | 105 |
| 0700 | Rubber, 1/2" thick, 5-1/2" wide | | 20 | .400 | | 38 | 11.65 | | 49.65 | 61.50 |
| 0800 | 2-3/4" wide | | 20 | .400 | | 16 | 11.65 | | 27.65 | 37 |

### 08 71 20.75 Door Hardware Accessories

| | | Crew | Daily Output | Labor-Hours | Unit | Material | Labor | Equipment | Total | Total Incl O&P |
|---|---|---|---|---|---|---|---|---|---|---|
| 0010 | **DOOR HARDWARE ACCESSORIES** | | | | | | | | | |
| 1000 | Knockers, brass, standard | 1 Carp | 16 | .500 | Ea. | 43.50 | 14.55 | | 58.05 | 72.50 |
| 1100 | Deluxe | | 10 | .800 | | 126 | 23.50 | | 149.50 | 177 |
| 4100 | Deluxe | | 18 | .444 | | 44 | 12.95 | | 56.95 | 70.50 |
| 4500 | Rubber door silencers | | 540 | .015 | | .33 | .43 | | .76 | 1.08 |

### 08 71 20.90 Hinges

| | | Crew | Daily Output | Labor-Hours | Unit | Material | Labor | Equipment | Total | Total Incl O&P |
|---|---|---|---|---|---|---|---|---|---|---|
| 0010 | **HINGES** | R087120-10 | | | | | | | | |
| 0012 | Full mortise, avg. freq., steel base, USP, 4-1/2" x 4-1/2" | | | | Pr. | 25.50 | | | 25.50 | 28 |
| 0100 | 5" x 5", USP | | | | | 42.50 | | | 42.50 | 46.50 |
| 0200 | 6" x 6", USP | | | | | 90 | | | 90 | 99 |
| 0400 | Brass base, 4-1/2" x 4-1/2", US10 | | | | | 52.50 | | | 52.50 | 57.50 |
| 0500 | 5" x 5", US10 | | | | | 76 | | | 76 | 84 |
| 0600 | 6" x 6", US10 | | | | | 130 | | | 130 | 143 |
| 0800 | Stainless steel base, 4-1/2" x 4-1/2", US32 | | | | | 77 | | | 77 | 85 |
| 0900 | For non removable pin, add (security item) | | | | Ea. | 4.47 | | | 4.47 | 4.92 |
| 0910 | For floating pin, driven tips, add | | | | | 3.15 | | | 3.15 | 3.47 |
| 0930 | For hospital type tip on pin, add | | | | | 13.80 | | | 13.80 | 15.20 |
| 0940 | For steeple type tip on pin, add | | | | | 12 | | | 12 | 13.20 |
| 0950 | Full mortise, high frequency, steel base, 3-1/2" x 3-1/2", US26D | | | | Pr. | 27 | | | 27 | 29.50 |
| 1000 | 4-1/2" x 4-1/2", USP | | | | | 61 | | | 61 | 67.50 |
| 1100 | 5" x 5", USP | | | | | 57 | | | 57 | 62.50 |
| 1200 | 6" x 6", USP | | | | | 140 | | | 140 | 154 |
| 1400 | Brass base, 3-1/2" x 3-1/2", US4 | | | | | 46.50 | | | 46.50 | 51.50 |
| 1430 | 4-1/2" x 4-1/2", US10 | | | | | 82 | | | 82 | 90.50 |
| 1500 | 5" x 5", US10 | | | | | 121 | | | 121 | 133 |
| 1600 | 6" x 6", US10 | | | | | 175 | | | 175 | 192 |
| 1800 | Stainless steel base, 4-1/2" x 4-1/2", US32 | | | | | 127 | | | 127 | 140 |
| 1810 | 5" x 4-1/2", US32 | | | | | 180 | | | 180 | 198 |
| 1930 | For hospital type tip on pin, add | | | | Ea. | 12.30 | | | 12.30 | 13.50 |
| 1950 | Full mortise, low frequency, steel base, 3-1/2" x 3-1/2", US26D | | | | Pr. | 11.20 | | | 11.20 | 12.35 |
| 2000 | 4-1/2" x 4-1/2", USP | | | | | 12.55 | | | 12.55 | 13.85 |
| 2100 | 5" x 5", USP | | | | | 31 | | | 31 | 34 |
| 2200 | 6" x 6", USP | | | | | 62 | | | 62 | 68 |
| 2300 | 4-1/2" x 4-1/2", US3 | | | | | 18.10 | | | 18.10 | 19.90 |
| 2310 | 5" x 5", US3 | | | | | 43.50 | | | 43.50 | 48 |
| 2400 | Brass bass, 4-1/2" x 4-1/2", US10 | | | | | 43.50 | | | 43.50 | 48 |
| 2500 | 5" x 5", US10 | | | | | 66 | | | 66 | 72.50 |
| 2800 | Stainless steel base, 4-1/2" x 4-1/2", US32 | | | | | 75 | | | 75 | 82.50 |

### 08 71 20.92 Mortised Hinges

| | | Crew | Daily Output | Labor-Hours | Unit | Material | Labor | Equipment | Total | Total Incl O&P |
|---|---|---|---|---|---|---|---|---|---|---|
| 0010 | **MORTISED HINGES** | | | | | | | | | |
| 0200 | Average frequency, steel plated, ball bearing, 3-1/2" x 3-1/2" | | | | Pr. | 25.50 | | | 25.50 | 28.50 |
| 0300 | Bronze, ball bearing | | | | | 32 | | | 32 | 35 |
| 0900 | High frequency, steel plated, ball bearing | | | | | 79.50 | | | 79.50 | 87.50 |
| 1100 | Bronze, ball bearing | | | | | 82 | | | 82 | 90.50 |
| 1300 | Average frequency, steel plated, ball bearing, 4-1/2" x 4-1/2" | | | | | 31.50 | | | 31.50 | 35 |
| 1500 | Bronze, ball bearing, to 36" wide | | | | | 34 | | | 34 | 37 |

# 08 71 Door Hardware

## 08 71 20 – Hardware

### 08 71 20.92 Mortised Hinges

| | | Crew | Daily Output | Labor-Hours | Unit | Material | 2010 Bare Costs Labor | Equipment | Total | Total Incl O&P |
|---|---|---|---|---|---|---|---|---|---|---|
| 1700 | Low frequency, steel, plated, plain bearing | | | | Pr. | 16.10 | | | 16.10 | 17.70 |
| 1900 | Bronze, plain bearing | | | | | 22.50 | | | 22.50 | 25 |

### 08 71 20.95 Kick Plates

| | | Crew | Daily Output | Labor-Hours | Unit | Material | 2010 Bare Costs Labor | Equipment | Total | Total Incl O&P |
|---|---|---|---|---|---|---|---|---|---|---|
| 0010 | **KICK PLATES** | | | | | | | | | |
| 0020 | Stainless steel, .050, 16 ga, 8" x 28", US32 | 1 Carp | 15 | .533 | Ea. | 34 | 15.50 | | 49.50 | 63.50 |
| 0080 | Mop/Kick, 4" x 28" | | 15 | .533 | | 29.50 | 15.50 | | 45 | 58 |
| 0090 | 4" x 30" | | 15 | .533 | | 31.50 | 15.50 | | 47 | 60.50 |
| 0100 | 4" x 34" | | 15 | .533 | | 35.50 | 15.50 | | 51 | 65 |
| 0110 | 6" x 28" | | 15 | .533 | | 38 | 15.50 | | 53.50 | 68 |
| 0120 | 6" x 30" | | 15 | .533 | | 40.50 | 15.50 | | 56 | 71 |
| 0130 | 6" x 34" | | 15 | .533 | | 46 | 15.50 | | 61.50 | 77 |
| 0590 | 6" x 28" | | 15 | .533 | | 43.50 | 15.50 | | 59 | 74 |
| 0600 | 6" x 30" | | 15 | .533 | | 50 | 15.50 | | 65.50 | 81 |
| 0610 | 6" x 34" | | 15 | .533 | | 50 | 15.50 | | 65.50 | 81 |

## 08 71 21 – Astragals

### 08 71 21.10 Exterior Mouldings, Astragals

| | | Crew | Daily Output | Labor-Hours | Unit | Material | 2010 Bare Costs Labor | Equipment | Total | Total Incl O&P |
|---|---|---|---|---|---|---|---|---|---|---|
| 0010 | **EXTERIOR MOULDINGS, ASTRAGALS** | | | | | | | | | |
| 4170 | Astragal for double doors, aluminum | 1 Carp | 4 | 2 | Opng. | 26 | 58 | | 84 | 127 |
| 4174 | Bronze | " | 4 | 2 | " | 36 | 58 | | 94 | 138 |

## 08 71 25 – Weatherstripping

### 08 71 25.10 Mechanical Seals, Weatherstripping

| | | Crew | Daily Output | Labor-Hours | Unit | Material | 2010 Bare Costs Labor | Equipment | Total | Total Incl O&P |
|---|---|---|---|---|---|---|---|---|---|---|
| 0010 | **MECHANICAL SEALS, WEATHERSTRIPPING** | | | | | | | | | |
| 1000 | Doors, wood frame, interlocking, for 3' x 7' door, zinc | 1 Carp | 3 | 2.667 | Opng. | 15.70 | 77.50 | | 93.20 | 148 |
| 1100 | Bronze | | 3 | 2.667 | | 25 | 77.50 | | 102.50 | 159 |
| 1300 | 6' x 7' opening, zinc | | 2 | 4 | | 17 | 116 | | 133 | 215 |
| 1400 | Bronze | | 2 | 4 | | 32 | 116 | | 148 | 232 |
| 1500 | Vinyl V strip | | 6.40 | 1.250 | Ea. | 8.25 | 36.50 | | 44.75 | 70 |
| 1700 | Wood frame, spring type, bronze | | | | | | | | | |
| 1800 | 3' x 7' door | 1 Carp | 7.60 | 1.053 | Opng. | 22 | 30.50 | | 52.50 | 75.50 |
| 1900 | 6' x 7' door | | 7 | 1.143 | | 28 | 33.50 | | 61.50 | 86.50 |
| 1920 | Felt, 3' x 7' door | | 14 | .571 | | 2.49 | 16.65 | | 19.14 | 30.50 |
| 1930 | 6' x 7' door | | 13 | .615 | | 2.85 | 17.90 | | 20.75 | 33 |
| 1950 | Rubber, 3' x 7' door | | 7.60 | 1.053 | | 5.35 | 30.50 | | 35.85 | 57.50 |
| 1960 | 6' x 7' door | | 7 | 1.143 | | 5.85 | 33.50 | | 39.35 | 62.50 |
| 2200 | Metal frame, spring type, bronze | | | | | | | | | |
| 2300 | 3' x 7' door | 1 Carp | 3 | 2.667 | Opng. | 36.50 | 77.50 | | 114 | 172 |
| 2400 | 6' x 7' door | " | 2.50 | 3.200 | " | 46.50 | 93 | | 139.50 | 208 |
| 2500 | For stainless steel, spring type, add | | | | | 133% | | | | |
| 2700 | Metal frame, extruded sections, 3' x 7' door, aluminum | 1 Carp | 3 | 2.667 | Opng. | 45 | 77.50 | | 122.50 | 181 |
| 2800 | Bronze | | 3 | 2.667 | | 114 | 77.50 | | 191.50 | 256 |
| 3100 | 6' x 7' door, aluminum | | 1.50 | 5.333 | | 57.50 | 155 | | 212.50 | 325 |
| 3200 | Bronze | | 1.50 | 5.333 | | 136 | 155 | | 291 | 410 |
| 3500 | Threshold weatherstripping | | | | | | | | | |
| 3650 | Door sweep, flush mounted, aluminum | 1 Carp | 25 | .320 | Ea. | 13.50 | 9.30 | | 22.80 | 30.50 |
| 3700 | Vinyl | | 25 | .320 | | 15.90 | 9.30 | | 25.20 | 33 |
| 5000 | Garage door bottom weatherstrip, 12' aluminum, clear | | 14 | .571 | | 21.50 | 16.65 | | 38.15 | 51.50 |
| 5010 | Bronze | | 14 | .571 | | 83 | 16.65 | | 99.65 | 120 |
| 5050 | Bottom protection, Rubber | | 14 | .571 | | 22 | 16.65 | | 38.65 | 52.50 |
| 5100 | Threshold | | 14 | .571 | | 90.50 | 16.65 | | 107.15 | 128 |

# 08 75 Window Hardware

## 08 75 10 – Window Handles and Latches

### 08 75 10.10 Handles and Latches

| | | Crew | Daily Output | Labor-Hours | Unit | Material | 2010 Bare Costs Labor | Equipment | Total | Total Incl O&P |
|---|---|---|---|---|---|---|---|---|---|---|
| 0010 | **HANDLES AND LATCHES** | | | | | | | | | |
| 1000 | Handles, surface mounted, aluminum | 1 Carp | 24 | .333 | Ea. | 3.98 | 9.70 | | 13.68 | 20.50 |
| 1020 | Brass | | 24 | .333 | | 7.40 | 9.70 | | 17.10 | 24.50 |
| 1040 | Chrome | | 24 | .333 | | 6.20 | 9.70 | | 15.90 | 23 |
| 1500 | Recessed, aluminum | | 12 | .667 | | 2.19 | 19.40 | | 21.59 | 35 |
| 1520 | Brass | | 12 | .667 | | 2.73 | 19.40 | | 22.13 | 35.50 |
| 1540 | Chrome | | 12 | .667 | | 2.26 | 19.40 | | 21.66 | 35 |
| 2000 | Latches, aluminum | | 20 | .400 | | 2.89 | 11.65 | | 14.54 | 23 |
| 2020 | Brass | | 20 | .400 | | 3.97 | 11.65 | | 15.62 | 24 |
| 2040 | Chrome | | 20 | .400 | | 2.47 | 11.65 | | 14.12 | 22.50 |

## 08 75 30 – Weatherstripping

### 08 75 30.10 Mechanical Weather Seals

| | | Crew | Daily Output | Labor-Hours | Unit | Material | 2010 Bare Costs Labor | Equipment | Total | Total Incl O&P |
|---|---|---|---|---|---|---|---|---|---|---|
| 0010 | **MECHANICAL WEATHER SEALS**, Window, double hung, 3' X 5' | | | | | | | | | |
| 0020 | Zinc | 1 Carp | 7.20 | 1.111 | Opng. | 12.80 | 32.50 | | 45.30 | 68.50 |
| 0100 | Bronze | | 7.20 | 1.111 | | 27 | 32.50 | | 59.50 | 84 |
| 0200 | Vinyl V strip | | 7 | 1.143 | | 4.95 | 33.50 | | 38.45 | 61.50 |
| 0500 | As above but heavy duty, zinc | | 4.60 | 1.739 | | 17.60 | 50.50 | | 68.10 | 104 |
| 0600 | Bronze | | 4.60 | 1.739 | | 30 | 50.50 | | 80.50 | 118 |
| 9000 | Minimum labor/equipment charge | 1 Clab | 4.60 | 1.739 | Job | | 37.50 | | 37.50 | 63 |

# 08 79 Hardware Accessories

## 08 79 20 – Door Accessories

### 08 79 20.10 Door Hardware Accessories

| | | Crew | Daily Output | Labor-Hours | Unit | Material | 2010 Bare Costs Labor | Equipment | Total | Total Incl O&P |
|---|---|---|---|---|---|---|---|---|---|---|
| 0010 | **DOOR HARDWARE ACCESSORIES** | | | | | | | | | |
| 0140 | Door bolt, surface, 4" | 1 Carp | 32 | .250 | Ea. | 9 | 7.30 | | 16.30 | 22 |
| 0160 | Door latch | " | 12 | .667 | " | 8.35 | 19.40 | | 27.75 | 41.50 |
| 0200 | Sliding closet door | | | | | | | | | |
| 0220 | Track and hanger, single | 1 Carp | 10 | .800 | Ea. | 54 | 23.50 | | 77.50 | 98.50 |
| 0240 | Double | | 8 | 1 | | 73 | 29 | | 102 | 130 |
| 0260 | Door guide, single | | 48 | .167 | | 24 | 4.85 | | 28.85 | 34.50 |
| 0280 | Double | | 48 | .167 | | 33 | 4.85 | | 37.85 | 44.50 |
| 0600 | Deadbolt and lock cover plate, brass or stainless steel | | 30 | .267 | | 27 | 7.75 | | 34.75 | 42.50 |
| 0620 | Hole cover plate, brass or chrome | | 35 | .229 | | 7.15 | 6.65 | | 13.80 | 19.05 |
| 2240 | Mortise lockset, passage, lever handle | | 9 | .889 | | 194 | 26 | | 220 | 257 |
| 4000 | Security chain, standard | | 18 | .444 | | 7.90 | 12.95 | | 20.85 | 30.50 |

# 08 81 Glass Glazing

## 08 81 10 – Float Glass

### 08 81 10.10 Various Types and Thickness of Float Glass

| | | Crew | Daily Output | Labor-Hours | Unit | Material | 2010 Bare Costs Labor | Equipment | Total | Total Incl O&P |
|---|---|---|---|---|---|---|---|---|---|---|
| 0010 | **VARIOUS TYPES AND THICKNESS OF FLOAT GLASS** | | | | | | | | | |
| 0020 | 3/16" Plain | 2 Glaz | 130 | .123 | S.F. | 4.58 | 3.51 | | 8.09 | 10.85 |
| 0200 | Tempered, clear | | 130 | .123 | | 6.15 | 3.51 | | 9.66 | 12.60 |
| 0300 | Tinted | | 130 | .123 | | 7.25 | 3.51 | | 10.76 | 13.75 |
| 0600 | 1/4" thick, clear, plain | | 120 | .133 | | 5.35 | 3.81 | | 9.16 | 12.15 |
| 0700 | Tinted | | 120 | .133 | | 7.40 | 3.81 | | 11.21 | 14.40 |
| 0800 | Tempered, clear | | 120 | .133 | | 7.60 | 3.81 | | 11.41 | 14.60 |
| 0900 | Tinted | | 120 | .133 | | 9.90 | 3.81 | | 13.71 | 17.15 |
| 1600 | 3/8" thick, clear, plain | | 75 | .213 | | 9.35 | 6.10 | | 15.45 | 20.50 |
| 1700 | Tinted | | 75 | .213 | | 14.80 | 6.10 | | 20.90 | 26.50 |

# 08 81 Glass Glazing

## 08 81 10 – Float Glass

### 08 81 10.10 Various Types and Thickness of Float Glass

| | | Crew | Daily Output | Labor-Hours | Unit | Material | 2010 Bare Costs Labor | Equipment | Total | Total Incl O&P |
|---|---|---|---|---|---|---|---|---|---|---|
| 1800 | Tempered, clear | 2 Glaz | 75 | .213 | S.F. | 15.40 | 6.10 | | 21.50 | 27 |
| 1900 | Tinted | | 75 | .213 | | 17.15 | 6.10 | | 23.25 | 29 |
| 2200 | 1/2" thick, clear, plain | | 55 | .291 | | 18.50 | 8.30 | | 26.80 | 34 |
| 2300 | Tinted | | 55 | .291 | | 26 | 8.30 | | 34.30 | 42 |
| 2400 | Tempered, clear | | 55 | .291 | | 22.50 | 8.30 | | 30.80 | 38.50 |
| 2500 | Tinted | | 55 | .291 | | 26.50 | 8.30 | | 34.80 | 42.50 |
| 2800 | 5/8" thick, clear, plain | | 45 | .356 | | 26 | 10.15 | | 36.15 | 45 |
| 2900 | Tempered, clear | | 45 | .356 | | 29.50 | 10.15 | | 39.65 | 49 |
| 8900 | For low emissivity coating for 3/16" & 1/4" only, add to above | | | | | 15% | | | | |

## 08 81 25 – Glazing Variables

### 08 81 25.10 Applications of Glazing

| | | Crew | Daily Output | Labor-Hours | Unit | Material | 2010 Bare Costs Labor | Equipment | Total | Total Incl O&P |
|---|---|---|---|---|---|---|---|---|---|---|
| 0010 | **APPLICATIONS OF GLAZING** | | | | | | | | | |
| 0600 | For glass replacement, add | | | | S.F. | | 100% | | | |
| 0700 | For gasket settings, add | | | | L.F. | 5.55 | | | 5.55 | 6.10 |
| 0900 | For sloped glazing, add | | | | S.F. | | 25% | | | |
| 2000 | Fabrication, polished edges, 1/4" thick | | | | Inch | .48 | | | .48 | .53 |
| 2100 | 1/2" thick | | | | | 1.21 | | | 1.21 | 1.33 |
| 2500 | Mitered edges, 1/4" thick | | | | | 1.21 | | | 1.21 | 1.33 |
| 2600 | 1/2" thick | | | | | 1.96 | | | 1.96 | 2.16 |

## 08 81 30 – Insulating Glass

### 08 81 30.10 Reduce Heat Transfer Glass

| | | | Crew | Daily Output | Labor-Hours | Unit | Material | 2010 Bare Costs Labor | Equipment | Total | Total Incl O&P |
|---|---|---|---|---|---|---|---|---|---|---|---|
| 0010 | **REDUCE HEAT TRANSFER GLASS** | | | | | | | | | | |
| 0015 | 2 lites 1/8" float, /2" thk under 15 S.F. | | | | | | | | | | |
| 0100 | Tinted | G | 2 Glaz | 95 | .168 | S.F. | 12.90 | 4.81 | | 17.71 | 22 |
| 0280 | Double glazed, 5/8" thk unit, 3/16" float, 15-30 S.F., clear | | | 90 | .178 | | 12.95 | 5.10 | | 18.05 | 22.50 |
| 0400 | 1" thk, dbl. glazed, 1/4" float, 30-70 S.F., clear | G | | 75 | .213 | | 15.50 | 6.10 | | 21.60 | 27 |
| 0500 | Tinted | G | | 75 | .213 | | 22 | 6.10 | | 28.10 | 34.50 |
| 2000 | Both lites, light & heat reflective | G | | 85 | .188 | | 29.50 | 5.35 | | 34.85 | 41.50 |
| 2500 | Heat reflective, film inside, 1" thick unit, clear | G | | 85 | .188 | | 26 | 5.35 | | 31.35 | 37.50 |
| 2600 | Tinted | G | | 85 | .188 | | 28 | 5.35 | | 33.35 | 40 |
| 3000 | Film on weatherside, clear, 1/2" thick unit | G | | 95 | .168 | | 18.50 | 4.81 | | 23.31 | 28.50 |
| 3100 | 5/8" thick unit | G | | 90 | .178 | | 18.50 | 5.10 | | 23.60 | 29 |
| 3200 | 1" thick unit | G | | 85 | .188 | | 25.50 | 5.35 | | 30.85 | 37 |
| 5000 | Spectrally selective film, on ext, blocks solar gain/allows 70% of light | G | | 95 | .168 | | 9.80 | 4.81 | | 14.61 | 18.70 |

## 08 81 40 – Plate Glass

### 08 81 40.10 Plate Glass

| | | Crew | Daily Output | Labor-Hours | Unit | Material | 2010 Bare Costs Labor | Equipment | Total | Total Incl O&P |
|---|---|---|---|---|---|---|---|---|---|---|---|
| 0010 | **PLATE GLASS** Twin ground, polished, | | | | | | | | | |
| 0015 | 3/16" thick, material | | | | S.F. | 4.83 | | | 4.83 | 5.30 |
| 0020 | 3/16" thick | 2 Glaz | 100 | .160 | | 4.83 | 4.57 | | 9.40 | 12.80 |
| 0100 | 1/4" thick | | 94 | .170 | | 6.60 | 4.86 | | 11.46 | 15.30 |
| 0200 | 3/8" thick | | 60 | .267 | | 11.40 | 7.60 | | 19 | 25 |
| 0300 | 1/2" thick | | 40 | .400 | | 22 | 11.40 | | 33.40 | 43.50 |

## 08 81 55 – Window Glass

### 08 81 55.10 Sheet Glass

| | | Crew | Daily Output | Labor-Hours | Unit | Material | 2010 Bare Costs Labor | Equipment | Total | Total Incl O&P |
|---|---|---|---|---|---|---|---|---|---|---|---|
| 0010 | **SHEET GLASS** (window), clear float, stops, putty bed | | | | | | | | | |
| 0015 | 1/8" thick, clear float | 2 Glaz | 480 | .033 | S.F. | 4.35 | .95 | | 5.30 | 6.35 |
| 0500 | 3/16" thick, clear | | 480 | .033 | | 5.35 | .95 | | 6.30 | 7.45 |
| 0600 | Tinted | | 480 | .033 | | 7.15 | .95 | | 8.10 | 9.40 |
| 0700 | Tempered | | 480 | .033 | | 8.65 | .95 | | 9.60 | 11.05 |

# 08 83 Mirrors

## 08 83 13 – Mirrored Glass Glazing

### 08 83 13.10 Mirrors

| | | Crew | Daily Output | Labor-Hours | Unit | Material | 2010 Bare Costs Labor | Equipment | Total | Total Incl O&P |
|---|---|---|---|---|---|---|---|---|---|---|
| 0010 | **MIRRORS**, No frames, wall type, 1/4" plate glass, polished edge | | | | | | | | | |
| 0100 | Up to 5 S.F. | 2 Glaz | 125 | .128 | S.F. | 9.10 | 3.65 | | 12.75 | 16 |
| 0200 | Over 5 S.F. | | 160 | .100 | | 8.80 | 2.86 | | 11.66 | 14.40 |
| 0500 | Door type, 1/4" plate glass, up to 12 S.F. | | 160 | .100 | | 8 | 2.86 | | 10.86 | 13.50 |
| 1000 | Float glass, up to 10 S.F., 1/8" thick | | 160 | .100 | | 5.25 | 2.86 | | 8.11 | 10.45 |
| 1100 | 3/16" thick | | 150 | .107 | | 6.35 | 3.05 | | 9.40 | 12 |
| 1500 | 12" x 12" wall tiles, square edge, clear | | 195 | .082 | | 1.90 | 2.34 | | 4.24 | 5.95 |
| 1600 | Veined | | 195 | .082 | | 4.86 | 2.34 | | 7.20 | 9.20 |
| 2010 | Bathroom, unframed, laminated | | 160 | .100 | | 15 | 2.86 | | 17.86 | 21 |

# 08 87 Glazing Surface Films

## 08 87 53 – Security Films

### 08 87 53.10 Security Film

| | | Crew | Daily Output | Labor-Hours | Unit | Material | 2010 Bare Costs Labor | Equipment | Total | Total Incl O&P |
|---|---|---|---|---|---|---|---|---|---|---|
| 0010 | **SECURITY FILM**, clear, 32000 psi tensile strength, adhered to glass | | | | | | | | | |
| 0100 | .002" thick, daylight installation | H-2 | 950 | .025 | S.F. | 1.85 | .66 | | 2.51 | 3.14 |
| 0150 | .004" thick, daylight installation | | 800 | .030 | | 2 | .79 | | 2.79 | 3.50 |
| 0200 | .006" thick, daylight installation | | 700 | .034 | | 2.15 | .90 | | 3.05 | 3.86 |
| 0210 | Install for anchorage | | 600 | .040 | | 2.39 | 1.05 | | 3.44 | 4.37 |
| 0400 | .007" thick, daylight installation | | 600 | .040 | | 2.25 | 1.05 | | 3.30 | 4.22 |
| 0410 | Install for anchorage | | 500 | .048 | | 2.50 | 1.26 | | 3.76 | 4.83 |
| 0500 | .008" thick, daylight installation | | 500 | .048 | | 2.65 | 1.26 | | 3.91 | 5 |
| 0510 | Install for anchorage | | 500 | .048 | | 2.94 | 1.26 | | 4.20 | 5.30 |
| 0600 | .015" thick, daylight installation | | 400 | .060 | | 4.40 | 1.57 | | 5.97 | 7.45 |
| 0610 | Install for anchorage | | 400 | .060 | | 2.94 | 1.57 | | 4.51 | 5.85 |
| 0900 | Security film anchorage, mechanical attachment and cover plate | H-3 | 370 | .043 | L.F. | 8.70 | 1.09 | | 9.79 | 11.40 |
| 0950 | Security film anchorage, wet glaze structural caulking | 1 Glaz | 225 | .036 | " | .83 | 1.02 | | 1.85 | 2.58 |
| 1000 | Adhered security film removal | 1 Clab | 275 | .029 | S.F. | | .63 | | .63 | 1.05 |

# 08 91 Louvers

## 08 91 19 – Fixed Louvers

### 08 91 19.10 Aluminum Louvers

| | | Crew | Daily Output | Labor-Hours | Unit | Material | 2010 Bare Costs Labor | Equipment | Total | Total Incl O&P |
|---|---|---|---|---|---|---|---|---|---|---|
| 0010 | **ALUMINUM LOUVERS** | | | | | | | | | |
| 0020 | Aluminum with screen, residential, 8" x 8" | 1 Carp | 38 | .211 | Ea. | 10.95 | 6.15 | | 17.10 | 22.50 |
| 0100 | 12" x 12" | | 38 | .211 | | 14 | 6.15 | | 20.15 | 25.50 |
| 0200 | 12" x 18" | | 35 | .229 | | 13.95 | 6.65 | | 20.60 | 26.50 |
| 0250 | 14" x 24" | | 30 | .267 | | 25 | 7.75 | | 32.75 | 40.50 |
| 0300 | 18" x 24" | | 27 | .296 | | 27 | 8.60 | | 35.60 | 44 |
| 0500 | 24" x 30" | | 24 | .333 | | 32 | 9.70 | | 41.70 | 51.50 |
| 0700 | Triangle, adjustable, small | | 20 | .400 | | 32.50 | 11.65 | | 44.15 | 55.50 |
| 0800 | Large | | 15 | .533 | | 40.50 | 15.50 | | 56 | 70.50 |
| 2100 | Midget, aluminum, 3/4" deep, 1" diameter | | 85 | .094 | | .73 | 2.74 | | 3.47 | 5.40 |
| 2150 | 3" diameter | | 60 | .133 | | 1.78 | 3.88 | | 5.66 | 8.50 |
| 2200 | 4" diameter | | 50 | .160 | | 3.64 | 4.66 | | 8.30 | 11.85 |
| 2250 | 6" diameter | | 30 | .267 | | 3.74 | 7.75 | | 11.49 | 17.15 |

# 08 95 Vents

## 08 95 13 – Soffit Vents

| 08 95 13.10 Wall Louvers | Crew | Daily Output | Labor-Hours | Unit | Material | 2010 Bare Costs Labor | Equipment | Total | Total Incl O&P |
|---|---|---|---|---|---|---|---|---|---|
| 0010 **WALL LOUVERS** | | | | | | | | | |
| 2400     Under eaves vent, aluminum, mill finish, 16" x 4" | 1 Carp | 48 | .167 | Ea. | 1.33 | 4.85 | | 6.18 | 9.60 |
| 2500        16" x 8" | " | 48 | .167 | " | 1.54 | 4.85 | | 6.39 | 9.85 |

## 08 95 16 – Wall Vents

### 08 95 16.10 Louvers

| | Crew | Daily Output | Labor-Hours | Unit | Material | 2010 Bare Costs Labor | Equipment | Total | Total Incl O&P |
|---|---|---|---|---|---|---|---|---|---|
| 0010 **LOUVERS** | | | | | | | | | |
| 0020   Redwood, 2'-0" diameter, full circle | 1 Carp | 16 | .500 | Ea. | 169 | 14.55 | | 183.55 | 211 |
| 0100     Half circle | | 16 | .500 | | 189 | 14.55 | | 203.55 | 233 |
| 0200     Octagonal | | 16 | .500 | | 129 | 14.55 | | 143.55 | 167 |
| 0300     Triangular, 5/12 pitch, 5'-0" at base | | 16 | .500 | | 189 | 14.55 | | 203.55 | 233 |
| 7000   Vinyl gable vent, 8" x 8" | | 38 | .211 | | 11.55 | 6.15 | | 17.70 | 23 |
| 7020     12" x 12" | | 38 | .211 | | 24 | 6.15 | | 30.15 | 37 |
| 7080     12" x 18" | | 35 | .229 | | 31 | 6.65 | | 37.65 | 45 |
| 7200     18" x 24" | | 30 | .267 | | 37.50 | 7.75 | | 45.25 | 54.50 |

# Division Notes

| | CREW | DAILY OUTPUT | LABOR-HOURS | UNIT | 2010 BARE COSTS | | | | TOTAL INCL O&P |
|---|---|---|---|---|---|---|---|---|---|
| | | | | | MAT. | LABOR | EQUIP. | TOTAL | |
| | | | | | | | | | |
| | | | | | | | | | |
| | | | | | | | | | |
| | | | | | | | | | |
| | | | | | | | | | |
| | | | | | | | | | |
| | | | | | | | | | |
| | | | | | | | | | |
| | | | | | | | | | |
| | | | | | | | | | |
| | | | | | | | | | |
| | | | | | | | | | |
| | | | | | | | | | |
| | | | | | | | | | |
| | | | | | | | | | |
| | | | | | | | | | |
| | | | | | | | | | |
| | | | | | | | | | |
| | | | | | | | | | |
| | | | | | | | | | |

# Estimating Tips

## General

- Room Finish Schedule: A complete set of plans should contain a room finish schedule. If one is not available, it would be well worth the time and effort to obtain one.

## 09 20 00 Plaster and Gypsum Board

- Lath is estimated by the square yard plus a 5% allowance for waste. Furring, channels, and accessories are measured by the linear foot. An extra foot should be allowed for each accessory miter or stop.
- Plaster is also estimated by the square yard. Deductions for openings vary by preference, from zero deduction to 50% of all openings over 2 feet in width. The estimator should allow one extra square foot for each linear foot of horizontal interior or exterior angle located below the ceiling level. Also, double the areas of small radius work.
- Drywall accessories, studs, track, and acoustical caulking are all measured by the linear foot. Drywall taping is figured by the square foot. Gypsum wallboard is estimated by the square foot. No material deductions should be made for door or window openings under 32 S.F.

## 09 60 00 Flooring

- Tile and terrazzo areas are taken off on a square foot basis. Trim and base materials are measured by the linear foot. Accent tiles are listed per each. Two basic methods of installation are used. Mud set is approximately 30% more expensive than thin set. In terrazzo work, be sure to include the linear footage of embedded decorative strips, grounds, machine rubbing, and power cleanup.
- Wood flooring is available in strip, parquet, or block configuration. The latter two types are set in adhesives with quantities estimated by the square foot. The laying pattern will influence labor costs and material waste. In addition to the material and labor for laying wood floors, the estimator must make allowances for sanding and finishing these areas unless the flooring is prefinished.
- Sheet flooring is measured by the square yard. Roll widths vary, so consideration should be given to use the most economical width, as waste must be figured into the total quantity. Consider also the installation methods available, direct glue down or stretched.

## 09 70 00 Wall Finishes

- Wall coverings are estimated by the square foot. The area to be covered is measured, length by height of wall above baseboards, to calculate the square footage of each wall. This figure is divided by the number of square feet in the single roll which is being used. Deduct, in full, the areas of openings such as doors and windows. Where a pattern match is required allow 25%–30% waste.

## 09 80 00 Acoustic Treatment

- Acoustical systems fall into several categories. The takeoff of these materials should be by the square foot of area with a 5% allowance for waste. Do not forget about scaffolding, if applicable, when estimating these systems.

## 09 90 00 Painting and Coating

- A major portion of the work in painting involves surface preparation. Be sure to include cleaning, sanding, filling, and masking costs in the estimate.
- Protection of adjacent surfaces is not included in painting costs. When considering the method of paint application, an important factor is the amount of protection and masking required. These must be estimated separately and may be the determining factor in choosing the method of application.

# Reference Numbers

Reference numbers are shown in shaded boxes at the beginning of some major classifications. These numbers refer to related items in the Reference Section. The reference information may be an estimating procedure, an alternate pricing method, or technical information.

*Note:* Not all subdivisions listed here necessarily appear in this publication.

Division 9 - Finishes

# 09 01 Maintenance of Finishes

## 09 01 70 – Maintenance of Wall Finishes

| 09 01 70.10 Gypsum Wallboard Repairs | Crew | Daily Output | Labor-Hours | Unit | Material | 2010 Bare Costs Labor | Equipment | Total | Total Incl O&P |
|---|---|---|---|---|---|---|---|---|---|
| 0010 | **GYPSUM WALLBOARD REPAIRS** | | | | | | | | | |
| 0100 | Fill and sand, pin/nail holes | 1 Carp | 960 | .008 | Ea. | | .24 | | .24 | .41 |
| 0110 | Screw head pops | | 480 | .017 | | | .49 | | .49 | .82 |
| 0120 | Dents, up to 2" square | | 48 | .167 | | .01 | 4.85 | | 4.86 | 8.15 |
| 0130 | 2" to 4" square | | 24 | .333 | | .03 | 9.70 | | 9.73 | 16.35 |
| 0140 | Cut square, patch, sand and finish, holes, up to 2" square | | 12 | .667 | | .04 | 19.40 | | 19.44 | 32.50 |
| 0150 | 2" to 4" square | | 11 | .727 | | .09 | 21 | | 21.09 | 35.50 |
| 0160 | 4" to 8" square | | 10 | .800 | | .22 | 23.50 | | 23.72 | 39 |
| 0170 | 8" to 12" square | | 8 | 1 | | .42 | 29 | | 29.42 | 49.50 |
| 0180 | 12" to 32" square | | 6 | 1.333 | | 2.62 | 39 | | 41.62 | 68.50 |
| 0210 | 16" by 48" | | 5 | 1.600 | | 2.01 | 46.50 | | 48.51 | 80.50 |
| 0220 | 32" by 48" | | 4 | 2 | | 3.36 | 58 | | 61.36 | 102 |
| 0230 | 48" square | | 3.50 | 2.286 | | 4.73 | 66.50 | | 71.23 | 117 |
| 0240 | 60" square | | 3.20 | 2.500 | | 8.30 | 73 | | 81.30 | 131 |
| 0500 | Skim coat surface with joint compound | | 1600 | .005 | S.F. | .03 | .15 | | .18 | .27 |

# 09 05 Common Work Results for Finishes

## 09 05 05 – Selective Finishes Demolition

### 09 05 05.10 Selective Demolition, Ceilings

| | | Crew | Daily Output | Labor-Hours | Unit | Material | 2010 Bare Costs Labor | Equipment | Total | Total Incl O&P |
|---|---|---|---|---|---|---|---|---|---|---|
| 0010 | **SELECTIVE DEMOLITION, CEILINGS** R024119-10 | | | | | | | | | |
| 0200 | Ceiling, drywall, furred and nailed or screwed | 2 Clab | 800 | .020 | S.F. | | .43 | | .43 | .72 |
| 1000 | Plaster, lime and horse hair, on wood lath, incl. lath | | 700 | .023 | | | .49 | | .49 | .83 |
| 1200 | Suspended ceiling, mineral fiber, 2' x 2' or 2' x 4' | | 1500 | .011 | | | .23 | | .23 | .39 |
| 1250 | On suspension system, incl. system | | 1200 | .013 | | | .29 | | .29 | .48 |
| 1500 | Tile, wood fiber, 12" x 12", glued | | 900 | .018 | | | .38 | | .38 | .64 |
| 1540 | Stapled | | 1500 | .011 | | | .23 | | .23 | .39 |
| 2000 | Wood, tongue and groove, 1" x 4" | | 1000 | .016 | | | .34 | | .34 | .58 |
| 2040 | 1" x 8" | | 1100 | .015 | | | .31 | | .31 | .53 |
| 2400 | Plywood or wood fiberboard, 4' x 8' sheets | | 1200 | .013 | | | .29 | | .29 | .48 |

### 09 05 05.20 Selective Demolition, Flooring

| | | Crew | Daily Output | Labor-Hours | Unit | Material | 2010 Bare Costs Labor | Equipment | Total | Total Incl O&P |
|---|---|---|---|---|---|---|---|---|---|---|
| 0010 | **SELECTIVE DEMOLITION, FLOORING** R024119-10 | | | | | | | | | |
| 0200 | Brick with mortar | 2 Clab | 475 | .034 | S.F. | | .72 | | .72 | 1.22 |
| 0400 | Carpet, bonded, including surface scraping | | 2000 | .008 | | | .17 | | .17 | .29 |
| 0480 | Tackless | | 9000 | .002 | | | .04 | | .04 | .06 |
| 0550 | Carpet tile, releasable adhesive | | 5000 | .003 | | | .07 | | .07 | .12 |
| 0560 | Permanent adhesive | | 1850 | .009 | | | .19 | | .19 | .31 |
| 0800 | Resilient, sheet goods | | 1400 | .011 | | | .25 | | .25 | .41 |
| 0850 | Vinyl or rubber cove base | 1 Clab | 1000 | .008 | L.F. | | .17 | | .17 | .29 |
| 0860 | Vinyl or rubber cove base, molded corner | " | 1000 | .008 | Ea. | | .17 | | .17 | .29 |
| 0870 | For glued and caulked installation, add to labor | | | | | | 50% | | | |
| 0900 | Vinyl composition tile, 12" x 12" | 2 Clab | 1000 | .016 | S.F. | | .34 | | .34 | .58 |
| 2000 | Tile, ceramic, thin set | | 675 | .024 | | | .51 | | .51 | .86 |
| 2020 | Mud set | | 625 | .026 | | | .55 | | .55 | .93 |
| 3000 | Wood, block, on end | 1 Carp | 400 | .020 | | | .58 | | .58 | .98 |
| 3200 | Parquet | | 450 | .018 | | | .52 | | .52 | .87 |
| 3400 | Strip flooring, interior, 2-1/4" x 25/32" thick | | 325 | .025 | | | .72 | | .72 | 1.21 |
| 3500 | Exterior, porch flooring, 1" x 4" | | 220 | .036 | | | 1.06 | | 1.06 | 1.78 |
| 3800 | Subfloor, tongue and groove, 1" x 6" | | 325 | .025 | | | .72 | | .72 | 1.21 |
| 3820 | 1" x 8" | | 430 | .019 | | | .54 | | .54 | .91 |
| 3840 | 1" x 10" | | 520 | .015 | | | .45 | | .45 | .75 |
| 4000 | Plywood, nailed | | 600 | .013 | | | .39 | | .39 | .65 |

# 09 05 Common Work Results for Finishes

## 09 05 05 – Selective Finishes Demolition

### 09 05 05.20 Selective Demolition, Flooring

| | | Crew | Daily Output | Labor-Hours | Unit | Material | 2010 Bare Costs Labor | Equipment | Total | Total Incl O&P |
|---|---|---|---|---|---|---|---|---|---|---|
| 4100 | Glued and nailed | 1 Carp | 400 | .020 | S.F. | | .58 | | .58 | .98 |
| 4200 | Hardboard, 1/4" thick | ↓ | 760 | .011 | ↓ | | .31 | | .31 | .52 |

### 09 05 05.30 Selective Demolition, Walls and Partitions

| | | | Crew | Daily Output | Labor-Hours | Unit | Material | 2010 Bare Costs Labor | Equipment | Total | Total Incl O&P |
|---|---|---|---|---|---|---|---|---|---|---|---|
| 0010 | **SELECTIVE DEMOLITION, WALLS AND PARTITIONS** | R024119-10 | | | | | | | | | |
| 0020 | Walls, concrete, reinforced | | B-39 | 120 | .400 | C.F. | | 8.75 | 1.87 | 10.62 | 16.75 |
| 0025 | Plain | | " | 160 | .300 | " | | 6.55 | 1.40 | 7.95 | 12.55 |
| 1000 | Drywall, nailed or screwed | | 1 Clab | 1000 | .008 | S.F. | | .17 | | .17 | .29 |
| 1010 | 2 layers | | | 400 | .020 | | | .43 | | .43 | .72 |
| 1500 | Fiberboard, nailed | | | 900 | .009 | | | .19 | | .19 | .32 |
| 1568 | Plenum barrier, sheet lead | | ↓ | 300 | .027 | | | .57 | | .57 | .96 |
| 2200 | Metal or wood studs, finish 2 sides, fiberboard | | B-1 | 520 | .046 | | | 1.02 | | 1.02 | 1.72 |
| 2250 | Lath and plaster | | | 260 | .092 | | | 2.05 | | 2.05 | 3.44 |
| 2300 | Plasterboard (drywall) | | | 520 | .046 | | | 1.02 | | 1.02 | 1.72 |
| 2350 | Plywood | | ↓ | 450 | .053 | | | 1.18 | | 1.18 | 1.99 |
| 2800 | Paneling, 4' x 8' sheets | | 1 Clab | 475 | .017 | | | .36 | | .36 | .61 |
| 3000 | Plaster, lime and horsehair, on wood lath | | | 400 | .020 | | | .43 | | .43 | .72 |
| 3020 | On metal lath | | | 335 | .024 | ↓ | | .51 | | .51 | .86 |
| 3450 | Plaster, interior gypsum, acoustic, or cement | | | 60 | .133 | S.Y. | | 2.87 | | 2.87 | 4.82 |
| 3500 | Stucco, on masonry | | | 145 | .055 | | | 1.19 | | 1.19 | 1.99 |
| 3510 | Commercial 3-coat | | | 80 | .100 | | | 2.15 | | 2.15 | 3.62 |
| 3520 | Interior stucco | | | 25 | .320 | ↓ | | 6.90 | | 6.90 | 11.55 |
| 3760 | Tile, ceramic, on walls, thin set | | | 300 | .027 | S.F. | | .57 | | .57 | .96 |
| 3765 | Mud set | | ↓ | 250 | .032 | " | | .69 | | .69 | 1.16 |

# 09 22 Supports for Plaster and Gypsum Board

## 09 22 03 – Fastening Methods for Finishes

### 09 22 03.20 Drilling Plaster/Drywall

| | | Crew | Daily Output | Labor-Hours | Unit | Material | 2010 Bare Costs Labor | Equipment | Total | Total Incl O&P |
|---|---|---|---|---|---|---|---|---|---|---|
| 0010 | **DRILLING PLASTER/DRYWALL** | | | | | | | | | |
| 1100 | Drilling & layout for drywall/plaster walls, up to 1" deep, no anchor | | | | | | | | | |
| 1200 | Holes, 1/4" diameter | 1 Carp | 150 | .053 | Ea. | .01 | 1.55 | | 1.56 | 2.62 |
| 1300 | 3/8" diameter | | 140 | .057 | | .01 | 1.66 | | 1.67 | 2.81 |
| 1400 | 1/2" diameter | | 130 | .062 | | .01 | 1.79 | | 1.80 | 3.02 |
| 1500 | 3/4" diameter | | 120 | .067 | | .01 | 1.94 | | 1.95 | 3.28 |
| 1600 | 1" diameter | | 110 | .073 | | .02 | 2.12 | | 2.14 | 3.58 |
| 1700 | 1-1/4" diameter | | 100 | .080 | | .03 | 2.33 | | 2.36 | 3.95 |
| 1800 | 1-1/2" diameter | ↓ | 90 | .089 | | .04 | 2.59 | | 2.63 | 4.39 |
| 1900 | For ceiling installations, add | | | | ↓ | | 40% | | | |

## 09 22 13 – Metal Furring

### 09 22 13.13 Metal Channel Furring

| | | Crew | Daily Output | Labor-Hours | Unit | Material | 2010 Bare Costs Labor | Equipment | Total | Total Incl O&P |
|---|---|---|---|---|---|---|---|---|---|---|
| 0010 | **METAL CHANNEL FURRING** | | | | | | | | | |
| 0030 | Beams and columns, 7/8" channels, galvanized, 12" O.C. | 1 Lath | 155 | .052 | S.F. | .34 | 1.33 | | 1.67 | 2.52 |
| 0050 | 16" O.C. | | 170 | .047 | | .28 | 1.22 | | 1.50 | 2.27 |
| 0070 | 24" O.C. | | 185 | .043 | | .19 | 1.12 | | 1.31 | 2 |
| 0100 | Ceilings, on steel, 7/8" channels, galvanized, 12" O.C. | | 210 | .038 | | .31 | .98 | | 1.29 | 1.93 |
| 0300 | 16" O.C. | | 290 | .028 | | .28 | .71 | | .99 | 1.46 |
| 0400 | 24" O.C. | | 420 | .019 | | .19 | .49 | | .68 | .99 |
| 0600 | 1-5/8" channels, galvanized, 12" O.C. | | 190 | .042 | | .41 | 1.09 | | 1.50 | 2.21 |
| 0700 | 16" O.C. | | 260 | .031 | | .37 | .80 | | 1.17 | 1.69 |
| 0900 | 24" O.C. | | 390 | .021 | | .25 | .53 | | .78 | 1.12 |
| 0930 | 7/8" channels with sound isolation clips, 12" O.C. | ↓ | 120 | .067 | ↓ | 1.37 | 1.72 | | 3.09 | 4.29 |

# 09 22 Supports for Plaster and Gypsum Board

## 09 22 13 – Metal Furring

### 09 22 13.13 Metal Channel Furring

| | | Crew | Daily Output | Labor-Hours | Unit | Material | 2010 Bare Costs Labor | Equipment | Total | Total Incl O&P |
|---|---|---|---|---|---|---|---|---|---|---|
| 0940 | 16" O.C. | 1 Lath | 100 | .080 | S.F. | 1.91 | 2.07 | | 3.98 | 5.45 |
| 0950 | 24" O.C. | | 165 | .048 | | 1.25 | 1.25 | | 2.50 | 3.39 |
| 0960 | 1-5/8" channels, galvanized, 12" O.C. | | 110 | .073 | | 1.48 | 1.88 | | 3.36 | 4.66 |
| 0970 | 16" O.C. | | 100 | .080 | | 2 | 2.07 | | 4.07 | 5.55 |
| 0980 | 24" O.C. | | 155 | .052 | | 1.31 | 1.33 | | 2.64 | 3.59 |
| 1000 | Walls, 7/8" channels, galvanized, 12" O.C. | | 235 | .034 | | .31 | .88 | | 1.19 | 1.76 |
| 1200 | 16" O.C. | | 265 | .030 | | .28 | .78 | | 1.06 | 1.57 |
| 1300 | 24" O.C. | | 350 | .023 | | .19 | .59 | | .78 | 1.15 |
| 1500 | 1-5/8" channels, galvanized, 12" O.C. | | 210 | .038 | | .41 | .98 | | 1.39 | 2.05 |
| 1600 | 16" O.C. | | 240 | .033 | | .37 | .86 | | 1.23 | 1.80 |
| 1800 | 24" O.C. | | 305 | .026 | | .25 | .68 | | .93 | 1.36 |
| 1920 | 7/8" channels with sound isolation clips, 12" O.C. | | 125 | .064 | | 1.37 | 1.65 | | 3.02 | 4.18 |
| 1940 | 16" O.C. | | 100 | .080 | | 1.91 | 2.07 | | 3.98 | 5.45 |
| 1950 | 24" O.C. | | 150 | .053 | | 1.25 | 1.38 | | 2.63 | 3.59 |
| 1960 | 1-5/8" channels, galvanized, 12" O.C. | | 115 | .070 | | 1.48 | 1.80 | | 3.28 | 4.53 |
| 1970 | 16" O.C. | | 95 | .084 | | 2 | 2.18 | | 4.18 | 5.70 |
| 1980 | 24" O.C. | | 140 | .057 | | 1.31 | 1.48 | | 2.79 | 3.82 |

## 09 22 16 – Non-Structural Metal Framing

### 09 22 16.13 Metal Studs and Track

| | | Crew | Daily Output | Labor-Hours | Unit | Material | 2010 Bare Costs Labor | Equipment | Total | Total Incl O&P |
|---|---|---|---|---|---|---|---|---|---|---|
| 0010 | **METAL STUDS AND TRACK** | | | | | | | | | |
| 1600 | Non-load bearing, galv, 8' high, 25 ga. 1-5/8" wide, 16" O.C. | 1 Carp | 619 | .013 | S.F. | .25 | .38 | | .63 | .90 |
| 1610 | 24" O.C. | | 950 | .008 | | .18 | .25 | | .43 | .61 |
| 1620 | 2-1/2" wide, 16" O.C. | | 613 | .013 | | .30 | .38 | | .68 | .97 |
| 1630 | 24" O.C. | | 938 | .009 | | .22 | .25 | | .47 | .67 |
| 1640 | 3-5/8" wide, 16" O.C. | | 600 | .013 | | .34 | .39 | | .73 | 1.03 |
| 1650 | 24" O.C. | | 925 | .009 | | .26 | .25 | | .51 | .70 |
| 1660 | 4" wide, 16" O.C. | | 594 | .013 | | .35 | .39 | | .74 | 1.04 |
| 1670 | 24" O.C. | | 925 | .009 | | .26 | .25 | | .51 | .70 |
| 1680 | 6" wide, 16" O.C. | | 588 | .014 | | .51 | .40 | | .91 | 1.24 |
| 1690 | 24" O.C. | | 906 | .009 | | .39 | .26 | | .65 | .85 |
| 1700 | 20 ga. studs, 1-5/8" wide, 16" O.C. | | 494 | .016 | | .34 | .47 | | .81 | 1.17 |
| 1710 | 24" O.C. | | 763 | .010 | | .26 | .31 | | .57 | .79 |
| 1720 | 2-1/2" wide, 16" O.C. | | 488 | .016 | | .39 | .48 | | .87 | 1.23 |
| 1730 | 24" O.C. | | 750 | .011 | | .30 | .31 | | .61 | .85 |
| 1740 | 3-5/8" wide, 16" O.C. | | 481 | .017 | | .43 | .48 | | .91 | 1.28 |
| 1750 | 24" O.C. | | 738 | .011 | | .32 | .32 | | .64 | .88 |
| 1760 | 4" wide, 16" O.C. | | 475 | .017 | | .50 | .49 | | .99 | 1.37 |
| 1770 | 24" O.C. | | 738 | .011 | | .38 | .32 | | .70 | .95 |
| 1780 | 6" wide, 16" O.C. | | 469 | .017 | | .60 | .50 | | 1.10 | 1.49 |
| 1790 | 24" O.C. | | 725 | .011 | | .45 | .32 | | .77 | 1.03 |
| 2000 | Non-load bearing, galv, 10' high, 25 ga. 1-5/8" wide, 16" O.C. | | 495 | .016 | | .23 | .47 | | .70 | 1.05 |
| 2100 | 24" O.C. | | 760 | .011 | | .17 | .31 | | .48 | .71 |
| 2200 | 2-1/2" wide, 16" O.C. | | 490 | .016 | | .28 | .48 | | .76 | 1.11 |
| 2250 | 24" O.C. | | 750 | .011 | | .21 | .31 | | .52 | .75 |
| 2300 | 3-5/8" wide, 16" O.C. | | 480 | .017 | | .32 | .49 | | .81 | 1.18 |
| 2350 | 24" O.C. | | 740 | .011 | | .24 | .31 | | .55 | .79 |
| 2400 | 4" wide, 16" O.C. | | 475 | .017 | | .33 | .49 | | .82 | 1.18 |
| 2450 | 24" O.C. | | 740 | .011 | | .24 | .31 | | .55 | .80 |
| 2500 | 6" wide, 16" O.C. | | 470 | .017 | | .49 | .50 | | .99 | 1.37 |
| 2550 | 24" O.C. | | 725 | .011 | | .36 | .32 | | .68 | .94 |
| 2600 | 20 ga. studs, 1-5/8" wide, 16" O.C. | | 395 | .020 | | .33 | .59 | | .92 | 1.35 |
| 2650 | 24" O.C. | | 610 | .013 | | .24 | .38 | | .62 | .90 |

# 09 22 Supports for Plaster and Gypsum Board

## 09 22 16 – Non-Structural Metal Framing

### 09 22 16.13 Metal Studs and Track

| | | Crew | Daily Output | Labor-Hours | Unit | Material | 2010 Bare Costs Labor | Equipment | Total | Total Incl O&P |
|---|---|---|---|---|---|---|---|---|---|---|
| 2700 | 2-1/2" wide, 16" O.C. | 1 Carp | 390 | .021 | S.F. | .37 | .60 | | .97 | 1.41 |
| 2750 | 24" O.C. | | 600 | .013 | | .28 | .39 | | .67 | .95 |
| 2800 | 3-5/8" wide, 16" OC | | 385 | .021 | | .40 | .60 | | 1 | 1.46 |
| 2850 | 24" O.C. | | 590 | .014 | | .30 | .39 | | .69 | .99 |
| 2900 | 4" wide, 16" O.C. | | 380 | .021 | | .48 | .61 | | 1.09 | 1.56 |
| 2950 | 24" O.C. | | 590 | .014 | | .35 | .39 | | .74 | 1.05 |
| 3000 | 6" wide, 16" O.C. | | 375 | .021 | | .56 | .62 | | 1.18 | 1.66 |
| 3050 | 24" O.C. | | 580 | .014 | | .42 | .40 | | .82 | 1.14 |
| 3060 | Non-load bearing, galv, 12' high, 25 ga. 1-5/8" wide, 16" O.C. | | 413 | .019 | | .22 | .56 | | .78 | 1.19 |
| 3070 | 24" O.C. | | 633 | .013 | | .16 | .37 | | .53 | .80 |
| 3080 | 2-1/2" wide, 16" O.C. | | 408 | .020 | | .27 | .57 | | .84 | 1.26 |
| 3090 | 24" O.C. | | 625 | .013 | | .20 | .37 | | .57 | .85 |
| 3100 | 3-5/8" wide, 16" O.C. | | 400 | .020 | | .31 | .58 | | .89 | 1.32 |
| 3110 | 24" O.C. | | 617 | .013 | | .23 | .38 | | .61 | .88 |
| 3120 | 4" wide, 16" O.C. | | 396 | .020 | | .31 | .59 | | .90 | 1.34 |
| 3130 | 24" O.C. | | 617 | .013 | | .23 | .38 | | .61 | .88 |
| 3140 | 6" wide, 16" O.C. | | 392 | .020 | | .47 | .59 | | 1.06 | 1.51 |
| 3150 | 24" O.C. | | 604 | .013 | | .34 | .39 | | .73 | 1.02 |
| 3160 | 20 ga. studs, 1-5/8" wide, 16" O.C. | | 329 | .024 | | .31 | .71 | | 1.02 | 1.53 |
| 3170 | 24" O.C. | | 508 | .016 | | .23 | .46 | | .69 | 1.02 |
| 3180 | 2-1/2" wide, 16" O.C. | | 325 | .025 | | .36 | .72 | | 1.08 | 1.60 |
| 3190 | 24" O.C. | | 500 | .016 | | .26 | .47 | | .73 | 1.07 |
| 3200 | 3-5/8" wide, 16" O.C. | | 321 | .025 | | .39 | .73 | | 1.12 | 1.64 |
| 3210 | 24" O.C. | | 492 | .016 | | .28 | .47 | | .75 | 1.11 |
| 3220 | 4" wide, 16" O.C. | | 317 | .025 | | .46 | .73 | | 1.19 | 1.74 |
| 3230 | 24" O.C. | | 492 | .016 | | .33 | .47 | | .80 | 1.17 |
| 3240 | 6" wide, 16" O.C. | | 313 | .026 | | .54 | .74 | | 1.28 | 1.84 |
| 3250 | 24" O.C. | ↓ | 483 | .017 | ↓ | .39 | .48 | | .87 | 1.24 |
| 5000 | Load bearing studs, see Div. 05 41 13.30 | | | | | | | | | |

## 09 22 26 – Suspension Systems

### 09 22 26.13 Ceiling Suspension Systems

| | | Crew | Daily Output | Labor-Hours | Unit | Material | 2010 Bare Costs Labor | Equipment | Total | Total Incl O&P |
|---|---|---|---|---|---|---|---|---|---|---|
| 0010 | **CEILING SUSPENSION SYSTEMS** For gypsum board or plaster | | | | | | | | | |
| 8000 | Suspended ceilings, including carriers | | | | | | | | | |
| 8200 | 1-1/2" carriers, 24" O.C. with: | | | | | | | | | |
| 8300 | 7/8" channels, 16" O.C. | 1 Lath | 275 | .029 | S.F. | .47 | .75 | | 1.22 | 1.73 |
| 8320 | 24" O.C. | | 310 | .026 | | .38 | .67 | | 1.05 | 1.50 |
| 8400 | 1-5/8" channels, 16" O.C. | | 205 | .039 | | .57 | 1.01 | | 1.58 | 2.25 |
| 8420 | 24" O.C. | ↓ | 250 | .032 | ↓ | .44 | .83 | | 1.27 | 1.82 |
| 8600 | 2" carriers, 24" O.C. with: | | | | | | | | | |
| 8700 | 7/8" channels, 16" O.C. | 1 Lath | 250 | .032 | S.F. | .53 | .83 | | 1.36 | 1.91 |
| 8720 | 24" O.C. | | 285 | .028 | | .44 | .73 | | 1.17 | 1.65 |
| 8800 | 1-5/8" channels, 16" O.C. | | 190 | .042 | | .62 | 1.09 | | 1.71 | 2.43 |
| 8820 | 24" O.C. | ↓ | 225 | .036 | ↓ | .50 | .92 | | 1.42 | 2.03 |

## 09 22 36 – Lath

### 09 22 36.13 Gypsum Lath

| | | Crew | Daily Output | Labor-Hours | Unit | Material | 2010 Bare Costs Labor | Equipment | Total | Total Incl O&P |
|---|---|---|---|---|---|---|---|---|---|---|
| 0011 | **GYPSUM LATH** Plain or perforated, nailed, 3/8" thick | 1 Lath | 765 | .010 | S.F. | .56 | .27 | | .83 | 1.06 |
| 0101 | 1/2" thick, nailed | | 720 | .011 | | .55 | .29 | | .84 | 1.07 |
| 0301 | Clipped to steel studs, 3/8" thick | | 675 | .012 | | .56 | .31 | | .87 | 1.11 |
| 0401 | 1/2" thick | | 630 | .013 | | .55 | .33 | | .88 | 1.14 |
| 0601 | Firestop gypsum base, to steel studs, 3/8" thick | | 630 | .013 | | .27 | .33 | | .60 | .83 |
| 0701 | 1/2" thick | | 585 | .014 | | .27 | .35 | | .62 | .87 |
| 0901 | Foil back, to steel studs, 3/8" thick | ↓ | 675 | .012 | | .33 | .31 | | .64 | .85 |

459

# 09 22 Supports for Plaster and Gypsum Board

## 09 22 36 – Lath

### 09 22 36.13 Gypsum Lath

| | | Crew | Daily Output | Labor-Hours | Unit | Material | 2010 Bare Costs Labor | 2010 Bare Costs Equipment | Total | Total Incl O&P |
|---|---|---|---|---|---|---|---|---|---|---|
| 1001 | 1/2" thick | 1 Lath | 630 | .013 | S.F. | .34 | .33 | | .67 | .90 |
| 1501 | For ceiling installations, add | | 1950 | .004 | | | .11 | | .11 | .17 |
| 1601 | For columns and beams, add | | 1550 | .005 | | | .13 | | .13 | .21 |

### 09 22 36.23 Metal Lath

| | | | Crew | Daily Output | Labor-Hours | Unit | Material | 2010 Bare Costs Labor | 2010 Bare Costs Equipment | Total | Total Incl O&P |
|---|---|---|---|---|---|---|---|---|---|---|---|
| 0010 | **METAL LATH** | R092000-50 | | | | | | | | | |
| 3601 | 2.5 lb. diamond painted, on wood framing, on walls | | 1 Lath | 765 | .010 | S.F. | .45 | .27 | | .72 | .94 |
| 3701 | On ceilings | | | 675 | .012 | | .45 | .31 | | .76 | .99 |
| 4201 | 3.4 lb. diamond painted, wired to steel framing, on walls | | | 675 | .012 | | .47 | .31 | | .78 | 1.01 |
| 4301 | On ceilings | | | 540 | .015 | | .47 | .38 | | .85 | 1.14 |
| 5101 | Rib lath, painted, wired to steel, on walls, 2.75 lb. | | | 675 | .012 | | .37 | .31 | | .68 | .90 |
| 5201 | 3.4 lb. | | | 630 | .013 | | .57 | .33 | | .90 | 1.16 |
| 5701 | Suspended ceiling system, incl. 3.4 lb. diamond lath, painted | | | 135 | .059 | | .51 | 1.53 | | 2.04 | 3.03 |
| 5801 | Galvanized | | | 135 | .059 | | .51 | 1.53 | | 2.04 | 3.03 |

### 09 22 36.83 Accessories, Plaster

| | | Crew | Daily Output | Labor-Hours | Unit | Material | 2010 Bare Costs Labor | 2010 Bare Costs Equipment | Total | Total Incl O&P |
|---|---|---|---|---|---|---|---|---|---|---|
| 0010 | **ACCESSORIES, PLASTER** | | | | | | | | | |
| 0020 | Casing bead, expanded flange, galvanized | 1 Lath | 2.70 | 2.963 | C.L.F. | 46.50 | 76.50 | | 123 | 174 |
| 0900 | Channels, cold rolled, 16 ga., 3/4" deep, galvanized | | | | | 31 | | | 31 | 34 |
| 1620 | Corner bead, expanded bullnose, 3/4" radius, #10, galvanized | 1 Lath | 2.60 | 3.077 | | 33.50 | 79.50 | | 113 | 165 |
| 1650 | #1, galvanized | | 2.55 | 3.137 | | 56 | 81 | | 137 | 193 |
| 1670 | Expanded wing, 2-3/4" wide, #1, galvanized | | 2.65 | 3.019 | | 34 | 78 | | 112 | 163 |
| 1700 | Inside corner (corner rite), 3" x 3", painted | | 2.60 | 3.077 | | 30 | 79.50 | | 109.50 | 161 |
| 1750 | Strip-ex, 4" wide, painted | | 2.55 | 3.137 | | 30 | 81 | | 111 | 164 |
| 1800 | Expansion joint, 3/4" grounds, limited expansion, galv., 1 piece | | 2.70 | 2.963 | | 108 | 76.50 | | 184.50 | 242 |
| 2100 | Extreme expansion, galvanized, 2 piece | | 2.60 | 3.077 | | 174 | 79.50 | | 253.50 | 320 |

# 09 23 Gypsum Plastering

## 09 23 13 – Acoustical Gypsum Plastering

### 09 23 13.10 Perlite or Vermiculite Plaster

| | | | Crew | Daily Output | Labor-Hours | Unit | Material | 2010 Bare Costs Labor | 2010 Bare Costs Equipment | Total | Total Incl O&P |
|---|---|---|---|---|---|---|---|---|---|---|---|
| 0010 | **PERLITE OR VERMICULITE PLASTER** | R092000-50 | | | | | | | | | |
| 0020 | In 100 lb. bags, under 200 bags | | | | | Bag | 14.10 | | | 14.10 | 15.50 |
| 0301 | 2 coats, no lath included, on walls | | J-1 | 830 | .048 | S.F. | .42 | 1.21 | .16 | 1.79 | 2.62 |
| 0401 | On ceilings | | | 710 | .056 | | .42 | 1.42 | .19 | 2.03 | 2.98 |
| 0901 | 3 coats, no lath included, on walls | | | 665 | .060 | | .70 | 1.51 | .21 | 2.42 | 3.47 |
| 1001 | On ceilings | | | 565 | .071 | | .70 | 1.78 | .24 | 2.72 | 3.95 |
| 1700 | For irregular or curved surfaces, add to above | | | | | S.Y. | | 30% | | | |
| 1800 | For columns and beams, add to above | | | | | | | 50% | | | |
| 1900 | For soffits, add to ceiling prices | | | | | | | 40% | | | |

## 09 23 20 – Gypsum Plaster

### 09 23 20.10 Gypsum Plaster On Walls and Ceilings

| | | | Crew | Daily Output | Labor-Hours | Unit | Material | 2010 Bare Costs Labor | 2010 Bare Costs Equipment | Total | Total Incl O&P |
|---|---|---|---|---|---|---|---|---|---|---|---|
| 0010 | **GYPSUM PLASTER ON WALLS AND CEILINGS** | R092000-50 | | | | | | | | | |
| 0020 | 80# bag, less than 1 ton | | | | | Bag | 15 | | | 15 | 16.50 |
| 0302 | 2 coats, no lath included, on walls | | J-1 | 750 | .053 | S.F. | .42 | 1.34 | .18 | 1.94 | 2.85 |
| 0402 | On ceilings | | | 660 | .061 | | .42 | 1.52 | .21 | 2.15 | 3.18 |
| 0903 | 3 coats, no lath included, on walls | | | 620 | .065 | | .60 | 1.62 | .22 | 2.44 | 3.55 |
| 1002 | On ceilings | | | 560 | .071 | | 1.10 | 1.80 | .24 | 3.14 | 4.41 |
| 1600 | For irregular or curved surfaces, add | | | | | | | 30% | | | |
| 1800 | For columns & beams, add | | | | | | | 50% | | | |

# 09 24 Portland Cement Plastering

## 09 24 23 – Portland Cement Stucco

### 09 24 23.40 Stucco

| | | Crew | Daily Output | Labor-Hours | Unit | Material | 2010 Bare Costs Labor | Equipment | Total | Total Incl O&P |
|---|---|---|---|---|---|---|---|---|---|---|
| 0010 | **STUCCO**  R092000-50 | | | | | | | | | |
| 0011 | 3 coats 1" thick, float finish, with mesh, on wood frame | J-2 | 470 | .102 | S.F. | .77 | 2.58 | .29 | 3.64 | 5.35 |
| 0101 | On masonry construction | J-1 | 495 | .081 | | .23 | 2.03 | .28 | 2.54 | 3.87 |
| 0151 | 2 coats, 3/4" thick, float finish, no lath incl. | " | 980 | .041 | | .24 | 1.03 | .14 | 1.41 | 2.09 |
| 0301 | For trowel finish, add | 1 Plas | 1530 | .005 | ↓ | | .14 | | .14 | .22 |
| 0600 | For coloring and special finish, add, minimum | J-1 | 685 | .058 | S.Y. | .39 | 1.47 | .20 | 2.06 | 3.05 |
| 0700 | Maximum | | 200 | .200 | " | 1.36 | 5.05 | .68 | 7.09 | 10.45 |
| 1001 | Exterior stucco, with bonding agent, 3 coats, on walls | | 1800 | .022 | S.F. | .35 | .56 | .08 | .99 | 1.38 |
| 1201 | Ceilings | | 1620 | .025 | | .35 | .62 | .08 | 1.05 | 1.49 |
| 1301 | Beams | | 720 | .056 | | .35 | 1.40 | .19 | 1.94 | 2.88 |
| 1501 | Columns | ↓ | 900 | .044 | | .35 | 1.12 | .15 | 1.62 | 2.38 |
| 1601 | Mesh, painted, nailed to wood, 1.8 lb. | 1 Lath | 540 | .015 | | .65 | .38 | | 1.03 | 1.34 |
| 1801 | 3.6 lb. | | 495 | .016 | | .37 | .42 | | .79 | 1.08 |
| 1901 | Wired to steel, painted, 1.8 lb. | | 477 | .017 | | .65 | .43 | | 1.08 | 1.42 |
| 2101 | 3.6 lb. | ↓ | 450 | .018 | ↓ | .37 | .46 | | .83 | 1.15 |

# 09 26 Veneer Plastering

## 09 26 13 – Gypsum Veneer Plastering

### 09 26 13.20 Blueboard

| | | Crew | Daily Output | Labor-Hours | Unit | Material | 2010 Bare Costs Labor | Equipment | Total | Total Incl O&P |
|---|---|---|---|---|---|---|---|---|---|---|
| 0010 | **BLUEBOARD** For use with thin coat | | | | | | | | | |
| 0100 | plaster application (see Div. 09 26 13.80) | | | | | | | | | |
| 1000 | 3/8" thick, on walls or ceilings, standard, no finish included | 2 Carp | 1900 | .008 | S.F. | .26 | .25 | | .51 | .70 |
| 1100 | With thin coat plaster finish | | 875 | .018 | | .34 | .53 | | .87 | 1.28 |
| 1400 | On beams, columns, or soffits, standard, no finish included | | 675 | .024 | | .30 | .69 | | .99 | 1.49 |
| 1450 | With thin coat plaster finish | | 475 | .034 | | .38 | .98 | | 1.36 | 2.07 |
| 3000 | 1/2" thick, on walls or ceilings, standard, no finish included | | 1900 | .008 | | .29 | .25 | | .54 | .73 |
| 3100 | With thin coat plaster finish | | 875 | .018 | | .37 | .53 | | .90 | 1.31 |
| 3300 | Fire resistant, no finish included | | 1900 | .008 | | .29 | .25 | | .54 | .73 |
| 3400 | With thin coat plaster finish | | 875 | .018 | | .37 | .53 | | .90 | 1.31 |
| 3450 | On beams, columns, or soffits, standard, no finish included | | 675 | .024 | | .33 | .69 | | 1.02 | 1.53 |
| 3500 | With thin coat plaster finish | | 475 | .034 | | .42 | .98 | | 1.40 | 2.11 |
| 3700 | Fire resistant, no finish included | | 675 | .024 | | .33 | .69 | | 1.02 | 1.53 |
| 3800 | With thin coat plaster finish | | 475 | .034 | | .42 | .98 | | 1.40 | 2.11 |
| 5000 | 5/8" thick, on walls or ceilings, fire resistant, no finish included | | 1900 | .008 | | .29 | .25 | | .54 | .73 |
| 5100 | With thin coat plaster finish | | 875 | .018 | | .37 | .53 | | .90 | 1.31 |
| 5500 | On beams, columns, or soffits, no finish included | | 675 | .024 | | .33 | .69 | | 1.02 | 1.53 |
| 5600 | With thin coat plaster finish | | 475 | .034 | | .42 | .98 | | 1.40 | 2.11 |
| 6000 | For high ceilings, over 8' high, add | | 3060 | .005 | | | .15 | | .15 | .26 |
| 6500 | For over 3 stories high, add per story | ↓ | 6100 | .003 | ↓ | | .08 | | .08 | .13 |

### 09 26 13.80 Thin Coat Plaster

| | | Crew | Daily Output | Labor-Hours | Unit | Material | 2010 Bare Costs Labor | Equipment | Total | Total Incl O&P |
|---|---|---|---|---|---|---|---|---|---|---|
| 0010 | **THIN COAT PLASTER**  R092000-50 | | | | | | | | | |
| 0012 | 1 coat veneer, not incl. lath | J-1 | 3600 | .011 | S.F. | .08 | .28 | .04 | .40 | .59 |
| 1000 | In 50 lb. bags | | | | Bag | 11.30 | | | 11.30 | 12.45 |

# 09 28 Backing Boards and Underlayments

## 09 28 13 – Cementitious Backing Boards

| | 09 28 13.10 Cementitious Backerboard | Crew | Daily Output | Labor-Hours | Unit | Material | 2010 Bare Costs Labor | Equipment | Total | Total Incl O&P |
|---|---|---|---|---|---|---|---|---|---|---|
| 0010 | **CEMENTITIOUS BACKERBOARD** | | | | | | | | | |
| 0070 | Cementitious backerboard, on floor, 3' x 4' x 1/2" sheets | 2 Carp | 525 | .030 | S.F. | .69 | .89 | | 1.58 | 2.25 |
| 0080 | 3' x 5' x 1/2" sheets | | 525 | .030 | | .72 | .89 | | 1.61 | 2.28 |
| 0090 | 3' x 6' x 1/2" sheets | | 525 | .030 | | .64 | .89 | | 1.53 | 2.20 |
| 0100 | 3' x 4' x 5/8" sheets | | 525 | .030 | | .93 | .89 | | 1.82 | 2.51 |
| 0110 | 3' x 5' x 5/8" sheets | | 525 | .030 | | .92 | .89 | | 1.81 | 2.50 |
| 0120 | 3' x 6' x 5/8" sheets | | 525 | .030 | | .75 | .89 | | 1.64 | 2.31 |
| 0150 | On wall, 3' x 4' x 1/2" sheets | | 350 | .046 | | .69 | 1.33 | | 2.02 | 3 |
| 0160 | 3' x 5' x 1/2" sheets | | 350 | .046 | | .72 | 1.33 | | 2.05 | 3.03 |
| 0170 | 3' x 6' x 1/2" sheets | | 350 | .046 | | .64 | 1.33 | | 1.97 | 2.95 |
| 0180 | 3' x 4' x 5/8" sheets | | 350 | .046 | | .93 | 1.33 | | 2.26 | 3.26 |
| 0190 | 3' x 5' x 5/8" sheets | | 350 | .046 | | .92 | 1.33 | | 2.25 | 3.25 |
| 0200 | 3' x 6' x 5/8" sheets | | 350 | .046 | | .75 | 1.33 | | 2.08 | 3.06 |
| 0250 | On counter, 3' x 4' x 1/2" sheets | | 180 | .089 | | .69 | 2.59 | | 3.28 | 5.10 |
| 0260 | 3' x 5' x 1/2" sheets | | 180 | .089 | | .72 | 2.59 | | 3.31 | 5.15 |
| 0270 | 3' x 6' x 1/2" sheets | | 180 | .089 | | .64 | 2.59 | | 3.23 | 5.05 |
| 0300 | 3' x 4' x 5/8" sheets | | 180 | .089 | | .93 | 2.59 | | 3.52 | 5.35 |
| 0310 | 3' x 5' x 5/8" sheets | | 180 | .089 | | .92 | 2.59 | | 3.51 | 5.35 |
| 0320 | 3' x 6' x 5/8" sheets | | 180 | .089 | | .75 | 2.59 | | 3.34 | 5.15 |

# 09 29 Gypsum Board

## 09 29 10 – Gypsum Board Panels

### 09 29 10.20 Taping and Finishing

| | | Crew | Daily Output | Labor-Hours | Unit | Material | 2010 Bare Costs Labor | Equipment | Total | Total Incl O&P |
|---|---|---|---|---|---|---|---|---|---|---|
| 0010 | **TAPING AND FINISHING** | | | | | | | | | |
| 3600 | For taping and finishing joints, add | 2 Carp | 2000 | .008 | S.F. | .04 | .23 | | .27 | .44 |
| 4500 | For thin coat plaster instead of taping, add | J-1 | 3600 | .011 | " | .08 | .28 | .04 | .40 | .59 |

### 09 29 10.30 Gypsum Board

| | | | Crew | Daily Output | Labor-Hours | Unit | Material | 2010 Bare Costs Labor | Equipment | Total | Total Incl O&P |
|---|---|---|---|---|---|---|---|---|---|---|---|
| 0010 | **GYPSUM BOARD** on walls & ceilings | R092910-10 | | | | | | | | | |
| 0100 | Nailed or screwed to studs unless otherwise noted | | | | | | | | | | |
| 0150 | 3/8" thick, on walls, standard, no finish included | | 2 Carp | 2000 | .008 | S.F. | .24 | .23 | | .47 | .65 |
| 0200 | On ceilings, standard, no finish included | | | 1800 | .009 | | .24 | .26 | | .50 | .70 |
| 0250 | On beams, columns, or soffits, no finish included | | | 675 | .024 | | .24 | .69 | | .93 | 1.42 |
| 0300 | 1/2" thick, on walls, standard, no finish included | | | 2000 | .008 | | .24 | .23 | | .47 | .65 |
| 0350 | Taped and finished (level 4 finish) | | | 965 | .017 | | .28 | .48 | | .76 | 1.12 |
| 0390 | With compound skim coat (level 5 finish) | | | 775 | .021 | | .33 | .60 | | .93 | 1.37 |
| 0400 | Fire resistant, no finish included | | | 2000 | .008 | | .28 | .23 | | .51 | .70 |
| 0450 | Taped and finished (level 4 finish) | | | 965 | .017 | | .32 | .48 | | .80 | 1.16 |
| 0490 | With compound skim coat (level 5 finish) | | | 775 | .021 | | .37 | .60 | | .97 | 1.41 |
| 0500 | Water resistant, no finish included | | | 2000 | .008 | | .35 | .23 | | .58 | .78 |
| 0550 | Taped and finished (level 4 finish) | | | 965 | .017 | | .39 | .48 | | .87 | 1.24 |
| 0590 | With compound skim coat (level 5 finish) | | | 775 | .021 | | .44 | .60 | | 1.04 | 1.49 |
| 0600 | Prefinished, vinyl, clipped to studs | | | 900 | .018 | | .60 | .52 | | 1.12 | 1.53 |
| 0700 | Mold resistant, no finish included | | | 2000 | .008 | | .42 | .23 | | .65 | .85 |
| 0710 | Taped and finished (level 4 finish) | | | 965 | .017 | | .46 | .48 | | .94 | 1.32 |
| 0720 | With compound skim coat (level 5 finish) | | | 775 | .021 | | .51 | .60 | | 1.11 | 1.57 |
| 1000 | On ceilings, standard, no finish included | | | 1800 | .009 | | .24 | .26 | | .50 | .70 |
| 1050 | Taped and finished (level 4 finish) | | | 765 | .021 | | .28 | .61 | | .89 | 1.33 |
| 1090 | With compound skim coat (level 5 finish) | | | 610 | .026 | | .33 | .76 | | 1.09 | 1.64 |
| 1100 | Fire resistant, no finish included | | | 1800 | .009 | | .28 | .26 | | .54 | .75 |
| 1150 | Taped and finished (level 4 finish) | | | 765 | .021 | | .32 | .61 | | .93 | 1.37 |
| 1195 | With compound skim coat (level 5 finish) | | | 610 | .026 | | .37 | .76 | | 1.13 | 1.68 |

# 09 29 Gypsum Board

## 09 29 10 – Gypsum Board Panels

| 09 29 10.30 Gypsum Board | | Crew | Daily Output | Labor-Hours | Unit | Material | 2010 Bare Costs Labor | Equipment | Total | Total Incl O&P |
|---|---|---|---|---|---|---|---|---|---|---|
| 1200 | Water resistant, no finish included | 2 Carp | 1800 | .009 | S.F. | .35 | .26 | | .61 | .83 |
| 1250 | Taped and finished (level 4 finish) | | 765 | .021 | | .39 | .61 | | 1 | 1.45 |
| 1290 | With compound skim coat (level 5 finish) | | 610 | .026 | | .44 | .76 | | 1.20 | 1.76 |
| 1310 | Mold resistant, no finish included | | 1800 | .009 | | .42 | .26 | | .68 | .90 |
| 1320 | Taped and finished (level 4 finish) | | 765 | .021 | | .46 | .61 | | 1.07 | 1.53 |
| 1330 | With compound skim coat (level 5 finish) | | 610 | .026 | | .51 | .76 | | 1.27 | 1.84 |
| 1500 | On beams, columns, or soffits, standard, no finish included | | 675 | .024 | | .28 | .69 | | .97 | 1.46 |
| 1550 | Taped and finished (level 4 finish) | | 475 | .034 | | .28 | .98 | | 1.26 | 1.96 |
| 1590 | With compound skim coat (level 5 finish) | | 540 | .030 | | .33 | .86 | | 1.19 | 1.81 |
| 1600 | Fire resistant, no finish included | | 675 | .024 | | .28 | .69 | | .97 | 1.47 |
| 1650 | Taped and finished (level 4 finish) | | 475 | .034 | | .32 | .98 | | 1.30 | 2 |
| 1690 | With compound skim coat (level 5 finish) | | 540 | .030 | | .37 | .86 | | 1.23 | 1.85 |
| 1700 | Water resistant, no finish included | | 675 | .024 | | .40 | .69 | | 1.09 | 1.60 |
| 1750 | Taped and finished (level 4 finish) | | 475 | .034 | | .39 | .98 | | 1.37 | 2.08 |
| 1790 | With compound skim coat (level 5 finish) | | 540 | .030 | | .44 | .86 | | 1.30 | 1.93 |
| 1800 | Mold resistant, no finish included | | 675 | .024 | | .48 | .69 | | 1.17 | 1.69 |
| 1810 | Taped and finished (level 4 finish) | | 475 | .034 | | .46 | .98 | | 1.44 | 2.16 |
| 1820 | With compound skim coat (level 5 finish) | | 540 | .030 | | .51 | .86 | | 1.37 | 2.01 |
| 2000 | 5/8" thick, on walls, standard, no finish included | | 2000 | .008 | | .28 | .23 | | .51 | .70 |
| 2050 | Taped and finished (level 4 finish) | | 965 | .017 | | .32 | .48 | | .80 | 1.16 |
| 2090 | With compound skim coat (level 5 finish) | | 775 | .021 | | .37 | .60 | | .97 | 1.41 |
| 2100 | Fire resistant, no finish included | | 2000 | .008 | | .27 | .23 | | .50 | .69 |
| 2150 | Taped and finished (level 4 finish) | | 965 | .017 | | .31 | .48 | | .79 | 1.15 |
| 2195 | With compound skim coat (level 5 finish) | | 775 | .021 | | .36 | .60 | | .96 | 1.40 |
| 2200 | Water resistant, no finish included | | 2000 | .008 | | .43 | .23 | | .66 | .86 |
| 2250 | Taped and finished (level 4 finish) | | 965 | .017 | | .47 | .48 | | .95 | 1.33 |
| 2290 | With compound skim coat (level 5 finish) | | 775 | .021 | | .52 | .60 | | 1.12 | 1.58 |
| 2300 | Prefinished, vinyl, clipped to studs | | 900 | .018 | | .71 | .52 | | 1.23 | 1.65 |
| 2510 | Mold resistant, no finish included | | 2000 | .008 | | .49 | .23 | | .72 | .93 |
| 2520 | Taped and finished (level 4 finish) | | 965 | .017 | | .53 | .48 | | 1.01 | 1.40 |
| 2530 | With compound skim coat (level 5 finish) | | 775 | .021 | | .58 | .60 | | 1.18 | 1.64 |
| 3000 | On ceilings, standard, no finish included | | 1800 | .009 | | .28 | .26 | | .54 | .75 |
| 3050 | Taped and finished (level 4 finish) | | 765 | .021 | | .32 | .61 | | .93 | 1.37 |
| 3090 | With compound skim coat (level 5 finish) | | 615 | .026 | | .37 | .76 | | 1.13 | 1.67 |
| 3100 | Fire resistant, no finish included | | 1800 | .009 | | .27 | .26 | | .53 | .74 |
| 3150 | Taped and finished (level 4 finish) | | 765 | .021 | | .31 | .61 | | .92 | 1.36 |
| 3190 | With compound skim coat (level 5 finish) | | 615 | .026 | | .36 | .76 | | 1.12 | 1.66 |
| 3200 | Water resistant, no finish included | | 1800 | .009 | | .43 | .26 | | .69 | .91 |
| 3250 | Taped and finished (level 4 finish) | | 765 | .021 | | .47 | .61 | | 1.08 | 1.54 |
| 3290 | With compound skim coat (level 5 finish) | | 615 | .026 | | .52 | .76 | | 1.28 | 1.84 |
| 3300 | Mold resistant, no finish included | | 1800 | .009 | | .49 | .26 | | .75 | .98 |
| 3310 | Taped and finished (level 4 finish) | | 765 | .021 | | .53 | .61 | | 1.14 | 1.61 |
| 3320 | With compound skim coat (level 5 finish) | | 615 | .026 | | .58 | .76 | | 1.34 | 1.90 |
| 3500 | On beams, columns, or soffits, no finish included | | 675 | .024 | | .32 | .69 | | 1.01 | 1.51 |
| 3550 | Taped and finished (level 4 finish) | | 475 | .034 | | .37 | .98 | | 1.35 | 2.06 |
| 3590 | With compound skim coat (level 5 finish) | | 380 | .042 | | .42 | 1.23 | | 1.65 | 2.52 |
| 3600 | Fire resistant, no finish included | | 675 | .024 | | .31 | .69 | | 1 | 1.50 |
| 3650 | Taped and finished (level 4 finish) | | 475 | .034 | | .36 | .98 | | 1.34 | 2.04 |
| 3690 | With compound skim coat (level 5 finish) | | 380 | .042 | | .36 | 1.23 | | 1.59 | 2.45 |
| 3700 | Water resistant, no finish included | | 675 | .024 | | .49 | .69 | | 1.18 | 1.70 |
| 3750 | Taped and finished (level 4 finish) | | 475 | .034 | | .54 | .98 | | 1.52 | 2.25 |
| 3790 | With compound skim coat (level 5 finish) | | 380 | .042 | | .52 | 1.23 | | 1.75 | 2.63 |
| 3800 | Mold resistant, no finish included | | 675 | .024 | | .56 | .69 | | 1.25 | 1.78 |

# 09 29 Gypsum Board

## 09 29 10 – Gypsum Board Panels

| 09 29 10.30 Gypsum Board | | Crew | Daily Output | Labor-Hours | Unit | Material | 2010 Bare Costs Labor | Equipment | Total | Total Incl O&P |
|---|---|---|---|---|---|---|---|---|---|---|
| 3810 | Taped and finished (level 4 finish) | 2 Carp | 475 | .034 | S.F. | .61 | .98 | | 1.59 | 2.32 |
| 3820 | With compound skim coat (level 5 finish) | | 380 | .042 | | .58 | 1.23 | | 1.81 | 2.69 |
| 4000 | Fireproofing, beams or columns, 2 layers, 1/2" thick, incl finish | | 330 | .048 | | .60 | 1.41 | | 2.01 | 3.03 |
| 4010 | Mold resistant | | 330 | .048 | | .88 | 1.41 | | 2.29 | 3.34 |
| 4050 | 5/8" thick | | 300 | .053 | | .62 | 1.55 | | 2.17 | 3.30 |
| 4060 | Mold resistant | | 300 | .053 | | 1.06 | 1.55 | | 2.61 | 3.78 |
| 4100 | 3 layers, 1/2" thick | | 225 | .071 | | .88 | 2.07 | | 2.95 | 4.45 |
| 4110 | Mold resistant | | 225 | .071 | | 1.30 | 2.07 | | 3.37 | 4.91 |
| 4150 | 5/8" thick | | 210 | .076 | | .94 | 2.22 | | 3.16 | 4.76 |
| 4160 | Mold resistant | | 210 | .076 | | 1.60 | 2.22 | | 3.82 | 5.50 |
| 5200 | For work over 8' high, add | ↓ | 3060 | .005 | | | .15 | | .15 | .26 |
| 5270 | For textured spray, add | 2 Lath | 1600 | .010 | ↓ | .05 | .26 | | .31 | .48 |
| 5350 | For finishing inner corners, add | 2 Carp | 950 | .017 | L.F. | .09 | .49 | | .58 | .92 |
| 5355 | For finishing outer corners, add | " | 1250 | .013 | | .21 | .37 | | .58 | .86 |
| 5500 | For acoustical sealant, add per bead | 1 Carp | 500 | .016 | ↓ | .04 | .47 | | .51 | .83 |
| 5550 | Sealant, 1 quart tube | | | | Ea. | 6.85 | | | 6.85 | 7.55 |
| 5600 | Sound deadening board, 1/4" gypsum | 2 Carp | 1800 | .009 | S.F. | .33 | .26 | | .59 | .80 |
| 5650 | 1/2" wood fiber | " | 1800 | .009 | " | .82 | .26 | | 1.08 | 1.34 |

## 09 29 15 – Gypsum Board Accessories

### 09 29 15.10 Accessories, Drywall

| | | Crew | Daily Output | Labor-Hours | Unit | Material | 2010 Bare Costs Labor | Equipment | Total | Total Incl O&P |
|---|---|---|---|---|---|---|---|---|---|---|
| 0011 | **ACCESSORIES, DRYWALL** Casing bead, galvanized steel | 1 Carp | 290 | .028 | L.F. | .24 | .80 | | 1.04 | 1.61 |
| 0101 | Vinyl | | 290 | .028 | | .22 | .80 | | 1.02 | 1.60 |
| 0401 | Corner bead, galvanized steel, 1-1/4" x 1-1/4" | | 350 | .023 | ↓ | .17 | .67 | | .84 | 1.30 |
| 0411 | 1-1/4" x 1-1/4", 10' long | | 35 | .229 | Ea. | 1.66 | 6.65 | | 8.31 | 13 |
| 0601 | Vinyl corner bead | | 400 | .020 | L.F. | .18 | .58 | | .76 | 1.18 |
| 0901 | Furring channel, galv. steel, 7/8" deep, standard | | 260 | .031 | | .25 | .90 | | 1.15 | 1.78 |
| 1001 | Resilient | | 260 | .031 | | .25 | .90 | | 1.15 | 1.79 |
| 1101 | J trim, galvanized steel, 1/2" wide | | 300 | .027 | | | .78 | | .78 | 1.31 |
| 1121 | 5/8" wide | | 300 | .027 | ↓ | .24 | .78 | | 1.02 | 1.57 |
| 1160 | Screws #6 x 1" A | | | | M | 7.35 | | | 7.35 | 8.10 |
| 1170 | #6 x 1-5/8" A | | | | " | 10.80 | | | 10.80 | 11.85 |
| 1501 | Z stud, galvanized steel, 1-1/2" wide | 1 Carp | 260 | .031 | L.F. | .36 | .90 | | 1.26 | 1.90 |

# 09 30 Tiling

## 09 30 13 – Ceramic Tiling

### 09 30 13.10 Ceramic Tile

| | | Crew | Daily Output | Labor-Hours | Unit | Material | 2010 Bare Costs Labor | Equipment | Total | Total Incl O&P |
|---|---|---|---|---|---|---|---|---|---|---|
| 0010 | **CERAMIC TILE** | | | | | | | | | |
| 0050 | Base, using 1' x 4" high pc. with 1" x 1" tiles, mud set | D-7 | 82 | .195 | L.F. | 4.95 | 4.82 | | 9.77 | 13.15 |
| 0100 | Thin set | " | 128 | .125 | | 4.45 | 3.09 | | 7.54 | 9.85 |
| 0300 | For 6" high base, 1" x 1" tile face, add | | | | | .72 | | | .72 | .79 |
| 0400 | For 2" x 2" tile face, add to above | | | | | .38 | | | .38 | .42 |
| 0600 | Cove base, 4-1/4" x 4-1/4" high, mud set | D-7 | 91 | .176 | | 3.75 | 4.34 | | 8.09 | 11.05 |
| 0700 | Thin set | | 128 | .125 | | 3.64 | 3.09 | | 6.73 | 8.95 |
| 0900 | 6" x 4-1/4" high, mud set | | 100 | .160 | | 3.34 | 3.95 | | 7.29 | 10 |
| 1000 | Thin set | | 137 | .117 | | 3.06 | 2.88 | | 5.94 | 8 |
| 1200 | Sanitary cove base, 6" x 4-1/4" high, mud set | | 93 | .172 | | 3.84 | 4.25 | | 8.09 | 11 |
| 1300 | Thin set | | 124 | .129 | | 3.59 | 3.19 | | 6.78 | 9.05 |
| 1500 | 6" x 6" high, mud set | | 84 | .190 | | 4.48 | 4.70 | | 9.18 | 12.50 |
| 1600 | Thin set | | 117 | .137 | | 4.20 | 3.38 | | 7.58 | 10 |
| 1800 | Bathroom accessories, average | ↓ | 82 | .195 | Ea. | 10.70 | 4.82 | | 15.52 | 19.45 |

464

## 09 30 13 – Ceramic Tiling

| 09 30 13.10 Ceramic Tile | | Crew | Daily Output | Labor-Hours | Unit | Material | 2010 Bare Costs Labor | Equipment | Total | Total Incl O&P |
|---|---|---|---|---|---|---|---|---|---|---|
| 1900 | Bathtub, 5', rec. 4-1/4" x 4-1/4" tile wainscot, adhesive set 6' high | D-7 | 2.90 | 5.517 | Ea. | 156 | 136 | | 292 | 390 |
| 2100 | 7' high wainscot | | 2.50 | 6.400 | | 179 | 158 | | 337 | 450 |
| 2200 | 8' high wainscot | | 2.20 | 7.273 | | 190 | 180 | | 370 | 495 |
| 2400 | Bullnose trim, 4-1/4" x 4-1/4", mud set | | 82 | .195 | L.F. | 3.55 | 4.82 | | 8.37 | 11.60 |
| 2500 | Thin set | | 128 | .125 | | 3.11 | 3.09 | | 6.20 | 8.35 |
| 2700 | 6" x 4-1/4" bullnose trim, mud set | | 84 | .190 | | 2.70 | 4.70 | | 7.40 | 10.50 |
| 2800 | Thin set | | 124 | .129 | | 2.50 | 3.19 | | 5.69 | 7.85 |
| 3000 | Floors, natural clay, random or uniform, thin set, color group 1 | | 183 | .087 | S.F. | 4.19 | 2.16 | | 6.35 | 8.05 |
| 3100 | Color group 2 | | 183 | .087 | | 4.51 | 2.16 | | 6.67 | 8.40 |
| 3255 | Floors, glazed, thin set, 6" x 6", color group 1 | | 200 | .080 | | 3.58 | 1.98 | | 5.56 | 7.10 |
| 3260 | 8" x 8" tile | | 250 | .064 | | 3.58 | 1.58 | | 5.16 | 6.45 |
| 3270 | 12" x 12" tile | | 325 | .049 | | 4.47 | 1.22 | | 5.69 | 6.85 |
| 3280 | 16" x 16" tile | | 550 | .029 | | 6.15 | .72 | | 6.87 | 7.90 |
| 3285 | Border, 6" x 12" tile | | 275 | .058 | | 11.55 | 1.44 | | 12.99 | 15 |
| 3290 | 3" x 12" tile | | 200 | .080 | | 34 | 1.98 | | 35.98 | 40 |
| 3300 | Porcelain type, 1 color, color group 2, 1" x 1" | | 183 | .087 | | 4.71 | 2.16 | | 6.87 | 8.65 |
| 3310 | 2" x 2" or 2" x 1", thin set | | 190 | .084 | | 4.98 | 2.08 | | 7.06 | 8.85 |
| 3350 | For random blend, 2 colors, add | | | | | .88 | | | .88 | .97 |
| 3360 | 4 colors, add | | | | | 1.24 | | | 1.24 | 1.36 |
| 4300 | Specialty tile, 4-1/4" x 4-1/4" x 1/2", decorator finish | D-7 | 183 | .087 | | 10 | 2.16 | | 12.16 | 14.45 |
| 4500 | Add for epoxy grout, 1/16" joint, 1" x 1" tile | | 800 | .020 | | .62 | .49 | | 1.11 | 1.47 |
| 4600 | 2" x 2" tile | | 820 | .020 | | .59 | .48 | | 1.07 | 1.42 |
| 4800 | Pregrouted sheets, walls, 4-1/4" x 4-1/4", 6" x 4-1/4" | | | | | | | | | |
| 4810 | and 8-1/2" x 4-1/4", 4 S.F. sheets, silicone grout | D-7 | 240 | .067 | S.F. | 4.73 | 1.65 | | 6.38 | 7.85 |
| 5100 | Floors, unglazed, 2 S.F. sheets, | | | | | | | | | |
| 5110 | Urethane adhesive | D-7 | 180 | .089 | S.F. | 4.71 | 2.20 | | 6.91 | 8.70 |
| 5400 | Walls, interior, thin set, 4-1/4" x 4-1/4" tile | | 190 | .084 | | 2.34 | 2.08 | | 4.42 | 5.90 |
| 5500 | 6" x 4-1/4" tile | | 190 | .084 | | 2.71 | 2.08 | | 4.79 | 6.30 |
| 5700 | 8-1/2" x 4-1/4" tile | | 190 | .084 | | 3.78 | 2.08 | | 5.86 | 7.50 |
| 5800 | 6" x 6" tile | | 200 | .080 | | 3.04 | 1.98 | | 5.02 | 6.50 |
| 5810 | 8" x 8" tile | | 225 | .071 | | 4.06 | 1.76 | | 5.82 | 7.30 |
| 5820 | 12" x 12" tile | | 300 | .053 | | 3.47 | 1.32 | | 4.79 | 5.95 |
| 5830 | 16" x 16" tile | | 500 | .032 | | 3.75 | .79 | | 4.54 | 5.40 |
| 6000 | Decorated wall tile, 4-1/4" x 4-1/4", minimum | | 270 | .059 | | 3.51 | 1.46 | | 4.97 | 6.20 |
| 6100 | Maximum | | 180 | .089 | | 41.50 | 2.20 | | 43.70 | 49.50 |
| 6600 | Crystalline glazed, 4-1/4" x 4-1/4", mud set, plain | | 100 | .160 | | 4.28 | 3.95 | | 8.23 | 11.05 |
| 6700 | 4-1/4" x 4-1/4", scored tile | | 100 | .160 | | 5.25 | 3.95 | | 9.20 | 12.10 |
| 6900 | 6" x 6" plain | | 93 | .172 | | 5.30 | 4.25 | | 9.55 | 12.60 |
| 7000 | For epoxy grout, 1/16" joints, 4-1/4" tile, add | | 800 | .020 | | .39 | .49 | | .88 | 1.22 |
| 7200 | For tile set in dry mortar, add | | 1735 | .009 | | | .23 | | .23 | .36 |
| 7300 | For tile set in Portland cement mortar, add | | 290 | .055 | | .27 | 1.36 | | 1.63 | 2.48 |
| 9300 | Ceramic tiles, recycled glass, standard colors, 2" x 2" thru 6" x 6" [G] | | 190 | .084 | | 17 | 2.08 | | 19.08 | 22 |
| 9310 | 6" x 6" [G] | | 200 | .080 | | 17 | 1.98 | | 18.98 | 22 |
| 9320 | 8" x 8" [G] | | 225 | .071 | | 18.45 | 1.76 | | 20.21 | 23.50 |
| 9330 | 12"x12" [G] | | 300 | .053 | | 18.45 | 1.32 | | 19.77 | 22.50 |
| 9340 | Earthtones, 2" x 2" to 4" x 8" [G] | | 190 | .084 | | 21.50 | 2.08 | | 23.58 | 27 |
| 9350 | 6" x 6" [G] | | 200 | .080 | | 21.50 | 1.98 | | 23.48 | 26.50 |
| 9360 | 8" x 8" [G] | | 225 | .071 | | 23 | 1.76 | | 24.76 | 28 |
| 9370 | 12" x 12" [G] | | 300 | .053 | | 23 | 1.32 | | 24.32 | 27 |
| 9380 | Deep colors, 2" x 2" to 4" x 8" [G] | | 190 | .084 | | 31 | 2.08 | | 33.08 | 37.50 |
| 9390 | 6" x 6" [G] | | 200 | .080 | | 31 | 1.98 | | 32.98 | 37 |
| 9400 | 8" x 8" [G] | | 225 | .071 | | 32 | 1.76 | | 33.76 | 38.50 |
| 9410 | 12" x 12" [G] | | 300 | .053 | | 32 | 1.32 | | 33.32 | 37.50 |

# 09 30 Tiling

## 09 30 16 – Quarry Tiling

| 09 30 16.10 Quarry Tile | Crew | Daily Output | Labor-Hours | Unit | Material | Labor | Equipment | Total | Total Incl O&P |
|---|---|---|---|---|---|---|---|---|---|
| 0010 **QUARRY TILE** | | | | | | | | | |
| 0100 Base, cove or sanitary, mud set, to 5" high, 1/2" thick | D-7 | 110 | .145 | L.F. | 5.30 | 3.59 | | 8.89 | 11.60 |
| 0300 Bullnose trim, red, mud set, 6" x 6" x 1/2" thick | | 120 | .133 | | 4.36 | 3.29 | | 7.65 | 10.05 |
| 0400 4" x 4" x 1/2" thick | | 110 | .145 | | 4.78 | 3.59 | | 8.37 | 11 |
| 0600 4" x 8" x 1/2" thick, using 8" as edge | | 130 | .123 | | 4.24 | 3.04 | | 7.28 | 9.55 |
| 0700 Floors, mud set, 1,000 S.F. lots, red, 4" x 4" x 1/2" thick | | 120 | .133 | S.F. | 7.50 | 3.29 | | 10.79 | 13.50 |
| 0900 6" x 6" x 1/2" thick | | 140 | .114 | | 6.85 | 2.82 | | 9.67 | 12 |
| 1000 4" x 8" x 1/2" thick | | 130 | .123 | | 7.50 | 3.04 | | 10.54 | 13.10 |
| 1300 For waxed coating, add | | | | | .67 | | | .67 | .74 |
| 1500 For non-standard colors, add | | | | | .40 | | | .40 | .44 |
| 1600 For abrasive surface, add | | | | | .47 | | | .47 | .52 |
| 1800 Brown tile, imported, 6" x 6" x 3/4" | D-7 | 120 | .133 | | 8.40 | 3.29 | | 11.69 | 14.50 |
| 1900 8" x 8" x 1" | | 110 | .145 | | 9.05 | 3.59 | | 12.64 | 15.70 |
| 2100 For thin set mortar application, deduct | | 700 | .023 | | | .56 | | .56 | .90 |
| 2700 Stair tread, 6" x 6" x 3/4", plain | | 50 | .320 | | 5.05 | 7.90 | | 12.95 | 18.20 |
| 2800 Abrasive | | 47 | .340 | | 5.30 | 8.40 | | 13.70 | 19.30 |
| 3000 Wainscot, 6" x 6" x 1/2", thin set, red | | 105 | .152 | | 4.09 | 3.76 | | 7.85 | 10.55 |
| 3100 Non-standard colors | | 105 | .152 | | 4.54 | 3.76 | | 8.30 | 11.05 |
| 3300 Window sill, 6" wide, 3/4" thick | | 90 | .178 | L.F. | 5.10 | 4.39 | | 9.49 | 12.65 |
| 3400 Corners | | 80 | .200 | Ea. | 5.70 | 4.94 | | 10.64 | 14.15 |

## 09 30 29 – Metal Tiling

### 09 30 29.10 Metal Tile

| | Crew | Daily Output | Labor-Hours | Unit | Material | Labor | Equipment | Total | Total Incl O&P |
|---|---|---|---|---|---|---|---|---|---|
| 0010 **METAL TILE** 4' x 4' sheet, 24 ga., tile pattern, nailed | | | | | | | | | |
| 0200 Stainless steel | 2 Carp | 512 | .031 | S.F. | 24.50 | .91 | | 25.41 | 28.50 |
| 0400 Aluminized steel | " | 512 | .031 | " | 13.15 | .91 | | 14.06 | 16 |

# 09 51 Acoustical Ceilings

## 09 51 23 – Acoustical Tile Ceilings

### 09 51 23.10 Suspended Acoustic Ceiling Tiles

| | Crew | Daily Output | Labor-Hours | Unit | Material | Labor | Equipment | Total | Total Incl O&P |
|---|---|---|---|---|---|---|---|---|---|
| 0010 **SUSPENDED ACOUSTIC CEILING TILES**, not including | | | | | | | | | |
| 0100 suspension system | | | | | | | | | |
| 0300 Fiberglass boards, film faced, 2' x 2' or 2' x 4', 5/8" thick | 1 Carp | 625 | .013 | S.F. | .70 | .37 | | 1.07 | 1.40 |
| 0400 3/4" thick | | 600 | .013 | | 1.61 | .39 | | 2 | 2.42 |
| 0500 3" thick, thermal, R11 | | 450 | .018 | | 1.53 | .52 | | 2.05 | 2.55 |
| 0600 Glass cloth faced fiberglass, 3/4" thick | | 500 | .016 | | 2.87 | .47 | | 3.34 | 3.94 |
| 0700 1" thick | | 485 | .016 | | 2.18 | .48 | | 2.66 | 3.21 |
| 0820 1-1/2" thick, nubby face | | 475 | .017 | | 2.66 | .49 | | 3.15 | 3.75 |
| 1110 Mineral fiber tile, lay-in, 2' x 2' or 2' x 4', 5/8" thick, fine texture | | 625 | .013 | | .55 | .37 | | .92 | 1.24 |
| 1115 Rough textured | | 625 | .013 | | 1.23 | .37 | | 1.60 | 1.98 |
| 1125 3/4" thick, fine textured | | 600 | .013 | | 1.50 | .39 | | 1.89 | 2.30 |
| 1130 Rough textured | | 600 | .013 | | 1.79 | .39 | | 2.18 | 2.62 |
| 1135 Fissured | | 600 | .013 | | 2.45 | .39 | | 2.84 | 3.35 |
| 1150 Tegular, 5/8" thick, fine textured | | 470 | .017 | | 1.45 | .50 | | 1.95 | 2.43 |
| 1155 Rough textured | | 470 | .017 | | 1.90 | .50 | | 2.40 | 2.92 |
| 1165 3/4" thick, fine textured | | 450 | .018 | | 2.08 | .52 | | 2.60 | 3.16 |
| 1170 Rough textured | | 450 | .018 | | 2.35 | .52 | | 2.87 | 3.46 |
| 1175 Fissured | | 450 | .018 | | 3.63 | .52 | | 4.15 | 4.86 |
| 1180 For aluminum face, add | | | | | 6.05 | | | 6.05 | 6.65 |
| 1185 For plastic film face, add | | | | | .94 | | | .94 | 1.03 |
| 1190 For fire rating, add | | | | | .45 | | | .45 | .50 |

# 09 51 Acoustical Ceilings

## 09 51 23 – Acoustical Tile Ceilings

### 09 51 23.10 Suspended Acoustic Ceiling Tiles

| | | Crew | Daily Output | Labor-Hours | Unit | Material | 2010 Bare Costs Labor | Equipment | Total | Total Incl O&P |
|---|---|---|---|---|---|---|---|---|---|---|
| 1900 | Eggcrate, acrylic, 1/2" x 1/2" x 1/2" cubes | 1 Carp | 500 | .016 | S.F. | 1.82 | .47 | | 2.29 | 2.78 |
| 2100 | Polystyrene eggcrate, 3/8" x 3/8" x 1/2" cubes | | 510 | .016 | | 1.53 | .46 | | 1.99 | 2.45 |
| 2200 | 1/2" x 1/2" x 1/2" cubes | | 500 | .016 | | 1.75 | .47 | | 2.22 | 2.71 |
| 2400 | Luminous panels, prismatic, acrylic | | 400 | .020 | | 2.22 | .58 | | 2.80 | 3.42 |
| 2500 | Polystyrene | | 400 | .020 | | 1.14 | .58 | | 1.72 | 2.23 |
| 2700 | Flat white acrylic | | 400 | .020 | | 3.86 | .58 | | 4.44 | 5.25 |
| 2800 | Polystyrene | | 400 | .020 | | 2.65 | .58 | | 3.23 | 3.90 |
| 3000 | Drop pan, white, acrylic | | 400 | .020 | | 5.65 | .58 | | 6.23 | 7.25 |
| 3100 | Polystyrene | | 400 | .020 | | 4.73 | .58 | | 5.31 | 6.20 |
| 3600 | Perforated aluminum sheets, .024" thick, corrugated, painted | | 490 | .016 | | 2.25 | .48 | | 2.73 | 3.28 |
| 3700 | Plain | | 500 | .016 | | 3.76 | .47 | | 4.23 | 4.92 |
| 3750 | Wood fiber in cementitious binder, 2' x 2' or 4', painted, 1" thick | | 600 | .013 | | 1.54 | .39 | | 1.93 | 2.34 |
| 3760 | 2" thick | | 550 | .015 | | 2.53 | .42 | | 2.95 | 3.49 |
| 3770 | 2-1/2" thick | | 500 | .016 | | 3.47 | .47 | | 3.94 | 4.60 |
| 3780 | 3" thick | | 450 | .018 | | 3.90 | .52 | | 4.42 | 5.15 |

### 09 51 23.30 Suspended Ceilings, Complete

| | | Crew | Daily Output | Labor-Hours | Unit | Material | 2010 Bare Costs Labor | Equipment | Total | Total Incl O&P |
|---|---|---|---|---|---|---|---|---|---|---|
| 0010 | **SUSPENDED CEILINGS, COMPLETE** Including standard | | | | | | | | | |
| 0100 | suspension system but not incl. 1-1/2" carrier channels | | | | | | | | | |
| 0600 | Fiberglass ceiling board, 2' x 4' x 5/8", plain faced | 1 Carp | 500 | .016 | S.F. | 1.38 | .47 | | 1.85 | 2.30 |
| 0700 | Offices, 2' x 4' x 3/4" | | 380 | .021 | | 2.29 | .61 | | 2.90 | 3.55 |
| 1800 | Tile, Z bar suspension, 5/8" mineral fiber tile | | 150 | .053 | | 2.16 | 1.55 | | 3.71 | 4.99 |
| 1900 | 3/4" mineral fiber tile | | 150 | .053 | | 2.31 | 1.55 | | 3.86 | 5.15 |

## 09 51 53 – Direct-Applied Acoustical Ceilings

### 09 51 53.10 Ceiling Tile

| | | Crew | Daily Output | Labor-Hours | Unit | Material | 2010 Bare Costs Labor | Equipment | Total | Total Incl O&P |
|---|---|---|---|---|---|---|---|---|---|---|
| 0010 | **CEILING TILE**, Stapled or cemented | | | | | | | | | |
| 0100 | 12" x 12" or 12" x 24", not including furring | | | | | | | | | |
| 0600 | Mineral fiber, vinyl coated, 5/8" thick | 1 Carp | 300 | .027 | S.F. | 1.79 | .78 | | 2.57 | 3.28 |
| 0700 | 3/4" thick | | 300 | .027 | | 1.91 | .78 | | 2.69 | 3.41 |
| 0900 | Fire rated, 3/4" thick, plain faced | | 300 | .027 | | 1.40 | .78 | | 2.18 | 2.85 |
| 1000 | Plastic coated face | | 300 | .027 | | 1.18 | .78 | | 1.96 | 2.61 |
| 1200 | Aluminum faced, 5/8" thick, plain | | 300 | .027 | | 1.51 | .78 | | 2.29 | 2.97 |
| 3300 | For flameproofing, add | | | | | .10 | | | .10 | .11 |
| 3400 | For sculptured 3 dimensional, add | | | | | .29 | | | .29 | .32 |
| 3900 | For ceiling primer, add | | | | | .13 | | | .13 | .14 |
| 4000 | For ceiling cement, add | | | | | .37 | | | .37 | .41 |

# 09 53 Acoustical Ceiling Suspension Assemblies

## 09 53 23 – Metal Acoustical Ceiling Suspension Assemblies

### 09 53 23.30 Ceiling Suspension Systems

| | | Crew | Daily Output | Labor-Hours | Unit | Material | 2010 Bare Costs Labor | Equipment | Total | Total Incl O&P |
|---|---|---|---|---|---|---|---|---|---|---|
| 0010 | **CEILING SUSPENSION SYSTEMS** for boards and tile | | | | | | | | | |
| 0050 | Class A suspension system, 15/16" T bar, 2' x 4' grid | 1 Carp | 800 | .010 | S.F. | .68 | .29 | | .97 | 1.24 |
| 0300 | 2' x 2' grid | " | 650 | .012 | | .85 | .36 | | 1.21 | 1.53 |
| 0350 | For 9/16" grid, add | | | | | .16 | | | .16 | .18 |
| 0360 | For fire rated grid, add | | | | | .09 | | | .09 | .10 |
| 0370 | For colored grid, add | | | | | .21 | | | .21 | .23 |
| 0400 | Concealed Z bar suspension system, 12" module | 1 Carp | 520 | .015 | | .69 | .45 | | 1.14 | 1.51 |
| 0600 | 1-1/2" carrier channels, 4' O.C., add | | 470 | .017 | | .11 | .50 | | .61 | .95 |
| 0650 | 1-1/2" x 3-1/2" channels | | 470 | .017 | | .27 | .50 | | .77 | 1.13 |
| 0700 | Carrier channels for ceilings with | | | | | | | | | |
| 0900 | recessed lighting fixtures, add | 1 Carp | 460 | .017 | S.F. | .19 | .51 | | .70 | 1.06 |

# 09 53 Acoustical Ceiling Suspension Assemblies

## 09 53 23 – Metal Acoustical Ceiling Suspension Assemblies

| 09 53 23.30 Ceiling Suspension Systems | Crew | Daily Output | Labor-Hours | Unit | Material | 2010 Bare Costs Labor | 2010 Bare Costs Equipment | Total | Total Incl O&P |
|---|---|---|---|---|---|---|---|---|---|
| 5000     Wire hangers, #12 wire | 1 Carp | 300 | .027 | Ea. | 1.31 | .78 | | 2.09 | 2.75 |

# 09 62 Specialty Flooring

## 09 62 19 – Laminate Flooring

### 09 62 19.10 Floating Floor

| | | | | | | | | | |
|---|---|---|---|---|---|---|---|---|---|
| 0010 **FLOATING FLOOR** | | | | | | | | | |
| 8300    Floating floor, laminate, wood pattern strip, complete | 1 Clab | 133 | .060 | S.F. | 4.25 | 1.29 | | 5.54 | 6.85 |
| 8310      Components, T & G wood composite strips | | | | | 3.66 | | | 3.66 | 4.03 |
| 8320      Film | | | | | .15 | | | .15 | .16 |
| 8330      Foam | | | | | .30 | | | .30 | .33 |
| 8340      Adhesive | | | | | .17 | | | .17 | .18 |
| 8350      Installation kit | | | | | .17 | | | .17 | .19 |
| 8360      Trim, 2" wide x 3' long | | | | L.F. | 2.79 | | | 2.79 | 3.07 |
| 8370      Reducer moulding | | | | " | 5.85 | | | 5.85 | 6.40 |

## 09 62 23 – Bamboo Flooring

### 09 62 23.10 Flooring, Bamboo

| | | | | | | | | | |
|---|---|---|---|---|---|---|---|---|---|
| 0010 **FLOORING, BAMBOO** | | | | | | | | | |
| 8600    Flooring, wood, bamboo strips, unfinished, 5/8" x 4" x 3' | [G] 1 Carp | 255 | .031 | S.F. | 4.44 | .91 | | 5.35 | 6.40 |
| 8610      5/8" x 4" x 4' | [G] | 275 | .029 | | 4.61 | .85 | | 5.46 | 6.45 |
| 8620      5/8" x 4" x 6' | [G] | 295 | .027 | | 5.05 | .79 | | 5.84 | 6.90 |
| 8630      Finished, 5/8" x 4" x 3' | [G] | 255 | .031 | | 4.89 | .91 | | 5.80 | 6.95 |
| 8640      5/8" x 4" x 4' | [G] | 275 | .029 | | 5.10 | .85 | | 5.95 | 7.05 |
| 8650      5/8" x 4" x 6' | [G] | 295 | .027 | | 4.96 | .79 | | 5.75 | 6.80 |
| 8660    Stair treads, unfinished, 1-1/16" x 11-1/2" x 4' | [G] | 18 | .444 | Ea. | 42.50 | 12.95 | | 55.45 | 69 |
| 8670      Finished, 1-1/16" x 11-1/2" x 4' | [G] | 18 | .444 | | 75.50 | 12.95 | | 88.45 | 105 |
| 8680    Stair risers, unfinished, 5/8" x 7-1/2" x 4' | [G] | 18 | .444 | | 15.75 | 12.95 | | 28.70 | 39.50 |
| 8690      Finished, 5/8" x 7-1/2" x 4' | [G] | 18 | .444 | | 30 | 12.95 | | 42.95 | 55 |
| 8700    Stair nosing, unfinished, 6' long | [G] | 16 | .500 | | 35 | 14.55 | | 49.55 | 63 |
| 8710      Finished, 6' long | [G] | 16 | .500 | | 40 | 14.55 | | 54.55 | 68.50 |

# 09 63 Masonry Flooring

## 09 63 13 – Brick Flooring

### 09 63 13.10 Miscellaneous Brick Flooring

| | | | | | | | | | |
|---|---|---|---|---|---|---|---|---|---|
| 0010 **MISCELLANEOUS BRICK FLOORING** | | | | | | | | | |
| 0020    Acid-proof shales, red, 8" x 3-3/4" x 1-1/4" thick | D-7 | .43 | 37.209 | M | 860 | 920 | | 1,780 | 2,425 |
| 0050      2-1/4" thick | D-1 | .40 | 40 | | 1,000 | 1,050 | | 2,050 | 2,850 |
| 0200    Acid-proof clay brick, 8" x 3-3/4" x 2-1/4" thick | [G] " | .40 | 40 | | 895 | 1,050 | | 1,945 | 2,725 |
| 0260    Cast ceramic, pressed, 4" x 8" x 1/2", unglazed | D-7 | 100 | .160 | S.F. | 6.25 | 3.95 | | 10.20 | 13.25 |
| 0270      Glazed | | 100 | .160 | | 8.35 | 3.95 | | 12.30 | 15.50 |
| 0280    Hand molded flooring, 4" x 8" x 3/4", unglazed | | 95 | .168 | | 8.25 | 4.16 | | 12.41 | 15.75 |
| 0290      Glazed | | 95 | .168 | | 10.35 | 4.16 | | 14.51 | 18.05 |
| 0300      8" hexagonal, 3/4" thick, unglazed | | 85 | .188 | | 9.05 | 4.65 | | 13.70 | 17.40 |
| 0310      Glazed | | 85 | .188 | | 16.35 | 4.65 | | 21 | 25.50 |
| 0450      Acid-proof joints, 1/4" wide | D-1 | 65 | .246 | | 1.44 | 6.50 | | 7.94 | 12.30 |
| 0500    Pavers, 8" x 4", 1" to 1-1/4" thick, red | D-7 | 95 | .168 | | 3.64 | 4.16 | | 7.80 | 10.65 |
| 0510      Ironspot | " | 95 | .168 | | 5.15 | 4.16 | | 9.31 | 12.30 |
| 0540      1-3/8" to 1-3/4" thick, red | D-1 | 95 | .168 | | 3.51 | 4.45 | | 7.96 | 11.20 |
| 0560      Ironspot | | 95 | .168 | | 5.10 | 4.45 | | 9.55 | 12.95 |
| 0580      2-1/4" thick, red | | 90 | .178 | | 3.57 | 4.69 | | 8.26 | 11.70 |

# 09 63 Masonry Flooring

## 09 63 13 – Brick Flooring

### 09 63 13.10 Miscellaneous Brick Flooring

| | | Crew | Daily Output | Labor-Hours | Unit | Material | 2010 Bare Costs Labor | Equipment | Total | Total Incl O&P |
|---|---|---|---|---|---|---|---|---|---|---|
| 0590 | Ironspot | D-1 | 90 | .178 | S.F. | 5.55 | 4.69 | | 10.24 | 13.85 |
| 0700 | Paver, adobe brick, 6" x 12", 1/2" joint  G | ↓ | 42 | .381 | | .90 | 10.05 | | 10.95 | 17.55 |
| 0710 | Mexican red, 12" x 12"  G | 1 Tilf | 48 | .167 | | 1.61 | 4.59 | | 6.20 | 9.10 |
| 0720 | Saltillo, 12" x 12"  G | " | 48 | .167 | ↓ | 1.13 | 4.59 | | 5.72 | 8.60 |
| 0800 | For sidewalks and patios with pavers, see Div. 32 14 16.10 | | | | | | | | | |
| 0870 | For epoxy joints, add | D-1 | 600 | .027 | S.F. | 2.72 | .70 | | 3.42 | 4.15 |
| 0880 | For Furan underlayment, add | " | 600 | .027 | | 2.25 | .70 | | 2.95 | 3.64 |
| 0890 | For waxed surface, steam cleaned, add | A-1H | 1000 | .008 | ↓ | .20 | .17 | .06 | .43 | .58 |

## 09 63 40 – Stone Flooring

### 09 63 40.10 Marble

| | | Crew | Daily Output | Labor-Hours | Unit | Material | 2010 Bare Costs Labor | Equipment | Total | Total Incl O&P |
|---|---|---|---|---|---|---|---|---|---|---|
| 0010 | **MARBLE** | | | | | | | | | |
| 0020 | Thin gauge tile, 12" x 6", 3/8", white Carara | D-7 | 60 | .267 | S.F. | 11.15 | 6.60 | | 17.75 | 23 |
| 0100 | Travertine | | 60 | .267 | | 12.20 | 6.60 | | 18.80 | 24 |
| 0200 | 12" x 12" x 3/8", thin set, floors | | 60 | .267 | | 6.05 | 6.60 | | 12.65 | 17.20 |
| 0300 | On walls | | 52 | .308 | ↓ | 9.35 | 7.60 | | 16.95 | 22.50 |
| 1000 | Marble threshold, 4" wide x 36" long x 5/8" thick, white | ↓ | 60 | .267 | Ea. | 6.05 | 6.60 | | 12.65 | 17.20 |

### 09 63 40.20 Slate Tile

| | | Crew | Daily Output | Labor-Hours | Unit | Material | 2010 Bare Costs Labor | Equipment | Total | Total Incl O&P |
|---|---|---|---|---|---|---|---|---|---|---|
| 0010 | **SLATE TILE** | | | | | | | | | |
| 0020 | Vermont, 6" x 6" x 1/4" thick, thin set | D-7 | 180 | .089 | S.F. | 6.80 | 2.20 | | 9 | 10.95 |

# 09 64 Wood Flooring

## 09 64 23 – Wood Parquet Flooring

### 09 64 23.10 Wood Parquet

| | | Crew | Daily Output | Labor-Hours | Unit | Material | 2010 Bare Costs Labor | Equipment | Total | Total Incl O&P |
|---|---|---|---|---|---|---|---|---|---|---|
| 0010 | **WOOD PARQUET** flooring | | | | | | | | | |
| 5200 | Parquetry, standard, 5/16" thick, not incl. finish, oak, minimum | 1 Carp | 160 | .050 | S.F. | 4.41 | 1.46 | | 5.87 | 7.30 |
| 5300 | Maximum | | 100 | .080 | | 4.95 | 2.33 | | 7.28 | 9.35 |
| 5500 | Teak, minimum | | 160 | .050 | | 4.79 | 1.46 | | 6.25 | 7.70 |
| 5600 | Maximum | | 100 | .080 | | 8.35 | 2.33 | | 10.68 | 13.10 |
| 5650 | 13/16" thick, select grade oak, minimum | | 160 | .050 | | 9.20 | 1.46 | | 10.66 | 12.60 |
| 5700 | Maximum | | 100 | .080 | | 14 | 2.33 | | 16.33 | 19.30 |
| 5800 | Custom parquetry, including finish, minimum | | 100 | .080 | | 15.45 | 2.33 | | 17.78 | 21 |
| 5900 | Maximum | | 50 | .160 | | 20.50 | 4.66 | | 25.16 | 30.50 |
| 6700 | Parquetry, prefinished white oak, 5/16" thick, minimum | | 160 | .050 | | 3.06 | 1.46 | | 4.52 | 5.80 |
| 6800 | Maximum | | 100 | .080 | | 6.55 | 2.33 | | 8.88 | 11.10 |
| 7000 | Walnut or teak, parquetry, minimum | | 160 | .050 | | 5.35 | 1.46 | | 6.81 | 8.35 |
| 7100 | Maximum | ↓ | 100 | .080 | ↓ | 9.35 | 2.33 | | 11.68 | 14.20 |
| 7200 | Acrylic wood parquet blocks, 12" x 12" x 5/16", | | | | | | | | | |
| 7210 | Irradiated, set in epoxy | 1 Carp | 160 | .050 | S.F. | 7.80 | 1.46 | | 9.26 | 11.05 |

## 09 64 29 – Wood Strip and Plank Flooring

### 09 64 29.10 Wood

| | | Crew | Daily Output | Labor-Hours | Unit | Material | 2010 Bare Costs Labor | Equipment | Total | Total Incl O&P |
|---|---|---|---|---|---|---|---|---|---|---|
| 0010 | **WOOD** | | | | | | | | | |
| 0020 | Fir, vertical grain, 1" x 4", not incl. finish, grade B & better | 1 Carp | 255 | .031 | S.F. | 2.74 | .91 | | 3.65 | 4.55 |
| 0100 | C grade & better | | 255 | .031 | | 2.58 | .91 | | 3.49 | 4.38 |
| 0300 | Flat grain, 1" x 4", not incl. finish, B & better | | 255 | .031 | | 3.13 | .91 | | 4.04 | 4.98 |
| 0400 | C & better | | 255 | .031 | | 3.01 | .91 | | 3.92 | 4.85 |
| 4000 | Maple, strip, 25/32" x 2-1/4", not incl. finish, select | | 170 | .047 | | 5.25 | 1.37 | | 6.62 | 8.10 |
| 4100 | #2 & better | | 170 | .047 | | 3.32 | 1.37 | | 4.69 | 5.95 |
| 4300 | 33/32" x 3-1/4", not incl. finish, #1 grade | | 170 | .047 | | 4.19 | 1.37 | | 5.56 | 6.90 |
| 4400 | #2 & better | ↓ | 170 | .047 | ↓ | 3.73 | 1.37 | | 5.10 | 6.40 |
| 4600 | Oak, white or red, 25/32" x 2-1/4", not incl. finish | | | | | | | | | |

# 09 64 Wood Flooring

## 09 64 29 - Wood Strip and Plank Flooring

| 09 64 29.10 Wood | | Crew | Daily Output | Labor-Hours | Unit | Material | 2010 Bare Costs Labor | Equipment | Total | Total Incl O&P |
|---|---|---|---|---|---|---|---|---|---|---|
| 4700 | #1 common | 1 Carp | 170 | .047 | S.F. | 2.40 | 1.37 | | 3.77 | 4.94 |
| 4900 | Select quartered, 2-1/4" wide | | 170 | .047 | | 2.94 | 1.37 | | 4.31 | 5.55 |
| 5000 | Clear | | 170 | .047 | | 3.83 | 1.37 | | 5.20 | 6.50 |
| 6100 | Prefinished, white oak, prime grade, 2-1/4" wide | | 170 | .047 | | 4.79 | 1.37 | | 6.16 | 7.55 |
| 6200 | 3-1/4" wide | | 185 | .043 | | 6.15 | 1.26 | | 7.41 | 8.85 |
| 6400 | Ranch plank | | 145 | .055 | | 6.75 | 1.61 | | 8.36 | 10.10 |
| 6500 | Hardwood blocks, 9" x 9", 25/32" thick | | 160 | .050 | | 5.75 | 1.46 | | 7.21 | 8.80 |
| 7400 | Yellow pine, 3/4" x 3-1/8", T & G, C & better, not incl. finish | ↓ | 200 | .040 | | 1.99 | 1.16 | | 3.15 | 4.15 |
| 7500 | Refinish wood floor, sand, 2 cts poly, wax, soft wood, min. | 1 Clab | 400 | .020 | | .78 | .43 | | 1.21 | 1.58 |
| 7600 | Hard wood, max | | 130 | .062 | | 1.16 | 1.32 | | 2.48 | 3.50 |
| 7800 | Sanding and finishing, 2 coats polyurethane | ↓ | 295 | .027 | ↓ | .78 | .58 | | 1.36 | 1.84 |
| 7900 | Subfloor and underlayment, see Div. 06 16 | | | | | | | | | |
| 8015 | Transition molding, 2 1/4" wide, 5' long | 1 Carp | 19.20 | .417 | Ea. | 15 | 12.15 | | 27.15 | 37 |

# 09 65 Resilient Flooring

## 09 65 10 - Resilient Tile Underlayment

### 09 65 10.10 Latex Underlayment

| | | Crew | Daily Output | Labor-Hours | Unit | Material | Labor | Equipment | Total | Total Incl O&P |
|---|---|---|---|---|---|---|---|---|---|---|
| 0010 | **LATEX UNDERLAYMENT** | | | | | | | | | |
| 3600 | Latex underlayment, 1/8" thk., cementitious for resilient flooring | 1 Tilf | 160 | .050 | S.F. | .79 | 1.38 | | 2.17 | 3.08 |
| 4000 | Liquid, fortified | | | | Gal. | 38.50 | | | 38.50 | 42 |

## 09 65 13 - Resilient Base and Accessories

### 09 65 13.13 Resilient Base

| | | Crew | Daily Output | Labor-Hours | Unit | Material | Labor | Equipment | Total | Total Incl O&P |
|---|---|---|---|---|---|---|---|---|---|---|
| 0010 | **RESILIENT BASE** | | | | | | | | | |
| 0800 | Base, cove, rubber or vinyl | | | | | | | | | |
| 1100 | Standard colors, 0.080" thick, 2-1/2" high | 1 Tilf | 315 | .025 | L.F. | .80 | .70 | | 1.50 | 2 |
| 1150 | 4" high | | 315 | .025 | | .94 | .70 | | 1.64 | 2.15 |
| 1200 | 6" high | | 315 | .025 | | 1.30 | .70 | | 2 | 2.55 |
| 1450 | 1/8" thick, 2-1/2" high | | 315 | .025 | | .80 | .70 | | 1.50 | 2 |
| 1500 | 4" high | | 315 | .025 | | .73 | .70 | | 1.43 | 1.92 |
| 1550 | 6" high | | 315 | .025 | ↓ | 1.35 | .70 | | 2.05 | 2.61 |
| 1600 | Corners, 2-1/2" high | | 315 | .025 | Ea. | 1.50 | .70 | | 2.20 | 2.77 |
| 1630 | 4" high | | 315 | .025 | | 2.85 | .70 | | 3.55 | 4.26 |
| 1660 | 6" high | ↓ | 315 | .025 | ↓ | 2.95 | .70 | | 3.65 | 4.37 |

## 09 65 16 - Resilient Sheet Flooring

### 09 65 16.10 Rubber and Vinyl Sheet Flooring

| | | | Crew | Daily Output | Labor-Hours | Unit | Material | Labor | Equipment | Total | Total Incl O&P |
|---|---|---|---|---|---|---|---|---|---|---|---|
| 0010 | **RUBBER AND VINYL SHEET FLOORING** | | | | | | | | | | |
| 5500 | Linoleum, sheet goods | G | 1 Tilf | 360 | .022 | S.F. | 4.55 | .61 | | 5.16 | 6 |
| 5900 | Rubber, sheet goods, 36" wide, 1/8" thick | | | 120 | .067 | | 6.45 | 1.84 | | 8.29 | 10.05 |
| 5950 | 3/16" thick | | | 100 | .080 | | 8.75 | 2.20 | | 10.95 | 13.20 |
| 6000 | 1/4" thick | | | 90 | .089 | | 10.30 | 2.45 | | 12.75 | 15.25 |
| 8000 | Vinyl sheet goods, backed, .065" thick, minimum | | | 250 | .032 | | 3.50 | .88 | | 4.38 | 5.25 |
| 8050 | Maximum | | | 200 | .040 | | 3.61 | 1.10 | | 4.71 | 5.75 |
| 8100 | .080" thick, minimum | | | 230 | .035 | | 3.60 | .96 | | 4.56 | 5.50 |
| 8150 | Maximum | | | 200 | .040 | | 5.10 | 1.10 | | 6.20 | 7.35 |
| 8200 | .125" thick, minimum | | | 230 | .035 | | 4.10 | .96 | | 5.06 | 6.05 |
| 8250 | Maximum | | | 200 | .040 | ↓ | 6.10 | 1.10 | | 7.20 | 8.45 |
| 8700 | Adhesive cement, 1 gallon per 200 to 300 S.F. | | | | | Gal. | 25 | | | 25 | 27.50 |
| 8800 | Asphalt primer, 1 gallon per 300 S.F. | | | | | | 12 | | | 12 | 13.20 |
| 8900 | Emulsion, 1 gallon per 140 S.F. | | | | | ↓ | 15.50 | | | 15.50 | 17.05 |

470

# 09 65 Resilient Flooring

## 09 65 19 – Resilient Tile Flooring

| 09 65 19.10 Miscellaneous Resilient Tile Flooring | | Crew | Daily Output | Labor-Hours | Unit | Material | 2010 Bare Costs Labor | Equipment | Total | Total Incl O&P |
|---|---|---|---|---|---|---|---|---|---|---|
| 0010 | **MISCELLANEOUS RESILIENT TILE FLOORING** | | | | | | | | | |
| 2200 | Cork tile, standard finish, 1/8" thick [G] | 1 Tilf | 315 | .025 | S.F. | 6 | .70 | | 6.70 | 7.70 |
| 2250 | 3/16" thick [G] | | 315 | .025 | | 6 | .70 | | 6.70 | 7.70 |
| 2300 | 5/16" thick [G] | | 315 | .025 | | 7.45 | .70 | | 8.15 | 9.30 |
| 2350 | 1/2" thick [G] | | 315 | .025 | | 8.80 | .70 | | 9.50 | 10.75 |
| 2500 | Urethane finish, 1/8" thick [G] | | 315 | .025 | | 7.10 | .70 | | 7.80 | 8.95 |
| 2550 | 3/16" thick [G] | | 315 | .025 | | 7.45 | .70 | | 8.15 | 9.30 |
| 2600 | 5/16" thick [G] | | 315 | .025 | | 9.55 | .70 | | 10.25 | 11.60 |
| 2650 | 1/2" thick [G] | | 315 | .025 | | 12.85 | .70 | | 13.55 | 15.25 |
| 6050 | Rubber tile, marbleized colors, 12" x 12", 1/8" thick | | 400 | .020 | | 6.45 | .55 | | 7 | 7.95 |
| 6100 | 3/16" thick | | 400 | .020 | | 9.50 | .55 | | 10.05 | 11.35 |
| 6300 | Special tile, plain colors, 1/8" thick | | 400 | .020 | | 9.50 | .55 | | 10.05 | 11.35 |
| 6350 | 3/16" thick | | 400 | .020 | | 9.65 | .55 | | 10.20 | 11.50 |
| 7000 | Vinyl composition tile, 12" x 12", 1/16" thick | | 500 | .016 | | .92 | .44 | | 1.36 | 1.72 |
| 7050 | Embossed | | 500 | .016 | | 2.17 | .44 | | 2.61 | 3.10 |
| 7100 | Marbleized | | 500 | .016 | | 2.17 | .44 | | 2.61 | 3.10 |
| 7150 | Solid | | 500 | .016 | | 2.79 | .44 | | 3.23 | 3.78 |
| 7200 | 3/32" thick, embossed | | 500 | .016 | | 1.38 | .44 | | 1.82 | 2.23 |
| 7250 | Marbleized | | 500 | .016 | | 2.49 | .44 | | 2.93 | 3.45 |
| 7300 | Solid | | 500 | .016 | | 2.31 | .44 | | 2.75 | 3.25 |
| 7350 | 1/8" thick, marbleized | | 500 | .016 | | 1.64 | .44 | | 2.08 | 2.51 |
| 7400 | Solid | | 500 | .016 | | 1.80 | .44 | | 2.24 | 2.69 |
| 7450 | Conductive | | 500 | .016 | | 5.45 | .44 | | 5.89 | 6.65 |
| 7500 | Vinyl tile, 12" x 12", .050" thick, minimum | | 500 | .016 | | 3 | .44 | | 3.44 | 4.01 |
| 7550 | Maximum | | 500 | .016 | | 6 | .44 | | 6.44 | 7.30 |
| 7600 | 1/8" thick, minimum | | 500 | .016 | | 4.35 | .44 | | 4.79 | 5.50 |
| 7650 | Solid colors | | 500 | .016 | | 4.95 | .44 | | 5.39 | 6.15 |
| 7700 | Marbleized or Travertine pattern | | 500 | .016 | | 5.65 | .44 | | 6.09 | 6.90 |
| 7750 | Florentine pattern | | 500 | .016 | | 6 | .44 | | 6.44 | 7.30 |
| 7800 | Maximum | | 500 | .016 | | 12.70 | .44 | | 13.14 | 14.65 |

## 09 65 33 – Conductive Resilient Flooring

### 09 65 33.10 Conductive Rubber and Vinyl Flooring

| | | Crew | Daily Output | Labor-Hours | Unit | Material | Labor | Equipment | Total | Total Incl O&P |
|---|---|---|---|---|---|---|---|---|---|---|
| 0010 | **CONDUCTIVE RUBBER AND VINYL FLOORING** | | | | | | | | | |
| 1700 | Conductive flooring, rubber tile, 1/8" thick | 1 Tilf | 315 | .025 | S.F. | 5.10 | .70 | | 5.80 | 6.70 |
| 1800 | Homogeneous vinyl tile, 1/8" thick | " | 315 | .025 | " | 7.15 | .70 | | 7.85 | 8.95 |

# 09 66 Terrazzo Flooring

## 09 66 13 – Portland Cement Terrazzo Flooring

### 09 66 13.10 Portland Cement Terrazzo

| | | Crew | Daily Output | Labor-Hours | Unit | Material | Labor | Equipment | Total | Total Incl O&P |
|---|---|---|---|---|---|---|---|---|---|---|
| 0010 | **PORTLAND CEMENT TERRAZZO**, cast-in-place | | | | | | | | | |
| 4300 | Stone chips, onyx gemstone, per 50 lb. bag | | | | Bag | 16.30 | | | 16.30 | 17.95 |

### 09 66 13.30 Terrazzo, Precast

| | | Crew | Daily Output | Labor-Hours | Unit | Material | Labor | Equipment | Total | Total Incl O&P |
|---|---|---|---|---|---|---|---|---|---|---|
| 0010 | **TERRAZZO, PRECAST** | | | | | | | | | |
| 0020 | Base, 6" high, straight | 1 Mstz | 70 | .114 | L.F. | 10.40 | 3.12 | | 13.52 | 16.45 |
| 0100 | Cove | | 60 | .133 | | 12.15 | 3.64 | | 15.79 | 19.20 |
| 0300 | 8" high, straight | | 60 | .133 | | 10.85 | 3.64 | | 14.49 | 17.75 |
| 0400 | Cove | | 50 | .160 | | 15.95 | 4.37 | | 20.32 | 24.50 |
| 0600 | For white cement, add | | | | | .43 | | | .43 | .47 |
| 0700 | For 16 ga. zinc toe strip, add | | | | | 1.63 | | | 1.63 | 1.79 |
| 0900 | Curbs, 4" x 4" high | 1 Mstz | 40 | .200 | | 30.50 | 5.45 | | 35.95 | 42.50 |

# 09 66 Terrazzo Flooring

## 09 66 13 – Portland Cement Terrazzo Flooring

### 09 66 13.30 Terrazzo, Precast

| | | Crew | Daily Output | Labor-Hours | Unit | Material | 2010 Bare Costs Labor | Equipment | Total | Total Incl O&P |
|---|---|---|---|---|---|---|---|---|---|---|
| 1000 | 8" x 8" high | 1 Mstz | 30 | .267 | L.F. | 35.50 | 7.30 | | 42.80 | 50.50 |
| 1200 | Floor tiles, non-slip, 1" thick, 12" x 12" | D-1 | 60 | .267 | S.F. | 18.30 | 7.05 | | 25.35 | 31.50 |
| 1300 | 1-1/4" thick, 12" x 12" | | 60 | .267 | | 19.60 | 7.05 | | 26.65 | 33 |
| 1500 | 16" x 16" | | 50 | .320 | | 21.50 | 8.45 | | 29.95 | 37.50 |
| 1600 | 1-1/2" thick, 16" x 16" | | 45 | .356 | | 19.45 | 9.40 | | 28.85 | 37 |
| 4800 | Wainscot, 12" x 12" x 1" tiles | 1 Mstz | 12 | .667 | | 6.50 | 18.20 | | 24.70 | 36 |
| 4900 | 16" x 16" x 1-1/2" tiles | " | 8 | 1 | | 13.70 | 27.50 | | 41.20 | 58.50 |

# 09 68 Carpeting

## 09 68 05 – Carpet Accessories

### 09 68 05.11 Flooring Transition Strip

| | | Crew | Daily Output | Labor-Hours | Unit | Material | 2010 Bare Costs Labor | Equipment | Total | Total Incl O&P |
|---|---|---|---|---|---|---|---|---|---|---|
| 0010 | **FLOORING TRANSITION STRIP** | | | | | | | | | |
| 0107 | Clamp down brass divider, 12' strip, vinyl to carpet | 1 Tilf | 31.25 | .256 | Ea. | 20.50 | 7.05 | | 27.55 | 34 |
| 0117 | Vinyl to hard surface | " | 31.25 | .256 | " | 20.50 | 7.05 | | 27.55 | 34 |

## 09 68 10 – Carpet Pad

### 09 68 10.10 Commercial Grade Carpet Pad

| | | Crew | Daily Output | Labor-Hours | Unit | Material | 2010 Bare Costs Labor | Equipment | Total | Total Incl O&P |
|---|---|---|---|---|---|---|---|---|---|---|
| 0010 | **COMMERCIAL GRADE CARPET PAD** | | | | | | | | | |
| 9001 | Sponge rubber pad, minimum | 1 Tilf | 1350 | .006 | S.F. | .44 | .16 | | .60 | .75 |
| 9101 | Maximum | | 1350 | .006 | | 1.11 | .16 | | 1.27 | 1.48 |
| 9201 | Felt pad, minimum | | 1350 | .006 | | .46 | .16 | | .62 | .77 |
| 9301 | Maximum | | 1350 | .006 | | .78 | .16 | | .94 | 1.12 |
| 9401 | Bonded urethane pad, minimum | | 1350 | .006 | | .51 | .16 | | .67 | .82 |
| 9501 | Maximum | | 1350 | .006 | | .87 | .16 | | 1.03 | 1.21 |
| 9601 | Prime urethane pad, minimum | | 1350 | .006 | | .29 | .16 | | .45 | .58 |
| 9701 | Maximum | | 1350 | .006 | | .54 | .16 | | .70 | .85 |

## 09 68 13 – Tile Carpeting

### 09 68 13.10 Carpet Tile

| | | Crew | Daily Output | Labor-Hours | Unit | Material | 2010 Bare Costs Labor | Equipment | Total | Total Incl O&P |
|---|---|---|---|---|---|---|---|---|---|---|
| 0010 | **CARPET TILE** | | | | | | | | | |
| 0100 | Tufted nylon, 18" x 18", hard back, 20 oz. | 1 Tilf | 150 | .053 | S.Y. | 22 | 1.47 | | 23.47 | 27 |
| 0110 | 26 oz. | | 150 | .053 | | 38 | 1.47 | | 39.47 | 44 |
| 0200 | Cushion back, 20 oz. | | 150 | .053 | | 28 | 1.47 | | 29.47 | 33 |
| 0210 | 26 oz. | | 150 | .053 | | 43.50 | 1.47 | | 44.97 | 50.50 |

## 09 68 16 – Sheet Carpeting

### 09 68 16.10 Sheet Carpet

| | | Crew | Daily Output | Labor-Hours | Unit | Material | 2010 Bare Costs Labor | Equipment | Total | Total Incl O&P |
|---|---|---|---|---|---|---|---|---|---|---|
| 0010 | **SHEET CARPET** | | | | | | | | | |
| 0701 | Nylon, level loop, 26 oz., light to medium traffic | 1 Tilf | 445 | .018 | S.F. | 2.97 | .50 | | 3.47 | 4.06 |
| 0901 | 32 oz., medium traffic | | 445 | .018 | | 3.69 | .50 | | 4.19 | 4.85 |
| 1101 | 40 oz., medium to heavy traffic | | 445 | .018 | | 5.50 | .50 | | 6 | 6.85 |
| 2101 | Nylon, plush, 20 oz., light traffic | | 445 | .018 | | 1.92 | .50 | | 2.42 | 2.90 |
| 2801 | 24 oz., light to medium traffic | | 445 | .018 | | 1.92 | .50 | | 2.42 | 2.90 |
| 2901 | 30 oz., medium traffic | | 445 | .018 | | 2.83 | .50 | | 3.33 | 3.91 |
| 3001 | 36 oz., medium traffic | | 445 | .018 | | 3.77 | .50 | | 4.27 | 4.93 |
| 3101 | 42 oz., medium to heavy traffic | | 370 | .022 | | 4.22 | .60 | | 4.82 | 5.60 |
| 3201 | 46 oz., medium to heavy traffic | | 370 | .022 | | 4.94 | .60 | | 5.54 | 6.40 |
| 3301 | 54 oz., heavy traffic | | 370 | .022 | | 5.40 | .60 | | 6 | 6.90 |
| 3501 | Olefin, 15 oz., light traffic | | 445 | .018 | | 1 | .50 | | 1.50 | 1.89 |
| 3651 | 22 oz., light traffic | | 445 | .018 | | 1.21 | .50 | | 1.71 | 2.12 |
| 4501 | 50 oz., medium to heavy traffic, level loop | | 445 | .018 | | 12.90 | .50 | | 13.40 | 15 |
| 4701 | 32 oz., medium to heavy traffic, patterned | | 400 | .020 | | 12.80 | .55 | | 13.35 | 14.95 |

# 09 68 Carpeting

## 09 68 16 – Sheet Carpeting

### 09 68 16.10 Sheet Carpet

| | | Crew | Daily Output | Labor-Hours | Unit | Material | 2010 Bare Costs Labor | 2010 Bare Costs Equipment | Total | Total Incl O&P |
|---|---|---|---|---|---|---|---|---|---|---|
| 4901 | 48 oz., heavy traffic, patterned | 1 Tilf | 400 | .020 | S.F. | 13.10 | .55 | | 13.65 | 15.30 |
| 5000 | For less than full roll (approx. 1500 S.F.), add | | | | | 25% | | | | |
| 5100 | For small rooms, less than 12' wide, add | | | | | | 25% | | | |
| 5200 | For large open areas (no cuts), deduct | | | | | | 25% | | | |
| 5600 | For bound carpet baseboard, add | 1 Tilf | 300 | .027 | L.F. | 2.40 | .73 | | 3.13 | 3.82 |
| 5610 | For stairs, not incl. price of carpet, add | " | 30 | .267 | Riser | | 7.35 | | 7.35 | 11.75 |
| 8950 | For tackless, stretched installation, add padding to above | | | | | | | | | |
| 9850 | For brand-named specific fiber, add | | | | S.Y. | 25% | | | | |

## 09 68 20 – Athletic Carpet

### 09 68 20.10 Indoor Athletic Carpet

| | | Crew | Daily Output | Labor-Hours | Unit | Material | 2010 Bare Costs Labor | 2010 Bare Costs Equipment | Total | Total Incl O&P |
|---|---|---|---|---|---|---|---|---|---|---|
| 0010 | **INDOOR ATHLETIC CARPET** | | | | | | | | | |
| 3700 | Polyethylene, in rolls, no base incl., landscape surfaces | 1 Tilf | 275 | .029 | S.F. | 3.20 | .80 | | 4 | 4.80 |
| 3800 | Nylon action surface, 1/8" thick | | 275 | .029 | | 3.36 | .80 | | 4.16 | 4.98 |
| 3900 | 1/4" thick | | 275 | .029 | | 4.84 | .80 | | 5.64 | 6.60 |
| 4000 | 3/8" thick | | 275 | .029 | | 6.10 | .80 | | 6.90 | 8 |

# 09 72 Wall Coverings

## 09 72 23 – Wallpapering

### 09 72 23.10 Wallpaper

| | | Crew | Daily Output | Labor-Hours | Unit | Material | 2010 Bare Costs Labor | 2010 Bare Costs Equipment | Total | Total Incl O&P |
|---|---|---|---|---|---|---|---|---|---|---|
| 0010 | **WALLPAPER** including sizing; add 10-30 percent waste @ takeoff R097223-10 | | | | | | | | | |
| 0050 | Aluminum foil | 1 Pape | 275 | .029 | S.F. | 1.02 | .75 | | 1.77 | 2.35 |
| 0100 | Copper sheets, .025" thick, vinyl backing | | 240 | .033 | | 5.45 | .86 | | 6.31 | 7.40 |
| 0300 | Phenolic backing | | 240 | .033 | | 7.05 | .86 | | 7.91 | 9.20 |
| 0600 | Cork tiles, light or dark, 12" x 12" x 3/16" | | 240 | .033 | | 4.47 | .86 | | 5.33 | 6.35 |
| 0700 | 5/16" thick | | 235 | .034 | | 3.80 | .88 | | 4.68 | 5.60 |
| 0900 | 1/4" basketweave | | 240 | .033 | | 5.85 | .86 | | 6.71 | 7.85 |
| 1000 | 1/2" natural, non-directional pattern | | 240 | .033 | | 7.85 | .86 | | 8.71 | 10.05 |
| 1100 | 3/4" natural, non-directional pattern | | 240 | .033 | | 10.80 | .86 | | 11.66 | 13.25 |
| 1200 | Granular surface, 12" x 36", 1/2" thick | | 385 | .021 | | 1.26 | .54 | | 1.80 | 2.27 |
| 1300 | 1" thick | | 370 | .022 | | 1.63 | .56 | | 2.19 | 2.70 |
| 1500 | Polyurethane coated, 12" x 12" x 3/16" thick | | 240 | .033 | | 3.95 | .86 | | 4.81 | 5.75 |
| 1600 | 5/16" thick | | 235 | .034 | | 5.65 | .88 | | 6.53 | 7.65 |
| 1800 | Cork wallpaper, paperbacked, natural | | 480 | .017 | | 1.99 | .43 | | 2.42 | 2.89 |
| 1900 | Colors | | 480 | .017 | | 2.78 | .43 | | 3.21 | 3.76 |
| 2100 | Flexible wood veneer, 1/32" thick, plain woods | | 100 | .080 | | 2.36 | 2.08 | | 4.44 | 6 |
| 2200 | Exotic woods | | 95 | .084 | | 3.58 | 2.19 | | 5.77 | 7.50 |
| 2400 | Gypsum-based, fabric-backed, fire resistant | | | | | | | | | |
| 2500 | for masonry walls, minimum, 21 oz./S.Y. | 1 Pape | 800 | .010 | S.F. | .82 | .26 | | 1.08 | 1.32 |
| 2600 | Average | | 720 | .011 | | 1.23 | .29 | | 1.52 | 1.82 |
| 2700 | Maximum (small quantities) | | 640 | .013 | | 1.37 | .32 | | 1.69 | 2.04 |
| 2750 | Acrylic, modified, semi-rigid PVC, .028" thick | 2 Carp | 330 | .048 | | 1.13 | 1.41 | | 2.54 | 3.61 |
| 2800 | .040" thick | " | 320 | .050 | | 1.49 | 1.46 | | 2.95 | 4.09 |
| 3000 | Vinyl wall covering, fabric-backed, lightweight, type 1 (12-15 oz./S.Y.) | 1 Pape | 640 | .013 | | .69 | .32 | | 1.01 | 1.29 |
| 3300 | Medium weight, type 2 (20-24 oz./S.Y.) | | 480 | .017 | | .82 | .43 | | 1.25 | 1.60 |
| 3400 | Heavy weight, type 3 (28 oz./S.Y.) | | 435 | .018 | | 1.64 | .48 | | 2.12 | 2.58 |
| 3600 | Adhesive, 5 gal. lots (18SY/Gal.) | | | | Gal. | 10.50 | | | 10.50 | 11.55 |
| 3700 | Wallpaper, average workmanship, solid pattern, low cost paper | 1 Pape | 640 | .013 | S.F. | .37 | .32 | | .69 | .94 |
| 3900 | basic patterns (matching required), avg. cost paper | | 535 | .015 | | .71 | .39 | | 1.10 | 1.41 |
| 4000 | Paper at $85 per double roll, quality workmanship | | 435 | .018 | | 2.47 | .48 | | 2.95 | 3.50 |
| 4100 | Linen wall covering, paper backed | | | | | | | | | |

# 09 72 Wall Coverings

## 09 72 23 – Wallpapering

| 09 72 23.10 Wallpaper | Crew | Daily Output | Labor-Hours | Unit | Material | 2010 Bare Costs Labor | Equipment | Total | Total Incl O&P |
|---|---|---|---|---|---|---|---|---|---|
| 4150 | Flame treatment, minimum | | | | S.F. | 1.05 | | | 1.05 | 1.16 |
| 4180 | Maximum | | | | | 1.55 | | | 1.55 | 1.71 |
| 4200 | Grass cloths with lining paper, minimum | 1 Pape | 400 | .020 | | .78 | .52 | | 1.30 | 1.71 |
| 4300 | Maximum | " | 350 | .023 | | 2.49 | .59 | | 3.08 | 3.71 |

# 09 91 Painting

## 09 91 03 – Paint Restoration

### 09 91 03.20 Sanding

| | | Crew | Daily Output | Labor-Hours | Unit | Material | 2010 Bare Costs Labor | Equipment | Total | Total Incl O&P |
|---|---|---|---|---|---|---|---|---|---|---|
| 0010 | **SANDING** and puttying interior trim, compared to | | | | | | | | | |
| 0100 | Painting 1 coat, on quality work | | | | L.F. | 100% | | | | |
| 0300 | Medium work | | | | | 50% | | | | |
| 0400 | Industrial grade | | | | | 25% | | | | |
| 0500 | Surface protection, placement and removal | | | | | | | | | |
| 0510 | Basic drop cloths | 1 Pord | 6400 | .001 | S.F. | | .03 | | .03 | .05 |
| 0520 | Masking with paper | | 800 | .010 | | .06 | .26 | | .32 | .49 |
| 0530 | Volume cover up (using plastic sheathing, or building paper) | | 16000 | .001 | | | .01 | | .01 | .02 |

### 09 91 03.30 Exterior Surface Preparation

| | | Crew | Daily Output | Labor-Hours | Unit | Material | 2010 Bare Costs Labor | Equipment | Total | Total Incl O&P |
|---|---|---|---|---|---|---|---|---|---|---|
| 0010 | **EXTERIOR SURFACE PREPARATION** | | | | | | | | | |
| 0015 | Doors, per side, not incl. frames or trim | | | | | | | | | |
| 0020 | Scrape & sand | | | | | | | | | |
| 0030 | Wood, flush | 1 Pord | 616 | .013 | S.F. | | .34 | | .34 | .55 |
| 0040 | Wood, detail | | 496 | .016 | | | .42 | | .42 | .68 |
| 0050 | Wood, louvered | | 280 | .029 | | | .74 | | .74 | 1.20 |
| 0060 | Wood, overhead | | 616 | .013 | | | .34 | | .34 | .55 |
| 0070 | Wire brush | | | | | | | | | |
| 0080 | Metal, flush | 1 Pord | 640 | .013 | S.F. | | .32 | | .32 | .53 |
| 0090 | Metal, detail | | 520 | .015 | | | .40 | | .40 | .65 |
| 0100 | Metal, louvered | | 360 | .022 | | | .57 | | .57 | .93 |
| 0110 | Metal or fibr., overhead | | 640 | .013 | | | .32 | | .32 | .53 |
| 0120 | Metal, roll up | | 560 | .014 | | | .37 | | .37 | .60 |
| 0130 | Metal, bulkhead | | 640 | .013 | | | .32 | | .32 | .53 |
| 0140 | Power wash, based on 2500 lb. operating pressure | | | | | | | | | |
| 0150 | Metal, flush | A-1H | 2240 | .004 | S.F. | | .08 | .03 | .11 | .16 |
| 0160 | Metal, detail | | 2120 | .004 | | | .08 | .03 | .11 | .17 |
| 0170 | Metal, louvered | | 2000 | .004 | | | .09 | .03 | .12 | .17 |
| 0180 | Metal or fibr., overhead | | 2400 | .003 | | | .07 | .03 | .10 | .15 |
| 0190 | Metal, roll up | | 2400 | .003 | | | .07 | .03 | .10 | .15 |
| 0200 | Metal, bulkhead | | 2200 | .004 | | | .08 | .03 | .11 | .16 |
| 0400 | Windows, per side, not incl. trim | | | | | | | | | |
| 0410 | Scrape & sand | | | | | | | | | |
| 0420 | Wood, 1-2 lite | 1 Pord | 320 | .025 | S.F. | | .65 | | .65 | 1.05 |
| 0430 | Wood, 3-6 lite | | 280 | .029 | | | .74 | | .74 | 1.20 |
| 0440 | Wood, 7-10 lite | | 240 | .033 | | | .86 | | .86 | 1.40 |
| 0450 | Wood, 12 lite | | 200 | .040 | | | 1.03 | | 1.03 | 1.68 |
| 0460 | Wood, Bay/Bow | | 320 | .025 | | | .65 | | .65 | 1.05 |
| 0470 | Wire brush | | | | | | | | | |
| 0480 | Metal, 1-2 lite | 1 Pord | 480 | .017 | S.F. | | .43 | | .43 | .70 |
| 0490 | Metal, 3-6 lite | | 400 | .020 | | | .52 | | .52 | .84 |
| 0500 | Metal, Bay/Bow | | 480 | .017 | | | .43 | | .43 | .70 |
| 0510 | Power wash, based on 2500 lb. operating pressure | | | | | | | | | |
| 0520 | 1-2 lite | A-1H | 4400 | .002 | S.F. | | .04 | .01 | .05 | .09 |

# 09 91 Painting

## 09 91 03 – Paint Restoration

### 09 91 03.30 Exterior Surface Preparation

| | Crew | Daily Output | Labor-Hours | Unit | Material | 2010 Bare Costs Labor | Equipment | Total | Total Incl O&P |
|---|---|---|---|---|---|---|---|---|---|
| 0530 | 3-6 lite | A-1H | 4320 | .002 | S.F. | | .04 | .01 | .05 | .09 |
| 0540 | 7-10 lite | | 4240 | .002 | | | .04 | .01 | .05 | .09 |
| 0550 | 12 lite | | 4160 | .002 | | | .04 | .01 | .05 | .09 |
| 0560 | Bay/Bow | ↓ | 4400 | .002 | ↓ | | .04 | .01 | .05 | .09 |
| 0600 | Siding, scrape and sand, light=10-30%, med.=30-70% | | | | | | | | | |
| 0610 | Heavy=70-100% of surface to sand | | | | | | | | | |
| 0650 | Texture 1-11, light | 1 Pord | 480 | .017 | S.F. | | .43 | | .43 | .70 |
| 0660 | Med. | | 440 | .018 | | | .47 | | .47 | .76 |
| 0670 | Heavy | | 360 | .022 | | | .57 | | .57 | .93 |
| 0680 | Wood shingles, shakes, light | | 440 | .018 | | | .47 | | .47 | .76 |
| 0690 | Med. | | 360 | .022 | | | .57 | | .57 | .93 |
| 0700 | Heavy | | 280 | .029 | | | .74 | | .74 | 1.20 |
| 0710 | Clapboard, light | | 520 | .015 | | | .40 | | .40 | .65 |
| 0720 | Med. | | 480 | .017 | | | .43 | | .43 | .70 |
| 0730 | Heavy | ↓ | 400 | .020 | ↓ | | .52 | | .52 | .84 |
| 0740 | Wire brush | | | | | | | | | |
| 0750 | Aluminum, light | 1 Pord | 600 | .013 | S.F. | | .34 | | .34 | .56 |
| 0760 | Med. | | 520 | .015 | | | .40 | | .40 | .65 |
| 0770 | Heavy | ↓ | 440 | .018 | ↓ | | .47 | | .47 | .76 |
| 0780 | Pressure wash, based on 2500 lb. operating pressure | | | | | | | | | |
| 0790 | Stucco | A-1H | 3080 | .003 | S.F. | | .06 | .02 | .08 | .11 |
| 0800 | Aluminum or vinyl | | 3200 | .003 | | | .05 | .02 | .07 | .11 |
| 0810 | Siding, masonry, brick & block | ↓ | 2400 | .003 | ↓ | | .07 | .03 | .10 | .15 |
| 1300 | Miscellaneous, wire brush | | | | | | | | | |
| 1310 | Metal, pedestrian gate | 1 Pord | 100 | .080 | S.F. | | 2.06 | | 2.06 | 3.36 |

### 09 91 03.40 Interior Surface Preparation

| | Crew | Daily Output | Labor-Hours | Unit | Material | 2010 Bare Costs Labor | Equipment | Total | Total Incl O&P |
|---|---|---|---|---|---|---|---|---|---|
| 0010 | **INTERIOR SURFACE PREPARATION** | | | | | | | | | |
| 0020 | Doors, per side, not incl. frames or trim | | | | | | | | | |
| 0030 | Scrape & sand | | | | | | | | | |
| 0040 | Wood, flush | 1 Pord | 616 | .013 | S.F. | | .34 | | .34 | .55 |
| 0050 | Wood, detail | | 496 | .016 | | | .42 | | .42 | .68 |
| 0060 | Wood, louvered | ↓ | 280 | .029 | ↓ | | .74 | | .74 | 1.20 |
| 0070 | Wire brush | | | | | | | | | |
| 0080 | Metal, flush | 1 Pord | 640 | .013 | S.F. | | .32 | | .32 | .53 |
| 0090 | Metal, detail | | 520 | .015 | | | .40 | | .40 | .65 |
| 0100 | Metal, louvered | ↓ | 360 | .022 | ↓ | | .57 | | .57 | .93 |
| 0110 | Hand wash | | | | | | | | | |
| 0120 | Wood, flush | 1 Pord | 2160 | .004 | S.F. | | .10 | | .10 | .16 |
| 0130 | Wood, detailed | | 2000 | .004 | | | .10 | | .10 | .17 |
| 0140 | Wood, louvered | | 1360 | .006 | | | .15 | | .15 | .25 |
| 0150 | Metal, flush | | 2160 | .004 | | | .10 | | .10 | .16 |
| 0160 | Metal, detail | | 2000 | .004 | | | .10 | | .10 | .17 |
| 0170 | Metal, louvered | ↓ | 1360 | .006 | ↓ | | .15 | | .15 | .25 |
| 0400 | Windows, per side, not incl. trim | | | | | | | | | |
| 0410 | Scrape & sand | | | | | | | | | |
| 0420 | Wood, 1-2 lite | 1 Pord | 360 | .022 | S.F. | | .57 | | .57 | .93 |
| 0430 | Wood, 3-6 lite | | 320 | .025 | | | .65 | | .65 | 1.05 |
| 0440 | Wood, 7-10 lite | | 280 | .029 | | | .74 | | .74 | 1.20 |
| 0450 | Wood, 12 lite | | 240 | .033 | | | .86 | | .86 | 1.40 |
| 0460 | Wood, Bay/Bow | | 360 | .022 | ↓ | | .57 | | .57 | .93 |
| 0470 | Wire brush | | | | | | | | | |
| 0480 | Metal, 1-2 lite | 1 Pord | 520 | .015 | S.F. | | .40 | | .40 | .65 |

# 09 91 Painting

## 09 91 03 – Paint Restoration

### 09 91 03.40 Interior Surface Preparation

| | Crew | Daily Output | Labor-Hours | Unit | Material | 2010 Bare Costs Labor | Equipment | Total | Total Incl O&P |
|---|---|---|---|---|---|---|---|---|---|
| 0490 | Metal, 3-6 lite | 1 Pord | 440 | .018 | S.F. | | .47 | | .47 | .76 |
| 0500 | Metal, Bay/Bow | ↓ | 520 | .015 | ↓ | | .40 | | .40 | .65 |
| 0600 | Walls, sanding, light=10-30%, medium - 30-70%, | | | | | | | | | |
| 0610 | heavy=70-100% of surface to sand | | | | | | | | | |
| 0650 | Walls, sand | | | | | | | | | |
| 0660 | Gypsum board or plaster, light | 1 Pord | 3077 | .003 | S.F. | | .07 | | .07 | .11 |
| 0670 | Gypsum board or plaster, medium | | 2160 | .004 | | | .10 | | .10 | .16 |
| 0680 | Gypsum board or plaster, heavy | | 923 | .009 | | | .22 | | .22 | .36 |
| 0690 | Wood, T&G, light | | 2400 | .003 | | | .09 | | .09 | .14 |
| 0700 | Wood, T&G, med. | | 1600 | .005 | | | .13 | | .13 | .21 |
| 0710 | Wood, T&G, heavy | ↓ | 800 | .010 | ↓ | | .26 | | .26 | .42 |
| 0720 | Walls, wash | | | | | | | | | |
| 0730 | Gypsum board or plaster | 1 Pord | 3200 | .003 | S.F. | | .06 | | .06 | .11 |
| 0740 | Wood, T&G | | 3200 | .003 | | | .06 | | .06 | .11 |
| 0750 | Masonry, brick & block, smooth | | 2800 | .003 | | | .07 | | .07 | .12 |
| 0760 | Masonry, brick & block, coarse | ↓ | 2000 | .004 | ↓ | | .10 | | .10 | .17 |
| 8000 | For chemical washing, see Div. 04 01 30 | | | | | | | | | |

### 09 91 03.41 Scrape After Fire Damage

| | Crew | Daily Output | Labor-Hours | Unit | Material | 2010 Bare Costs Labor | Equipment | Total | Total Incl O&P |
|---|---|---|---|---|---|---|---|---|---|
| 0010 | **SCRAPE AFTER FIRE DAMAGE** | | | | | | | | | |
| 0050 | Boards, 1" x 4" | 1 Pord | 336 | .024 | L.F. | | .61 | | .61 | 1 |
| 0060 | 1" x 6" | | 260 | .031 | | | .79 | | .79 | 1.29 |
| 0070 | 1" x 8" | | 207 | .039 | | | 1 | | 1 | 1.62 |
| 0080 | 1" x 10" | | 174 | .046 | | | 1.19 | | 1.19 | 1.93 |
| 0500 | Framing, 2" x 4" | | 265 | .030 | | | .78 | | .78 | 1.27 |
| 0510 | 2" x 6" | | 221 | .036 | | | .93 | | .93 | 1.52 |
| 0520 | 2" x 8" | | 190 | .042 | | | 1.09 | | 1.09 | 1.77 |
| 0530 | 2" x 10" | | 165 | .048 | | | 1.25 | | 1.25 | 2.04 |
| 0540 | 2" x 12" | | 144 | .056 | | | 1.43 | | 1.43 | 2.33 |
| 1000 | Heavy framing, 3" x 4" | | 226 | .035 | | | .91 | | .91 | 1.49 |
| 1010 | 4" x 4" | | 210 | .038 | | | .98 | | .98 | 1.60 |
| 1020 | 4" x 6" | | 191 | .042 | | | 1.08 | | 1.08 | 1.76 |
| 1030 | 4" x 8" | | 165 | .048 | | | 1.25 | | 1.25 | 2.04 |
| 1040 | 4" x 10" | | 144 | .056 | | | 1.43 | | 1.43 | 2.33 |
| 1060 | 4" x 12" | | 131 | .061 | ↓ | | 1.58 | | 1.58 | 2.56 |
| 2900 | For sealing, minimum | | 825 | .010 | S.F. | .14 | .25 | | .39 | .56 |
| 2920 | Maximum | ↓ | 460 | .017 | " | .28 | .45 | | .73 | 1.04 |

## 09 91 13 – Exterior Painting

### 09 91 13.30 Fences

| | Crew | Daily Output | Labor-Hours | Unit | Material | 2010 Bare Costs Labor | Equipment | Total | Total Incl O&P |
|---|---|---|---|---|---|---|---|---|---|
| 0010 | **FENCES**          R099100-20 | | | | | | | | | |
| 0100 | Chain link or wire metal, one side, water base | | | | | | | | | |
| 0110 | Roll & brush, first coat | 1 Pord | 960 | .008 | S.F. | .05 | .21 | | .26 | .41 |
| 0120 | Second coat | | 1280 | .006 | | .05 | .16 | | .21 | .32 |
| 0130 | Spray, first coat | | 2275 | .004 | | .05 | .09 | | .14 | .21 |
| 0140 | Second coat | ↓ | 2600 | .003 | ↓ | .05 | .08 | | .13 | .19 |
| 0150 | Picket, water base | | | | | | | | | |
| 0160 | Roll & brush, first coat | 1 Pord | 865 | .009 | S.F. | .06 | .24 | | .30 | .45 |
| 0170 | Second coat | | 1050 | .008 | | .06 | .20 | | .26 | .38 |
| 0180 | Spray, first coat | | 2275 | .004 | | .06 | .09 | | .15 | .21 |
| 0190 | Second coat | ↓ | 2600 | .003 | ↓ | .06 | .08 | | .14 | .19 |
| 0200 | Stockade, water base | | | | | | | | | |
| 0210 | Roll & brush, first coat | 1 Pord | 1040 | .008 | S.F. | .06 | .20 | | .26 | .38 |
| 0220 | Second coat | ↓ | 1200 | .007 | ↓ | .06 | .17 | | .23 | .34 |

# 09 91 Painting

## 09 91 13 – Exterior Painting

### 09 91 13.30 Fences

| | | Crew | Daily Output | Labor-Hours | Unit | Material | 2010 Bare Costs Labor | Equipment | Total | Total Incl O&P |
|---|---|---|---|---|---|---|---|---|---|---|
| 0230 | Spray, first coat | 1 Pord | 2275 | .004 | S.F. | .06 | .09 | | .15 | .21 |
| 0240 | Second coat | ↓ | 2600 | .003 | ↓ | .06 | .08 | | .14 | .19 |

### 09 91 13.42 Miscellaneous, Exterior

| | | | Crew | Daily Output | Labor-Hours | Unit | Material | Labor | Equipment | Total | Total Incl O&P |
|---|---|---|---|---|---|---|---|---|---|---|---|
| 0010 | **MISCELLANEOUS, EXTERIOR** | R099100-20 | | | | | | | | | |
| 0100 | Railing, ext., decorative wood, incl. cap & baluster | | | | | | | | | | |
| 0110 | Newels & spindles @ 12" O.C. | | | | | | | | | | |
| 0120 | Brushwork, stain, sand, seal & varnish | | | | | | | | | | |
| 0130 | First coat | | 1 Pord | 90 | .089 | L.F. | .69 | 2.29 | | 2.98 | 4.49 |
| 0140 | Second coat | | " | 120 | .067 | " | .69 | 1.72 | | 2.41 | 3.56 |
| 0150 | Rough sawn wood, 42" high, 2" x 2" verticals, 6" O.C. | | | | | | | | | | |
| 0160 | Brushwork, stain, each coat | | 1 Pord | 90 | .089 | L.F. | .22 | 2.29 | | 2.51 | 3.98 |
| 0170 | Wrought iron, 1" rail, 1/2" sq. verticals | | | | | | | | | | |
| 0180 | Brushwork, zinc chromate, 60" high, bars 6" O.C. | | | | | | | | | | |
| 0190 | Primer | | 1 Pord | 130 | .062 | L.F. | .59 | 1.59 | | 2.18 | 3.23 |
| 0200 | Finish coat | | | 130 | .062 | | .18 | 1.59 | | 1.77 | 2.78 |
| 0210 | Additional coat | | ↓ | 190 | .042 | ↓ | .21 | 1.09 | | 1.30 | 2 |
| 0220 | Shutters or blinds, single panel, 2' x 4', paint all sides | | | | | | | | | | |
| 0230 | Brushwork, primer | | 1 Pord | 20 | .400 | Ea. | .60 | 10.30 | | 10.90 | 17.45 |
| 0240 | Finish coat, exterior latex | | | 20 | .400 | | .43 | 10.30 | | 10.73 | 17.25 |
| 0250 | Primer & 1 coat, exterior latex | | | 13 | .615 | | .89 | 15.90 | | 16.79 | 27 |
| 0260 | Spray, primer | | | 35 | .229 | | .88 | 5.90 | | 6.78 | 10.55 |
| 0270 | Finish coat, exterior latex | | | 35 | .229 | | .90 | 5.90 | | 6.80 | 10.60 |
| 0280 | Primer & 1 coat, exterior latex | | ↓ | 20 | .400 | ↓ | .93 | 10.30 | | 11.23 | 17.85 |
| 0290 | For louvered shutters, add | | | | | S.F. | 10% | | | | |
| 0300 | Stair stringers, exterior, metal | | | | | | | | | | |
| 0310 | Roll & brush, zinc chromate, to 14", each coat | | 1 Pord | 320 | .025 | L.F. | .06 | .65 | | .71 | 1.12 |
| 0320 | Rough sawn wood, 4" x 12" | | | | | | | | | | |
| 0330 | Roll & brush, exterior latex, each coat | | 1 Pord | 215 | .037 | L.F. | .06 | .96 | | 1.02 | 1.63 |
| 0340 | Trellis/lattice, 2" x 2" @ 3" O.C. with 2" x 8" supports | | | | | | | | | | |
| 0350 | Spray, latex, per side, each coat | | 1 Pord | 475 | .017 | S.F. | .06 | .43 | | .49 | .78 |
| 0450 | Decking, ext., sealer, alkyd, brushwork, sealer coat | | | 1140 | .007 | | .09 | .18 | | .27 | .39 |
| 0460 | 1st coat | | | 1140 | .007 | | .09 | .18 | | .27 | .38 |
| 0470 | 2nd coat | | | 1300 | .006 | | .06 | .16 | | .22 | .33 |
| 0500 | Paint, alkyd, brushwork, primer coat | | | 1140 | .007 | | .07 | .18 | | .25 | .37 |
| 0510 | 1st coat | | | 1140 | .007 | | .16 | .18 | | .34 | .46 |
| 0520 | 2nd coat | | | 1300 | .006 | | .12 | .16 | | .28 | .39 |
| 0600 | Sand paint, alkyd, brushwork, 1 coat | | ↓ | 150 | .053 | | .11 | 1.38 | | 1.49 | 2.36 |

### 09 91 13.60 Siding Exterior

| | | Crew | Daily Output | Labor-Hours | Unit | Material | Labor | Equipment | Total | Total Incl O&P |
|---|---|---|---|---|---|---|---|---|---|---|
| 0010 | **SIDING EXTERIOR**, Alkyd (oil base) | | | | | | | | | |
| 0450 | Steel siding, oil base, paint 1 coat, brushwork | 2 Pord | 2015 | .008 | S.F. | .13 | .20 | | .33 | .47 |
| 0500 | Spray | | 4550 | .004 | | .19 | .09 | | .28 | .36 |
| 0800 | Paint 2 coats, brushwork | | 1300 | .012 | | .25 | .32 | | .57 | .80 |
| 1000 | Spray | | 2750 | .006 | | .17 | .15 | | .32 | .43 |
| 1200 | Stucco, rough, oil base, paint 2 coats, brushwork | | 1300 | .012 | | .25 | .32 | | .57 | .80 |
| 1400 | Roller | | 1625 | .010 | | .27 | .25 | | .52 | .70 |
| 1600 | Spray | | 2925 | .005 | | .28 | .14 | | .42 | .54 |
| 1800 | Texture 1-11 or clapboard, oil base, primer coat, brushwork | | 1300 | .012 | | .10 | .32 | | .42 | .63 |
| 2000 | Spray | | 4550 | .004 | | .10 | .09 | | .19 | .26 |
| 2100 | Paint 1 coat, brushwork | | 1300 | .012 | | .18 | .32 | | .50 | .72 |
| 2200 | Spray | | 4550 | .004 | | .18 | .09 | | .27 | .35 |
| 2400 | Paint 2 coats, brushwork | | 810 | .020 | | .37 | .51 | | .88 | 1.23 |
| 2600 | Spray | ↓ | 2600 | .006 | ↓ | .41 | .16 | | .57 | .71 |

# 09 91 Painting

## 09 91 13 – Exterior Painting

### 09 91 13.60 Siding Exterior

| | | Crew | Daily Output | Labor-Hours | Unit | Material | 2010 Bare Costs Labor | Equipment | Total | Total Incl O&P |
|---|---|---|---|---|---|---|---|---|---|---|
| 3000 | Stain 1 coat, brushwork | 2 Pord | 1520 | .011 | S.F. | .07 | .27 | | .34 | .52 |
| 3200 | Spray | | 5320 | .003 | | .08 | .08 | | .16 | .22 |
| 3400 | Stain 2 coats, brushwork | | 950 | .017 | | .15 | .43 | | .58 | .87 |
| 4000 | Spray | | 3050 | .005 | | .17 | .14 | | .31 | .40 |
| 4200 | Wood shingles, oil base primer coat, brushwork | | 1300 | .012 | | .09 | .32 | | .41 | .62 |
| 4400 | Spray | | 3900 | .004 | | .08 | .11 | | .19 | .26 |
| 4600 | Paint 1 coat, brushwork | | 1300 | .012 | | .15 | .32 | | .47 | .69 |
| 4800 | Spray | | 3900 | .004 | | .19 | .11 | | .30 | .38 |
| 5000 | Paint 2 coats, brushwork | | 810 | .020 | | .31 | .51 | | .82 | 1.17 |
| 5200 | Spray | | 2275 | .007 | | .29 | .18 | | .47 | .62 |
| 5800 | Stain 1 coat, brushwork | | 1500 | .011 | | .07 | .28 | | .35 | .53 |
| 6000 | Spray | | 3900 | .004 | | .07 | .11 | | .18 | .25 |
| 6500 | Stain 2 coats, brushwork | | 950 | .017 | | .15 | .43 | | .58 | .87 |
| 7000 | Spray | | 2660 | .006 | | .21 | .16 | | .37 | .48 |
| 8000 | For latex paint, deduct | | | | | 10% | | | | |
| 8100 | For work over 12' H, from pipe scaffolding, add | | | | | | 15% | | | |
| 8200 | For work over 12' H, from extension ladder, add | | | | | | 25% | | | |
| 8300 | For work over 12' H, from swing staging, add | | | | | | 35% | | | |

### 09 91 13.62 Siding, Misc.

| | | Crew | Daily Output | Labor-Hours | Unit | Material | 2010 Bare Costs Labor | Equipment | Total | Total Incl O&P |
|---|---|---|---|---|---|---|---|---|---|---|
| 0010 | **SIDING, MISC.**, latex paint    R099100-10 | | | | | | | | | |
| 0100 | Aluminum siding | | | | | | | | | |
| 0110 | Brushwork, primer | 2 Pord | 2275 | .007 | S.F. | .05 | .18 | | .23 | .36 |
| 0120 | Finish coat, exterior latex | | 2275 | .007 | | .04 | .18 | | .22 | .35 |
| 0130 | Primer & 1 coat exterior latex | | 1300 | .012 | | .11 | .32 | | .43 | .64 |
| 0140 | Primer & 2 coats exterior latex | | 975 | .016 | | .15 | .42 | | .57 | .86 |
| 0150 | Mineral fiber shingles | | | | | | | | | |
| 0160 | Brushwork, primer | 2 Pord | 1495 | .011 | S.F. | .10 | .28 | | .38 | .56 |
| 0170 | Finish coat, industrial enamel | | 1495 | .011 | | .15 | .28 | | .43 | .61 |
| 0180 | Primer & 1 coat enamel | | 810 | .020 | | .25 | .51 | | .76 | 1.10 |
| 0190 | Primer & 2 coats enamel | | 540 | .030 | | .39 | .76 | | 1.15 | 1.67 |
| 0200 | Roll, primer | | 1625 | .010 | | .11 | .25 | | .36 | .53 |
| 0210 | Finish coat, industrial enamel | | 1625 | .010 | | .16 | .25 | | .41 | .59 |
| 0220 | Primer & 1 coat enamel | | 975 | .016 | | .27 | .42 | | .69 | .98 |
| 0230 | Primer & 2 coats enamel | | 650 | .025 | | .43 | .64 | | 1.07 | 1.50 |
| 0240 | Spray, primer | | 3900 | .004 | | .08 | .11 | | .19 | .26 |
| 0250 | Finish coat, industrial enamel | | 3900 | .004 | | .13 | .11 | | .24 | .32 |
| 0260 | Primer & 1 coat enamel | | 2275 | .007 | | .22 | .18 | | .40 | .54 |
| 0270 | Primer & 2 coats enamel | | 1625 | .010 | | .35 | .25 | | .60 | .80 |
| 0280 | Waterproof sealer, first coat | | 4485 | .004 | | .07 | .09 | | .16 | .22 |
| 0290 | Second coat | | 5235 | .003 | | .06 | .08 | | .14 | .20 |
| 0300 | Rough wood incl. shingles, shakes or rough sawn siding | | | | | | | | | |
| 0310 | Brushwork, primer | 2 Pord | 1280 | .013 | S.F. | .12 | .32 | | .44 | .66 |
| 0320 | Finish coat, exterior latex | | 1280 | .013 | | .08 | .32 | | .40 | .62 |
| 0330 | Primer & 1 coat exterior latex | | 960 | .017 | | .20 | .43 | | .63 | .92 |
| 0340 | Primer & 2 coats exterior latex | | 700 | .023 | | .28 | .59 | | .87 | 1.27 |
| 0350 | Roll, primer | | 2925 | .005 | | .16 | .14 | | .30 | .41 |
| 0360 | Finish coat, exterior latex | | 2925 | .005 | | .09 | .14 | | .23 | .33 |
| 0370 | Primer & 1 coat exterior latex | | 1790 | .009 | | .26 | .23 | | .49 | .66 |
| 0380 | Primer & 2 coats exterior latex | | 1300 | .012 | | .35 | .32 | | .67 | .91 |
| 0390 | Spray, primer | | 3900 | .004 | | .14 | .11 | | .25 | .32 |
| 0400 | Finish coat, exterior latex | | 3900 | .004 | | .07 | .11 | | .18 | .25 |
| 0410 | Primer & 1 coat exterior latex | | 2600 | .006 | | .21 | .16 | | .37 | .49 |

# 09 91 Painting

## 09 91 13 – Exterior Painting

### 09 91 13.62 Siding, Misc.

| | | Crew | Daily Output | Labor-Hours | Unit | Material | 2010 Bare Costs Labor | Equipment | Total | Total Incl O&P |
|---|---|---|---|---|---|---|---|---|---|---|
| 0420 | Primer & 2 coats exterior latex | 2 Pord | 2080 | .008 | S.F. | .28 | .20 | | .48 | .63 |
| 0430 | Waterproof sealer, first coat | | 4485 | .004 | | .12 | .09 | | .21 | .28 |
| 0440 | Second coat | ↓ | 4485 | .004 | ↓ | .07 | .09 | | .16 | .22 |
| 0450 | Smooth wood incl. butt, T&G, beveled, drop or B&B siding | | | | | | | | | |
| 0460 | Brushwork, primer | 2 Pord | 2325 | .007 | S.F. | .09 | .18 | | .27 | .39 |
| 0470 | Finish coat, exterior latex | | 1280 | .013 | | .08 | .32 | | .40 | .62 |
| 0480 | Primer & 1 coat exterior latex | | 800 | .020 | | .17 | .52 | | .69 | 1.02 |
| 0490 | Primer & 2 coats exterior latex | | 630 | .025 | | .24 | .66 | | .90 | 1.34 |
| 0500 | Roll, primer | | 2275 | .007 | | .10 | .18 | | .28 | .41 |
| 0510 | Finish coat, exterior latex | | 2275 | .007 | | .08 | .18 | | .26 | .39 |
| 0520 | Primer & 1 coat exterior latex | | 1300 | .012 | | .18 | .32 | | .50 | .72 |
| 0530 | Primer & 2 coats exterior latex | | 975 | .016 | | .27 | .42 | | .69 | .98 |
| 0540 | Spray, primer | | 4550 | .004 | | .08 | .09 | | .17 | .23 |
| 0550 | Finish coat, exterior latex | | 4550 | .004 | | .07 | .09 | | .16 | .23 |
| 0560 | Primer & 1 coat exterior latex | | 2600 | .006 | | .15 | .16 | | .31 | .42 |
| 0570 | Primer & 2 coats exterior latex | | 1950 | .008 | | .22 | .21 | | .43 | .58 |
| 0580 | Waterproof sealer, first coat | | 5230 | .003 | | .07 | .08 | | .15 | .20 |
| 0590 | Second coat | ↓ | 5980 | .003 | | .07 | .07 | | .14 | .18 |
| 0600 | For oil base paint, add | | | | ↓ | 10% | | | | |

### 09 91 13.70 Doors and Windows, Exterior

| | | Crew | Daily Output | Labor-Hours | Unit | Material | 2010 Bare Costs Labor | Equipment | Total | Total Incl O&P |
|---|---|---|---|---|---|---|---|---|---|---|
| 0010 | **DOORS AND WINDOWS, EXTERIOR** R099100-10 | | | | | | | | | |
| 0100 | Door frames & trim, only | | | | | | | | | |
| 0110 | Brushwork, primer R099100-20 | 1 Pord | 512 | .016 | L.F. | .05 | .40 | | .45 | .72 |
| 0120 | Finish coat, exterior latex | | 512 | .016 | | .05 | .40 | | .45 | .72 |
| 0130 | Primer & 1 coat, exterior latex | | 300 | .027 | | .11 | .69 | | .80 | 1.24 |
| 0140 | Primer & 2 coats, exterior latex | ↓ | 265 | .030 | ↓ | .16 | .78 | | .94 | 1.45 |
| 0150 | Doors, flush, both sides, incl. frame & trim | | | | | | | | | |
| 0160 | Roll & brush, primer | 1 Pord | 10 | .800 | Ea. | 4.16 | 20.50 | | 24.66 | 38 |
| 0170 | Finish coat, exterior latex | | 10 | .800 | | 4.04 | 20.50 | | 24.54 | 38 |
| 0180 | Primer & 1 coat, exterior latex | | 7 | 1.143 | | 8.20 | 29.50 | | 37.70 | 57 |
| 0190 | Primer & 2 coats, exterior latex | | 5 | 1.600 | | 12.25 | 41.50 | | 53.75 | 80.50 |
| 0200 | Brushwork, stain, sealer & 2 coats polyurethane | ↓ | 4 | 2 | ↓ | 24 | 51.50 | | 75.50 | 111 |
| 0210 | Doors, French, both sides, 10-15 lite, incl. frame & trim | | | | | | | | | |
| 0220 | Brushwork, primer | 1 Pord | 6 | 1.333 | Ea. | 2.08 | 34.50 | | 36.58 | 58.50 |
| 0230 | Finish coat, exterior latex | | 6 | 1.333 | | 2.02 | 34.50 | | 36.52 | 58 |
| 0240 | Primer & 1 coat, exterior latex | | 3 | 2.667 | | 4.10 | 69 | | 73.10 | 117 |
| 0250 | Primer & 2 coats, exterior latex | | 2 | 4 | | 6 | 103 | | 109 | 175 |
| 0260 | Brushwork, stain, sealer & 2 coats polyurethane | ↓ | 2.50 | 3.200 | | 8.80 | 82.50 | | 91.30 | 144 |
| 0270 | Doors, louvered, both sides, incl. frame & trim | | | | | | | | | |
| 0280 | Brushwork, primer | 1 Pord | 7 | 1.143 | Ea. | 4.16 | 29.50 | | 33.66 | 52.50 |
| 0290 | Finish coat, exterior latex | | 7 | 1.143 | | 4.04 | 29.50 | | 33.54 | 52.50 |
| 0300 | Primer & 1 coat, exterior latex | | 4 | 2 | | 8.20 | 51.50 | | 59.70 | 93 |
| 0310 | Primer & 2 coats, exterior latex | | 3 | 2.667 | | 12 | 69 | | 81 | 125 |
| 0320 | Brushwork, stain, sealer & 2 coats polyurethane | ↓ | 4.50 | 1.778 | | 24 | 46 | | 70 | 101 |
| 0330 | Doors, panel, both sides, incl. frame & trim | | | | | | | | | |
| 0340 | Roll & brush, primer | 1 Pord | 6 | 1.333 | Ea. | 4.16 | 34.50 | | 38.66 | 60.50 |
| 0350 | Finish coat, exterior latex | | 6 | 1.333 | | 4.04 | 34.50 | | 38.54 | 60.50 |
| 0360 | Primer & 1 coat, exterior latex | | 3 | 2.667 | | 8.20 | 69 | | 77.20 | 121 |
| 0370 | Primer & 2 coats, exterior latex | | 2.50 | 3.200 | | 12 | 82.50 | | 94.50 | 147 |
| 0380 | Brushwork, stain, sealer & 2 coats polyurethane | ↓ | 3 | 2.667 | | 24 | 69 | | 93 | 139 |
| 0400 | Windows, per ext. side, based on 15 SF | | | | | | | | | |
| 0410 | 1 to 6 lite | | | | | | | | | |

479

| 09 91 13.70 Doors and Windows, Exterior | | Crew | Daily Output | Labor-Hours | Unit | Material | 2010 Bare Costs Labor | Equipment | Total | Total Incl O&P |
|---|---|---|---|---|---|---|---|---|---|---|
| 0420 | Brushwork, primer | 1 Pord | 13 | .615 | Ea. | .82 | 15.90 | | 16.72 | 27 |
| 0430 | Finish coat, exterior latex | | 13 | .615 | | .80 | 15.90 | | 16.70 | 27 |
| 0440 | Primer & 1 coat, exterior latex | | 8 | 1 | | 1.62 | 26 | | 27.62 | 44 |
| 0450 | Primer & 2 coats, exterior latex | | 6 | 1.333 | | 2.37 | 34.50 | | 36.87 | 58.50 |
| 0460 | Stain, sealer & 1 coat varnish | | 7 | 1.143 | | 3.47 | 29.50 | | 32.97 | 52 |
| 0470 | 7 to 10 lite | | | | | | | | | |
| 0480 | Brushwork, primer | 1 Pord | 11 | .727 | Ea. | .82 | 18.75 | | 19.57 | 31.50 |
| 0490 | Finish coat, exterior latex | | 11 | .727 | | .80 | 18.75 | | 19.55 | 31.50 |
| 0500 | Primer & 1 coat, exterior latex | | 7 | 1.143 | | 1.62 | 29.50 | | 31.12 | 50 |
| 0510 | Primer & 2 coats, exterior latex | | 5 | 1.600 | | 2.37 | 41.50 | | 43.87 | 69.50 |
| 0520 | Stain, sealer & 1 coat varnish | | 6 | 1.333 | | 3.47 | 34.50 | | 37.97 | 60 |
| 0530 | 12 lite | | | | | | | | | |
| 0540 | Brushwork, primer | 1 Pord | 10 | .800 | Ea. | .82 | 20.50 | | 21.32 | 34.50 |
| 0550 | Finish coat, exterior latex | | 10 | .800 | | .80 | 20.50 | | 21.30 | 34.50 |
| 0560 | Primer & 1 coat, exterior latex | | 6 | 1.333 | | 1.62 | 34.50 | | 36.12 | 58 |
| 0570 | Primer & 2 coats, exterior latex | | 5 | 1.600 | | 2.37 | 41.50 | | 43.87 | 69.50 |
| 0580 | Stain, sealer & 1 coat varnish | | 6 | 1.333 | | 3.40 | 34.50 | | 37.90 | 59.50 |
| 0590 | For oil base paint, add | | | | | 10% | | | | |

## 09 91 13.80 Trim, Exterior

| 09 91 13.80 Trim, Exterior | | Crew | Daily Output | Labor-Hours | Unit | Material | 2010 Bare Costs Labor | Equipment | Total | Total Incl O&P |
|---|---|---|---|---|---|---|---|---|---|---|
| 0010 | TRIM, EXTERIOR | R099100-10 | | | | | | | | |
| 0100 | Door frames & trim (see Doors, interior or exterior) | | | | | | | | | |
| 0110 | Fascia, latex paint, one coat coverage | | | | | | | | | |
| 0120 | 1" x 4", brushwork | 1 Pord | 640 | .013 | L.F. | .02 | .32 | | .34 | .55 |
| 0130 | Roll | | 1280 | .006 | | .02 | .16 | | .18 | .28 |
| 0140 | Spray | | 2080 | .004 | | .01 | .10 | | .11 | .18 |
| 0150 | 1" x 6" to 1" x 10", brushwork | | 640 | .013 | | .06 | .32 | | .38 | .59 |
| 0160 | Roll | | 1230 | .007 | | .06 | .17 | | .23 | .34 |
| 0170 | Spray | | 2100 | .004 | | .05 | .10 | | .15 | .21 |
| 0180 | 1" x 12", brushwork | | 640 | .013 | | .06 | .32 | | .38 | .59 |
| 0190 | Roll | | 1050 | .008 | | .06 | .20 | | .26 | .39 |
| 0200 | Spray | | 2200 | .004 | | .05 | .09 | | .14 | .20 |
| 0210 | Gutters & downspouts, metal, zinc chromate paint | | | | | | | | | |
| 0220 | Brushwork, gutters, 5", first coat | 1 Pord | 640 | .013 | L.F. | .06 | .32 | | .38 | .60 |
| 0230 | Second coat | | 960 | .008 | | .06 | .21 | | .27 | .42 |
| 0240 | Third coat | | 1280 | .006 | | .05 | .16 | | .21 | .31 |
| 0250 | Downspouts, 4", first coat | | 640 | .013 | | .06 | .32 | | .38 | .60 |
| 0260 | Second coat | | 960 | .008 | | .06 | .21 | | .27 | .42 |
| 0270 | Third coat | | 1280 | .006 | | .05 | .16 | | .21 | .31 |
| 0280 | Gutters & downspouts, wood | | | | | | | | | |
| 0290 | Brushwork, gutters, 5", primer | 1 Pord | 640 | .013 | L.F. | .05 | .32 | | .37 | .59 |
| 0300 | Finish coat, exterior latex | | 640 | .013 | | .05 | .32 | | .37 | .58 |
| 0310 | Primer & 1 coat exterior latex | | 400 | .020 | | .11 | .52 | | .63 | .96 |
| 0320 | Primer & 2 coats exterior latex | | 325 | .025 | | .16 | .64 | | .80 | 1.21 |
| 0330 | Downspouts, 4", primer | | 640 | .013 | | .05 | .32 | | .37 | .59 |
| 0340 | Finish coat, exterior latex | | 640 | .013 | | .05 | .32 | | .37 | .58 |
| 0350 | Primer & 1 coat exterior latex | | 400 | .020 | | .11 | .52 | | .63 | .96 |
| 0360 | Primer & 2 coats exterior latex | | 325 | .025 | | .08 | .64 | | .72 | 1.12 |
| 0370 | Molding, exterior, up to 14" wide | | | | | | | | | |
| 0380 | Brushwork, primer | 1 Pord | 640 | .013 | L.F. | .07 | .32 | | .39 | .60 |
| 0390 | Finish coat, exterior latex | | 640 | .013 | | .06 | .32 | | .38 | .59 |
| 0400 | Primer & 1 coat exterior latex | | 400 | .020 | | .13 | .52 | | .65 | .98 |
| 0410 | Primer & 2 coats exterior latex | | 315 | .025 | | .13 | .66 | | .79 | 1.21 |

# 09 91 Painting

## 09 91 13 – Exterior Painting

| 09 91 13.80 Trim, Exterior | | Crew | Daily Output | Labor-Hours | Unit | Material | 2010 Bare Costs Labor | Equipment | Total | Total Incl O&P |
|---|---|---|---|---|---|---|---|---|---|---|
| 0420 | Stain & fill | 1 Pord | 1050 | .008 | L.F. | .09 | .20 | | .29 | .42 |
| 0430 | Shellac | | 1850 | .004 | | .09 | .11 | | .20 | .28 |
| 0440 | Varnish | | 1275 | .006 | | .10 | .16 | | .26 | .37 |

### 09 91 13.90 Walls, Masonry (CMU), Exterior

| | | Crew | Daily Output | Labor-Hours | Unit | Material | 2010 Bare Costs Labor | Equipment | Total | Total Incl O&P |
|---|---|---|---|---|---|---|---|---|---|---|
| 0350 | **WALLS, MASONRY (CMU), EXTERIOR** | | | | | | | | | |
| 0360 | Concrete masonry units (CMU), smooth surface | | | | | | | | | |
| 0370 | Brushwork, latex, first coat | 1 Pord | 640 | .013 | S.F. | .06 | .32 | | .38 | .59 |
| 0380 | Second coat | | 960 | .008 | | .05 | .21 | | .26 | .40 |
| 0390 | Waterproof sealer, first coat | | 736 | .011 | | .24 | .28 | | .52 | .73 |
| 0400 | Second coat | | 1104 | .007 | | .24 | .19 | | .43 | .57 |
| 0410 | Roll, latex, paint, first coat | | 1465 | .005 | | .07 | .14 | | .21 | .31 |
| 0420 | Second coat | | 1790 | .004 | | .05 | .12 | | .17 | .25 |
| 0430 | Waterproof sealer, first coat | | 1680 | .005 | | .24 | .12 | | .36 | .47 |
| 0440 | Second coat | | 2060 | .004 | | .24 | .10 | | .34 | .43 |
| 0450 | Spray, latex, paint, first coat | | 1950 | .004 | | .05 | .11 | | .16 | .23 |
| 0460 | Second coat | | 2600 | .003 | | .04 | .08 | | .12 | .18 |
| 0470 | Waterproof sealer, first coat | | 2245 | .004 | | .24 | .09 | | .33 | .42 |
| 0480 | Second coat | | 2990 | .003 | | .24 | .07 | | .31 | .38 |
| 0490 | Concrete masonry unit (CMU), porous | | | | | | | | | |
| 0500 | Brushwork, latex, first coat | 1 Pord | 640 | .013 | S.F. | .12 | .32 | | .44 | .66 |
| 0510 | Second coat | | 960 | .008 | | .06 | .21 | | .27 | .41 |
| 0520 | Waterproof sealer, first coat | | 736 | .011 | | .24 | .28 | | .52 | .73 |
| 0530 | Second coat | | 1104 | .007 | | .24 | .19 | | .43 | .57 |
| 0540 | Roll latex, first coat | | 1465 | .005 | | .09 | .14 | | .23 | .33 |
| 0550 | Second coat | | 1790 | .004 | | .06 | .12 | | .18 | .25 |
| 0560 | Waterproof sealer, first coat | | 1680 | .005 | | .24 | .12 | | .36 | .47 |
| 0570 | Second coat | | 2060 | .004 | | .24 | .10 | | .34 | .43 |
| 0580 | Spray latex, first coat | | 1950 | .004 | | .06 | .11 | | .17 | .24 |
| 0590 | Second coat | | 2600 | .003 | | .04 | .08 | | .12 | .18 |
| 0600 | Waterproof sealer, first coat | | 2245 | .004 | | .24 | .09 | | .33 | .42 |
| 0610 | Second coat | | 2990 | .003 | | .24 | .07 | | .31 | .38 |

## 09 91 23 – Interior Painting

### 09 91 23.20 Cabinets and Casework

| | | Crew | Daily Output | Labor-Hours | Unit | Material | 2010 Bare Costs Labor | Equipment | Total | Total Incl O&P |
|---|---|---|---|---|---|---|---|---|---|---|
| 0010 | **CABINETS AND CASEWORK** | | | | | | | | | |
| 1000 | Primer coat, oil base, brushwork | 1 Pord | 650 | .012 | S.F. | .07 | .32 | | .39 | .60 |
| 2000 | Paint, oil base, brushwork, 1 coat | | 650 | .012 | | .10 | .32 | | .42 | .64 |
| 2500 | 2 coats | | 400 | .020 | | .20 | .52 | | .72 | 1.06 |
| 3000 | Stain, brushwork, wipe off | | 650 | .012 | | .07 | .32 | | .39 | .60 |
| 4000 | Shellac, 1 coat, brushwork | | 650 | .012 | | .07 | .32 | | .39 | .60 |
| 4500 | Varnish, 3 coats, brushwork, sand after 1st coat | | 325 | .025 | | .24 | .64 | | .88 | 1.29 |
| 5000 | For latex paint, deduct | | | | | 10% | | | | |

### 09 91 23.33 Doors and Windows, Interior Alkyd (Oil Base)

| | | Crew | Daily Output | Labor-Hours | Unit | Material | 2010 Bare Costs Labor | Equipment | Total | Total Incl O&P |
|---|---|---|---|---|---|---|---|---|---|---|
| 0010 | **DOORS AND WINDOWS, INTERIOR ALKYD (OIL BASE)** | | | | | | | | | |
| 0500 | Flush door & frame, 3' x 7', oil, primer, brushwork | 1 Pord | 10 | .800 | Ea. | 2.90 | 20.50 | | 23.40 | 36.50 |
| 1000 | Paint, 1 coat | | 10 | .800 | | 4.03 | 20.50 | | 24.53 | 38 |
| 1200 | 2 coats | | 6 | 1.333 | | 5.10 | 34.50 | | 39.60 | 61.50 |
| 1400 | Stain, brushwork, wipe off | | 18 | .444 | | 1.57 | 11.45 | | 13.02 | 20.50 |
| 1600 | Shellac, 1 coat, brushwork | | 25 | .320 | | 1.52 | 8.25 | | 9.77 | 15.10 |
| 1800 | Varnish, 3 coats, brushwork, sand after 1st coat | | 9 | .889 | | 5 | 23 | | 28 | 43 |
| 2000 | Panel door & frame, 3' x 7', oil, primer, brushwork | | 6 | 1.333 | | 2.72 | 34.50 | | 37.22 | 59 |
| 2200 | Paint, 1 coat | | 6 | 1.333 | | 4.03 | 34.50 | | 38.53 | 60.50 |
| 2400 | 2 coats | | 3 | 2.667 | | 10.75 | 69 | | 79.75 | 124 |

# 09 91 Painting

## 09 91 23 - Interior Painting

| 09 91 23.33 Doors and Windows, Interior Alkyd (Oil Base) | Crew | Daily Output | Labor-Hours | Unit | Material | Labor | 2010 Bare Costs Equipment | Total | Total Incl O&P |
|---|---|---|---|---|---|---|---|---|---|
| 2600 Stain, brushwork, panel door, 3' x 7', not incl. frame | 1 Pord | 16 | .500 | Ea. | 1.57 | 12.90 | | 14.47 | 22.50 |
| 2800 Shellac, 1 coat, brushwork | | 22 | .364 | | 1.52 | 9.40 | | 10.92 | 16.90 |
| 3000 Varnish, 3 coats, brushwork, sand after 1st coat | | 7.50 | 1.067 | | 5 | 27.50 | | 32.50 | 50.50 |
| 3020 French door, incl. 3' x 7', 6 lites, frame & trim | | | | | | | | | |
| 3022 Paint, 1 coat, over existing paint | 1 Pord | 5 | 1.600 | Ea. | 8.05 | 41.50 | | 49.55 | 76 |
| 3024 2 coats, over existing paint | | 5 | 1.600 | | 15.65 | 41.50 | | 57.15 | 84 |
| 3026 Primer & 1 coat | | 3.50 | 2.286 | | 13.50 | 59 | | 72.50 | 111 |
| 3028 Primer & 2 coats | | 3 | 2.667 | | 21.50 | 69 | | 90.50 | 136 |
| 3032 Varnish or polyurethane, 1 coat | | 5 | 1.600 | | 6.40 | 41.50 | | 47.90 | 74 |
| 3034 2 coats, sanding between | | 3 | 2.667 | | 12.80 | 69 | | 81.80 | 126 |
| 4400 Windows, including frame and trim, per side | | | | | | | | | |
| 4600 Colonial type, 6/6 lites, 2' x 3', oil, primer, brushwork | 1 Pord | 14 | .571 | Ea. | .43 | 14.75 | | 15.18 | 24.50 |
| 5800 Paint, 1 coat | | 14 | .571 | | .64 | 14.75 | | 15.39 | 24.50 |
| 6000 2 coats | | 9 | .889 | | 1.24 | 23 | | 24.24 | 39 |
| 6200 3' x 5' opening, 6/6 lites, primer coat, brushwork | | 12 | .667 | | 1.07 | 17.20 | | 18.27 | 29 |
| 6400 Paint, 1 coat | | 12 | .667 | | 1.59 | 17.20 | | 18.79 | 30 |
| 6600 2 coats | | 7 | 1.143 | | 3.09 | 29.50 | | 32.59 | 51.50 |
| 6800 4' x 8' opening, 6/6 lites, primer coat, brushwork | | 8 | 1 | | 2.29 | 26 | | 28.29 | 44.50 |
| 7000 Paint, 1 coat | | 8 | 1 | | 3.39 | 26 | | 29.39 | 45.50 |
| 7200 2 coats | | 5 | 1.600 | | 6.60 | 41.50 | | 48.10 | 74.50 |
| 8000 Single lite type, 2' x 3', oil base, primer coat, brushwork | | 33 | .242 | | .43 | 6.25 | | 6.68 | 10.65 |
| 8200 Paint, 1 coat | | 33 | .242 | | .64 | 6.25 | | 6.89 | 10.90 |
| 8400 2 coats | | 20 | .400 | | 1.24 | 10.30 | | 11.54 | 18.15 |
| 8600 3' x 5' opening, primer coat, brushwork | | 20 | .400 | | 1.07 | 10.30 | | 11.37 | 18 |
| 8800 Paint, 1 coat | | 20 | .400 | | 1.59 | 10.30 | | 11.89 | 18.55 |
| 8900 2 coats | | 13 | .615 | | 3.09 | 15.90 | | 18.99 | 29.50 |
| 9200 4' x 8' opening, primer coat, brushwork | | 14 | .571 | | 2.29 | 14.75 | | 17.04 | 26.50 |
| 9400 Paint, 1 coat | | 14 | .571 | | 3.39 | 14.75 | | 18.14 | 27.50 |
| 9600 2 coats | | 8 | 1 | | 6.60 | 26 | | 32.60 | 49.50 |

## 09 91 23.35 Doors and Windows, Interior Latex

| | Crew | Daily Output | Labor-Hours | Unit | Material | Labor | 2010 Bare Costs Equipment | Total | Total Incl O&P |
|---|---|---|---|---|---|---|---|---|---|
| 0010 **DOORS & WINDOWS, INTERIOR LATEX**        R099100-10 | | | | | | | | | |
| 0100 Doors, flush, both sides, incl. frame & trim | | | | | | | | | |
| 0110 Roll & brush, primer | 1 Pord | 10 | .800 | Ea. | 3.78 | 20.50 | | 24.28 | 37.50 |
| 0120 Finish coat, latex | | 10 | .800 | | 4.09 | 20.50 | | 24.59 | 38 |
| 0130 Primer & 1 coat latex | | 7 | 1.143 | | 7.85 | 29.50 | | 37.35 | 56.50 |
| 0140 Primer & 2 coats latex | | 5 | 1.600 | | 11.75 | 41.50 | | 53.25 | 80 |
| 0160 Spray, both sides, primer | | 20 | .400 | | 3.98 | 10.30 | | 14.28 | 21 |
| 0170 Finish coat, latex | | 20 | .400 | | 4.30 | 10.30 | | 14.60 | 21.50 |
| 0180 Primer & 1 coat latex | | 11 | .727 | | 8.35 | 18.75 | | 27.10 | 39.50 |
| 0190 Primer & 2 coats latex | | 8 | 1 | | 12.40 | 26 | | 38.40 | 55.50 |
| 0200 Doors, French, both sides, 10-15 lite, incl. frame & trim | | | | | | | | | |
| 0210 Roll & brush, primer | 1 Pord | 6 | 1.333 | Ea. | 1.89 | 34.50 | | 36.39 | 58 |
| 0220 Finish coat, latex | | 6 | 1.333 | | 2.05 | 34.50 | | 36.55 | 58.50 |
| 0230 Primer & 1 coat latex | | 3 | 2.667 | | 3.94 | 69 | | 72.94 | 116 |
| 0240 Primer & 2 coats latex | | 2 | 4 | | 5.85 | 103 | | 108.85 | 174 |
| 0260 Doors, louvered, both sides, incl. frame & trim | | | | | | | | | |
| 0270 Roll & brush, primer | 1 Pord | 7 | 1.143 | Ea. | 3.78 | 29.50 | | 33.28 | 52 |
| 0280 Finish coat, latex | | 7 | 1.143 | | 4.09 | 29.50 | | 33.59 | 52.50 |
| 0290 Primer & 1 coat, latex | | 4 | 2 | | 7.65 | 51.50 | | 59.15 | 92.50 |
| 0300 Primer & 2 coats, latex | | 3 | 2.667 | | 11.95 | 69 | | 80.95 | 125 |
| 0320 Spray, both sides, primer | | 20 | .400 | | 3.98 | 10.30 | | 14.28 | 21 |
| 0330 Finish coat, latex | | 20 | .400 | | 4.30 | 10.30 | | 14.60 | 21.50 |

# 09 91 Painting

## 09 91 23 – Interior Painting

| 09 91 23.35 Doors and Windows, Interior Latex | | Crew | Daily Output | Labor-Hours | Unit | Material | 2010 Bare Costs Labor | Equipment | Total | Total Incl O&P |
|---|---|---|---|---|---|---|---|---|---|---|
| 0340 | Primer & 1 coat, latex | 1 Pord | 11 | .727 | Ea. | 8.35 | 18.75 | | 27.10 | 39.50 |
| 0350 | Primer & 2 coats, latex | | 8 | 1 | | 12.70 | 26 | | 38.70 | 56 |
| 0360 | Doors, panel, both sides, incl. frame & trim | | | | | | | | | |
| 0370 | Roll & brush, primer | 1 Pord | 6 | 1.333 | Ea. | 3.98 | 34.50 | | 38.48 | 60.50 |
| 0380 | Finish coat, latex | | 6 | 1.333 | | 4.09 | 34.50 | | 38.59 | 60.50 |
| 0390 | Primer & 1 coat, latex | | 3 | 2.667 | | 7.85 | 69 | | 76.85 | 121 |
| 0400 | Primer & 2 coats, latex | | 2.50 | 3.200 | | 11.95 | 82.50 | | 94.45 | 147 |
| 0420 | Spray, both sides, primer | | 10 | .800 | | 3.98 | 20.50 | | 24.48 | 38 |
| 0430 | Finish coat, latex | | 10 | .800 | | 4.30 | 20.50 | | 24.80 | 38 |
| 0440 | Primer & 1 coat, latex | | 5 | 1.600 | | 8.35 | 41.50 | | 49.85 | 76 |
| 0450 | Primer & 2 coats, latex | | 4 | 2 | | 12.70 | 51.50 | | 64.20 | 98 |
| 0460 | Windows, per interior side, based on 15 SF | | | | | | | | | |
| 0470 | 1 to 6 lite | | | | | | | | | |
| 0480 | Brushwork, primer | 1 Pord | 13 | .615 | Ea. | .75 | 15.90 | | 16.65 | 27 |
| 0490 | Finish coat, enamel | | 13 | .615 | | .81 | 15.90 | | 16.71 | 27 |
| 0500 | Primer & 1 coat enamel | | 8 | 1 | | 1.55 | 26 | | 27.55 | 43.50 |
| 0510 | Primer & 2 coats enamel | | 6 | 1.333 | | 2.36 | 34.50 | | 36.86 | 58.50 |
| 0530 | 7 to 10 lite | | | | | | | | | |
| 0540 | Brushwork, primer | 1 Pord | 11 | .727 | Ea. | .75 | 18.75 | | 19.50 | 31.50 |
| 0550 | Finish coat, enamel | | 11 | .727 | | .81 | 18.75 | | 19.56 | 31.50 |
| 0560 | Primer & 1 coat enamel | | 7 | 1.143 | | 1.55 | 29.50 | | 31.05 | 49.50 |
| 0570 | Primer & 2 coats enamel | | 5 | 1.600 | | 2.36 | 41.50 | | 43.86 | 69.50 |
| 0590 | 12 lite | | | | | | | | | |
| 0600 | Brushwork, primer | 1 Pord | 10 | .800 | Ea. | .75 | 20.50 | | 21.25 | 34.50 |
| 0610 | Finish coat, enamel | | 10 | .800 | | .81 | 20.50 | | 21.31 | 34.50 |
| 0620 | Primer & 1 coat enamel | | 6 | 1.333 | | 1.55 | 34.50 | | 36.05 | 57.50 |
| 0630 | Primer & 2 coats enamel | | 5 | 1.600 | | 2.36 | 41.50 | | 43.86 | 69.50 |
| 0650 | For oil base paint, add | | | | | 10% | | | | |

| 09 91 23.39 Doors and Windows, Interior Latex, Zero Voc | | | Crew | Daily Output | Labor-Hours | Unit | Material | 2010 Bare Costs Labor | Equipment | Total | Total Incl O&P |
|---|---|---|---|---|---|---|---|---|---|---|---|
| 0010 | **DOORS & WINDOWS, INTERIOR LATEX, ZERO VOC** | | | | | | | | | | |
| 0100 | Doors flush, both sides, incl. frame & trim | | | | | | | | | | |
| 0110 | Roll & brush, primer | G | 1 Pord | 10 | .800 | Ea. | 5.05 | 20.50 | | 25.55 | 39 |
| 0120 | Finish coat, latex | G | | 10 | .800 | | 5.25 | 20.50 | | 25.75 | 39.50 |
| 0130 | Primer & 1 coat latex | G | | 7 | 1.143 | | 10.30 | 29.50 | | 39.80 | 59.50 |
| 0140 | Primer & 2 coats latex | G | | 5 | 1.600 | | 15.25 | 41.50 | | 56.75 | 84 |
| 0160 | Spray, both sides, primer | G | | 20 | .400 | | 5.35 | 10.30 | | 15.65 | 22.50 |
| 0170 | Finish coat, latex | G | | 20 | .400 | | 5.50 | 10.30 | | 15.80 | 23 |
| 0180 | Primer & 1 coat latex | G | | 11 | .727 | | 10.90 | 18.75 | | 29.65 | 42.50 |
| 0190 | Primer & 2 coats latex | G | | 8 | 1 | | 16.15 | 26 | | 42.15 | 60 |
| 0200 | Doors, French, both sides, 10-15 lite, incl. frame & trim | | | | | | | | | | |
| 0210 | Roll & brush, primer | G | 1 Pord | 6 | 1.333 | Ea. | 2.53 | 34.50 | | 37.03 | 59 |
| 0220 | Finish coat, latex | G | | 6 | 1.333 | | 2.62 | 34.50 | | 37.12 | 59 |
| 0230 | Primer & 1 coat latex | G | | 3 | 2.667 | | 5.15 | 69 | | 74.15 | 118 |
| 0240 | Primer & 2 coats latex | G | | 2 | 4 | | 7.60 | 103 | | 110.60 | 176 |
| 0360 | Doors, panel, both sides, incl. frame & trim | | | | | | | | | | |
| 0370 | Roll & brush, primer | G | 1 Pord | 6 | 1.333 | Ea. | 5.35 | 34.50 | | 39.85 | 62 |
| 0380 | Finish coat, latex | G | | 6 | 1.333 | | 5.25 | 34.50 | | 39.75 | 62 |
| 0390 | Primer & 1 coat, latex | G | | 3 | 2.667 | | 10.30 | 69 | | 79.30 | 123 |
| 0400 | Primer & 2 coats, latex | G | | 2.50 | 3.200 | | 15.55 | 82.50 | | 98.05 | 151 |
| 0420 | Spray, both sides, primer | G | | 10 | .800 | | 5.35 | 20.50 | | 25.85 | 39.50 |
| 0430 | Finish coat, latex | G | | 10 | .800 | | 5.50 | 20.50 | | 26 | 39.50 |
| 0440 | Primer & 1 coat, latex | G | | 5 | 1.600 | | 10.90 | 41.50 | | 52.40 | 79 |

# 09 91 Painting

## 09 91 23 – Interior Painting

### 09 91 23.39 Doors and Windows, Interior Latex, Zero Voc

| | | Crew | Daily Output | Labor-Hours | Unit | Material | 2010 Bare Costs Labor | Equipment | Total | Total Incl O&P |
|---|---|---|---|---|---|---|---|---|---|---|
| 0450 | Primer & 2 coats, latex [G] | 1 Pord | 4 | 2 | Ea. | 16.45 | 51.50 | | 67.95 | 102 |
| 0460 | Windows, per interior side, based on 15 SF | | | | | | | | | |
| 0470 | 1 to 6 lite | | | | | | | | | |
| 0480 | Brushwork, primer [G] | 1 Pord | 13 | .615 | Ea. | 1 | 15.90 | | 16.90 | 27 |
| 0490 | Finish coat, enamel [G] | | 13 | .615 | | 1.03 | 15.90 | | 16.93 | 27 |
| 0500 | Primer & 1 coat enamel [G] | | 8 | 1 | | 2.03 | 26 | | 28.03 | 44 |
| 0510 | Primer & 2 coats enamel [G] | | 6 | 1.333 | | 3.07 | 34.50 | | 37.57 | 59.50 |

### 09 91 23.40 Floors, Interior

| | | Crew | Daily Output | Labor-Hours | Unit | Material | 2010 Bare Costs Labor | Equipment | Total | Total Incl O&P |
|---|---|---|---|---|---|---|---|---|---|---|
| 0010 | **FLOORS, INTERIOR** | | | | | | | | | |
| 0100 | Concrete paint, latex | | | | | | | | | |
| 0110 | Brushwork | | | | | | | | | |
| 0120 | 1st coat | 1 Pord | 975 | .008 | S.F. | .15 | .21 | | .36 | .51 |
| 0130 | 2nd coat | | 1150 | .007 | | .10 | .18 | | .28 | .40 |
| 0140 | 3rd coat | | 1300 | .006 | | .08 | .16 | | .24 | .35 |
| 0150 | Roll | | | | | | | | | |
| 0160 | 1st coat | 1 Pord | 2600 | .003 | S.F. | .20 | .08 | | .28 | .35 |
| 0170 | 2nd coat | | 3250 | .002 | | .12 | .06 | | .18 | .23 |
| 0180 | 3rd coat | | 3900 | .002 | | .09 | .05 | | .14 | .19 |
| 0190 | Spray | | | | | | | | | |
| 0200 | 1st coat | 1 Pord | 2600 | .003 | S.F. | .17 | .08 | | .25 | .32 |
| 0210 | 2nd coat | | 3250 | .002 | | .09 | .06 | | .15 | .20 |
| 0220 | 3rd coat | | 3900 | .002 | | .08 | .05 | | .13 | .17 |
| 0300 | Acid stain and sealer | | | | | | | | | |
| 0310 | Stain, one coat | 1 Pord | 650 | .012 | S.F. | .11 | .32 | | .43 | .64 |
| 0320 | Two coats | | 570 | .014 | | .22 | .36 | | .58 | .83 |
| 0330 | Acrylic sealer, one coat | | 2600 | .003 | | .15 | .08 | | .23 | .30 |
| 0340 | Two coats | | 1400 | .006 | | .30 | .15 | | .45 | .57 |

### 09 91 23.52 Miscellaneous, Interior

| | | Crew | Daily Output | Labor-Hours | Unit | Material | 2010 Bare Costs Labor | Equipment | Total | Total Incl O&P |
|---|---|---|---|---|---|---|---|---|---|---|
| 0010 | **MISCELLANEOUS, INTERIOR** | | | | | | | | | |
| 2400 | Floors, conc./wood, oil base, primer/sealer coat, brushwork | 2 Pord | 1950 | .008 | S.F. | .06 | .21 | | .27 | .41 |
| 2450 | Roller | | 5200 | .003 | | .06 | .08 | | .14 | .20 |
| 2600 | Spray | | 6000 | .003 | | .06 | .07 | | .13 | .18 |
| 2650 | Paint 1 coat, brushwork | | 1950 | .008 | | .10 | .21 | | .31 | .45 |
| 2800 | Roller | | 5200 | .003 | | .10 | .08 | | .18 | .24 |
| 2850 | Spray | | 6000 | .003 | | .11 | .07 | | .18 | .23 |
| 3000 | Stain, wood floor, brushwork, 1 coat | | 4550 | .004 | | .07 | .09 | | .16 | .23 |
| 3200 | Roller | | 5200 | .003 | | .08 | .08 | | .16 | .22 |
| 3250 | Spray | | 6000 | .003 | | .08 | .07 | | .15 | .20 |
| 3400 | Varnish, wood floor, brushwork | | 4550 | .004 | | .08 | .09 | | .17 | .24 |
| 3450 | Roller | | 5200 | .003 | | .08 | .08 | | .16 | .22 |
| 3600 | Spray | | 6000 | .003 | | .09 | .07 | | .16 | .21 |
| 3800 | Grilles, per side, oil base, primer coat, brushwork | 1 Pord | 520 | .015 | | .14 | .40 | | .54 | .81 |
| 3850 | Spray | | 1140 | .007 | | .15 | .18 | | .33 | .45 |
| 3880 | Paint 1 coat, brushwork | | 520 | .015 | | .21 | .40 | | .61 | .88 |
| 3900 | Spray | | 1140 | .007 | | .24 | .18 | | .42 | .55 |
| 3920 | Paint 2 coats, brushwork | | 325 | .025 | | .41 | .64 | | 1.05 | 1.48 |
| 3940 | Spray | | 650 | .012 | | .47 | .32 | | .79 | 1.04 |
| 4500 | Louvers, one side, primer, brushwork | | 524 | .015 | | .06 | .39 | | .45 | .71 |
| 4520 | Paint one coat, brushwork | | 520 | .015 | | .07 | .40 | | .47 | .73 |
| 4530 | Spray | | 1140 | .007 | | .08 | .18 | | .26 | .38 |
| 4540 | Paint two coats, brushwork | | 325 | .025 | | .14 | .64 | | .78 | 1.18 |
| 4550 | Spray | | 650 | .012 | | .15 | .32 | | .47 | .69 |

# 09 91 Painting

## 09 91 23 – Interior Painting

### 09 91 23.52 Miscellaneous, Interior

| | | Crew | Daily Output | Labor-Hours | Unit | Material | 2010 Bare Costs Labor | Equipment | Total | Total Incl O&P |
|---|---|---|---|---|---|---|---|---|---|---|
| 4560 | Paint three coats, brushwork | 1 Pord | 270 | .030 | S.F. | .21 | .76 | | .97 | 1.47 |
| 4570 | Spray | | 500 | .016 | | .23 | .41 | | .64 | .92 |
| 5000 | Pipe, 1" - 4" diameter, primer or sealer coat, oil base, brushwork | 2 Pord | 1250 | .013 | L.F. | .06 | .33 | | .39 | .61 |
| 5100 | Spray | | 2165 | .007 | | .06 | .19 | | .25 | .38 |
| 5200 | Paint 1 coat, brushwork | | 1250 | .013 | | .08 | .33 | | .41 | .63 |
| 5300 | Spray | | 2165 | .007 | | .07 | .19 | | .26 | .39 |
| 5350 | Paint 2 coats, brushwork | | 775 | .021 | | .15 | .53 | | .68 | 1.03 |
| 5400 | Spray | | 1240 | .013 | | .16 | .33 | | .49 | .72 |
| 5450 | 5" - 8" diameter, primer or sealer coat, brushwork | | 620 | .026 | | .13 | .67 | | .80 | 1.22 |
| 5500 | Spray | | 1085 | .015 | | .21 | .38 | | .59 | .85 |
| 5550 | Paint 1 coat, brushwork | | 620 | .026 | | .22 | .67 | | .89 | 1.32 |
| 5600 | Spray | | 1085 | .015 | | .25 | .38 | | .63 | .89 |
| 5650 | Paint 2 coats, brushwork | | 385 | .042 | | .29 | 1.07 | | 1.36 | 2.07 |
| 5700 | Spray | | 620 | .026 | | .32 | .67 | | .99 | 1.44 |
| 6600 | Radiators, per side, primer, brushwork | 1 Pord | 520 | .015 | S.F. | .06 | .40 | | .46 | .72 |
| 6620 | Paint, one coat | | 520 | .015 | | .06 | .40 | | .46 | .71 |
| 6640 | Two coats | | 340 | .024 | | .14 | .61 | | .75 | 1.14 |
| 6660 | Three coats | | 283 | .028 | | .21 | .73 | | .94 | 1.42 |
| 7000 | Trim, wood, incl. puttying, under 6" wide | | | | | | | | | |
| 7200 | Primer coat, oil base, brushwork | 1 Pord | 650 | .012 | L.F. | .04 | .32 | | .36 | .56 |
| 7250 | Paint, 1 coat, brushwork | | 650 | .012 | | .05 | .32 | | .37 | .58 |
| 7400 | 2 coats | | 400 | .020 | | .10 | .52 | | .62 | .95 |
| 7450 | 3 coats | | 325 | .025 | | .15 | .64 | | .79 | 1.20 |
| 7500 | Over 6" wide, primer coat, brushwork | | 650 | .012 | | .07 | .32 | | .39 | .60 |
| 7550 | Paint, 1 coat, brushwork | | 650 | .012 | | .11 | .32 | | .43 | .64 |
| 7600 | 2 coats | | 400 | .020 | | .21 | .52 | | .73 | 1.07 |
| 7650 | 3 coats | | 325 | .025 | | .31 | .64 | | .95 | 1.37 |
| 8000 | Cornice, simple design, primer coat, oil base, brushwork | | 650 | .012 | S.F. | .07 | .32 | | .39 | .60 |
| 8250 | Paint, 1 coat | | 650 | .012 | | .11 | .32 | | .43 | .64 |
| 8300 | 2 coats | | 400 | .020 | | .21 | .52 | | .73 | 1.07 |
| 8350 | Ornate design, primer coat | | 350 | .023 | | .07 | .59 | | .66 | 1.04 |
| 8400 | Paint, 1 coat | | 350 | .023 | | .11 | .59 | | .70 | 1.08 |
| 8450 | 2 coats | | 400 | .020 | | .21 | .52 | | .73 | 1.07 |
| 8600 | Balustrades, primer coat, oil base, brushwork | | 520 | .015 | | .07 | .40 | | .47 | .73 |
| 8650 | Paint, 1 coat | | 520 | .015 | | .11 | .40 | | .51 | .77 |
| 8700 | 2 coats | | 325 | .025 | | .21 | .64 | | .85 | 1.26 |
| 8900 | Trusses and wood frames, primer coat, oil base, brushwork | | 800 | .010 | | .07 | .26 | | .33 | .50 |
| 8950 | Spray | | 1200 | .007 | | .07 | .17 | | .24 | .36 |
| 9000 | Paint 1 coat, brushwork | | 750 | .011 | | .11 | .28 | | .39 | .57 |
| 9200 | Spray | | 1200 | .007 | | .12 | .17 | | .29 | .41 |
| 9220 | Paint 2 coats, brushwork | | 500 | .016 | | .21 | .41 | | .62 | .90 |
| 9240 | Spray | | 600 | .013 | | .23 | .34 | | .57 | .81 |
| 9260 | Stain, brushwork, wipe off | | 600 | .013 | | .07 | .34 | | .41 | .64 |
| 9280 | Varnish, 3 coats, brushwork | | 275 | .029 | | .24 | .75 | | .99 | 1.48 |
| 9350 | For latex paint, deduct | | | | | 10% | | | | |

### 09 91 23.72 Walls and Ceilings, Interior

| | | Crew | Daily Output | Labor-Hours | Unit | Material | 2010 Bare Costs Labor | Equipment | Total | Total Incl O&P |
|---|---|---|---|---|---|---|---|---|---|---|
| 0010 | **WALLS AND CEILINGS, INTERIOR** | | | | | | | | | |
| 0100 | Concrete, drywall or plaster, oil base, primer or sealer coat | | | | | | | | | |
| 0200 | Smooth finish, brushwork | 1 Pord | 1150 | .007 | S.F. | .07 | .18 | | .25 | .37 |
| 0240 | Roller | | 1350 | .006 | | .07 | .15 | | .22 | .32 |
| 0280 | Spray | | 2750 | .003 | | .05 | .08 | | .13 | .18 |
| 0300 | Sand finish, brushwork | | 975 | .008 | | .07 | .21 | | .28 | .41 |

| 09 91 23.72 Walls and Ceilings, Interior | Crew | Daily Output | Labor-Hours | Unit | Material | 2010 Bare Costs Labor | Equipment | Total | Total Incl O&P |
|---|---|---|---|---|---|---|---|---|---|
| 0340 | Roller | 1 Pord | 1150 | .007 | S.F. | .08 | .18 | | .26 | .37 |
| 0380 | Spray | | 2275 | .004 | | .06 | .09 | | .15 | .21 |
| 0400 | Paint 1 coat, smooth finish, brushwork | | 1200 | .007 | | .09 | .17 | | .26 | .38 |
| 0440 | Roller | | 1300 | .006 | | .09 | .16 | | .25 | .36 |
| 0480 | Spray | | 2275 | .004 | | .08 | .09 | | .17 | .24 |
| 0500 | Sand finish, brushwork | | 1050 | .008 | | .09 | .20 | | .29 | .42 |
| 0540 | Roller | | 1600 | .005 | | .09 | .13 | | .22 | .31 |
| 0580 | Spray | | 2100 | .004 | | .08 | .10 | | .18 | .25 |
| 0800 | Paint 2 coats, smooth finish, brushwork | | 680 | .012 | | .18 | .30 | | .48 | .69 |
| 0840 | Roller | | 800 | .010 | | .19 | .26 | | .45 | .63 |
| 0880 | Spray | | 1625 | .005 | | .16 | .13 | | .29 | .39 |
| 0900 | Sand finish, brushwork | | 605 | .013 | | .18 | .34 | | .52 | .76 |
| 0940 | Roller | | 1020 | .008 | | .19 | .20 | | .39 | .54 |
| 0980 | Spray | | 1700 | .005 | | .16 | .12 | | .28 | .38 |
| 1200 | Paint 3 coats, smooth finish, brushwork | | 510 | .016 | | .27 | .40 | | .67 | .95 |
| 1240 | Roller | | 650 | .012 | | .28 | .32 | | .60 | .83 |
| 1280 | Spray | | 1625 | .005 | | .24 | .13 | | .37 | .48 |
| 1300 | Sand finish, brushwork | | 454 | .018 | | .27 | .45 | | .72 | 1.03 |
| 1340 | Roller | | 680 | .012 | | .28 | .30 | | .58 | .80 |
| 1380 | Spray | | 1133 | .007 | | .24 | .18 | | .42 | .57 |
| 1600 | Glaze coating, 2 coats, spray, clear | | 1200 | .007 | | .49 | .17 | | .66 | .82 |
| 1640 | Multicolor | | 1200 | .007 | | .95 | .17 | | 1.12 | 1.33 |
| 1660 | Painting walls, complete, including surface prep, primer & | | | | | | | | | |
| 1670 | 2 coats finish, on drywall or plaster, with roller | 1 Pord | 325 | .025 | S.F. | .18 | .64 | | .82 | 1.23 |
| 1700 | For latex paint, deduct | | | | | 10% | | | | |
| 1800 | For ceiling installations, add | | | | | | 25% | | | |
| 2000 | Masonry or concrete block, oil base, primer or sealer coat | | | | | | | | | |
| 2100 | Smooth finish, brushwork | 1 Pord | 1224 | .007 | S.F. | .06 | .17 | | .23 | .34 |
| 2180 | Spray | | 2400 | .003 | | .09 | .09 | | .18 | .24 |
| 2200 | Sand finish, brushwork | | 1089 | .007 | | .10 | .19 | | .29 | .42 |
| 2280 | Spray | | 2400 | .003 | | .09 | .09 | | .18 | .24 |
| 2400 | Paint 1 coat, smooth finish, brushwork | | 1100 | .007 | | .10 | .19 | | .29 | .42 |
| 2480 | Spray | | 2400 | .003 | | .09 | .09 | | .18 | .24 |
| 2500 | Sand finish, brushwork | | 979 | .008 | | .10 | .21 | | .31 | .45 |
| 2580 | Spray | | 2400 | .003 | | .09 | .09 | | .18 | .24 |
| 2800 | Paint 2 coats, smooth finish, brushwork | | 756 | .011 | | .20 | .27 | | .47 | .66 |
| 2880 | Spray | | 1360 | .006 | | .18 | .15 | | .33 | .45 |
| 2900 | Sand finish, brushwork | | 672 | .012 | | .20 | .31 | | .51 | .72 |
| 2980 | Spray | | 1360 | .006 | | .18 | .15 | | .33 | .45 |
| 3200 | Paint 3 coats, smooth finish, brushwork | | 560 | .014 | | .30 | .37 | | .67 | .93 |
| 3280 | Spray | | 1088 | .007 | | .28 | .19 | | .47 | .61 |
| 3300 | Sand finish, brushwork | | 498 | .016 | | .30 | .41 | | .71 | 1 |
| 3380 | Spray | | 1088 | .007 | | .28 | .19 | | .47 | .61 |
| 3600 | Glaze coating, 3 coats, spray, clear | | 900 | .009 | | .70 | .23 | | .93 | 1.14 |
| 3620 | Multicolor | | 900 | .009 | | 1.10 | .23 | | 1.33 | 1.58 |
| 4000 | Block filler, 1 coat, brushwork | | 425 | .019 | | .13 | .49 | | .62 | .94 |
| 4100 | Silicone, water repellent, 2 coats, spray | | 2000 | .004 | | .26 | .10 | | .36 | .45 |
| 4120 | For latex paint, deduct | | | | | 10% | | | | |
| 8200 | For work 8' - 15' H, add | | | | | | 10% | | | |
| 8300 | For work over 15' H, add | | | | | | 20% | | | |
| 8400 | For light textured surfaces, add | | | | | | 10% | | | |
| 8410 | Heavy textured, add | | | | | | 25% | | | |

# 09 91 Painting

## 09 91 23 – Interior Painting

| 09 91 23.74 Walls and Ceilings, Interior, Zero VOC Latex | | Crew | Daily Output | Labor-Hours | Unit | Material | 2010 Bare Costs Labor | Equipment | Total | Total Incl O&P |
|---|---|---|---|---|---|---|---|---|---|---|
| 0010 | **WALLS AND CEILINGS, INTERIOR, ZERO VOC LATEX** | | | | | | | | | |
| 0100 | Concrete, dry wall or plaster, latex, primer or sealer coat | | | | | | | | | |
| 0200 | Smooth finish, brushwork | G | 1 Pord | 1150 | .007 | S.F. | .07 | .18 | | .25 | .36 |
| 0240 | Roller | G | | 1350 | .006 | | .06 | .15 | | .21 | .32 |
| 0280 | Spray | G | | 2750 | .003 | | .05 | .08 | | .13 | .17 |
| 0300 | Sand finish, brushwork | G | | 975 | .008 | | .06 | .21 | | .27 | .41 |
| 0340 | Roller | G | | 1150 | .007 | | .07 | .18 | | .25 | .37 |
| 0380 | Spray | G | | 2275 | .004 | | .05 | .09 | | .14 | .21 |
| 0400 | Paint 1 coat, smooth finish, brushwork | G | | 1200 | .007 | | .06 | .17 | | .23 | .35 |
| 0440 | Roller | G | | 1300 | .006 | | .06 | .16 | | .22 | .33 |
| 0480 | Spray | G | | 2275 | .004 | | .06 | .09 | | .15 | .21 |
| 0500 | Sand finish, brushwork | G | | 1050 | .008 | | .06 | .20 | | .26 | .39 |
| 0540 | Roller | G | | 1600 | .005 | | .06 | .13 | | .19 | .28 |
| 0580 | Spray | G | | 2100 | .004 | | .06 | .10 | | .16 | .22 |
| 0800 | Paint 2 coats, smooth finish, brushwork | G | | 680 | .012 | | .13 | .30 | | .43 | .63 |
| 0840 | Roller | G | | 800 | .010 | | .13 | .26 | | .39 | .56 |
| 0880 | Spray | G | | 1625 | .005 | | .11 | .13 | | .24 | .33 |
| 0900 | Sand finish, brushwork | G | | 605 | .013 | | .12 | .34 | | .46 | .69 |
| 0940 | Roller | G | | 1020 | .008 | | .13 | .20 | | .33 | .47 |
| 0980 | Spray | G | | 1700 | .005 | | .11 | .12 | | .23 | .32 |
| 1200 | Paint 3 coats, smooth finish, brushwork | G | | 510 | .016 | | .18 | .40 | | .58 | .86 |
| 1240 | Roller | G | | 650 | .012 | | .19 | .32 | | .51 | .73 |
| 1280 | Spray | G | | 1625 | .005 | | .17 | .13 | | .30 | .39 |
| 1800 | For ceiling installations, add | G | | | | | | 25% | | | |
| 8200 | For work 8' - 15' H, add | | | | | | | 10% | | | |
| 8300 | For work over 15' H, add | | | | | | | 20% | | | |

## 09 91 23.75 Dry Fall Painting

| | | Crew | Daily Output | Labor-Hours | Unit | Material | Labor | Equipment | Total | Total Incl O&P |
|---|---|---|---|---|---|---|---|---|---|---|
| 0010 | **DRY FALL PAINTING** | | | | | | | | | |
| 0100 | Sprayed on walls, gypsum board or plaster | | | | | | | | | |
| 0220 | One coat | 1 Pord | 2600 | .003 | S.F. | .05 | .08 | | .13 | .18 |
| 0250 | Two coats | | 1560 | .005 | | .10 | .13 | | .23 | .33 |
| 0280 | Concrete or textured plaster, one coat | | 1560 | .005 | | .05 | .13 | | .18 | .27 |
| 0310 | Two coats | | 1300 | .006 | | .10 | .16 | | .26 | .37 |
| 0340 | Concrete block, one coat | | 1560 | .005 | | .05 | .13 | | .18 | .27 |
| 0370 | Two coats | | 1300 | .006 | | .10 | .16 | | .26 | .37 |
| 0400 | Wood, one coat | | 877 | .009 | | .05 | .24 | | .29 | .43 |
| 0430 | Two coats | | 650 | .012 | | .10 | .32 | | .42 | .63 |
| 0440 | On ceilings, gypsum board or plaster | | | | | | | | | |
| 0470 | One coat | 1 Pord | 1560 | .005 | S.F. | .05 | .13 | | .18 | .27 |
| 0500 | Two coats | | 1300 | .006 | | .10 | .16 | | .26 | .37 |
| 0530 | Concrete or textured plaster, one coat | | 1560 | .005 | | .05 | .13 | | .18 | .27 |
| 0560 | Two coats | | 1300 | .006 | | .10 | .16 | | .26 | .37 |
| 0570 | Structural steel, bar joists or metal deck, one coat | | 1560 | .005 | | .05 | .13 | | .18 | .27 |
| 0580 | Two coats | | 1040 | .008 | | .10 | .20 | | .30 | .43 |

# 09 93 Staining and Transparent Finishing

## 09 93 23 – Interior Staining and Finishing

| 09 93 23.10 Varnish | Crew | Daily Output | Labor-Hours | Unit | Material | 2010 Bare Costs Labor | Equipment | Total | Total Incl O&P |
|---|---|---|---|---|---|---|---|---|---|
| 0010 **VARNISH** | | | | | | | | | |
| 0012   1 coat + sealer, on wood trim, brush, no sanding included | 1 Pord | 400 | .020 | S.F. | .07 | .52 | | .59 | .92 |
| 0100   Hardwood floors, 2 coats, no sanding included, roller | " | 1890 | .004 | " | .15 | .11 | | .26 | .35 |

# 09 96 High-Performance Coatings

## 09 96 56 – Epoxy Coatings

| 09 96 56.20 Wall Coatings | Crew | Daily Output | Labor-Hours | Unit | Material | 2010 Bare Costs Labor | Equipment | Total | Total Incl O&P |
|---|---|---|---|---|---|---|---|---|---|
| 0010 **WALL COATINGS** | | | | | | | | | |
| 0100   Acrylic glazed coatings, minimum | 1 Pord | 525 | .015 | S.F. | .28 | .39 | | .67 | .95 |
| 0200     Maximum | | 305 | .026 | | .60 | .68 | | 1.28 | 1.76 |
| 0300   Epoxy coatings, minimum | | 525 | .015 | | .37 | .39 | | .76 | 1.05 |
| 0400     Maximum | | 170 | .047 | | 1.12 | 1.21 | | 2.33 | 3.21 |
| 0600   Exposed aggregate, troweled on, 1/16" to 1/4", minimum | | 235 | .034 | | .56 | .88 | | 1.44 | 2.05 |
| 0700     Maximum (epoxy or polyacrylate) | | 130 | .062 | | 1.20 | 1.59 | | 2.79 | 3.90 |
| 0900     1/2" to 5/8" aggregate, minimum | | 130 | .062 | | 1.11 | 1.59 | | 2.70 | 3.80 |
| 1000     Maximum | | 80 | .100 | | 1.90 | 2.58 | | 4.48 | 6.30 |
| 1200     1" aggregate size, minimum | | 90 | .089 | | 1.93 | 2.29 | | 4.22 | 5.85 |
| 1300     Maximum | | 55 | .145 | | 2.95 | 3.75 | | 6.70 | 9.35 |
| 1500   Exposed aggregate, sprayed on, 1/8" aggregate, minimum | | 295 | .027 | | .51 | .70 | | 1.21 | 1.70 |
| 1600     Maximum | | 145 | .055 | | .96 | 1.42 | | 2.38 | 3.38 |

# Estimating Tips

## General

- The items in this division are usually priced per square foot or each.

- Many items in Division 10 require some type of support system or special anchors that are not usually furnished with the item. The required anchors must be added to the estimate in the appropriate division.

- Some items in Division 10, such as lockers, may require assembly before installation. Verify the amount of assembly required. Assembly can often exceed installation time.

## 10 20 00 Interior Specialties

- Support angles and blocking are not included in the installation of toilet compartments, shower/dressing compartments, or cubicles. Appropriate line items from Divisions 5 or 6 may need to be added to support the installations.

- Toilet partitions are priced by the stall. A stall consists of a side wall, pilaster, and door with hardware. Toilet tissue holders and grab bars are extra.

- The required acoustical rating of a folding partition can have a significant impact on costs. Verify the sound transmission coefficient rating of the panel priced to the specification requirements.

- Grab bar installation does not include supplemental blocking or backing to support the required load. When grab bars are installed at an existing facility, provisions must be made to attach the grab bars to solid structure.

## Reference Numbers

Reference numbers are shown in shaded boxes at the beginning of some major classifications. These numbers refer to related items in the Reference Section. The reference information may be an estimating procedure, an alternate pricing method, or technical information.

*Note:* Not all subdivisions listed here necessarily appear in this publication.

**Division 10 - Specialties**

# 10 21 Compartments and Cubicles

## 10 21 16 – Shower and Dressing Compartments

| 10 21 16.10 Partitions, Shower | Crew | Daily Output | Labor-Hours | Unit | Material | 2010 Bare Costs Labor | Equipment | Total | Total Incl O&P |
|---|---|---|---|---|---|---|---|---|---|
| 0010 **PARTITIONS, SHOWER** Floor mounted, no plumbing | | | | | | | | | |
| 0400 Cabinet, one piece, fiberglass, 32" x 32" | 2 Carp | 5 | 3.200 | Ea. | 475 | 93 | | 568 | 675 |
| 0420 36" x 36" | | 5 | 3.200 | | 530 | 93 | | 623 | 735 |
| 0440 36" x 48" | | 5 | 3.200 | | 1,375 | 93 | | 1,468 | 1,675 |
| 0460 Acrylic, 32" x 32" | | 5 | 3.200 | | 325 | 93 | | 418 | 510 |
| 0480 36" x 36" | | 5 | 3.200 | | 980 | 93 | | 1,073 | 1,225 |
| 0500 36" x 48" | | 5 | 3.200 | | 2,100 | 93 | | 2,193 | 2,475 |
| 0520 Shower door for above, clear plastic, 24" wide | 1 Carp | 8 | 1 | | 162 | 29 | | 191 | 227 |
| 0540 28" wide | | 8 | 1 | | 184 | 29 | | 213 | 251 |
| 0560 Tempered glass, 24" wide | | 8 | 1 | | 175 | 29 | | 204 | 241 |
| 0580 28" wide | | 8 | 1 | | 197 | 29 | | 226 | 266 |
| 2400 Glass stalls, with doors, no receptors, chrome on brass | 2 Shee | 3 | 5.333 | | 1,525 | 173 | | 1,698 | 1,950 |
| 2700 Anodized aluminum | " | 4 | 4 | | 1,050 | 130 | | 1,180 | 1,375 |
| 3200 Receptors, precast terrazzo, 32" x 32" | 2 Marb | 14 | 1.143 | | 147 | 32 | | 179 | 215 |
| 3300 48" x 34" | | 9.50 | 1.684 | | 203 | 47 | | 250 | 300 |
| 3500 Plastic, simulated terrazzo receptor, 32" x 32" | | 14 | 1.143 | | 120 | 32 | | 152 | 185 |
| 3600 32" x 48" | | 12 | 1.333 | | 204 | 37.50 | | 241.50 | 287 |
| 3800 Precast concrete, colors, 32" x 32" | | 14 | 1.143 | | 221 | 32 | | 253 | 296 |
| 3900 48" x 48" | | 8 | 2 | | 395 | 56 | | 451 | 525 |
| 4100 Shower doors, economy plastic, 24" wide | 1 Shee | 9 | .889 | | 132 | 29 | | 161 | 193 |
| 4200 Tempered glass door, economy | | 8 | 1 | | 219 | 32.50 | | 251.50 | 295 |
| 4400 Folding, tempered glass, aluminum frame | | 6 | 1.333 | | 395 | 43 | | 438 | 505 |
| 4700 Deluxe, tempered glass, chrome on brass frame, minimum | | 8 | 1 | | 235 | 32.50 | | 267.50 | 315 |
| 4800 Maximum | | 1 | 8 | | 910 | 259 | | 1,169 | 1,425 |
| 4850 On anodized aluminum frame, minimum | | 2 | 4 | | 148 | 130 | | 278 | 375 |
| 4900 Maximum | | 1 | 8 | | 535 | 259 | | 794 | 1,025 |
| 5100 Shower enclosure, tempered glass, anodized alum. frame | | | | | | | | | |
| 5120 2 panel & door, corner unit, 32" x 32" | 1 Shee | 2 | 4 | Ea. | 520 | 130 | | 650 | 790 |
| 5140 Neo-angle corner unit, 16" x 24" x 16" | " | 2 | 4 | | 960 | 130 | | 1,090 | 1,275 |
| 5200 Shower surround, 3 wall, polypropylene, 32" x 32" | 1 Carp | 4 | 2 | | 385 | 58 | | 443 | 525 |
| 5220 PVC, 32" x 32" | | 4 | 2 | | 350 | 58 | | 408 | 485 |
| 5240 Fiberglass | | 4 | 2 | | 385 | 58 | | 443 | 520 |
| 5250 2 wall, polypropylene, 32" x 32" | | 4 | 2 | | 290 | 58 | | 348 | 420 |
| 5270 PVC | | 4 | 2 | | 360 | 58 | | 418 | 495 |
| 5290 Fiberglass | | 4 | 2 | | 365 | 58 | | 423 | 505 |
| 5300 Tub doors, tempered glass & frame, minimum | 1 Shee | 8 | 1 | | 210 | 32.50 | | 242.50 | 285 |
| 5400 Maximum | | 6 | 1.333 | | 490 | 43 | | 533 | 610 |
| 5600 Chrome plated, brass frame, minimum | | 8 | 1 | | 278 | 32.50 | | 310.50 | 360 |
| 5700 Maximum | | 6 | 1.333 | | 680 | 43 | | 723 | 820 |
| 5900 Tub/shower enclosure, temp. glass, alum. frame, minimum | | 2 | 4 | | 375 | 130 | | 505 | 630 |
| 6200 Maximum | | 1.50 | 5.333 | | 785 | 173 | | 958 | 1,150 |
| 6500 On chrome-plated brass frame, minimum | | 2 | 4 | | 520 | 130 | | 650 | 785 |
| 6600 Maximum | | 1.50 | 5.333 | | 1,100 | 173 | | 1,273 | 1,500 |
| 6800 Tub surround, 3 wall, polypropylene | 1 Carp | 4 | 2 | | 235 | 58 | | 293 | 355 |
| 6900 PVC | | 4 | 2 | | 355 | 58 | | 413 | 495 |
| 7000 Fiberglass, minimum | | 4 | 2 | | 370 | 58 | | 428 | 505 |
| 7100 Maximum | | 3 | 2.667 | | 625 | 77.50 | | 702.50 | 815 |

# 10 28 Toilet, Bath, and Laundry Accessories

## 10 28 13 – Toilet Accessories

| 10 28 13.13 Commercial Toilet Accessories | Crew | Daily Output | Labor-Hours | Unit | Material | 2010 Bare Costs Labor | Equipment | Total | Total Incl O&P |
|---|---|---|---|---|---|---|---|---|---|
| 0010 **COMMERCIAL TOILET ACCESSORIES** | | | | | | | | | |
| 0200 Curtain rod, stainless steel, 5' long, 1" diameter | 1 Carp | 13 | .615 | Ea. | 34.50 | 17.90 | | 52.40 | 68 |
| 0300 1-1/4" diameter | | 13 | .615 | | 24 | 17.90 | | 41.90 | 56.50 |
| 0800 Grab bar, straight, 1-1/4" diameter, stainless steel, 18" long | | 24 | .333 | | 30 | 9.70 | | 39.70 | 50 |
| 1100 36" long | | 20 | .400 | | 34.50 | 11.65 | | 46.15 | 57.50 |
| 1105 42" long | | 20 | .400 | | 37.50 | 11.65 | | 49.15 | 61 |
| 3000 Mirror, with stainless steel 3/4" square frame, 18" x 24" | | 20 | .400 | | 56.50 | 11.65 | | 68.15 | 82 |
| 3100 36" x 24" | | 15 | .533 | | 105 | 15.50 | | 120.50 | 142 |
| 3300 72" x 24" | | 6 | 1.333 | | 210 | 39 | | 249 | 297 |
| 4300 Robe hook, single, regular | | 36 | .222 | | 11.65 | 6.45 | | 18.10 | 23.50 |
| 4400 Heavy duty, concealed mounting | | 36 | .222 | | 13.35 | 6.45 | | 19.80 | 25.50 |
| 6400 Towel bar, stainless steel, 18" long | | 23 | .348 | | 39.50 | 10.10 | | 49.60 | 60.50 |
| 6500 30" long | | 21 | .381 | | 111 | 11.10 | | 122.10 | 142 |
| 7400 Tumbler holder, tumbler only | | 30 | .267 | | 40 | 7.75 | | 47.75 | 57 |
| 7500 Soap, tumbler & toothbrush | | 30 | .267 | | 18.30 | 7.75 | | 26.05 | 33 |

## 10 28 16 – Bath Accessories

### 10 28 16.20 Medicine Cabinets

| | Crew | Daily Output | Labor-Hours | Unit | Material | Labor | Equipment | Total | Total Incl O&P |
|---|---|---|---|---|---|---|---|---|---|
| 0010 **MEDICINE CABINETS** | | | | | | | | | |
| 0020 With mirror, st. st. frame, 16" x 22", unlighted | 1 Carp | 14 | .571 | Ea. | 66.50 | 16.65 | | 83.15 | 101 |
| 0100 Wood frame | | 14 | .571 | | 119 | 16.65 | | 135.65 | 159 |
| 0300 Sliding mirror doors, 20" x 16" x 4-3/4", unlighted | | 7 | 1.143 | | 110 | 33.50 | | 143.50 | 177 |
| 0400 24" x 19" x 8-1/2", lighted | | 5 | 1.600 | | 159 | 46.50 | | 205.50 | 254 |
| 0600 Triple door, 30" x 32", unlighted, plywood body | | 7 | 1.143 | | 279 | 33.50 | | 312.50 | 360 |
| 0700 Steel body | | 7 | 1.143 | | 310 | 33.50 | | 343.50 | 395 |
| 0900 Oak door, wood body, beveled mirror, single door | | 7 | 1.143 | | 160 | 33.50 | | 193.50 | 232 |
| 1000 Double door | | 6 | 1.333 | | 375 | 39 | | 414 | 475 |

## 10 28 23 – Laundry Accessories

### 10 28 23.13 Built-In Ironing Boards

| | Crew | Daily Output | Labor-Hours | Unit | Material | Labor | Equipment | Total | Total Incl O&P |
|---|---|---|---|---|---|---|---|---|---|
| 0010 **BUILT-IN IRONING BOARDS** | | | | | | | | | |
| 0020 Including cabinet, board & light, minimum | 1 Carp | 2 | 4 | Ea. | 315 | 116 | | 431 | 540 |

# 10 31 Manufactured Fireplaces

## 10 31 13 – Manufactured Fireplace Chimneys

### 10 31 13.10 Fireplace Chimneys

| | Crew | Daily Output | Labor-Hours | Unit | Material | Labor | Equipment | Total | Total Incl O&P |
|---|---|---|---|---|---|---|---|---|---|
| 0010 **FIREPLACE CHIMNEYS** | | | | | | | | | |
| 0500 Chimney dbl. wall, all stainless, over 8'-6", 7" diam., add to fireplace | 1 Carp | 33 | .242 | V.L.F. | 71.50 | 7.05 | | 78.55 | 90.50 |
| 0600 10" diameter, add to fireplace | | 32 | .250 | | 109 | 7.30 | | 116.30 | 132 |
| 0700 12" diameter, add to fireplace | | 31 | .258 | | 136 | 7.50 | | 143.50 | 162 |
| 0800 14" diameter, add to fireplace | | 30 | .267 | | 183 | 7.75 | | 190.75 | 214 |
| 1000 Simulated brick chimney top, 4' high, 16" x 16" | | 10 | .800 | Ea. | 258 | 23.50 | | 281.50 | 325 |
| 1100 24" x 24" | | 7 | 1.143 | " | 480 | 33.50 | | 513.50 | 585 |

### 10 31 13.20 Chimney Accessories

| | Crew | Daily Output | Labor-Hours | Unit | Material | Labor | Equipment | Total | Total Incl O&P |
|---|---|---|---|---|---|---|---|---|---|
| 0010 **CHIMNEY ACCESSORIES** | | | | | | | | | |
| 0020 Chimney screens, galv., 13" x 13" flue | 1 Bric | 8 | 1 | Ea. | 54 | 29.50 | | 83.50 | 107 |
| 0050 24" x 24" flue | | 5 | 1.600 | | 124 | 47 | | 171 | 214 |
| 0200 Stainless steel, 13" x 13" flue | | 8 | 1 | | 330 | 29.50 | | 359.50 | 410 |
| 0250 20" x 20" flue | | 5 | 1.600 | | 450 | 47 | | 497 | 570 |
| 2400 Squirrel and bird screens, galvanized, 8" x 8" flue | | 16 | .500 | | 46.50 | 14.65 | | 61.15 | 75.50 |
| 2450 13" x 13" flue | | 12 | .667 | | 50.50 | 19.50 | | 70 | 87.50 |

# 10 31 Manufactured Fireplaces

## 10 31 16 – Manufactured Fireplace Forms

| 10 31 16.10 Fireplace Forms | Crew | Daily Output | Labor-Hours | Unit | Material | 2010 Bare Costs Labor | Equipment | Total | Total Incl O&P |
|---|---|---|---|---|---|---|---|---|---|
| 0010 **FIREPLACE FORMS** | | | | | | | | | |
| 1800 Fireplace forms, no accessories, 32" opening | 1 Bric | 3 | 2.667 | Ea. | 650 | 78 | | 728 | 845 |
| 1900 36" opening | | 2.50 | 3.200 | | 830 | 93.50 | | 923.50 | 1,075 |
| 2000 40" opening | | 2 | 4 | | 1,100 | 117 | | 1,217 | 1,400 |
| 2100 78" opening | | 1.50 | 5.333 | | 1,600 | 156 | | 1,756 | 2,000 |

## 10 31 23 – Prefabricated Fireplaces

| 10 31 23.10 Fireplace, Prefabricated | Crew | Daily Output | Labor-Hours | Unit | Material | 2010 Bare Costs Labor | Equipment | Total | Total Incl O&P |
|---|---|---|---|---|---|---|---|---|---|
| 0010 **FIREPLACE, PREFABRICATED**, free standing or wall hung | | | | | | | | | |
| 0100 With hood & screen, minimum | 1 Carp | 1.30 | 6.154 | Ea. | 1,200 | 179 | | 1,379 | 1,625 |
| 0150 Average | | 1 | 8 | | 1,700 | 233 | | 1,933 | 2,250 |
| 0200 Maximum | | .90 | 8.889 | | 3,375 | 259 | | 3,634 | 4,125 |
| 1500 Simulated logs, gas fired, 40,000 BTU, 2' long, minimum | | 7 | 1.143 | Set | 450 | 33.50 | | 483.50 | 550 |
| 1600 Maximum | | 6 | 1.333 | | 980 | 39 | | 1,019 | 1,150 |
| 1700 Electric, 1,500 BTU, 1'-6" long, minimum | | 7 | 1.143 | | 175 | 33.50 | | 208.50 | 249 |
| 1800 11,500 BTU, maximum | | 6 | 1.333 | | 395 | 39 | | 434 | 495 |
| 2000 Fireplace, built-in, 36" hearth, radiant | | 1.30 | 6.154 | Ea. | 595 | 179 | | 774 | 955 |
| 2100 Recirculating, small fan | | 1 | 8 | | 925 | 233 | | 1,158 | 1,425 |
| 2150 Large fan | | .90 | 8.889 | | 1,925 | 259 | | 2,184 | 2,525 |
| 2200 42" hearth, radiant | | 1.20 | 6.667 | | 835 | 194 | | 1,029 | 1,250 |
| 2300 Recirculating, small fan | | .90 | 8.889 | | 1,075 | 259 | | 1,334 | 1,625 |
| 2350 Large fan | | .80 | 10 | | 1,925 | 291 | | 2,216 | 2,600 |
| 2400 48" hearth, radiant | | 1.10 | 7.273 | | 1,800 | 212 | | 2,012 | 2,325 |
| 2500 Recirculating, small fan | | .80 | 10 | | 2,225 | 291 | | 2,516 | 2,950 |
| 2550 Large fan | | .70 | 11.429 | | 3,450 | 335 | | 3,785 | 4,350 |
| 3000 See through, including doors | | .80 | 10 | | 2,925 | 291 | | 3,216 | 3,725 |
| 3200 Corner (2 wall) | | 1 | 8 | | 2,950 | 233 | | 3,183 | 3,625 |

# 10 32 Fireplace Specialties

## 10 32 13 – Fireplace Dampers

| 10 32 13.10 Dampers | Crew | Daily Output | Labor-Hours | Unit | Material | 2010 Bare Costs Labor | Equipment | Total | Total Incl O&P |
|---|---|---|---|---|---|---|---|---|---|
| 0010 **DAMPERS** | | | | | | | | | |
| 0800 Damper, rotary control, steel, 30" opening | 1 Bric | 6 | 1.333 | Ea. | 79.50 | 39 | | 118.50 | 152 |
| 0850 Cast iron, 30" opening | | 6 | 1.333 | | 88.50 | 39 | | 127.50 | 162 |
| 1200 Steel plate, poker control, 60" opening | | 8 | 1 | | 281 | 29.50 | | 310.50 | 360 |
| 1250 84" opening, special order | | 5 | 1.600 | | 510 | 47 | | 557 | 640 |
| 1400 "Universal" type, chain operated, 32" x 20" opening | | 8 | 1 | | 218 | 29.50 | | 247.50 | 288 |
| 1450 48" x 24" opening | | 5 | 1.600 | | 325 | 47 | | 372 | 435 |

## 10 32 23 – Fireplace Doors

| 10 32 23.10 Doors | Crew | Daily Output | Labor-Hours | Unit | Material | 2010 Bare Costs Labor | Equipment | Total | Total Incl O&P |
|---|---|---|---|---|---|---|---|---|---|
| 0010 **DOORS** | | | | | | | | | |
| 0400 Cleanout doors and frames, cast iron, 8" x 8" | 1 Bric | 12 | .667 | Ea. | 37.50 | 19.50 | | 57 | 73 |
| 0450 12" x 12" | | 10 | .800 | | 45.50 | 23.50 | | 69 | 88.50 |
| 0500 18" x 24" | | 8 | 1 | | 131 | 29.50 | | 160.50 | 192 |
| 0550 Cast iron frame, steel door, 24" x 30" | | 5 | 1.600 | | 283 | 47 | | 330 | 385 |
| 1600 Dutch Oven door and frame, cast iron, 12" x 15" opening | | 13 | .615 | | 115 | 18 | | 133 | 156 |
| 1650 Copper plated, 12" x 15" opening | | 13 | .615 | | 224 | 18 | | 242 | 277 |

# 10 35 Stoves

## 10 35 13 – Heating Stoves

| 10 35 13.10 Woodburning Stoves | Crew | Daily Output | Labor-Hours | Unit | Material | 2010 Bare Costs Labor | Equipment | Total | Total Incl O&P |
|---|---|---|---|---|---|---|---|---|---|
| 0010 **WOODBURNING STOVES** | | | | | | | | | |
| 0015 Cast iron, minimum | 2 Carp | 1.30 | 12.308 | Ea. | 1,175 | 360 | | 1,535 | 1,900 |
| 0020 Average | | 1 | 16 | | 1,600 | 465 | | 2,065 | 2,525 |
| 0030 Maximum | | .80 | 20 | | 2,850 | 580 | | 3,430 | 4,125 |
| 0050 For gas log lighter, add | | | | | 42 | | | 42 | 46.50 |

# 10 44 Fire Protection Specialties

## 10 44 16 – Fire Extinguishers

| 10 44 16.13 Portable Fire Extinguishers | Crew | Daily Output | Labor-Hours | Unit | Material | 2010 Bare Costs Labor | Equipment | Total | Total Incl O&P |
|---|---|---|---|---|---|---|---|---|---|
| 0010 **PORTABLE FIRE EXTINGUISHERS** | | | | | | | | | |
| 0140 $CO_2$, with hose and "H" horn, 10 lb. | | | | Ea. | 191 | | | 191 | 210 |
| 1000 Dry chemical, pressurized | | | | | | | | | |
| 1040 Standard type, portable, painted, 2-1/2 lb. | | | | Ea. | 31.50 | | | 31.50 | 34.50 |
| 1080 10 lb. | | | | | 69.50 | | | 69.50 | 76.50 |
| 1100 20 lb. | | | | | 113 | | | 113 | 124 |
| 1120 30 lb. | | | | | 375 | | | 375 | 415 |
| 2000 ABC all purpose type, portable, 2-1/2 lb. | | | | | 21 | | | 21 | 23.50 |
| 2080 9-1/2 lb. | | | | | 44 | | | 44 | 48 |

# 10 55 Postal Specialties

## 10 55 23 – Mail Boxes

| 10 55 23.10 Mail Boxes | Crew | Daily Output | Labor-Hours | Unit | Material | 2010 Bare Costs Labor | Equipment | Total | Total Incl O&P |
|---|---|---|---|---|---|---|---|---|---|
| 0011 **MAIL BOXES** | | | | | | | | | |
| 1900 Letter slot, residential | 1 Carp | 20 | .400 | Ea. | 88 | 11.65 | | 99.65 | 117 |
| 2400 Residential, galv. steel, small 20" x 7" x 9" | 1 Clab | 16 | .500 | | 149 | 10.75 | | 159.75 | 182 |
| 2410 With galv. steel post, 54" long | | 6 | 1.333 | | 225 | 28.50 | | 253.50 | 296 |
| 2420 Large, 24" x 12" x 15" | | 16 | .500 | | 170 | 10.75 | | 180.75 | 205 |
| 2430 With galv. steel post, 54" long | | 6 | 1.333 | | 225 | 28.50 | | 253.50 | 296 |
| 2440 Decorative, polyethylene, 22" x 10" x 10" | | 16 | .500 | | 43 | 10.75 | | 53.75 | 65 |
| 2450 With alum. post, decorative, 54" long | | 6 | 1.333 | | 170 | 28.50 | | 198.50 | 235 |

# 10 56 Storage Assemblies

## 10 56 13 – Metal Storage Shelving

| 10 56 13.10 Shelving | Crew | Daily Output | Labor-Hours | Unit | Material | 2010 Bare Costs Labor | Equipment | Total | Total Incl O&P |
|---|---|---|---|---|---|---|---|---|---|
| 0010 **SHELVING** | | | | | | | | | |
| 0020 Metal, industrial, cross-braced, 3' wide, 12" deep | 1 Sswk | 175 | .046 | SF Shlf | 6.60 | 1.44 | | 8.04 | 9.95 |
| 0100 24" deep | | 330 | .024 | | 4.71 | .76 | | 5.47 | 6.65 |
| 2200 Wide span, 1600 lb. capacity per shelf, 6' wide, 24" deep | | 380 | .021 | | 13.35 | .66 | | 14.01 | 15.90 |
| 2400 36" deep | | 440 | .018 | | 8.25 | .57 | | 8.82 | 10.15 |
| 3000 Residential, vinyl covered wire, wardrobe, 12" deep | 1 Carp | 195 | .041 | L.F. | 5.90 | 1.19 | | 7.09 | 8.50 |
| 3100 16" deep | | 195 | .041 | | 8 | 1.19 | | 9.19 | 10.80 |
| 3200 Standard, 6" deep | | 195 | .041 | | 3.23 | 1.19 | | 4.42 | 5.55 |
| 3300 9" deep | | 195 | .041 | | 4.86 | 1.19 | | 6.05 | 7.35 |
| 3400 12" deep | | 195 | .041 | | 6.45 | 1.19 | | 7.64 | 9.10 |
| 3500 16" deep | | 195 | .041 | | 9.90 | 1.19 | | 11.09 | 12.90 |
| 3600 20" deep | | 195 | .041 | | 13.15 | 1.19 | | 14.34 | 16.45 |
| 3700 Support bracket | | 80 | .100 | Ea. | 4.10 | 2.91 | | 7.01 | 9.40 |

# 10 57 Wardrobe and Closet Specialties

## 10 57 23 – Closet and Utility Shelving

| 10 57 23.19 Wood Closet and Utility Shelving | Crew | Daily Output | Labor-Hours | Unit | Material | 2010 Bare Costs Labor | Equipment | Total | Total Incl O&P |
|---|---|---|---|---|---|---|---|---|---|
| 0010 **WOOD CLOSET AND UTILITY SHELVING** | | | | | | | | | |
| 0020    Pine, clear grade, no edge band, 1" x 8" | 1 Carp | 115 | .070 | L.F. | 2.79 | 2.02 | | 4.81 | 6.50 |
| 0100       1" x 10" | | 110 | .073 | | 3.48 | 2.12 | | 5.60 | 7.40 |
| 0200       1" x 12" | | 105 | .076 | | 4.19 | 2.22 | | 6.41 | 8.35 |
| 0450       1" x 18" | | 95 | .084 | | 6.30 | 2.45 | | 8.75 | 11 |
| 0460       1" x 24" | | 85 | .094 | | 8.40 | 2.74 | | 11.14 | 13.80 |
| 0600    Plywood, 3/4" thick with lumber edge, 12" wide | | 75 | .107 | | 1.58 | 3.10 | | 4.68 | 6.95 |
| 0700       24" wide | | 70 | .114 | ▼ | 2.81 | 3.33 | | 6.14 | 8.70 |
| 0900    Bookcase, clear grade pine, shelves 12" O.C., 8" deep, per SF shelf | | 70 | .114 | S.F. | 9.10 | 3.33 | | 12.43 | 15.60 |
| 1000       12" deep shelves | | 65 | .123 | " | 13.60 | 3.58 | | 17.18 | 21 |
| 1200    Adjustable closet rod and shelf, 12" wide, 3' long | | 20 | .400 | Ea. | 7.80 | 11.65 | | 19.45 | 28 |
| 1300       8' long | | 15 | .533 | " | 16.40 | 15.50 | | 31.90 | 44 |
| 1500    Prefinished shelves with supports, stock, 8" wide | | 75 | .107 | L.F. | 3.14 | 3.10 | | 6.24 | 8.65 |
| 1600       10" wide | ▼ | 70 | .114 | " | 4.27 | 3.33 | | 7.60 | 10.30 |

# 10 73 Protective Covers

## 10 73 16 – Canopies

| 10 73 16.10 Canopies, Residential | Crew | Daily Output | Labor-Hours | Unit | Material | 2010 Bare Costs Labor | Equipment | Total | Total Incl O&P |
|---|---|---|---|---|---|---|---|---|---|
| 0010 **CANOPIES, RESIDENTIAL** Prefabricated | | | | | | | | | |
| 0500    Carport, free standing, baked enamel, alum., .032", 40 psf | | | | | | | | | |
| 0520       16' x 8', 4 posts | 2 Carp | 3 | 5.333 | Ea. | 4,275 | 155 | | 4,430 | 4,950 |
| 0600       20' x 10', 6 posts | | 2 | 8 | | 4,450 | 233 | | 4,683 | 5,300 |
| 0605       30' x 10', 8 posts | ▼ | 2 | 8 | | 6,700 | 233 | | 6,933 | 7,750 |
| 1000    Door canopies, extruded alum., .032", 42" projection, 4' wide | 1 Carp | 8 | 1 | | 274 | 29 | | 303 | 350 |
| 1020       6' wide | " | 6 | 1.333 | | 355 | 39 | | 394 | 460 |
| 1040       8' wide | 2 Carp | 9 | 1.778 | | 480 | 51.50 | | 531.50 | 615 |
| 1060       10' wide | | 7 | 2.286 | | 705 | 66.50 | | 771.50 | 885 |
| 1080       12' wide | | 5 | 3.200 | | 810 | 93 | | 903 | 1,050 |
| 1200       54" projection, 4' wide | 1 Carp | 8 | 1 | | 320 | 29 | | 349 | 405 |
| 1220       6' wide | " | 6 | 1.333 | | 400 | 39 | | 439 | 505 |
| 1240       8' wide | 2 Carp | 9 | 1.778 | | 460 | 51.50 | | 511.50 | 590 |
| 1260       10' wide | | 7 | 2.286 | | 760 | 66.50 | | 826.50 | 945 |
| 1280       12' wide | ▼ | 5 | 3.200 | | 810 | 93 | | 903 | 1,050 |
| 1300       Painted, add | | | | | 20% | | | | |
| 1310       Bronze anodized, add | | | | | 50% | | | | |
| 3000    Window awnings, aluminum, window 3' high, 4' wide | 1 Carp | 10 | .800 | | 217 | 23.50 | | 240.50 | 278 |
| 3020       6' wide | " | 8 | 1 | | 263 | 29 | | 292 | 340 |
| 3040       9' wide | 2 Carp | 9 | 1.778 | | 310 | 51.50 | | 361.50 | 425 |
| 3060       12' wide | " | 5 | 3.200 | | 360 | 93 | | 453 | 550 |
| 3100       Window, 4' high, 4' wide | 1 Carp | 10 | .800 | | 162 | 23.50 | | 185.50 | 217 |
| 3120       6' wide | " | 8 | 1 | | 230 | 29 | | 259 | 300 |
| 3140       9' wide | 2 Carp | 9 | 1.778 | | 385 | 51.50 | | 436.50 | 505 |
| 3160       12' wide | " | 5 | 3.200 | | 410 | 93 | | 503 | 610 |
| 3200       Window, 6' high, 4' wide | 1 Carp | 10 | .800 | | 222 | 23.50 | | 245.50 | 284 |
| 3220       6' wide | " | 8 | 1 | | 340 | 29 | | 369 | 425 |
| 3240       9' wide | 2 Carp | 9 | 1.778 | | 900 | 51.50 | | 951.50 | 1,075 |
| 3260       12' wide | " | 5 | 3.200 | | 1,375 | 93 | | 1,468 | 1,675 |
| 3400    Roll-up aluminum, 2'-6" wide | 1 Carp | 14 | .571 | | 190 | 16.65 | | 206.65 | 237 |
| 3420       3' wide | | 12 | .667 | | 195 | 19.40 | | 214.40 | 247 |
| 3440       4' wide | | 10 | .800 | | 234 | 23.50 | | 257.50 | 296 |
| 3460       6' wide | ▼ | 8 | 1 | ▼ | 261 | 29 | | 290 | 335 |

# 10 73 Protective Covers

## 10 73 16 – Canopies

| 10 73 16.10 Canopies, Residential | | Crew | Daily Output | Labor-Hours | Unit | Material | 2010 Bare Costs Labor | 2010 Bare Costs Equipment | Total | Total Incl O&P |
|---|---|---|---|---|---|---|---|---|---|---|
| 3480 | 9' wide | 2 Carp | 9 | 1.778 | Ea. | 370 | 51.50 | | 421.50 | 495 |
| 3500 | 12' wide | " | 5 | 3.200 | ↓ | 475 | 93 | | 568 | 680 |
| 3600 | Window awnings, canvas, 24" drop, 3' wide | 1 Carp | 30 | .267 | L.F. | 48.50 | 7.75 | | 56.25 | 66.50 |
| 3620 | 4' wide | | 40 | .200 | | 42 | 5.80 | | 47.80 | 56 |
| 3700 | 30" drop, 3' wide | | 30 | .267 | | 51.50 | 7.75 | | 59.25 | 70 |
| 3720 | 4' wide | | 40 | .200 | | 44.50 | 5.80 | | 50.30 | 59 |
| 3740 | 5' wide | | 45 | .178 | | 40 | 5.15 | | 45.15 | 52.50 |
| 3760 | 6' wide | | 48 | .167 | | 37 | 4.85 | | 41.85 | 48.50 |
| 3780 | 8' wide | | 48 | .167 | | 33.50 | 4.85 | | 38.35 | 44.50 |
| 3800 | 10' wide | ↓ | 50 | .160 | ↓ | 41 | 4.66 | | 45.66 | 53.50 |

# 10 74 Manufactured Exterior Specialties

## 10 74 23 – Cupolas

### 10 74 23.10 Wood Cupolas

| | | Crew | Daily Output | Labor-Hours | Unit | Material | 2010 Bare Costs Labor | 2010 Bare Costs Equipment | Total | Total Incl O&P |
|---|---|---|---|---|---|---|---|---|---|---|
| 0010 | **WOOD CUPOLAS** | | | | | | | | | |
| 0020 | Stock units, pine, painted, 18" sq., 28" high, alum. roof | 1 Carp | 4.10 | 1.951 | Ea. | 162 | 57 | | 219 | 274 |
| 0100 | Copper roof | | 3.80 | 2.105 | | 208 | 61.50 | | 269.50 | 330 |
| 0300 | 23" square, 33" high, aluminum roof | | 3.70 | 2.162 | | 345 | 63 | | 408 | 485 |
| 0400 | Copper roof | | 3.30 | 2.424 | | 465 | 70.50 | | 535.50 | 630 |
| 0600 | 30" square, 37" high, aluminum roof | | 3.70 | 2.162 | | 495 | 63 | | 558 | 650 |
| 0700 | Copper roof | | 3.30 | 2.424 | | 590 | 70.50 | | 660.50 | 770 |
| 0900 | Hexagonal, 31" wide, 46" high, copper roof | | 4 | 2 | | 730 | 58 | | 788 | 905 |
| 1000 | 36" wide, 50" high, copper roof | ↓ | 3.50 | 2.286 | | 1,275 | 66.50 | | 1,341.50 | 1,500 |
| 1200 | For deluxe stock units, add to above | | | | | 25% | | | | |
| 1400 | For custom built units, add to above | | | | ↓ | 50% | 50% | | | |

## 10 74 33 – Weathervanes

### 10 74 33.10 Residential Weathervanes

| | | Crew | Daily Output | Labor-Hours | Unit | Material | 2010 Bare Costs Labor | 2010 Bare Costs Equipment | Total | Total Incl O&P |
|---|---|---|---|---|---|---|---|---|---|---|
| 0010 | **RESIDENTIAL WEATHERVANES** | | | | | | | | | |
| 0020 | Residential types, minimum | 1 Carp | 8 | 1 | Ea. | 205 | 29 | | 234 | 274 |
| 0100 | Maximum | " | 2 | 4 | " | 1,700 | 116 | | 1,816 | 2,075 |

# 10 75 Flagpoles

## 10 75 16 – Ground-Set Flagpoles

### 10 75 16.10 Flagpoles

| | | Crew | Daily Output | Labor-Hours | Unit | Material | 2010 Bare Costs Labor | 2010 Bare Costs Equipment | Total | Total Incl O&P |
|---|---|---|---|---|---|---|---|---|---|---|
| 0010 | **FLAGPOLES**, Ground set | | | | | | | | | |
| 0050 | Not including base or foundation | | | | | | | | | |
| 0100 | Aluminum, tapered, ground set 20' high | K-1 | 2 | 8 | Ea. | 990 | 208 | 148 | 1,346 | 1,600 |
| 0200 | 25' high | | 1.70 | 9.412 | | 1,275 | 245 | 174 | 1,694 | 2,000 |
| 0300 | 30' high | | 1.50 | 10.667 | | 1,250 | 277 | 197 | 1,724 | 2,050 |
| 0500 | 40' high | ↓ | 1.20 | 13.333 | ↓ | 2,350 | 345 | 247 | 2,942 | 3,425 |

# Division Notes

| | CREW | DAILY OUTPUT | LABOR-HOURS | UNIT | 2010 BARE COSTS | | | | TOTAL INCL O&P |
|---|---|---|---|---|---|---|---|---|---|
| | | | | | MAT. | LABOR | EQUIP. | TOTAL | |
| | | | | | | | | | |
| | | | | | | | | | |
| | | | | | | | | | |
| | | | | | | | | | |
| | | | | | | | | | |
| | | | | | | | | | |
| | | | | | | | | | |
| | | | | | | | | | |
| | | | | | | | | | |
| | | | | | | | | | |
| | | | | | | | | | |
| | | | | | | | | | |
| | | | | | | | | | |
| | | | | | | | | | |
| | | | | | | | | | |
| | | | | | | | | | |
| | | | | | | | | | |
| | | | | | | | | | |
| | | | | | | | | | |
| | | | | | | | | | |
| | | | | | | | | | |
| | | | | | | | | | |
| | | | | | | | | | |

## Estimating Tips

### General

- The items in this division are usually priced per square foot or each. Many of these items are purchased by the owner for installation by the contractor. Check the specifications for responsibilities and include time for receiving, storage, installation, and mechanical and electrical hookups in the appropriate divisions.

- Many items in Division 11 require some type of support system that is not usually furnished with the item. Examples of these systems include blocking for the attachment of casework and support angles for ceiling-hung projection screens. The required blocking or supports must be added to the estimate in the appropriate division.

- Some items in Division 11 may require assembly or electrical hookups. Verify the amount of assembly required or the need for a hard electrical connection and add the appropriate costs.

## Reference Numbers

Reference numbers are shown in shaded boxes at the beginning of some major classifications. These numbers refer to related items in the Reference Section. The reference information may be an estimating procedure, an alternate pricing method, or technical information.

*Note:* Not all subdivisions listed here necessarily appear in this publication.

# 11 24 Maintenance Equipment

## 11 24 19 – Vacuum Cleaning Systems

| 11 24 19.10 Vacuum Cleaning | Crew | Daily Output | Labor-Hours | Unit | Material | 2010 Bare Costs Labor | Equipment | Total | Total Incl O&P |
|---|---|---|---|---|---|---|---|---|---|
| 0010 **VACUUM CLEANING** | | | | | | | | | |
| 0020 Central, 3 inlet, residential | 1 Skwk | .90 | 8.889 | Total | 1,025 | 260 | | 1,285 | 1,575 |
| 0400 5 inlet system, residential | | .50 | 16 | | 1,450 | 470 | | 1,920 | 2,375 |
| 0600 7 inlet system, commercial | | .40 | 20 | | 1,625 | 585 | | 2,210 | 2,750 |
| 0800 9 inlet system, residential | | .30 | 26.667 | | 3,600 | 780 | | 4,380 | 5,250 |
| 4010 Rule of thumb: First 1200 S.F., installed | | | | | | | | | 1,180 |
| 4020 For each additional S.F., add | | | | S.F. | | | | | .19 |

# 11 26 Unit Kitchens

## 11 26 13 – Metal Unit Kitchens

### 11 26 13.10 Commercial Unit Kitchens

| | Crew | Daily Output | Labor-Hours | Unit | Material | 2010 Bare Costs Labor | Equipment | Total | Total Incl O&P |
|---|---|---|---|---|---|---|---|---|---|
| 0010 **COMMERCIAL UNIT KITCHENS** | | | | | | | | | |
| 1500 Combination range, refrigerator and sink, 30" wide, minimum | L-1 | 2 | 5 | Ea. | 925 | 170 | | 1,095 | 1,300 |
| 1550 Maximum | | 1 | 10 | | 3,675 | 340 | | 4,015 | 4,600 |
| 1570 60" wide, average | | 1.40 | 7.143 | | 3,225 | 243 | | 3,468 | 3,925 |
| 1590 72" wide, average | | 1.20 | 8.333 | | 4,200 | 284 | | 4,484 | 5,100 |

# 11 31 Residential Appliances

## 11 31 13 – Residential Kitchen Appliances

### 11 31 13.13 Cooking Equipment

| | Crew | Daily Output | Labor-Hours | Unit | Material | 2010 Bare Costs Labor | Equipment | Total | Total Incl O&P |
|---|---|---|---|---|---|---|---|---|---|
| 0010 **COOKING EQUIPMENT** | | | | | | | | | |
| 0020 Cooking range, 30" free standing, 1 oven, minimum | 2 Clab | 10 | 1.600 | Ea. | 345 | 34.50 | | 379.50 | 440 |
| 0050 Maximum | | 4 | 4 | | 1,900 | 86 | | 1,986 | 2,250 |
| 0150 2 oven, minimum | | 10 | 1.600 | | 1,400 | 34.50 | | 1,434.50 | 1,575 |
| 0200 Maximum | | 10 | 1.600 | | 1,600 | 34.50 | | 1,634.50 | 1,825 |
| 0350 Built-in, 30" wide, 1 oven, minimum | 1 Elec | 6 | 1.333 | | 680 | 44 | | 724 | 820 |
| 0400 Maximum | 2 Carp | 2 | 8 | | 1,500 | 233 | | 1,733 | 2,050 |
| 0500 2 oven, conventional, minimum | | 4 | 4 | | 1,550 | 116 | | 1,666 | 1,900 |
| 0550 1 conventional, 1 microwave, maximum | | 2 | 8 | | 1,375 | 233 | | 1,608 | 1,925 |
| 0700 Free-standing, 1 oven, 21" wide range, minimum | 2 Clab | 10 | 1.600 | | 330 | 34.50 | | 364.50 | 420 |
| 0750 21" wide, maximum | " | 4 | 4 | | 335 | 86 | | 421 | 515 |
| 0900 Countertop cooktops, 4 burner, standard, minimum | 1 Elec | 6 | 1.333 | | 300 | 44 | | 344 | 400 |
| 0950 Maximum | | 3 | 2.667 | | 600 | 87.50 | | 687.50 | 805 |
| 1050 As above, but with grill and griddle attachment, minimum | | 6 | 1.333 | | 1,375 | 44 | | 1,419 | 1,600 |
| 1100 Maximum | | 3 | 2.667 | | 3,350 | 87.50 | | 3,437.50 | 3,825 |
| 1250 Microwave oven, minimum | | 4 | 2 | | 110 | 65.50 | | 175.50 | 228 |
| 1300 Maximum | | 2 | 4 | | 420 | 131 | | 551 | 675 |
| 5380 Oven, built in, standard | | 4 | 2 | | 485 | 65.50 | | 550.50 | 635 |
| 5390 Deluxe | | 2 | 4 | | 2,000 | 131 | | 2,131 | 2,425 |

### 11 31 13.23 Refrigeration Equipment

| | Crew | Daily Output | Labor-Hours | Unit | Material | 2010 Bare Costs Labor | Equipment | Total | Total Incl O&P |
|---|---|---|---|---|---|---|---|---|---|
| 0010 **REFRIGERATION EQUIPMENT** | | | | | | | | | |
| 2000 Deep freeze, 15 to 23 C.F., minimum | 2 Clab | 10 | 1.600 | Ea. | 530 | 34.50 | | 564.50 | 645 |
| 2050 Maximum | | 5 | 3.200 | | 660 | 69 | | 729 | 845 |
| 2200 30 C.F., minimum | | 8 | 2 | | 830 | 43 | | 873 | 990 |
| 2250 Maximum | | 3 | 5.333 | | 940 | 115 | | 1,055 | 1,225 |
| 5200 Icemaker, automatic, 20 lb. per day | 1 Plum | 7 | 1.143 | | 880 | 39.50 | | 919.50 | 1,025 |
| 5350 51 lb. per day | " | 2 | 4 | | 1,250 | 137 | | 1,387 | 1,600 |
| 5450 Refrigerator, no frost, 6 C.F. | 2 Clab | 15 | 1.067 | | 230 | 23 | | 253 | 291 |
| 5500 Refrigerator, no frost, 10 C.F. to 12 C.F. minimum | | 10 | 1.600 | | 445 | 34.50 | | 479.50 | 550 |

# 11 31 Residential Appliances

## 11 31 13 - Residential Kitchen Appliances

### 11 31 13.23 Refrigeration Equipment

| | | Crew | Daily Output | Labor-Hours | Unit | Material | 2010 Bare Costs Labor | Equipment | Total | Total Incl O&P |
|---|---|---|---|---|---|---|---|---|---|---|
| 5600 | Maximum | 2 Clab | 6 | 2.667 | Ea. | 450 | 57.50 | | 507.50 | 590 |
| 5750 | 14 C.F. to 16 C.F., minimum | | 9 | 1.778 | | 475 | 38 | | 513 | 585 |
| 5800 | Maximum | | 5 | 3.200 | | 710 | 69 | | 779 | 895 |
| 5950 | 18 C.F. to 20 C.F., minimum | | 8 | 2 | | 590 | 43 | | 633 | 725 |
| 6000 | Maximum | | 4 | 4 | | 1,100 | 86 | | 1,186 | 1,350 |
| 6150 | 21 C.F. to 29 C.F., minimum | | 7 | 2.286 | | 940 | 49 | | 989 | 1,100 |
| 6200 | Maximum | | 3 | 5.333 | | 3,075 | 115 | | 3,190 | 3,575 |
| 6790 | Energy-star qualified, 18 CF, minimum Ⓖ | 2 Carp | 4 | 4 | | 495 | 116 | | 611 | 740 |
| 6795 | Maximum Ⓖ | | 2 | 8 | | 1,300 | 233 | | 1,533 | 1,825 |
| 6797 | 21.7 CF, minimum Ⓖ | | 4 | 4 | | 815 | 116 | | 931 | 1,100 |
| 6799 | Maximum Ⓖ | | 4 | 4 | | 1,300 | 116 | | 1,416 | 1,625 |

### 11 31 13.33 Kitchen Cleaning Equipment

| | | Crew | Daily Output | Labor-Hours | Unit | Material | 2010 Bare Costs Labor | Equipment | Total | Total Incl O&P |
|---|---|---|---|---|---|---|---|---|---|---|
| 0010 | **KITCHEN CLEANING EQUIPMENT** | | | | | | | | | |
| 2750 | Dishwasher, built-in, 2 cycles, minimum | L-1 | 4 | 2.500 | Ea. | 212 | 85 | | 297 | 375 |
| 2800 | Maximum | | 2 | 5 | | 320 | 170 | | 490 | 630 |
| 2950 | 4 or more cycles, minimum | | 4 | 2.500 | | 279 | 85 | | 364 | 445 |
| 2960 | Average | | 4 | 2.500 | | 370 | 85 | | 455 | 550 |
| 3000 | Maximum | | 2 | 5 | | 1,050 | 170 | | 1,220 | 1,425 |
| 3100 | Energy-star qualified, minimum Ⓖ | | 4 | 2.500 | | 340 | 85 | | 425 | 515 |
| 3110 | Maximum Ⓖ | | 2 | 5 | | 1,250 | 170 | | 1,420 | 1,650 |

### 11 31 13.43 Waste Disposal Equipment

| | | Crew | Daily Output | Labor-Hours | Unit | Material | 2010 Bare Costs Labor | Equipment | Total | Total Incl O&P |
|---|---|---|---|---|---|---|---|---|---|---|
| 0010 | **WASTE DISPOSAL EQUIPMENT** | | | | | | | | | |
| 1750 | Compactor, residential size, 4 to 1 compaction, minimum | 1 Carp | 5 | 1.600 | Ea. | 535 | 46.50 | | 581.50 | 665 |
| 1800 | Maximum | " | 3 | 2.667 | | 830 | 77.50 | | 907.50 | 1,050 |
| 3300 | Garbage disposal, sink type, minimum | L-1 | 10 | 1 | | 72.50 | 34 | | 106.50 | 135 |
| 3350 | Maximum | " | 10 | 1 | | 191 | 34 | | 225 | 266 |

### 11 31 13.53 Kitchen Ventilation Equipment

| | | Crew | Daily Output | Labor-Hours | Unit | Material | 2010 Bare Costs Labor | Equipment | Total | Total Incl O&P |
|---|---|---|---|---|---|---|---|---|---|---|
| 0010 | **KITCHEN VENTILATION EQUIPMENT** | | | | | | | | | |
| 4150 | Hood for range, 2 speed, vented, 30" wide, minimum | L-3 | 5 | 2 | Ea. | 53.50 | 59.50 | | 113 | 159 |
| 4200 | Maximum | | 3 | 3.333 | | 820 | 99.50 | | 919.50 | 1,075 |
| 4300 | 42" wide, minimum | | 5 | 2 | | 234 | 59.50 | | 293.50 | 355 |
| 4330 | Custom | | 5 | 2 | | 1,500 | 59.50 | | 1,559.50 | 1,775 |
| 4350 | Maximum | | 3 | 3.333 | | 1,850 | 99.50 | | 1,949.50 | 2,200 |
| 4500 | For ventless hood, 2 speed, add | | | | | 17.05 | | | 17.05 | 18.75 |
| 4650 | For vented 1 speed, deduct from maximum | | | | | 45.50 | | | 45.50 | 50 |

## 11 31 23 - Residential Laundry Appliances

### 11 31 23.13 Washers

| | | Crew | Daily Output | Labor-Hours | Unit | Material | 2010 Bare Costs Labor | Equipment | Total | Total Incl O&P |
|---|---|---|---|---|---|---|---|---|---|---|
| 0010 | **WASHERS** | | | | | | | | | |
| 6650 | Washing machine, automatic, minimum | 1 Plum | 3 | 2.667 | Ea. | 355 | 91.50 | | 446.50 | 540 |
| 6700 | Maximum | | 1 | 8 | | 1,000 | 275 | | 1,275 | 1,575 |
| 6750 | Energy star qualified, front loading, minimum Ⓖ | | 3 | 2.667 | | 480 | 91.50 | | 571.50 | 680 |
| 6760 | Maximum Ⓖ | | 1 | 8 | | 1,700 | 275 | | 1,975 | 2,325 |
| 6764 | Top loading, minimum Ⓖ | | 3 | 2.667 | | 575 | 91.50 | | 666.50 | 785 |
| 6766 | Maximum Ⓖ | | 3 | 2.667 | | 1,050 | 91.50 | | 1,141.50 | 1,300 |

### 11 31 23.23 Dryers

| | | Crew | Daily Output | Labor-Hours | Unit | Material | 2010 Bare Costs Labor | Equipment | Total | Total Incl O&P |
|---|---|---|---|---|---|---|---|---|---|---|
| 0010 | **DRYERS** | | | | | | | | | |
| 6770 | Electric, front loading, energy-star qualified, minimum Ⓖ | L-2 | 3 | 5.333 | Ea. | 360 | 136 | | 496 | 625 |
| 6780 | Maximum Ⓖ | " | 2 | 8 | | 1,300 | 203 | | 1,503 | 1,775 |
| 7450 | Vent kits for dryers | 1 Carp | 10 | .800 | | 25.50 | 23.50 | | 49 | 67 |

# 11 31 Residential Appliances

## 11 31 33 - Miscellaneous Residential Appliances

### 11 31 33.13 Sump Pumps

| | 11 31 33.13 Sump Pumps | Crew | Daily Output | Labor-Hours | Unit | Material | 2010 Bare Costs Labor | Equipment | Total | Total Incl O&P |
|---|---|---|---|---|---|---|---|---|---|---|
| 0010 | **SUMP PUMPS** | | | | | | | | | |
| 6400 | Cellar drainer, pedestal, 1/3 H.P., molded PVC base | 1 Plum | 3 | 2.667 | Ea. | 119 | 91.50 | | 210.50 | 281 |
| 6450 | Solid brass | " | 2 | 4 | " | 263 | 137 | | 400 | 515 |
| 6460 | Sump pump, see also Div. 22 14 29.16 | | | | | | | | | |

### 11 31 33.23 Water Heaters

| | | Crew | Daily Output | Labor-Hours | Unit | Material | 2010 Bare Costs Labor | Equipment | Total | Total Incl O&P |
|---|---|---|---|---|---|---|---|---|---|---|
| 0010 | **WATER HEATERS** | | | | | | | | | |
| 6900 | Electric, glass lined, 30 gallon, minimum | L-1 | 5 | 2 | Ea. | 520 | 68 | | 588 | 680 |
| 6950 | Maximum | | 3 | 3.333 | | 720 | 114 | | 834 | 975 |
| 7100 | 80 gallon, minimum | | 2 | 5 | | 935 | 170 | | 1,105 | 1,300 |
| 7150 | Maximum | | 1 | 10 | | 1,300 | 340 | | 1,640 | 1,975 |
| 7180 | Gas, glass lined, 30 gallon, minimum | 2 Plum | 5 | 3.200 | | 805 | 110 | | 915 | 1,075 |
| 7220 | Maximum | | 3 | 5.333 | | 1,125 | 183 | | 1,308 | 1,525 |
| 7260 | 50 gallon, minimum | | 2.50 | 6.400 | | 845 | 220 | | 1,065 | 1,275 |
| 7300 | Maximum | | 1.50 | 10.667 | | 1,175 | 365 | | 1,540 | 1,875 |
| 7310 | Water heater, see also Div. 22 33 30.13 | | | | | | | | | |

### 11 31 33.43 Air Quality

| | | Crew | Daily Output | Labor-Hours | Unit | Material | 2010 Bare Costs Labor | Equipment | Total | Total Incl O&P |
|---|---|---|---|---|---|---|---|---|---|---|
| 0010 | **AIR QUALITY** | | | | | | | | | |
| 2450 | Dehumidifier, portable, automatic, 15 pint | | | | Ea. | 154 | | | 154 | 170 |
| 2550 | 40 pint | | | | | 171 | | | 171 | 188 |
| 3550 | Heater, electric, built-in, 1250 watt, ceiling type, minimum | 1 Elec | 4 | 2 | | 96 | 65.50 | | 161.50 | 212 |
| 3600 | Maximum | | 3 | 2.667 | | 156 | 87.50 | | 243.50 | 315 |
| 3700 | Wall type, minimum | | 4 | 2 | | 154 | 65.50 | | 219.50 | 277 |
| 3750 | Maximum | | 3 | 2.667 | | 166 | 87.50 | | 253.50 | 325 |
| 3900 | 1500 watt wall type, with blower | | 4 | 2 | | 154 | 65.50 | | 219.50 | 277 |
| 3950 | 3000 watt | | 3 | 2.667 | | 315 | 87.50 | | 402.50 | 490 |
| 4850 | Humidifier, portable, 8 gallons per day | | | | | 165 | | | 165 | 182 |
| 5000 | 15 gallons per day | | | | | 198 | | | 198 | 218 |

# 11 33 Retractable Stairs

## 11 33 10 - Disappearing Stairs

### 11 33 10.10 Disappearing Stairway

| | | Crew | Daily Output | Labor-Hours | Unit | Material | 2010 Bare Costs Labor | Equipment | Total | Total Incl O&P |
|---|---|---|---|---|---|---|---|---|---|---|
| 0010 | **DISAPPEARING STAIRWAY** No trim included | | | | | | | | | |
| 0020 | One piece, yellow pine, 8'-0" ceiling | 2 Carp | 4 | 4 | Ea. | 240 | 116 | | 356 | 460 |
| 0030 | 9'-0" ceiling | | 4 | 4 | | 273 | 116 | | 389 | 495 |
| 0040 | 10'-0" ceiling | | 3 | 5.333 | | 335 | 155 | | 490 | 625 |
| 0050 | 11'-0" ceiling | | 3 | 5.333 | | 455 | 155 | | 610 | 760 |
| 0060 | 12'-0" ceiling | | 3 | 5.333 | | 455 | 155 | | 610 | 760 |
| 0100 | Custom grade, pine, 8'-6" ceiling, minimum | 1 Carp | 4 | 2 | | 138 | 58 | | 196 | 249 |
| 0150 | Average | | 3.50 | 2.286 | | 174 | 66.50 | | 240.50 | 305 |
| 0200 | Maximum | | 3 | 2.667 | | 257 | 77.50 | | 334.50 | 415 |
| 0500 | Heavy duty, pivoted, from 7'-7" to 12'-10" floor to floor | | 3 | 2.667 | | 650 | 77.50 | | 727.50 | 845 |
| 0600 | 16'-0" ceiling | | 2 | 4 | | 1,325 | 116 | | 1,441 | 1,650 |
| 0800 | Economy folding, pine, 8'-6" ceiling | | 4 | 2 | | 121 | 58 | | 179 | 231 |
| 0900 | 9'-6" ceiling | | 4 | 2 | | 130 | 58 | | 188 | 241 |
| 1100 | Automatic electric, aluminum, floor to floor height, 8' to 9' | 2 Carp | 1 | 16 | | 8,250 | 465 | | 8,715 | 9,850 |

# 11 41 Food Storage Equipment

## 11 41 13 – Refrigerated Food Storage Cases

| 11 41 13.30 Wine Cellar | Crew | Daily Output | Labor-Hours | Unit | Material | 2010 Bare Costs Labor | Equipment | Total | Total Incl O&P |
|---|---|---|---|---|---|---|---|---|---|
| 0010 **WINE CELLAR**, refrigerated, Redwood interior, carpeted, walk-in type | | | | | | | | | |
| 0020   6'-8" high, including racks | | | | | | | | | |
| 0200     80" W x 48" D for 900 bottles | 2 Carp | 1.50 | 10.667 | Ea. | 3,350 | 310 | | 3,660 | 4,200 |
| 0250     80" W x 72" D for 1300 bottles | | 1.33 | 12.030 | | 4,425 | 350 | | 4,775 | 5,450 |
| 0300     80" W x 94" D for 1900 bottles | | 1.17 | 13.675 | | 5,725 | 400 | | 6,125 | 6,975 |

# Division Notes

| | CREW | DAILY OUTPUT | LABOR-HOURS | UNIT | 2010 BARE COSTS | | | | TOTAL INCL O&P |
|---|---|---|---|---|---|---|---|---|---|
| | | | | | MAT. | LABOR | EQUIP. | TOTAL | |
| | | | | | | | | | |
| | | | | | | | | | |
| | | | | | | | | | |
| | | | | | | | | | |
| | | | | | | | | | |
| | | | | | | | | | |
| | | | | | | | | | |
| | | | | | | | | | |
| | | | | | | | | | |
| | | | | | | | | | |
| | | | | | | | | | |
| | | | | | | | | | |
| | | | | | | | | | |
| | | | | | | | | | |
| | | | | | | | | | |
| | | | | | | | | | |
| | | | | | | | | | |
| | | | | | | | | | |
| | | | | | | | | | |
| | | | | | | | | | |
| | | | | | | | | | |
| | | | | | | | | | |
| | | | | | | | | | |

# Estimating Tips

## General

- The items in this division are usually priced per square foot or each. Most of these items are purchased by the owner and placed by the contractor. Do not assume the items in Division 12 will be purchased and installed by the contractor. Check the specifications for responsibilities and include receiving, storage, installation, and mechanical and electrical hookups in the appropriate divisions.

- Some items in this division require some type of support system that is not usually furnished with the item. Examples of these systems include blocking for the attachment of casework and heavy drapery rods. The required blocking must be added to the estimate in the appropriate division.

# Reference Numbers

Reference numbers are shown in shaded boxes at the beginning of some major classifications. These numbers refer to related items in the Reference Section. The reference information may be an estimating procedure, an alternate pricing method, or technical information.

*Note:* Not all subdivisions listed here necessarily appear in this publication.

**Division 12 - Furnishings**

# 12 21 Window Blinds

## 12 21 13 – Horizontal Louver Blinds

| 12 21 13.13 Metal Horizontal Louver Blinds | Crew | Daily Output | Labor-Hours | Unit | Material | 2010 Bare Costs Labor | Equipment | Total | Total Incl O&P |
|---|---|---|---|---|---|---|---|---|---|
| 0010 **METAL HORIZONTAL LOUVER BLINDS** | | | | | | | | | |
| 0020 Horizontal, 1" aluminum slats, solid color, stock | 1 Carp | 590 | .014 | S.F. | 4.75 | .39 | | 5.14 | 5.90 |
| 0090 Custom, minimum | | 590 | .014 | | 5.25 | .39 | | 5.64 | 6.45 |
| 0100 Maximum | | 440 | .018 | | 7.15 | .53 | | 7.68 | 8.75 |
| 0450 Stock, minimum | | 590 | .014 | | 4.86 | .39 | | 5.25 | 6 |
| 0500 Maximum | | 440 | .018 | | 7.90 | .53 | | 8.43 | 9.60 |

# 12 22 Curtains and Drapes

## 12 22 16 – Drapery Track and Accessories

### 12 22 16.10 Drapery Hardware

| | Crew | Daily Output | Labor-Hours | Unit | Material | 2010 Bare Costs Labor | Equipment | Total | Total Incl O&P |
|---|---|---|---|---|---|---|---|---|---|
| 0010 **DRAPERY HARDWARE** | | | | | | | | | |
| 0030 Standard traverse, per foot, minimum | 1 Carp | 59 | .136 | L.F. | 3.42 | 3.95 | | 7.37 | 10.40 |
| 0100 Maximum | | 51 | .157 | " | 8.05 | 4.56 | | 12.61 | 16.55 |
| 0200 Decorative traverse, 28"-48", minimum | | 22 | .364 | Ea. | 25.50 | 10.60 | | 36.10 | 46.50 |
| 0220 Maximum | | 21 | .381 | | 44 | 11.10 | | 55.10 | 66.50 |
| 0300 48"-84", minimum | | 20 | .400 | | 21 | 11.65 | | 32.65 | 42.50 |
| 0320 Maximum | | 19 | .421 | | 59.50 | 12.25 | | 71.75 | 86 |
| 0400 66"-120", minimum | | 18 | .444 | | 60 | 12.95 | | 72.95 | 88 |
| 0420 Maximum | | 17 | .471 | | 95.50 | 13.70 | | 109.20 | 128 |
| 0500 84"-156", minimum | | 16 | .500 | | 66.50 | 14.55 | | 81.05 | 97.50 |
| 0520 Maximum | | 15 | .533 | | 123 | 15.50 | | 138.50 | 162 |
| 0600 130"-240", minimum | | 14 | .571 | | 31.50 | 16.65 | | 48.15 | 62.50 |
| 0620 Maximum | | 13 | .615 | | 164 | 17.90 | | 181.90 | 210 |
| 0700 Slide rings, each, minimum | | | | | 1.44 | | | 1.44 | 1.58 |
| 0720 Maximum | | | | | 2.37 | | | 2.37 | 2.61 |
| 3000 Ripplefold, snap-a-pleat system, 3' or less, minimum | 1 Carp | 15 | .533 | | 46.50 | 15.50 | | 62 | 77 |
| 3020 Maximum | " | 14 | .571 | | 81 | 16.65 | | 97.65 | 117 |
| 3200 Each additional foot, add, minimum | | | | L.F. | 2.23 | | | 2.23 | 2.45 |
| 3220 Maximum | | | | " | 6.80 | | | 6.80 | 7.45 |
| 4000 Traverse rods, adjustable, 28" to 48" | 1 Carp | 22 | .364 | Ea. | 21 | 10.60 | | 31.60 | 41 |
| 4020 48" to 84" | | 20 | .400 | | 29.50 | 11.65 | | 41.15 | 52 |
| 4040 66" to 120" | | 18 | .444 | | 30.50 | 12.95 | | 43.45 | 55.50 |
| 4060 84" to 156" | | 16 | .500 | | 33 | 14.55 | | 47.55 | 60.50 |
| 4080 100" to 180" | | 14 | .571 | | 42.50 | 16.65 | | 59.15 | 74.50 |
| 4100 228" to 312" | | 13 | .615 | | 59.50 | 17.90 | | 77.40 | 95.50 |
| 4500 Curtain rod, 28" to 48", single | | 22 | .364 | | 5.10 | 10.60 | | 15.70 | 23.50 |
| 4510 Double | | 22 | .364 | | 8.75 | 10.60 | | 19.35 | 27.50 |
| 4520 48" to 86", single | | 20 | .400 | | 8.75 | 11.65 | | 20.40 | 29.50 |
| 4530 Double | | 20 | .400 | | 14.60 | 11.65 | | 26.25 | 35.50 |
| 4540 66" to 120", single | | 18 | .444 | | 14.70 | 12.95 | | 27.65 | 38 |
| 4550 Double | | 18 | .444 | | 23 | 12.95 | | 35.95 | 47 |
| 4600 Valance, pinch pleated fabric, 12" deep, up to 54" long, minimum | | | | | 36.50 | | | 36.50 | 40.50 |
| 4610 Maximum | | | | | 91.50 | | | 91.50 | 101 |
| 4620 Up to 77" long, minimum | | | | | 56.50 | | | 56.50 | 62 |
| 4630 Maximum | | | | | 148 | | | 148 | 163 |
| 5000 Stationary rods, first 2' | | | | | 9.35 | | | 9.35 | 10.25 |

# 12 23 Interior Shutters

## 12 23 10 – Wood Interior Shutters

### 12 23 10.10 Wood Interior Shutters

| | | Crew | Daily Output | Labor-Hours | Unit | Material | 2010 Bare Costs Labor | 2010 Bare Costs Equipment | Total | Total Incl O&P |
|---|---|---|---|---|---|---|---|---|---|---|
| 0010 | **WOOD INTERIOR SHUTTERS**, louvered | | | | | | | | | |
| 0200 | Two panel, 27" wide, 36" high | 1 Carp | 5 | 1.600 | Set | 124 | 46.50 | | 170.50 | 215 |
| 0300 | 33" wide, 36" high | | 5 | 1.600 | | 162 | 46.50 | | 208.50 | 258 |
| 0500 | 47" wide, 36" high | | 5 | 1.600 | | 216 | 46.50 | | 262.50 | 315 |
| 1000 | Four panel, 27" wide, 36" high | | 5 | 1.600 | | 147 | 46.50 | | 193.50 | 240 |
| 1100 | 33" wide, 36" high | | 5 | 1.600 | | 180 | 46.50 | | 226.50 | 277 |
| 1300 | 47" wide, 36" high | | 5 | 1.600 | | 255 | 46.50 | | 301.50 | 360 |

### 12 23 10.13 Wood Panels

| | | Crew | Daily Output | Labor-Hours | Unit | Material | Labor | Equipment | Total | Total Incl O&P |
|---|---|---|---|---|---|---|---|---|---|---|
| 0010 | **WOOD PANELS** | | | | | | | | | |
| 3000 | Wood folding panels with movable louvers, 7" x 20" each | 1 Carp | 17 | .471 | Pr. | 47 | 13.70 | | 60.70 | 74.50 |
| 3300 | 8" x 28" each | | 17 | .471 | | 61 | 13.70 | | 74.70 | 90.50 |
| 3450 | 9" x 36" each | | 17 | .471 | | 75.50 | 13.70 | | 89.20 | 106 |
| 3600 | 10" x 40" each | | 17 | .471 | | 81.50 | 13.70 | | 95.20 | 113 |
| 4000 | Fixed louver type, stock units, 8" x 20" each | | 17 | .471 | | 84 | 13.70 | | 97.70 | 116 |
| 4150 | 10" x 28" each | | 17 | .471 | | 90 | 13.70 | | 103.70 | 122 |
| 4300 | 12" x 36" each | | 17 | .471 | | 106 | 13.70 | | 119.70 | 140 |
| 4450 | 18" x 40" each | | 17 | .471 | | 118 | 13.70 | | 131.70 | 153 |
| 5000 | Insert panel type, stock, 7" x 20" each | | 17 | .471 | | 19.65 | 13.70 | | 33.35 | 44.50 |
| 5150 | 8" x 28" each | | 17 | .471 | | 36 | 13.70 | | 49.70 | 62.50 |
| 5300 | 9" x 36" each | | 17 | .471 | | 46 | 13.70 | | 59.70 | 73.50 |
| 5450 | 10" x 40" each | | 17 | .471 | | 49 | 13.70 | | 62.70 | 77 |
| 5600 | Raised panel type, stock, 10" x 24" each | | 17 | .471 | | 116 | 13.70 | | 129.70 | 151 |
| 5650 | 12" x 26" each | | 17 | .471 | | 116 | 13.70 | | 129.70 | 151 |
| 5700 | 14" x 30" each | | 17 | .471 | | 214 | 13.70 | | 227.70 | 259 |
| 5750 | 16" x 36" each | | 17 | .471 | | 294 | 13.70 | | 307.70 | 350 |
| 6000 | For custom built pine, add | | | | | 22% | | | | |
| 6500 | For custom built hardwood blinds, add | | | | | 42% | | | | |

# 12 24 Window Shades

## 12 24 13 – Roller Window Shades

### 12 24 13.10 Shades

| | | | Crew | Daily Output | Labor-Hours | Unit | Material | Labor | Equipment | Total | Total Incl O&P |
|---|---|---|---|---|---|---|---|---|---|---|---|
| 0010 | **SHADES** | | | | | | | | | | |
| 0020 | Basswood, roll-up, stain finish, 3/8" slats | | 1 Carp | 300 | .027 | S.F. | 13.95 | .78 | | 14.73 | 16.65 |
| 5011 | Insulative shades | G | | 125 | .064 | | 11 | 1.86 | | 12.86 | 15.25 |
| 6011 | Solar screening, fiberglass | G | | 85 | .094 | | 4.69 | 2.74 | | 7.43 | 9.75 |
| 8011 | Interior insulative shutter | | | | | | | | | | |
| 8111 | Stock unit, 15" x 60" | G | 1 Carp | 17 | .471 | Pr. | 11 | 13.70 | | 24.70 | 35 |

# 12 32 Manufactured Wood Casework

## 12 32 16 – Manufactured Plastic-Laminate-Clad Casework

### 12 32 16.20 Plastic Laminate Casework Doors

| | | Crew | Daily Output | Labor-Hours | Unit | Material | Labor | Equipment | Total | Total Incl O&P |
|---|---|---|---|---|---|---|---|---|---|---|
| 0010 | **PLASTIC LAMINATE CASEWORK DOORS** | | | | | | | | | |
| 1000 | For casework frames, see Div. 12 32 23.15 | | | | | | | | | |
| 1100 | For casework hardware, see Div. 12 32 23.35 | | | | | | | | | |
| 6000 | Plastic laminate on particle board | | | | | | | | | |
| 6100 | 12" wide, 18" high | 1 Carp | 25 | .320 | Ea. | 10.50 | 9.30 | | 19.80 | 27 |
| 6120 | 24" high | | 24 | .333 | | 14 | 9.70 | | 23.70 | 31.50 |
| 6140 | 30" high | | 23 | .348 | | 17.50 | 10.10 | | 27.60 | 36.50 |
| 6160 | 36" high | | 21 | .381 | | 21 | 11.10 | | 32.10 | 41.50 |

# 12 32 Manufactured Wood Casework

## 12 32 16 – Manufactured Plastic-Laminate-Clad Casework

### 12 32 16.20 Plastic Laminate Casework Doors

| | | Crew | Daily Output | Labor-Hours | Unit | Material | 2010 Bare Costs Labor | Equipment | Total | Total Incl O&P |
|---|---|---|---|---|---|---|---|---|---|---|
| 6200 | 48" high | 1 Carp | 16 | .500 | Ea. | 28 | 14.55 | | 42.55 | 55.50 |
| 6250 | 60" high | | 13 | .615 | | 35 | 17.90 | | 52.90 | 68.50 |
| 6300 | 72" high | | 12 | .667 | | 42 | 19.40 | | 61.40 | 78.50 |
| 6320 | 15" wide, 18" high | | 24.50 | .327 | | 13.10 | 9.50 | | 22.60 | 30.50 |
| 6340 | 24" high | | 23.50 | .340 | | 17.50 | 9.90 | | 27.40 | 36 |
| 6360 | 30" high | | 22.50 | .356 | | 22 | 10.35 | | 32.35 | 41.50 |
| 6380 | 36" high | | 20.50 | .390 | | 26.50 | 11.35 | | 37.85 | 48 |
| 6400 | 48" high | | 15.50 | .516 | | 35 | 15 | | 50 | 64 |
| 6450 | 60" high | | 12.50 | .640 | | 44 | 18.60 | | 62.60 | 80 |
| 6480 | 72" high | | 11.50 | .696 | | 52.50 | 20 | | 72.50 | 92 |
| 6500 | 18" wide, 18" high | | 24 | .333 | | 15.75 | 9.70 | | 25.45 | 33.50 |
| 6550 | 24" high | | 23 | .348 | | 21 | 10.10 | | 31.10 | 40 |
| 6600 | 30" high | | 22 | .364 | | 26.50 | 10.60 | | 37.10 | 47 |
| 6650 | 36" high | | 20 | .400 | | 31.50 | 11.65 | | 43.15 | 54 |
| 6700 | 48" high | | 15 | .533 | | 42 | 15.50 | | 57.50 | 72 |
| 6750 | 60" high | | 12 | .667 | | 52.50 | 19.40 | | 71.90 | 90.50 |
| 6800 | 72" high | | 11 | .727 | | 63 | 21 | | 84 | 105 |

### 12 32 16.25 Plastic Laminate Drawer Fronts

| | | Crew | Daily Output | Labor-Hours | Unit | Material | 2010 Bare Costs Labor | Equipment | Total | Total Incl O&P |
|---|---|---|---|---|---|---|---|---|---|---|
| 0010 | **PLASTIC LAMINATE DRAWER FRONTS** | | | | | | | | | |
| 2800 | Plastic laminate on particle board front | | | | | | | | | |
| 3000 | 4" high, 12" wide | 1 Carp | 17 | .471 | Ea. | 3.51 | 13.70 | | 17.21 | 27 |
| 3200 | 18" wide | | 16 | .500 | | 5.25 | 14.55 | | 19.80 | 30.50 |
| 3600 | 24" wide | | 15 | .533 | | 7 | 15.50 | | 22.50 | 33.50 |
| 3800 | 6" high, 12" wide | | 16 | .500 | | 5.25 | 14.55 | | 19.80 | 30.50 |
| 4000 | 18" wide | | 15 | .533 | | 7.90 | 15.50 | | 23.40 | 34.50 |
| 4500 | 24" wide | | 14 | .571 | | 10.55 | 16.65 | | 27.20 | 39.50 |
| 4800 | 9" high, 12" wide | | 15 | .533 | | 8 | 15.50 | | 23.50 | 35 |
| 5000 | 18" wide | | 14 | .571 | | 11.95 | 16.65 | | 28.60 | 41 |
| 5200 | 24" wide | | 13 | .615 | | 15.95 | 17.90 | | 33.85 | 47.50 |

## 12 32 23 – Hardwood Casework

### 12 32 23.10 Manufactured Wood Casework, Stock Units

| | | Crew | Daily Output | Labor-Hours | Unit | Material | 2010 Bare Costs Labor | Equipment | Total | Total Incl O&P |
|---|---|---|---|---|---|---|---|---|---|---|
| 0010 | **MANUFACTURED WOOD CASEWORK, STOCK UNITS** | | | | | | | | | |
| 0700 | Kitchen base cabinets, hardwood, not incl. counter tops, | | | | | | | | | |
| 0710 | 24" deep, 35" high, prefinished | | | | | | | | | |
| 0800 | One top drawer, one door below, 12" wide | 2 Carp | 24.80 | .645 | Ea. | 229 | 18.75 | | 247.75 | 284 |
| 0820 | 15" wide | | 24 | .667 | | 238 | 19.40 | | 257.40 | 295 |
| 0840 | 18" wide | | 23.30 | .687 | | 259 | 20 | | 279 | 320 |
| 0860 | 21" wide | | 22.70 | .705 | | 272 | 20.50 | | 292.50 | 335 |
| 0880 | 24" wide | | 22.30 | .717 | | 310 | 21 | | 331 | 380 |
| 1000 | Four drawers, 12" wide | | 24.80 | .645 | | 240 | 18.75 | | 258.75 | 296 |
| 1020 | 15" wide | | 24 | .667 | | 243 | 19.40 | | 262.40 | 300 |
| 1040 | 18" wide | | 23.30 | .687 | | 268 | 20 | | 288 | 330 |
| 1060 | 24" wide | | 22.30 | .717 | | 305 | 21 | | 326 | 370 |
| 1200 | Two top drawers, two doors below, 27" wide | | 22 | .727 | | 330 | 21 | | 351 | 400 |
| 1220 | 30" wide | | 21.40 | .748 | | 365 | 22 | | 387 | 435 |
| 1240 | 33" wide | | 20.90 | .766 | | 385 | 22.50 | | 407.50 | 460 |
| 1260 | 36" wide | | 20.30 | .788 | | 400 | 23 | | 423 | 480 |
| 1280 | 42" wide | | 19.80 | .808 | | 425 | 23.50 | | 448.50 | 510 |
| 1300 | 48" wide | | 18.90 | .847 | | 460 | 24.50 | | 484.50 | 545 |
| 1500 | Range or sink base, two doors below, 30" wide | | 21.40 | .748 | | 305 | 22 | | 327 | 370 |
| 1520 | 33" wide | | 20.90 | .766 | | 330 | 22.50 | | 352.50 | 400 |
| 1540 | 36" wide | | 20.30 | .788 | | 345 | 23 | | 368 | 420 |

# 12 32 Manufactured Wood Casework

## 12 32 23 – Hardwood Casework

| 12 32 23.10 Manufactured Wood Casework, Stock Units | | Crew | Daily Output | Labor-Hours | Unit | Material | 2010 Bare Costs Labor | Equipment | Total | Total Incl O&P |
|---|---|---|---|---|---|---|---|---|---|---|
| 1560 | 42" wide | 2 Carp | 19.80 | .808 | Ea. | 370 | 23.50 | | 393.50 | 445 |
| 1580 | 48" wide | ↓ | 18.90 | .847 | | 385 | 24.50 | | 409.50 | 465 |
| 1800 | For sink front units, deduct | | | | | 145 | | | 145 | 160 |
| 2000 | Corner base cabinets, 36" wide, standard | 2 Carp | 18 | .889 | | 540 | 26 | | 566 | 640 |
| 2100 | Lazy Susan with revolving door | " | 16.50 | .970 | ↓ | 725 | 28 | | 753 | 845 |
| 4000 | Kitchen wall cabinets, hardwood, 12" deep with two doors | | | | | | | | | |
| 4050 | 12" high, 30" wide | 2 Carp | 24.80 | .645 | Ea. | 205 | 18.75 | | 223.75 | 257 |
| 4100 | 36" wide | | 24 | .667 | | 240 | 19.40 | | 259.40 | 297 |
| 4400 | 15" high, 30" wide | | 24 | .667 | | 165 | 19.40 | | 184.40 | 214 |
| 4420 | 33" wide | | 23.30 | .687 | | 226 | 20 | | 246 | 283 |
| 4440 | 36" wide | | 22.70 | .705 | | 240 | 20.50 | | 260.50 | 299 |
| 4450 | 42" wide | | 22.70 | .705 | | 288 | 20.50 | | 308.50 | 350 |
| 4700 | 24" high, 30" wide | | 23.30 | .687 | | 275 | 20 | | 295 | 340 |
| 4720 | 36" wide | | 22.70 | .705 | | 305 | 20.50 | | 325.50 | 370 |
| 4740 | 42" wide | | 22.30 | .717 | | 350 | 21 | | 371 | 420 |
| 5000 | 30" high, one door, 12" wide | | 22 | .727 | | 185 | 21 | | 206 | 240 |
| 5020 | 15" wide | | 21.40 | .748 | | 208 | 22 | | 230 | 265 |
| 5040 | 18" wide | | 20.90 | .766 | | 229 | 22.50 | | 251.50 | 290 |
| 5060 | 24" wide | | 20.30 | .788 | | 267 | 23 | | 290 | 330 |
| 5300 | Two doors, 27" wide | | 19.80 | .808 | | 294 | 23.50 | | 317.50 | 365 |
| 5320 | 30" wide | | 19.30 | .829 | | 305 | 24 | | 329 | 375 |
| 5340 | 36" wide | | 18.80 | .851 | | 350 | 25 | | 375 | 425 |
| 5360 | 42" wide | | 18.50 | .865 | | 380 | 25 | | 405 | 465 |
| 5380 | 48" wide | | 18.40 | .870 | | 430 | 25.50 | | 455.50 | 520 |
| 6000 | Corner wall, 30" high, 24" wide | | 18 | .889 | | 233 | 26 | | 259 | 300 |
| 6050 | 30" wide | | 17.20 | .930 | | 264 | 27 | | 291 | 335 |
| 6100 | 36" wide | | 16.50 | .970 | | 295 | 28 | | 323 | 375 |
| 6500 | Revolving Lazy Susan | | 15.20 | 1.053 | | 415 | 30.50 | | 445.50 | 505 |
| 7000 | Broom cabinet, 84" high, 24" deep, 18" wide | | 10 | 1.600 | | 575 | 46.50 | | 621.50 | 715 |
| 7500 | Oven cabinets, 84" high, 24" deep, 27" wide | | 8 | 2 | ↓ | 860 | 58 | | 918 | 1,050 |
| 7750 | Valance board trim | ↓ | 396 | .040 | L.F. | 12.40 | 1.18 | | 13.58 | 15.65 |
| 9000 | For deluxe models of all cabinets, add | | | | | 40% | | | | |
| 9500 | For custom built in place, add | | | | | 25% | 10% | | | |
| 9550 | Rule of thumb, kitchen cabinets not including | | | | | | | | | |
| 9560 | appliances & counter top, minimum | 2 Carp | 30 | .533 | L.F. | 146 | 15.50 | | 161.50 | 187 |
| 9600 | Maximum | " | 25 | .640 | " | 310 | 18.60 | | 328.60 | 375 |

## 12 32 23.15 Manufactured Wood Casework Frames

| | | Crew | Daily Output | Labor-Hours | Unit | Material | 2010 Bare Costs Labor | Equipment | Total | Total Incl O&P |
|---|---|---|---|---|---|---|---|---|---|---|
| 0010 | **MANUFACTURED WOOD CASEWORK FRAMES** | | | | | | | | | |
| 0050 | Base cabinets, counter storage, 36" high | | | | | | | | | |
| 0100 | One bay, 18" wide | 1 Carp | 2.70 | 2.963 | Ea. | 134 | 86 | | 220 | 292 |
| 0400 | Two bay, 36" wide | | 2.20 | 3.636 | | 204 | 106 | | 310 | 400 |
| 1100 | Three bay, 54" wide | | 1.50 | 5.333 | | 243 | 155 | | 398 | 530 |
| 2800 | Bookcases, one bay, 7' high, 18" wide | | 2.40 | 3.333 | | 157 | 97 | | 254 | 335 |
| 3500 | Two bay, 36" wide | | 1.60 | 5 | | 228 | 146 | | 374 | 495 |
| 4100 | Three bay, 54" wide | | 1.20 | 6.667 | | 375 | 194 | | 569 | 740 |
| 6100 | Wall mounted cabinet, one bay, 24" high, 18" wide | | 3.60 | 2.222 | | 86.50 | 64.50 | | 151 | 204 |
| 6800 | Two bay, 36" wide | | 2.20 | 3.636 | | 126 | 106 | | 232 | 315 |
| 7400 | Three bay, 54" wide | | 1.70 | 4.706 | | 157 | 137 | | 294 | 405 |
| 8400 | 30" high, one bay, 18" wide | | 3.60 | 2.222 | | 94 | 64.50 | | 158.50 | 212 |
| 9000 | Two bay, 36" wide | | 2.15 | 3.721 | | 125 | 108 | | 233 | 320 |
| 9400 | Three bay, 54" wide | | 1.60 | 5 | | 156 | 146 | | 302 | 415 |
| 9800 | Wardrobe, 7' high, single, 24" wide | ↓ | 2.70 | 2.963 | ↓ | 173 | 86 | | 259 | 335 |

# 12 32 Manufactured Wood Casework

## 12 32 23 – Hardwood Casework

| 12 32 23.15 Manufactured Wood Casework Frames | Crew | Daily Output | Labor-Hours | Unit | Material | 2010 Bare Costs Labor | Equipment | Total | Total Incl O&P |
|---|---|---|---|---|---|---|---|---|---|
| 9950 | Partition, adjustable shelves & drawers, 48" wide | 1 Carp | 1.40 | 5.714 | Ea. | 330 | 166 | | 496 | 645 |

### 12 32 23.20 Manufactured Hardwood Casework Doors

| | | Crew | Daily Output | Labor-Hours | Unit | Material | Labor | Equipment | Total | Total Incl O&P |
|---|---|---|---|---|---|---|---|---|---|---|
| 0010 | **MANUFACTURED HARDWOOD CASEWORK DOORS** | | | | | | | | | |
| 2000 | Glass panel, hardwood frame | | | | | | | | | |
| 2200 | 12" wide, 18" high | 1 Carp | 34 | .235 | Ea. | 18.75 | 6.85 | | 25.60 | 32 |
| 2400 | 24" high | | 33 | .242 | | 25 | 7.05 | | 32.05 | 39.50 |
| 2600 | 30" high | | 32 | .250 | | 31.50 | 7.30 | | 38.80 | 47 |
| 2800 | 36" high | | 30 | .267 | | 37.50 | 7.75 | | 45.25 | 54.50 |
| 3000 | 48" high | | 23 | .348 | | 50 | 10.10 | | 60.10 | 72 |
| 3200 | 60" high | | 17 | .471 | | 62.50 | 13.70 | | 76.20 | 92 |
| 3400 | 72" high | | 15 | .533 | | 75 | 15.50 | | 90.50 | 109 |
| 3600 | 15" wide, 18" high | | 33 | .242 | | 23.50 | 7.05 | | 30.55 | 38 |
| 3800 | 24" high | | 32 | .250 | | 31.50 | 7.30 | | 38.80 | 47 |
| 4000 | 30" high | | 30 | .267 | | 39 | 7.75 | | 46.75 | 56 |
| 4250 | 36" high | | 28 | .286 | | 47 | 8.30 | | 55.30 | 65.50 |
| 4300 | 48" high | | 22 | .364 | | 62.50 | 10.60 | | 73.10 | 87 |
| 4350 | 60" high | | 16 | .500 | | 78 | 14.55 | | 92.55 | 111 |
| 4400 | 72" high | | 14 | .571 | | 94 | 16.65 | | 110.65 | 131 |
| 4450 | 18" wide, 18" high | | 32 | .250 | | 28 | 7.30 | | 35.30 | 43.50 |
| 4500 | 24" high | | 30 | .267 | | 37.50 | 7.75 | | 45.25 | 54.50 |
| 4550 | 30" high | | 29 | .276 | | 47 | 8.05 | | 55.05 | 65 |
| 4600 | 36" high | | 27 | .296 | | 56.50 | 8.60 | | 65.10 | 76.50 |
| 4650 | 48" high | | 21 | .381 | | 75 | 11.10 | | 86.10 | 101 |
| 4700 | 60" high | | 15 | .533 | | 94 | 15.50 | | 109.50 | 129 |
| 4750 | 72" high | | 13 | .615 | | 113 | 17.90 | | 130.90 | 154 |
| 5000 | Hardwood, raised panel | | | | | | | | | |
| 5100 | 12" wide, 18" high | 1 Carp | 16 | .500 | Ea. | 24 | 14.55 | | 38.55 | 51 |
| 5150 | 24" high | | 15.50 | .516 | | 32 | 15 | | 47 | 60.50 |
| 5200 | 30" high | | 15 | .533 | | 40 | 15.50 | | 55.50 | 70 |
| 5250 | 36" high | | 14 | .571 | | 48 | 16.65 | | 64.65 | 81 |
| 5300 | 48" high | | 11 | .727 | | 64 | 21 | | 85 | 106 |
| 5320 | 60" high | | 8 | 1 | | 80 | 29 | | 109 | 137 |
| 5340 | 72" high | | 7 | 1.143 | | 96 | 33.50 | | 129.50 | 162 |
| 5360 | 15" wide, 18" high | | 15.50 | .516 | | 30 | 15 | | 45 | 58.50 |
| 5380 | 24" high | | 15 | .533 | | 40 | 15.50 | | 55.50 | 70 |
| 5400 | 30" high | | 14.50 | .552 | | 50 | 16.05 | | 66.05 | 82 |
| 5420 | 36" high | | 13.50 | .593 | | 60 | 17.25 | | 77.25 | 95 |
| 5440 | 48" high | | 10.50 | .762 | | 80 | 22 | | 102 | 126 |
| 5460 | 60" high | | 7.50 | 1.067 | | 100 | 31 | | 131 | 162 |
| 5480 | 72" high | | 6.50 | 1.231 | | 120 | 36 | | 156 | 193 |
| 5500 | 18" wide, 18" high | | 15 | .533 | | 36 | 15.50 | | 51.50 | 65.50 |
| 5550 | 24" high | | 14.50 | .552 | | 48 | 16.05 | | 64.05 | 80 |
| 5600 | 30" high | | 14 | .571 | | 60 | 16.65 | | 76.65 | 94 |
| 5650 | 36" high | | 13 | .615 | | 72 | 17.90 | | 89.90 | 109 |
| 5700 | 48" high | | 10 | .800 | | 96 | 23.50 | | 119.50 | 145 |
| 5750 | 60" high | | 7 | 1.143 | | 120 | 33.50 | | 153.50 | 188 |
| 5800 | 72" high | | 6 | 1.333 | | 144 | 39 | | 183 | 224 |

### 12 32 23.25 Manufactured Wood Casework Drawer Fronts

| | | Crew | Daily Output | Labor-Hours | Unit | Material | Labor | Equipment | Total | Total Incl O&P |
|---|---|---|---|---|---|---|---|---|---|---|
| 0010 | **MANUFACTURED WOOD CASEWORK DRAWER FRONTS** | | | | | | | | | |
| 0100 | Solid hardwood front | | | | | | | | | |
| 1000 | 4" high, 12" wide | 1 Carp | 17 | .471 | Ea. | 2.83 | 13.70 | | 16.53 | 26 |
| 1200 | 18" wide | | 16 | .500 | | 4.25 | 14.55 | | 18.80 | 29 |

# 12 32 Manufactured Wood Casework

## 12 32 23 – Hardwood Casework

| 12 32 23.25 Manufactured Wood Casework Drawer Fronts | Crew | Daily Output | Labor-Hours | Unit | Material | 2010 Bare Costs Labor | Equipment | Total | Total Incl O&P |
|---|---|---|---|---|---|---|---|---|---|
| 1400 | 24" wide | 1 Carp | 15 | .533 | Ea. | 5.65 | 15.50 | | 21.15 | 32.50 |
| 1600 | 6" high, 12" wide | | 16 | .500 | | 4.25 | 14.55 | | 18.80 | 29 |
| 1800 | 18" wide | | 15 | .533 | | 6.40 | 15.50 | | 21.90 | 33 |
| 2000 | 24" wide | | 14 | .571 | | 8.50 | 16.65 | | 25.15 | 37.50 |
| 2200 | 9" high, 12" wide | | 15 | .533 | | 6.40 | 15.50 | | 21.90 | 33 |
| 2400 | 18" wide | | 14 | .571 | | 9.55 | 16.65 | | 26.20 | 38.50 |
| 2600 | 24" wide | | 13 | .615 | | 12.75 | 17.90 | | 30.65 | 44 |

### 12 32 23.30 Manufactured Wood Casework Vanities

| | | Crew | Daily Output | Labor-Hours | Unit | Material | 2010 Bare Costs Labor | Equipment | Total | Total Incl O&P |
|---|---|---|---|---|---|---|---|---|---|---|
| 0010 | **MANUFACTURED WOOD CASEWORK VANITIES** | | | | | | | | | |
| 8000 | Vanity bases, 2 doors, 30" high, 21" deep, 24" wide | 2 Carp | 20 | .800 | Ea. | 227 | 23.50 | | 250.50 | 289 |
| 8050 | 30" wide | | 16 | 1 | | 262 | 29 | | 291 | 335 |
| 8100 | 36" wide | | 13.33 | 1.200 | | 350 | 35 | | 385 | 445 |
| 8150 | 48" wide | | 11.43 | 1.400 | | 415 | 40.50 | | 455.50 | 530 |
| 9000 | For deluxe models of all vanities, add to above | | | | | 40% | | | | |
| 9500 | For custom built in place, add to above | | | | | 25% | 10% | | | |

### 12 32 23.35 Manufactured Wood Casework Hardware

| | | Crew | Daily Output | Labor-Hours | Unit | Material | 2010 Bare Costs Labor | Equipment | Total | Total Incl O&P |
|---|---|---|---|---|---|---|---|---|---|---|
| 0010 | **MANUFACTURED WOOD CASEWORK HARDWARE** | | | | | | | | | |
| 1000 | Catches, minimum | 1 Carp | 235 | .034 | Ea. | 1 | .99 | | 1.99 | 2.77 |
| 1020 | Average | | 119.40 | .067 | | 3.29 | 1.95 | | 5.24 | 6.90 |
| 1040 | Maximum | | 80 | .100 | | 6.25 | 2.91 | | 9.16 | 11.75 |
| 2000 | Door/drawer pulls, handles | | | | | | | | | |
| 2200 | Handles and pulls, projecting, metal, minimum | 1 Carp | 160 | .050 | Ea. | 4.52 | 1.46 | | 5.98 | 7.40 |
| 2220 | Average | | 95.24 | .084 | | 7 | 2.44 | | 9.44 | 11.80 |
| 2240 | Maximum | | 68 | .118 | | 9.55 | 3.42 | | 12.97 | 16.30 |
| 2300 | Wood, minimum | | 160 | .050 | | 4.76 | 1.46 | | 6.22 | 7.70 |
| 2320 | Average | | 95.24 | .084 | | 6.35 | 2.44 | | 8.79 | 11.10 |
| 2340 | Maximum | | 68 | .118 | | 8.75 | 3.42 | | 12.17 | 15.35 |
| 2600 | Flush, metal, minimum | | 160 | .050 | | 4.76 | 1.46 | | 6.22 | 7.70 |
| 2620 | Average | | 95.24 | .084 | | 6.35 | 2.44 | | 8.79 | 11.10 |
| 2640 | Maximum | | 68 | .118 | | 8.75 | 3.42 | | 12.17 | 15.35 |
| 3000 | Drawer tracks/glides, minimum | | 48 | .167 | Pr. | 8.05 | 4.85 | | 12.90 | 17.05 |
| 3020 | Average | | 32 | .250 | | 13.70 | 7.30 | | 21 | 27.50 |
| 3040 | Maximum | | 24 | .333 | | 23.50 | 9.70 | | 33.20 | 42.50 |
| 4000 | Cabinet hinges, minimum | | 160 | .050 | | 2.74 | 1.46 | | 4.20 | 5.45 |
| 4020 | Average | | 95.24 | .084 | | 6.10 | 2.44 | | 8.54 | 10.80 |
| 4040 | Maximum | | 68 | .118 | | 10.35 | 3.42 | | 13.77 | 17.15 |

# 12 34 Manufactured Plastic Casework

## 12 34 16 – Manufactured Solid-Plastic Casework

### 12 34 16.10 Outdoor Casework

| | | Crew | Daily Output | Labor-Hours | Unit | Material | 2010 Bare Costs Labor | Equipment | Total | Total Incl O&P |
|---|---|---|---|---|---|---|---|---|---|---|
| 0010 | **OUTDOOR CASEWORK** | | | | | | | | | |
| 0020 | Cabinet, base, sink/range, 36" | 2 Carp | 20.30 | .788 | Ea. | 1,625 | 23 | | 1,648 | 1,825 |
| 0100 | Base, 36" | | 20.30 | .788 | | 2,325 | 23 | | 2,348 | 2,600 |
| 0200 | Filler strip, 1" x 30" | | 158 | .101 | | 35 | 2.95 | | 37.95 | 43.50 |

# 12 36 Countertops

## 12 36 16 – Metal Countertops

| 12 36 16.10 Stainless Steel Countertops | Crew | Daily Output | Labor-Hours | Unit | Material | 2010 Bare Costs Labor | 2010 Bare Costs Equipment | Total | Total Incl O&P |
|---|---|---|---|---|---|---|---|---|---|
| 0010 **STAINLESS STEEL COUNTERTOPS** | | | | | | | | | |
| 3200 Stainless steel, custom | 1 Carp | 24 | .333 | S.F. | 143 | 9.70 | | 152.70 | 173 |

## 12 36 19 – Wood Countertops

### 12 36 19.10 Maple Countertops

| | Crew | Daily Output | Labor-Hours | Unit | Material | Labor | Equipment | Total | Total Incl O&P |
|---|---|---|---|---|---|---|---|---|---|
| 0010 **MAPLE COUNTERTOPS** | | | | | | | | | |
| 2900 Solid, laminated, 1-1/2" thick, no splash | 1 Carp | 28 | .286 | L.F. | 62.50 | 8.30 | | 70.80 | 82.50 |
| 3000 With square splash | | 28 | .286 | " | 74 | 8.30 | | 82.30 | 95.50 |
| 3400 Recessed cutting block with trim, 16" x 20" x 1" | | 8 | 1 | Ea. | 72.50 | 29 | | 101.50 | 129 |
| 3411 Replace cutting block only | ↓ | 16 | .500 | " | 35.50 | 14.55 | | 50.05 | 64 |

## 12 36 23 – Plastic Countertops

### 12 36 23.13 Plastic-Laminate-Clad Countertops

| | Crew | Daily Output | Labor-Hours | Unit | Material | Labor | Equipment | Total | Total Incl O&P |
|---|---|---|---|---|---|---|---|---|---|
| 0010 **PLASTIC-LAMINATE-CLAD COUNTERTOPS** | | | | | | | | | |
| 0020 Stock, 24" wide w/backsplash, minimum | 1 Carp | 30 | .267 | L.F. | 9.10 | 7.75 | | 16.85 | 23 |
| 0100 Maximum | | 25 | .320 | | 19.50 | 9.30 | | 28.80 | 37 |
| 0300 Custom plastic, 7/8" thick, aluminum molding, no splash | | 30 | .267 | | 21 | 7.75 | | 28.75 | 36 |
| 0400 Cove splash | | 30 | .267 | | 27.50 | 7.75 | | 35.25 | 43 |
| 0600 1-1/4" thick, no splash | | 28 | .286 | | 31 | 8.30 | | 39.30 | 48 |
| 0700 Square splash | | 28 | .286 | | 30 | 8.30 | | 38.30 | 47 |
| 0900 Square edge, plastic face, 7/8" thick, no splash | | 30 | .267 | | 26 | 7.75 | | 33.75 | 42 |
| 1000 With splash | ↓ | 30 | .267 | | 33.50 | 7.75 | | 41.25 | 49.50 |
| 1200 For stainless channel edge, 7/8" thick, add | | | | | 2.75 | | | 2.75 | 3.03 |
| 1300 1-1/4" thick, add | | | | | 3.22 | | | 3.22 | 3.54 |
| 1500 For solid color suede finish, add | | | | ↓ | 2.68 | | | 2.68 | 2.95 |
| 1700 For end splash, add | | | | Ea. | 17.85 | | | 17.85 | 19.65 |
| 1901 For cut outs, standard, add, minimum | 1 Carp | 32 | .250 | | | 7.30 | | 7.30 | 12.25 |
| 2000 Maximum | | 8 | 1 | | 5.95 | 29 | | 34.95 | 55.50 |
| 2010 Cut out in backsplash for elec. wall outlet | | 38 | .211 | | | 6.15 | | 6.15 | 10.30 |
| 2020 Cut out for sink | | 20 | .400 | | | 11.65 | | 11.65 | 19.60 |
| 2030 Cut out for stove top | | 18 | .444 | ↓ | | 12.95 | | 12.95 | 22 |
| 2100 Postformed, including backsplash and front edge | | 30 | .267 | L.F. | 10.70 | 7.75 | | 18.45 | 25 |
| 2110 Mitred, add | | 12 | .667 | Ea. | | 19.40 | | 19.40 | 32.50 |
| 2200 Built-in place, 25" wide, plastic laminate | ↓ | 25 | .320 | L.F. | 14.30 | 9.30 | | 23.60 | 31.50 |

## 12 36 33 – Tile Countertops

### 12 36 33.10 Ceramic Tile Countertops

| | Crew | Daily Output | Labor-Hours | Unit | Material | Labor | Equipment | Total | Total Incl O&P |
|---|---|---|---|---|---|---|---|---|---|
| 0010 **CERAMIC TILE COUNTERTOPS** | | | | | | | | | |
| 2300 Ceramic tile mosaic | 1 Carp | 25 | .320 | L.F. | 31 | 9.30 | | 40.30 | 49.50 |

## 12 36 40 – Stone Countertops

### 12 36 40.10 Natural Stone Countertops

| | Crew | Daily Output | Labor-Hours | Unit | Material | Labor | Equipment | Total | Total Incl O&P |
|---|---|---|---|---|---|---|---|---|---|
| 0010 **NATURAL STONE COUNTERTOPS** | | | | | | | | | |
| 2500 Marble, stock, with splash, 1/2" thick, minimum | 1 Bric | 17 | .471 | L.F. | 38 | 13.75 | | 51.75 | 64.50 |
| 2700 3/4" thick, maximum | | 13 | .615 | | 95.50 | 18 | | 113.50 | 135 |
| 2800 Granite, average, 1-1/4" thick, 24" wide, no splash | ↓ | 13.01 | .615 | ↓ | 131 | 18 | | 149 | 174 |

## 12 36 61 – Simulated Stone Countertops

### 12 36 61.16 Solid Surface Countertops

| | Crew | Daily Output | Labor-Hours | Unit | Material | Labor | Equipment | Total | Total Incl O&P |
|---|---|---|---|---|---|---|---|---|---|
| 0010 **SOLID SURFACE COUNTERTOPS**, Acrylic polymer | | | | | | | | | |
| 2000 Pricing for order of 1 – 50 L.F. | | | | | | | | | |
| 2100 25" wide, solid colors | 2 Carp | 20 | .800 | L.F. | 60 | 23.50 | | 83.50 | 105 |
| 2200 Patterned colors | | 20 | .800 | | 76.50 | 23.50 | | 100 | 123 |
| 2300 Premium patterned colors | | 20 | .800 | | 95.50 | 23.50 | | 119 | 144 |
| 2400 With silicone attached 4" backsplash, solid colors | ↓ | 19 | .842 | ↓ | 66 | 24.50 | | 90.50 | 114 |

# 12 36 Countertops

## 12 36 61 – Simulated Stone Countertops

| 12 36 61.16 Solid Surface Countertops | | Crew | Daily Output | Labor-Hours | Unit | Material | 2010 Bare Costs Labor | Equipment | Total | Total Incl O&P |
|---|---|---|---|---|---|---|---|---|---|---|
| 2500 | Patterned colors | 2 Carp | 19 | .842 | L.F. | 83.50 | 24.50 | | 108 | 133 |
| 2600 | Premium patterned colors | | 19 | .842 | | 104 | 24.50 | | 128.50 | 156 |
| 2700 | With hard seam attached 4" backsplash, solid colors | | 15 | 1.067 | | 66 | 31 | | 97 | 125 |
| 2800 | Patterned colors | | 15 | 1.067 | | 83.50 | 31 | | 114.50 | 144 |
| 2900 | Premium patterned colors | | 15 | 1.067 | | 104 | 31 | | 135 | 167 |
| 3800 | Sinks, pricing for order of 1 – 50 units | | | | | | | | | |
| 3900 | Single bowl, hard seamed, solid colors, 13" x 17" | 1 Carp | 2 | 4 | Ea. | 405 | 116 | | 521 | 640 |
| 4000 | 10" x 15" | | 4.55 | 1.758 | | 188 | 51 | | 239 | 293 |
| 4100 | Cutouts for sinks | | 5.25 | 1.524 | | | 44.50 | | 44.50 | 74.50 |

## 12 36 61.17 Solid Surface Vanity Tops

| | | Crew | Daily Output | Labor-Hours | Unit | Material | Labor | Equipment | Total | Total Incl O&P |
|---|---|---|---|---|---|---|---|---|---|---|
| 0010 | **SOLID SURFACE VANITY TOPS** | | | | | | | | | |
| 0015 | Solid surface, center bowl, 17" x 19" | 1 Carp | 12 | .667 | Ea. | 189 | 19.40 | | 208.40 | 241 |
| 0020 | 19" x 25" | | 12 | .667 | | 229 | 19.40 | | 248.40 | 285 |
| 0030 | 19" x 31" | | 12 | .667 | | 278 | 19.40 | | 297.40 | 340 |
| 0040 | 19" x 37" | | 12 | .667 | | 325 | 19.40 | | 344.40 | 390 |
| 0050 | 22" x 25" | | 10 | .800 | | 202 | 23.50 | | 225.50 | 261 |
| 0060 | 22" x 31" | | 10 | .800 | | 236 | 23.50 | | 259.50 | 298 |
| 0070 | 22" x 37" | | 10 | .800 | | 274 | 23.50 | | 297.50 | 340 |
| 0080 | 22" x 43" | | 10 | .800 | | 315 | 23.50 | | 338.50 | 385 |
| 0090 | 22" x 49" | | 10 | .800 | | 345 | 23.50 | | 368.50 | 420 |
| 0110 | 22" x 55" | | 8 | 1 | | 395 | 29 | | 424 | 485 |
| 0120 | 22" x 61" | | 8 | 1 | | 450 | 29 | | 479 | 545 |
| 0220 | Double bowl, 22" x 61" | | 8 | 1 | | 505 | 29 | | 534 | 610 |
| 0230 | Double bowl, 22" x 73" | | 8 | 1 | | 705 | 29 | | 734 | 825 |
| 0240 | For aggregate colors, add | | | | | 35% | | | | |
| 0250 | For faucets and fittings, see Div. 22 41 39.10 | | | | | | | | | |

## 12 36 61.19 Engineered Stone Countertops

| | | Crew | Daily Output | Labor-Hours | Unit | Material | Labor | Equipment | Total | Total Incl O&P |
|---|---|---|---|---|---|---|---|---|---|---|
| 0010 | **ENGINEERED STONE COUNTERTOPS** | | | | | | | | | |
| 0100 | 25" wide, 4" backsplash, color group A, minimum | 2 Carp | 15 | 1.067 | L.F. | 17 | 31 | | 48 | 70.50 |
| 0110 | Maximum | | 15 | 1.067 | | 42 | 31 | | 73 | 98 |
| 0120 | Color group B, minimum | | 15 | 1.067 | | 22 | 31 | | 53 | 76 |
| 0130 | Maximum | | 15 | 1.067 | | 49 | 31 | | 80 | 106 |
| 0140 | Color group C, minimum | | 15 | 1.067 | | 29.50 | 31 | | 60.50 | 84.50 |
| 0150 | Maximum | | 15 | 1.067 | | 60 | 31 | | 91 | 118 |
| 0160 | Color group D, minimum | | 15 | 1.067 | | 37 | 31 | | 68 | 92.50 |
| 0170 | Maximum | | 15 | 1.067 | | 70 | 31 | | 101 | 129 |

# 12 93 Site Furnishings

## 12 93 33 – Manufactured Planters

| 12 93 33.10 Planters | | Crew | Daily Output | Labor-Hours | Unit | Material | Labor | Equipment | Total | Total Incl O&P |
|---|---|---|---|---|---|---|---|---|---|---|
| 0010 | **PLANTERS** | | | | | | | | | |
| 0012 | Concrete, sandblasted, precast, 48" diameter, 24" high | 2 Clab | 15 | 1.067 | Ea. | 655 | 23 | | 678 | 760 |
| 0300 | Fiberglass, circular, 36" diameter, 24" high | | 15 | 1.067 | | 475 | 23 | | 498 | 560 |
| 1200 | Wood, square, 48" side, 24" high | | 15 | 1.067 | | 1,000 | 23 | | 1,023 | 1,150 |
| 1300 | Circular, 48" diameter, 30" high | | 10 | 1.600 | | 825 | 34.50 | | 859.50 | 970 |
| 1600 | Planter/bench, 72" | | 5 | 3.200 | | 3,225 | 69 | | 3,294 | 3,675 |

## 12 93 43 – Site Seating and Tables

| 12 93 43.13 Site Seating | | Crew | Daily Output | Labor-Hours | Unit | Material | Labor | Equipment | Total | Total Incl O&P |
|---|---|---|---|---|---|---|---|---|---|---|
| 0010 | **SITE SEATING** | | | | | | | | | |
| 0012 | Seating, benches, park, precast conc, w/backs, wood rails, 4' long | 2 Clab | 5 | 3.200 | Ea. | 420 | 69 | | 489 | 580 |

# 12 93 Site Furnishings

## 12 93 43 – Site Seating and Tables

| 12 93 43.13 Site Seating | | Crew | Daily Output | Labor-Hours | Unit | Material | 2010 Bare Costs Labor | Equipment | Total | Total Incl O&P |
|---|---|---|---|---|---|---|---|---|---|---|
| 0100 | 8' long | 2 Clab | 4 | 4 | Ea. | 800 | 86 | | 886 | 1,025 |
| 0500 | Steel barstock pedestals w/backs, 2" x 3" wood rails, 4' long | | 10 | 1.600 | | 1,050 | 34.50 | | 1,084.50 | 1,200 |
| 0510 | 8' long | | 7 | 2.286 | | 1,250 | 49 | | 1,299 | 1,450 |
| 0800 | Cast iron pedestals, back & arms, wood slats, 4' long | | 8 | 2 | | 295 | 43 | | 338 | 400 |
| 0820 | 8' long | | 5 | 3.200 | | 980 | 69 | | 1,049 | 1,200 |
| 1700 | Steel frame, fir seat, 10' long | | 10 | 1.600 | | 240 | 34.50 | | 274.50 | 320 |

# Estimating Tips

## General

- The items and systems in this division are usually estimated, purchased, supplied, and installed as a unit by one or more subcontractors. The estimator must ensure that all parties are operating from the same set of specifications and assumptions, and that all necessary items are estimated and will be provided. Many times the complex items and systems are covered, but the more common ones, such as excavation or a crane, are overlooked for the very reason that everyone assumes nobody could miss them. The estimator should be the central focus and be able to ensure that all systems are complete.

- Another area where problems can develop in this division is at the interface between systems. The estimator must ensure, for instance, that anchor bolts, nuts, and washers are estimated and included for the air-supported structures and pre-engineered buildings to be bolted to their foundations. Utility supply is a common area where essential items or pieces of equipment can be missed or overlooked due to the fact that each subcontractor may feel it is another's responsibility. The estimator should also be aware of certain items which may be supplied as part of a package but installed by others, and ensure that the installing contractor's estimate includes the cost of installation. Conversely, the estimator must also ensure that items are not costed by two different subcontractors, resulting in an inflated overall estimate.

## 13 30 00 Special Structures

- The foundations and floor slab, as well as rough mechanical and electrical, should be estimated, as this work is required for the assembly and erection of the structure.

Generally, as noted in the book, the pre-engineered building comes as a shell. Pricing is based on the size and structural design parameters stated in the reference section. Additional features, such as windows and doors, must also be included by the estimator. Here again, the estimator must have a clear understanding of the scope of each portion of the work and all the necessary interfaces.

## Reference Numbers

Reference numbers are shown in shaded boxes at the beginning of some major classifications. These numbers refer to related items in the Reference Section. The reference information may be an estimating procedure, an alternate pricing method, or technical information.

*Note:* Not all subdivisions listed here necessarily appear in this publication.

# 13 11 Swimming Pools

## 13 11 13 – Below-Grade Swimming Pools

### 13 11 13.50 Swimming Pools

| | | Crew | Daily Output | Labor-Hours | Unit | Material | 2010 Bare Costs | | Total | Total Incl O&P |
|---|---|---|---|---|---|---|---|---|---|---|
| | | | | | | | Labor | Equipment | | |
| 0010 | **SWIMMING POOLS** Residential in-ground, vinyl lined, concrete | | | | | | | | | |
| 0020 | Sides including equipment, sand bottom | B-52 | 300 | .187 | SF Surf | 13.90 | 4.51 | 1.80 | 20.21 | 25 |
| 0100 | Metal or polystyrene sides | B-14 | 410 | .117 | | 11.60 | 2.69 | .82 | 15.11 | 18.15 |
| 0200 | Add for vermiculite bottom | | | | | .89 | | | .89 | .98 |
| 0500 | Gunite bottom and sides, white plaster finish | B-52 | 145 | .386 | SF Surf | 26 | 9.35 | 3.72 | 39.07 | 48.50 |
| 0600 | 12' x 30' pool | | 155 | .361 | | 23.50 | 8.75 | 3.48 | 35.73 | 44 |
| 0720 | 16' x 32' pool | | 250 | .224 | | 21 | 5.40 | 2.15 | 28.55 | 34.50 |
| 0750 | 20' x 40' pool | | | | | | | | | |
| 0810 | Concrete bottom and sides, tile finish | B-52 | 80 | .700 | SF Surf | 26 | 16.90 | 6.75 | 49.65 | 64.50 |
| 0820 | 12' x 30' pool | | 95 | .589 | | 21.50 | 14.25 | 5.65 | 41.40 | 54 |
| 0830 | 16' x 32' pool | | 130 | .431 | | 17.15 | 10.40 | 4.14 | 31.69 | 41 |
| 0840 | 20' x 40' pool | | | | | | | | | |
| 1600 | For water heating system, see Div. 23 52 28.10 | | | | | | | | | |
| 1700 | Filtration and deck equipment only, as % of total | | | | Total | | | | 20% | 20% |
| 1800 | Deck equipment, rule of thumb, 20' x 40' pool | | | | SF Pool | | | | | 1.30 |
| 3000 | Painting pools, preparation + 3 coats, 20' x 40' pool, epoxy | 2 Pord | .33 | 48.485 | Total | 1,625 | 1,250 | | 2,875 | 3,800 |
| 3100 | Rubber base paint, 18 gallons | " | .33 | 48.485 | " | 1,100 | 1,250 | | 2,350 | 3,225 |

R131113-20

## 13 11 46 – Swimming Pool Accessories

### 13 11 46.50 Swimming Pool Equipment

| | | Crew | Daily Output | Labor-Hours | Unit | Material | Labor | Equipment | Total | Total Incl O&P |
|---|---|---|---|---|---|---|---|---|---|---|
| 0010 | **SWIMMING POOL EQUIPMENT** | | | | | | | | | |
| 0020 | Diving stand, stainless steel, 3 meter | 2 Carp | .40 | 40 | Ea. | 10,500 | 1,175 | | 11,675 | 13,500 |
| 0600 | Diving boards, 16' long, aluminum | | 2.70 | 5.926 | | 3,375 | 172 | | 3,547 | 4,000 |
| 0700 | Fiberglass | | 2.70 | 5.926 | | 2,550 | 172 | | 2,722 | 3,100 |
| 1200 | Ladders, heavy duty, stainless steel, 2 tread | | 7 | 2.286 | | 585 | 66.50 | | 651.50 | 755 |
| 1500 | 4 tread | | 6 | 2.667 | | 775 | 77.50 | | 852.50 | 985 |
| 2100 | Lights, underwater, 12 volt, with transformer, 300 watt | 1 Elec | 1 | 8 | | 263 | 263 | | 526 | 720 |
| 2200 | 110 volt, 500 watt, standard | " | 1 | 8 | | 209 | 263 | | 472 | 660 |
| 3000 | Pool covers, reinforced vinyl | 3 Clab | 1800 | .013 | S.F. | .36 | .29 | | .65 | .88 |
| 3100 | Vinyl water tube | | 3200 | .008 | | .50 | .16 | | .66 | .82 |
| 3200 | Maximum | | 3000 | .008 | | .63 | .17 | | .80 | .98 |
| 3300 | Slides, tubular, fiberglass, aluminum handrails & ladder, 5'-0", straight | 2 Carp | 1.60 | 10 | Ea. | 3,625 | 291 | | 3,916 | 4,500 |
| 3320 | 8'-0", curved | " | 3 | 5.333 | " | 6,375 | 155 | | 6,530 | 7,275 |

# 13 12 Fountains

## 13 12 13 – Exterior Fountains

### 13 12 13.10 Yard Fountains

| | | Crew | Daily Output | Labor-Hours | Unit | Material | Labor | Equipment | Total | Total Incl O&P |
|---|---|---|---|---|---|---|---|---|---|---|
| 0010 | **YARD FOUNTAINS** | | | | | | | | | |
| 0100 | Outdoor fountain, 48" high with bowl and figures | 2 Clab | 2 | 8 | Ea. | 253 | 172 | | 425 | 565 |

# 13 17 Tubs and Pools

## 13 17 13 – Redwood Hot Tub System

### 13 17 13.10 Redwood Hot Tub System

| | | Crew | Daily Output | Labor-Hours | Unit | Material | 2010 Bare Costs Labor | Equipment | Total | Total Incl O&P |
|---|---|---|---|---|---|---|---|---|---|---|
| 0010 | **REDWOOD HOT TUB SYSTEM** | | | | | | | | | |
| 7050 | 4' diameter x 4' deep | Q-1 | 1 | 16 | Ea. | 1,900 | 495 | | 2,395 | 2,900 |
| 7150 | 6' diameter x 4' deep | | .80 | 20 | | 2,950 | 620 | | 3,570 | 4,275 |
| 7200 | 8' diameter x 4' deep | | .80 | 20 | | 4,100 | 620 | | 4,720 | 5,525 |

## 13 17 33 – Whirlpool Tubs

### 13 17 33.10 Whirlpool Bath

| | | Crew | Daily Output | Labor-Hours | Unit | Material | 2010 Bare Costs Labor | Equipment | Total | Total Incl O&P |
|---|---|---|---|---|---|---|---|---|---|---|
| 0010 | **WHIRLPOOL BATH** | | | | | | | | | |
| 6000 | Whirlpool, bath with vented overflow, molded fiberglass | | | | | | | | | |
| 6100 | 66" x 48" x 24" | Q-1 | 1 | 16 | Ea. | 3,225 | 495 | | 3,720 | 4,350 |
| 6400 | 72" x 36" x 24" | | 1 | 16 | | 3,175 | 495 | | 3,670 | 4,275 |
| 6500 | 60" x 30" x 21" | | 1 | 16 | | 2,725 | 495 | | 3,220 | 3,800 |
| 6600 | 72" x 42" x 22" | | 1 | 16 | | 4,250 | 495 | | 4,745 | 5,475 |
| 6700 | 83" x 65" | | .30 | 53.333 | | 5,550 | 1,650 | | 7,200 | 8,800 |

# 13 24 Special Activity Rooms

## 13 24 16 – Saunas

### 13 24 16.50 Saunas and Heaters

| | | Crew | Daily Output | Labor-Hours | Unit | Material | 2010 Bare Costs Labor | Equipment | Total | Total Incl O&P |
|---|---|---|---|---|---|---|---|---|---|---|
| 0010 | **SAUNAS AND HEATERS** | | | | | | | | | |
| 0020 | Prefabricated, incl. heater & controls, 7' high, 6' x 4', C/C | L-7 | 2.20 | 11.818 | Ea. | 4,625 | 294 | | 4,919 | 5,600 |
| 0050 | 6' x 4', C/P | | 2 | 13 | | 4,275 | 325 | | 4,600 | 5,250 |
| 0400 | 6' x 5', C/C | | 2 | 13 | | 5,175 | 325 | | 5,500 | 6,225 |
| 0450 | 6' x 5', C/P | | 2 | 13 | | 4,800 | 325 | | 5,125 | 5,850 |
| 0600 | 6' x 6', C/C | | 1.80 | 14.444 | | 5,475 | 360 | | 5,835 | 6,625 |
| 0650 | 6' x 6', C/P | | 1.80 | 14.444 | | 5,125 | 360 | | 5,485 | 6,225 |
| 0800 | 6' x 9', C/C | | 1.60 | 16.250 | | 6,800 | 405 | | 7,205 | 8,150 |
| 0850 | 6' x 9', C/P | | 1.60 | 16.250 | | 6,300 | 405 | | 6,705 | 7,625 |
| 1000 | 8' x 12', C/C | | 1.10 | 23.636 | | 10,600 | 590 | | 11,190 | 12,700 |
| 1050 | 8' x 12', C/P | | 1.10 | 23.636 | | 9,725 | 590 | | 10,315 | 11,700 |
| 1400 | 8' x 10', C/C | | 1.20 | 21.667 | | 8,975 | 540 | | 9,515 | 10,800 |
| 1450 | 8' x 10', C/P | | 1.20 | 21.667 | | 8,350 | 540 | | 8,890 | 10,100 |
| 1600 | 10' x 12', C/C | | 1 | 26 | | 11,200 | 645 | | 11,845 | 13,400 |
| 1650 | 10' x 12', C/P | | 1 | 26 | | 10,100 | 645 | | 10,745 | 12,200 |
| 1700 | Door only, cedar, 2' x 6', with tempered insulated glass window | 2 Carp | 3.40 | 4.706 | | 610 | 137 | | 747 | 900 |
| 1800 | Prehung, incl. jambs, pulls & hardware | " | 12 | 1.333 | | 615 | 39 | | 654 | 740 |
| 2500 | Heaters only (incl. above), wall mounted, to 200 C.F. | | | | | 605 | | | 605 | 665 |
| 2750 | To 300 C.F. | | | | | 770 | | | 770 | 845 |
| 3000 | Floor standing, to 720 C.F., 10,000 watts, w/controls | 1 Elec | 3 | 2.667 | | 2,025 | 87.50 | | 2,112.50 | 2,375 |
| 3250 | To 1,000 C.F., 16,000 watts | " | 3 | 2.667 | | 2,525 | 87.50 | | 2,612.50 | 2,925 |

## 13 24 26 – Steam Baths

### 13 24 26.50 Steam Baths and Components

| | | Crew | Daily Output | Labor-Hours | Unit | Material | 2010 Bare Costs Labor | Equipment | Total | Total Incl O&P |
|---|---|---|---|---|---|---|---|---|---|---|
| 0010 | **STEAM BATHS AND COMPONENTS** | | | | | | | | | |
| 0020 | Heater, timer & head, single, to 140 C.F. | 1 Plum | 1.20 | 6.667 | Ea. | 1,400 | 229 | | 1,629 | 1,925 |
| 0500 | To 300 C.F. | " | 1.10 | 7.273 | | 1,625 | 250 | | 1,875 | 2,175 |
| 2700 | Conversion unit for residential tub, including door | | | | | 4,100 | | | 4,100 | 4,500 |

# 13 34 Fabricated Engineered Structures

## 13 34 13 – Glazed Structures

### 13 34 13.13 Greenhouses

| | | Crew | Daily Output | Labor-Hours | Unit | Material | 2010 Bare Costs Labor | Equipment | Total | Total Incl O&P |
|---|---|---|---|---|---|---|---|---|---|---|
| 0010 | **GREENHOUSES**, Shell only, stock units, not incl. 2' stub walls, | | | | | | | | | |
| 0020 | foundation, floors, heat or compartments | | | | | | | | | |
| 0300 | Residential type, free standing, 8'-6" long x 7'-6" wide | 2 Carp | 59 | .271 | SF Flr. | 38 | 7.90 | | 45.90 | 55 |
| 0400 | 10'-6" wide | | 85 | .188 | | 27 | 5.50 | | 32.50 | 38.50 |
| 0600 | 13'-6" wide | | 108 | .148 | | 23 | 4.31 | | 27.31 | 33 |
| 0700 | 17'-0" wide | | 160 | .100 | | 27 | 2.91 | | 29.91 | 35 |
| 0900 | Lean-to type, 3'-10" wide | | 34 | .471 | | 33.50 | 13.70 | | 47.20 | 60 |
| 1000 | 6'-10" wide | ↓ | 58 | .276 | ↓ | 38 | 8.05 | | 46.05 | 55.50 |
| 1100 | Wall mounted to existing window, 3' x 3' | 1 Carp | 4 | 2 | Ea. | 1,500 | 58 | | 1,558 | 1,750 |
| 1120 | 4' x 5' | " | 3 | 2.667 | " | 1,900 | 77.50 | | 1,977.50 | 2,225 |
| 1200 | Deluxe quality, free standing, 7'-6" wide | 2 Carp | 55 | .291 | SF Flr. | 79.50 | 8.45 | | 87.95 | 102 |
| 1220 | 10'-6" wide | | 81 | .198 | | 56.50 | 5.75 | | 62.25 | 71.50 |
| 1240 | 13'-6" wide | | 104 | .154 | | 51.50 | 4.48 | | 55.98 | 64.50 |
| 1260 | 17'-0" wide | | 150 | .107 | | 51 | 3.10 | | 54.10 | 61 |
| 1400 | Lean-to type, 3'-10" wide | | 31 | .516 | | 77.50 | 15 | | 92.50 | 111 |
| 1420 | 6'-10" wide | | 55 | .291 | | 56.50 | 8.45 | | 64.95 | 77 |
| 1440 | 8'-0" wide | ↓ | 97 | .165 | ↓ | 59 | 4.80 | | 63.80 | 73 |

### 13 34 13.19 Swimming Pool Enclosures

| | | Crew | Daily Output | Labor-Hours | Unit | Material | 2010 Bare Costs Labor | Equipment | Total | Total Incl O&P |
|---|---|---|---|---|---|---|---|---|---|---|
| 0010 | **SWIMMING POOL ENCLOSURES** Translucent, free standing | | | | | | | | | |
| 0020 | not including foundations, heat or light | | | | | | | | | |
| 0200 | Economy, minimum | 2 Carp | 200 | .080 | SF Hor. | 14.80 | 2.33 | | 17.13 | 20 |
| 0300 | Maximum | | 100 | .160 | | 43 | 4.66 | | 47.66 | 55.50 |
| 0400 | Deluxe, minimum | | 100 | .160 | | 50.50 | 4.66 | | 55.16 | 63.50 |
| 0600 | Maximum | ↓ | 70 | .229 | ↓ | 227 | 6.65 | | 233.65 | 261 |

## 13 34 63 – Natural Fiber Construction

### 13 34 63.50 Straw Bale Construction

| | | | Crew | Daily Output | Labor-Hours | Unit | Material | 2010 Bare Costs Labor | Equipment | Total | Total Incl O&P |
|---|---|---|---|---|---|---|---|---|---|---|---|
| 0010 | **STRAW BALE CONSTRUCTION** | | | | | | | | | | |
| 2000 | Straw bales wall, incl labor & material complete, minimum | G | | | | SF Flr. | | | | | 130 |
| 2010 | Maximum | G | | | | " | | | | | 160 |
| 2020 | Straw bales in walls w/modified post and beam frame | G | 2 Carp | 320 | .050 | S.F. | 4.11 | 1.46 | | 5.57 | 6.95 |

# Estimating Tips

## General

- Many products in Division 14 will require some type of support or blocking for installation not included with the item itself. Examples are supports for conveyors or tube systems, attachment points for lifts, and footings for hoists or cranes. Add these supports in the appropriate division.

## 14 10 00 Dumbwaiters
## 14 20 00 Elevators

- Dumbwaiters and elevators are estimated and purchased in a method similar to buying a car. The manufacturer has a base unit with standard features. Added to this base unit price will be whatever options the owner or specifications require. Increased load capacity, additional vertical travel, additional stops, higher speed, and cab finish options are items to be considered. When developing an estimate for dumbwaiters and elevators, remember that some items needed by the installers may have to be included as part of the general contract.

Examples are:
  - shaftway
  - rail support brackets
  - machine room
  - electrical supply
  - sill angles
  - electrical connections
  - pits
  - roof penthouses
  - pit ladders

Check the job specifications and drawings before pricing.

- Installation of elevators and handicapped lifts in historic structures can require significant additional costs. The associated structural requirements may involve cutting into and repairing finishes, mouldings, flooring, etc. The estimator must account for these special conditions.

## 14 30 00 Escalators and Moving Walks

- Escalators and moving walks are specialty items installed by specialty contractors. There are numerous options associated with these items. For specific options, contact a manufacturer or contractor. In a method similar to estimating dumbwaiters and elevators, you should verify the extent of general contract work and add items as necessary.

## 14 40 00 Lifts
## 14 90 00 Other Conveying Equipment

- Products such as correspondence lifts, chutes, and pneumatic tube systems, as well as other items specified in this subdivision, may require trained installers. The general contractor might not have any choice as to who will perform the installation or when it will be performed. Long lead times are often required for these products, making early decisions in scheduling necessary.

## Reference Numbers

Reference numbers are shown in shaded boxes at the beginning of some major classifications. These numbers refer to related items in the Reference Section. The reference information may be an estimating procedure, an alternate pricing method, or technical information.

*Note:* Not all subdivisions listed here necessarily appear in this publication.

**Division 14 - Conveying Equipment**

# 14 21 Electric Traction Elevators

## 14 21 33 – Electric Traction Residential Elevators

| 14 21 33.20 Residential Elevators | Crew | Daily Output | Labor-Hours | Unit | Material | 2010 Bare Costs Labor | Equipment | Total | Total Incl O&P |
|---|---|---|---|---|---|---|---|---|---|
| 0010 **RESIDENTIAL ELEVATORS** | | | | | | | | | |
| 7000    Residential, cab type, 1 floor, 2 stop, minimum | 2 Elev | .20 | 80 | Ea. | 11,000 | 3,300 | | 14,300 | 17,500 |
| 7100          Maximum | | .10 | 160 | | 18,600 | 6,625 | | 25,225 | 31,300 |
| 7200      2 floor, 3 stop, minimum | | .12 | 133 | | 16,400 | 5,525 | | 21,925 | 27,000 |
| 7300          Maximum | ↓ | .06 | 266 | ↓ | 26,700 | 11,000 | | 37,700 | 47,300 |

# 14 42 Wheelchair Lifts

## 14 42 13 – Inclined Wheelchair Lifts

### 14 42 13.10 Inclined Wheelchair Lifts and Stairclimbers

| | Crew | Daily Output | Labor-Hours | Unit | Material | 2010 Bare Costs Labor | Equipment | Total | Total Incl O&P |
|---|---|---|---|---|---|---|---|---|---|
| 0010 **INCLINED WHEELCHAIR LIFTS AND STAIRCLIMBERS** | | | | | | | | | |
| 7700    Stair climber (chair lift), single seat, minimum | 2 Elev | 1 | 16 | Ea. | 5,325 | 660 | | 5,985 | 6,950 |
| 7800          Maximum | " | .20 | 80 | " | 7,350 | 3,300 | | 10,650 | 13,500 |

# Estimating Tips

## 22 10 00 Plumbing Piping and Pumps

This subdivision is primarily basic pipe and related materials. The pipe may be used by any of the mechanical disciplines, i.e., plumbing, fire protection, heating, and air conditioning.

- The labor adjustment factors listed in Subdivision 22 01 02.20 apply throughout Divisions 21, 22, and 23. CAUTION: the correct percentage may vary for the same items. For example, the percentage add for the basic pipe installation should be based on the maximum height that the craftsman must install for that particular section. If the pipe is to be located 14' above the floor but it is suspended on threaded rod from beams, the bottom flange of which is 18' high (4' rods), then the height is actually 18' and the add is 20%. The pipe coverer, however, does not have to go above the 14', and so his or her add should be 10%.

- Most pipe is priced first as straight pipe with a joint (coupling, weld, etc.) every 10' and a hanger usually every 10'.

There are exceptions with hanger spacing such as for cast iron pipe (5') and plastic pipe (3 per 10'). Following each type of pipe there are several lines listing sizes and the amount to be subtracted to delete couplings and hangers. This is for pipe that is to be buried or supported together on trapeze hangers. The reason that the couplings are deleted is that these runs are usually long, and frequently longer lengths of pipe are used. By deleting the couplings, the estimator is expected to look up and add back the correct reduced number of couplings.

- When preparing an estimate, it may be necessary to approximate the fittings. Fittings usually run between 25% and 50% of the cost of the pipe. The lower percentage is for simpler runs, and the higher number is for complex areas, such as mechanical rooms.

- For historic restoration projects, the systems must be as invisible as possible, and pathways must be sought for pipes, conduit, and ductwork. While installations in accessible spaces (such as basements and attics) are relatively straightforward to estimate, labor costs may be more difficult to determine when delivery systems must be concealed.

## 22 40 00 Plumbing Fixtures

- Plumbing fixture costs usually require two lines: the fixture itself and its "rough-in, supply, and waste."

- In the Assemblies Section (Plumbing D2010) for the desired fixture, the System Components Group at the center of the page shows the fixture on the first line. The rest of the list (fittings, pipe, tubing, etc.) will total up to what we refer to in the Unit Price section as "Rough-in, supply, waste, and vent." Note that for most fixtures we allow a nominal 5' of tubing to reach from the fixture to a main or riser.

- Remember that gas- and oil-fired units need venting.

# Reference Numbers

Reference numbers are shown in shaded boxes at the beginning of some major classifications. These numbers refer to related items in the Reference Section. The reference information may be an estimating procedure, an alternate pricing method, or technical information.

*Note:* Not all subdivisions listed here necessarily appear in this publication.

*Note:* **Trade Service,** *in part, has been used as a reference source for some of the material prices used in Division 22.*

# 22 05 Common Work Results for Plumbing

## 22 05 05 – Selective Plumbing Demolition

### 22 05 05.10 Plumbing Demolition

| | | Crew | Daily Output | Labor-Hours | Unit | Material | 2010 Bare Costs Labor | 2010 Bare Costs Equipment | Total | Total Incl O&P |
|---|---|---|---|---|---|---|---|---|---|---|
| 0010 | **PLUMBING DEMOLITION** | | | | | | | | | |
| 1020 | Fixtures, including 10' piping | | | | | | | | | |
| 1101 | Bathtubs, cast iron | 1 Clab | 4 | 2 | Ea. | | 43 | | 43 | 72.50 |
| 1121 | Fiberglass | | 6 | 1.333 | | | 28.50 | | 28.50 | 48 |
| 1141 | Steel | ↓ | 5 | 1.600 | | | 34.50 | | 34.50 | 58 |
| 1200 | Lavatory, wall hung | 1 Plum | 10 | .800 | | | 27.50 | | 27.50 | 45 |
| 1221 | Counter top | 1 Clab | 16 | .500 | | | 10.75 | | 10.75 | 18.10 |
| 1301 | Sink, single compartment | | 16 | .500 | | | 10.75 | | 10.75 | 18.10 |
| 1321 | Double | ↓ | 10 | .800 | | | 17.20 | | 17.20 | 29 |
| 1400 | Water closet, floor mounted | 1 Plum | 8 | 1 | | | 34.50 | | 34.50 | 56.50 |
| 1421 | Wall mounted | 1 Clab | 7 | 1.143 | ↓ | | 24.50 | | 24.50 | 41.50 |
| 2001 | Piping, metal, to 1-1/2" diameter | | 200 | .040 | L.F. | | .86 | | .86 | 1.45 |
| 2051 | 2" thru 3-1/2" diameter | | 150 | .053 | | | 1.15 | | 1.15 | 1.93 |
| 2101 | 4" thru 6" diameter | ↓ | 100 | .080 | ↓ | | 1.72 | | 1.72 | 2.89 |
| 3000 | Submersible sump pump | 1 Plum | 24 | .333 | Ea. | | 11.45 | | 11.45 | 18.75 |
| 6000 | Remove and reset fixtures, minimum | | 6 | 1.333 | | | 46 | | 46 | 75 |
| 6100 | Maximum | ↓ | 4 | 2 | ↓ | | 68.50 | | 68.50 | 113 |
| 9000 | Minimum labor/equipment charge | ↓ | 2 | 4 | Job | | 137 | | 137 | 225 |

## 22 05 23 – General-Duty Valves for Plumbing Piping

### 22 05 23.20 Valves, Bronze

| | | Crew | Daily Output | Labor-Hours | Unit | Material | 2010 Bare Costs Labor | 2010 Bare Costs Equipment | Total | Total Incl O&P |
|---|---|---|---|---|---|---|---|---|---|---|
| 0010 | **VALVES, BRONZE** | | | | | | | | | |
| 1750 | Check, swing, class 150, regrinding disc, threaded | | | | | | | | | |
| 1860 | 3/4" | 1 Plum | 20 | .400 | Ea. | 65.50 | 13.75 | | 79.25 | 94.50 |
| 1870 | 1" | " | 19 | .421 | " | 94.50 | 14.45 | | 108.95 | 128 |
| 2850 | Gate, N.R.S., soldered, 125 psi | | | | | | | | | |
| 2940 | 3/4" | 1 Plum | 20 | .400 | Ea. | 36.50 | 13.75 | | 50.25 | 62.50 |
| 2950 | 1" | " | 19 | .421 | " | 52 | 14.45 | | 66.45 | 80.50 |
| 5600 | Relief, pressure & temperature, self-closing, ASME, threaded | | | | | | | | | |
| 5650 | 1" | 1 Plum | 24 | .333 | Ea. | 190 | 11.45 | | 201.45 | 227 |
| 5660 | 1-1/4" | " | 20 | .400 | " | 360 | 13.75 | | 373.75 | 420 |
| 6400 | Pressure, water, ASME, threaded | | | | | | | | | |
| 6440 | 3/4" | 1 Plum | 28 | .286 | Ea. | 70 | 9.80 | | 79.80 | 93 |
| 6450 | 1" | " | 24 | .333 | " | 149 | 11.45 | | 160.45 | 183 |
| 6900 | Reducing, water pressure | | | | | | | | | |
| 6940 | 1/2" | 1 Plum | 24 | .333 | Ea. | 225 | 11.45 | | 236.45 | 266 |
| 6960 | 1" | " | 19 | .421 | " | 350 | 14.45 | | 364.45 | 410 |
| 8350 | Tempering, water, sweat connections | | | | | | | | | |
| 8400 | 1/2" | 1 Plum | 24 | .333 | Ea. | 74.50 | 11.45 | | 85.95 | 101 |
| 8440 | 3/4" | " | 20 | .400 | " | 91 | 13.75 | | 104.75 | 123 |
| 8650 | Threaded connections | | | | | | | | | |
| 8700 | 1/2" | 1 Plum | 24 | .333 | Ea. | 112 | 11.45 | | 123.45 | 142 |
| 8740 | 3/4" | " | 20 | .400 | " | 390 | 13.75 | | 403.75 | 455 |

## 22 05 48 – Vibration and Seismic Controls for Plumbing Piping and Equipment

### 22 05 48.10 Seismic Bracing Supports

| | | Crew | Daily Output | Labor-Hours | Unit | Material | 2010 Bare Costs Labor | 2010 Bare Costs Equipment | Total | Total Incl O&P |
|---|---|---|---|---|---|---|---|---|---|---|
| 0010 | **SEISMIC BRACING SUPPORTS** | | | | | | | | | |
| 0020 | Clamps | | | | | | | | | |
| 0030 | C-clamp, for mounting on steel beam | | | | | | | | | |
| 0040 | 3/8" threaded rod | 1 Skwk | 160 | .050 | Ea. | 2.83 | 1.46 | | 4.29 | 5.55 |
| 0050 | 1/2" threaded rod | | 160 | .050 | | 3.50 | 1.46 | | 4.96 | 6.30 |
| 0060 | 5/8" threaded rod | | 160 | .050 | | 5.35 | 1.46 | | 6.81 | 8.35 |
| 0070 | 3/4" threaded rod | ↓ | 160 | .050 | ↓ | 7.25 | 1.46 | | 8.71 | 10.45 |
| 0100 | Brackets | | | | | | | | | |

## 22 05 48 – Vibration and Seismic Controls for Plumbing Piping and Equipment

| 22 05 48.10 Seismic Bracing Supports | Crew | Daily Output | Labor-Hours | Unit | Material | 2010 Bare Costs Labor | Equipment | Total | Total Incl O&P |
|---|---|---|---|---|---|---|---|---|---|
| 0110 | Beam side or wall mallable iron | | | | | | | | | |
| 0120 | 3/8" threaded rod | 1 Skwk | 48 | .167 | Ea. | 3.01 | 4.88 | | 7.89 | 11.50 |
| 0130 | 1/2" threaded rod | | 48 | .167 | | 5.35 | 4.88 | | 10.23 | 14.05 |
| 0140 | 5/8" threaded rod | | 48 | .167 | | 8.20 | 4.88 | | 13.08 | 17.25 |
| 0150 | 3/4" threaded rod | | 48 | .167 | | 9.85 | 4.88 | | 14.73 | 19.05 |
| 0160 | 7/8" threaded rod | | 48 | .167 | | 11.50 | 4.88 | | 16.38 | 21 |
| 0170 | For concrete installation, add | | | | | | 30% | | | |
| 0180 | Wall, welded steel | | | | | | | | | |
| 0190 | 0 size 12" wide 18" deep | 1 Skwk | 34 | .235 | Ea. | 204 | 6.90 | | 210.90 | 236 |
| 0200 | 1 size 18" wide 24" deep | | 34 | .235 | | 242 | 6.90 | | 248.90 | 279 |
| 0210 | 2 size 24" wide 30" deep | | 34 | .235 | | 320 | 6.90 | | 326.90 | 365 |
| 0300 | Rod, carbon steel | | | | | | | | | |
| 0310 | Continuous thread | | | | | | | | | |
| 0320 | 1/4" thread | 1 Skwk | 144 | .056 | L.F. | .16 | 1.63 | | 1.79 | 2.91 |
| 0330 | 3/8" thread | | 144 | .056 | | .25 | 1.63 | | 1.88 | 3.01 |
| 0340 | 1/2" thread | | 144 | .056 | | .45 | 1.63 | | 2.08 | 3.23 |
| 0350 | 5/8" thread | | 144 | .056 | | .82 | 1.63 | | 2.45 | 3.63 |
| 0360 | 3/4" thread | | 144 | .056 | | 1.20 | 1.63 | | 2.83 | 4.05 |
| 0370 | 7/8" thread | | 144 | .056 | | 1.73 | 1.63 | | 3.36 | 4.63 |
| 0380 | For galvanized, add | | | | | 30% | | | | |
| 0400 | Channel, steel | | | | | | | | | |
| 0410 | 3/4" x 1-1/2" | 1 Skwk | 80 | .100 | L.F. | 8 | 2.93 | | 10.93 | 13.70 |
| 0420 | 1-1/2" x 1-1/2" | | 70 | .114 | | 10.70 | 3.34 | | 14.04 | 17.35 |
| 0430 | 1-7/8" x 1-1/2" | | 60 | .133 | | 26 | 3.90 | | 29.90 | 35 |
| 0440 | 3" x 1-1/2" | | 50 | .160 | | 30 | 4.68 | | 34.68 | 41 |
| 0450 | Spring nuts | | | | | | | | | |
| 0460 | 3/8" | 1 Skwk | 100 | .080 | Ea. | 3 | 2.34 | | 5.34 | 7.20 |
| 0470 | 1/2" | " | 80 | .100 | " | 3.70 | 2.93 | | 6.63 | 9 |
| 0500 | Welding, field | | | | | | | | | |
| 0510 | Cleaning and welding plates, bars, or rods | | | | | | | | | |
| 0520 | To existing beams, columns, or trusses | | | | | | | | | |
| 0530 | 1" weld | 1 Skwk | 144 | .056 | Ea. | .19 | 1.63 | | 1.82 | 2.94 |
| 0540 | 2" weld | | 72 | .111 | | .34 | 3.25 | | 3.59 | 5.80 |
| 0550 | 3" weld | | 54 | .148 | | .52 | 4.33 | | 4.85 | 7.80 |
| 0560 | 4" weld | | 36 | .222 | | .73 | 6.50 | | 7.23 | 11.70 |
| 0570 | 5" weld | | 30 | .267 | | .91 | 7.80 | | 8.71 | 14.10 |
| 0580 | 6" weld | | 24 | .333 | | 1.04 | 9.75 | | 10.79 | 17.50 |
| 0600 | Vibration absorbers | | | | | | | | | |
| 0610 | Hangers, neoprene flex | | | | | | | | | |
| 0620 | 10-120 lb. capacity | 1 Skwk | 8 | 1 | Ea. | 22.50 | 29.50 | | 52 | 73.50 |
| 0630 | 75-550 lb. capacity | | 8 | 1 | | 29 | 29.50 | | 58.50 | 81 |
| 0640 | 250-1100 lb. capacity | | 6 | 1.333 | | 59 | 39 | | 98 | 131 |
| 0650 | 1000-4000 lb. capacity | | 6 | 1.333 | | 93.50 | 39 | | 132.50 | 169 |

## 22 05 76 – Facility Drainage Piping Cleanouts

### 22 05 76.10 Cleanouts

| | | | | | | | | | | |
|---|---|---|---|---|---|---|---|---|---|---|
| 0010 | **CLEANOUTS** | | | | | | | | | |
| 0080 | Round or square, scoriated nickel bronze top | | | | | | | | | |
| 0100 | 2" pipe size | 1 Plum | 10 | .800 | Ea. | 155 | 27.50 | | 182.50 | 215 |
| 0140 | 4" pipe size | " | 6 | 1.333 | " | 232 | 46 | | 278 | 330 |

### 22 05 76.20 Cleanout Tees

| | | |
|---|---|---|
| 0010 | **CLEANOUT TEES** | |
| 0100 | Cast iron, B&S, with countersunk plug | |

# 22 05 Common Work Results for Plumbing

## 22 05 76 – Facility Drainage Piping Cleanouts

| 22 05 76.20 Cleanout Tees | | Crew | Daily Output | Labor-Hours | Unit | Material | 2010 Bare Costs Labor | Equipment | Total | Total Incl O&P |
|---|---|---|---|---|---|---|---|---|---|---|
| 0220 | 3" pipe size | 1 Plum | 3.60 | 2.222 | Ea. | 230 | 76.50 | | 306.50 | 380 |
| 0240 | 4" pipe size | " | 3.30 | 2.424 | " | 286 | 83.50 | | 369.50 | 450 |
| 0500 | For round smooth access cover, same price | | | | | | | | | |
| 4000 | Plastic, tees and adapters. Add plugs | | | | | | | | | |
| 4010 | ABS, DWV | | | | | | | | | |
| 4020 | Cleanout tee, 1-1/2" pipe size | 1 Plum | 15 | .533 | Ea. | 4.62 | 18.30 | | 22.92 | 35 |

# 22 07 Plumbing Insulation

## 22 07 16 – Plumbing Equipment Insulation

### 22 07 16.10 Insulation for Plumbing Equipment

| | | | Crew | Daily Output | Labor-Hours | Unit | Material | Labor | Equipment | Total | Total Incl O&P |
|---|---|---|---|---|---|---|---|---|---|---|---|
| 0010 | **INSULATION FOR PLUMBING EQUIPMENT** | | | | | | | | | | |
| 2900 | Domestic water heater wrap kit | | | | | | | | | | |
| 2920 | 1-1/2" with vinyl jacket, 20-60 gal. | G | 1 Plum | 8 | 1 | Ea. | 16.05 | 34.50 | | 50.55 | 74 |

## 22 07 19 – Plumbing Piping Insulation

### 22 07 19.10 Piping Insulation

| | | | Crew | Daily Output | Labor-Hours | Unit | Material | Labor | Equipment | Total | Total Incl O&P |
|---|---|---|---|---|---|---|---|---|---|---|---|
| 0010 | **PIPING INSULATION** | | | | | | | | | | |
| 2930 | Insulated protectors, (ADA) | | | | | | | | | | |
| 2935 | For exposed piping under sinks or lavatories | | | | | | | | | | |
| 2940 | Vinyl coated foam, velcro tabs | | | | | | | | | | |
| 2945 | P Trap, 1-1/4" or 1-1/2" | | 1 Plum | 32 | .250 | Ea. | 18.50 | 8.60 | | 27.10 | 34.50 |
| 2960 | Valve and supply cover | | | | | | | | | | |
| 2965 | 1/2", 3/8", and 7/16" pipe size | | 1 Plum | 32 | .250 | Ea. | 17.60 | 8.60 | | 26.20 | 33.50 |
| 2970 | Extension drain cover | | | | | | | | | | |
| 2975 | 1-1/4", or 1-1/2" pipe size | | 1 Plum | 32 | .250 | Ea. | 19.30 | 8.60 | | 27.90 | 35.50 |
| 2985 | 1-1/4" pipe size | | " | 32 | .250 | " | 21.50 | 8.60 | | 30.10 | 37.50 |
| 4000 | Pipe covering (price copper tube one size less than IPS) | | | | | | | | | | |
| 6600 | Fiberglass, with all service jacket | | | | | | | | | | |
| 6840 | 1" wall, 1/2" iron pipe size | G | Q-14 | 240 | .067 | L.F. | .95 | 1.80 | | 2.75 | 4.11 |
| 6860 | 3/4" iron pipe size | G | | 230 | .070 | | 1.04 | 1.88 | | 2.92 | 4.33 |
| 6870 | 1" iron pipe size | G | | 220 | .073 | | 1.12 | 1.97 | | 3.09 | 4.56 |
| 6900 | 2" iron pipe size | G | | 200 | .080 | | 1.41 | 2.16 | | 3.57 | 5.20 |
| 7879 | Rubber tubing, flexible closed cell foam | | | | | | | | | | |
| 8100 | 1/2" wall, 1/4" iron pipe size | G | 1 Asbe | 90 | .089 | L.F. | .50 | 2.67 | | 3.17 | 5.05 |
| 8130 | 1/2" iron pipe size | G | | 89 | .090 | | .61 | 2.70 | | 3.31 | 5.25 |
| 8140 | 3/4" iron pipe size | G | | 89 | .090 | | .68 | 2.70 | | 3.38 | 5.35 |
| 8150 | 1" iron pipe size | G | | 88 | .091 | | .75 | 2.73 | | 3.48 | 5.45 |
| 8170 | 1-1/2" iron pipe size | G | | 87 | .092 | | 1.06 | 2.76 | | 3.82 | 5.85 |
| 8180 | 2" iron pipe size | G | | 86 | .093 | | 1.38 | 2.80 | | 4.18 | 6.25 |
| 8300 | 3/4" wall, 1/4" iron pipe size | G | | 90 | .089 | | .77 | 2.67 | | 3.44 | 5.35 |
| 8330 | 1/2" iron pipe size | G | | 89 | .090 | | 1.01 | 2.70 | | 3.71 | 5.70 |
| 8340 | 3/4" iron pipe size | G | | 89 | .090 | | 1.23 | 2.70 | | 3.93 | 5.95 |
| 8350 | 1" iron pipe size | G | | 88 | .091 | | 1.41 | 2.73 | | 4.14 | 6.20 |
| 8380 | 2" iron pipe size | G | | 86 | .093 | | 2.52 | 2.80 | | 5.32 | 7.50 |
| 8444 | 1" wall, 1/2" iron pipe size | G | | 86 | .093 | | 1.93 | 2.80 | | 4.73 | 6.85 |
| 8445 | 3/4" iron pipe size | G | | 84 | .095 | | 2.34 | 2.86 | | 5.20 | 7.40 |
| 8446 | 1" iron pipe size | G | | 84 | .095 | | 2.72 | 2.86 | | 5.58 | 7.85 |
| 8447 | 1-1/4" iron pipe size | G | | 82 | .098 | | 3.08 | 2.93 | | 6.01 | 8.35 |
| 8448 | 1-1/2" iron pipe size | G | | 82 | .098 | | 3.58 | 2.93 | | 6.51 | 8.90 |
| 8449 | 2" iron pipe size | G | | 80 | .100 | | 4.78 | 3.01 | | 7.79 | 10.35 |
| 8450 | 2-1/2" iron pipe size | G | | 80 | .100 | | 6.25 | 3.01 | | 9.26 | 11.95 |

# 22 07 Plumbing Insulation

## 22 07 19 – Plumbing Piping Insulation

| 22 07 19.10 Piping Insulation | Crew | Daily Output | Labor-Hours | Unit | Material | 2010 Bare Costs Labor | Equipment | Total | Total Incl O&P |
|---|---|---|---|---|---|---|---|---|---|
| 8456 | Rubber insulation tape, 1/8" x 2" x 30' | G | | | Ea. | 11.40 | | | 11.40 | 12.50 |

# 22 11 Facility Water Distribution

## 22 11 13 – Facility Water Distribution Piping

### 22 11 13.23 Pipe/Tube, Copper

| | | Crew | Daily Output | Labor-Hours | Unit | Material | 2010 Bare Costs Labor | Equipment | Total | Total Incl O&P |
|---|---|---|---|---|---|---|---|---|---|---|
| 0010 | **PIPE/TUBE, COPPER**, Solder joints | | | | | | | | | |
| 1000 | Type K tubing, couplings & clevis hanger assemblies 10' O.C. | | | | | | | | | |
| 1180 | 3/4" diameter | 1 Plum | 74 | .108 | L.F. | 6 | 3.71 | | 9.71 | 12.70 |
| 1200 | 1" diameter | " | 66 | .121 | " | 7.95 | 4.16 | | 12.11 | 15.55 |
| 2000 | Type L tubing, couplings & clevis hanger assemblies 10' O.C. | | | | | | | | | |
| 2140 | 1/2" diameter | 1 Plum | 81 | .099 | L.F. | 2.49 | 3.39 | | 5.88 | 8.30 |
| 2160 | 5/8" diameter | | 79 | .101 | | 3.87 | 3.48 | | 7.35 | 9.95 |
| 2180 | 3/4" diameter | | 76 | .105 | | 3.83 | 3.62 | | 7.45 | 10.15 |
| 2200 | 1" diameter | | 68 | .118 | | 5.95 | 4.04 | | 9.99 | 13.15 |
| 2220 | 1-1/4" diameter | | 58 | .138 | | 8.35 | 4.74 | | 13.09 | 16.95 |
| 3000 | Type M tubing, couplings & clevis hanger assemblies 10' O.C. | | | | | | | | | |
| 3140 | 1/2" diameter | 1 Plum | 84 | .095 | L.F. | 1.86 | 3.27 | | 5.13 | 7.40 |
| 3180 | 3/4" diameter | | 78 | .103 | | 2.93 | 3.52 | | 6.45 | 8.95 |
| 3200 | 1" diameter | | 70 | .114 | | 4.72 | 3.93 | | 8.65 | 11.65 |
| 3220 | 1-1/4" diameter | | 60 | .133 | | 6.95 | 4.58 | | 11.53 | 15.15 |
| 3240 | 1-1/2" diameter | | 54 | .148 | | 9.45 | 5.10 | | 14.55 | 18.70 |
| 3260 | 2" diameter | | 44 | .182 | | 14.80 | 6.25 | | 21.05 | 26.50 |
| 4000 | Type DWV tubing, couplings & clevis hanger assemblies 10' O.C. | | | | | | | | | |
| 4100 | 1-1/4" diameter | 1 Plum | 60 | .133 | L.F. | 9.80 | 4.58 | | 14.38 | 18.30 |
| 4120 | 1-1/2" diameter | | 54 | .148 | | 9.25 | 5.10 | | 14.35 | 18.55 |
| 4140 | 2" diameter | | 44 | .182 | | 12.55 | 6.25 | | 18.80 | 24 |
| 4160 | 3" diameter | Q-1 | 58 | .276 | | 23.50 | 8.55 | | 32.05 | 40 |
| 4180 | 4" diameter | " | 40 | .400 | | 42 | 12.35 | | 54.35 | 66.50 |

### 22 11 13.25 Pipe/Tube Fittings, Copper

| | | Crew | Daily Output | Labor-Hours | Unit | Material | 2010 Bare Costs Labor | Equipment | Total | Total Incl O&P |
|---|---|---|---|---|---|---|---|---|---|---|
| 0010 | **PIPE/TUBE FITTINGS, COPPER**, Wrought unless otherwise noted | | | | | | | | | |
| 0040 | Solder joints, copper x copper | | | | | | | | | |
| 0100 | 1/2" | 1 Plum | 20 | .400 | Ea. | 1.45 | 13.75 | | 15.20 | 24 |
| 0120 | 3/4" | | 19 | .421 | | 3.27 | 14.45 | | 17.72 | 27 |
| 0250 | 45° elbow, 1/4" | | 22 | .364 | | 8.60 | 12.50 | | 21.10 | 30 |
| 0280 | 1/2" | | 20 | .400 | | 2.67 | 13.75 | | 16.42 | 25.50 |
| 0290 | 5/8" | | 19 | .421 | | 13.35 | 14.45 | | 27.80 | 38 |
| 0300 | 3/4" | | 19 | .421 | | 4.68 | 14.45 | | 19.13 | 28.50 |
| 0310 | 1" | | 16 | .500 | | 11.75 | 17.20 | | 28.95 | 41 |
| 0320 | 1-1/4" | | 15 | .533 | | 15.90 | 18.30 | | 34.20 | 47.50 |
| 0450 | Tee, 1/4" | | 14 | .571 | | 9.65 | 19.65 | | 29.30 | 42.50 |
| 0480 | 1/2" | | 13 | .615 | | 2.49 | 21 | | 23.49 | 37 |
| 0490 | 5/8" | | 12 | .667 | | 16 | 23 | | 39 | 55 |
| 0500 | 3/4" | | 12 | .667 | | 6 | 23 | | 29 | 44 |
| 0510 | 1" | | 10 | .800 | | 18.55 | 27.50 | | 46.05 | 65.50 |
| 0520 | 1-1/4" | | 9 | .889 | | 25 | 30.50 | | 55.50 | 77.50 |
| 0612 | Tee, reducing on the outlet, 1/4" | | 15 | .533 | | 17.65 | 18.30 | | 35.95 | 49.50 |
| 0613 | 3/8" | | 15 | .533 | | 14.55 | 18.30 | | 32.85 | 46 |
| 0614 | 1/2" | | 14 | .571 | | 15.15 | 19.65 | | 34.80 | 48.50 |
| 0615 | 5/8" | | 13 | .615 | | 26 | 21 | | 47 | 63 |
| 0616 | 3/4" | | 12 | .667 | | 8.50 | 23 | | 31.50 | 47 |
| 0617 | 1" | | 11 | .727 | | 23 | 25 | | 48 | 66 |

### 22 11 13.25 Pipe/Tube Fittings, Copper

| | | Crew | Daily Output | Labor-Hours | Unit | Material | 2010 Bare Costs Labor | 2010 Bare Costs Equipment | Total | Total Incl O&P |
|---|---|---|---|---|---|---|---|---|---|---|
| 0618 | 1-1/4" | 1 Plum | 10 | .800 | Ea. | 32 | 27.50 | | 59.50 | 80 |
| 0619 | 1-1/2" | | 9 | .889 | | 29 | 30.50 | | 59.50 | 82 |
| 0620 | 2" | ▼ | 8 | 1 | | 52.50 | 34.50 | | 87 | 115 |
| 0621 | 2-1/2" | Q-1 | 9 | 1.778 | | 143 | 55 | | 198 | 248 |
| 0622 | 3" | | 8 | 2 | | 158 | 62 | | 220 | 274 |
| 0623 | 4" | | 6 | 2.667 | | 305 | 82.50 | | 387.50 | 470 |
| 0624 | 5" | ▼ | 5 | 3.200 | | 1,475 | 99 | | 1,574 | 1,775 |
| 0625 | 6" | Q-2 | 7 | 3.429 | | 1,925 | 102 | | 2,027 | 2,300 |
| 0626 | 8" | " | 6 | 4 | | 7,825 | 119 | | 7,944 | 8,825 |
| 0630 | Tee, reducing on the run, 1/4" | 1 Plum | 15 | .533 | | 19.45 | 18.30 | | 37.75 | 51.50 |
| 0631 | 3/8" | | 15 | .533 | | 26 | 18.30 | | 44.30 | 58.50 |
| 0632 | 1/2" | | 14 | .571 | | 17.90 | 19.65 | | 37.55 | 51.50 |
| 0633 | 5/8" | | 13 | .615 | | 26 | 21 | | 47 | 63 |
| 0634 | 3/4" | | 12 | .667 | | 7.05 | 23 | | 30.05 | 45.50 |
| 0635 | 1" | | 11 | .727 | | 22 | 25 | | 47 | 65.50 |
| 0636 | 1-1/4" | | 10 | .800 | | 36 | 27.50 | | 63.50 | 84.50 |
| 0637 | 1-1/2" | | 9 | .889 | | 62 | 30.50 | | 92.50 | 118 |
| 0638 | 2" | | 8 | 1 | | 86 | 34.50 | | 120.50 | 151 |
| 0639 | 2-1/2" | Q-1 | 9 | 1.778 | | 186 | 55 | | 241 | 294 |
| 0640 | 3" | | 8 | 2 | | 287 | 62 | | 349 | 415 |
| 0641 | 4" | | 6 | 2.667 | | 605 | 82.50 | | 687.50 | 800 |
| 0642 | 5" | ▼ | 5 | 3.200 | | 1,400 | 99 | | 1,499 | 1,700 |
| 0643 | 6" | Q-2 | 7 | 3.429 | | 2,150 | 102 | | 2,252 | 2,525 |
| 0644 | 8" | " | 6 | 4 | | 7,825 | 119 | | 7,944 | 8,825 |
| 0650 | Coupling, 1/4" | 1 Plum | 24 | .333 | | 1.06 | 11.45 | | 12.51 | 19.90 |
| 0680 | 1/2" | | 22 | .364 | | 1.10 | 12.50 | | 13.60 | 21.50 |
| 0690 | 5/8" | | 21 | .381 | | 3.32 | 13.10 | | 16.42 | 25 |
| 0700 | 3/4" | | 21 | .381 | | 2.36 | 13.10 | | 15.46 | 24 |
| 0710 | 1" | | 18 | .444 | | 4.41 | 15.25 | | 19.66 | 30 |
| 0715 | 1-1/4" | ▼ | 17 | .471 | ▼ | 7.85 | 16.15 | | 24 | 35 |
| 2000 | DWV, solder joints, copper x copper | | | | | | | | | |
| 2030 | 90° Elbow, 1-1/4" | 1 Plum | 13 | .615 | Ea. | 14.05 | 21 | | 35.05 | 50 |
| 2050 | 1-1/2" | | 12 | .667 | | 21 | 23 | | 44 | 60.50 |
| 2070 | 2" | ▼ | 10 | .800 | | 27.50 | 27.50 | | 55 | 75.50 |
| 2090 | 3" | Q-1 | 10 | 1.600 | | 68 | 49.50 | | 117.50 | 156 |
| 2100 | 4" | " | 9 | 1.778 | | 390 | 55 | | 445 | 520 |
| 2250 | Tee, Sanitary, 1-1/4" | 1 Plum | 9 | .889 | | 28 | 30.50 | | 58.50 | 80.50 |
| 2270 | 1-1/2" | | 8 | 1 | | 34.50 | 34.50 | | 69 | 94.50 |
| 2290 | 2" | ▼ | 7 | 1.143 | | 40.50 | 39.50 | | 80 | 109 |
| 2310 | 3" | Q-1 | 7 | 2.286 | | 164 | 70.50 | | 234.50 | 296 |
| 2330 | 4" | " | 6 | 2.667 | | 415 | 82.50 | | 497.50 | 595 |
| 2400 | Coupling, 1-1/4" | 1 Plum | 14 | .571 | | 6.60 | 19.65 | | 26.25 | 39.50 |
| 2420 | 1-1/2" | | 13 | .615 | | 8.20 | 21 | | 29.20 | 43.50 |
| 2440 | 2" | ▼ | 11 | .727 | | 11.35 | 25 | | 36.35 | 53.50 |
| 2460 | 3" | Q-1 | 11 | 1.455 | | 22 | 45 | | 67 | 97.50 |
| 2480 | 4" | " | 10 | 1.600 | ▼ | 70 | 49.50 | | 119.50 | 158 |

### 22 11 13.44 Pipe, Steel

| | | Crew | Daily Output | Labor-Hours | Unit | Material | 2010 Bare Costs Labor | 2010 Bare Costs Equipment | Total | Total Incl O&P |
|---|---|---|---|---|---|---|---|---|---|---|
| 0010 | **PIPE, STEEL** | | | | | | | | | |
| 0050 | Schedule 40, threaded, with couplings, and clevis hanger | | | | | | | | | |
| 0060 | assemblies sized for covering, 10' O.C. | | | | | | | | | |
| 0540 | Black, 1/4" diameter | 1 Plum | 66 | .121 | L.F. | 2.78 | 4.16 | | 6.94 | 9.85 |
| 0570 | 3/4" diameter | ▼ | 61 | .131 | ▼ | 4.28 | 4.51 | | 8.79 | 12.10 |

# 22 11 Facility Water Distribution

## 22 11 13 – Facility Water Distribution Piping

### 22 11 13.44 Pipe, Steel

| | | Crew | Daily Output | Labor-Hours | Unit | Material | 2010 Bare Costs Labor | 2010 Bare Costs Equipment | Total | Total Incl O&P |
|---|---|---|---|---|---|---|---|---|---|---|
| 0580 | 1" diameter | 1 Plum | 53 | .151 | L.F. | 6.25 | 5.20 | | 11.45 | 15.40 |
| 0590 | 1-1/4" diameter | Q-1 | 89 | .180 | | 7.95 | 5.55 | | 13.50 | 17.85 |
| 0600 | 1-1/2" diameter | | 80 | .200 | | 9.45 | 6.20 | | 15.65 | 20.50 |
| 0610 | 2" diameter | | 64 | .250 | | 12.60 | 7.75 | | 20.35 | 26.50 |

### 22 11 13.45 Pipe Fittings, Steel, Threaded

| | | Crew | Daily Output | Labor-Hours | Unit | Material | 2010 Bare Costs Labor | 2010 Bare Costs Equipment | Total | Total Incl O&P |
|---|---|---|---|---|---|---|---|---|---|---|
| 0010 | **PIPE FITTINGS, STEEL, THREADED** | | | | | | | | | |
| 5000 | Malleable iron, 150 lb. | | | | | | | | | |
| 5020 | Black | | | | | | | | | |
| 5040 | 90° elbow, straight | | | | | | | | | |
| 5090 | 3/4" | 1 Plum | 14 | .571 | Ea. | 2.87 | 19.65 | | 22.52 | 35 |
| 5100 | 1" | " | 13 | .615 | | 4.98 | 21 | | 25.98 | 40 |
| 5120 | 1-1/2" | Q-1 | 20 | .800 | | 10.80 | 24.50 | | 35.30 | 52.50 |
| 5130 | 2" | " | 18 | .889 | | 18.60 | 27.50 | | 46.10 | 65.50 |
| 5450 | Tee, straight | | | | | | | | | |
| 5500 | 3/4" | 1 Plum | 9 | .889 | Ea. | 4.55 | 30.50 | | 35.05 | 55 |
| 5510 | 1" | " | 8 | 1 | | 7.80 | 34.50 | | 42.30 | 65 |
| 5520 | 1-1/4" | Q-1 | 14 | 1.143 | | 12.65 | 35.50 | | 48.15 | 72 |
| 5530 | 1-1/2" | | 13 | 1.231 | | 15.70 | 38 | | 53.70 | 80 |
| 5540 | 2" | | 11 | 1.455 | | 27 | 45 | | 72 | 103 |
| 5650 | Coupling | | | | | | | | | |
| 5700 | 3/4" | 1 Plum | 18 | .444 | Ea. | 3.84 | 15.25 | | 19.09 | 29 |
| 5710 | 1" | " | 15 | .533 | | 5.75 | 18.30 | | 24.05 | 36.50 |
| 5730 | 1-1/2" | Q-1 | 24 | .667 | | 10.05 | 20.50 | | 30.55 | 45 |
| 5740 | 2" | " | 21 | .762 | | 14.90 | 23.50 | | 38.40 | 55 |

### 22 11 13.74 Pipe, Plastic

| | | Crew | Daily Output | Labor-Hours | Unit | Material | 2010 Bare Costs Labor | 2010 Bare Costs Equipment | Total | Total Incl O&P |
|---|---|---|---|---|---|---|---|---|---|---|
| 0010 | **PIPE, PLASTIC** | | | | | | | | | |
| 1800 | PVC, couplings 10' O.C., clevis hanger assemblies, 3 per 10' | | | | | | | | | |
| 1820 | Schedule 40 | | | | | | | | | |
| 1860 | 1/2" diameter | 1 Plum | 54 | .148 | L.F. | 1.65 | 5.10 | | 6.75 | 10.15 |
| 1870 | 3/4" diameter | | 51 | .157 | | 1.89 | 5.40 | | 7.29 | 10.95 |
| 1880 | 1" diameter | | 46 | .174 | | 2.18 | 5.95 | | 8.13 | 12.20 |
| 1890 | 1-1/4" diameter | | 42 | .190 | | 2.72 | 6.55 | | 9.27 | 13.70 |
| 1900 | 1-1/2" diameter | | 36 | .222 | | 2.92 | 7.65 | | 10.57 | 15.70 |
| 1910 | 2" diameter | Q-1 | 59 | .271 | | 3.51 | 8.40 | | 11.91 | 17.60 |
| 1920 | 2-1/2" diameter | | 56 | .286 | | 5.40 | 8.85 | | 14.25 | 20.50 |
| 1930 | 3" diameter | | 53 | .302 | | 6.95 | 9.35 | | 16.30 | 23 |
| 1940 | 4" diameter | | 48 | .333 | | 9.60 | 10.30 | | 19.90 | 27.50 |
| 4100 | DWV type, schedule 40, couplings 10' O.C., clevis hanger assy's, 3 per 10' | | | | | | | | | |
| 4210 | ABS, schedule 40, foam core type | | | | | | | | | |
| 4212 | Plain end black | | | | | | | | | |
| 4214 | 1-1/2" diameter | 1 Plum | 39 | .205 | L.F. | 1.93 | 7.05 | | 8.98 | 13.70 |
| 4216 | 2" diameter | Q-1 | 62 | .258 | | 2.35 | 8 | | 10.35 | 15.70 |
| 4218 | 3" diameter | | 56 | .286 | | 4.42 | 8.85 | | 13.27 | 19.35 |
| 4220 | 4" diameter | | 51 | .314 | | 6.10 | 9.70 | | 15.80 | 22.50 |
| 4222 | 6" diameter | | 42 | .381 | | 12.35 | 11.80 | | 24.15 | 33 |
| 4240 | To delete coupling & hangers, subtract | | | | | | | | | |
| 4244 | 1-1/2" diam. to 6" diam. | | | | | 43% | 48% | | | |
| 4400 | PVC | | | | | | | | | |
| 4410 | 1-1/4" diameter | 1 Plum | 42 | .190 | L.F. | 1.99 | 6.55 | | 8.54 | 12.90 |
| 4420 | 1-1/2" diameter | " | 36 | .222 | | 2 | 7.65 | | 9.65 | 14.70 |
| 4460 | 2" diameter | Q-1 | 59 | .271 | | 2.41 | 8.40 | | 10.81 | 16.40 |
| 4470 | 3" diameter | | 53 | .302 | | 4.51 | 9.35 | | 13.86 | 20.50 |

525

## 22 11 13 – Facility Water Distribution Piping

| 22 11 13.74 Pipe, Plastic | | Crew | Daily Output | Labor-Hours | Unit | Material | 2010 Bare Costs Labor | Equipment | Total | Total Incl O&P |
|---|---|---|---|---|---|---|---|---|---|---|
| 4480 | 4" diameter | Q-1 | 48 | .333 | L.F. | 6.10 | 10.30 | | 16.40 | 23.50 |
| 5300 | CPVC, socket joint, couplings 10' O.C., clevis hanger assemblies, 3 per 10' | | | | | | | | | |
| 5302 | Schedule 40 | | | | | | | | | |
| 5304 | 1/2" diameter | 1 Plum | 54 | .148 | L.F. | 2.35 | 5.10 | | 7.45 | 10.95 |
| 5305 | 3/4" diameter | | 51 | .157 | | 2.85 | 5.40 | | 8.25 | 12 |
| 5306 | 1" diameter | | 46 | .174 | | 3.76 | 5.95 | | 9.71 | 13.95 |
| 5307 | 1-1/4" diameter | | 42 | .190 | | 4.88 | 6.55 | | 11.43 | 16.05 |
| 5308 | 1-1/2" diameter | ▼ | 36 | .222 | | 5.75 | 7.65 | | 13.40 | 18.80 |
| 5309 | 2" diameter | Q-1 | 59 | .271 | ▼ | 7.15 | 8.40 | | 15.55 | 21.50 |
| 5360 | CPVC, threaded, couplings 10' O.C., clevis hanger assemblies, 3 per 10' | | | | | | | | | |
| 5380 | Schedule 40 | | | | | | | | | |
| 5460 | 1/2" diameter | 1 Plum | 54 | .148 | L.F. | 3.28 | 5.10 | | 8.38 | 11.95 |
| 5470 | 3/4" diameter | | 51 | .157 | | 3.88 | 5.40 | | 9.28 | 13.10 |
| 5480 | 1" diameter | | 46 | .174 | | 4.76 | 5.95 | | 10.71 | 15.05 |
| 5490 | 1-1/4" diameter | | 42 | .190 | | 5.85 | 6.55 | | 12.40 | 17.15 |
| 5500 | 1-1/2" diameter | ▼ | 36 | .222 | | 6.60 | 7.65 | | 14.25 | 19.75 |
| 5510 | 2" diameter | Q-1 | 59 | .271 | ▼ | 8.20 | 8.40 | | 16.60 | 23 |
| 6500 | Residential installation, plastic pipe | | | | | | | | | |
| 6510 | Couplings 10' O.C., strap hangers 3 per 10' | | | | | | | | | |
| 6520 | PVC, Schedule 40 | | | | | | | | | |
| 6530 | 1/2" diameter | 1 Plum | 138 | .058 | L.F. | 1.52 | 1.99 | | 3.51 | 4.93 |
| 6540 | 3/4" diameter | | 128 | .063 | | 1.66 | 2.15 | | 3.81 | 5.35 |
| 6550 | 1" diameter | | 119 | .067 | | 1.97 | 2.31 | | 4.28 | 5.95 |
| 6560 | 1-1/4" diameter | | 111 | .072 | | 2.34 | 2.48 | | 4.82 | 6.65 |
| 6570 | 1-1/2" diameter | ▼ | 104 | .077 | | 2.81 | 2.64 | | 5.45 | 7.40 |
| 6580 | 2" diameter | Q-1 | 197 | .081 | | 3.25 | 2.51 | | 5.76 | 7.70 |
| 6590 | 2-1/2" diameter | | 162 | .099 | | 5.85 | 3.06 | | 8.91 | 11.45 |
| 6600 | 4" diameter | ▼ | 123 | .130 | ▼ | 8.90 | 4.02 | | 12.92 | 16.40 |
| 6700 | PVC, DWV, Schedule 40 | | | | | | | | | |
| 6720 | 1-1/4" diameter | 1 Plum | 100 | .080 | L.F. | 2.33 | 2.75 | | 5.08 | 7.05 |
| 6730 | 1-1/2" diameter | " | 94 | .085 | | 2.68 | 2.92 | | 5.60 | 7.75 |
| 6740 | 2" diameter | Q-1 | 178 | .090 | | 3.03 | 2.78 | | 5.81 | 7.90 |
| 6760 | 4" diameter | " | 110 | .145 | ▼ | 8.05 | 4.50 | | 12.55 | 16.20 |
| 7280 | PEX, flexible, no couplings or hangers | | | | | | | | | |
| 7282 | Note: For labor costs add 25% to the couplings and fittings labor total. | | | | | | | | | |
| 7300 | Non-barrier type, hot/cold tubing rolls | | | | | | | | | |
| 7310 | 1/4" diameter x 100' | | | | L.F. | .44 | | | .44 | .48 |
| 7350 | 3/8" diameter x 100' | | | | | .49 | | | .49 | .54 |
| 7360 | 1/2" diameter x 100' | | | | | .55 | | | .55 | .61 |
| 7370 | 1/2" diameter x 500' | | | | | .55 | | | .55 | .61 |
| 7380 | 1/2" diameter x 1000' | | | | | .55 | | | .55 | .61 |
| 7400 | 3/4" diameter x 100' | | | | | 1 | | | 1 | 1.10 |
| 7410 | 3/4" diameter x 500' | | | | | 1 | | | 1 | 1.10 |
| 7420 | 3/4" diameter x 1000' | | | | | 1 | | | 1 | 1.10 |
| 7460 | 1" diameter x 100' | | | | | 1.71 | | | 1.71 | 1.88 |
| 7470 | 1" diameter x 300' | | | | | 1.71 | | | 1.71 | 1.88 |
| 7480 | 1" diameter x 500' | | | | | 1.71 | | | 1.71 | 1.88 |
| 7500 | 1-1/4" diameter x 100' | | | | | 2.90 | | | 2.90 | 3.19 |
| 7510 | 1-1/4" diameter x 300' | | | | | 2.90 | | | 2.90 | 3.19 |
| 7540 | 1-1/2" diameter x 100' | | | | | 3.64 | | | 3.64 | 4 |
| 7550 | 1-1/2" diameter x 300' | | | | ▼ | 3.40 | | | 3.40 | 3.74 |
| 7596 | Most sizes available in red or blue | | | | | | | | | |
| 7700 | Non-barrier type, hot/cold tubing straight lengths | | | | | | | | | |

### 22 11 13.74 Pipe, Plastic

| | | Crew | Daily Output | Labor-Hours | Unit | Material | 2010 Bare Costs Labor | Equipment | Total | Total Incl O&P |
|---|---|---|---|---|---|---|---|---|---|---|
| 7710 | 1/2" diameter x 20' | | | | L.F. | .55 | | | .55 | .61 |
| 7750 | 3/4" diameter x 20' | | | | | .99 | | | .99 | 1.09 |
| 7760 | 1" diameter x 20' | | | | | 1.71 | | | 1.71 | 1.88 |
| 7770 | 1-1/4" diameter x 20' | | | | | 2.90 | | | 2.90 | 3.19 |
| 7780 | 1-1/2" diameter x 20' | | | | | 3.64 | | | 3.64 | 4 |
| 7790 | 2" diameter | | | | | 5.05 | | | 5.05 | 5.55 |
| 7796 | Most sizes available in red or blue | | | | | | | | | |

### 22 11 13.76 Pipe Fittings, Plastic

| | | Crew | Daily Output | Labor-Hours | Unit | Material | 2010 Bare Costs Labor | Equipment | Total | Total Incl O&P |
|---|---|---|---|---|---|---|---|---|---|---|
| 0010 | **PIPE FITTINGS, PLASTIC** | | | | | | | | | |
| 2700 | PVC (white), schedule 40, socket joints | | | | | | | | | |
| 2760 | 90° elbow, 1/2" | 1 Plum | 33.30 | .240 | Ea. | .41 | 8.25 | | 8.66 | 14 |
| 2770 | 3/4" | | 28.60 | .280 | | .46 | 9.60 | | 10.06 | 16.25 |
| 2780 | 1" | | 25 | .320 | | .83 | 11 | | 11.83 | 18.90 |
| 2790 | 1-1/4" | | 22.20 | .360 | | 1.47 | 12.40 | | 13.87 | 22 |
| 2800 | 1-1/2" | | 20 | .400 | | 1.58 | 13.75 | | 15.33 | 24 |
| 2810 | 2" | Q-1 | 36.40 | .440 | | 2.47 | 13.60 | | 16.07 | 25 |
| 2820 | 2-1/2" | | 26.70 | .599 | | 7.55 | 18.55 | | 26.10 | 39 |
| 2830 | 3" | | 22.90 | .699 | | 9 | 21.50 | | 30.50 | 45.50 |
| 2840 | 4" | | 18.20 | .879 | | 16.10 | 27 | | 43.10 | 62.50 |
| 3180 | Tee, 1/2" | 1 Plum | 22.20 | .360 | | .51 | 12.40 | | 12.91 | 21 |
| 3190 | 3/4" | | 19 | .421 | | .59 | 14.45 | | 15.04 | 24 |
| 3200 | 1" | | 16.70 | .479 | | 1.10 | 16.45 | | 17.55 | 28 |
| 3210 | 1-1/4" | | 14.80 | .541 | | 1.71 | 18.55 | | 20.26 | 32.50 |
| 3220 | 1-1/2" | | 13.30 | .602 | | 2.09 | 20.50 | | 22.59 | 36.50 |
| 3230 | 2" | Q-1 | 24.20 | .661 | | 3.05 | 20.50 | | 23.55 | 37 |
| 3240 | 2-1/2" | | 17.80 | .899 | | 10.05 | 28 | | 38.05 | 56.50 |
| 3250 | 3" | | 15.20 | 1.053 | | 13.25 | 32.50 | | 45.75 | 68 |
| 3260 | 4" | | 12.10 | 1.322 | | 24 | 41 | | 65 | 93.50 |
| 3380 | Coupling, 1/2" | 1 Plum | 33.30 | .240 | | .28 | 8.25 | | 8.53 | 13.85 |
| 3390 | 3/4" | | 28.60 | .280 | | .38 | 9.60 | | 9.98 | 16.15 |
| 3400 | 1" | | 25 | .320 | | .68 | 11 | | 11.68 | 18.75 |
| 3410 | 1-1/4" | | 22.20 | .360 | | .90 | 12.40 | | 13.30 | 21.50 |
| 3420 | 1-1/2" | | 20 | .400 | | .97 | 13.75 | | 14.72 | 23.50 |
| 3430 | 2" | Q-1 | 36.40 | .440 | | 1.48 | 13.60 | | 15.08 | 24 |
| 3440 | 2-1/2" | | 26.70 | .599 | | 3.27 | 18.55 | | 21.82 | 34 |
| 3450 | 3" | | 22.90 | .699 | | 5.10 | 21.50 | | 26.60 | 41 |
| 3460 | 4" | | 18.20 | .879 | | 7.40 | 27 | | 34.40 | 52.50 |
| 4500 | DWV, ABS, non pressure, socket joints | | | | | | | | | |
| 4540 | 1/4 Bend, 1-1/4" | 1 Plum | 20.20 | .396 | Ea. | 2.16 | 13.60 | | 15.76 | 25 |
| 4560 | 1-1/2" | " | 18.20 | .440 | | 1.56 | 15.10 | | 16.66 | 26.50 |
| 4570 | 2" | Q-1 | 33.10 | .483 | | 2.30 | 14.95 | | 17.25 | 27 |
| 4800 | Tee, sanitary | | | | | | | | | |
| 4820 | 1-1/4" | 1 Plum | 13.50 | .593 | Ea. | 2.58 | 20.50 | | 23.08 | 36.50 |
| 4830 | 1-1/2" | " | 12.10 | .661 | | 2.08 | 22.50 | | 24.58 | 39.50 |
| 4840 | 2" | Q-1 | 20 | .800 | | 3.21 | 24.50 | | 27.71 | 44 |
| 5000 | DWV, PVC, schedule 40, socket joints | | | | | | | | | |
| 5040 | 1/4 bend, 1-1/4" | 1 Plum | 20.20 | .396 | Ea. | 3.69 | 13.60 | | 17.29 | 26.50 |
| 5060 | 1-1/2" | " | 18.20 | .440 | | 1.10 | 15.10 | | 16.20 | 26 |
| 5070 | 2" | Q-1 | 33.10 | .483 | | 1.74 | 14.95 | | 16.69 | 26.50 |
| 5080 | 3" | | 20.80 | .769 | | 5.15 | 24 | | 29.15 | 44.50 |
| 5090 | 4" | | 16.50 | .970 | | 10.10 | 30 | | 40.10 | 60 |
| 5110 | 1/4 bend, long sweep, 1-1/2" | 1 Plum | 18.20 | .440 | | 2.65 | 15.10 | | 17.75 | 28 |

| 22 11 13.76 Pipe Fittings, Plastic | | Crew | Daily Output | Labor-Hours | Unit | Material | 2010 Bare Costs Labor | Equipment | Total | Total Incl O&P |
|---|---|---|---|---|---|---|---|---|---|---|
| 5112 | 2" | Q-1 | 33.10 | .483 | Ea. | 2.86 | 14.95 | | 17.81 | 27.50 |
| 5114 | 3" | | 20.80 | .769 | | 6.75 | 24 | | 30.75 | 46.50 |
| 5116 | 4" | ↓ | 16.50 | .970 | | 12.90 | 30 | | 42.90 | 63 |
| 5250 | Tee, sanitary 1-1/4" | 1 Plum | 13.50 | .593 | | 3.19 | 20.50 | | 23.69 | 37 |
| 5254 | 1-1/2" | " | 12.10 | .661 | | 2 | 22.50 | | 24.50 | 39 |
| 5255 | 2" | Q-1 | 20 | .800 | | 2.94 | 24.50 | | 27.44 | 43.50 |
| 5256 | 3" | | 13.90 | 1.151 | | 7.55 | 35.50 | | 43.05 | 67 |
| 5257 | 4" | | 11 | 1.455 | | 13.10 | 45 | | 58.10 | 88 |
| 5259 | 6" | ↓ | 6.70 | 2.388 | | 57.50 | 74 | | 131.50 | 184 |
| 5261 | 8" | Q-2 | 6.20 | 3.871 | | 190 | 115 | | 305 | 400 |
| 5264 | 2" x 1-1/2" | Q-1 | 22 | .727 | | 2.42 | 22.50 | | 24.92 | 39.50 |
| 5266 | 3" x 1-1/2" | | 15.50 | 1.032 | | 5.45 | 32 | | 37.45 | 58.50 |
| 5268 | 4" x 3" | | 12.10 | 1.322 | | 16.65 | 41 | | 57.65 | 85.50 |
| 5271 | 6" x 4" | ↓ | 6.90 | 2.319 | | 61.50 | 71.50 | | 133 | 186 |
| 5314 | Combination Y & 1/8 bend, 1-1/2" | 1 Plum | 12.10 | .661 | | 4.34 | 22.50 | | 26.84 | 42 |
| 5315 | 2" | Q-1 | 20 | .800 | | 5.75 | 24.50 | | 30.25 | 47 |
| 5317 | 3" | | 13.90 | 1.151 | | 14.30 | 35.50 | | 49.80 | 74 |
| 5318 | 4" | ↓ | 11 | 1.455 | ↓ | 28.50 | 45 | | 73.50 | 105 |
| 5324 | Combination Y & 1/8 bend, reducing | | | | | | | | | |
| 5325 | 2" x 2" x 1-1/2" | Q-1 | 22 | .727 | Ea. | 6.25 | 22.50 | | 28.75 | 44 |
| 5327 | 3" x 3" x 1-1/2" | | 15.50 | 1.032 | | 10.80 | 32 | | 42.80 | 64.50 |
| 5328 | 3" x 3" x 2" | | 15.30 | 1.046 | | 8.50 | 32.50 | | 41 | 62.50 |
| 5329 | 4" x 4" x 2" | ↓ | 12.20 | 1.311 | | 13.80 | 40.50 | | 54.30 | 81.50 |
| 5331 | Wye, 1-1/4" | 1 Plum | 13.50 | .593 | | 4.06 | 20.50 | | 24.56 | 38 |
| 5332 | 1-1/2" | " | 12.10 | .661 | | 3.06 | 22.50 | | 25.56 | 40.50 |
| 5333 | 2" | Q-1 | 20 | .800 | | 3.58 | 24.50 | | 28.08 | 44.50 |
| 5334 | 3" | | 13.90 | 1.151 | | 9.65 | 35.50 | | 45.15 | 69 |
| 5335 | 4" | | 11 | 1.455 | | 17.55 | 45 | | 62.55 | 93 |
| 5336 | 6" | ↓ | 6.70 | 2.388 | | 53 | 74 | | 127 | 179 |
| 5337 | 8" | Q-2 | 6.20 | 3.871 | | 155 | 115 | | 270 | 360 |
| 5341 | 2" x 1-1/2" | Q-1 | 22 | .727 | | 4.39 | 22.50 | | 26.89 | 42 |
| 5342 | 3" x 1-1/2" | | 15.50 | 1.032 | | 6.30 | 32 | | 38.30 | 59.50 |
| 5343 | 4" x 3" | | 12.10 | 1.322 | | 14.25 | 41 | | 55.25 | 82.50 |
| 5344 | 6" x 4" | ↓ | 6.90 | 2.319 | | 39 | 71.50 | | 110.50 | 161 |
| 5345 | 8" x 6" | Q-2 | 6.40 | 3.750 | | 117 | 112 | | 229 | 310 |
| 5347 | Double wye, 1-1/2" | 1 Plum | 9.10 | .879 | | 6.90 | 30 | | 36.90 | 57 |
| 5348 | 2" | Q-1 | 16.60 | .964 | | 7.45 | 30 | | 37.45 | 57 |
| 5349 | 3" | | 10.40 | 1.538 | | 19.20 | 47.50 | | 66.70 | 99 |
| 5350 | 4" | ↓ | 8.25 | 1.939 | ↓ | 39 | 60 | | 99 | 142 |
| 5353 | Double wye, reducing | | | | | | | | | |
| 5354 | 2" x 2" x 1-1/2" x 1-1/2" | Q-1 | 16.80 | .952 | Ea. | 6.80 | 29.50 | | 36.30 | 56 |
| 5355 | 3" x 3" x 2" x 2" | | 10.60 | 1.509 | | 14.35 | 46.50 | | 60.85 | 92.50 |
| 5356 | 4" x 4" x 3" x 3" | | 8.45 | 1.893 | | 31 | 58.50 | | 89.50 | 130 |
| 5357 | 6" x 6" x 4" x 4" | | 7.25 | 2.207 | | 81.50 | 68.50 | | 150 | 202 |
| 5410 | Reducer bushing, 2" x 1-1/4" | | 36.50 | .438 | | 1.95 | 13.55 | | 15.50 | 24 |
| 5412 | 3" x 1-1/2" | | 27.30 | .586 | | 4.53 | 18.15 | | 22.68 | 34.50 |
| 5414 | 4" x 2" | | 18.20 | .879 | | 8.75 | 27 | | 35.75 | 54 |
| 5416 | 6" x 4" | ↓ | 11.10 | 1.441 | | 23.50 | 44.50 | | 68 | 98.50 |
| 5418 | 8" x 6" | Q-2 | 10.20 | 2.353 | ↓ | 50.50 | 70 | | 120.50 | 171 |
| 5500 | CPVC, Schedule 80, threaded joints | | | | | | | | | |
| 5540 | 90° Elbow, 1/4" | 1 Plum | 32 | .250 | Ea. | 10.40 | 8.60 | | 19 | 25.50 |
| 5560 | 1/2" | | 30.30 | .264 | | 6.05 | 9.05 | | 15.10 | 21.50 |
| 5570 | 3/4" | ↓ | 26 | .308 | | 9.05 | 10.55 | | 19.60 | 27.50 |

# 22 11 Facility Water Distribution

## 22 11 13 – Facility Water Distribution Piping

| 22 11 13.76 Pipe Fittings, Plastic | | Crew | Daily Output | Labor-Hours | Unit | Material | 2010 Bare Costs Labor | Equipment | Total | Total Incl O&P |
|---|---|---|---|---|---|---|---|---|---|---|
| 5580 | 1" | 1 Plum | 22.70 | .352 | Ea. | 12.65 | 12.10 | | 24.75 | 34 |
| 5590 | 1-1/4" | | 20.20 | .396 | | 24.50 | 13.60 | | 38.10 | 49.50 |
| 5600 | 1-1/2" | ↓ | 18.20 | .440 | | 26.50 | 15.10 | | 41.60 | 54 |
| 5610 | 2" | Q-1 | 33.10 | .483 | | 35 | 14.95 | | 49.95 | 63 |
| 5730 | Coupling, 1/4" | 1 Plum | 32 | .250 | | 13.25 | 8.60 | | 21.85 | 28.50 |
| 5732 | 1/2" | | 30.30 | .264 | | 13.25 | 9.05 | | 22.30 | 29.50 |
| 5734 | 3/4" | | 26 | .308 | | 15.90 | 10.55 | | 26.45 | 35 |
| 5736 | 1" | | 22.70 | .352 | | 17.60 | 12.10 | | 29.70 | 39 |
| 5738 | 1-1/4" | | 20.20 | .396 | | 21 | 13.60 | | 34.60 | 46 |
| 5740 | 1-1/2" | ↓ | 18.20 | .440 | | 23 | 15.10 | | 38.10 | 50 |
| 5742 | 2" | Q-1 | 33.10 | .483 | ↓ | 27 | 14.95 | | 41.95 | 54 |
| 5900 | CPVC, Schedule 80, socket joints | | | | | | | | | |
| 5904 | 90° Elbow, 1/4" | 1 Plum | 32 | .250 | Ea. | 9.70 | 8.60 | | 18.30 | 25 |
| 5906 | 1/2" | | 30.30 | .264 | | 3.81 | 9.05 | | 12.86 | 19.05 |
| 5908 | 3/4" | | 26 | .308 | | 4.85 | 10.55 | | 15.40 | 22.50 |
| 5910 | 1" | | 22.70 | .352 | | 7.70 | 12.10 | | 19.80 | 28.50 |
| 5912 | 1-1/4" | | 20.20 | .396 | | 16.65 | 13.60 | | 30.25 | 41 |
| 5914 | 1-1/2" | ↓ | 18.20 | .440 | | 18.60 | 15.10 | | 33.70 | 45.50 |
| 5916 | 2" | Q-1 | 33.10 | .483 | | 22.50 | 14.95 | | 37.45 | 49 |
| 5930 | 45° Elbow, 1/4" | 1 Plum | 32 | .250 | | 14.40 | 8.60 | | 23 | 30 |
| 5932 | 1/2" | | 30.30 | .264 | | 4.65 | 9.05 | | 13.70 | 19.95 |
| 5934 | 3/4" | | 26 | .308 | | 6.70 | 10.55 | | 17.25 | 24.50 |
| 5936 | 1" | | 22.70 | .352 | | 10.70 | 12.10 | | 22.80 | 31.50 |
| 5938 | 1-1/4" | | 20.20 | .396 | | 21 | 13.60 | | 34.60 | 45.50 |
| 5940 | 1-1/2" | ↓ | 18.20 | .440 | | 21.50 | 15.10 | | 36.60 | 48.50 |
| 5942 | 2" | Q-1 | 33.10 | .483 | | 24 | 14.95 | | 38.95 | 51 |
| 5990 | Coupling, 1/4" | 1 Plum | 32 | .250 | | 10.35 | 8.60 | | 18.95 | 25.50 |
| 5992 | 1/2" | | 30.30 | .264 | | 4.02 | 9.05 | | 13.07 | 19.25 |
| 5994 | 3/4" | | 26 | .308 | | 5.60 | 10.55 | | 16.15 | 23.50 |
| 5996 | 1" | | 22.70 | .352 | | 7.55 | 12.10 | | 19.65 | 28 |
| 5998 | 1-1/4" | | 20.20 | .396 | | 11.35 | 13.60 | | 24.95 | 35 |
| 6000 | 1-1/2" | ↓ | 18.20 | .440 | | 14.25 | 15.10 | | 29.35 | 40.50 |
| 6002 | 2" | Q-1 | 33.10 | .483 | ↓ | 16.55 | 14.95 | | 31.50 | 43 |

## 22 11 19 – Domestic Water Piping Specialties

### 22 11 19.38 Water Supply Meters

| | | Crew | Daily Output | Labor-Hours | Unit | Material | 2010 Bare Costs Labor | Equipment | Total | Total Incl O&P |
|---|---|---|---|---|---|---|---|---|---|---|
| 0010 | **WATER SUPPLY METERS** | | | | | | | | | |
| 2000 | Domestic/commercial, bronze | | | | | | | | | |
| 2020 | Threaded | | | | | | | | | |
| 2060 | 5/8" diameter, to 20 GPM | 1 Plum | 16 | .500 | Ea. | 42 | 17.20 | | 59.20 | 74 |
| 2080 | 3/4" diameter, to 30 GPM | | 14 | .571 | | 76.50 | 19.65 | | 96.15 | 116 |
| 2100 | 1" diameter, to 50 GPM | ↓ | 12 | .667 | ↓ | 116 | 23 | | 139 | 166 |

### 22 11 19.42 Backflow Preventers

| | | Crew | Daily Output | Labor-Hours | Unit | Material | 2010 Bare Costs Labor | Equipment | Total | Total Incl O&P |
|---|---|---|---|---|---|---|---|---|---|---|
| 0010 | **BACKFLOW PREVENTERS**, Includes valves | | | | | | | | | |
| 0020 | and four test cocks, corrosion resistant, automatic operation | | | | | | | | | |
| 4100 | Threaded, bronze, valves are ball | | | | | | | | | |
| 4120 | 3/4" pipe size | 1 Plum | 16 | .500 | Ea. | 365 | 17.20 | | 382.20 | 430 |

### 22 11 19.50 Vacuum Breakers

| | | | | | | | | | | |
|---|---|---|---|---|---|---|---|---|---|---|
| 0010 | **VACUUM BREAKERS** | | | | | | | | | |
| 0013 | See also backflow preventers Div. 22 11 19.42 | | | | | | | | | |
| 1000 | Anti-siphon continuous pressure type | | | | | | | | | |
| 1010 | Max. 150 PSI - 210°F | | | | | | | | | |
| 1020 | Bronze body | | | | | | | | | |

# 22 11 Facility Water Distribution

## 22 11 19 – Domestic Water Piping Specialties

### 22 11 19.50 Vacuum Breakers

| | | Crew | Daily Output | Labor-Hours | Unit | Material | 2010 Bare Costs Labor | 2010 Bare Costs Equipment | Total | Total Incl O&P |
|---|---|---|---|---|---|---|---|---|---|---|
| 1030 | 1/2" size | 1 Stpi | 24 | .333 | Ea. | 172 | 11.40 | | 183.40 | 208 |
| 1040 | 3/4" size | | 20 | .400 | | 172 | 13.70 | | 185.70 | 212 |
| 1050 | 1" size | | 19 | .421 | | 178 | 14.40 | | 192.40 | 219 |
| 1060 | 1-1/4" size | | 15 | .533 | | 355 | 18.25 | | 373.25 | 420 |
| 1070 | 1-1/2" size | | 13 | .615 | | 425 | 21 | | 446 | 505 |
| 1080 | 2" size | | 11 | .727 | | 440 | 25 | | 465 | 525 |
| 1200 | Max. 125 PSI with atmospheric vent | | | | | | | | | |
| 1210 | Brass, in-line construction | | | | | | | | | |
| 1220 | 1/4" size | 1 Stpi | 24 | .333 | Ea. | 59.50 | 11.40 | | 70.90 | 84 |
| 1230 | 3/8" size | " | 24 | .333 | | 59.50 | 11.40 | | 70.90 | 84 |
| 1260 | For polished chrome finish, add | | | | | 13% | | | | |
| 2000 | Anti-siphon, non-continuous pressure type | | | | | | | | | |
| 2010 | Hot or cold water 125 PSI - 210°F | | | | | | | | | |
| 2020 | Bronze body | | | | | | | | | |
| 2030 | 1/4" size | 1 Stpi | 24 | .333 | Ea. | 38 | 11.40 | | 49.40 | 60 |
| 2040 | 3/8" size | | 24 | .333 | | 38 | 11.40 | | 49.40 | 60 |
| 2050 | 1/2" size | | 24 | .333 | | 43 | 11.40 | | 54.40 | 66 |
| 2060 | 3/4" size | | 20 | .400 | | 52.50 | 13.70 | | 66.20 | 80 |
| 2070 | 1" size | | 19 | .421 | | 79.50 | 14.40 | | 93.90 | 111 |
| 2080 | 1-1/4" size | | 15 | .533 | | 139 | 18.25 | | 157.25 | 183 |
| 2090 | 1-1/2" size | | 13 | .615 | | 164 | 21 | | 185 | 215 |
| 2100 | 2" size | | 11 | .727 | | 255 | 25 | | 280 | 320 |
| 2110 | 2-1/2" size | | 8 | 1 | | 730 | 34.50 | | 764.50 | 860 |
| 2120 | 3" size | | 6 | 1.333 | | 975 | 45.50 | | 1,020.50 | 1,150 |
| 2150 | For polished chrome finish, add | | | | | 50% | | | | |

### 22 11 19.54 Water Hammer Arresters/Shock Absorbers

| | | Crew | Daily Output | Labor-Hours | Unit | Material | 2010 Bare Costs Labor | 2010 Bare Costs Equipment | Total | Total Incl O&P |
|---|---|---|---|---|---|---|---|---|---|---|
| 0010 | **WATER HAMMER ARRESTERS/SHOCK ABSORBERS** | | | | | | | | | |
| 0490 | Copper | | | | | | | | | |
| 0500 | 3/4" male I.P.S. For 1 to 11 fixtures | 1 Plum | 12 | .667 | Ea. | 20.50 | 23 | | 43.50 | 60 |

# 22 13 Facility Sanitary Sewerage

## 22 13 16 – Sanitary Waste and Vent Piping

### 22 13 16.20 Pipe, Cast Iron

| | | | Crew | Daily Output | Labor-Hours | Unit | Material | 2010 Bare Costs Labor | 2010 Bare Costs Equipment | Total | Total Incl O&P |
|---|---|---|---|---|---|---|---|---|---|---|---|
| 0010 | **PIPE, CAST IRON**, Soil, on clevis hanger assemblies, 5' O.C. | R221113-50 | | | | | | | | | |
| 0020 | Single hub, service wt., lead & oakum joints 10' O.C. | | | | | | | | | | |
| 2120 | 2" diameter | | Q-1 | 63 | .254 | L.F. | 7 | 7.85 | | 14.85 | 20.50 |
| 2140 | 3" diameter | | | 60 | .267 | | 9.80 | 8.25 | | 18.05 | 24.50 |
| 2160 | 4" diameter | | | 55 | .291 | | 12.70 | 9 | | 21.70 | 28.50 |
| 4000 | No hub, couplings 10' O.C. | | | | | | | | | | |
| 4100 | 1-1/2" diameter | | Q-1 | 71 | .225 | L.F. | 7.05 | 6.95 | | 14 | 19.15 |
| 4120 | 2" diameter | | | 67 | .239 | | 7.35 | 7.40 | | 14.75 | 20 |
| 4140 | 3" diameter | | | 64 | .250 | | 10.15 | 7.75 | | 17.90 | 24 |
| 4160 | 4" diameter | | | 58 | .276 | | 13.20 | 8.55 | | 21.75 | 28.50 |

### 22 13 16.30 Pipe Fittings, Cast Iron

| | | Crew | Daily Output | Labor-Hours | Unit | Material | 2010 Bare Costs Labor | 2010 Bare Costs Equipment | Total | Total Incl O&P |
|---|---|---|---|---|---|---|---|---|---|---|
| 0010 | **PIPE FITTINGS, CAST IRON**, Soil | | | | | | | | | |
| 0040 | Hub and spigot, service weight, lead & oakum joints | | | | | | | | | |
| 0080 | 1/4 bend, 2" | Q-1 | 16 | 1 | Ea. | 14.85 | 31 | | 45.85 | 67 |
| 0120 | 3" | | 14 | 1.143 | | 19.90 | 35.50 | | 55.40 | 80 |
| 0140 | 4" | | 13 | 1.231 | | 31 | 38 | | 69 | 96.50 |
| 0340 | 1/8 bend, 2" | | 16 | 1 | | 10.55 | 31 | | 41.55 | 62 |

# 22 13 Facility Sanitary Sewerage

## 22 13 16 - Sanitary Waste and Vent Piping

### 22 13 16.30 Pipe Fittings, Cast Iron

| | | Crew | Daily Output | Labor-Hours | Unit | Material | 2010 Bare Costs Labor | Equipment | Total | Total Incl O&P |
|---|---|---|---|---|---|---|---|---|---|---|
| 0350 | 3" | Q-1 | 14 | 1.143 | Ea. | 16.60 | 35.50 | | 52.10 | 76.50 |
| 0360 | 4" | | 13 | 1.231 | | 24 | 38 | | 62 | 89 |
| 0500 | Sanitary tee, 2" | | 10 | 1.600 | | 21 | 49.50 | | 70.50 | 104 |
| 0540 | 3" | | 9 | 1.778 | | 33.50 | 55 | | 88.50 | 127 |
| 0620 | 4" | | 8 | 2 | | 41 | 62 | | 103 | 146 |
| 5990 | No hub | | | | | | | | | |
| 6000 | Cplg. & labor required at joints not incl. in fitting | | | | | | | | | |
| 6010 | price. Add 1 coupling per joint for installed price | | | | | | | | | |
| 6020 | 1/4 Bend, 1-1/2" | | | | Ea. | 7.70 | | | 7.70 | 8.45 |
| 6060 | 2" | | | | | 8.45 | | | 8.45 | 9.30 |
| 6080 | 3" | | | | | 11.60 | | | 11.60 | 12.80 |
| 6120 | 4" | | | | | 16.80 | | | 16.80 | 18.50 |
| 6184 | 1/4 Bend, long sweep, 1-1/2" | | | | | 18.20 | | | 18.20 | 20 |
| 6186 | 2" | | | | | 18.20 | | | 18.20 | 20 |
| 6188 | 3" | | | | | 21.50 | | | 21.50 | 23.50 |
| 6189 | 4" | | | | | 34.50 | | | 34.50 | 38 |
| 6190 | 5" | | | | | 63.50 | | | 63.50 | 70 |
| 6191 | 6" | | | | | 77.50 | | | 77.50 | 85 |
| 6192 | 8" | | | | | 187 | | | 187 | 206 |
| 6193 | 10" | | | | | 335 | | | 335 | 370 |
| 6200 | 1/8 Bend, 1-1/2" | | | | | 6.45 | | | 6.45 | 7.10 |
| 6210 | 2" | | | | | 7.20 | | | 7.20 | 7.95 |
| 6212 | 3" | | | | | 9.75 | | | 9.75 | 10.70 |
| 6214 | 4" | | | | | 12.30 | | | 12.30 | 13.55 |
| 6380 | Sanitary Tee, tapped, 1-1/2" | | | | | 14.20 | | | 14.20 | 15.65 |
| 6382 | 2" x 1-1/2" | | | | | 12.80 | | | 12.80 | 14.10 |
| 6384 | 2" | | | | | 14.35 | | | 14.35 | 15.80 |
| 6386 | 3" x 2" | | | | | 20 | | | 20 | 22 |
| 6388 | 3" | | | | | 37 | | | 37 | 40.50 |
| 6390 | 4" x 1-1/2" | | | | | 17.70 | | | 17.70 | 19.50 |
| 6392 | 4" x 2" | | | | | 20 | | | 20 | 22 |
| 6393 | 4" | | | | | 20 | | | 20 | 22 |
| 6394 | 6" x 1-1/2" | | | | | 44 | | | 44 | 48.50 |
| 6396 | 6" x 2" | | | | | 45 | | | 45 | 49.50 |
| 6459 | Sanitary Tee, 1-1/2" | | | | | 10.70 | | | 10.70 | 11.80 |
| 6460 | 2" | | | | | 11.60 | | | 11.60 | 12.80 |
| 6470 | 3" | | | | | 14.20 | | | 14.20 | 15.65 |
| 6472 | 4" | | | | | 26 | | | 26 | 28.50 |
| 8000 | Coupling, standard (by CISPI Mfrs.) | | | | | | | | | |
| 8020 | 1-1/2" | Q-1 | 48 | .333 | Ea. | 14.45 | 10.30 | | 24.75 | 33 |
| 8040 | 2" | | 44 | .364 | | 14.45 | 11.25 | | 25.70 | 34.50 |
| 8080 | 3" | | 38 | .421 | | 17.25 | 13 | | 30.25 | 40.50 |
| 8120 | 4" | | 33 | .485 | | 20.50 | 15 | | 35.50 | 47 |

### 22 13 16.60 Traps

| | | Crew | Daily Output | Labor-Hours | Unit | Material | 2010 Bare Costs Labor | Equipment | Total | Total Incl O&P |
|---|---|---|---|---|---|---|---|---|---|---|
| 0010 | **TRAPS** | | | | | | | | | |
| 0030 | Cast iron, service weight | | | | | | | | | |
| 0050 | Running P trap, without vent | | | | | | | | | |
| 1100 | 2" | Q-1 | 16 | 1 | Ea. | 107 | 31 | | 138 | 169 |
| 1150 | 4" | " | 13 | 1.231 | | 107 | 38 | | 145 | 181 |
| 1160 | 6" | Q-2 | 17 | 1.412 | | 465 | 42 | | 507 | 585 |
| 3000 | P trap, B&S, 2" pipe size | Q-1 | 16 | 1 | | 25.50 | 31 | | 56.50 | 78.50 |
| 3040 | 3" pipe size | " | 14 | 1.143 | | 38 | 35.50 | | 73.50 | 99.50 |

531

# 22 13 Facility Sanitary Sewerage

## 22 13 16 – Sanitary Waste and Vent Piping

### 22 13 16.60 Traps

| | | Crew | Daily Output | Labor-Hours | Unit | Material | 2010 Bare Costs Labor | Equipment | Total | Total Incl O&P |
|---|---|---|---|---|---|---|---|---|---|---|
| 4700 | Copper, drainage, drum trap | | | | | | | | | |
| 4840 | 3" x 6" swivel, 1-1/2" pipe size | 1 Plum | 16 | .500 | Ea. | 201 | 17.20 | | 218.20 | 249 |
| 5100 | P trap, standard pattern | | | | | | | | | |
| 5200 | 1-1/4" pipe size | 1 Plum | 18 | .444 | Ea. | 93.50 | 15.25 | | 108.75 | 128 |
| 5240 | 1-1/2" pipe size | | 17 | .471 | | 90 | 16.15 | | 106.15 | 126 |
| 5260 | 2" pipe size | | 15 | .533 | | 194 | 18.30 | | 212.30 | 243 |
| 5280 | 3" pipe size | | 11 | .727 | | 335 | 25 | | 360 | 410 |
| 6710 | ABS DWV P trap, solvent weld joint | | | | | | | | | |
| 6720 | 1-1/2" pipe size | 1 Plum | 18 | .444 | Ea. | 4.74 | 15.25 | | 19.99 | 30 |
| 6722 | 2" pipe size | | 17 | .471 | | 6.40 | 16.15 | | 22.55 | 33.50 |
| 6724 | 3" pipe size | | 15 | .533 | | 24.50 | 18.30 | | 42.80 | 57 |
| 6726 | 4" pipe size | | 14 | .571 | | 50.50 | 19.65 | | 70.15 | 87.50 |
| 6860 | PVC DWV hub x hub, basin trap, 1-1/4" pipe size | | 18 | .444 | | 7.50 | 15.25 | | 22.75 | 33.50 |
| 6870 | Sink P trap, 1-1/2" pipe size | | 18 | .444 | | 7.50 | 15.25 | | 22.75 | 33.50 |
| 6880 | Tubular S trap, 1-1/2" pipe size | | 17 | .471 | | 13.90 | 16.15 | | 30.05 | 42 |
| 6890 | PVC sch. 40 DWV, drum trap | | | | | | | | | |
| 6900 | 1-1/2" pipe size | 1 Plum | 16 | .500 | Ea. | 17.25 | 17.20 | | 34.45 | 47 |
| 6910 | P trap, 1-1/2" pipe size | | 18 | .444 | | 4.26 | 15.25 | | 19.51 | 29.50 |
| 6920 | 2" pipe size | | 17 | .471 | | 5.75 | 16.15 | | 21.90 | 33 |
| 6930 | 3" pipe size | | 15 | .533 | | 19.45 | 18.30 | | 37.75 | 51.50 |
| 6940 | 4" pipe size | | 14 | .571 | | 44.50 | 19.65 | | 64.15 | 81 |
| 6950 | P trap w/clean out, 1-1/2" pipe size | | 18 | .444 | | 7.05 | 15.25 | | 22.30 | 33 |
| 6960 | 2" pipe size | | 17 | .471 | | 11.90 | 16.15 | | 28.05 | 39.50 |

### 22 13 16.80 Vent Flashing and Caps

| | | Crew | Daily Output | Labor-Hours | Unit | Material | 2010 Bare Costs Labor | Equipment | Total | Total Incl O&P |
|---|---|---|---|---|---|---|---|---|---|---|
| 0010 | **VENT FLASHING AND CAPS** | | | | | | | | | |
| 0120 | Vent caps | | | | | | | | | |
| 0140 | Cast iron | | | | | | | | | |
| 0160 | 1-1/4" - 1-1/2" pipe | 1 Plum | 23 | .348 | Ea. | 30.50 | 11.95 | | 42.45 | 53 |
| 0170 | 2" - 2-1/8" pipe | | 22 | .364 | | 35.50 | 12.50 | | 48 | 59.50 |
| 0180 | 2-1/2" - 3-5/8" pipe | | 21 | .381 | | 40 | 13.10 | | 53.10 | 65.50 |
| 0190 | 4" - 4-1/8" pipe | | 19 | .421 | | 48 | 14.45 | | 62.45 | 76.50 |
| 0200 | 5" - 6" pipe | | 17 | .471 | | 71.50 | 16.15 | | 87.65 | 105 |
| 0300 | PVC | | | | | | | | | |
| 0320 | 1-1/4" - 1-1/2" pipe | 1 Plum | 24 | .333 | Ea. | 8 | 11.45 | | 19.45 | 27.50 |
| 0330 | 2" - 2-1/8" pipe | " | 23 | .348 | " | 8.65 | 11.95 | | 20.60 | 29 |

## 22 13 19 – Sanitary Waste Piping Specialties

### 22 13 19.13 Sanitary Drains

| | | Crew | Daily Output | Labor-Hours | Unit | Material | 2010 Bare Costs Labor | Equipment | Total | Total Incl O&P |
|---|---|---|---|---|---|---|---|---|---|---|
| 0010 | **SANITARY DRAINS** | | | | | | | | | |
| 2000 | Floor, medium duty, C.I., deep flange, 7" dia top | | | | | | | | | |
| 2040 | 2" and 3" pipe size | Q-1 | 12 | 1.333 | Ea. | 158 | 41 | | 199 | 242 |
| 2080 | For galvanized body, add | | | | | 75.50 | | | 75.50 | 83 |
| 2120 | For polished bronze top, add | | | | | 89 | | | 89 | 98 |

# 22 14 Facility Storm Drainage

## 22 14 26 – Facility Storm Drains

| 22 14 26.13 Roof Drains | Crew | Daily Output | Labor-Hours | Unit | Material | 2010 Bare Costs Labor | Equipment | Total | Total Incl O&P |
|---|---|---|---|---|---|---|---|---|---|
| 0010 **ROOF DRAINS** | | | | | | | | | |
| 3860 Roof, flat metal deck, C.I. body, 12" C.I. dome | | | | | | | | | |
| 3890      3" pipe size | Q-1 | 14 | 1.143 | Ea. | 310 | 35.50 | | 345.50 | 400 |

## 22 14 29 – Sump Pumps

### 22 14 29.16 Submersible Sump Pumps

| | Crew | Daily Output | Labor-Hours | Unit | Material | Labor | Equipment | Total | Total Incl O&P |
|---|---|---|---|---|---|---|---|---|---|
| 0010 **SUBMERSIBLE SUMP PUMPS** | | | | | | | | | |
| 7000 Sump pump, automatic | | | | | | | | | |
| 7100      Plastic, 1-1/4" discharge, 1/4 HP | 1 Plum | 6 | 1.333 | Ea. | 215 | 46 | | 261 | 310 |
| 7500      Cast iron, 1-1/4" discharge, 1/4 HP | " | 6 | 1.333 | " | 166 | 46 | | 212 | 257 |

# 22 31 Domestic Water Softeners

## 22 31 13 – Residential Domestic Water Softeners

### 22 31 13.10 Residential Water Softeners

| | Crew | Daily Output | Labor-Hours | Unit | Material | Labor | Equipment | Total | Total Incl O&P |
|---|---|---|---|---|---|---|---|---|---|
| 0010 **RESIDENTIAL WATER SOFTENERS** | | | | | | | | | |
| 7350 Water softener, automatic, to 30 grains per gallon | 2 Plum | 5 | 3.200 | Ea. | 380 | 110 | | 490 | 600 |
| 7400      To 100 grains per gallon | " | 4 | 4 | " | 750 | 137 | | 887 | 1,050 |

# 22 33 Electric Domestic Water Heaters

## 22 33 30 – Residential, Electric Domestic Water Heaters

### 22 33 30.13 Residential, Small-Capacity Elec. Water Heaters

| | Crew | Daily Output | Labor-Hours | Unit | Material | Labor | Equipment | Total | Total Incl O&P |
|---|---|---|---|---|---|---|---|---|---|
| 0010 **RESIDENTIAL, SMALL-CAPACITY ELECTRIC DOMESTIC WATER HEATERS** | | | | | | | | | |
| 1000 Residential, electric, glass lined tank, 5 yr, 10 gal., single element | 1 Plum | 2.30 | 3.478 | Ea. | 385 | 119 | | 504 | 620 |
| 1060      30 gallon, double element | | 2.20 | 3.636 | | 575 | 125 | | 700 | 840 |
| 1080      40 gallon, double element | | 2 | 4 | | 615 | 137 | | 752 | 900 |
| 1100      52 gallon, double element | | 2 | 4 | | 690 | 137 | | 827 | 980 |
| 1120      66 gallon, double element | | 1.80 | 4.444 | | 930 | 153 | | 1,083 | 1,275 |
| 1140      80 gallon, double element | | 1.60 | 5 | | 1,025 | 172 | | 1,197 | 1,425 |

# 22 34 Fuel-Fired Domestic Water Heaters

## 22 34 13 – Instantaneous, Tankless, Gas Domestic Water Heaters

### 22 34 13.10 Instantaneous, Tankless, Gas Water Heaters

| | | Crew | Daily Output | Labor-Hours | Unit | Material | Labor | Equipment | Total | Total Incl O&P |
|---|---|---|---|---|---|---|---|---|---|---|
| 0010 **INSTANTANEOUS, TANKLESS, GAS WATER HEATERS** | | | | | | | | | | |
| 9410      Natural gas/propane, incl vent, 3.2 GPM | G | 1 Plum | 2 | 4 | Ea. | 535 | 137 | | 672 | 815 |

## 22 34 30 – Residential Gas Domestic Water Heaters

### 22 34 30.13 Residential, Atmos, Gas Domestic Wtr Heaters

| | Crew | Daily Output | Labor-Hours | Unit | Material | Labor | Equipment | Total | Total Incl O&P |
|---|---|---|---|---|---|---|---|---|---|
| 0010 **RESIDENTIAL, ATMOSPHERIC, GAS DOMESTIC WATER HEATERS** | | | | | | | | | |
| 2000 Gas fired, foam lined tank, 10 yr, vent not incl. | | | | | | | | | |
| 2040      30 gallon | 1 Plum | 2 | 4 | Ea. | 895 | 137 | | 1,032 | 1,200 |
| 2100      75 gallon | " | 1.50 | 5.333 | " | 1,225 | 183 | | 1,408 | 1,650 |

## 22 34 46 – Oil-Fired Domestic Water Heaters

### 22 34 46.10 Residential Oil-Fired Water Heaters

| | Crew | Daily Output | Labor-Hours | Unit | Material | Labor | Equipment | Total | Total Incl O&P |
|---|---|---|---|---|---|---|---|---|---|
| 0010 **RESIDENTIAL OIL-FIRED WATER HEATERS** | | | | | | | | | |
| 3000 Oil fired, glass lined tank, 5 yr, vent not included, 30 gallon | 1 Plum | 2 | 4 | Ea. | 665 | 137 | | 802 | 955 |
| 3040      50 gallon | " | 1.80 | 4.444 | " | 1,050 | 153 | | 1,203 | 1,400 |

# 22 41 Residential Plumbing Fixtures

## 22 41 13 – Residential Water Closets, Urinals, and Bidets

| 22 41 13.40 Water Closets | | Crew | Daily Output | Labor-Hours | Unit | Material | 2010 Bare Costs Labor | Equipment | Total | Total Incl O&P |
|---|---|---|---|---|---|---|---|---|---|---|
| 0010 | **WATER CLOSETS** | | | | | | | | | |
| 0150 | Tank type, vitreous china, incl. seat, supply pipe w/stop | | | | | | | | | |
| 0200 | Wall hung | | | | | | | | | |
| 0400 | Two piece, close coupled | Q-1 | 5.30 | 3.019 | Ea. | 595 | 93.50 | | 688.50 | 810 |
| 0960 | For rough-in, supply, waste, vent and carrier | | 2.73 | 5.861 | | 910 | 181 | | 1,091 | 1,300 |
| 1000 | Floor mounted | | 5.30 | 3.019 | | 540 | 93.50 | | 633.50 | 745 |
| 1020 | One piece, low profile | | 5.30 | 3.019 | | 570 | 93.50 | | 663.50 | 785 |
| 1100 | Two piece, close coupled | | 5.30 | 3.019 | | 258 | 93.50 | | 351.50 | 435 |
| 1110 | Two piece, close coupled, dual flush | | 5.30 | 3.019 | | 256 | 93.50 | | 349.50 | 435 |
| 1140 | Two piece, close coupled, 1.28 gpf, ADA ⬜G | | 5.30 | 3.019 | | 295 | 93.50 | | 388.50 | 480 |
| 1960 | For color, add | | | | | 30% | | | | |
| 1980 | For rough-in, supply, waste and vent | Q-1 | 3.05 | 5.246 | Ea. | 283 | 162 | | 445 | 575 |

## 22 41 16 – Residential Lavatories and Sinks

### 22 41 16.10 Lavatories

| | | Crew | Daily Output | Labor-Hours | Unit | Material | Labor | Equipment | Total | Total Incl O&P |
|---|---|---|---|---|---|---|---|---|---|---|
| 0010 | **LAVATORIES**, With trim, white unless noted otherwise | | | | | | | | | |
| 0500 | Vanity top, porcelain enamel on cast iron | | | | | | | | | |
| 0600 | 20" x 18" | Q-1 | 6.40 | 2.500 | Ea. | 260 | 77.50 | | 337.50 | 415 |
| 0640 | 33" x 19" oval | | 6.40 | 2.500 | | 610 | 77.50 | | 687.50 | 800 |
| 0720 | 19" round | | 6.40 | 2.500 | | 246 | 77.50 | | 323.50 | 395 |
| 0860 | For color, add | | | | | 25% | | | | |
| 1000 | Cultured marble, 19" x 17", single bowl | Q-1 | 6.40 | 2.500 | Ea. | 190 | 77.50 | | 267.50 | 335 |
| 1120 | 25" x 22", single bowl | | 6.40 | 2.500 | | 238 | 77.50 | | 315.50 | 390 |
| 1160 | 37" x 22", single bowl | | 6.40 | 2.500 | | 257 | 77.50 | | 334.50 | 410 |
| 1560 | | | | | | | | | | |
| 1900 | Stainless steel, self-rimming, 25" x 22", single bowl, ledge | Q-1 | 6.40 | 2.500 | Ea. | 345 | 77.50 | | 422.50 | 505 |
| 1960 | 17" x 22", single bowl | | 6.40 | 2.500 | | 340 | 77.50 | | 417.50 | 495 |
| 2600 | Steel, enameled, 20" x 17", single bowl | | 5.80 | 2.759 | | 184 | 85.50 | | 269.50 | 345 |
| 2900 | Vitreous china, 20" x 16", single bowl | | 5.40 | 2.963 | | 278 | 91.50 | | 369.50 | 455 |
| 3200 | 22" x 13", single bowl | | 5.40 | 2.963 | | 285 | 91.50 | | 376.50 | 465 |
| 3580 | Rough-in, supply, waste and vent for all above lavatories | | 2.30 | 6.957 | | 252 | 215 | | 467 | 630 |
| 4000 | Wall hung | | | | | | | | | |
| 4040 | Porcelain enamel on cast iron, 16" x 14", single bowl | Q-1 | 8 | 2 | Ea. | 455 | 62 | | 517 | 600 |
| 4180 | 20" x 18", single bowl | " | 8 | 2 | " | 355 | 62 | | 417 | 490 |
| 4580 | For color, add | | | | | 30% | | | | |
| 6000 | Vitreous china, 18" x 15", single bowl with backsplash | Q-1 | 7 | 2.286 | Ea. | 249 | 70.50 | | 319.50 | 390 |
| 6060 | 19" x 17", single bowl | | 7 | 2.286 | | 198 | 70.50 | | 268.50 | 335 |
| 6960 | Rough-in, supply, waste and vent for above lavatories | | 1.66 | 9.639 | | 385 | 298 | | 683 | 915 |
| 7000 | Pedestal type | | | | | | | | | |
| 7600 | Vitreous china, 27" x 21", white | Q-1 | 6.60 | 2.424 | Ea. | 565 | 75 | | 640 | 745 |
| 7610 | 27" x 21", colored | | 6.60 | 2.424 | | 675 | 75 | | 750 | 865 |
| 7620 | 27" x 21", premium color | | 6.60 | 2.424 | | 740 | 75 | | 815 | 935 |
| 7660 | 26" x 20", white | | 6.60 | 2.424 | | 515 | 75 | | 590 | 690 |
| 7670 | 26" x 20", colored | | 6.60 | 2.424 | | 610 | 75 | | 685 | 795 |
| 7680 | 26" x 20", premium color | | 6.60 | 2.424 | | 670 | 75 | | 745 | 860 |
| 7700 | 24" x 18", white | | 6.60 | 2.424 | | 480 | 75 | | 555 | 655 |
| 7710 | 24" x 18", colored | | 6.60 | 2.424 | | 570 | 75 | | 645 | 750 |
| 7720 | 24" x 18", premium color | | 6.60 | 2.424 | | 625 | 75 | | 700 | 810 |
| 7760 | 21" x 18", white | | 6.60 | 2.424 | | 233 | 75 | | 308 | 380 |
| 7770 | 21" x 18", colored | | 6.60 | 2.424 | | 250 | 75 | | 325 | 400 |
| 7990 | Rough-in, supply, waste and vent for pedestal lavatories | | 1.66 | 9.639 | | 385 | 298 | | 683 | 915 |

# 22 41 Residential Plumbing Fixtures

## 22 41 16 – Residential Lavatories and Sinks

### 22 41 16.30 Sinks

| | | Crew | Daily Output | Labor-Hours | Unit | Material | 2010 Bare Costs Labor | 2010 Bare Costs Equipment | Total | Total Incl O&P |
|---|---|---|---|---|---|---|---|---|---|---|
| 0010 | **SINKS**, With faucets and drain | | | | | | | | | |
| 2000 | Kitchen, counter top style, P.E. on C.I., 24" x 21" single bowl | Q-1 | 5.60 | 2.857 | Ea. | 257 | 88.50 | | 345.50 | 425 |
| 2100 | 31" x 22" single bowl | | 5.60 | 2.857 | | 300 | 88.50 | | 388.50 | 475 |
| 2200 | 32" x 21" double bowl | | 4.80 | 3.333 | | 385 | 103 | | 488 | 595 |
| 3000 | Stainless steel, self rimming, 19" x 18" single bowl | | 5.60 | 2.857 | | 555 | 88.50 | | 643.50 | 755 |
| 3100 | 25" x 22" single bowl | | 5.60 | 2.857 | | 615 | 88.50 | | 703.50 | 825 |
| 3200 | 33" x 22" double bowl | | 4.80 | 3.333 | | 895 | 103 | | 998 | 1,150 |
| 3300 | 43" x 22" double bowl | | 4.80 | 3.333 | | 1,050 | 103 | | 1,153 | 1,325 |
| 4000 | Steel, enameled, with ledge, 24" x 21" single bowl | | 5.60 | 2.857 | | 180 | 88.50 | | 268.50 | 345 |
| 4100 | 32" x 21" double bowl | | 4.80 | 3.333 | | 207 | 103 | | 310 | 395 |
| 4960 | For color sinks except stainless steel, add | | | | | 10% | | | | |
| 4980 | For rough-in, supply, waste and vent, counter top sinks | Q-1 | 2.14 | 7.477 | | 272 | 231 | | 503 | 680 |
| 5000 | Kitchen, raised deck, P.E. on C.I. | | | | | | | | | |
| 5100 | 32" x 21", dual level, double bowl | Q-1 | 2.60 | 6.154 | Ea. | 325 | 190 | | 515 | 670 |
| 5790 | For rough-in, supply, waste & vent, sinks | " | 1.85 | 8.649 | " | 272 | 268 | | 540 | 740 |

## 22 41 19 – Residential Bathtubs

### 22 41 19.10 Baths

| | | Crew | Daily Output | Labor-Hours | Unit | Material | 2010 Bare Costs Labor | 2010 Bare Costs Equipment | Total | Total Incl O&P |
|---|---|---|---|---|---|---|---|---|---|---|
| 0010 | **BATHS** R224000-40 | | | | | | | | | |
| 0100 | Tubs, recessed porcelain enamel on cast iron, with trim | | | | | | | | | |
| 0180 | 48" x 42" | Q-1 | 4 | 4 | Ea. | 1,650 | 124 | | 1,774 | 2,025 |
| 0220 | 72" x 36" | " | 3 | 5.333 | " | 2,225 | 165 | | 2,390 | 2,725 |
| 0300 | Mat bottom | | | | | | | | | |
| 0380 | 5' long | Q-1 | 4.40 | 3.636 | Ea. | 945 | 112 | | 1,057 | 1,225 |
| 0480 | Above floor drain, 5' long | | 4 | 4 | | 825 | 124 | | 949 | 1,125 |
| 0560 | Corner 48" x 44" | | 4.40 | 3.636 | | 2,150 | 112 | | 2,262 | 2,550 |
| 2000 | Enameled formed steel, 4'-6" long | | 5.80 | 2.759 | | 385 | 85.50 | | 470.50 | 565 |
| 4600 | Module tub & showerwall surround, molded fiberglass | | | | | | | | | |
| 4610 | 5' long x 34" wide x 76" high | Q-1 | 4 | 4 | Ea. | 755 | 124 | | 879 | 1,025 |
| 9600 | Rough-in, supply, waste and vent, for all above tubs, add | " | 2.07 | 7.729 | " | 315 | 239 | | 554 | 735 |

## 22 41 23 – Residential Shower Receptors and Basins

### 22 41 23.20 Showers

| | | Crew | Daily Output | Labor-Hours | Unit | Material | 2010 Bare Costs Labor | 2010 Bare Costs Equipment | Total | Total Incl O&P |
|---|---|---|---|---|---|---|---|---|---|---|
| 0010 | **SHOWERS** | | | | | | | | | |
| 1500 | Stall, with drain only. Add for valve and door/curtain | | | | | | | | | |
| 1520 | 32" square | Q-1 | 5 | 3.200 | Ea. | 885 | 99 | | 984 | 1,125 |
| 1530 | 36" square | | 4.80 | 3.333 | | 2,175 | 103 | | 2,278 | 2,550 |
| 1540 | Terrazzo receptor, 32" square | | 5 | 3.200 | | 1,300 | 99 | | 1,399 | 1,575 |
| 1560 | 36" square | | 4.80 | 3.333 | | 1,425 | 103 | | 1,528 | 1,750 |
| 1580 | 36" corner angle | | 4.80 | 3.333 | | 1,675 | 103 | | 1,778 | 2,000 |
| 3000 | Fiberglass, one piece, with 3 walls, 32" x 32" square | | 5.50 | 2.909 | | 515 | 90 | | 605 | 715 |
| 3100 | 36" x 36" square | | 5.50 | 2.909 | | 530 | 90 | | 620 | 730 |
| 4200 | Rough-in, supply, waste and vent for above showers | | 2.05 | 7.805 | | 390 | 241 | | 631 | 825 |

## 22 41 36 – Residential Laundry Trays

### 22 41 36.10 Laundry Sinks

| | | Crew | Daily Output | Labor-Hours | Unit | Material | 2010 Bare Costs Labor | 2010 Bare Costs Equipment | Total | Total Incl O&P |
|---|---|---|---|---|---|---|---|---|---|---|
| 0010 | **LAUNDRY SINKS**, With trim | | | | | | | | | |
| 0020 | Porcelain enamel on cast iron, black iron frame | | | | | | | | | |
| 0050 | 24" x 21", single compartment | Q-1 | 6 | 2.667 | Ea. | 465 | 82.50 | | 547.50 | 645 |
| 0100 | 26" x 21", single compartment | " | 6 | 2.667 | " | 450 | 82.50 | | 532.50 | 630 |
| 3000 | Plastic, on wall hanger or legs | | | | | | | | | |
| 3020 | 18" x 23", single compartment | Q-1 | 6.50 | 2.462 | Ea. | 141 | 76 | | 217 | 280 |
| 3100 | 20" x 24", single compartment | | 6.50 | 2.462 | | 141 | 76 | | 217 | 280 |

# 22 41 Residential Plumbing Fixtures

## 22 41 36 – Residential Laundry Trays

### 22 41 36.10 Laundry Sinks

| | | Crew | Daily Output | Labor-Hours | Unit | Material | 2010 Bare Costs Labor | Equipment | Total | Total Incl O&P |
|---|---|---|---|---|---|---|---|---|---|---|
| 3200 | 36" x 23", double compartment | Q-1 | 5.50 | 2.909 | Ea. | 167 | 90 | | 257 | 330 |
| 3300 | 40" x 24", double compartment | | 5.50 | 2.909 | | 248 | 90 | | 338 | 420 |
| 5000 | Stainless steel, counter top, 22" x 17" single compartment | | 6 | 2.667 | | 61.50 | 82.50 | | 144 | 203 |
| 5200 | 33" x 22", double compartment | | 5 | 3.200 | | 73.50 | 99 | | 172.50 | 243 |
| 9600 | Rough-in, supply, waste and vent, for all laundry sinks | ↓ | 2.14 | 7.477 | ↓ | 272 | 231 | | 503 | 680 |

## 22 41 39 – Residential Faucets, Supplies and Trim

### 22 41 39.10 Faucets and Fittings

| | | Crew | Daily Output | Labor-Hours | Unit | Material | 2010 Bare Costs Labor | Equipment | Total | Total Incl O&P |
|---|---|---|---|---|---|---|---|---|---|---|
| 0010 | **FAUCETS AND FITTINGS** | | | | | | | | | |
| 0150 | Bath, faucets, diverter spout combination, sweat | 1 Plum | 8 | 1 | Ea. | 86.50 | 34.50 | | 121 | 152 |
| 0200 | For integral stops, IPS unions, add | | | | | 109 | | | 109 | 120 |
| 0420 | Bath, press-bal mix valve w/diverter, spout, shower hd, arm/flange | 1 Plum | 8 | 1 | | 155 | 34.50 | | 189.50 | 228 |
| 0500 | Drain, central lift, 1-1/2" IPS male | | 20 | .400 | | 44.50 | 13.75 | | 58.25 | 71 |
| 0600 | Trip lever, 1-1/2" IPS male | | 20 | .400 | | 45 | 13.75 | | 58.75 | 72 |
| 1000 | Kitchen sink faucets, top mount, cast spout | | 10 | .800 | | 61.50 | 27.50 | | 89 | 113 |
| 1100 | For spray, add | ↓ | 24 | .333 | ↓ | 16.15 | 11.45 | | 27.60 | 36.50 |
| 1300 | Single control lever handle | | | | | | | | | |
| 1310 | With pull out spray | | | | | | | | | |
| 1320 | Polished chrome | 1 Plum | 10 | .800 | Ea. | 157 | 27.50 | | 184.50 | 217 |
| 2000 | Laundry faucets, shelf type, IPS or copper unions | " | 12 | .667 | " | 49.50 | 23 | | 72.50 | 92 |
| 2020 | | | | | | | | | | |
| 2100 | Lavatory faucet, centerset, without drain | 1 Plum | 10 | .800 | Ea. | 44.50 | 27.50 | | 72 | 94 |
| 2120 | With pop-up drain | " | 6.66 | 1.201 | " | 80.50 | 41.50 | | 122 | 156 |
| 2210 | Porcelain cross handles and pop-up drain | | | | | | | | | |
| 2220 | Polished chrome | 1 Plum | 6.66 | 1.201 | Ea. | 126 | 41.50 | | 167.50 | 207 |
| 2230 | Polished brass | " | 6.66 | 1.201 | " | 189 | 41.50 | | 230.50 | 276 |
| 2260 | Single lever handle and pop-up drain | | | | | | | | | |
| 2270 | Black nickel | 1 Plum | 6.66 | 1.201 | Ea. | 220 | 41.50 | | 261.50 | 310 |
| 2280 | Polished brass | | 6.66 | 1.201 | | 220 | 41.50 | | 261.50 | 310 |
| 2290 | Polished chrome | | 6.66 | 1.201 | | 172 | 41.50 | | 213.50 | 257 |
| 2800 | Self-closing, center set | | 10 | .800 | | 131 | 27.50 | | 158.50 | 189 |
| 4000 | Shower by-pass valve with union | | 18 | .444 | | 85.50 | 15.25 | | 100.75 | 119 |
| 4200 | Shower thermostatic mixing valve, concealed | ↓ | 8 | 1 | | 365 | 34.50 | | 399.50 | 460 |
| 4204 | For inlet strainer, check, and stops, add | | | | ↓ | 45 | | | 45 | 49.50 |
| 4220 | Shower pressure balancing mixing valve, | | | | | | | | | |
| 4230 | With shower head, arm, flange and diverter tub spout | | | | | | | | | |
| 4240 | Chrome | 1 Plum | 6.14 | 1.303 | Ea. | 222 | 45 | | 267 | 320 |
| 4250 | Polished brass | | 6.14 | 1.303 | | 279 | 45 | | 324 | 380 |
| 4260 | Satin | | 6.14 | 1.303 | | 279 | 45 | | 324 | 380 |
| 4270 | Polished chrome/brass | | 6.14 | 1.303 | | 229 | 45 | | 274 | 325 |
| 5000 | Sillcock, compact, brass, IPS or copper to hose | ↓ | 24 | .333 | ↓ | 8.05 | 11.45 | | 19.50 | 27.50 |

# 22 42 Commercial Plumbing Fixtures

## 22 42 13 – Commercial Water Closets, Urinals, and Bidets

### 22 42 13.40 Water Closets

| | | Crew | Daily Output | Labor-Hours | Unit | Material | 2010 Bare Costs Labor | 2010 Bare Costs Equipment | Total | Total Incl O&P |
|---|---|---|---|---|---|---|---|---|---|---|
| 0010 | **WATER CLOSETS** | | | | | | | | | |
| 3000 | Bowl only, with flush valve, seat, 1.6 gpf unless noted | | | | | | | | | |
| 3100 | Wall hung | Q-1 | 5.80 | 2.759 | Ea. | 305 | 85.50 | | 390.50 | 475 |
| 3200 | For rough-in, supply, waste and vent, single WC | | 2.56 | 6.250 | | 950 | 193 | | 1,143 | 1,375 |
| 3300 | Floor mounted | | 5.80 | 2.759 | | 325 | 85.50 | | 410.50 | 500 |
| 3400 | For rough-in, supply, waste and vent, single WC | ↓ | 2.84 | 5.634 | ↓ | 325 | 174 | | 499 | 645 |

## 22 42 16 – Commercial Lavatories and Sinks

### 22 42 16.14 Lavatories

| | | | | | | | | | | |
|---|---|---|---|---|---|---|---|---|---|---|
| 0010 | **LAVATORIES**, With trim, white unless noted otherwise | | | | | | | | | |
| 0020 | Commercial lavatories same as residential. See Div. 22 41 16.10 | | | | | | | | | |

### 22 42 16.40 Service Sinks

| | | Crew | Daily Output | Labor-Hours | Unit | Material | 2010 Bare Costs Labor | 2010 Bare Costs Equipment | Total | Total Incl O&P |
|---|---|---|---|---|---|---|---|---|---|---|
| 0010 | **SERVICE SINKS** | | | | | | | | | |
| 6650 | Service, floor, corner, P.E. on C.I., 28" x 28" | Q-1 | 4.40 | 3.636 | Ea. | 695 | 112 | | 807 | 950 |
| 6750 | Vinyl coated rim guard, add | | | | | 67.50 | | | 67.50 | 74 |
| 6760 | Mop sink, molded stone, 24" x 36" | 1 Plum | 3.33 | 2.402 | | 233 | 82.50 | | 315.50 | 390 |
| 6770 | Mop sink, molded stone, 24" x 36", w/rim 3 sides | " | 3.33 | 2.402 | | 248 | 82.50 | | 330.50 | 410 |
| 6790 | For rough-in, supply, waste & vent, floor service sinks | Q-1 | 1.64 | 9.756 | ↓ | 730 | 300 | | 1,030 | 1,300 |

## 22 42 39 – Commercial Faucets, Supplies, and Trim

### 22 42 39.10 Faucets and Fittings

| | | Crew | Daily Output | Labor-Hours | Unit | Material | 2010 Bare Costs Labor | 2010 Bare Costs Equipment | Total | Total Incl O&P |
|---|---|---|---|---|---|---|---|---|---|---|
| 0010 | **FAUCETS AND FITTINGS** | | | | | | | | | |
| 2790 | Faucets for lavatories | | | | | | | | | |
| 2800 | Self-closing, center set | 1 Plum | 10 | .800 | Ea. | 131 | 27.50 | | 158.50 | 189 |
| 2810 | Automatic sensor and operator, with faucet head | | 6.15 | 1.301 | | 370 | 44.50 | | 414.50 | 485 |
| 3000 | Service sink faucet, cast spout, pail hook, hose end | ↓ | 14 | .571 | ↓ | 80 | 19.65 | | 99.65 | 120 |

### 22 42 39.30 Carriers and Supports

| | | Crew | Daily Output | Labor-Hours | Unit | Material | 2010 Bare Costs Labor | 2010 Bare Costs Equipment | Total | Total Incl O&P |
|---|---|---|---|---|---|---|---|---|---|---|
| 0010 | **CARRIERS AND SUPPORTS**, For plumbing fixtures | | | | | | | | | |
| 0600 | Plate type with studs, top back plate | 1 Plum | 7 | 1.143 | Ea. | 70.50 | 39.50 | | 110 | 143 |
| 3000 | Lavatory, concealed arm | | | | | | | | | |
| 3050 | Floor mounted, single | | | | | | | | | |
| 3100 | High back fixture | 1 Plum | 6 | 1.333 | Ea. | 395 | 46 | | 441 | 505 |
| 3200 | Flat slab fixture | " | 6 | 1.333 | " | 340 | 46 | | 386 | 450 |
| 8200 | Water closet, residential | | | | | | | | | |
| 8220 | Vertical centerline, floor mount | | | | | | | | | |
| 8240 | Single, 3" caulk, 2" or 3" vent | 1 Plum | 6 | 1.333 | Ea. | 455 | 46 | | 501 | 575 |
| 8260 | 4" caulk, 2" or 4" vent | " | 6 | 1.333 | " | 575 | 46 | | 621 | 710 |

# 22 51 Swimming Pool Plumbing Systems

## 22 51 19 – Swimming Pool Water Treatment Equipment

### 22 51 19.50 Swimming Pool Filtration Equipment

| | | Crew | Daily Output | Labor-Hours | Unit | Material | 2010 Bare Costs Labor | 2010 Bare Costs Equipment | Total | Total Incl O&P |
|---|---|---|---|---|---|---|---|---|---|---|
| 0010 | **SWIMMING POOL FILTRATION EQUIPMENT** | | | | | | | | | |
| 0900 | Filter system, sand or diatomite type, incl. pump, 6,000 gal./hr. | 2 Plum | 1.80 | 8.889 | Total | 1,700 | 305 | | 2,005 | 2,375 |
| 1020 | Add for chlorination system, 800 S.F. pool | " | 3 | 5.333 | Ea. | 103 | 183 | | 286 | 415 |

# Division Notes

| | CREW | DAILY OUTPUT | LABOR-HOURS | UNIT | 2010 BARE COSTS | | | | TOTAL INCL O&P |
|---|---|---|---|---|---|---|---|---|---|
| | | | | | MAT. | LABOR | EQUIP. | TOTAL | |
| | | | | | | | | | |
| | | | | | | | | | |
| | | | | | | | | | |
| | | | | | | | | | |
| | | | | | | | | | |
| | | | | | | | | | |
| | | | | | | | | | |
| | | | | | | | | | |
| | | | | | | | | | |
| | | | | | | | | | |
| | | | | | | | | | |
| | | | | | | | | | |
| | | | | | | | | | |
| | | | | | | | | | |
| | | | | | | | | | |
| | | | | | | | | | |
| | | | | | | | | | |
| | | | | | | | | | |
| | | | | | | | | | |
| | | | | | | | | | |

# Estimating Tips

The labor adjustment factors listed in Subdivision 22 01 02.20 also apply to Division 23.

## 23 10 00 Facility Fuel Systems

- The prices in this subdivision for above- and below-ground storage tanks do not include foundations or hold-down slabs, unless noted. The estimator should refer to Divisions 3 and 31 for foundation system pricing. In addition to the foundations, required tank accessories, such as tank gauges, leak detection devices, and additional manholes and piping, must be added to the tank prices.

## 23 50 00 Central Heating Equipment

- When estimating the cost of an HVAC system, check to see who is responsible for providing and installing the temperature control system. It is possible to overlook controls, assuming that they would be included in the electrical estimate.
- When looking up a boiler, be careful on specified capacity. Some manufacturers rate their products on output while others use input.
- Include HVAC insulation for pipe, boiler, and duct (wrap and liner).
- Be careful when looking up mechanical items to get the correct pressure rating and connection type (thread, weld, flange).

## 23 70 00 Central HVAC Equipment

- Combination heating and cooling units are sized by the air conditioning requirements. (See Reference No. R236000-20 for preliminary sizing guide.)
- A ton of air conditioning is nominally 400 CFM.
- Rectangular duct is taken off by the linear foot for each size, but its cost is usually estimated by the pound. Remember that SMACNA standards now base duct on internal pressure.
- Prefabricated duct is estimated and purchased like pipe: straight sections and fittings.
- Note that cranes or other lifting equipment are not included on any lines in Division 23. For example, if a crane is required to lift a heavy piece of pipe into place high above a gym floor, or to put a rooftop unit on the roof of a four-story building, etc., it must be added. Due to the potential for extreme variation—from nothing additional required to a major crane or helicopter—we feel that including a nominal amount for "lifting contingency" would be useless and detract from the accuracy of the estimate. When using equipment rental cost data from RSMeans, do not forget to include the cost of the operator(s).

# Reference Numbers

Reference numbers are shown in shaded boxes at the beginning of some major classifications. These numbers refer to related items in the Reference Section. The reference information may be an estimating procedure, an alternate pricing method, or technical information.

*Note:* Not all subdivisions listed here necessarily appear in this publication.

*Note:* **Trade Service,** *in part, has been used as a reference source for some of the material prices used in Division 23.*

Division 23 - Heating, Ventilating, and AC

# 23 05 Common Work Results for HVAC

## 23 05 05 – Selective HVAC Demolition

| 23 05 05.10 HVAC Demolition | | Crew | Daily Output | Labor-Hours | Unit | Material | 2010 Bare Costs Labor | Equipment | Total | Total Incl O&P |
|---|---|---|---|---|---|---|---|---|---|---|
| 0010 | **HVAC DEMOLITION** | | | | | | | | | |
| 0100 | Air conditioner, split unit, 3 ton | Q-5 | 2 | 8 | Ea. | | 247 | | 247 | 405 |
| 0150 | Package unit, 3 ton | Q-6 | 3 | 8 | " | | 237 | | 237 | 390 |
| 0260 | Baseboard, hydronic fin tube, 1/2" | Q-5 | 117 | .137 | L.F. | | 4.22 | | 4.22 | 6.90 |
| 0298 | Boilers | | | | | | | | | |
| 0300 | Electric, up thru 148 kW | Q-19 | 2 | 12 | Ea. | | 380 | | 380 | 620 |
| 0310 | 150 thru 518 kW | " | 1 | 24 | | | 755 | | 755 | 1,225 |
| 0320 | 550 thru 2000 kW | Q-21 | .40 | 80 | | | 2,575 | | 2,575 | 4,225 |
| 0330 | 2070 kW and up | " | .30 | 106 | | | 3,425 | | 3,425 | 5,625 |
| 0340 | Gas and/or oil, up thru 150 MBH | Q-7 | 2.20 | 14.545 | | | 450 | | 450 | 735 |
| 0350 | 160 thru 2000 MBH | | .80 | 40 | | | 1,225 | | 1,225 | 2,025 |
| 0360 | 2100 thru 4500 MBH | | .50 | 64 | | | 1,975 | | 1,975 | 3,225 |
| 0370 | 4600 thru 7000 MBH | | .30 | 106 | | | 3,300 | | 3,300 | 5,400 |
| 0390 | 12,200 thru 25,000 MBH | | .12 | 266 | | | 8,225 | | 8,225 | 13,500 |
| 1000 | Ductwork, 4" high, 8" wide | 1 Clab | 200 | .040 | L.F. | | .86 | | .86 | 1.45 |
| 1100 | 6" high, 8" wide | | 165 | .048 | | | 1.04 | | 1.04 | 1.75 |
| 1200 | 10" high, 12" wide | | 125 | .064 | | | 1.38 | | 1.38 | 2.31 |
| 1300 | 12"-14" high, 16"-18" wide | | 85 | .094 | | | 2.02 | | 2.02 | 3.40 |
| 1500 | 30" high, 36" wide | | 56 | .143 | | | 3.07 | | 3.07 | 5.15 |
| 2200 | Furnace, electric | Q-20 | 2 | 10 | Ea. | | 299 | | 299 | 495 |
| 2300 | Gas or oil, under 120 MBH | Q-9 | 4 | 4 | | | 117 | | 117 | 193 |
| 2340 | Over 120 MBH | " | 3 | 5.333 | | | 155 | | 155 | 257 |
| 2800 | Heat pump, package unit, 3 ton | Q-5 | 2.40 | 6.667 | | | 206 | | 206 | 335 |
| 2840 | Split unit, 3 ton | | 2 | 8 | | | 247 | | 247 | 405 |
| 2950 | Tank, steel, oil, 275 gal., above ground | | 10 | 1.600 | | | 49.50 | | 49.50 | 81 |
| 2960 | Remove and reset | | 3 | 5.333 | | | 164 | | 164 | 269 |
| 9000 | Minimum labor/equipment charge | Q-6 | 3 | 8 | Job | | 237 | | 237 | 390 |

# 23 07 HVAC Insulation

## 23 07 13 – Duct Insulation

### 23 07 13.10 Duct Thermal Insulation

| 23 07 13.10 Duct Thermal Insulation | | | Crew | Daily Output | Labor-Hours | Unit | Material | 2010 Bare Costs Labor | Equipment | Total | Total Incl O&P |
|---|---|---|---|---|---|---|---|---|---|---|---|
| 0010 | **DUCT THERMAL INSULATION** | | | | | | | | | | |
| 3000 | Ductwork | | | | | | | | | | |
| 3020 | Blanket type, fiberglass, flexible | | | | | | | | | | |
| 3140 | FSK vapor barrier wrap, .75 lb. density | | | | | | | | | | |
| 3160 | 1" thick | G | Q-14 | 350 | .046 | S.F. | .20 | 1.24 | | 1.44 | 2.31 |
| 3170 | 1-1/2" thick | G | | 320 | .050 | | .23 | 1.35 | | 1.58 | 2.54 |
| 3212 | Vinyl Jacket, .75 lb. density, 1-1/2" thick | G | | 320 | .050 | | .23 | 1.35 | | 1.58 | 2.54 |
| 9600 | Minimum labor/equipment charge | | 1 Stpi | 4 | 2 | Job | | 68.50 | | 68.50 | 112 |

# 23 09 Instrumentation and Control for HVAC

## 23 09 53 – Pneumatic and Electric Control System for HVAC

| 23 09 53.10 Control Components | | Crew | Daily Output | Labor-Hours | Unit | Material | 2010 Bare Costs Labor | Equipment | Total | Total Incl O&P |
|---|---|---|---|---|---|---|---|---|---|---|
| 0010 | **CONTROL COMPONENTS** | | | | | | | | | |
| 5000 | Thermostats | | | | | | | | | |
| 5030 | Manual | 1 Shee | 8 | 1 | Ea. | 44 | 32.50 | | 76.50 | 102 |
| 5040 | 1 set back, electric, timed | G | 8 | 1 | | 33.50 | 32.50 | | 66 | 90 |
| 5050 | 2 set back, electric, timed | G | 8 | 1 | | 143 | 32.50 | | 175.50 | 211 |

# 23 13 Facility Fuel-Storage Tanks

## 23 13 13 – Facility Underground Fuel-Oil, Storage Tanks

### 23 13 13.09 Single-Wall Steel Fuel-Oil Tanks

| | | Crew | Daily Output | Labor-Hours | Unit | Material | 2010 Bare Costs Labor | Equipment | Total | Total Incl O&P |
|---|---|---|---|---|---|---|---|---|---|---|
| 0010 | **SINGLE-WALL STEEL FUEL-OIL TANKS** | | | | | | | | | |
| 5000 | Steel underground, sti-P3, set in place, not incl. hold-down bars. | | | | | | | | | |
| 5500 | Excavation, pad, pumps and piping not included | | | | | | | | | |
| 5510 | Single wall, 500 gallon capacity, 7 gauge shell | Q-5 | 2.70 | 5.926 | Ea. | 1,975 | 183 | | 2,158 | 2,475 |
| 5520 | 1,000 gallon capacity, 7 gauge shell | " | 2.50 | 6.400 | | 3,150 | 197 | | 3,347 | 3,800 |
| 5530 | 2,000 gallon capacity, 1/4" thick shell | Q-7 | 4.60 | 6.957 | | 5,125 | 214 | | 5,339 | 5,975 |
| 5535 | 2,500 gallon capacity, 7 gauge shell | Q-5 | 3 | 5.333 | | 5,650 | 164 | | 5,814 | 6,500 |
| 5610 | 25,000 gallon capacity, 3/8" thick shell | Q-7 | 1.30 | 24.615 | | 25,700 | 760 | | 26,460 | 29,600 |
| 5630 | 40,000 gallon capacity, 3/8" thick shell | | .90 | 35.556 | | 34,600 | 1,100 | | 35,700 | 39,800 |
| 5640 | 50,000 gallon capacity, 3/8" thick shell | | .80 | 40 | | 38,400 | 1,225 | | 39,625 | 44,200 |

### 23 13 13.23 Glass-Fiber-Reinfcd-Plastic, Fuel-Oil, Storage

| | | Crew | Daily Output | Labor-Hours | Unit | Material | 2010 Bare Costs Labor | Equipment | Total | Total Incl O&P |
|---|---|---|---|---|---|---|---|---|---|---|
| 0010 | **GLASS-FIBER-REINFCD-PLASTIC, UNDERGRND FUEL-OIL, STORAGE** | | | | | | | | | |
| 0210 | Fiberglass, underground, single wall, U.L. listed, not including | | | | | | | | | |
| 0220 | manway or hold-down strap | | | | | | | | | |
| 0230 | 1,000 gallon capacity | Q-5 | 2.46 | 6.504 | Ea. | 3,650 | 201 | | 3,851 | 4,350 |
| 0240 | 2,000 gallon capacity | Q-7 | 4.57 | 7.002 | | 5,750 | 216 | | 5,966 | 6,675 |
| 0500 | For manway, fittings and hold-downs, add | | | | | 20% | 15% | | | |
| 2210 | Fiberglass, underground, single wall, U.L. listed, including | | | | | | | | | |
| 2220 | hold-down straps, no manways | | | | | | | | | |
| 2230 | 1,000 gallon capacity | Q-5 | 1.88 | 8.511 | Ea. | 4,075 | 262 | | 4,337 | 4,900 |
| 2240 | 2,000 gallon capacity | Q-7 | 3.55 | 9.014 | " | 6,175 | 278 | | 6,453 | 7,225 |

## 23 13 23 – Facility Aboveground Fuel-Oil, Storage Tanks

### 23 13 23.16 Steel

| | | Crew | Daily Output | Labor-Hours | Unit | Material | 2010 Bare Costs Labor | Equipment | Total | Total Incl O&P |
|---|---|---|---|---|---|---|---|---|---|---|
| 3001 | **STEEL**, storage, above ground, including supports, coating | | | | | | | | | |
| 3020 | fittings, not including foundation, pumps or piping | | | | | | | | | |
| 3040 | Single wall, 275 gallon | Q-5 | 5 | 3.200 | Ea. | 375 | 98.50 | | 473.50 | 570 |
| 3060 | 550 gallon | " | 2.70 | 5.926 | | 2,250 | 183 | | 2,433 | 2,775 |
| 3080 | 1,000 gallon | Q-7 | 5 | 6.400 | | 2,825 | 197 | | 3,022 | 3,450 |
| 3320 | Double wall, 500 gallon capacity | Q-5 | 2.40 | 6.667 | | 2,375 | 206 | | 2,581 | 2,925 |
| 3330 | 2000 gallon capacity | Q-7 | 4.15 | 7.711 | | 8,250 | 238 | | 8,488 | 9,475 |
| 3340 | 4000 gallon capacity | | 3.60 | 8.889 | | 14,700 | 274 | | 14,974 | 16,700 |
| 3350 | 6000 gallon capacity | | 2.40 | 13.333 | | 17,400 | 410 | | 17,810 | 19,800 |
| 3360 | 8000 gallon capacity | | 2 | 16 | | 22,300 | 495 | | 22,795 | 25,300 |
| 3370 | 10000 gallon capacity | | 1.80 | 17.778 | | 25,000 | 550 | | 25,550 | 28,400 |
| 3380 | 15000 gallon capacity | | 1.50 | 21.333 | | 37,900 | 660 | | 38,560 | 42,800 |
| 3390 | 20000 gallon capacity | | 1.30 | 24.615 | | 43,200 | 760 | | 43,960 | 48,800 |
| 3400 | 25000 gallon capacity | | 1.15 | 27.826 | | 52,500 | 860 | | 53,360 | 59,000 |
| 3410 | 30000 gallon capacity | | 1 | 32 | | 57,500 | 985 | | 58,485 | 65,000 |

# 23 21 Hydronic Piping and Pumps

## 23 21 20 – Hydronic HVAC Piping Specialties

### 23 21 20.46 Expansion Tanks

| | | Crew | Daily Output | Labor-Hours | Unit | Material | 2010 Bare Costs Labor | Equipment | Total | Total Incl O&P |
|---|---|---|---|---|---|---|---|---|---|---|
| 0010 | **EXPANSION TANKS** | | | | | | | | | |
| 1507 | Fiberglass and steel single/double wall storage, see Div. 23 13 13 | | | | | | | | | |
| 2000 | Steel, liquid expansion, ASME, painted, 15 gallon capacity | Q-5 | 17 | .941 | Ea. | 520 | 29 | | 549 | 625 |
| 2040 | 30 gallon capacity | | 12 | 1.333 | | 580 | 41 | | 621 | 710 |
| 3000 | Steel ASME expansion, rubber diaphragm, 19 gal. cap. accept. | | 12 | 1.333 | | 2,150 | 41 | | 2,191 | 2,450 |
| 3020 | 31 gallon capacity | ↓ | 8 | 2 | ↓ | 2,375 | 61.50 | | 2,436.50 | 2,725 |

## 23 21 23 – Hydronic Pumps

### 23 21 23.13 In-Line Centrifugal Hydronic Pumps

| | | Crew | Daily Output | Labor-Hours | Unit | Material | 2010 Bare Costs Labor | Equipment | Total | Total Incl O&P |
|---|---|---|---|---|---|---|---|---|---|---|
| 0010 | **IN-LINE CENTRIFUGAL HYDRONIC PUMPS** | | | | | | | | | |
| 0600 | Bronze, sweat connections, 1/40 HP, in line | | | | | | | | | |
| 0640 | 3/4" size | Q-1 | 16 | 1 | Ea. | 192 | 31 | | 223 | 262 |
| 1000 | Flange connection, 3/4" to 1-1/2" size | | | | | | | | | |
| 1040 | 1/12 HP | Q-1 | 6 | 2.667 | Ea. | 495 | 82.50 | | 577.50 | 680 |
| 1060 | 1/8 HP | | 6 | 2.667 | | 855 | 82.50 | | 937.50 | 1,075 |
| 2101 | Pumps, circulating, 3/4" to 1-1/2" size, 1/3 HP | ↓ | 6 | 2.667 | ↓ | 695 | 82.50 | | 777.50 | 900 |

# 23 31 HVAC Ducts and Casings

## 23 31 13 – Metal Ducts

### 23 31 13.13 Rectangular Metal Ducts

| | | Crew | Daily Output | Labor-Hours | Unit | Material | 2010 Bare Costs Labor | Equipment | Total | Total Incl O&P |
|---|---|---|---|---|---|---|---|---|---|---|
| 0010 | **RECTANGULAR METAL DUCTS** | | | | | | | | | |
| 0020 | Fabricated rectangular, includes fittings, joints, supports, | | | | | | | | | |
| 0030 | allowance for flexible connections, no insulation | | | | | | | | | |
| 0031 | NOTE: Fabrication and installation are combined | | | | | | | | | |
| 0040 | as LABOR cost. Approx. 25% fittings assumed. | | | | | | | | | |
| 0100 | Aluminum, alloy 3003-H14, under 100 lb. | Q-10 | 75 | .320 | Lb. | 3.72 | 9.65 | | 13.37 | 20 |
| 0110 | 100 to 500 lb. | | 80 | .300 | | 2.48 | 9.05 | | 11.53 | 17.75 |
| 0120 | 500 to 1,000 lb. | | 95 | .253 | | 2.31 | 7.65 | | 9.96 | 15.20 |
| 0140 | 1,000 to 2,000 lb. | | 120 | .200 | | 2.15 | 6.05 | | 8.20 | 12.35 |
| 0500 | Galvanized steel, under 200 lb. | | 235 | .102 | | .47 | 3.09 | | 3.56 | 5.60 |
| 0520 | 200 to 500 lb. | | 245 | .098 | | .46 | 2.96 | | 3.42 | 5.40 |
| 0540 | 500 to 1,000 lb. | ↓ | 255 | .094 | ↓ | .45 | 2.85 | | 3.30 | 5.20 |

### 23 31 13.19 Metal Duct Fittings

| | | Crew | Daily Output | Labor-Hours | Unit | Material | 2010 Bare Costs Labor | Equipment | Total | Total Incl O&P |
|---|---|---|---|---|---|---|---|---|---|---|
| 0010 | **METAL DUCT FITTINGS** | | | | | | | | | |
| 0050 | Air extractors, 12" x 4" | 1 Shee | 24 | .333 | Ea. | 16.10 | 10.80 | | 26.90 | 35.50 |
| 0100 | 8" x 6" | " | 22 | .364 | " | 16.10 | 11.80 | | 27.90 | 37.50 |

# 23 33 Air Duct Accessories

## 23 33 13 – Dampers

### 23 33 13.13 Volume-Control Dampers

| | | Crew | Daily Output | Labor-Hours | Unit | Material | 2010 Bare Costs Labor | Equipment | Total | Total Incl O&P |
|---|---|---|---|---|---|---|---|---|---|---|
| 0010 | **VOLUME-CONTROL DAMPERS** | | | | | | | | | |
| 6000 | 12" x 12" | 1 Shee | 21 | .381 | Ea. | 27.50 | 12.35 | | 39.85 | 50.50 |
| 8000 | Multi-blade dampers, parallel blade | | | | | | | | | |
| 8100 | 8" x 8" | 1 Shee | 24 | .333 | Ea. | 73 | 10.80 | | 83.80 | 98.50 |

### 23 33 13.16 Fire Dampers

| | | Crew | Daily Output | Labor-Hours | Unit | Material | 2010 Bare Costs Labor | Equipment | Total | Total Incl O&P |
|---|---|---|---|---|---|---|---|---|---|---|
| 0010 | **FIRE DAMPERS** | | | | | | | | | |
| 3000 | Fire damper, curtain type, 1-1/2 hr rated, vertical, 6" x 6" | 1 Shee | 24 | .333 | Ea. | 21.50 | 10.80 | | 32.30 | 42 |
| 3020 | 8" x 6" | " | 22 | .364 | " | 21.50 | 11.80 | | 33.30 | 43.50 |

# 23 33 Air Duct Accessories

## 23 33 46 – Flexible Ducts

### 23 33 46.10 Flexible Air Ducts

| | | Crew | Daily Output | Labor-Hours | Unit | Material | 2010 Bare Costs Labor | Equipment | Total | Total Incl O&P |
|---|---|---|---|---|---|---|---|---|---|---|
| 0010 | **FLEXIBLE AIR DUCTS** | | | | | | | | | |
| 1300 | Flexible, coated fiberglass fabric on corr. resist. metal helix | | | | | | | | | |
| 1400 | pressure to 12" (WG) UL-181 | | | | | | | | | |
| 1500 | Non-insulated, 3" diameter | Q-9 | 400 | .040 | L.F. | 1.02 | 1.17 | | 2.19 | 3.05 |
| 1540 | 5" diameter | | 320 | .050 | | 1.25 | 1.46 | | 2.71 | 3.79 |
| 1561 | Ductwork, flexible, non-insulated, 6" diameter | | 280 | .057 | | 1.53 | 1.67 | | 3.20 | 4.44 |
| 1580 | 7" diameter | | 240 | .067 | | 1.82 | 1.94 | | 3.76 | 5.20 |
| 1900 | Insulated, 1" thick, PE jacket, 3" diameter G | | 380 | .042 | | 2.15 | 1.23 | | 3.38 | 4.40 |
| 1910 | 4" diameter G | | 340 | .047 | | 2.15 | 1.37 | | 3.52 | 4.64 |
| 1920 | 5" diameter G | | 300 | .053 | | 2.15 | 1.55 | | 3.70 | 4.94 |
| 1940 | 6" diameter G | | 260 | .062 | | 2.38 | 1.79 | | 4.17 | 5.60 |
| 1960 | 7" diameter G | | 220 | .073 | | 2.78 | 2.12 | | 4.90 | 6.55 |
| 1980 | 8" diameter G | | 180 | .089 | | 3 | 2.59 | | 5.59 | 7.60 |
| 2040 | 12" diameter G | | 100 | .160 | | 4.36 | 4.66 | | 9.02 | 12.50 |

## 23 33 53 – Duct Liners

### 23 33 53.10 Duct Liner Board

| | | Crew | Daily Output | Labor-Hours | Unit | Material | 2010 Bare Costs Labor | Equipment | Total | Total Incl O&P |
|---|---|---|---|---|---|---|---|---|---|---|
| 0010 | **DUCT LINER BOARD** | | | | | | | | | |
| 3490 | Board type, fiberglass liner, 3 lb. density | | | | | | | | | |
| 3500 | Fire resistant, black pigmented, 1 side | | | | | | | | | |
| 3520 | 1" thick G | Q-14 | 150 | .107 | S.F. | .77 | 2.89 | | 3.66 | 5.75 |
| 3540 | 1-1/2" thick G | " | 130 | .123 | " | .97 | 3.33 | | 4.30 | 6.70 |
| 3940 | Board type, non-fibrous foam | | | | | | | | | |
| 3950 | Temperature, bacteria and fungi resistant | | | | | | | | | |
| 3960 | 1" thick G | Q-14 | 150 | .107 | S.F. | 2.25 | 2.89 | | 5.14 | 7.35 |
| 3970 | 1-1/2" thick G | | 130 | .123 | | 3 | 3.33 | | 6.33 | 8.95 |
| 3980 | 2" thick G | | 120 | .133 | | 3.60 | 3.61 | | 7.21 | 10.05 |

# 23 34 HVAC Fans

## 23 34 23 – HVAC Power Ventilators

### 23 34 23.10 HVAC Power Circulators and Ventilators

| | | Crew | Daily Output | Labor-Hours | Unit | Material | 2010 Bare Costs Labor | Equipment | Total | Total Incl O&P |
|---|---|---|---|---|---|---|---|---|---|---|
| 0010 | **HVAC POWER CIRCULATORS AND VENTILATORS** | | | | | | | | | |
| 8020 | Attic, roof type | | | | | | | | | |
| 8030 | Aluminum dome, damper & curb | | | | | | | | | |
| 8040 | 6" diameter, 300 CFM | 1 Elec | 16 | .500 | Ea. | 400 | 16.45 | | 416.45 | 465 |
| 8050 | 7" diameter, 450 CFM | | 15 | .533 | | 435 | 17.50 | | 452.50 | 510 |
| 8060 | 9" diameter, 900 CFM | | 14 | .571 | | 480 | 18.75 | | 498.75 | 555 |
| 8080 | 12" diameter, 1000 CFM (gravity) | | 10 | .800 | | 495 | 26.50 | | 521.50 | 590 |
| 8090 | 16" diameter, 1500 CFM (gravity) | | 9 | .889 | | 595 | 29 | | 624 | 705 |
| 8100 | 20" diameter, 2500 CFM (gravity) | | 8 | 1 | | 730 | 33 | | 763 | 860 |
| 8160 | Plastic, ABS dome | | | | | | | | | |
| 8180 | 1050 CFM | 1 Elec | 14 | .571 | Ea. | 146 | 18.75 | | 164.75 | 191 |
| 8200 | 1600 CFM | " | 12 | .667 | " | 218 | 22 | | 240 | 276 |
| 8240 | Attic, wall type, with shutter, one speed | | | | | | | | | |
| 8250 | 12" diameter, 1000 CFM | 1 Elec | 14 | .571 | Ea. | 315 | 18.75 | | 333.75 | 375 |
| 8260 | 14" diameter, 1500 CFM | | 12 | .667 | | 340 | 22 | | 362 | 410 |
| 8270 | 16" diameter, 2000 CFM | | 9 | .889 | | 385 | 29 | | 414 | 475 |
| 8290 | Whole house, wall type, with shutter, one speed | | | | | | | | | |
| 8300 | 30" diameter, 4800 CFM | 1 Elec | 7 | 1.143 | Ea. | 825 | 37.50 | | 862.50 | 965 |
| 8310 | 36" diameter, 7000 CFM | | 6 | 1.333 | | 900 | 44 | | 944 | 1,050 |
| 8320 | 42" diameter, 10,000 CFM | | 5 | 1.600 | | 1,000 | 52.50 | | 1,052.50 | 1,175 |

# 23 34 HVAC Fans

## 23 34 23 – HVAC Power Ventilators

| 23 34 23.10 HVAC Power Circulators and Ventilators | Crew | Daily Output | Labor-Hours | Unit | Material | 2010 Bare Costs Labor | Equipment | Total | Total Incl O&P |
|---|---|---|---|---|---|---|---|---|---|
| 8330 | 48" diameter, 16,000 CFM | 1 Elec | 4 | 2 | Ea. | 1,250 | 65.50 | | 1,315.50 | 1,475 |
| 8340 | For two speed, add | | | ↓ | | 75.50 | | | 75.50 | 83 |
| 8350 | Whole house, lay-down type, with shutter, one speed | | | | | | | | | |
| 8360 | 30" diameter, 4500 CFM | 1 Elec | 8 | 1 | Ea. | 880 | 33 | | 913 | 1,025 |
| 8370 | 36" diameter, 6500 CFM | | 7 | 1.143 | | 945 | 37.50 | | 982.50 | 1,100 |
| 8380 | 42" diameter, 9000 CFM | | 6 | 1.333 | | 1,050 | 44 | | 1,094 | 1,225 |
| 8390 | 48" diameter, 12,000 CFM | ↓ | 5 | 1.600 | | 1,175 | 52.50 | | 1,227.50 | 1,375 |
| 8440 | For two speed, add | | | | | 56.50 | | | 56.50 | 62 |
| 8450 | For 12 hour timer switch, add | 1 Elec | 32 | .250 | ↓ | 56.50 | 8.20 | | 64.70 | 75.50 |

# 23 37 Air Outlets and Inlets

## 23 37 13 – Diffusers, Registers, and Grilles

### 23 37 13.10 Diffusers

| | | Crew | Daily Output | Labor-Hours | Unit | Material | 2010 Bare Costs Labor | Equipment | Total | Total Incl O&P |
|---|---|---|---|---|---|---|---|---|---|---|
| 0010 | **DIFFUSERS**, Aluminum, opposed blade damper unless noted | | | | | | | | | |
| 0100 | Ceiling, linear, also for sidewall | | | | | | | | | |
| 0120 | 2" wide | 1 Shee | 32 | .250 | L.F. | 43 | 8.10 | | 51.10 | 60.50 |
| 0160 | 4" wide | | 26 | .308 | " | 57.50 | 9.95 | | 67.45 | 80 |
| 0500 | Perforated, 24" x 24" lay-in panel size, 6" x 6" | | 16 | .500 | Ea. | 57.50 | 16.20 | | 73.70 | 90.50 |
| 0520 | 8" x 8" | | 15 | .533 | | 59 | 17.30 | | 76.30 | 93.50 |
| 0530 | 9" x 9" | | 14 | .571 | | 63 | 18.50 | | 81.50 | 100 |
| 0590 | 16" x 16" | | 11 | .727 | | 109 | 23.50 | | 132.50 | 159 |
| 1000 | Rectangular, 1 to 4 way blow, 6" x 6" | | 16 | .500 | | 46.50 | 16.20 | | 62.70 | 78 |
| 1010 | 8" x 8" | | 15 | .533 | | 55.50 | 17.30 | | 72.80 | 89.50 |
| 1014 | 9" x 9" | | 15 | .533 | | 61 | 17.30 | | 78.30 | 96 |
| 1016 | 10" x 10" | | 15 | .533 | | 65 | 17.30 | | 82.30 | 100 |
| 1020 | 12" x 6" | | 15 | .533 | | 67.50 | 17.30 | | 84.80 | 103 |
| 1040 | 12" x 9" | | 14 | .571 | | 73.50 | 18.50 | | 92 | 112 |
| 1060 | 12" x 12" | | 12 | .667 | | 73 | 21.50 | | 94.50 | 116 |
| 1070 | 14" x 6" | | 13 | .615 | | 73 | 19.95 | | 92.95 | 114 |
| 1074 | 14" x 14" | | 12 | .667 | | 103 | 21.50 | | 124.50 | 149 |
| 1150 | 18" x 18" | | 9 | .889 | | 128 | 29 | | 157 | 189 |
| 1170 | 24" x 12" | | 10 | .800 | | 136 | 26 | | 162 | 193 |
| 1180 | 24" x 24" | | 7 | 1.143 | | 263 | 37 | | 300 | 350 |
| 1500 | Round, butterfly damper, steel, diffuser size, 6" diameter | | 18 | .444 | | 23 | 14.40 | | 37.40 | 49.50 |
| 1520 | 8" diameter | | 16 | .500 | | 25 | 16.20 | | 41.20 | 54.50 |
| 2000 | T bar mounting, 24" x 24" lay-in frame, 6" x 6" | | 16 | .500 | | 42.50 | 16.20 | | 58.70 | 74 |
| 2020 | 8" x 8" | | 14 | .571 | | 44.50 | 18.50 | | 63 | 79 |
| 2040 | 12" x 12" | | 12 | .667 | | 52 | 21.50 | | 73.50 | 93 |
| 2060 | 16" x 16" | | 11 | .727 | | 70 | 23.50 | | 93.50 | 116 |
| 2080 | 18" x 18" | ↓ | 10 | .800 | | 78 | 26 | | 104 | 129 |
| 6000 | For steel diffusers instead of aluminum, deduct | | | | ↓ | 10% | | | | |

### 23 37 13.30 Grilles

| | | Crew | Daily Output | Labor-Hours | Unit | Material | 2010 Bare Costs Labor | Equipment | Total | Total Incl O&P |
|---|---|---|---|---|---|---|---|---|---|---|
| 0010 | **GRILLES** | | | | | | | | | |
| 0020 | Aluminum | | | | | | | | | |
| 1000 | Air return, 6" x 6" | 1 Shee | 26 | .308 | Ea. | 17.55 | 9.95 | | 27.50 | 36 |
| 1020 | 10" x 6" | | 24 | .333 | | 17.55 | 10.80 | | 28.35 | 37 |
| 1080 | 16" x 8" | | 22 | .364 | | 22 | 11.80 | | 33.80 | 44 |
| 1100 | 12" x 12" | | 22 | .364 | | 24 | 11.80 | | 35.80 | 45.50 |
| 1120 | 24" x 12" | | 18 | .444 | | 33 | 14.40 | | 47.40 | 60 |
| 1180 | 16" x 16" | ↓ | 22 | .364 | ↓ | 31.50 | 11.80 | | 43.30 | 54.50 |

## 23 37 13 – Diffusers, Registers, and Grilles

| 23 37 13.60 Registers | | Crew | Daily Output | Labor-Hours | Unit | Material | 2010 Bare Costs Labor | Equipment | Total | Total Incl O&P |
|---|---|---|---|---|---|---|---|---|---|---|
| 0010 | **REGISTERS** | | | | | | | | | |
| 0980 | Air supply | | | | | | | | | |
| 3000 | Baseboard, hand adj. damper, enameled steel | | | | | | | | | |
| 3012 | 8" x 6" | 1 Shee | 26 | .308 | Ea. | 13.90 | 9.95 | | 23.85 | 32 |
| 3020 | 10" x 6" | | 24 | .333 | | 15.10 | 10.80 | | 25.90 | 34.50 |
| 3040 | 12" x 5" | | 23 | .348 | | 16.40 | 11.25 | | 27.65 | 36.50 |
| 3060 | 12" x 6" | ↓ | 23 | .348 | ↓ | 16.40 | 11.25 | | 27.65 | 36.50 |
| 4000 | Floor, toe operated damper, enameled steel | | | | | | | | | |
| 4020 | 4" x 8" | 1 Shee | 32 | .250 | Ea. | 25.50 | 8.10 | | 33.60 | 42 |
| 4040 | 4" x 12" | " | 26 | .308 | " | 30 | 9.95 | | 39.95 | 49.50 |
| 4300 | Spiral pipe supply register | | | | | | | | | |
| 4310 | Aluminum, double deflection, w/damper extractor | | | | | | | | | |
| 4320 | 4" x 12", for 6" thru 10" diameter duct | 1 Shee | 25 | .320 | Ea. | 58 | 10.35 | | 68.35 | 81 |
| 4330 | 4" x 18", for 6" thru 10" diameter duct | | 18 | .444 | | 72.50 | 14.40 | | 86.90 | 104 |
| 4340 | 6" x 12", for 8" thru 12" diameter duct | | 19 | .421 | | 63.50 | 13.65 | | 77.15 | 92.50 |
| 4350 | 6" x 18", for 8" thru 12" diameter duct | | 18 | .444 | | 82.50 | 14.40 | | 96.90 | 115 |
| 4360 | 6" x 24", for 8" thru 12" diameter duct | | 16 | .500 | | 102 | 16.20 | | 118.20 | 140 |
| 4370 | 6" x 30", for 8" thru 12" diameter duct | | 15 | .533 | | 130 | 17.30 | | 147.30 | 172 |
| 4380 | 8" x 18", for 10" thru 14" diameter duct | | 18 | .444 | | 88 | 14.40 | | 102.40 | 121 |
| 4390 | 8" x 24", for 10" thru 14" diameter duct | | 15 | .533 | | 110 | 17.30 | | 127.30 | 150 |
| 4400 | 8" x 30", for 10" thru 14" diameter duct | | 14 | .571 | | 146 | 18.50 | | 164.50 | 192 |
| 4410 | 10" x 24", for 12" thru 18" diameter duct | | 13 | .615 | | 121 | 19.95 | | 140.95 | 166 |
| 4420 | 10" x 30", for 12" thru 18" diameter duct | | 12 | .667 | | 160 | 21.50 | | 181.50 | 212 |
| 4430 | 10" x 36", for 12" thru 18" diameter duct | ↓ | 11 | .727 | ↓ | 198 | 23.50 | | 221.50 | 257 |

# 23 41 Particulate Air Filtration

## 23 41 13 – Panel Air Filters

### 23 41 13.10 Panel Type Air Filters

| | | | Crew | Daily Output | Labor-Hours | Unit | Material | Labor | Equipment | Total | Total Incl O&P |
|---|---|---|---|---|---|---|---|---|---|---|---|
| 0010 | **PANEL TYPE AIR FILTERS** | | | | | | | | | | |
| 2950 | Mechanical media filtration units | | | | | | | | | | |
| 3000 | High efficiency type, with frame, non-supported | G | | | | MCFM | 45 | | | 45 | 49.50 |
| 3100 | Supported type | G | | | | " | 60 | | | 60 | 66 |
| 5500 | Throwaway glass or paper media type | | | | | Ea. | 3.35 | | | 3.35 | 3.69 |

## 23 41 16 – Renewable-Media Air Filters

### 23 41 16.10 Disposable Media Air Filters

| | | | | | | Unit | Material | | | Total | Total Incl O&P |
|---|---|---|---|---|---|---|---|---|---|---|---|
| 0010 | **DISPOSABLE MEDIA AIR FILTERS** | | | | | | | | | | |
| 5000 | Renewable disposable roll | | | | | MCFM | 250 | | | 250 | 275 |

## 23 41 19 – Washable Air Filters

### 23 41 19.10 Permanent Air Filters

| | | | | | | Unit | Material | | | Total | Total Incl O&P |
|---|---|---|---|---|---|---|---|---|---|---|---|
| 0010 | **PERMANENT AIR FILTERS** | | | | | | | | | | |
| 4500 | Permanent washable | G | | | | MCFM | 20 | | | 20 | 22 |

## 23 41 23 – Extended Surface Filters

### 23 41 23.10 Expanded Surface Filters

| | | | | | | Unit | Material | | | Total | Total Incl O&P |
|---|---|---|---|---|---|---|---|---|---|---|---|
| 0010 | **EXPANDED SURFACE FILTERS** | | | | | | | | | | |
| 4000 | Medium efficiency, extended surface | G | | | | MCFM | 5.50 | | | 5.50 | 6.05 |

# 23 42 Gas-Phase Air Filtration

## 23 42 13 – Activated-Carbon Air Filtration

| 23 42 13.10 Charcoal Type Air Filtration | Crew | Daily Output | Labor-Hours | Unit | Material | 2010 Bare Costs Labor | Equipment | Total | Total Incl O&P |
|---|---|---|---|---|---|---|---|---|---|
| 0010 **CHARCOAL TYPE AIR FILTRATION** | | | | | | | | | |
| 0050 Activated charcoal type, full flow | | | | MCFM | 600 | | | 600 | 660 |
| 0060 Full flow, impregnated media 12" deep | | | | | 225 | | | 225 | 248 |
| 0070 HEPA filter & frame for field erection | | | | | 300 | | | 300 | 330 |
| 0080 HEPA filter-diffuser, ceiling install. | | | | | 275 | | | 275 | 305 |

# 23 43 Electronic Air Cleaners

## 23 43 13 – Washable Electronic Air Cleaners

### 23 43 13.10 Electronic Air Cleaners

| | Crew | Daily Output | Labor-Hours | Unit | Material | Labor | Equipment | Total | Total Incl O&P |
|---|---|---|---|---|---|---|---|---|---|
| 0010 **ELECTRONIC AIR CLEANERS** | | | | | | | | | |
| 2000 Electronic air cleaner, duct mounted | | | | | | | | | |
| 2150 400 – 1000 CFM | 1 Shee | 2.30 | 3.478 | Ea. | 1,675 | 113 | | 1,788 | 2,025 |
| 2200 1000 – 1400 CFM | | 2.20 | 3.636 | | 1,525 | 118 | | 1,643 | 1,875 |
| 2250 1400 – 2000 CFM | | 2.10 | 3.810 | | 1,525 | 123 | | 1,648 | 1,875 |

# 23 51 Breechings, Chimneys, and Stacks

## 23 51 23 – Gas Vents

### 23 51 23.10 Gas Chimney Vents

| | Crew | Daily Output | Labor-Hours | Unit | Material | Labor | Equipment | Total | Total Incl O&P |
|---|---|---|---|---|---|---|---|---|---|
| 0010 **GAS CHIMNEY VENTS,** Prefab metal, U.L. listed | | | | | | | | | |
| 0020 Gas, double wall, galvanized steel | | | | | | | | | |
| 0080 3" diameter | Q-9 | 72 | .222 | V.L.F. | 5.35 | 6.50 | | 11.85 | 16.60 |
| 0100 4" diameter | " | 68 | .235 | " | 6.70 | 6.85 | | 13.55 | 18.70 |

# 23 52 Heating Boilers

## 23 52 13 – Electric Boilers

### 23 52 13.10 Electric Boilers, ASME

| | Crew | Daily Output | Labor-Hours | Unit | Material | Labor | Equipment | Total | Total Incl O&P |
|---|---|---|---|---|---|---|---|---|---|
| 0010 **ELECTRIC BOILERS, ASME,** Standard controls and trim | | | | | | | | | |
| 1000 Steam, 6 KW, 20.5 MBH | Q-19 | 1.20 | 20 | Ea. | 3,500 | 630 | | 4,130 | 4,875 |
| 1160 60 KW, 205 MBH | | 1 | 24 | | 6,025 | 755 | | 6,780 | 7,850 |
| 2000 Hot water, 7.5 KW, 25.6 MBH | | 1.30 | 18.462 | | 3,750 | 580 | | 4,330 | 5,075 |
| 2040 30 KW, 102 MBH | | 1.20 | 20 | | 3,975 | 630 | | 4,605 | 5,400 |
| 2060 45 KW, 164 MBH | | 1.20 | 20 | | 4,475 | 630 | | 5,105 | 5,950 |

## 23 52 23 – Cast-Iron Boilers

### 23 52 23.20 Gas-Fired Boilers

| | Crew | Daily Output | Labor-Hours | Unit | Material | Labor | Equipment | Total | Total Incl O&P |
|---|---|---|---|---|---|---|---|---|---|
| 0010 **GAS-FIRED BOILERS,** Natural or propane, standard controls, packaged | | | | | | | | | |
| 1000 Cast iron, with insulated jacket | | | | | | | | | |
| 3000 Hot water, gross output, 80 MBH | Q-7 | 1.46 | 21.918 | Ea. | 1,775 | 675 | | 2,450 | 3,075 |
| 3020 100 MBH | " | 1.35 | 23.704 | | 2,300 | 730 | | 3,030 | 3,725 |
| 7000 For tankless water heater, add | | | | | 10% | | | | |
| 7050 For additional zone valves up to 312 MBH add | | | | | 150 | | | 150 | 165 |

### 23 52 23.30 Gas/Oil Fired Boilers

| | Crew | Daily Output | Labor-Hours | Unit | Material | Labor | Equipment | Total | Total Incl O&P |
|---|---|---|---|---|---|---|---|---|---|
| 0010 **GAS/OIL FIRED BOILERS,** Combination with burners and controls, packaged | | | | | | | | | |
| 1000 Cast iron with insulated jacket | | | | | | | | | |
| 2000 Steam, gross output, 720 MBH | Q-7 | .43 | 74.074 | Ea. | 13,900 | 2,275 | | 16,175 | 19,100 |
| 2900 Hot water, gross output | | | | | | | | | |
| 2910 200 MBH | Q-6 | .62 | 39.024 | Ea. | 7,775 | 1,150 | | 8,925 | 10,500 |
| 2920 300 MBH | | .49 | 49.080 | | 7,775 | 1,450 | | 9,225 | 11,000 |

# 23 52 Heating Boilers

## 23 52 23 – Cast-Iron Boilers

### 23 52 23.30 Gas/Oil Fired Boilers

| | | Crew | Daily Output | Labor- Hours | Unit | Material | 2010 Bare Costs Labor | 2010 Bare Costs Equipment | Total | Total Incl O&P |
|---|---|---|---|---|---|---|---|---|---|---|
| 2930 | 400 MBH | Q-6 | .41 | 57.971 | Ea. | 9,100 | 1,725 | | 10,825 | 12,800 |
| 2940 | 500 MBH | ↓ | .36 | 67.039 | | 9,800 | 2,000 | | 11,800 | 14,100 |
| 3000 | 584 MBH | Q-7 | .44 | 72.072 | ↓ | 8,125 | 2,225 | | 10,350 | 12,600 |

### 23 52 23.40 Oil-Fired Boilers

| | | Crew | Daily Output | Labor- Hours | Unit | Material | Labor | Equipment | Total | Total Incl O&P |
|---|---|---|---|---|---|---|---|---|---|---|
| 0010 | **OIL-FIRED BOILERS,** Standard controls, flame retention burner, packaged | | | | | | | | | |
| 1000 | Cast iron, with insulated flush jacket | | | | | | | | | |
| 2000 | Steam, gross output, 109 MBH | Q-7 | 1.20 | 26.667 | Ea. | 1,975 | 820 | | 2,795 | 3,525 |
| 2060 | 207 MBH | " | .90 | 35.556 | " | 2,700 | 1,100 | | 3,800 | 4,775 |
| 3000 | Hot water, same price as steam | | | | | | | | | |

## 23 52 26 – Steel Boilers

### 23 52 26.40 Oil-Fired Boilers

| | | Crew | Daily Output | Labor- Hours | Unit | Material | Labor | Equipment | Total | Total Incl O&P |
|---|---|---|---|---|---|---|---|---|---|---|
| 0010 | **OIL-FIRED BOILERS,** Standard controls, flame retention burner | | | | | | | | | |
| 5000 | Steel, with insulated flush jacket | | | | | | | | | |
| 7000 | Hot water, gross output, 103 MBH | Q-6 | 1.60 | 15 | Ea. | 1,725 | 445 | | 2,170 | 2,625 |
| 7020 | 122 MBH | | 1.45 | 16.506 | | 1,825 | 490 | | 2,315 | 2,800 |
| 7060 | 168 MBH | | 1.30 | 18.405 | | 2,025 | 545 | | 2,570 | 3,125 |
| 7080 | 225 MBH | ↓ | 1.22 | 19.704 | ↓ | 2,700 | 585 | | 3,285 | 3,900 |

## 23 52 28 – Swimming Pool Boilers

### 23 52 28.10 Swimming Pool Heaters

| | | Crew | Daily Output | Labor- Hours | Unit | Material | Labor | Equipment | Total | Total Incl O&P |
|---|---|---|---|---|---|---|---|---|---|---|
| 0010 | **SWIMMING POOL HEATERS,** Not including wiring, external | | | | | | | | | |
| 0020 | piping, base or pad, | | | | | | | | | |
| 0160 | Gas fired, input, 155 MBH | Q-6 | 1.50 | 16 | Ea. | 1,575 | 475 | | 2,050 | 2,525 |
| 0200 | 199 MBH | | 1 | 24 | | 1,700 | 710 | | 2,410 | 3,050 |
| 0280 | 500 MBH | ↓ | .40 | 60 | | 7,225 | 1,775 | | 9,000 | 10,900 |
| 2000 | Electric, 12 KW, 4,800 gallon pool | Q-19 | 3 | 8 | | 2,025 | 252 | | 2,277 | 2,625 |
| 2020 | 15 KW, 7,200 gallon pool | | 2.80 | 8.571 | | 2,050 | 270 | | 2,320 | 2,700 |
| 2040 | 24 KW, 9,600 gallon pool | | 2.40 | 10 | | 2,375 | 315 | | 2,690 | 3,125 |
| 2100 | 57 KW, 24,000 gallon pool | ↓ | 1.20 | 20 | ↓ | 3,475 | 630 | | 4,105 | 4,850 |

## 23 52 88 – Burners

### 23 52 88.10 Replacement Type Burners

| | | Crew | Daily Output | Labor- Hours | Unit | Material | Labor | Equipment | Total | Total Incl O&P |
|---|---|---|---|---|---|---|---|---|---|---|
| 0010 | **REPLACEMENT TYPE BURNERS** | | | | | | | | | |
| 0990 | Residential, conversion, gas fired, LP or natural | | | | | | | | | |
| 1000 | Gun type, atmospheric input 50 to 225 MBH | Q-1 | 2.50 | 6.400 | Ea. | 650 | 198 | | 848 | 1,025 |
| 1020 | 100 to 400 MBH | | 2 | 8 | | 1,075 | 247 | | 1,322 | 1,575 |
| 1040 | 300 to 1000 MBH | ↓ | 1.70 | 9.412 | ↓ | 3,300 | 291 | | 3,591 | 4,100 |

# 23 54 Furnaces

## 23 54 13 – Electric-Resistance Furnaces

### 23 54 13.10 Electric Furnaces

| | | Crew | Daily Output | Labor- Hours | Unit | Material | Labor | Equipment | Total | Total Incl O&P |
|---|---|---|---|---|---|---|---|---|---|---|
| 0010 | **ELECTRIC FURNACES,** Hot air, blowers, std. controls | | | | | | | | | |
| 0011 | not including gas, oil or flue piping | | | | | | | | | |
| 1000 | Electric, UL listed | | | | | | | | | |
| 1020 | 10.2 MBH | Q-20 | 5 | 4 | Ea. | 475 | 120 | | 595 | 715 |
| 1100 | 34.1 MBH | " | 4.40 | 4.545 | " | 615 | 136 | | 751 | 900 |

## 23 54 16 – Fuel-Fired Furnaces

### 23 54 16.13 Gas-Fired Furnaces

| | | Crew | Daily Output | Labor- Hours | Unit | Material | Labor | Equipment | Total | Total Incl O&P |
|---|---|---|---|---|---|---|---|---|---|---|
| 0010 | **GAS-FIRED FURNACES** | | | | | | | | | |
| 3000 | Gas, AGA certified, upflow, direct drive models | | | | | | | | | |

# 23 54 Furnaces

## 23 54 16 – Fuel-Fired Furnaces

| | 23 54 16.13 Gas-Fired Furnaces | Crew | Daily Output | Labor-Hours | Unit | Material | 2010 Bare Costs Labor | Equipment | Total | Total Incl O&P |
|---|---|---|---|---|---|---|---|---|---|---|
| 3020 | 45 MBH input | Q-9 | 4 | 4 | Ea. | 575 | 117 | | 692 | 830 |
| 3040 | 60 MBH input | | 3.80 | 4.211 | | 615 | 123 | | 738 | 880 |
| 3060 | 75 MBH input | | 3.60 | 4.444 | | 685 | 130 | | 815 | 970 |
| 3100 | 100 MBH input | | 3.20 | 5 | | 695 | 146 | | 841 | 1,000 |
| 3120 | 125 MBH input | | 3 | 5.333 | | 700 | 155 | | 855 | 1,025 |
| 3130 | 150 MBH input | | 2.80 | 5.714 | | 705 | 167 | | 872 | 1,050 |
| 3140 | 200 MBH input | | 2.60 | 6.154 | | 2,425 | 179 | | 2,604 | 2,950 |
| 4000 | For starter plenum, add | | 16 | 1 | | 80 | 29 | | 109 | 136 |

## 23 54 16.16 Oil-Fired Furnaces

| | | Crew | Daily Output | Labor-Hours | Unit | Material | 2010 Bare Costs Labor | Equipment | Total | Total Incl O&P |
|---|---|---|---|---|---|---|---|---|---|---|
| 0010 | **OIL-FIRED FURNACES** | | | | | | | | | |
| 6000 | Oil, UL listed, atomizing gun type burner | | | | | | | | | |
| 6020 | 56 MBH output | Q-9 | 3.60 | 4.444 | Ea. | 1,850 | 130 | | 1,980 | 2,250 |
| 6030 | 84 MBH output | | 3.50 | 4.571 | | 1,850 | 133 | | 1,983 | 2,275 |
| 6040 | 95 MBH output | | 3.40 | 4.706 | | 1,875 | 137 | | 2,012 | 2,300 |
| 6060 | 134 MBH output | | 3.20 | 5 | | 1,950 | 146 | | 2,096 | 2,400 |
| 6080 | 151 MBH output | | 3 | 5.333 | | 2,275 | 155 | | 2,430 | 2,750 |
| 6100 | 200 MBH input | | 2.60 | 6.154 | | 2,325 | 179 | | 2,504 | 2,850 |

## 23 54 16.21 Solid Fuel-Fired Furnaces

| | | | Crew | Daily Output | Labor-Hours | Unit | Material | 2010 Bare Costs Labor | Equipment | Total | Total Incl O&P |
|---|---|---|---|---|---|---|---|---|---|---|---|
| 0010 | **SOLID FUEL-FIRED FURNACES** | | | | | | | | | | |
| 6020 | Wood fired furnaces | | | | | | | | | | |
| 6030 | Includes hot water coil, thermostat, and auto draft control | | | | | | | | | | |
| 6040 | 24" long firebox | G | Q-9 | 4 | 4 | Ea. | 3,975 | 117 | | 4,092 | 4,550 |
| 6050 | 30" long firebox | G | | 3.60 | 4.444 | | 4,675 | 130 | | 4,805 | 5,350 |
| 6060 | With fireplace glass doors | G | | 3.20 | 5 | | 6,000 | 146 | | 6,146 | 6,850 |
| 6200 | Wood/oil fired furnaces, includes two thermostats | | | | | | | | | | |
| 6210 | Includes hot water coil and auto draft control | | | | | | | | | | |
| 6240 | 24" long firebox | G | Q-9 | 3.40 | 4.706 | Ea. | 4,825 | 137 | | 4,962 | 5,525 |
| 6250 | 30" long firebox | G | | 3 | 5.333 | | 5,400 | 155 | | 5,555 | 6,200 |
| 6260 | With fireplace glass doors | G | | 2.80 | 5.714 | | 6,000 | 167 | | 6,167 | 6,875 |
| 6400 | Wood/gas fired furnaces, includes two thermostats | | | | | | | | | | |
| 6410 | Includes hot water coil and auto draft control | | | | | | | | | | |
| 6440 | 24" long firebox | G | Q-9 | 2.80 | 5.714 | Ea. | 5,450 | 167 | | 5,617 | 6,275 |
| 6450 | 30" long firebox | G | | 2.40 | 6.667 | | 6,150 | 194 | | 6,344 | 7,100 |
| 6460 | With fireplace glass doors | G | | 2 | 8 | | 7,425 | 233 | | 7,658 | 8,525 |
| 6600 | Wood/oil/gas fired furnaces, optional accessories | | | | | | | | | | |
| 6610 | Hot air plenum | | Q-9 | 16 | 1 | Ea. | 93 | 29 | | 122 | 150 |
| 6620 | Safety heat dump | | | 24 | .667 | | 82 | 19.45 | | 101.45 | 122 |
| 6630 | Auto air intake | | | 18 | .889 | | 132 | 26 | | 158 | 188 |
| 6640 | Cold air return package | | | 14 | 1.143 | | 142 | 33.50 | | 175.50 | 211 |
| 6650 | Wood fork | | | | | | 44 | | | 44 | 48.50 |
| 6700 | Wood fired outdoor furnace | | | | | | | | | | |
| 6740 | 24" long firebox | G | Q-9 | 3.80 | 4.211 | Ea. | 4,200 | 123 | | 4,323 | 4,800 |
| 6760 | Wood fired outdoor furnace, optional accessories | | | | | | | | | | |
| 6770 | Chimney section, stainless steel, 6" ID x 3' lg. | G | Q-9 | 36 | .444 | Ea. | 121 | 12.95 | | 133.95 | 155 |
| 6780 | Chimney cap, stainless steel | G | " | 40 | .400 | " | 66 | 11.65 | | 77.65 | 92 |
| 6800 | Wood fired hot water furnace | | | | | | | | | | |
| 6820 | Includes 200 gal. hot water storage, thermostat, and auto draft control | | | | | | | | | | |
| 6840 | 30" long firebox | G | Q-9 | 2.10 | 7.619 | Ea. | 8,275 | 222 | | 8,497 | 9,475 |
| 6850 | Water to air heat exchanger | | | | | | | | | | |
| 6870 | Includes mounting kit and blower relay | | | | | | | | | | |
| 6880 | 140 MBH, 18.75" W x 18.75" L | | Q-9 | 7.50 | 2.133 | Ea. | 370 | 62 | | 432 | 510 |
| 6890 | 200 MBH, 24" W x 24" L | | " | 7 | 2.286 | " | 525 | 66.50 | | 591.50 | 690 |

# 23 54 Furnaces

## 23 54 16 – Fuel-Fired Furnaces

### 23 54 16.21 Solid Fuel-Fired Furnaces

| | | Crew | Daily Output | Labor-Hours | Unit | Material | 2010 Bare Costs Labor | Equipment | Total | Total Incl O&P |
|---|---|---|---|---|---|---|---|---|---|---|
| 6900 | Water to water heat exchanger | | | | | | | | | |
| 6940 | 100 MBH | Q-9 | 6.50 | 2.462 | Ea. | 370 | 72 | | 442 | 530 |
| 6960 | 290 MBH | " | 6 | 2.667 | " | 535 | 77.50 | | 612.50 | 720 |
| 7000 | Optional accessories | | | | | | | | | |
| 7010 | Large volume circulation pump, (2 Included) | Q-9 | 14 | 1.143 | Ea. | 242 | 33.50 | | 275.50 | 320 |
| 7020 | Air bleed fittings, (package) | | 24 | .667 | | 49 | 19.45 | | 68.45 | 86 |
| 7030 | Domestic water preheater | | 6 | 2.667 | | 219 | 77.50 | | 296.50 | 370 |
| 7040 | Smoke pipe kit | | 4 | 4 | | 74 | 117 | | 191 | 275 |

## 23 54 24 – Furnace Components for Cooling

### 23 54 24.10 Furnace Components and Combinations

| | | Crew | Daily Output | Labor-Hours | Unit | Material | 2010 Bare Costs Labor | Equipment | Total | Total Incl O&P |
|---|---|---|---|---|---|---|---|---|---|---|
| 0010 | **FURNACE COMPONENTS AND COMBINATIONS** | | | | | | | | | |
| 0080 | Coils, A/C evaporator, for gas or oil furnaces | | | | | | | | | |
| 0090 | Add-on, with holding charge | | | | | | | | | |
| 0100 | Upflow | | | | | | | | | |
| 0120 | 1-1/2 ton cooling | Q-5 | 4 | 4 | Ea. | 158 | 123 | | 281 | 375 |
| 0130 | 2 ton cooling | | 3.70 | 4.324 | | 188 | 133 | | 321 | 425 |
| 0140 | 3 ton cooling | | 3.30 | 4.848 | | 238 | 149 | | 387 | 505 |
| 0150 | 4 ton cooling | | 3 | 5.333 | | 330 | 164 | | 494 | 630 |
| 0160 | 5 ton cooling | | 2.70 | 5.926 | | 385 | 183 | | 568 | 725 |
| 0300 | Downflow | | | | | | | | | |
| 0330 | 2-1/2 ton cooling | Q-5 | 3 | 5.333 | Ea. | 232 | 164 | | 396 | 525 |
| 0340 | 3-1/2 ton cooling | | 2.60 | 6.154 | | 276 | 190 | | 466 | 615 |
| 0350 | 5 ton cooling | | 2.20 | 7.273 | | 385 | 224 | | 609 | 790 |
| 0600 | Horizontal | | | | | | | | | |
| 0630 | 2 ton cooling | Q-5 | 3.90 | 4.103 | Ea. | 260 | 126 | | 386 | 495 |
| 0640 | 3 ton cooling | | 3.50 | 4.571 | | 296 | 141 | | 437 | 555 |
| 0650 | 4 ton cooling | | 3.20 | 5 | | 375 | 154 | | 529 | 665 |
| 0660 | 5 ton cooling | | 2.90 | 5.517 | | 375 | 170 | | 545 | 690 |
| 2000 | Cased evaporator coils for air handlers | | | | | | | | | |
| 2100 | 1-1/2 ton cooling | Q-5 | 4.40 | 3.636 | Ea. | 325 | 112 | | 437 | 540 |
| 2110 | 2 ton cooling | | 4.10 | 3.902 | | 325 | 120 | | 445 | 555 |
| 2120 | 2-1/2 ton cooling | | 3.90 | 4.103 | | 345 | 126 | | 471 | 585 |
| 2130 | 3 ton cooling | | 3.70 | 4.324 | | 385 | 133 | | 518 | 640 |
| 2140 | 3-1/2 ton cooling | | 3.50 | 4.571 | | 400 | 141 | | 541 | 670 |
| 2150 | 4 ton cooling | | 3.20 | 5 | | 480 | 154 | | 634 | 785 |
| 2160 | 5 ton cooling | | 2.90 | 5.517 | | 555 | 170 | | 725 | 890 |
| 3010 | Air handler, modular | | | | | | | | | |
| 3100 | With cased evaporator cooling coil | | | | | | | | | |
| 3120 | 1-1/2 ton cooling | Q-5 | 3.80 | 4.211 | Ea. | 1,025 | 130 | | 1,155 | 1,350 |
| 3130 | 2 ton cooling | | 3.50 | 4.571 | | 1,175 | 141 | | 1,316 | 1,500 |
| 3140 | 2-1/2 ton cooling | | 3.30 | 4.848 | | 1,175 | 149 | | 1,324 | 1,525 |
| 3150 | 3 ton cooling | | 3.10 | 5.161 | | 1,275 | 159 | | 1,434 | 1,650 |
| 3160 | 3-1/2 ton cooling | | 2.90 | 5.517 | | 1,325 | 170 | | 1,495 | 1,725 |
| 3170 | 4 ton cooling | | 2.50 | 6.400 | | 1,475 | 197 | | 1,672 | 1,950 |
| 3180 | 5 ton cooling | | 2.10 | 7.619 | | 1,675 | 235 | | 1,910 | 2,200 |
| 3500 | With no cooling coil | | | | | | | | | |
| 3520 | 1-1/2 ton coil size | Q-5 | 12 | 1.333 | Ea. | 795 | 41 | | 836 | 945 |
| 3530 | 2 ton coil size | | 10 | 1.600 | | 815 | 49.50 | | 864.50 | 980 |
| 3540 | 2-1/2 ton coil size | | 10 | 1.600 | | 890 | 49.50 | | 939.50 | 1,050 |
| 3554 | 3 ton coil size | | 9 | 1.778 | | 905 | 55 | | 960 | 1,075 |
| 3560 | 3-1/2 ton coil size | | 9 | 1.778 | | 970 | 55 | | 1,025 | 1,175 |
| 3570 | 4 ton coil size | | 8.50 | 1.882 | | 1,150 | 58 | | 1,208 | 1,350 |

# 23 54 Furnaces

## 23 54 24 – Furnace Components for Cooling

| 23 54 24.10 Furnace Components and Combinations | Crew | Daily Output | Labor-Hours | Unit | Material | 2010 Bare Costs Labor | Equipment | Total | Total Incl O&P |
|---|---|---|---|---|---|---|---|---|---|
| 3580 | 5 ton coil size | Q-5 | 8 | 2 | Ea. | 1,300 | 61.50 | | 1,361.50 | 1,550 |
| 4000 | With heater | | | | | | | | | |
| 4120 | 5 kW, 17.1 MBH | Q-5 | 16 | 1 | Ea. | 690 | 31 | | 721 | 810 |
| 4130 | 7.5 kW, 25.6 MBH | | 15.60 | 1.026 | | 810 | 31.50 | | 841.50 | 940 |
| 4140 | 10 kW, 34.2 MBH | | 15.20 | 1.053 | | 930 | 32.50 | | 962.50 | 1,075 |
| 4150 | 12.5 KW, 42.7 MBH | | 14.80 | 1.081 | | 1,050 | 33.50 | | 1,083.50 | 1,200 |
| 4160 | 15 KW, 51.2 MBH | | 14.40 | 1.111 | | 1,200 | 34.50 | | 1,234.50 | 1,350 |
| 4170 | 25 KW, 85.4 MBH | | 14 | 1.143 | | 1,325 | 35 | | 1,360 | 1,500 |
| 4180 | 30 KW, 102 MBH | | 13 | 1.231 | | 1,525 | 38 | | 1,563 | 1,725 |

# 23 62 Packaged Compressor and Condenser Units

## 23 62 13 – Packaged Air-Cooled Refrigerant Compressor and Condenser Units

| 23 62 13.10 Packaged Air-Cooled Refrig. Condensing Units | Crew | Daily Output | Labor-Hours | Unit | Material | 2010 Bare Costs Labor | Equipment | Total | Total Incl O&P |
|---|---|---|---|---|---|---|---|---|---|
| 0010 | **PACKAGED AIR-COOLED REFRIGERANT CONDENSING UNITS** | | | | | | | | | |
| 0030 | Air cooled, compressor, standard controls | | | | | | | | | |
| 0050 | 1.5 ton | Q-5 | 2.50 | 6.400 | Ea. | 1,175 | 197 | | 1,372 | 1,625 |
| 0100 | 2 ton | | 2.10 | 7.619 | | 1,200 | 235 | | 1,435 | 1,700 |
| 0200 | 2.5 ton | | 1.70 | 9.412 | | 1,300 | 290 | | 1,590 | 1,925 |
| 0300 | 3 ton | | 1.30 | 12.308 | | 1,325 | 380 | | 1,705 | 2,100 |
| 0350 | 3.5 ton | | 1.10 | 14.545 | | 1,575 | 450 | | 2,025 | 2,450 |
| 0400 | 4 ton | | .90 | 17.778 | | 1,775 | 550 | | 2,325 | 2,850 |
| 0500 | 5 ton | | .60 | 26.667 | | 2,125 | 820 | | 2,945 | 3,700 |

# 23 74 Packaged Outdoor HVAC Equipment

## 23 74 33 – Packaged, Outdoor, Heating and Cooling Makeup Air-Conditioners

| 23 74 33.10 Roof Top Air Conditioners | Crew | Daily Output | Labor-Hours | Unit | Material | 2010 Bare Costs Labor | Equipment | Total | Total Incl O&P |
|---|---|---|---|---|---|---|---|---|---|
| 0010 | **ROOF TOP AIR CONDITIONERS**, Standard controls, curb, economizer | | | | | | | | | |
| 1000 | Single zone, electric cool, gas heat | | | | | | | | | |
| 1140 | 5 ton cooling, 112 MBH heating | Q-5 | .56 | 28.521 | Ea. | 4,850 | 880 | | 5,730 | 6,800 |
| 1160 | 10 ton cooling, 200 MBH heating | Q-6 | .67 | 35.982 | " | 10,600 | 1,075 | | 11,675 | 13,400 |

# 23 81 Decentralized Unitary HVAC Equipment

## 23 81 13 – Packaged Terminal Air-Conditioners

| 23 81 13.10 Packaged Cabinet Type Air-Conditioners | Crew | Daily Output | Labor-Hours | Unit | Material | 2010 Bare Costs Labor | Equipment | Total | Total Incl O&P |
|---|---|---|---|---|---|---|---|---|---|
| 0010 | **PACKAGED CABINET TYPE AIR-CONDITIONERS**, Cabinet, wall sleeve, | | | | | | | | | |
| 0100 | louver, electric heat, thermostat, manual changeover, 208 V | | | | | | | | | |
| 0200 | 6,000 BTUH cooling, 8800 BTU heat | Q-5 | 6 | 2.667 | Ea. | 680 | 82 | | 762 | 885 |
| 0220 | 9,000 BTUH cooling, 13,900 BTU heat | | 5 | 3.200 | | 790 | 98.50 | | 888.50 | 1,025 |
| 0240 | 12,000 BTUH cooling, 13,900 BTU heat | | 4 | 4 | | 850 | 123 | | 973 | 1,125 |
| 0260 | 15,000 BTUH cooling, 13,900 BTU heat | | 3 | 5.333 | | 915 | 164 | | 1,079 | 1,275 |

## 23 81 19 – Self-Contained Air-Conditioners

| 23 81 19.10 Window Unit Air Conditioners | Crew | Daily Output | Labor-Hours | Unit | Material | 2010 Bare Costs Labor | Equipment | Total | Total Incl O&P |
|---|---|---|---|---|---|---|---|---|---|
| 0010 | **WINDOW UNIT AIR CONDITIONERS** | | | | | | | | | |
| 4000 | Portable/window, 15 amp 125V grounded receptacle required | | | | | | | | | |
| 4060 | 5000 BTUH | 1 Carp | 8 | 1 | Ea. | 199 | 29 | | 228 | 268 |
| 4340 | 6000 BTUH | | 8 | 1 | | 241 | 29 | | 270 | 315 |
| 4480 | 8000 BTUH | | 6 | 1.333 | | 405 | 39 | | 444 | 510 |

# 23 81 Decentralized Unitary HVAC Equipment

## 23 81 19 - Self-Contained Air-Conditioners

### 23 81 19.10 Window Unit Air Conditioners

| | | Crew | Daily Output | Labor-Hours | Unit | Material | 2010 Bare Costs Labor | 2010 Bare Costs Equipment | Total | Total Incl O&P |
|---|---|---|---|---|---|---|---|---|---|---|
| 4500 | 10,000 BTUH | 1 Carp | 6 | 1.333 | Ea. | 515 | 39 | | 554 | 630 |
| 4520 | 12,000 BTUH | L-2 | 8 | 2 | ↓ | 630 | 51 | | 681 | 780 |
| 4600 | Window/thru-the-wall, 15 amp 230V grounded receptacle required | | | | | | | | | |
| 4780 | 17,000 BTUH | L-2 | 6 | 2.667 | Ea. | 845 | 68 | | 913 | 1,050 |
| 4940 | 25,000 BTUH | ↓ | 4 | 4 | ↓ | 1,075 | 102 | | 1,177 | 1,350 |
| 4960 | 29,000 BTUH | ↓ | 4 | 4 | ↓ | 1,200 | 102 | | 1,302 | 1,500 |

### 23 81 19.20 Self-Contained Single Package

| | | Crew | Daily Output | Labor-Hours | Unit | Material | 2010 Bare Costs Labor | 2010 Bare Costs Equipment | Total | Total Incl O&P |
|---|---|---|---|---|---|---|---|---|---|---|
| 0010 | **SELF-CONTAINED SINGLE PACKAGE** | | | | | | | | | |
| 0100 | Air cooled, for free blow or duct, not incl. remote condenser | | | | | | | | | |
| 0200 | 3 ton cooling | Q-5 | 1 | 16 | Ea. | 3,300 | 495 | | 3,795 | 4,425 |
| 0210 | 4 ton cooling | " | .80 | 20 | " | 3,575 | 615 | | 4,190 | 4,950 |
| 1000 | Water cooled for free blow or duct, not including tower | | | | | | | | | |
| 1100 | 3 ton cooling | Q-6 | 1 | 24 | Ea. | 3,250 | 710 | | 3,960 | 4,750 |

## 23 81 26 - Split-System Air-Conditioners

### 23 81 26.10 Split Ductless Systems

| | | Crew | Daily Output | Labor-Hours | Unit | Material | 2010 Bare Costs Labor | 2010 Bare Costs Equipment | Total | Total Incl O&P |
|---|---|---|---|---|---|---|---|---|---|---|
| 0010 | **SPLIT DUCTLESS SYSTEMS** | | | | | | | | | |
| 0100 | Cooling only, single zone | | | | | | | | | |
| 0110 | Wall mount | | | | | | | | | |
| 0120 | 3/4 ton cooling | Q-5 | 2 | 8 | Ea. | 655 | 247 | | 902 | 1,125 |
| 0130 | 1 ton cooling | ↓ | 1.80 | 8.889 | | 730 | 274 | | 1,004 | 1,250 |
| 0140 | 1-1/2 ton cooling | | 1.60 | 10 | | 1,150 | 310 | | 1,460 | 1,750 |
| 0150 | 2 ton cooling | ↓ | 1.40 | 11.429 | ↓ | 1,300 | 350 | | 1,650 | 2,000 |
| 1000 | Ceiling mount | | | | | | | | | |
| 1020 | 2 ton cooling | Q-5 | 1.40 | 11.429 | Ea. | 2,475 | 350 | | 2,825 | 3,300 |
| 1030 | 3 ton cooling | " | 1.20 | 13.333 | " | 3,200 | 410 | | 3,610 | 4,200 |
| 3000 | Multizone | | | | | | | | | |
| 3010 | Wall mount | | | | | | | | | |
| 3020 | 2 @ 3/4 ton cooling | Q-5 | 1.80 | 8.889 | Ea. | 2,100 | 274 | | 2,374 | 2,775 |
| 5000 | Cooling/Heating | | | | | | | | | |
| 5110 | 1 ton cooling | Q-5 | 1.70 | 9.412 | Ea. | 765 | 290 | | 1,055 | 1,325 |
| 5120 | 1-1/2 ton cooling | " | 1.50 | 10.667 | " | 1,175 | 330 | | 1,505 | 1,850 |
| 7000 | Accessories for all split ductless systems | | | | | | | | | |
| 7010 | Add for ambient frost control | Q-5 | 8 | 2 | Ea. | 179 | 61.50 | | 240.50 | 298 |
| 7020 | Add for tube/wiring kit | | | | | | | | | |
| 7030 | 15' kit | Q-5 | 32 | .500 | Ea. | 40 | 15.40 | | 55.40 | 69.50 |
| 7036 | 25' kit | | 28 | .571 | | 95 | 17.60 | | 112.60 | 134 |
| 7040 | 35' kit | | 24 | .667 | | 129 | 20.50 | | 149.50 | 176 |
| 7050 | 50' kit | ↓ | 20 | .800 | ↓ | 167 | 24.50 | | 191.50 | 225 |

## 23 81 43 - Air-Source Unitary Heat Pumps

### 23 81 43.10 Air-Source Heat Pumps

| | | Crew | Daily Output | Labor-Hours | Unit | Material | 2010 Bare Costs Labor | 2010 Bare Costs Equipment | Total | Total Incl O&P |
|---|---|---|---|---|---|---|---|---|---|---|
| 0010 | **AIR-SOURCE HEAT PUMPS**, Not including interconnecting tubing | | | | | | | | | |
| 1000 | Air to air, split system, not including curbs, pads, fan coil and ductwork | | | | | | | | | |
| 1012 | Outside condensing unit only, for fan coil see Div. 23 82 19.10 | | | | | | | | | |
| 1020 | 2 ton cooling, 8.5 MBH heat @ 0°F | Q-5 | 2 | 8 | Ea. | 2,125 | 247 | | 2,372 | 2,725 |
| 1054 | 4 ton cooling, 24 MBH heat @ 0°F | " | .80 | 20 | " | 3,150 | 615 | | 3,765 | 4,450 |
| 1500 | Single package, not including curbs, pads, or plenums | | | | | | | | | |
| 1520 | 2 ton cooling, 6.5 MBH heat @ 0°F | Q-5 | 1.50 | 10.667 | Ea. | 2,750 | 330 | | 3,080 | 3,575 |
| 1580 | 4 ton cooling, 13 MBH heat @ 0°F | " | .96 | 16.667 | " | 3,850 | 515 | | 4,365 | 5,100 |

# 23 81 Decentralized Unitary HVAC Equipment

## 23 81 46 – Water-Source Unitary Heat Pumps

| 23 81 46.10 Water Source Heat Pumps | Crew | Daily Output | Labor-Hours | Unit | Material | 2010 Bare Costs Labor | 2010 Bare Costs Equipment | Total | Total Incl O&P |
|---|---|---|---|---|---|---|---|---|---|
| 0010 **WATER SOURCE HEAT PUMPS**, Not incl. connecting tubing or water source | | | | | | | | | |
| 2000 Water source to air, single package | | | | | | | | | |
| 2100 1 ton cooling, 13 MBH heat @ 75°F | Q-5 | 2 | 8 | Ea. | 1,475 | 247 | | 1,722 | 2,025 |
| 2200 4 ton cooling, 31 MBH heat @ 75°F | " | 1.20 | 13.333 | " | 2,250 | 410 | | 2,660 | 3,150 |

# 23 82 Convection Heating and Cooling Units

## 23 82 19 – Fan Coil Units

### 23 82 19.10 Fan Coil Air Conditioning

| | Crew | Daily Output | Labor-Hours | Unit | Material | Labor | Equipment | Total | Total Incl O&P |
|---|---|---|---|---|---|---|---|---|---|
| 0010 **FAN COIL AIR CONDITIONING** Cabinet mounted, filters, controls | | | | | | | | | |
| 0100 Chilled water, 1/2 ton cooling | Q-5 | 8 | 2 | Ea. | 710 | 61.50 | | 771.50 | 880 |
| 0110 3/4 ton cooling | | 7 | 2.286 | | 735 | 70.50 | | 805.50 | 925 |
| 0120 1 ton cooling | | 6 | 2.667 | | 815 | 82 | | 897 | 1,025 |

## 23 82 29 – Radiators

### 23 82 29.10 Hydronic Heating

| | Crew | Daily Output | Labor-Hours | Unit | Material | Labor | Equipment | Total | Total Incl O&P |
|---|---|---|---|---|---|---|---|---|---|
| 0010 **HYDRONIC HEATING**, Terminal units, not incl. main supply pipe | | | | | | | | | |
| 1000 Radiation | | | | | | | | | |
| 3000 Radiators, cast iron | | | | | | | | | |
| 3100 Free standing or wall hung, 6 tube, 25" high | Q-5 | 96 | .167 | Section | 36 | 5.15 | | 41.15 | 48 |

## 23 82 36 – Finned-Tube Radiation Heaters

### 23 82 36.10 Finned Tube Radiation

| | Crew | Daily Output | Labor-Hours | Unit | Material | Labor | Equipment | Total | Total Incl O&P |
|---|---|---|---|---|---|---|---|---|---|
| 0010 **FINNED TUBE RADIATION**, Terminal units, not incl. main supply pipe | | | | | | | | | |
| 1310 Baseboard, pkgd, 1/2" copper tube, alum. fin, 7" high | Q-5 | 60 | .267 | L.F. | 7.55 | 8.20 | | 15.75 | 22 |
| 1320 3/4" copper tube, alum. fin, 7" high | | 58 | .276 | | 8 | 8.50 | | 16.50 | 23 |
| 1340 1" copper tube, alum. fin, 8-7/8" high | | 56 | .286 | | 25 | 8.80 | | 33.80 | 42 |
| 1360 1-1/4" copper tube, alum. fin, 8-7/8" high | | 54 | .296 | | 26 | 9.15 | | 35.15 | 43.50 |

# 23 83 Radiant Heating Units

## 23 83 16 – Radiant-Heating Hydronic Piping

### 23 83 16.10 Radiant Floor Heating

| | Crew | Daily Output | Labor-Hours | Unit | Material | Labor | Equipment | Total | Total Incl O&P |
|---|---|---|---|---|---|---|---|---|---|
| 0010 **RADIANT FLOOR HEATING** | | | | | | | | | |
| 0100 Tubing, PEX (cross-linked polyethylene) | | | | | | | | | |
| 0110 Oxygen barrier type for systems with ferrous materials | | | | | | | | | |
| 0120 1/2" | Q-5 | 800 | .020 | L.F. | 1.01 | .62 | | 1.63 | 2.12 |
| 0130 3/4" | | 535 | .030 | | 1.29 | .92 | | 2.21 | 2.93 |
| 0140 1" | | 400 | .040 | | 2.21 | 1.23 | | 3.44 | 4.45 |
| 0200 Non barrier type for ferrous free systems | | | | | | | | | |
| 0210 1/2" | Q-5 | 800 | .020 | L.F. | .55 | .62 | | 1.17 | 1.62 |
| 0220 3/4" | | 535 | .030 | | 1 | .92 | | 1.92 | 2.61 |
| 0230 1" | | 400 | .040 | | 1.71 | 1.23 | | 2.94 | 3.90 |
| 1000 Manifolds | | | | | | | | | |
| 1110 Brass | | | | | | | | | |
| 1120 With supply and return valves, flow meter, thermometer, | | | | | | | | | |
| 1122 auto air vent and drain/fill valve. | | | | | | | | | |
| 1130 1", 2 circuit | Q-5 | 14 | 1.143 | Ea. | 181 | 35 | | 216 | 257 |
| 1140 1", 3 circuit | | 13.50 | 1.185 | | 207 | 36.50 | | 243.50 | 287 |
| 1150 1", 4 circuit | | 13 | 1.231 | | 225 | 38 | | 263 | 310 |
| 1154 1", 5 circuit | | 12.50 | 1.280 | | 268 | 39.50 | | 307.50 | 360 |
| 1158 1", 6 circuit | | 12 | 1.333 | | 292 | 41 | | 333 | 390 |

| 23 83 16.10 Radiant Floor Heating | | Crew | Daily Output | Labor-Hours | Unit | Material | 2010 Bare Costs Labor | 2010 Bare Costs Equipment | Total | Total Incl O&P |
|---|---|---|---|---|---|---|---|---|---|---|
| 1162 | 1", 7 circuit | Q-5 | 11.50 | 1.391 | Ea. | 320 | 43 | | 363 | 420 |
| 1166 | 1", 8 circuit | | 11 | 1.455 | | 355 | 45 | | 400 | 465 |
| 1172 | 1", 9 circuit | | 10.50 | 1.524 | | 380 | 47 | | 427 | 495 |
| 1174 | 1", 10 circuit | | 10 | 1.600 | | 410 | 49.50 | | 459.50 | 530 |
| 1178 | 1", 11 circuit | | 9.50 | 1.684 | | 425 | 52 | | 477 | 555 |
| 1182 | 1", 12 circuit | | 9 | 1.778 | | 470 | 55 | | 525 | 605 |
| 1610 | Copper manifold header, (cut to size) | | | | | | | | | |
| 1620 | 1" header, 12 – 1/2" sweat outlets | Q-5 | 3.33 | 4.805 | Ea. | 72.50 | 148 | | 220.50 | 325 |
| 1630 | 1-1/4" header, 12 – 1/2" sweat outlets | | 3.20 | 5 | | 84 | 154 | | 238 | 345 |
| 1640 | 1-1/4" header, 12 – 3/4" sweat outlets | | 3 | 5.333 | | 90.50 | 164 | | 254.50 | 370 |
| 1650 | 1-1/2" header, 12 – 3/4" sweat outlets | | 3.10 | 5.161 | | 109 | 159 | | 268 | 380 |
| 1660 | 2" header, 12 – 3/4" sweat outlets | | 2.90 | 5.517 | | 160 | 170 | | 330 | 455 |
| 3000 | Valves | | | | | | | | | |
| 3110 | Thermostatic zone valve actuator with end switch | Q-5 | 40 | .400 | Ea. | 36.50 | 12.35 | | 48.85 | 60 |
| 3114 | Thermostatic zone valve actuator | " | 36 | .444 | " | 81 | 13.70 | | 94.70 | 112 |
| 3120 | Motorized straight zone valve with operator complete | | | | | | | | | |
| 3130 | 3/4" | Q-5 | 35 | .457 | Ea. | 125 | 14.10 | | 139.10 | 161 |
| 3140 | 1" | | 32 | .500 | | 137 | 15.40 | | 152.40 | 177 |
| 3150 | 1-1/4" | | 29.60 | .541 | | 165 | 16.65 | | 181.65 | 210 |
| 3500 | 4 Way mixing valve, manual, brass | | | | | | | | | |
| 3530 | 1" | Q-5 | 13.30 | 1.203 | Ea. | 126 | 37 | | 163 | 200 |
| 3540 | 1-1/4" | | 11.40 | 1.404 | | 137 | 43.50 | | 180.50 | 222 |
| 3550 | 1-1/2" | | 11 | 1.455 | | 203 | 45 | | 248 | 298 |
| 3560 | 2" | | 10.60 | 1.509 | | 288 | 46.50 | | 334.50 | 390 |
| 3800 | Mixing valve motor, 4 way for valves, 1" and 1-1/4" | | 34 | .471 | | 310 | 14.50 | | 324.50 | 365 |
| 3810 | Mixing valve motor, 4 way for valves, 1-1/2" and 2" | | 30 | .533 | | 355 | 16.45 | | 371.45 | 415 |
| 5000 | Radiant floor heating, zone control panel | | | | | | | | | |
| 5120 | 4 Zone actuator valve control, expandable | Q-5 | 20 | .800 | Ea. | 163 | 24.50 | | 187.50 | 220 |
| 5130 | 6 Zone actuator valve control, expandable | | 18 | .889 | | 199 | 27.50 | | 226.50 | 264 |
| 6070 | Thermal track, straight panel for long continuous runs, 5.333 S.F. | | 40 | .400 | | 16.60 | 12.35 | | 28.95 | 38.50 |
| 6080 | Thermal track, utility panel, for direction reverse at run end, 5.333 S.F. | | 40 | .400 | | 16.60 | 12.35 | | 28.95 | 38.50 |
| 6090 | Combination panel, for direction reverse plus straight run, 5.333 S.F. | | 40 | .400 | | 16.60 | 12.35 | | 28.95 | 38.50 |
| 7000 | PEX tubing fittings | | | | | | | | | |
| 7100 | Compression type | | | | | | | | | |
| 7116 | Coupling | | | | | | | | | |
| 7120 | 1/2" x 1/2" | 1 Stpi | 27 | .296 | Ea. | 6.40 | 10.15 | | 16.55 | 23.50 |
| 7124 | 3/4" x 3/4" | " | 23 | .348 | " | 10.10 | 11.90 | | 22 | 30.50 |
| 7130 | Adapter | | | | | | | | | |
| 7132 | 1/2" x female sweat 1/2" | 1 Stpi | 27 | .296 | Ea. | 4.15 | 10.15 | | 14.30 | 21 |
| 7134 | 1/2" x female sweat 3/4" | | 26 | .308 | | 4.88 | 10.55 | | 15.43 | 22.50 |
| 7136 | 5/8" x female sweat 3/4" | | 24 | .333 | | 6.65 | 11.40 | | 18.05 | 26 |
| 7140 | Elbow | | | | | | | | | |
| 7142 | 1/2" x female sweat 1/2" | 1 Stpi | 27 | .296 | Ea. | 6.35 | 10.15 | | 16.50 | 23.50 |
| 7144 | 1/2" x female sweat 3/4" | | 26 | .308 | | 7.40 | 10.55 | | 17.95 | 25.50 |
| 7146 | 5/8" x female sweat 3/4" | | 24 | .333 | | 8.75 | 11.40 | | 20.15 | 28.50 |
| 7200 | Insert type | | | | | | | | | |
| 7206 | PEX x male NPT | | | | | | | | | |
| 7210 | 1/2" x 1/2" | 1 Stpi | 29 | .276 | Ea. | 1.43 | 9.45 | | 10.88 | 17.05 |
| 7220 | 3/4" x 3/4" | | 27 | .296 | | 2.10 | 10.15 | | 12.25 | 18.95 |
| 7230 | 1" x 1" | | 26 | .308 | | 2.66 | 10.55 | | 13.21 | 20 |
| 7300 | PEX coupling | | | | | | | | | |
| 7310 | 1/2" x 1/2" | 1 Stpi | 30 | .267 | Ea. | .58 | 9.15 | | 9.73 | 15.60 |
| 7320 | 3/4" x 3/4" | | 29 | .276 | | .71 | 9.45 | | 10.16 | 16.30 |

# 23 83 Radiant Heating Units

## 23 83 16 – Radiant-Heating Hydronic Piping

| 23 83 16.10 Radiant Floor Heating | Crew | Daily Output | Labor-Hours | Unit | Material | 2010 Bare Costs Labor | Equipment | Total | Total Incl O&P |
|---|---|---|---|---|---|---|---|---|---|
| 7330 | 1" x 1" | 1 Stpi | 28 | .286 | Ea. | 1.41 | 9.80 | | 11.21 | 17.60 |
| 7400 | PEX stainless crimp ring | | | | | | | | | |
| 7410 | 1/2" | 1 Stpi | 86 | .093 | Ea. | .25 | 3.19 | | 3.44 | 5.50 |
| 7420 | 3/4" x 3/4" | | 84 | .095 | | .34 | 3.26 | | 3.60 | 5.70 |
| 7430 | 1" x 1" | ↓ | 82 | .098 | ↓ | .40 | 3.34 | | 3.74 | 5.95 |

## 23 83 33 – Electric Radiant Heaters

### 23 83 33.10 Electric Heating

| | | Crew | Daily Output | Labor-Hours | Unit | Material | 2010 Bare Costs Labor | Equipment | Total | Total Incl O&P |
|---|---|---|---|---|---|---|---|---|---|---|
| 0010 | **ELECTRIC HEATING**, not incl. conduit or feed wiring | | | | | | | | | |
| 1100 | Rule of thumb: Baseboard units, including control | 1 Elec | 4.40 | 1.818 | kW | 92.50 | 59.50 | | 152 | 199 |
| 1300 | Baseboard heaters, 2' long, 375 watt | | 8 | 1 | Ea. | 40 | 33 | | 73 | 97.50 |
| 1400 | 3' long, 500 watt | | 8 | 1 | | 46 | 33 | | 79 | 104 |
| 1600 | 4' long, 750 watt | | 6.70 | 1.194 | | 54 | 39 | | 93 | 124 |
| 1800 | 5' long, 935 watt | | 5.70 | 1.404 | | 68 | 46 | | 114 | 150 |
| 2000 | 6' long, 1125 watt | | 5 | 1.600 | | 74 | 52.50 | | 126.50 | 167 |
| 2400 | 8' long, 1500 watt | | 4 | 2 | | 92 | 65.50 | | 157.50 | 208 |
| 2800 | 10' long, 1875 watt | ↓ | 3.30 | 2.424 | ↓ | 193 | 79.50 | | 272.50 | 340 |
| 2950 | Wall heaters with fan, 120 to 277 volt | | | | | | | | | |
| 3600 | Thermostats, integral | 1 Elec | 16 | .500 | Ea. | 30 | 16.45 | | 46.45 | 59.50 |
| 3800 | Line voltage, 1 pole | | 8 | 1 | | 31 | 33 | | 64 | 87.50 |
| 5000 | Radiant heating ceiling panels, 2' x 4', 500 watt | | 16 | .500 | | 253 | 16.45 | | 269.45 | 305 |
| 5050 | 750 watt | | 16 | .500 | | 279 | 16.45 | | 295.45 | 330 |
| 5300 | Infrared quartz heaters, 120 volts, 1000 watts | | 6.70 | 1.194 | | 222 | 39 | | 261 | 310 |
| 5350 | 1500 watt | | 5 | 1.600 | | 222 | 52.50 | | 274.50 | 330 |
| 5400 | 240 volts, 1500 watt | | 5 | 1.600 | | 222 | 52.50 | | 274.50 | 330 |
| 5450 | 2000 watt | | 4 | 2 | | 222 | 65.50 | | 287.50 | 350 |
| 5500 | 3000 watt | ↓ | 3 | 2.667 | ↓ | 246 | 87.50 | | 333.50 | 415 |

# Estimating Tips

## 26 05 00 Common Work Results for Electrical

- Conduit should be taken off in three main categories—power distribution, branch power, and branch lighting—so the estimator can concentrate on systems and components, therefore making it easier to ensure all items have been accounted for.

- For cost modifications for elevated conduit installation, add the percentages to labor according to the height of installation, and only to the quantities exceeding the different height levels, not to the total conduit quantities.

- Remember that aluminum wiring of equal ampacity is larger in diameter than copper and may require larger conduit.

- If more than three wires at a time are being pulled, deduct percentages from the labor hours of that grouping of wires.

- When taking off grounding systems, identify separately the type and size of wire, and list each unique type of ground connection.

- The estimator should take the weights of materials into consideration when completing a takeoff. Topics to consider include: How will the materials be supported? What methods of support are available? How high will the support structure have to reach? Will the final support structure be able to withstand the total burden? Is the support material included or separate from the fixture, equipment, and material specified?

- Do not overlook the costs for equipment used in the installation. If scaffolding or highlifts are available in the field, contractors may use them in lieu of the proposed ladders and rolling staging.

## 26 20 00 Low-Voltage Electrical Transmission

- Supports and concrete pads may be shown on drawings for the larger equipment, or the support system may be only a piece of plywood for the back of a panelboard. In either case, it must be included in the costs.

## 26 40 00 Electrical and Cathodic Protection

- When taking off cathodic protections systems, identify the type and size of cable, and list each unique type of anode connection.

## 26 50 00 Lighting

- Fixtures should be taken off room by room, using the fixture schedule, specifications, and the ceiling plan. For large concentrations of lighting fixtures in the same area, deduct the percentages from labor hours.

# Reference Numbers

Reference numbers are shown in shaded boxes at the beginning of some major classifications. These numbers refer to related items in the Reference Section. The reference information may be an estimating procedure, an alternate pricing method, or technical information.

*Note:* Not all subdivisions listed here necessarily appear in this publication.

*Note:* **Trade Service,** *in part, has been used as a reference source for some of the material prices used in Division 26.*

## 26 05 05 – Selective Electrical Demolition

| 26 05 05.10 Electrical Demolition | Crew | Daily Output | Labor-Hours | Unit | Material | 2010 Bare Costs Labor | 2010 Bare Costs Equipment | Total | Total Incl O&P |
|---|---|---|---|---|---|---|---|---|---|
| 0010 | **ELECTRICAL DEMOLITION** | | | | | | | | |
| 0020 | Conduit to 15' high, including fittings & hangers | | | | | | | | |
| 0100 | Rigid galvanized steel, 1/2" to 1" diameter | 1 Elec | 242 | .033 | L.F. | | 1.09 | | 1.09 | 1.77 |
| 0120 | 1-1/4" to 2" | " | 200 | .040 | " | | 1.31 | | 1.31 | 2.14 |
| 0270 | Armored cable, (BX) avg. 50' runs | | | | | | | | |
| 0290 | #14, 3 wire | 1 Elec | 571 | .014 | L.F. | | .46 | | .46 | .75 |
| 0300 | #12, 2 wire | | 605 | .013 | | | .43 | | .43 | .71 |
| 0310 | #12, 3 wire | | 514 | .016 | | | .51 | | .51 | .83 |
| 0320 | #10, 2 wire | | 514 | .016 | | | .51 | | .51 | .83 |
| 0330 | #10, 3 wire | | 425 | .019 | | | .62 | | .62 | 1.01 |
| 0340 | #8, 3 wire | | 342 | .023 | | | .77 | | .77 | 1.25 |
| 0350 | Non metallic sheathed cable (Romex) | | | | | | | | |
| 0360 | #14, 2 wire | 1 Elec | 720 | .011 | L.F. | | .37 | | .37 | .59 |
| 0370 | #14, 3 wire | | 657 | .012 | | | .40 | | .40 | .65 |
| 0380 | #12, 2 wire | | 629 | .013 | | | .42 | | .42 | .68 |
| 0390 | #10, 3 wire | | 450 | .018 | | | .58 | | .58 | .95 |
| 0400 | Wiremold raceway, including fittings & hangers | | | | | | | | |
| 0420 | No. 3000 | 1 Elec | 250 | .032 | L.F. | | 1.05 | | 1.05 | 1.71 |
| 0440 | No. 4000 | | 217 | .037 | | | 1.21 | | 1.21 | 1.97 |
| 0460 | No. 6000 | | 166 | .048 | | | 1.58 | | 1.58 | 2.58 |
| 0465 | Telephone/power pole | | 12 | .667 | Ea. | | 22 | | 22 | 35.50 |
| 0470 | Non-metallic, straight section | | 480 | .017 | L.F. | | .55 | | .55 | .89 |
| 0500 | Channels, steel, including fittings & hangers | | | | | | | | |
| 0520 | 3/4" x 1-1/2" | 1 Elec | 308 | .026 | L.F. | | .85 | | .85 | 1.39 |
| 0540 | 1-1/2" x 1-1/2" | | 269 | .030 | | | .98 | | .98 | 1.59 |
| 0560 | 1-1/2" x 1-7/8" | | 229 | .035 | | | 1.15 | | 1.15 | 1.87 |
| 1210 | Panel boards, incl. removal of all breakers, | | | | | | | | |
| 1220 | conduit terminations & wire connections | | | | | | | | |
| 1230 | 3 wire, 120/240V, 100A, to 20 circuits | 1 Elec | 2.60 | 3.077 | Ea. | | 101 | | 101 | 164 |
| 1240 | 200 amps, to 42 circuits | 2 Elec | 2.60 | 6.154 | | | 202 | | 202 | 330 |
| 1260 | 4 wire, 120/208V, 125A, to 20 circuits | 1 Elec | 2.40 | 3.333 | | | 110 | | 110 | 178 |
| 1270 | 200 amps, to 42 circuits | 2 Elec | 2.40 | 6.667 | | | 219 | | 219 | 355 |
| 1720 | Junction boxes, 4" sq. & oct. | 1 Elec | 80 | .100 | | | 3.29 | | 3.29 | 5.35 |
| 1760 | Switch box | | 107 | .075 | | | 2.46 | | 2.46 | 4 |
| 1780 | Receptacle & switch plates | | 257 | .031 | | | 1.02 | | 1.02 | 1.66 |
| 1800 | Wire, THW-THWN-THHN, removed from | | | | | | | | |
| 1810 | in place conduit, to 15' high | | | | | | | | |
| 1830 | #14 | 1 Elec | 65 | .123 | C.L.F. | | 4.04 | | 4.04 | 6.60 |
| 1840 | #12 | | 55 | .145 | | | 4.78 | | 4.78 | 7.75 |
| 1850 | #10 | | 45.50 | .176 | | | 5.80 | | 5.80 | 9.40 |
| 2000 | Interior fluorescent fixtures, incl. supports | | | | | | | | |
| 2010 | & whips, to 15' high | | | | | | | | |
| 2100 | Recessed drop-in 2' x 2', 2 lamp | 2 Elec | 35 | .457 | Ea. | | 15 | | 15 | 24.50 |
| 2140 | 2' x 4', 4 lamp | " | 30 | .533 | " | | 17.50 | | 17.50 | 28.50 |
| 2180 | Surface mount, acrylic lens & hinged frame | | | | | | | | |
| 2220 | 2' x 2', 2 lamp | 2 Elec | 44 | .364 | Ea. | | 11.95 | | 11.95 | 19.45 |
| 2260 | 2' x 4', 4 lamp | " | 33 | .485 | " | | 15.95 | | 15.95 | 26 |
| 2300 | Strip fixtures, surface mount | | | | | | | | |
| 2320 | 4' long, 1 lamp | 2 Elec | 53 | .302 | Ea. | | 9.90 | | 9.90 | 16.15 |
| 2380 | 8' long, 2 lamp | " | 40 | .400 | " | | 13.15 | | 13.15 | 21.50 |
| 2460 | Interior incandescent, surface, ceiling | | | | | | | | |
| 2470 | or wall mount, to 12' high | | | | | | | | |
| 2480 | Metal cylinder type, 75 Watt | 2 Elec | 62 | .258 | Ea. | | 8.50 | | 8.50 | 13.80 |

# 26 05 Common Work Results for Electrical

## 26 05 05 – Selective Electrical Demolition

| 26 05 05.10 Electrical Demolition | | Crew | Daily Output | Labor-Hours | Unit | Material | 2010 Bare Costs Labor | Equipment | Total | Total Incl O&P |
|---|---|---|---|---|---|---|---|---|---|---|
| 2600 | Exterior fixtures, incandescent, wall mount | | | | | | | | | |
| 2620 | 100 Watt | 2 Elec | 50 | .320 | Ea. | | 10.50 | | 10.50 | 17.10 |
| 3000 | Ceiling fan, tear out and remove | 1 Elec | 18 | .444 | " | | 14.60 | | 14.60 | 24 |
| 9000 | Minimum labor/equipment charge | " | 4 | 2 | Job | | 65.50 | | 65.50 | 107 |

## 26 05 19 – Low-Voltage Electrical Power Conductors and Cables

### 26 05 19.20 Armored Cable

| | | Crew | Daily Output | Labor-Hours | Unit | Material | 2010 Bare Costs Labor | Equipment | Total | Total Incl O&P |
|---|---|---|---|---|---|---|---|---|---|---|
| 0010 | **ARMORED CABLE** | | | | | | | | | |
| 0051 | 600 volt, copper (BX), #14, 2 conductor, solid | 1 Elec | 240 | .033 | L.F. | .70 | 1.09 | | 1.79 | 2.56 |
| 0101 | 3 conductor, solid | | 200 | .040 | | 1.11 | 1.31 | | 2.42 | 3.36 |
| 0151 | #12, 2 conductor, solid | | 210 | .038 | | .71 | 1.25 | | 1.96 | 2.83 |
| 0201 | 3 conductor, solid | | 180 | .044 | | 1.14 | 1.46 | | 2.60 | 3.63 |
| 0251 | #10, 2 conductor, solid | | 180 | .044 | | 1.30 | 1.46 | | 2.76 | 3.81 |
| 0301 | 3 conductor, solid | | 150 | .053 | | 1.79 | 1.75 | | 3.54 | 4.82 |
| 0351 | #8, 3 conductor, solid | | 120 | .067 | | 3.36 | 2.19 | | 5.55 | 7.25 |

### 26 05 19.55 Non-Metallic Sheathed Cable

| | | Crew | Daily Output | Labor-Hours | Unit | Material | 2010 Bare Costs Labor | Equipment | Total | Total Incl O&P |
|---|---|---|---|---|---|---|---|---|---|---|
| 0010 | **NON-METALLIC SHEATHED CABLE** 600 volt | | | | | | | | | |
| 0100 | Copper with ground wire, (Romex) | | | | | | | | | |
| 0151 | #14, 2 wire | 1 Elec | 250 | .032 | L.F. | .23 | 1.05 | | 1.28 | 1.96 |
| 0201 | 3 wire | | 230 | .035 | | .32 | 1.14 | | 1.46 | 2.21 |
| 0251 | #12, 2 wire | | 220 | .036 | | .34 | 1.19 | | 1.53 | 2.32 |
| 0301 | 3 wire | | 200 | .040 | | .49 | 1.31 | | 1.80 | 2.67 |
| 0351 | #10, 2 wire | | 200 | .040 | | .54 | 1.31 | | 1.85 | 2.73 |
| 0401 | 3 wire | | 140 | .057 | | .77 | 1.88 | | 2.65 | 3.90 |
| 0451 | #8, 3 conductor | | 130 | .062 | | 1.21 | 2.02 | | 3.23 | 4.62 |
| 0501 | #6, 3 wire | | 120 | .067 | | 1.96 | 2.19 | | 4.15 | 5.70 |
| 0550 | SE type SER aluminum cable, 3 RHW and | | | | | | | | | |
| 0601 | 1 bare neutral, 3 #8 & 1 #8 | 1 Elec | 150 | .053 | L.F. | 1.20 | 1.75 | | 2.95 | 4.17 |
| 0651 | 3 #6 & 1 #6 | " | 130 | .062 | | 1.36 | 2.02 | | 3.38 | 4.78 |
| 0701 | 3 #4 & 1 #6 | 2 Elec | 220 | .073 | | 1.52 | 2.39 | | 3.91 | 5.55 |
| 0751 | 3 #2 & 1 #4 | | 200 | .080 | | 2.24 | 2.63 | | 4.87 | 6.75 |
| 0801 | 3 #1/0 & 1 #2 | | 180 | .089 | | 3.39 | 2.92 | | 6.31 | 8.50 |
| 0851 | 3 #2/0 & 1 #1 | | 160 | .100 | | 3.99 | 3.29 | | 7.28 | 9.75 |
| 0901 | 3 #4/0 & 1 #2/0 | | 140 | .114 | | 5.70 | 3.75 | | 9.45 | 12.35 |
| 2401 | SEU service entrance cable, copper 2 conductors, #8 + #8 neutral | 1 Elec | 150 | .053 | | 1.15 | 1.75 | | 2.90 | 4.12 |
| 2601 | #6 + #8 neutral | | 130 | .062 | | 1.73 | 2.02 | | 3.75 | 5.20 |
| 2801 | #6 + #6 neutral | | 130 | .062 | | 1.97 | 2.02 | | 3.99 | 5.45 |
| 3001 | #4 + #6 neutral | 2 Elec | 220 | .073 | | 2.73 | 2.39 | | 5.12 | 6.90 |
| 3201 | #4 + #4 neutral | | 220 | .073 | | 3.08 | 2.39 | | 5.47 | 7.30 |
| 3401 | #3 + #5 neutral | | 210 | .076 | | 3.61 | 2.50 | | 6.11 | 8.05 |
| 6500 | Service entrance cap for copper SEU | | | | | | | | | |
| 6600 | 100 amp | 1 Elec | 12 | .667 | Ea. | 13 | 22 | | 35 | 50 |
| 6700 | 150 amp | | 10 | .800 | | 23.50 | 26.50 | | 50 | 69 |
| 6800 | 200 amp | | 8 | 1 | | 36 | 33 | | 69 | 93 |

### 26 05 19.90 Wire

| | | Crew | Daily Output | Labor-Hours | Unit | Material | 2010 Bare Costs Labor | Equipment | Total | Total Incl O&P |
|---|---|---|---|---|---|---|---|---|---|---|
| 0010 | **WIRE** | | | | | | | | | |
| 0021 | 600 volt type THW, copper solid, #14 | 1 Elec | 1300 | .006 | L.F. | .08 | .20 | | .28 | .42 |
| 0031 | #12 | | 1100 | .007 | | .12 | .24 | | .36 | .52 |
| 0041 | #10 | | 1000 | .008 | | .18 | .26 | | .44 | .63 |
| 0161 | #6 | | 650 | .012 | | .55 | .40 | | .95 | 1.26 |
| 0181 | #4 | 2 Elec | 1060 | .015 | | .86 | .50 | | 1.36 | 1.76 |
| 0201 | #3 | | 1000 | .016 | | 1.07 | .53 | | 1.60 | 2.03 |
| 0221 | #2 | | 900 | .018 | | 1.34 | .58 | | 1.92 | 2.43 |

# 26 05 Common Work Results for Electrical

## 26 05 19 – Low-Voltage Electrical Power Conductors and Cables

### 26 05 19.90 Wire

| | | Crew | Daily Output | Labor-Hours | Unit | Material | 2010 Bare Costs Labor | Equipment | Total | Total Incl O&P |
|---|---|---|---|---|---|---|---|---|---|---|
| 0241 | #1 | 2 Elec | 800 | .020 | L.F. | 1.74 | .66 | | 2.40 | 2.98 |
| 0261 | 1/0 | | 660 | .024 | | 2.11 | .80 | | 2.91 | 3.62 |
| 0281 | 2/0 | | 580 | .028 | | 2.65 | .91 | | 3.56 | 4.39 |
| 0301 | 3/0 | | 500 | .032 | | 3.33 | 1.05 | | 4.38 | 5.35 |
| 0351 | 4/0 | | 440 | .036 | | 4.19 | 1.19 | | 5.38 | 6.55 |

## 26 05 26 – Grounding and Bonding for Electrical Systems

### 26 05 26.80 Grounding

| | | Crew | Daily Output | Labor-Hours | Unit | Material | 2010 Bare Costs Labor | Equipment | Total | Total Incl O&P |
|---|---|---|---|---|---|---|---|---|---|---|
| 0010 | **GROUNDING** | | | | | | | | | |
| 0030 | Rod, copper clad, 8' long, 1/2" diameter | 1 Elec | 5.50 | 1.455 | Ea. | 16.75 | 48 | | 64.75 | 96.50 |
| 0050 | 3/4" diameter | | 5.30 | 1.509 | | 30.50 | 49.50 | | 80 | 114 |
| 0080 | 10' long, 1/2" diameter | | 4.80 | 1.667 | | 19.65 | 55 | | 74.65 | 111 |
| 0100 | 3/4" diameter | | 4.40 | 1.818 | | 36.50 | 59.50 | | 96 | 137 |
| 0261 | Wire, ground bare armored, #8-1 conductor | | 200 | .040 | L.F. | 1.19 | 1.31 | | 2.50 | 3.45 |
| 0271 | #6-1 conductor | | 180 | .044 | " | 1.41 | 1.46 | | 2.87 | 3.93 |
| 0390 | Bare copper wire, stranded, #8 | | 11 | .727 | C.L.F. | 30.50 | 24 | | 54.50 | 72.50 |
| 0401 | Bare copper, #6 wire | | 1000 | .008 | L.F. | .53 | .26 | | .79 | 1.02 |
| 0601 | #2 stranded | 2 Elec | 1000 | .016 | " | 1.34 | .53 | | 1.87 | 2.34 |
| 1800 | Water pipe ground clamps, heavy duty | | | | | | | | | |
| 2000 | Bronze, 1/2" to 1" diameter | 1 Elec | 8 | 1 | Ea. | 26 | 33 | | 59 | 82 |

## 26 05 33 – Raceway and Boxes for Electrical Systems

### 26 05 33.05 Conduit

| | | Crew | Daily Output | Labor-Hours | Unit | Material | 2010 Bare Costs Labor | Equipment | Total | Total Incl O&P |
|---|---|---|---|---|---|---|---|---|---|---|
| 0010 | **CONDUIT** To 15' high, includes 2 terminations, 2 elbows, | | | | | | | | | |
| 0020 | 11 beam clamps, and 11 couplings per 100 L.F. | | | | | | | | | |
| 1750 | Rigid galvanized steel, 1/2" diameter | 1 Elec | 90 | .089 | L.F. | 2.62 | 2.92 | | 5.54 | 7.65 |
| 1770 | 3/4" diameter | | 80 | .100 | | 2.86 | 3.29 | | 6.15 | 8.50 |
| 1800 | 1" diameter | | 65 | .123 | | 3.90 | 4.04 | | 7.94 | 10.90 |
| 1830 | 1-1/4" diameter | | 60 | .133 | | 5.35 | 4.38 | | 9.73 | 13.05 |
| 1850 | 1-1/2" diameter | | 55 | .145 | | 6.25 | 4.78 | | 11.03 | 14.65 |
| 1870 | 2" diameter | | 45 | .178 | | 8.15 | 5.85 | | 14 | 18.45 |
| 5000 | Electric metallic tubing (EMT), 1/2" diameter | | 170 | .047 | | .62 | 1.55 | | 2.17 | 3.20 |
| 5020 | 3/4" diameter | | 130 | .062 | | .96 | 2.02 | | 2.98 | 4.35 |
| 5040 | 1" diameter | | 115 | .070 | | 1.70 | 2.29 | | 3.99 | 5.60 |
| 5060 | 1-1/4" diameter | | 100 | .080 | | 2.77 | 2.63 | | 5.40 | 7.30 |
| 5080 | 1-1/2" diameter | | 90 | .089 | | 3.59 | 2.92 | | 6.51 | 8.70 |
| 9100 | PVC, schedule 40, 1/2" diameter | | 190 | .042 | | 1.01 | 1.38 | | 2.39 | 3.36 |
| 9110 | 3/4" diameter | | 145 | .055 | | 1.20 | 1.81 | | 3.01 | 4.27 |
| 9120 | 1" diameter | | 125 | .064 | | 2.13 | 2.10 | | 4.23 | 5.75 |
| 9130 | 1-1/4" diameter | | 110 | .073 | | 2.79 | 2.39 | | 5.18 | 6.95 |
| 9140 | 1-1/2" diameter | | 100 | .080 | | 3.15 | 2.63 | | 5.78 | 7.75 |
| 9150 | 2" diameter | | 90 | .089 | | 3.94 | 2.92 | | 6.86 | 9.10 |

### 26 05 33.25 Conduit Fittings for Rigid Galvanized Steel

| | | Crew | Daily Output | Labor-Hours | Unit | Material | 2010 Bare Costs Labor | Equipment | Total | Total Incl O&P |
|---|---|---|---|---|---|---|---|---|---|---|
| 0010 | **CONDUIT FITTINGS FOR RIGID GALVANIZED STEEL** | | | | | | | | | |
| 2280 | LB, LR or LL fittings & covers, 1/2" diameter | 1 Elec | 16 | .500 | Ea. | 12.30 | 16.45 | | 28.75 | 40 |
| 2290 | 3/4" diameter | | 13 | .615 | | 14.35 | 20 | | 34.35 | 49 |
| 2300 | 1" diameter | | 11 | .727 | | 21.50 | 24 | | 45.50 | 62.50 |
| 2330 | 1-1/4" diameter | | 8 | 1 | | 32.50 | 33 | | 65.50 | 89.50 |
| 2350 | 1-1/2" diameter | | 6 | 1.333 | | 40.50 | 44 | | 84.50 | 116 |
| 2370 | 2" diameter | | 5 | 1.600 | | 67 | 52.50 | | 119.50 | 159 |
| 5280 | Service entrance cap, 1/2" diameter | | 16 | .500 | | 9.05 | 16.45 | | 25.50 | 36.50 |
| 5300 | 3/4" diameter | | 13 | .615 | | 10.50 | 20 | | 30.50 | 44.50 |
| 5320 | 1" diameter | | 10 | .800 | | 12.55 | 26.50 | | 39.05 | 57 |

# 26 05 Common Work Results for Electrical

## 26 05 33 – Raceway and Boxes for Electrical Systems

| 26 05 33.25 Conduit Fittings for Rigid Galvanized Steel | | Crew | Daily Output | Labor-Hours | Unit | Material | 2010 Bare Costs Labor | Equipment | Total | Total Incl O&P |
|---|---|---|---|---|---|---|---|---|---|---|
| 5340 | 1-1/4" diameter | 1 Elec | 8 | 1 | Ea. | 18.35 | 33 | | 51.35 | 73.50 |
| 5360 | 1-1/2" diameter | | 6.50 | 1.231 | | 35.50 | 40.50 | | 76 | 105 |
| 5380 | 2" diameter | | 5.50 | 1.455 | | 50.50 | 48 | | 98.50 | 134 |

### 26 05 33.35 Flexible Metallic Conduit

| | | Crew | Daily Output | Labor-Hours | Unit | Material | 2010 Bare Costs Labor | Equipment | Total | Total Incl O&P |
|---|---|---|---|---|---|---|---|---|---|---|
| 0010 | **FLEXIBLE METALLIC CONDUIT** | | | | | | | | | |
| 0050 | Steel, 3/8" diameter | 1 Elec | 200 | .040 | L.F. | .51 | 1.31 | | 1.82 | 2.70 |
| 0100 | 1/2" diameter | | 200 | .040 | | .58 | 1.31 | | 1.89 | 2.78 |
| 0200 | 3/4" diameter | | 160 | .050 | | .78 | 1.64 | | 2.42 | 3.53 |
| 0250 | 1" diameter | | 100 | .080 | | 1.43 | 2.63 | | 4.06 | 5.85 |
| 0300 | 1-1/4" diameter | | 70 | .114 | | 1.84 | 3.75 | | 5.59 | 8.10 |
| 0350 | 1-1/2" diameter | | 50 | .160 | | 3.02 | 5.25 | | 8.27 | 11.85 |
| 0370 | 2" diameter | | 40 | .200 | | 3.69 | 6.55 | | 10.24 | 14.75 |

### 26 05 33.50 Outlet Boxes

| | | Crew | Daily Output | Labor-Hours | Unit | Material | 2010 Bare Costs Labor | Equipment | Total | Total Incl O&P |
|---|---|---|---|---|---|---|---|---|---|---|
| 0010 | **OUTLET BOXES** | | | | | | | | | |
| 0021 | Pressed steel, octagon, 4" | 1 Elec | 18 | .444 | Ea. | 3.36 | 14.60 | | 17.96 | 27.50 |
| 0060 | Covers, blank | | 64 | .125 | | 1.40 | 4.11 | | 5.51 | 8.25 |
| 0100 | Extension rings | | 40 | .200 | | 5.60 | 6.55 | | 12.15 | 16.85 |
| 0151 | Square 4" | | 18 | .444 | | 2.38 | 14.60 | | 16.98 | 26.50 |
| 0200 | Extension rings | | 40 | .200 | | 5.65 | 6.55 | | 12.20 | 16.90 |
| 0250 | Covers, blank | | 64 | .125 | | 1.53 | 4.11 | | 5.64 | 8.40 |
| 0300 | Plaster rings | | 64 | .125 | | 3.09 | 4.11 | | 7.20 | 10.10 |
| 0651 | Switchbox | | 24 | .333 | | 5.40 | 10.95 | | 16.35 | 24 |
| 1100 | Concrete, floor, 1 gang | | 5.30 | 1.509 | | 89.50 | 49.50 | | 139 | 179 |

### 26 05 33.60 Outlet Boxes, Plastic

| | | Crew | Daily Output | Labor-Hours | Unit | Material | 2010 Bare Costs Labor | Equipment | Total | Total Incl O&P |
|---|---|---|---|---|---|---|---|---|---|---|
| 0010 | **OUTLET BOXES, PLASTIC** | | | | | | | | | |
| 0051 | 4" diameter, round, with 2 mounting nails | 1 Elec | 23 | .348 | Ea. | 3.28 | 11.45 | | 14.73 | 22 |
| 0101 | Bar hanger mounted | | 23 | .348 | | 6 | 11.45 | | 17.45 | 25 |
| 0201 | Square with 2 mounting nails | | 23 | .348 | | 4.96 | 11.45 | | 16.41 | 24 |
| 0300 | Plaster ring | | 64 | .125 | | 2.08 | 4.11 | | 6.19 | 9 |
| 0401 | Switch box with 2 mounting nails, 1 gang | | 27 | .296 | | 2.24 | 9.75 | | 11.99 | 18.30 |
| 0501 | 2 gang | | 23 | .348 | | 4.56 | 11.45 | | 16.01 | 23.50 |
| 0601 | 3 gang | | 18 | .444 | | 7.30 | 14.60 | | 21.90 | 32 |

### 26 05 33.65 Pull Boxes

| | | Crew | Daily Output | Labor-Hours | Unit | Material | 2010 Bare Costs Labor | Equipment | Total | Total Incl O&P |
|---|---|---|---|---|---|---|---|---|---|---|
| 0010 | **PULL BOXES** | | | | | | | | | |
| 0100 | Sheet metal, pull box, NEMA 1, type SC, 6" W x 6" H x 4" D | 1 Elec | 8 | 1 | Ea. | 13.65 | 33 | | 46.65 | 68.50 |
| 0200 | 8" W x 8" H x 4" D | | 8 | 1 | | 18.70 | 33 | | 51.70 | 74 |
| 0300 | 10" W x 12" H x 6" D | | 5.30 | 1.509 | | 33 | 49.50 | | 82.50 | 117 |

## 26 05 39 – Underfloor Raceways for Electrical Systems

### 26 05 39.30 Conduit In Concrete Slab

| | | Crew | Daily Output | Labor-Hours | Unit | Material | 2010 Bare Costs Labor | Equipment | Total | Total Incl O&P |
|---|---|---|---|---|---|---|---|---|---|---|
| 0010 | **CONDUIT IN CONCRETE SLAB** Including terminations, | | | | | | | | | |
| 0020 | fittings and supports | | | | | | | | | |
| 3230 | PVC, schedule 40, 1/2" diameter | 1 Elec | 270 | .030 | L.F. | .67 | .97 | | 1.64 | 2.32 |
| 3250 | 3/4" diameter | | 230 | .035 | | .81 | 1.14 | | 1.95 | 2.75 |
| 3270 | 1" diameter | | 200 | .040 | | 1.11 | 1.31 | | 2.42 | 3.36 |
| 3300 | 1-1/4" diameter | | 170 | .047 | | 1.55 | 1.55 | | 3.10 | 4.22 |
| 3330 | 1-1/2" diameter | | 140 | .057 | | 1.85 | 1.88 | | 3.73 | 5.10 |
| 3350 | 2" diameter | | 120 | .067 | | 2.38 | 2.19 | | 4.57 | 6.20 |
| 4350 | Rigid galvanized steel, 1/2" diameter | | 200 | .040 | | 2.26 | 1.31 | | 3.57 | 4.63 |
| 4400 | 3/4" diameter | | 170 | .047 | | 2.50 | 1.55 | | 4.05 | 5.25 |
| 4450 | 1" diameter | | 130 | .062 | | 3.54 | 2.02 | | 5.56 | 7.20 |
| 4500 | 1-1/4" diameter | | 110 | .073 | | 4.73 | 2.39 | | 7.12 | 9.10 |

559

## 26 05 39 – Underfloor Raceways for Electrical Systems

| 26 05 39.30 Conduit In Concrete Slab | | Crew | Daily Output | Labor-Hours | Unit | Material | 2010 Bare Costs Labor | 2010 Bare Costs Equipment | Total | Total Incl O&P |
|---|---|---|---|---|---|---|---|---|---|---|
| 4600 | 1-1/2" diameter | 1 Elec | 100 | .080 | L.F. | 5.65 | 2.63 | | 8.28 | 10.50 |
| 4800 | 2" diameter | ↓ | 90 | .089 | ↓ | 7.30 | 2.92 | | 10.22 | 12.75 |

### 26 05 39.40 Conduit In Trench

| | | Crew | Daily Output | Labor-Hours | Unit | Material | Labor | Equipment | Total | Total Incl O&P |
|---|---|---|---|---|---|---|---|---|---|---|
| 0010 | **CONDUIT IN TRENCH** Includes terminations and fittings | | | | | | | | | |
| 0200 | Rigid galvanized steel, 2" diameter | 1 Elec | 150 | .053 | L.F. | 7.05 | 1.75 | | 8.80 | 10.60 |
| 0400 | 2-1/2" diameter | " | 100 | .080 | | 14.05 | 2.63 | | 16.68 | 19.75 |
| 0600 | 3" diameter | 2 Elec | 160 | .100 | | 17.35 | 3.29 | | 20.64 | 24.50 |
| 0800 | 3-1/2" diameter | " | 140 | .114 | ↓ | 22.50 | 3.75 | | 26.25 | 31 |

## 26 05 80 – Wiring Connections

### 26 05 80.10 Motor Connections

| | | Crew | Daily Output | Labor-Hours | Unit | Material | Labor | Equipment | Total | Total Incl O&P |
|---|---|---|---|---|---|---|---|---|---|---|
| 0010 | **MOTOR CONNECTIONS** | | | | | | | | | |
| 0020 | Flexible conduit and fittings, 115 volt, 1 phase, up to 1 HP motor | 1 Elec | 8 | 1 | Ea. | 9.55 | 33 | | 42.55 | 64 |

## 26 05 90 – Residential Applications

### 26 05 90.10 Residential Wiring

| | | Crew | Daily Output | Labor-Hours | Unit | Material | Labor | Equipment | Total | Total Incl O&P |
|---|---|---|---|---|---|---|---|---|---|---|
| 0010 | **RESIDENTIAL WIRING** | | | | | | | | | |
| 0020 | 20' avg. runs and #14/2 wiring incl. unless otherwise noted | | | | | | | | | |
| 1000 | Service & panel, includes 24' SE-AL cable, service eye, meter, | | | | | | | | | |
| 1010 | Socket, panel board, main bkr., ground rod, 15 or 20 amp | | | | | | | | | |
| 1020 | 1-pole circuit breakers, and misc. hardware | | | | | | | | | |
| 1100 | 100 amp, with 10 branch breakers | 1 Elec | 1.19 | 6.723 | Ea. | 565 | 221 | | 786 | 985 |
| 1110 | With PVC conduit and wire | | .92 | 8.696 | | 630 | 286 | | 916 | 1,150 |
| 1120 | With RGS conduit and wire | | .73 | 10.959 | | 805 | 360 | | 1,165 | 1,475 |
| 1150 | 150 amp, with 14 branch breakers | | 1.03 | 7.767 | | 880 | 255 | | 1,135 | 1,375 |
| 1170 | With PVC conduit and wire | | .82 | 9.756 | | 1,025 | 320 | | 1,345 | 1,650 |
| 1180 | With RGS conduit and wire | | .67 | 11.940 | | 1,350 | 390 | | 1,740 | 2,150 |
| 1200 | 200 amp, with 18 branch breakers | 2 Elec | 1.80 | 8.889 | | 1,150 | 292 | | 1,442 | 1,750 |
| 1220 | With PVC conduit and wire | | 1.46 | 10.959 | | 1,300 | 360 | | 1,660 | 2,000 |
| 1230 | With RGS conduit and wire | ↓ | 1.24 | 12.903 | | 1,750 | 425 | | 2,175 | 2,625 |
| 1800 | Lightning surge suppressor for above services, add | 1 Elec | 32 | .250 | ↓ | 51.50 | 8.20 | | 59.70 | 70 |
| 2000 | Switch devices | | | | | | | | | |
| 2100 | Single pole, 15 amp, Ivory, with a 1-gang box, cover plate, | | | | | | | | | |
| 2110 | Type NM (Romex) cable | 1 Elec | 17.10 | .468 | Ea. | 10.05 | 15.35 | | 25.40 | 36 |
| 2120 | Type MC (BX) cable | | 14.30 | .559 | | 27.50 | 18.40 | | 45.90 | 60.50 |
| 2130 | EMT & wire | | 5.71 | 1.401 | | 32.50 | 46 | | 78.50 | 111 |
| 2150 | 3-way, #14/3, type NM cable | | 14.55 | .550 | | 14.05 | 18.05 | | 32.10 | 45 |
| 2170 | Type MC cable | | 12.31 | .650 | | 38 | 21.50 | | 59.50 | 76 |
| 2180 | EMT & wire | | 5 | 1.600 | | 36 | 52.50 | | 88.50 | 126 |
| 2200 | 4-way, #14/3, type NM cable | | 14.55 | .550 | | 30.50 | 18.05 | | 48.55 | 63 |
| 2220 | Type MC cable | | 12.31 | .650 | | 54 | 21.50 | | 75.50 | 94 |
| 2230 | EMT & wire | | 5 | 1.600 | | 52.50 | 52.50 | | 105 | 143 |
| 2250 | S.P., 20 amp, #12/2, type NM cable | | 13.33 | .600 | | 16.85 | 19.70 | | 36.55 | 50.50 |
| 2270 | Type MC cable | | 11.43 | .700 | | 32 | 23 | | 55 | 73 |
| 2280 | EMT & wire | | 4.85 | 1.649 | | 41 | 54 | | 95 | 133 |
| 2290 | S.P. rotary dimmer, 600W, no wiring | | 17 | .471 | | 20.50 | 15.45 | | 35.95 | 48 |
| 2300 | S.P. rotary dimmer, 600W, type NM cable | | 14.55 | .550 | | 25.50 | 18.05 | | 43.55 | 57.50 |
| 2320 | Type MC cable | | 12.31 | .650 | | 43 | 21.50 | | 64.50 | 81.50 |
| 2330 | EMT & wire | | 5 | 1.600 | | 49 | 52.50 | | 101.50 | 140 |
| 2350 | 3-way rotary dimmer, type NM cable | | 13.33 | .600 | | 32.50 | 19.70 | | 52.20 | 68 |
| 2370 | Type MC cable | | 11.43 | .700 | | 50 | 23 | | 73 | 92.50 |
| 2380 | EMT & wire | ↓ | 4.85 | 1.649 | ↓ | 56.50 | 54 | | 110.50 | 150 |
| 2400 | Interval timer wall switch, 20 amp, 1-30 min., #12/2 | | | | | | | | | |

| 26 05 90.10 Residential Wiring | Crew | Daily Output | Labor-Hours | Unit | Material | 2010 Bare Costs Labor | Equipment | Total | Total Incl O&P |
|---|---|---|---|---|---|---|---|---|---|
| 2410     Type NM cable | 1 Elec | 14.55 | .550 | Ea. | 50 | 18.05 | | 68.05 | 84.50 |
| 2420     Type MC cable | | 12.31 | .650 | | 58.50 | 21.50 | | 80 | 99 |
| 2430     EMT & wire | | 5 | 1.600 | | 74 | 52.50 | | 126.50 | 167 |
| 2500   Decorator style | | | | | | | | | |
| 2510     S.P., 15 amp, type NM cable | 1 Elec | 17.10 | .468 | Ea. | 14.90 | 15.35 | | 30.25 | 41.50 |
| 2520     Type MC cable | | 14.30 | .559 | | 32.50 | 18.40 | | 50.90 | 65.50 |
| 2530     EMT & wire | | 5.71 | 1.401 | | 37.50 | 46 | | 83.50 | 116 |
| 2550     3-way, #14/3, type NM cable | | 14.55 | .550 | | 18.95 | 18.05 | | 37 | 50.50 |
| 2570     Type MC cable | | 12.31 | .650 | | 43 | 21.50 | | 64.50 | 81.50 |
| 2580     EMT & wire | | 5 | 1.600 | | 41 | 52.50 | | 93.50 | 131 |
| 2600     4-way, #14/3, type NM cable | | 14.55 | .550 | | 35 | 18.05 | | 53.05 | 68 |
| 2620     Type MC cable | | 12.31 | .650 | | 59 | 21.50 | | 80.50 | 99.50 |
| 2630     EMT & wire | | 5 | 1.600 | | 57.50 | 52.50 | | 110 | 149 |
| 2650     S.P., 20 amp, #12/2, type NM cable | | 13.33 | .600 | | 21.50 | 19.70 | | 41.20 | 56 |
| 2670     Type MC cable | | 11.43 | .700 | | 37 | 23 | | 60 | 78.50 |
| 2680     EMT & wire | | 4.85 | 1.649 | | 45.50 | 54 | | 99.50 | 138 |
| 2700     S.P., slide dimmer, type NM cable | | 17.10 | .468 | | 33 | 15.35 | | 48.35 | 61.50 |
| 2720     Type MC cable | | 14.30 | .559 | | 50.50 | 18.40 | | 68.90 | 85.50 |
| 2730     EMT & wire | | 5.71 | 1.401 | | 57 | 46 | | 103 | 138 |
| 2750     S.P., touch dimmer, type NM cable | | 17.10 | .468 | | 27 | 15.35 | | 42.35 | 54.50 |
| 2770     Type MC cable | | 14.30 | .559 | | 44.50 | 18.40 | | 62.90 | 79 |
| 2780     EMT & wire | | 5.71 | 1.401 | | 51 | 46 | | 97 | 131 |
| 2800     3-way touch dimmer, type NM cable | | 13.33 | .600 | | 45.50 | 19.70 | | 65.20 | 82 |
| 2820     Type MC cable | | 11.43 | .700 | | 63 | 23 | | 86 | 107 |
| 2830     EMT & wire | | 4.85 | 1.649 | | 69.50 | 54 | | 123.50 | 164 |
| 3000   Combination devices | | | | | | | | | |
| 3100     S.P. switch/15 amp recpt., Ivory, 1-gang box, plate | | | | | | | | | |
| 3110     Type NM cable | 1 Elec | 11.43 | .700 | Ea. | 21.50 | 23 | | 44.50 | 61 |
| 3120     Type MC cable | | 10 | .800 | | 39 | 26.50 | | 65.50 | 86 |
| 3130     EMT & wire | | 4.40 | 1.818 | | 45.50 | 59.50 | | 105 | 147 |
| 3150     S.P. switch/pilot light, type NM cable | | 11.43 | .700 | | 22 | 23 | | 45 | 62 |
| 3170     Type MC cable | | 10 | .800 | | 39.50 | 26.50 | | 66 | 86.50 |
| 3180     EMT & wire | | 4.43 | 1.806 | | 46 | 59.50 | | 105.50 | 147 |
| 3190     2-S.P. switches, 2-#14/2, no wiring | | 14 | .571 | | 8.25 | 18.75 | | 27 | 39.50 |
| 3200     2-S.P. switches, 2-#14/2, type NM cables | | 10 | .800 | | 25 | 26.50 | | 51.50 | 70.50 |
| 3220     Type MC cable | | 8.89 | .900 | | 52 | 29.50 | | 81.50 | 106 |
| 3230     EMT & wire | | 4.10 | 1.951 | | 49 | 64 | | 113 | 158 |
| 3250     3-way switch/15 amp recpt., #14/3, type NM cable | | 10 | .800 | | 29 | 26.50 | | 55.50 | 75 |
| 3270     Type MC cable | | 8.89 | .900 | | 53 | 29.50 | | 82.50 | 107 |
| 3280     EMT & wire | | 4.10 | 1.951 | | 51 | 64 | | 115 | 161 |
| 3300     2-3 way switches, 2-#14/3, type NM cables | | 8.89 | .900 | | 38 | 29.50 | | 67.50 | 90 |
| 3320     Type MC cable | | 8 | 1 | | 78 | 33 | | 111 | 140 |
| 3330     EMT & wire | | 4 | 2 | | 58.50 | 65.50 | | 124 | 172 |
| 3350     S.P. switch/20 amp recpt., #12/2, type NM cable | | 10 | .800 | | 33.50 | 26.50 | | 60 | 80 |
| 3370     Type MC cable | | 8.89 | .900 | | 42.50 | 29.50 | | 72 | 94.50 |
| 3380     EMT & wire | | 4.10 | 1.951 | | 57.50 | 64 | | 121.50 | 168 |
| 3400   Decorator style | | | | | | | | | |
| 3410     S.P. switch/15 amp recpt., type NM cable | 1 Elec | 11.43 | .700 | Ea. | 26.50 | 23 | | 49.50 | 66.50 |
| 3420     Type MC cable | | 10 | .800 | | 44 | 26.50 | | 70.50 | 91 |
| 3430     EMT & wire | | 4.40 | 1.818 | | 50 | 59.50 | | 109.50 | 152 |
| 3450     S.P. switch/pilot light, type NM cable | | 11.43 | .700 | | 27 | 23 | | 50 | 67.50 |
| 3470     Type MC cable | | 10 | .800 | | 44.50 | 26.50 | | 71 | 92 |
| 3480     EMT & wire | | 4.40 | 1.818 | | 51 | 59.50 | | 110.50 | 153 |

## 26 05 90 – Residential Applications

| 26 05 90.10 Residential Wiring | Crew | Daily Output | Labor-Hours | Unit | Material | 2010 Bare Costs Labor | Equipment | Total | Total Incl O&P |
|---|---|---|---|---|---|---|---|---|---|
| 3500 | 2-S.P. switches, 2-#14/2, type NM cables | 1 Elec | 10 | .800 | Ea. | 30 | 26.50 | | 56.50 | 76 |
| 3520 | Type MC cable | | 8.89 | .900 | | 57 | 29.50 | | 86.50 | 111 |
| 3530 | EMT & wire | | 4.10 | 1.951 | | 54 | 64 | | 118 | 164 |
| 3550 | 3-way/15 amp recpt., #14/3, type NM cable | | 10 | .800 | | 34 | 26.50 | | 60.50 | 80.50 |
| 3570 | Type MC cable | | 8.89 | .900 | | 58 | 29.50 | | 87.50 | 112 |
| 3580 | EMT & wire | | 4.10 | 1.951 | | 56 | 64 | | 120 | 166 |
| 3650 | 2-3 way switches, 2-#14/3, type NM cables | | 8.89 | .900 | | 43 | 29.50 | | 72.50 | 95.50 |
| 3670 | Type MC cable | | 8 | 1 | | 83 | 33 | | 116 | 145 |
| 3680 | EMT & wire | | 4 | 2 | | 63.50 | 65.50 | | 129 | 177 |
| 3700 | S.P. switch/20 amp recpt., #12/2, type NM cable | | 10 | .800 | | 38.50 | 26.50 | | 65 | 85.50 |
| 3720 | Type MC cable | | 8.89 | .900 | | 47 | 29.50 | | 76.50 | 100 |
| 3730 | EMT & wire | ▼ | 4.10 | 1.951 | ▼ | 62.50 | 64 | | 126.50 | 173 |
| 4000 | Receptacle devices | | | | | | | | | |
| 4010 | Duplex outlet, 15 amp recpt., Ivory, 1-gang box, plate | | | | | | | | | |
| 4015 | Type NM cable | 1 Elec | 14.55 | .550 | Ea. | 8.55 | 18.05 | | 26.60 | 39 |
| 4020 | Type MC cable | | 12.31 | .650 | | 26 | 21.50 | | 47.50 | 63 |
| 4030 | EMT & wire | | 5.33 | 1.501 | | 31 | 49.50 | | 80.50 | 114 |
| 4050 | With #12/2, type NM cable | | 12.31 | .650 | | 10.80 | 21.50 | | 32.30 | 46.50 |
| 4070 | Type MC cable | | 10.67 | .750 | | 26 | 24.50 | | 50.50 | 69 |
| 4080 | EMT & wire | | 4.71 | 1.699 | | 34.50 | 56 | | 90.50 | 129 |
| 4100 | 20 amp recpt., #12/2, type NM cable | | 12.31 | .650 | | 19.85 | 21.50 | | 41.35 | 56.50 |
| 4120 | Type MC cable | | 10.67 | .750 | | 35 | 24.50 | | 59.50 | 79 |
| 4130 | EMT & wire | ▼ | 4.71 | 1.699 | ▼ | 44 | 56 | | 100 | 139 |
| 4140 | For GFI see Div. 26 05 90.10 line 4300 below | | | | | | | | | |
| 4150 | Decorator style, 15 amp recpt., type NM cable | 1 Elec | 14.55 | .550 | Ea. | 13.40 | 18.05 | | 31.45 | 44.50 |
| 4170 | Type MC cable | | 12.31 | .650 | | 31 | 21.50 | | 52.50 | 68.50 |
| 4180 | EMT & wire | | 5.33 | 1.501 | | 36 | 49.50 | | 85.50 | 120 |
| 4200 | With #12/2, type NM cable | | 12.31 | .650 | | 15.70 | 21.50 | | 37.20 | 52 |
| 4220 | Type MC cable | | 10.67 | .750 | | 31 | 24.50 | | 55.50 | 74 |
| 4230 | EMT & wire | | 4.71 | 1.699 | | 39.50 | 56 | | 95.50 | 135 |
| 4250 | 20 amp recpt. #12/2, type NM cable | | 12.31 | .650 | | 24.50 | 21.50 | | 46 | 61.50 |
| 4270 | Type MC cable | | 10.67 | .750 | | 40 | 24.50 | | 64.50 | 84 |
| 4280 | EMT & wire | | 4.71 | 1.699 | | 48.50 | 56 | | 104.50 | 145 |
| 4300 | GFI, 15 amp recpt., type NM cable | | 12.31 | .650 | | 43 | 21.50 | | 64.50 | 82 |
| 4320 | Type MC cable | | 10.67 | .750 | | 60.50 | 24.50 | | 85 | 107 |
| 4330 | EMT & wire | | 4.71 | 1.699 | | 65.50 | 56 | | 121.50 | 163 |
| 4350 | GFI with #12/2, type NM cable | | 10.67 | .750 | | 45.50 | 24.50 | | 70 | 90 |
| 4370 | Type MC cable | | 9.20 | .870 | | 61 | 28.50 | | 89.50 | 114 |
| 4380 | EMT & wire | | 4.21 | 1.900 | | 69.50 | 62.50 | | 132 | 178 |
| 4400 | 20 amp recpt., #12/2 type NM cable | | 10.67 | .750 | | 47.50 | 24.50 | | 72 | 92 |
| 4420 | Type MC cable | | 9.20 | .870 | | 63 | 28.50 | | 91.50 | 116 |
| 4430 | EMT & wire | | 4.21 | 1.900 | | 71.50 | 62.50 | | 134 | 181 |
| 4500 | Weather-proof cover for above receptacles, add | ▼ | 32 | .250 | ▼ | 5.25 | 8.20 | | 13.45 | 19.10 |
| 4550 | Air conditioner outlet, 20 amp-240 volt recpt. | | | | | | | | | |
| 4560 | 30' of #12/2, 2 pole circuit breaker | | | | | | | | | |
| 4570 | Type NM cable | 1 Elec | 10 | .800 | Ea. | 60.50 | 26.50 | | 87 | 110 |
| 4580 | Type MC cable | | 9 | .889 | | 79.50 | 29 | | 108.50 | 135 |
| 4590 | EMT & wire | | 4 | 2 | | 84.50 | 65.50 | | 150 | 200 |
| 4600 | Decorator style, type NM cable | | 10 | .800 | | 65 | 26.50 | | 91.50 | 115 |
| 4620 | Type MC cable | | 9 | .889 | | 84.50 | 29 | | 113.50 | 141 |
| 4630 | EMT & wire | ▼ | 4 | 2 | ▼ | 89 | 65.50 | | 154.50 | 205 |
| 4650 | Dryer outlet, 30 amp-240 volt recpt., 20' of #10/3 | | | | | | | | | |
| 4660 | 2 pole circuit breaker | | | | | | | | | |

| 26 05 90.10 Residential Wiring | | Crew | Daily Output | Labor-Hours | Unit | Material | 2010 Bare Costs Labor | Equipment | Total | Total Incl O&P |
|---|---|---|---|---|---|---|---|---|---|---|
| 4670 | Type NM cable | 1 Elec | 6.41 | 1.248 | Ea. | 66 | 41 | | 107 | 139 |
| 4680 | Type MC cable | | 5.71 | 1.401 | | 80 | 46 | | 126 | 163 |
| 4690 | EMT & wire | | 3.48 | 2.299 | | 81 | 75.50 | | 156.50 | 212 |
| 4700 | Range outlet, 50 amp-240 volt recpt., 30' of #8/3 | | | | | | | | | |
| 4710 | Type NM cable | 1 Elec | 4.21 | 1.900 | Ea. | 93 | 62.50 | | 155.50 | 204 |
| 4720 | Type MC cable | | 4 | 2 | | 163 | 65.50 | | 228.50 | 287 |
| 4730 | EMT & wire | | 2.96 | 2.703 | | 111 | 89 | | 200 | 266 |
| 4750 | Central vacuum outlet, Type NM cable | | 6.40 | 1.250 | | 62.50 | 41 | | 103.50 | 136 |
| 4770 | Type MC cable | | 5.71 | 1.401 | | 90 | 46 | | 136 | 174 |
| 4780 | EMT & wire | | 3.48 | 2.299 | | 88.50 | 75.50 | | 164 | 221 |
| 4800 | 30 amp-110 volt locking recpt., #10/2 circ. bkr. | | | | | | | | | |
| 4810 | Type NM cable | 1 Elec | 6.20 | 1.290 | Ea. | 72.50 | 42.50 | | 115 | 149 |
| 4820 | Type MC cable | | 5.40 | 1.481 | | 104 | 48.50 | | 152.50 | 194 |
| 4830 | EMT & wire | | 3.20 | 2.500 | | 99 | 82 | | 181 | 243 |
| 4900 | Low voltage outlets | | | | | | | | | |
| 4910 | Telephone recpt., 20' of 4/C phone wire | 1 Elec | 26 | .308 | Ea. | 10.35 | 10.10 | | 20.45 | 28 |
| 4920 | TV recpt., 20' of RG59U coax wire, F type connector | " | 16 | .500 | " | 19.30 | 16.45 | | 35.75 | 47.50 |
| 4950 | Door bell chime, transformer, 2 buttons, 60' of bellwire | | | | | | | | | |
| 4970 | Economy model | 1 Elec | 11.50 | .696 | Ea. | 75 | 23 | | 98 | 120 |
| 4980 | Custom model | | 11.50 | .696 | | 119 | 23 | | 142 | 168 |
| 4990 | Luxury model, 3 buttons | | 9.50 | .842 | | 320 | 27.50 | | 347.50 | 400 |
| 6000 | Lighting outlets | | | | | | | | | |
| 6050 | Wire only (for fixture), type NM cable | 1 Elec | 32 | .250 | Ea. | 6.45 | 8.20 | | 14.65 | 20.50 |
| 6070 | Type MC cable | | 24 | .333 | | 17.05 | 10.95 | | 28 | 36.50 |
| 6080 | EMT & wire | | 10 | .800 | | 20.50 | 26.50 | | 47 | 65.50 |
| 6100 | Box (4"), and wire (for fixture), type NM cable | | 25 | .320 | | 16.25 | 10.50 | | 26.75 | 35 |
| 6120 | Type MC cable | | 20 | .400 | | 27 | 13.15 | | 40.15 | 51 |
| 6130 | EMT & wire | | 11 | .727 | | 30.50 | 24 | | 54.50 | 72.50 |
| 6200 | Fixtures (use with lines 6050 or 6100 above) | | | | | | | | | |
| 6210 | Canopy style, economy grade | 1 Elec | 40 | .200 | Ea. | 34 | 6.55 | | 40.55 | 48 |
| 6220 | Custom grade | | 40 | .200 | | 52.50 | 6.55 | | 59.05 | 68.50 |
| 6250 | Dining room chandelier, economy grade | | 19 | .421 | | 85 | 13.85 | | 98.85 | 116 |
| 6260 | Custom grade | | 19 | .421 | | 250 | 13.85 | | 263.85 | 298 |
| 6270 | Luxury grade | | 15 | .533 | | 565 | 17.50 | | 582.50 | 650 |
| 6310 | Kitchen fixture (fluorescent), economy grade | | 30 | .267 | | 63.50 | 8.75 | | 72.25 | 84.50 |
| 6320 | Custom grade | | 25 | .320 | | 173 | 10.50 | | 183.50 | 207 |
| 6350 | Outdoor, wall mounted, economy grade | | 30 | .267 | | 32 | 8.75 | | 40.75 | 49.50 |
| 6360 | Custom grade | | 30 | .267 | | 111 | 8.75 | | 119.75 | 136 |
| 6370 | Luxury grade | | 25 | .320 | | 250 | 10.50 | | 260.50 | 292 |
| 6410 | Outdoor PAR floodlights, 1 lamp, 150 watt | | 20 | .400 | | 35 | 13.15 | | 48.15 | 60 |
| 6420 | 2 lamp, 150 watt each | | 20 | .400 | | 58 | 13.15 | | 71.15 | 85.50 |
| 6425 | Motion sensing, 2 lamp, 150 watt each | | 20 | .400 | | 70 | 13.15 | | 83.15 | 98.50 |
| 6430 | For infrared security sensor, add | | 32 | .250 | | 117 | 8.20 | | 125.20 | 142 |
| 6450 | Outdoor, quartz-halogen, 300 watt flood | | 20 | .400 | | 42 | 13.15 | | 55.15 | 68 |
| 6600 | Recessed downlight, round, pre-wired, 50 or 75 watt trim | | 30 | .267 | | 43.50 | 8.75 | | 52.25 | 62 |
| 6610 | With shower light trim | | 30 | .267 | | 53.50 | 8.75 | | 62.25 | 73.50 |
| 6620 | With wall washer trim | | 28 | .286 | | 64.50 | 9.40 | | 73.90 | 86.50 |
| 6630 | With eye-ball trim | | 28 | .286 | | 64.50 | 9.40 | | 73.90 | 86.50 |
| 6640 | For direct contact with insulation, add | | | | | 2.20 | | | 2.20 | 2.42 |
| 6700 | Porcelain lamp holder | 1 Elec | 40 | .200 | | 4.20 | 6.55 | | 10.75 | 15.30 |
| 6710 | With pull switch | | 40 | .200 | | 5.05 | 6.55 | | 11.60 | 16.25 |
| 6750 | Fluorescent strip, 1-20 watt tube, wrap around diffuser, 24" | | 24 | .333 | | 54 | 10.95 | | 64.95 | 77.50 |
| 6760 | 1-34 watt tube, 48" | | 24 | .333 | | 69.50 | 10.95 | | 80.45 | 94.50 |

563

# 26 05 Common Work Results for Electrical

## 26 05 90 – Residential Applications

| | | | Daily | Labor- | | | 2010 Bare Costs | | | | Total |
|---|---|---|---|---|---|---|---|---|---|---|---|
| **26 05 90.10 Residential Wiring** | | Crew | Output | Hours | Unit | Material | Labor | Equipment | Total | | Incl O&P |
| 6770 | 2-34 watt tubes, 48" | 1 Elec | 20 | .400 | Ea. | 82.50 | 13.15 | | 95.65 | | 113 |
| 6780 | With residential ballast | | 20 | .400 | | 92.50 | 13.15 | | 105.65 | | 124 |
| 6800 | Bathroom heat lamp, 1-250 watt | | 28 | .286 | | 46 | 9.40 | | 55.40 | | 66 |
| 6810 | 2-250 watt lamps | | 28 | .286 | | 71.50 | 9.40 | | 80.90 | | 94 |
| 6820 | For timer switch, see Div. 26 05 90.10 line 2400 | | | | | | | | | | |
| 6900 | Outdoor post lamp, incl. post, fixture, 35' of #14/2 | | | | | | | | | | |
| 6910 | Type NMC cable | 1 Elec | 3.50 | 2.286 | Ea. | 202 | 75 | | 277 | | 345 |
| 6920 | Photo-eye, add | | 27 | .296 | | 35 | 9.75 | | 44.75 | | 54.50 |
| 6950 | Clock dial time switch, 24 hr., w/enclosure, type NM cable | | 11.43 | .700 | | 61 | 23 | | 84 | | 105 |
| 6970 | Type MC cable | | 11 | .727 | | 78.50 | 24 | | 102.50 | | 126 |
| 6980 | EMT & wire | | 4.85 | 1.649 | | 83.50 | 54 | | 137.50 | | 180 |
| 7000 | Alarm systems | | | | | | | | | | |
| 7050 | Smoke detectors, box, #14/3, type NM cable | 1 Elec | 14.55 | .550 | Ea. | 34 | 18.05 | | 52.05 | | 67 |
| 7070 | Type MC cable | | 12.31 | .650 | | 51.50 | 21.50 | | 73 | | 91 |
| 7080 | EMT & wire | | 5 | 1.600 | | 49.50 | 52.50 | | 102 | | 140 |
| 7090 | For relay output to security system, add | | | | | 13 | | | 13 | | 14.30 |
| 8000 | Residential equipment | | | | | | | | | | |
| 8050 | Disposal hook-up, incl. switch, outlet box, 3' of flex | | | | | | | | | | |
| 8060 | 20 amp-1 pole circ. bkr., and 25' of #12/2 | | | | | | | | | | |
| 8070 | Type NM cable | 1 Elec | 10 | .800 | Ea. | 30.50 | 26.50 | | 57 | | 76.50 |
| 8080 | Type MC cable | | 8 | 1 | | 48 | 33 | | 81 | | 106 |
| 8090 | EMT & wire | | 5 | 1.600 | | 56.50 | 52.50 | | 109 | | 148 |
| 8100 | Trash compactor or dishwasher hook-up, incl. outlet box, | | | | | | | | | | |
| 8110 | 3' of flex, 15 amp-1 pole circ. bkr., and 25' of #14/2 | | | | | | | | | | |
| 8130 | Type MC cable | 1 Elec | 8 | 1 | Ea. | 43 | 33 | | 76 | | 101 |
| 8140 | EMT & wire | " | 5 | 1.600 | " | 49 | 52.50 | | 101.50 | | 139 |
| 8150 | Hot water sink dispensor hook-up, use line 8100 | | | | | | | | | | |
| 8200 | Vent/exhaust fan hook-up, type NM cable | 1 Elec | 32 | .250 | Ea. | 6.45 | 8.20 | | 14.65 | | 20.50 |
| 8220 | Type MC cable | | 24 | .333 | | 17.05 | 10.95 | | 28 | | 36.50 |
| 8230 | EMT & wire | | 10 | .800 | | 20.50 | 26.50 | | 47 | | 65.50 |
| 8250 | Bathroom vent fan, 50 CFM (use with above hook-up) | | | | | | | | | | |
| 8260 | Economy model | 1 Elec | 15 | .533 | Ea. | 25 | 17.50 | | 42.50 | | 56 |
| 8270 | Low noise model | | 15 | .533 | | 32 | 17.50 | | 49.50 | | 63.50 |
| 8280 | Custom model | | 12 | .667 | | 117 | 22 | | 139 | | 165 |
| 8300 | Bathroom or kitchen vent fan, 110 CFM | | | | | | | | | | |
| 8310 | Economy model | 1 Elec | 15 | .533 | Ea. | 69.50 | 17.50 | | 87 | | 105 |
| 8320 | Low noise model | " | 15 | .533 | " | 86 | 17.50 | | 103.50 | | 123 |
| 8350 | Paddle fan, variable speed (w/o lights) | | | | | | | | | | |
| 8360 | Economy model (AC motor) | 1 Elec | 10 | .800 | Ea. | 106 | 26.50 | | 132.50 | | 160 |
| 8370 | Custom model (AC motor) | | 10 | .800 | | 182 | 26.50 | | 208.50 | | 243 |
| 8380 | Luxury model (DC motor) | | 8 | 1 | | 360 | 33 | | 393 | | 450 |
| 8390 | Remote speed switch for above, add | | 12 | .667 | | 30 | 22 | | 52 | | 68.50 |
| 8500 | Whole house exhaust fan, ceiling mount, 36", variable speed | | | | | | | | | | |
| 8510 | Remote switch, incl. shutters, 20 amp-1 pole circ. bkr. | | | | | | | | | | |
| 8520 | 30' of #12/2, type NM cable | 1 Elec | 4 | 2 | Ea. | 1,025 | 65.50 | | 1,090.50 | | 1,225 |
| 8530 | Type MC cable | | 3.50 | 2.286 | | 1,050 | 75 | | 1,125 | | 1,275 |
| 8540 | EMT & wire | | 3 | 2.667 | | 1,050 | 87.50 | | 1,137.50 | | 1,325 |
| 8600 | Whirlpool tub hook-up, incl. timer switch, outlet box | | | | | | | | | | |
| 8610 | 3' of flex, 20 amp-1 pole GFI circ. bkr. | | | | | | | | | | |
| 8620 | 30' of #12/2, type NM cable | 1 Elec | 5 | 1.600 | Ea. | 124 | 52.50 | | 176.50 | | 222 |
| 8630 | Type MC cable | | 4.20 | 1.905 | | 136 | 62.50 | | 198.50 | | 251 |
| 8640 | EMT & wire | | 3.40 | 2.353 | | 144 | 77.50 | | 221.50 | | 285 |
| 8650 | Hot water heater hook-up, incl. 1-2 pole circ. bkr., box; | | | | | | | | | | |

# 26 05 Common Work Results for Electrical

## 26 05 90 – Residential Applications

| 26 05 90.10 Residential Wiring | Crew | Daily Output | Labor-Hours | Unit | Material | 2010 Bare Costs Labor | Equipment | Total | Total Incl O&P |
|---|---|---|---|---|---|---|---|---|---|
| 8660 | 3' of flex, 20' of #10/2, type NM cable | 1 Elec | 5 | 1.600 | Ea. | 32 | 52.50 | | 84.50 | 121 |
| 8670 | Type MC cable | | 4.20 | 1.905 | | 55.50 | 62.50 | | 118 | 163 |
| 8680 | EMT & wire | ▼ | 3.40 | 2.353 | ▼ | 52 | 77.50 | | 129.50 | 184 |
| 9000 | Heating/air conditioning | | | | | | | | | |
| 9050 | Furnace/boiler hook-up, incl. firestat, local on-off switch | | | | | | | | | |
| 9060 | Emergency switch, and 40' of type NM cable | 1 Elec | 4 | 2 | Ea. | 54.50 | 65.50 | | 120 | 167 |
| 9070 | Type MC cable | | 3.50 | 2.286 | | 81.50 | 75 | | 156.50 | 212 |
| 9080 | EMT & wire | ▼ | 1.50 | 5.333 | ▼ | 89.50 | 175 | | 264.50 | 385 |
| 9100 | Air conditioner hook-up, incl. local 60 amp disc. switch | | | | | | | | | |
| 9110 | 3' sealtite, 40 amp, 2 pole circuit breaker | | | | | | | | | |
| 9130 | 40' of #8/2, type NM cable | 1 Elec | 3.50 | 2.286 | Ea. | 216 | 75 | | 291 | 360 |
| 9140 | Type MC cable | | 3 | 2.667 | | 315 | 87.50 | | 402.50 | 490 |
| 9150 | EMT & wire | ▼ | 1.30 | 6.154 | ▼ | 252 | 202 | | 454 | 610 |
| 9200 | Heat pump hook-up, 1-40 & 1-100 amp 2 pole circ. bkr. | | | | | | | | | |
| 9210 | Local disconnect switch, 3' sealtite | | | | | | | | | |
| 9220 | 40' of #8/2 & 30' of #3/2 | | | | | | | | | |
| 9230 | Type NM cable | 1 Elec | 1.30 | 6.154 | Ea. | 545 | 202 | | 747 | 930 |
| 9240 | Type MC cable | | 1.08 | 7.407 | | 745 | 243 | | 988 | 1,225 |
| 9250 | EMT & wire | ▼ | .94 | 8.511 | ▼ | 615 | 280 | | 895 | 1,125 |
| 9500 | Thermostat hook-up, using low voltage wire | | | | | | | | | |
| 9520 | Heating only, 25' of #18-3 | 1 Elec | 24 | .333 | Ea. | 9.85 | 10.95 | | 20.80 | 28.50 |
| 9530 | Heating/cooling, 25' of #18-4 | " | 20 | .400 | " | 12.30 | 13.15 | | 25.45 | 35 |

# 26 24 Switchboards and Panelboards

## 26 24 16 – Panelboards

### 26 24 16.10 Load Centers

| | | Crew | Daily Output | Labor-Hours | Unit | Material | 2010 Bare Costs Labor | Equipment | Total | Total Incl O&P |
|---|---|---|---|---|---|---|---|---|---|---|
| 0010 | **LOAD CENTERS** (residential type) | | | | | | | | | |
| 0100 | 3 wire, 120/240V, 1 phase, including 1 pole plug-in breakers | | | | | | | | | |
| 0200 | 100 amp main lugs, indoor, 8 circuits | 1 Elec | 1.40 | 5.714 | Ea. | 180 | 188 | | 368 | 505 |
| 0300 | 12 circuits | | 1.20 | 6.667 | | 252 | 219 | | 471 | 630 |
| 0400 | Rainproof, 8 circuits | | 1.40 | 5.714 | | 216 | 188 | | 404 | 545 |
| 0500 | 12 circuits | ▼ | 1.20 | 6.667 | | 305 | 219 | | 524 | 690 |
| 0600 | 200 amp main lugs, indoor, 16 circuits | R-1A | 1.80 | 8.889 | | 350 | 243 | | 593 | 785 |
| 0700 | 20 circuits | | 1.50 | 10.667 | | 435 | 291 | | 726 | 960 |
| 0800 | 24 circuits | | 1.30 | 12.308 | | 575 | 335 | | 910 | 1,175 |
| 1200 | Rainproof, 16 circuits | | 1.80 | 8.889 | | 415 | 243 | | 658 | 855 |
| 1300 | 20 circuits | | 1.50 | 10.667 | | 495 | 291 | | 786 | 1,025 |
| 1400 | 24 circuits | ▼ | 1.30 | 12.308 | ▼ | 745 | 335 | | 1,080 | 1,375 |

# 26 27 Low-Voltage Distribution Equipment

## 26 27 13 – Electricity Metering

### 26 27 13.10 Meter Centers and Sockets

| | | Crew | Daily Output | Labor-Hours | Unit | Material | 2010 Bare Costs Labor | Equipment | Total | Total Incl O&P |
|---|---|---|---|---|---|---|---|---|---|---|
| 0010 | **METER CENTERS AND SOCKETS** | | | | | | | | | |
| 0100 | Sockets, single position, 4 terminal, 100 amp | 1 Elec | 3.20 | 2.500 | Ea. | 44 | 82 | | 126 | 183 |
| 0200 | 150 amp | | 2.30 | 3.478 | | 51 | 114 | | 165 | 243 |
| 0300 | 200 amp | | 1.90 | 4.211 | | 74 | 138 | | 212 | 305 |
| 0500 | Double position, 4 terminal, 100 amp | | 2.80 | 2.857 | | 180 | 94 | | 274 | 350 |
| 0600 | 150 amp | | 2.10 | 3.810 | | 212 | 125 | | 337 | 435 |
| 0700 | 200 amp | ▼ | 1.70 | 4.706 | ▼ | 435 | 155 | | 590 | 730 |

565

# 26 27 Low-Voltage Distribution Equipment

## 26 27 13 – Electricity Metering

| 26 27 13.10 Meter Centers and Sockets | Crew | Daily Output | Labor-Hours | Unit | Material | 2010 Bare Costs Labor | Equipment | Total | Total Incl O&P |
|---|---|---|---|---|---|---|---|---|---|
| 2590 | Basic meter device | | | | | | | | | |
| 2600 | 1P 3W 120/240V 4 jaw 125A sockets, 3 meter | 2 Elec | 1 | 16 | Ea. | 665 | 525 | | 1,190 | 1,575 |
| 2620 | 5 meter | | .80 | 20 | | 995 | 655 | | 1,650 | 2,175 |
| 2640 | 7 meter | | .56 | 28.571 | | 1,450 | 940 | | 2,390 | 3,125 |
| 2660 | 10 meter | | .48 | 33.333 | | 2,000 | 1,100 | | 3,100 | 3,975 |
| 2680 | Rainproof 1P 3W 120/240V 4 jaw 125A sockets | | | | | | | | | |
| 2690 | 3 meter | 2 Elec | 1 | 16 | Ea. | 665 | 525 | | 1,190 | 1,575 |
| 2710 | 6 meter | | .60 | 26.667 | | 1,150 | 875 | | 2,025 | 2,675 |
| 2730 | 8 meter | | .52 | 30.769 | | 1,600 | 1,000 | | 2,600 | 3,400 |
| 2750 | 1P 3W 120/240V 4 jaw sockets | | | | | | | | | |
| 2760 | with 125A circuit breaker, 3 meter | 2 Elec | 1 | 16 | Ea. | 1,250 | 525 | | 1,775 | 2,225 |
| 2780 | 5 meter | | .80 | 20 | | 1,950 | 655 | | 2,605 | 3,225 |
| 2800 | 7 meter | | .56 | 28.571 | | 2,800 | 940 | | 3,740 | 4,625 |
| 2820 | 10 meter | | .48 | 33.333 | | 3,925 | 1,100 | | 5,025 | 6,100 |
| 2830 | Rainproof 1P 3W 120/240V 4 jaw sockets | | | | | | | | | |
| 2840 | with 125A circuit breaker, 3 meter | 2 Elec | 1 | 16 | Ea. | 1,250 | 525 | | 1,775 | 2,225 |
| 2870 | 6 meter | | .60 | 26.667 | | 2,300 | 875 | | 3,175 | 3,950 |
| 2890 | 8 meter | | .52 | 30.769 | | 3,125 | 1,000 | | 4,125 | 5,100 |
| 3250 | 1P 3W 120/240V 4 jaw sockets | | | | | | | | | |
| 3260 | with 200A circuit breaker, 3 meter | 2 Elec | 1 | 16 | Ea. | 1,875 | 525 | | 2,400 | 2,900 |
| 3290 | 6 meter | | .60 | 26.667 | | 3,725 | 875 | | 4,600 | 5,525 |
| 3310 | 8 meter | | .56 | 28.571 | | 5,050 | 940 | | 5,990 | 7,075 |
| 3330 | Rainproof 1P 3W 120/240V 4 jaw sockets | | | | | | | | | |
| 3350 | with 200A circuit breaker, 3 meter | 2 Elec | 1 | 16 | Ea. | 1,875 | 525 | | 2,400 | 2,900 |
| 3380 | 6 meter | | .60 | 26.667 | | 3,725 | 875 | | 4,600 | 5,525 |
| 3400 | 8 meter | | .52 | 30.769 | | 5,050 | 1,000 | | 6,050 | 7,200 |

## 26 27 23 – Indoor Service Poles

### 26 27 23.40 Surface Raceway

| | | Crew | Daily Output | Labor-Hours | Unit | Material | 2010 Bare Costs Labor | Equipment | Total | Total Incl O&P |
|---|---|---|---|---|---|---|---|---|---|---|
| 0010 | **SURFACE RACEWAY** | | | | | | | | | |
| 0100 | No. 500 | 1 Elec | 100 | .080 | L.F. | 1.03 | 2.63 | | 3.66 | 5.40 |
| 0110 | No. 700 | | 100 | .080 | | 1.16 | 2.63 | | 3.79 | 5.55 |
| 0200 | No. 1000 | | 90 | .089 | | 1.96 | 2.92 | | 4.88 | 6.90 |
| 0400 | No. 1500, small pancake | | 90 | .089 | | 2.10 | 2.92 | | 5.02 | 7.05 |
| 0600 | No. 2000, base & cover, blank | | 90 | .089 | | 2.15 | 2.92 | | 5.07 | 7.10 |
| 0800 | No. 3000, base & cover, blank | | 75 | .107 | | 4.10 | 3.50 | | 7.60 | 10.20 |
| 2400 | Fittings, elbows, No. 500 | | 40 | .200 | Ea. | 1.85 | 6.55 | | 8.40 | 12.75 |
| 2800 | Elbow cover, No. 2000 | | 40 | .200 | | 3.50 | 6.55 | | 10.05 | 14.55 |
| 2880 | Tee, No. 500 | | 42 | .190 | | 3.60 | 6.25 | | 9.85 | 14.15 |
| 2900 | No. 2000 | | 27 | .296 | | 11.70 | 9.75 | | 21.45 | 28.50 |
| 3000 | Switch box, No. 500 | | 16 | .500 | | 12.40 | 16.45 | | 28.85 | 40 |
| 3400 | Telephone outlet, No. 1500 | | 16 | .500 | | 14.50 | 16.45 | | 30.95 | 42.50 |
| 3600 | Junction box, No. 1500 | | 16 | .500 | | 9.90 | 16.45 | | 26.35 | 37.50 |
| 3800 | Plugmold wired sections, No. 2000 | | | | | | | | | |
| 4000 | 1 circuit, 6 outlets, 3 ft. long | 1 Elec | 8 | 1 | Ea. | 36 | 33 | | 69 | 93 |
| 4100 | 2 circuits, 8 outlets, 6 ft. long | " | 5.30 | 1.509 | " | 59.50 | 49.50 | | 109 | 146 |

## 26 27 26 – Wiring Devices

### 26 27 26.10 Low Voltage Switching

| | | Crew | Daily Output | Labor-Hours | Unit | Material | 2010 Bare Costs Labor | Equipment | Total | Total Incl O&P |
|---|---|---|---|---|---|---|---|---|---|---|
| 0010 | **LOW VOLTAGE SWITCHING** | | | | | | | | | |
| 3600 | Relays, 120 V or 277 V standard | 1 Elec | 12 | .667 | Ea. | 37.50 | 22 | | 59.50 | 76.50 |
| 3800 | Flush switch, standard | | 40 | .200 | | 11.30 | 6.55 | | 17.85 | 23 |
| 4000 | Interchangeable | | 40 | .200 | | 14.75 | 6.55 | | 21.30 | 27 |
| 4100 | Surface switch, standard | | 40 | .200 | | 8 | 6.55 | | 14.55 | 19.50 |

# 26 27 Low-Voltage Distribution Equipment

## 26 27 26 – Wiring Devices

### 26 27 26.10 Low Voltage Switching

| | | Crew | Daily Output | Labor-Hours | Unit | Material | 2010 Bare Costs Labor | Equipment | Total | Total Incl O&P |
|---|---|---|---|---|---|---|---|---|---|---|
| 4200 | Transformer 115 V to 25 V | 1 Elec | 12 | .667 | Ea. | 128 | 22 | | 150 | 177 |
| 4400 | Master control, 12 circuit, manual | | 4 | 2 | | 118 | 65.50 | | 183.50 | 237 |
| 4500 | 25 circuit, motorized | | 4 | 2 | | 131 | 65.50 | | 196.50 | 251 |
| 4600 | Rectifier, silicon | | 12 | .667 | | 38.50 | 22 | | 60.50 | 77.50 |
| 4800 | Switchplates, 1 gang, 1, 2 or 3 switch, plastic | | 80 | .100 | | 3.60 | 3.29 | | 6.89 | 9.30 |
| 5000 | Stainless steel | | 80 | .100 | | 9.65 | 3.29 | | 12.94 | 15.95 |
| 5400 | 2 gang, 3 switch, stainless steel | | 53 | .151 | | 18.60 | 4.96 | | 23.56 | 28.50 |
| 5500 | 4 switch, plastic | | 53 | .151 | | 8 | 4.96 | | 12.96 | 16.85 |
| 5600 | 2 gang, 4 switch, stainless steel | | 53 | .151 | | 19.45 | 4.96 | | 24.41 | 29.50 |
| 5700 | 6 switch, stainless steel | | 53 | .151 | | 43 | 4.96 | | 47.96 | 55.50 |
| 5800 | 3 gang, 9 switch, stainless steel | | 32 | .250 | | 59.50 | 8.20 | | 67.70 | 79 |

### 26 27 26.20 Wiring Devices Elements

| | | Crew | Daily Output | Labor-Hours | Unit | Material | 2010 Bare Costs Labor | Equipment | Total | Total Incl O&P |
|---|---|---|---|---|---|---|---|---|---|---|
| 0010 | **WIRING DEVICES ELEMENTS** | | | | | | | | | |
| 0200 | Toggle switch, quiet type, single pole, 15 amp | 1 Elec | 40 | .200 | Ea. | 5.30 | 6.55 | | 11.85 | 16.55 |
| 0600 | 3 way, 15 amp | | 23 | .348 | | 7.65 | 11.45 | | 19.10 | 27 |
| 0900 | 4 way, 15 amp | | 15 | .533 | | 25 | 17.50 | | 42.50 | 56 |
| 1650 | Dimmer switch, 120 volt, incandescent, 600 watt, 1 pole  G | | 16 | .500 | | 13.25 | 16.45 | | 29.70 | 41 |
| 2460 | Receptacle, duplex, 120 volt, grounded, 15 amp | | 40 | .200 | | 1.37 | 6.55 | | 7.92 | 12.20 |
| 2470 | 20 amp | | 27 | .296 | | 10.40 | 9.75 | | 20.15 | 27.50 |
| 2490 | Dryer, 30 amp | | 15 | .533 | | 6.25 | 17.50 | | 23.75 | 35.50 |
| 2500 | Range, 50 amp | | 11 | .727 | | 14.60 | 24 | | 38.60 | 55 |
| 2600 | Wall plates, stainless steel, 1 gang | | 80 | .100 | | 2.50 | 3.29 | | 5.79 | 8.10 |
| 2800 | 2 gang | | 53 | .151 | | 4.25 | 4.96 | | 9.21 | 12.75 |
| 3200 | Lampholder, keyless | | 26 | .308 | | 12.80 | 10.10 | | 22.90 | 30.50 |
| 3400 | Pullchain with receptacle | | 22 | .364 | | 13.60 | 11.95 | | 25.55 | 34.50 |

## 26 27 73 – Door Chimes

### 26 27 73.10 Doorbell System

| | | Crew | Daily Output | Labor-Hours | Unit | Material | 2010 Bare Costs Labor | Equipment | Total | Total Incl O&P |
|---|---|---|---|---|---|---|---|---|---|---|
| 0010 | **DOORBELL SYSTEM**, incl. transformer, button & signal | | | | | | | | | |
| 1000 | Door chimes, 2 notes, minimum | 1 Elec | 16 | .500 | Ea. | 30 | 16.45 | | 46.45 | 59.50 |
| 1020 | Maximum | | 12 | .667 | | 158 | 22 | | 180 | 210 |
| 1100 | Tube type, 3 tube system | | 12 | .667 | | 234 | 22 | | 256 | 293 |
| 1180 | 4 tube system | | 10 | .800 | | 375 | 26.50 | | 401.50 | 455 |
| 1900 | For transformer & button, minimum add | | 5 | 1.600 | | 17 | 52.50 | | 69.50 | 104 |
| 1960 | Maximum, add | | 4.50 | 1.778 | | 51 | 58.50 | | 109.50 | 151 |
| 3000 | For push button only, minimum | | 24 | .333 | | 3.44 | 10.95 | | 14.39 | 21.50 |
| 3100 | Maximum | | 20 | .400 | | 27 | 13.15 | | 40.15 | 51 |

# 26 28 Low-Voltage Circuit Protective Devices

## 26 28 16 – Enclosed Switches and Circuit Breakers

### 26 28 16.10 Circuit Breakers

| | | Crew | Daily Output | Labor-Hours | Unit | Material | 2010 Bare Costs Labor | Equipment | Total | Total Incl O&P |
|---|---|---|---|---|---|---|---|---|---|---|
| 0010 | **CIRCUIT BREAKERS** (in enclosure) | | | | | | | | | |
| 0100 | Enclosed (NEMA 1), 600 volt, 3 pole, 30 amp | 1 Elec | 3.20 | 2.500 | Ea. | 630 | 82 | | 712 | 830 |
| 0200 | 60 amp | | 2.80 | 2.857 | | 630 | 94 | | 724 | 850 |
| 0400 | 100 amp | | 2.30 | 3.478 | | 720 | 114 | | 834 | 980 |

### 26 28 16.20 Safety Switches

| | | Crew | Daily Output | Labor-Hours | Unit | Material | 2010 Bare Costs Labor | Equipment | Total | Total Incl O&P |
|---|---|---|---|---|---|---|---|---|---|---|
| 0010 | **SAFETY SWITCHES** | | | | | | | | | |
| 0100 | General duty 240 volt, 3 pole NEMA 1, fusible, 30 amp | 1 Elec | 3.20 | 2.500 | Ea. | 113 | 82 | | 195 | 259 |
| 0200 | 60 amp | | 2.30 | 3.478 | | 192 | 114 | | 306 | 395 |
| 0300 | 100 amp | | 1.90 | 4.211 | | 330 | 138 | | 468 | 585 |
| 0400 | 200 amp | | 1.30 | 6.154 | | 710 | 202 | | 912 | 1,100 |

# 26 28 Low-Voltage Circuit Protective Devices

## 26 28 16 – Enclosed Switches and Circuit Breakers

### 26 28 16.20 Safety Switches

| | | Crew | Daily Output | Labor-Hours | Unit | Material | 2010 Bare Costs Labor | Equipment | Total | Total Incl O&P |
|---|---|---|---|---|---|---|---|---|---|---|
| 0500 | 400 amp | 2 Elec | 1.80 | 8.889 | Ea. | 1,775 | 292 | | 2,067 | 2,450 |
| 9010 | Disc. switch, 600V 3 pole fusible, 30 amp, to 10 HP motor | 1 Elec | 3.20 | 2.500 | | 330 | 82 | | 412 | 500 |
| 9050 | 60 amp, to 30 HP motor | | 2.30 | 3.478 | | 760 | 114 | | 874 | 1,025 |
| 9070 | 100 amp, to 60 HP motor | | 1.90 | 4.211 | | 760 | 138 | | 898 | 1,050 |

### 26 28 16.40 Time Switches

| | | Crew | Daily Output | Labor-Hours | Unit | Material | 2010 Bare Costs Labor | Equipment | Total | Total Incl O&P |
|---|---|---|---|---|---|---|---|---|---|---|
| 0010 | **TIME SWITCHES** | | | | | | | | | |
| 0100 | Single pole, single throw, 24 hour dial | 1 Elec | 4 | 2 | Ea. | 107 | 65.50 | | 172.50 | 225 |
| 0200 | 24 hour dial with reserve power | | 3.60 | 2.222 | | 460 | 73 | | 533 | 625 |
| 0300 | Astronomic dial | | 3.60 | 2.222 | | 184 | 73 | | 257 | 320 |
| 0400 | Astronomic dial with reserve power | | 3.30 | 2.424 | | 595 | 79.50 | | 674.50 | 785 |
| 0500 | 7 day calendar dial | | 3.30 | 2.424 | | 146 | 79.50 | | 225.50 | 291 |
| 0600 | 7 day calendar dial with reserve power | | 3.20 | 2.500 | | 655 | 82 | | 737 | 855 |
| 0700 | Photo cell 2000 watt | | 8 | 1 | | 19 | 33 | | 52 | 74.50 |

# 26 32 Packaged Generator Assemblies

## 26 32 13 – Engine Generators

### 26 32 13.16 Gas-Engine-Driven Generator Sets

| | | Crew | Daily Output | Labor-Hours | Unit | Material | 2010 Bare Costs Labor | Equipment | Total | Total Incl O&P |
|---|---|---|---|---|---|---|---|---|---|---|
| 0010 | **GAS-ENGINE-DRIVEN GENERATOR SETS** | | | | | | | | | |
| 0020 | Gas or gasoline operated, includes battery, | | | | | | | | | |
| 0050 | charger, muffler & transfer switch | | | | | | | | | |
| 0200 | 3 phase 4 wire, 277/480 volt, 7.5 kW | R-3 | .83 | 24.096 | Ea. | 7,925 | 785 | 167 | 8,877 | 10,200 |
| 0300 | 11.5 kW | | .71 | 28.169 | | 11,200 | 920 | 195 | 12,315 | 14,100 |
| 0400 | 20 kW | | .63 | 31.746 | | 13,200 | 1,025 | 219 | 14,444 | 16,500 |
| 0500 | 35 kW | | .55 | 36.364 | | 15,800 | 1,175 | 251 | 17,226 | 19,500 |

# 26 36 Transfer Switches

## 26 36 23 – Automatic Transfer Switches

### 26 36 23.10 Automatic Transfer Switch Devices

| | | Crew | Daily Output | Labor-Hours | Unit | Material | 2010 Bare Costs Labor | Equipment | Total | Total Incl O&P |
|---|---|---|---|---|---|---|---|---|---|---|
| 0010 | **AUTOMATIC TRANSFER SWITCH DEVICES** | | | | | | | | | |
| 0100 | Switches, enclosed 480 volt, 3 pole, 30 amp | 1 Elec | 2.30 | 3.478 | Ea. | 3,050 | 114 | | 3,164 | 3,525 |
| 0200 | 60 amp | " | 1.90 | 4.211 | " | 3,050 | 138 | | 3,188 | 3,575 |

# 26 41 Facility Lightning Protection

## 26 41 13 – Lightning Protection for Structures

### 26 41 13.13 Lightning Protection for Buildings

| | | Crew | Daily Output | Labor-Hours | Unit | Material | 2010 Bare Costs Labor | Equipment | Total | Total Incl O&P |
|---|---|---|---|---|---|---|---|---|---|---|
| 0010 | **LIGHTNING PROTECTION FOR BUILDINGS** | | | | | | | | | |
| 0200 | Air terminals & base, copper | | | | | | | | | |
| 0400 | 3/8" diameter x 10" (to 75' high) | 1 Elec | 8 | 1 | Ea. | 21 | 33 | | 54 | 77 |
| 1000 | Aluminum, 1/2" diameter x 12" (to 75' high) | | 8 | 1 | | 14.05 | 33 | | 47.05 | 69 |
| 1020 | 1/2" diameter x 24" | | 7.30 | 1.096 | | 16.70 | 36 | | 52.70 | 77 |
| 1040 | 1/2" diameter x 60" | | 6.70 | 1.194 | | 25.50 | 39 | | 64.50 | 92.50 |
| 2000 | Cable, copper, 220 lb. per thousand ft. (to 75' high) | | 320 | .025 | L.F. | 3.05 | .82 | | 3.87 | 4.70 |
| 2500 | Aluminum, 101 lb. per thousand ft. (to 75' high) | | 280 | .029 | " | .85 | .94 | | 1.79 | 2.47 |
| 3000 | Arrester, 175 volt AC to ground | | 8 | 1 | Ea. | 78.50 | 33 | | 111.50 | 140 |

# 26 51 Interior Lighting

## 26 51 13 – Interior Lighting Fixtures, Lamps, and Ballasts

| 26 51 13.50 Interior Lighting Fixtures | | Crew | Daily Output | Labor-Hours | Unit | Material | 2010 Bare Costs Labor | Equipment | Total | Total Incl O&P |
|---|---|---|---|---|---|---|---|---|---|---|
| 0010 | **INTERIOR LIGHTING FIXTURES** Including lamps, mounting | | | | | | | | | |
| 0030 | hardware and connections | | | | | | | | | |
| 0100 | Fluorescent, C.W. lamps, troffer, recess mounted in grid, RS | | | | | | | | | |
| 0130 | Grid ceiling mount | | | | | | | | | |
| 0200 | Acrylic lens, 1'W x 4'L, two 40 watt | 1 Elec | 5.70 | 1.404 | Ea. | 53.50 | 46 | | 99.50 | 134 |
| 0300 | 2'W x 2'L, two U40 watt | | 5.70 | 1.404 | | 57 | 46 | | 103 | 138 |
| 0600 | 2'W x 4'L, four 40 watt | | 4.70 | 1.702 | | 65.50 | 56 | | 121.50 | 163 |
| 1000 | Surface mounted, RS | | | | | | | | | |
| 1030 | Acrylic lens with hinged & latched door frame | | | | | | | | | |
| 1100 | 1'W x 4'L, two 40 watt | 1 Elec | 7 | 1.143 | Ea. | 74 | 37.50 | | 111.50 | 143 |
| 1200 | 2'W x 2'L, two U40 watt | | 7 | 1.143 | | 79.50 | 37.50 | | 117 | 148 |
| 1500 | 2'W x 4'L, four 40 watt | | 5.30 | 1.509 | | 94.50 | 49.50 | | 144 | 185 |
| 2100 | Strip fixture | | | | | | | | | |
| 2200 | 4' long, one 40 watt, RS | 1 Elec | 8.50 | .941 | Ea. | 31.50 | 31 | | 62.50 | 85 |
| 2300 | 4' long, two 40 watt, RS | " | 8 | 1 | | 34.50 | 33 | | 67.50 | 91.50 |
| 2600 | 8' long, one 75 watt, SL | 2 Elec | 13.40 | 1.194 | | 47 | 39 | | 86 | 116 |
| 2700 | 8' long, two 75 watt, SL | " | 12.40 | 1.290 | | 57 | 42.50 | | 99.50 | 132 |
| 4450 | Incandescent, high hat can, round alzak reflector, prewired | | | | | | | | | |
| 4470 | 100 watt | 1 Elec | 8 | 1 | Ea. | 70 | 33 | | 103 | 131 |
| 4480 | 150 watt | " | 8 | 1 | " | 102 | 33 | | 135 | 166 |
| 5200 | Ceiling, surface mounted, opal glass drum | | | | | | | | | |
| 5300 | 8", one 60 watt lamp | 1 Elec | 10 | .800 | Ea. | 43.50 | 26.50 | | 70 | 91 |
| 5400 | 10", two 60 watt lamps | | 8 | 1 | | 49 | 33 | | 82 | 108 |
| 5500 | 12", four 60 watt lamps | | 6.70 | 1.194 | | 69 | 39 | | 108 | 140 |
| 6900 | Mirror light, fluorescent, RS, acrylic enclosure, two 40 watt | | 8 | 1 | | 116 | 33 | | 149 | 182 |
| 6910 | One 40 watt | | 8 | 1 | | 94 | 33 | | 127 | 157 |
| 6920 | One 20 watt | | 12 | .667 | | 74 | 22 | | 96 | 117 |

## 26 51 13.70 Residential Fixtures

| 26 51 13.70 Residential Fixtures | | Crew | Daily Output | Labor-Hours | Unit | Material | 2010 Bare Costs Labor | Equipment | Total | Total Incl O&P |
|---|---|---|---|---|---|---|---|---|---|---|
| 0010 | **RESIDENTIAL FIXTURES** | | | | | | | | | |
| 0400 | Fluorescent, interior, surface, circline, 32 watt & 40 watt | 1 Elec | 20 | .400 | Ea. | 103 | 13.15 | | 116.15 | 135 |
| 0500 | 2' x 2', two U 32 watt T8 | | 8 | 1 | | 138 | 33 | | 171 | 205 |
| 0700 | Shallow under cabinet, two 20 watt | | 16 | .500 | | 47.50 | 16.45 | | 63.95 | 79 |
| 0900 | Wall mounted, 4'L, two 32 watt T8, with baffle | | 10 | .800 | | 155 | 26.50 | | 181.50 | 214 |
| 2000 | Incandescent, exterior lantern, wall mounted, 60 watt | | 16 | .500 | | 40 | 16.45 | | 56.45 | 70.50 |
| 2100 | Post light, 150W, with 7' post | | 4 | 2 | | 117 | 65.50 | | 182.50 | 236 |
| 2500 | Lamp holder, weatherproof with 150W PAR | | 16 | .500 | | 30.50 | 16.45 | | 46.95 | 60 |
| 2550 | With reflector and guard | | 12 | .667 | | 64 | 22 | | 86 | 106 |
| 2600 | Interior pendent, globe with shade, 150 watt | | 20 | .400 | | 174 | 13.15 | | 187.15 | 213 |

# 26 55 Special Purpose Lighting

## 26 55 59 – Display Lighting

### 26 55 59.10 Track Lighting

| 26 55 59.10 Track Lighting | | Crew | Daily Output | Labor-Hours | Unit | Material | 2010 Bare Costs Labor | Equipment | Total | Total Incl O&P |
|---|---|---|---|---|---|---|---|---|---|---|
| 0010 | **TRACK LIGHTING** | | | | | | | | | |
| 0100 | 8' section | 2 Elec | 10.60 | 1.509 | Ea. | 81 | 49.50 | | 130.50 | 170 |
| 0300 | 3 circuits, 4' section | 1 Elec | 6.70 | 1.194 | | 68 | 39 | | 107 | 139 |
| 0400 | 8' section | 2 Elec | 10.60 | 1.509 | | 106 | 49.50 | | 155.50 | 198 |
| 0500 | 12' section | " | 8.80 | 1.818 | | 176 | 59.50 | | 235.50 | 291 |
| 1000 | Feed kit, surface mounting | 1 Elec | 16 | .500 | | 12.20 | 16.45 | | 28.65 | 40 |
| 1100 | End cover | | 24 | .333 | | 4.75 | 10.95 | | 15.70 | 23 |
| 1200 | Feed kit, stem mounting, 1 circuit | | 16 | .500 | | 36.50 | 16.45 | | 52.95 | 67 |
| 1300 | 3 circuit | | 16 | .500 | | 36.50 | 16.45 | | 52.95 | 67 |

# 26 55 Special Purpose Lighting

## 26 55 59 – Display Lighting

| 26 55 59.10 Track Lighting | | Crew | Daily Output | Labor-Hours | Unit | Material | 2010 Bare Costs Labor | Equipment | Total | Total Incl O&P |
|---|---|---|---|---|---|---|---|---|---|---|
| 2000 | Electrical joiner, for continuous runs, 1 circuit | 1 Elec | 32 | .250 | Ea. | 17.60 | 8.20 | | 25.80 | 32.50 |
| 2100 | 3 circuit | | 32 | .250 | | 42.50 | 8.20 | | 50.70 | 60 |
| 2200 | Fixtures, spotlight, 75W PAR halogen | | 16 | .500 | | 105 | 16.45 | | 121.45 | 143 |
| 2210 | 50W MR16 halogen | | 16 | .500 | | 128 | 16.45 | | 144.45 | 168 |
| 3000 | Wall washer, 250 watt tungsten halogen | | 16 | .500 | | 122 | 16.45 | | 138.45 | 161 |
| 3100 | Low voltage, 25/50 watt, 1 circuit | | 16 | .500 | | 123 | 16.45 | | 139.45 | 162 |
| 3120 | 3 circuit | | 16 | .500 | | 127 | 16.45 | | 143.45 | 167 |

# 26 56 Exterior Lighting

## 26 56 13 – Lighting Poles and Standards

### 26 56 13.10 Lighting Poles

| | | Crew | Daily Output | Labor-Hours | Unit | Material | 2010 Bare Costs Labor | Equipment | Total | Total Incl O&P |
|---|---|---|---|---|---|---|---|---|---|---|
| 0010 | **LIGHTING POLES** | | | | | | | | | |
| 6420 | Wood pole, 4-1/2" x 5-1/8", 8' high | 1 Elec | 6 | 1.333 | Ea. | 320 | 44 | | 364 | 420 |
| 6440 | 12' high | | 5.70 | 1.404 | | 435 | 46 | | 481 | 555 |
| 6460 | 20' high | | 4 | 2 | | 615 | 65.50 | | 680.50 | 780 |

## 26 56 23 – Area Lighting

### 26 56 23.10 Exterior Fixtures

| | | Crew | Daily Output | Labor-Hours | Unit | Material | 2010 Bare Costs Labor | Equipment | Total | Total Incl O&P |
|---|---|---|---|---|---|---|---|---|---|---|
| 0010 | **EXTERIOR FIXTURES** With lamps | | | | | | | | | |
| 0400 | Quartz, 500 watt | 1 Elec | 5.30 | 1.509 | Ea. | 56 | 49.50 | | 105.50 | 143 |
| 1100 | Wall pack, low pressure sodium, 35 watt | | 4 | 2 | | 234 | 65.50 | | 299.50 | 365 |
| 1150 | 55 watt | | 4 | 2 | | 278 | 65.50 | | 343.50 | 410 |

## 26 56 26 – Landscape Lighting

### 26 56 26.20 Landscape Fixtures

| | | Crew | Daily Output | Labor-Hours | Unit | Material | 2010 Bare Costs Labor | Equipment | Total | Total Incl O&P |
|---|---|---|---|---|---|---|---|---|---|---|
| 0010 | **LANDSCAPE FIXTURES** | | | | | | | | | |
| 7380 | Landscape recessed uplight, incl. housing, ballast, transformer | | | | | | | | | |
| 7390 | & reflector, not incl. conduit, wire, trench | | | | | | | | | |
| 7420 | Incandescent, 250 watt | 1 Elec | 5 | 1.600 | Ea. | 565 | 52.50 | | 617.50 | 705 |
| 7440 | Quartz, 250 watt | " | 5 | 1.600 | " | 535 | 52.50 | | 587.50 | 675 |

## 26 56 33 – Walkway Lighting

### 26 56 33.10 Walkway Luminaire

| | | Crew | Daily Output | Labor-Hours | Unit | Material | 2010 Bare Costs Labor | Equipment | Total | Total Incl O&P |
|---|---|---|---|---|---|---|---|---|---|---|
| 0010 | **WALKWAY LUMINAIRE** | | | | | | | | | |
| 6500 | Bollard light, lamp & ballast, 42" high with polycarbonate lens | | | | | | | | | |
| 7200 | Incandescent, 150 watt | 1 Elec | 3 | 2.667 | Ea. | 555 | 87.50 | | 642.50 | 755 |

# 26 61 Lighting Systems and Accessories

## 26 61 23 – Lamps Applications

### 26 61 23.10 Lamps

| | | Crew | Daily Output | Labor-Hours | Unit | Material | 2010 Bare Costs Labor | Equipment | Total | Total Incl O&P |
|---|---|---|---|---|---|---|---|---|---|---|
| 0010 | **LAMPS** | | | | | | | | | |
| 0081 | Fluorescent, rapid start, cool white, 2' long, 20 watt | 1 Elec | 100 | .080 | Ea. | 3.54 | 2.63 | | 6.17 | 8.20 |
| 0101 | 4' long, 40 watt | | 90 | .089 | | 3.01 | 2.92 | | 5.93 | 8.05 |
| 1351 | High pressure sodium, 70 watt | | 30 | .267 | | 48 | 8.75 | | 56.75 | 67.50 |
| 1371 | 150 watt | | 30 | .267 | | 51.50 | 8.75 | | 60.25 | 71 |

# Estimating Tips

## 27 20 00 Data Communications
## 27 30 00 Voice Communications
## 27 40 00 Audio-Video Communications

When estimating material costs for special systems, it is always prudent to obtain manufacturers' quotations for equipment prices and special installation requirements which will affect the total costs.

# Reference Numbers

Reference numbers are shown in shaded boxes at the beginning of some major classifications. These numbers refer to related items in the Reference Section. The reference information may be an estimating procedure, an alternate pricing method, or technical information.

*Note:* Not all subdivisions listed here necessarily appear in this publication.

*Note:* **Trade Service,** *in part, has been used as a reference source for some of the material prices used in Division 27.*

# 27 41 Audio-Video Systems

## 27 41 19 – Portable Audio-Video Equipment

| 27 41 19.10 T.V. Systems | Crew | Daily Output | Labor-Hours | Unit | Material | 2010 Bare Costs Labor | Equipment | Total | Total Incl O&P |
|---|---|---|---|---|---|---|---|---|---|
| 0010 **T.V. SYSTEMS**, not including rough-in wires, cables & conduits | | | | | | | | | |
| 0100 Master TV antenna system | | | | | | | | | |
| 0200 VHF reception & distribution, 12 outlets | 1 Elec | 6 | 1.333 | Outlet | 205 | 44 | | 249 | 297 |
| 0800 VHF & UHF reception & distribution, 12 outlets | | 6 | 1.333 | " | 203 | 44 | | 247 | 296 |
| 5000 T.V. Antenna only, minimum | | 6 | 1.333 | Ea. | 45 | 44 | | 89 | 121 |
| 5100 Maximum | | 4 | 2 | " | 189 | 65.50 | | 254.50 | 315 |

# Estimating Tips

- When estimating material costs for electronic safety and security systems, it is always prudent to obtain manufacturers' quotations for equipment prices and special installation requirements that affect the total cost.
- Fire alarm systems consist of control panels, annunciator panels, battery with rack, charger, and fire alarm actuating and indicating devices. Some fire alarm systems include speakers, telephone lines, door closer controls, and other components. Be careful not to overlook the costs related to installation for these items.

Also be aware of costs for integrated automation instrumentation and terminal devices, control equipment, control wiring, and programming.

- Security equipment includes items such as CCTV, access control, and other detection and identification systems to perform alert and alarm functions. Be sure to consider the costs related to installation for this security equipment, such as for integrated automation instrumentation and terminal devices, control equipment, control wiring, and programming.

# Reference Numbers

Reference numbers are shown in shaded boxes at the beginning of some major classifications. These numbers refer to related items in the Reference Section. The reference information may be an estimating procedure, an alternate pricing method, or technical information.

*Note:* Not all subdivisions listed here necessarily appear in this publication.

# 28 16 Intrusion Detection

## 28 16 16 – Intrusion Detection Systems Infrastructure

| 28 16 16.50 Intrusion Detection | Crew | Daily Output | Labor-Hours | Unit | Material | 2010 Bare Costs Labor | Equipment | Total | Total Incl O&P |
|---|---|---|---|---|---|---|---|---|---|
| 0010 **INTRUSION DETECTION**, not including wires & conduits | | | | | | | | | |
| 0100 Burglar alarm, battery operated, mechanical trigger | 1 Elec | 4 | 2 | Ea. | 272 | 65.50 | | 337.50 | 405 |
| 0200 Electrical trigger | | 4 | 2 | | 325 | 65.50 | | 390.50 | 460 |
| 0400 For outside key control, add | | 8 | 1 | | 82 | 33 | | 115 | 144 |
| 0600 For remote signaling circuitry, add | | 8 | 1 | | 122 | 33 | | 155 | 189 |
| 0800 Card reader, flush type, standard | | 2.70 | 2.963 | | 910 | 97.50 | | 1,007.50 | 1,150 |
| 1000 Multi-code | | 2.70 | 2.963 | | 1,175 | 97.50 | | 1,272.50 | 1,450 |
| 1200 Door switches, hinge switch | | 5.30 | 1.509 | | 57.50 | 49.50 | | 107 | 144 |
| 1400 Magnetic switch | | 5.30 | 1.509 | | 67.50 | 49.50 | | 117 | 155 |
| 2800 Ultrasonic motion detector, 12 volt | | 2.30 | 3.478 | | 225 | 114 | | 339 | 435 |
| 3000 Infrared photoelectric detector | | 2.30 | 3.478 | | 186 | 114 | | 300 | 390 |
| 3200 Passive infrared detector | | 2.30 | 3.478 | | 278 | 114 | | 392 | 490 |
| 3420 Switchmats, 30" x 5' | | 5.30 | 1.509 | | 83 | 49.50 | | 132.50 | 172 |
| 3440 30" x 25' | | 4 | 2 | | 199 | 65.50 | | 264.50 | 325 |
| 3460 Police connect panel | | 4 | 2 | | 239 | 65.50 | | 304.50 | 370 |
| 3480 Telephone dialer | | 5.30 | 1.509 | | 375 | 49.50 | | 424.50 | 495 |
| 3500 Alarm bell | | 4 | 2 | | 102 | 65.50 | | 167.50 | 220 |
| 3520 Siren | ▼ | 4 | 2 | ▼ | 143 | 65.50 | | 208.50 | 264 |

# 28 31 Fire Detection and Alarm

## 28 31 23 – Fire Detection and Alarm Annunciation Panels and Fire Stations

### 28 31 23.50 Alarm Panels and Devices

| | Crew | Daily Output | Labor-Hours | Unit | Material | 2010 Bare Costs Labor | Equipment | Total | Total Incl O&P |
|---|---|---|---|---|---|---|---|---|---|
| 0010 **ALARM PANELS AND DEVICES**, not including wires & conduits | | | | | | | | | |
| 5600 Strobe and horn | 1 Elec | 5.30 | 1.509 | Ea. | 147 | 49.50 | | 196.50 | 242 |
| 5800 Fire alarm horn | | 6.70 | 1.194 | | 58.50 | 39 | | 97.50 | 129 |
| 6600 Drill switch | | 8 | 1 | | 360 | 33 | | 393 | 450 |
| 6800 Master box | | 2.70 | 2.963 | | 6,175 | 97.50 | | 6,272.50 | 6,950 |
| 7800 Remote annunciator, 8 zone lamp | | 1.80 | 4.444 | | 201 | 146 | | 347 | 460 |
| 8000 12 zone lamp | 2 Elec | 2.60 | 6.154 | | 345 | 202 | | 547 | 710 |
| 8200 16 zone lamp | " | 2.20 | 7.273 | | 345 | 239 | | 584 | 770 |

## 28 31 46 – Smoke Detection Sensors

### 28 31 46.50 Smoke Detectors

| | Crew | Daily Output | Labor-Hours | Unit | Material | 2010 Bare Costs Labor | Equipment | Total | Total Incl O&P |
|---|---|---|---|---|---|---|---|---|---|
| 0010 **SMOKE DETECTORS** | | | | | | | | | |
| 5200 Smoke detector, ceiling type | 1 Elec | 6.20 | 1.290 | Ea. | 126 | 42.50 | | 168.50 | 208 |

# Estimating Tips

## 31 05 00 Common Work Results for Earthwork

- Estimating the actual cost of performing earthwork requires careful consideration of the variables involved. This includes items such as type of soil, whether water will be encountered, dewatering, whether banks need bracing, disposal of excavated earth, and length of haul to fill or spoil sites, etc. If the project has large quantities of cut or fill, consider raising or lowering the site to reduce costs, while paying close attention to the effect on site drainage and utilities.

- If the project has large quantities of fill, creating a borrow pit on the site can significantly lower the costs.

- It is very important to consider what time of year the project is scheduled for completion. Bad weather can create large cost overruns from dewatering, site repair, and lost productivity from cold weather.

# Reference Numbers

Reference numbers are shown in shaded boxes at the beginning of some major classifications. These numbers refer to related items in the Reference Section. The reference information may be an estimating procedure, an alternate pricing method, or technical information.

*Note:* Not all subdivisions listed here necessarily appear in this publication.

# 31 05 Common Work Results for Earthwork

## 31 05 13 – Soils for Earthwork

| 31 05 13.10 Borrow | Crew | Daily Output | Labor-Hours | Unit | Material | 2010 Bare Costs Labor | Equipment | Total | Total Incl O&P |
|---|---|---|---|---|---|---|---|---|---|
| 0010 **BORROW** | | | | | | | | | |
| 0020 Spread, 200 H.P. dozer, no compaction, 2 mi. RT haul | | | | | | | | | |
| 0200 Common borrow | B-15 | 600 | .047 | C.Y. | 7.40 | 1.17 | 4.21 | 12.78 | 14.70 |

## 31 05 16 – Aggregates for Earthwork

| 31 05 16.10 Borrow | Crew | Daily Output | Labor-Hours | Unit | Material | 2010 Bare Costs Labor | Equipment | Total | Total Incl O&P |
|---|---|---|---|---|---|---|---|---|---|
| 0010 **BORROW** | | | | | | | | | |
| 0020 Spread, with 200 H.P. dozer, no compaction, 2 mi. RT haul | | | | | | | | | |
| 0100 Bank run gravel | B-15 | 600 | .047 | C.Y. | 22 | 1.17 | 4.21 | 27.38 | 30.50 |
| 0300 Crushed stone (1.40 tons per CY) , 1-1/2" | | 600 | .047 | | 35 | 1.17 | 4.21 | 40.38 | 45 |
| 0320 3/4" | | 600 | .047 | | 35 | 1.17 | 4.21 | 40.38 | 45 |
| 0340 1/2" | | 600 | .047 | | 30 | 1.17 | 4.21 | 35.38 | 39.50 |
| 0360 3/8" | | 600 | .047 | | 29.50 | 1.17 | 4.21 | 34.88 | 39 |
| 0400 Sand, washed, concrete | | 600 | .047 | | 33 | 1.17 | 4.21 | 38.38 | 42.50 |
| 0500 Dead or bank sand | ↓ | 600 | .047 | ↓ | 10.55 | 1.17 | 4.21 | 15.93 | 18.15 |

# 31 11 Clearing and Grubbing Land

## 31 11 10 – Clearing and Grubbing Land

| 31 11 10.10 Clear and Grub Site | Crew | Daily Output | Labor-Hours | Unit | Material | 2010 Bare Costs Labor | Equipment | Total | Total Incl O&P |
|---|---|---|---|---|---|---|---|---|---|
| 0010 **CLEAR AND GRUB SITE** | | | | | | | | | |
| 0020 Cut & chip light trees to 6" diam. | B-7 | 1 | 48 | Acre | | 1,125 | 1,400 | 2,525 | 3,400 |
| 0150 Grub stumps and remove | B-30 | 2 | 12 | | | 305 | 1,175 | 1,480 | 1,800 |
| 0200 Cut & chip medium, trees to 12" diam. | B-7 | .70 | 68.571 | | | 1,600 | 2,025 | 3,625 | 4,875 |
| 0250 Grub stumps and remove | B-30 | 1 | 24 | | | 615 | 2,350 | 2,965 | 3,625 |
| 0300 Cut & chip heavy, trees to 24" diam. | B-7 | .30 | 160 | | | 3,700 | 4,700 | 8,400 | 11,400 |
| 0350 Grub stumps and remove | B-30 | .50 | 48 | | | 1,225 | 4,700 | 5,925 | 7,200 |
| 0400 If burning is allowed, reduce cut & chip | | | | ↓ | | | | | 40% |

# 31 13 Selective Tree and Shrub Removal and Trimming

## 31 13 13 – Selective Tree and Shrub Removal

| 31 13 13.10 Selective Clearing | Crew | Daily Output | Labor-Hours | Unit | Material | 2010 Bare Costs Labor | Equipment | Total | Total Incl O&P |
|---|---|---|---|---|---|---|---|---|---|
| 0010 **SELECTIVE CLEARING** | | | | | | | | | |
| 0020 Clearing brush with brush saw | A-1C | .25 | 32 | Acre | | 690 | 113 | 803 | 1,275 |
| 0100 By hand | 1 Clab | .12 | 66.667 | | | 1,425 | | 1,425 | 2,400 |
| 0300 With dozer, ball and chain, light clearing | B-11A | 2 | 8 | | | 205 | 595 | 800 | 995 |
| 0400 Medium clearing | " | 1.50 | 10.667 | ↓ | | 273 | 795 | 1,068 | 1,325 |

# 31 14 Earth Stripping and Stockpiling

## 31 14 13 – Soil Stripping and Stockpiling

| 31 14 13.23 Topsoil Stripping and Stockpiling | Crew | Daily Output | Labor-Hours | Unit | Material | 2010 Bare Costs Labor | Equipment | Total | Total Incl O&P |
|---|---|---|---|---|---|---|---|---|---|
| 0010 **TOPSOIL STRIPPING AND STOCKPILING** | | | | | | | | | |
| 1400 Loam or topsoil, remove and stockpile on site | | | | | | | | | |
| 1420 6" deep, 200' haul | B-10B | 865 | .009 | C.Y. | | .27 | 1.38 | 1.65 | 1.97 |
| 1430 300' haul | | 520 | .015 | | | .46 | 2.29 | 2.75 | 3.27 |
| 1440 500' haul | | 225 | .036 | ↓ | | 1.05 | 5.30 | 6.35 | 7.60 |
| 1450 Alternate method: 6" deep, 200' haul | | 5090 | .002 | S.Y. | | .05 | .23 | .28 | .34 |
| 1460 500' haul | ↓ | 1325 | .006 | " | | .18 | .90 | 1.08 | 1.28 |

# 31 22 Grading

## 31 22 16 – Fine Grading

| 31 22 16.10 Finish Grading | Crew | Daily Output | Labor-Hours | Unit | Material | 2010 Bare Costs Labor | Equipment | Total | Total Incl O&P |
|---|---|---|---|---|---|---|---|---|---|
| 0010 **FINISH GRADING** | | | | | | | | | |
| 0012 Finish grading area to be paved with grader, small area | B-11L | 400 | .040 | S.Y. | | 1.02 | 1.56 | 2.58 | 3.40 |
| 0100 Large area | | 2000 | .008 | | | .20 | .31 | .51 | .68 |
| 0200 Grade subgrade for base course, roadways | ↓ | 3500 | .005 | | | .12 | .18 | .30 | .39 |
| 1020 For large parking lots | B-32C | 5000 | .010 | | | .25 | .41 | .66 | .86 |
| 1050 For small irregular areas | " | 2000 | .024 | | | .62 | 1.02 | 1.64 | 2.16 |
| 1100 Fine grade for slab on grade, machine | B-11L | 1040 | .015 | | | .39 | .60 | .99 | 1.31 |
| 1150 Hand grading | B-18 | 700 | .034 | | | .76 | .06 | .82 | 1.35 |
| 1200 Fine grade granular base for sidewalks and bikeways | B-62 | 1200 | .020 | ↓ | | .48 | .13 | .61 | .94 |
| 2550 Hand grade select gravel | 2 Clab | 60 | .267 | C.S.F. | | 5.75 | | 5.75 | 9.65 |
| 3000 Hand grade select gravel, including compaction, 4" deep | B-18 | 555 | .043 | S.Y. | | .96 | .08 | 1.04 | 1.70 |
| 3100 6" deep | | 400 | .060 | | | 1.33 | .11 | 1.44 | 2.36 |
| 3120 8" deep | ↓ | 300 | .080 | | | 1.77 | .15 | 1.92 | 3.14 |
| 3300 Finishing grading slopes, gentle | B-11L | 8900 | .002 | | | .05 | .07 | .12 | .16 |
| 3310 Steep slopes | " | 7100 | .002 | ↓ | | .06 | .09 | .15 | .20 |

# 31 23 Excavation and Fill

## 31 23 16 – Excavation

### 31 23 16.13 Excavating, Trench

| | Crew | Daily Output | Labor-Hours | Unit | Material | 2010 Bare Costs Labor | Equipment | Total | Total Incl O&P |
|---|---|---|---|---|---|---|---|---|---|
| 0010 **EXCAVATING, TRENCH** | | | | | | | | | |
| 0011 Or continuous footing | | | | | | | | | |
| 0050 1' to 4' deep, 3/8 C.Y. excavator | B-11C | 150 | .107 | B.C.Y. | | 2.73 | 2.25 | 4.98 | 7 |
| 0060 1/2 C.Y. excavator | B-11M | 200 | .080 | | | 2.05 | 1.94 | 3.99 | 5.50 |
| 0090 4' to 6' deep, 1/2 C.Y. excavator | " | 200 | .080 | | | 2.05 | 1.94 | 3.99 | 5.50 |
| 0100 5/8 C.Y. excavator | B-12Q | 250 | .064 | | | 1.67 | 2.26 | 3.93 | 5.25 |
| 0300 1/2 C.Y. excavator, truck mounted | B-12J | 200 | .080 | | | 2.09 | 4.06 | 6.15 | 7.90 |
| 1352 4' to 6' deep, 1/2 C.Y. excavator w/trench box | B-13H | 188 | .085 | | | 2.22 | 4.93 | 7.15 | 9.05 |
| 1354 5/8 C.Y. excavator | " | 235 | .068 | | | 1.78 | 3.94 | 5.72 | 7.30 |
| 1400 By hand with pick and shovel 2' to 6' deep, light soil | 1 Clab | 8 | 1 | | | 21.50 | | 21.50 | 36 |
| 1500 Heavy soil | " | 4 | 2 | ↓ | | 43 | | 43 | 72.50 |
| 5020 Loam & Sandy clay with no sheeting or dewatering included | | | | | | | | | |
| 5050 1' to 4' deep, 3/8 C.Y. tractor loader/backhoe | B-11C | 162 | .099 | B.C.Y. | | 2.53 | 2.09 | 4.62 | 6.45 |
| 5060 1/2 C.Y. excavator | B-11M | 216 | .074 | | | 1.89 | 1.79 | 3.68 | 5.10 |
| 5080 4' to 6' deep, 1/2 C.Y. excavator | " | 216 | .074 | | | 1.89 | 1.79 | 3.68 | 5.10 |
| 5090 5/8 C.Y. excavator | B-12Q | 276 | .058 | | | 1.51 | 2.05 | 3.56 | 4.75 |
| 5130 1/2 C.Y. excavator, truck mounted | B-12J | 216 | .074 | | | 1.93 | 3.76 | 5.69 | 7.35 |
| 5352 4' to 6' deep, 1/2 C.Y. excavator w/trench box | B-13H | 205 | .078 | | | 2.04 | 4.52 | 6.56 | 8.35 |
| 5354 5/8 C.Y. excavator | " | 257 | .062 | ↓ | | 1.62 | 3.60 | 5.22 | 6.65 |
| 6020 Sand & gravel with no sheeting or dewatering included | | | | | | | | | |
| 6050 1' to 4' deep, 3/8 C.Y. excavator | B-11C | 165 | .097 | B.C.Y. | | 2.48 | 2.05 | 4.53 | 6.35 |
| 6060 1/2 C.Y. excavator | B-11M | 220 | .073 | | | 1.86 | 1.76 | 3.62 | 5 |
| 6080 4' to 6' deep, 1/2 C.Y. excavator | " | 220 | .073 | | | 1.86 | 1.76 | 3.62 | 5 |
| 6090 5/8 C.Y. excavator | B-12Q | 275 | .058 | | | 1.52 | 2.05 | 3.57 | 4.77 |
| 6130 1/2 C.Y. excavator, truck mounted | B-12J | 220 | .073 | | | 1.90 | 3.69 | 5.59 | 7.20 |
| 6352 4' to 6' deep, 1/2 C.Y. excavator w/trench box | B-13H | 209 | .077 | | | 2 | 4.43 | 6.43 | 8.20 |
| 6354 5/8 C.Y. excavator | " | 261 | .061 | ↓ | | 1.60 | 3.55 | 5.15 | 6.55 |
| 7020 Dense hard clay with no sheeting or dewatering included | | | | | | | | | |
| 7050 1' to 4' deep, 3/8 C.Y. excavator | B-11C | 132 | .121 | B.C.Y. | | 3.10 | 2.56 | 5.66 | 7.95 |
| 7060 1/2 C.Y. excavator | B-11M | 176 | .091 | | | 2.33 | 2.20 | 4.53 | 6.25 |
| 7080 4' to 6' deep, 1/2 C.Y. excavator | " | 176 | .091 | | | 2.33 | 2.20 | 4.53 | 6.25 |
| 7090 5/8 C.Y. excavator | B-12Q | 220 | .073 | | | 1.90 | 2.57 | 4.47 | 5.95 |

# 31 23 Excavation and Fill

## 31 23 16 – Excavation

| | | Crew | Daily Output | Labor-Hours | Unit | Material | 2010 Bare Costs Labor | 2010 Bare Costs Equipment | Total | Total Incl O&P |
|---|---|---|---|---|---|---|---|---|---|---|
| **31 23 16.13** | **Excavating, Trench** | | | | | | | | | |
| 7130 | 1/2 C.Y. excavator, truck mounted | B-12J | 176 | .091 | B.C.Y. | | 2.37 | 4.62 | 6.99 | 9 |
| **31 23 16.14** | **Excavating, Utility Trench** | | | | | | | | | |
| 0010 | **EXCAVATING, UTILITY TRENCH** | | | | | | | | | |
| 0011 | Common earth | | | | | | | | | |
| 0050 | Trenching with chain trencher, 12 H.P., operator walking | | | | | | | | | |
| 0100 | 4" wide trench, 12" deep | B-53 | 800 | .010 | L.F. | | .22 | .08 | .30 | .45 |
| 1000 | Backfill by hand including compaction, add | | | | | | | | | |
| 1050 | 4" wide trench, 12" deep | A-1G | 800 | .010 | L.F. | | .22 | .06 | .28 | .43 |
| **31 23 16.16** | **Structural Excavation for Minor Structures** | | | | | | | | | |
| 0010 | **STRUCTURAL EXCAVATION FOR MINOR STRUCTURES** | | | | | | | | | |
| 0015 | Hand, pits to 6' deep, sandy soil | 1 Clab | 8 | 1 | B.C.Y. | | 21.50 | | 21.50 | 36 |
| 0100 | Heavy soil or clay | | 4 | 2 | | | 43 | | 43 | 72.50 |
| 1100 | Hand loading trucks from stock pile, sandy soil | | 12 | .667 | | | 14.35 | | 14.35 | 24 |
| 1300 | Heavy soil or clay | ↓ | 8 | 1 | ↓ | | 21.50 | | 21.50 | 36 |
| 1500 | For wet or muck hand excavation, add to above | | | | % | | | | 50% | 50% |
| **31 23 16.42** | **Excavating, Bulk Bank Measure** | | | | | | | | | |
| 0010 | **EXCAVATING, BULK BANK MEASURE** | | | | | | | | | |
| 0011 | Common earth piled | | | | | | | | | |
| 0020 | For loading onto trucks, add | | | | | | | | 15% | 15% |
| 0200 | Excavator, hydraulic, crawler mtd., 1 C.Y. cap. = 100 C.Y./hr. | B-12A | 800 | .020 | B.C.Y. | | .52 | 1 | 1.52 | 1.96 |
| 0310 | Wheel mounted, 1/2 C.Y. cap. = 40 C.Y./hr. | B-12E | 320 | .050 | | | 1.30 | 1.21 | 2.51 | 3.49 |
| 1200 | Front end loader, track mtd., 1-1/2 C.Y. cap. = 70 C.Y./hr. | B-10N | 560 | .014 | | | .42 | .77 | 1.19 | 1.54 |
| 1500 | Wheel mounted, 3/4 C.Y. cap. = 45 C.Y./hr. | B-10R | 360 | .022 | ↓ | | .66 | .75 | 1.41 | 1.90 |
| 5000 | Excavating, bulk bank measure, sandy clay & loam piled | | | | | | | | | |
| 5020 | For loading onto trucks, add | | | | | | | | 15% | 15% |
| 5100 | Excavator, hydraulic, crawler mtd., 1 C.Y. cap. = 120 C.Y./hr. | B-12A | 960 | .017 | B.C.Y. | | .43 | .84 | 1.27 | 1.64 |
| 5610 | Wheel mounted, 1/2 C.Y. cap. = 44 C.Y./hr. | B-12E | 352 | .045 | " | | 1.19 | 1.10 | 2.29 | 3.17 |
| 8000 | For hauling excavated material, see Div. 31 23 23.20 | | | | | | | | | |

## 31 23 23 – Fill

| | | Crew | Daily Output | Labor-Hours | Unit | Material | 2010 Bare Costs Labor | 2010 Bare Costs Equipment | Total | Total Incl O&P |
|---|---|---|---|---|---|---|---|---|---|---|
| **31 23 23.13** | **Backfill** | | | | | | | | | |
| 0010 | **BACKFILL** | | | | | | | | | |
| 0015 | By hand, no compaction, light soil | 1 Clab | 14 | .571 | L.C.Y. | | 12.30 | | 12.30 | 20.50 |
| 0100 | Heavy soil | | 11 | .727 | " | | 15.65 | | 15.65 | 26.50 |
| 0300 | Compaction in 6" layers, hand tamp, add to above | ↓ | 20.60 | .388 | E.C.Y. | | 8.35 | | 8.35 | 14.05 |
| 0500 | Air tamp, add | B-9D | 190 | .211 | | | 4.61 | 1.35 | 5.96 | 9.25 |
| 0600 | Vibrating plate, add | A-1D | 60 | .133 | | | 2.87 | .57 | 3.44 | 5.45 |
| 0800 | Compaction in 12" layers, hand tamp, add to above | 1 Clab | 34 | .235 | ↓ | | 5.05 | | 5.05 | 8.50 |
| 1300 | Dozer backfilling, bulk, up to 300' haul, no compaction | B-10B | 1200 | .007 | L.C.Y. | | .20 | .99 | 1.19 | 1.41 |
| 1400 | Air tamped, add | B-11B | 80 | .200 | E.C.Y. | | 5 | 3.67 | 8.67 | 12.35 |
| **31 23 23.16** | **Fill By Borrow and Utility Bedding** | | | | | | | | | |
| 0010 | **FILL BY BORROW AND UTILITY BEDDING** | | | | | | | | | |
| 0049 | Utility bedding, for pipe & conduit, not incl. compaction | | | | | | | | | |
| 0050 | Crushed or screened bank run gravel | B-6 | 150 | .160 | L.C.Y. | 25 | 3.81 | 2.25 | 31.06 | 36.50 |
| 0100 | Crushed stone 3/4" to 1/2" | | 150 | .160 | | 35 | 3.81 | 2.25 | 41.06 | 47.50 |
| 0200 | Sand, dead or bank | ↓ | 150 | .160 | ↓ | 10.55 | 3.81 | 2.25 | 16.61 | 20.50 |
| 0500 | Compacting bedding in trench | A-1D | 90 | .089 | E.C.Y. | | 1.91 | .38 | 2.29 | 3.63 |
| 0600 | If material source exceeds 2 miles, add for extra mileage. | | | | | | | | | |
| 0610 | See Div. 31 23 23 .20 for hauling mileage add. | | | | | | | | | |
| **31 23 23.17** | **General Fill** | | | | | | | | | |
| 0010 | **GENERAL FILL** | | | | | | | | | |
| 0011 | Spread dumped material, no compaction | | | | | | | | | |

# 31 23 Excavation and Fill

## 31 23 23 – Fill

| 31 23 23.17 General Fill | Crew | Daily Output | Labor-Hours | Unit | Material | 2010 Bare Costs Labor | Equipment | Total | Total Incl O&P |
|---|---|---|---|---|---|---|---|---|---|
| 0020 By dozer, no compaction | B-10B | 1000 | .008 | L.C.Y. | | .24 | 1.19 | 1.43 | 1.70 |
| 0100     By hand | 1 Clab | 12 | .667 | " | | 14.35 | | 14.35 | 24 |
| 0500 Gravel fill, compacted, under floor slabs, 4" deep | B-37 | 10000 | .005 | S.F. | .25 | .11 | .02 | .38 | .48 |
| 0600     6" deep | | 8600 | .006 | | .38 | .13 | .02 | .53 | .65 |
| 0700     9" deep | | 7200 | .007 | | .63 | .15 | .02 | .80 | .98 |
| 0800     12" deep | | 6000 | .008 | | .89 | .18 | .03 | 1.10 | 1.31 |
| 1000 Alternate pricing method, 4" deep | | 120 | .400 | E.C.Y. | 19 | 9.20 | 1.27 | 29.47 | 38 |
| 1100     6" deep | | 160 | .300 | | 19 | 6.90 | .95 | 26.85 | 33.50 |
| 1200     9" deep | | 200 | .240 | | 19 | 5.50 | .76 | 25.26 | 31 |
| 1300     12" deep | | 220 | .218 | | 19 | 5 | .69 | 24.69 | 30 |

## 31 23 23.20 Hauling

| | Crew | Daily Output | Labor-Hours | Unit | Material | 2010 Bare Costs Labor | Equipment | Total | Total Incl O&P |
|---|---|---|---|---|---|---|---|---|---|
| 0010 **HAULING** | | | | | | | | | |
| 0011 Excavated or borrow, loose cubic yards | | | | | | | | | |
| 0012 no loading equipment, including hauling,waiting, loading/dumping | | | | | | | | | |
| 0013 time per cycle (wait, load, travel, unload or dump & return) | | | | | | | | | |
| 0014 8 CY truck, 15 MPH ave, cycle 0.5 miles, 10 min. wait/Ld./Uld. | B-34A | 320 | .025 | L.C.Y. | | .59 | 1.26 | 1.85 | 2.36 |
| 0016     cycle 1 mile | | 272 | .029 | | | .69 | 1.48 | 2.17 | 2.77 |
| 0018     cycle 2 miles | | 208 | .038 | | | .91 | 1.93 | 2.84 | 3.63 |
| 0020     cycle 4 miles | | 144 | .056 | | | 1.31 | 2.79 | 4.10 | 5.25 |
| 0022     cycle 6 miles | | 112 | .071 | | | 1.68 | 3.59 | 5.27 | 6.75 |
| 0024     cycle 8 miles | | 88 | .091 | | | 2.14 | 4.57 | 6.71 | 8.55 |
| 0026     20 MPH ave,cycle 0.5 mile | | 336 | .024 | | | .56 | 1.20 | 1.76 | 2.25 |
| 0028     cycle 1 mile | | 296 | .027 | | | .64 | 1.36 | 2 | 2.55 |
| 0030     cycle 2 miles | | 240 | .033 | | | .78 | 1.67 | 2.45 | 3.15 |
| 0032     cycle 4 miles | | 176 | .045 | | | 1.07 | 2.28 | 3.35 | 4.29 |
| 0034     cycle 6 miles | | 136 | .059 | | | 1.39 | 2.95 | 4.34 | 5.55 |
| 0036     cycle 8 miles | | 112 | .071 | | | 1.68 | 3.59 | 5.27 | 6.75 |
| 0044     25 MPH ave, cycle 4 miles | | 192 | .042 | | | .98 | 2.09 | 3.07 | 3.93 |
| 0046     cycle 6 miles | | 160 | .050 | | | 1.18 | 2.51 | 3.69 | 4.72 |
| 0048     cycle 8 miles | | 128 | .063 | | | 1.47 | 3.14 | 4.61 | 5.90 |
| 0050     30 MPH ave, cycle 4 miles | | 216 | .037 | | | .87 | 1.86 | 2.73 | 3.50 |
| 0052     cycle 6 miles | | 176 | .045 | | | 1.07 | 2.28 | 3.35 | 4.29 |
| 0054     cycle 8 miles | | 144 | .056 | | | 1.31 | 2.79 | 4.10 | 5.25 |
| 0114     15 MPH ave, cycle 0.5 mile, 15 min. wait/Ld./Uld. | | 224 | .036 | | | .84 | 1.79 | 2.63 | 3.37 |
| 0116     cycle 1 mile | | 200 | .040 | | | .94 | 2.01 | 2.95 | 3.78 |
| 0118     cycle 2 miles | | 168 | .048 | | | 1.12 | 2.39 | 3.51 | 4.50 |
| 0120     cycle 4 miles | | 120 | .067 | | | 1.57 | 3.35 | 4.92 | 6.30 |
| 0122     cycle 6 miles | | 96 | .083 | | | 1.96 | 4.19 | 6.15 | 7.85 |
| 0124     cycle 8 miles | | 80 | .100 | | | 2.36 | 5 | 7.36 | 9.45 |
| 0126     20 MPH ave, cycle 0.5 mile | | 232 | .034 | | | .81 | 1.73 | 2.54 | 3.26 |
| 0128     cycle 1 mile | | 208 | .038 | | | .91 | 1.93 | 2.84 | 3.63 |
| 0130     cycle 2 miles | | 184 | .043 | | | 1.02 | 2.18 | 3.20 | 4.10 |
| 0132     cycle 4 miles | | 144 | .056 | | | 1.31 | 2.79 | 4.10 | 5.25 |
| 0134     cycle 6 miles | | 112 | .071 | | | 1.68 | 3.59 | 5.27 | 6.75 |
| 0136     cycle 8 miles | | 96 | .083 | | | 1.96 | 4.19 | 6.15 | 7.85 |
| 0144     25 MPH ave, cycle 4 miles | | 152 | .053 | | | 1.24 | 2.64 | 3.88 | 4.97 |
| 0146     cycle 6 miles | | 128 | .063 | | | 1.47 | 3.14 | 4.61 | 5.90 |
| 0148     cycle 8 miles | | 112 | .071 | | | 1.68 | 3.59 | 5.27 | 6.75 |
| 0150     30 MPH ave, cycle 4 miles | | 168 | .048 | | | 1.12 | 2.39 | 3.51 | 4.50 |
| 0152     cycle 6 miles | | 144 | .056 | | | 1.31 | 2.79 | 4.10 | 5.25 |
| 0154     cycle 8 miles | | 120 | .067 | | | 1.57 | 3.35 | 4.92 | 6.30 |
| 0214     15 MPH ave, cycle 0.5 mile, 20 min wait/Ld./Uld. | | 176 | .045 | | | 1.07 | 2.28 | 3.35 | 4.29 |

# 31 23 Excavation and Fill

## 31 23 23 – Fill

| 31 23 23.20 Hauling | | Crew | Daily Output | Labor-Hours | Unit | Material | 2010 Bare Costs Labor | 2010 Bare Costs Equipment | Total | Total Incl O&P |
|---|---|---|---|---|---|---|---|---|---|---|
| 0216 | cycle 1 mile | B-34A | 160 | .050 | L.C.Y. | | 1.18 | 2.51 | 3.69 | 4.72 |
| 0218 | cycle 2 miles | | 136 | .059 | | | 1.39 | 2.95 | 4.34 | 5.55 |
| 0220 | cycle 4 miles | | 104 | .077 | | | 1.81 | 3.86 | 5.67 | 7.25 |
| 0222 | cycle 6 miles | | 88 | .091 | | | 2.14 | 4.57 | 6.71 | 8.55 |
| 0224 | cycle 8 miles | | 72 | .111 | | | 2.62 | 5.60 | 8.22 | 10.50 |
| 0226 | 20 MPH ave, cycle 0.5 mile | | 176 | .045 | | | 1.07 | 2.28 | 3.35 | 4.29 |
| 0228 | cycle 1 mile | | 168 | .048 | | | 1.12 | 2.39 | 3.51 | 4.50 |
| 0230 | cycle 2 miles | | 144 | .056 | | | 1.31 | 2.79 | 4.10 | 5.25 |
| 0232 | cycle 4 miles | | 120 | .067 | | | 1.57 | 3.35 | 4.92 | 6.30 |
| 0234 | cycle 6 miles | | 96 | .083 | | | 1.96 | 4.19 | 6.15 | 7.85 |
| 0236 | cycle 8 miles | | 88 | .091 | | | 2.14 | 4.57 | 6.71 | 8.55 |
| 0244 | 25 MPH ave, cycle 4 miles | | 128 | .063 | | | 1.47 | 3.14 | 4.61 | 5.90 |
| 0246 | cycle 6 miles | | 112 | .071 | | | 1.68 | 3.59 | 5.27 | 6.75 |
| 0248 | cycle 8 miles | | 96 | .083 | | | 1.96 | 4.19 | 6.15 | 7.85 |
| 0250 | 30 MPH ave, cycle 4 miles | | 136 | .059 | | | 1.39 | 2.95 | 4.34 | 5.55 |
| 0252 | cycle 6 miles | | 120 | .067 | | | 1.57 | 3.35 | 4.92 | 6.30 |
| 0254 | cycle 8 miles | | 104 | .077 | | | 1.81 | 3.86 | 5.67 | 7.25 |
| 0314 | 15 MPH ave, cycle 0.5 mile, 25 min wait/Ld./Uld. | | 144 | .056 | | | 1.31 | 2.79 | 4.10 | 5.25 |
| 0316 | cycle 1 mile | | 128 | .063 | | | 1.47 | 3.14 | 4.61 | 5.90 |
| 0318 | cycle 2 miles | | 112 | .071 | | | 1.68 | 3.59 | 5.27 | 6.75 |
| 0320 | cycle 4 miles | | 96 | .083 | | | 1.96 | 4.19 | 6.15 | 7.85 |
| 0322 | cycle 6 miles | | 80 | .100 | | | 2.36 | 5 | 7.36 | 9.45 |
| 0324 | cycle 8 miles | | 64 | .125 | | | 2.94 | 6.30 | 9.24 | 11.80 |
| 0326 | 20 MPH ave, cycle 0.5 mile | | 144 | .056 | | | 1.31 | 2.79 | 4.10 | 5.25 |
| 0328 | cycle 1 mile | | 136 | .059 | | | 1.39 | 2.95 | 4.34 | 5.55 |
| 0330 | cycle 2 miles | | 120 | .067 | | | 1.57 | 3.35 | 4.92 | 6.30 |
| 0332 | cycle 4 miles | | 104 | .077 | | | 1.81 | 3.86 | 5.67 | 7.25 |
| 0334 | cycle 6 miles | | 88 | .091 | | | 2.14 | 4.57 | 6.71 | 8.55 |
| 0336 | cycle 8 miles | | 80 | .100 | | | 2.36 | 5 | 7.36 | 9.45 |
| 0344 | 25 MPH ave, cycle 4 miles | | 112 | .071 | | | 1.68 | 3.59 | 5.27 | 6.75 |
| 0346 | cycle 6 miles | | 96 | .083 | | | 1.96 | 4.19 | 6.15 | 7.85 |
| 0348 | cycle 8 miles | | 88 | .091 | | | 2.14 | 4.57 | 6.71 | 8.55 |
| 0350 | 30 MPH ave, cycle 4 miles | | 112 | .071 | | | 1.68 | 3.59 | 5.27 | 6.75 |
| 0352 | cycle 6 miles | | 104 | .077 | | | 1.81 | 3.86 | 5.67 | 7.25 |
| 0354 | cycle 8 miles | | 96 | .083 | | | 1.96 | 4.19 | 6.15 | 7.85 |
| 0414 | 15 MPH ave, cycle 0.5 mile, 30 min wait/Ld./Uld. | | 120 | .067 | | | 1.57 | 3.35 | 4.92 | 6.30 |
| 0416 | cycle 1 mile | | 112 | .071 | | | 1.68 | 3.59 | 5.27 | 6.75 |
| 0418 | cycle 2 miles | | 96 | .083 | | | 1.96 | 4.19 | 6.15 | 7.85 |
| 0420 | cycle 4 miles | | 80 | .100 | | | 2.36 | 5 | 7.36 | 9.45 |
| 0422 | cycle 6 miles | | 72 | .111 | | | 2.62 | 5.60 | 8.22 | 10.50 |
| 0424 | cycle 8 miles | | 64 | .125 | | | 2.94 | 6.30 | 9.24 | 11.80 |
| 0426 | 20 MPH ave, cycle 0.5 mile | | 120 | .067 | | | 1.57 | 3.35 | 4.92 | 6.30 |
| 0428 | cycle 1 mile | | 112 | .071 | | | 1.68 | 3.59 | 5.27 | 6.75 |
| 0430 | cycle 2 miles | | 104 | .077 | | | 1.81 | 3.86 | 5.67 | 7.25 |
| 0432 | cycle 4 miles | | 88 | .091 | | | 2.14 | 4.57 | 6.71 | 8.55 |
| 0434 | cycle 6 miles | | 80 | .100 | | | 2.36 | 5 | 7.36 | 9.45 |
| 0436 | cycle 8 miles | | 72 | .111 | | | 2.62 | 5.60 | 8.22 | 10.50 |
| 0444 | 25 MPH ave, cycle 4 miles | | 96 | .083 | | | 1.96 | 4.19 | 6.15 | 7.85 |
| 0446 | cycle 6 miles | | 88 | .091 | | | 2.14 | 4.57 | 6.71 | 8.55 |
| 0448 | cycle 8 miles | | 80 | .100 | | | 2.36 | 5 | 7.36 | 9.45 |
| 0450 | 30 MPH ave, cycle 4 miles | | 96 | .083 | | | 1.96 | 4.19 | 6.15 | 7.85 |
| 0452 | cycle 6 miles | | 88 | .091 | | | 2.14 | 4.57 | 6.71 | 8.55 |
| 0454 | cycle 8 miles | | 80 | .100 | | | 2.36 | 5 | 7.36 | 9.45 |

# 31 23 Excavation and Fill

## 31 23 23 – Fill

| 31 23 23.20 Hauling | | Crew | Daily Output | Labor-Hours | Unit | Material | 2010 Bare Costs Labor | 2010 Bare Costs Equipment | Total | Total Incl O&P |
|---|---|---|---|---|---|---|---|---|---|---|
| 0514 | 15 MPH ave, cycle 0.5 mile, 35 min wait/Ld./Uld. | B-34A | 104 | .077 | L.C.Y. | | 1.81 | 3.86 | 5.67 | 7.25 |
| 0516 | cycle 1 mile | | 96 | .083 | | | 1.96 | 4.19 | 6.15 | 7.85 |
| 0518 | cycle 2 miles | | 88 | .091 | | | 2.14 | 4.57 | 6.71 | 8.55 |
| 0520 | cycle 4 miles | | 72 | .111 | | | 2.62 | 5.60 | 8.22 | 10.50 |
| 0522 | cycle 6 miles | | 64 | .125 | | | 2.94 | 6.30 | 9.24 | 11.80 |
| 0524 | cycle 8 miles | | 56 | .143 | | | 3.36 | 7.20 | 10.56 | 13.50 |
| 0526 | 20 MPH ave, cycle 0.5 mile | | 104 | .077 | | | 1.81 | 3.86 | 5.67 | 7.25 |
| 0528 | cycle 1 mile | | 96 | .083 | | | 1.96 | 4.19 | 6.15 | 7.85 |
| 0530 | cycle 2 miles | | 96 | .083 | | | 1.96 | 4.19 | 6.15 | 7.85 |
| 0532 | cycle 4 miles | | 80 | .100 | | | 2.36 | 5 | 7.36 | 9.45 |
| 0534 | cycle 6 miles | | 72 | .111 | | | 2.62 | 5.60 | 8.22 | 10.50 |
| 0536 | cycle 8 miles | | 64 | .125 | | | 2.94 | 6.30 | 9.24 | 11.80 |
| 0544 | 25 MPH ave, cycle 4 miles | | 88 | .091 | | | 2.14 | 4.57 | 6.71 | 8.55 |
| 0546 | cycle 6 miles | | 80 | .100 | | | 2.36 | 5 | 7.36 | 9.45 |
| 0548 | cycle 8 miles | | 72 | .111 | | | 2.62 | 5.60 | 8.22 | 10.50 |
| 0550 | 30 MPH ave, cycle 4 miles | | 88 | .091 | | | 2.14 | 4.57 | 6.71 | 8.55 |
| 0552 | cycle 6 miles | | 80 | .100 | | | 2.36 | 5 | 7.36 | 9.45 |
| 0554 | cycle 8 miles | | 72 | .111 | | | 2.62 | 5.60 | 8.22 | 10.50 |
| 1014 | 12 CY truck, cycle 0.5 mile, 15 MPH ave, 15 min. wait/Ld./Uld. | B-34B | 336 | .024 | | | .56 | 1.99 | 2.55 | 3.12 |
| 1016 | cycle 1 mile | | 300 | .027 | | | .63 | 2.23 | 2.86 | 3.50 |
| 1018 | cycle 2 miles | | 252 | .032 | | | .75 | 2.65 | 3.40 | 4.16 |
| 1020 | cycle 4 miles | | 180 | .044 | | | 1.05 | 3.71 | 4.76 | 5.80 |
| 1022 | cycle 6 miles | | 144 | .056 | | | 1.31 | 4.64 | 5.95 | 7.30 |
| 1024 | cycle 8 miles | | 120 | .067 | | | 1.57 | 5.55 | 7.12 | 8.70 |
| 1025 | cycle 10 miles | | 96 | .083 | | | 1.96 | 6.95 | 8.91 | 10.90 |
| 1026 | 20 MPH ave, cycle 0.5 mile | | 348 | .023 | | | .54 | 1.92 | 2.46 | 3.01 |
| 1028 | cycle 1 mile | | 312 | .026 | | | .60 | 2.14 | 2.74 | 3.36 |
| 1030 | cycle 2 miles | | 276 | .029 | | | .68 | 2.42 | 3.10 | 3.80 |
| 1032 | cycle 4 miles | | 216 | .037 | | | .87 | 3.09 | 3.96 | 4.85 |
| 1034 | cycle 6 miles | | 168 | .048 | | | 1.12 | 3.98 | 5.10 | 6.25 |
| 1036 | cycle 8 miles | | 144 | .056 | | | 1.31 | 4.64 | 5.95 | 7.30 |
| 1038 | cycle 10 miles | | 120 | .067 | | | 1.57 | 5.55 | 7.12 | 8.70 |
| 1040 | 25 MPH ave, cycle 4 miles | | 228 | .035 | | | .83 | 2.93 | 3.76 | 4.60 |
| 1042 | cycle 6 miles | | 192 | .042 | | | .98 | 3.48 | 4.46 | 5.45 |
| 1044 | cycle 8 miles | | 168 | .048 | | | 1.12 | 3.98 | 5.10 | 6.25 |
| 1046 | cycle 10 miles | | 144 | .056 | | | 1.31 | 4.64 | 5.95 | 7.30 |
| 1050 | 30 MPH ave, cycle 4 miles | | 252 | .032 | | | .75 | 2.65 | 3.40 | 4.16 |
| 1052 | cycle 6 miles | | 216 | .037 | | | .87 | 3.09 | 3.96 | 4.85 |
| 1054 | cycle 8 miles | | 180 | .044 | | | 1.05 | 3.71 | 4.76 | 5.80 |
| 1056 | cycle 10 miles | | 156 | .051 | | | 1.21 | 4.28 | 5.49 | 6.70 |
| 1060 | 35 MPH ave, cycle 4 miles | | 264 | .030 | | | .71 | 2.53 | 3.24 | 3.97 |
| 1062 | cycle 6 miles | | 228 | .035 | | | .83 | 2.93 | 3.76 | 4.60 |
| 1064 | cycle 8 miles | | 204 | .039 | | | .92 | 3.27 | 4.19 | 5.15 |
| 1066 | cycle 10 miles | | 180 | .044 | | | 1.05 | 3.71 | 4.76 | 5.80 |
| 1068 | cycle 20 miles | | 120 | .067 | | | 1.57 | 5.55 | 7.12 | 8.70 |
| 1069 | cycle 30 miles | | 84 | .095 | | | 2.24 | 7.95 | 10.19 | 12.50 |
| 1070 | cycle 40 miles | | 72 | .111 | | | 2.62 | 9.30 | 11.92 | 14.55 |
| 1072 | 40 MPH ave, cycle 6 miles | | 240 | .033 | | | .78 | 2.78 | 3.56 | 4.37 |
| 1074 | cycle 8 miles | | 216 | .037 | | | .87 | 3.09 | 3.96 | 4.85 |
| 1076 | cycle 10 miles | | 192 | .042 | | | .98 | 3.48 | 4.46 | 5.45 |
| 1078 | cycle 20 miles | | 120 | .067 | | | 1.57 | 5.55 | 7.12 | 8.70 |
| 1080 | cycle 30 miles | | 96 | .083 | | | 1.96 | 6.95 | 8.91 | 10.90 |
| 1082 | cycle 40 miles | | 72 | .111 | | | 2.62 | 9.30 | 11.92 | 14.55 |

## 31 23 23 – Fill

| 31 23 23.20 Hauling | | Crew | Daily Output | Labor-Hours | Unit | Material | 2010 Bare Costs | | Total | Total Incl O&P |
|---|---|---|---|---|---|---|---|---|---|---|
| | | | | | | | Labor | Equipment | | |
| 1084 | cycle 50 miles | B-34B | 60 | .133 | L.C.Y. | | 3.14 | 11.15 | 14.29 | 17.50 |
| 1094 | 45 MPH ave, cycle 8 miles | | 216 | .037 | | | .87 | 3.09 | 3.96 | 4.85 |
| 1096 | cycle 10 miles | | 204 | .039 | | | .92 | 3.27 | 4.19 | 5.15 |
| 1098 | cycle 20 miles | | 132 | .061 | | | 1.43 | 5.05 | 6.48 | 7.95 |
| 1100 | cycle 30 miles | | 108 | .074 | | | 1.74 | 6.20 | 7.94 | 9.70 |
| 1102 | cycle 40 miles | | 84 | .095 | | | 2.24 | 7.95 | 10.19 | 12.50 |
| 1104 | cycle 50 miles | | 72 | .111 | | | 2.62 | 9.30 | 11.92 | 14.55 |
| 1106 | 50 MPH ave, cycle 10 miles | | 216 | .037 | | | .87 | 3.09 | 3.96 | 4.85 |
| 1108 | cycle 20 miles | | 144 | .056 | | | 1.31 | 4.64 | 5.95 | 7.30 |
| 1110 | cycle 30 miles | | 108 | .074 | | | 1.74 | 6.20 | 7.94 | 9.70 |
| 1112 | cycle 40 miles | | 84 | .095 | | | 2.24 | 7.95 | 10.19 | 12.50 |
| 1114 | cycle 50 miles | | 72 | .111 | | | 2.62 | 9.30 | 11.92 | 14.55 |
| 1214 | 15 MPH ave, cycle 0.5 mile, 20 min. wait/Ld./Uld. | | 264 | .030 | | | .71 | 2.53 | 3.24 | 3.97 |
| 1216 | cycle 1 mile | | 240 | .033 | | | .78 | 2.78 | 3.56 | 4.37 |
| 1218 | cycle 2 miles | | 204 | .039 | | | .92 | 3.27 | 4.19 | 5.15 |
| 1220 | cycle 4 miles | | 156 | .051 | | | 1.21 | 4.28 | 5.49 | 6.70 |
| 1222 | cycle 6 miles | | 132 | .061 | | | 1.43 | 5.05 | 6.48 | 7.95 |
| 1224 | cycle 8 miles | | 108 | .074 | | | 1.74 | 6.20 | 7.94 | 9.70 |
| 1225 | cycle 10 miles | | 96 | .083 | | | 1.96 | 6.95 | 8.91 | 10.90 |
| 1226 | 20 MPH ave, cycle 0.5 mile | | 264 | .030 | | | .71 | 2.53 | 3.24 | 3.97 |
| 1228 | cycle 1 mile | | 252 | .032 | | | .75 | 2.65 | 3.40 | 4.16 |
| 1230 | cycle 2 miles | | 216 | .037 | | | .87 | 3.09 | 3.96 | 4.85 |
| 1232 | cycle 4 miles | | 180 | .044 | | | 1.05 | 3.71 | 4.76 | 5.80 |
| 1234 | cycle 6 miles | | 144 | .056 | | | 1.31 | 4.64 | 5.95 | 7.30 |
| 1236 | cycle 8 miles | | 132 | .061 | | | 1.43 | 5.05 | 6.48 | 7.95 |
| 1238 | cycle 10 miles | | 108 | .074 | | | 1.74 | 6.20 | 7.94 | 9.70 |
| 1240 | 25 MPH ave, cycle 4 miles | | 192 | .042 | | | .98 | 3.48 | 4.46 | 5.45 |
| 1242 | cycle 6 miles | | 168 | .048 | | | 1.12 | 3.98 | 5.10 | 6.25 |
| 1244 | cycle 8 miles | | 144 | .056 | | | 1.31 | 4.64 | 5.95 | 7.30 |
| 1246 | cycle 10 miles | | 132 | .061 | | | 1.43 | 5.05 | 6.48 | 7.95 |
| 1250 | 30 MPH ave, cycle 4 miles | | 204 | .039 | | | .92 | 3.27 | 4.19 | 5.15 |
| 1252 | cycle 6 miles | | 180 | .044 | | | 1.05 | 3.71 | 4.76 | 5.80 |
| 1254 | cycle 8 miles | | 156 | .051 | | | 1.21 | 4.28 | 5.49 | 6.70 |
| 1256 | cycle 10 miles | | 144 | .056 | | | 1.31 | 4.64 | 5.95 | 7.30 |
| 1260 | 35 MPH ave, cycle 4 miles | | 216 | .037 | | | .87 | 3.09 | 3.96 | 4.85 |
| 1262 | cycle 6 miles | | 192 | .042 | | | .98 | 3.48 | 4.46 | 5.45 |
| 1264 | cycle 8 miles | | 168 | .048 | | | 1.12 | 3.98 | 5.10 | 6.25 |
| 1266 | cycle 10 miles | | 156 | .051 | | | 1.21 | 4.28 | 5.49 | 6.70 |
| 1268 | cycle 20 miles | | 108 | .074 | | | 1.74 | 6.20 | 7.94 | 9.70 |
| 1269 | cycle 30 miles | | 72 | .111 | | | 2.62 | 9.30 | 11.92 | 14.55 |
| 1270 | cycle 40 miles | | 60 | .133 | | | 3.14 | 11.15 | 14.29 | 17.50 |
| 1272 | 40 MPH ave, cycle 6 miles | | 192 | .042 | | | .98 | 3.48 | 4.46 | 5.45 |
| 1274 | cycle 8 miles | | 180 | .044 | | | 1.05 | 3.71 | 4.76 | 5.80 |
| 1276 | cycle 10 miles | | 156 | .051 | | | 1.21 | 4.28 | 5.49 | 6.70 |
| 1278 | cycle 20 miles | | 108 | .074 | | | 1.74 | 6.20 | 7.94 | 9.70 |
| 1280 | cycle 30 miles | | 84 | .095 | | | 2.24 | 7.95 | 10.19 | 12.50 |
| 1282 | cycle 40 miles | | 72 | .111 | | | 2.62 | 9.30 | 11.92 | 14.55 |
| 1284 | cycle 50 miles | | 60 | .133 | | | 3.14 | 11.15 | 14.29 | 17.50 |
| 1294 | 45 MPH ave, cycle 8 miles | | 180 | .044 | | | 1.05 | 3.71 | 4.76 | 5.80 |
| 1296 | cycle 10 miles | | 168 | .048 | | | 1.12 | 3.98 | 5.10 | 6.25 |
| 1298 | cycle 20 miles | | 120 | .067 | | | 1.57 | 5.55 | 7.12 | 8.70 |
| 1300 | cycle 30 miles | | 96 | .083 | | | 1.96 | 6.95 | 8.91 | 10.90 |
| 1302 | cycle 40 miles | | 72 | .111 | | | 2.62 | 9.30 | 11.92 | 14.55 |

# 31 23 Excavation and Fill

## 31 23 23 – Fill

| 31 23 23.20 Hauling | | Crew | Daily Output | Labor-Hours | Unit | Material | 2010 Bare Costs Labor | 2010 Bare Costs Equipment | Total | Total Incl O&P |
|---|---|---|---|---|---|---|---|---|---|---|
| 1304 | cycle 50 miles | B-34B | 60 | .133 | L.C.Y. | | 3.14 | 11.15 | 14.29 | 17.50 |
| 1306 | 50 MPH ave, cycle 10 miles | | 180 | .044 | | | 1.05 | 3.71 | 4.76 | 5.80 |
| 1308 | cycle 20 miles | | 132 | .061 | | | 1.43 | 5.05 | 6.48 | 7.95 |
| 1310 | cycle 30 miles | | 96 | .083 | | | 1.96 | 6.95 | 8.91 | 10.90 |
| 1312 | cycle 40 miles | | 84 | .095 | | | 2.24 | 7.95 | 10.19 | 12.50 |
| 1314 | cycle 50 miles | | 72 | .111 | | | 2.62 | 9.30 | 11.92 | 14.55 |
| 1414 | 15 MPH ave, cycle 0.5 mile, 25 min. wait/Ld./Uld. | | 204 | .039 | | | .92 | 3.27 | 4.19 | 5.15 |
| 1416 | cycle 1 mile | | 192 | .042 | | | .98 | 3.48 | 4.46 | 5.45 |
| 1418 | cycle 2 miles | | 168 | .048 | | | 1.12 | 3.98 | 5.10 | 6.25 |
| 1420 | cycle 4 miles | | 132 | .061 | | | 1.43 | 5.05 | 6.48 | 7.95 |
| 1422 | cycle 6 miles | | 120 | .067 | | | 1.57 | 5.55 | 7.12 | 8.70 |
| 1424 | cycle 8 miles | | 96 | .083 | | | 1.96 | 6.95 | 8.91 | 10.90 |
| 1425 | cycle 10 miles | | 84 | .095 | | | 2.24 | 7.95 | 10.19 | 12.50 |
| 1426 | 20 MPH ave, cycle 0.5 mile | | 216 | .037 | | | .87 | 3.09 | 3.96 | 4.85 |
| 1428 | cycle 1 mile | | 204 | .039 | | | .92 | 3.27 | 4.19 | 5.15 |
| 1430 | cycle 2 miles | | 180 | .044 | | | 1.05 | 3.71 | 4.76 | 5.80 |
| 1432 | cycle 4 miles | | 156 | .051 | | | 1.21 | 4.28 | 5.49 | 6.70 |
| 1434 | cycle 6 miles | | 132 | .061 | | | 1.43 | 5.05 | 6.48 | 7.95 |
| 1436 | cycle 8 miles | | 120 | .067 | | | 1.57 | 5.55 | 7.12 | 8.70 |
| 1438 | cycle 10 miles | | 96 | .083 | | | 1.96 | 6.95 | 8.91 | 10.90 |
| 1440 | 25 MPH ave, cycle 4 miles | | 168 | .048 | | | 1.12 | 3.98 | 5.10 | 6.25 |
| 1442 | cycle 6 miles | | 144 | .056 | | | 1.31 | 4.64 | 5.95 | 7.30 |
| 1444 | cycle 8 miles | | 132 | .061 | | | 1.43 | 5.05 | 6.48 | 7.95 |
| 1446 | cycle 10 miles | | 108 | .074 | | | 1.74 | 6.20 | 7.94 | 9.70 |
| 1450 | 30 MPH ave, cycle 4 miles | | 168 | .048 | | | 1.12 | 3.98 | 5.10 | 6.25 |
| 1452 | cycle 6 miles | | 156 | .051 | | | 1.21 | 4.28 | 5.49 | 6.70 |
| 1454 | cycle 8 miles | | 132 | .061 | | | 1.43 | 5.05 | 6.48 | 7.95 |
| 1456 | cycle 10 miles | | 120 | .067 | | | 1.57 | 5.55 | 7.12 | 8.70 |
| 1460 | 35 MPH ave, cycle 4 miles | | 180 | .044 | | | 1.05 | 3.71 | 4.76 | 5.80 |
| 1462 | cycle 6 miles | | 156 | .051 | | | 1.21 | 4.28 | 5.49 | 6.70 |
| 1464 | cycle 8 miles | | 144 | .056 | | | 1.31 | 4.64 | 5.95 | 7.30 |
| 1466 | cycle 10 miles | | 132 | .061 | | | 1.43 | 5.05 | 6.48 | 7.95 |
| 1468 | cycle 20 miles | | 96 | .083 | | | 1.96 | 6.95 | 8.91 | 10.90 |
| 1469 | cycle 30 miles | | 72 | .111 | | | 2.62 | 9.30 | 11.92 | 14.55 |
| 1470 | cycle 40 miles | | 60 | .133 | | | 3.14 | 11.15 | 14.29 | 17.50 |
| 1472 | 40 MPH ave, cycle 6 miles | | 168 | .048 | | | 1.12 | 3.98 | 5.10 | 6.25 |
| 1474 | cycle 8 miles | | 156 | .051 | | | 1.21 | 4.28 | 5.49 | 6.70 |
| 1476 | cycle 10 miles | | 144 | .056 | | | 1.31 | 4.64 | 5.95 | 7.30 |
| 1478 | cycle 20 miles | | 96 | .083 | | | 1.96 | 6.95 | 8.91 | 10.90 |
| 1480 | cycle 30 miles | | 84 | .095 | | | 2.24 | 7.95 | 10.19 | 12.50 |
| 1482 | cycle 40 miles | | 60 | .133 | | | 3.14 | 11.15 | 14.29 | 17.50 |
| 1484 | cycle 50 miles | | 60 | .133 | | | 3.14 | 11.15 | 14.29 | 17.50 |
| 1494 | 45 MPH ave, cycle 8 miles | | 156 | .051 | | | 1.21 | 4.28 | 5.49 | 6.70 |
| 1496 | cycle 10 miles | | 144 | .056 | | | 1.31 | 4.64 | 5.95 | 7.30 |
| 1498 | cycle 20 miles | | 108 | .074 | | | 1.74 | 6.20 | 7.94 | 9.70 |
| 1500 | cycle 30 miles | | 84 | .095 | | | 2.24 | 7.95 | 10.19 | 12.50 |
| 1502 | cycle 40 miles | | 72 | .111 | | | 2.62 | 9.30 | 11.92 | 14.55 |
| 1504 | cycle 50 miles | | 60 | .133 | | | 3.14 | 11.15 | 14.29 | 17.50 |
| 1506 | 50 MPH ave, cycle 10 miles | | 156 | .051 | | | 1.21 | 4.28 | 5.49 | 6.70 |
| 1508 | cycle 20 miles | | 120 | .067 | | | 1.57 | 5.55 | 7.12 | 8.70 |
| 1510 | cycle 30 miles | | 96 | .083 | | | 1.96 | 6.95 | 8.91 | 10.90 |
| 1512 | cycle 40 miles | | 72 | .111 | | | 2.62 | 9.30 | 11.92 | 14.55 |
| 1514 | cycle 50 miles | | 60 | .133 | | | 3.14 | 11.15 | 14.29 | 17.50 |

# 31 23 Excavation and Fill

## 31 23 23 – Fill

| 31 23 23.20 Hauling | | Crew | Daily Output | Labor-Hours | Unit | Material | 2010 Bare Costs | | Total | Total Incl O&P |
|---|---|---|---|---|---|---|---|---|---|---|
| | | | | | | | Labor | Equipment | | |
| 1614 | 15 MPH, cycle 0.5 mile, 30 min. wait/Ld./Uld. | B-34B | 180 | .044 | L.C.Y. | | 1.05 | 3.71 | 4.76 | 5.80 |
| 1616 | cycle 1 mile | | 168 | .048 | | | 1.12 | 3.98 | 5.10 | 6.25 |
| 1618 | cycle 2 miles | | 144 | .056 | | | 1.31 | 4.64 | 5.95 | 7.30 |
| 1620 | cycle 4 miles | | 120 | .067 | | | 1.57 | 5.55 | 7.12 | 8.70 |
| 1622 | cycle 6 miles | | 108 | .074 | | | 1.74 | 6.20 | 7.94 | 9.70 |
| 1624 | cycle 8 miles | | 84 | .095 | | | 2.24 | 7.95 | 10.19 | 12.50 |
| 1625 | cycle 10 miles | | 84 | .095 | | | 2.24 | 7.95 | 10.19 | 12.50 |
| 1626 | 20 MPH ave, cycle 0.5 mile | | 180 | .044 | | | 1.05 | 3.71 | 4.76 | 5.80 |
| 1628 | cycle 1 mile | | 168 | .048 | | | 1.12 | 3.98 | 5.10 | 6.25 |
| 1630 | cycle 2 miles | | 156 | .051 | | | 1.21 | 4.28 | 5.49 | 6.70 |
| 1632 | cycle 4 miles | | 132 | .061 | | | 1.43 | 5.05 | 6.48 | 7.95 |
| 1634 | cycle 6 miles | | 120 | .067 | | | 1.57 | 5.55 | 7.12 | 8.70 |
| 1636 | cycle 8 miles | | 108 | .074 | | | 1.74 | 6.20 | 7.94 | 9.70 |
| 1638 | cycle 10 miles | | 96 | .083 | | | 1.96 | 6.95 | 8.91 | 10.90 |
| 1640 | 25 MPH ave, cycle 4 miles | | 144 | .056 | | | 1.31 | 4.64 | 5.95 | 7.30 |
| 1642 | cycle 6 miles | | 132 | .061 | | | 1.43 | 5.05 | 6.48 | 7.95 |
| 1644 | cycle 8 miles | | 108 | .074 | | | 1.74 | 6.20 | 7.94 | 9.70 |
| 1646 | cycle 10 miles | | 108 | .074 | | | 1.74 | 6.20 | 7.94 | 9.70 |
| 1650 | 30 MPH ave, cycle 4 miles | | 144 | .056 | | | 1.31 | 4.64 | 5.95 | 7.30 |
| 1652 | cycle 6 miles | | 132 | .061 | | | 1.43 | 5.05 | 6.48 | 7.95 |
| 1654 | cycle 8 miles | | 120 | .067 | | | 1.57 | 5.55 | 7.12 | 8.70 |
| 1656 | cycle 10 miles | | 108 | .074 | | | 1.74 | 6.20 | 7.94 | 9.70 |
| 1660 | 35 MPH ave, cycle 4 miles | | 156 | .051 | | | 1.21 | 4.28 | 5.49 | 6.70 |
| 1662 | cycle 6 miles | | 144 | .056 | | | 1.31 | 4.64 | 5.95 | 7.30 |
| 1664 | cycle 8 miles | | 132 | .061 | | | 1.43 | 5.05 | 6.48 | 7.95 |
| 1666 | cycle 10 miles | | 120 | .067 | | | 1.57 | 5.55 | 7.12 | 8.70 |
| 1668 | cycle 20 miles | | 84 | .095 | | | 2.24 | 7.95 | 10.19 | 12.50 |
| 1669 | cycle 30 miles | | 72 | .111 | | | 2.62 | 9.30 | 11.92 | 14.55 |
| 1670 | cycle 40 miles | | 60 | .133 | | | 3.14 | 11.15 | 14.29 | 17.50 |
| 1672 | 40 MPH, cycle 6 miles | | 144 | .056 | | | 1.31 | 4.64 | 5.95 | 7.30 |
| 1674 | cycle 8 miles | | 132 | .061 | | | 1.43 | 5.05 | 6.48 | 7.95 |
| 1676 | cycle 10 miles | | 120 | .067 | | | 1.57 | 5.55 | 7.12 | 8.70 |
| 1678 | cycle 20 miles | | 96 | .083 | | | 1.96 | 6.95 | 8.91 | 10.90 |
| 1680 | cycle 30 miles | | 72 | .111 | | | 2.62 | 9.30 | 11.92 | 14.55 |
| 1682 | cycle 40 miles | | 60 | .133 | | | 3.14 | 11.15 | 14.29 | 17.50 |
| 1684 | cycle 50 miles | | 48 | .167 | | | 3.93 | 13.90 | 17.83 | 22 |
| 1694 | 45 MPH ave, cycle 8 miles | | 144 | .056 | | | 1.31 | 4.64 | 5.95 | 7.30 |
| 1696 | cycle 10 miles | | 132 | .061 | | | 1.43 | 5.05 | 6.48 | 7.95 |
| 1698 | cycle 20 miles | | 96 | .083 | | | 1.96 | 6.95 | 8.91 | 10.90 |
| 1700 | cycle 30 miles | | 84 | .095 | | | 2.24 | 7.95 | 10.19 | 12.50 |
| 1702 | cycle 40 miles | | 60 | .133 | | | 3.14 | 11.15 | 14.29 | 17.50 |
| 1704 | cycle 50 miles | | 60 | .133 | | | 3.14 | 11.15 | 14.29 | 17.50 |
| 1706 | 50 MPH ave, cycle 10 miles | | 132 | .061 | | | 1.43 | 5.05 | 6.48 | 7.95 |
| 1708 | cycle 20 miles | | 108 | .074 | | | 1.74 | 6.20 | 7.94 | 9.70 |
| 1710 | cycle 30 miles | | 84 | .095 | | | 2.24 | 7.95 | 10.19 | 12.50 |
| 1712 | cycle 40 miles | | 72 | .111 | | | 2.62 | 9.30 | 11.92 | 14.55 |
| 1714 | cycle 50 miles | ↓ | 60 | .133 | ↓ | | 3.14 | 11.15 | 14.29 | 17.50 |
| 2000 | Hauling, 8 CY truck, small project cost per hour | B-34A | 8 | 1 | Hr. | | 23.50 | 50 | 73.50 | 94.50 |
| 2100 | 12 CY Truck | B-34B | 8 | 1 | | | 23.50 | 83.50 | 107 | 131 |
| 2150 | 16.5 CY Truck | B-34C | 8 | 1 | | | 23.50 | 89 | 112.50 | 137 |
| 2175 | 18 CY 8 wheel Truck | B-34I | 8 | 1 | | | 23.50 | 105 | 128.50 | 154 |
| 2200 | 20 CY Truck | B-34D | 8 | 1 | ↓ | | 23.50 | 91 | 114.50 | 139 |
| 9014 | 18 CY truck, 8 wheels,15 min. wait/Ld./Uld.,15 MPH, cycle 0.5 mi. | B-34I | 504 | .016 | L.C.Y. | | .37 | 1.66 | 2.03 | 2.45 |

584

## 31 23 23 – Fill

| 31 23 23.20 Hauling | | Crew | Daily Output | Labor-Hours | Unit | Material | 2010 Bare Costs | | Total | Total Incl O&P |
|---|---|---|---|---|---|---|---|---|---|---|
| | | | | | | | Labor | Equipment | | |
| 9016 | cycle 1 mile | B-34I | 450 | .018 | L.C.Y. | | .42 | 1.86 | 2.28 | 2.75 |
| 9018 | cycle 2 miles | | 378 | .021 | | | .50 | 2.22 | 2.72 | 3.27 |
| 9020 | cycle 4 miles | | 270 | .030 | | | .70 | 3.11 | 3.81 | 4.58 |
| 9022 | cycle 6 miles | | 216 | .037 | | | .87 | 3.88 | 4.75 | 5.70 |
| 9024 | cycle 8 miles | | 180 | .044 | | | 1.05 | 4.66 | 5.71 | 6.85 |
| 9025 | cycle 10 miles | | 144 | .056 | | | 1.31 | 5.80 | 7.11 | 8.60 |
| 9026 | 20 MPH ave, cycle 0.5 mile | | 522 | .015 | | | .36 | 1.61 | 1.97 | 2.37 |
| 9028 | cycle 1 mile | | 468 | .017 | | | .40 | 1.79 | 2.19 | 2.64 |
| 9030 | cycle 2 miles | | 414 | .019 | | | .46 | 2.02 | 2.48 | 2.99 |
| 9032 | cycle 4 miles | | 324 | .025 | | | .58 | 2.59 | 3.17 | 3.82 |
| 9034 | cycle 6 miles | | 252 | .032 | | | .75 | 3.33 | 4.08 | 4.90 |
| 9036 | cycle 8 miles | | 216 | .037 | | | .87 | 3.88 | 4.75 | 5.70 |
| 9038 | cycle 10 miles | | 180 | .044 | | | 1.05 | 4.66 | 5.71 | 6.85 |
| 9040 | 25 MPH ave, cycle 4 miles | | 342 | .023 | | | .55 | 2.45 | 3 | 3.62 |
| 9042 | cycle 6 miles | | 288 | .028 | | | .65 | 2.91 | 3.56 | 4.29 |
| 9044 | cycle 8 miles | | 252 | .032 | | | .75 | 3.33 | 4.08 | 4.90 |
| 9046 | cycle 10 miles | | 216 | .037 | | | .87 | 3.88 | 4.75 | 5.70 |
| 9050 | 30 MPH ave, cycle 4 miles | | 378 | .021 | | | .50 | 2.22 | 2.72 | 3.27 |
| 9052 | cycle 6 miles | | 324 | .025 | | | .58 | 2.59 | 3.17 | 3.82 |
| 9054 | cycle 8 miles | | 270 | .030 | | | .70 | 3.11 | 3.81 | 4.58 |
| 9056 | cycle 10 miles | | 234 | .034 | | | .81 | 3.58 | 4.39 | 5.30 |
| 9060 | 35 MPH ave, cycle 4 miles | | 396 | .020 | | | .48 | 2.12 | 2.60 | 3.12 |
| 9062 | cycle 6 miles | | 342 | .023 | | | .55 | 2.45 | 3 | 3.62 |
| 9064 | cycle 8 miles | | 288 | .028 | | | .65 | 2.91 | 3.56 | 4.29 |
| 9066 | cycle 10 miles | | 270 | .030 | | | .70 | 3.11 | 3.81 | 4.58 |
| 9068 | cycle 20 miles | | 162 | .049 | | | 1.16 | 5.20 | 6.36 | 7.65 |
| 9070 | cycle 30 miles | | 126 | .063 | | | 1.50 | 6.65 | 8.15 | 9.80 |
| 9072 | cycle 40 miles | | 90 | .089 | | | 2.09 | 9.30 | 11.39 | 13.75 |
| 9074 | 40 MPH ave, cycle 6 miles | | 360 | .022 | | | .52 | 2.33 | 2.85 | 3.43 |
| 9076 | cycle 8 miles | | 324 | .025 | | | .58 | 2.59 | 3.17 | 3.82 |
| 9078 | cycle 10 miles | | 288 | .028 | | | .65 | 2.91 | 3.56 | 4.29 |
| 9080 | cycle 20 miles | | 180 | .044 | | | 1.05 | 4.66 | 5.71 | 6.85 |
| 9082 | cycle 30 miles | | 144 | .056 | | | 1.31 | 5.80 | 7.11 | 8.60 |
| 9084 | cycle 40 miles | | 108 | .074 | | | 1.74 | 7.75 | 9.49 | 11.45 |
| 9086 | cycle 50 miles | | 90 | .089 | | | 2.09 | 9.30 | 11.39 | 13.75 |
| 9094 | 45 MPH ave, cycle 8 miles | | 324 | .025 | | | .58 | 2.59 | 3.17 | 3.82 |
| 9096 | cycle 10 miles | | 306 | .026 | | | .62 | 2.74 | 3.36 | 4.03 |
| 9098 | cycle 20 miles | | 198 | .040 | | | .95 | 4.23 | 5.18 | 6.25 |
| 9100 | cycle 30 miles | | 144 | .056 | | | 1.31 | 5.80 | 7.11 | 8.60 |
| 9102 | cycle 40 miles | | 126 | .063 | | | 1.50 | 6.65 | 8.15 | 9.80 |
| 9104 | cycle 50 miles | | 108 | .074 | | | 1.74 | 7.75 | 9.49 | 11.45 |
| 9106 | 50 MPH ave, cycle 10 miles | | 324 | .025 | | | .58 | 2.59 | 3.17 | 3.82 |
| 9108 | cycle 20 miles | | 216 | .037 | | | .87 | 3.88 | 4.75 | 5.70 |
| 9110 | cycle 30 miles | | 162 | .049 | | | 1.16 | 5.20 | 6.36 | 7.65 |
| 9112 | cycle 40 miles | | 126 | .063 | | | 1.50 | 6.65 | 8.15 | 9.80 |
| 9114 | cycle 50 miles | | 108 | .074 | | | 1.74 | 7.75 | 9.49 | 11.45 |
| 9214 | 20 min. wait/Ld./Uld.,15 MPH, cycle 0.5 mi. | | 396 | .020 | | | .48 | 2.12 | 2.60 | 3.12 |
| 9216 | cycle 1 mile | | 360 | .022 | | | .52 | 2.33 | 2.85 | 3.43 |
| 9218 | cycle 2 miles | | 306 | .026 | | | .62 | 2.74 | 3.36 | 4.03 |
| 9220 | cycle 4 miles | | 234 | .034 | | | .81 | 3.58 | 4.39 | 5.30 |
| 9222 | cycle 6 miles | | 198 | .040 | | | .95 | 4.23 | 5.18 | 6.25 |
| 9224 | cycle 8 miles | | 162 | .049 | | | 1.16 | 5.20 | 6.36 | 7.65 |
| 9225 | cycle 10 miles | | 144 | .056 | | | 1.31 | 5.80 | 7.11 | 8.60 |

## 31 23 23 – Fill

| 31 23 23.20 Hauling | | Crew | Daily Output | Labor-Hours | Unit | Material | Labor | Equipment | Total | Total Incl O&P |
|---|---|---|---|---|---|---|---|---|---|---|
| | | | | | | | | 2010 Bare Costs | | |
| 9226 | 20 MPH ave, cycle 0.5 mile | B-34I | 396 | .020 | L.C.Y. | | .48 | 2.12 | 2.60 | 3.12 |
| 9228 | cycle 1 mile | | 378 | .021 | | | .50 | 2.22 | 2.72 | 3.27 |
| 9230 | cycle 2 miles | | 324 | .025 | | | .58 | 2.59 | 3.17 | 3.82 |
| 9232 | cycle 4 miles | | 270 | .030 | | | .70 | 3.11 | 3.81 | 4.58 |
| 9234 | cycle 6 miles | | 216 | .037 | | | .87 | 3.88 | 4.75 | 5.70 |
| 9236 | cycle 8 miles | | 198 | .040 | | | .95 | 4.23 | 5.18 | 6.25 |
| 9238 | cycle 10 miles | | 162 | .049 | | | 1.16 | 5.20 | 6.36 | 7.65 |
| 9240 | 25 MPH ave, cycle 4 miles | | 288 | .028 | | | .65 | 2.91 | 3.56 | 4.29 |
| 9242 | cycle 6 miles | | 252 | .032 | | | .75 | 3.33 | 4.08 | 4.90 |
| 9244 | cycle 8 miles | | 216 | .037 | | | .87 | 3.88 | 4.75 | 5.70 |
| 9246 | cycle 10 miles | | 198 | .040 | | | .95 | 4.23 | 5.18 | 6.25 |
| 9250 | 30 MPH ave, cycle 4 miles | | 306 | .026 | | | .62 | 2.74 | 3.36 | 4.03 |
| 9252 | cycle 6 miles | | 270 | .030 | | | .70 | 3.11 | 3.81 | 4.58 |
| 9254 | cycle 8 miles | | 234 | .034 | | | .81 | 3.58 | 4.39 | 5.30 |
| 9256 | cycle 10 miles | | 216 | .037 | | | .87 | 3.88 | 4.75 | 5.70 |
| 9260 | 35 MPH ave, cycle 4 miles | | 324 | .025 | | | .58 | 2.59 | 3.17 | 3.82 |
| 9262 | cycle 6 miles | | 288 | .028 | | | .65 | 2.91 | 3.56 | 4.29 |
| 9264 | cycle 8 miles | | 252 | .032 | | | .75 | 3.33 | 4.08 | 4.90 |
| 9266 | cycle 10 miles | | 234 | .034 | | | .81 | 3.58 | 4.39 | 5.30 |
| 9268 | cycle 20 miles | | 162 | .049 | | | 1.16 | 5.20 | 6.36 | 7.65 |
| 9270 | cycle 30 miles | | 108 | .074 | | | 1.74 | 7.75 | 9.49 | 11.45 |
| 9272 | cycle 40 miles | | 90 | .089 | | | 2.09 | 9.30 | 11.39 | 13.75 |
| 9274 | 40 MPH ave, cycle 6 miles | | 288 | .028 | | | .65 | 2.91 | 3.56 | 4.29 |
| 9276 | cycle 8 miles | | 270 | .030 | | | .70 | 3.11 | 3.81 | 4.58 |
| 9278 | cycle 10 miles | | 234 | .034 | | | .81 | 3.58 | 4.39 | 5.30 |
| 9280 | cycle 20 miles | | 162 | .049 | | | 1.16 | 5.20 | 6.36 | 7.65 |
| 9282 | cycle 30 miles | | 126 | .063 | | | 1.50 | 6.65 | 8.15 | 9.80 |
| 9284 | cycle 40 miles | | 108 | .074 | | | 1.74 | 7.75 | 9.49 | 11.45 |
| 9286 | cycle 50 miles | | 90 | .089 | | | 2.09 | 9.30 | 11.39 | 13.75 |
| 9294 | 45 MPH ave, cycle 8 miles | | 270 | .030 | | | .70 | 3.11 | 3.81 | 4.58 |
| 9296 | cycle 10 miles | | 252 | .032 | | | .75 | 3.33 | 4.08 | 4.90 |
| 9298 | cycle 20 miles | | 180 | .044 | | | 1.05 | 4.66 | 5.71 | 6.85 |
| 9300 | cycle 30 miles | | 144 | .056 | | | 1.31 | 5.80 | 7.11 | 8.60 |
| 9302 | cycle 40 miles | | 108 | .074 | | | 1.74 | 7.75 | 9.49 | 11.45 |
| 9304 | cycle 50 miles | | 90 | .089 | | | 2.09 | 9.30 | 11.39 | 13.75 |
| 9306 | 50 MPH ave, cycle 10 miles | | 270 | .030 | | | .70 | 3.11 | 3.81 | 4.58 |
| 9308 | cycle 20 miles | | 198 | .040 | | | .95 | 4.23 | 5.18 | 6.25 |
| 9310 | cycle 30 miles | | 144 | .056 | | | 1.31 | 5.80 | 7.11 | 8.60 |
| 9312 | cycle 40 miles | | 126 | .063 | | | 1.50 | 6.65 | 8.15 | 9.80 |
| 9314 | cycle 50 miles | | 108 | .074 | | | 1.74 | 7.75 | 9.49 | 11.45 |
| 9414 | 25 min. wait/Ld./Uld.,15 MPH, cycle 0.5 mi. | | 306 | .026 | | | .62 | 2.74 | 3.36 | 4.03 |
| 9416 | cycle 1 mile | | 288 | .028 | | | .65 | 2.91 | 3.56 | 4.29 |
| 9418 | cycle 2 miles | | 252 | .032 | | | .75 | 3.33 | 4.08 | 4.90 |
| 9420 | cycle 4 miles | | 198 | .040 | | | .95 | 4.23 | 5.18 | 6.25 |
| 9422 | cycle 6 miles | | 180 | .044 | | | 1.05 | 4.66 | 5.71 | 6.85 |
| 9424 | cycle 8 miles | | 144 | .056 | | | 1.31 | 5.80 | 7.11 | 8.60 |
| 9425 | cycle 10 miles | | 126 | .063 | | | 1.50 | 6.65 | 8.15 | 9.80 |
| 9426 | 20 MPH ave, cycle 0.5 mile | | 324 | .025 | | | .58 | 2.59 | 3.17 | 3.82 |
| 9428 | cycle 1 mile | | 306 | .026 | | | .62 | 2.74 | 3.36 | 4.03 |
| 9430 | cycle 2 miles | | 270 | .030 | | | .70 | 3.11 | 3.81 | 4.58 |
| 9432 | cycle 4 miles | | 234 | .034 | | | .81 | 3.58 | 4.39 | 5.30 |
| 9434 | cycle 6 miles | | 198 | .040 | | | .95 | 4.23 | 5.18 | 6.25 |
| 9436 | cycle 8 miles | | 180 | .044 | | | 1.05 | 4.66 | 5.71 | 6.85 |

| 31 23 23.20 Hauling | | Crew | Daily Output | Labor-Hours | Unit | Material | 2010 Bare Costs Labor | 2010 Bare Costs Equipment | Total | Total Incl O&P |
|---|---|---|---|---|---|---|---|---|---|---|
| 9438 | cycle 10 miles | B-34I | 144 | .056 | L.C.Y. | | 1.31 | 5.80 | 7.11 | 8.60 |
| 9440 | 25 MPH ave, cycle 4 miles | | 252 | .032 | | | .75 | 3.33 | 4.08 | 4.90 |
| 9442 | cycle 6 miles | | 216 | .037 | | | .87 | 3.88 | 4.75 | 5.70 |
| 9444 | cycle 8 miles | | 198 | .040 | | | .95 | 4.23 | 5.18 | 6.25 |
| 9446 | cycle 10 miles | | 180 | .044 | | | 1.05 | 4.66 | 5.71 | 6.85 |
| 9450 | 30 MPH ave, cycle 4 miles | | 252 | .032 | | | .75 | 3.33 | 4.08 | 4.90 |
| 9452 | cycle 6 miles | | 234 | .034 | | | .81 | 3.58 | 4.39 | 5.30 |
| 9454 | cycle 8 miles | | 198 | .040 | | | .95 | 4.23 | 5.18 | 6.25 |
| 9456 | cycle 10 miles | | 180 | .044 | | | 1.05 | 4.66 | 5.71 | 6.85 |
| 9460 | 35 MPH ave, cycle 4 miles | | 270 | .030 | | | .70 | 3.11 | 3.81 | 4.58 |
| 9462 | cycle 6 miles | | 234 | .034 | | | .81 | 3.58 | 4.39 | 5.30 |
| 9464 | cycle 8 miles | | 216 | .037 | | | .87 | 3.88 | 4.75 | 5.70 |
| 9466 | cycle 10 miles | | 198 | .040 | | | .95 | 4.23 | 5.18 | 6.25 |
| 9468 | cycle 20 miles | | 144 | .056 | | | 1.31 | 5.80 | 7.11 | 8.60 |
| 9470 | cycle 30 miles | | 108 | .074 | | | 1.74 | 7.75 | 9.49 | 11.45 |
| 9472 | cycle 40 miles | | 90 | .089 | | | 2.09 | 9.30 | 11.39 | 13.75 |
| 9474 | 40 MPH ave, cycle 6 miles | | 252 | .032 | | | .75 | 3.33 | 4.08 | 4.90 |
| 9476 | cycle 8 miles | | 234 | .034 | | | .81 | 3.58 | 4.39 | 5.30 |
| 9478 | cycle 10 miles | | 216 | .037 | | | .87 | 3.88 | 4.75 | 5.70 |
| 9480 | cycle 20 miles | | 144 | .056 | | | 1.31 | 5.80 | 7.11 | 8.60 |
| 9482 | cycle 30 miles | | 126 | .063 | | | 1.50 | 6.65 | 8.15 | 9.80 |
| 9484 | cycle 40 miles | | 90 | .089 | | | 2.09 | 9.30 | 11.39 | 13.75 |
| 9486 | cycle 50 miles | | 90 | .089 | | | 2.09 | 9.30 | 11.39 | 13.75 |
| 9494 | 45 MPH ave, cycle 8 miles | | 234 | .034 | | | .81 | 3.58 | 4.39 | 5.30 |
| 9496 | cycle 10 miles | | 216 | .037 | | | .87 | 3.88 | 4.75 | 5.70 |
| 9498 | cycle 20 miles | | 162 | .049 | | | 1.16 | 5.20 | 6.36 | 7.65 |
| 9500 | cycle 30 miles | | 126 | .063 | | | 1.50 | 6.65 | 8.15 | 9.80 |
| 9502 | cycle 40 miles | | 108 | .074 | | | 1.74 | 7.75 | 9.49 | 11.45 |
| 9504 | cycle 50 miles | | 90 | .089 | | | 2.09 | 9.30 | 11.39 | 13.75 |
| 9506 | 50 MPH ave, cycle 10 miles | | 234 | .034 | | | .81 | 3.58 | 4.39 | 5.30 |
| 9508 | cycle 20 miles | | 180 | .044 | | | 1.05 | 4.66 | 5.71 | 6.85 |
| 9510 | cycle 30 miles | | 144 | .056 | | | 1.31 | 5.80 | 7.11 | 8.60 |
| 9512 | cycle 40 miles | | 108 | .074 | | | 1.74 | 7.75 | 9.49 | 11.45 |
| 9514 | cycle 50 miles | | 90 | .089 | | | 2.09 | 9.30 | 11.39 | 13.75 |
| 9614 | 25 min. wait/Ld./Uld.,15 MPH, cycle 0.5 mi. | | 270 | .030 | | | .70 | 3.11 | 3.81 | 4.58 |
| 9616 | cycle 1 mile | | 252 | .032 | | | .75 | 3.33 | 4.08 | 4.90 |
| 9618 | cycle 2 miles | | 216 | .037 | | | .87 | 3.88 | 4.75 | 5.70 |
| 9620 | cycle 4 miles | | 180 | .044 | | | 1.05 | 4.66 | 5.71 | 6.85 |
| 9622 | cycle 6 miles | | 162 | .049 | | | 1.16 | 5.20 | 6.36 | 7.65 |
| 9624 | cycle 8 miles | | 126 | .063 | | | 1.50 | 6.65 | 8.15 | 9.80 |
| 9625 | cycle 10 miles | | 126 | .063 | | | 1.50 | 6.65 | 8.15 | 9.80 |
| 9626 | 20 MPH ave, cycle 0.5 mile | | 270 | .030 | | | .70 | 3.11 | 3.81 | 4.58 |
| 9628 | cycle 1 mile | | 252 | .032 | | | .75 | 3.33 | 4.08 | 4.90 |
| 9630 | cycle 2 miles | | 234 | .034 | | | .81 | 3.58 | 4.39 | 5.30 |
| 9632 | cycle 4 miles | | 198 | .040 | | | .95 | 4.23 | 5.18 | 6.25 |
| 9634 | cycle 6 miles | | 180 | .044 | | | 1.05 | 4.66 | 5.71 | 6.85 |
| 9636 | cycle 8 miles | | 162 | .049 | | | 1.16 | 5.20 | 6.36 | 7.65 |
| 9638 | cycle 10 miles | | 144 | .056 | | | 1.31 | 5.80 | 7.11 | 8.60 |
| 9640 | 25 MPH ave, cycle 4 miles | | 216 | .037 | | | .87 | 3.88 | 4.75 | 5.70 |
| 9642 | cycle 6 miles | | 198 | .040 | | | .95 | 4.23 | 5.18 | 6.25 |
| 9644 | cycle 8 miles | | 180 | .044 | | | 1.05 | 4.66 | 5.71 | 6.85 |
| 9646 | cycle 10 miles | | 162 | .049 | | | 1.16 | 5.20 | 6.36 | 7.65 |
| 9650 | 30 MPH ave, cycle 4 miles | | 216 | .037 | | | .87 | 3.88 | 4.75 | 5.70 |

# 31 23 Excavation and Fill

## 31 23 23 – Fill

| | | Crew | Daily Output | Labor-Hours | Unit | Material | 2010 Bare Costs Labor | 2010 Bare Costs Equipment | Total | Total Incl O&P |
|---|---|---|---|---|---|---|---|---|---|---|
| 9652 | cycle 6 miles | B-34I | 198 | .040 | L.C.Y. | | .95 | 4.23 | 5.18 | 6.25 |
| 9654 | cycle 8 miles | | 180 | .044 | | | 1.05 | 4.66 | 5.71 | 6.85 |
| 9656 | cycle 10 miles | | 162 | .049 | | | 1.16 | 5.20 | 6.36 | 7.65 |
| 9660 | 35 MPH ave, cycle 4 miles | | 234 | .034 | | | .81 | 3.58 | 4.39 | 5.30 |
| 9662 | cycle 6 miles | | 216 | .037 | | | .87 | 3.88 | 4.75 | 5.70 |
| 9664 | cycle 8 miles | | 198 | .040 | | | .95 | 4.23 | 5.18 | 6.25 |
| 9666 | cycle 10 miles | | 180 | .044 | | | 1.05 | 4.66 | 5.71 | 6.85 |
| 9668 | cycle 20 miles | | 126 | .063 | | | 1.50 | 6.65 | 8.15 | 9.80 |
| 9670 | cycle 30 miles | | 108 | .074 | | | 1.74 | 7.75 | 9.49 | 11.45 |
| 9672 | cycle 40 miles | | 90 | .089 | | | 2.09 | 9.30 | 11.39 | 13.75 |
| 9674 | 40 MPH ave, cycle 6 miles | | 216 | .037 | | | .87 | 3.88 | 4.75 | 5.70 |
| 9676 | cycle 8 miles | | 198 | .040 | | | .95 | 4.23 | 5.18 | 6.25 |
| 9678 | cycle 10 miles | | 180 | .044 | | | 1.05 | 4.66 | 5.71 | 6.85 |
| 9680 | cycle 20 miles | | 144 | .056 | | | 1.31 | 5.80 | 7.11 | 8.60 |
| 9682 | cycle 30 miles | | 108 | .074 | | | 1.74 | 7.75 | 9.49 | 11.45 |
| 9684 | cycle 40 miles | | 90 | .089 | | | 2.09 | 9.30 | 11.39 | 13.75 |
| 9686 | cycle 50 miles | | 72 | .111 | | | 2.62 | 11.65 | 14.27 | 17.15 |
| 9694 | 45 MPH ave, cycle 8 miles | | 216 | .037 | | | .87 | 3.88 | 4.75 | 5.70 |
| 9696 | cycle 10 miles | | 198 | .040 | | | .95 | 4.23 | 5.18 | 6.25 |
| 9698 | cycle 20 miles | | 144 | .056 | | | 1.31 | 5.80 | 7.11 | 8.60 |
| 9700 | cycle 30 miles | | 126 | .063 | | | 1.50 | 6.65 | 8.15 | 9.80 |
| 9702 | cycle 40 miles | | 108 | .074 | | | 1.74 | 7.75 | 9.49 | 11.45 |
| 9704 | cycle 50 miles | | 90 | .089 | | | 2.09 | 9.30 | 11.39 | 13.75 |
| 9706 | 50 MPH ave, cycle 10 miles | | 198 | .040 | | | .95 | 4.23 | 5.18 | 6.25 |
| 9708 | cycle 20 miles | | 162 | .049 | | | 1.16 | 5.20 | 6.36 | 7.65 |
| 9710 | cycle 30 miles | | 126 | .063 | | | 1.50 | 6.65 | 8.15 | 9.80 |
| 9712 | cycle 40 miles | | 108 | .074 | | | 1.74 | 7.75 | 9.49 | 11.45 |
| 9714 | cycle 50 miles | | 90 | .089 | | | 2.09 | 9.30 | 11.39 | 13.75 |

### 31 23 23.24 Compaction, Structural

| | | Crew | Daily Output | Labor-Hours | Unit | Material | Labor | Equipment | Total | Total Incl O&P |
|---|---|---|---|---|---|---|---|---|---|---|
| 0010 | **COMPACTION, STRUCTURAL** | | | | | | | | | |
| 0020 | Steel wheel tandem roller, 5 tons | B-10E | 8 | 1 | Hr. | | 29.50 | 19 | 48.50 | 69.50 |
| 0050 | Air tamp, 6" to 8" lifts, common fill | B-9 | 250 | .160 | E.C.Y. | | 3.50 | .90 | 4.40 | 6.90 |
| 0060 | Select fill | " | 300 | .133 | | | 2.92 | .75 | 3.67 | 5.75 |
| 0600 | Vibratory plate, 8" lifts, common fill | A-1D | 200 | .040 | | | .86 | .17 | 1.03 | 1.64 |
| 0700 | Select fill | " | 216 | .037 | | | .80 | .16 | .96 | 1.51 |

# 31 25 Erosion and Sedimentation Controls

## 31 25 13 – Erosion Controls

### 31 25 13.10 Synthetic Erosion Control

| | | | Crew | Daily Output | Labor-Hours | Unit | Material | Labor | Equipment | Total | Total Incl O&P |
|---|---|---|---|---|---|---|---|---|---|---|---|
| 0010 | **SYNTHETIC EROSION CONTROL** | | | | | | | | | | |
| 0020 | Jute mesh, 100 SY per roll, 4' wide, stapled | G | B-80A | 2400 | .010 | S.Y. | 1.04 | .22 | .12 | 1.38 | 1.64 |
| 0100 | Plastic netting, stapled, 2" x 1" mesh, 20 mil | G | B-1 | 2500 | .010 | | .79 | .21 | | 1 | 1.23 |
| 0200 | Polypropylene mesh, stapled, 6.5 oz./S.Y. | G | | 2500 | .010 | | 1.70 | .21 | | 1.91 | 2.23 |
| 0300 | Tobacco netting, or jute mesh #2, stapled | G | | 2500 | .010 | | .10 | .21 | | .31 | .47 |
| 1000 | Silt fence, polypropylene, 3' high, ideal conditions | G | 2 Clab | 1600 | .010 | L.F. | .40 | .22 | | .62 | .80 |
| 1100 | Adverse conditions | G | " | 950 | .017 | " | .40 | .36 | | .76 | 1.05 |

# 31 31 Soil Treatment

## 31 31 16 – Termite Control

| 31 31 16.13 Chemical Termite Control | Crew | Daily Output | Labor-Hours | Unit | Material | 2010 Bare Costs Labor | Equipment | Total | Total Incl O&P |
|---|---|---|---|---|---|---|---|---|---|
| 0010 **CHEMICAL TERMITE CONTROL** | | | | | | | | | |
| 0020　Slab and walls, residential | 1 Skwk | 1200 | .007 | SF Flr. | .31 | .20 | | .51 | .67 |
| 0400　Insecticides for termite control, minimum | | 14.20 | .563 | Gal. | 12.75 | 16.50 | | 29.25 | 41.50 |
| 0500　　　Maximum | | 11 | .727 | " | 22 | 21.50 | | 43.50 | 59.50 |

# Division Notes

| | CREW | DAILY OUTPUT | LABOR-HOURS | UNIT | 2010 BARE COSTS | | | | TOTAL INCL O&P |
|---|---|---|---|---|---|---|---|---|---|
| | | | | | MAT. | LABOR | EQUIP. | TOTAL | |
| | | | | | | | | | |
| | | | | | | | | | |
| | | | | | | | | | |
| | | | | | | | | | |
| | | | | | | | | | |
| | | | | | | | | | |
| | | | | | | | | | |
| | | | | | | | | | |
| | | | | | | | | | |
| | | | | | | | | | |
| | | | | | | | | | |
| | | | | | | | | | |
| | | | | | | | | | |
| | | | | | | | | | |
| | | | | | | | | | |
| | | | | | | | | | |
| | | | | | | | | | |
| | | | | | | | | | |
| | | | | | | | | | |

# Estimating Tips

## 32 01 00 Operations and Maintenance of Exterior Improvements

- Recycling of asphalt pavement is becoming very popular and is an alternative to removal and replacement of asphalt pavement. It can be a good value engineering proposal if removed pavement can be recycled either at the site or another site that is reasonably close to the project site.

## 32 10 00 Bases, Ballasts, and Paving

- When estimating paving, keep in mind the project schedule. If an asphaltic paving project is in a colder climate and runs through to the spring, consider placing the base course in the autumn and then topping it in the spring, just prior to completion. This could save considerable costs in spring repair. Keep in mind that prices for asphalt and concrete are generally higher in the cold seasons.

## 32 90 00 Planting

- The timing of planting and guarantee specifications often dictate the costs for establishing tree and shrub growth and a stand of grass or ground cover. Establish the work performance schedule to coincide with the local planting season. Maintenance and growth guarantees can add from 20%–100% to the total landscaping cost. The cost to replace trees and shrubs can be as high as 5% of the total cost, depending on the planting zone, soil conditions, and time of year.

# Reference Numbers

Reference numbers are shown in shaded boxes at the beginning of some major classifications. These numbers refer to related items in the Reference Section. The reference information may be an estimating procedure, an alternate pricing method, or technical information.

*Note:* Not all subdivisions listed here necessarily appear in this publication.

**Division 32 - Exterior Improvements**

# 32 01 Operation and Maintenance of Exterior Improvements

## 32 01 13 – Flexible Paving Surface Treatment

| 32 01 13.66 Fog Seal | Crew | Daily Output | Labor-Hours | Unit | Material | 2010 Bare Costs Labor | Equipment | Total | Total Incl O&P |
|---|---|---|---|---|---|---|---|---|---|
| 0010 **FOG SEAL** | | | | | | | | | |
| 0012 Sealcoating, 2 coat coal tar pitch emulsion over 10,000 SY | B-45 | 5000 | .003 | S.Y. | 1.05 | .07 | .06 | 1.18 | 1.35 |
| 0030     1000 to 10,000 S.Y. | " | 3000 | .005 | | 1.05 | .12 | .10 | 1.27 | 1.47 |
| 0100     Under 1000 S.Y. | B-1 | 1050 | .023 | | 1.05 | .51 | | 1.56 | 2.01 |
| 0300 Petroleum resistant, over 10,000 S.Y. | B-45 | 5000 | .003 | | 1.30 | .07 | .06 | 1.43 | 1.62 |
| 0320     1000 to 10,000 S.Y. | " | 3000 | .005 | | 1.30 | .12 | .10 | 1.52 | 1.74 |
| 0400     Under 1000 S.Y. | B-1 | 1050 | .023 | | 1.30 | .51 | | 1.81 | 2.28 |

# 32 06 Schedules for Exterior Improvements

## 32 06 10 – Schedules for Bases, Ballasts, and Paving

### 32 06 10.10 Sidewalks, Driveways and Patios

| | Crew | Daily Output | Labor-Hours | Unit | Material | Labor | Equipment | Total | Total Incl O&P |
|---|---|---|---|---|---|---|---|---|---|
| 0010 **SIDEWALKS, DRIVEWAYS AND PATIOS** No base | | | | | | | | | |
| 0021   Asphaltic concrete, 2" thick | B-37 | 6480 | .007 | S.F. | .76 | .17 | .02 | .95 | 1.16 |
| 0101     2-1/2" thick | " | 5950 | .008 | " | .97 | .19 | .03 | 1.19 | 1.41 |
| 0300   Concrete, 3000 psi, CIP, 6 x 6 - W1.4 x W1.4 mesh, | | | | | | | | | |
| 0310     broomed finish, no base, 4" thick | B-24 | 600 | .040 | S.F. | 1.62 | 1.05 | | 2.67 | 3.51 |
| 0350       5" thick | | 545 | .044 | | 2.16 | 1.15 | | 3.31 | 4.27 |
| 0400       6" thick | | 510 | .047 | | 2.51 | 1.23 | | 3.74 | 4.80 |
| 0450     For bank run gravel base, 4" thick, add | B-18 | 2500 | .010 | | .51 | .21 | .02 | .74 | .94 |
| 0520       8" thick, add | " | 1600 | .015 | | 1.03 | .33 | .03 | 1.39 | 1.73 |
| 1000   Crushed stone, 1" thick, white marble | 2 Clab | 1700 | .009 | | .22 | .20 | | .42 | .58 |
| 1050     Bluestone | " | 1700 | .009 | | .24 | .20 | | .44 | .60 |
| 1700   Redwood, prefabricated, 4' x 4' sections | 2 Carp | 316 | .051 | | 4.74 | 1.47 | | 6.21 | 7.70 |
| 1750     Redwood planks, 1" thick, on sleepers | " | 240 | .067 | | 4.74 | 1.94 | | 6.68 | 8.45 |
| 2250   Stone dust, 4" thick | B-62 | 900 | .027 | S.Y. | 3.27 | .64 | .18 | 4.09 | 4.85 |

### 32 06 10.20 Steps

| | Crew | Daily Output | Labor-Hours | Unit | Material | Labor | Equipment | Total | Total Incl O&P |
|---|---|---|---|---|---|---|---|---|---|
| 0010 **STEPS** | | | | | | | | | |
| 0011   Incl. excav., borrow & concrete base as required | | | | | | | | | |
| 0100     Brick steps | B-24 | 35 | .686 | LF Riser | 12.85 | 17.90 | | 30.75 | 43.50 |
| 0200     Railroad ties | 2 Clab | 25 | .640 | | 3.17 | 13.75 | | 16.92 | 26.50 |
| 0300     Bluestone treads, 12" x 2" or 12" x 1-1/2" | B-24 | 30 | .800 | | 28 | 21 | | 49 | 65.50 |
| 0600     Precast concrete, see Div. 03 41 23.50 | | | | | | | | | |
| 4025   Steel edge strips, incl. stakes, 1/4" x 5" | B-1 | 390 | .062 | L.F. | 4.20 | 1.36 | | 5.56 | 6.90 |
| 4050   Edging, landscape timber or railroad ties, 6" x 8" | 2 Carp | 170 | .094 | " | 3.15 | 2.74 | | 5.89 | 8.10 |

# 32 11 Base Courses

## 32 11 23 – Aggregate Base Courses

### 32 11 23.23 Base Course Drainage Layers

| | Crew | Daily Output | Labor-Hours | Unit | Material | Labor | Equipment | Total | Total Incl O&P |
|---|---|---|---|---|---|---|---|---|---|
| 0010 **BASE COURSE DRAINAGE LAYERS** | | | | | | | | | |
| 0011   For roadways and large areas | | | | | | | | | |
| 0051     3/4" stone compacted to 3" deep | B-36 | 36000 | .001 | S.F. | .38 | .03 | .04 | .45 | .50 |
| 0101       6" deep | | 35100 | .001 | | .75 | .03 | .04 | .82 | .93 |
| 0201       9" deep | | 25875 | .002 | | 1.10 | .04 | .06 | 1.20 | 1.33 |
| 0305       12" deep | | 21150 | .002 | | 1.55 | .05 | .07 | 1.67 | 1.87 |
| 0306     Crushed 1-1/2" stone base, compacted to 4" deep | | 47000 | .001 | | .06 | .02 | .03 | .11 | .13 |
| 0307       6" deep | | 35100 | .001 | | .78 | .03 | .04 | .85 | .95 |
| 0308       8" deep | | 27000 | .001 | | 1.04 | .04 | .05 | 1.13 | 1.26 |
| 0309       12" deep | | 16200 | .002 | | 1.55 | .06 | .09 | 1.70 | 1.91 |
| 0350     Bank run gravel, spread and compacted | | | | | | | | | |

# 32 11 Base Courses

## 32 11 23 – Aggregate Base Courses

| 32 11 23.23 Base Course Drainage Layers | | Crew | Daily Output | Labor-Hours | Unit | Material | 2010 Bare Costs Labor | 2010 Bare Costs Equipment | Total | Total Incl O&P |
|---|---|---|---|---|---|---|---|---|---|---|
| 0371 | 6" deep | B-32 | 54000 | .001 | S.F. | .48 | .02 | .04 | .54 | .59 |
| 0391 | 9" deep | ↓ | 39600 | .001 | | .69 | .02 | .05 | .76 | .86 |
| 0401 | 12" deep | ↓ | 32400 | .001 | ↓ | .95 | .03 | .06 | 1.04 | 1.17 |
| 6900 | For small and irregular areas, add | | | | | | 50% | 50% | | |

## 32 11 26 – Asphaltic Base Courses

### 32 11 26.19 Bituminous-Stabilized Base Courses

| | | Crew | Daily Output | Labor-Hours | Unit | Material | 2010 Bare Costs Labor | 2010 Bare Costs Equipment | Total | Total Incl O&P |
|---|---|---|---|---|---|---|---|---|---|---|
| 0010 | **BITUMINOUS-STABILIZED BASE COURSES** | | | | | | | | | |
| 0020 | And large paved areas | | | | | | | | | |
| 0700 | Liquid application to gravel base, asphalt emulsion | B-45 | 6000 | .003 | Gal. | 6 | .06 | .05 | 6.11 | 6.75 |
| 0800 | Prime and seal, cut back asphalt | | 6000 | .003 | " | 7.10 | .06 | .05 | 7.21 | 7.95 |
| 1000 | Macadam penetration crushed stone, 2 gal. per S.Y., 4" thick | | 6000 | .003 | S.Y. | 12 | .06 | .05 | 12.11 | 13.35 |
| 1100 | 6" thick, 3 gal. per S.Y. | | 4000 | .004 | | 18 | .09 | .08 | 18.17 | 20 |
| 1200 | 8" thick, 4 gal. per S.Y. | ↓ | 3000 | .005 | ↓ | 24 | .12 | .10 | 24.22 | 27 |
| 8900 | For small and irregular areas, add | | | | | | 50% | 50% | | |

# 32 12 Flexible Paving

## 32 12 16 – Asphalt Paving

### 32 12 16.14 Asphaltic Concrete Paving

| | | Crew | Daily Output | Labor-Hours | Unit | Material | 2010 Bare Costs Labor | 2010 Bare Costs Equipment | Total | Total Incl O&P |
|---|---|---|---|---|---|---|---|---|---|---|
| 0010 | **ASPHALTIC CONCRETE** Paving, parking lots & driveways | | | | | | | | | |
| 0020 | 6" stone base, 2" binder course, 1" topping | B-25C | 9000 | .005 | S.F. | 1.82 | .13 | .25 | 2.20 | 2.50 |
| 0025 | 2" binder course, 2" topping | | 9000 | .005 | | 2.24 | .13 | .25 | 2.62 | 2.95 |
| 0030 | 3" binder course, 2" topping | | 9000 | .005 | | 2.63 | .13 | .25 | 3.01 | 3.38 |
| 0035 | 4" binder course, 2" topping | | 9000 | .005 | | 3.02 | .13 | .25 | 3.40 | 3.81 |
| 0040 | 1.5" binder course, 1" topping | | 9000 | .005 | | 1.63 | .13 | .25 | 2.01 | 2.28 |
| 0042 | 3" binder course, 1" topping | | 9000 | .005 | | 2.22 | .13 | .25 | 2.60 | 2.93 |
| 0045 | 3" binder course, 3" topping | | 9000 | .005 | | 3.05 | .13 | .25 | 3.43 | 3.84 |
| 0050 | 4" binder course, 3" topping | | 9000 | .005 | | 3.44 | .13 | .25 | 3.82 | 4.27 |
| 0055 | 4" binder course, 4" topping | | 9000 | .005 | | 3.84 | .13 | .25 | 4.22 | 4.72 |
| 0300 | Binder course, 1-1/2" thick | | 35000 | .001 | | .59 | .03 | .06 | .68 | .78 |
| 0400 | 2" thick | | 25000 | .002 | | .76 | .05 | .09 | .90 | 1.02 |
| 0500 | 3" thick | | 15000 | .003 | | 1.18 | .08 | .15 | 1.41 | 1.59 |
| 0600 | 4" thick | | 10800 | .004 | | 1.55 | .11 | .21 | 1.87 | 2.11 |
| 0800 | Sand finish course, 3/4" thick | | 41000 | .001 | | .32 | .03 | .05 | .40 | .47 |
| 0900 | 1" thick | ↓ | 34000 | .001 | | .40 | .03 | .07 | .50 | .57 |
| 1000 | Fill pot holes, hot mix, 2" thick | B-16 | 4200 | .008 | | .84 | .17 | .16 | 1.17 | 1.39 |
| 1100 | 4" thick | | 3500 | .009 | | 1.23 | .21 | .19 | 1.63 | 1.91 |
| 1120 | 6" thick | ↓ | 3100 | .010 | | 1.65 | .23 | .22 | 2.10 | 2.45 |
| 1140 | Cold patch, 2" thick | B-51 | 3000 | .016 | | .85 | .35 | .08 | 1.28 | 1.62 |
| 1160 | 4" thick | | 2700 | .018 | | 1.62 | .39 | .09 | 2.10 | 2.54 |
| 1180 | 6" thick | ↓ | 1900 | .025 | ↓ | 2.52 | .56 | .13 | 3.21 | 3.85 |

# 32 13 Rigid Paving

## 32 13 13 – Concrete Paving

### 32 13 13.23 Concrete Paving Surface Treatment

| | | Crew | Daily Output | Labor-Hours | Unit | Material | 2010 Bare Costs Labor | Equipment | Total | Total Incl O&P |
|---|---|---|---|---|---|---|---|---|---|---|
| 0010 | **CONCRETE PAVING SURFACE TREATMENT** | | | | | | | | | |
| 0015 | Including joints, finishing and curing | | | | | | | | | |
| 0021 | Fixed form, 12' pass, unreinforced, 6" thick | B-26 | 18000 | .005 | S.F. | 3.05 | .12 | .18 | 3.35 | 3.76 |
| 0101 | 8" thick | " | 13500 | .007 | | 4.11 | .16 | .24 | 4.51 | 5.05 |
| 0701 | Finishing, broom finish small areas | 2 Cefi | 1215 | .013 | | | .37 | | .37 | .59 |

# 32 14 Unit Paving

## 32 14 16 – Brick Unit Paving

### 32 14 16.10 Brick Paving

| | | Crew | Daily Output | Labor-Hours | Unit | Material | Labor | Equipment | Total | Total Incl O&P |
|---|---|---|---|---|---|---|---|---|---|---|
| 0010 | **BRICK PAVING** | | | | | | | | | |
| 0012 | 4" x 8" x 1-1/2", without joints (4.5 brick/S.F.) | D-1 | 110 | .145 | S.F. | 3.27 | 3.84 | | 7.11 | 9.95 |
| 0100 | Grouted, 3/8" joint (3.9 brick/S.F.) | | 90 | .178 | | 3.38 | 4.69 | | 8.07 | 11.45 |
| 0200 | 4" x 8" x 2-1/4", without joints (4.5 bricks/S.F.) | | 110 | .145 | | 3.74 | 3.84 | | 7.58 | 10.45 |
| 0300 | Grouted, 3/8" joint (3.9 brick/S.F.) | | 90 | .178 | | 3.45 | 4.69 | | 8.14 | 11.55 |
| 0500 | Bedding, asphalt, 3/4" thick | B-25 | 5130 | .017 | | .65 | .41 | .50 | 1.56 | 1.95 |
| 0540 | Course washed sand bed, 1" thick | B-18 | 5000 | .005 | | .30 | .11 | .01 | .42 | .52 |
| 0580 | Mortar, 1" thick | D-1 | 300 | .053 | | .66 | 1.41 | | 2.07 | 3.04 |
| 0620 | 2" thick | | 200 | .080 | | 1.31 | 2.11 | | 3.42 | 4.92 |
| 1500 | Brick on 1" thick sand bed laid flat, 4.5 per S.F. | | 100 | .160 | | 3 | 4.22 | | 7.22 | 10.25 |
| 2000 | Brick pavers, laid on edge, 7.2 per S.F. | | 70 | .229 | | 3.18 | 6.05 | | 9.23 | 13.45 |

## 32 14 23 – Asphalt Unit Paving

### 32 14 23.10 Asphalt Blocks

| | | Crew | Daily Output | Labor-Hours | Unit | Material | Labor | Equipment | Total | Total Incl O&P |
|---|---|---|---|---|---|---|---|---|---|---|
| 0010 | **ASPHALT BLOCKS** | | | | | | | | | |
| 0020 | Rectangular, 6" x 12" x 1-1/4", w/bed & neopr. adhesive | D-1 | 135 | .119 | S.F. | 7.80 | 3.13 | | 10.93 | 13.75 |
| 0100 | 3" thick | | 130 | .123 | | 10.95 | 3.25 | | 14.20 | 17.40 |
| 0300 | Hexagonal tile, 8" wide, 1-1/4" thick | | 135 | .119 | | 7.80 | 3.13 | | 10.93 | 13.75 |
| 0400 | 2" thick | | 130 | .123 | | 10.95 | 3.25 | | 14.20 | 17.40 |
| 0500 | Square, 8" x 8", 1-1/4" thick | | 135 | .119 | | 7.80 | 3.13 | | 10.93 | 13.75 |
| 0600 | 2" thick | | 130 | .123 | | 10.95 | 3.25 | | 14.20 | 17.40 |

## 32 14 40 – Stone Paving

### 32 14 40.10 Stone Pavers

| | | Crew | Daily Output | Labor-Hours | Unit | Material | Labor | Equipment | Total | Total Incl O&P |
|---|---|---|---|---|---|---|---|---|---|---|
| 0010 | **STONE PAVERS** | | | | | | | | | |
| 1100 | Flagging, bluestone, irregular, 1" thick, | D-1 | 81 | .198 | S.F. | 5.95 | 5.20 | | 11.15 | 15.15 |
| 1150 | Snapped random rectangular, 1" thick | | 92 | .174 | | 9.05 | 4.59 | | 13.64 | 17.50 |
| 1200 | 1-1/2" thick | | 85 | .188 | | 10.85 | 4.97 | | 15.82 | 20 |
| 1250 | 2" thick | | 83 | .193 | | 12.65 | 5.10 | | 17.75 | 22.50 |
| 1300 | Slate, natural cleft, irregular, 3/4" thick | | 92 | .174 | | 7 | 4.59 | | 11.59 | 15.25 |
| 1310 | 1" thick | | 85 | .188 | | 8.15 | 4.97 | | 13.12 | 17.15 |
| 1351 | Random rectangular, gauged, 1/2" thick | | 105 | .152 | | 15.15 | 4.02 | | 19.17 | 23.50 |
| 1400 | Random rectangular, butt joint, gauged, 1/4" thick | | 150 | .107 | | 16.30 | 2.82 | | 19.12 | 22.50 |
| 1450 | For sand rubbed finish, add | | | | | 7.60 | | | 7.60 | 8.35 |
| 1500 | For interior setting, add | | | | | 25% | | | 25% | 25% |
| 1550 | Granite blocks, 3-1/2" x 3-1/2" x 3-1/2" | D-1 | 92 | .174 | S.F. | 10.05 | 4.59 | | 14.64 | 18.60 |

# 32 16 Curbs and Gutters

## 32 16 13 – Concrete Curbs and Gutters

| 32 16 13.13 Cast-in-Place Concrete Curbs and Gutters | Crew | Daily Output | Labor-Hours | Unit | Material | 2010 Bare Costs Labor | Equipment | Total | Total Incl O&P |
|---|---|---|---|---|---|---|---|---|---|
| 0010 **CAST-IN-PLACE CONCRETE CURBS AND GUTTERS** | | | | | | | | | |
| 0300 Concrete, wood forms, 6" x 18", straight | C-2 | 500 | .096 | L.F. | 3.63 | 2.47 | | 6.10 | 8.15 |
| 0400 6" x 18", radius | " | 200 | .240 | | 3.70 | 6.15 | | 9.85 | 14.40 |
| 0404 Concrete, wood forms, 6" x 18", straight & concrete | C-2A | 500 | .096 | | 6.35 | 2.68 | | 9.03 | 11.50 |
| 0406 6" x 18", radius | " | 200 | .240 | | 6.40 | 6.70 | | 13.10 | 18.25 |

### 32 16 13.26 Precast Concrete Curbs

| | Crew | Daily Output | Labor-Hours | Unit | Material | Labor | Equipment | Total | Total Incl O&P |
|---|---|---|---|---|---|---|---|---|---|
| 0010 **PRECAST CONCRETE CURBS** | | | | | | | | | |
| 0550 Precast, 6" x 18", straight | B-29 | 700 | .069 | L.F. | 10.85 | 1.60 | 1.16 | 13.61 | 15.85 |
| 0600 6" x 18", radius | " | 325 | .148 | " | 12.45 | 3.45 | 2.50 | 18.40 | 22 |

## 32 16 19 – Asphalt Curbs

### 32 16 19.10 Bituminous Concrete Curbs

| | Crew | Daily Output | Labor-Hours | Unit | Material | Labor | Equipment | Total | Total Incl O&P |
|---|---|---|---|---|---|---|---|---|---|
| 0010 **BITUMINOUS CONCRETE CURBS** | | | | | | | | | |
| 0012 Curbs, asphaltic, machine formed, 8" wide, 6" high, 40 L.F./ton | B-27 | 1000 | .032 | L.F. | 1.36 | .70 | .29 | 2.35 | 2.99 |
| 0100 8" wide, 8" high, 30 L.F. per ton | | 900 | .036 | | 1.56 | .78 | .32 | 2.66 | 3.39 |
| 0150 Asphaltic berm, 12" W, 3"-6" H, 35 L.F./ton, before pavement | | 700 | .046 | | 1.61 | 1.01 | .41 | 3.03 | 3.91 |
| 0200 12" W, 1-1/2" to 4" H, 60 L.F. per ton, laid with pavement | B-2 | 1050 | .038 | | .98 | .83 | | 1.81 | 2.48 |

## 32 16 40 – Stone Curbs

### 32 16 40.13 Cut Stone Curbs

| | Crew | Daily Output | Labor-Hours | Unit | Material | Labor | Equipment | Total | Total Incl O&P |
|---|---|---|---|---|---|---|---|---|---|
| 0010 **CUT STONE CURBS** | | | | | | | | | |
| 1000 Granite, split face, straight, 5" x 16" | D-13 | 500 | .096 | L.F. | 12.05 | 2.68 | 1.31 | 16.04 | 19.10 |
| 1100 6" x 18" | " | 450 | .107 | | 15.85 | 2.98 | 1.46 | 20.29 | 24 |
| 1300 Radius curbing, 6" x 18", over 10' radius | B-29 | 260 | .185 | | 19.40 | 4.31 | 3.13 | 26.84 | 32 |
| 1400 Corners, 2' radius | | 80 | .600 | Ea. | 65 | 14 | 10.15 | 89.15 | 106 |
| 1600 Edging, 4-1/2" x 12", straight | | 300 | .160 | L.F. | 6.05 | 3.74 | 2.71 | 12.50 | 15.90 |
| 1800 Curb inlets, (guttermouth) straight | | 41 | 1.171 | Ea. | 145 | 27.50 | 19.80 | 192.30 | 227 |
| 2000 Indian granite (belgian block) | | | | | | | | | |
| 2100 Jumbo, 10-1/2" x 7-1/2" x 4", grey | D-1 | 150 | .107 | L.F. | 2.21 | 2.82 | | 5.03 | 7.05 |
| 2150 Pink | | 150 | .107 | | 2.88 | 2.82 | | 5.70 | 7.80 |
| 2200 Regular, 9" x 4-1/2" x 4-1/2", grey | | 160 | .100 | | 2 | 2.64 | | 4.64 | 6.55 |
| 2250 Pink | | 160 | .100 | | 2.76 | 2.64 | | 5.40 | 7.40 |
| 2300 Cubes, 4" x 4" x 4", grey | | 175 | .091 | | 1.91 | 2.41 | | 4.32 | 6.10 |
| 2350 Pink | | 175 | .091 | | 2 | 2.41 | | 4.41 | 6.20 |
| 2400 6" x 6" x 6", pink | | 155 | .103 | | 4.96 | 2.73 | | 7.69 | 9.95 |
| 2500 Alternate pricing method for indian granite | | | | | | | | | |
| 2550 Jumbo, 10-1/2" x 7-1/2" x 4" (30 lb), grey | | | | Ton | 126 | | | 126 | 139 |
| 2600 Pink | | | | | 167 | | | 167 | 184 |
| 2650 Regular, 9" x 4-1/2" x 4-1/2" (20 lb), grey | | | | | 141 | | | 141 | 156 |
| 2700 Pink | | | | | 193 | | | 193 | 212 |
| 2750 Cubes, 4" x 4" x 4" (5 lb), grey | | | | | 231 | | | 231 | 255 |
| 2800 Pink | | | | | 257 | | | 257 | 283 |
| 2850 6" x 6" x 6" (25 lb), pink | | | | | 193 | | | 193 | 212 |
| 2900 For pallets, add | | | | | 20 | | | 20 | 22 |

# 32 31 Fences and Gates

## 32 31 13 – Chain Link Fences and Gates

### 32 31 13.15 Chain Link Fence

| | | Crew | Daily Output | Labor-Hours | Unit | Material | 2010 Bare Costs Labor | Equipment | Total | Total Incl O&P |
|---|---|---|---|---|---|---|---|---|---|---|
| 0010 | **CHAIN LINK FENCE** | | | | | | | | | |
| 0020 | 1-5/8" post 10' O.C., 1-3/8" top rail, 2" corner post galv. stl., 3' high | B-1 | 185 | .130 | L.F. | 8.60 | 2.88 | | 11.48 | 14.30 |
| 0050 | 4' high | | 170 | .141 | | 10.30 | 3.13 | | 13.43 | 16.60 |
| 0100 | 6' high | | 115 | .209 | | 11.70 | 4.63 | | 16.33 | 20.50 |
| 0150 | Add for gate 3' wide, 1-3/8" frame 3' high | | 12 | 2 | Ea. | 62.50 | 44.50 | | 107 | 144 |
| 0170 | 4' high | | 10 | 2.400 | | 60.50 | 53 | | 113.50 | 157 |
| 0190 | 6' high | | 10 | 2.400 | | 66 | 53 | | 119 | 162 |
| 0200 | Add for gate 4' wide, 1-3/8" frame 3' high | | 9 | 2.667 | | 64 | 59 | | 123 | 170 |
| 0220 | 4' high | | 9 | 2.667 | | 69 | 59 | | 128 | 176 |
| 0240 | 6' high | | 8 | 3 | | 173 | 66.50 | | 239.50 | 300 |
| 0350 | Aluminized steel, 9 ga. wire, 3' high | | 185 | .130 | L.F. | 10.15 | 2.88 | | 13.03 | 16.05 |
| 0380 | 4' high | | 170 | .141 | | 11.55 | 3.13 | | 14.68 | 18 |
| 0400 | 6' high | | 115 | .209 | | 14.85 | 4.63 | | 19.48 | 24 |
| 0450 | Add for gate 3' wide, 1-3/8" frame 3' high | | 12 | 2 | Ea. | 99 | 44.50 | | 143.50 | 184 |
| 0470 | 4' high | | 10 | 2.400 | | 135 | 53 | | 188 | 239 |
| 0490 | 6' high | | 10 | 2.400 | | 203 | 53 | | 256 | 315 |
| 0500 | Add for gate 4' wide, 1-3/8" frame 3' high | | 10 | 2.400 | | 135 | 53 | | 188 | 239 |
| 0520 | 4' high | | 9 | 2.667 | | 180 | 59 | | 239 | 298 |
| 0540 | 6' high | | 8 | 3 | | 281 | 66.50 | | 347.50 | 420 |
| 0620 | Vinyl covered 9 ga. wire, 3' high | | 185 | .130 | L.F. | 9 | 2.88 | | 11.88 | 14.75 |
| 0640 | 4' high | | 170 | .141 | | 13.55 | 3.13 | | 16.68 | 20 |
| 0660 | 6' high | | 115 | .209 | | 15.45 | 4.63 | | 20.08 | 25 |
| 0720 | Add for gate 3' wide, 1-3/8" frame 3' high | | 12 | 2 | Ea. | 96.50 | 44.50 | | 141 | 181 |
| 0740 | 4' high | | 10 | 2.400 | | 126 | 53 | | 179 | 228 |
| 0760 | 6' high | | 10 | 2.400 | | 193 | 53 | | 246 | 305 |
| 0780 | Add for gate 4' wide, 1-3/8" frame 3' high | | 10 | 2.400 | | 132 | 53 | | 185 | 235 |
| 0800 | 4' high | | 9 | 2.667 | | 174 | 59 | | 233 | 292 |
| 0820 | 6' high | | 8 | 3 | | 251 | 66.50 | | 317.50 | 390 |
| 0860 | Tennis courts, 11 ga. wire, 2 1/2" post 10' O.C., 1-5/8" top rail | | | | | | | | | |
| 0900 | 2-1/2" corner post, 10' high | B-1 | 95 | .253 | L.F. | 19.30 | 5.60 | | 24.90 | 31 |
| 0920 | 12' high | | 80 | .300 | " | 23 | 6.65 | | 29.65 | 36.50 |
| 1000 | Add for gate 3' wide, 1-5/8" frame 10' high | | 10 | 2.400 | Ea. | 242 | 53 | | 295 | 355 |
| 1040 | Aluminized, 11 ga. wire 10' high | | 95 | .253 | L.F. | 31.50 | 5.60 | | 37.10 | 44 |
| 1100 | 12' high | | 80 | .300 | " | 32.50 | 6.65 | | 39.15 | 47 |
| 1140 | Add for gate 3' wide, 1-5/8" frame, 10' high | | 10 | 2.400 | Ea. | 360 | 53 | | 413 | 485 |
| 1250 | Vinyl covered 11 ga. wire, 10' high | | 95 | .253 | L.F. | 24.50 | 5.60 | | 30.10 | 36 |
| 1300 | 12' high | | 80 | .300 | " | 28.50 | 6.65 | | 35.15 | 42 |
| 1400 | Add for gate 3' wide, 1-3/8" frame, 10' high | | 10 | 2.400 | Ea. | 365 | 53 | | 418 | 490 |

## 32 31 23 – Plastic Fences and Gates

### 32 31 23.10 Fence, Vinyl

| | | Crew | Daily Output | Labor-Hours | Unit | Material | 2010 Bare Costs Labor | Equipment | Total | Total Incl O&P |
|---|---|---|---|---|---|---|---|---|---|---|
| 0010 | **FENCE, VINYL** | | | | | | | | | |
| 0011 | White, steel reinforced, stainless steel fasteners | | | | | | | | | |
| 0020 | Picket, 4" x 4" posts @ 6' - 0" OC, 3' high | B-1 | 140 | .171 | L.F. | 19.30 | 3.80 | | 23.10 | 27.50 |
| 0030 | 4' high | | 130 | .185 | | 22 | 4.09 | | 26.09 | 31.50 |
| 0040 | 5' high | | 120 | .200 | | 26 | 4.43 | | 30.43 | 36 |
| 0100 | Board (semi-privacy), 5" x 5" posts @ 7' - 6" OC, 5' high | | 130 | .185 | | 27 | 4.09 | | 31.09 | 36.50 |
| 0120 | 6' high | | 125 | .192 | | 30.50 | 4.26 | | 34.76 | 40.50 |
| 0200 | Basket weave, 5" x 5" posts @ 7' - 6" OC, 5' high | | 160 | .150 | | 23.50 | 3.33 | | 26.83 | 31.50 |
| 0220 | 6' high | | 150 | .160 | | 27.50 | 3.55 | | 31.05 | 36.50 |
| 0300 | Privacy, 5" x 5" posts @ 7' - 6" OC, 5' high | | 130 | .185 | | 29 | 4.09 | | 33.09 | 39 |
| 0320 | 6' high | | 150 | .160 | | 33 | 3.55 | | 36.55 | 42.50 |
| 0350 | Gate, 5' high | | 9 | 2.667 | Ea. | 415 | 59 | | 474 | 555 |

# 32 31 Fences and Gates

## 32 31 23 – Plastic Fences and Gates

| 32 31 23.10 Fence, Vinyl | Crew | Daily Output | Labor-Hours | Unit | Material | 2010 Bare Costs Labor | Equipment | Total | Total Incl O&P |
|---|---|---|---|---|---|---|---|---|---|
| 0360 | 6' high | B-1 | 9 | 2.667 | Ea. | 425 | 59 | | 484 | 565 |
| 0400 | For posts set in concrete, add | ↓ | 25 | .960 | ↓ | 7.95 | 21.50 | | 29.45 | 45 |

## 32 31 26 – Wire Fences and Gates

### 32 31 26.10 Fences, Misc. Metal

| | | Crew | Daily Output | Labor-Hours | Unit | Material | Labor | Equipment | Total | Total Incl O&P |
|---|---|---|---|---|---|---|---|---|---|---|
| 0010 | **FENCES, MISC. METAL** | | | | | | | | | |
| 0012 | Chicken wire, posts @ 4', 1" mesh, 4' high | B-80C | 410 | .059 | L.F. | 2.10 | 1.29 | .60 | 3.99 | 5.15 |
| 0100 | 2" mesh, 6' high | | 350 | .069 | | 1.89 | 1.51 | .71 | 4.11 | 5.40 |
| 0200 | Galv. steel, 12 ga., 2" x 4" mesh, posts 5' O.C., 3' high | | 300 | .080 | | 3.03 | 1.76 | .83 | 5.62 | 7.20 |
| 0300 | 5' high | | 300 | .080 | | 4.04 | 1.76 | .83 | 6.63 | 8.30 |
| 0400 | 14 ga., 1" x 2" mesh, 3' high | | 300 | .080 | | 3.21 | 1.76 | .83 | 5.80 | 7.40 |
| 0500 | 5' high | ↓ | 300 | .080 | ↓ | 4.44 | 1.76 | .83 | 7.03 | 8.75 |
| 1000 | Kennel fencing, 1-1/2" mesh, 6' long, 3'-6" wide, 6'-2" high | 2 Clab | 4 | 4 | Ea. | 505 | 86 | | 591 | 700 |
| 1050 | 12' long | | 4 | 4 | | 605 | 86 | | 691 | 810 |
| 1200 | Top covers, 1-1/2" mesh, 6' long | | 15 | 1.067 | | 102 | 23 | | 125 | 152 |
| 1250 | 12' long | ↓ | 12 | 1.333 | ↓ | 164 | 28.50 | | 192.50 | 228 |

## 32 31 29 – Wood Fences and Gates

### 32 31 29.10 Fence, Wood

| | | Crew | Daily Output | Labor-Hours | Unit | Material | Labor | Equipment | Total | Total Incl O&P |
|---|---|---|---|---|---|---|---|---|---|---|
| 0010 | **FENCE, WOOD** | | | | | | | | | |
| 0011 | Basket weave, 3/8" x 4" boards, 2" x 4" | | | | | | | | | |
| 0020 | stringers on spreaders, 4" x 4" posts | | | | | | | | | |
| 0050 | No. 1 cedar, 6' high | B-80C | 160 | .150 | L.F. | 8.85 | 3.30 | 1.55 | 13.70 | 16.90 |
| 0070 | Treated pine, 6' high | | 150 | .160 | | 10.65 | 3.52 | 1.65 | 15.82 | 19.40 |
| 0090 | Vertical weave 6' high | ↓ | 145 | .166 | ↓ | 12.60 | 3.64 | 1.71 | 17.95 | 22 |
| 0200 | Board fence, 1" x 4" boards, 2" x 4" rails, 4" x 4" post | | | | | | | | | |
| 0220 | Preservative treated, 2 rail, 3' high | B-80C | 145 | .166 | L.F. | 6.55 | 3.64 | 1.71 | 11.90 | 15.20 |
| 0240 | 4' high | | 135 | .178 | | 7.20 | 3.91 | 1.83 | 12.94 | 16.45 |
| 0260 | 3 rail, 5' high | | 130 | .185 | | 8.10 | 4.06 | 1.91 | 14.07 | 17.85 |
| 0300 | 6' high | | 125 | .192 | | 9.40 | 4.22 | 1.98 | 15.60 | 19.60 |
| 0320 | No. 2 grade western cedar, 2 rail, 3' high | | 145 | .166 | | 7.15 | 3.64 | 1.71 | 12.50 | 15.85 |
| 0340 | 4' high | | 135 | .178 | | 8.55 | 3.91 | 1.83 | 14.29 | 17.95 |
| 0360 | 3 rail, 5' high | | 130 | .185 | | 9.85 | 4.06 | 1.91 | 15.82 | 19.75 |
| 0400 | 6' high | | 125 | .192 | | 10.75 | 4.22 | 1.98 | 16.95 | 21 |
| 0420 | No. 1 grade cedar, 2 rail, 3' high | | 145 | .166 | | 10.85 | 3.64 | 1.71 | 16.20 | 19.90 |
| 0440 | 4' high | | 135 | .178 | | 12.25 | 3.91 | 1.83 | 17.99 | 22 |
| 0460 | 3 rail, 5' high | | 130 | .185 | | 14.40 | 4.06 | 1.91 | 20.37 | 25 |
| 0500 | 6' high | ↓ | 125 | .192 | ↓ | 16.10 | 4.22 | 1.98 | 22.30 | 27 |
| 0540 | Shadow box, 1" x 6" board, 2" x 4" rail, 4" x 4"post | | | | | | | | | |
| 0560 | Pine, pressure treated, 3 rail, 6' high | B-80C | 150 | .160 | L.F. | 12.05 | 3.52 | 1.65 | 17.22 | 21 |
| 0600 | Gate, 3'-6" wide | | 8 | 3 | Ea. | 73 | 66 | 31 | 170 | 225 |
| 0620 | No. 1 cedar, 3 rail, 4' high | | 130 | .185 | L.F. | 14.75 | 4.06 | 1.91 | 20.72 | 25 |
| 0640 | 6' high | | 125 | .192 | | 18.30 | 4.22 | 1.98 | 24.50 | 29 |
| 0860 | Open rail fence, split rails, 2 rail 3' high, no. 1 cedar | | 160 | .150 | | 6 | 3.30 | 1.55 | 10.85 | 13.80 |
| 0870 | No. 2 cedar | | 160 | .150 | | 4.72 | 3.30 | 1.55 | 9.57 | 12.40 |
| 0880 | 3 rail, 4' high, no. 1 cedar | | 150 | .160 | | 8 | 3.52 | 1.65 | 13.17 | 16.50 |
| 0890 | No. 2 cedar | | 150 | .160 | | 5.65 | 3.52 | 1.65 | 10.82 | 13.90 |
| 0920 | Rustic rails, 2 rail 3' high, no. 1 cedar | | 160 | .150 | | 3.86 | 3.30 | 1.55 | 8.71 | 11.45 |
| 0930 | No. 2 cedar | | 160 | .150 | | 3.83 | 3.30 | 1.55 | 8.68 | 11.40 |
| 0940 | 3 rail, 4' high | | 150 | .160 | | 5.20 | 3.52 | 1.65 | 10.37 | 13.45 |
| 0950 | No. 2 cedar | ↓ | 150 | .160 | ↓ | 3.98 | 3.52 | 1.65 | 9.15 | 12.10 |
| 0960 | Picket fence, gothic, pressure treated pine | | | | | | | | | |
| 1000 | 2 rail, 3' high | B-80C | 140 | .171 | L.F. | 4.46 | 3.77 | 1.77 | 10 | 13.15 |
| 1020 | 3 rail, 4' high | ↓ | 130 | .185 | " | 5.30 | 4.06 | 1.91 | 11.27 | 14.70 |

# 32 31 Fences and Gates

## 32 31 29 – Wood Fences and Gates

### 32 31 29.10 Fence, Wood

| | | Crew | Daily Output | Labor-Hours | Unit | Material | 2010 Bare Costs Labor | Equipment | Total | Total Incl O&P |
|---|---|---|---|---|---|---|---|---|---|---|
| 1040 | Gate, 3'-6" wide | B-80C | 9 | 2.667 | Ea. | 47 | 58.50 | 27.50 | 133 | 180 |
| 1060 | No. 2 cedar, 2 rail, 3' high | | 140 | .171 | L.F. | 5.60 | 3.77 | 1.77 | 11.14 | 14.40 |
| 1100 | 3 rail, 4' high | | 130 | .185 | " | 5.70 | 4.06 | 1.91 | 11.67 | 15.20 |
| 1120 | Gate, 3'-6" wide | | 9 | 2.667 | Ea. | 55.50 | 58.50 | 27.50 | 141.50 | 190 |
| 1140 | No. 1 cedar, 2 rail 3' high | | 140 | .171 | L.F. | 11.15 | 3.77 | 1.77 | 16.69 | 20.50 |
| 1160 | 3 rail, 4' high | | 130 | .185 | | 13 | 4.06 | 1.91 | 18.97 | 23 |
| 1200 | Rustic picket, molded pine, 2 rail, 3' high | | 140 | .171 | | 5.35 | 3.77 | 1.77 | 10.89 | 14.10 |
| 1220 | No. 1 cedar, 2 rail, 3' high | | 140 | .171 | | 7.10 | 3.77 | 1.77 | 12.64 | 16.10 |
| 1240 | Stockade fence, no. 1 cedar, 3-1/4" rails, 6' high | | 160 | .150 | | 10.50 | 3.30 | 1.55 | 15.35 | 18.75 |
| 1260 | 8' high | | 155 | .155 | | 13.60 | 3.40 | 1.60 | 18.60 | 22.50 |
| 1300 | No. 2 cedar, treated wood rails, 6' high | | 160 | .150 | ↓ | 10.50 | 3.30 | 1.55 | 15.35 | 18.75 |
| 1320 | Gate, 3'-6" wide | | 8 | 3 | Ea. | 61.50 | 66 | 31 | 158.50 | 212 |
| 1360 | Treated pine, treated rails, 6' high | | 160 | .150 | L.F. | 10.30 | 3.30 | 1.55 | 15.15 | 18.50 |
| 1400 | 8' high | ↓ | 150 | .160 | " | 15.40 | 3.52 | 1.65 | 20.57 | 24.50 |

### 32 31 29.20 Fence, Wood Rail

| | | Crew | Daily Output | Labor-Hours | Unit | Material | 2010 Bare Costs Labor | Equipment | Total | Total Incl O&P |
|---|---|---|---|---|---|---|---|---|---|---|
| 0010 | **FENCE, WOOD RAIL** | | | | | | | | | |
| 0012 | Picket, No. 2 cedar, Gothic, 2 rail, 3' high | B-1 | 160 | .150 | L.F. | 6.05 | 3.33 | | 9.38 | 12.25 |
| 0050 | Gate, 3'-6" wide | B-80C | 9 | 2.667 | Ea. | 52 | 58.50 | 27.50 | 138 | 186 |
| 0400 | 3 rail, 4' high | | 150 | .160 | L.F. | 6.95 | 3.52 | 1.65 | 12.12 | 15.30 |
| 0500 | Gate, 3'-6" wide | | 9 | 2.667 | Ea. | 62.50 | 58.50 | 27.50 | 148.50 | 197 |
| 1200 | Stockade, No. 2 cedar, treated wood rails, 6' high | | 160 | .150 | L.F. | 7.50 | 3.30 | 1.55 | 12.35 | 15.45 |
| 1250 | Gate, 3' wide | | 9 | 2.667 | Ea. | 61.50 | 58.50 | 27.50 | 147.50 | 197 |
| 1300 | No. 1 cedar, 3-1/4" cedar rails, 6' high | | 160 | .150 | L.F. | 18.60 | 3.30 | 1.55 | 23.45 | 27.50 |
| 1500 | Gate, 3' wide | | 9 | 2.667 | Ea. | 156 | 58.50 | 27.50 | 242 | 300 |
| 2700 | Prefabricated redwood or cedar, 4' high | | 160 | .150 | L.F. | 13.10 | 3.30 | 1.55 | 17.95 | 21.50 |
| 2800 | 6' high | | 150 | .160 | | 17.35 | 3.52 | 1.65 | 22.52 | 27 |
| 3300 | Board, shadow box, 1" x 6", treated pine, 6' high | | 160 | .150 | | 10.20 | 3.30 | 1.55 | 15.05 | 18.40 |
| 3400 | No. 1 cedar, 6' high | | 150 | .160 | | 20 | 3.52 | 1.65 | 25.17 | 29.50 |
| 3900 | Basket weave, No. 1 cedar, 6' high | ↓ | 160 | .150 | ↓ | 19.95 | 3.30 | 1.55 | 24.80 | 29 |
| 4200 | Gate, 3'-6" wide | B-1 | 9 | 2.667 | Ea. | 63.50 | 59 | | 122.50 | 169 |
| 5000 | Fence rail, redwood, 2" x 4", merch grade 8' | " | 2400 | .010 | L.F. | 1.17 | .22 | | 1.39 | 1.66 |

# 32 32 Retaining Walls

## 32 32 13 – Cast-in-Place Concrete Retaining Walls

### 32 32 13.10 Retaining Walls, Cast Concrete

| | | Crew | Daily Output | Labor-Hours | Unit | Material | 2010 Bare Costs Labor | Equipment | Total | Total Incl O&P |
|---|---|---|---|---|---|---|---|---|---|---|
| 0010 | **RETAINING WALLS, CAST CONCRETE** | | | | | | | | | |
| 1800 | Concrete gravity wall with vertical face including excavation & backfill | | | | | | | | | |
| 1850 | No reinforcing | | | | | | | | | |
| 1900 | 6' high, level embankment | C-17C | 36 | 2.306 | L.F. | 70.50 | 68.50 | 16.10 | 155.10 | 210 |
| 2000 | 33° slope embankment | " | 32 | 2.594 | " | 64.50 | 77 | 18.10 | 159.60 | 220 |
| 2800 | Reinforced concrete cantilever, incl. excavation, backfill & reinf. | | | | | | | | | |
| 2900 | 6' high, 33° slope embankment | C-17C | 35 | 2.371 | L.F. | 64.50 | 70.50 | 16.55 | 151.55 | 207 |

## 32 32 23 – Segmental Retaining Walls

### 32 32 23.13 Segmental Conc. Unit Masonry Retaining Walls

| | | Crew | Daily Output | Labor-Hours | Unit | Material | 2010 Bare Costs Labor | Equipment | Total | Total Incl O&P |
|---|---|---|---|---|---|---|---|---|---|---|
| 0010 | **SEGMENTAL CONC. UNIT MASONRY RETAINING WALLS** | | | | | | | | | |
| 7100 | Segmental Retaining Wall system, incl pins, and void fill | | | | | | | | | |
| 7120 | base not included | | | | | | | | | |
| 7140 | Large unit, 8" high x 18" wide x 20" deep, 3 plane split | B-62 | 300 | .080 | S.F. | 10.10 | 1.91 | .54 | 12.55 | 14.85 |
| 7150 | Straight split | | 300 | .080 | | 10.10 | 1.91 | .54 | 12.55 | 14.85 |
| 7160 | Medium, ltwt, 8" high x 18" wide x 12" deep, 3 plane split | ↓ | 400 | .060 | | 11.30 | 1.43 | .40 | 13.13 | 15.20 |

# 32 32 Retaining Walls

## 32 32 23 – Segmental Retaining Walls

| 32 32 23.13 Segmental Conc. Unit Masonry Retaining Walls | Crew | Daily Output | Labor-Hours | Unit | Material | 2010 Bare Costs Labor | Equipment | Total | Total Incl O&P |
|---|---|---|---|---|---|---|---|---|---|
| 7170 | Straight split | B-62 | 400 | .060 | S.F. | 8.50 | 1.43 | .40 | 10.33 | 12.15 |
| 7180 | Small unit, 4" x 18" x 10" deep, 3 plane split | | 400 | .060 | | 12 | 1.43 | .40 | 13.83 | 16 |
| 7190 | Straight split | | 400 | .060 | | 12.70 | 1.43 | .40 | 14.53 | 16.75 |
| 7200 | Cap unit, 3 plane split | | 300 | .080 | | 14.20 | 1.91 | .54 | 16.65 | 19.40 |
| 7210 | Cap unit, straight split | | 300 | .080 | | 14.20 | 1.91 | .54 | 16.65 | 19.40 |
| 7260 | For reinforcing, add | | | | | | | | 4.25 | 4.68 |
| 8000 | For higher walls, add components as necessary | | | | | | | | | |

## 32 32 26 – Metal Crib Retaining Walls

### 32 32 26.10 Metal Bin Retaining Walls

| | | Crew | Daily Output | Labor-Hours | Unit | Material | Labor | Equipment | Total | Total Incl O&P |
|---|---|---|---|---|---|---|---|---|---|---|
| 0010 | **METAL BIN RETAINING WALLS** | | | | | | | | | |
| 0011 | Aluminized steel bin, excavation | | | | | | | | | |
| 0020 | and backfill not included, 10' wide | | | | | | | | | |
| 0100 | 4' high, 5.5' deep | B-13 | 650 | .074 | S.F. | 23 | 1.73 | 1.15 | 25.88 | 29.50 |
| 0200 | 8' high, 5.5' deep | | 615 | .078 | | 26.50 | 1.82 | 1.22 | 29.54 | 33.50 |
| 0300 | 10' high, 7.7' deep | | 580 | .083 | | 28 | 1.93 | 1.29 | 31.22 | 35 |
| 0400 | 12' high, 7.7' deep | | 530 | .091 | | 30 | 2.12 | 1.41 | 33.53 | 38 |
| 0500 | 16' high, 7.7' deep | | 515 | .093 | | 31.50 | 2.18 | 1.45 | 35.13 | 40 |

## 32 32 60 – Stone Retaining Walls

### 32 32 60.10 Retaining Walls, Stone

| | | Crew | Daily Output | Labor-Hours | Unit | Material | Labor | Equipment | Total | Total Incl O&P |
|---|---|---|---|---|---|---|---|---|---|---|
| 0010 | **RETAINING WALLS, STONE** | | | | | | | | | |
| 0015 | Including excavation, concrete footing and | | | | | | | | | |
| 0020 | stone 3' below grade. Price is exposed face area. | | | | | | | | | |
| 0200 | Decorative random stone, to 6' high, 1'-6" thick, dry set | D-1 | 35 | .457 | S.F. | 46 | 12.05 | | 58.05 | 71 |
| 0300 | Mortar set | | 40 | .400 | | 46 | 10.55 | | 56.55 | 68.50 |
| 0500 | Cut stone, to 6' high, 1'-6" thick, dry set | | 35 | .457 | | 46 | 12.05 | | 58.05 | 71 |
| 0600 | Mortar set | | 40 | .400 | | 46 | 10.55 | | 56.55 | 68.50 |
| 0800 | Random stone, 6' to 10' high, 2' thick, dry set | | 45 | .356 | | 46 | 9.40 | | 55.40 | 66.50 |
| 0900 | Mortar set | | 50 | .320 | | 46 | 8.45 | | 54.45 | 65 |
| 1100 | Cut stone, 6' to 10' high, 2' thick, dry set | | 45 | .356 | | 46 | 9.40 | | 55.40 | 66.50 |
| 1200 | Mortar set | | 50 | .320 | | 46 | 8.45 | | 54.45 | 65 |

# 32 84 Planting Irrigation

## 32 84 23 – Underground Sprinklers

### 32 84 23.10 Sprinkler Irrigation System

| | | Crew | Daily Output | Labor-Hours | Unit | Material | Labor | Equipment | Total | Total Incl O&P |
|---|---|---|---|---|---|---|---|---|---|---|
| 0010 | **SPRINKLER IRRIGATION SYSTEM** | | | | | | | | | |
| 0011 | For lawns | | | | | | | | | |
| 0800 | Residential system, custom, 1" supply | B-20 | 2000 | .012 | S.F. | .30 | .27 | | .57 | .78 |
| 0900 | 1-1/2" supply | " | 1800 | .013 | " | .35 | .30 | | .65 | .89 |

## 32 91 13 – Soil Preparation

### 32 91 13.16 Mulching

| | | Crew | Daily Output | Labor-Hours | Unit | Material | 2010 Bare Costs Labor | 2010 Bare Costs Equipment | Total | Total Incl O&P |
|---|---|---|---|---|---|---|---|---|---|---|
| 0010 | **MULCHING** | | | | | | | | | |
| 0100 | Aged barks, 3" deep, hand spread | 1 Clab | 100 | .080 | S.Y. | 2.93 | 1.72 | | 4.65 | 6.10 |
| 0150 | Skid steer loader | B-63 | 13.50 | 2.963 | M.S.F. | 325 | 63.50 | 11.95 | 400.45 | 480 |
| 0200 | Hay, 1" deep, hand spread | 1 Clab | 475 | .017 | S.Y. | .52 | .36 | | .88 | 1.18 |
| 0250 | Power mulcher, small | B-64 | 180 | .089 | M.S.F. | 58 | 1.97 | 2.17 | 62.14 | 69 |
| 0350 | Large | B-65 | 530 | .030 | " | 58 | .67 | 1.05 | 59.72 | 66 |
| 0400 | Humus peat, 1" deep, hand spread | 1 Clab | 700 | .011 | S.Y. | 4.55 | .25 | | 4.80 | 5.40 |
| 0450 | Push spreader | " | 2500 | .003 | " | 4.55 | .07 | | 4.62 | 5.10 |
| 0550 | Tractor spreader | B-66 | 700 | .011 | M.S.F. | 505 | .33 | .31 | 505.64 | 555 |
| 0600 | Oat straw, 1" deep, hand spread | 1 Clab | 475 | .017 | S.Y. | .49 | .36 | | .85 | 1.15 |
| 0650 | Power mulcher, small | B-64 | 180 | .089 | M.S.F. | 54.50 | 1.97 | 2.17 | 58.64 | 65.50 |
| 0700 | Large | B-65 | 530 | .030 | " | 54.50 | .67 | 1.05 | 56.22 | 62.50 |
| 0750 | Add for asphaltic emulsion | B-45 | 1770 | .009 | Gal. | 2.28 | .20 | .17 | 2.65 | 3.04 |
| 0800 | Peat moss, 1" deep, hand spread | 1 Clab | 900 | .009 | S.Y. | 1.90 | .19 | | 2.09 | 2.41 |
| 0850 | Push spreader | " | 2500 | .003 | " | 1.90 | .07 | | 1.97 | 2.21 |
| 0950 | Tractor spreader | B-66 | 700 | .011 | M.S.F. | 211 | .33 | .31 | 211.64 | 233 |
| 1000 | Polyethylene film, 6 mil. | 2 Clab | 2000 | .008 | S.Y. | .22 | .17 | | .39 | .53 |
| 1100 | Redwood nuggets, 3" deep, hand spread | 1 Clab | 150 | .053 | " | 4.70 | 1.15 | | 5.85 | 7.10 |
| 1150 | Skid steer loader | B-63 | 13.50 | 2.963 | M.S.F. | 520 | 63.50 | 11.95 | 595.45 | 695 |
| 1200 | Stone mulch, hand spread, ceramic chips, economy | 1 Clab | 125 | .064 | S.Y. | 6.95 | 1.38 | | 8.33 | 9.95 |
| 1250 | Deluxe | " | 95 | .084 | " | 10.60 | 1.81 | | 12.41 | 14.75 |
| 1300 | Granite chips | B-1 | 10 | 2.400 | C.Y. | 34.50 | 53 | | 87.50 | 128 |
| 1400 | Marble chips | | 10 | 2.400 | | 129 | 53 | | 182 | 232 |
| 1600 | Pea gravel | | 28 | .857 | | 68.50 | 19 | | 87.50 | 108 |
| 1700 | Quartz | | 10 | 2.400 | | 166 | 53 | | 219 | 272 |
| 1800 | Tar paper, 15 Lb. felt | 1 Clab | 800 | .010 | S.Y. | .53 | .22 | | .75 | .94 |
| 1900 | Wood chips, 2" deep, hand spread | " | 220 | .036 | " | 1.93 | .78 | | 2.71 | 3.43 |
| 1950 | Skid steer loader | B-63 | 20.30 | 1.970 | M.S.F. | 214 | 42.50 | 7.95 | 264.45 | 315 |

### 32 91 13.26 Planting Beds

| | | Crew | Daily Output | Labor-Hours | Unit | Material | 2010 Bare Costs Labor | 2010 Bare Costs Equipment | Total | Total Incl O&P |
|---|---|---|---|---|---|---|---|---|---|---|
| 0010 | **PLANTING BEDS** | | | | | | | | | |
| 0100 | Backfill planting pit, by hand, on site topsoil | 2 Clab | 18 | .889 | C.Y. | | 19.10 | | 19.10 | 32 |
| 0200 | Prepared planting mix, by hand | " | 24 | .667 | | | 14.35 | | 14.35 | 24 |
| 0300 | Skid steer loader, on site topsoil | B-62 | 340 | .071 | | | 1.68 | .48 | 2.16 | 3.32 |
| 0400 | Prepared planting mix | " | 410 | .059 | | | 1.40 | .39 | 1.79 | 2.75 |
| 1000 | Excavate planting pit, by hand, sandy soil | 2 Clab | 16 | 1 | | | 21.50 | | 21.50 | 36 |
| 1100 | Heavy soil or clay | " | 8 | 2 | | | 43 | | 43 | 72.50 |
| 1200 | 1/2 C.Y. backhoe, sandy soil | B-11C | 150 | .107 | | | 2.73 | 2.25 | 4.98 | 7 |
| 1300 | Heavy soil or clay | " | 115 | .139 | | | 3.56 | 2.94 | 6.50 | 9.15 |
| 2000 | Mix planting soil, incl. loam, manure, peat, by hand | 2 Clab | 60 | .267 | | 40.50 | 5.75 | | 46.25 | 54 |
| 2100 | Skid steer loader | B-62 | 150 | .160 | | 40.50 | 3.81 | 1.08 | 45.39 | 52 |
| 3000 | Pile sod, skid steer loader | " | 2800 | .009 | S.Y. | | .20 | .06 | .26 | .40 |
| 3100 | By hand | 2 Clab | 400 | .040 | | | .86 | | .86 | 1.45 |
| 4000 | Remove sod, F.E. loader | B-10S | 2000 | .004 | | | .12 | .18 | .30 | .39 |
| 4100 | Sod cutter | B-12K | 3200 | .005 | | | .13 | .30 | .43 | .55 |
| 4200 | By hand | 2 Clab | 240 | .067 | | | 1.43 | | 1.43 | 2.41 |

## 32 91 19 – Landscape Grading

### 32 91 19.13 Topsoil Placement and Grading

| | | Crew | Daily Output | Labor-Hours | Unit | Material | 2010 Bare Costs Labor | 2010 Bare Costs Equipment | Total | Total Incl O&P |
|---|---|---|---|---|---|---|---|---|---|---|
| 0010 | **TOPSOIL PLACEMENT AND GRADING** | | | | | | | | | |
| 0300 | Fine grade, base course for paving, see Div. 32 11 23.23 | | | | | | | | | |
| 0701 | Furnish and place, truck dumped, unscreened, 4" deep | B-10S | 12000 | .001 | S.F. | .38 | .02 | .03 | .43 | .48 |
| 0801 | 6" deep | " | 7400 | .001 | " | .53 | .03 | .05 | .61 | .69 |
| 0900 | Fine grading and seeding, incl. lime, fertilizer & seed, | | | | | | | | | |

# 32 91 Planting Preparation

## 32 91 19 – Landscape Grading

| 32 91 19.13 Topsoil Placement and Grading | Crew | Daily Output | Labor-Hours | Unit | Material | 2010 Bare Costs Labor | Equipment | Total | Total Incl O&P |
|---|---|---|---|---|---|---|---|---|---|
| 1001　　With equipment | B-14 | 9000 | .005 | S.F. | .08 | .12 | .04 | .24 | .34 |

# 32 92 Turf and Grasses

## 32 92 19 – Seeding

### 32 92 19.13 Mechanical Seeding

| | | Crew | Daily Output | Labor-Hours | Unit | Material | 2010 Bare Costs Labor | Equipment | Total | Total Incl O&P |
|---|---|---|---|---|---|---|---|---|---|---|
| 0010 | MECHANICAL SEEDING　　R329219-50 | | | | | | | | | |
| 0020 | Mechanical seeding, 215 lb./acre | B-66 | 1.50 | 5.333 | Acre | 565 | 152 | 146 | 863 | 1,025 |
| 0101 | $2.00/lb., 44 lb./M.S.Y. | 1 Clab | 13950 | .001 | S.F. | .02 | .01 | | .03 | .04 |
| 0300 | Fine grading and seeding incl. lime, fertilizer & seed, | | | | | | | | | |
| 0310 | 　with equipment | B-14 | 1000 | .048 | S.Y. | .20 | 1.10 | .34 | 1.64 | 2.44 |
| 0600 | Limestone hand push spreader, 50 lbs. per M.S.F. | 1 Clab | 180 | .044 | M.S.F. | 4.02 | .96 | | 4.98 | 6.05 |
| 0800 | Grass seed hand push spreader, 4.5 lbs. per M.S.F. | " | 180 | .044 | " | 20 | .96 | | 20.96 | 23.50 |

## 32 92 23 – Sodding

### 32 92 23.10 Sodding Systems

| | | Crew | Daily Output | Labor-Hours | Unit | Material | 2010 Bare Costs Labor | Equipment | Total | Total Incl O&P |
|---|---|---|---|---|---|---|---|---|---|---|
| 0010 | SODDING SYSTEMS | | | | | | | | | |
| 0020 | Sodding, 1" deep, bluegrass sod, on level ground, over 8 MSF | B-63 | 22 | 1.818 | M.S.F. | 246 | 39 | 7.35 | 292.35 | 345 |
| 0200 | 　4 M.S.F. | | 17 | 2.353 | | 273 | 50.50 | 9.50 | 333 | 395 |
| 0300 | 　1000 S.F. | | 13.50 | 2.963 | | 297 | 63.50 | 11.95 | 372.45 | 445 |
| 0500 | 　Sloped ground, over 8 M.S.F. | | 6 | 6.667 | | 246 | 143 | 27 | 416 | 540 |
| 0600 | 　4 M.S.F. | | 5 | 8 | | 273 | 172 | 32.50 | 477.50 | 625 |
| 0700 | 　1000 S.F. | | 4 | 10 | | 297 | 215 | 40.50 | 552.50 | 730 |
| 1000 | Bent grass sod, on level ground, over 6 M.S.F. | | 20 | 2 | | 525 | 43 | 8.10 | 576.10 | 660 |
| 1100 | 　3 M.S.F. | | 18 | 2.222 | | 605 | 48 | 9 | 662 | 755 |
| 1200 | 　Sodding 1000 S.F. or less | | 14 | 2.857 | | 695 | 61.50 | 11.55 | 768.05 | 880 |
| 1500 | 　Sloped ground, over 6 M.S.F. | | 15 | 2.667 | | 525 | 57.50 | 10.75 | 593.25 | 690 |
| 1600 | 　3 M.S.F. | | 13.50 | 2.963 | | 605 | 63.50 | 11.95 | 680.45 | 785 |
| 1700 | 　1000 S.F. | | 12 | 3.333 | | 695 | 71.50 | 13.45 | 779.95 | 900 |

# 32 93 Plants

## 32 93 13 – Ground Covers

### 32 93 13.10 Ground Cover Plants

| | | Crew | Daily Output | Labor-Hours | Unit | Material | 2010 Bare Costs Labor | Equipment | Total | Total Incl O&P |
|---|---|---|---|---|---|---|---|---|---|---|
| 0010 | GROUND COVER PLANTS | | | | | | | | | |
| 0012 | Plants, pachysandra, in prepared beds | B-1 | 15 | 1.600 | C | 27 | 35.50 | | 62.50 | 89.50 |
| 0200 | 　Vinca minor, 1 yr, bare root, in prepared beds | | 12 | 2 | " | 40 | 44.50 | | 84.50 | 119 |
| 0600 | Stone chips, in 50 lb. bags, Georgia marble | | 520 | .046 | Bag | 5.25 | 1.02 | | 6.27 | 7.50 |
| 0700 | 　Onyx gemstone | | 260 | .092 | | 22.50 | 2.05 | | 24.55 | 28.50 |
| 0800 | 　Quartz | | 260 | .092 | | 8.50 | 2.05 | | 10.55 | 12.80 |
| 0900 | Pea gravel, truckload lots | | 28 | .857 | Ton | 27.50 | 19 | | 46.50 | 62 |

## 32 93 33 – Shrubs

### 32 93 33.10 Shrubs and Trees

| | | Crew | Daily Output | Labor-Hours | Unit | Material | 2010 Bare Costs Labor | Equipment | Total | Total Incl O&P |
|---|---|---|---|---|---|---|---|---|---|---|
| 0010 | SHRUBS AND TREES | | | | | | | | | |
| 0011 | Evergreen, in prepared beds, B & B | | | | | | | | | |
| 0100 | 　Arborvitae pyramidal, 4'-5' | B-17 | 30 | 1.067 | Ea. | 48.50 | 25.50 | 24.50 | 98.50 | 122 |
| 0150 | 　　Globe, 12"-15" | B-1 | 96 | .250 | | 21 | 5.55 | | 26.55 | 32.50 |
| 0300 | 　Cedar, blue, 8'-10' | B-17 | 18 | 1.778 | | 219 | 42 | 41 | 302 | 355 |
| 0500 | 　Hemlock, canadian, 2-1/2'-3' | B-1 | 36 | .667 | | 33.50 | 14.80 | | 48.30 | 62 |
| 0550 | 　Holly, Savannah, 8' - 10' H | | 9.68 | 2.479 | | 485 | 55 | | 540 | 630 |
| 0600 | 　Juniper, andorra, 18"-24" | | 80 | .300 | | 16.80 | 6.65 | | 23.45 | 29.50 |

# 32 93 Plants

## 32 93 33 – Shrubs

### 32 93 33.10 Shrubs and Trees

| 32 93 33.10 Shrubs and Trees | | Crew | Daily Output | Labor-Hours | Unit | Material | 2010 Bare Costs Labor | Equipment | Total | Total Incl O&P |
|---|---|---|---|---|---|---|---|---|---|---|
| 0620 | Wiltoni, 15"-18" | B-1 | 80 | .300 | Ea. | 21 | 6.65 | | 27.65 | 34 |
| 0640 | Skyrocket, 4-1/2'-5' | B-17 | 55 | .582 | | 56 | 13.80 | 13.45 | 83.25 | 99.50 |
| 0660 | Blue pfitzer, 2'-2-1/2' | B-1 | 44 | .545 | | 28 | 12.10 | | 40.10 | 51.50 |
| 0680 | Ketleerie, 2-1/2'-3' | | 50 | .480 | | 34 | 10.65 | | 44.65 | 55 |
| 0700 | Pine, black, 2-1/2'-3' | | 50 | .480 | | 45.50 | 10.65 | | 56.15 | 68 |
| 0720 | Mugo, 18"-24" | | 60 | .400 | | 36 | 8.85 | | 44.85 | 54.50 |
| 0740 | White, 4'-5' | B-17 | 75 | .427 | | 58.50 | 10.15 | 9.85 | 78.50 | 91.50 |
| 0800 | Spruce, blue, 18"-24" | B-1 | 60 | .400 | | 42.50 | 8.85 | | 51.35 | 62 |
| 0840 | Norway, 4'-5' | B-17 | 75 | .427 | | 67 | 10.15 | 9.85 | 87 | 101 |
| 0900 | Yew, denisforma, 12"-15" | B-1 | 60 | .400 | | 26 | 8.85 | | 34.85 | 43.50 |
| 1000 | Capitata, 18"-24" | | 30 | .800 | | 24 | 17.75 | | 41.75 | 56 |
| 1100 | Hicksi, 2'-2-1/2' | | 30 | .800 | | 31.50 | 17.75 | | 49.25 | 65 |

### 32 93 33.20 Shrubs

| 32 93 33.20 Shrubs | | Crew | Daily Output | Labor-Hours | Unit | Material | 2010 Bare Costs Labor | Equipment | Total | Total Incl O&P |
|---|---|---|---|---|---|---|---|---|---|---|
| 0010 | **SHRUBS** | | | | | | | | | |
| 0011 | Broadleaf Evergreen, planted in prepared beds | | | | | | | | | |
| 0100 | Andromeda, 15"-18", container | B-1 | 96 | .250 | Ea. | 26.50 | 5.55 | | 32.05 | 38.50 |
| 0200 | Azalea, 15" - 18", container | | 96 | .250 | | 33 | 5.55 | | 38.55 | 45.50 |
| 0300 | Barberry, 9"-12", container | | 130 | .185 | | 11.75 | 4.09 | | 15.84 | 19.85 |
| 0400 | Boxwood, 15"-18", B&B | | 96 | .250 | | 30 | 5.55 | | 35.55 | 42 |
| 0500 | Euonymus, emerald gaiety, 12" to 15", container | | 115 | .209 | | 20.50 | 4.63 | | 25.13 | 30.50 |
| 0600 | Holly, 15"-18", B & B | | 96 | .250 | | 18.65 | 5.55 | | 24.20 | 30 |
| 0900 | Mount laurel, 18" - 24", B & B | | 80 | .300 | | 56.50 | 6.65 | | 63.15 | 73 |
| 1000 | Paxistema, 9 – 12" high | | 130 | .185 | | 18.30 | 4.09 | | 22.39 | 27 |
| 1100 | Rhododendron, 18"-24", container | | 48 | .500 | | 31.50 | 11.10 | | 42.60 | 53 |
| 1200 | Rosemary, 1 gal container | | 600 | .040 | | 62.50 | .89 | | 63.39 | 70.50 |
| 2000 | Deciduous, planted in prepared beds, amelanchier, 2'-3', B & B | | 57 | .421 | | 90.50 | 9.35 | | 99.85 | 115 |
| 2100 | Azalea, 15"-18", B & B | | 96 | .250 | | 24.50 | 5.55 | | 30.05 | 36.50 |
| 2300 | Bayberry, 2'-3', B & B | | 57 | .421 | | 28 | 9.35 | | 37.35 | 46 |
| 2600 | Cotoneaster, 15"-18", B & B | | 80 | .300 | | 16.75 | 6.65 | | 23.40 | 29.50 |
| 2800 | Dogwood, 3'-4', B & B | B-17 | 40 | .800 | | 26.50 | 19 | 18.50 | 64 | 81 |
| 2900 | Euonymus, alatus compacta, 15" to 18", container | B-1 | 80 | .300 | | 22.50 | 6.65 | | 29.15 | 35.50 |
| 3200 | Forsythia, 2'-3', container | " | 60 | .400 | | 20 | 8.85 | | 28.85 | 37 |
| 3300 | Hibiscus, 3'-4', B & B | B-17 | 75 | .427 | | 15.05 | 10.15 | 9.85 | 35.05 | 44.50 |
| 3400 | Honeysuckle, 3'-4', B & B | B-1 | 60 | .400 | | 22 | 8.85 | | 30.85 | 39.50 |
| 3500 | Hydrangea, 2'-3', B & B | " | 57 | .421 | | 26 | 9.35 | | 35.35 | 44.50 |
| 3600 | Lilac, 3'-4', B & B | B-17 | 40 | .800 | | 23 | 19 | 18.50 | 60.50 | 77 |
| 3900 | Privet, bare root, 18"-24" | B-1 | 80 | .300 | | 12.55 | 6.65 | | 19.20 | 25 |
| 4100 | Quince, 2'-3', B & B | " | 57 | .421 | | 24 | 9.35 | | 33.35 | 42 |
| 4200 | Russian olive, 3'-4', B & B | B-17 | 75 | .427 | | 24 | 10.15 | 9.85 | 44 | 53.50 |
| 4400 | Spirea, 3'-4', B & B | B-1 | 70 | .343 | | 16 | 7.60 | | 23.60 | 30.50 |
| 4500 | Viburnum, 3'-4', B & B | B-17 | 40 | .800 | | 29.50 | 19 | 18.50 | 67 | 84.50 |

## 32 93 43 – Trees

### 32 93 43.20 Trees

| 32 93 43.20 Trees | | | Crew | Daily Output | Labor-Hours | Unit | Material | 2010 Bare Costs Labor | Equipment | Total | Total Incl O&P |
|---|---|---|---|---|---|---|---|---|---|---|---|
| 0010 | **TREES** | | | | | | | | | | |
| 0011 | Deciduous, in prep. beds, balled & burlapped (B&B) | | | | | | | | | | |
| 0100 | Ash, 2" caliper | G | B-17 | 8 | 4 | Ea. | 115 | 95 | 92.50 | 302.50 | 385 |
| 0200 | Beech, 5'-6' | G | | 50 | .640 | | 223 | 15.20 | 14.80 | 253 | 288 |
| 0300 | Birch, 6'-8', 3 stems | G | | 20 | 1.600 | | 114 | 38 | 37 | 189 | 229 |
| 0500 | Crabapple, 6'-8' | G | | 20 | 1.600 | | 160 | 38 | 37 | 235 | 280 |
| 0600 | Dogwood, 4'-5' | G | | 40 | .800 | | 63.50 | 19 | 18.50 | 101 | 122 |
| 0700 | Eastern redbud 4'-5' | G | | 40 | .800 | | 157 | 19 | 18.50 | 194.50 | 225 |
| 0800 | Elm, 8'-10' | G | | 20 | 1.600 | | 119 | 38 | 37 | 194 | 235 |

# 32 93 Plants

## 32 93 43 – Trees

| 32 93 43.20 Trees | | Crew | Daily Output | Labor-Hours | Unit | Material | 2010 Bare Costs Labor | Equipment | Total | Total Incl O&P |
|---|---|---|---|---|---|---|---|---|---|---|
| 0900 | Ginkgo, 6'-7' | G B-17 | 24 | 1.333 | Ea. | 163 | 31.50 | 31 | 225.50 | 267 |
| 1000 | Hawthorn, 8'-10', 1" caliper | G | 20 | 1.600 | | 135 | 38 | 37 | 210 | 252 |
| 1100 | Honeylocust, 10'-12', 1-1/2" caliper | G | 10 | 3.200 | | 145 | 76 | 74 | 295 | 370 |
| 1300 | Larch, 8' | G | 32 | 1 | | 105 | 24 | 23 | 152 | 181 |
| 1400 | Linden, 8'-10', 1" caliper | G | 20 | 1.600 | | 113 | 38 | 37 | 188 | 228 |
| 1500 | Magnolia, 4'-5' | G | 20 | 1.600 | | 71.50 | 38 | 37 | 146.50 | 183 |
| 1600 | Maple, red, 8'-10', 1-1/2" caliper | G | 10 | 3.200 | | 241 | 76 | 74 | 391 | 475 |
| 1700 | Mountain ash, 8'-10', 1" caliper | G | 16 | 2 | | 182 | 47.50 | 46 | 275.50 | 330 |
| 1800 | Oak, 2-1/2"-3" caliper | G | 6 | 5.333 | | 269 | 127 | 123 | 519 | 645 |
| 2100 | Planetree, 9'-11', 1-1/4" caliper | G | 10 | 3.200 | | 105 | 76 | 74 | 255 | 325 |
| 2200 | Plum, 6'-8', 1" caliper | G | 20 | 1.600 | | 95.50 | 38 | 37 | 170.50 | 209 |
| 2300 | Poplar, 9'-11', 1-1/4" caliper | G | 10 | 3.200 | | 90 | 76 | 74 | 240 | 310 |
| 2500 | Sumac, 2'-3' | G | 75 | .427 | | 23 | 10.15 | 9.85 | 43 | 52.50 |
| 2700 | Tulip, 5'-6' | G | 40 | .800 | | 53 | 19 | 18.50 | 90.50 | 110 |
| 2800 | Willow, 6'-8', 1" caliper | G | 20 | 1.600 | | 68.50 | 38 | 37 | 143.50 | 180 |

# 32 94 Planting Accessories

## 32 94 13 – Landscape Edging

| 32 94 13.20 Edging | | Crew | Daily Output | Labor-Hours | Unit | Material | 2010 Bare Costs Labor | Equipment | Total | Total Incl O&P |
|---|---|---|---|---|---|---|---|---|---|---|
| 0010 | **EDGING** | | | | | | | | | |
| 0050 | Aluminum alloy, including stakes, 1/8" x 4", mill finish | B-1 | 390 | .062 | L.F. | 3.15 | 1.36 | | 4.51 | 5.75 |
| 0051 | Black paint | | 390 | .062 | | 3.65 | 1.36 | | 5.01 | 6.30 |
| 0052 | Black anodized | | 390 | .062 | | 4.22 | 1.36 | | 5.58 | 6.95 |
| 0100 | Brick, set horizontally, 1-1/2 bricks per L.F. | D-1 | 370 | .043 | | 1.40 | 1.14 | | 2.54 | 3.42 |
| 0150 | Set vertically, 3 bricks per L.F. | " | 135 | .119 | | 4.24 | 3.13 | | 7.37 | 9.80 |
| 0200 | Corrugated aluminum, roll, 4" wide | 1 Carp | 650 | .012 | | .72 | .36 | | 1.08 | 1.39 |
| 0250 | 6" wide | " | 550 | .015 | | .90 | .42 | | 1.32 | 1.70 |
| 0600 | Railroad ties, 6" x 8" | 2 Carp | 170 | .094 | | 3.15 | 2.74 | | 5.89 | 8.10 |
| 0650 | 7" x 9" | | 136 | .118 | | 3.50 | 3.42 | | 6.92 | 9.60 |
| 0750 | Redwood 2" x 4" | | 330 | .048 | | 2.26 | 1.41 | | 3.67 | 4.86 |
| 0800 | Steel edge strips, incl. stakes, 1/4" x 5" | B-1 | 390 | .062 | | 4.20 | 1.36 | | 5.56 | 6.90 |
| 0850 | 3/16" x 4" | " | 390 | .062 | | 3.32 | 1.36 | | 4.68 | 5.95 |

## 32 94 50 – Tree Guying

| 32 94 50.10 Tree Guying Systems | | Crew | Daily Output | Labor-Hours | Unit | Material | 2010 Bare Costs Labor | Equipment | Total | Total Incl O&P |
|---|---|---|---|---|---|---|---|---|---|---|
| 0010 | **TREE GUYING SYSTEMS** | | | | | | | | | |
| 0015 | Tree guying Including stakes, guy wire and wrap | | | | | | | | | |
| 0100 | Less than 3" caliper, 2 stakes | 2 Clab | 35 | .457 | Ea. | 17.55 | 9.85 | | 27.40 | 36 |
| 0200 | 3" to 4" caliper, 3 stakes | " | 21 | .762 | " | 20 | 16.40 | | 36.40 | 49.50 |
| 1000 | Including arrowhead anchor, cable, turnbuckles and wrap | | | | | | | | | |
| 1100 | Less than 3" caliper, 3 anchors | 2 Clab | 20 | .800 | Ea. | 51 | 17.20 | | 68.20 | 85 |
| 1200 | 3" to 6" caliper, 4 anchors | | 15 | 1.067 | | 51 | 23 | | 74 | 94.50 |
| 1300 | 6" caliper, 6 anchors | | 12 | 1.333 | | 95.50 | 28.50 | | 124 | 153 |
| 1400 | 8" caliper, 8 anchors | | 9 | 1.778 | | 107 | 38 | | 145 | 183 |

# 32 96 Transplanting

## 32 96 23 – Plant and Bulb Transplanting

| 32 96 23.23 Planting | Crew | Daily Output | Labor-Hours | Unit | Material | 2010 Bare Costs Labor | Equipment | Total | Total Incl O&P |
|---|---|---|---|---|---|---|---|---|---|
| 0010 **PLANTING** | | | | | | | | | |
| 0012   Moving shrubs on site, 12" ball | B-62 | 28 | .857 | Ea. | | 20.50 | 5.75 | 26.25 | 40.50 |
| 0100   24" ball | " | 22 | 1.091 | " | | 26 | 7.35 | 33.35 | 51.50 |
| **32 96 23.43 Moving Trees** | | | | | | | | | |
| 0290 **MOVING TREES**, On site | | | | | | | | | |
| 0300   Moving trees on site, 36" ball | B-6 | 3.75 | 6.400 | Ea. | | 153 | 90 | 243 | 355 |
| 0400   60" ball | " | 1 | 24 | " | | 570 | 340 | 910 | 1,325 |

## Estimating Tips

### 33 10 00 Water Utilities
### 33 30 00 Sanitary Sewerage Utilities
### 33 40 00 Storm Drainage Utilities

• Never assume that the water, sewer, and drainage lines will go in at the early stages of the project. Consider the site access needs before dividing the site in half with open trenches, loose pipe, and machinery obstructions. Always inspect the site to establish that the site drawings are complete. Check off all existing utilities on your drawings as you locate them. Be especially careful with underground because appurtenances are sometimes buried during regrading or repaving operations. If you find any discrepancies, mark up the site plan for further research. Differing site conditions can be very costly if discovered later in the project.

• See also Section 33 01 00 for restoration of pipe where removal/replacement may be undesirable. Use of new types of piping materials can reduce the overall project cost. Owners/design engineers should consider the installing contractor as a valuable source of current information on utility products and local conditions that could lead to significant cost savings.

## Reference Numbers

Reference numbers are shown in shaded boxes at the beginning of some major classifications. These numbers refer to related items in the Reference Section. The reference information may be an estimating procedure, an alternate pricing method, or technical information.
*Note:* Not all subdivisions listed here necessarily appear in this publication.

**Division 33 - Utilities**

*Note:* **Trade Service,** *in part, has been used as a reference source for some of the material prices used in Division 33.*

# 33 05 Common Work Results for Utilities

## 33 05 16 – Utility Structures

| 33 05 16.13 Utility Boxes | Crew | Daily Output | Labor-Hours | Unit | Material | 2010 Bare Costs Labor | Equipment | Total | Total Incl O&P |
|---|---|---|---|---|---|---|---|---|---|
| 0010 **UTILITY BOXES** Precast concrete, 6" thick | | | | | | | | | |
| 0050      5' x 10' x 6' high, I.D. | B-13 | 2 | 24 | Ea. | 2,300 | 560 | 375 | 3,235 | 3,875 |
| 0350    Hand hole, precast concrete, 1-1/2" thick | | | | | | | | | |
| 0400      1'-0" x 2'-0" x 1'-9", I.D., light duty | B-1 | 4 | 6 | Ea. | 390 | 133 | | 523 | 655 |
| 0450      4'-6" x 3'-2" x 2'-0", O.D., heavy duty | B-6 | 3 | 8 | " | 1,200 | 191 | 113 | 1,504 | 1,775 |

## 33 05 23 – Trenchless Utility Installation

### 33 05 23.19 Microtunneling

| | Crew | Daily Output | Labor-Hours | Unit | Material | 2010 Bare Costs Labor | Equipment | Total | Total Incl O&P |
|---|---|---|---|---|---|---|---|---|---|
| 0010 **MICROTUNNELING** | | | | | | | | | |
| 0011    Not including excavation, backfill, shoring, | | | | | | | | | |
| 0020    or dewatering, average 50'/day, slurry method | | | | | | | | | |
| 0100      24" to 48" outside diameter, minimum | | | | L.F. | | | | 800 | 880 |
| 0110        Adverse conditions, add | | | | % | | | | 50% | 50% |
| 1000    Rent microtunneling machine, average monthly lease | | | | Month | | | | 90,000 | 99,000 |
| 1010    Operating technician | | | | Day | | | | 560 | 620 |
| 1100    Mobilization and demobilization, minimum | | | | Job | | | | 40,000 | 44,000 |
| 1110      Maximum | | | | " | | | | 400,000 | 440,000 |

# 33 11 Water Utility Distribution Piping

## 33 11 13 – Public Water Utility Distribution Piping

### 33 11 13.15 Water Supply, Ductile Iron Pipe

| | Crew | Daily Output | Labor-Hours | Unit | Material | 2010 Bare Costs Labor | Equipment | Total | Total Incl O&P |
|---|---|---|---|---|---|---|---|---|---|
| 0010 **WATER SUPPLY, DUCTILE IRON PIPE** | | | | | | | | | |
| 0020    Not including excavation or backfill | | | | | | | | | |
| 2000    Pipe, class 50 water piping, 18' lengths | | | | | | | | | |
| 2020      Mechanical joint, 4" diameter | B-21A | 200 | .200 | L.F. | 16.55 | 5.50 | 3.28 | 25.33 | 31 |
| 2040        6" diameter | | 160 | .250 | | 19.20 | 6.90 | 4.10 | 30.20 | 37 |
| 3000      Tyton, push-on joint, 4" diameter | | 400 | .100 | | 12.40 | 2.75 | 1.64 | 16.79 | 20 |
| 3020        6" diameter | ↓ | 333.33 | .120 | ↓ | 15.85 | 3.30 | 1.97 | 21.12 | 25 |
| 8000    Fittings, mechanical joint | | | | | | | | | |
| 8006      90° bend, 4" diameter | B-20A | 16 | 2 | Ea. | 230 | 53.50 | | 283.50 | 340 |
| 8020        6" diameter | | 12.80 | 2.500 | | 315 | 67 | | 382 | 455 |
| 8200      Wye or tee, 4" diameter | | 10.67 | 2.999 | | 350 | 80 | | 430 | 520 |
| 8220        6" diameter | | 8.53 | 3.751 | | 465 | 100 | | 565 | 680 |
| 8398      45° bends, 4" diameter | | 16 | 2 | | 180 | 53.50 | | 233.50 | 287 |
| 8400        6" diameter | | 12.80 | 2.500 | | 249 | 67 | | 316 | 385 |
| 8450      Decreaser, 6" x 4" diameter | | 14.22 | 2.250 | | 193 | 60 | | 253 | 315 |
| 8460        8" x 6" diameter | ↓ | 11.64 | 2.749 | ↓ | 247 | 73.50 | | 320.50 | 395 |
| 8550    Piping, butterfly valves, cast iron | | | | | | | | | |
| 8560      4" diameter | B-20 | 6 | 4 | Ea. | 900 | 88.50 | | 988.50 | 1,150 |
| 8700    Joint restraint, ductile iron mechanical joints | | | | | | | | | |
| 8710      4" diameter | B-20A | 32 | 1 | Ea. | 34 | 26.50 | | 60.50 | 82 |
| 8720      6" diameter | | 25.60 | 1.250 | | 41.50 | 33.50 | | 75 | 101 |
| 8730      8" diameter | | 21.33 | 1.500 | | 59 | 40 | | 99 | 132 |
| 8740      10" diameter | | 18.28 | 1.751 | | 86.50 | 47 | | 133.50 | 173 |
| 8750      12" diameter | | 16.84 | 1.900 | | 121 | 51 | | 172 | 217 |
| 8760      14" diameter | | 16 | 2 | | 165 | 53.50 | | 218.50 | 270 |
| 8770      16" diameter | | 11.64 | 2.749 | | 219 | 73.50 | | 292.50 | 360 |
| 8780      18" diameter | | 11.03 | 2.901 | | 305 | 77.50 | | 382.50 | 465 |
| 8785      20" diameter | | 9.14 | 3.501 | | 375 | 93.50 | | 468.50 | 565 |
| 8790      24" diameter | ↓ | 7.53 | 4.250 | | 445 | 114 | | 559 | 675 |
| 9600    Steel sleeve with tap, 4" diameter | B-20 | 3 | 8 | ↓ | 415 | 177 | | 592 | 755 |

606

# 33 11 Water Utility Distribution Piping

## 33 11 13 – Public Water Utility Distribution Piping

### 33 11 13.15 Water Supply, Ductile Iron Pipe

| | | Crew | Daily Output | Labor-Hours | Unit | Material | 2010 Bare Costs Labor | 2010 Bare Costs Equipment | Total | Total Incl O&P |
|---|---|---|---|---|---|---|---|---|---|---|
| 9620 | 6" diameter | B-20 | 2 | 12 | Ea. | 450 | 266 | | 716 | 940 |

### 33 11 13.25 Water Supply, Polyvinyl Chloride Pipe

| | | Crew | Daily Output | Labor-Hours | Unit | Material | 2010 Bare Costs Labor | 2010 Bare Costs Equipment | Total | Total Incl O&P |
|---|---|---|---|---|---|---|---|---|---|---|
| 0010 | **WATER SUPPLY, POLYVINYL CHLORIDE PIPE** | | | | | | | | | |
| 2100 | PVC pipe, Class 150, 1-1/2" diameter | Q-1A | 750 | .013 | L.F. | .30 | .46 | | .76 | 1.09 |
| 2120 | 2" diameter | | 686 | .015 | | .46 | .51 | | .97 | 1.34 |
| 2140 | 2-1/2" diameter | | 500 | .020 | | .68 | .70 | | 1.38 | 1.89 |
| 2160 | 3" diameter | B-20 | 430 | .056 | | 1.04 | 1.24 | | 2.28 | 3.22 |
| 8700 | PVC pipe, joint restraint | | | | | | | | | |
| 8710 | 4" diameter | B-20A | 32 | 1 | Ea. | 38.50 | 26.50 | | 65 | 86.50 |
| 8720 | 6" diameter | | 25.60 | 1.250 | | 46.50 | 33.50 | | 80 | 107 |
| 8730 | 8" diameter | | 21.33 | 1.500 | | 67 | 40 | | 107 | 140 |
| 8740 | 10" diameter | | 18.28 | 1.751 | | 124 | 47 | | 171 | 214 |
| 8750 | 12" diameter | | 16.84 | 1.900 | | 131 | 51 | | 182 | 228 |
| 8760 | 14" diameter | | 16 | 2 | | 206 | 53.50 | | 259.50 | 315 |
| 8770 | 16" diameter | | 11.64 | 2.749 | | 263 | 73.50 | | 336.50 | 410 |
| 8780 | 18" diameter | | 11.03 | 2.901 | | 325 | 77.50 | | 402.50 | 490 |
| 8785 | 20" diameter | | 9.14 | 3.501 | | 405 | 93.50 | | 498.50 | 600 |
| 8790 | 24" diameter | | 7.53 | 4.250 | | 470 | 114 | | 584 | 705 |

# 33 12 Water Utility Distribution Equipment

## 33 12 13 – Water Service Connections

### 33 12 13.15 Tapping, Crosses and Sleeves

| | | Crew | Daily Output | Labor-Hours | Unit | Material | 2010 Bare Costs Labor | 2010 Bare Costs Equipment | Total | Total Incl O&P |
|---|---|---|---|---|---|---|---|---|---|---|
| 0010 | **TAPPING, CROSSES AND SLEEVES** | | | | | | | | | |
| 4000 | Drill and tap pressurized main (labor only) | | | | | | | | | |
| 4100 | 6" main, 1" to 2" service | Q-1 | 3 | 5.333 | Ea. | | 165 | | 165 | 270 |
| 4150 | 8" main, 1" to 2" service | " | 2.75 | 5.818 | " | | 180 | | 180 | 295 |
| 4500 | Tap and insert gate valve | | | | | | | | | |
| 4600 | 8" main, 4" branch | B-21 | 3.20 | 8.750 | Ea. | | 205 | 43 | 248 | 390 |
| 4650 | 6" branch | | 2.70 | 10.370 | | | 242 | 51 | 293 | 460 |
| 4700 | 10" Main, 4" branch | | 2.70 | 10.370 | | | 242 | 51 | 293 | 460 |
| 4750 | 6" branch | | 2.35 | 11.915 | | | 279 | 58.50 | 337.50 | 530 |
| 4800 | 12" main, 6" branch | | 2.35 | 11.915 | | | 279 | 58.50 | 337.50 | 530 |

# 33 21 Water Supply Wells

## 33 21 13 – Public Water Supply Wells

### 33 21 13.10 Wells and Accessories

| | | Crew | Daily Output | Labor-Hours | Unit | Material | 2010 Bare Costs Labor | 2010 Bare Costs Equipment | Total | Total Incl O&P |
|---|---|---|---|---|---|---|---|---|---|---|
| 0010 | **WELLS & ACCESSORIES** | | | | | | | | | |
| 0011 | Domestic | | | | | | | | | |
| 0100 | Drilled, 4" to 6" diameter | B-23 | 120 | .333 | L.F. | | 7.30 | 24 | 31.30 | 39 |
| 1500 | Pumps, installed in wells to 100' deep, 4" submersible | | | | | | | | | |
| 1520 | 3/4 H.P. | Q-1 | 2.66 | 6.015 | Ea. | 620 | 186 | | 806 | 985 |
| 1600 | 1 H.P. | " | 2.29 | 6.987 | " | 840 | 216 | | 1,056 | 1,275 |

# 33 31 Sanitary Utility Sewerage Piping

## 33 31 13 – Public Sanitary Utility Sewerage Piping

| 33 31 13.15 Sewage Collection, Concrete Pipe | Crew | Daily Output | Labor-Hours | Unit | Material | 2010 Bare Costs Labor | Equipment | Total | Total Incl O&P |
|---|---|---|---|---|---|---|---|---|---|
| 0010 **SEWAGE COLLECTION, CONCRETE PIPE** | | | | | | | | | |
| 0020 See Div. 33 41 13.60 for sewage/drainage collection, concrete pipe | | | | | | | | | |

| 33 31 13.25 Sewage Collection, Polyvinyl Chloride Pipe | Crew | Daily Output | Labor-Hours | Unit | Material | 2010 Bare Costs Labor | Equipment | Total | Total Incl O&P |
|---|---|---|---|---|---|---|---|---|---|
| 0010 **SEWAGE COLLECTION, POLYVINYL CHLORIDE PIPE** | | | | | | | | | |
| 0020 Not including excavation or backfill | | | | | | | | | |
| 2000 20' lengths, S.D.R. 35, B&S, 4" diameter | B-20 | 375 | .064 | L.F. | 1.68 | 1.42 | | 3.10 | 4.24 |
| 2040 6" diameter | | 350 | .069 | | 3.64 | 1.52 | | 5.16 | 6.55 |
| 2080 13' lengths , S.D.R. 35, B&S, 8" diameter | ↓ | 335 | .072 | | 7.85 | 1.59 | | 9.44 | 11.30 |
| 2120 10" diameter | B-21 | 330 | .085 | | 11.90 | 1.98 | .42 | 14.30 | 16.90 |
| 4000 Piping, DWV PVC, no exc/bkfill, 10' L, Sch 40, 4" diameter | B-20 | 375 | .064 | | 3.71 | 1.42 | | 5.13 | 6.50 |
| 4010 6" diameter | | 350 | .069 | | 7.25 | 1.52 | | 8.77 | 10.50 |
| 4020 8" diameter | ↓ | 335 | .072 | ↓ | 12.35 | 1.59 | | 13.94 | 16.20 |

# 33 36 Utility Septic Tanks

## 33 36 13 – Utility Septic Tank and Effluent Wet Wells

### 33 36 13.10 Septic Tanks

| | Crew | Daily Output | Labor-Hours | Unit | Material | 2010 Bare Costs Labor | Equipment | Total | Total Incl O&P |
|---|---|---|---|---|---|---|---|---|---|
| 0010 **SEPTIC TANKS** | | | | | | | | | |
| 0011 Not including excavation or piping | | | | | | | | | |
| 0015 Septic tanks, precast, 1,000 gal | B-21 | 8 | 3.500 | Ea. | 750 | 82 | 17.25 | 849.25 | 980 |
| 0060 1,500 gallon | | 7 | 4 | | 1,175 | 93.50 | 19.70 | 1,288.20 | 1,450 |
| 0100 2,000 gallon | | 5 | 5.600 | | 1,675 | 131 | 27.50 | 1,833.50 | 2,100 |
| 0600 High density polyethylene, 1,000 gallon | | 6 | 4.667 | | 985 | 109 | 23 | 1,117 | 1,275 |
| 0700 1,500 gallon | ↓ | 4 | 7 | | 1,375 | 164 | 34.50 | 1,573.50 | 1,825 |
| 1000 Distribution boxes, concrete, 7 outlets | 2 Clab | 16 | 1 | | 80 | 21.50 | | 101.50 | 124 |
| 1100 9 outlets | " | 8 | 2 | | 445 | 43 | | 488 | 565 |
| 1150 Leaching field chambers, 13' x 3'-7" x 1'-4", standard | B-13 | 16 | 3 | | 525 | 70 | 46.50 | 641.50 | 750 |
| 1420 Leaching pit, 6', dia, 3' deep complete | | | | ↓ | 1,050 | | | 1,050 | 1,150 |
| 2200 Excavation for septic tank, 3/4 C.Y. backhoe | B-12F | 145 | .110 | C.Y. | | 2.88 | 4.67 | 7.55 | 9.90 |
| 2400 4' trench for disposal field, 3/4 C.Y. backhoe | " | 335 | .048 | L.F. | | 1.25 | 2.02 | 3.27 | 4.29 |
| 2600 Gravel fill, run of bank | B-6 | 150 | .160 | C.Y. | 20 | 3.81 | 2.25 | 26.06 | 31 |
| 2800 Crushed stone, 3/4" | " | 150 | .160 | " | 31 | 3.81 | 2.25 | 37.06 | 43 |
| 3000 Effluent filter, 4" dia. | B-21 | 4.70 | 5.957 | Ea. | 44.50 | 139 | 29.50 | 213 | 315 |

# 33 41 Storm Utility Drainage Piping

## 33 41 13 – Public Storm Utility Drainage Piping

### 33 41 13.60 Sewage/Drainage Collection, Concrete Pipe

| | Crew | Daily Output | Labor-Hours | Unit | Material | 2010 Bare Costs Labor | Equipment | Total | Total Incl O&P |
|---|---|---|---|---|---|---|---|---|---|
| 0010 **SEWAGE/DRAINAGE COLLECTION, CONCRETE PIPE** | | | | | | | | | |
| 0020 Not including excavation or backfill | | | | | | | | | |
| 1020 8" diameter | B-14 | 224 | .214 | L.F. | 6.90 | 4.93 | 1.51 | 13.34 | 17.45 |
| 1030 10" diameter | " | 216 | .222 | " | 7.65 | 5.10 | 1.56 | 14.31 | 18.65 |
| 3780 Concrete slotted pipe, class 4 mortar joint | | | | | | | | | |
| 3800 12" diameter | B-21 | 168 | .167 | L.F. | 12 | 3.90 | .82 | 16.72 | 20.50 |
| 3840 18" diameter | " | 152 | .184 | " | 18 | 4.31 | .91 | 23.22 | 28 |
| 3900 Class 4 O-ring | | | | | | | | | |
| 3940 12" diameter | B-21 | 168 | .167 | L.F. | 11 | 3.90 | .82 | 15.72 | 19.50 |
| 3960 18" diameter | " | 152 | .184 | " | 17.75 | 4.31 | .91 | 22.97 | 28 |

# 33 44 Storm Utility Water Drains

## 33 44 13 – Utility Area Drains

| 33 44 13.13 Catchbasins | | Crew | Daily Output | Labor-Hours | Unit | Material | 2010 Bare Costs Labor | Equipment | Total | Total Incl O&P |
|---|---|---|---|---|---|---|---|---|---|---|
| 0010 | **CATCHBASINS** | | | | | | | | | |
| 0011 | Not including footing & excavation | | | | | | | | | |
| 1600 | Frames & covers, C.I., 24" square, 500 lb. | B-6 | 7.80 | 3.077 | Ea. | 300 | 73.50 | 43.50 | 417 | 500 |

# 33 46 Subdrainage

## 33 46 16 – Subdrainage Piping

### 33 46 16.20 Piping, Subdrainage, Concrete

| | | Crew | Daily Output | Labor-Hours | Unit | Material | 2010 Bare Costs Labor | Equipment | Total | Total Incl O&P |
|---|---|---|---|---|---|---|---|---|---|---|
| 0010 | **PIPING, SUBDRAINAGE, CONCRETE** | | | | | | | | | |
| 0021 | Not including excavation and backfill | | | | | | | | | |
| 3000 | Porous wall concrete underdrain, std. strength, 4" diameter | B-20 | 335 | .072 | L.F. | 3.40 | 1.59 | | 4.99 | 6.40 |
| 3020 | 6" diameter | " | 315 | .076 | | 4.42 | 1.69 | | 6.11 | 7.70 |
| 3040 | 8" diameter | B-21 | 310 | .090 | ↓ | 5.45 | 2.11 | .45 | 8.01 | 10 |

### 33 46 16.25 Piping, Subdrainage, Corrugated Metal

| | | Crew | Daily Output | Labor-Hours | Unit | Material | 2010 Bare Costs Labor | Equipment | Total | Total Incl O&P |
|---|---|---|---|---|---|---|---|---|---|---|
| 0010 | **PIPING, SUBDRAINAGE, CORRUGATED METAL** | | | | | | | | | |
| 0021 | Not including excavation and backfill | | | | | | | | | |
| 2010 | Aluminum, perforated | | | | | | | | | |
| 2020 | 6" diameter, 18 ga. | B-14 | 380 | .126 | L.F. | 7.25 | 2.91 | .89 | 11.05 | 13.85 |
| 2200 | 8" diameter, 16 ga. | ↓ | 370 | .130 | | 10.50 | 2.98 | .91 | 14.39 | 17.55 |
| 2220 | 10" diameter, 16 ga. | ↓ | 360 | .133 | ↓ | 13.15 | 3.07 | .94 | 17.16 | 20.50 |
| 3000 | Uncoated galvanized, perforated | | | | | | | | | |
| 3020 | 6" diameter, 18 ga. | B-20 | 380 | .063 | L.F. | 7.25 | 1.40 | | 8.65 | 10.35 |
| 3200 | 8" diameter, 16 ga. | " | 370 | .065 | | 10.50 | 1.44 | | 11.94 | 13.95 |
| 3220 | 10" diameter, 16 ga. | B-21 | 360 | .078 | | 15.75 | 1.82 | .38 | 17.95 | 21 |
| 3240 | 12" diameter, 16 ga. | " | 285 | .098 | ↓ | 16.50 | 2.30 | .48 | 19.28 | 22.50 |
| 4000 | Steel, perforated, asphalt coated | | | | | | | | | |
| 4020 | 6" diameter 18 ga. | B-20 | 380 | .063 | L.F. | 7.25 | 1.40 | | 8.65 | 10.35 |
| 4030 | 8" diameter 18 ga. | " | 370 | .065 | | 10.50 | 1.44 | | 11.94 | 13.95 |
| 4040 | 10" diameter 16 ga. | B-21 | 360 | .078 | | 12.75 | 1.82 | .38 | 14.95 | 17.50 |
| 4050 | 12" diameter 16 ga. | ↓ | 285 | .098 | | 14.50 | 2.30 | .48 | 17.28 | 20.50 |
| 4060 | 18" diameter 16 ga. | ↓ | 205 | .137 | ↓ | 20.50 | 3.19 | .67 | 24.36 | 28.50 |

# 33 49 Storm Drainage Structures

## 33 49 13 – Storm Drainage Manholes, Frames, and Covers

### 33 49 13.10 Storm Drainage Manholes, Frames and Covers

| | | Crew | Daily Output | Labor-Hours | Unit | Material | 2010 Bare Costs Labor | Equipment | Total | Total Incl O&P |
|---|---|---|---|---|---|---|---|---|---|---|
| 0010 | **STORM DRAINAGE MANHOLES, FRAMES & COVERS** | | | | | | | | | |
| 0020 | Excludes footing, excavation, backfill (See line items for frame & cover) | | | | | | | | | |
| 0050 | Brick, 4' inside diameter, 4' deep | D-1 | 1 | 16 | Ea. | 440 | 420 | | 860 | 1,175 |
| 1110 | Precast, 4' I.D., 4' deep | B-22 | 4.10 | 7.317 | " | 450 | 175 | 50.50 | 675.50 | 845 |

# 33 51 Natural-Gas Distribution

## 33 51 13 – Natural-Gas Piping

| 33 51 13.10 Piping, Gas Service and Distribution, P.E. | Crew | Daily Output | Labor-Hours | Unit | Material | 2010 Bare Costs Labor | Equipment | Total | Total Incl O&P |
|---|---|---|---|---|---|---|---|---|---|
| 0010 **PIPING, GAS SERVICE AND DISTRIBUTION, POLYETHYLENE** | | | | | | | | | |
| 0020 Not including excavation or backfill | | | | | | | | | |
| 1000 60 psi coils, compression coupling @ 100', 1/2" diameter, SDR 11 | B-20A | 608 | .053 | L.F. | 1.66 | 1.41 | | 3.07 | 4.16 |
| 1010 1" diameter, SDR 11 | | 544 | .059 | | 1.83 | 1.57 | | 3.40 | 4.61 |
| 1040 1-1/4" diameter, SDR 11 | | 544 | .059 | | 2.57 | 1.57 | | 4.14 | 5.40 |
| 1100 2" diameter, SDR 11 | | 488 | .066 | | 3.18 | 1.75 | | 4.93 | 6.40 |
| 1160 3" diameter, SDR 11 | | 408 | .078 | | 6.65 | 2.09 | | 8.74 | 10.75 |
| 1500 60 PSI 40' joints with coupling, 3" diameter, SDR 11 | B-21A | 408 | .098 | | 6.65 | 2.70 | 1.61 | 10.96 | 13.50 |
| 1540 4" diameter, SDR 11 | | 352 | .114 | | 15.20 | 3.13 | 1.86 | 20.19 | 24 |
| 1600 6" diameter, SDR 11 | | 328 | .122 | | 47.50 | 3.35 | 2 | 52.85 | 60 |
| 1640 8" diameter, SDR 11 | | 272 | .147 | | 64.50 | 4.04 | 2.41 | 70.95 | 80.50 |

## 33 51 13.20 Piping, Gas Service and Distribution, Steel

| | Crew | Daily Output | Labor-Hours | Unit | Material | 2010 Bare Costs Labor | Equipment | Total | Total Incl O&P |
|---|---|---|---|---|---|---|---|---|---|
| 0010 **PIPING, GAS SERVICE & DISTRIBUTION, STEEL** | | | | | | | | | |
| 0020 Not including excavation or backfill, tar coated and wrapped | | | | | | | | | |
| 4000 Pipe schedule 40, plain end | | | | | | | | | |
| 4040 1" diameter | Q-4 | 300 | .107 | L.F. | 7.75 | 3.48 | .20 | 11.43 | 14.45 |
| 4080 2" diameter | Q-4 | 280 | .114 | L.F. | 12.20 | 3.73 | .21 | 16.14 | 19.75 |

# Reference Section

All the reference information is in one section, making it easy to find what you need to know ... and easy to use the book on a daily basis. This section is visually identified by a vertical gray bar on the page edges.

In this Reference Section, we've included Equipment Rental Costs, a listing of rental and operating costs; Crew Listings, a full listing of all crews, equipment, and their costs; Location Factors for adjusting costs to the region you are in; Reference Tables, where you will find explanations, estimating information and procedures, or technical data; an explanation of all the Abbreviations in the book; and sample Estimating Forms.

## Table of Contents

# Estimating Tips

- This section contains the average costs to rent and operate hundreds of pieces of construction equipment. This is useful information when estimating the time and material requirements of any particular operation in order to establish a unit or total cost. Equipment costs include not only rental, but also operating costs for equipment under normal use.

# Rental Costs

- Equipment rental rates are obtained from industry sources throughout North America-contractors, suppliers, dealers, manufacturers, and distributors.
- Rental rates vary throughout the country, with larger cities generally having lower rates. Lease plans for new equipment are available for periods in excess of six months, with a percentage of payments applying toward purchase.
- Monthly rental rates vary from 2% to 5% of the purchase price of the equipment depending on the anticipated life of the equipment and its wearing parts.
- Weekly rental rates are about 1/3 the monthly rates, and daily rental rates are about 1/3 the weekly rate.

# Operating Costs

- The operating costs include parts and labor for routine servicing, such as repair and replacement of pumps, filters and worn lines. Normal operating expendables, such as fuel, lubricants, tires and electricity (where applicable), are also included.
- Extraordinary operating expendables with highly variable wear patterns, such as diamond bits and blades, are excluded. These costs can be found as material costs in the Unit Price section.
- The hourly operating costs listed do not include the operator's wages.

# Equipment Cost/Day

- Any power equipment required by a crew is shown in the Crew Listings with a daily cost.
- The daily cost of equipment needed by a crew is based on dividing the weekly rental rate by 5 (number of working days in the week), and then adding the hourly operating cost times 8 (the number of hours in a day). This "Equipment Cost/Day" is shown in the far right column of the Equipment Rental pages.
- If equipment is needed for only one or two days, it is best to develop your own cost by including components for daily rent and hourly operating cost. This is important when the listed Crew for a task does not contain the equipment needed, such as a crane for lifting mechanical heating/cooling equipment up onto a roof.

- If the quantity of work is less than the crew's Daily Output shown for a Unit Price line item that includes a bare unit equipment cost, it is recommended to estimate one day's rental cost and operating cost for equipment shown in the Crew Listing for that line item.

# Mobilization/ Demobilization

- The cost to move construction equipment from an equipment yard or rental company to the jobsite and back again is not included in equipment rental costs listed in the Reference section, nor in the bare equipment cost of any Unit Price line item, nor in any equipment costs shown in the Crew listings.
- Mobilization (to the site) and demobilization (from the site) costs can be found in the Unit Price section.
- If a piece of equipment is already at the jobsite, it is not appropriate to utilize mobil./demob. costs again in an estimate.

## 01 54 33 | Equipment Rental

| | | | UNIT | HOURLY OPER. COST | RENT PER DAY | RENT PER WEEK | RENT PER MONTH | EQUIPMENT COST/DAY | |
|---|---|---|---|---|---|---|---|---|---|
| 10 | 0010 | **CONCRETE EQUIPMENT RENTAL** without operators | R015433 -10 | | | | | | 10 |
| | 0200 | Bucket, concrete lightweight, 1/2 C.Y. | Ea. | .70 | 20 | 60 | 180 | 17.60 | |
| | 0300 | 1 C.Y. | | .75 | 24.50 | 73 | 219 | 20.60 | |
| | 0400 | 1-1/2 C.Y. | | .95 | 33 | 99 | 297 | 27.40 | |
| | 0500 | 2 C.Y. | | 1.05 | 40 | 120 | 360 | 32.40 | |
| | 0580 | 8 C.Y. | | 5.65 | 260 | 780 | 2,350 | 201.20 | |
| | 0600 | Cart, concrete, self-propelled, operator walking, 10 C.F. | | 3.05 | 56.50 | 170 | 510 | 58.40 | |
| | 0700 | Operator riding, 18 C.F. | | 5.00 | 90 | 270 | 810 | 94 | |
| | 0800 | Conveyer for concrete, portable, gas, 16" wide, 26' long | | 11.95 | 123 | 370 | 1,100 | 169.60 | |
| | 0900 | 46' long | | 12.30 | 150 | 450 | 1,350 | 188.40 | |
| | 1000 | 56' long | | 12.45 | 158 | 475 | 1,425 | 194.60 | |
| | 1100 | Core drill, electric, 2-1/2 H.P., 1" to 8" bit diameter | | 1.75 | 65.50 | 197 | 590 | 53.40 | |
| | 1150 | 11 H.P., 8" to 18" cores | | 5.60 | 115 | 345 | 1,025 | 113.80 | |
| | 1200 | Finisher, concrete floor, gas, riding trowel, 96" wide | | 12.35 | 145 | 435 | 1,300 | 185.80 | |
| | 1300 | Gas, walk-behind, 3 blade, 36" trowel | | 2.05 | 19.65 | 59 | 177 | 28.20 | |
| | 1400 | 4 blade, 48" trowel | | 4.10 | 27 | 81 | 243 | 49 | |
| | 1500 | Float, hand-operated (Bull float) 48" wide | | .08 | 13.65 | 41 | 123 | 8.85 | |
| | 1570 | Curb builder, 14 H.P., gas, single screw | | 13.55 | 247 | 740 | 2,225 | 256.40 | |
| | 1590 | Double screw | | 14.20 | 287 | 860 | 2,575 | 285.60 | |
| | 1600 | Grinder, concrete and terrazzo, electric, floor | | 2.48 | 104 | 312 | 935 | 82.25 | |
| | 1700 | Wall grinder | | 1.24 | 52 | 156 | 470 | 41.10 | |
| | 1800 | Mixer, powered, mortar and concrete, gas, 6 C.F., 18 H.P. | | 8.20 | 118 | 355 | 1,075 | 136.60 | |
| | 1900 | 10 C.F., 25 H.P. | | 10.30 | 143 | 430 | 1,300 | 168.40 | |
| | 2000 | 16 C.F. | | 10.60 | 167 | 500 | 1,500 | 184.80 | |
| | 2100 | Concrete, stationary, tilt drum, 2 C.Y. | | 6.30 | 232 | 695 | 2,075 | 189.40 | |
| | 2120 | Pump, concrete, truck mounted 4" line 80' boom | | 23.35 | 920 | 2,760 | 8,275 | 738.80 | |
| | 2140 | 5" line, 110' boom | | 30.30 | 1,225 | 3,670 | 11,000 | 976.40 | |
| | 2160 | Mud jack, 50 C.F. per hr | | 6.95 | 128 | 385 | 1,150 | 132.60 | |
| | 2180 | 225 C.F. per hr | | 9.00 | 147 | 440 | 1,325 | 160 | |
| | 2190 | Shotcrete pump rig, 12 C.Y./hr | | 14.15 | 227 | 680 | 2,050 | 249.20 | |
| | 2200 | 35 C.Y./hr | | 16.75 | 243 | 730 | 2,200 | 280 | |
| | 2600 | Saw, concrete, manual, gas, 18 H.P. | | 6.35 | 38.50 | 115 | 345 | 73.80 | |
| | 2650 | Self-propelled, gas, 30 H.P. | | 12.80 | 98.50 | 295 | 885 | 161.40 | |
| | 2700 | Vibrators, concrete, electric, 60 cycle, 2 H.P. | | .45 | 7.35 | 22 | 66 | 8 | |
| | 2800 | 3 H.P. | | .67 | 10.35 | 31 | 93 | 11.55 | |
| | 2900 | Gas engine, 5 H.P. | | 1.95 | 14.35 | 43 | 129 | 24.20 | |
| | 3000 | 8 H.P. | | 2.65 | 15.35 | 46 | 138 | 30.40 | |
| | 3050 | Vibrating screed, gas engine, 8 H.P. | | 2.72 | 72.50 | 217 | 650 | 65.15 | |
| | 3120 | Concrete transit mixer, 6 x 4, 250 H.P., 8 C.Y., rear discharge | | 59.20 | 575 | 1,725 | 5,175 | 818.60 | |
| | 3200 | Front discharge | | 69.95 | 710 | 2,125 | 6,375 | 984.60 | |
| | 3300 | 6 x 6, 285 H.P., 12 C.Y., rear discharge | | 69.00 | 665 | 2,000 | 6,000 | 952 | |
| | 3400 | Front discharge | | 72.20 | 715 | 2,150 | 6,450 | 1,008 | |
| 20 | 0010 | **EARTHWORK EQUIPMENT RENTAL** without operators | R015433 -10 | | | | | | 20 |
| | 0040 | Aggregate spreader, push type 8' to 12' wide | Ea. | 2.90 | 25.50 | 77 | 231 | 38.60 | |
| | 0045 | Tailgate type, 8' wide | | 2.75 | 33.50 | 100 | 300 | 42 | |
| | 0055 | Earth auger, truck-mounted, for fence & sign posts, utility poles | | 18.90 | 495 | 1,490 | 4,475 | 449.20 | |
| | 0060 | For borings and monitoring wells | | 43.85 | 665 | 1,995 | 5,975 | 749.80 | |
| | 0070 | Portable, trailer mounted | | 3.05 | 25.50 | 77 | 231 | 39.80 | |
| | 0075 | Truck-mounted, for caissons, water wells | | 96.05 | 3,050 | 9,115 | 27,300 | 2,591 | |
| | 0080 | Horizontal boring machine, 12" to 36" diameter, 45 H.P. | | 22.80 | 200 | 600 | 1,800 | 302.40 | |
| | 0090 | 12" to 48" diameter, 65 H.P. | | 32.65 | 355 | 1,060 | 3,175 | 473.20 | |
| | 0095 | Auger, for fence posts, gas engine, hand held | | .55 | 5.65 | 17 | 51 | 7.80 | |
| | 0100 | Excavator, diesel hydraulic, crawler mounted, 1/2 C.Y. cap. | | 20.20 | 375 | 1,125 | 3,375 | 386.60 | |
| | 0120 | 5/8 C.Y. capacity | | 30.30 | 535 | 1,610 | 4,825 | 564.40 | |
| | 0140 | 3/4 C.Y. capacity | | 37.85 | 625 | 1,875 | 5,625 | 677.80 | |
| | 0150 | 1 C.Y. capacity | | 47.70 | 700 | 2,100 | 6,300 | 801.60 | |
| | 0200 | 1-1/2 C.Y. capacity | | 57.00 | 935 | 2,805 | 8,425 | 1,017 | |
| | 0300 | 2 C.Y. capacity | | 76.90 | 1,175 | 3,530 | 10,600 | 1,321 | |

## 01 54 33 | Equipment Rental

| | | UNIT | HOURLY OPER. COST | RENT PER DAY | RENT PER WEEK | RENT PER MONTH | EQUIPMENT COST/DAY | |
|---|---|---|---|---|---|---|---|---|
| 20 | 0320 | 2-1/2 C.Y. capacity | Ea. | 104.45 | 1,575 | 4,740 | 14,200 | 1,784 | 20 |
| | 0325 | 3-1/2 C.Y. capacity | | 138.85 | 2,075 | 6,240 | 18,700 | 2,359 | |
| | 0330 | 4-1/2 C.Y. capacity | | 166.15 | 2,575 | 7,705 | 23,100 | 2,870 | |
| | 0335 | 6 C.Y. capacity | | 211.30 | 2,825 | 8,500 | 25,500 | 3,390 | |
| | 0340 | 7 C.Y. capacity | | 216.05 | 3,050 | 9,125 | 27,400 | 3,553 | |
| | 0342 | Excavator attachments, bucket thumbs | | 2.95 | 238 | 715 | 2,150 | 166.60 | |
| | 0345 | Grapples | | 2.65 | 207 | 620 | 1,850 | 145.20 | |
| | 0347 | Hydraulic hammer for boom mounting, 5000 ft lbs | | 12.45 | 410 | 1,225 | 3,675 | 344.60 | |
| | 0349 | 11,000 ft lbs | | 21.05 | 735 | 2,200 | 6,600 | 608.40 | |
| | 0350 | Gradall type, truck mounted, 3 ton @ 15' radius, 5/8 C.Y. | | 38.60 | 840 | 2,520 | 7,550 | 812.80 | |
| | 0370 | 1 C.Y. capacity | | 43.55 | 1,025 | 3,050 | 9,150 | 958.40 | |
| | 0400 | Backhoe-loader, 40 to 45 H.P., 5/8 C.Y. capacity | | 12.80 | 193 | 580 | 1,750 | 218.40 | |
| | 0450 | 45 H.P. to 60 H.P., 3/4 C.Y. capacity | | 20.35 | 292 | 875 | 2,625 | 337.80 | |
| | 0460 | 80 H.P., 1-1/4 C.Y. capacity | | 24.45 | 320 | 960 | 2,875 | 387.60 | |
| | 0470 | 112 H.P., 1-1/2 C.Y. capacity | | 38.55 | 525 | 1,570 | 4,700 | 622.40 | |
| | 0482 | Backhoe-loader attachment, compactor, 20,000 lb. | | 5.25 | 142 | 425 | 1,275 | 127 | |
| | 0485 | Hydraulic hammer, 750 ft lbs | | 2.95 | 91.50 | 275 | 825 | 78.60 | |
| | 0486 | Hydraulic hammer, 1200 ft lbs | | 5.40 | 185 | 555 | 1,675 | 154.20 | |
| | 0500 | Brush chipper, gas engine, 6" cutter head, 35 H.P. | | 10.65 | 108 | 325 | 975 | 150.20 | |
| | 0550 | 12" cutter head, 130 H.P. | | 18.15 | 180 | 540 | 1,625 | 253.20 | |
| | 0600 | 15" cutter head, 165 H.P. | | 27.75 | 217 | 650 | 1,950 | 352 | |
| | 0750 | Bucket, clamshell, general purpose, 3/8 C.Y. | | 1.15 | 36.50 | 110 | 330 | 31.20 | |
| | 0800 | 1/2 C.Y. | | 1.25 | 45 | 135 | 405 | 37 | |
| | 0850 | 3/4 C.Y. | | 1.40 | 55 | 165 | 495 | 44.20 | |
| | 0900 | 1 C.Y. | | 1.45 | 58.50 | 175 | 525 | 46.60 | |
| | 0950 | 1-1/2 C.Y. | | 2.35 | 80 | 240 | 720 | 66.80 | |
| | 1000 | 2 C.Y. | | 2.45 | 90 | 270 | 810 | 73.60 | |
| | 1010 | Bucket, dragline, medium duty, 1/2 C.Y. | | .65 | 23.50 | 71 | 213 | 19.40 | |
| | 1020 | 3/4 C.Y. | | .70 | 24.50 | 74 | 222 | 20.40 | |
| | 1030 | 1 C.Y. | | .70 | 26.50 | 80 | 240 | 21.60 | |
| | 1040 | 1-1/2 C.Y. | | 1.10 | 40 | 120 | 360 | 32.80 | |
| | 1050 | 2 C.Y. | | 1.20 | 45 | 135 | 405 | 36.60 | |
| | 1070 | 3 C.Y. | | 1.80 | 63.50 | 190 | 570 | 52.40 | |
| | 1200 | Compactor, manually guided 2-drum vibratory smooth roller, 7.5 H.P. | | 6.20 | 167 | 500 | 1,500 | 149.60 | |
| | 1250 | Rammer/tamper, gas, 8" | | 2.60 | 43.50 | 130 | 390 | 46.80 | |
| | 1260 | 15" | | 2.85 | 48.50 | 145 | 435 | 51.80 | |
| | 1300 | Vibratory plate, gas, 18" plate, 3000 lb. blow | | 2.55 | 23 | 69 | 207 | 34.20 | |
| | 1350 | 21" plate, 5000 lb. blow | | 3.20 | 30 | 90 | 270 | 43.60 | |
| | 1370 | Curb builder/extruder, 14 H.P., gas, single screw | | 13.55 | 247 | 740 | 2,225 | 256.40 | |
| | 1390 | Double screw | | 14.20 | 287 | 860 | 2,575 | 285.60 | |
| | 1500 | Disc harrow attachment, for tractor | | .40 | 67 | 201 | 605 | 43.40 | |
| | 1810 | Feller buncher, shearing & accumulating trees, 100 H.P. | | 34.20 | 560 | 1,680 | 5,050 | 609.60 | |
| | 1860 | Grader, self-propelled, 25,000 lb. | | 31.75 | 475 | 1,420 | 4,250 | 538 | |
| | 1910 | 30,000 lb. | | 36.65 | 550 | 1,645 | 4,925 | 622.20 | |
| | 1920 | 40,000 lb. | | 55.90 | 1,050 | 3,120 | 9,350 | 1,071 | |
| | 1930 | 55,000 lb. | | 72.55 | 1,375 | 4,155 | 12,500 | 1,411 | |
| | 1950 | Hammer, pavement breaker, self-propelled, diesel, 1000 to 1250 lb. | | 28.25 | 345 | 1,040 | 3,125 | 434 | |
| | 2000 | 1300 to 1500 lb. | | 42.38 | 695 | 2,080 | 6,250 | 755.05 | |
| | 2050 | Pile driving hammer, steam or air, 4150 ft lbs @ 225 bpm | | 9.65 | 470 | 1,405 | 4,225 | 358.20 | |
| | 2100 | 8750 ft lbs @ 145 bpm | | 11.65 | 650 | 1,945 | 5,825 | 482.20 | |
| | 2150 | 15,000 ft lbs @ 60 bpm | | 13.20 | 785 | 2,360 | 7,075 | 577.60 | |
| | 2200 | 24,450 ft lbs @ 111 bpm | | 14.25 | 880 | 2,635 | 7,900 | 641 | |
| | 2250 | Leads, 60' high for pile driving hammers up to 20,000 ft lbs | | 3.00 | 78 | 234 | 700 | 70.80 | |
| | 2300 | 90' high for hammers over 20,000 ft lbs | | 4.50 | 141 | 422 | 1,275 | 120.40 | |
| | 2350 | Diesel type hammer, 22,400 ft lbs | | 29.80 | 635 | 1,905 | 5,725 | 619.40 | |
| | 2400 | 41,300 ft lbs | | 38.60 | 690 | 2,070 | 6,200 | 722.80 | |
| | 2450 | 141,000 ft lbs | | 56.40 | 1,175 | 3,540 | 10,600 | 1,159 | |
| | 2500 | Vib. elec. hammer/extractor, 200 kW diesel generator, 34 H.P. | | 53.70 | 660 | 1,980 | 5,950 | 825.60 | |

## 01 54 33 | Equipment Rental

| | | | UNIT | HOURLY OPER. COST | RENT PER DAY | RENT PER WEEK | RENT PER MONTH | EQUIPMENT COST/DAY | |
|---|---|---|---|---|---|---|---|---|---|
| 20 | 2550 | 80 H.P. | Ea. | 99.00 | 970 | 2,910 | 8,725 | 1,374 | 20 |
| | 2600 | 150 H.P. | | 188.90 | 1,875 | 5,650 | 17,000 | 2,641 | |
| | 2700 | Extractor, steam or air, 700 ft lbs | | 17.50 | 510 | 1,525 | 4,575 | 445 | |
| | 2750 | 1000 ft lbs | | 19.95 | 625 | 1,870 | 5,600 | 533.60 | |
| | 2800 | Log chipper, up to 22" diameter, 600 H.P. | | 52.70 | 445 | 1,340 | 4,025 | 689.60 | |
| | 2850 | Logger, for skidding & stacking logs, 150 H.P. | | 50.90 | 835 | 2,500 | 7,500 | 907.20 | |
| | 2860 | Mulcher, diesel powered, trailer mounted | | 23.50 | 218 | 655 | 1,975 | 319 | |
| | 2900 | Rake, spring tooth, with tractor | | 14.34 | 285 | 855 | 2,575 | 285.70 | |
| | 3000 | Roller, vibratory, tandem, smooth drum, 20 H.P. | | 8.25 | 143 | 430 | 1,300 | 152 | |
| | 3050 | 35 H.P. | | 10.40 | 253 | 760 | 2,275 | 235.20 | |
| | 3100 | Towed type vibratory compactor, smooth drum, 50 H.P. | | 25.90 | 380 | 1,135 | 3,400 | 434.20 | |
| | 3150 | Sheepsfoot, 50 H.P. | | 28.15 | 440 | 1,320 | 3,950 | 489.20 | |
| | 3170 | Landfill compactor, 220 H.P. | | 82.85 | 1,475 | 4,390 | 13,200 | 1,541 | |
| | 3200 | Pneumatic tire roller, 80 H.P. | | 16.15 | 345 | 1,040 | 3,125 | 337.20 | |
| | 3250 | 120 H.P. | | 24.20 | 610 | 1,835 | 5,500 | 560.60 | |
| | 3300 | Sheepsfoot vibratory roller, 240 H.P. | | 69.85 | 1,150 | 3,420 | 10,300 | 1,243 | |
| | 3320 | 340 H.P. | | 94.00 | 1,400 | 4,220 | 12,700 | 1,596 | |
| | 3350 | Smooth drum vibratory roller, 75 H.P. | | 23.20 | 550 | 1,655 | 4,975 | 516.60 | |
| | 3400 | 125 H.P. | | 29.90 | 655 | 1,970 | 5,900 | 633.20 | |
| | 3410 | Rotary mower, brush, 60", with tractor | | 18.25 | 260 | 780 | 2,350 | 302 | |
| | 3420 | Rototiller, walk-behind, gas, 5 H.P. | | 2.12 | 65.50 | 196 | 590 | 56.15 | |
| | 3422 | 8 H.P. | | 3.30 | 100 | 300 | 900 | 86.40 | |
| | 3440 | Scrapers, towed type, 7 C.Y. capacity | | 5.15 | 107 | 320 | 960 | 105.20 | |
| | 3450 | 10 C.Y. capacity | | 6.45 | 175 | 525 | 1,575 | 156.60 | |
| | 3500 | 15 C.Y. capacity | | 7.15 | 192 | 575 | 1,725 | 172.20 | |
| | 3525 | Self-propelled, single engine, 14 C.Y. capacity | | 103.95 | 1,475 | 4,425 | 13,300 | 1,717 | |
| | 3550 | Dual engine, 21 C.Y. capacity | | 153.65 | 1,700 | 5,065 | 15,200 | 2,242 | |
| | 3600 | 31 C.Y. capacity | | 208.65 | 2,575 | 7,750 | 23,300 | 3,219 | |
| | 3640 | 44 C.Y. capacity | | 264.30 | 3,625 | 10,910 | 32,700 | 4,296 | |
| | 3650 | Elevating type, single engine, 11 C.Y. capacity | | 66.70 | 1,075 | 3,255 | 9,775 | 1,185 | |
| | 3700 | 22 C.Y. capacity | | 126.05 | 2,125 | 6,375 | 19,100 | 2,283 | |
| | 3710 | Screening plant 110 H.P. w/5' x 10' screen | | 36.90 | 415 | 1,240 | 3,725 | 543.20 | |
| | 3720 | 5' x 16' screen | | 39.05 | 515 | 1,550 | 4,650 | 622.40 | |
| | 3850 | Shovel, crawler-mounted, front-loading, 7 C.Y. capacity | | 228.10 | 2,850 | 8,555 | 25,700 | 3,536 | |
| | 3855 | 12 C.Y. capacity | | 305.30 | 3,625 | 10,860 | 32,600 | 4,614 | |
| | 3860 | Shovel/backhoe bucket, 1/2 C.Y. | | 2.20 | 63.50 | 190 | 570 | 55.60 | |
| | 3870 | 3/4 C.Y. | | 2.25 | 70 | 210 | 630 | 60 | |
| | 3880 | 1 C.Y. | | 2.35 | 78.50 | 235 | 705 | 65.80 | |
| | 3890 | 1-1/2 C.Y. | | 2.50 | 93.50 | 280 | 840 | 76 | |
| | 3910 | 3 C.Y. | | 2.80 | 127 | 380 | 1,150 | 98.40 | |
| | 3950 | Stump chipper, 18" deep, 30 H.P. | | 7.56 | 217 | 652 | 1,950 | 190.90 | |
| | 4110 | Tractor, crawler, with bulldozer, torque converter, diesel 80 H.P. | | 26.45 | 375 | 1,125 | 3,375 | 436.60 | |
| | 4150 | 105 H.P. | | 39.30 | 575 | 1,730 | 5,200 | 660.40 | |
| | 4200 | 140 H.P. | | 42.45 | 715 | 2,150 | 6,450 | 769.60 | |
| | 4260 | 200 H.P. | | 68.60 | 1,075 | 3,215 | 9,650 | 1,192 | |
| | 4310 | 300 H.P. | | 82.50 | 1,550 | 4,660 | 14,000 | 1,592 | |
| | 4360 | 410 H.P. | | 109.70 | 2,000 | 6,005 | 18,000 | 2,079 | |
| | 4370 | 500 H.P. | | 147.85 | 2,700 | 8,135 | 24,400 | 2,810 | |
| | 4380 | 700 H.P. | | 245.45 | 4,400 | 13,170 | 39,500 | 4,598 | |
| | 4400 | Loader, crawler, torque conv., diesel, 1-1/2 C.Y., 80 H.P. | | 24.10 | 400 | 1,205 | 3,625 | 433.80 | |
| | 4450 | 1-1/2 to 1-3/4 C.Y., 95 H.P. | | 28.20 | 515 | 1,545 | 4,625 | 534.60 | |
| | 4510 | 1-3/4 to 2-1/4 C.Y., 130 H.P. | | 42.30 | 835 | 2,505 | 7,525 | 839.40 | |
| | 4530 | 2-1/2 to 3-1/4 C.Y., 190 H.P. | | 56.50 | 1,050 | 3,125 | 9,375 | 1,077 | |
| | 4560 | 3-1/2 to 5 C.Y., 275 H.P. | | 81.25 | 1,500 | 4,490 | 13,500 | 1,548 | |
| | 4610 | Front end loader, 4WD, articulated frame, 1 to 1-1/4 C.Y., 70 H.P. | | 18.05 | 208 | 625 | 1,875 | 269.40 | |
| | 4620 | 1-1/2 to 1-3/4 C.Y., 95 H.P. | | 23.95 | 293 | 880 | 2,650 | 367.60 | |
| | 4650 | 1-3/4 to 2 C.Y., 130 H.P. | | 27.65 | 345 | 1,035 | 3,100 | 428.20 | |
| | 4710 | 2-1/2 to 3-1/2 C.Y., 145 H.P. | | 26.35 | 375 | 1,125 | 3,375 | 435.80 | |

| | | | | | UNIT | HOURLY OPER. COST | RENT PER DAY | RENT PER WEEK | RENT PER MONTH | EQUIPMENT COST/DAY | |
|---|---|---|---|---|---|---|---|---|---|---|---|
| **01 54 33 \| Equipment Rental** | | | | | | | | | | | |
| 20 | 4730 | 3 to 4-1/2 C.Y., 185 H.P. | | | Ea. | 35.85 | 570 | 1,705 | 5,125 | 627.80 | 20 |
| | 4760 | 5-1/4 to 5-3/4 C.Y., 270 H.P. | | | | 56.30 | 905 | 2,720 | 8,150 | 994.40 | |
| | 4810 | 7 to 9 C.Y., 475 H.P. | | | | 97.15 | 1,625 | 4,900 | 14,700 | 1,757 | |
| | 4870 | 9 - 11 C.Y., 620 H.P. | | | | 129.55 | 2,600 | 7,825 | 23,500 | 2,601 | |
| | 4880 | Skid steer loader, wheeled, 10 C.F., 30 H.P. gas | | | | 9.30 | 145 | 435 | 1,300 | 161.40 | |
| | 4890 | 1 C.Y., 78 H.P., diesel | | | | 19.00 | 232 | 695 | 2,075 | 291 | |
| | 4892 | Skid-steer attachment, auger | | | | .55 | 91.50 | 275 | 825 | 59.40 | |
| | 4893 | Backhoe | | | | .67 | 112 | 336 | 1,000 | 72.55 | |
| | 4894 | Broom | | | | .73 | 121 | 364 | 1,100 | 78.65 | |
| | 4895 | Forks | | | | .24 | 40 | 120 | 360 | 25.90 | |
| | 4896 | Grapple | | | | .57 | 95.50 | 286 | 860 | 61.75 | |
| | 4897 | Concrete hammer | | | | 1.06 | 177 | 532 | 1,600 | 114.90 | |
| | 4898 | Tree spade | | | | .82 | 136 | 408 | 1,225 | 88.15 | |
| | 4899 | Trencher | | | | .79 | 131 | 393 | 1,175 | 84.90 | |
| | 4900 | Trencher, chain, boom type, gas, operator walking, 12 H.P. | | | | 4.75 | 46.50 | 140 | 420 | 66 | |
| | 4910 | Operator riding, 40 H.P. | | | | 19.55 | 297 | 890 | 2,675 | 334.40 | |
| | 5000 | Wheel type, diesel, 4' deep, 12" wide | | | | 82.05 | 825 | 2,480 | 7,450 | 1,152 | |
| | 5100 | 6' deep, 20" wide | | | | 86.95 | 1,900 | 5,735 | 17,200 | 1,843 | |
| | 5150 | Chain type, diesel, 5' deep, 8" wide | | | | 36.25 | 580 | 1,745 | 5,225 | 639 | |
| | 5200 | Diesel, 8' deep, 16" wide | | | | 88.95 | 2,300 | 6,890 | 20,700 | 2,090 | |
| | 5202 | Rock trencher, wheel type, 6" wide x 18" deep | | | | 19.55 | 315 | 940 | 2,825 | 344.40 | |
| | 5206 | Chain type, 18" wide x 7' deep | | | | 106.25 | 2,875 | 8,605 | 25,800 | 2,571 | |
| | 5210 | Tree spade, self-propelled | | | | 13.10 | 267 | 800 | 2,400 | 264.80 | |
| | 5250 | Truck, dump, 2-axle, 12 ton, 8 C.Y. payload, 220 H.P. | | | | 33.35 | 225 | 675 | 2,025 | 401.80 | |
| | 5300 | Three axle dump, 16 ton, 12 C.Y. payload, 400 H.P. | | | | 59.35 | 320 | 965 | 2,900 | 667.80 | |
| | 5310 | Four axle dump, 25 ton, 18 C.Y. payload, 450 H.P. | | | | 69.55 | 470 | 1,410 | 4,225 | 838.40 | |
| | 5350 | Dump trailer only, rear dump, 16-1/2 C.Y. | | | | 4.90 | 135 | 405 | 1,225 | 120.20 | |
| | 5400 | 20 C.Y. | | | | 5.35 | 153 | 460 | 1,375 | 134.80 | |
| | 5450 | Flatbed, single axle, 1-1/2 ton rating | | | | 24.85 | 68.50 | 205 | 615 | 239.80 | |
| | 5500 | 3 ton rating | | | | 29.75 | 96.50 | 290 | 870 | 296 | |
| | 5550 | Off highway rear dump, 25 ton capacity | | | | 74.80 | 1,325 | 4,005 | 12,000 | 1,399 | |
| | 5600 | 35 ton capacity | | | | 70.50 | 1,175 | 3,515 | 10,500 | 1,267 | |
| | 5610 | 50 ton capacity | | | | 95.65 | 1,625 | 4,895 | 14,700 | 1,744 | |
| | 5620 | 65 ton capacity | | | | 99.70 | 1,625 | 4,860 | 14,600 | 1,770 | |
| | 5630 | 100 ton capacity | | | | 128.25 | 2,125 | 6,350 | 19,100 | 2,296 | |
| | 6000 | Vibratory plow, 25 H.P., walking | | | | 8.15 | 61.50 | 185 | 555 | 102.20 | |
| 40 | 0010 | **GENERAL EQUIPMENT RENTAL** without operators | R015433 -10 | | | | | | | | 40 |
| | 0150 | Aerial lift, scissor type, to 15' high, 1000 lb. cap., electric | | | Ea. | 2.80 | 55 | 165 | 495 | 55.40 | |
| | 0160 | To 25' high, 2000 lb. capacity | | | | 3.20 | 70 | 210 | 630 | 67.60 | |
| | 0170 | Telescoping boom to 40' high, 500 lb. capacity, gas | | | | 19.30 | 320 | 965 | 2,900 | 347.40 | |
| | 0180 | To 45' high, 500 lb. capacity | | | | 20.35 | 370 | 1,115 | 3,350 | 385.80 | |
| | 0190 | To 60' high, 600 lb. capacity | | | | 22.55 | 490 | 1,465 | 4,400 | 473.40 | |
| | 0195 | Air compressor, portable, 6.5 cfm, electric | | | | .50 | 13 | 39 | 117 | 11.80 | |
| | 0196 | Gasoline | | | | .75 | 19.65 | 59 | 177 | 17.80 | |
| | 0200 | Towed type, gas engine, 60 cfm | | | | 13.70 | 48.50 | 145 | 435 | 138.60 | |
| | 0300 | 160 cfm | | | | 16.00 | 50 | 150 | 450 | 158 | |
| | 0400 | Diesel engine, rotary screw, 250 cfm | | | | 16.30 | 105 | 315 | 945 | 193.40 | |
| | 0500 | 365 cfm | | | | 22.20 | 130 | 390 | 1,175 | 255.60 | |
| | 0550 | 450 cfm | | | | 28.25 | 163 | 490 | 1,475 | 324 | |
| | 0600 | 600 cfm | | | | 49.20 | 228 | 685 | 2,050 | 530.60 | |
| | 0700 | 750 cfm | | | | 50.10 | 237 | 710 | 2,125 | 542.80 | |
| | 0800 | For silenced models, small sizes, add to rent | | | | 3% | 5% | 5% | 5% | | |
| | 0900 | Large sizes, add to rent | | | | 5% | 7% | 7% | 7% | | |
| | 0930 | Air tools, breaker, pavement, 60 lb. | | | Ea. | .45 | 9.65 | 29 | 87 | 9.40 | |
| | 0940 | 80 lb. | | | | .45 | 10.35 | 31 | 93 | 9.80 | |
| | 0950 | Drills, hand (jackhammer) 65 lb. | | | | .55 | 17.35 | 52 | 156 | 14.80 | |
| | 0960 | Track or wagon, swing boom, 4" drifter | | | | 57.35 | 765 | 2,295 | 6,875 | 917.80 | |
| | 0970 | 5" drifter | | | | 71.65 | 825 | 2,480 | 7,450 | 1,069 | |

## 01 54 33 | Equipment Rental

| | | UNIT | HOURLY OPER. COST | RENT PER DAY | RENT PER WEEK | RENT PER MONTH | EQUIPMENT COST/DAY | |
|---|---|---|---|---|---|---|---|---|
| **40** | 0975 | Track mounted quarry drill, 6" diameter drill | Ea. | 96.10 | 1,275 | 3,790 | 11,400 | 1,527 | **40** |
| | 0980 | Dust control per drill | | 1.04 | 19 | 57 | 171 | 19.70 | |
| | 0990 | Hammer, chipping, 12 lb. | | .50 | 23.50 | 70 | 210 | 18 | |
| | 1000 | Hose, air with couplings, 50' long, 3/4" diameter | | .03 | 4.33 | 13 | 39 | 2.85 | |
| | 1100 | 1" diameter | | .04 | 6.35 | 19 | 57 | 4.10 | |
| | 1200 | 1-1/2" diameter | | .06 | 9.65 | 29 | 87 | 6.30 | |
| | 1300 | 2" diameter | | .11 | 19 | 57 | 171 | 12.30 | |
| | 1400 | 2-1/2" diameter | | .12 | 20 | 60 | 180 | 12.95 | |
| | 1410 | 3" diameter | | .15 | 25 | 75 | 225 | 16.20 | |
| | 1450 | Drill, steel, 7/8" x 2' | | .05 | 8 | 24 | 72 | 5.20 | |
| | 1460 | 7/8" x 6' | | .05 | 9 | 27 | 81 | 5.80 | |
| | 1520 | Moil points | | .02 | 4 | 12 | 36 | 2.55 | |
| | 1525 | Pneumatic nailer w/accessories | | .46 | 30.50 | 91 | 273 | 21.90 | |
| | 1530 | Sheeting driver for 60 lb. breaker | | .04 | 6 | 18 | 54 | 3.90 | |
| | 1540 | For 90 lb. breaker | | .12 | 8 | 24 | 72 | 5.75 | |
| | 1550 | Spade, 25 lb. | | .40 | 6 | 18 | 54 | 6.80 | |
| | 1560 | Tamper, single, 35 lb. | | .53 | 35 | 105 | 315 | 25.25 | |
| | 1570 | Triple, 140 lb. | | .79 | 52.50 | 158 | 475 | 37.90 | |
| | 1580 | Wrenches, impact, air powered, up to 3/4" bolt | | .40 | 9 | 27 | 81 | 8.60 | |
| | 1590 | Up to 1-1/4" bolt | | .50 | 23 | 69 | 207 | 17.80 | |
| | 1600 | Barricades, barrels, reflectorized, 1 to 50 barrels | | .03 | 4.60 | 13.80 | 41.50 | 3 | |
| | 1610 | 100 to 200 barrels | | .02 | 3.53 | 10.60 | 32 | 2.30 | |
| | 1620 | Barrels with flashers, 1 to 50 barrels | | .03 | 5.25 | 15.80 | 47.50 | 3.40 | |
| | 1630 | 100 to 200 barrels | | .03 | 4.20 | 12.60 | 38 | 2.75 | |
| | 1640 | Barrels with steady burn type C lights | | .04 | 7 | 21 | 63 | 4.50 | |
| | 1650 | Illuminated board, trailer mounted, with generator | | .75 | 118 | 355 | 1,075 | 77 | |
| | 1670 | Portable barricade, stock, with flashers, 1 to 6 units | | .03 | 5.25 | 15.80 | 47.50 | 3.40 | |
| | 1680 | 25 to 50 units | | .03 | 4.90 | 14.70 | 44 | 3.20 | |
| | 1690 | Butt fusion machine, electric | | 12.80 | 53.50 | 160 | 480 | 134.40 | |
| | 1695 | Electro fusion machine | | 9.45 | 38.50 | 115 | 345 | 98.60 | |
| | 1700 | Carts, brick, hand powered, 1000 lb. capacity | | .36 | 60.50 | 182 | 545 | 39.30 | |
| | 1800 | Gas engine, 1500 lb., 7-1/2' lift | | 4.01 | 120 | 359 | 1,075 | 103.90 | |
| | 1822 | Dehumidifier, medium, 6 lb/hr, 150 cfm | | .98 | 60 | 180 | 540 | 43.85 | |
| | 1824 | Large, 18 lb/hr, 600 cfm | | 1.98 | 122 | 366 | 1,100 | 89.05 | |
| | 1830 | Distributor, asphalt, trailer mounted, 2000 gal., 38 H.P. diesel | | 9.40 | 340 | 1,015 | 3,050 | 278.20 | |
| | 1840 | 3000 gal., 38 H.P. diesel | | 10.75 | 370 | 1,105 | 3,325 | 307 | |
| | 1850 | Drill, rotary hammer, electric | | .88 | 25 | 75 | 225 | 22.05 | |
| | 1860 | Carbide bit, 1-1/2" diameter, add to electric rotary hammer | | .04 | 7.60 | 22.75 | 68.50 | 4.85 | |
| | 1865 | Rotary, crawler, 250 H.P. | | 141.75 | 2,075 | 6,245 | 18,700 | 2,383 | |
| | 1870 | Emulsion sprayer, 65 gal., 5 H.P. gas engine | | 2.83 | 99 | 297 | 890 | 82.05 | |
| | 1880 | 200 gal., 5 H.P. engine | | 7.45 | 165 | 495 | 1,475 | 158.60 | |
| | 1930 | Floodlight, mercury vapor, or quartz, on tripod, 1000 watt | | .36 | 14 | 42 | 126 | 11.30 | |
| | 1940 | 2000 watt | | .63 | 26 | 78 | 234 | 20.65 | |
| | 1950 | Floodlights, trailer mounted with generator, 1 - 300 watt light | | 3.35 | 71.50 | 215 | 645 | 69.80 | |
| | 1960 | 2 - 1000 watt lights | | 4.45 | 90 | 270 | 810 | 89.60 | |
| | 2000 | 4 - 300 watt lights | | 4.20 | 88.50 | 265 | 795 | 86.60 | |
| | 2005 | Foam spray rig, incl. box trailer, compressor, generator, proportioner | | 32.33 | 490 | 1,465 | 4,400 | 551.65 | |
| | 2020 | Forklift, straight mast, 12' lift, 5000 lb., 2 wheel drive, gas | | 25.20 | 200 | 600 | 1,800 | 321.60 | |
| | 2040 | 21' lift, 5000 lb., 4 wheel drive, diesel | | 20.20 | 247 | 740 | 2,225 | 309.60 | |
| | 2050 | For rough terrain, 42' lift, 35' reach, 9000 lb., 110 H.P. | | 26.40 | 445 | 1,335 | 4,000 | 478.20 | |
| | 2060 | For plant, 4 ton capacity, 80 H.P., 2 wheel drive, gas | | 15.50 | 102 | 305 | 915 | 185 | |
| | 2080 | 10 ton capacity, 120 H.P., 2 wheel drive, diesel | | 23.40 | 178 | 535 | 1,600 | 294.20 | |
| | 2100 | Generator, electric, gas engine, 1.5 kW to 3 kW | | 3.55 | 11.35 | 34 | 102 | 35.20 | |
| | 2200 | 5 kW | | 4.60 | 15.35 | 46 | 138 | 46 | |
| | 2300 | 10 kW | | 8.70 | 36.50 | 110 | 330 | 91.60 | |
| | 2400 | 25 kW | | 10.20 | 75 | 225 | 675 | 126.60 | |
| | 2500 | Diesel engine, 20 kW | | 11.50 | 75 | 225 | 675 | 137 | |
| | 2600 | 50 kW | | 21.55 | 103 | 310 | 930 | 234.40 | |

## 01 54 33 | Equipment Rental

| | | UNIT | HOURLY OPER. COST | RENT PER DAY | RENT PER WEEK | RENT PER MONTH | EQUIPMENT COST/DAY | |
|---|---|---|---|---|---|---|---|---|
| 2700 | 100 kW | Ea. | 42.45 | 132 | 395 | 1,175 | 418.60 | 40 |
| 2800 | 250 kW | | 82.90 | 233 | 700 | 2,100 | 803.20 | |
| 2850 | Hammer, hydraulic, for mounting on boom, to 500 ft lbs | | 2.25 | 68.50 | 205 | 615 | 59 | |
| 2860 | 1000 ft lbs | | 3.80 | 112 | 335 | 1,000 | 97.40 | |
| 2900 | Heaters, space, oil or electric, 50 MBH | | 1.69 | 7 | 21 | 63 | 17.70 | |
| 3000 | 100 MBH | | 3.06 | 9.35 | 28 | 84 | 30.10 | |
| 3100 | 300 MBH | | 9.79 | 31.50 | 94 | 282 | 97.10 | |
| 3150 | 500 MBH | | 19.75 | 41.50 | 125 | 375 | 183 | |
| 3200 | Hose, water, suction with coupling, 20' long, 2" diameter | | .02 | 3 | 9 | 27 | 1.95 | |
| 3210 | 3" diameter | | .03 | 4.67 | 14 | 42 | 3.05 | |
| 3220 | 4" diameter | | .03 | 5.35 | 16 | 48 | 3.45 | |
| 3230 | 6" diameter | | .11 | 18.35 | 55 | 165 | 11.90 | |
| 3240 | 8" diameter | | .20 | 33.50 | 100 | 300 | 21.60 | |
| 3250 | Discharge hose with coupling, 50' long, 2" diameter | | .01 | 1.33 | 4 | 12 | .90 | |
| 3260 | 3" diameter | | .02 | 2.67 | 8 | 24 | 1.75 | |
| 3270 | 4" diameter | | .02 | 3.67 | 11 | 33 | 2.35 | |
| 3280 | 6" diameter | | .06 | 9.65 | 29 | 87 | 6.30 | |
| 3290 | 8" diameter | | .20 | 33.50 | 100 | 300 | 21.60 | |
| 3295 | Insulation blower | | .22 | 6 | 18 | 54 | 5.35 | |
| 3300 | Ladders, extension type, 16' to 36' long | | .14 | 23 | 69 | 207 | 14.90 | |
| 3400 | 40' to 60' long | | .20 | 33.50 | 100 | 300 | 21.60 | |
| 3405 | Lance for cutting concrete | | 3.07 | 104 | 313 | 940 | 87.15 | |
| 3407 | Lawn mower, rotary, 22", 5 H.P. | | 2.12 | 65 | 195 | 585 | 55.95 | |
| 3408 | 48" self propelled | | 3.28 | 114 | 341 | 1,025 | 94.45 | |
| 3410 | Level, laser type, for pipe and sewer leveling | | 1.46 | 97 | 291 | 875 | 69.90 | |
| 3430 | Electronic | | .75 | 50 | 150 | 450 | 36 | |
| 3440 | Laser type, rotating beam for grade control | | 1.17 | 78 | 234 | 700 | 56.15 | |
| 3460 | Builders level with tripod and rod | | .09 | 14.65 | 44 | 132 | 9.50 | |
| 3500 | Light towers, towable, with diesel generator, 2000 watt | | 4.20 | 88.50 | 265 | 795 | 86.60 | |
| 3600 | 4000 watt | | 4.45 | 98.50 | 295 | 885 | 94.60 | |
| 3700 | Mixer, powered, plaster and mortar, 6 C.F., 7 H.P. | | 2.55 | 18.65 | 56 | 168 | 31.60 | |
| 3800 | 10 C.F., 9 H.P. | | 2.70 | 30 | 90 | 270 | 39.60 | |
| 3850 | Nailer, pneumatic | | .46 | 30.50 | 91 | 273 | 21.90 | |
| 3900 | Paint sprayers complete, 8 cfm | | .69 | 45.50 | 137 | 410 | 32.90 | |
| 4000 | 17 cfm | | 1.28 | 85 | 255 | 765 | 61.25 | |
| 4020 | Pavers, bituminous, rubber tires, 8' wide, 50 H.P., diesel | | 39.45 | 1,050 | 3,165 | 9,500 | 948.60 | |
| 4030 | 10' wide, 150 H.P. | | 85.85 | 1,700 | 5,070 | 15,200 | 1,701 | |
| 4050 | Crawler, 8' wide, 100 H.P., diesel | | 83.90 | 1,800 | 5,420 | 16,300 | 1,755 | |
| 4060 | 10' wide, 150 H.P. | | 96.80 | 2,125 | 6,365 | 19,100 | 2,047 | |
| 4070 | Concrete paver, 12' to 24' wide, 250 H.P. | | 96.25 | 1,575 | 4,750 | 14,300 | 1,720 | |
| 4080 | Placer-spreader-trimmer, 24' wide, 300 H.P. | | 140.15 | 2,600 | 7,785 | 23,400 | 2,678 | |
| 4100 | Pump, centrifugal gas pump, 1-1/2" diam., 65 GPM | | 3.60 | 45 | 135 | 405 | 55.80 | |
| 4200 | 2" diameter, 130 GPM | | 5.00 | 51.50 | 155 | 465 | 71 | |
| 4300 | 3" diameter, 250 GPM | | 5.30 | 53.50 | 160 | 480 | 74.40 | |
| 4400 | 6" diameter, 1500 GPM | | 29.25 | 177 | 530 | 1,600 | 340 | |
| 4500 | Submersible electric pump, 1-1/4" diameter, 55 GPM | | .41 | 16 | 48 | 144 | 12.90 | |
| 4600 | 1-1/2" diameter, 83 GPM | | .44 | 18.35 | 55 | 165 | 14.50 | |
| 4700 | 2" diameter, 120 GPM | | 1.25 | 23 | 69 | 207 | 23.80 | |
| 4800 | 3" diameter, 300 GPM | | 2.15 | 41.50 | 125 | 375 | 42.20 | |
| 4900 | 4" diameter, 560 GPM | | 9.55 | 163 | 490 | 1,475 | 174.40 | |
| 5000 | 6" diameter, 1590 GPM | | 14.05 | 220 | 660 | 1,975 | 244.40 | |
| 5100 | Diaphragm pump, gas, single, 1-1/2" diameter | | 1.10 | 48 | 144 | 430 | 37.60 | |
| 5200 | 2" diameter | | 4.00 | 60 | 180 | 540 | 68 | |
| 5300 | 3" diameter | | 4.00 | 60 | 180 | 540 | 68 | |
| 5400 | Double, 4" diameter | | 5.35 | 80 | 240 | 720 | 90.80 | |
| 5450 | Pressure Washer 5 GPM, 3000 psi | | 4.60 | 40 | 120 | 360 | 60.80 | |
| 5500 | Trash pump, self-priming, gas, 2" diameter | | 4.35 | 20.50 | 62 | 186 | 47.20 | |
| 5600 | Diesel, 4" diameter | | 11.90 | 58.50 | 175 | 525 | 130.20 | |

## 01 54 33 | Equipment Rental

| | | UNIT | HOURLY OPER. COST | RENT PER DAY | RENT PER WEEK | RENT PER MONTH | EQUIPMENT COST/DAY | |
|---|---|---|---|---|---|---|---|---|
| 40 | 5650 | Diesel, 6" diameter | Ea. | 40.15 | 130 | 390 | 1,175 | 399.20 | 40 |
| | 5655 | Grout Pump | | 18.10 | 95 | 285 | 855 | 201.80 | |
| | 5700 | Salamanders, L.P. gas fired, 100,000 Btu | | 3.10 | 16 | 48 | 144 | 34.40 | |
| | 5705 | 50,000 Btu | | 2.31 | 9.35 | 28 | 84 | 24.10 | |
| | 5720 | Sandblaster, portable, open top, 3 C.F. capacity | | .55 | 27 | 81 | 243 | 20.60 | |
| | 5730 | 6 C.F. capacity | | .85 | 40 | 120 | 360 | 30.80 | |
| | 5740 | Accessories for above | | .12 | 20 | 60 | 180 | 12.95 | |
| | 5750 | Sander, floor | | .85 | 19 | 57 | 171 | 18.20 | |
| | 5760 | Edger | | .81 | 28 | 84 | 252 | 23.30 | |
| | 5800 | Saw, chain, gas engine, 18" long | | 2.15 | 18.35 | 55 | 165 | 28.20 | |
| | 5900 | Hydraulic powered, 36" long | | .65 | 56.50 | 170 | 510 | 39.20 | |
| | 5950 | 60" long | | .65 | 56.50 | 170 | 510 | 39.20 | |
| | 6000 | Masonry, table mounted, 14" diameter, 5 H.P. | | 1.34 | 56.50 | 170 | 510 | 44.70 | |
| | 6050 | Portable cut-off, 8 H.P. | | 2.40 | 32.50 | 98 | 294 | 38.80 | |
| | 6100 | Circular, hand held, electric, 7-1/4" diameter | | .21 | 4.67 | 14 | 42 | 4.50 | |
| | 6200 | 12" diameter | | .27 | 7.65 | 23 | 69 | 6.75 | |
| | 6250 | Wall saw, w/hydraulic power, 10 H.P | | 9.30 | 60 | 180 | 540 | 110.40 | |
| | 6275 | Shot blaster, walk-behind, 20" wide | | 4.60 | 298 | 895 | 2,675 | 215.80 | |
| | 6280 | Sidewalk broom, walk-behind | | 2.05 | 61.50 | 185 | 555 | 53.40 | |
| | 6300 | Steam cleaner, 100 gallons per hour | | 3.50 | 53.50 | 161 | 485 | 60.20 | |
| | 6310 | 200 gallons per hour | | 5.05 | 63.50 | 190 | 570 | 78.40 | |
| | 6340 | Tar Kettle/Pot, 400 gallons | | 4.68 | 80 | 240 | 720 | 85.45 | |
| | 6350 | Torch, cutting, acetylene-oxygen, 150' hose | | .50 | 25 | 75 | 225 | 19 | |
| | 6360 | Hourly operating cost includes tips and gas | | 9.90 | | | | 79.20 | |
| | 6410 | Toilet, portable chemical | | .12 | 19.35 | 58 | 174 | 12.55 | |
| | 6420 | Recycle flush type | | .14 | 23.50 | 70 | 210 | 15.10 | |
| | 6430 | Toilet, fresh water flush, garden hose, | | .16 | 27 | 81 | 243 | 17.50 | |
| | 6440 | Hoisted, non-flush, for high rise | | .14 | 23 | 69 | 207 | 14.90 | |
| | 6450 | Toilet, trailers, minimum | | .24 | 40 | 120 | 360 | 25.90 | |
| | 6460 | Maximum | | .73 | 122 | 365 | 1,100 | 78.85 | |
| | 6465 | Tractor, farm with attachment | | 17.10 | 267 | 800 | 2,400 | 296.80 | |
| | 6500 | Trailers, platform, flush deck, 2 axle, 25 ton capacity | | 4.95 | 110 | 330 | 990 | 105.60 | |
| | 6600 | 40 ton capacity | | 6.40 | 153 | 460 | 1,375 | 143.20 | |
| | 6700 | 3 axle, 50 ton capacity | | 6.95 | 170 | 510 | 1,525 | 157.60 | |
| | 6800 | 75 ton capacity | | 8.65 | 223 | 670 | 2,000 | 203.20 | |
| | 6810 | Trailer mounted cable reel for high voltage line work | | 4.94 | 235 | 706 | 2,125 | 180.70 | |
| | 6820 | Trailer mounted cable tensioning rig | | 9.80 | 465 | 1,400 | 4,200 | 358.40 | |
| | 6830 | Cable pulling rig | | 65.52 | 2,625 | 7,860 | 23,600 | 2,096 | |
| | 6900 | Water tank trailer, engine driven discharge, 5000 gallons | | 6.45 | 147 | 440 | 1,325 | 139.60 | |
| | 6925 | 10,000 gallons | | 8.80 | 203 | 610 | 1,825 | 192.40 | |
| | 6950 | Water truck, off highway, 6000 gallons | | 84.65 | 805 | 2,420 | 7,250 | 1,161 | |
| | 7010 | Tram car for high voltage line work, powered, 2 conductor | | 6.81 | 128 | 383 | 1,150 | 131.10 | |
| | 7020 | Transit (builder's level) with tripod | | .09 | 14.65 | 44 | 132 | 9.50 | |
| | 7030 | Trench box, 3000 lbs. 6' x 8' | | .56 | 93 | 279 | 835 | 60.30 | |
| | 7040 | 7200 lbs. 6' x 20' | | 1.05 | 175 | 525 | 1,575 | 113.40 | |
| | 7050 | 8000 lbs., 8' x 16' | | .95 | 158 | 475 | 1,425 | 102.60 | |
| | 7060 | 9500 lbs., 8' x 20' | | 1.19 | 199 | 596 | 1,800 | 128.70 | |
| | 7065 | 11,000 lbs., 8' x 24' | | 1.27 | 212 | 637 | 1,900 | 137.55 | |
| | 7070 | 12,000 lbs., 10' x 20' | | 1.71 | 285 | 855 | 2,575 | 184.70 | |
| | 7100 | Truck, pickup, 3/4 ton, 2 wheel drive | | 13.25 | 56.50 | 170 | 510 | 140 | |
| | 7200 | 4 wheel drive | | 13.50 | 71.50 | 215 | 645 | 151 | |
| | 7250 | Crew carrier, 9 passenger | | 18.80 | 86.50 | 260 | 780 | 202.40 | |
| | 7290 | Flat bed truck, 20,000 lbs. GVW | | 21.20 | 127 | 380 | 1,150 | 245.60 | |
| | 7300 | Tractor, 4 x 2, 220 H.P. | | 29.50 | 197 | 590 | 1,775 | 354 | |
| | 7410 | 330 H.P. | | 43.80 | 270 | 810 | 2,425 | 512.40 | |
| | 7500 | 6 x 4, 380 H.P. | | 50.30 | 315 | 950 | 2,850 | 592.40 | |
| | 7600 | 450 H.P. | | 60.85 | 380 | 1,145 | 3,425 | 715.80 | |
| | 7620 | Vacuum truck, hazardous material, 2500 gallons | | 11.15 | 305 | 920 | 2,750 | 273.20 | |

## 01 54 33 | Equipment Rental

| | | UNIT | HOURLY OPER. COST | RENT PER DAY | RENT PER WEEK | RENT PER MONTH | EQUIPMENT COST/DAY | |
|---|---|---|---|---|---|---|---|---|
| **40** | 7625 | 5,000 gallons | Ea. | 13.23 | 430 | 1,290 | 3,875 | 363.85 | **40** |
| | 7640 | Tractor, with A frame, boom and winch, 225 H.P. | | 32.15 | 273 | 820 | 2,450 | 421.20 | |
| | 7650 | Vacuum, HEPA, 16 gallon, wet/dry | | .84 | 18 | 54 | 162 | 17.50 | |
| | 7655 | 55 gallon, wet/dry | | .86 | 27 | 81 | 243 | 23.10 | |
| | 7660 | Water tank, portable | | .17 | 28.50 | 85.50 | 257 | 18.45 | |
| | 7690 | Sewer/catch basin vacuum, 14 C.Y., 1500 gallons | | 17.78 | 645 | 1,940 | 5,825 | 530.25 | |
| | 7700 | Welder, electric, 200 amp | | 3.86 | 17.35 | 52 | 156 | 41.30 | |
| | 7800 | 300 amp | | 5.72 | 21.50 | 64 | 192 | 58.55 | |
| | 7900 | Gas engine, 200 amp | | 14.15 | 25.50 | 76 | 228 | 128.40 | |
| | 8000 | 300 amp | | 16.20 | 27 | 81 | 243 | 145.80 | |
| | 8100 | Wheelbarrow, any size | | .07 | 11.65 | 35 | 105 | 7.55 | |
| | 8200 | Wrecking ball, 4000 lbs. | | 2.15 | 71.50 | 215 | 645 | 60.20 | |
| **50** | 0010 | **HIGHWAY EQUIPMENT RENTAL** without operators | | | | | | | **50** |
| | 0050 | Asphalt batch plant, portable drum mixer, 100 ton/hr | Ea. | 66.15 | 1,450 | 4,355 | 13,100 | 1,400 | |
| | 0060 | 200 ton/hr | | 73.90 | 1,525 | 4,600 | 13,800 | 1,511 | |
| | 0070 | 300 ton/hr | | 85.75 | 1,800 | 5,425 | 16,300 | 1,771 | |
| | 0100 | Backhoe attachment, long stick, up to 185 H.P., 10.5' long | | .33 | 21.50 | 65 | 195 | 15.65 | |
| | 0140 | Up to 250 H.P., 12' long | | .35 | 23.50 | 70 | 210 | 16.80 | |
| | 0180 | Over 250 H.P., 15' long | | .48 | 31.50 | 95 | 285 | 22.85 | |
| | 0200 | Special dipper arm, up to 100 H.P., 32' long | | .98 | 65 | 195 | 585 | 46.85 | |
| | 0240 | Over 100 H.P., 33' long | | 1.22 | 81 | 243 | 730 | 58.35 | |
| | 0280 | Catch basin/sewer cleaning truck, 3 ton, 9 C.Y., 1000 gal | | 40.90 | 405 | 1,210 | 3,625 | 569.20 | |
| | 0300 | Concrete batch plant, portable, electric, 200 C.Y./hr | | 17.80 | 515 | 1,540 | 4,625 | 450.40 | |
| | 0520 | Grader/dozer attachment, ripper/scarifier, rear mounted, up to 135 H.P. | | 3.20 | 65 | 195 | 585 | 64.60 | |
| | 0540 | Up to 180 H.P. | | 3.75 | 83.50 | 250 | 750 | 80 | |
| | 0580 | Up to 250 H.P. | | 4.15 | 95 | 285 | 855 | 90.20 | |
| | 0700 | Pvmt. removal bucket, for hyd. excavator, up to 90 H.P. | | 1.70 | 50 | 150 | 450 | 43.60 | |
| | 0740 | Up to 200 H.P. | | 1.90 | 71.50 | 215 | 645 | 58.20 | |
| | 0780 | Over 200 H.P. | | 2.05 | 83.50 | 250 | 750 | 66.40 | |
| | 0900 | Aggregate spreader, self-propelled, 187 H.P. | | 50.35 | 695 | 2,090 | 6,275 | 820.80 | |
| | 1000 | Chemical spreader, 3 C.Y. | | 3.05 | 43.50 | 130 | 390 | 50.40 | |
| | 1900 | Hammermill, traveling, 250 H.P. | | 63.25 | 1,875 | 5,650 | 17,000 | 1,636 | |
| | 2000 | Horizontal borer, 3" diameter, 13 H.P. gas driven | | 6.00 | 56.50 | 170 | 510 | 82 | |
| | 2150 | Horizontal directional drill, 20,000 lb. thrust, 78 H.P. diesel | | 29.70 | 690 | 2,070 | 6,200 | 651.60 | |
| | 2160 | 30,000 lb. thrust, 115 H.P. | | 37.15 | 1,050 | 3,155 | 9,475 | 928.20 | |
| | 2170 | 50,000 lb. thrust, 170 H.P. | | 53.00 | 1,350 | 4,040 | 12,100 | 1,232 | |
| | 2190 | Mud trailer for HDD, 1500 gallons, 175 H.P., gas | | 30.75 | 153 | 460 | 1,375 | 338 | |
| | 2200 | Hydromulchers, gas power, 3000 gallons, for truck mounting | | 22.90 | 258 | 775 | 2,325 | 338.20 | |
| | 2400 | Joint & crack cleaner, walk behind, 25 H.P. | | 3.80 | 50 | 150 | 450 | 60.40 | |
| | 2500 | Filler, trailer mounted, 400 gallons, 20 H.P. | | 9.15 | 217 | 650 | 1,950 | 203.20 | |
| | 3000 | Paint striper, self-propelled, double line, 30 H.P. | | 6.95 | 162 | 485 | 1,450 | 152.60 | |
| | 3200 | Post drivers, 6" I-Beam frame, for truck mounting | | 18.75 | 425 | 1,280 | 3,850 | 406 | |
| | 3400 | Road sweeper, self-propelled, 8' wide, 90 H.P. | | 37.80 | 580 | 1,740 | 5,225 | 650.40 | |
| | 3450 | Road sweeper, vacuum assisted, 4 C.Y., 220 gallons | | 73.55 | 635 | 1,905 | 5,725 | 969.40 | |
| | 4000 | Road mixer, self-propelled, 130 H.P. | | 44.05 | 775 | 2,325 | 6,975 | 817.40 | |
| | 4100 | 310 H.P. | | 79.75 | 2,200 | 6,585 | 19,800 | 1,955 | |
| | 4220 | Cold mix paver, incl. pug mill and bitumen tank, 165 H.P. | | 96.80 | 2,150 | 6,440 | 19,300 | 2,062 | |
| | 4250 | Paver, asphalt, wheel or crawler, 130 H.P., diesel | | 95.35 | 2,050 | 6,155 | 18,500 | 1,994 | |
| | 4300 | Paver, road widener, gas 1' to 6', 67 H.P. | | 44.65 | 835 | 2,500 | 7,500 | 857.20 | |
| | 4400 | Diesel, 2' to 14', 88 H.P. | | 59.80 | 1,075 | 3,190 | 9,575 | 1,116 | |
| | 4600 | Slipform pavers, curb and gutter, 2 track, 75 H.P. | | 44.25 | 785 | 2,355 | 7,075 | 825 | |
| | 4700 | 4 track, 165 H.P. | | 54.95 | 825 | 2,475 | 7,425 | 934.60 | |
| | 4800 | Median barrier, 215 H.P. | | 55.65 | 855 | 2,570 | 7,700 | 959.20 | |
| | 4901 | Trailer, low bed, 75 ton capacity | | 9.35 | 218 | 655 | 1,975 | 205.80 | |
| | 5000 | Road planer, walk behind, 10" cutting width, 10 H.P. | | 3.45 | 30.50 | 91 | 273 | 45.80 | |
| | 5100 | Self-propelled, 12" cutting width, 64 H.P. | | 10.20 | 127 | 380 | 1,150 | 157.60 | |
| | 5120 | Traffic line remover, metal ball blaster, truck mounted, 115 H.P. | | 52.80 | 770 | 2,305 | 6,925 | 883.40 | |
| | 5140 | Grinder, truck mounted, 115 H.P. | | 56.60 | 835 | 2,505 | 7,525 | 953.80 | |

R015433 -10

## 01 54 33 | Equipment Rental

| | | UNIT | HOURLY OPER. COST | RENT PER DAY | RENT PER WEEK | RENT PER MONTH | EQUIPMENT COST/DAY | |
|---|---|---|---|---|---|---|---|---|
| **50** | 5160 | Walk-behind, 11 H.P. | Ea. | 3.90 | 46.50 | 140 | 420 | 59.20 | **50** |
| | 5200 | Pavement profiler, 4' to 6' wide, 450 H.P. | | 244.25 | 3,400 | 10,220 | 30,700 | 3,998 | |
| | 5300 | 8' to 10' wide, 750 H.P. | | 391.35 | 4,950 | 14,865 | 44,600 | 6,104 | |
| | 5400 | Roadway plate, steel, 1" x 8' x 20' | | .07 | 11.65 | 35 | 105 | 7.55 | |
| | 5600 | Stabilizer, self-propelled, 150 H.P. | | 47.20 | 615 | 1,850 | 5,550 | 747.60 | |
| | 5700 | 310 H.P. | | 81.20 | 1,350 | 4,070 | 12,200 | 1,464 | |
| | 5800 | Striper, thermal, truck mounted 120 gallon paint, 150 H.P. | | 62.30 | 505 | 1,520 | 4,550 | 802.40 | |
| | 6000 | Tar kettle, 330 gallon, trailer mounted | | 4.30 | 61.50 | 185 | 555 | 71.40 | |
| | 7000 | Tunnel locomotive, diesel, 8 to 12 ton | | 30.00 | 580 | 1,745 | 5,225 | 589 | |
| | 7005 | Electric, 10 ton | | 24.00 | 665 | 1,995 | 5,975 | 591 | |
| | 7010 | Muck cars, 1/2 C.Y. capacity | | 1.85 | 23.50 | 70 | 210 | 28.80 | |
| | 7020 | 1 C.Y. capacity | | 2.05 | 31.50 | 95 | 285 | 35.40 | |
| | 7030 | 2 C.Y. capacity | | 2.15 | 36.50 | 110 | 330 | 39.20 | |
| | 7040 | Side dump, 2 C.Y. capacity | | 2.35 | 45 | 135 | 405 | 45.80 | |
| | 7050 | 3 C.Y. capacity | | 3.20 | 51.50 | 155 | 465 | 56.60 | |
| | 7060 | 5 C.Y. capacity | | 4.55 | 65 | 195 | 585 | 75.40 | |
| | 7100 | Ventilating blower for tunnel, 7-1/2 H.P. | | 1.39 | 51.50 | 155 | 465 | 42.10 | |
| | 7110 | 10 H.P. | | .83 | .52 | 1.55 | 4.65 | 6.95 | |
| | 7120 | 20 H.P. | | 1.66 | .67 | 2 | 6 | 13.70 | |
| | 7140 | 40 H.P. | | 3.31 | .97 | 2.90 | 8.70 | 27.05 | |
| | 7160 | 60 H.P. | | 7.23 | 152 | 455 | 1,375 | 148.85 | |
| | 7175 | 75 H.P. | | 9.22 | 202 | 607 | 1,825 | 195.15 | |
| | 7180 | 200 H.P. | | 21.05 | 305 | 910 | 2,725 | 350.40 | |
| | 7800 | Windrow loader, elevating | | 52.00 | 1,350 | 4,060 | 12,200 | 1,228 | |
| **60** | 0010 | **LIFTING AND HOISTING EQUIPMENT RENTAL** without operators | | | | | | | **60** |
| | 0120 | Aerial lift truck, 2 person, to 80' | Ea. | 28.05 | 735 | 2,205 | 6,625 | 665.40 | |
| | 0140 | Boom work platform, 40' snorkel | | 17.60 | 265 | 795 | 2,375 | 299.80 | |
| | 0150 | Crane, flatbed mounted, 3 ton capacity | | 15.70 | 195 | 585 | 1,750 | 242.60 | |
| | 0200 | Crane, climbing, 106' jib, 6000 lb. capacity, 410 fpm | | 38.95 | 1,500 | 4,490 | 13,500 | 1,210 | |
| | 0300 | 101' jib, 10,250 lb. capacity, 270 fpm | | 44.95 | 1,900 | 5,690 | 17,100 | 1,498 | |
| | 0500 | Tower, static, 130' high, 106' jib, 6200 lb. capacity at 400 fpm | | 42.45 | 1,725 | 5,190 | 15,600 | 1,378 | |
| | 0600 | Crawler mounted, lattice boom, 1/2 C.Y., 15 tons at 12' radius | | 35.47 | 685 | 2,050 | 6,150 | 693.75 | |
| | 0700 | 3/4 C.Y., 20 tons at 12' radius | | 47.29 | 855 | 2,570 | 7,700 | 892.30 | |
| | 0800 | 1 C.Y., 25 tons at 12' radius | | 63.05 | 1,150 | 3,420 | 10,300 | 1,188 | |
| | 0900 | 1-1/2 C.Y., 40 tons at 12' radius | | 63.05 | 1,150 | 3,445 | 10,300 | 1,193 | |
| | 1000 | 2 C.Y., 50 tons at 12' radius | | 66.90 | 1,350 | 4,055 | 12,200 | 1,346 | |
| | 1100 | 3 C.Y., 75 tons at 12' radius | | 71.80 | 1,575 | 4,710 | 14,100 | 1,516 | |
| | 1200 | 100 ton capacity, 60' boom | | 81.40 | 1,800 | 5,405 | 16,200 | 1,732 | |
| | 1300 | 165 ton capacity, 60' boom | | 103.75 | 2,100 | 6,320 | 19,000 | 2,094 | |
| | 1400 | 200 ton capacity, 70' boom | | 125.80 | 2,675 | 7,990 | 24,000 | 2,604 | |
| | 1500 | 350 ton capacity, 80' boom | | 177.05 | 4,075 | 12,195 | 36,600 | 3,855 | |
| | 1600 | Truck mounted, lattice boom, 6 x 4, 20 tons at 10' radius | | 36.33 | 1,225 | 3,690 | 11,100 | 1,029 | |
| | 1700 | 25 tons at 10' radius | | 39.34 | 1,350 | 4,020 | 12,100 | 1,119 | |
| | 1800 | 8 x 4, 30 tons at 10' radius | | 42.56 | 1,425 | 4,280 | 12,800 | 1,196 | |
| | 1900 | 40 tons at 12' radius | | 45.29 | 1,500 | 4,470 | 13,400 | 1,256 | |
| | 2000 | 60 tons at 15' radius | | 50.61 | 1,575 | 4,730 | 14,200 | 1,351 | |
| | 2050 | 82 tons at 15' radius | | 56.35 | 1,675 | 5,050 | 15,200 | 1,461 | |
| | 2100 | 90 tons at 15' radius | | 63.07 | 1,825 | 5,510 | 16,500 | 1,607 | |
| | 2200 | 115 tons at 15' radius | | 71.12 | 2,050 | 6,160 | 18,500 | 1,801 | |
| | 2300 | 150 tons at 18' radius | | 88.35 | 2,150 | 6,480 | 19,400 | 2,003 | |
| | 2350 | 165 tons at 18' radius | | 83.09 | 2,300 | 6,870 | 20,600 | 2,039 | |
| | 2400 | Truck mounted, hydraulic, 12 ton capacity | | 41.45 | 540 | 1,620 | 4,850 | 655.60 | |
| | 2500 | 25 ton capacity | | 43.70 | 665 | 1,990 | 5,975 | 747.60 | |
| | 2550 | 33 ton capacity | | 44.25 | 680 | 2,045 | 6,125 | 763 | |
| | 2560 | 40 ton capacity | | 57.20 | 800 | 2,405 | 7,225 | 938.60 | |
| | 2600 | 55 ton capacity | | 75.80 | 1,000 | 3,015 | 9,050 | 1,209 | |
| | 2700 | 80 ton capacity | | 97.75 | 1,275 | 3,815 | 11,400 | 1,545 | |
| | 2720 | 100 ton capacity | | 91.65 | 1,525 | 4,600 | 13,800 | 1,653 | |

Reference notes:
- R015433 -10
- R015433 -15
- R312316 -45

## 01 54 33 | Equipment Rental

| | | UNIT | HOURLY OPER. COST | RENT PER DAY | RENT PER WEEK | RENT PER MONTH | EQUIPMENT COST/DAY | |
|---|---|---|---|---|---|---|---|---|
| 2740 | 120 ton capacity | Ea. | 106.15 | 1,650 | 4,920 | 14,800 | 1,833 | 60 |
| 2760 | 150 ton capacity | | 124.30 | 2,250 | 6,735 | 20,200 | 2,341 | |
| 2800 | Self-propelled, 4 x 4, with telescoping boom, 5 ton | | 16.90 | 235 | 705 | 2,125 | 276.20 | |
| 2900 | 12-1/2 ton capacity | | 41.45 | 540 | 1,620 | 4,850 | 655.60 | |
| 3000 | 15 ton capacity | | 39.70 | 585 | 1,755 | 5,275 | 668.60 | |
| 3050 | 20 ton capacity | | 35.20 | 575 | 1,720 | 5,150 | 625.60 | |
| 3100 | 25 ton capacity | | 36.45 | 605 | 1,820 | 5,450 | 655.60 | |
| 3150 | 40 ton capacity | | 57.95 | 915 | 2,750 | 8,250 | 1,014 | |
| 3200 | Derricks, guy, 20 ton capacity, 60' boom, 75' mast | | 21.70 | 365 | 1,100 | 3,300 | 393.60 | |
| 3300 | 100' boom, 115' mast | | 34.23 | 630 | 1,890 | 5,675 | 651.85 | |
| 3400 | Stiffleg, 20 ton capacity, 70' boom, 37' mast | | 24.01 | 475 | 1,430 | 4,300 | 478.10 | |
| 3500 | 100' boom, 47' mast | | 36.96 | 760 | 2,280 | 6,850 | 751.70 | |
| 3550 | Helicopter, small, lift to 1250 lbs. maximum, w/pilot | | 92.16 | 2,950 | 8,880 | 26,600 | 2,513 | |
| 3600 | Hoists, chain type, overhead, manual, 3/4 ton | | .10 | 1 | 3 | 9 | 1.40 | |
| 3900 | 10 ton | | .75 | 9.35 | 28 | 84 | 11.60 | |
| 4000 | Hoist and tower, 5000 lb. cap., portable electric, 40' high | | 4.82 | 211 | 633 | 1,900 | 165.15 | |
| 4100 | For each added 10' section, add | | .10 | 16.65 | 50 | 150 | 10.80 | |
| 4200 | Hoist and single tubular tower, 5000 lb. electric, 100' high | | 6.48 | 295 | 884 | 2,650 | 228.65 | |
| 4300 | For each added 6'-6" section, add | | .17 | 28.50 | 85 | 255 | 18.35 | |
| 4400 | Hoist and double tubular tower, 5000 lb., 100' high | | 6.93 | 325 | 974 | 2,925 | 250.25 | |
| 4500 | For each added 6'-6" section, add | | .19 | 31.50 | 95 | 285 | 20.50 | |
| 4550 | Hoist and tower, mast type, 6000 lb., 100' high | | 7.53 | 335 | 1,010 | 3,025 | 262.25 | |
| 4570 | For each added 10' section, add | | .12 | 20 | 60 | 180 | 12.95 | |
| 4600 | Hoist and tower, personnel, electric, 2000 lb., 100' @ 125 fpm | | 15.10 | 895 | 2,690 | 8,075 | 658.80 | |
| 4700 | 3000 lb., 100' @ 200 fpm | | 17.31 | 1,025 | 3,050 | 9,150 | 748.50 | |
| 4800 | 3000 lb., 150' @ 300 fpm | | 19.11 | 1,125 | 3,410 | 10,200 | 834.90 | |
| 4900 | 4000 lb., 100' @ 300 fpm | | 19.88 | 1,150 | 3,480 | 10,400 | 855.05 | |
| 5000 | 6000 lb., 100' @ 275 fpm | | 21.55 | 1,225 | 3,650 | 11,000 | 902.40 | |
| 5100 | For added heights up to 500', add | L.F. | .01 | 1.67 | 5 | 15 | 1.10 | |
| 5200 | Jacks, hydraulic, 20 ton | Ea. | .05 | 2 | 6 | 18 | 1.60 | |
| 5500 | 100 ton | | .35 | 11.35 | 34 | 102 | 9.60 | |
| 6100 | Jacks, hydraulic, climbing w/ 50' jackrods, control console, 30 ton cap. | | 1.82 | 121 | 364 | 1,100 | 87.35 | |
| 6150 | For each added 10' jackrod section, add | | .05 | 3.33 | 10 | 30 | 2.40 | |
| 6300 | 50 ton capacity | | 2.93 | 195 | 585 | 1,750 | 140.45 | |
| 6350 | For each added 10' jackrod section, add | | .06 | 4 | 12 | 36 | 2.90 | |
| 6500 | 125 ton capacity | | 7.70 | 515 | 1,540 | 4,625 | 369.60 | |
| 6550 | For each added 10' jackrod section, add | | .53 | 35 | 105 | 315 | 25.25 | |
| 6600 | Cable jack, 10 ton capacity with 200' cable | | 1.53 | 102 | 305 | 915 | 73.25 | |
| 6650 | For each added 50' of cable, add | | .18 | 11.65 | 35 | 105 | 8.45 | |
| 0010 | **WELLPOINT EQUIPMENT RENTAL** without operators | R015433 -10 | | | | | | 70 |
| 0020 | Based on 2 months rental | | | | | | | |
| 0100 | Combination jetting & wellpoint pump, 60 H.P. diesel | Ea. | 14.71 | 300 | 902 | 2,700 | 298.10 | |
| 0200 | High pressure gas jet pump, 200 H.P., 300 psi | " | 33.40 | 257 | 771 | 2,325 | 421.40 | |
| 0300 | Discharge pipe, 8" diameter | L.F. | .01 | .49 | 1.47 | 4.41 | .35 | |
| 0350 | 12" diameter | | .01 | .72 | 2.16 | 6.50 | .50 | |
| 0400 | Header pipe, flows up to 150 GPM, 4" diameter | | .01 | .44 | 1.32 | 3.96 | .35 | |
| 0500 | 400 GPM, 6" diameter | | .01 | .52 | 1.57 | 4.71 | .40 | |
| 0600 | 800 GPM, 8" diameter | | .01 | .72 | 2.16 | 6.50 | .50 | |
| 0700 | 1500 GPM, 10" diameter | | .01 | .75 | 2.26 | 6.80 | .55 | |
| 0800 | 2500 GPM, 12" diameter | | .02 | 1.43 | 4.29 | 12.85 | 1 | |
| 0900 | 4500 GPM, 16" diameter | | .03 | 1.83 | 5.50 | 16.50 | 1.35 | |
| 0950 | For quick coupling aluminum and plastic pipe, add | | .03 | 1.90 | 5.69 | 17.05 | 1.40 | |
| 1100 | Wellpoint, 25' long, with fittings & riser pipe, 1-1/2" or 2" diameter | Ea. | .06 | 3.78 | 11.35 | 34 | 2.75 | |
| 1200 | Wellpoint pump, diesel powered, 4" suction, 20 H.P. | | 6.44 | 173 | 520 | 1,550 | 155.50 | |
| 1300 | 6" suction, 30 H.P. | | 8.72 | 215 | 645 | 1,925 | 198.75 | |
| 1400 | 8" suction, 40 H.P. | | 11.79 | 295 | 884 | 2,650 | 271.10 | |
| 1500 | 10" suction, 75 H.P. | | 17.73 | 345 | 1,033 | 3,100 | 348.45 | |

| | | 01 54 33 | Equipment Rental | UNIT | HOURLY OPER. COST | RENT PER DAY | RENT PER WEEK | RENT PER MONTH | EQUIPMENT COST/DAY | |
|---|---|---|---|---|---|---|---|---|---|---|
| 70 | 1600 | | 12" suction, 100 H.P. | Ea. | 25.55 | 550 | 1,650 | 4,950 | 534.40 | 70 |
| | 1700 | | 12" suction, 175 H.P. | " | 37.17 | 605 | 1,810 | 5,425 | 659.35 | |
| 80 | 0010 | **MARINE EQUIPMENT RENTAL** without operators | R015433 -10 | | | | | | | 80 |
| | 0200 | | Barge, 400 Ton, 30' wide x 90' long | Ea. | 15.50 | 1,075 | 3,220 | 9,650 | 768 | |
| | 0240 | | 800 Ton, 45' wide x 90' long | | 18.80 | 1,300 | 3,900 | 11,700 | 930.40 | |
| | 2000 | | Tugboat, diesel, 100 H.P. | | 36.45 | 203 | 610 | 1,825 | 413.60 | |
| | 2040 | | 250 H.P. | | 77.10 | 375 | 1,120 | 3,350 | 840.80 | |
| | 2080 | | 380 H.P. | | 149.05 | 1,100 | 3,325 | 9,975 | 1,857 | |

# Crews

| Crew A-1 | Hr. | Daily | Hr. | Daily | Bare Costs | Incl. O&P |
|---|---|---|---|---|---|---|
| 1 Building Laborer | $21.50 | $172.00 | $36.15 | $289.20 | $21.50 | $36.15 |
| 1 Concrete saw, gas manual | | 73.80 | | 81.18 | 9.22 | 10.15 |
| 8 L.H., Daily Totals | | $245.80 | | $370.38 | $30.73 | $46.30 |

| Crew A-1A | Hr. | Daily | Hr. | Daily | Bare Costs | Incl. O&P |
|---|---|---|---|---|---|---|
| 1 Skilled Worker | $29.25 | $234.00 | $49.05 | $392.40 | $29.25 | $49.05 |
| 1 Shot Blaster, 20" | | 215.80 | | 237.38 | 26.98 | 29.67 |
| 8 L.H., Daily Totals | | $449.80 | | $629.78 | $56.23 | $78.72 |

| Crew A-1B | Hr. | Daily | Hr. | Daily | Bare Costs | Incl. O&P |
|---|---|---|---|---|---|---|
| 1 Building Laborer | $21.50 | $172.00 | $36.15 | $289.20 | $21.50 | $36.15 |
| 1 Concrete Saw | | 161.40 | | 177.54 | 20.18 | 22.19 |
| 8 L.H., Daily Totals | | $333.40 | | $466.74 | $41.67 | $58.34 |

| Crew A-1C | Hr. | Daily | Hr. | Daily | Bare Costs | Incl. O&P |
|---|---|---|---|---|---|---|
| 1 Building Laborer | $21.50 | $172.00 | $36.15 | $289.20 | $21.50 | $36.15 |
| 1 Chain Saw, gas, 18" | | 28.20 | | 31.02 | 3.52 | 3.88 |
| 8 L.H., Daily Totals | | $200.20 | | $320.22 | $25.02 | $40.03 |

| Crew A-1D | Hr. | Daily | Hr. | Daily | Bare Costs | Incl. O&P |
|---|---|---|---|---|---|---|
| 1 Building Laborer | $21.50 | $172.00 | $36.15 | $289.20 | $21.50 | $36.15 |
| 1 Vibrating plate, gas, 18" | | 34.20 | | 37.62 | 4.28 | 4.70 |
| 8 L.H., Daily Totals | | $206.20 | | $326.82 | $25.77 | $40.85 |

| Crew A-1E | Hr. | Daily | Hr. | Daily | Bare Costs | Incl. O&P |
|---|---|---|---|---|---|---|
| 1 Building Laborer | $21.50 | $172.00 | $36.15 | $289.20 | $21.50 | $36.15 |
| 1 Vibratory Plate, gas, 21" | | 43.60 | | 47.96 | 5.45 | 6.00 |
| 8 L.H., Daily Totals | | $215.60 | | $337.16 | $26.95 | $42.15 |

| Crew A-1F | Hr. | Daily | Hr. | Daily | Bare Costs | Incl. O&P |
|---|---|---|---|---|---|---|
| 1 Building Laborer | $21.50 | $172.00 | $36.15 | $289.20 | $21.50 | $36.15 |
| 1 Rammer/tamper, gas, 8" | | 46.80 | | 51.48 | 5.85 | 6.43 |
| 8 L.H., Daily Totals | | $218.80 | | $340.68 | $27.35 | $42.59 |

| Crew A-1G | Hr. | Daily | Hr. | Daily | Bare Costs | Incl. O&P |
|---|---|---|---|---|---|---|
| 1 Building Laborer | $21.50 | $172.00 | $36.15 | $289.20 | $21.50 | $36.15 |
| 1 Rammer/tamper, gas, 15" | | 51.80 | | 56.98 | 6.47 | 7.12 |
| 8 L.H., Daily Totals | | $223.80 | | $346.18 | $27.98 | $43.27 |

| Crew A-1H | Hr. | Daily | Hr. | Daily | Bare Costs | Incl. O&P |
|---|---|---|---|---|---|---|
| 1 Building Laborer | $21.50 | $172.00 | $36.15 | $289.20 | $21.50 | $36.15 |
| 1 Exterior Steam Cleaner | | 60.20 | | 66.22 | 7.53 | 8.28 |
| 8 L.H., Daily Totals | | $232.20 | | $355.42 | $29.02 | $44.43 |

| Crew A-1J | Hr. | Daily | Hr. | Daily | Bare Costs | Incl. O&P |
|---|---|---|---|---|---|---|
| 1 Building Laborer | $21.50 | $172.00 | $36.15 | $289.20 | $21.50 | $36.15 |
| 1 Cultivator, Walk-Behind, 5 H.P. | | 56.15 | | 61.77 | 7.02 | 7.72 |
| 8 L.H., Daily Totals | | $228.15 | | $350.96 | $28.52 | $43.87 |

| Crew A-1K | Hr. | Daily | Hr. | Daily | Bare Costs | Incl. O&P |
|---|---|---|---|---|---|---|
| 1 Building Laborer | $21.50 | $172.00 | $36.15 | $289.20 | $21.50 | $36.15 |
| 1 Cultivator, Walk-Behind, 8 H.P. | | 86.40 | | 95.04 | 10.80 | 11.88 |
| 8 L.H., Daily Totals | | $258.40 | | $384.24 | $32.30 | $48.03 |

| Crew A-1M | Hr. | Daily | Hr. | Daily | Bare Costs | Incl. O&P |
|---|---|---|---|---|---|---|
| 1 Building Laborer | $21.50 | $172.00 | $36.15 | $289.20 | $21.50 | $36.15 |
| 1 Snow Blower, Walk-Behind | | 53.40 | | 58.74 | 6.67 | 7.34 |
| 8 L.H., Daily Totals | | $225.40 | | $347.94 | $28.18 | $43.49 |

| Crew A-2 | Hr. | Daily | Hr. | Daily | Bare Costs | Incl. O&P |
|---|---|---|---|---|---|---|
| 2 Laborers | $21.50 | $344.00 | $36.15 | $578.40 | $21.97 | $36.82 |
| 1 Truck Driver (light) | 22.90 | 183.20 | 38.15 | 305.20 | | |
| 1 Flatbed Truck, Gas, 1.5 Ton | | 239.80 | | 263.78 | 9.99 | 10.99 |
| 24 L.H., Daily Totals | | $767.00 | | $1147.38 | $31.96 | $47.81 |

| Crew A-2A | Hr. | Daily | Hr. | Daily | Bare Costs | Incl. O&P |
|---|---|---|---|---|---|---|
| 2 Laborers | $21.50 | $344.00 | $36.15 | $578.40 | $21.97 | $36.82 |
| 1 Truck Driver (light) | 22.90 | 183.20 | 38.15 | 305.20 | | |
| 1 Flatbed Truck, Gas, 1.5 Ton | | 239.80 | | 263.78 | | |
| 1 Concrete Saw | | 161.40 | | 177.54 | 16.72 | 18.39 |
| 24 L.H., Daily Totals | | $928.40 | | $1324.92 | $38.68 | $55.20 |

| Crew A-2B | Hr. | Daily | Hr. | Daily | Bare Costs | Incl. O&P |
|---|---|---|---|---|---|---|
| 1 Truck Driver (light) | $22.90 | $183.20 | $38.15 | $305.20 | $22.90 | $38.15 |
| 1 Flatbed Truck, Gas, 1.5 Ton | | 239.80 | | 263.78 | 29.98 | 32.97 |
| 8 L.H., Daily Totals | | $423.00 | | $568.98 | $52.88 | $71.12 |

| Crew A-3A | Hr. | Daily | Hr. | Daily | Bare Costs | Incl. O&P |
|---|---|---|---|---|---|---|
| 1 Truck Driver (light) | $22.90 | $183.20 | $38.15 | $305.20 | $22.90 | $38.15 |
| 1 Pickup truck, 4 x 4, 3/4 ton | | 151.00 | | 166.10 | 18.88 | 20.76 |
| 8 L.H., Daily Totals | | $334.20 | | $471.30 | $41.77 | $58.91 |

| Crew A-3B | Hr. | Daily | Hr. | Daily | Bare Costs | Incl. O&P |
|---|---|---|---|---|---|---|
| 1 Equip. Oper. (med.) | $29.65 | $237.20 | $48.55 | $388.40 | $26.60 | $43.88 |
| 1 Truck Driver (heav.) | 23.55 | 188.40 | 39.20 | 313.60 | | |
| 1 Dump Truck, 12 C.Y., 400 H.P. | | 667.80 | | 734.58 | | |
| 1 F.E. Loader, W.M., 2.5 C.Y. | | 435.80 | | 479.38 | 68.97 | 75.87 |
| 16 L.H., Daily Totals | | $1529.20 | | $1915.96 | $95.58 | $119.75 |

| Crew A-3C | Hr. | Daily | Hr. | Daily | Bare Costs | Incl. O&P |
|---|---|---|---|---|---|---|
| 1 Equip. Oper. (light) | $28.50 | $228.00 | $46.65 | $373.20 | $28.50 | $46.65 |
| 1 Loader, Skid Steer, 78 H.P. | | 291.00 | | 320.10 | 36.38 | 40.01 |
| 8 L.H., Daily Totals | | $519.00 | | $693.30 | $64.88 | $86.66 |

| Crew A-3D | Hr. | Daily | Hr. | Daily | Bare Costs | Incl. O&P |
|---|---|---|---|---|---|---|
| 1 Truck Driver, Light | $22.90 | $183.20 | $38.15 | $305.20 | $22.90 | $38.15 |
| 1 Pickup truck, 4 x 4, 3/4 ton | | 151.00 | | 166.10 | | |
| 1 Flatbed Trailer, 25 Ton | | 105.60 | | 116.16 | 32.08 | 35.28 |
| 8 L.H., Daily Totals | | $439.80 | | $587.46 | $54.98 | $73.43 |

| Crew A-3E | Hr. | Daily | Hr. | Daily | Bare Costs | Incl. O&P |
|---|---|---|---|---|---|---|
| 1 Equip. Oper. (crane) | $30.65 | $245.20 | $50.15 | $401.20 | $27.10 | $44.67 |
| 1 Truck Driver (heavy) | 23.55 | 188.40 | 39.20 | 313.60 | | |
| 1 Pickup truck, 4 x 4, 3/4 ton | | 151.00 | | 166.10 | 9.44 | 10.38 |
| 16 L.H., Daily Totals | | $584.60 | | $880.90 | $36.54 | $55.06 |

| Crew A-3F | Hr. | Daily | Hr. | Daily | Bare Costs | Incl. O&P |
|---|---|---|---|---|---|---|
| 1 Equip. Oper. (crane) | $30.65 | $245.20 | $50.15 | $401.20 | $27.10 | $44.67 |
| 1 Truck Driver (heavy) | 23.55 | 188.40 | 39.20 | 313.60 | | |
| 1 Pickup truck, 4 x 4, 3/4 ton | | 151.00 | | 166.10 | | |
| 1 Truck Tractor, 6x4, 380 H.P. | | 592.40 | | 651.64 | | |
| 1 Lowbed Trailer, 75 Ton | | 205.80 | | 226.38 | 59.33 | 65.26 |
| 16 L.H., Daily Totals | | $1382.80 | | $1758.92 | $86.42 | $109.93 |

# Crews

## Crew A-3G

| Crew No. | Hr. | Daily | Hr. | Daily | Bare Costs | Incl. O&P |
|---|---|---|---|---|---|---|
| 1 Equip. Oper. (crane) | $30.65 | $245.20 | $50.15 | $401.20 | $27.10 | $44.67 |
| 1 Truck Driver (heavy) | 23.55 | 188.40 | 39.20 | 313.60 | | |
| 1 Pickup truck, 4 x 4, 3/4 ton | | 151.00 | | 166.10 | | |
| 1 Truck Tractor, 6x4, 450 H.P. | | 715.80 | | 787.38 | | |
| 1 Lowbed Trailer, 75 Ton | | 205.80 | | 226.38 | 67.04 | 73.74 |
| 16 L.H., Daily Totals | | $1506.20 | | $1894.66 | $94.14 | $118.42 |

## Crew A-3H

| Crew No. | Hr. | Daily | Hr. | Daily | Bare Costs | Incl. O&P |
|---|---|---|---|---|---|---|
| 1 Equip. Oper. (crane) | $30.65 | $245.20 | $50.15 | $401.20 | $30.65 | $50.15 |
| 1 Hyd. crane, 12 Ton (daily) | | 871.60 | | 958.76 | 108.95 | 119.85 |
| 8 L.H., Daily Totals | | $1116.80 | | $1359.96 | $139.60 | $170.00 |

## Crew A-3I

| Crew No. | Hr. | Daily | Hr. | Daily | Bare Costs | Incl. O&P |
|---|---|---|---|---|---|---|
| 1 Equip. Oper. (crane) | $30.65 | $245.20 | $50.15 | $401.20 | $30.65 | $50.15 |
| 1 Hyd. crane, 25 Ton (daily) | | 1015.00 | | 1116.50 | 126.88 | 139.56 |
| 8 L.H., Daily Totals | | $1260.20 | | $1517.70 | $157.53 | $189.71 |

## Crew A-3J

| Crew No. | Hr. | Daily | Hr. | Daily | Bare Costs | Incl. O&P |
|---|---|---|---|---|---|---|
| 1 Equip. Oper. (crane) | $30.65 | $245.20 | $50.15 | $401.20 | $30.65 | $50.15 |
| 1 Hyd. crane, 40 Ton (daily) | | 1258.00 | | 1383.80 | 157.25 | 172.97 |
| 8 L.H., Daily Totals | | $1503.20 | | $1785.00 | $187.90 | $223.13 |

## Crew A-3K

| Crew No. | Hr. | Daily | Hr. | Daily | Bare Costs | Incl. O&P |
|---|---|---|---|---|---|---|
| 1 Equip. Oper. (crane) | $30.65 | $245.20 | $50.15 | $401.20 | $28.55 | $46.73 |
| 1 Equip. Oper. Oiler | 26.45 | 211.60 | 43.30 | 346.40 | | |
| 1 Hyd. crane, 55 Ton (daily) | | 1611.00 | | 1772.10 | | |
| 1 P/U Truck, 3/4 Ton (daily) | | 161.00 | | 177.10 | 110.75 | 121.83 |
| 16 L.H., Daily Totals | | $2228.80 | | $2696.80 | $139.30 | $168.55 |

## Crew A-3L

| Crew No. | Hr. | Daily | Hr. | Daily | Bare Costs | Incl. O&P |
|---|---|---|---|---|---|---|
| 1 Equip. Oper. (crane) | $30.65 | $245.20 | $50.15 | $401.20 | $28.55 | $46.73 |
| 1 Equip. Oper. Oiler | 26.45 | 211.60 | 43.30 | 346.40 | | |
| 1 Hyd. crane, 80 Ton (daily) | | 2052.00 | | 2257.20 | | |
| 1 P/U Truck, 3/4 Ton (daily) | | 161.00 | | 177.10 | 138.31 | 152.14 |
| 16 L.H., Daily Totals | | $2669.80 | | $3181.90 | $166.86 | $198.87 |

## Crew A-3M

| Crew No. | Hr. | Daily | Hr. | Daily | Bare Costs | Incl. O&P |
|---|---|---|---|---|---|---|
| 1 Equip. Oper. (crane) | $30.65 | $245.20 | $50.15 | $401.20 | $28.55 | $46.73 |
| 1 Equip. Oper. Oiler | 26.45 | 211.60 | 43.30 | 346.40 | | |
| 1 Hyd. crane, 100 Ton (daily) | | 2268.00 | | 2494.80 | | |
| 1 P/U Truck, 3/4 Ton (daily) | | 161.00 | | 177.10 | 151.81 | 166.99 |
| 16 L.H., Daily Totals | | $2885.80 | | $3419.50 | $180.36 | $213.72 |

## Crew A-3N

| Crew No. | Hr. | Daily | Hr. | Daily | Bare Costs | Incl. O&P |
|---|---|---|---|---|---|---|
| 1 Equip. Oper. (crane) | $30.65 | $245.20 | $50.15 | $401.20 | $30.65 | $50.15 |
| 1 Tower crane (monthly) | | 1049.00 | | 1153.90 | 131.13 | 144.24 |
| 8 L.H., Daily Totals | | $1294.20 | | $1555.10 | $161.78 | $194.39 |

## Crew A-3P

| Crew No. | Hr. | Daily | Hr. | Daily | Bare Costs | Incl. O&P |
|---|---|---|---|---|---|---|
| 1 Equip. Oper., Light | $28.50 | $228.00 | $46.65 | $373.20 | $28.50 | $46.65 |
| 1 A.T. Forklift, 42' lift | | 478.20 | | 526.02 | 59.77 | 65.75 |
| 8 L.H., Daily Totals | | $706.20 | | $899.22 | $88.28 | $112.40 |

## Crew A-4

| Crew No. | Hr. | Daily | Hr. | Daily | Bare Costs | Incl. O&P |
|---|---|---|---|---|---|---|
| 2 Carpenters | $29.10 | $465.60 | $48.95 | $783.20 | $28.00 | $46.63 |
| 1 Painter, Ordinary | 25.80 | 206.40 | 42.00 | 336.00 | | |
| 24 L.H., Daily Totals | | $672.00 | | $1119.20 | $28.00 | $46.63 |

## Crew A-5

| Crew No. | Hr. | Daily | Hr. | Daily | Bare Costs | Incl. O&P |
|---|---|---|---|---|---|---|
| 2 Laborers | $21.50 | $344.00 | $36.15 | $578.40 | $21.66 | $36.37 |
| .25 Truck Driver (light) | 22.90 | 45.80 | 38.15 | 76.30 | | |
| .25 Flatbed Truck, Gas, 1.5 Ton | | 59.95 | | 65.94 | 3.33 | 3.66 |
| 18 L.H., Daily Totals | | $449.75 | | $720.64 | $24.99 | $40.04 |

## Crew A-6

| Crew No. | Hr. | Daily | Hr. | Daily | Bare Costs | Incl. O&P |
|---|---|---|---|---|---|---|
| 1 Instrument Man | $29.25 | $234.00 | $49.05 | $392.40 | $28.90 | $48.02 |
| 1 Rodman/Chainman | 28.55 | 228.40 | 47.00 | 376.00 | | |
| 1 Laser Transit/Level | | 69.90 | | 76.89 | 4.37 | 4.81 |
| 16 L.H., Daily Totals | | $532.30 | | $845.29 | $33.27 | $52.83 |

## Crew A-7

| Crew No. | Hr. | Daily | Hr. | Daily | Bare Costs | Incl. O&P |
|---|---|---|---|---|---|---|
| 1 Chief Of Party | $34.50 | $276.00 | $57.60 | $460.80 | $30.77 | $51.22 |
| 1 Instrument Man | 29.25 | 234.00 | 49.05 | 392.40 | | |
| 1 Rodman/Chainman | 28.55 | 228.40 | 47.00 | 376.00 | | |
| 1 Laser Transit/Level | | 69.90 | | 76.89 | 2.91 | 3.20 |
| 24 L.H., Daily Totals | | $808.30 | | $1306.09 | $33.68 | $54.42 |

## Crew A-8

| Crew No. | Hr. | Daily | Hr. | Daily | Bare Costs | Incl. O&P |
|---|---|---|---|---|---|---|
| 1 Chief of Party | $34.50 | $276.00 | $57.60 | $460.80 | $30.21 | $50.16 |
| 1 Instrument Man | 29.25 | 234.00 | 49.05 | 392.40 | | |
| 2 Rodmen/Chainmen | 28.55 | 456.80 | 47.00 | 752.00 | | |
| 1 Laser Transit/Level | | 69.90 | | 76.89 | 2.18 | 2.40 |
| 32 L.H., Daily Totals | | $1036.70 | | $1682.09 | $32.40 | $52.57 |

## Crew A-9

| Crew No. | Hr. | Daily | Hr. | Daily | Bare Costs | Incl. O&P |
|---|---|---|---|---|---|---|
| 1 Asbestos Foreman | $30.55 | $244.40 | $51.75 | $414.00 | $30.11 | $51.01 |
| 7 Asbestos Workers | 30.05 | 1682.80 | 50.90 | 2850.40 | | |
| 64 L.H., Daily Totals | | $1927.20 | | $3264.40 | $30.11 | $51.01 |

## Crew A-10A

| Crew No. | Hr. | Daily | Hr. | Daily | Bare Costs | Incl. O&P |
|---|---|---|---|---|---|---|
| 1 Asbestos Foreman | $30.55 | $244.40 | $51.75 | $414.00 | $30.22 | $51.18 |
| 2 Asbestos Workers | 30.05 | 480.80 | 50.90 | 814.40 | | |
| 24 L.H., Daily Totals | | $725.20 | | $1228.40 | $30.22 | $51.18 |

## Crew A-10B

| Crew No. | Hr. | Daily | Hr. | Daily | Bare Costs | Incl. O&P |
|---|---|---|---|---|---|---|
| 1 Asbestos Foreman | $30.55 | $244.40 | $51.75 | $414.00 | $30.18 | $51.11 |
| 3 Asbestos Workers | 30.05 | 721.20 | 50.90 | 1221.60 | | |
| 32 L.H., Daily Totals | | $965.60 | | $1635.60 | $30.18 | $51.11 |

## Crew A-10C

| Crew No. | Hr. | Daily | Hr. | Daily | Bare Costs | Incl. O&P |
|---|---|---|---|---|---|---|
| 3 Asbestos Workers | $30.05 | $721.20 | $50.90 | $1221.60 | $30.05 | $50.90 |
| 1 Flatbed Truck, Gas, 1.5 Ton | | 239.80 | | 263.78 | 9.99 | 10.99 |
| 24 L.H., Daily Totals | | $961.00 | | $1485.38 | $40.04 | $61.89 |

## Crew A-10D

| Crew No. | Hr. | Daily | Hr. | Daily | Bare Costs | Incl. O&P |
|---|---|---|---|---|---|---|
| 2 Asbestos Workers | $30.05 | $480.80 | $50.90 | $814.40 | $29.30 | $48.81 |
| 1 Equip. Oper. (crane) | 30.65 | 245.20 | 50.15 | 401.20 | | |
| 1 Equip. Oper. Oiler | 26.45 | 211.60 | 43.30 | 346.40 | | |
| 1 Hydraulic Crane, 33 Ton | | 763.00 | | 839.30 | 23.84 | 26.23 |
| 32 L.H., Daily Totals | | $1700.60 | | $2401.30 | $53.14 | $75.04 |

## Crew A-11

| Crew No. | Hr. | Daily | Hr. | Daily | Bare Costs | Incl. O&P |
|---|---|---|---|---|---|---|
| 1 Asbestos Foreman | $30.55 | $244.40 | $51.75 | $414.00 | $30.11 | $51.01 |
| 7 Asbestos Workers | 30.05 | 1682.80 | 50.90 | 2850.40 | | |
| 2 Chip. Hammers, 12 Lb., Elec. | | 36.00 | | 39.60 | 0.56 | 0.62 |
| 64 L.H., Daily Totals | | $1963.20 | | $3304.00 | $30.68 | $51.63 |

# Crews

| Crew No. | Bare Costs Hr. | Daily | Incl. Subs O&P Hr. | Daily | Cost Per Labor-Hour Bare Costs | Incl. O&P |
|---|---|---|---|---|---|---|
| **Crew A-12** | | | | | | |
| 1 Asbestos Foreman | $30.55 | $244.40 | $51.75 | $414.00 | $30.11 | $51.01 |
| 7 Asbestos Workers | 30.05 | 1682.80 | 50.90 | 2850.40 | | |
| 1 Trk-mtd vac, 14 CY, 1500 Gal. | | 530.25 | | 583.27 | | |
| 1 Flatbed Truck, 20,000 GVW | | 245.60 | | 270.16 | 12.12 | 13.33 |
| 64 L.H., Daily Totals | | $2703.05 | | $4117.84 | $42.24 | $64.34 |
| **Crew A-13** | | | | | | |
| 1 Equip. Oper. (light) | $28.50 | $228.00 | $46.65 | $373.20 | $28.50 | $46.65 |
| 1 Trk-mtd vac, 14 CY, 1500 Gal. | | 530.25 | | 583.27 | | |
| 1 Flatbed Truck, 20,000 GVW | | 245.60 | | 270.16 | 96.98 | 106.68 |
| 8 L.H., Daily Totals | | $1003.85 | | $1226.64 | $125.48 | $153.33 |
| **Crew B-1** | | | | | | |
| 1 Labor Foreman (outside) | $23.50 | $188.00 | $39.55 | $316.40 | $22.17 | $37.28 |
| 2 Laborers | 21.50 | 344.00 | 36.15 | 578.40 | | |
| 24 L.H., Daily Totals | | $532.00 | | $894.80 | $22.17 | $37.28 |
| **Crew B-1A** | | | | | | |
| 1 Laborer Foreman | $23.50 | $188.00 | $39.55 | $316.40 | $22.17 | $37.28 |
| 2 Laborers | 21.50 | 344.00 | 36.15 | 578.40 | | |
| 2 Cutting Torches | | 38.00 | | 41.80 | | |
| 2 Set of Gases | | 158.40 | | 174.24 | 8.18 | 9.00 |
| 24 L.H., Daily Totals | | $728.40 | | $1110.84 | $30.35 | $46.28 |
| **Crew B-1B** | | | | | | |
| 1 Laborer Foreman | $23.50 | $188.00 | $39.55 | $316.40 | $24.29 | $40.50 |
| 2 Laborers | 21.50 | 344.00 | 36.15 | 578.40 | | |
| 1 Equip. Oper. (crane) | 30.65 | 245.20 | 50.15 | 401.20 | | |
| 2 Cutting Torches | | 38.00 | | 41.80 | | |
| 2 Set of Gases | | 158.40 | | 174.24 | | |
| 1 Hyd. Crane, 12 Ton | | 655.60 | | 721.16 | 26.63 | 29.29 |
| 32 L.H., Daily Totals | | $1629.20 | | $2233.20 | $50.91 | $69.79 |
| **Crew B-2** | | | | | | |
| 1 Labor Foreman (outside) | $23.50 | $188.00 | $39.55 | $316.40 | $21.90 | $36.83 |
| 4 Laborers | 21.50 | 688.00 | 36.15 | 1156.80 | | |
| 40 L.H., Daily Totals | | $876.00 | | $1473.20 | $21.90 | $36.83 |
| **Crew B-3** | | | | | | |
| 1 Labor Foreman (outside) | $23.50 | $188.00 | $39.55 | $316.40 | $23.88 | $39.80 |
| 2 Laborers | 21.50 | 344.00 | 36.15 | 578.40 | | |
| 1 Equip. Oper. (med.) | 29.65 | 237.20 | 48.55 | 388.40 | | |
| 2 Truck Drivers (heavy) | 23.55 | 376.80 | 39.20 | 627.20 | | |
| 1 Crawler Loader, 3 C.Y. | | 1077.00 | | 1184.70 | | |
| 2 Dump Trucks 12 C.Y., 400 H.P. | | 1335.60 | | 1469.16 | 50.26 | 55.29 |
| 48 L.H., Daily Totals | | $3558.60 | | $4564.26 | $74.14 | $95.09 |
| **Crew B-3A** | | | | | | |
| 4 Laborers | $21.50 | $688.00 | $36.15 | $1156.80 | $23.13 | $38.63 |
| 1 Equip. Oper. (med.) | 29.65 | 237.20 | 48.55 | 388.40 | | |
| 1 Hyd. Excavator, 1.5 C.Y. | | 1017.00 | | 1118.70 | 25.43 | 27.97 |
| 40 L.H., Daily Totals | | $1942.20 | | $2663.90 | $48.56 | $66.60 |
| **Crew B-3B** | | | | | | |
| 2 Laborers | $21.50 | $344.00 | $36.15 | $578.40 | $24.05 | $40.01 |
| 1 Equip. Oper. (med.) | 29.65 | 237.20 | 48.55 | 388.40 | | |
| 1 Truck Driver (heavy) | 23.55 | 188.40 | 39.20 | 313.60 | | |
| 1 Backhoe Loader, 80 H.P. | | 387.60 | | 426.36 | | |
| 1 Dump Truck, 12 C.Y., 400 H.P. | | 667.80 | | 734.58 | 32.98 | 36.28 |
| 32 L.H., Daily Totals | | $1825.00 | | $2441.34 | $57.03 | $76.29 |

| Crew No. | Bare Costs Hr. | Daily | Incl. Subs O&P Hr. | Daily | Cost Per Labor-Hour Bare Costs | Incl. O&P |
|---|---|---|---|---|---|---|
| **Crew B-3C** | | | | | | |
| 3 Laborers | $21.50 | $516.00 | $36.15 | $867.60 | $23.54 | $39.25 |
| 1 Equip. Oper. (med.) | 29.65 | 237.20 | 48.55 | 388.40 | | |
| 1 Crawler Loader, 4 C.Y. | | 1548.00 | | 1702.80 | 48.38 | 53.21 |
| 32 L.H., Daily Totals | | $2301.20 | | $2958.80 | $71.91 | $92.46 |
| **Crew B-4** | | | | | | |
| 1 Labor Foreman (outside) | $23.50 | $188.00 | $39.55 | $316.40 | $22.18 | $37.23 |
| 4 Laborers | 21.50 | 688.00 | 36.15 | 1156.80 | | |
| 1 Truck Driver (heavy) | 23.55 | 188.40 | 39.20 | 313.60 | | |
| 1 Truck Tractor, 220 H.P. | | 354.00 | | 389.40 | | |
| 1 Flatbed Trailer, 40 Ton | | 143.20 | | 157.52 | 10.36 | 11.39 |
| 48 L.H., Daily Totals | | $1561.60 | | $2333.72 | $32.53 | $48.62 |
| **Crew B-5** | | | | | | |
| 1 Labor Foreman (outside) | $23.50 | $188.00 | $39.55 | $316.40 | $23.53 | $39.31 |
| 3 Laborers | 21.50 | 516.00 | 36.15 | 867.60 | | |
| 1 Equip. Oper. (med.) | 29.65 | 237.20 | 48.55 | 388.40 | | |
| 1 Air Compressor, 250 cfm | | 193.40 | | 212.74 | | |
| 2 Breakers, Pavement, 60 lb. | | 18.80 | | 20.68 | | |
| 2 -50' Air Hoses, 1.5" | | 12.60 | | 13.86 | | |
| 1 Crawler Loader, 3 C.Y. | | 1077.00 | | 1184.70 | 32.55 | 35.80 |
| 40 L.H., Daily Totals | | $2243.00 | | $3004.38 | $56.08 | $75.11 |
| **Crew B-5A** | | | | | | |
| 1 Foreman | $23.50 | $188.00 | $39.55 | $316.40 | $23.95 | $39.88 |
| 6 Laborers | 21.50 | 1032.00 | 36.15 | 1735.20 | | |
| 2 Equip. Oper. (med.) | 29.65 | 474.40 | 48.55 | 776.80 | | |
| 1 Equip. Oper. (light) | 28.50 | 228.00 | 46.65 | 373.20 | | |
| 2 Truck Drivers (heavy) | 23.55 | 376.80 | 39.20 | 627.20 | | |
| 1 Air Compressor, 365 cfm | | 255.60 | | 281.16 | | |
| 2 Breakers, Pavement, 60 lb. | | 18.80 | | 20.68 | | |
| 8 -50' Air Hoses, 1" | | 32.80 | | 36.08 | | |
| 2 Dump Trucks, 8 C.Y., 220 H.P. | | 803.60 | | 883.96 | 11.57 | 12.73 |
| 96 L.H., Daily Totals | | $3410.00 | | $5050.68 | $35.52 | $52.61 |
| **Crew B-5B** | | | | | | |
| 1 Powderman | $29.25 | $234.00 | $49.05 | $392.40 | $26.53 | $43.96 |
| 2 Equip. Oper. (med.) | 29.65 | 474.40 | 48.55 | 776.80 | | |
| 3 Truck Drivers (heavy) | 23.55 | 565.20 | 39.20 | 940.80 | | |
| 1 F.E. Loader, W.M.,2.5 C.Y. | | 435.80 | | 479.38 | | |
| 3 Dump Trucks, 12 C.Y., 400 H.P. | | 2003.40 | | 2203.74 | | |
| 1 Air Compressor, 365 cfm | | 255.60 | | 281.16 | 56.14 | 61.76 |
| 48 L.H., Daily Totals | | $3968.40 | | $5074.28 | $82.67 | $105.71 |
| **Crew B-5C** | | | | | | |
| 3 Laborers | $21.50 | $516.00 | $36.15 | $867.60 | $24.79 | $41.11 |
| 1 Equip. Oper. (med.) | 29.65 | 237.20 | 48.55 | 388.40 | | |
| 2 Truck Drivers (heav.) | 23.55 | 376.80 | 39.20 | 627.20 | | |
| 1 Equip. Oper. (crane) | 30.65 | 245.20 | 50.15 | 401.20 | | |
| 1 Equip. Oper. Oiler | 26.45 | 211.60 | 43.30 | 346.40 | | |
| 2 Dump Trucks, 12 C.Y., 400 H.P. | | 1335.60 | | 1469.16 | | |
| 1 Crawler Loader, 4 C.Y. | | 1548.00 | | 1702.80 | | |
| 1 S.P. Crane, 4x4, 25 Ton | | 655.60 | | 721.16 | 55.30 | 60.83 |
| 64 L.H., Daily Totals | | $5126.00 | | $6523.92 | $80.09 | $101.94 |
| **Crew B-6** | | | | | | |
| 2 Laborers | $21.50 | $344.00 | $36.15 | $578.40 | $23.83 | $39.65 |
| 1 Equip. Oper. (light) | 28.50 | 228.00 | 46.65 | 373.20 | | |
| 1 Backhoe Loader, 48 H.P. | | 337.80 | | 371.58 | 14.07 | 15.48 |
| 24 L.H., Daily Totals | | $909.80 | | $1323.18 | $37.91 | $55.13 |

627

| Crew No. | Bare Costs | | Incl. Subs O&P | | Cost Per Labor-Hour | |
|---|---|---|---|---|---|---|

**Crew B-6B**

| Crew B-6B | Hr. | Daily | Hr. | Daily | Bare Costs | Incl. O&P |
|---|---|---|---|---|---|---|
| 2 Labor Foremen (out) | $23.50 | $376.00 | $39.55 | $632.80 | $22.17 | $37.28 |
| 4 Laborers | 21.50 | 688.00 | 36.15 | 1156.80 | | |
| 1 S.P. Crane, 4x4, 5 Ton | | 276.20 | | 303.82 | | |
| 1 Flatbed Truck, Gas, 1.5 Ton | | 239.80 | | 263.78 | | |
| 1 Butt Fusion Machine | | 134.40 | | 147.84 | 13.55 | 14.90 |
| 48 L.H., Daily Totals | | $1714.40 | | $2505.04 | $35.72 | $52.19 |

**Crew B-7**

| Crew B-7 | Hr. | Daily | Hr. | Daily | Bare Costs | Incl. O&P |
|---|---|---|---|---|---|---|
| 1 Labor Foreman (outside) | $23.50 | $188.00 | $39.55 | $316.40 | $23.19 | $38.78 |
| 4 Laborers | 21.50 | 688.00 | 36.15 | 1156.80 | | |
| 1 Equip. Oper. (med.) | 29.65 | 237.20 | 48.55 | 388.40 | | |
| 1 Brush Chipper, 12", 130 H.P. | | 253.20 | | 278.52 | | |
| 1 Crawler Loader, 3 C.Y. | | 1077.00 | | 1184.70 | | |
| 2 Chain Saws, gas, 36" Long | | 78.40 | | 86.24 | 29.35 | 32.28 |
| 48 L.H., Daily Totals | | $2521.80 | | $3411.06 | $52.54 | $71.06 |

**Crew B-7A**

| Crew B-7A | Hr. | Daily | Hr. | Daily | Bare Costs | Incl. O&P |
|---|---|---|---|---|---|---|
| 2 Laborers | $21.50 | $344.00 | $36.15 | $578.40 | $23.83 | $39.65 |
| 1 Equip. Oper. (light) | 28.50 | 228.00 | 46.65 | 373.20 | | |
| 1 Rake w/Tractor | | 285.70 | | 314.27 | | |
| 2 Chain Saws, gas, 18" | | 56.40 | | 62.04 | 14.25 | 15.68 |
| 24 L.H., Daily Totals | | $914.10 | | $1327.91 | $38.09 | $55.33 |

**Crew B-8**

| Crew B-8 | Hr. | Daily | Hr. | Daily | Bare Costs | Incl. O&P |
|---|---|---|---|---|---|---|
| 1 Labor Foreman (outside) | $23.50 | $188.00 | $39.55 | $316.40 | $24.70 | $41.05 |
| 2 Laborers | 21.50 | 344.00 | 36.15 | 578.40 | | |
| 2 Equip. Oper. (med.) | 29.65 | 474.40 | 48.55 | 776.80 | | |
| 2 Truck Drivers (heavy) | 23.55 | 376.80 | 39.20 | 627.20 | | |
| 1 Hyd. Crane, 25 Ton | | 747.60 | | 822.36 | | |
| 1 Crawler Loader, 3 C.Y. | | 1077.00 | | 1184.70 | | |
| 2 Dump Trucks, 12 C.Y., 400 H.P. | | 1335.60 | | 1469.16 | 56.43 | 62.08 |
| 56 L.H., Daily Totals | | $4543.40 | | $5775.02 | $81.13 | $103.13 |

**Crew B-9**

| Crew B-9 | Hr. | Daily | Hr. | Daily | Bare Costs | Incl. O&P |
|---|---|---|---|---|---|---|
| 1 Labor Foreman (outside) | $23.50 | $188.00 | $39.55 | $316.40 | $21.90 | $36.83 |
| 4 Laborers | 21.50 | 688.00 | 36.15 | 1156.80 | | |
| 1 Air Compressor, 250 cfm | | 193.40 | | 212.74 | | |
| 2 Breakers, Pavement, 60 lb. | | 18.80 | | 20.68 | | |
| 2 -50' Air Hoses, 1.5" | | 12.60 | | 13.86 | 5.62 | 6.18 |
| 40 L.H., Daily Totals | | $1100.80 | | $1720.48 | $27.52 | $43.01 |

**Crew B-9A**

| Crew B-9A | Hr. | Daily | Hr. | Daily | Bare Costs | Incl. O&P |
|---|---|---|---|---|---|---|
| 2 Laborers | $21.50 | $344.00 | $36.15 | $578.40 | $22.18 | $37.17 |
| 1 Truck Driver (heavy) | 23.55 | 188.40 | 39.20 | 313.60 | | |
| 1 Water Tank Trailer, 5000 Gal. | | 139.60 | | 153.56 | | |
| 1 Truck Tractor, 220 H.P. | | 354.00 | | 389.40 | | |
| 2 -50' Discharge Hoses, 3" | | 3.50 | | 3.85 | 20.71 | 22.78 |
| 24 L.H., Daily Totals | | $1029.50 | | $1438.81 | $42.90 | $59.95 |

**Crew B-9B**

| Crew B-9B | Hr. | Daily | Hr. | Daily | Bare Costs | Incl. O&P |
|---|---|---|---|---|---|---|
| 2 Laborers | $21.50 | $344.00 | $36.15 | $578.40 | $22.18 | $37.17 |
| 1 Truck Driver (heavy) | 23.55 | 188.40 | 39.20 | 313.60 | | |
| 2 -50' Discharge Hoses, 3" | | 3.50 | | 3.85 | | |
| 1 Water Tank Trailer, 5000 Gal. | | 139.60 | | 153.56 | | |
| 1 Truck Tractor, 220 H.P. | | 354.00 | | 389.40 | | |
| 1 Pressure Washer | | 60.80 | | 66.88 | 23.25 | 25.57 |
| 24 L.H., Daily Totals | | $1090.30 | | $1505.69 | $45.43 | $62.74 |

**Crew B-9D**

| Crew B-9D | Hr. | Daily | Hr. | Daily | Bare Costs | Incl. O&P |
|---|---|---|---|---|---|---|
| 1 Labor Foreman (Outside) | $23.50 | $188.00 | $39.55 | $316.40 | $21.90 | $36.83 |
| 4 Common Laborers | 21.50 | 688.00 | 36.15 | 1156.80 | | |
| 1 Air Compressor, 250 cfm | | 193.40 | | 212.74 | | |
| 2 -50' Air Hoses, 1.5" | | 12.60 | | 13.86 | | |
| 2 Air Powered Tampers | | 50.50 | | 55.55 | 6.41 | 7.05 |
| 40 L.H., Daily Totals | | $1132.50 | | $1755.35 | $28.31 | $43.88 |

**Crew B-10**

| Crew B-10 | Hr. | Daily | Hr. | Daily | Bare Costs | Incl. O&P |
|---|---|---|---|---|---|---|
| 1 Equip. Oper. (med.) | $29.65 | $237.20 | $48.55 | $388.40 | $29.65 | $48.55 |
| 8 L.H., Daily Totals | | $237.20 | | $388.40 | $29.65 | $48.55 |

**Crew B-10A**

| Crew B-10A | Hr. | Daily | Hr. | Daily | Bare Costs | Incl. O&P |
|---|---|---|---|---|---|---|
| 1 Equip. Oper. (med.) | $29.65 | $237.20 | $48.55 | $388.40 | $29.65 | $48.55 |
| 1 Roller, 2-Drum, W.B., 7.5 H.P. | | 149.60 | | 164.56 | 18.70 | 20.57 |
| 8 L.H., Daily Totals | | $386.80 | | $552.96 | $48.35 | $69.12 |

**Crew B-10B**

| Crew B-10B | Hr. | Daily | Hr. | Daily | Bare Costs | Incl. O&P |
|---|---|---|---|---|---|---|
| 1 Equip. Oper. (med.) | $29.65 | $237.20 | $48.55 | $388.40 | $29.65 | $48.55 |
| 1 Dozer, 200 H.P. | | 1192.00 | | 1311.20 | 149.00 | 163.90 |
| 8 L.H., Daily Totals | | $1429.20 | | $1699.60 | $178.65 | $212.45 |

**Crew B-10C**

| Crew B-10C | Hr. | Daily | Hr. | Daily | Bare Costs | Incl. O&P |
|---|---|---|---|---|---|---|
| 1 Equip. Oper. (med.) | $29.65 | $237.20 | $48.55 | $388.40 | $29.65 | $48.55 |
| 1 Dozer, 200 H.P. | | 1192.00 | | 1311.20 | | |
| 1 Vibratory Roller, Towed, 23 Ton | | 434.20 | | 477.62 | 203.28 | 223.60 |
| 8 L.H., Daily Totals | | $1863.40 | | $2177.22 | $232.93 | $272.15 |

**Crew B-10D**

| Crew B-10D | Hr. | Daily | Hr. | Daily | Bare Costs | Incl. O&P |
|---|---|---|---|---|---|---|
| 1 Equip. Oper. (med.) | $29.65 | $237.20 | $48.55 | $388.40 | $29.65 | $48.55 |
| 1 Dozer, 200 H.P. | | 1192.00 | | 1311.20 | | |
| 1 Sheepsft. Roller, Towed | | 489.20 | | 538.12 | 210.15 | 231.16 |
| 8 L.H., Daily Totals | | $1918.40 | | $2237.72 | $239.80 | $279.71 |

**Crew B-10E**

| Crew B-10E | Hr. | Daily | Hr. | Daily | Bare Costs | Incl. O&P |
|---|---|---|---|---|---|---|
| 1 Equip. Oper. (med.) | $29.65 | $237.20 | $48.55 | $388.40 | $29.65 | $48.55 |
| 1 Tandem Roller, 5 Ton | | 152.00 | | 167.20 | 19.00 | 20.90 |
| 8 L.H., Daily Totals | | $389.20 | | $555.60 | $48.65 | $69.45 |

**Crew B-10F**

| Crew B-10F | Hr. | Daily | Hr. | Daily | Bare Costs | Incl. O&P |
|---|---|---|---|---|---|---|
| 1 Equip. Oper. (med.) | $29.65 | $237.20 | $48.55 | $388.40 | $29.65 | $48.55 |
| 1 Tandem Roller, 10 Ton | | 235.20 | | 258.72 | 29.40 | 32.34 |
| 8 L.H., Daily Totals | | $472.40 | | $647.12 | $59.05 | $80.89 |

**Crew B-10G**

| Crew B-10G | Hr. | Daily | Hr. | Daily | Bare Costs | Incl. O&P |
|---|---|---|---|---|---|---|
| 1 Equip. Oper. (med.) | $29.65 | $237.20 | $48.55 | $388.40 | $29.65 | $48.55 |
| 1 Sheepsft. Roll., 240 H.P. | | 1243.00 | | 1367.30 | 155.38 | 170.91 |
| 8 L.H., Daily Totals | | $1480.20 | | $1755.70 | $185.03 | $219.46 |

**Crew B-10H**

| Crew B-10H | Hr. | Daily | Hr. | Daily | Bare Costs | Incl. O&P |
|---|---|---|---|---|---|---|
| 1 Equip. Oper. (med.) | $29.65 | $237.20 | $48.55 | $388.40 | $29.65 | $48.55 |
| 1 Diaphragm Water Pump, 2" | | 68.00 | | 74.80 | | |
| 1 -20' Suction Hose, 2" | | 1.95 | | 2.15 | | |
| 2 -50' Discharge Hoses, 2" | | 1.80 | | 1.98 | 8.97 | 9.87 |
| 8 L.H., Daily Totals | | $308.95 | | $467.32 | $38.62 | $58.42 |

## Crew B-10I

| | Bare Costs Hr. | Daily | Incl. Subs O&P Hr. | Daily | Cost Per Labor-Hour Bare Costs | Incl. O&P |
|---|---|---|---|---|---|---|
| 1 Equip. Oper. (med.) | $29.65 | $237.20 | $48.55 | $388.40 | $29.65 | $48.55 |
| 1 Diaphragm Water Pump, 4" | | 90.80 | | 99.88 | | |
| 1 -20' Suction Hose, 4" | | 3.45 | | 3.79 | | |
| 2 -50' Discharge Hoses, 4" | | 4.70 | | 5.17 | 12.37 | 13.61 |
| 8 L.H., Daily Totals | | $336.15 | | $497.25 | $42.02 | $62.16 |

## Crew B-10J

| | Bare Costs Hr. | Daily | Incl. Subs O&P Hr. | Daily | Cost Per Labor-Hour Bare Costs | Incl. O&P |
|---|---|---|---|---|---|---|
| 1 Equip. Oper. (med.) | $29.65 | $237.20 | $48.55 | $388.40 | $29.65 | $48.55 |
| 1 Centrifugal Water Pump, 3" | | 74.40 | | 81.84 | | |
| 1 -20' Suction Hose, 3" | | 3.05 | | 3.36 | | |
| 2 -50' Discharge Hoses, 3" | | 3.50 | | 3.85 | 10.12 | 11.13 |
| 8 L.H., Daily Totals | | $318.15 | | $477.44 | $39.77 | $59.68 |

## Crew B-10K

| | Bare Costs Hr. | Daily | Incl. Subs O&P Hr. | Daily | Cost Per Labor-Hour Bare Costs | Incl. O&P |
|---|---|---|---|---|---|---|
| 1 Equip. Oper. (med.) | $29.65 | $237.20 | $48.55 | $388.40 | $29.65 | $48.55 |
| 1 Centr. Water Pump, 6" | | 340.00 | | 374.00 | | |
| 1 -20' Suction Hose, 6" | | 11.90 | | 13.09 | | |
| 2 -50' Discharge Hoses, 6" | | 12.60 | | 13.86 | 45.56 | 50.12 |
| 8 L.H., Daily Totals | | $601.70 | | $789.35 | $75.21 | $98.67 |

## Crew B-10L

| | Bare Costs Hr. | Daily | Incl. Subs O&P Hr. | Daily | Cost Per Labor-Hour Bare Costs | Incl. O&P |
|---|---|---|---|---|---|---|
| 1 Equip. Oper. (med.) | $29.65 | $237.20 | $48.55 | $388.40 | $29.65 | $48.55 |
| 1 Dozer, 80 H.P. | | 436.60 | | 480.26 | 54.58 | 60.03 |
| 8 L.H., Daily Totals | | $673.80 | | $868.66 | $84.22 | $108.58 |

## Crew B-10M

| | Bare Costs Hr. | Daily | Incl. Subs O&P Hr. | Daily | Cost Per Labor-Hour Bare Costs | Incl. O&P |
|---|---|---|---|---|---|---|
| 1 Equip. Oper. (med.) | $29.65 | $237.20 | $48.55 | $388.40 | $29.65 | $48.55 |
| 1 Dozer, 300 H.P. | | 1592.00 | | 1751.20 | 199.00 | 218.90 |
| 8 L.H., Daily Totals | | $1829.20 | | $2139.60 | $228.65 | $267.45 |

## Crew B-10N

| | Bare Costs Hr. | Daily | Incl. Subs O&P Hr. | Daily | Cost Per Labor-Hour Bare Costs | Incl. O&P |
|---|---|---|---|---|---|---|
| 1 Equip. Oper. (med.) | $29.65 | $237.20 | $48.55 | $388.40 | $29.65 | $48.55 |
| 1 F.E. Loader, T.M., 1.5 C.Y. | | 433.80 | | 477.18 | 54.23 | 59.65 |
| 8 L.H., Daily Totals | | $671.00 | | $865.58 | $83.88 | $108.20 |

## Crew B-10O

| | Bare Costs Hr. | Daily | Incl. Subs O&P Hr. | Daily | Cost Per Labor-Hour Bare Costs | Incl. O&P |
|---|---|---|---|---|---|---|
| 1 Equip. Oper. (med.) | $29.65 | $237.20 | $48.55 | $388.40 | $29.65 | $48.55 |
| 1 F.E. Loader, T.M., 2.25 C.Y. | | 839.40 | | 923.34 | 104.93 | 115.42 |
| 8 L.H., Daily Totals | | $1076.60 | | $1311.74 | $134.57 | $163.97 |

## Crew B-10P

| | Bare Costs Hr. | Daily | Incl. Subs O&P Hr. | Daily | Cost Per Labor-Hour Bare Costs | Incl. O&P |
|---|---|---|---|---|---|---|
| 1 Equip. Oper. (med.) | $29.65 | $237.20 | $48.55 | $388.40 | $29.65 | $48.55 |
| 1 Crawler Loader, 3 C.Y. | | 1077.00 | | 1184.70 | 134.63 | 148.09 |
| 8 L.H., Daily Totals | | $1314.20 | | $1573.10 | $164.28 | $196.64 |

## Crew B-10Q

| | Bare Costs Hr. | Daily | Incl. Subs O&P Hr. | Daily | Cost Per Labor-Hour Bare Costs | Incl. O&P |
|---|---|---|---|---|---|---|
| 1 Equip. Oper. (med.) | $29.65 | $237.20 | $48.55 | $388.40 | $29.65 | $48.55 |
| 1 Crawler Loader, 4 C.Y. | | 1548.00 | | 1702.80 | 193.50 | 212.85 |
| 8 L.H., Daily Totals | | $1785.20 | | $2091.20 | $223.15 | $261.40 |

## Crew B-10R

| | Bare Costs Hr. | Daily | Incl. Subs O&P Hr. | Daily | Cost Per Labor-Hour Bare Costs | Incl. O&P |
|---|---|---|---|---|---|---|
| 1 Equip. Oper. (med.) | $29.65 | $237.20 | $48.55 | $388.40 | $29.65 | $48.55 |
| 1 F.E. Loader, W.M., 1 C.Y. | | 269.40 | | 296.34 | 33.67 | 37.04 |
| 8 L.H., Daily Totals | | $506.60 | | $684.74 | $63.33 | $85.59 |

## Crew B-10S

| | Bare Costs Hr. | Daily | Incl. Subs O&P Hr. | Daily | Cost Per Labor-Hour Bare Costs | Incl. O&P |
|---|---|---|---|---|---|---|
| 1 Equip. Oper. (med.) | $29.65 | $237.20 | $48.55 | $388.40 | $29.65 | $48.55 |
| 1 F.E. Loader, W.M., 1.5 C.Y. | | 367.60 | | 404.36 | 45.95 | 50.55 |
| 8 L.H., Daily Totals | | $604.80 | | $792.76 | $75.60 | $99.09 |

## Crew B-10T

| | Bare Costs Hr. | Daily | Incl. Subs O&P Hr. | Daily | Cost Per Labor-Hour Bare Costs | Incl. O&P |
|---|---|---|---|---|---|---|
| 1 Equip. Oper. (med.) | $29.65 | $237.20 | $48.55 | $388.40 | $29.65 | $48.55 |
| 1 F.E. Loader, W.M., 2.5 C.Y. | | 435.80 | | 479.38 | 54.48 | 59.92 |
| 8 L.H., Daily Totals | | $673.00 | | $867.78 | $84.13 | $108.47 |

## Crew B-10U

| | Bare Costs Hr. | Daily | Incl. Subs O&P Hr. | Daily | Cost Per Labor-Hour Bare Costs | Incl. O&P |
|---|---|---|---|---|---|---|
| 1 Equip. Oper. (med.) | $29.65 | $237.20 | $48.55 | $388.40 | $29.65 | $48.55 |
| 1 F.E. Loader, W.M., 5.5 C.Y. | | 994.40 | | 1093.84 | 124.30 | 136.73 |
| 8 L.H., Daily Totals | | $1231.60 | | $1482.24 | $153.95 | $185.28 |

## Crew B-10V

| | Bare Costs Hr. | Daily | Incl. Subs O&P Hr. | Daily | Cost Per Labor-Hour Bare Costs | Incl. O&P |
|---|---|---|---|---|---|---|
| 1 Equip. Oper. (med.) | $29.65 | $237.20 | $48.55 | $388.40 | $29.65 | $48.55 |
| 1 Dozer, 700 H.P. | | 4598.00 | | 5057.80 | 574.75 | 632.23 |
| 8 L.H., Daily Totals | | $4835.20 | | $5446.20 | $604.40 | $680.77 |

## Crew B-10W

| | Bare Costs Hr. | Daily | Incl. Subs O&P Hr. | Daily | Cost Per Labor-Hour Bare Costs | Incl. O&P |
|---|---|---|---|---|---|---|
| 1 Equip. Oper. (med.) | $29.65 | $237.20 | $48.55 | $388.40 | $29.65 | $48.55 |
| 1 Dozer, 105 H.P. | | 660.40 | | 726.44 | 82.55 | 90.81 |
| 8 L.H., Daily Totals | | $897.60 | | $1114.84 | $112.20 | $139.35 |

## Crew B-10X

| | Bare Costs Hr. | Daily | Incl. Subs O&P Hr. | Daily | Cost Per Labor-Hour Bare Costs | Incl. O&P |
|---|---|---|---|---|---|---|
| 1 Equip. Oper. (med.) | $29.65 | $237.20 | $48.55 | $388.40 | $29.65 | $48.55 |
| 1 Dozer, 410 H.P. | | 2079.00 | | 2286.90 | 259.88 | 285.86 |
| 8 L.H., Daily Totals | | $2316.20 | | $2675.30 | $289.52 | $334.41 |

## Crew B-10Y

| | Bare Costs Hr. | Daily | Incl. Subs O&P Hr. | Daily | Cost Per Labor-Hour Bare Costs | Incl. O&P |
|---|---|---|---|---|---|---|
| 1 Equip. Oper. (med.) | $29.65 | $237.20 | $48.55 | $388.40 | $29.65 | $48.55 |
| 1 Vibr. Roller, Towed, 12 Ton | | 516.60 | | 568.26 | 64.58 | 71.03 |
| 8 L.H., Daily Totals | | $753.80 | | $956.66 | $94.22 | $119.58 |

## Crew B-11A

| | Bare Costs Hr. | Daily | Incl. Subs O&P Hr. | Daily | Cost Per Labor-Hour Bare Costs | Incl. O&P |
|---|---|---|---|---|---|---|
| 1 Equipment Oper. (med.) | $29.65 | $237.20 | $48.55 | $388.40 | $25.57 | $42.35 |
| 1 Laborer | 21.50 | 172.00 | 36.15 | 289.20 | | |
| 1 Dozer, 200 H.P. | | 1192.00 | | 1311.20 | 74.50 | 81.95 |
| 16 L.H., Daily Totals | | $1601.20 | | $1988.80 | $100.08 | $124.30 |

## Crew B-11B

| | Bare Costs Hr. | Daily | Incl. Subs O&P Hr. | Daily | Cost Per Labor-Hour Bare Costs | Incl. O&P |
|---|---|---|---|---|---|---|
| 1 Equipment Oper. (light) | $28.50 | $228.00 | $46.65 | $373.20 | $25.00 | $41.40 |
| 1 Laborer | 21.50 | 172.00 | 36.15 | 289.20 | | |
| 1 Air Powered Tamper | | 25.25 | | 27.77 | | |
| 1 Air Compressor, 365 cfm | | 255.60 | | 281.16 | | |
| 2 -50' Air Hoses, 1.5" | | 12.60 | | 13.86 | 18.34 | 20.17 |
| 16 L.H., Daily Totals | | $693.45 | | $985.20 | $43.34 | $61.57 |

## Crew B-11C

| | Bare Costs Hr. | Daily | Incl. Subs O&P Hr. | Daily | Cost Per Labor-Hour Bare Costs | Incl. O&P |
|---|---|---|---|---|---|---|
| 1 Equipment Oper. (med.) | $29.65 | $237.20 | $48.55 | $388.40 | $25.57 | $42.35 |
| 1 Laborer | 21.50 | 172.00 | 36.15 | 289.20 | | |
| 1 Backhoe Loader, 48 H.P. | | 337.80 | | 371.58 | 21.11 | 23.22 |
| 16 L.H., Daily Totals | | $747.00 | | $1049.18 | $46.69 | $65.57 |

## Crew B-11K

| | Bare Costs Hr. | Daily | Incl. Subs O&P Hr. | Daily | Cost Per Labor-Hour Bare Costs | Incl. O&P |
|---|---|---|---|---|---|---|
| 1 Equipment Oper. (med.) | $29.65 | $237.20 | $48.55 | $388.40 | $25.57 | $42.35 |
| 1 Laborer | 21.50 | 172.00 | 36.15 | 289.20 | | |
| 1 Trencher, Chain Type, 8' D | | 2090.00 | | 2299.00 | 130.63 | 143.69 |
| 16 L.H., Daily Totals | | $2499.20 | | $2976.60 | $156.20 | $186.04 |

# Crews

### Crew B-11L

| | \[Bare Costs\] Hr. | Daily | \[Incl. Subs O&P\] Hr. | Daily | Bare Costs | Incl. O&P |
|---|---|---|---|---|---|---|
| 1 Equipment Oper. (med.) | $29.65 | $237.20 | $48.55 | $388.40 | $25.57 | $42.35 |
| 1 Laborer | 21.50 | 172.00 | 36.15 | 289.20 | | |
| 1 Grader, 30,000 Lbs. | | 622.20 | | 684.42 | 38.89 | 42.78 |
| 16 L.H., Daily Totals | | $1031.40 | | $1362.02 | $64.46 | $85.13 |

### Crew B-11M

| | \[Bare Costs\] Hr. | Daily | \[Incl. Subs O&P\] Hr. | Daily | Bare Costs | Incl. O&P |
|---|---|---|---|---|---|---|
| 1 Equipment Oper. (med.) | $29.65 | $237.20 | $48.55 | $388.40 | $25.57 | $42.35 |
| 1 Laborer | 21.50 | 172.00 | 36.15 | 289.20 | | |
| 1 Backhoe Loader, 80 H.P. | | 387.60 | | 426.36 | 24.23 | 26.65 |
| 16 L.H., Daily Totals | | $796.80 | | $1103.96 | $49.80 | $69.00 |

### Crew B-11W

| | \[Bare Costs\] Hr. | Daily | \[Incl. Subs O&P\] Hr. | Daily | Bare Costs | Incl. O&P |
|---|---|---|---|---|---|---|
| 1 Equipment Operator (med.) | $29.65 | $237.20 | $48.55 | $388.40 | $23.89 | $39.73 |
| 1 Common Laborer | 21.50 | 172.00 | 36.15 | 289.20 | | |
| 10 Truck Drivers (hvy.) | 23.55 | 1884.00 | 39.20 | 3136.00 | | |
| 1 Dozer, 200 H.P. | | 1192.00 | | 1311.20 | | |
| 1 Vibratory Roller, Towed, 23 Ton | | 434.20 | | 477.62 | | |
| 10 Dump Trucks, 8 C.Y., 220 H.P. | | 4018.00 | | 4419.80 | 58.79 | 64.67 |
| 96 L.H., Daily Totals | | $7937.40 | | $10022.22 | $82.68 | $104.40 |

### Crew B-11Y

| | \[Bare Costs\] Hr. | Daily | \[Incl. Subs O&P\] Hr. | Daily | Bare Costs | Incl. O&P |
|---|---|---|---|---|---|---|
| 1 Labor Foreman (Outside) | $23.50 | $188.00 | $39.55 | $316.40 | $24.44 | $40.66 |
| 5 Common Laborers | 21.50 | 860.00 | 36.15 | 1446.00 | | |
| 3 Equipment Operators (med.) | 29.65 | 711.60 | 48.55 | 1165.20 | | |
| 1 Dozer, 80 H.P. | | 436.60 | | 480.26 | | |
| 2 Rollers, 2-Drum, W.B., 7.5 H.P. | | 299.20 | | 329.12 | | |
| 4 Vibratory Plates, gas, 21" | | 174.40 | | 191.84 | 12.64 | 13.91 |
| 72 L.H., Daily Totals | | $2669.80 | | $3928.82 | $37.08 | $54.57 |

### Crew B-12A

| | \[Bare Costs\] Hr. | Daily | \[Incl. Subs O&P\] Hr. | Daily | Bare Costs | Incl. O&P |
|---|---|---|---|---|---|---|
| 1 Equip. Oper. (crane) | $30.65 | $245.20 | $50.15 | $401.20 | $26.07 | $43.15 |
| 1 Laborer | 21.50 | 172.00 | 36.15 | 289.20 | | |
| 1 Hyd. Excavator, 1 C.Y. | | 801.60 | | 881.76 | 50.10 | 55.11 |
| 16 L.H., Daily Totals | | $1218.80 | | $1572.16 | $76.17 | $98.26 |

### Crew B-12B

| | \[Bare Costs\] Hr. | Daily | \[Incl. Subs O&P\] Hr. | Daily | Bare Costs | Incl. O&P |
|---|---|---|---|---|---|---|
| 1 Equip. Oper. (crane) | $30.65 | $245.20 | $50.15 | $401.20 | $26.07 | $43.15 |
| 1 Laborer | 21.50 | 172.00 | 36.15 | 289.20 | | |
| 1 Hyd. Excavator, 1.5 C.Y. | | 1017.00 | | 1118.70 | 63.56 | 69.92 |
| 16 L.H., Daily Totals | | $1434.20 | | $1809.10 | $89.64 | $113.07 |

### Crew B-12C

| | \[Bare Costs\] Hr. | Daily | \[Incl. Subs O&P\] Hr. | Daily | Bare Costs | Incl. O&P |
|---|---|---|---|---|---|---|
| 1 Equip. Oper. (crane) | $30.65 | $245.20 | $50.15 | $401.20 | $26.07 | $43.15 |
| 1 Laborer | 21.50 | 172.00 | 36.15 | 289.20 | | |
| 1 Hyd. Excavator, 2 C.Y. | | 1321.00 | | 1453.10 | 82.56 | 90.82 |
| 16 L.H., Daily Totals | | $1738.20 | | $2143.50 | $108.64 | $133.97 |

### Crew B-12D

| | \[Bare Costs\] Hr. | Daily | \[Incl. Subs O&P\] Hr. | Daily | Bare Costs | Incl. O&P |
|---|---|---|---|---|---|---|
| 1 Equip. Oper. (crane) | $30.65 | $245.20 | $50.15 | $401.20 | $26.07 | $43.15 |
| 1 Laborer | 21.50 | 172.00 | 36.15 | 289.20 | | |
| 1 Hyd. Excavator, 3.5 C.Y. | | 2359.00 | | 2594.90 | 147.44 | 162.18 |
| 16 L.H., Daily Totals | | $2776.20 | | $3285.30 | $173.51 | $205.33 |

### Crew B-12E

| | \[Bare Costs\] Hr. | Daily | \[Incl. Subs O&P\] Hr. | Daily | Bare Costs | Incl. O&P |
|---|---|---|---|---|---|---|
| 1 Equip. Oper. (crane) | $30.65 | $245.20 | $50.15 | $401.20 | $26.07 | $43.15 |
| 1 Laborer | 21.50 | 172.00 | 36.15 | 289.20 | | |
| 1 Hyd. Excavator, .5 C.Y. | | 386.60 | | 425.26 | 24.16 | 26.58 |
| 16 L.H., Daily Totals | | $803.80 | | $1115.66 | $50.24 | $69.73 |

### Crew B-12F

| | \[Bare Costs\] Hr. | Daily | \[Incl. Subs O&P\] Hr. | Daily | Bare Costs | Incl. O&P |
|---|---|---|---|---|---|---|
| 1 Equip. Oper. (crane) | $30.65 | $245.20 | $50.15 | $401.20 | $26.07 | $43.15 |
| 1 Laborer | 21.50 | 172.00 | 36.15 | 289.20 | | |
| 1 Hyd. Excavator, .75 C.Y. | | 677.80 | | 745.58 | 42.36 | 46.60 |
| 16 L.H., Daily Totals | | $1095.00 | | $1435.98 | $68.44 | $89.75 |

### Crew B-12G

| | \[Bare Costs\] Hr. | Daily | \[Incl. Subs O&P\] Hr. | Daily | Bare Costs | Incl. O&P |
|---|---|---|---|---|---|---|
| 1 Equip. Oper. (crane) | $30.65 | $245.20 | $50.15 | $401.20 | $26.07 | $43.15 |
| 1 Laborer | 21.50 | 172.00 | 36.15 | 289.20 | | |
| 1 Crawler Crane, 15 Ton | | 693.75 | | 763.13 | | |
| 1 Clamshell Bucket, .5 C.Y. | | 37.00 | | 40.70 | 45.67 | 50.24 |
| 16 L.H., Daily Totals | | $1147.95 | | $1494.22 | $71.75 | $93.39 |

### Crew B-12H

| | \[Bare Costs\] Hr. | Daily | \[Incl. Subs O&P\] Hr. | Daily | Bare Costs | Incl. O&P |
|---|---|---|---|---|---|---|
| 1 Equip. Oper. (crane) | $30.65 | $245.20 | $50.15 | $401.20 | $26.07 | $43.15 |
| 1 Laborer | 21.50 | 172.00 | 36.15 | 289.20 | | |
| 1 Crawler Crane, 25 Ton | | 1188.00 | | 1306.80 | | |
| 1 Clamshell Bucket, 1 C.Y. | | 46.60 | | 51.26 | 77.16 | 84.88 |
| 16 L.H., Daily Totals | | $1651.80 | | $2048.46 | $103.24 | $128.03 |

### Crew B-12I

| | \[Bare Costs\] Hr. | Daily | \[Incl. Subs O&P\] Hr. | Daily | Bare Costs | Incl. O&P |
|---|---|---|---|---|---|---|
| 1 Equip. Oper. (crane) | $30.65 | $245.20 | $50.15 | $401.20 | $26.07 | $43.15 |
| 1 Laborer | 21.50 | 172.00 | 36.15 | 289.20 | | |
| 1 Crawler Crane, 20 Ton | | 892.30 | | 981.53 | | |
| 1 Dragline Bucket, .75 C.Y. | | 20.40 | | 22.44 | 57.04 | 62.75 |
| 16 L.H., Daily Totals | | $1329.90 | | $1694.37 | $83.12 | $105.90 |

### Crew B-12J

| | \[Bare Costs\] Hr. | Daily | \[Incl. Subs O&P\] Hr. | Daily | Bare Costs | Incl. O&P |
|---|---|---|---|---|---|---|
| 1 Equip. Oper. (crane) | $30.65 | $245.20 | $50.15 | $401.20 | $26.07 | $43.15 |
| 1 Laborer | 21.50 | 172.00 | 36.15 | 289.20 | | |
| 1 Gradall, 5/8 C.Y. | | 812.80 | | 894.08 | 50.80 | 55.88 |
| 16 L.H., Daily Totals | | $1230.00 | | $1584.48 | $76.88 | $99.03 |

### Crew B-12K

| | \[Bare Costs\] Hr. | Daily | \[Incl. Subs O&P\] Hr. | Daily | Bare Costs | Incl. O&P |
|---|---|---|---|---|---|---|
| 1 Equip. Oper. (crane) | $30.65 | $245.20 | $50.15 | $401.20 | $26.07 | $43.15 |
| 1 Laborer | 21.50 | 172.00 | 36.15 | 289.20 | | |
| 1 Gradall, 3 Ton, 1 C.Y. | | 958.40 | | 1054.24 | 59.90 | 65.89 |
| 16 L.H., Daily Totals | | $1375.60 | | $1744.64 | $85.97 | $109.04 |

### Crew B-12L

| | \[Bare Costs\] Hr. | Daily | \[Incl. Subs O&P\] Hr. | Daily | Bare Costs | Incl. O&P |
|---|---|---|---|---|---|---|
| 1 Equip. Oper. (crane) | $30.65 | $245.20 | $50.15 | $401.20 | $26.07 | $43.15 |
| 1 Laborer | 21.50 | 172.00 | 36.15 | 289.20 | | |
| 1 Crawler Crane, 15 Ton | | 693.75 | | 763.13 | | |
| 1 F.E. Attachment, .5 C.Y. | | 55.60 | | 61.16 | 46.83 | 51.52 |
| 16 L.H., Daily Totals | | $1166.55 | | $1514.68 | $72.91 | $94.67 |

### Crew B-12M

| | \[Bare Costs\] Hr. | Daily | \[Incl. Subs O&P\] Hr. | Daily | Bare Costs | Incl. O&P |
|---|---|---|---|---|---|---|
| 1 Equip. Oper. (crane) | $30.65 | $245.20 | $50.15 | $401.20 | $26.07 | $43.15 |
| 1 Laborer | 21.50 | 172.00 | 36.15 | 289.20 | | |
| 1 Crawler Crane, 20 Ton | | 892.30 | | 981.53 | | |
| 1 F.E. Attachment, .75 C.Y. | | 60.00 | | 66.00 | 59.52 | 65.47 |
| 16 L.H., Daily Totals | | $1369.50 | | $1737.93 | $85.59 | $108.62 |

### Crew B-12N

| | \[Bare Costs\] Hr. | Daily | \[Incl. Subs O&P\] Hr. | Daily | Bare Costs | Incl. O&P |
|---|---|---|---|---|---|---|
| 1 Equip. Oper. (crane) | $30.65 | $245.20 | $50.15 | $401.20 | $26.07 | $43.15 |
| 1 Laborer | 21.50 | 172.00 | 36.15 | 289.20 | | |
| 1 Crawler Crane, 25 Ton | | 1188.00 | | 1306.80 | | |
| 1 F.E. Attachment, 1 C.Y. | | 65.80 | | 72.38 | 78.36 | 86.20 |
| 16 L.H., Daily Totals | | $1671.00 | | $2069.58 | $104.44 | $129.35 |

| Crew No. | Bare Costs | | Incl. Subs O&P | | Cost Per Labor-Hour | |
|---|---|---|---|---|---|---|
| **Crew B-120** | Hr. | Daily | Hr. | Daily | Bare Costs | Incl. O&P |
| 1 Equip. Oper. (crane) | $30.65 | $245.20 | $50.15 | $401.20 | $26.07 | $43.15 |
| 1 Laborer | 21.50 | 172.00 | 36.15 | 289.20 | | |
| 1 Crawler Crane, 40 Ton | | 1193.00 | | 1312.30 | | |
| 1 F.E. Attachment, 1.5 C.Y. | | 76.00 | | 83.60 | 79.31 | 87.24 |
| 16 L.H., Daily Totals | | $1686.20 | | $2086.30 | $105.39 | $130.39 |
| **Crew B-12P** | Hr. | Daily | Hr. | Daily | Bare Costs | Incl. O&P |
| 1 Equip. Oper. (crane) | $30.65 | $245.20 | $50.15 | $401.20 | $26.07 | $43.15 |
| 1 Laborer | 21.50 | 172.00 | 36.15 | 289.20 | | |
| 1 Crawler Crane, 40 Ton | | 1193.00 | | 1312.30 | | |
| 1 Dragline Bucket, 1.5 C.Y. | | 32.80 | | 36.08 | 76.61 | 84.27 |
| 16 L.H., Daily Totals | | $1643.00 | | $2038.78 | $102.69 | $127.42 |
| **Crew B-12Q** | Hr. | Daily | Hr. | Daily | Bare Costs | Incl. O&P |
| 1 Equip. Oper. (crane) | $30.65 | $245.20 | $50.15 | $401.20 | $26.07 | $43.15 |
| 1 Laborer | 21.50 | 172.00 | 36.15 | 289.20 | | |
| 1 Hyd. Excavator, 5/8 C.Y. | | 564.40 | | 620.84 | 35.27 | 38.80 |
| 16 L.H., Daily Totals | | $981.60 | | $1311.24 | $61.35 | $81.95 |
| **Crew B-12S** | Hr. | Daily | Hr. | Daily | Bare Costs | Incl. O&P |
| 1 Equip. Oper. (crane) | $30.65 | $245.20 | $50.15 | $401.20 | $26.07 | $43.15 |
| 1 Laborer | 21.50 | 172.00 | 36.15 | 289.20 | | |
| 1 Hyd. Excavator, 2.5 C.Y. | | 1784.00 | | 1962.40 | 111.50 | 122.65 |
| 16 L.H., Daily Totals | | $2201.20 | | $2652.80 | $137.57 | $165.80 |
| **Crew B-12T** | Hr. | Daily | Hr. | Daily | Bare Costs | Incl. O&P |
| 1 Equip. Oper. (crane) | $30.65 | $245.20 | $50.15 | $401.20 | $26.07 | $43.15 |
| 1 Laborer | 21.50 | 172.00 | 36.15 | 289.20 | | |
| 1 Crawler Crane, 75 Ton | | 1516.00 | | 1667.60 | | |
| 1 F.E. Attachment, 3 C.Y. | | 98.40 | | 108.24 | 100.90 | 110.99 |
| 16 L.H., Daily Totals | | $2031.60 | | $2466.24 | $126.97 | $154.14 |
| **Crew B-12V** | Hr. | Daily | Hr. | Daily | Bare Costs | Incl. O&P |
| 1 Equip. Oper. (crane) | $30.65 | $245.20 | $50.15 | $401.20 | $26.07 | $43.15 |
| 1 Laborer | 21.50 | 172.00 | 36.15 | 289.20 | | |
| 1 Crawler Crane, 75 Ton | | 1516.00 | | 1667.60 | | |
| 1 Dragline Bucket, 3 C.Y. | | 52.40 | | 57.64 | 98.03 | 107.83 |
| 16 L.H., Daily Totals | | $1985.60 | | $2415.64 | $124.10 | $150.98 |
| **Crew B-13** | Hr. | Daily | Hr. | Daily | Bare Costs | Incl. O&P |
| 1 Labor Foreman (outside) | $23.50 | $188.00 | $39.55 | $316.40 | $23.36 | $39.05 |
| 4 Laborers | 21.50 | 688.00 | 36.15 | 1156.80 | | |
| 1 Equip. Oper. (crane) | 30.65 | 245.20 | 50.15 | 401.20 | | |
| 1 Hyd. Crane, 25 Ton | | 747.60 | | 822.36 | 15.57 | 17.13 |
| 48 L.H., Daily Totals | | $1868.80 | | $2696.76 | $38.93 | $56.18 |
| **Crew B-13A** | Hr. | Daily | Hr. | Daily | Bare Costs | Incl. O&P |
| 1 Foreman | $23.50 | $188.00 | $39.55 | $316.40 | $24.70 | $41.05 |
| 2 Laborers | 21.50 | 344.00 | 36.15 | 578.40 | | |
| 2 Equipment Operators(med.) | 29.65 | 474.40 | 48.55 | 776.80 | | |
| 2 Truck Drivers (heavy) | 23.55 | 376.80 | 39.20 | 627.20 | | |
| 1 Crawler Crane, 75 Ton | | 1516.00 | | 1667.60 | | |
| 1 Crawler Loader, 4 C.Y. | | 1548.00 | | 1702.80 | | |
| 2 Dump Trucks, 8 C.Y., 220 H.P. | | 803.60 | | 883.96 | 69.06 | 75.97 |
| 56 L.H., Daily Totals | | $5250.80 | | $6553.16 | $93.76 | $117.02 |

| Crew No. | Bare Costs | | Incl. Subs O&P | | Cost Per Labor-Hour | |
|---|---|---|---|---|---|---|
| **Crew B-13B** | Hr. | Daily | Hr. | Daily | Bare Costs | Incl. O&P |
| 1 Labor Foreman (outside) | $23.50 | $188.00 | $39.55 | $316.40 | $23.80 | $39.66 |
| 4 Laborers | 21.50 | 688.00 | 36.15 | 1156.80 | | |
| 1 Equip. Oper. (crane) | 30.65 | 245.20 | 50.15 | 401.20 | | |
| 1 Equip. Oper. Oiler | 26.45 | 211.60 | 43.30 | 346.40 | | |
| 1 Hyd. Crane, 55 Ton | | 1209.00 | | 1329.90 | 21.59 | 23.75 |
| 56 L.H., Daily Totals | | $2541.80 | | $3550.70 | $45.39 | $63.41 |
| **Crew B-13C** | Hr. | Daily | Hr. | Daily | Bare Costs | Incl. O&P |
| 1 Labor Foreman (outside) | $23.50 | $188.00 | $39.55 | $316.40 | $23.80 | $39.66 |
| 4 Laborers | 21.50 | 688.00 | 36.15 | 1156.80 | | |
| 1 Equip. Oper. (crane) | 30.65 | 245.20 | 50.15 | 401.20 | | |
| 1 Equip. Oper. Oiler | 26.45 | 211.60 | 43.30 | 346.40 | | |
| 1 Crawler Crane, 100 Ton | | 1732.00 | | 1905.20 | 30.93 | 34.02 |
| 56 L.H., Daily Totals | | $3064.80 | | $4126.00 | $54.73 | $73.68 |
| **Crew B-13D** | Hr. | Daily | Hr. | Daily | Bare Costs | Incl. O&P |
| 1 Laborer | $21.50 | $172.00 | $36.15 | $289.20 | $26.07 | $43.15 |
| 1 Equip. Oper. (crane) | 30.65 | 245.20 | 50.15 | 401.20 | | |
| 1 Hyd. Excavator, 1 C.Y. | | 801.60 | | 881.76 | | |
| 1 Trench Box | | 113.40 | | 124.74 | 57.19 | 62.91 |
| 16 L.H., Daily Totals | | $1332.20 | | $1696.90 | $83.26 | $106.06 |
| **Crew B-13E** | Hr. | Daily | Hr. | Daily | Bare Costs | Incl. O&P |
| 1 Laborer | $21.50 | $172.00 | $36.15 | $289.20 | $26.07 | $43.15 |
| 1 Equip. Oper. (crane) | 30.65 | 245.20 | 50.15 | 401.20 | | |
| 1 Hyd. Excavator, 1.5 C.Y. | | 1017.00 | | 1118.70 | | |
| 1 Trench Box | | 113.40 | | 124.74 | 70.65 | 77.72 |
| 16 L.H., Daily Totals | | $1547.60 | | $1933.84 | $96.72 | $120.86 |
| **Crew B-13F** | Hr. | Daily | Hr. | Daily | Bare Costs | Incl. O&P |
| 1 Laborer | $21.50 | $172.00 | $36.15 | $289.20 | $26.07 | $43.15 |
| 1 Equip. Oper. (crane) | 30.65 | 245.20 | 50.15 | 401.20 | | |
| 1 Hyd. Excavator, 3.5 C.Y. | | 2359.00 | | 2594.90 | | |
| 1 Trench Box | | 113.40 | | 124.74 | 154.53 | 169.98 |
| 16 L.H., Daily Totals | | $2889.60 | | $3410.04 | $180.60 | $213.13 |
| **Crew B-13G** | Hr. | Daily | Hr. | Daily | Bare Costs | Incl. O&P |
| 1 Laborer | $21.50 | $172.00 | $36.15 | $289.20 | $26.07 | $43.15 |
| 1 Equip. Oper. (crane) | 30.65 | 245.20 | 50.15 | 401.20 | | |
| 1 Hyd. Excavator, .75 C.Y. | | 677.80 | | 745.58 | | |
| 1 Trench Box | | 113.40 | | 124.74 | 49.45 | 54.40 |
| 16 L.H., Daily Totals | | $1208.40 | | $1560.72 | $75.53 | $97.55 |
| **Crew B-13H** | Hr. | Daily | Hr. | Daily | Bare Costs | Incl. O&P |
| 1 Laborer | $21.50 | $172.00 | $36.15 | $289.20 | $26.07 | $43.15 |
| 1 Equip. Oper. (crane) | 30.65 | 245.20 | 50.15 | 401.20 | | |
| 1 Gradall, 5/8 C.Y. | | 812.80 | | 894.08 | | |
| 1 Trench Box | | 113.40 | | 124.74 | 57.89 | 63.68 |
| 16 L.H., Daily Totals | | $1343.40 | | $1709.22 | $83.96 | $106.83 |
| **Crew B-13I** | Hr. | Daily | Hr. | Daily | Bare Costs | Incl. O&P |
| 1 Laborer | $21.50 | $172.00 | $36.15 | $289.20 | $26.07 | $43.15 |
| 1 Equip. Oper. (crane) | 30.65 | 245.20 | 50.15 | 401.20 | | |
| 1 Gradall, 3 Ton, 1 C.Y. | | 958.40 | | 1054.24 | | |
| 1 Trench Box | | 113.40 | | 124.74 | 66.99 | 73.69 |
| 16 L.H., Daily Totals | | $1489.00 | | $1869.38 | $93.06 | $116.84 |

## Crew B-13J

| Crew No. | Hr. | Daily | Hr. | Daily | Bare Costs | Incl. O&P |
|---|---|---|---|---|---|---|
| 1 Laborer | $21.50 | $172.00 | $36.15 | $289.20 | $26.07 | $43.15 |
| 1 Equip. Oper. (crane) | 30.65 | 245.20 | 50.15 | 401.20 | | |
| 1 Hyd. Excavator, 2.5 C.Y. | | 1784.00 | | 1962.40 | | |
| 1 Trench Box | | 113.40 | | 124.74 | 118.59 | 130.45 |
| 16 L.H., Daily Totals | | $2314.60 | | $2777.54 | $144.66 | $173.60 |

## Crew B-14

| Crew No. | Hr. | Daily | Hr. | Daily | Bare Costs | Incl. O&P |
|---|---|---|---|---|---|---|
| 1 Labor Foreman (outside) | $23.50 | $188.00 | $39.55 | $316.40 | $23.00 | $38.47 |
| 4 Laborers | 21.50 | 688.00 | 36.15 | 1156.80 | | |
| 1 Equip. Oper. (light) | 28.50 | 228.00 | 46.65 | 373.20 | | |
| 1 Backhoe Loader, 48 H.P. | | 337.80 | | 371.58 | 7.04 | 7.74 |
| 48 L.H., Daily Totals | | $1441.80 | | $2217.98 | $30.04 | $46.21 |

## Crew B-14A

| Crew No. | Hr. | Daily | Hr. | Daily | Bare Costs | Incl. O&P |
|---|---|---|---|---|---|---|
| 1 Equip. Oper. (crane) | $30.65 | $245.20 | $50.15 | $401.20 | $27.60 | $45.48 |
| .5 Laborer | 21.50 | 86.00 | 36.15 | 144.60 | | |
| 1 Hyd. Excavator, 4.5 C.Y. | | 2870.00 | | 3157.00 | 239.17 | 263.08 |
| 12 L.H., Daily Totals | | $3201.20 | | $3702.80 | $266.77 | $308.57 |

## Crew B-14B

| Crew No. | Hr. | Daily | Hr. | Daily | Bare Costs | Incl. O&P |
|---|---|---|---|---|---|---|
| 1 Equip. Oper. (crane) | $30.65 | $245.20 | $50.15 | $401.20 | $27.60 | $45.48 |
| .5 Laborer | 21.50 | 86.00 | 36.15 | 144.60 | | |
| 1 Hyd. Excavator, 6 C.Y. | | 3390.00 | | 3729.00 | 282.50 | 310.75 |
| 12 L.H., Daily Totals | | $3721.20 | | $4274.80 | $310.10 | $356.23 |

## Crew B-14C

| Crew No. | Hr. | Daily | Hr. | Daily | Bare Costs | Incl. O&P |
|---|---|---|---|---|---|---|
| 1 Equip. Oper. (crane) | $30.65 | $245.20 | $50.15 | $401.20 | $27.60 | $45.48 |
| .5 Laborer | 21.50 | 86.00 | 36.15 | 144.60 | | |
| 1 Hyd. Excavator, 7 C.Y. | | 3553.00 | | 3908.30 | 296.08 | 325.69 |
| 12 L.H., Daily Totals | | $3884.20 | | $4454.10 | $323.68 | $371.18 |

## Crew B-14F

| Crew No. | Hr. | Daily | Hr. | Daily | Bare Costs | Incl. O&P |
|---|---|---|---|---|---|---|
| 1 Equip. Oper. (crane) | $30.65 | $245.20 | $50.15 | $401.20 | $27.60 | $45.48 |
| .5 Laborer | 21.50 | 86.00 | 36.15 | 144.60 | | |
| 1 Hyd. Shovel, 7 C.Y. | | 3536.00 | | 3889.60 | 294.67 | 324.13 |
| 12 L.H., Daily Totals | | $3867.20 | | $4435.40 | $322.27 | $369.62 |

## Crew B-14G

| Crew No. | Hr. | Daily | Hr. | Daily | Bare Costs | Incl. O&P |
|---|---|---|---|---|---|---|
| 1 Equip. Oper. (crane) | $30.65 | $245.20 | $50.15 | $401.20 | $27.60 | $45.48 |
| .5 Laborer | 21.50 | 86.00 | 36.15 | 144.60 | | |
| 1 Hyd. Shovel, 12 C.Y. | | 4614.00 | | 5075.40 | 384.50 | 422.95 |
| 12 L.H., Daily Totals | | $4945.20 | | $5621.20 | $412.10 | $468.43 |

## Crew B-14J

| Crew No. | Hr. | Daily | Hr. | Daily | Bare Costs | Incl. O&P |
|---|---|---|---|---|---|---|
| 1 Equip. Oper. (med.) | $29.65 | $237.20 | $48.55 | $388.40 | $26.93 | $44.42 |
| .5 Laborer | 21.50 | 86.00 | 36.15 | 144.60 | | |
| 1 F.E. Loader, 8 C.Y. | | 1757.00 | | 1932.70 | 146.42 | 161.06 |
| 12 L.H., Daily Totals | | $2080.20 | | $2465.70 | $173.35 | $205.47 |

## Crew B-14K

| Crew No. | Hr. | Daily | Hr. | Daily | Bare Costs | Incl. O&P |
|---|---|---|---|---|---|---|
| 1 Equip. Oper. (med.) | $29.65 | $237.20 | $48.55 | $388.40 | $26.93 | $44.42 |
| .5 Laborer | 21.50 | 86.00 | 36.15 | 144.60 | | |
| 1 F.E. Loader, 10 C.Y. | | 2601.00 | | 2861.10 | 216.75 | 238.43 |
| 12 L.H., Daily Totals | | $2924.20 | | $3394.10 | $243.68 | $282.84 |

## Crew B-15

| Crew No. | Hr. | Daily | Hr. | Daily | Bare Costs | Incl. O&P |
|---|---|---|---|---|---|---|
| 1 Equipment Oper. (med.) | $29.65 | $237.20 | $48.55 | $388.40 | $25.00 | $41.44 |
| .5 Laborer | 21.50 | 86.00 | 36.15 | 144.60 | | |
| 2 Truck Drivers (heavy) | 23.55 | 376.80 | 39.20 | 627.20 | | |
| 2 Dump Trucks, 12 C.Y., 400 H.P. | | 1335.60 | | 1469.16 | | |
| 1 Dozer, 200 H.P. | | 1192.00 | | 1311.20 | 90.27 | 99.30 |
| 28 L.H., Daily Totals | | $3227.60 | | $3940.56 | $115.27 | $140.73 |

## Crew B-16

| Crew No. | Hr. | Daily | Hr. | Daily | Bare Costs | Incl. O&P |
|---|---|---|---|---|---|---|
| 1 Labor Foreman (outside) | $23.50 | $188.00 | $39.55 | $316.40 | $22.51 | $37.76 |
| 2 Laborers | 21.50 | 344.00 | 36.15 | 578.40 | | |
| 1 Truck Driver (heavy) | 23.55 | 188.40 | 39.20 | 313.60 | | |
| 1 Dump Truck, 12 C.Y., 400 H.P. | | 667.80 | | 734.58 | 20.87 | 22.96 |
| 32 L.H., Daily Totals | | $1388.20 | | $1942.98 | $43.38 | $60.72 |

## Crew B-17

| Crew No. | Hr. | Daily | Hr. | Daily | Bare Costs | Incl. O&P |
|---|---|---|---|---|---|---|
| 2 Laborers | $21.50 | $344.00 | $36.15 | $578.40 | $23.76 | $39.54 |
| 1 Equip. Oper. (light) | 28.50 | 228.00 | 46.65 | 373.20 | | |
| 1 Truck Driver (heavy) | 23.55 | 188.40 | 39.20 | 313.60 | | |
| 1 Backhoe Loader, 48 H.P. | | 337.80 | | 371.58 | | |
| 1 Dump Truck, 8 C.Y., 220 H.P. | | 401.80 | | 441.98 | 23.11 | 25.42 |
| 32 L.H., Daily Totals | | $1500.00 | | $2078.76 | $46.88 | $64.96 |

## Crew B-17A

| Crew No. | Hr. | Daily | Hr. | Daily | Bare Costs | Incl. O&P |
|---|---|---|---|---|---|---|
| 2 Laborer Foremen | $23.50 | $376.00 | $39.55 | $632.80 | $23.65 | $39.74 |
| 6 Laborers | 21.50 | 1032.00 | 36.15 | 1735.20 | | |
| 1 Skilled Worker Foreman | 31.25 | 250.00 | 52.40 | 419.20 | | |
| 1 Skilled Worker | 29.25 | 234.00 | 49.05 | 392.40 | | |
| 80 L.H., Daily Totals | | $1892.00 | | $3179.60 | $23.65 | $39.74 |

## Crew B-18

| Crew No. | Hr. | Daily | Hr. | Daily | Bare Costs | Incl. O&P |
|---|---|---|---|---|---|---|
| 1 Labor Foreman (outside) | $23.50 | $188.00 | $39.55 | $316.40 | $22.17 | $37.28 |
| 2 Laborers | 21.50 | 344.00 | 36.15 | 578.40 | | |
| 1 Vibratory Plate, gas, 21" | | 43.60 | | 47.96 | 1.82 | 2.00 |
| 24 L.H., Daily Totals | | $575.60 | | $942.76 | $23.98 | $39.28 |

## Crew B-19

| Crew No. | Hr. | Daily | Hr. | Daily | Bare Costs | Incl. O&P |
|---|---|---|---|---|---|---|
| 1 Pile Driver Foreman | $30.20 | $241.60 | $52.80 | $422.40 | $27.88 | $48.04 |
| 4 Pile Drivers | 28.20 | 902.40 | 49.30 | 1577.60 | | |
| 1 Equip. Oper. (crane) | 30.65 | 245.20 | 50.15 | 401.20 | | |
| 1 Building Laborer | 21.50 | 172.00 | 36.15 | 289.20 | | |
| 1 Crawler Crane, 40 Ton | | 1193.00 | | 1312.30 | | |
| 1 Lead, 90' high | | 120.40 | | 132.44 | | |
| 1 Hammer, Diesel, 22k ft-lb | | 619.40 | | 681.34 | 34.51 | 37.97 |
| 56 L.H., Daily Totals | | $3494.00 | | $4816.48 | $62.39 | $86.01 |

## Crew B-19A

| Crew No. | Hr. | Daily | Hr. | Daily | Bare Costs | Incl. O&P |
|---|---|---|---|---|---|---|
| 1 Pile Driver Foreman | $30.20 | $241.60 | $52.80 | $422.40 | $28.84 | $49.20 |
| 4 Pile Drivers | 28.20 | 902.40 | 49.30 | 1577.60 | | |
| 2 Equip. Oper. (crane) | 30.65 | 490.40 | 50.15 | 802.40 | | |
| 1 Equip. Oper. Oiler | 26.45 | 211.60 | 43.30 | 346.40 | | |
| 1 Crawler Crane, 75 Ton | | 1516.00 | | 1667.60 | | |
| 1 Lead, 90' high | | 120.40 | | 132.44 | | |
| 1 Hammer, Diesel, 41k ft-lb | | 722.80 | | 795.08 | 36.86 | 40.55 |
| 64 L.H., Daily Totals | | $4205.20 | | $5743.92 | $65.71 | $89.75 |

## Crew B-20

| Crew No. | Hr. | Daily | Hr. | Daily | Bare Costs | Incl. O&P |
|---|---|---|---|---|---|---|
| 1 Labor Foreman (out) | $23.50 | $188.00 | $39.55 | $316.40 | $22.17 | $37.28 |
| 2 Laborers | 21.50 | 344.00 | 36.15 | 578.40 | | |
| 24 L.H., Daily Totals | | $532.00 | | $894.80 | $22.17 | $37.28 |

# Crews

| Crew No. | Bare Costs | | Incl. Subs O&P | | Cost Per Labor-Hour | |
|---|---|---|---|---|---|---|
| **Crew B-20A** | **Hr.** | **Daily** | **Hr.** | **Daily** | **Bare Costs** | **Incl. O&P** |
| 1 Labor Foreman | $23.50 | $188.00 | $39.55 | $316.40 | $26.71 | $44.26 |
| 1 Laborer | 21.50 | 172.00 | 36.15 | 289.20 | | |
| 1 Plumber | 34.35 | 274.80 | 56.30 | 450.40 | | |
| 1 Plumber Apprentice | 27.50 | 220.00 | 45.05 | 360.40 | | |
| 32 L.H., Daily Totals | | $854.80 | | $1416.40 | $26.71 | $44.26 |
| **Crew B-21** | **Hr.** | **Daily** | **Hr.** | **Daily** | **Bare Costs** | **Incl. O&P** |
| 1 Labor Foreman (out) | $23.50 | $188.00 | $39.55 | $316.40 | $23.38 | $39.12 |
| 2 Laborers | 21.50 | 344.00 | 36.15 | 578.40 | | |
| .5 Equip. Oper. (crane) | 30.65 | 122.60 | 50.15 | 200.60 | | |
| .5 S.P. Crane, 4x4, 5 Ton | | 138.10 | | 151.91 | 4.93 | 5.43 |
| 28 L.H., Daily Totals | | $792.70 | | $1247.31 | $28.31 | $44.55 |
| **Crew B-21A** | **Hr.** | **Daily** | **Hr.** | **Daily** | **Bare Costs** | **Incl. O&P** |
| 1 Labor Foreman | $23.50 | $188.00 | $39.55 | $316.40 | $27.50 | $45.44 |
| 1 Laborer | 21.50 | 172.00 | 36.15 | 289.20 | | |
| 1 Plumber | 34.35 | 274.80 | 56.30 | 450.40 | | |
| 1 Plumber Apprentice | 27.50 | 220.00 | 45.05 | 360.40 | | |
| 1 Equip. Oper. (crane) | 30.65 | 245.20 | 50.15 | 401.20 | | |
| 1 S.P. Crane, 4x4, 12 Ton | | 655.60 | | 721.16 | 16.39 | 18.03 |
| 40 L.H., Daily Totals | | $1755.60 | | $2538.76 | $43.89 | $63.47 |
| **Crew B-21B** | **Hr.** | **Daily** | **Hr.** | **Daily** | **Bare Costs** | **Incl. O&P** |
| 1 Laborer Foreman | $23.50 | $188.00 | $39.55 | $316.40 | $23.73 | $39.63 |
| 3 Laborers | 21.50 | 516.00 | 36.15 | 867.60 | | |
| 1 Equip. Oper. (crane) | 30.65 | 245.20 | 50.15 | 401.20 | | |
| 1 Hyd. Crane, 12 Ton | | 655.60 | | 721.16 | 16.39 | 18.03 |
| 40 L.H., Daily Totals | | $1604.80 | | $2306.36 | $40.12 | $57.66 |
| **Crew B-21C** | **Hr.** | **Daily** | **Hr.** | **Daily** | **Bare Costs** | **Incl. O&P** |
| 1 Laborer Foreman | $23.50 | $188.00 | $39.55 | $316.40 | $23.80 | $39.66 |
| 4 Laborers | 21.50 | 688.00 | 36.15 | 1156.80 | | |
| 1 Equip. Oper. (crane) | 30.65 | 245.20 | 50.15 | 401.20 | | |
| 1 Equip. Oper. Oiler | 26.45 | 211.60 | 43.30 | 346.40 | | |
| 2 Cutting Torches | | 38.00 | | 41.80 | | |
| 2 Set of Gases | | 158.40 | | 174.24 | | |
| 1 Lattice Boom Crane, 90 Ton | | 1607.00 | | 1767.70 | 32.20 | 35.42 |
| 56 L.H., Daily Totals | | $3136.20 | | $4204.54 | $56.00 | $75.08 |
| **Crew B-22** | **Hr.** | **Daily** | **Hr.** | **Daily** | **Bare Costs** | **Incl. O&P** |
| 1 Labor Foreman (out) | $23.50 | $188.00 | $39.55 | $316.40 | $23.86 | $39.86 |
| 2 Laborers | 21.50 | 344.00 | 36.15 | 578.40 | | |
| .75 Equip. Oper. (crane) | 30.65 | 183.90 | 50.15 | 300.90 | | |
| .75 S.P. Crane, 4x4, 5 Ton | | 207.15 | | 227.87 | 6.91 | 7.60 |
| 30 L.H., Daily Totals | | $923.05 | | $1423.57 | $30.77 | $47.45 |
| **Crew B-22A** | **Hr.** | **Daily** | **Hr.** | **Daily** | **Bare Costs** | **Incl. O&P** |
| 1 Labor Foreman (out) | $23.50 | $188.00 | $39.55 | $316.40 | $25.00 | $41.79 |
| 1 Skilled Worker | 29.25 | 234.00 | 49.05 | 392.40 | | |
| 2 Laborers | 21.50 | 344.00 | 36.15 | 578.40 | | |
| .75 Equipment Oper. (crane) | 30.65 | 183.90 | 50.15 | 300.90 | | |
| .75 S.P. Crane, 4x4, 5 Ton | | 207.15 | | 227.87 | | |
| 1 Generator, 5 kW | | 46.00 | | 50.60 | | |
| 1 Butt Fusion Machine | | 134.40 | | 147.84 | 10.20 | 11.22 |
| 38 L.H., Daily Totals | | $1337.45 | | $2014.41 | $35.20 | $53.01 |
| **Crew B-22B** | **Hr.** | **Daily** | **Hr.** | **Daily** | **Bare Costs** | **Incl. O&P** |
| 1 Skilled Worker | $29.25 | $234.00 | $49.05 | $392.40 | $25.38 | $42.60 |
| 1 Laborer | 21.50 | 172.00 | 36.15 | 289.20 | | |
| 1 Electro Fusion Machine | | 98.60 | | 108.46 | 6.16 | 6.78 |
| 16 L.H., Daily Totals | | $504.60 | | $790.06 | $31.54 | $49.38 |

| Crew No. | Bare Costs | | Incl. Subs O&P | | Cost Per Labor-Hour | |
|---|---|---|---|---|---|---|
| **Crew B-23** | **Hr.** | **Daily** | **Hr.** | **Daily** | **Bare Costs** | **Incl. O&P** |
| 1 Labor Foreman (outside) | $23.50 | $188.00 | $39.55 | $316.40 | $21.90 | $36.83 |
| 4 Laborers | 21.50 | 688.00 | 36.15 | 1156.80 | | |
| 1 Drill Rig, Truck-Mounted | | 2591.00 | | 2850.10 | | |
| 1 Flatbed Truck, Gas, 3 Ton | | 296.00 | | 325.60 | 72.17 | 79.39 |
| 40 L.H., Daily Totals | | $3763.00 | | $4648.90 | $94.08 | $116.22 |
| **Crew B-23A** | **Hr.** | **Daily** | **Hr.** | **Daily** | **Bare Costs** | **Incl. O&P** |
| 1 Labor Foreman (outside) | $23.50 | $188.00 | $39.55 | $316.40 | $24.88 | $41.42 |
| 1 Laborer | 21.50 | 172.00 | 36.15 | 289.20 | | |
| 1 Equip. Operator (med.) | 29.65 | 237.20 | 48.55 | 388.40 | | |
| 1 Drill Rig, Truck-Mounted | | 2591.00 | | 2850.10 | | |
| 1 Pickup Truck, 3/4 Ton | | 140.00 | | 154.00 | 113.79 | 125.17 |
| 24 L.H., Daily Totals | | $3328.20 | | $3998.10 | $138.68 | $166.59 |
| **Crew B-23B** | **Hr.** | **Daily** | **Hr.** | **Daily** | **Bare Costs** | **Incl. O&P** |
| 1 Labor Foreman (outside) | $23.50 | $188.00 | $39.55 | $316.40 | $24.88 | $41.42 |
| 1 Laborer | 21.50 | 172.00 | 36.15 | 289.20 | | |
| 1 Equip. Operator (med.) | 29.65 | 237.20 | 48.55 | 388.40 | | |
| 1 Drill Rig, Truck-Mounted | | 2591.00 | | 2850.10 | | |
| 1 Pickup Truck, 3/4 Ton | | 140.00 | | 154.00 | | |
| 1 Centr. Water Pump, 6" | | 340.00 | | 374.00 | 127.96 | 140.75 |
| 24 L.H., Daily Totals | | $3668.20 | | $4372.10 | $152.84 | $182.17 |
| **Crew B-24** | **Hr.** | **Daily** | **Hr.** | **Daily** | **Bare Costs** | **Incl. O&P** |
| 1 Cement Finisher | $27.80 | $222.40 | $44.50 | $356.00 | $26.13 | $43.20 |
| 1 Laborer | 21.50 | 172.00 | 36.15 | 289.20 | | |
| 1 Carpenter | 29.10 | 232.80 | 48.95 | 391.60 | | |
| 24 L.H., Daily Totals | | $627.20 | | $1036.80 | $26.13 | $43.20 |
| **Crew B-25** | **Hr.** | **Daily** | **Hr.** | **Daily** | **Bare Costs** | **Incl. O&P** |
| 1 Labor Foreman | $23.50 | $188.00 | $39.55 | $316.40 | $23.90 | $39.84 |
| 7 Laborers | 21.50 | 1204.00 | 36.15 | 2024.40 | | |
| 3 Equip. Oper. (med.) | 29.65 | 711.60 | 48.55 | 1165.20 | | |
| 1 Asphalt Paver, 130 H.P. | | 1994.00 | | 2193.40 | | |
| 1 Tandem Roller, 10 Ton | | 235.20 | | 258.72 | | |
| 1 Roller, Pneum. Whl, 12 Ton | | 337.20 | | 370.92 | 29.16 | 32.08 |
| 88 L.H., Daily Totals | | $4670.00 | | $6329.04 | $53.07 | $71.92 |
| **Crew B-25B** | **Hr.** | **Daily** | **Hr.** | **Daily** | **Bare Costs** | **Incl. O&P** |
| 1 Labor Foreman | $23.50 | $188.00 | $39.55 | $316.40 | $24.38 | $40.57 |
| 7 Laborers | 21.50 | 1204.00 | 36.15 | 2024.40 | | |
| 4 Equip. Oper. (med.) | 29.65 | 948.80 | 48.55 | 1553.60 | | |
| 1 Asphalt Paver, 130 H.P. | | 1994.00 | | 2193.40 | | |
| 2 Tandem Rollers, 10 Ton | | 470.40 | | 517.44 | | |
| 1 Roller, Pneum. Whl, 12 Ton | | 337.20 | | 370.92 | 29.18 | 32.10 |
| 96 L.H., Daily Totals | | $5142.40 | | $6976.16 | $53.57 | $72.67 |
| **Crew B-25C** | **Hr.** | **Daily** | **Hr.** | **Daily** | **Bare Costs** | **Incl. O&P** |
| 1 Labor Foreman | $23.50 | $188.00 | $39.55 | $316.40 | $24.55 | $40.85 |
| 3 Laborers | 21.50 | 516.00 | 36.15 | 867.60 | | |
| 2 Equip. Oper. (med.) | 29.65 | 474.40 | 48.55 | 776.80 | | |
| 1 Asphalt Paver, 130 H.P. | | 1994.00 | | 2193.40 | | |
| 1 Tandem Roller, 10 Ton | | 235.20 | | 258.72 | 46.44 | 51.09 |
| 48 L.H., Daily Totals | | $3407.60 | | $4412.92 | $70.99 | $91.94 |

# Crews

| Crew No. | Bare Costs | | Incl. Subs O&P | | Cost Per Labor-Hour | |
|---|---|---|---|---|---|---|

| Crew B-26 | Hr. | Daily | Hr. | Daily | Bare Costs | Incl. O&P |
|---|---|---|---|---|---|---|
| 1 Labor Foreman (outside) | $23.50 | $188.00 | $39.55 | $316.40 | $24.63 | $41.18 |
| 6 Laborers | 21.50 | 1032.00 | 36.15 | 1735.20 | | |
| 2 Equip. Oper. (med.) | 29.65 | 474.40 | 48.55 | 776.80 | | |
| 1 Rodman (reinf.) | 31.35 | 250.80 | 54.90 | 439.20 | | |
| 1 Cement Finisher | 27.80 | 222.40 | 44.50 | 356.00 | | |
| 1 Grader, 30,000 Lbs. | | 622.20 | | 684.42 | | |
| 1 Paving Mach. & Equip. | | 2678.00 | | 2945.80 | 37.50 | 41.25 |
| 88 L.H., Daily Totals | | $5467.80 | | $7253.82 | $62.13 | $82.43 |

| Crew B-26A | Hr. | Daily | Hr. | Daily | Bare Costs | Incl. O&P |
|---|---|---|---|---|---|---|
| 1 Labor Foreman (outside) | $23.50 | $188.00 | $39.55 | $316.40 | $24.63 | $41.18 |
| 6 Laborers | 21.50 | 1032.00 | 36.15 | 1735.20 | | |
| 2 Equip. Oper. (med.) | 29.65 | 474.40 | 48.55 | 776.80 | | |
| 1 Rodman (reinf.) | 31.35 | 250.80 | 54.90 | 439.20 | | |
| 1 Cement Finisher | 27.80 | 222.40 | 44.50 | 356.00 | | |
| 1 Grader, 30,000 Lbs. | | 622.20 | | 684.42 | | |
| 1 Paving Mach. & Equip. | | 2678.00 | | 2945.80 | | |
| 1 Concrete Saw | | 161.40 | | 177.54 | 39.34 | 43.27 |
| 88 L.H., Daily Totals | | $5629.20 | | $7431.36 | $63.97 | $84.45 |

| Crew B-26B | Hr. | Daily | Hr. | Daily | Bare Costs | Incl. O&P |
|---|---|---|---|---|---|---|
| 1 Labor Foreman (outside) | $23.50 | $188.00 | $39.55 | $316.40 | $25.05 | $41.79 |
| 6 Laborers | 21.50 | 1032.00 | 36.15 | 1735.20 | | |
| 3 Equip. Oper. (med.) | 29.65 | 711.60 | 48.55 | 1165.20 | | |
| 1 Rodman (reinf.) | 31.35 | 250.80 | 54.90 | 439.20 | | |
| 1 Cement Finisher | 27.80 | 222.40 | 44.50 | 356.00 | | |
| 1 Grader, 30,000 Lbs. | | 622.20 | | 684.42 | | |
| 1 Paving Mach. & Equip. | | 2678.00 | | 2945.80 | | |
| 1 Concrete Pump, 110' Boom | | 976.40 | | 1074.04 | 44.55 | 49.00 |
| 96 L.H., Daily Totals | | $6681.40 | | $8716.26 | $69.60 | $90.79 |

| Crew B-27 | Hr. | Daily | Hr. | Daily | Bare Costs | Incl. O&P |
|---|---|---|---|---|---|---|
| 1 Labor Foreman (outside) | $23.50 | $188.00 | $39.55 | $316.40 | $22.00 | $37.00 |
| 3 Laborers | 21.50 | 516.00 | 36.15 | 867.60 | | |
| 1 Berm Machine | | 285.60 | | 314.16 | 8.93 | 9.82 |
| 32 L.H., Daily Totals | | $989.60 | | $1498.16 | $30.93 | $46.82 |

| Crew B-28 | Hr. | Daily | Hr. | Daily | Bare Costs | Incl. O&P |
|---|---|---|---|---|---|---|
| 2 Carpenters | $29.10 | $465.60 | $48.95 | $783.20 | $26.57 | $44.68 |
| 1 Laborer | 21.50 | 172.00 | 36.15 | 289.20 | | |
| 24 L.H., Daily Totals | | $637.60 | | $1072.40 | $26.57 | $44.68 |

| Crew B-29 | Hr. | Daily | Hr. | Daily | Bare Costs | Incl. O&P |
|---|---|---|---|---|---|---|
| 1 Labor Foreman (outside) | $23.50 | $188.00 | $39.55 | $316.40 | $23.36 | $39.05 |
| 4 Laborers | 21.50 | 688.00 | 36.15 | 1156.80 | | |
| 1 Equip. Oper. (crane) | 30.65 | 245.20 | 50.15 | 401.20 | | |
| 1 Gradall, 5/8 C.Y. | | 812.80 | | 894.08 | 16.93 | 18.63 |
| 48 L.H., Daily Totals | | $1934.00 | | $2768.48 | $40.29 | $57.68 |

| Crew B-30 | Hr. | Daily | Hr. | Daily | Bare Costs | Incl. O&P |
|---|---|---|---|---|---|---|
| 1 Equip. Oper. (med.) | $29.65 | $237.20 | $48.55 | $388.40 | $25.58 | $42.32 |
| 2 Truck Drivers (heavy) | 23.55 | 376.80 | 39.20 | 627.20 | | |
| 1 Hyd. Excavator, 1.5 C.Y. | | 1017.00 | | 1118.70 | | |
| 2 Dump Trucks, 12 C.Y., 400 H.P. | | 1335.60 | | 1469.16 | 98.03 | 107.83 |
| 24 L.H., Daily Totals | | $2966.60 | | $3603.46 | $123.61 | $150.14 |

| Crew B-31 | Hr. | Daily | Hr. | Daily | Bare Costs | Incl. O&P |
|---|---|---|---|---|---|---|
| 1 Labor Foreman (outside) | $23.50 | $188.00 | $39.55 | $316.40 | $21.90 | $36.83 |
| 4 Laborers | 21.50 | 688.00 | 36.15 | 1156.80 | | |
| 1 Air Compressor, 250 cfm | | 193.40 | | 212.74 | | |
| 1 Sheeting Driver | | 5.75 | | 6.33 | | |
| 2 -50' Air Hoses, 1.5" | | 12.60 | | 13.86 | 5.29 | 5.82 |
| 40 L.H., Daily Totals | | $1087.75 | | $1706.13 | $27.19 | $42.65 |

| Crew B-32 | Hr. | Daily | Hr. | Daily | Bare Costs | Incl. O&P |
|---|---|---|---|---|---|---|
| 1 Laborer | $21.50 | $172.00 | $36.15 | $289.20 | $27.61 | $45.45 |
| 3 Equip. Oper. (med.) | 29.65 | 711.60 | 48.55 | 1165.20 | | |
| 1 Grader, 30,000 Lbs. | | 622.20 | | 684.42 | | |
| 1 Tandem Roller, 10 Ton | | 235.20 | | 258.72 | | |
| 1 Dozer, 200 H.P. | | 1192.00 | | 1311.20 | 64.04 | 70.45 |
| 32 L.H., Daily Totals | | $2933.00 | | $3708.74 | $91.66 | $115.90 |

| Crew B-32A | Hr. | Daily | Hr. | Daily | Bare Costs | Incl. O&P |
|---|---|---|---|---|---|---|
| 1 Laborer | $21.50 | $172.00 | $36.15 | $289.20 | $26.93 | $44.42 |
| 2 Equip. Oper. (med.) | 29.65 | 474.40 | 48.55 | 776.80 | | |
| 1 Grader, 30,000 Lbs. | | 622.20 | | 684.42 | | |
| 1 Roller, Vibratory, 25 Ton | | 633.20 | | 696.52 | 52.31 | 57.54 |
| 24 L.H., Daily Totals | | $1901.80 | | $2446.94 | $79.24 | $101.96 |

| Crew B-32B | Hr. | Daily | Hr. | Daily | Bare Costs | Incl. O&P |
|---|---|---|---|---|---|---|
| 1 Laborer | $21.50 | $172.00 | $36.15 | $289.20 | $26.93 | $44.42 |
| 2 Equip. Oper. (med.) | 29.65 | 474.40 | 48.55 | 776.80 | | |
| 1 Dozer, 200 H.P. | | 1192.00 | | 1311.20 | | |
| 1 Roller, Vibratory, 25 Ton | | 633.20 | | 696.52 | 76.05 | 83.66 |
| 24 L.H., Daily Totals | | $2471.60 | | $3073.72 | $102.98 | $128.07 |

| Crew B-32C | Hr. | Daily | Hr. | Daily | Bare Costs | Incl. O&P |
|---|---|---|---|---|---|---|
| 1 Labor Foreman | $23.50 | $188.00 | $39.55 | $316.40 | $25.91 | $42.92 |
| 2 Laborers | 21.50 | 344.00 | 36.15 | 578.40 | | |
| 3 Equip. Oper. (med.) | 29.65 | 711.60 | 48.55 | 1165.20 | | |
| 1 Grader, 30,000 Lbs. | | 622.20 | | 684.42 | | |
| 1 Tandem Roller, 10 Ton | | 235.20 | | 258.72 | | |
| 1 Dozer, 200 H.P. | | 1192.00 | | 1311.20 | 42.70 | 46.97 |
| 48 L.H., Daily Totals | | $3293.00 | | $4314.34 | $68.60 | $89.88 |

| Crew B-33A | Hr. | Daily | Hr. | Daily | Bare Costs | Incl. O&P |
|---|---|---|---|---|---|---|
| 1 Equip. Oper. (med.) | $29.65 | $237.20 | $48.55 | $388.40 | $29.65 | $48.55 |
| .25 Equip. Oper. (med.) | 29.65 | 59.30 | 48.55 | 97.10 | | |
| 1 Scraper, Towed, 7 C.Y. | | 105.20 | | 115.72 | | |
| 1.250 Dozers, 300 H.P. | | 1990.00 | | 2189.00 | 209.52 | 230.47 |
| 10 L.H., Daily Totals | | $2391.70 | | $2790.22 | $239.17 | $279.02 |

| Crew B-33B | Hr. | Daily | Hr. | Daily | Bare Costs | Incl. O&P |
|---|---|---|---|---|---|---|
| 1 Equip. Oper. (med.) | $29.65 | $237.20 | $48.55 | $388.40 | $29.65 | $48.55 |
| .25 Equip. Oper. (med.) | 29.65 | 59.30 | 48.55 | 97.10 | | |
| 1 Scraper, Towed, 10 C.Y. | | 156.60 | | 172.26 | | |
| 1.250 Dozers, 300 H.P. | | 1990.00 | | 2189.00 | 214.66 | 236.13 |
| 10 L.H., Daily Totals | | $2443.10 | | $2846.76 | $244.31 | $284.68 |

| Crew B-33C | Hr. | Daily | Hr. | Daily | Bare Costs | Incl. O&P |
|---|---|---|---|---|---|---|
| 1 Equip. Oper. (med.) | $29.65 | $237.20 | $48.55 | $388.40 | $29.65 | $48.55 |
| .25 Equip. Oper. (med.) | 29.65 | 59.30 | 48.55 | 97.10 | | |
| 1 Scraper, Towed, 15 C.Y. | | 172.20 | | 189.42 | | |
| 1.250 Dozers, 300 H.P. | | 1990.00 | | 2189.00 | 216.22 | 237.84 |
| 10 L.H., Daily Totals | | $2458.70 | | $2863.92 | $245.87 | $286.39 |

## Crew B-33D

| Crew No. | Bare Costs Hr. | Daily | Incl. Subs O&P Hr. | Daily | Cost Per Labor-Hour Bare Costs | Incl. O&P |
|---|---|---|---|---|---|---|
| 1 Equip. Oper. (med.) | $29.65 | $237.20 | $48.55 | $388.40 | $29.65 | $48.55 |
| .25 Equip. Oper. (med.) | 29.65 | 59.30 | 48.55 | 97.10 | | |
| 1 S.P. Scraper, 14 C.Y. | | 1717.00 | | 1888.70 | | |
| .25 Dozer, 300 H.P. | | 398.00 | | 437.80 | 211.50 | 232.65 |
| 10 L.H., Daily Totals | | $2411.50 | | $2812.00 | $241.15 | $281.20 |

## Crew B-33E

| Crew No. | Bare Costs Hr. | Daily | Incl. Subs O&P Hr. | Daily | Cost Per Labor-Hour Bare Costs | Incl. O&P |
|---|---|---|---|---|---|---|
| 1 Equip. Oper. (med.) | $29.65 | $237.20 | $48.55 | $388.40 | $29.65 | $48.55 |
| .25 Equip. Oper. (med.) | 29.65 | 59.30 | 48.55 | 97.10 | | |
| 1 S.P. Scraper, 21 C.Y. | | 2242.00 | | 2466.20 | | |
| .25 Dozer, 300 H.P. | | 398.00 | | 437.80 | 264.00 | 290.40 |
| 10 L.H., Daily Totals | | $2936.50 | | $3389.50 | $293.65 | $338.95 |

## Crew B-33F

| Crew No. | Bare Costs Hr. | Daily | Incl. Subs O&P Hr. | Daily | Cost Per Labor-Hour Bare Costs | Incl. O&P |
|---|---|---|---|---|---|---|
| 1 Equip. Oper. (med.) | $29.65 | $237.20 | $48.55 | $388.40 | $29.65 | $48.55 |
| .25 Equip. Oper. (med.) | 29.65 | 59.30 | 48.55 | 97.10 | | |
| 1 Elev. Scraper, 11 C.Y. | | 1185.00 | | 1303.50 | | |
| .25 Dozer, 300 H.P. | | 398.00 | | 437.80 | 158.30 | 174.13 |
| 10 L.H., Daily Totals | | $1879.50 | | $2226.80 | $187.95 | $222.68 |

## Crew B-33G

| Crew No. | Bare Costs Hr. | Daily | Incl. Subs O&P Hr. | Daily | Cost Per Labor-Hour Bare Costs | Incl. O&P |
|---|---|---|---|---|---|---|
| 1 Equip. Oper. (med.) | $29.65 | $237.20 | $48.55 | $388.40 | $29.65 | $48.55 |
| .25 Equip. Oper. (med.) | 29.65 | 59.30 | 48.55 | 97.10 | | |
| 1 Elev. Scraper, 22 C.Y. | | 2283.00 | | 2511.30 | | |
| .25 Dozer, 300 H.P. | | 398.00 | | 437.80 | 268.10 | 294.91 |
| 10 L.H., Daily Totals | | $2977.50 | | $3434.60 | $297.75 | $343.46 |

## Crew B-33K

| Crew No. | Bare Costs Hr. | Daily | Incl. Subs O&P Hr. | Daily | Cost Per Labor-Hour Bare Costs | Incl. O&P |
|---|---|---|---|---|---|---|
| 1 Equipment Operator (med.) | $29.65 | $237.20 | $48.55 | $388.40 | $27.32 | $45.01 |
| .25 Equipment Operator (med.) | 29.65 | 59.30 | 48.55 | 97.10 | | |
| .5 Laborer | 21.50 | 86.00 | 36.15 | 144.60 | | |
| 1 S.P. Scraper, 31 C.Y. | | 3219.00 | | 3540.90 | | |
| .25 Dozer, 410 H.P. | | 519.75 | | 571.73 | 267.05 | 293.76 |
| 14 L.H., Daily Totals | | $4121.25 | | $4742.73 | $294.38 | $338.77 |

## Crew B-34A

| Crew No. | Bare Costs Hr. | Daily | Incl. Subs O&P Hr. | Daily | Cost Per Labor-Hour Bare Costs | Incl. O&P |
|---|---|---|---|---|---|---|
| 1 Truck Driver (heavy) | $23.55 | $188.40 | $39.20 | $313.60 | $23.55 | $39.20 |
| 1 Dump Truck, 8 C.Y., 220 H.P. | | 401.80 | | 441.98 | 50.23 | 55.25 |
| 8 L.H., Daily Totals | | $590.20 | | $755.58 | $73.78 | $94.45 |

## Crew B-34B

| Crew No. | Bare Costs Hr. | Daily | Incl. Subs O&P Hr. | Daily | Cost Per Labor-Hour Bare Costs | Incl. O&P |
|---|---|---|---|---|---|---|
| 1 Truck Driver (heavy) | $23.55 | $188.40 | $39.20 | $313.60 | $23.55 | $39.20 |
| 1 Dump Truck, 12 C.Y., 400 H.P. | | 667.80 | | 734.58 | 83.47 | 91.82 |
| 8 L.H., Daily Totals | | $856.20 | | $1048.18 | $107.03 | $131.02 |

## Crew B-34C

| Crew No. | Bare Costs Hr. | Daily | Incl. Subs O&P Hr. | Daily | Cost Per Labor-Hour Bare Costs | Incl. O&P |
|---|---|---|---|---|---|---|
| 1 Truck Driver (heavy) | $23.55 | $188.40 | $39.20 | $313.60 | $23.55 | $39.20 |
| 1 Truck Tractor, 6x4, 380 H.P. | | 592.40 | | 651.64 | | |
| 1 Dump Trailer, 16.5 C.Y. | | 120.20 | | 132.22 | 89.08 | 97.98 |
| 8 L.H., Daily Totals | | $901.00 | | $1097.46 | $112.63 | $137.18 |

## Crew B-34D

| Crew No. | Bare Costs Hr. | Daily | Incl. Subs O&P Hr. | Daily | Cost Per Labor-Hour Bare Costs | Incl. O&P |
|---|---|---|---|---|---|---|
| 1 Truck Driver (heavy) | $23.55 | $188.40 | $39.20 | $313.60 | $23.55 | $39.20 |
| 1 Truck Tractor, 6x4, 380 H.P. | | 592.40 | | 651.64 | | |
| 1 Dump Trailer, 20 C.Y. | | 134.80 | | 148.28 | 90.90 | 99.99 |
| 8 L.H., Daily Totals | | $915.60 | | $1113.52 | $114.45 | $139.19 |

## Crew B-34E

| Crew No. | Bare Costs Hr. | Daily | Incl. Subs O&P Hr. | Daily | Cost Per Labor-Hour Bare Costs | Incl. O&P |
|---|---|---|---|---|---|---|
| 1 Truck Driver (heavy) | $23.55 | $188.40 | $39.20 | $313.60 | $23.55 | $39.20 |
| 1 Dump Truck, Off Hwy., 25 Ton | | 1399.00 | | 1538.90 | 174.88 | 192.36 |
| 8 L.H., Daily Totals | | $1587.40 | | $1852.50 | $198.43 | $231.56 |

## Crew B-34F

| Crew No. | Bare Costs Hr. | Daily | Incl. Subs O&P Hr. | Daily | Cost Per Labor-Hour Bare Costs | Incl. O&P |
|---|---|---|---|---|---|---|
| 1 Truck Driver (heavy) | $23.55 | $188.40 | $39.20 | $313.60 | $23.55 | $39.20 |
| 1 Dump Truck, Off Hwy., 35 Ton | | 1267.00 | | 1393.70 | 158.38 | 174.21 |
| 8 L.H., Daily Totals | | $1455.40 | | $1707.30 | $181.93 | $213.41 |

## Crew B-34G

| Crew No. | Bare Costs Hr. | Daily | Incl. Subs O&P Hr. | Daily | Cost Per Labor-Hour Bare Costs | Incl. O&P |
|---|---|---|---|---|---|---|
| 1 Truck Driver (heavy) | $23.55 | $188.40 | $39.20 | $313.60 | $23.55 | $39.20 |
| 1 Dump Truck, Off Hwy., 50 Ton | | 1744.00 | | 1918.40 | 218.00 | 239.80 |
| 8 L.H., Daily Totals | | $1932.40 | | $2232.00 | $241.55 | $279.00 |

## Crew B-34H

| Crew No. | Bare Costs Hr. | Daily | Incl. Subs O&P Hr. | Daily | Cost Per Labor-Hour Bare Costs | Incl. O&P |
|---|---|---|---|---|---|---|
| 1 Truck Driver (heavy) | $23.55 | $188.40 | $39.20 | $313.60 | $23.55 | $39.20 |
| 1 Dump Truck, Off Hwy., 65 Ton | | 1770.00 | | 1947.00 | 221.25 | 243.38 |
| 8 L.H., Daily Totals | | $1958.40 | | $2260.60 | $244.80 | $282.57 |

## Crew B-34I

| Crew No. | Bare Costs Hr. | Daily | Incl. Subs O&P Hr. | Daily | Cost Per Labor-Hour Bare Costs | Incl. O&P |
|---|---|---|---|---|---|---|
| 1 Truck Driver (heavy) | $23.55 | $188.40 | $39.20 | $313.60 | $23.55 | $39.20 |
| 1 Dump Truck, 18 C.Y., 450 H.P. | | 838.40 | | 922.24 | 104.80 | 115.28 |
| 8 L.H., Daily Totals | | $1026.80 | | $1235.84 | $128.35 | $154.48 |

## Crew B-34J

| Crew No. | Bare Costs Hr. | Daily | Incl. Subs O&P Hr. | Daily | Cost Per Labor-Hour Bare Costs | Incl. O&P |
|---|---|---|---|---|---|---|
| 1 Truck Driver (heavy) | $23.55 | $188.40 | $39.20 | $313.60 | $23.55 | $39.20 |
| 1 Dump Truck, Off Hwy., 100 Ton | | 2296.00 | | 2525.60 | 287.00 | 315.70 |
| 8 L.H., Daily Totals | | $2484.40 | | $2839.20 | $310.55 | $354.90 |

## Crew B-34K

| Crew No. | Bare Costs Hr. | Daily | Incl. Subs O&P Hr. | Daily | Cost Per Labor-Hour Bare Costs | Incl. O&P |
|---|---|---|---|---|---|---|
| 1 Truck Driver (heavy) | $23.55 | $188.40 | $39.20 | $313.60 | $23.55 | $39.20 |
| 1 Truck Tractor, 6x4, 450 H.P. | | 715.80 | | 787.38 | | |
| 1 Lowbed Trailer, 75 Ton | | 205.80 | | 226.38 | 115.20 | 126.72 |
| 8 L.H., Daily Totals | | $1110.00 | | $1327.36 | $138.75 | $165.92 |

## Crew B-34L

| Crew No. | Bare Costs Hr. | Daily | Incl. Subs O&P Hr. | Daily | Cost Per Labor-Hour Bare Costs | Incl. O&P |
|---|---|---|---|---|---|---|
| 1 Equip. Oper. (light) | $28.50 | $228.00 | $46.65 | $373.20 | $28.50 | $46.65 |
| 1 Flatbed Truck, Gas, 1.5 Ton | | 239.80 | | 263.78 | 29.98 | 32.97 |
| 8 L.H., Daily Totals | | $467.80 | | $636.98 | $58.48 | $79.62 |

## Crew B-34N

| Crew No. | Bare Costs Hr. | Daily | Incl. Subs O&P Hr. | Daily | Cost Per Labor-Hour Bare Costs | Incl. O&P |
|---|---|---|---|---|---|---|
| 1 Truck Driver (heavy) | $23.55 | $188.40 | $39.20 | $313.60 | $23.55 | $39.20 |
| 1 Dump Truck, 8 C.Y., 220 H.P. | | 401.80 | | 441.98 | | |
| 1 Flatbed Trailer, 40 Ton | | 143.20 | | 157.52 | 68.13 | 74.94 |
| 8 L.H., Daily Totals | | $733.40 | | $913.10 | $91.67 | $114.14 |

## Crew B-34P

| Crew No. | Bare Costs Hr. | Daily | Incl. Subs O&P Hr. | Daily | Cost Per Labor-Hour Bare Costs | Incl. O&P |
|---|---|---|---|---|---|---|
| 1 Pipe Fitter | $34.25 | $274.00 | $56.15 | $449.20 | $28.93 | $47.62 |
| 1 Truck Driver (light) | 22.90 | 183.20 | 38.15 | 305.20 | | |
| 1 Equip. Oper. (med.) | 29.65 | 237.20 | 48.55 | 388.40 | | |
| 1 Flatbed Truck, Gas, 3 Ton | | 296.00 | | 325.60 | | |
| 1 Backhoe Loader, 48 H.P. | | 337.80 | | 371.58 | 26.41 | 29.05 |
| 24 L.H., Daily Totals | | $1328.20 | | $1839.98 | $55.34 | $76.67 |

# Crews

| Crew No. | Bare Costs | | Incl. Subs O&P | | Cost Per Labor-Hour | |
|---|---|---|---|---|---|---|
| **Crew B-34Q** | Hr. | Daily | Hr. | Daily | Bare Costs | Incl. O&P |
| 1 Pipe Fitter | $34.25 | $274.00 | $56.15 | $449.20 | $29.27 | $48.15 |
| 1 Truck Driver (light) | 22.90 | 183.20 | 38.15 | 305.20 | | |
| 1 Eqip. Oper. (crane) | 30.65 | 245.20 | 50.15 | 401.20 | | |
| 1 Flatbed Trailer, 25 Ton | | 105.60 | | 116.16 | | |
| 1 Dump Truck, 8 C.Y., 220 H.P. | | 401.80 | | 441.98 | | |
| 1 Hyd. Crane, 25 Ton | | 747.60 | | 822.36 | 52.29 | 57.52 |
| 24 L.H., Daily Totals | | $1957.40 | | $2536.10 | $81.56 | $105.67 |
| **Crew B-34R** | Hr. | Daily | Hr. | Daily | Bare Costs | Incl. O&P |
| 1 Pipe Fitter | $34.25 | $274.00 | $56.15 | $449.20 | $29.27 | $48.15 |
| 1 Truck Driver (light) | 22.90 | 183.20 | 38.15 | 305.20 | | |
| 1 Eqip. Oper. (crane) | 30.65 | 245.20 | 50.15 | 401.20 | | |
| 1 Flatbed Trailer, 25 Ton | | 105.60 | | 116.16 | | |
| 1 Dump Truck, 8 C.Y., 220 H.P. | | 401.80 | | 441.98 | | |
| 1 Hyd. Crane, 25 Ton | | 747.60 | | 822.36 | | |
| 1 Hyd. Excavator, 1 C.Y. | | 801.60 | | 881.76 | 85.69 | 94.26 |
| 24 L.H., Daily Totals | | $2759.00 | | $3417.86 | $114.96 | $142.41 |
| **Crew B-34S** | Hr. | Daily | Hr. | Daily | Bare Costs | Incl. O&P |
| 2 Pipe Fitters | $34.25 | $548.00 | $56.15 | $898.40 | $30.68 | $50.41 |
| 1 Truck Driver (heavy) | 23.55 | 188.40 | 39.20 | 313.60 | | |
| 1 Eqip. Oper. (crane) | 30.65 | 245.20 | 50.15 | 401.20 | | |
| 1 Flatbed Trailer, 40 Ton | | 143.20 | | 157.52 | | |
| 1 Truck Tractor, 6x4, 380 H.P. | | 592.40 | | 651.64 | | |
| 1 Hyd. Crane, 80 Ton | | 1545.00 | | 1699.50 | | |
| 1 Hyd. Excavator, 2 C.Y. | | 1321.00 | | 1453.10 | 112.55 | 123.81 |
| 32 L.H., Daily Totals | | $4583.20 | | $5574.96 | $143.22 | $174.22 |
| **Crew B-34T** | Hr. | Daily | Hr. | Daily | Bare Costs | Incl. O&P |
| 2 Pipe Fitters | $34.25 | $548.00 | $56.15 | $898.40 | $30.68 | $50.41 |
| 1 Truck Driver (heavy) | 23.55 | 188.40 | 39.20 | 313.60 | | |
| 1 Eqip. Oper. (crane) | 30.65 | 245.20 | 50.15 | 401.20 | | |
| 1 Flatbed Trailer, 40 Ton | | 143.20 | | 157.52 | | |
| 1 Truck Tractor, 6x4, 380 H.P. | | 592.40 | | 651.64 | | |
| 1 Hyd. Crane, 80 Ton | | 1545.00 | | 1699.50 | 71.27 | 78.40 |
| 32 L.H., Daily Totals | | $3262.20 | | $4121.86 | $101.94 | $128.81 |
| **Crew B-35** | Hr. | Daily | Hr. | Daily | Bare Costs | Incl. O&P |
| 1 Laborer Foreman (out) | $23.50 | $188.00 | $39.55 | $316.40 | $27.85 | $46.24 |
| 1 Skilled Worker | 29.25 | 234.00 | 49.05 | 392.40 | | |
| 1 Welder (plumber) | 34.35 | 274.80 | 56.30 | 450.40 | | |
| 1 Laborer | 21.50 | 172.00 | 36.15 | 289.20 | | |
| 1 Equip. Oper. (crane) | 30.65 | 245.20 | 50.15 | 401.20 | | |
| 1 Welder, electric, 300 amp | | 58.55 | | 64.41 | | |
| 1 Hyd. Excavator, .75 C.Y. | | 677.80 | | 745.58 | 18.41 | 20.25 |
| 40 L.H., Daily Totals | | $1850.35 | | $2659.59 | $46.26 | $66.49 |
| **Crew B-35A** | Hr. | Daily | Hr. | Daily | Bare Costs | Incl. O&P |
| 1 Laborer Foreman (out) | $23.50 | $188.00 | $39.55 | $316.40 | $26.74 | $44.38 |
| 2 Laborers | 21.50 | 344.00 | 36.15 | 578.40 | | |
| 1 Skilled Worker | 29.25 | 234.00 | 49.05 | 392.40 | | |
| 1 Welder (plumber) | 34.35 | 274.80 | 56.30 | 450.40 | | |
| 1 Equip. Oper. (crane) | 30.65 | 245.20 | 50.15 | 401.20 | | |
| 1 Equip. Oper. Oiler | 26.45 | 211.60 | 43.30 | 346.40 | | |
| 1 Welder, gas engine, 300 amp | | 145.80 | | 160.38 | | |
| 1 Crawler Crane, 75 Ton | | 1516.00 | | 1667.60 | 29.68 | 32.64 |
| 56 L.H., Daily Totals | | $3159.40 | | $4313.18 | $56.42 | $77.02 |
| **Crew B-36** | Hr. | Daily | Hr. | Daily | Bare Costs | Incl. O&P |
| 1 Labor Foreman (outside) | $23.50 | $188.00 | $39.55 | $316.40 | $25.16 | $41.79 |
| 2 Laborers | 21.50 | 344.00 | 36.15 | 578.40 | | |
| 2 Equip. Oper. (med.) | 29.65 | 474.40 | 48.55 | 776.80 | | |
| 1 Dozer, 200 H.P. | | 1192.00 | | 1311.20 | | |
| 1 Aggregate Spreader | | 38.60 | | 42.46 | | |
| 1 Tandem Roller, 10 Ton | | 235.20 | | 258.72 | 36.65 | 40.31 |
| 40 L.H., Daily Totals | | $2472.20 | | $3283.98 | $61.81 | $82.10 |
| **Crew B-36A** | Hr. | Daily | Hr. | Daily | Bare Costs | Incl. O&P |
| 1 Labor Foreman (outside) | $23.50 | $188.00 | $39.55 | $316.40 | $26.44 | $43.72 |
| 2 Laborers | 21.50 | 344.00 | 36.15 | 578.40 | | |
| 4 Equip. Oper. (med.) | 29.65 | 948.80 | 48.55 | 1553.60 | | |
| 1 Dozer, 200 H.P. | | 1192.00 | | 1311.20 | | |
| 1 Aggregate Spreader | | 38.60 | | 42.46 | | |
| 1 Tandem Roller, 10 Ton | | 235.20 | | 258.72 | | |
| 1 Roller, Pneum. Whl, 12 Ton | | 337.20 | | 370.92 | 32.20 | 35.42 |
| 56 L.H., Daily Totals | | $3283.80 | | $4431.70 | $58.64 | $79.14 |
| **Crew B-36B** | Hr. | Daily | Hr. | Daily | Bare Costs | Incl. O&P |
| 1 Labor Foreman (outside) | $23.50 | $188.00 | $39.55 | $316.40 | $26.08 | $43.16 |
| 2 Laborers | 21.50 | 344.00 | 36.15 | 578.40 | | |
| 4 Equip. Oper. (med.) | 29.65 | 948.80 | 48.55 | 1553.60 | | |
| 1 Truck Driver, Heavy | 23.55 | 188.40 | 39.20 | 313.60 | | |
| 1 Grader, 30,000 Lbs. | | 622.20 | | 684.42 | | |
| 1 F.E. Loader, crl, 1.5 C.Y. | | 534.60 | | 588.06 | | |
| 1 Dozer, 300 H.P. | | 1592.00 | | 1751.20 | | |
| 1 Roller, Vibratory, 25 Ton | | 633.20 | | 696.52 | | |
| 1 Truck Tractor, 6x4, 450 H.P. | | 715.80 | | 787.38 | | |
| 1 Water Tank Trailer, 5000 Gal. | | 139.60 | | 153.56 | 66.21 | 72.83 |
| 64 L.H., Daily Totals | | $5906.60 | | $7423.14 | $92.29 | $115.99 |
| **Crew B-36C** | Hr. | Daily | Hr. | Daily | Bare Costs | Incl. O&P |
| 1 Labor Foreman (outside) | $23.50 | $188.00 | $39.55 | $316.40 | $27.20 | $44.88 |
| 3 Equip. Oper. (med.) | 29.65 | 711.60 | 48.55 | 1165.20 | | |
| 1 Truck Driver, Heavy | 23.55 | 188.40 | 39.20 | 313.60 | | |
| 1 Grader, 30,000 Lbs. | | 622.20 | | 684.42 | | |
| 1 Dozer, 300 H.P. | | 1592.00 | | 1751.20 | | |
| 1 Roller, Vibratory, 25 Ton | | 633.20 | | 696.52 | | |
| 1 Truck Tractor, 6x4, 450 H.P. | | 715.80 | | 787.38 | | |
| 1 Water Tank Trailer, 5000 Gal. | | 139.60 | | 153.56 | 92.57 | 101.83 |
| 40 L.H., Daily Totals | | $4790.80 | | $5868.28 | $119.77 | $146.71 |
| **Crew B-36E** | Hr. | Daily | Hr. | Daily | Bare Costs | Incl. O&P |
| 1 Labor Foreman (outside) | $23.50 | $188.00 | $39.55 | $316.40 | $27.61 | $45.49 |
| 4 Equip. Oper. (med.) | 29.65 | 948.80 | 48.55 | 1553.60 | | |
| 1 Truck Driver, Heavy | 23.55 | 188.40 | 39.20 | 313.60 | | |
| 1 Grader, 30,000 Lbs. | | 622.20 | | 684.42 | | |
| 1 Dozer, 300 H.P. | | 1592.00 | | 1751.20 | | |
| 1 Roller, Vibratory, 25 Ton | | 633.20 | | 696.52 | | |
| 1 Truck Tractor, 6x4, 380 H.P. | | 592.40 | | 651.64 | | |
| 1 Dist. Tanker, 3000 Gallon | | 307.00 | | 337.70 | 78.06 | 85.86 |
| 48 L.H., Daily Totals | | $5072.00 | | $6305.08 | $105.67 | $131.36 |
| **Crew B-37** | Hr. | Daily | Hr. | Daily | Bare Costs | Incl. O&P |
| 1 Labor Foreman (outside) | $23.50 | $188.00 | $39.55 | $316.40 | $23.00 | $38.47 |
| 4 Laborers | 21.50 | 688.00 | 36.15 | 1156.80 | | |
| 1 Equip. Oper. (light) | 28.50 | 228.00 | 46.65 | 373.20 | | |
| 1 Tandem Roller, 5 Ton | | 152.00 | | 167.20 | 3.17 | 3.48 |
| 48 L.H., Daily Totals | | $1256.00 | | $2013.60 | $26.17 | $41.95 |

# Crews

| Crew No. | Bare Costs Hr. | Daily | Incl. Subs O&P Hr. | Daily | Cost Per Labor-Hour Bare Costs | Incl. O&P |
|---|---|---|---|---|---|---|
| **Crew B-38** | Hr. | Daily | Hr. | Daily | Bare Costs | Incl. O&P |
| 2 Laborers | $21.50 | $344.00 | $36.15 | $578.40 | $23.83 | $39.65 |
| 1 Equip. Oper. (light) | 28.50 | 228.00 | 46.65 | 373.20 | | |
| 1 Backhoe Loader, 48 H.P. | | 337.80 | | 371.58 | | |
| 1 Hyd.Hammer, (1200 lb.) | | 154.20 | | 169.62 | 20.50 | 22.55 |
| 24 L.H., Daily Totals | | $1064.00 | | $1492.80 | $44.33 | $62.20 |
| **Crew B-39** | Hr. | Daily | Hr. | Daily | Bare Costs | Incl. O&P |
| 1 Labor Foreman (outside) | $23.50 | $188.00 | $39.55 | $316.40 | $21.83 | $36.72 |
| 5 Laborers | 21.50 | 860.00 | 36.15 | 1446.00 | | |
| 1 Air Compressor, 250 cfm | | 193.40 | | 212.74 | | |
| 2 Breakers, Pavement, 60 lb. | | 18.80 | | 20.68 | | |
| 2 -50' Air Hoses, 1.5" | | 12.60 | | 13.86 | 4.68 | 5.15 |
| 48 L.H., Daily Totals | | $1272.80 | | $2009.68 | $26.52 | $41.87 |
| **Crew B-40** | Hr. | Daily | Hr. | Daily | Bare Costs | Incl. O&P |
| 1 Pile Driver Foreman (out) | $30.20 | $241.60 | $52.80 | $422.40 | $27.88 | $48.04 |
| 4 Pile Drivers | 28.20 | 902.40 | 49.30 | 1577.60 | | |
| 1 Building Laborer | 21.50 | 172.00 | 36.15 | 289.20 | | |
| 1 Equip. Oper. (crane) | 30.65 | 245.20 | 50.15 | 401.20 | | |
| 1 Crawler Crane, 40 Ton | | 1193.00 | | 1312.30 | | |
| 1 Vibratory Hammer & Gen. | | 2641.00 | | 2905.10 | 68.46 | 75.31 |
| 56 L.H., Daily Totals | | $5395.20 | | $6907.80 | $96.34 | $123.35 |
| **Crew B-40B** | Hr. | Daily | Hr. | Daily | Bare Costs | Incl. O&P |
| 1 Laborer Foreman | $23.50 | $188.00 | $39.55 | $316.40 | $24.18 | $40.24 |
| 3 Laborers | 21.50 | 516.00 | 36.15 | 867.60 | | |
| 1 Equip. Oper. (crane) | 30.65 | 245.20 | 50.15 | 401.20 | | |
| 1 Equip. Oper. Oiler | 26.45 | 211.60 | 43.30 | 346.40 | | |
| 1 Lattice Boom Crane, 40 Ton | | 1256.00 | | 1381.60 | 26.17 | 28.78 |
| 48 L.H., Daily Totals | | $2416.80 | | $3313.20 | $50.35 | $69.03 |
| **Crew B-41** | Hr. | Daily | Hr. | Daily | Bare Costs | Incl. O&P |
| 1 Labor Foreman (outside) | $23.50 | $188.00 | $39.55 | $316.40 | $22.50 | $37.73 |
| 4 Laborers | 21.50 | 688.00 | 36.15 | 1156.80 | | |
| .25 Equip. Oper. (crane) | 30.65 | 61.30 | 50.15 | 100.30 | | |
| .25 Equip. Oper. Oiler | 26.45 | 52.90 | 43.30 | 86.60 | | |
| .25 Crawler Crane, 40 Ton | | 298.25 | | 328.07 | 6.78 | 7.46 |
| 44 L.H., Daily Totals | | $1288.45 | | $1988.18 | $29.28 | $45.19 |
| **Crew B-42** | Hr. | Daily | Hr. | Daily | Bare Costs | Incl. O&P |
| 1 Labor Foreman (outside) | $23.50 | $188.00 | $39.55 | $316.40 | $24.93 | $41.51 |
| 4 Laborers | 21.50 | 688.00 | 36.15 | 1156.80 | | |
| 1 Equip. Oper. (crane) | 30.65 | 245.20 | 50.15 | 401.20 | | |
| 1 Welder (plumber) | 34.35 | 274.80 | 56.30 | 450.40 | | |
| 1 Hyd. Crane, 25 Ton | | 747.60 | | 822.36 | | |
| 1 Welder, gas engine, 300 amp | | 145.80 | | 160.38 | | |
| 1 Horz. Boring Csg. Mch. | | 473.20 | | 520.52 | 24.40 | 26.84 |
| 56 L.H., Daily Totals | | $2762.60 | | $3828.06 | $49.33 | $68.36 |
| **Crew B-43** | Hr. | Daily | Hr. | Daily | Bare Costs | Incl. O&P |
| 1 Labor Foreman (outside) | $23.50 | $188.00 | $39.55 | $316.40 | $21.90 | $36.83 |
| 4 Laborers | 21.50 | 688.00 | 36.15 | 1156.80 | | |
| 1 Drill Rig, Truck-Mounted | | 2591.00 | | 2850.10 | 64.78 | 71.25 |
| 40 L.H., Daily Totals | | $3467.00 | | $4323.30 | $86.67 | $108.08 |

| Crew No. | Bare Costs Hr. | Daily | Incl. Subs O&P Hr. | Daily | Cost Per Labor-Hour Bare Costs | Incl. O&P |
|---|---|---|---|---|---|---|
| **Crew B-44** | Hr. | Daily | Hr. | Daily | Bare Costs | Incl. O&P |
| 1 Pile Driver Foreman | $30.20 | $241.60 | $52.80 | $422.40 | $27.08 | $46.56 |
| 4 Pile Drivers | 28.20 | 902.40 | 49.30 | 1577.60 | | |
| 1 Equip. Oper. (crane) | 30.65 | 245.20 | 50.15 | 401.20 | | |
| 2 Laborers | 21.50 | 344.00 | 36.15 | 578.40 | | |
| 1 Crawler Crane, 40 Ton | | 1193.00 | | 1312.30 | | |
| 1 Lead, 60' high | | 70.80 | | 77.88 | | |
| 1 Hammer, diesel, 15K ft.-lbs. | | 577.60 | | 635.36 | 28.77 | 31.65 |
| 64 L.H., Daily Totals | | $3574.60 | | $5005.14 | $55.85 | $78.21 |
| **Crew B-45** | Hr. | Daily | Hr. | Daily | Bare Costs | Incl. O&P |
| 1 Building Laborer | $21.50 | $172.00 | $36.15 | $289.20 | $22.52 | $37.67 |
| 1 Truck Driver (heavy) | 23.55 | 188.40 | 39.20 | 313.60 | | |
| 1 Dist. Tanker, 3000 Gallon | | 307.00 | | 337.70 | 19.19 | 21.11 |
| 16 L.H., Daily Totals | | $667.40 | | $940.50 | $41.71 | $58.78 |
| **Crew B-46** | Hr. | Daily | Hr. | Daily | Bare Costs | Incl. O&P |
| 1 Pile Driver Foreman | $30.20 | $241.60 | $52.80 | $422.40 | $25.18 | $43.31 |
| 2 Pile Drivers | 28.20 | 451.20 | 49.30 | 788.80 | | |
| 3 Laborers | 21.50 | 516.00 | 36.15 | 867.60 | | |
| 1 Chain Saw, gas, 36" Long | | 39.20 | | 43.12 | 0.82 | 0.90 |
| 48 L.H., Daily Totals | | $1248.00 | | $2121.92 | $26.00 | $44.21 |
| **Crew B-47** | Hr. | Daily | Hr. | Daily | Bare Costs | Incl. O&P |
| 1 Blast Foreman | $23.50 | $188.00 | $39.55 | $316.40 | $22.50 | $37.85 |
| 1 Driller | 21.50 | 172.00 | 36.15 | 289.20 | | |
| 1 Air Track Drill, 4" | | 917.80 | | 1009.58 | | |
| 1 Air Compressor, 600 cfm | | 530.60 | | 583.66 | | |
| 2 -50' Air Hoses, 3" | | 32.40 | | 35.64 | 92.55 | 101.81 |
| 16 L.H., Daily Totals | | $1840.80 | | $2234.48 | $115.05 | $139.66 |
| **Crew B-47A** | Hr. | Daily | Hr. | Daily | Bare Costs | Incl. O&P |
| 1 Drilling Foreman | $23.50 | $188.00 | $39.55 | $316.40 | $26.87 | $44.33 |
| 1 Equip. Oper. (heavy) | 30.65 | 245.20 | 50.15 | 401.20 | | |
| 1 Oiler | 26.45 | 211.60 | 43.30 | 346.40 | | |
| 1 Air Track Drill, 5" | | 1069.00 | | 1175.90 | 44.54 | 49.00 |
| 24 L.H., Daily Totals | | $1713.80 | | $2239.90 | $71.41 | $93.33 |
| **Crew B-47C** | Hr. | Daily | Hr. | Daily | Bare Costs | Incl. O&P |
| 1 Laborer | $21.50 | $172.00 | $36.15 | $289.20 | $25.00 | $41.40 |
| 1 Equip. Oper. (light) | 28.50 | 228.00 | 46.65 | 373.20 | | |
| 1 Air Compressor, 750 cfm | | 542.80 | | 597.08 | | |
| 2 -50' Air Hoses, 3" | | 32.40 | | 35.64 | | |
| 1 Air Track Drill, 4" | | 917.80 | | 1009.58 | 93.31 | 102.64 |
| 16 L.H., Daily Totals | | $1893.00 | | $2304.70 | $118.31 | $144.04 |
| **Crew B-47E** | Hr. | Daily | Hr. | Daily | Bare Costs | Incl. O&P |
| 1 Laborer Foreman | $23.50 | $188.00 | $39.55 | $316.40 | $22.00 | $37.00 |
| 3 Laborers | 21.50 | 516.00 | 36.15 | 867.60 | | |
| 1 Flatbed Truck, Gas, 3 Ton | | 296.00 | | 325.60 | 9.25 | 10.18 |
| 32 L.H., Daily Totals | | $1000.00 | | $1509.60 | $31.25 | $47.17 |
| **Crew B-47G** | Hr. | Daily | Hr. | Daily | Bare Costs | Incl. O&P |
| 1 Laborer Foreman | $23.50 | $188.00 | $39.55 | $316.40 | $22.17 | $37.28 |
| 2 Laborers | 21.50 | 344.00 | 36.15 | 578.40 | | |
| 1 Air Track Drill, 4" | | 917.80 | | 1009.58 | | |
| 1 Air Compressor, 600 cfm | | 530.60 | | 583.66 | | |
| 2 -50' Air Hoses, 3" | | 32.40 | | 35.64 | | |
| 1 Grout Pump | | 201.80 | | 221.98 | 70.11 | 77.12 |
| 24 L.H., Daily Totals | | $2214.60 | | $2745.66 | $92.28 | $114.40 |

# Crews

| Crew No. | Bare Costs | | Incl. Subs O&P | | Cost Per Labor-Hour | |
|---|---|---|---|---|---|---|

| Crew B-47H | Hr. | Daily | Hr. | Daily | Bare Costs | Incl. O&P |
|---|---|---|---|---|---|---|
| 1 Skilled Worker Foreman | $31.25 | $250.00 | $52.40 | $419.20 | $29.75 | $49.89 |
| 3 Skilled Workers | 29.25 | 702.00 | 49.05 | 1177.20 | | |
| 1 Flatbed Truck, Gas, 3 Ton | | 296.00 | | 325.60 | 9.25 | 10.18 |
| 32 L.H., Daily Totals | | $1248.00 | | $1922.00 | $39.00 | $60.06 |

| Crew B-48 | Hr. | Daily | Hr. | Daily | Bare Costs | Incl. O&P |
|---|---|---|---|---|---|---|
| 1 Labor Foreman (outside) | $23.50 | $188.00 | $39.55 | $316.40 | $23.36 | $39.05 |
| 4 Laborers | 21.50 | 688.00 | 36.15 | 1156.80 | | |
| 1 Equip. Oper. (crane) | 30.65 | 245.20 | 50.15 | 401.20 | | |
| 1 Centr. Water Pump, 6" | | 340.00 | | 374.00 | | |
| 1 -20' Suction Hose, 6" | | 11.90 | | 13.09 | | |
| 1 -50' Discharge Hose, 6" | | 6.30 | | 6.93 | | |
| 1 Drill Rig, Truck-Mounted | | 2591.00 | | 2850.10 | 61.44 | 67.59 |
| 48 L.H., Daily Totals | | $4070.40 | | $5118.52 | $84.80 | $106.64 |

| Crew B-49 | Hr. | Daily | Hr. | Daily | Bare Costs | Incl. O&P |
|---|---|---|---|---|---|---|
| 1 Labor Foreman (outside) | $23.50 | $188.00 | $39.55 | $316.40 | $24.23 | $41.01 |
| 5 Laborers | 21.50 | 860.00 | 36.15 | 1446.00 | | |
| 1 Equip. Oper. (crane) | 30.65 | 245.20 | 50.15 | 401.20 | | |
| 2 Pile Drivers | 28.20 | 451.20 | 49.30 | 788.80 | | |
| 1 Hyd. Crane, 25 Ton | | 747.60 | | 822.36 | | |
| 1 Centr. Water Pump, 6" | | 340.00 | | 374.00 | | |
| 1 -20' Suction Hose, 6" | | 11.90 | | 13.09 | | |
| 1 -50' Discharge Hose, 6" | | 6.30 | | 6.93 | | |
| 1 Drill Rig, Truck-Mounted | | 2591.00 | | 2850.10 | 51.34 | 56.48 |
| 72 L.H., Daily Totals | | $5441.20 | | $7018.88 | $75.57 | $97.48 |

| Crew B-50 | Hr. | Daily | Hr. | Daily | Bare Costs | Incl. O&P |
|---|---|---|---|---|---|---|
| 1 Pile Driver Foreman | $30.20 | $241.60 | $52.80 | $422.40 | $25.97 | $44.58 |
| 6 Pile Drivers | 28.20 | 1353.60 | 49.30 | 2366.40 | | |
| 1 Equip. Oper. (crane) | 30.65 | 245.20 | 50.15 | 401.20 | | |
| 5 Laborers | 21.50 | 860.00 | 36.15 | 1446.00 | | |
| 1 Crawler Crane, 40 Ton | | 1193.00 | | 1312.30 | | |
| 1 Lead, 60' high | | 70.80 | | 77.88 | | |
| 1 Hammer, diesel, 15K ft.-lbs. | | 577.60 | | 635.36 | | |
| 1 Air Compressor, 600 cfm | | 530.60 | | 583.66 | | |
| 2 -50' Air Hoses, 3" | | 32.40 | | 35.64 | | |
| 1 Chain Saw, gas, 36" Long | | 39.20 | | 43.12 | 23.50 | 25.85 |
| 104 L.H., Daily Totals | | $5144.00 | | $7323.96 | $49.46 | $70.42 |

| Crew B-51 | Hr. | Daily | Hr. | Daily | Bare Costs | Incl. O&P |
|---|---|---|---|---|---|---|
| 1 Labor Foreman (outside) | $23.50 | $188.00 | $39.55 | $316.40 | $22.07 | $37.05 |
| 4 Laborers | 21.50 | 688.00 | 36.15 | 1156.80 | | |
| 1 Truck Driver (light) | 22.90 | 183.20 | 38.15 | 305.20 | | |
| 1 Flatbed Truck, Gas, 1.5 Ton | | 239.80 | | 263.78 | 5.00 | 5.50 |
| 48 L.H., Daily Totals | | $1299.00 | | $2042.18 | $27.06 | $42.55 |

| Crew B-52 | Hr. | Daily | Hr. | Daily | Bare Costs | Incl. O&P |
|---|---|---|---|---|---|---|
| 1 Labor Foreman | $23.50 | $188.00 | $39.55 | $316.40 | $24.16 | $40.69 |
| 1 Carpenter | 29.10 | 232.80 | 48.95 | 391.60 | | |
| 4 Laborers | 21.50 | 688.00 | 36.15 | 1156.80 | | |
| .5 Rodman (reinf.) | 31.35 | 125.40 | 54.90 | 219.60 | | |
| .5 Equip. Oper. (med.) | 29.65 | 118.60 | 48.55 | 194.20 | | |
| .5 Crawler Loader, 3 C.Y. | | 538.50 | | 592.35 | 9.62 | 10.58 |
| 56 L.H., Daily Totals | | $1891.30 | | $2870.95 | $33.77 | $51.27 |

| Crew B-53 | Hr. | Daily | Hr. | Daily | Bare Costs | Incl. O&P |
|---|---|---|---|---|---|---|
| 1 Building Laborer | $21.50 | $172.00 | $36.15 | $289.20 | $21.50 | $36.15 |
| 1 Trencher, Chain, 12 H.P. | | 66.00 | | 72.60 | 8.25 | 9.07 |
| 8 L.H., Daily Totals | | $238.00 | | $361.80 | $29.75 | $45.23 |

| Crew B-54 | Hr. | Daily | Hr. | Daily | Bare Costs | Incl. O&P |
|---|---|---|---|---|---|---|
| 1 Equip. Oper. (light) | $28.50 | $228.00 | $46.65 | $373.20 | $28.50 | $46.65 |
| 1 Trencher, Chain, 40 H.P. | | 334.40 | | 367.84 | 41.80 | 45.98 |
| 8 L.H., Daily Totals | | $562.40 | | $741.04 | $70.30 | $92.63 |

| Crew B-54A | Hr. | Daily | Hr. | Daily | Bare Costs | Incl. O&P |
|---|---|---|---|---|---|---|
| .17 Labor Foreman (outside) | $23.50 | $31.96 | $39.55 | $53.79 | $28.76 | $47.24 |
| 1 Equipment Operator (med.) | 29.65 | 237.20 | 48.55 | 388.40 | | |
| 1 Wheel Trencher, 67 H.P. | | 1152.00 | | 1267.20 | 123.08 | 135.38 |
| 9.36 L.H., Daily Totals | | $1421.16 | | $1709.39 | $151.83 | $182.63 |

| Crew B-54B | Hr. | Daily | Hr. | Daily | Bare Costs | Incl. O&P |
|---|---|---|---|---|---|---|
| .25 Labor Foreman (outside) | $23.50 | $47.00 | $39.55 | $79.10 | $28.42 | $46.75 |
| 1 Equipment Operator (med.) | 29.65 | 237.20 | 48.55 | 388.40 | | |
| 1 Wheel Trencher, 150 H.P. | | 1843.00 | | 2027.30 | 184.30 | 202.73 |
| 10 L.H., Daily Totals | | $2127.20 | | $2494.80 | $212.72 | $249.48 |

| Crew B-54D | Hr. | Daily | Hr. | Daily | Bare Costs | Incl. O&P |
|---|---|---|---|---|---|---|
| 1 Laborer | $21.50 | $172.00 | $36.15 | $289.20 | $25.57 | $42.35 |
| 1 Equipment Operator (med.) | 29.65 | 237.20 | 48.55 | 388.40 | | |
| 1 Rock trencher, 6" width | | 344.40 | | 378.84 | 21.52 | 23.68 |
| 16 L.H., Daily Totals | | $753.60 | | $1056.44 | $47.10 | $66.03 |

| Crew B-54E | Hr. | Daily | Hr. | Daily | Bare Costs | Incl. O&P |
|---|---|---|---|---|---|---|
| 1 Laborer | $21.50 | $172.00 | $36.15 | $289.20 | $25.57 | $42.35 |
| 1 Equipment Operator (med.) | 29.65 | 237.20 | 48.55 | 388.40 | | |
| 1 Rock trencher, 18" width | | 2571.00 | | 2828.10 | 160.69 | 176.76 |
| 16 L.H., Daily Totals | | $2980.20 | | $3505.70 | $186.26 | $219.11 |

| Crew B-55 | Hr. | Daily | Hr. | Daily | Bare Costs | Incl. O&P |
|---|---|---|---|---|---|---|
| 1 Laborer | $21.50 | $172.00 | $36.15 | $289.20 | $22.20 | $37.15 |
| 1 Truck Driver (light) | 22.90 | 183.20 | 38.15 | 305.20 | | |
| 1 Truck-mounted earth auger | | 749.80 | | 824.78 | | |
| 1 Flatbed Truck, Gas, 3 Ton | | 296.00 | | 325.60 | 65.36 | 71.90 |
| 16 L.H., Daily Totals | | $1401.00 | | $1744.78 | $87.56 | $109.05 |

| Crew B-56 | Hr. | Daily | Hr. | Daily | Bare Costs | Incl. O&P |
|---|---|---|---|---|---|---|
| 2 Laborers | $21.50 | $344.00 | $36.15 | $578.40 | $21.50 | $36.15 |
| 1 Air Track Drill, 4" | | 917.80 | | 1009.58 | | |
| 1 Air Compressor, 600 cfm | | 530.60 | | 583.66 | | |
| 1 -50' Air Hose, 3" | | 16.20 | | 17.82 | 91.54 | 100.69 |
| 16 L.H., Daily Totals | | $1808.60 | | $2189.46 | $113.04 | $136.84 |

| Crew B-57 | Hr. | Daily | Hr. | Daily | Bare Costs | Incl. O&P |
|---|---|---|---|---|---|---|
| 1 Labor Foreman (outside) | $23.50 | $188.00 | $39.55 | $316.40 | $23.73 | $39.63 |
| 3 Laborers | 21.50 | 516.00 | 36.15 | 867.60 | | |
| 1 Equip. Oper. (crane) | 30.65 | 245.20 | 50.15 | 401.20 | | |
| 1 Barge, 400 Ton | | 768.00 | | 844.80 | | |
| 1 Crawler Crane, 25 Ton | | 1188.00 | | 1306.80 | | |
| 1 Clamshell Bucket, 1 C.Y. | | 46.60 | | 51.26 | | |
| 1 Centr. Water Pump, 6" | | 340.00 | | 374.00 | | |
| 1 -20' Suction Hose, 6" | | 11.90 | | 13.09 | | |
| 20 -50' Discharge Hoses, 6" | | 126.00 | | 138.60 | 62.01 | 68.21 |
| 40 L.H., Daily Totals | | $3429.70 | | $4313.75 | $85.74 | $107.84 |

| Crew B-58 | Hr. | Daily | Hr. | Daily | Bare Costs | Incl. O&P |
|---|---|---|---|---|---|---|
| 2 Laborers | $21.50 | $344.00 | $36.15 | $578.40 | $23.83 | $39.65 |
| 1 Equip. Oper. (light) | 28.50 | 228.00 | 46.65 | 373.20 | | |
| 1 Backhoe Loader, 48 H.P. | | 337.80 | | 371.58 | | |
| 1 Small Helicopter, w/pilot | | 2513.00 | | 2764.30 | 118.78 | 130.66 |
| 24 L.H., Daily Totals | | $3422.80 | | $4087.48 | $142.62 | $170.31 |

# Crews

| Crew No. | Bare Costs | | Incl. Subs O&P | | Cost Per Labor-Hour | |
|---|---|---|---|---|---|---|

| Crew B-59 | Hr. | Daily | Hr. | Daily | Bare Costs | Incl. O&P |
|---|---|---|---|---|---|---|
| 1 Truck Driver (heavy) | $23.55 | $188.40 | $39.20 | $313.60 | $23.55 | $39.20 |
| 1 Truck Tractor, 220 H.P. | | 354.00 | | 389.40 | | |
| 1 Water Tank Trailer, 5000 Gal. | | 139.60 | | 153.56 | 61.70 | 67.87 |
| 8 L.H., Daily Totals | | $682.00 | | $856.56 | $85.25 | $107.07 |

| Crew B-60 | Hr. | Daily | Hr. | Daily | Bare Costs | Incl. O&P |
|---|---|---|---|---|---|---|
| 1 Labor Foreman (outside) | $23.50 | $188.00 | $39.55 | $316.40 | $24.52 | $40.80 |
| 3 Laborers | 21.50 | 516.00 | 36.15 | 867.60 | | |
| 1 Equip. Oper. (crane) | 30.65 | 245.20 | 50.15 | 401.20 | | |
| 1 Equip. Oper. (light) | 28.50 | 228.00 | 46.65 | 373.20 | | |
| 1 Crawler Crane, 40 Ton | | 1193.00 | | 1312.30 | | |
| 1 Lead, 60' high | | 70.80 | | 77.88 | | |
| 1 Hammer, diesel, 15K ft.-lbs. | | 577.60 | | 635.36 | | |
| 1 Backhoe Loader, 48 H.P. | | 337.80 | | 371.58 | 45.40 | 49.94 |
| 48 L.H., Daily Totals | | $3356.40 | | $4355.52 | $69.92 | $90.74 |

| Crew B-61 | Hr. | Daily | Hr. | Daily | Bare Costs | Incl. O&P |
|---|---|---|---|---|---|---|
| 1 Labor Foreman (outside) | $23.50 | $188.00 | $39.55 | $316.40 | $21.90 | $36.83 |
| 4 Laborers | 21.50 | 688.00 | 36.15 | 1156.80 | | |
| 1 Cement Mixer, 2 C.Y. | | 189.40 | | 208.34 | | |
| 1 Air Compressor, 160 cfm | | 158.00 | | 173.80 | 8.69 | 9.55 |
| 40 L.H., Daily Totals | | $1223.40 | | $1855.34 | $30.59 | $46.38 |

| Crew B-62 | Hr. | Daily | Hr. | Daily | Bare Costs | Incl. O&P |
|---|---|---|---|---|---|---|
| 2 Laborers | $21.50 | $344.00 | $36.15 | $578.40 | $23.83 | $39.65 |
| 1 Equip. Oper. (light) | 28.50 | 228.00 | 46.65 | 373.20 | | |
| 1 Loader, Skid Steer, 30 H.P., gas | | 161.40 | | 177.54 | 6.72 | 7.40 |
| 24 L.H., Daily Totals | | $733.40 | | $1129.14 | $30.56 | $47.05 |

| Crew B-63 | Hr. | Daily | Hr. | Daily | Bare Costs | Incl. O&P |
|---|---|---|---|---|---|---|
| 5 Laborers | $21.50 | $860.00 | $36.15 | $1446.00 | $21.50 | $36.15 |
| 1 Loader, Skid Steer, 30 H.P., gas | | 161.40 | | 177.54 | 4.04 | 4.44 |
| 40 L.H., Daily Totals | | $1021.40 | | $1623.54 | $25.54 | $40.59 |

| Crew B-64 | Hr. | Daily | Hr. | Daily | Bare Costs | Incl. O&P |
|---|---|---|---|---|---|---|
| 1 Laborer | $21.50 | $172.00 | $36.15 | $289.20 | $22.20 | $37.15 |
| 1 Truck Driver (light) | 22.90 | 183.20 | 38.15 | 305.20 | | |
| 1 Power Mulcher (small) | | 150.20 | | 165.22 | | |
| 1 Flatbed Truck, Gas, 1.5 Ton | | 239.80 | | 263.78 | 24.38 | 26.81 |
| 16 L.H., Daily Totals | | $745.20 | | $1023.40 | $46.58 | $63.96 |

| Crew B-65 | Hr. | Daily | Hr. | Daily | Bare Costs | Incl. O&P |
|---|---|---|---|---|---|---|
| 1 Laborer | $21.50 | $172.00 | $36.15 | $289.20 | $22.20 | $37.15 |
| 1 Truck Driver (light) | 22.90 | 183.20 | 38.15 | 305.20 | | |
| 1 Power Mulcher (large) | | 319.00 | | 350.90 | | |
| 1 Flatbed Truck, Gas, 1.5 Ton | | 239.80 | | 263.78 | 34.92 | 38.42 |
| 16 L.H., Daily Totals | | $914.00 | | $1209.08 | $57.13 | $75.57 |

| Crew B-66 | Hr. | Daily | Hr. | Daily | Bare Costs | Incl. O&P |
|---|---|---|---|---|---|---|
| 1 Equip. Oper. (light) | $28.50 | $228.00 | $46.65 | $373.20 | $28.50 | $46.65 |
| 1 Loader-Backhoe | | 218.40 | | 240.24 | 27.30 | 30.03 |
| 8 L.H., Daily Totals | | $446.40 | | $613.44 | $55.80 | $76.68 |

| Crew B-67 | Hr. | Daily | Hr. | Daily | Bare Costs | Incl. O&P |
|---|---|---|---|---|---|---|
| 1 Millwright | $30.05 | $240.40 | $48.10 | $384.80 | $29.27 | $47.38 |
| 1 Equip. Oper. (light) | 28.50 | 228.00 | 46.65 | 373.20 | | |
| 1 Forklift, R/T, 4,000 Lb. | | 309.60 | | 340.56 | 19.35 | 21.29 |
| 16 L.H., Daily Totals | | $778.00 | | $1098.56 | $48.63 | $68.66 |

| Crew B-68 | Hr. | Daily | Hr. | Daily | Bare Costs | Incl. O&P |
|---|---|---|---|---|---|---|
| 2 Millwrights | $30.05 | $480.80 | $48.10 | $769.60 | $29.53 | $47.62 |
| 1 Equip. Oper. (light) | 28.50 | 228.00 | 46.65 | 373.20 | | |
| 1 Forklift, R/T, 4,000 Lb. | | 309.60 | | 340.56 | 12.90 | 14.19 |
| 24 L.H., Daily Totals | | $1018.40 | | $1483.36 | $42.43 | $61.81 |

| Crew B-69 | Hr. | Daily | Hr. | Daily | Bare Costs | Incl. O&P |
|---|---|---|---|---|---|---|
| 1 Labor Foreman (outside) | $23.50 | $188.00 | $39.55 | $316.40 | $24.18 | $40.24 |
| 3 Laborers | 21.50 | 516.00 | 36.15 | 867.60 | | |
| 1 Equip Oper. (crane) | 30.65 | 245.20 | 50.15 | 401.20 | | |
| 1 Equip Oper. Oiler | 26.45 | 211.60 | 43.30 | 346.40 | | |
| 1 Hyd. Crane, 80 Ton | | 1545.00 | | 1699.50 | 32.19 | 35.41 |
| 48 L.H., Daily Totals | | $2705.80 | | $3631.10 | $56.37 | $75.65 |

| Crew B-69A | Hr. | Daily | Hr. | Daily | Bare Costs | Incl. O&P |
|---|---|---|---|---|---|---|
| 1 Labor Foreman | $23.50 | $188.00 | $39.55 | $316.40 | $24.24 | $40.17 |
| 3 Laborers | 21.50 | 516.00 | 36.15 | 867.60 | | |
| 1 Equip. Oper. (med.) | 29.65 | 237.20 | 48.55 | 388.40 | | |
| 1 Concrete Finisher | 27.80 | 222.40 | 44.50 | 356.00 | | |
| 1 Curb/Gutter Paver, 2-Track | | 825.00 | | 907.50 | 17.19 | 18.91 |
| 48 L.H., Daily Totals | | $1988.60 | | $2835.90 | $41.43 | $59.08 |

| Crew B-69B | Hr. | Daily | Hr. | Daily | Bare Costs | Incl. O&P |
|---|---|---|---|---|---|---|
| 1 Labor Foreman | $23.50 | $188.00 | $39.55 | $316.40 | $24.24 | $40.17 |
| 3 Laborers | 21.50 | 516.00 | 36.15 | 867.60 | | |
| 1 Equip. Oper. (med.) | 29.65 | 237.20 | 48.55 | 388.40 | | |
| 1 Cement Finisher | 27.80 | 222.40 | 44.50 | 356.00 | | |
| 1 Curb/Gutter Paver, 4-Track | | 934.60 | | 1028.06 | 19.47 | 21.42 |
| 48 L.H., Daily Totals | | $2098.20 | | $2956.46 | $43.71 | $61.59 |

| Crew B-70 | Hr. | Daily | Hr. | Daily | Bare Costs | Incl. O&P |
|---|---|---|---|---|---|---|
| 1 Labor Foreman (outside) | $23.50 | $188.00 | $39.55 | $316.40 | $25.28 | $41.95 |
| 3 Laborers | 21.50 | 516.00 | 36.15 | 867.60 | | |
| 3 Equip. Oper. (med.) | 29.65 | 711.60 | 48.55 | 1165.20 | | |
| 1 Grader, 30,000 Lbs. | | 622.20 | | 684.42 | | |
| 1 Ripper, beam & 1 shank | | 80.00 | | 88.00 | | |
| 1 Road Sweeper, S.P., 8' wide | | 650.40 | | 715.44 | | |
| 1 F.E. Loader, W.M., 1.5 C.Y. | | 367.60 | | 404.36 | 30.72 | 33.79 |
| 56 L.H., Daily Totals | | $3135.80 | | $4241.42 | $56.00 | $75.74 |

| Crew B-71 | Hr. | Daily | Hr. | Daily | Bare Costs | Incl. O&P |
|---|---|---|---|---|---|---|
| 1 Labor Foreman (outside) | $23.50 | $188.00 | $39.55 | $316.40 | $25.28 | $41.95 |
| 3 Laborers | 21.50 | 516.00 | 36.15 | 867.60 | | |
| 3 Equip. Oper. (med.) | 29.65 | 711.60 | 48.55 | 1165.20 | | |
| 1 Pvmt. Profiler, 750 H.P. | | 6104.00 | | 6714.40 | | |
| 1 Road Sweeper, S.P., 8' wide | | 650.40 | | 715.44 | | |
| 1 F.E. Loader, W.M., 1.5 C.Y. | | 367.60 | | 404.36 | 127.18 | 139.90 |
| 56 L.H., Daily Totals | | $8537.60 | | $10183.40 | $152.46 | $181.85 |

| Crew B-72 | Hr. | Daily | Hr. | Daily | Bare Costs | Incl. O&P |
|---|---|---|---|---|---|---|
| 1 Labor Foreman (outside) | $23.50 | $188.00 | $39.55 | $316.40 | $25.82 | $42.77 |
| 3 Laborers | 21.50 | 516.00 | 36.15 | 867.60 | | |
| 4 Equip. Oper. (med.) | 29.65 | 948.80 | 48.55 | 1553.60 | | |
| 1 Pvmt. Profiler, 750 H.P. | | 6104.00 | | 6714.40 | | |
| 1 Hammermill, 250 H.P. | | 1636.00 | | 1799.60 | | |
| 1 Windrow Loader | | 1228.00 | | 1350.80 | | |
| 1 Mix Paver 165 H.P. | | 2062.00 | | 2268.20 | | |
| 1 Roller, Pneum. Whl, 12 Ton | | 337.20 | | 370.92 | 177.61 | 195.37 |
| 64 L.H., Daily Totals | | $13020.00 | | $15241.52 | $203.44 | $238.15 |

| Crew No. | Bare Costs | | Incl. Subs O&P | | Cost Per Labor-Hour | |
|---|---|---|---|---|---|---|

| Crew B-73 | Hr. | Daily | Hr. | Daily | Bare Costs | Incl. O&P |
|---|---|---|---|---|---|---|
| 1 Labor Foreman (outside) | $23.50 | $188.00 | $39.55 | $316.40 | $26.84 | $44.33 |
| 2 Laborers | 21.50 | 344.00 | 36.15 | 578.40 | | |
| 5 Equip. Oper. (med.) | 29.65 | 1186.00 | 48.55 | 1942.00 | | |
| 1 Road Mixer, 310 H.P. | | 1955.00 | | 2150.50 | | |
| 1 Tandem Roller, 10 Ton | | 235.20 | | 258.72 | | |
| 1 Hammermill, 250 H.P. | | 1636.00 | | 1799.60 | | |
| 1 Grader, 30,000 Lbs. | | 622.20 | | 684.42 | | |
| .5 F.E. Loader, W.M., 1.5 C.Y. | | 183.80 | | 202.18 | | |
| .5 Truck Tractor, 220 H.P. | | 177.00 | | 194.70 | | |
| .5 Water Tank Trailer, 5000 Gal. | | 69.80 | | 76.78 | 76.23 | 83.86 |
| 64 L.H., Daily Totals | | $6597.00 | | $8203.70 | $103.08 | $128.18 |

| Crew B-74 | Hr. | Daily | Hr. | Daily | Bare Costs | Incl. O&P |
|---|---|---|---|---|---|---|
| 1 Labor Foreman (outside) | $23.50 | $188.00 | $39.55 | $316.40 | $26.34 | $43.54 |
| 1 Laborer | 21.50 | 172.00 | 36.15 | 289.20 | | |
| 4 Equip. Oper. (med.) | 29.65 | 948.80 | 48.55 | 1553.60 | | |
| 2 Truck Drivers (heavy) | 23.55 | 376.80 | 39.20 | 627.20 | | |
| 1 Grader, 30,000 Lbs. | | 622.20 | | 684.42 | | |
| 1 Ripper, beam & 1 shank | | 80.00 | | 88.00 | | |
| 2 Stabilizers, 310 H.P. | | 2928.00 | | 3220.80 | | |
| 1 Flatbed Truck, Gas, 3 Ton | | 296.00 | | 325.60 | | |
| 1 Chem. Spreader, Towed | | 50.40 | | 55.44 | | |
| 1 Roller, Vibratory, 25 Ton | | 633.20 | | 696.52 | | |
| 1 Water Tank Trailer, 5000 Gal. | | 139.60 | | 153.56 | | |
| 1 Truck Tractor, 220 H.P. | | 354.00 | | 389.40 | 79.74 | 87.71 |
| 64 L.H., Daily Totals | | $6789.00 | | $8400.14 | $106.08 | $131.25 |

| Crew B-75 | Hr. | Daily | Hr. | Daily | Bare Costs | Incl. O&P |
|---|---|---|---|---|---|---|
| 1 Labor Foreman (outside) | $23.50 | $188.00 | $39.55 | $316.40 | $26.74 | $44.16 |
| 1 Laborer | 21.50 | 172.00 | 36.15 | 289.20 | | |
| 4 Equip. Oper. (med.) | 29.65 | 948.80 | 48.55 | 1553.60 | | |
| 1 Truck Driver (heavy) | 23.55 | 188.40 | 39.20 | 313.60 | | |
| 1 Grader, 30,000 Lbs. | | 622.20 | | 684.42 | | |
| 1 Ripper, beam & 1 shank | | 80.00 | | 88.00 | | |
| 2 Stabilizers, 310 H.P. | | 2928.00 | | 3220.80 | | |
| 1 Dist. Tanker, 3000 Gallon | | 307.00 | | 337.70 | | |
| 1 Truck Tractor, 6x4, 380 H.P. | | 592.40 | | 651.64 | | |
| 1 Roller, Vibratory, 25 Ton | | 633.20 | | 696.52 | 92.19 | 101.41 |
| 56 L.H., Daily Totals | | $6660.00 | | $8151.88 | $118.93 | $145.57 |

| Crew B-76 | Hr. | Daily | Hr. | Daily | Bare Costs | Incl. O&P |
|---|---|---|---|---|---|---|
| 1 Dock Builder Foreman | $30.20 | $241.60 | $52.80 | $422.40 | $28.77 | $49.21 |
| 5 Dock Builders | 28.20 | 1128.00 | 49.30 | 1972.00 | | |
| 2 Equip. Oper. (crane) | 30.65 | 490.40 | 50.15 | 802.40 | | |
| 1 Equip. Oper. Oiler | 26.45 | 211.60 | 43.30 | 346.40 | | |
| 1 Crawler Crane, 50 Ton | | 1346.00 | | 1480.60 | | |
| 1 Barge, 400 Ton | | 768.00 | | 844.80 | | |
| 1 Hammer, diesel, 15K ft.-lbs. | | 577.60 | | 635.36 | | |
| 1 Lead, 60' high | | 70.80 | | 77.88 | | |
| 1 Air Compressor, 600 cfm | | 530.60 | | 583.66 | | |
| 2 -50' Air Hoses, 3" | | 32.40 | | 35.64 | 46.19 | 50.80 |
| 72 L.H., Daily Totals | | $5397.00 | | $7201.14 | $74.96 | $100.02 |

| Crew B-76A | Hr. | Daily | Hr. | Daily | Bare Costs | Incl. O&P |
|---|---|---|---|---|---|---|
| 1 Laborer Foreman | $23.50 | $188.00 | $39.55 | $316.40 | $23.51 | $39.22 |
| 5 Laborers | 21.50 | 860.00 | 36.15 | 1446.00 | | |
| 1 Equip. Oper. (crane) | 30.65 | 245.20 | 50.15 | 401.20 | | |
| 1 Equip. Oper. Oiler | 26.45 | 211.60 | 43.30 | 346.40 | | |
| 1 Crawler Crane, 50 Ton | | 1346.00 | | 1480.60 | | |
| 1 Barge, 400 Ton | | 768.00 | | 844.80 | 33.03 | 36.33 |
| 64 L.H., Daily Totals | | $3618.80 | | $4835.40 | $56.54 | $75.55 |

| Crew B-77 | Hr. | Daily | Hr. | Daily | Bare Costs | Incl. O&P |
|---|---|---|---|---|---|---|
| 1 Labor Foreman | $23.50 | $188.00 | $39.55 | $316.40 | $22.18 | $37.23 |
| 3 Laborers | 21.50 | 516.00 | 36.15 | 867.60 | | |
| 1 Truck Driver (light) | 22.90 | 183.20 | 38.15 | 305.20 | | |
| 1 Crack Cleaner, 25 H.P. | | 60.40 | | 66.44 | | |
| 1 Crack Filler, Trailer Mtd. | | 203.20 | | 223.52 | | |
| 1 Flatbed Truck, Gas, 3 Ton | | 296.00 | | 325.60 | 13.99 | 15.39 |
| 40 L.H., Daily Totals | | $1446.80 | | $2104.76 | $36.17 | $52.62 |

| Crew B-78 | Hr. | Daily | Hr. | Daily | Bare Costs | Incl. O&P |
|---|---|---|---|---|---|---|
| 1 Labor Foreman | $23.50 | $188.00 | $39.55 | $316.40 | $21.90 | $36.83 |
| 4 Laborers | 21.50 | 688.00 | 36.15 | 1156.80 | | |
| 1 Paint Striper, S.P. | | 152.60 | | 167.86 | | |
| 1 Flatbed Truck, Gas, 3 Ton | | 296.00 | | 325.60 | | |
| 1 Pickup Truck, 3/4 Ton | | 140.00 | | 154.00 | 14.72 | 16.19 |
| 40 L.H., Daily Totals | | $1464.60 | | $2120.66 | $36.62 | $53.02 |

| Crew B-78B | Hr. | Daily | Hr. | Daily | Bare Costs | Incl. O&P |
|---|---|---|---|---|---|---|
| 2 Laborers | $21.50 | $344.00 | $36.15 | $578.40 | $22.28 | $37.32 |
| .25 Equip. Oper. (light) | 28.50 | 57.00 | 46.65 | 93.30 | | |
| 1 Pickup Truck, 3/4 Ton | | 140.00 | | 154.00 | | |
| 1 Line Rem., 11 H.P., walk behind | | 59.20 | | 65.12 | | |
| .25 Road Sweeper, S.P., 8' wide | | 162.60 | | 178.86 | 20.10 | 22.11 |
| 18 L.H., Daily Totals | | $762.80 | | $1069.68 | $42.38 | $59.43 |

| Crew B-79 | Hr. | Daily | Hr. | Daily | Bare Costs | Incl. O&P |
|---|---|---|---|---|---|---|
| 1 Labor Foreman | $23.50 | $188.00 | $39.55 | $316.40 | $22.00 | $37.00 |
| 3 Laborers | 21.50 | 516.00 | 36.15 | 867.60 | | |
| 1 Thermo. Striper, T.M. | | 802.40 | | 882.64 | | |
| 1 Flatbed Truck, Gas, 3 Ton | | 296.00 | | 325.60 | | |
| 2 Pickup Trucks, 3/4 Ton | | 280.00 | | 308.00 | 43.08 | 47.38 |
| 32 L.H., Daily Totals | | $2082.40 | | $2700.24 | $65.08 | $84.38 |

| Crew B-80 | Hr. | Daily | Hr. | Daily | Bare Costs | Incl. O&P |
|---|---|---|---|---|---|---|
| 1 Labor Foreman | $23.50 | $188.00 | $39.55 | $316.40 | $22.17 | $37.28 |
| 2 Laborers | 21.50 | 344.00 | 36.15 | 578.40 | | |
| 1 Flatbed Truck, Gas, 3 Ton | | 296.00 | | 325.60 | | |
| 1 Earth Auger, Truck-Mtd. | | 449.20 | | 494.12 | 31.05 | 34.16 |
| 24 L.H., Daily Totals | | $1277.20 | | $1714.52 | $53.22 | $71.44 |

| Crew B-80A | Hr. | Daily | Hr. | Daily | Bare Costs | Incl. O&P |
|---|---|---|---|---|---|---|
| 3 Laborers | $21.50 | $516.00 | $36.15 | $867.60 | $21.50 | $36.15 |
| 1 Flatbed Truck, Gas, 3 Ton | | 296.00 | | 325.60 | 12.33 | 13.57 |
| 24 L.H., Daily Totals | | $812.00 | | $1193.20 | $33.83 | $49.72 |

| Crew B-80B | Hr. | Daily | Hr. | Daily | Bare Costs | Incl. O&P |
|---|---|---|---|---|---|---|
| 3 Laborers | $21.50 | $516.00 | $36.15 | $867.60 | $23.25 | $38.77 |
| 1 Equip. Oper. (light) | 28.50 | 228.00 | 46.65 | 373.20 | | |
| 1 Crane, Flatbed Mounted, 3 Ton | | 242.60 | | 266.86 | 7.58 | 8.34 |
| 32 L.H., Daily Totals | | $986.60 | | $1507.66 | $30.83 | $47.11 |

| Crew B-80C | Hr. | Daily | Hr. | Daily | Bare Costs | Incl. O&P |
|---|---|---|---|---|---|---|
| 2 Laborers | $21.50 | $344.00 | $36.15 | $578.40 | $21.97 | $36.82 |
| 1 Truck Driver (light) | 22.90 | 183.20 | 38.15 | 305.20 | | |
| 1 Flatbed Truck, Gas, 1.5 Ton | | 239.80 | | 263.78 | | |
| 1 Manual fence post auger, gas | | 7.80 | | 8.58 | 10.32 | 11.35 |
| 24 L.H., Daily Totals | | $774.80 | | $1155.96 | $32.28 | $48.16 |

# Crews

| Crew No. | Bare Costs Hr. | Daily | Incl. Subs O&P Hr. | Daily | Cost Per Labor-Hour Bare Costs | Incl. O&P |
|---|---|---|---|---|---|---|
| **Crew B-81** | | | | | | |
| 1 Laborer | $21.50 | $172.00 | $36.15 | $289.20 | $22.52 | $37.67 |
| 1 Truck Driver (heavy) | 23.55 | 188.40 | 39.20 | 313.60 | | |
| 1 Hydromulcher, T.M. | | 338.20 | | 372.02 | | |
| 1 Truck Tractor, 220 H.P. | | 354.00 | | 389.40 | 43.26 | 47.59 |
| 16 L.H., Daily Totals | | $1052.60 | | $1364.22 | $65.79 | $85.26 |
| **Crew B-82** | | | | | | |
| 1 Laborer | $21.50 | $172.00 | $36.15 | $289.20 | $25.00 | $41.40 |
| 1 Equip. Oper. (light) | 28.50 | 228.00 | 46.65 | 373.20 | | |
| 1 Horiz. Borer, 6 H.P. | | 82.00 | | 90.20 | 5.13 | 5.64 |
| 16 L.H., Daily Totals | | $482.00 | | $752.60 | $30.13 | $47.04 |
| **Crew B-82A** | | | | | | |
| 1 Laborer | $21.50 | $172.00 | $36.15 | $289.20 | $25.00 | $41.40 |
| 1 Equip. Oper. (light) | 28.50 | 228.00 | 46.65 | 373.20 | | |
| 1 Flatbed Truck, Gas, 3 Ton | | 296.00 | | 325.60 | | |
| 1 Flatbed Trailer, 25 Ton | | 105.60 | | 116.16 | | |
| 1 Horiz. Dir. Drill, 20k lb. thrust | | 651.60 | | 716.76 | 65.83 | 72.41 |
| 16 L.H., Daily Totals | | $1453.20 | | $1820.92 | $90.83 | $113.81 |
| **Crew B-82B** | | | | | | |
| 2 Laborers | $21.50 | $344.00 | $36.15 | $578.40 | $23.83 | $39.65 |
| 1 Equip. Oper. (light) | 28.50 | 228.00 | 46.65 | 373.20 | | |
| 1 Flatbed Truck, Gas, 3 Ton | | 296.00 | | 325.60 | | |
| 1 Flatbed Trailer, 25 Ton | | 105.60 | | 116.16 | | |
| 1 Horiz. Dir. Drill, 30k lb. thrust | | 928.20 | | 1021.02 | 55.41 | 60.95 |
| 24 L.H., Daily Totals | | $1901.80 | | $2414.38 | $79.24 | $100.60 |
| **Crew B-82C** | | | | | | |
| 2 Laborers | $21.50 | $344.00 | $36.15 | $578.40 | $23.83 | $39.65 |
| 1 Equip. Oper. (light) | 28.50 | 228.00 | 46.65 | 373.20 | | |
| 1 Flatbed Truck, Gas, 3 Ton | | 296.00 | | 325.60 | | |
| 1 Flatbed Trailer, 25 Ton | | 105.60 | | 116.16 | | |
| 1 Horiz. Dir. Drill, 50k lb. thrust | | 1232.00 | | 1355.20 | 68.07 | 74.87 |
| 24 L.H., Daily Totals | | $2205.60 | | $2748.56 | $91.90 | $114.52 |
| **Crew B-82D** | | | | | | |
| 1 Equip. Oper. (light) | $28.50 | $228.00 | $46.65 | $373.20 | $28.50 | $46.65 |
| 1 Mud Trailer for HDD, 1500 gallon | | 338.00 | | 371.80 | 42.25 | 46.48 |
| 8 L.H., Daily Totals | | $566.00 | | $745.00 | $70.75 | $93.13 |
| **Crew B-83** | | | | | | |
| 1 Tugboat Captain | $29.65 | $237.20 | $48.55 | $388.40 | $25.57 | $42.35 |
| 1 Tugboat Hand | 21.50 | 172.00 | 36.15 | 289.20 | | |
| 1 Tugboat, 250 H.P. | | 840.80 | | 924.88 | 52.55 | 57.81 |
| 16 L.H., Daily Totals | | $1250.00 | | $1602.48 | $78.13 | $100.16 |
| **Crew B-84** | | | | | | |
| 1 Equip. Oper. (med.) | $29.65 | $237.20 | $48.55 | $388.40 | $29.65 | $48.55 |
| 1 Rotary Mower/Tractor | | 302.00 | | 332.20 | 37.75 | 41.52 |
| 8 L.H., Daily Totals | | $539.20 | | $720.60 | $67.40 | $90.08 |
| **Crew B-85** | | | | | | |
| 3 Laborers | $21.50 | $516.00 | $36.15 | $867.60 | $23.54 | $39.24 |
| 1 Equip. Oper. (med.) | 29.65 | 237.20 | 48.55 | 388.40 | | |
| 1 Truck Driver (heavy) | 23.55 | 188.40 | 39.20 | 313.60 | | |
| 1 Aerial Lift Truck, 80' | | 665.40 | | 731.94 | | |
| 1 Brush Chipper, 12", 130 H.P. | | 253.20 | | 278.52 | | |
| 1 Pruning Saw, Rotary | | 6.75 | | 7.42 | 23.13 | 25.45 |
| 40 L.H., Daily Totals | | $1866.95 | | $2587.49 | $46.67 | $64.69 |

| Crew No. | Bare Costs Hr. | Daily | Incl. Subs O&P Hr. | Daily | Cost Per Labor-Hour Bare Costs | Incl. O&P |
|---|---|---|---|---|---|---|
| **Crew B-86** | | | | | | |
| 1 Equip. Oper. (med.) | $29.65 | $237.20 | $48.55 | $388.40 | $29.65 | $48.55 |
| 1 Stump Chipper, S.P. | | 190.90 | | 209.99 | 23.86 | 26.25 |
| 8 L.H., Daily Totals | | $428.10 | | $598.39 | $53.51 | $74.80 |
| **Crew B-86A** | | | | | | |
| 1 Equip. Oper. (med.) | $29.65 | $237.20 | $48.55 | $388.40 | $29.65 | $48.55 |
| 1 Grader, 30,000 Lbs. | | 622.20 | | 684.42 | 77.78 | 85.55 |
| 8 L.H., Daily Totals | | $859.40 | | $1072.82 | $107.43 | $134.10 |
| **Crew B-86B** | | | | | | |
| 1 Equip. Oper. (med.) | $29.65 | $237.20 | $48.55 | $388.40 | $29.65 | $48.55 |
| 1 Dozer, 200 H.P. | | 1192.00 | | 1311.20 | 149.00 | 163.90 |
| 8 L.H., Daily Totals | | $1429.20 | | $1699.60 | $178.65 | $212.45 |
| **Crew B-87** | | | | | | |
| 1 Laborer | $21.50 | $172.00 | $36.15 | $289.20 | $28.02 | $46.07 |
| 4 Equip. Oper. (med.) | 29.65 | 948.80 | 48.55 | 1553.60 | | |
| 2 Feller Bunchers, 100 H.P. | | 1219.20 | | 1341.12 | | |
| 1 Log Chipper, 22" Tree | | 689.60 | | 758.56 | | |
| 1 Dozer, 105 H.P. | | 660.40 | | 726.44 | | |
| 1 Chain Saw, gas, 36" Long | | 39.20 | | 43.12 | 65.21 | 71.73 |
| 40 L.H., Daily Totals | | $3729.20 | | $4712.04 | $93.23 | $117.80 |
| **Crew B-88** | | | | | | |
| 1 Laborer | $21.50 | $172.00 | $36.15 | $289.20 | $28.49 | $46.78 |
| 6 Equip. Oper. (med.) | 29.65 | 1423.20 | 48.55 | 2330.40 | | |
| 2 Feller Bunchers, 100 H.P. | | 1219.20 | | 1341.12 | | |
| 1 Log Chipper, 22" Tree | | 689.60 | | 758.56 | | |
| 2 Log Skidders, 50 H.P. | | 1814.40 | | 1995.84 | | |
| 1 Dozer, 105 H.P. | | 660.40 | | 726.44 | | |
| 1 Chain Saw, gas, 36" Long | | 39.20 | | 43.12 | 78.98 | 86.88 |
| 56 L.H., Daily Totals | | $6018.00 | | $7484.68 | $107.46 | $133.66 |
| **Crew B-89** | | | | | | |
| 1 Skilled Worker | $29.25 | $234.00 | $49.05 | $392.40 | $25.38 | $42.60 |
| 1 Building Laborer | 21.50 | 172.00 | 36.15 | 289.20 | | |
| 1 Flatbed Truck, Gas, 3 Ton | | 296.00 | | 325.60 | | |
| 1 Concrete Saw | | 161.40 | | 177.54 | | |
| 1 Water Tank, 65 Gal. | | 18.45 | | 20.30 | 29.74 | 32.71 |
| 16 L.H., Daily Totals | | $881.85 | | $1205.04 | $55.12 | $75.31 |
| **Crew B-89A** | | | | | | |
| 1 Skilled Worker | $29.25 | $234.00 | $49.05 | $392.40 | $25.38 | $42.60 |
| 1 Laborer | 21.50 | 172.00 | 36.15 | 289.20 | | |
| 1 Core Drill (large) | | 113.80 | | 125.18 | 7.11 | 7.82 |
| 16 L.H., Daily Totals | | $519.80 | | $806.78 | $32.49 | $50.42 |
| **Crew B-89B** | | | | | | |
| 1 Equip. Oper. (light) | $28.50 | $228.00 | $46.65 | $373.20 | $25.70 | $42.40 |
| 1 Truck Driver, Light | 22.90 | 183.20 | 38.15 | 305.20 | | |
| 1 Wall Saw, Hydraulic, 10 H.P. | | 110.40 | | 121.44 | | |
| 1 Generator, Diesel, 100 kW | | 418.60 | | 460.46 | | |
| 1 Water Tank, 65 Gal. | | 18.45 | | 20.30 | | |
| 1 Flatbed Truck, Gas, 3 Ton | | 296.00 | | 325.60 | 52.72 | 57.99 |
| 16 L.H., Daily Totals | | $1254.65 | | $1606.19 | $78.42 | $100.39 |

# Crews

| Crew No. | Bare Costs | | Incl. Subs O&P | | Cost Per Labor-Hour | |
|---|---|---|---|---|---|---|

### Crew B-90

| | Hr. | Daily | Hr. | Daily | Bare Costs | Incl. O&P |
|---|---|---|---|---|---|---|
| 1 Labor Foreman (outside) | $23.50 | $188.00 | $39.55 | $316.40 | $24.01 | $39.96 |
| 3 Laborers | 21.50 | 516.00 | 36.15 | 867.60 | | |
| 2 Equip. Oper. (light) | 28.50 | 456.00 | 46.65 | 746.40 | | |
| 2 Truck Drivers (heavy) | 23.55 | 376.80 | 39.20 | 627.20 | | |
| 1 Road Mixer, 310 H.P. | | 1955.00 | | 2150.50 | | |
| 1 Dist. Truck, 2000 Gal. | | 278.20 | | 306.02 | 34.89 | 38.38 |
| 64 L.H., Daily Totals | | $3770.00 | | $5014.12 | $58.91 | $78.35 |

### Crew B-90A

| | Hr. | Daily | Hr. | Daily | Bare Costs | Incl. O&P |
|---|---|---|---|---|---|---|
| 1 Labor Foreman | $23.50 | $188.00 | $39.55 | $316.40 | $26.44 | $43.72 |
| 2 Laborers | 21.50 | 344.00 | 36.15 | 578.40 | | |
| 4 Equip. Oper. (med.) | 29.65 | 948.80 | 48.55 | 1553.60 | | |
| 2 Graders, 30,000 Lbs. | | 1244.40 | | 1368.84 | | |
| 1 Tandem Roller, 10 Ton | | 235.20 | | 258.72 | | |
| 1 Roller, Pneum. Whl, 12 Ton | | 337.20 | | 370.92 | 32.44 | 35.69 |
| 56 L.H., Daily Totals | | $3297.60 | | $4446.88 | $58.89 | $79.41 |

### Crew B-90B

| | Hr. | Daily | Hr. | Daily | Bare Costs | Incl. O&P |
|---|---|---|---|---|---|---|
| 1 Labor Foreman | $23.50 | $188.00 | $39.55 | $316.40 | $25.91 | $42.92 |
| 2 Laborers | 21.50 | 344.00 | 36.15 | 578.40 | | |
| 3 Equip. Oper. (med.) | 29.65 | 711.60 | 48.55 | 1165.20 | | |
| 1 Tandem Roller, 10 Ton | | 235.20 | | 258.72 | | |
| 1 Roller, Pneum. Whl, 12 Ton | | 337.20 | | 370.92 | | |
| 1 Road Mixer, 310 H.P. | | 1955.00 | | 2150.50 | 52.65 | 57.92 |
| 48 L.H., Daily Totals | | $3771.00 | | $4840.14 | $78.56 | $100.84 |

### Crew B-91

| | Hr. | Daily | Hr. | Daily | Bare Costs | Incl. O&P |
|---|---|---|---|---|---|---|
| 1 Labor Foreman (outside) | $23.50 | $188.00 | $39.55 | $316.40 | $26.08 | $43.16 |
| 2 Laborers | 21.50 | 344.00 | 36.15 | 578.40 | | |
| 4 Equip. Oper. (med.) | 29.65 | 948.80 | 48.55 | 1553.60 | | |
| 1 Truck Driver (heavy) | 23.55 | 188.40 | 39.20 | 313.60 | | |
| 1 Dist. Tanker, 3000 Gallon | | 307.00 | | 337.70 | | |
| 1 Truck Tractor, 6x4, 380 H.P. | | 592.40 | | 651.64 | | |
| 1 Aggreg. Spreader, S.P. | | 820.80 | | 902.88 | | |
| 1 Roller, Pneum. Whl, 12 Ton | | 337.20 | | 370.92 | | |
| 1 Tandem Roller, 10 Ton | | 235.20 | | 258.72 | 35.82 | 39.40 |
| 64 L.H., Daily Totals | | $3961.80 | | $5283.86 | $61.90 | $82.56 |

### Crew B-92

| | Hr. | Daily | Hr. | Daily | Bare Costs | Incl. O&P |
|---|---|---|---|---|---|---|
| 1 Labor Foreman (outside) | $23.50 | $188.00 | $39.55 | $316.40 | $22.00 | $37.00 |
| 3 Laborers | 21.50 | 516.00 | 36.15 | 867.60 | | |
| 1 Crack Cleaner, 25 H.P. | | 60.40 | | 66.44 | | |
| 1 Air Compressor, 60 cfm | | 138.60 | | 152.46 | | |
| 1 Tar Kettle, T.M. | | 71.40 | | 78.54 | | |
| 1 Flatbed Truck, Gas, 3 Ton | | 296.00 | | 325.60 | 17.70 | 19.47 |
| 32 L.H., Daily Totals | | $1270.40 | | $1807.04 | $39.70 | $56.47 |

### Crew B-93

| | Hr. | Daily | Hr. | Daily | Bare Costs | Incl. O&P |
|---|---|---|---|---|---|---|
| 1 Equip. Oper. (med.) | $29.65 | $237.20 | $48.55 | $388.40 | $29.65 | $48.55 |
| 1 Feller Buncher, 100 H.P. | | 609.60 | | 670.56 | 76.20 | 83.82 |
| 8 L.H., Daily Totals | | $846.80 | | $1058.96 | $105.85 | $132.37 |

### Crew B-94A

| | Hr. | Daily | Hr. | Daily | Bare Costs | Incl. O&P |
|---|---|---|---|---|---|---|
| 1 Laborer | $21.50 | $172.00 | $36.15 | $289.20 | $21.50 | $36.15 |
| 1 Diaphragm Water Pump, 2" | | 68.00 | | 74.80 | | |
| 1 -20' Suction Hose, 2" | | 1.95 | | 2.15 | | |
| 2 -50' Discharge Hoses, 2" | | 1.80 | | 1.98 | 8.97 | 9.87 |
| 8 L.H., Daily Totals | | $243.75 | | $368.13 | $30.47 | $46.02 |

### Crew B-94B

| | Hr. | Daily | Hr. | Daily | Bare Costs | Incl. O&P |
|---|---|---|---|---|---|---|
| 1 Laborer | $21.50 | $172.00 | $36.15 | $289.20 | $21.50 | $36.15 |
| 1 Diaphragm Water Pump, 4" | | 90.80 | | 99.88 | | |
| 1 -20' Suction Hose, 4" | | 3.45 | | 3.79 | | |
| 2 -50' Discharge Hoses, 4" | | 4.70 | | 5.17 | 12.37 | 13.61 |
| 8 L.H., Daily Totals | | $270.95 | | $398.05 | $33.87 | $49.76 |

### Crew B-94C

| | Hr. | Daily | Hr. | Daily | Bare Costs | Incl. O&P |
|---|---|---|---|---|---|---|
| 1 Laborer | $21.50 | $172.00 | $36.15 | $289.20 | $21.50 | $36.15 |
| 1 Centrifugal Water Pump, 3" | | 74.40 | | 81.84 | | |
| 1 -20' Suction Hose, 3" | | 3.05 | | 3.36 | | |
| 2 -50' Discharge Hoses, 3" | | 3.50 | | 3.85 | 10.12 | 11.13 |
| 8 L.H., Daily Totals | | $252.95 | | $378.25 | $31.62 | $47.28 |

### Crew B-94D

| | Hr. | Daily | Hr. | Daily | Bare Costs | Incl. O&P |
|---|---|---|---|---|---|---|
| 1 Laborer | $21.50 | $172.00 | $36.15 | $289.20 | $21.50 | $36.15 |
| 1 Centr. Water Pump, 6" | | 340.00 | | 374.00 | | |
| 1 -20' Suction Hose, 6" | | 11.90 | | 13.09 | | |
| 2 -50' Discharge Hoses, 6" | | 12.60 | | 13.86 | 45.56 | 50.12 |
| 8 L.H., Daily Totals | | $536.50 | | $690.15 | $67.06 | $86.27 |

### Crew C-1

| | Hr. | Daily | Hr. | Daily | Bare Costs | Incl. O&P |
|---|---|---|---|---|---|---|
| 2 Carpenters | $29.10 | $465.60 | $48.95 | $783.20 | $25.36 | $42.61 |
| 1 Carpenter Helper | 21.75 | 174.00 | 36.40 | 291.20 | | |
| 1 Laborer | 21.50 | 172.00 | 36.15 | 289.20 | | |
| 32 L.H., Daily Totals | | $811.60 | | $1363.60 | $25.36 | $42.61 |

### Crew C-2

| | Hr. | Daily | Hr. | Daily | Bare Costs | Incl. O&P |
|---|---|---|---|---|---|---|
| 1 Carpenter Foreman (out) | $31.10 | $248.80 | $52.30 | $418.40 | $25.72 | $43.19 |
| 2 Carpenters | 29.10 | 465.60 | 48.95 | 783.20 | | |
| 2 Carpenter Helpers | 21.75 | 348.00 | 36.40 | 582.40 | | |
| 1 Laborer | 21.50 | 172.00 | 36.15 | 289.20 | | |
| 48 L.H., Daily Totals | | $1234.40 | | $2073.20 | $25.72 | $43.19 |

### Crew C-2A

| | Hr. | Daily | Hr. | Daily | Bare Costs | Incl. O&P |
|---|---|---|---|---|---|---|
| 1 Carpenter Foreman (out) | $31.10 | $248.80 | $52.30 | $418.40 | $27.95 | $46.63 |
| 3 Carpenters | 29.10 | 698.40 | 48.95 | 1174.80 | | |
| 1 Cement Finisher | 27.80 | 222.40 | 44.50 | 356.00 | | |
| 1 Laborer | 21.50 | 172.00 | 36.15 | 289.20 | | |
| 48 L.H., Daily Totals | | $1341.60 | | $2238.40 | $27.95 | $46.63 |

### Crew C-3

| | Hr. | Daily | Hr. | Daily | Bare Costs | Incl. O&P |
|---|---|---|---|---|---|---|
| 1 Rodman Foreman | $33.35 | $266.80 | $58.40 | $467.20 | $27.55 | $47.27 |
| 3 Rodmen (reinf.) | 31.35 | 752.40 | 54.90 | 1317.60 | | |
| 1 Equip. Oper. (light) | 28.50 | 228.00 | 46.65 | 373.20 | | |
| 3 Laborers | 21.50 | 516.00 | 36.15 | 867.60 | | |
| 3 Stressing Equipment | | 28.80 | | 31.68 | | |
| .5 Grouting Equipment | | 80.00 | | 88.00 | 1.70 | 1.87 |
| 64 L.H., Daily Totals | | $1872.00 | | $3145.28 | $29.25 | $49.15 |

### Crew C-4

| | Hr. | Daily | Hr. | Daily | Bare Costs | Incl. O&P |
|---|---|---|---|---|---|---|
| 1 Rodman Foreman | $33.35 | $266.80 | $58.40 | $467.20 | $29.39 | $51.09 |
| 2 Rodmen (reinf.) | 31.35 | 501.60 | 54.90 | 878.40 | | |
| 1 Building Laborer | 21.50 | 172.00 | 36.15 | 289.20 | | |
| 3 Stressing Equipment | | 28.80 | | 31.68 | 0.90 | 0.99 |
| 32 L.H., Daily Totals | | $969.20 | | $1666.48 | $30.29 | $52.08 |

### Crew C-4A

| | Hr. | Daily | Hr. | Daily | Bare Costs | Incl. O&P |
|---|---|---|---|---|---|---|
| 2 Rodmen (reinf.) | $31.35 | $501.60 | $54.90 | $878.40 | $31.35 | $54.90 |
| 4 Stressing Equipment | | 38.40 | | 42.24 | 2.40 | 2.64 |
| 16 L.H., Daily Totals | | $540.00 | | $920.64 | $33.75 | $57.54 |

642

# Crews

| Crew No. | Bare Costs | | Incl. Subs O&P | | Cost Per Labor-Hour | |
|---|---|---|---|---|---|---|

**Crew C-5**

| Crew C-5 | Hr. | Daily | Hr. | Daily | Bare Costs | Incl. O&P |
|---|---|---|---|---|---|---|
| 1 Rodman Foreman | $33.35 | $266.80 | $58.40 | $467.20 | $28.28 | $48.44 |
| 2 Rodmen (reinf.) | 31.35 | 501.60 | 54.90 | 878.40 | | |
| 1 Equip. Oper. (crane) | 30.65 | 245.20 | 50.15 | 401.20 | | |
| 2 Building Laborers | 21.50 | 344.00 | 36.15 | 578.40 | | |
| 1 Hyd. Crane, 25 Ton | | 747.60 | | 822.36 | 15.57 | 17.13 |
| 48 L.H., Daily Totals | | $2105.20 | | $3147.56 | $43.86 | $65.57 |

| Crew C-6 | Hr. | Daily | Hr. | Daily | Bare Costs | Incl. O&P |
|---|---|---|---|---|---|---|
| 1 Labor Foreman (outside) | $23.50 | $188.00 | $39.55 | $316.40 | $22.88 | $38.11 |
| 4 Laborers | 21.50 | 688.00 | 36.15 | 1156.80 | | |
| 1 Cement Finisher | 27.80 | 222.40 | 44.50 | 356.00 | | |
| 2 Gas Engine Vibrators | | 60.80 | | 66.88 | 1.27 | 1.39 |
| 48 L.H., Daily Totals | | $1159.20 | | $1896.08 | $24.15 | $39.50 |

| Crew C-7 | Hr. | Daily | Hr. | Daily | Bare Costs | Incl. O&P |
|---|---|---|---|---|---|---|
| 1 Labor Foreman (outside) | $23.50 | $188.00 | $39.55 | $316.40 | $23.88 | $39.63 |
| 5 Laborers | 21.50 | 860.00 | 36.15 | 1446.00 | | |
| 1 Cement Finisher | 27.80 | 222.40 | 44.50 | 356.00 | | |
| 1 Equip. Oper. (med.) | 29.65 | 237.20 | 48.55 | 388.40 | | |
| 1 Equip. Oper. (oiler) | 26.45 | 211.60 | 43.30 | 346.40 | | |
| 2 Gas Engine Vibrators | | 60.80 | | 66.88 | | |
| 1 Concrete Bucket, 1 C.Y. | | 20.60 | | 22.66 | | |
| 1 Hyd. Crane, 55 Ton | | 1209.00 | | 1329.90 | 17.92 | 19.71 |
| 72 L.H., Daily Totals | | $3009.60 | | $4272.64 | $41.80 | $59.34 |

| Crew C-8 | Hr. | Daily | Hr. | Daily | Bare Costs | Incl. O&P |
|---|---|---|---|---|---|---|
| 1 Labor Foreman (outside) | $23.50 | $188.00 | $39.55 | $316.40 | $24.75 | $40.79 |
| 3 Laborers | 21.50 | 516.00 | 36.15 | 867.60 | | |
| 2 Cement Finishers | 27.80 | 444.80 | 44.50 | 712.00 | | |
| 1 Equip. Oper. (med.) | 29.65 | 237.20 | 48.55 | 388.40 | | |
| 1 Concrete Pump (small) | | 738.80 | | 812.68 | 13.19 | 14.51 |
| 56 L.H., Daily Totals | | $2124.80 | | $3097.08 | $37.94 | $55.31 |

| Crew C-8A | Hr. | Daily | Hr. | Daily | Bare Costs | Incl. O&P |
|---|---|---|---|---|---|---|
| 1 Labor Foreman (outside) | $23.50 | $188.00 | $39.55 | $316.40 | $23.93 | $39.50 |
| 3 Laborers | 21.50 | 516.00 | 36.15 | 867.60 | | |
| 2 Cement Finishers | 27.80 | 444.80 | 44.50 | 712.00 | | |
| 48 L.H., Daily Totals | | $1148.80 | | $1896.00 | $23.93 | $39.50 |

| Crew C-8B | Hr. | Daily | Hr. | Daily | Bare Costs | Incl. O&P |
|---|---|---|---|---|---|---|
| 1 Labor Foreman (outside) | $23.50 | $188.00 | $39.55 | $316.40 | $23.53 | $39.31 |
| 3 Laborers | 21.50 | 516.00 | 36.15 | 867.60 | | |
| 1 Equip. Oper. (med.) | 29.65 | 237.20 | 48.55 | 388.40 | | |
| 1 Vibrating Power Screed | | 65.15 | | 71.67 | | |
| 1 Roller, Vibratory, 25 Ton | | 633.20 | | 696.52 | | |
| 1 Dozer, 200 H.P. | | 1192.00 | | 1311.20 | 47.26 | 51.98 |
| 40 L.H., Daily Totals | | $2831.55 | | $3651.78 | $70.79 | $91.29 |

| Crew C-8C | Hr. | Daily | Hr. | Daily | Bare Costs | Incl. O&P |
|---|---|---|---|---|---|---|
| 1 Labor Foreman (outside) | $23.50 | $188.00 | $39.55 | $316.40 | $24.24 | $40.17 |
| 3 Laborers | 21.50 | 516.00 | 36.15 | 867.60 | | |
| 1 Cement Finisher | 27.80 | 222.40 | 44.50 | 356.00 | | |
| 1 Equip. Oper. (med.) | 29.65 | 237.20 | 48.55 | 388.40 | | |
| 1 Shotcrete Rig, 12 C.Y./hr | | 249.20 | | 274.12 | 5.19 | 5.71 |
| 48 L.H., Daily Totals | | $1412.80 | | $2202.52 | $29.43 | $45.89 |

| Crew C-8D | Hr. | Daily | Hr. | Daily | Bare Costs | Incl. O&P |
|---|---|---|---|---|---|---|
| 1 Labor Foreman (outside) | $23.50 | $188.00 | $39.55 | $316.40 | $25.32 | $41.71 |
| 1 Laborer | 21.50 | 172.00 | 36.15 | 289.20 | | |
| 1 Cement Finisher | 27.80 | 222.40 | 44.50 | 356.00 | | |
| 1 Equipment Oper. (light) | 28.50 | 228.00 | 46.65 | 373.20 | | |
| 1 Air Compressor, 250 cfm | | 193.40 | | 212.74 | | |
| 2 -50' Air Hoses, 1" | | 8.20 | | 9.02 | 6.30 | 6.93 |
| 32 L.H., Daily Totals | | $1012.00 | | $1556.56 | $31.63 | $48.64 |

| Crew C-8E | Hr. | Daily | Hr. | Daily | Bare Costs | Incl. O&P |
|---|---|---|---|---|---|---|
| 1 Labor Foreman (outside) | $23.50 | $188.00 | $39.55 | $316.40 | $25.32 | $41.71 |
| 1 Laborer | 21.50 | 172.00 | 36.15 | 289.20 | | |
| 1 Cement Finisher | 27.80 | 222.40 | 44.50 | 356.00 | | |
| 1 Equipment Oper. (light) | 28.50 | 228.00 | 46.65 | 373.20 | | |
| 1 Air Compressor, 250 cfm | | 193.40 | | 212.74 | | |
| 2 -50' Air Hoses, 1" | | 8.20 | | 9.02 | | |
| 1 Concrete Pump (small) | | 738.80 | | 812.68 | 29.39 | 32.33 |
| 32 L.H., Daily Totals | | $1750.80 | | $2369.24 | $54.71 | $74.04 |

| Crew C-10 | Hr. | Daily | Hr. | Daily | Bare Costs | Incl. O&P |
|---|---|---|---|---|---|---|
| 1 Laborer | $21.50 | $172.00 | $36.15 | $289.20 | $25.70 | $41.72 |
| 2 Cement Finishers | 27.80 | 444.80 | 44.50 | 712.00 | | |
| 24 L.H., Daily Totals | | $616.80 | | $1001.20 | $25.70 | $41.72 |

| Crew C-10B | Hr. | Daily | Hr. | Daily | Bare Costs | Incl. O&P |
|---|---|---|---|---|---|---|
| 3 Laborers | $21.50 | $516.00 | $36.15 | $867.60 | $24.02 | $39.49 |
| 2 Cement Finishers | 27.80 | 444.80 | 44.50 | 712.00 | | |
| 1 Concrete Mixer, 10 C.F. | | 168.40 | | 185.24 | | |
| 2 Trowels, 48" Walk-Behind | | 98.00 | | 107.80 | 6.66 | 7.33 |
| 40 L.H., Daily Totals | | $1227.20 | | $1872.64 | $30.68 | $46.82 |

| Crew C-10C | Hr. | Daily | Hr. | Daily | Bare Costs | Incl. O&P |
|---|---|---|---|---|---|---|
| 1 Laborer | $21.50 | $172.00 | $36.15 | $289.20 | $25.70 | $41.72 |
| 2 Cement Finishers | 27.80 | 444.80 | 44.50 | 712.00 | | |
| 1 Trowel, 48" Walk-Behind | | 49.00 | | 53.90 | 2.04 | 2.25 |
| 24 L.H., Daily Totals | | $665.80 | | $1055.10 | $27.74 | $43.96 |

| Crew C-10D | Hr. | Daily | Hr. | Daily | Bare Costs | Incl. O&P |
|---|---|---|---|---|---|---|
| 1 Laborer | $21.50 | $172.00 | $36.15 | $289.20 | $25.70 | $41.72 |
| 2 Cement Finishers | 27.80 | 444.80 | 44.50 | 712.00 | | |
| 1 Vibrating Power Screed | | 65.15 | | 71.67 | | |
| 1 Trowel, 48" Walk-Behind | | 49.00 | | 53.90 | 4.76 | 5.23 |
| 24 L.H., Daily Totals | | $730.95 | | $1126.77 | $30.46 | $46.95 |

| Crew C-10E | Hr. | Daily | Hr. | Daily | Bare Costs | Incl. O&P |
|---|---|---|---|---|---|---|
| 1 Laborer | $21.50 | $172.00 | $36.15 | $289.20 | $25.70 | $41.72 |
| 2 Cement Finishers | 27.80 | 444.80 | 44.50 | 712.00 | | |
| 1 Vibrating Power Screed | | 65.15 | | 71.67 | | |
| 1 Cement Trowel, 96" Ride-On | | 185.80 | | 204.38 | 10.46 | 11.50 |
| 24 L.H., Daily Totals | | $867.75 | | $1277.24 | $36.16 | $53.22 |

| Crew C-11 | Hr. | Daily | Hr. | Daily | Bare Costs | Incl. O&P |
|---|---|---|---|---|---|---|
| 1 Skilled Worker Foreman | $31.25 | $250.00 | $52.40 | $419.20 | $29.74 | $49.69 |
| 5 Skilled Workers | 29.25 | 1170.00 | 49.05 | 1962.00 | | |
| 1 Equip. Oper. (crane) | 30.65 | 245.20 | 50.15 | 401.20 | | |
| 1 Lattice Boom Crane, 150 Ton | | 2003.00 | | 2203.30 | 35.77 | 39.34 |
| 56 L.H., Daily Totals | | $3668.20 | | $4985.70 | $65.50 | $89.03 |

643

## Crew C-12

| | Hr. | Daily | Hr. | Daily | Bare Costs | Incl. O&P |
|---|---|---|---|---|---|---|
| 1 Carpenter Foreman (out) | $31.10 | $248.80 | $52.30 | $418.40 | $28.43 | $47.58 |
| 3 Carpenters | 29.10 | 698.40 | 48.95 | 1174.80 | | |
| 1 Laborer | 21.50 | 172.00 | 36.15 | 289.20 | | |
| 1 Equip. Oper. (crane) | 30.65 | 245.20 | 50.15 | 401.20 | | |
| 1 Hyd. Crane, 12 Ton | | 655.60 | | 721.16 | 13.66 | 15.02 |
| 48 L.H., Daily Totals | | $2020.00 | | $3004.76 | $42.08 | $62.60 |

## Crew C-13

| | Hr. | Daily | Hr. | Daily | Bare Costs | Incl. O&P |
|---|---|---|---|---|---|---|
| 2 Struc. Steel Workers | $31.40 | $502.40 | $59.60 | $953.60 | $30.63 | $56.05 |
| 1 Carpenter | 29.10 | 232.80 | 48.95 | 391.60 | | |
| 1 Welder, gas engine, 300 amp | | 145.80 | | 160.38 | 6.08 | 6.68 |
| 24 L.H., Daily Totals | | $881.00 | | $1505.58 | $36.71 | $62.73 |

## Crew C-14

| | Hr. | Daily | Hr. | Daily | Bare Costs | Incl. O&P |
|---|---|---|---|---|---|---|
| 1 Carpenter Foreman (out) | $31.10 | $248.80 | $52.30 | $418.40 | $25.90 | $43.43 |
| 3 Carpenters | 29.10 | 698.40 | 48.95 | 1174.80 | | |
| 2 Carpenter Helpers | 21.75 | 348.00 | 36.40 | 582.40 | | |
| 4 Laborers | 21.50 | 688.00 | 36.15 | 1156.80 | | |
| 2 Rodmen (reinf.) | 31.35 | 501.60 | 54.90 | 878.40 | | |
| 2 Rodman Helpers | 21.75 | 348.00 | 36.40 | 582.40 | | |
| 2 Cement Finishers | 27.80 | 444.80 | 44.50 | 712.00 | | |
| 1 Equip. Oper. (crane) | 30.65 | 245.20 | 50.15 | 401.20 | | |
| 1 Hyd. Crane, 80 Ton | | 1545.00 | | 1699.50 | 11.36 | 12.50 |
| 136 L.H., Daily Totals | | $5067.80 | | $7605.90 | $37.26 | $55.93 |

## Crew C-14A

| | Hr. | Daily | Hr. | Daily | Bare Costs | Incl. O&P |
|---|---|---|---|---|---|---|
| 1 Carpenter Foreman (out) | $31.10 | $248.80 | $52.30 | $418.40 | $28.90 | $48.82 |
| 16 Carpenters | 29.10 | 3724.80 | 48.95 | 6265.60 | | |
| 4 Rodmen (reinf.) | 31.35 | 1003.20 | 54.90 | 1756.80 | | |
| 2 Laborers | 21.50 | 344.00 | 36.15 | 578.40 | | |
| 1 Cement Finisher | 27.80 | 222.40 | 44.50 | 356.00 | | |
| 1 Equip. Oper. (med.) | 29.65 | 237.20 | 48.55 | 388.40 | | |
| 1 Gas Engine Vibrator | | 30.40 | | 33.44 | | |
| 1 Concrete Pump (small) | | 738.80 | | 812.68 | 3.85 | 4.23 |
| 200 L.H., Daily Totals | | $6549.60 | | $10609.72 | $32.75 | $53.05 |

## Crew C-14B

| | Hr. | Daily | Hr. | Daily | Bare Costs | Incl. O&P |
|---|---|---|---|---|---|---|
| 1 Carpenter Foreman (out) | $31.10 | $248.80 | $52.30 | $418.40 | $28.86 | $48.65 |
| 16 Carpenters | 29.10 | 3724.80 | 48.95 | 6265.60 | | |
| 4 Rodmen (reinf.) | 31.35 | 1003.20 | 54.90 | 1756.80 | | |
| 2 Laborers | 21.50 | 344.00 | 36.15 | 578.40 | | |
| 2 Cement Finishers | 27.80 | 444.80 | 44.50 | 712.00 | | |
| 1 Equip. Oper. (med.) | 29.65 | 237.20 | 48.55 | 388.40 | | |
| 1 Gas Engine Vibrator | | 30.40 | | 33.44 | | |
| 1 Concrete Pump (small) | | 738.80 | | 812.68 | 3.70 | 4.07 |
| 208 L.H., Daily Totals | | $6772.00 | | $10965.72 | $32.56 | $52.72 |

## Crew C-14C

| | Hr. | Daily | Hr. | Daily | Bare Costs | Incl. O&P |
|---|---|---|---|---|---|---|
| 1 Carpenter Foreman (out) | $31.10 | $248.80 | $52.30 | $418.40 | $27.30 | $46.06 |
| 6 Carpenters | 29.10 | 1396.80 | 48.95 | 2349.60 | | |
| 2 Rodmen (reinf.) | 31.35 | 501.60 | 54.90 | 878.40 | | |
| 4 Laborers | 21.50 | 688.00 | 36.15 | 1156.80 | | |
| 1 Cement Finisher | 27.80 | 222.40 | 44.50 | 356.00 | | |
| 1 Gas Engine Vibrator | | 30.40 | | 33.44 | 0.27 | 0.30 |
| 112 L.H., Daily Totals | | $3088.00 | | $5192.64 | $27.57 | $46.36 |

## Crew C-14D

| | Hr. | Daily | Hr. | Daily | Bare Costs | Incl. O&P |
|---|---|---|---|---|---|---|
| 1 Carpenter Foreman (out) | $31.10 | $248.80 | $52.30 | $418.40 | $28.72 | $48.34 |
| 18 Carpenters | 29.10 | 4190.40 | 48.95 | 7048.80 | | |
| 2 Rodmen (reinf.) | 31.35 | 501.60 | 54.90 | 878.40 | | |
| 2 Laborers | 21.50 | 344.00 | 36.15 | 578.40 | | |
| 1 Cement Finisher | 27.80 | 222.40 | 44.50 | 356.00 | | |
| 1 Equip. Oper. (med.) | 29.65 | 237.20 | 48.55 | 388.40 | | |
| 1 Gas Engine Vibrator | | 30.40 | | 33.44 | | |
| 1 Concrete Pump (small) | | 738.80 | | 812.68 | 3.85 | 4.23 |
| 200 L.H., Daily Totals | | $6513.60 | | $10514.52 | $32.57 | $52.57 |

## Crew C-14E

| | Hr. | Daily | Hr. | Daily | Bare Costs | Incl. O&P |
|---|---|---|---|---|---|---|
| 1 Carpenter Foreman (out) | $31.10 | $248.80 | $52.30 | $418.40 | $27.91 | $47.52 |
| 2 Carpenters | 29.10 | 465.60 | 48.95 | 783.20 | | |
| 4 Rodmen (reinf.) | 31.35 | 1003.20 | 54.90 | 1756.80 | | |
| 3 Laborers | 21.50 | 516.00 | 36.15 | 867.60 | | |
| 1 Cement Finisher | 27.80 | 222.40 | 44.50 | 356.00 | | |
| 1 Gas Engine Vibrator | | 30.40 | | 33.44 | 0.35 | 0.38 |
| 88 L.H., Daily Totals | | $2486.40 | | $4215.44 | $28.25 | $47.90 |

## Crew C-14F

| | Hr. | Daily | Hr. | Daily | Bare Costs | Incl. O&P |
|---|---|---|---|---|---|---|
| 1 Laborer Foreman (out) | $23.50 | $188.00 | $39.55 | $316.40 | $25.92 | $42.09 |
| 2 Laborers | 21.50 | 344.00 | 36.15 | 578.40 | | |
| 6 Cement Finishers | 27.80 | 1334.40 | 44.50 | 2136.00 | | |
| 1 Gas Engine Vibrator | | 30.40 | | 33.44 | 0.42 | 0.46 |
| 72 L.H., Daily Totals | | $1896.80 | | $3064.24 | $26.34 | $42.56 |

## Crew C-14G

| | Hr. | Daily | Hr. | Daily | Bare Costs | Incl. O&P |
|---|---|---|---|---|---|---|
| 1 Laborer Foreman (out) | $23.50 | $188.00 | $39.55 | $316.40 | $25.39 | $41.41 |
| 2 Laborers | 21.50 | 344.00 | 36.15 | 578.40 | | |
| 4 Cement Finishers | 27.80 | 889.60 | 44.50 | 1424.00 | | |
| 1 Gas Engine Vibrator | | 30.40 | | 33.44 | 0.54 | 0.60 |
| 56 L.H., Daily Totals | | $1452.00 | | $2352.24 | $25.93 | $42.00 |

## Crew C-14H

| | Hr. | Daily | Hr. | Daily | Bare Costs | Incl. O&P |
|---|---|---|---|---|---|---|
| 1 Carpenter Foreman (out) | $31.10 | $248.80 | $52.30 | $418.40 | $28.32 | $47.63 |
| 2 Carpenters | 29.10 | 465.60 | 48.95 | 783.20 | | |
| 1 Rodman (reinf.) | 31.35 | 250.80 | 54.90 | 439.20 | | |
| 1 Laborer | 21.50 | 172.00 | 36.15 | 289.20 | | |
| 1 Cement Finisher | 27.80 | 222.40 | 44.50 | 356.00 | | |
| 1 Gas Engine Vibrator | | 30.40 | | 33.44 | 0.63 | 0.70 |
| 48 L.H., Daily Totals | | $1390.00 | | $2319.44 | $28.96 | $48.32 |

## Crew C-14L

| | Hr. | Daily | Hr. | Daily | Bare Costs | Incl. O&P |
|---|---|---|---|---|---|---|
| 1 Carpenter Foreman (out) | $31.10 | $248.80 | $52.30 | $418.40 | $26.63 | $44.59 |
| 6 Carpenters | 29.10 | 1396.80 | 48.95 | 2349.60 | | |
| 4 Laborers | 21.50 | 688.00 | 36.15 | 1156.80 | | |
| 1 Cement Finisher | 27.80 | 222.40 | 44.50 | 356.00 | | |
| 1 Gas Engine Vibrator | | 30.40 | | 33.44 | 0.32 | 0.35 |
| 96 L.H., Daily Totals | | $2586.40 | | $4314.24 | $26.94 | $44.94 |

## Crew C-15

| | Hr. | Daily | Hr. | Daily | Bare Costs | Incl. O&P |
|---|---|---|---|---|---|---|
| 1 Carpenter Foreman (out) | $31.10 | $248.80 | $52.30 | $418.40 | $26.75 | $44.73 |
| 2 Carpenters | 29.10 | 465.60 | 48.95 | 783.20 | | |
| 3 Laborers | 21.50 | 516.00 | 36.15 | 867.60 | | |
| 2 Cement Finishers | 27.80 | 444.80 | 44.50 | 712.00 | | |
| 1 Rodman (reinf.) | 31.35 | 250.80 | 54.90 | 439.20 | | |
| 72 L.H., Daily Totals | | $1926.00 | | $3220.40 | $26.75 | $44.73 |

# Crews

## Crew C-16

| Crew No. | Hr. | Daily | Hr. | Daily | Bare Costs | Incl. O&P |
|---|---|---|---|---|---|---|
| 1 Labor Foreman (outside) | $23.50 | $188.00 | $39.55 | $316.40 | $26.22 | $43.93 |
| 3 Laborers | 21.50 | 516.00 | 36.15 | 867.60 | | |
| 2 Cement Finishers | 27.80 | 444.80 | 44.50 | 712.00 | | |
| 1 Equip. Oper. (med.) | 29.65 | 237.20 | 48.55 | 388.40 | | |
| 2 Rodmen (reinf.) | 31.35 | 501.60 | 54.90 | 878.40 | | |
| 1 Concrete Pump (small) | | 738.80 | | 812.68 | 10.26 | 11.29 |
| 72 L.H., Daily Totals | | $2626.40 | | $3975.48 | $36.48 | $55.22 |

## Crew C-17

| Crew No. | Hr. | Daily | Hr. | Daily | Bare Costs | Incl. O&P |
|---|---|---|---|---|---|---|
| 2 Skilled Worker Foremen | $31.25 | $500.00 | $52.40 | $838.40 | $29.65 | $49.72 |
| 8 Skilled Workers | 29.25 | 1872.00 | 49.05 | 3139.20 | | |
| 80 L.H., Daily Totals | | $2372.00 | | $3977.60 | $29.65 | $49.72 |

## Crew C-17A

| Crew No. | Hr. | Daily | Hr. | Daily | Bare Costs | Incl. O&P |
|---|---|---|---|---|---|---|
| 2 Skilled Worker Foremen | $31.25 | $500.00 | $52.40 | $838.40 | $29.66 | $49.73 |
| 8 Skilled Workers | 29.25 | 1872.00 | 49.05 | 3139.20 | | |
| .125 Equip. Oper. (crane) | 30.65 | 30.65 | 50.15 | 50.15 | | |
| .125 Hyd. Crane, 80 Ton | | 193.13 | | 212.44 | 2.38 | 2.62 |
| 81 L.H., Daily Totals | | $2595.78 | | $4240.19 | $32.05 | $52.35 |

## Crew C-17B

| Crew No. | Hr. | Daily | Hr. | Daily | Bare Costs | Incl. O&P |
|---|---|---|---|---|---|---|
| 2 Skilled Worker Foremen | $31.25 | $500.00 | $52.40 | $838.40 | $29.67 | $49.73 |
| 8 Skilled Workers | 29.25 | 1872.00 | 49.05 | 3139.20 | | |
| .25 Equip. Oper. (crane) | 30.65 | 61.30 | 50.15 | 100.30 | | |
| .25 Hyd. Crane, 80 Ton | | 386.25 | | 424.88 | | |
| .25 Trowel, 48" Walk-Behind | | 12.25 | | 13.48 | 4.86 | 5.35 |
| 82 L.H., Daily Totals | | $2831.80 | | $4516.25 | $34.53 | $55.08 |

## Crew C-17C

| Crew No. | Hr. | Daily | Hr. | Daily | Bare Costs | Incl. O&P |
|---|---|---|---|---|---|---|
| 2 Skilled Worker Foremen | $31.25 | $500.00 | $52.40 | $838.40 | $29.69 | $49.74 |
| 8 Skilled Workers | 29.25 | 1872.00 | 49.05 | 3139.20 | | |
| .375 Equip. Oper. (crane) | 30.65 | 91.95 | 50.15 | 150.45 | | |
| .375 Hyd. Crane, 80 Ton | | 579.38 | | 637.31 | 6.98 | 7.68 |
| 83 L.H., Daily Totals | | $3043.32 | | $4765.36 | $36.67 | $57.41 |

## Crew C-17D

| Crew No. | Hr. | Daily | Hr. | Daily | Bare Costs | Incl. O&P |
|---|---|---|---|---|---|---|
| 2 Skilled Worker Foremen | $31.25 | $500.00 | $52.40 | $838.40 | $29.70 | $49.74 |
| 8 Skilled Workers | 29.25 | 1872.00 | 49.05 | 3139.20 | | |
| .5 Equip. Oper. (crane) | 30.65 | 122.60 | 50.15 | 200.60 | | |
| .5 Hyd. Crane, 80 Ton | | 772.50 | | 849.75 | 9.20 | 10.12 |
| 84 L.H., Daily Totals | | $3267.10 | | $5027.95 | $38.89 | $59.86 |

## Crew C-17E

| Crew No. | Hr. | Daily | Hr. | Daily | Bare Costs | Incl. O&P |
|---|---|---|---|---|---|---|
| 2 Skilled Worker Foremen | $31.25 | $500.00 | $52.40 | $838.40 | $29.65 | $49.72 |
| 8 Skilled Workers | 29.25 | 1872.00 | 49.05 | 3139.20 | | |
| 1 Hyd. Jack with Rods | | 87.35 | | 96.08 | 1.09 | 1.20 |
| 80 L.H., Daily Totals | | $2459.35 | | $4073.68 | $30.74 | $50.92 |

## Crew C-18

| Crew No. | Hr. | Daily | Hr. | Daily | Bare Costs | Incl. O&P |
|---|---|---|---|---|---|---|
| .125 Labor Foreman (out) | $23.50 | $23.50 | $39.55 | $39.55 | $21.72 | $36.53 |
| 1 Laborer | 21.50 | 172.00 | 36.15 | 289.20 | | |
| 1 Concrete Cart, 10 C.F. | | 58.40 | | 64.24 | 6.49 | 7.14 |
| 9 L.H., Daily Totals | | $253.90 | | $392.99 | $28.21 | $43.67 |

## Crew C-19

| Crew No. | Hr. | Daily | Hr. | Daily | Bare Costs | Incl. O&P |
|---|---|---|---|---|---|---|
| .125 Labor Foreman (out) | $23.50 | $23.50 | $39.55 | $39.55 | $21.72 | $36.53 |
| 1 Laborer | 21.50 | 172.00 | 36.15 | 289.20 | | |
| 1 Concrete Cart, 18 C.F. | | 94.00 | | 103.40 | 10.44 | 11.49 |
| 9 L.H., Daily Totals | | $289.50 | | $432.15 | $32.17 | $48.02 |

## Crew C-20

| Crew No. | Hr. | Daily | Hr. | Daily | Bare Costs | Incl. O&P |
|---|---|---|---|---|---|---|
| 1 Labor Foreman (outside) | $23.50 | $188.00 | $39.55 | $316.40 | $23.56 | $39.17 |
| 5 Laborers | 21.50 | 860.00 | 36.15 | 1446.00 | | |
| 1 Cement Finisher | 27.80 | 222.40 | 44.50 | 356.00 | | |
| 1 Equip. Oper. (med.) | 29.65 | 237.20 | 48.55 | 388.40 | | |
| 2 Gas Engine Vibrators | | 60.80 | | 66.88 | | |
| 1 Concrete Pump (small) | | 738.80 | | 812.68 | 12.49 | 13.74 |
| 64 L.H., Daily Totals | | $2307.20 | | $3386.36 | $36.05 | $52.91 |

## Crew C-21

| Crew No. | Hr. | Daily | Hr. | Daily | Bare Costs | Incl. O&P |
|---|---|---|---|---|---|---|
| 1 Labor Foreman (outside) | $23.50 | $188.00 | $39.55 | $316.40 | $23.56 | $39.17 |
| 5 Laborers | 21.50 | 860.00 | 36.15 | 1446.00 | | |
| 1 Cement Finisher | 27.80 | 222.40 | 44.50 | 356.00 | | |
| 1 Equip. Oper. (med.) | 29.65 | 237.20 | 48.55 | 388.40 | | |
| 2 Gas Engine Vibrators | | 60.80 | | 66.88 | | |
| 1 Concrete Conveyer | | 194.60 | | 214.06 | 3.99 | 4.39 |
| 64 L.H., Daily Totals | | $1763.00 | | $2787.74 | $27.55 | $43.56 |

## Crew C-22

| Crew No. | Hr. | Daily | Hr. | Daily | Bare Costs | Incl. O&P |
|---|---|---|---|---|---|---|
| 1 Rodman Foreman | $33.35 | $266.80 | $58.40 | $467.20 | $31.60 | $55.18 |
| 4 Rodmen (reinf.) | 31.35 | 1003.20 | 54.90 | 1756.80 | | |
| .125 Equip. Oper. (crane) | 30.65 | 30.65 | 50.15 | 50.15 | | |
| .125 Equip. Oper. Oiler | 26.45 | 26.45 | 43.30 | 43.30 | | |
| .125 Hyd. Crane, 25 Ton | | 93.45 | | 102.80 | 2.23 | 2.45 |
| 42 L.H., Daily Totals | | $1420.55 | | $2420.24 | $33.82 | $57.62 |

## Crew C-23

| Crew No. | Hr. | Daily | Hr. | Daily | Bare Costs | Incl. O&P |
|---|---|---|---|---|---|---|
| 2 Skilled Worker Foremen | $31.25 | $500.00 | $52.40 | $838.40 | $29.51 | $49.26 |
| 6 Skilled Workers | 29.25 | 1404.00 | 49.05 | 2354.40 | | |
| 1 Equip. Oper. (crane) | 30.65 | 245.20 | 50.15 | 401.20 | | |
| 1 Equip. Oper. Oiler | 26.45 | 211.60 | 43.30 | 346.40 | | |
| 1 Lattice Boom Crane, 90 Ton | | 1607.00 | | 1767.70 | 20.09 | 22.10 |
| 80 L.H., Daily Totals | | $3967.80 | | $5708.10 | $49.60 | $71.35 |

## Crew C-24

| Crew No. | Hr. | Daily | Hr. | Daily | Bare Costs | Incl. O&P |
|---|---|---|---|---|---|---|
| 2 Skilled Worker Foremen | $31.25 | $500.00 | $52.40 | $838.40 | $29.51 | $49.26 |
| 6 Skilled Workers | 29.25 | 1404.00 | 49.05 | 2354.40 | | |
| 1 Equip. Oper. (crane) | 30.65 | 245.20 | 50.15 | 401.20 | | |
| 1 Equip. Oper. Oiler | 26.45 | 211.60 | 43.30 | 346.40 | | |
| 1 Lattice Boom Crane, 150 Ton | | 2003.00 | | 2203.30 | 25.04 | 27.54 |
| 80 L.H., Daily Totals | | $4363.80 | | $6143.70 | $54.55 | $76.80 |

## Crew C-25

| Crew No. | Hr. | Daily | Hr. | Daily | Bare Costs | Incl. O&P |
|---|---|---|---|---|---|---|
| 2 Rodmen (reinf.) | $31.35 | $501.60 | $54.90 | $878.40 | $24.73 | $43.75 |
| 2 Rodmen Helpers | 18.10 | 289.60 | 32.60 | 521.60 | | |
| 32 L.H., Daily Totals | | $791.20 | | $1400.00 | $24.73 | $43.75 |

## Crew C-27

| Crew No. | Hr. | Daily | Hr. | Daily | Bare Costs | Incl. O&P |
|---|---|---|---|---|---|---|
| 2 Cement Finishers | $27.80 | $444.80 | $44.50 | $712.00 | $27.80 | $44.50 |
| 1 Concrete Saw | | 161.40 | | 177.54 | 10.09 | 11.10 |
| 16 L.H., Daily Totals | | $606.20 | | $889.54 | $37.89 | $55.60 |

## Crew C-28

| Crew No. | Hr. | Daily | Hr. | Daily | Bare Costs | Incl. O&P |
|---|---|---|---|---|---|---|
| 1 Cement Finisher | $27.80 | $222.40 | $44.50 | $356.00 | $27.80 | $44.50 |
| 1 Portable Air Compressor, Gas | | 17.80 | | 19.58 | 2.23 | 2.45 |
| 8 L.H., Daily Totals | | $240.20 | | $375.58 | $30.02 | $46.95 |

## Crew D-1

| Crew No. | Hr. | Daily | Hr. | Daily | Bare Costs | Incl. O&P |
|---|---|---|---|---|---|---|
| 1 Bricklayer | $29.25 | $234.00 | $48.20 | $385.60 | $26.40 | $43.50 |
| 1 Bricklayer Helper | 23.55 | 188.40 | 38.80 | 310.40 | | |
| 16 L.H., Daily Totals | | $422.40 | | $696.00 | $26.40 | $43.50 |

| Crew No. | Bare Costs | | Incl. Subs O&P | | Cost Per Labor-Hour | |
|---|---|---|---|---|---|---|

**Crew D-2**

| Crew D-2 | Hr. | Daily | Hr. | Daily | Bare Costs | Incl. O&P |
|---|---|---|---|---|---|---|
| 3 Bricklayers | $29.25 | $702.00 | $48.20 | $1156.80 | $26.97 | $44.44 |
| 2 Bricklayer Helpers | 23.55 | 376.80 | 38.80 | 620.80 | | |
| 40 L.H., Daily Totals | | $1078.80 | | $1777.60 | $26.97 | $44.44 |

**Crew D-3**

| Crew D-3 | Hr. | Daily | Hr. | Daily | Bare Costs | Incl. O&P |
|---|---|---|---|---|---|---|
| 3 Bricklayers | $29.25 | $702.00 | $48.20 | $1156.80 | $27.07 | $44.65 |
| 2 Bricklayer Helpers | 23.55 | 376.80 | 38.80 | 620.80 | | |
| .25 Carpenter | 29.10 | 58.20 | 48.95 | 97.90 | | |
| 42 L.H., Daily Totals | | $1137.00 | | $1875.50 | $27.07 | $44.65 |

**Crew D-4**

| Crew D-4 | Hr. | Daily | Hr. | Daily | Bare Costs | Incl. O&P |
|---|---|---|---|---|---|---|
| 1 Bricklayer | $29.25 | $234.00 | $48.20 | $385.60 | $24.28 | $40.15 |
| 3 Bricklayer Helpers | 23.55 | 565.20 | 38.80 | 931.20 | | |
| 1 Building Laborer | 21.50 | 172.00 | 36.15 | 289.20 | | |
| 1 Grout Pump, 50 C.F./hr. | | 132.60 | | 145.86 | 3.31 | 3.65 |
| 40 L.H., Daily Totals | | $1103.80 | | $1751.86 | $27.59 | $43.80 |

**Crew D-5**

| Crew D-5 | Hr. | Daily | Hr. | Daily | Bare Costs | Incl. O&P |
|---|---|---|---|---|---|---|
| 1 Block Mason Helper | $23.55 | $188.40 | $38.80 | $310.40 | $23.55 | $38.80 |
| 8 L.H., Daily Totals | | $188.40 | | $310.40 | $23.55 | $38.80 |

**Crew D-6**

| Crew D-6 | Hr. | Daily | Hr. | Daily | Bare Costs | Incl. O&P |
|---|---|---|---|---|---|---|
| 3 Bricklayers | $29.25 | $702.00 | $48.20 | $1156.80 | $26.40 | $43.50 |
| 3 Bricklayer Helpers | 23.55 | 565.20 | 38.80 | 931.20 | | |
| 48 L.H., Daily Totals | | $1267.20 | | $2088.00 | $26.40 | $43.50 |

**Crew D-7**

| Crew D-7 | Hr. | Daily | Hr. | Daily | Bare Costs | Incl. O&P |
|---|---|---|---|---|---|---|
| 1 Tile Layer | $27.55 | $220.40 | $44.10 | $352.80 | $24.70 | $39.55 |
| 1 Tile Layer Helper | 21.85 | 174.80 | 35.00 | 280.00 | | |
| 16 L.H., Daily Totals | | $395.20 | | $632.80 | $24.70 | $39.55 |

**Crew D-8**

| Crew D-8 | Hr. | Daily | Hr. | Daily | Bare Costs | Incl. O&P |
|---|---|---|---|---|---|---|
| 3 Bricklayers | $29.25 | $702.00 | $48.20 | $1156.80 | $26.97 | $44.44 |
| 2 Bricklayer Helpers | 23.55 | 376.80 | 38.80 | 620.80 | | |
| 40 L.H., Daily Totals | | $1078.80 | | $1777.60 | $26.97 | $44.44 |

**Crew D-9**

| Crew D-9 | Hr. | Daily | Hr. | Daily | Bare Costs | Incl. O&P |
|---|---|---|---|---|---|---|
| 3 Bricklayers | $29.25 | $702.00 | $48.20 | $1156.80 | $26.40 | $43.50 |
| 3 Bricklayer Helpers | 23.55 | 565.20 | 38.80 | 931.20 | | |
| 48 L.H., Daily Totals | | $1267.20 | | $2088.00 | $26.40 | $43.50 |

**Crew D-10**

| Crew D-10 | Hr. | Daily | Hr. | Daily | Bare Costs | Incl. O&P |
|---|---|---|---|---|---|---|
| 1 Bricklayer Foreman | $31.25 | $250.00 | $51.50 | $412.00 | $28.68 | $47.16 |
| 1 Bricklayer | 29.25 | 234.00 | 48.20 | 385.60 | | |
| 1 Bricklayer Helper | 23.55 | 188.40 | 38.80 | 310.40 | | |
| 1 Equip. Oper. (crane) | 30.65 | 245.20 | 50.15 | 401.20 | | |
| 1 S.P. Crane, 4x4, 12 Ton | | 655.60 | | 721.16 | 20.49 | 22.54 |
| 32 L.H., Daily Totals | | $1573.20 | | $2230.36 | $49.16 | $69.70 |

**Crew D-11**

| Crew D-11 | Hr. | Daily | Hr. | Daily | Bare Costs | Incl. O&P |
|---|---|---|---|---|---|---|
| 2 Bricklayers | $29.25 | $468.00 | $48.20 | $771.20 | $27.35 | $45.07 |
| 1 Bricklayer Helper | 23.55 | 188.40 | 38.80 | 310.40 | | |
| 24 L.H., Daily Totals | | $656.40 | | $1081.60 | $27.35 | $45.07 |

**Crew D-12**

| Crew D-12 | Hr. | Daily | Hr. | Daily | Bare Costs | Incl. O&P |
|---|---|---|---|---|---|---|
| 2 Bricklayers | $29.25 | $468.00 | $48.20 | $771.20 | $26.40 | $43.50 |
| 2 Bricklayer Helpers | 23.55 | 376.80 | 38.80 | 620.80 | | |
| 32 L.H., Daily Totals | | $844.80 | | $1392.00 | $26.40 | $43.50 |

**Crew D-13**

| Crew D-13 | Hr. | Daily | Hr. | Daily | Bare Costs | Incl. O&P |
|---|---|---|---|---|---|---|
| 1 Bricklayer Foreman | $31.25 | $250.00 | $51.50 | $412.00 | $27.92 | $45.94 |
| 2 Bricklayers | 29.25 | 468.00 | 48.20 | 771.20 | | |
| 2 Bricklayer Helpers | 23.55 | 376.80 | 38.80 | 620.80 | | |
| 1 Equip. Oper. (crane) | 30.65 | 245.20 | 50.15 | 401.20 | | |
| 1 S.P. Crane, 4x4, 12 Ton | | 655.60 | | 721.16 | 13.66 | 15.02 |
| 48 L.H., Daily Totals | | $1995.60 | | $2926.36 | $41.58 | $60.97 |

**Crew E-1**

| Crew E-1 | Hr. | Daily | Hr. | Daily | Bare Costs | Incl. O&P |
|---|---|---|---|---|---|---|
| 2 Struc. Steel Workers | $31.40 | $502.40 | $59.60 | $953.60 | $31.40 | $59.60 |
| 1 Welder, gas engine, 300 amp | | 145.80 | | 160.38 | 9.11 | 10.02 |
| 16 L.H., Daily Totals | | $648.20 | | $1113.98 | $40.51 | $69.62 |

**Crew E-2**

| Crew E-2 | Hr. | Daily | Hr. | Daily | Bare Costs | Incl. O&P |
|---|---|---|---|---|---|---|
| 1 Struc. Steel Foreman | $33.40 | $267.20 | $63.40 | $507.20 | $31.61 | $58.66 |
| 4 Struc. Steel Workers | 31.40 | 1004.80 | 59.60 | 1907.20 | | |
| 1 Equip. Oper. (crane) | 30.65 | 245.20 | 50.15 | 401.20 | | |
| 1 Lattice Boom Crane, 90 Ton | | 1607.00 | | 1767.70 | 33.48 | 36.83 |
| 48 L.H., Daily Totals | | $3124.20 | | $4583.30 | $65.09 | $95.49 |

**Crew E-3**

| Crew E-3 | Hr. | Daily | Hr. | Daily | Bare Costs | Incl. O&P |
|---|---|---|---|---|---|---|
| 1 Struc. Steel Foreman | $33.40 | $267.20 | $63.40 | $507.20 | $32.07 | $60.87 |
| 2 Struc. Steel Workers | 31.40 | 502.40 | 59.60 | 953.60 | | |
| 1 Welder, gas engine, 300 amp | | 145.80 | | 160.38 | 6.08 | 6.68 |
| 24 L.H., Daily Totals | | $915.40 | | $1621.18 | $38.14 | $67.55 |

**Crew E-4**

| Crew E-4 | Hr. | Daily | Hr. | Daily | Bare Costs | Incl. O&P |
|---|---|---|---|---|---|---|
| 1 Struc. Steel Foreman | $33.40 | $267.20 | $63.40 | $507.20 | $31.90 | $60.55 |
| 3 Struc. Steel Workers | 31.40 | 753.60 | 59.60 | 1430.40 | | |
| 1 Welder, gas engine, 300 amp | | 145.80 | | 160.38 | 4.56 | 5.01 |
| 32 L.H., Daily Totals | | $1166.60 | | $2097.98 | $36.46 | $65.56 |

**Crew E-5**

| Crew E-5 | Hr. | Daily | Hr. | Daily | Bare Costs | Incl. O&P |
|---|---|---|---|---|---|---|
| 1 Struc. Steel Foreman | $33.40 | $267.20 | $63.40 | $507.20 | $31.54 | $58.97 |
| 7 Struc. Steel Workers | 31.40 | 1758.40 | 59.60 | 3337.60 | | |
| 1 Equip. Oper. (crane) | 30.65 | 245.20 | 50.15 | 401.20 | | |
| 1 Lattice Boom Crane, 90 Ton | | 1607.00 | | 1767.70 | | |
| 1 Welder, gas engine, 300 amp | | 145.80 | | 160.38 | 24.34 | 26.78 |
| 72 L.H., Daily Totals | | $4023.60 | | $6174.08 | $55.88 | $85.75 |

**Crew E-6**

| Crew E-6 | Hr. | Daily | Hr. | Daily | Bare Costs | Incl. O&P |
|---|---|---|---|---|---|---|
| 1 Struc. Steel Foreman | $33.40 | $267.20 | $63.40 | $507.20 | $31.29 | $58.36 |
| 12 Struc. Steel Workers | 31.40 | 3014.40 | 59.60 | 5721.60 | | |
| 1 Equip. Oper. (crane) | 30.65 | 245.20 | 50.15 | 401.20 | | |
| 1 Equip. Oper. (light) | 28.50 | 228.00 | 46.65 | 373.20 | | |
| 1 Lattice Boom Crane, 90 Ton | | 1607.00 | | 1767.70 | | |
| 1 Welder, gas engine, 300 amp | | 145.80 | | 160.38 | | |
| 1 Air Compressor, 160 cfm | | 158.00 | | 173.80 | | |
| 2 Impact Wrenches | | 35.60 | | 39.16 | 16.22 | 17.84 |
| 120 L.H., Daily Totals | | $5701.20 | | $9144.24 | $47.51 | $76.20 |

**Crew E-7**

| Crew E-7 | Hr. | Daily | Hr. | Daily | Bare Costs | Incl. O&P |
|---|---|---|---|---|---|---|
| 1 Struc. Steel Foreman | $33.40 | $267.20 | $63.40 | $507.20 | $31.54 | $58.97 |
| 7 Struc. Steel Workers | 31.40 | 1758.40 | 59.60 | 3337.60 | | |
| 1 Equip. Oper. (crane) | 30.65 | 245.20 | 50.15 | 401.20 | | |
| 1 Lattice Boom Crane, 90 Ton | | 1607.00 | | 1767.70 | | |
| 2 Welders, gas engine, 300 amp | | 291.60 | | 320.76 | 26.37 | 29.01 |
| 72 L.H., Daily Totals | | $4169.40 | | $6334.46 | $57.91 | $87.98 |

| Crew No. | Bare Costs Hr. | Daily | Incl. Subs O&P Hr. | Daily | Cost Per Labor-Hour Bare Costs | Incl. O&P |
|---|---|---|---|---|---|---|
| **Crew E-8** | Hr. | Daily | Hr. | Daily | Bare Costs | Incl. O&P |
| 1 Struc. Steel Foreman | $33.40 | $267.20 | $63.40 | $507.20 | $31.51 | $59.09 |
| 9 Struc. Steel Workers | 31.40 | 2260.80 | 59.60 | 4291.20 | | |
| 1 Equip. Oper. (crane) | 30.65 | 245.20 | 50.15 | 401.20 | | |
| 1 Lattice Boom Crane, 90 Ton | | 1607.00 | | 1767.70 | | |
| 4 Welders, gas engine, 300 amp | | 583.20 | | 641.52 | 24.89 | 27.38 |
| 88 L.H., Daily Totals | | $4963.40 | | $7608.82 | $56.40 | $86.46 |

| **Crew E-9** | Hr. | Daily | Hr. | Daily | Bare Costs | Incl. O&P |
|---|---|---|---|---|---|---|
| 2 Struc. Steel Foremen | $33.40 | $534.40 | $63.40 | $1014.40 | $31.24 | $57.89 |
| 5 Struc. Steel Workers | 31.40 | 1256.00 | 59.60 | 2384.00 | | |
| 1 Welder Foreman | 33.40 | 267.20 | 63.40 | 507.20 | | |
| 5 Welders | 31.40 | 1256.00 | 59.60 | 2384.00 | | |
| 1 Equip. Oper. (crane) | 30.65 | 245.20 | 50.15 | 401.20 | | |
| 1 Equip. Oper. Oiler | 26.45 | 211.60 | 43.30 | 346.40 | | |
| 1 Equip. Oper. (light) | 28.50 | 228.00 | 46.65 | 373.20 | | |
| 1 Lattice Boom Crane, 90 Ton | | 1607.00 | | 1767.70 | | |
| 5 Welders, gas engine, 300 amp | | 729.00 | | 801.90 | 18.25 | 20.07 |
| 128 L.H., Daily Totals | | $6334.40 | | $9980.00 | $49.49 | $77.97 |

| **Crew E-10** | Hr. | Daily | Hr. | Daily | Bare Costs | Incl. O&P |
|---|---|---|---|---|---|---|
| 1 Struc. Steel Foreman | $33.40 | $267.20 | $63.40 | $507.20 | $32.07 | $60.87 |
| 2 Struc. Steel Workers | 31.40 | 502.40 | 59.60 | 953.60 | | |
| 1 Welder, gas engine, 300 amp | | 145.80 | | 160.38 | | |
| 1 Flatbed Truck, Gas, 3 Ton | | 296.00 | | 325.60 | 18.41 | 20.25 |
| 24 L.H., Daily Totals | | $1211.40 | | $1946.78 | $50.48 | $81.12 |

| **Crew E-11** | Hr. | Daily | Hr. | Daily | Bare Costs | Incl. O&P |
|---|---|---|---|---|---|---|
| 2 Painters, Struc. Steel | $26.55 | $424.80 | $51.20 | $819.20 | $25.77 | $46.30 |
| 1 Building Laborer | 21.50 | 172.00 | 36.15 | 289.20 | | |
| 1 Equip. Oper. (light) | 28.50 | 228.00 | 46.65 | 373.20 | | |
| 1 Air Compressor, 250 cfm | | 193.40 | | 212.74 | | |
| 1 Sandblaster, portable, 3 C.F. | | 20.60 | | 22.66 | | |
| 1 Set Sand Blasting Accessories | | 12.95 | | 14.24 | 7.09 | 7.80 |
| 32 L.H., Daily Totals | | $1051.75 | | $1731.24 | $32.87 | $54.10 |

| **Crew E-12** | Hr. | Daily | Hr. | Daily | Bare Costs | Incl. O&P |
|---|---|---|---|---|---|---|
| 1 Welder Foreman | $33.40 | $267.20 | $63.40 | $507.20 | $30.95 | $55.02 |
| 1 Equip. Oper. (light) | 28.50 | 228.00 | 46.65 | 373.20 | | |
| 1 Welder, gas engine, 300 amp | | 145.80 | | 160.38 | 9.11 | 10.02 |
| 16 L.H., Daily Totals | | $641.00 | | $1040.78 | $40.06 | $65.05 |

| **Crew E-13** | Hr. | Daily | Hr. | Daily | Bare Costs | Incl. O&P |
|---|---|---|---|---|---|---|
| 1 Welder Foreman | $33.40 | $267.20 | $63.40 | $507.20 | $31.77 | $57.82 |
| .5 Equip. Oper. (light) | 28.50 | 114.00 | 46.65 | 186.60 | | |
| 1 Welder, gas engine, 300 amp | | 145.80 | | 160.38 | 12.15 | 13.37 |
| 12 L.H., Daily Totals | | $527.00 | | $854.18 | $43.92 | $71.18 |

| **Crew E-14** | Hr. | Daily | Hr. | Daily | Bare Costs | Incl. O&P |
|---|---|---|---|---|---|---|
| 1 Struc. Steel Worker | $31.40 | $251.20 | $59.60 | $476.80 | $31.40 | $59.60 |
| 1 Welder, gas engine, 300 amp | | 145.80 | | 160.38 | 18.23 | 20.05 |
| 8 L.H., Daily Totals | | $397.00 | | $637.18 | $49.63 | $79.65 |

| **Crew E-16** | Hr. | Daily | Hr. | Daily | Bare Costs | Incl. O&P |
|---|---|---|---|---|---|---|
| 1 Welder Foreman | $33.40 | $267.20 | $63.40 | $507.20 | $32.40 | $61.50 |
| 1 Welder | 31.40 | 251.20 | 59.60 | 476.80 | | |
| 1 Welder, gas engine, 300 amp | | 145.80 | | 160.38 | 9.11 | 10.02 |
| 16 L.H., Daily Totals | | $664.20 | | $1144.38 | $41.51 | $71.52 |

| **Crew E-17** | Hr. | Daily | Hr. | Daily | Bare Costs | Incl. O&P |
|---|---|---|---|---|---|---|
| 1 Structural Steel Foreman | $33.40 | $267.20 | $63.40 | $507.20 | $32.40 | $61.50 |
| 1 Structural Steel Worker | 31.40 | 251.20 | 59.60 | 476.80 | | |
| 16 L.H., Daily Totals | | $518.40 | | $984.00 | $32.40 | $61.50 |

| **Crew E-18** | Hr. | Daily | Hr. | Daily | Bare Costs | Incl. O&P |
|---|---|---|---|---|---|---|
| 1 Structural Steel Foreman | $33.40 | $267.20 | $63.40 | $507.20 | $31.45 | $58.15 |
| 3 Structural Steel Workers | 31.40 | 753.60 | 59.60 | 1430.40 | | |
| 1 Equipment Operator (med.) | 29.65 | 237.20 | 48.55 | 388.40 | | |
| 1 Lattice Boom Crane, 20 Ton | | 1029.00 | | 1131.90 | 25.73 | 28.30 |
| 40 L.H., Daily Totals | | $2287.00 | | $3457.90 | $57.17 | $86.45 |

| **Crew E-19** | Hr. | Daily | Hr. | Daily | Bare Costs | Incl. O&P |
|---|---|---|---|---|---|---|
| 1 Structural Steel Worker | $31.40 | $251.20 | $59.60 | $476.80 | $31.10 | $56.55 |
| 1 Structural Steel Foreman | 33.40 | 267.20 | 63.40 | 507.20 | | |
| 1 Equip. Oper. (light) | 28.50 | 228.00 | 46.65 | 373.20 | | |
| 1 Lattice Boom Crane, 20 Ton | | 1029.00 | | 1131.90 | 42.88 | 47.16 |
| 24 L.H., Daily Totals | | $1775.40 | | $2489.10 | $73.97 | $103.71 |

| **Crew E-20** | Hr. | Daily | Hr. | Daily | Bare Costs | Incl. O&P |
|---|---|---|---|---|---|---|
| 1 Structural Steel Foreman | $33.40 | $267.20 | $63.40 | $507.20 | $30.94 | $56.86 |
| 5 Structural Steel Workers | 31.40 | 1256.00 | 59.60 | 2384.00 | | |
| 1 Equip. Oper. (crane) | 30.65 | 245.20 | 50.15 | 401.20 | | |
| 1 Oiler | 26.45 | 211.60 | 43.30 | 346.40 | | |
| 1 Lattice Boom Crane, 40 Ton | | 1256.00 | | 1381.60 | 19.63 | 21.59 |
| 64 L.H., Daily Totals | | $3236.00 | | $5020.40 | $50.56 | $78.44 |

| **Crew E-22** | Hr. | Daily | Hr. | Daily | Bare Costs | Incl. O&P |
|---|---|---|---|---|---|---|
| 1 Skilled Worker Foreman | $31.25 | $250.00 | $52.40 | $419.20 | $29.92 | $50.17 |
| 2 Skilled Workers | 29.25 | 468.00 | 49.05 | 784.80 | | |
| 24 L.H., Daily Totals | | $718.00 | | $1204.00 | $29.92 | $50.17 |

| **Crew E-24** | Hr. | Daily | Hr. | Daily | Bare Costs | Incl. O&P |
|---|---|---|---|---|---|---|
| 3 Structural Steel Workers | $31.40 | $753.60 | $59.60 | $1430.40 | $30.96 | $56.84 |
| 1 Equipment Operator (med.) | 29.65 | 237.20 | 48.55 | 388.40 | | |
| 1 Hyd. Crane, 25 Ton | | 747.60 | | 822.36 | 23.36 | 25.70 |
| 32 L.H., Daily Totals | | $1738.40 | | $2641.16 | $54.33 | $82.54 |

| **Crew E-25** | Hr. | Daily | Hr. | Daily | Bare Costs | Incl. O&P |
|---|---|---|---|---|---|---|
| 1 Welder | $31.40 | $251.20 | $59.60 | $476.80 | $31.40 | $59.60 |
| 1 Cutting Torch | | 19.00 | | 20.90 | | |
| 1 Set of Gases | | 79.20 | | 87.12 | 12.28 | 13.50 |
| 8 L.H., Daily Totals | | $349.40 | | $584.82 | $43.67 | $73.10 |

| **Crew F-3** | Hr. | Daily | Hr. | Daily | Bare Costs | Incl. O&P |
|---|---|---|---|---|---|---|
| 2 Carpenters | $29.10 | $465.60 | $48.95 | $783.20 | $26.47 | $44.17 |
| 2 Carpenter Helpers | 21.75 | 348.00 | 36.40 | 582.40 | | |
| 1 Equip. Oper. (crane) | 30.65 | 245.20 | 50.15 | 401.20 | | |
| 1 Hyd. Crane, 12 Ton | | 655.60 | | 721.16 | 16.39 | 18.03 |
| 40 L.H., Daily Totals | | $1714.40 | | $2487.96 | $42.86 | $62.20 |

| **Crew F-4** | Hr. | Daily | Hr. | Daily | Bare Costs | Incl. O&P |
|---|---|---|---|---|---|---|
| 2 Carpenters | $29.10 | $465.60 | $48.95 | $783.20 | $26.47 | $44.17 |
| 2 Carpenter Helpers | 21.75 | 348.00 | 36.40 | 582.40 | | |
| 1 Equip. Oper. (crane) | 30.65 | 245.20 | 50.15 | 401.20 | | |
| 1 Hyd. Crane, 55 Ton | | 1209.00 | | 1329.90 | 30.23 | 33.25 |
| 40 L.H., Daily Totals | | $2267.80 | | $3096.70 | $56.70 | $77.42 |

# Crews

## Crew F-5

| Crew F-5 | Hr. | Daily | Hr. | Daily | Bare Costs | Incl. O&P |
|---|---|---|---|---|---|---|
| 2 Carpenters | $29.10 | $465.60 | $48.95 | $783.20 | $25.43 | $42.67 |
| 2 Carpenter Helpers | 21.75 | 348.00 | 36.40 | 582.40 | | |
| 32 L.H., Daily Totals | | $813.60 | | $1365.60 | $25.43 | $42.67 |

## Crew F-6

| Crew F-6 | Hr. | Daily | Hr. | Daily | Bare Costs | Incl. O&P |
|---|---|---|---|---|---|---|
| 2 Carpenters | $29.10 | $465.60 | $48.95 | $783.20 | $26.37 | $44.07 |
| 2 Building Laborers | 21.50 | 344.00 | 36.15 | 578.40 | | |
| 1 Equip. Oper. (crane) | 30.65 | 245.20 | 50.15 | 401.20 | | |
| 1 Hyd. Crane, 12 Ton | | 655.60 | | 721.16 | 16.39 | 18.03 |
| 40 L.H., Daily Totals | | $1710.40 | | $2483.96 | $42.76 | $62.10 |

## Crew F-7

| Crew F-7 | Hr. | Daily | Hr. | Daily | Bare Costs | Incl. O&P |
|---|---|---|---|---|---|---|
| 2 Carpenters | $29.10 | $465.60 | $48.95 | $783.20 | $25.30 | $42.55 |
| 2 Building Laborers | 21.50 | 344.00 | 36.15 | 578.40 | | |
| 32 L.H., Daily Totals | | $809.60 | | $1361.60 | $25.30 | $42.55 |

## Crew G-1

| Crew G-1 | Hr. | Daily | Hr. | Daily | Bare Costs | Incl. O&P |
|---|---|---|---|---|---|---|
| 1 Roofer Foreman | $26.45 | $211.60 | $47.65 | $381.20 | $22.92 | $41.29 |
| 4 Roofers, Composition | 24.45 | 782.40 | 44.05 | 1409.60 | | |
| 2 Roofer Helpers | 18.10 | 289.60 | 32.60 | 521.60 | | |
| 1 Application Equipment | | 188.40 | | 207.24 | | |
| 1 Tar Kettle/Pot | | 85.45 | | 94.00 | | |
| 1 Crew Truck | | 202.40 | | 222.64 | 8.50 | 9.35 |
| 56 L.H., Daily Totals | | $1759.85 | | $2836.28 | $31.43 | $50.65 |

## Crew G-2

| Crew G-2 | Hr. | Daily | Hr. | Daily | Bare Costs | Incl. O&P |
|---|---|---|---|---|---|---|
| 1 Plasterer | $26.10 | $208.80 | $42.60 | $340.80 | $23.78 | $39.17 |
| 1 Plasterer Helper | 23.75 | 190.00 | 38.75 | 310.00 | | |
| 1 Building Laborer | 21.50 | 172.00 | 36.15 | 289.20 | | |
| 1 Grout Pump, 50 C.F./hr | | 132.60 | | 145.86 | 5.53 | 6.08 |
| 24 L.H., Daily Totals | | $703.40 | | $1085.86 | $29.31 | $45.24 |

## Crew G-2A

| Crew G-2A | Hr. | Daily | Hr. | Daily | Bare Costs | Incl. O&P |
|---|---|---|---|---|---|---|
| 1 Roofer, composition | $24.45 | $195.60 | $44.05 | $352.40 | $21.35 | $37.60 |
| 1 Roofer Helper | 18.10 | 144.80 | 32.60 | 260.80 | | |
| 1 Building Laborer | 21.50 | 172.00 | 36.15 | 289.20 | | |
| 1 Foam spray rig, trailer-mtd. | | 551.65 | | 606.82 | | |
| 1 Pickup Truck, 3/4 Ton | | 140.00 | | 154.00 | 28.82 | 31.70 |
| 24 L.H., Daily Totals | | $1204.05 | | $1663.21 | $50.17 | $69.30 |

## Crew G-3

| Crew G-3 | Hr. | Daily | Hr. | Daily | Bare Costs | Incl. O&P |
|---|---|---|---|---|---|---|
| 2 Sheet Metal Workers | $32.40 | $518.40 | $53.60 | $857.60 | $26.95 | $44.88 |
| 2 Building Laborers | 21.50 | 344.00 | 36.15 | 578.40 | | |
| 32 L.H., Daily Totals | | $862.40 | | $1436.00 | $26.95 | $44.88 |

## Crew G-4

| Crew G-4 | Hr. | Daily | Hr. | Daily | Bare Costs | Incl. O&P |
|---|---|---|---|---|---|---|
| 1 Labor Foreman (outside) | $23.50 | $188.00 | $39.55 | $316.40 | $22.17 | $37.28 |
| 2 Building Laborers | 21.50 | 344.00 | 36.15 | 578.40 | | |
| 1 Flatbed Truck, Gas, 1.5 Ton | | 239.80 | | 263.78 | | |
| 1 Air Compressor, 160 cfm | | 158.00 | | 173.80 | 16.57 | 18.23 |
| 24 L.H., Daily Totals | | $929.80 | | $1332.38 | $38.74 | $55.52 |

## Crew G-5

| Crew G-5 | Hr. | Daily | Hr. | Daily | Bare Costs | Incl. O&P |
|---|---|---|---|---|---|---|
| 1 Roofer Foreman | $26.45 | $211.60 | $47.65 | $381.20 | $22.31 | $40.19 |
| 2 Roofers, Composition | 24.45 | 391.20 | 44.05 | 704.80 | | |
| 2 Roofer Helpers | 18.10 | 289.60 | 32.60 | 521.60 | | |
| 1 Application Equipment | | 188.40 | | 207.24 | 4.71 | 5.18 |
| 40 L.H., Daily Totals | | $1080.80 | | $1814.84 | $27.02 | $45.37 |

## Crew G-6A

| Crew G-6A | Hr. | Daily | Hr. | Daily | Bare Costs | Incl. O&P |
|---|---|---|---|---|---|---|
| 2 Roofers Composition | $24.45 | $391.20 | $44.05 | $704.80 | $24.45 | $44.05 |
| 1 Small Compressor, Electric | | 11.80 | | 12.98 | | |
| 2 Pneumatic Nailers | | 43.80 | | 48.18 | 3.48 | 3.82 |
| 16 L.H., Daily Totals | | $446.80 | | $765.96 | $27.93 | $47.87 |

## Crew G-7

| Crew G-7 | Hr. | Daily | Hr. | Daily | Bare Costs | Incl. O&P |
|---|---|---|---|---|---|---|
| 1 Carpenter | $29.10 | $232.80 | $48.95 | $391.60 | $29.10 | $48.95 |
| 1 Small Compressor, Electric | | 11.80 | | 12.98 | | |
| 1 Pneumatic Nailer | | 21.90 | | 24.09 | 4.21 | 4.63 |
| 8 L.H., Daily Totals | | $266.50 | | $428.67 | $33.31 | $53.58 |

## Crew H-1

| Crew H-1 | Hr. | Daily | Hr. | Daily | Bare Costs | Incl. O&P |
|---|---|---|---|---|---|---|
| 2 Glaziers | $28.55 | $456.80 | $47.00 | $752.00 | $29.98 | $53.30 |
| 2 Struc. Steel Workers | 31.40 | 502.40 | 59.60 | 953.60 | | |
| 32 L.H., Daily Totals | | $959.20 | | $1705.60 | $29.98 | $53.30 |

## Crew H-2

| Crew H-2 | Hr. | Daily | Hr. | Daily | Bare Costs | Incl. O&P |
|---|---|---|---|---|---|---|
| 2 Glaziers | $28.55 | $456.80 | $47.00 | $752.00 | $26.20 | $43.38 |
| 1 Building Laborer | 21.50 | 172.00 | 36.15 | 289.20 | | |
| 24 L.H., Daily Totals | | $628.80 | | $1041.20 | $26.20 | $43.38 |

## Crew H-3

| Crew H-3 | Hr. | Daily | Hr. | Daily | Bare Costs | Incl. O&P |
|---|---|---|---|---|---|---|
| 1 Glazier | $28.55 | $228.40 | $47.00 | $376.00 | $25.15 | $41.70 |
| 1 Helper | 21.75 | 174.00 | 36.40 | 291.20 | | |
| 16 L.H., Daily Totals | | $402.40 | | $667.20 | $25.15 | $41.70 |

## Crew J-1

| Crew J-1 | Hr. | Daily | Hr. | Daily | Bare Costs | Incl. O&P |
|---|---|---|---|---|---|---|
| 3 Plasterers | $26.10 | $626.40 | $42.60 | $1022.40 | $25.16 | $41.06 |
| 2 Plasterer Helpers | 23.75 | 380.00 | 38.75 | 620.00 | | |
| 1 Mixing Machine, 6 C.F. | | 136.60 | | 150.26 | 3.42 | 3.76 |
| 40 L.H., Daily Totals | | $1143.00 | | $1792.66 | $28.57 | $44.82 |

## Crew J-2

| Crew J-2 | Hr. | Daily | Hr. | Daily | Bare Costs | Incl. O&P |
|---|---|---|---|---|---|---|
| 3 Plasterers | $26.10 | $626.40 | $42.60 | $1022.40 | $25.27 | $41.16 |
| 2 Plasterer Helpers | 23.75 | 380.00 | 38.75 | 620.00 | | |
| 1 Lather | 25.85 | 206.80 | 41.65 | 333.20 | | |
| 1 Mixing Machine, 6 C.F. | | 136.60 | | 150.26 | 2.85 | 3.13 |
| 48 L.H., Daily Totals | | $1349.80 | | $2125.86 | $28.12 | $44.29 |

## Crew J-3

| Crew J-3 | Hr. | Daily | Hr. | Daily | Bare Costs | Incl. O&P |
|---|---|---|---|---|---|---|
| 1 Terrazzo Worker | $27.30 | $218.40 | $43.70 | $349.60 | $24.82 | $39.75 |
| 1 Terrazzo Helper | 22.35 | 178.80 | 35.80 | 286.40 | | |
| 1 Terrazzo Grinder, Electric | | 82.25 | | 90.47 | | |
| 1 Terrazzo Mixer | | 184.80 | | 203.28 | 16.69 | 18.36 |
| 16 L.H., Daily Totals | | $664.25 | | $929.76 | $41.52 | $58.11 |

## Crew K-1

| Crew K-1 | Hr. | Daily | Hr. | Daily | Bare Costs | Incl. O&P |
|---|---|---|---|---|---|---|
| 1 Carpenter | $29.10 | $232.80 | $48.95 | $391.60 | $26.00 | $43.55 |
| 1 Truck Driver (light) | 22.90 | 183.20 | 38.15 | 305.20 | | |
| 1 Flatbed Truck, Gas, 3 Ton | | 296.00 | | 325.60 | 18.50 | 20.35 |
| 16 L.H., Daily Totals | | $712.00 | | $1022.40 | $44.50 | $63.90 |

## Crew K-2

| Crew K-2 | Hr. | Daily | Hr. | Daily | Bare Costs | Incl. O&P |
|---|---|---|---|---|---|---|
| 1 Struc. Steel Foreman | $33.40 | $267.20 | $63.40 | $507.20 | $29.23 | $53.72 |
| 1 Struc. Steel Worker | 31.40 | 251.20 | 59.60 | 476.80 | | |
| 1 Truck Driver (light) | 22.90 | 183.20 | 38.15 | 305.20 | | |
| 1 Flatbed Truck, Gas, 3 Ton | | 296.00 | | 325.60 | 12.33 | 13.57 |
| 24 L.H., Daily Totals | | $997.60 | | $1614.80 | $41.57 | $67.28 |

| Crew No. | Bare Costs | | Incl. Subs O&P | | Cost Per Labor-Hour | |
|---|---|---|---|---|---|---|
| **Crew L-1** | Hr. | Daily | Hr. | Daily | Bare Costs | Incl. O&P |
| .25 Electrician | $32.85 | $65.70 | $53.45 | $106.90 | $34.05 | $55.73 |
| 1 Plumber | 34.35 | 274.80 | 56.30 | 450.40 | | |
| 10 L.H., Daily Totals | | $340.50 | | $557.30 | $34.05 | $55.73 |
| **Crew L-2** | Hr. | Daily | Hr. | Daily | Bare Costs | Incl. O&P |
| 1 Carpenter | $29.10 | $232.80 | $48.95 | $391.60 | $25.43 | $42.67 |
| 1 Carpenter Helper | 21.75 | 174.00 | 36.40 | 291.20 | | |
| 16 L.H., Daily Totals | | $406.80 | | $682.80 | $25.43 | $42.67 |
| **Crew L-3** | Hr. | Daily | Hr. | Daily | Bare Costs | Incl. O&P |
| 1 Carpenter | $29.10 | $232.80 | $48.95 | $391.60 | $29.85 | $49.85 |
| .25 Electrician | 32.85 | 65.70 | 53.45 | 106.90 | | |
| 10 L.H., Daily Totals | | $298.50 | | $498.50 | $29.85 | $49.85 |
| **Crew L-3A** | Hr. | Daily | Hr. | Daily | Bare Costs | Incl. O&P |
| 1 Carpenter Foreman (outside) | $31.10 | $248.80 | $52.30 | $418.40 | $31.53 | $52.73 |
| .5 Sheet Metal Worker | 32.40 | 129.60 | 53.60 | 214.40 | | |
| 12 L.H., Daily Totals | | $378.40 | | $632.80 | $31.53 | $52.73 |
| **Crew L-4** | Hr. | Daily | Hr. | Daily | Bare Costs | Incl. O&P |
| 1 Skilled Worker | $29.25 | $234.00 | $49.05 | $392.40 | $25.50 | $42.73 |
| 1 Helper | 21.75 | 174.00 | 36.40 | 291.20 | | |
| 16 L.H., Daily Totals | | $408.00 | | $683.60 | $25.50 | $42.73 |
| **Crew L-5** | Hr. | Daily | Hr. | Daily | Bare Costs | Incl. O&P |
| 1 Struc. Steel Foreman | $33.40 | $267.20 | $63.40 | $507.20 | $31.58 | $58.79 |
| 5 Struc. Steel Workers | 31.40 | 1256.00 | 59.60 | 2384.00 | | |
| 1 Equip. Oper. (crane) | 30.65 | 245.20 | 50.15 | 401.20 | | |
| 1 Hyd. Crane, 25 Ton | | 747.60 | | 822.36 | 13.35 | 14.69 |
| 56 L.H., Daily Totals | | $2516.00 | | $4114.76 | $44.93 | $73.48 |
| **Crew L-5A** | Hr. | Daily | Hr. | Daily | Bare Costs | Incl. O&P |
| 1 Structural Steel Foreman | $33.40 | $267.20 | $63.40 | $507.20 | $31.71 | $58.19 |
| 2 Structural Steel Workers | 31.40 | 502.40 | 59.60 | 953.60 | | |
| 1 Equip. Oper. (crane) | 30.65 | 245.20 | 50.15 | 401.20 | | |
| 1 S.P. Crane, 4x4, 25 Ton | | 655.60 | | 721.16 | 20.49 | 22.54 |
| 32 L.H., Daily Totals | | $1670.40 | | $2583.16 | $52.20 | $80.72 |
| **Crew L-5B** | Hr. | Daily | Hr. | Daily | Bare Costs | Incl. O&P |
| 1 Structural Steel Foreman | $33.40 | $267.20 | $63.40 | $507.20 | $31.39 | $54.23 |
| 2 Structural Steel Workers | 31.40 | 502.40 | 59.60 | 953.60 | | |
| 2 Electricians | 32.85 | 525.60 | 53.45 | 855.20 | | |
| 2 Steamfitters/Pipefitters | 34.25 | 548.00 | 56.15 | 898.40 | | |
| 1 Equip. Oper. (crane) | 30.65 | 245.20 | 50.15 | 401.20 | | |
| 1 Common Building Laborer | 21.50 | 172.00 | 36.15 | 289.20 | | |
| 1 Hyd. Crane, 80 Ton | | 1545.00 | | 1699.50 | 21.46 | 23.60 |
| 72 L.H., Daily Totals | | $3805.40 | | $5604.30 | $52.85 | $77.84 |
| **Crew L-6** | Hr. | Daily | Hr. | Daily | Bare Costs | Incl. O&P |
| 1 Plumber | $34.35 | $274.80 | $56.30 | $450.40 | $33.85 | $55.35 |
| .5 Electrician | 32.85 | 131.40 | 53.45 | 213.80 | | |
| 12 L.H., Daily Totals | | $406.20 | | $664.20 | $33.85 | $55.35 |
| **Crew L-7** | Hr. | Daily | Hr. | Daily | Bare Costs | Incl. O&P |
| 1 Carpenter | $29.10 | $232.80 | $48.95 | $391.60 | $24.87 | $41.57 |
| 2 Carpenter Helpers | 21.75 | 348.00 | 36.40 | 582.40 | | |
| .25 Electrician | 32.85 | 65.70 | 53.45 | 106.90 | | |
| 26 L.H., Daily Totals | | $646.50 | | $1080.90 | $24.87 | $41.57 |

| Crew No. | Bare Costs | | Incl. Subs O&P | | Cost Per Labor-Hour | |
|---|---|---|---|---|---|---|
| **Crew L-8** | Hr. | Daily | Hr. | Daily | Bare Costs | Incl. O&P |
| 1 Carpenter | $29.10 | $232.80 | $48.95 | $391.60 | $27.21 | $45.40 |
| 1 Carpenter Helper | 21.75 | 174.00 | 36.40 | 291.20 | | |
| .5 Plumber | 34.35 | 137.40 | 56.30 | 225.20 | | |
| 20 L.H., Daily Totals | | $544.20 | | $908.00 | $27.21 | $45.40 |
| **Crew L-9** | Hr. | Daily | Hr. | Daily | Bare Costs | Incl. O&P |
| 1 Skilled Worker Foreman | $31.25 | $250.00 | $52.40 | $419.20 | $26.76 | $44.66 |
| 1 Skilled Worker | 29.25 | 234.00 | 49.05 | 392.40 | | |
| 2 Helpers | 21.75 | 348.00 | 36.40 | 582.40 | | |
| .5 Electrician | 32.85 | 131.40 | 53.45 | 213.80 | | |
| 36 L.H., Daily Totals | | $963.40 | | $1607.80 | $26.76 | $44.66 |
| **Crew L-10** | Hr. | Daily | Hr. | Daily | Bare Costs | Incl. O&P |
| 1 Structural Steel Foreman | $33.40 | $267.20 | $63.40 | $507.20 | $31.82 | $57.72 |
| 1 Structural Steel Worker | 31.40 | 251.20 | 59.60 | 476.80 | | |
| 1 Equip. Oper. (crane) | 30.65 | 245.20 | 50.15 | 401.20 | | |
| 1 Hyd. Crane, 12 Ton | | 655.60 | | 721.16 | 27.32 | 30.05 |
| 24 L.H., Daily Totals | | $1419.20 | | $2106.36 | $59.13 | $87.77 |
| **Crew L-11** | Hr. | Daily | Hr. | Daily | Bare Costs | Incl. O&P |
| 2 Wreckers | $22.20 | $355.20 | $40.30 | $644.80 | $25.89 | $44.35 |
| 1 Equip. Oper. (crane) | 30.65 | 245.20 | 50.15 | 401.20 | | |
| 1 Equip. Oper. (light) | 28.50 | 228.00 | 46.65 | 373.20 | | |
| 1 Hyd. Excavator, 2.5 C.Y. | | 1784.00 | | 1962.40 | | |
| 1 Loader, Skid Steer, 78 H.P. | | 291.00 | | 320.10 | 64.84 | 71.33 |
| 32 L.H., Daily Totals | | $2903.40 | | $3701.70 | $90.73 | $115.68 |
| **Crew M-1** | Hr. | Daily | Hr. | Daily | Bare Costs | Incl. O&P |
| 3 Elevator Constructors | $41.35 | $992.40 | $67.25 | $1614.00 | $39.29 | $63.89 |
| 1 Elevator Apprentice | 33.10 | 264.80 | 53.80 | 430.40 | | |
| 5 Hand Tools | | 58.00 | | 63.80 | 1.81 | 1.99 |
| 32 L.H., Daily Totals | | $1315.20 | | $2108.20 | $41.10 | $65.88 |
| **Crew M-3** | Hr. | Daily | Hr. | Daily | Bare Costs | Incl. O&P |
| 1 Electrician Foreman (out) | $34.85 | $278.80 | $56.70 | $453.60 | $32.52 | $53.19 |
| 1 Common Laborer | 21.50 | 172.00 | 36.15 | 289.20 | | |
| .25 Equipment Operator, Medium | 29.65 | 59.30 | 48.55 | 97.10 | | |
| 1 Elevator Constructor | 41.35 | 330.80 | 67.25 | 538.00 | | |
| 1 Elevator Apprentice | 33.10 | 264.80 | 53.80 | 430.40 | | |
| .25 S.P. Crane, 4x4, 20 Ton | | 156.40 | | 172.04 | 4.60 | 5.06 |
| 34 L.H., Daily Totals | | $1262.10 | | $1980.34 | $37.12 | $58.25 |
| **Crew M-4** | Hr. | Daily | Hr. | Daily | Bare Costs | Incl. O&P |
| 1 Electrician Foreman (out) | $34.85 | $278.80 | $56.70 | $453.60 | $32.24 | $52.73 |
| 1 Common Laborer | 21.50 | 172.00 | 36.15 | 289.20 | | |
| .25 Equipment Operator, Crane | 30.65 | 61.30 | 50.15 | 100.30 | | |
| .25 Equipment Operator, Oiler | 26.45 | 52.90 | 43.30 | 86.60 | | |
| 1 Elevator Constructor | 41.35 | 330.80 | 67.25 | 538.00 | | |
| 1 Elevator Apprentice | 33.10 | 264.80 | 53.80 | 430.40 | | |
| .25 S.P. Crane, 4x4, 40 Ton | | 253.50 | | 278.85 | 7.04 | 7.75 |
| 36 L.H., Daily Totals | | $1414.10 | | $2176.95 | $39.28 | $60.47 |
| **Crew Q-1** | Hr. | Daily | Hr. | Daily | Bare Costs | Incl. O&P |
| 1 Plumber | $34.35 | $274.80 | $56.30 | $450.40 | $30.93 | $50.67 |
| 1 Plumber Apprentice | 27.50 | 220.00 | 45.05 | 360.40 | | |
| 16 L.H., Daily Totals | | $494.80 | | $810.80 | $30.93 | $50.67 |

| Crew No. | Bare Costs Hr. | Daily | Incl. Subs O&P Hr. | Daily | Cost Per Labor-Hour Bare Costs | Incl. O&P |
|---|---|---|---|---|---|---|
| **Crew Q-1A** | Hr. | Daily | Hr. | Daily | Bare Costs | Incl. O&P |
| .25 Plumber Foreman (out) | $36.35 | $72.70 | $59.60 | $119.20 | $34.75 | $56.96 |
| 1 Plumber | 34.35 | 274.80 | 56.30 | 450.40 | | |
| 10 L.H., Daily Totals | | $347.50 | | $569.60 | $34.75 | $56.96 |
| **Crew Q-1C** | Hr. | Daily | Hr. | Daily | Bare Costs | Incl. O&P |
| 1 Plumber | $34.35 | $274.80 | $56.30 | $450.40 | $30.50 | $49.97 |
| 1 Plumber Apprentice | 27.50 | 220.00 | 45.05 | 360.40 | | |
| 1 Equip. Oper. (medium) | 29.65 | 237.20 | 48.55 | 388.40 | | |
| 1 Trencher, Chain Type, 8' D | | 2090.00 | | 2299.00 | 87.08 | 95.79 |
| 24 L.H., Daily Totals | | $2822.00 | | $3498.20 | $117.58 | $145.76 |
| **Crew Q-2** | Hr. | Daily | Hr. | Daily | Bare Costs | Incl. O&P |
| 1 Plumber | $34.35 | $274.80 | $56.30 | $450.40 | $29.78 | $48.80 |
| 2 Plumber Apprentices | 27.50 | 440.00 | 45.05 | 720.80 | | |
| 24 L.H., Daily Totals | | $714.80 | | $1171.20 | $29.78 | $48.80 |
| **Crew Q-3** | Hr. | Daily | Hr. | Daily | Bare Costs | Incl. O&P |
| 2 Plumbers | $34.35 | $549.60 | $56.30 | $900.80 | $30.93 | $50.67 |
| 2 Plumber Apprentices | 27.50 | 440.00 | 45.05 | 720.80 | | |
| 32 L.H., Daily Totals | | $989.60 | | $1621.60 | $30.93 | $50.67 |
| **Crew Q-4** | Hr. | Daily | Hr. | Daily | Bare Costs | Incl. O&P |
| 2 Plumbers | $34.35 | $549.60 | $56.30 | $900.80 | $32.64 | $53.49 |
| 1 Welder (plumber) | 34.35 | 274.80 | 56.30 | 450.40 | | |
| 1 Plumber Apprentice | 27.50 | 220.00 | 45.05 | 360.40 | | |
| 1 Welder, electric, 300 amp | | 58.55 | | 64.41 | 1.83 | 2.01 |
| 32 L.H., Daily Totals | | $1102.95 | | $1776.01 | $34.47 | $55.50 |
| **Crew Q-5** | Hr. | Daily | Hr. | Daily | Bare Costs | Incl. O&P |
| 1 Steamfitter | $34.25 | $274.00 | $56.15 | $449.20 | $30.82 | $50.52 |
| 1 Steamfitter Apprentice | 27.40 | 219.20 | 44.90 | 359.20 | | |
| 16 L.H., Daily Totals | | $493.20 | | $808.40 | $30.82 | $50.52 |
| **Crew Q-6** | Hr. | Daily | Hr. | Daily | Bare Costs | Incl. O&P |
| 1 Steamfitter | $34.25 | $274.00 | $56.15 | $449.20 | $29.68 | $48.65 |
| 2 Steamfitter Apprentices | 27.40 | 438.40 | 44.90 | 718.40 | | |
| 24 L.H., Daily Totals | | $712.40 | | $1167.60 | $29.68 | $48.65 |
| **Crew Q-7** | Hr. | Daily | Hr. | Daily | Bare Costs | Incl. O&P |
| 2 Steamfitters | $34.25 | $548.00 | $56.15 | $898.40 | $30.82 | $50.52 |
| 2 Steamfitter Apprentices | 27.40 | 438.40 | 44.90 | 718.40 | | |
| 32 L.H., Daily Totals | | $986.40 | | $1616.80 | $30.82 | $50.52 |
| **Crew Q-8** | Hr. | Daily | Hr. | Daily | Bare Costs | Incl. O&P |
| 2 Steamfitters | $34.25 | $548.00 | $56.15 | $898.40 | $32.54 | $53.34 |
| 1 Welder (steamfitter) | 34.25 | 274.00 | 56.15 | 449.20 | | |
| 1 Steamfitter Apprentice | 27.40 | 219.20 | 44.90 | 359.20 | | |
| 1 Welder, electric, 300 amp | | 58.55 | | 64.41 | 1.83 | 2.01 |
| 32 L.H., Daily Totals | | $1099.75 | | $1771.20 | $34.37 | $55.35 |
| **Crew Q-9** | Hr. | Daily | Hr. | Daily | Bare Costs | Incl. O&P |
| 1 Sheet Metal Worker | $32.40 | $259.20 | $53.60 | $428.80 | $29.15 | $48.23 |
| 1 Sheet Metal Apprentice | 25.90 | 207.20 | 42.85 | 342.80 | | |
| 16 L.H., Daily Totals | | $466.40 | | $771.60 | $29.15 | $48.23 |
| **Crew Q-10** | Hr. | Daily | Hr. | Daily | Bare Costs | Incl. O&P |
| 2 Sheet Metal Workers | $32.40 | $518.40 | $53.60 | $857.60 | $30.23 | $50.02 |
| 1 Sheet Metal Apprentice | 25.90 | 207.20 | 42.85 | 342.80 | | |
| 24 L.H., Daily Totals | | $725.60 | | $1200.40 | $30.23 | $50.02 |

| Crew No. | Bare Costs Hr. | Daily | Incl. Subs O&P Hr. | Daily | Cost Per Labor-Hour Bare Costs | Incl. O&P |
|---|---|---|---|---|---|---|
| **Crew Q-11** | Hr. | Daily | Hr. | Daily | Bare Costs | Incl. O&P |
| 2 Sheet Metal Workers | $32.40 | $518.40 | $53.60 | $857.60 | $29.15 | $48.23 |
| 2 Sheet Metal Apprentices | 25.90 | 414.40 | 42.85 | 685.60 | | |
| 32 L.H., Daily Totals | | $932.80 | | $1543.20 | $29.15 | $48.23 |
| **Crew Q-12** | Hr. | Daily | Hr. | Daily | Bare Costs | Incl. O&P |
| 1 Sprinkler Installer | $33.25 | $266.00 | $54.45 | $435.60 | $29.93 | $49.00 |
| 1 Sprinkler Apprentice | 26.60 | 212.80 | 43.55 | 348.40 | | |
| 16 L.H., Daily Totals | | $478.80 | | $784.00 | $29.93 | $49.00 |
| **Crew Q-13** | Hr. | Daily | Hr. | Daily | Bare Costs | Incl. O&P |
| 2 Sprinkler Installers | $33.25 | $532.00 | $54.45 | $871.20 | $29.93 | $49.00 |
| 2 Sprinkler Apprentices | 26.60 | 425.60 | 43.55 | 696.80 | | |
| 32 L.H., Daily Totals | | $957.60 | | $1568.00 | $29.93 | $49.00 |
| **Crew Q-14** | Hr. | Daily | Hr. | Daily | Bare Costs | Incl. O&P |
| 1 Asbestos Worker | $30.05 | $240.40 | $50.90 | $407.20 | $27.05 | $45.83 |
| 1 Asbestos Apprentice | 24.05 | 192.40 | 40.75 | 326.00 | | |
| 16 L.H., Daily Totals | | $432.80 | | $733.20 | $27.05 | $45.83 |
| **Crew Q-15** | Hr. | Daily | Hr. | Daily | Bare Costs | Incl. O&P |
| 1 Plumber | $34.35 | $274.80 | $56.30 | $450.40 | $30.93 | $50.67 |
| 1 Plumber Apprentice | 27.50 | 220.00 | 45.05 | 360.40 | | |
| 1 Welder, electric, 300 amp | | 58.55 | | 64.41 | 3.66 | 4.03 |
| 16 L.H., Daily Totals | | $553.35 | | $875.21 | $34.58 | $54.70 |
| **Crew Q-16** | Hr. | Daily | Hr. | Daily | Bare Costs | Incl. O&P |
| 2 Plumbers | $34.35 | $549.60 | $56.30 | $900.80 | $32.07 | $52.55 |
| 1 Plumber Apprentice | 27.50 | 220.00 | 45.05 | 360.40 | | |
| 1 Welder, electric, 300 amp | | 58.55 | | 64.41 | 2.44 | 2.68 |
| 24 L.H., Daily Totals | | $828.15 | | $1325.61 | $34.51 | $55.23 |
| **Crew Q-17** | Hr. | Daily | Hr. | Daily | Bare Costs | Incl. O&P |
| 1 Steamfitter | $34.25 | $274.00 | $56.15 | $449.20 | $30.82 | $50.52 |
| 1 Steamfitter Apprentice | 27.40 | 219.20 | 44.90 | 359.20 | | |
| 1 Welder, electric, 300 amp | | 58.55 | | 64.41 | 3.66 | 4.03 |
| 16 L.H., Daily Totals | | $551.75 | | $872.80 | $34.48 | $54.55 |
| **Crew Q-17A** | Hr. | Daily | Hr. | Daily | Bare Costs | Incl. O&P |
| 1 Steamfitter | $34.25 | $274.00 | $56.15 | $449.20 | $30.77 | $50.40 |
| 1 Steamfitter Apprentice | 27.40 | 219.20 | 44.90 | 359.20 | | |
| 1 Equip. Oper. (crane) | 30.65 | 245.20 | 50.15 | 401.20 | | |
| 1 Hyd. Crane, 12 Ton | | 655.60 | | 721.16 | | |
| 1 Welder, electric, 300 amp | | 58.55 | | 64.41 | 29.76 | 32.73 |
| 24 L.H., Daily Totals | | $1452.55 | | $1995.17 | $60.52 | $83.13 |
| **Crew Q-18** | Hr. | Daily | Hr. | Daily | Bare Costs | Incl. O&P |
| 2 Steamfitters | $34.25 | $548.00 | $56.15 | $898.40 | $31.97 | $52.52 |
| 1 Steamfitter Apprentice | 27.40 | 219.20 | 44.90 | 359.20 | | |
| 1 Welder, electric, 300 amp | | 58.55 | | 64.41 | 2.44 | 2.68 |
| 24 L.H., Daily Totals | | $825.75 | | $1322.01 | $34.41 | $55.08 |
| **Crew Q-19** | Hr. | Daily | Hr. | Daily | Bare Costs | Incl. O&P |
| 1 Steamfitter | $34.25 | $274.00 | $56.15 | $449.20 | $31.50 | $51.50 |
| 1 Steamfitter Apprentice | 27.40 | 219.20 | 44.90 | 359.20 | | |
| 1 Electrician | 32.85 | 262.80 | 53.45 | 427.60 | | |
| 24 L.H., Daily Totals | | $756.00 | | $1236.00 | $31.50 | $51.50 |

# Crews

| Crew No. | Bare Costs | | Incl. Subs O&P | | Cost Per Labor-Hour | |
|---|---|---|---|---|---|---|
| **Crew Q-20** | Hr. | Daily | Hr. | Daily | Bare Costs | Incl. O&P |
| 1 Sheet Metal Worker | $32.40 | $259.20 | $53.60 | $428.80 | $29.89 | $49.27 |
| 1 Sheet Metal Apprentice | 25.90 | 207.20 | 42.85 | 342.80 | | |
| .5 Electrician | 32.85 | 131.40 | 53.45 | 213.80 | | |
| 20 L.H., Daily Totals | | $597.80 | | $985.40 | $29.89 | $49.27 |
| **Crew Q-21** | Hr. | Daily | Hr. | Daily | Bare Costs | Incl. O&P |
| 2 Steamfitters | $34.25 | $548.00 | $56.15 | $898.40 | $32.19 | $52.66 |
| 1 Steamfitter Apprentice | 27.40 | 219.20 | 44.90 | 359.20 | | |
| 1 Electrician | 32.85 | 262.80 | 53.45 | 427.60 | | |
| 32 L.H., Daily Totals | | $1030.00 | | $1685.20 | $32.19 | $52.66 |
| **Crew Q-22** | Hr. | Daily | Hr. | Daily | Bare Costs | Incl. O&P |
| 1 Plumber | $34.35 | $274.80 | $56.30 | $450.40 | $30.93 | $50.67 |
| 1 Plumber Apprentice | 27.50 | 220.00 | 45.05 | 360.40 | | |
| 1 Hyd. Crane, 12 Ton | | 655.60 | | 721.16 | 40.98 | 45.07 |
| 16 L.H., Daily Totals | | $1150.40 | | $1531.96 | $71.90 | $95.75 |
| **Crew Q-22A** | Hr. | Daily | Hr. | Daily | Bare Costs | Incl. O&P |
| 1 Plumber | $34.35 | $274.80 | $56.30 | $450.40 | $28.50 | $46.91 |
| 1 Plumber Apprentice | 27.50 | 220.00 | 45.05 | 360.40 | | |
| 1 Laborer | 21.50 | 172.00 | 36.15 | 289.20 | | |
| 1 Equip. Oper. (crane) | 30.65 | 245.20 | 50.15 | 401.20 | | |
| 1 Hyd. Crane, 12 Ton | | 655.60 | | 721.16 | 20.49 | 22.54 |
| 32 L.H., Daily Totals | | $1567.60 | | $2222.36 | $48.99 | $69.45 |
| **Crew Q-23** | Hr. | Daily | Hr. | Daily | Bare Costs | Incl. O&P |
| 1 Plumber Foreman | $36.35 | $290.80 | $59.60 | $476.80 | $33.45 | $54.82 |
| 1 Plumber | 34.35 | 274.80 | 56.30 | 450.40 | | |
| 1 Equip. Oper. (med.) | 29.65 | 237.20 | 48.55 | 388.40 | | |
| 1 Lattice Boom Crane, 20 Ton | | 1029.00 | | 1131.90 | 42.88 | 47.16 |
| 24 L.H., Daily Totals | | $1831.80 | | $2447.50 | $76.33 | $101.98 |
| **Crew R-1** | Hr. | Daily | Hr. | Daily | Bare Costs | Incl. O&P |
| 1 Electrician Foreman | $33.35 | $266.80 | $54.25 | $434.00 | $29.23 | $47.90 |
| 3 Electricians | 32.85 | 788.40 | 53.45 | 1282.80 | | |
| 2 Helpers | 21.75 | 348.00 | 36.40 | 582.40 | | |
| 48 L.H., Daily Totals | | $1403.20 | | $2299.20 | $29.23 | $47.90 |
| **Crew R-1A** | Hr. | Daily | Hr. | Daily | Bare Costs | Incl. O&P |
| 1 Electrician | $32.85 | $262.80 | $53.45 | $427.60 | $27.30 | $44.92 |
| 1 Helper | 21.75 | 174.00 | 36.40 | 291.20 | | |
| 16 L.H., Daily Totals | | $436.80 | | $718.80 | $27.30 | $44.92 |
| **Crew R-2** | Hr. | Daily | Hr. | Daily | Bare Costs | Incl. O&P |
| 1 Electrician Foreman | $33.35 | $266.80 | $54.25 | $434.00 | $29.44 | $48.22 |
| 3 Electricians | 32.85 | 788.40 | 53.45 | 1282.80 | | |
| 2 Helpers | 21.75 | 348.00 | 36.40 | 582.40 | | |
| 1 Equip. Oper. (crane) | 30.65 | 245.20 | 50.15 | 401.20 | | |
| 1 S.P. Crane, 4x4, 5 Ton | | 276.20 | | 303.82 | 4.93 | 5.43 |
| 56 L.H., Daily Totals | | $1924.60 | | $3004.22 | $34.37 | $53.65 |
| **Crew R-3** | Hr. | Daily | Hr. | Daily | Bare Costs | Incl. O&P |
| 1 Electrician Foreman | $33.35 | $266.80 | $54.25 | $434.00 | $32.61 | $53.11 |
| 1 Electrician | 32.85 | 262.80 | 53.45 | 427.60 | | |
| .5 Equip. Oper. (crane) | 30.65 | 122.60 | 50.15 | 200.60 | | |
| .5 S.P. Crane, 4x4, 5 Ton | | 138.10 | | 151.91 | 6.91 | 7.60 |
| 20 L.H., Daily Totals | | $790.30 | | $1214.11 | $39.52 | $60.71 |

| Crew No. | Bare Costs | | Incl. Subs O&P | | Cost Per Labor-Hour | |
|---|---|---|---|---|---|---|
| **Crew R-4** | Hr. | Daily | Hr. | Daily | Bare Costs | Incl. O&P |
| 1 Struc. Steel Foreman | $33.40 | $267.20 | $63.40 | $507.20 | $32.09 | $59.13 |
| 3 Struc. Steel Workers | 31.40 | 753.60 | 59.60 | 1430.40 | | |
| 1 Electrician | 32.85 | 262.80 | 53.45 | 427.60 | | |
| 1 Welder, gas engine, 300 amp | | 145.80 | | 160.38 | 3.65 | 4.01 |
| 40 L.H., Daily Totals | | $1429.40 | | $2525.58 | $35.73 | $63.14 |
| **Crew R-5** | Hr. | Daily | Hr. | Daily | Bare Costs | Incl. O&P |
| 1 Electrician Foreman | $33.35 | $266.80 | $54.25 | $434.00 | $28.86 | $47.32 |
| 4 Electrician Linemen | 32.85 | 1051.20 | 53.45 | 1710.40 | | |
| 2 Electrician Operators | 32.85 | 525.60 | 53.45 | 855.20 | | |
| 4 Electrician Groundmen | 21.75 | 696.00 | 36.40 | 1164.80 | | |
| 1 Crew Truck | | 202.40 | | 222.64 | | |
| 1 Flatbed Truck, 20,000 GVW | | 245.60 | | 270.16 | | |
| 1 Pickup Truck, 3/4 Ton | | 140.00 | | 154.00 | | |
| .2 Hyd. Crane, 55 Ton | | 241.80 | | 265.98 | | |
| .2 Hyd. Crane, 12 Ton | | 131.12 | | 144.23 | | |
| .2 Earth Auger, Truck-Mtd. | | 89.84 | | 98.82 | | |
| 1 Tractor w/Winch | | 421.20 | | 463.32 | 16.73 | 18.40 |
| 88 L.H., Daily Totals | | $4011.56 | | $5783.56 | $45.59 | $65.72 |
| **Crew R-6** | Hr. | Daily | Hr. | Daily | Bare Costs | Incl. O&P |
| 1 Electrician Foreman | $33.35 | $266.80 | $54.25 | $434.00 | $28.86 | $47.32 |
| 4 Electrician Linemen | 32.85 | 1051.20 | 53.45 | 1710.40 | | |
| 2 Electrician Operators | 32.85 | 525.60 | 53.45 | 855.20 | | |
| 4 Electrician Groundmen | 21.75 | 696.00 | 36.40 | 1164.80 | | |
| 1 Crew Truck | | 202.40 | | 222.64 | | |
| 1 Flatbed Truck, 20,000 GVW | | 245.60 | | 270.16 | | |
| 1 Pickup Truck, 3/4 Ton | | 140.00 | | 154.00 | | |
| .2 Hyd. Crane, 55 Ton | | 241.80 | | 265.98 | | |
| .2 Hyd. Crane, 12 Ton | | 131.12 | | 144.23 | | |
| .2 Earth Auger, Truck-Mtd. | | 89.84 | | 98.82 | | |
| 1 Tractor w/Winch | | 421.20 | | 463.32 | | |
| 3 Cable Trailers | | 542.10 | | 596.31 | | |
| .5 Tensioning Rig | | 179.20 | | 197.12 | | |
| .5 Cable Pulling Rig | | 1048.00 | | 1152.80 | 36.83 | 40.52 |
| 88 L.H., Daily Totals | | $5780.86 | | $7729.79 | $65.69 | $87.84 |
| **Crew R-7** | Hr. | Daily | Hr. | Daily | Bare Costs | Incl. O&P |
| 1 Electrician Foreman | $33.35 | $266.80 | $54.25 | $434.00 | $23.68 | $39.38 |
| 5 Electrician Groundmen | 21.75 | 870.00 | 36.40 | 1456.00 | | |
| 1 Crew Truck | | 202.40 | | 222.64 | 4.22 | 4.64 |
| 48 L.H., Daily Totals | | $1339.20 | | $2112.64 | $27.90 | $44.01 |
| **Crew R-8** | Hr. | Daily | Hr. | Daily | Bare Costs | Incl. O&P |
| 1 Electrician Foreman | $33.35 | $266.80 | $54.25 | $434.00 | $29.23 | $47.90 |
| 3 Electrician Linemen | 32.85 | 788.40 | 53.45 | 1282.80 | | |
| 2 Electrician Groundmen | 21.75 | 348.00 | 36.40 | 582.40 | | |
| 1 Pickup Truck, 3/4 Ton | | 140.00 | | 154.00 | | |
| 1 Crew Truck | | 202.40 | | 222.64 | 7.13 | 7.85 |
| 48 L.H., Daily Totals | | $1745.60 | | $2675.84 | $36.37 | $55.75 |
| **Crew R-9** | Hr. | Daily | Hr. | Daily | Bare Costs | Incl. O&P |
| 1 Electrician Foreman | $33.35 | $266.80 | $54.25 | $434.00 | $27.36 | $45.02 |
| 1 Electrician Lineman | 32.85 | 262.80 | 53.45 | 427.60 | | |
| 2 Electrician Operators | 32.85 | 525.60 | 53.45 | 855.20 | | |
| 4 Electrician Groundmen | 21.75 | 696.00 | 36.40 | 1164.80 | | |
| 1 Pickup Truck, 3/4 Ton | | 140.00 | | 154.00 | | |
| 1 Crew Truck | | 202.40 | | 222.64 | 5.35 | 5.88 |
| 64 L.H., Daily Totals | | $2093.60 | | $3258.24 | $32.71 | $50.91 |

# Crews

| Crew No. | Bare Costs | | Incl. Subs O&P | | Cost Per Labor-Hour | |
|---|---|---|---|---|---|---|
| **Crew R-10** | Hr. | Daily | Hr. | Daily | Bare Costs | Incl. O&P |
| 1 Electrician Foreman | $33.35 | $266.80 | $54.25 | $434.00 | $31.08 | $50.74 |
| 4 Electrician Linemen | 32.85 | 1051.20 | 53.45 | 1710.40 | | |
| 1 Electrician Groundman | 21.75 | 174.00 | 36.40 | 291.20 | | |
| 1 Crew Truck | | 202.40 | | 222.64 | | |
| 3 Tram Cars | | 393.30 | | 432.63 | 12.41 | 13.65 |
| 48 L.H., Daily Totals | | $2087.70 | | $3090.87 | $43.49 | $64.39 |

| **Crew R-11** | Hr. | Daily | Hr. | Daily | Bare Costs | Incl. O&P |
|---|---|---|---|---|---|---|
| 1 Electrician Foreman | $33.35 | $266.80 | $54.25 | $434.00 | $30.99 | $50.62 |
| 4 Electricians | 32.85 | 1051.20 | 53.45 | 1710.40 | | |
| 1 Equip. Oper. (crane) | 30.65 | 245.20 | 50.15 | 401.20 | | |
| 1 Common Laborer | 21.50 | 172.00 | 36.15 | 289.20 | | |
| 1 Crew Truck | | 202.40 | | 222.64 | | |
| 1 Hyd. Crane, 12 Ton | | 655.60 | | 721.16 | 15.32 | 16.85 |
| 56 L.H., Daily Totals | | $2593.20 | | $3778.60 | $46.31 | $67.47 |

| **Crew R-12** | Hr. | Daily | Hr. | Daily | Bare Costs | Incl. O&P |
|---|---|---|---|---|---|---|
| 1 Carpenter Foreman | $29.60 | $236.80 | $49.80 | $398.40 | $26.64 | $45.30 |
| 4 Carpenters | 29.10 | 931.20 | 48.95 | 1566.40 | | |
| 4 Common Laborers | 21.50 | 688.00 | 36.15 | 1156.80 | | |
| 1 Equip. Oper. (med.) | 29.65 | 237.20 | 48.55 | 388.40 | | |
| 1 Steel Worker | 31.40 | 251.20 | 59.60 | 476.80 | | |
| 1 Dozer, 200 H.P. | | 1192.00 | | 1311.20 | | |
| 1 Pickup Truck, 3/4 Ton | | 140.00 | | 154.00 | 15.14 | 16.65 |
| 88 L.H., Daily Totals | | $3676.40 | | $5452.00 | $41.78 | $61.95 |

| **Crew R-15** | Hr. | Daily | Hr. | Daily | Bare Costs | Incl. O&P |
|---|---|---|---|---|---|---|
| 1 Electrician Foreman | $33.35 | $266.80 | $54.25 | $434.00 | $32.21 | $52.45 |
| 4 Electricians | 32.85 | 1051.20 | 53.45 | 1710.40 | | |
| 1 Equipment Oper. (light) | 28.50 | 228.00 | 46.65 | 373.20 | | |
| 1 Aerial Lift Truck | | 347.40 | | 382.14 | 7.24 | 7.96 |
| 48 L.H., Daily Totals | | $1893.40 | | $2899.74 | $39.45 | $60.41 |

| **Crew R-15A** | Hr. | Daily | Hr. | Daily | Bare Costs | Incl. O&P |
|---|---|---|---|---|---|---|
| 1 Electrician Foreman | $33.35 | $266.80 | $54.25 | $434.00 | $28.43 | $46.68 |
| 2 Electricians | 32.85 | 525.60 | 53.45 | 855.20 | | |
| 2 Common Laborers | 21.50 | 344.00 | 36.15 | 578.40 | | |
| 1 Equipment Oper. (light) | 28.50 | 228.00 | 46.65 | 373.20 | | |
| 1 Aerial Lift Truck | | 347.40 | | 382.14 | 7.24 | 7.96 |
| 48 L.H., Daily Totals | | $1711.80 | | $2622.94 | $35.66 | $54.64 |

| **Crew R-18** | Hr. | Daily | Hr. | Daily | Bare Costs | Incl. O&P |
|---|---|---|---|---|---|---|
| .25 Electrician Foreman | $33.35 | $66.70 | $54.25 | $108.50 | $26.06 | $43.02 |
| 1 Electrician | 32.85 | 262.80 | 53.45 | 427.60 | | |
| 2 Helpers | 21.75 | 348.00 | 36.40 | 582.40 | | |
| 26 L.H., Daily Totals | | $677.50 | | $1118.50 | $26.06 | $43.02 |

| **Crew R-19** | Hr. | Daily | Hr. | Daily | Bare Costs | Incl. O&P |
|---|---|---|---|---|---|---|
| .5 Electrician Foreman | $33.35 | $133.40 | $54.25 | $217.00 | $32.95 | $53.61 |
| 2 Electricians | 32.85 | 525.60 | 53.45 | 855.20 | | |
| 20 L.H., Daily Totals | | $659.00 | | $1072.20 | $32.95 | $53.61 |

| **Crew R-21** | Hr. | Daily | Hr. | Daily | Bare Costs | Incl. O&P |
|---|---|---|---|---|---|---|
| 1 Electrician Foreman | $33.35 | $266.80 | $54.25 | $434.00 | $32.89 | $53.53 |
| 3 Electricians | 32.85 | 788.40 | 53.45 | 1282.80 | | |
| .1 Equip. Oper. (med.) | 29.65 | 23.72 | 48.55 | 38.84 | | |
| .1 S.P. Crane, 4x4, 25 Ton | | 65.56 | | 72.12 | 2.00 | 2.20 |
| 32.8 L.H., Daily Totals | | $1144.48 | | $1827.76 | $34.89 | $55.72 |

| Crew No. | Bare Costs | | Incl. Subs O&P | | Cost Per Labor-Hour | |
|---|---|---|---|---|---|---|
| **Crew R-22** | Hr. | Daily | Hr. | Daily | Bare Costs | Incl. O&P |
| .66 Electrician Foreman | $33.35 | $176.09 | $54.25 | $286.44 | $28.16 | $46.25 |
| 2 Helpers | 21.75 | 348.00 | 36.40 | 582.40 | | |
| 2 Electricians | 32.85 | 525.60 | 53.45 | 855.20 | | |
| 37.28 L.H., Daily Totals | | $1049.69 | | $1724.04 | $28.16 | $46.25 |

| **Crew R-30** | Hr. | Daily | Hr. | Daily | Bare Costs | Incl. O&P |
|---|---|---|---|---|---|---|
| .25 Electrician Foreman (out) | $34.85 | $69.70 | $56.70 | $113.40 | $26.02 | $43.05 |
| 1 Electrician | 32.85 | 262.80 | 53.45 | 427.60 | | |
| 2 Laborers, (Semi-Skilled) | 21.50 | 344.00 | 36.15 | 578.40 | | |
| 26 L.H., Daily Totals | | $676.50 | | $1119.40 | $26.02 | $43.05 |

# Location Factors

Costs shown in *RSMeans Residential Cost Data* are based on national averages for materials and installation. To adjust these costs to a specific location, simply multiply the base cost by the factor for that city. The data is arranged alphabetically by state and postal zip code numbers. For a city not listed, use the factor for a nearby city with similar economic characteristics.

| STATE | CITY | Residential |
|---|---|---|
| **ALABAMA** | | |
| 350-352 | Birmingham | .86 |
| 354 | Tuscaloosa | .77 |
| 355 | Jasper | .72 |
| 356 | Decatur | .77 |
| 357-358 | Huntsville | .83 |
| 359 | Gadsden | .74 |
| 360-361 | Montgomery | .75 |
| 362 | Anniston | .77 |
| 363 | Dothan | .75 |
| 364 | Evergreen | .73 |
| 365-366 | Mobile | .81 |
| 367 | Selma | .72 |
| 368 | Phenix City | .73 |
| 369 | Butler | .73 |
| | | |
| **ALASKA** | | |
| 995-996 | Anchorage | 1.26 |
| 997 | Fairbanks | 1.27 |
| 998 | Juneau | 1.25 |
| 999 | Ketchikan | 1.29 |
| | | |
| **ARIZONA** | | |
| 850,853 | Phoenix | .86 |
| 851,852 | Mesa/Tempe | .81 |
| 855 | Globe | .77 |
| 856-857 | Tucson | .84 |
| 859 | Show Low | .79 |
| 860 | Flagstaff | .84 |
| 863 | Prescott | .77 |
| 864 | Kingman | .81 |
| 865 | Chambers | .77 |
| | | |
| **ARKANSAS** | | |
| 716 | Pine Bluff | .79 |
| 717 | Camden | .67 |
| 718 | Texarkana | .72 |
| 719 | Hot Springs | .68 |
| 720-722 | Little Rock | .83 |
| 723 | West Memphis | .77 |
| 724 | Jonesboro | .76 |
| 725 | Batesville | .73 |
| 726 | Harrison | .75 |
| 727 | Fayetteville | .70 |
| 728 | Russellville | .75 |
| 729 | Fort Smith | .76 |
| | | |
| **CALIFORNIA** | | |
| 900-902 | Los Angeles | 1.08 |
| 903-905 | Inglewood | 1.01 |
| 906-908 | Long Beach | 1.00 |
| 910-912 | Pasadena | 1.00 |
| 913-916 | Van Nuys | 1.03 |
| 917-918 | Alhambra | 1.04 |
| 919-921 | San Diego | 1.03 |
| 922 | Palm Springs | 1.00 |
| 923-924 | San Bernardino | 1.01 |
| 925 | Riverside | 1.07 |
| 926-927 | Santa Ana | 1.02 |
| 928 | Anaheim | 1.07 |
| 930 | Oxnard | 1.08 |
| 931 | Santa Barbara | 1.07 |
| 932-933 | Bakersfield | 1.06 |
| 934 | San Luis Obispo | 1.03 |
| 935 | Mojave | 1.01 |
| 936-938 | Fresno | 1.09 |
| 939 | Salinas | 1.11 |
| 940-941 | San Francisco | 1.26 |
| 942,956-958 | Sacramento | 1.12 |
| 943 | Palo Alto | 1.14 |
| 944 | San Mateo | 1.22 |
| 945 | Vallejo | 1.15 |
| 946 | Oakland | 1.22 |
| 947 | Berkeley | 1.20 |
| 948 | Richmond | 1.23 |
| 949 | San Rafael | 1.21 |
| 950 | Santa Cruz | 1.14 |
| 951 | San Jose | 1.21 |
| 952 | Stockton | 1.08 |
| 953 | Modesto | 1.08 |

| STATE | CITY | Residential |
|---|---|---|
| **CALIFORNIA (CONT'D)** | | |
| 954 | Santa Rosa | 1.16 |
| 955 | Eureka | 1.10 |
| 959 | Marysville | 1.09 |
| 960 | Redding | 1.09 |
| 961 | Susanville | 1.09 |
| | | |
| **COLORADO** | | |
| 800-802 | Denver | .92 |
| 803 | Boulder | .89 |
| 804 | Golden | .87 |
| 805 | Fort Collins | .86 |
| 806 | Greeley | .76 |
| 807 | Fort Morgan | .89 |
| 808-809 | Colorado Springs | .87 |
| 810 | Pueblo | .89 |
| 811 | Alamosa | .85 |
| 812 | Salida | .87 |
| 813 | Durango | .87 |
| 814 | Montrose | .84 |
| 815 | Grand Junction | .88 |
| 816 | Glenwood Springs | .87 |
| | | |
| **CONNECTICUT** | | |
| 060 | New Britain | 1.09 |
| 061 | Hartford | 1.09 |
| 062 | Willimantic | 1.10 |
| 063 | New London | 1.09 |
| 064 | Meriden | 1.09 |
| 065 | New Haven | 1.10 |
| 066 | Bridgeport | 1.10 |
| 067 | Waterbury | 1.10 |
| 068 | Norwalk | 1.10 |
| 069 | Stamford | 1.11 |
| | | |
| **D.C.** | | |
| 200-205 | Washington | .96 |
| | | |
| **DELAWARE** | | |
| 197 | Newark | 1.03 |
| 198 | Wilmington | 1.04 |
| 199 | Dover | 1.02 |
| | | |
| **FLORIDA** | | |
| 320,322 | Jacksonville | .81 |
| 321 | Daytona Beach | .88 |
| 323 | Tallahassee | .78 |
| 324 | Panama City | .75 |
| 325 | Pensacola | .82 |
| 326,344 | Gainesville | .81 |
| 327-328,347 | Orlando | .89 |
| 329 | Melbourne | .88 |
| 330-332,340 | Miami | .88 |
| 333 | Fort Lauderdale | .87 |
| 334,349 | West Palm Beach | .87 |
| 335-336,346 | Tampa | .92 |
| 337 | St. Petersburg | .79 |
| 338 | Lakeland | .89 |
| 339,341 | Fort Myers | .87 |
| 342 | Sarasota | .90 |
| | | |
| **GEORGIA** | | |
| 300-303,399 | Atlanta | .88 |
| 304 | Statesboro | .71 |
| 305 | Gainesville | .77 |
| 306 | Athens | .76 |
| 307 | Dalton | .75 |
| 308-309 | Augusta | .82 |
| 310-312 | Macon | .80 |
| 313-314 | Savannah | .80 |
| 315 | Waycross | .79 |
| 316 | Valdosta | .74 |
| 317,398 | Albany | .77 |
| 318-319 | Columbus | .81 |
| | | |
| **HAWAII** | | |
| 967 | Hilo | 1.19 |
| 968 | Honolulu | 1.21 |

# Location Factors

| STATE | CITY | Residential |
|---|---|---|
| **STATES & POSS.** | | |
| 969 | Guam | .94 |
| | | |
| **IDAHO** | | |
| 832 | Pocatello | .84 |
| 833 | Twin Falls | .71 |
| 834 | Idaho Falls | .73 |
| 835 | Lewiston | .94 |
| 836-837 | Boise | .84 |
| 838 | Coeur d'Alene | .92 |
| | | |
| **ILLINOIS** | | |
| 600-603 | North Suburban | 1.20 |
| 604 | Joliet | 1.22 |
| 605 | South Suburban | 1.20 |
| 606-608 | Chicago | 1.22 |
| 609 | Kankakee | 1.12 |
| 610-611 | Rockford | 1.11 |
| 612 | Rock Island | .98 |
| 613 | La Salle | 1.09 |
| 614 | Galesburg | 1.03 |
| 615-616 | Peoria | 1.05 |
| 617 | Bloomington | 1.03 |
| 618-619 | Champaign | 1.04 |
| 620-622 | East St. Louis | 1.02 |
| 623 | Quincy | 1.02 |
| 624 | Effingham | 1.03 |
| 625 | Decatur | 1.03 |
| 626-627 | Springfield | 1.02 |
| 628 | Centralia | 1.02 |
| 629 | Carbondale | .99 |
| | | |
| **INDIANA** | | |
| 460 | Anderson | .90 |
| 461-462 | Indianapolis | .92 |
| 463-464 | Gary | 1.04 |
| 465-466 | South Bend | .90 |
| 467-468 | Fort Wayne | .89 |
| 469 | Kokomo | .90 |
| 470 | Lawrenceburg | .87 |
| 471 | New Albany | .86 |
| 472 | Columbus | .92 |
| 473 | Muncie | .91 |
| 474 | Bloomington | .92 |
| 475 | Washington | .90 |
| 476-477 | Evansville | .90 |
| 478 | Terre Haute | .91 |
| 479 | Lafayette | .92 |
| | | |
| **IOWA** | | |
| 500-503,509 | Des Moines | .86 |
| 504 | Mason City | .74 |
| 505 | Fort Dodge | .74 |
| 506-507 | Waterloo | .76 |
| 508 | Creston | .78 |
| 510-511 | Sioux City | .82 |
| 512 | Sibley | .70 |
| 513 | Spencer | .72 |
| 514 | Carroll | .72 |
| 515 | Council Bluffs | .80 |
| 516 | Shenandoah | .72 |
| 520 | Dubuque | .83 |
| 521 | Decorah | .73 |
| 522-524 | Cedar Rapids | .90 |
| 525 | Ottumwa | .81 |
| 526 | Burlington | .83 |
| 527-528 | Davenport | .93 |
| | | |
| **KANSAS** | | |
| 660-662 | Kansas City | .98 |
| 664-666 | Topeka | .77 |
| 667 | Fort Scott | .85 |
| 668 | Emporia | .73 |
| 669 | Belleville | .77 |
| 670-672 | Wichita | .77 |
| 673 | Independence | .82 |
| 674 | Salina | .75 |
| 675 | Hutchinson | .77 |
| 676 | Hays | .79 |
| 677 | Colby | .81 |
| 678 | Dodge City | .79 |
| 679 | Liberal | .78 |
| | | |
| **KENTUCKY** | | |
| 400-402 | Louisville | .90 |
| 403-405 | Lexington | .87 |

| STATE | CITY | Residential |
|---|---|---|
| **KENTUCKY (CONT'D)** | | |
| 406 | Frankfort | .83 |
| 407-409 | Corbin | .74 |
| 410 | Covington | .96 |
| 411-412 | Ashland | .93 |
| 413-414 | Campton | .75 |
| 415-416 | Pikeville | .82 |
| 417-418 | Hazard | .70 |
| 420 | Paducah | .88 |
| 421-422 | Bowling Green | .88 |
| 423 | Owensboro | .85 |
| 424 | Henderson | .90 |
| 425-426 | Somerset | .74 |
| 427 | Elizabethtown | .86 |
| | | |
| **LOUISIANA** | | |
| 700-701 | New Orleans | .85 |
| 703 | Thibodaux | .81 |
| 704 | Hammond | .76 |
| 705 | Lafayette | .79 |
| 706 | Lake Charles | .81 |
| 707-708 | Baton Rouge | .83 |
| 710-711 | Shreveport | .77 |
| 712 | Monroe | .72 |
| 713-714 | Alexandria | .73 |
| | | |
| **MAINE** | | |
| 039 | Kittery | .91 |
| 040-041 | Portland | .90 |
| 042 | Lewiston | .90 |
| 043 | Augusta | .93 |
| 044 | Bangor | .89 |
| 045 | Bath | .91 |
| 046 | Machias | .91 |
| 047 | Houlton | .92 |
| 048 | Rockland | .92 |
| 049 | Waterville | .91 |
| | | |
| **MARYLAND** | | |
| 206 | Waldorf | .83 |
| 207-208 | College Park | .90 |
| 209 | Silver Spring | .85 |
| 210-212 | Baltimore | .90 |
| 214 | Annapolis | .83 |
| 215 | Cumberland | .87 |
| 216 | Easton | .66 |
| 217 | Hagerstown | .86 |
| 218 | Salisbury | .72 |
| 219 | Elkton | .85 |
| | | |
| **MASSACHUSETTS** | | |
| 010-011 | Springfield | 1.05 |
| 012 | Pittsfield | 1.05 |
| 013 | Greenfield | 1.03 |
| 014 | Fitchburg | 1.11 |
| 015-016 | Worcester | 1.13 |
| 017 | Framingham | 1.15 |
| 018 | Lowell | 1.15 |
| 019 | Lawrence | 1.15 |
| 020-022, 024 | Boston | 1.21 |
| 023 | Brockton | 1.15 |
| 025 | Buzzards Bay | 1.12 |
| 026 | Hyannis | 1.12 |
| 027 | New Bedford | 1.14 |
| | | |
| **MICHIGAN** | | |
| 480,483 | Royal Oak | 1.01 |
| 481 | Ann Arbor | 1.02 |
| 482 | Detroit | 1.06 |
| 484-485 | Flint | .97 |
| 486 | Saginaw | .94 |
| 487 | Bay City | .94 |
| 488-489 | Lansing | .96 |
| 490 | Battle Creek | .94 |
| 491 | Kalamazoo | .93 |
| 492 | Jackson | .93 |
| 493,495 | Grand Rapids | .84 |
| 494 | Muskegon | .90 |
| 496 | Traverse City | .84 |
| 497 | Gaylord | .81 |
| 498-499 | Iron mountain | .91 |
| | | |
| **MINNESOTA** | | |
| 550-551 | Saint Paul | 1.14 |
| 553-555 | Minneapolis | 1.16 |
| 556-558 | Duluth | 1.10 |

654

# Location Factors

| STATE | CITY | Residential |
|---|---|---|
| **MINNESOTA (CONT'd)** | | |
| 559 | Rochester | 1.06 |
| 560 | Mankato | 1.02 |
| 561 | Windom | .82 |
| 562 | Willmar | .84 |
| 563 | St. Cloud | 1.10 |
| 564 | Brainerd | 1.00 |
| 565 | Detroit Lakes | .95 |
| 566 | Bemidji | .97 |
| 567 | Thief River Falls | .96 |
| **MISSISSIPPI** | | |
| 386 | Clarksdale | .76 |
| 387 | Greenville | .83 |
| 388 | Tupelo | .77 |
| 389 | Greenwood | .78 |
| 390-392 | Jackson | .83 |
| 393 | Meridian | .82 |
| 394 | Laurel | .78 |
| 395 | Biloxi | .80 |
| 396 | Mccomb | .76 |
| 397 | Columbus | .77 |
| **MISSOURI** | | |
| 630-631 | St. Louis | 1.02 |
| 633 | Bowling Green | .93 |
| 634 | Hannibal | .84 |
| 635 | Kirksville | .79 |
| 636 | Flat River | .92 |
| 637 | Cape Girardeau | .86 |
| 638 | Sikeston | .81 |
| 639 | Poplar Bluff | .81 |
| 640-641 | Kansas City | 1.03 |
| 644-645 | St. Joseph | .91 |
| 646 | Chillicothe | .84 |
| 647 | Harrisonville | .94 |
| 648 | Joplin | .81 |
| 650-651 | Jefferson City | .86 |
| 652 | Columbia | .89 |
| 653 | Sedalia | .83 |
| 654-655 | Rolla | .88 |
| 656-658 | Springfield | .86 |
| **MONTANA** | | |
| 590-591 | Billings | .87 |
| 592 | Wolf Point | .82 |
| 593 | Miles City | .85 |
| 594 | Great Falls | .87 |
| 595 | Havre | .82 |
| 596 | Helena | .86 |
| 597 | Butte | .86 |
| 598 | Missoula | .85 |
| 599 | Kalispell | .83 |
| **NEBRASKA** | | |
| 680-681 | Omaha | .89 |
| 683-685 | Lincoln | .85 |
| 686 | Columbus | .85 |
| 687 | Norfolk | .90 |
| 688 | Grand Island | .90 |
| 689 | Hastings | .92 |
| 690 | Mccook | .83 |
| 691 | North Platte | .90 |
| 692 | Valentine | .84 |
| 693 | Alliance | .83 |
| **NEVADA** | | |
| 889-891 | Las Vegas | 1.05 |
| 893 | Ely | .84 |
| 894-895 | Reno | .92 |
| 897 | Carson City | .92 |
| 898 | Elko | .88 |
| **NEW HAMPSHIRE** | | |
| 030 | Nashua | .94 |
| 031 | Manchester | .94 |
| 032-033 | Concord | .92 |
| 034 | Keene | .73 |
| 035 | Littleton | .79 |
| 036 | Charleston | .72 |
| 037 | Claremont | .73 |
| 038 | Portsmouth | .94 |

| STATE | CITY | Residential |
|---|---|---|
| **NEW JERSEY** | | |
| 070-071 | Newark | 1.12 |
| 072 | Elizabeth | 1.14 |
| 073 | Jersey City | 1.11 |
| 074-075 | Paterson | 1.12 |
| 076 | Hackensack | 1.11 |
| 077 | Long Branch | 1.11 |
| 078 | Dover | 1.11 |
| 079 | Summit | 1.12 |
| 080,083 | Vineland | 1.09 |
| 081 | Camden | 1.10 |
| 082,084 | Atlantic City | 1.12 |
| 085-086 | Trenton | 1.10 |
| 087 | Point Pleasant | 1.09 |
| 088-089 | New Brunswick | 1.12 |
| **NEW MEXICO** | | |
| 870-872 | Albuquerque | .84 |
| 873 | Gallup | .84 |
| 874 | Farmington | .84 |
| 875 | Santa Fe | .85 |
| 877 | Las Vegas | .84 |
| 878 | Socorro | .84 |
| 879 | Truth/Consequences | .83 |
| 880 | Las Cruces | .82 |
| 881 | Clovis | .84 |
| 882 | Roswell | .84 |
| 883 | Carrizozo | .84 |
| 884 | Tucumcari | .85 |
| **NEW YORK** | | |
| 100-102 | New York | 1.39 |
| 103 | Staten Island | 1.32 |
| 104 | Bronx | 1.33 |
| 105 | Mount Vernon | 1.16 |
| 106 | White Plains | 1.19 |
| 107 | Yonkers | 1.20 |
| 108 | New Rochelle | 1.20 |
| 109 | Suffern | 1.16 |
| 110 | Queens | 1.32 |
| 111 | Long Island City | 1.34 |
| 112 | Brooklyn | 1.36 |
| 113 | Flushing | 1.34 |
| 114 | Jamaica | 1.33 |
| 115,117,118 | Hicksville | 1.21 |
| 116 | Far Rockaway | 1.33 |
| 119 | Riverhead | 1.22 |
| 120-122 | Albany | .97 |
| 123 | Schenectady | .98 |
| 124 | Kingston | 1.06 |
| 125-126 | Poughkeepsie | 1.20 |
| 127 | Monticello | 1.08 |
| 128 | Glens Falls | .88 |
| 129 | Plattsburgh | .94 |
| 130-132 | Syracuse | .96 |
| 133-135 | Utica | .93 |
| 136 | Watertown | .93 |
| 137-139 | Binghamton | .94 |
| 140-142 | Buffalo | 1.04 |
| 143 | Niagara Falls | 1.01 |
| 144-146 | Rochester | .98 |
| 147 | Jamestown | .90 |
| 148-149 | Elmira | .88 |
| **NORTH CAROLINA** | | |
| 270,272-274 | Greensboro | .81 |
| 271 | Winston-Salem | .81 |
| 275-276 | Raleigh | .83 |
| 277 | Durham | .82 |
| 278 | Rocky Mount | .72 |
| 279 | Elizabeth City | .73 |
| 280 | Gastonia | .82 |
| 281-282 | Charlotte | .83 |
| 283 | Fayetteville | .81 |
| 284 | Wilmington | .79 |
| 285 | Kinston | .72 |
| 286 | Hickory | .77 |
| 287-288 | Asheville | .80 |
| 289 | Murphy | .71 |
| **NORTH DAKOTA** | | |
| 580-581 | Fargo | .76 |
| 582 | Grand Forks | .73 |
| 583 | Devils Lake | .76 |
| 584 | Jamestown | .71 |
| 585 | Bismarck | .76 |

# Location Factors

| STATE | CITY | Residential |
|---|---|---|
| **NORTH DAKOTA (CONT'D)** | | |
| 586 | Dickinson | .74 |
| 587 | Minot | .79 |
| 588 | Williston | .74 |
| | | |
| **OHIO** | | |
| 430-432 | Columbus | .94 |
| 433 | Marion | .88 |
| 434-436 | Toledo | .99 |
| 437-438 | Zanesville | .87 |
| 439 | Steubenville | .93 |
| 440 | Lorain | .96 |
| 441 | Cleveland | 1.00 |
| 442-443 | Akron | .96 |
| 444-445 | Youngstown | .94 |
| 446-447 | Canton | .92 |
| 448-449 | Mansfield | .92 |
| 450 | Hamilton | .91 |
| 451-452 | Cincinnati | .91 |
| 453-454 | Dayton | .90 |
| 455 | Springfield | .92 |
| 456 | Chillicothe | .94 |
| 457 | Athens | .88 |
| 458 | Lima | .89 |
| | | |
| **OKLAHOMA** | | |
| 730-731 | Oklahoma City | .78 |
| 734 | Ardmore | .77 |
| 735 | Lawton | .80 |
| 736 | Clinton | .76 |
| 737 | Enid | .76 |
| 738 | Woodward | .75 |
| 739 | Guymon | .65 |
| 740-741 | Tulsa | .76 |
| 743 | Miami | .80 |
| 744 | Muskogee | .70 |
| 745 | Mcalester | .73 |
| 746 | Ponca City | .76 |
| 747 | Durant | .76 |
| 748 | Shawnee | .75 |
| 749 | Poteau | .77 |
| | | |
| **OREGON** | | |
| 970-972 | Portland | .98 |
| 973 | Salem | .96 |
| 974 | Eugene | .97 |
| 975 | Medford | .96 |
| 976 | Klamath Falls | .96 |
| 977 | Bend | .98 |
| 978 | Pendleton | .96 |
| 979 | Vale | .94 |
| | | |
| **PENNSYLVANIA** | | |
| 150-152 | Pittsburgh | .98 |
| 153 | Washington | .95 |
| 154 | Uniontown | .92 |
| 155 | Bedford | .88 |
| 156 | Greensburg | .95 |
| 157 | Indiana | .92 |
| 158 | Dubois | .90 |
| 159 | Johnstown | .90 |
| 160 | Butler | .94 |
| 161 | New Castle | .93 |
| 162 | Kittanning | .95 |
| 163 | Oil City | .90 |
| 164-165 | Erie | .93 |
| 166 | Altoona | .88 |
| 167 | Bradford | .90 |
| 168 | State College | .91 |
| 169 | Wellsboro | .92 |
| 170-171 | Harrisburg | .95 |
| 172 | Chambersburg | .89 |
| 173-174 | York | .93 |
| 175-176 | Lancaster | .92 |
| 177 | Williamsport | .85 |
| 178 | Sunbury | .93 |
| 179 | Pottsville | .93 |
| 180 | Lehigh Valley | 1.04 |
| 181 | Allentown | 1.05 |
| 182 | Hazleton | .93 |
| 183 | Stroudsburg | .93 |
| 184-185 | Scranton | .98 |
| 186-187 | Wilkes-Barre | .95 |
| 188 | Montrose | .92 |
| 189 | Doylestown | 1.08 |

| STATE | CITY | Residential |
|---|---|---|
| **PENNSYLVANIA (CONT'D)** | | |
| 190-191 | Philadelphia | 1.17 |
| 193 | Westchester | 1.13 |
| 194 | Norristown | 1.12 |
| 195-196 | Reading | .98 |
| | | |
| **PUERTO RICO** | | |
| 009 | San Juan | .73 |
| | | |
| **RHODE ISLAND** | | |
| 028 | Newport | 1.08 |
| 029 | Providence | 1.08 |
| | | |
| **SOUTH CAROLINA** | | |
| 290-292 | Columbia | .82 |
| 293 | Spartanburg | .82 |
| 294 | Charleston | .85 |
| 295 | Florence | .78 |
| 296 | Greenville | .81 |
| 297 | Rock Hill | .80 |
| 298 | Aiken | .99 |
| 299 | Beaufort | .80 |
| | | |
| **SOUTH DAKOTA** | | |
| 570-571 | Sioux Falls | .77 |
| 572 | Watertown | .74 |
| 573 | Mitchell | .75 |
| 574 | Aberdeen | .76 |
| 575 | Pierre | .75 |
| 576 | Mobridge | .74 |
| 577 | Rapid City | .76 |
| | | |
| **TENNESSEE** | | |
| 370-372 | Nashville | .84 |
| 373-374 | Chattanooga | .81 |
| 375,380-381 | Memphis | .81 |
| 376 | Johnson City | .70 |
| 377-379 | Knoxville | .74 |
| 382 | Mckenzie | .71 |
| 383 | Jackson | .73 |
| 384 | Columbia | .72 |
| 385 | Cookeville | .70 |
| | | |
| **TEXAS** | | |
| 750 | Mckinney | .74 |
| 751 | Waxahackie | .76 |
| 752-753 | Dallas | .83 |
| 754 | Greenville | .70 |
| 755 | Texarkana | .74 |
| 756 | Longview | .69 |
| 757 | Tyler | .75 |
| 758 | Palestine | .68 |
| 759 | Lufkin | .72 |
| 760-761 | Fort Worth | .82 |
| 762 | Denton | .75 |
| 763 | Wichita Falls | .78 |
| 764 | Eastland | .72 |
| 765 | Temple | .75 |
| 766-767 | Waco | .78 |
| 768 | Brownwood | .68 |
| 769 | San Angelo | .72 |
| 770-772 | Houston | .85 |
| 773 | Huntsville | .68 |
| 774 | Wharton | .70 |
| 775 | Galveston | .83 |
| 776-777 | Beaumont | .82 |
| 778 | Bryan | .74 |
| 779 | Victoria | .73 |
| 780 | Laredo | .72 |
| 781-782 | San Antonio | .78 |
| 783-784 | Corpus Christi | .77 |
| 785 | Mc Allen | .75 |
| 786-787 | Austin | .78 |
| 788 | Del Rio | .66 |
| 789 | Giddings | .69 |
| 790-791 | Amarillo | .79 |
| 792 | Childress | .77 |
| 793-794 | Lubbock | .76 |
| 795-796 | Abilene | .75 |
| 797 | Midland | .76 |
| 798-799,885 | El Paso | .75 |
| | | |
| **UTAH** | | |
| 840-841 | Salt Lake City | .79 |
| 842,844 | Ogden | .77 |
| 843 | Logan | .77 |

# Location Factors

| STATE | CITY | Residential |
|---|---|---|
| **UTAH (CONT'D)** | | |
| 845 | Price | .68 |
| 846-847 | Provo | .78 |
| **VERMONT** | | |
| 050 | White River Jct. | .74 |
| 051 | Bellows Falls | .78 |
| 052 | Bennington | .79 |
| 053 | Brattleboro | .80 |
| 054 | Burlington | .80 |
| 056 | Montpelier | .81 |
| 057 | Rutland | .80 |
| 058 | St. Johnsbury | .76 |
| 059 | Guildhall | .76 |
| **VIRGINIA** | | |
| 220-221 | Fairfax | 1.03 |
| 222 | Arlington | 1.04 |
| 223 | Alexandria | 1.07 |
| 224-225 | Fredericksburg | .93 |
| 226 | Winchester | .89 |
| 227 | Culpeper | .98 |
| 228 | Harrisonburg | .88 |
| 229 | Charlottesville | .89 |
| 230-232 | Richmond | .97 |
| 233-235 | Norfolk | .99 |
| 236 | Newport News | .98 |
| 237 | Portsmouth | .91 |
| 238 | Petersburg | .95 |
| 239 | Farmville | .87 |
| 240-241 | Roanoke | .95 |
| 242 | Bristol | .84 |
| 243 | Pulaski | .81 |
| 244 | Staunton | .89 |
| 245 | Lynchburg | .94 |
| 246 | Grundy | .82 |
| **WASHINGTON** | | |
| 980-981,987 | Seattle | 1.03 |
| 982 | Everett | 1.03 |
| 983-984 | Tacoma | 1.01 |
| 985 | Olympia | 1.00 |
| 986 | Vancouver | .94 |
| 988 | Wenatchee | .89 |
| 989 | Yakima | .95 |
| 990-992 | Spokane | .96 |
| 993 | Richland | .95 |
| 994 | Clarkston | .94 |
| **WEST VIRGINIA** | | |
| 247-248 | Bluefield | .88 |
| 249 | Lewisburg | .89 |
| 250-253 | Charleston | .95 |
| 254 | Martinsburg | .88 |
| 255-257 | Huntington | .97 |
| 258-259 | Beckley | .90 |
| 260 | Wheeling | .92 |
| 261 | Parkersburg | .90 |
| 262 | Buckhannon | .91 |
| 263-264 | Clarksburg | .90 |
| 265 | Morgantown | .92 |
| 266 | Gassaway | .91 |
| 267 | Romney | .89 |
| 268 | Petersburg | .91 |
| **WISCONSIN** | | |
| 530,532 | Milwaukee | 1.08 |
| 531 | Kenosha | 1.01 |
| 534 | Racine | 1.01 |
| 535 | Beloit | .97 |
| 537 | Madison | .98 |
| 538 | Lancaster | .95 |
| 539 | Portage | .94 |
| 540 | New Richmond | .97 |
| 541-543 | Green Bay | .99 |
| 544 | Wausau | .94 |
| 545 | Rhinelander | .93 |
| 546 | La Crosse | .93 |
| 547 | Eau Claire | .96 |
| 548 | Superior | .96 |
| 549 | Oshkosh | .93 |
| **WYOMING** | | |
| 820 | Cheyenne | .80 |
| 821 | Yellowstone Nat. Pk. | .73 |
| 822 | Wheatland | .73 |

| STATE | CITY | Residential |
|---|---|---|
| **WYOMING (CONT'D)** | | |
| 823 | Rawlins | .73 |
| 824 | Worland | .72 |
| 825 | Riverton | .72 |
| 826 | Casper | .75 |
| 827 | Newcastle | .72 |
| 828 | Sheridan | .77 |
| 829-831 | Rock Springs | .76 |
| **CANADIAN FACTORS (reflect Canadian currency)** | | |
| **ALBERTA** | | |
| | Calgary | 1.11 |
| | Edmonton | 1.10 |
| | Fort McMurray | 1.12 |
| | Lethbridge | 1.09 |
| | Lloydminster | 1.04 |
| | Medicine Hat | 1.04 |
| | Red Deer | 1.04 |
| **BRITISH COLUMBIA** | | |
| | Kamloops | 1.02 |
| | Prince George | 1.03 |
| | Vancouver | 1.04 |
| | Victoria | .98 |
| **MANITOBA** | | |
| | Brandon | 1.00 |
| | Portage la Prairie | .99 |
| | Winnipeg | .99 |
| **NEW BRUNSWICK** | | |
| | Bathurst | .92 |
| | Dalhousie | .92 |
| | Fredericton | .99 |
| | Moncton | .93 |
| | Newcastle | .92 |
| | St. John | .99 |
| **NEWFOUNDLAND** | | |
| | Corner Brook | .94 |
| | St Johns | .95 |
| **NORTHWEST TERRITORIES** | Yellowknife | 1.05 |
| **NOVA SCOTIA** | | |
| | Bridgewater | .95 |
| | Dartmouth | .95 |
| | Halifax | .98 |
| | New Glasgow | .95 |
| | Sydney | .94 |
| | Truro | .95 |
| | Yarmouth | .95 |
| **ONTARIO** | | |
| | Barrie | 1.10 |
| | Brantford | 1.12 |
| | Cornwall | 1.11 |
| | Hamilton | 1.13 |
| | Kingston | 1.11 |
| | Kitchener | 1.07 |
| | London | 1.11 |
| | North Bay | 1.08 |
| | Oshawa | 1.10 |
| | Ottawa | 1.12 |
| | Owen Sound | 1.09 |
| | Peterborough | 1.09 |
| | Sarnia | 1.12 |
| | Sault Ste Marie | 1.05 |
| | St. Catharines | 1.07 |
| | Sudbury | 1.05 |
| | Thunder Bay | 1.09 |
| | Timmins | 1.08 |
| | Toronto | 1.15 |
| | Windsor | 1.09 |
| **PRINCE EDWARD ISLAND** | | |
| | Charlottetown | .90 |
| | Summerside | .90 |
| **QUEBEC** | | |
| | Cap-de-la-Madeleine | 1.10 |
| | Charlesbourg | 1.10 |
| | Chicoutimi | 1.13 |
| | Gatineau | 1.09 |
| | Granby | 1.09 |

# Location Factors

| STATE | CITY | Residential |
|---|---|---|
| **QUEBEC (CONT'D)** | | |
| | Hull | 1.09 |
| | Joliette | 1.10 |
| | Laval | 1.09 |
| | Montreal | 1.15 |
| | Quebec | 1.15 |
| | Rimouski | 1.13 |
| | Rouyn-Noranda | 1.09 |
| | Saint Hyacinthe | 1.09 |
| | Sherbrooke | 1.09 |
| | Sorel | 1.10 |
| | St Jerome | 1.09 |
| | Trois Rivieres | 1.10 |
| **SASKATCHEWAN** | | |
| | Moose Jaw | .92 |
| | Prince Albert | .91 |
| | Regina | .94 |
| | Saskatoon | .92 |
| **YUKON** | | |
| | Whitehorse | .91 |

658

## R011105-05   Tips for Accurate Estimating

1. Use pre-printed or columnar forms for orderly sequence of dimensions and locations and for recording telephone quotations.

2. Use only the front side of each paper or form except for certain pre-printed summary forms.

3. Be consistent in listing dimensions: For example, length x width x height. This helps in rechecking to ensure that, the total length of partitions is appropriate for the building area.

4. Use printed (rather than measured) dimensions where given.

5. Add up multiple printed dimensions for a single entry where possible.

6. Measure all other dimensions carefully.

7. Use each set of dimensions to calculate multiple related quantities.

8. Convert foot and inch measurements to decimal feet when listing. Memorize decimal equivalents to .01 parts of a foot (1/8″ equals approximately .01′).

9. Do not "round off" quantities until the final summary.

10. Mark drawings with different colors as items are taken off.

11. Keep similar items together, different items separate.

12. Identify location and drawing numbers to aid in future checking for completeness.

13. Measure or list everything on the drawings or mentioned in the specifications.

14. It may be necessary to list items not called for to make the job complete.

15. Be alert for: Notes on plans such as N.T.S. (not to scale); changes in scale throughout the drawings; reduced size drawings; discrepancies between the specifications and the drawings.

16. Develop a consistent pattern of performing an estimate. For example:
    a. Start the quantity takeoff at the lower floor and move to the next higher floor.
    b. Proceed from the main section of the building to the wings.
    c. Proceed from south to north or vice versa, clockwise or counterclockwise.
    d. Take off floor plan quantities first, elevations next, then detail drawings.

17. List all gross dimensions that can be either used again for different quantities, or used as a rough check of other quantities for verification (exterior perimeter, gross floor area, individual floor areas, etc.).

18. Utilize design symmetry or repetition (repetitive floors, repetitive wings, symmetrical design around a center line, similar room layouts, etc.). Note: Extreme caution is needed here so as not to omit or duplicate an area.

19. Do not convert units until the final total is obtained. For instance, when estimating concrete work, keep all units to the nearest cubic foot, then summarize and convert to cubic yards.

20. When figuring alternatives, it is best to total all items involved in the basic system, then total all items involved in the alternates. Therefore you work with positive numbers in all cases. When adds and deducts are used, it is often confusing whether to add or subtract a portion of an item; especially on a complicated or involved alternate.

## R011110-10   Architectural Fees

Tabulated below are typical percentage fees by project size, for good professional architectural service. Fees may vary from those listed depending upon degree of design difficulty and economic conditions in any particular area.

Rates can be interpolated horizontally and vertically. Various portions of the same project requiring different rates should be adjusted proportionately. For alterations, add 50% to the fee for the first $500,000 of project cost and add 25% to the fee for project cost over $500,000.

Architectural fees tabulated below include Structural, Mechanical and Electrical Engineering Fees. They do not include the fees for special consultants such as kitchen planning, security, acoustical, interior design, etc.

Civil Engineering fees are included in the Architectural fee for project sites requiring minimal design such as city sites. However, separate Civil Engineering fees must be added when utility connections require design, drainage calculations are needed, stepped foundations are required, or provisions are required to protect adjacent wetlands.

| Building Types | Total Project Size in Thousands of Dollars | | | | | | |
|---|---|---|---|---|---|---|---|
| | 100 | 250 | 500 | 1,000 | 5,000 | 10,000 | 50,000 |
| Factories, garages, warehouses, repetitive housing | 9.0% | 8.0% | 7.0% | 6.2% | 5.3% | 4.9% | 4.5% |
| Apartments, banks, schools, libraries, offices, municipal buildings | 12.2 | 12.3 | 9.2 | 8.0 | 7.0 | 6.6 | 6.2 |
| Churches, hospitals, homes, laboratories, museums, research | 15.0 | 13.6 | 12.7 | 11.9 | 9.5 | 8.8 | 8.0 |
| Memorials, monumental work, decorative furnishings | — | 16.0 | 14.5 | 13.1 | 10.0 | 9.0 | 8.3 |

## R012909-80   Sales Tax by State

State sales tax on materials is tabulated below (5 states have no sales tax). Many states allow local jurisdictions, such as a county or city, to levy additional sales tax.

Some projects may be sales tax exempt, particularly those constructed with public funds.

| State | Tax (%) | State | Tax (%) | State | Tax (%) | State | Tax (%) |
|---|---|---|---|---|---|---|---|
| Alabama | 4 | Illinois | 6.25 | Montana | 0 | Rhode Island | 7 |
| Alaska | 0 | Indiana | 7 | Nebraska | 5.5 | South Carolina | 6 |
| Arizona | 5.6 | Iowa | 6 | Nevada | 6.5 | South Dakota | 4 |
| Arkansas | 6 | Kansas | 5.3 | New Hampshire | 0 | Tennessee | 7 |
| California | 8.25 | Kentucky | 6 | New Jersey | 7 | Texas | 6.25 |
| Colorado | 2.9 | Louisiana | 4 | New Mexico | 5 | Utah | 4.75 |
| Connecticut | 6 | Maine | 5 | New York | 4 | Vermont | 6 |
| Delaware | 0 | Maryland | 6 | North Carolina | 4.5 | Virginia | 4 |
| District of Columbia | 5.75 | Massachusetts | 6.25 | North Dakota | 5 | Washington | 6.5 |
| Florida | 6 | Michigan | 6 | Ohio | 7 | West Virginia | 6 |
| Georgia | 4 | Minnesota | 6.5 | Oklahoma | 4.5 | Wisconsin | 5 |
| Hawaii | 4 | Mississippi | 7 | Oregon | 0 | Wyoming | 4 |
| Idaho | 6 | Missouri | 4.225 | Pennsylvania | 6 | Average | 5.01 % |

## Sales Tax by Province (Canada)

GST - a value-added tax, which the government imposes on most goods and services provided in or imported into Canada. PST - a retail sales tax, which five of the provinces impose on the price of most goods and some

services. QST - a value-added tax, similar to the federal GST, which Quebec imposes. HST - Three provinces have combined their retail sales tax with the federal GST into one harmonized tax.

| Province | PST (%) | QST (%) | GST(%) | HST(%) |
|---|---|---|---|---|
| Alberta | 0 | 0 | 5 | 0 |
| British Columbia | 7 | 0 | 5 | 0 |
| Manitoba | 7 | 0 | 5 | 0 |
| New Brunswick | 0 | 0 | 0 | 13 |
| Newfoundland | 0 | 0 | 0 | 13 |
| Northwest Territories | 0 | 0 | 5 | 0 |
| Nova Scotia | 0 | 0 | 0 | 13 |
| Ontario | 8 | 0 | 5 | 0 |
| Prince Edward Island | 10 | 0 | 5 | 0 |
| Quebec | 0 | 7.5 | 5 | 0 |
| Saskatchewan | 5 | 0 | 5 | 0 |
| Yukon | 0 | 0 | 5 | 0 |

## R012909-85   Unemployment Taxes and Social Security Taxes

State Unemployment Tax rates vary not only from state to state, but also with the experience rating of the contractor. The Federal Unemployment Tax rate is 6.2% of the first $7,000 of wages. This is reduced by a credit of up to 5.4% for timely payment to the state. The minimum Federal Unemployment Tax is 0.8% after all credits.

Social Security (FICA) for 2010 is estimated at time of publication to be 7.65% of wages up to $106,800.

## R013113-40  Builder's Risk Insurance

Builder's Risk Insurance is insurance on a building during construction. Premiums are paid by the owner or the contractor. Blasting, collapse and underground insurance would raise total insurance costs above those listed. Floater policy for materials delivered to the job runs $.75 to $1.25 per $100 value. Contractor equipment insurance runs $.50 to $1.50 per $100 value. Insurance for miscellaneous tools to $1,500 value runs from $3.00 to $7.50 per $100 value.

Tabulated below are New England Builder's Risk insurance rates in dollars per $100 value for $1,000 deductible. For $25,000 deductible, rates can be reduced 13% to 34%. On contracts over $1,000,000, rates may be lower than those tabulated. Policies are written annually for the total completed value in place. For "all risk" insurance (excluding flood, earthquake and certain other perils) add $.025 to total rates below.

| Coverage | Frame Construction (Class 1) | | Average | Brick Construction (Class 4) | | Average | Fire Resistive (Class 6) | | Average |
|---|---|---|---|---|---|---|---|---|---|
| | Range | | | Range | | | Range | | |
| Fire Insurance | $.350 to | $.850 | $.600 | $.158 to | $.189 | $.174 | $.052 to | $.080 | $.070 |
| Extended Coverage | .115 to | .200 | .158 | .080 to | .105 | .101 | .081 to | .105 | .100 |
| Vandalism | .012 to | .016 | .014 | .008 to | .011 | .011 | .008 to | .011 | .010 |
| Total Annual Rate | $.477 to | $1.066 | $.772 | $.246 to | $.305 | $.286 | $.141 to | $.196 | $.180 |

## R013113-50  General Contractor's Overhead

There are two distinct types of overhead on a construction project: Project Overhead and Main Office Overhead. Project Overhead includes those costs at a construction site not directly associated with the installation of construction materials. Examples of Project Overhead costs include the following:

1. Superintendent
2. Construction office and storage trailers
3. Temporary sanitary facilities
4. Temporary utilities
5. Security fencing
6. Photographs
7. Clean up
8. Performance and payment bonds

The above Project Overhead items are also referred to as General Requirements and therefore are estimated in Division 1. Division 1 is the first division listed in the CSI MasterFormat but it is usually the last division estimated. The sum of the costs in Divisions 1 through 49 is referred to as the sum of the direct costs.

All construction projects also include indirect costs. The primary components of indirect costs are the contractor's Main Office Overhead and profit. The amount of the Main Office Overhead expense varies depending on the the following:

1. Owner's compensation
2. Project managers and estimator's wages
3. Clerical support wages
4. Office rent and utilities
5. Corporate legal and accounting costs
6. Advertising
7. Automobile expenses
8. Association dues
9. Travel and entertainment expenses

These costs are usually calculated as a percentage of annual sales volume. This percentage can range from 35% for a small contractor doing less than $500,000 to 5% for a large contractor with sales in excess of $100 million.

## R013113-60   Workers' Compensation Insurance Rates by Trade

The table below tabulates the national averages for Workers' Compensation insurance rates by trade and type of building. The average "Insurance Rate" is multiplied by the "% of Building Cost" for each trade. This produces the "Workers' Compensation Cost" by % of total labor cost, to be added for each trade by building type to determine the weighted average Workers' Compensation rate for the building types analyzed.

| Trade | Insurance Rate (% Labor Cost) Range | Average | % of Building Cost Office Bldgs. | Schools & Apts. | Mfg. | Workers' Compensation Office Bldgs. | Schools & Apts. | Mfg. |
|---|---|---|---|---|---|---|---|---|
| Excavation, Grading, etc. | 4.2 % to 17.5% | 9.4% | 4.8% | 4.9% | 4.5% | 0.45% | 0.46% | 0.42% |
| Piles & Foundations | 4.8 to 57.1 | 18.5 | 7.1 | 5.2 | 8.7 | 1.31 | 0.96 | 1.61 |
| Concrete | 4.8 to 29.9 | 13.7 | 5.0 | 14.8 | 3.7 | 0.69 | 2.03 | 0.51 |
| Masonry | 4.6 to 29.8 | 13.5 | 6.9 | 7.5 | 1.9 | 0.93 | 1.01 | 0.26 |
| Structural Steel | 4.8 to 170.8 | 36.0 | 10.7 | 3.9 | 17.6 | 3.85 | 1.40 | 6.34 |
| Miscellaneous & Ornamental Metals | 4 to 20.3 | 10.1 | 2.8 | 4.0 | 3.6 | 0.28 | 0.40 | 0.36 |
| Carpentry & Millwork | 4.8 to 53.2 | 16.9 | 3.7 | 4.0 | 0.5 | 0.63 | 0.68 | 0.08 |
| Metal or Composition Siding | 4.8 to 35.7 | 15.5 | 2.3 | 0.3 | 4.3 | 0.36 | 0.05 | 0.67 |
| Roofing | 4.8 to 77.1 | 28.9 | 2.3 | 2.6 | 3.1 | 0.66 | 0.75 | 0.90 |
| Doors & Hardware | 3.4 to 34.5 | 11.3 | 0.9 | 1.4 | 0.4 | 0.10 | 0.16 | 0.05 |
| Sash & Glazing | 4.8 to 36 | 13.3 | 3.5 | 4.0 | 1.0 | 0.47 | 0.53 | 0.13 |
| Lath & Plaster | 3.1 to 30.3 | 11.9 | 3.3 | 6.9 | 0.8 | 0.39 | 0.82 | 0.10 |
| Tile, Marble & Floors | 3.1 to 16.8 | 8.8 | 2.6 | 3.0 | 0.5 | 0.23 | 0.26 | 0.04 |
| Acoustical Ceilings | 4.4 to 32 | 9.8 | 2.4 | 0.2 | 0.3 | 0.24 | 0.02 | 0.03 |
| Painting | 4.8 to 29.6 | 11.5 | 1.5 | 1.6 | 1.6 | 0.17 | 0.18 | 0.18 |
| Interior Partitions | 4.8 to 53.2 | 16.9 | 3.9 | 4.3 | 4.4 | 0.66 | 0.73 | 0.74 |
| Miscellaneous Items | 2.4 to 134.5 | 14.9 | 5.2 | 3.7 | 9.7 | 0.78 | 0.55 | 1.45 |
| Elevators | 2.6 to 13.5 | 6.3 | 2.1 | 1.1 | 2.2 | 0.13 | 0.07 | 0.14 |
| Sprinklers | 2.5 to 13.6 | 7.4 | 0.5 | — | 2.0 | 0.04 | — | 0.15 |
| Plumbing | 3.9 to 13.3 | 7.6 | 4.9 | 7.2 | 5.2 | 0.37 | 0.55 | 0.40 |
| Heat., Vent., Air Conditioning | 3.9 to 21.2 | 9.1 | 13.5 | 11.0 | 12.9 | 1.23 | 1.00 | 1.17 |
| Electrical | 2.9 to 15.4 | 6.4 | 10.1 | 8.4 | 11.1 | 0.65 | 0.54 | 0.71 |
| Total | 2.4 % to 170.8% | — | 100.0% | 100.0% | 100.0% | 14.62% | 13.15% | 16.44% |

Overall Weighted Average   14.74%

## Workers' Compensation Insurance Rates by States

The table below lists the weighted average Workers' Compensation base rate for each state with a factor comparing this with the national average of 14.4%.

| State | Weighted Average | Factor | State | Weighted Average | Factor | State | Weighted Average | Factor |
|---|---|---|---|---|---|---|---|---|
| Alabama | 19.8% | 138 | Kentucky | 16.3% | 113 | North Dakota | 12.9% | 90 |
| Alaska | 19.6 | 136 | Louisiana | 28.2 | 196 | Ohio | 13.0 | 90 |
| Arizona | 9.7 | 67 | Maine | 14.2 | 99 | Oklahoma | 14.5 | 101 |
| Arkansas | 10.4 | 72 | Maryland | 14.5 | 101 | Oregon | 12.4 | 86 |
| California | 21.4 | 149 | Massachusetts | 12.1 | 84 | Pennsylvania | 14.7 | 102 |
| Colorado | 9.0 | 63 | Michigan | 19.0 | 132 | Rhode Island | 11.6 | 81 |
| Connecticut | 20.0 | 139 | Minnesota | 26.0 | 181 | South Carolina | 19.8 | 138 |
| Delaware | 11.5 | 80 | Mississippi | 15.3 | 106 | South Dakota | 17.2 | 119 |
| District of Columbia | 11.3 | 78 | Missouri | 17.5 | 122 | Tennessee | 14.2 | 99 |
| Florida | 12.6 | 88 | Montana | 15.0 | 104 | Texas | 11.2 | 78 |
| Georgia | 26.8 | 186 | Nebraska | 21.2 | 147 | Utah | 9.1 | 63 |
| Hawaii | 16.9 | 117 | Nevada | 10.3 | 72 | Vermont | 15.0 | 104 |
| Idaho | 9.9 | 69 | New Hampshire | 19.2 | 133 | Virginia | 10.9 | 76 |
| Illinois | 23.0 | 160 | New Jersey | 13.3 | 92 | Washington | 9.8 | 68 |
| Indiana | 7.2 | 50 | New Mexico | 18.4 | 128 | West Virginia | 12.0 | 83 |
| Iowa | 11.4 | 79 | New York | 6.9 | 48 | Wisconsin | 15.0 | 104 |
| Kansas | 8.6 | 60 | North Carolina | 16.9 | 117 | Wyoming | 5.3 | 37 |

Weighted Average for U.S. is   14.7% of payroll = 100%

Rates in the following table are the base or manual costs per $100 of payroll for Workers' Compensation in each state. Rates are usually applied to straight time wages only and not to premium time wages and bonuses.

The weighted average skilled worker rate for 35 trades is 14.4%. For bidding purposes, apply the full value of Workers' Compensation directly to total labor costs, or if labor is 38%, materials 42% and overhead and profit 20% of total cost, carry 38/80 x 14.4% =6.8% of cost (before overhead and profit) into overhead. Rates vary not only from state to state but also with the experience rating of the contractor.

Rates are the most current available at the time of publication.

## R013113-60 Workers' Compensation Insurance Rates by Trade and State (cont.)

| State | Carpentry — 3 stories or less 5651 | Carpentry — interior cab. work 5437 | Carpentry — general 5403 | Concrete Work — NOC 5213 | Concrete Work — flat (flr., sdwk.) 5221 | Electrical Wiring — inside 5190 | Excavation — earth NOC 6217 | Excavation — rock 6217 | Glaziers 5462 | Insulation Work 5479 | Lathing 5443 | Masonry 5022 | Painting & Decorating 5474 | Pile Driving 6003 | Plastering 5480 | Plumbing 5183 | Roofing 5551 | Sheet Metal Work (HVAC) 5538 | Steel Erection — door & sash 5102 | Steel Erection — inter., ornam. 5102 | Steel Erection — structure 5040 | Steel Erection — NOC 5057 | Tile Work — (interior ceramic) 5348 | Waterproofing 9014 | Wrecking 5701 |
|---|---|---|---|---|---|---|---|---|---|---|---|---|---|---|---|---|---|---|---|---|---|---|---|---|---|
| AL | 28.11 | 16.91 | 33.75 | 15.19 | 9.51 | 10.24 | 10.24 | 10.24 | 22.09 | 16.53 | 10.78 | 23.87 | 21.44 | 24.16 | 15.68 | 10.18 | 43.60 | 10.03 | 8.28 | 8.28 | 41.21 | 18.79 | 13.84 | 7.13 | 41.21 |
| AK | 11.41 | 14.35 | 15.47 | 11.20 | 10.66 | 8.55 | 12.54 | 12.54 | 35.96 | 31.60 | 8.46 | 29.81 | 16.71 | 31.00 | 30.26 | 10.01 | 35.75 | 8.86 | 8.04 | 8.04 | 29.65 | 32.73 | 6.25 | 6.29 | 29.65 |
| AZ | 11.55 | 6.95 | 17.61 | 9.58 | 5.16 | 4.96 | 5.32 | 5.32 | 7.21 | 14.50 | 5.56 | 7.35 | 6.53 | 11.22 | 5.24 | 5.77 | 15.08 | 6.92 | 9.96 | 9.96 | 17.31 | 14.27 | 3.56 | 3.13 | 17.31 |
| AR | 9.83 | 6.03 | 13.66 | 8.16 | 6.58 | 4.73 | 6.47 | 6.47 | 7.41 | 9.31 | 5.61 | 7.02 | 9.22 | 12.87 | 8.87 | 5.43 | 17.31 | 5.37 | 5.41 | 5.41 | 25.61 | 31.50 | 5.46 | 3.15 | 25.61 |
| CA | 34.52 | 34.52 | 34.52 | 12.92 | 12.92 | 9.65 | 15.56 | 15.56 | 18.87 | 14.65 | 12.69 | 21.99 | 16.27 | 16.32 | 24.72 | 13.26 | 47.80 | 16.92 | 13.77 | 13.77 | 22.36 | 17.89 | 8.82 | 16.27 | 17.89 |
| CO | 10.43 | 5.56 | 7.98 | 7.19 | 5.24 | 3.48 | 7.24 | 7.24 | 6.53 | 11.47 | 4.36 | 9.05 | 5.77 | 10.08 | 5.59 | 4.64 | 17.78 | 4.59 | 6.83 | 6.83 | 27.27 | 10.66 | 5.43 | 3.46 | 10.66 |
| CT | 14.94 | 15.49 | 24.99 | 28.69 | 11.11 | 8.50 | 13.15 | 13.15 | 20.92 | 17.38 | 17.82 | 23.28 | 16.39 | 20.36 | 16.27 | 10.08 | 34.95 | 12.68 | 15.41 | 15.41 | 41.41 | 23.21 | 13.64 | 5.64 | 41.41 |
| DE | 11.96 | 11.96 | 8.80 | 8.99 | 9.49 | 4.26 | 7.16 | 7.16 | 10.17 | 8.80 | 10.97 | 10.39 | 11.94 | 14.39 | 10.17 | 6.10 | 21.13 | 7.75 | 9.69 | 9.69 | 21.36 | 9.69 | 7.19 | 10.39 | 21.36 |
| DC | 10.70 | 10.28 | 7.97 | 9.28 | 7.58 | 6.22 | 9.12 | 9.12 | 16.60 | 6.06 | 6.77 | 8.27 | 6.06 | 12.61 | 10.50 | 8.51 | 14.67 | 8.61 | 11.03 | 11.03 | 24.14 | 13.86 | 13.64 | 3.40 | 24.14 |
| FL | 12.62 | 7.98 | 13.59 | 13.18 | 5.99 | 15.44 | 7.01 | 7.01 | 8.77 | 8.12 | 5.53 | 9.08 | 8.76 | 38.24 | 19.38 | 5.47 | 21.29 | 7.98 | 8.12 | 8.12 | 22.59 | 10.37 | 5.16 | 4.53 | 22.59 |
| GA | 35.73 | 21.35 | 25.92 | 17.90 | 15.31 | 10.45 | 16.30 | 16.30 | 19.14 | 22.15 | 14.61 | 24.16 | 24.99 | 26.75 | 24.86 | 12.18 | 63.28 | 17.45 | 20.26 | 20.26 | 71.30 | 39.53 | 13.97 | 8.92 | 71.30 |
| HI | 17.38 | 11.62 | 28.20 | 13.74 | 12.27 | 7.10 | 7.73 | 7.73 | 20.55 | 21.19 | 10.94 | 17.87 | 11.33 | 20.15 | 15.61 | 6.06 | 33.24 | 8.02 | 11.11 | 11.11 | 31.71 | 21.70 | 9.78 | 11.54 | 31.71 |
| ID | 9.41 | 6.65 | 10.29 | 10.24 | 5.84 | 3.48 | 5.84 | 5.84 | 8.87 | 8.06 | 9.22 | 7.35 | 7.88 | 11.56 | 5.48 | 5.01 | 26.07 | 6.56 | 7.00 | 7.00 | 24.33 | 9.22 | 9.07 | 4.91 | 24.33 |
| IL | 25.30 | 15.57 | 23.56 | 29.89 | 12.90 | 10.43 | 10.77 | 10.77 | 18.01 | 20.90 | 17.31 | 21.46 | 11.94 | 31.27 | 17.49 | 12.01 | 33.86 | 14.59 | 19.11 | 19.11 | 79.28 | 21.91 | 16.76 | 5.22 | 79.28 |
| IN | 11.86 | 4.44 | 6.93 | 5.02 | 3.12 | 2.85 | 4.38 | 4.38 | 6.11 | 7.10 | 22.54 | 4.56 | 4.86 | 5.84 | 3.09 | 12.76 | 10.06 | 4.48 | 3.95 | 3.95 | 12.69 | 6.07 | 3.12 | 2.39 | 12.69 |
| IA | 13.14 | 10.98 | 12.06 | 14.63 | 7.56 | 4.65 | 7.06 | 7.06 | 9.01 | 6.62 | 5.84 | 9.42 | 7.53 | 9.92 | 7.28 | 6.74 | 22.71 | 6.08 | 5.56 | 5.56 | 30.86 | 26.76 | 8.01 | 3.61 | 30.86 |
| KS | 12.20 | 7.16 | 9.07 | 6.95 | 5.58 | 3.39 | 5.22 | 5.22 | 9.12 | 7.26 | 4.46 | 7.09 | 7.12 | 9.74 | 5.27 | 4.53 | 12.45 | 5.13 | 4.53 | 4.53 | 24.78 | 16.44 | 6.24 | 4.25 | 16.44 |
| KY | 14.98 | 12.29 | 25.40 | 10.80 | 7.22 | 5.36 | 9.95 | 9.95 | 13.90 | 14.09 | 9.23 | 7.30 | 11.88 | 22.46 | 12.14 | 5.65 | 31.57 | 11.42 | 9.86 | 9.86 | 60.00 | 18.72 | 16.40 | 4.59 | 60.00 |
| LA | 22.02 | 24.93 | 53.17 | 26.43 | 15.61 | 9.88 | 17.49 | 17.49 | 20.14 | 21.43 | 24.51 | 28.33 | 29.58 | 31.25 | 22.37 | 8.64 | 77.12 | 21.20 | 18.98 | 18.98 | 51.76 | 24.21 | 13.77 | 13.78 | 66.41 |
| ME | 15.11 | 10.18 | 25.32 | 18.95 | 9.40 | 6.61 | 8.79 | 8.79 | 14.50 | 11.15 | 7.69 | 13.82 | 13.31 | 15.89 | 12.02 | 9.12 | 18.69 | 8.40 | 8.34 | 8.34 | 32.51 | 19.53 | 6.58 | 5.84 | 32.51 |
| MD | 14.33 | 11.61 | 13.75 | 15.69 | 5.67 | 5.60 | 7.82 | 7.82 | 11.43 | 13.56 | 8.01 | 9.92 | 7.12 | 20.15 | 12.77 | 5.69 | 29.53 | 6.93 | 8.31 | 8.31 | 52.61 | 26.15 | 7.99 | 5.44 | 26.15 |
| MA | 7.50 | 5.93 | 11.92 | 21.45 | 6.62 | 3.17 | 4.17 | 4.17 | 8.93 | 8.94 | 6.53 | 11.62 | 5.01 | 4.99 | 4.89 | 3.88 | 30.35 | 5.74 | 6.76 | 6.76 | 44.61 | 39.97 | 6.45 | 2.50 | 29.46 |
| MI | 20.53 | 10.95 | 22.88 | 15.72 | 9.41 | 5.27 | 10.95 | 10.95 | 14.98 | 13.04 | 13.59 | 14.45 | 13.57 | 57.09 | 12.36 | 7.21 | 32.64 | 11.89 | 11.07 | 11.07 | 57.09 | 19.42 | 10.83 | 6.26 | 57.09 |
| MN | 22.68 | 23.13 | 32.18 | 10.25 | 13.85 | 6.68 | 11.88 | 11.88 | 27.48 | 16.33 | 12.68 | 19.35 | 14.58 | 22.85 | 12.68 | 11.28 | 54.88 | 16.13 | 11.70 | 11.70 | 170.80 | 13.03 | 11.23 | 6.85 | 13.03 |
| MS | 16.49 | 10.30 | 17.28 | 10.71 | 7.75 | 6.48 | 11.17 | 11.17 | 10.34 | 10.46 | 6.84 | 13.96 | 12.78 | 30.91 | 19.04 | 7.94 | 34.45 | 7.79 | 12.45 | 12.45 | 33.05 | 15.81 | 8.83 | 3.94 | 33.05 |
| MO | 20.17 | 12.95 | 15.43 | 19.32 | 10.66 | 7.57 | 10.57 | 10.57 | 11.63 | 15.03 | 9.23 | 16.87 | 12.93 | 18.60 | 16.85 | 10.79 | 34.32 | 9.57 | 11.61 | 11.61 | 33.95 | 41.29 | 11.92 | 6.56 | 33.95 |
| MT | 13.10 | 10.20 | 23.32 | 12.63 | 10.84 | 5.93 | 14.51 | 14.51 | 8.57 | 24.07 | 7.98 | 12.12 | 8.43 | 22.50 | 10.60 | 9.71 | 37.56 | 10.63 | 9.09 | 9.09 | 22.59 | 11.57 | 9.08 | 7.91 | 11.57 |
| NE | 23.73 | 18.63 | 20.88 | 26.18 | 14.23 | 9.80 | 16.00 | 16.00 | 16.90 | 23.33 | 11.75 | 21.90 | 17.52 | 20.73 | 17.43 | 12.53 | 36.95 | 12.48 | 15.00 | 15.00 | 39.83 | 36.08 | 10.53 | 6.83 | 55.60 |
| NV | 14.08 | 7.98 | 12.08 | 9.61 | 8.20 | 6.12 | 7.77 | 7.77 | 10.06 | 7.54 | 4.60 | 7.35 | 7.54 | 11.58 | 6.73 | 6.12 | 12.82 | 9.04 | 8.35 | 8.35 | 22.13 | 16.86 | 5.83 | 5.36 | 16.86 |
| NH | 26.15 | 11.92 | 19.85 | 24.52 | 14.29 | 7.33 | 13.00 | 13.00 | 10.32 | 5.63 | 9.25 | 21.17 | 21.90 | 7.88 | 10.06 | 10.99 | 45.41 | 8.04 | 15.28 | 15.28 | 64.41 | 23.21 | 11.64 | 6.10 | 64.41 |
| NJ | 14.79 | 8.84 | 14.79 | 15.65 | 9.31 | 4.38 | 8.18 | 8.18 | 8.97 | 12.55 | 10.73 | 13.44 | 11.40 | 16.59 | 10.73 | 5.79 | 37.97 | 6.78 | 9.33 | 9.33 | 20.26 | 16.09 | 7.96 | 6.20 | 21.39 |
| NM | 20.42 | 7.36 | 18.00 | 14.67 | 12.11 | 8.39 | 9.67 | 9.67 | 21.18 | 13.47 | 8.06 | 15.88 | 11.90 | 20.37 | 15.53 | 8.71 | 39.03 | 11.93 | 13.94 | 13.94 | 44.89 | 47.45 | 7.36 | 6.06 | 44.89 |
| NY | 7.96 | 3.39 | 7.17 | 8.25 | 6.46 | 3.17 | 4.63 | 4.63 | 5.71 | 3.73 | 6.49 | 8.74 | 5.50 | 8.04 | 4.21 | 3.98 | 14.20 | 5.50 | 5.44 | 5.44 | 13.31 | 7.90 | 3.26 | 2.83 | 5.51 |
| NC | 16.57 | 12.67 | 16.19 | 18.29 | 8.30 | 10.73 | 11.86 | 11.86 | 14.23 | 12.38 | 11.28 | 11.33 | 11.44 | 17.48 | 14.68 | 9.46 | 26.41 | 11.87 | 10.88 | 10.88 | 62.71 | 20.69 | 9.08 | 5.75 | 62.71 |
| ND | 10.87 | 10.87 | 10.87 | 6.50 | 6.50 | 3.55 | 5.58 | 5.58 | 10.87 | 10.87 | 7.25 | 17.45 | 6.87 | 19.11 | 7.25 | 5.19 | 21.35 | 5.19 | 19.14 | 19.14 | 19.14 | 19.14 | 10.87 | 21.35 | 10.90 |
| OH | 13.61 | 7.75 | 11.13 | 9.75 | 9.79 | 5.67 | 8.20 | 8.20 | 8.42 | 15.84 | 31.95 | 11.77 | 13.74 | 13.44 | 4.26 | 6.07 | 30.45 | 6.93 | 8.35 | 8.35 | 20.46 | 11.61 | 9.82 | 6.91 | 11.61 |
| OK | 13.42 | 9.17 | 11.76 | 11.76 | 6.34 | 5.73 | 10.83 | 10.83 | 16.07 | 19.47 | 8.45 | 10.02 | 8.47 | 20.25 | 12.19 | 7.09 | 21.13 | 9.05 | 13.76 | 13.76 | 39.72 | 23.97 | 6.50 | 5.71 | 39.72 |
| OR | 16.06 | 7.50 | 14.54 | 11.48 | 7.70 | 4.95 | 9.25 | 9.25 | 12.89 | 11.25 | 7.90 | 12.08 | 9.99 | 16.97 | 11.59 | 5.41 | 21.99 | 7.70 | 6.54 | 6.54 | 22.55 | 21.87 | 8.85 | 5.56 | 22.55 |
| PA | 14.68 | 14.68 | 12.10 | 15.30 | 11.22 | 6.32 | 9.13 | 9.13 | 12.06 | 12.10 | 12.06 | 13.10 | 14.00 | 16.59 | 12.06 | 7.77 | 29.88 | 8.29 | 15.11 | 15.11 | 22.64 | 15.11 | 8.45 | 13.10 | 22.64 |
| RI | 10.79 | 8.37 | 10.96 | 13.14 | 10.29 | 5.15 | 7.50 | 7.50 | 13.33 | 17.64 | 6.04 | 11.62 | 9.27 | 27.21 | 9.50 | 4.42 | 14.82 | 7.75 | 5.68 | 5.68 | 20.92 | 14.98 | 5.62 | 4.72 | 14.98 |
| SC | 21.43 | 18.13 | 22.49 | 16.89 | 9.59 | 11.45 | 11.78 | 11.78 | 16.99 | 18.58 | 11.06 | 13.93 | 15.50 | 20.61 | 15.75 | 12.36 | 50.08 | 13.06 | 13.91 | 13.91 | 41.22 | 32.53 | 10.50 | 6.33 | 41.22 |
| SD | 21.47 | 9.62 | 21.86 | 25.23 | 7.35 | 5.33 | 9.54 | 9.54 | 15.06 | 13.87 | 8.26 | 11.62 | 10.45 | 20.56 | 11.87 | 10.92 | 26.74 | 12.70 | 8.86 | 8.86 | 59.15 | 31.01 | 7.69 | 5.99 | 59.15 |
| TN | 14.91 | 11.20 | 13.03 | 12.97 | 6.75 | 5.79 | 13.34 | 13.34 | 12.18 | 9.21 | 8.32 | 12.35 | 11.84 | 28.35 | 13.71 | 6.79 | 24.19 | 9.81 | 8.15 | 8.15 | 25.81 | 25.53 | 8.36 | 4.08 | 25.81 |
| TX | 9.17 | 8.39 | 9.17 | 9.00 | 7.06 | 5.76 | 7.88 | 7.88 | 8.56 | 11.97 | 5.74 | 10.31 | 8.18 | 16.38 | 8.18 | 5.88 | 19.42 | 12.05 | 7.87 | 7.87 | 33.20 | 11.24 | 5.53 | 6.19 | 8.70 |
| UT | 11.93 | 6.73 | 9.82 | 7.43 | 6.42 | 3.47 | 8.78 | 8.78 | 11.14 | 9.47 | 4.81 | 8.51 | 6.34 | 9.45 | 5.50 | 4.68 | 18.93 | 6.11 | 5.43 | 5.43 | 19.45 | 11.11 | 5.16 | 3.24 | 13.92 |
| VT | 11.28 | 10.68 | 17.87 | 12.39 | 7.41 | 6.20 | 12.96 | 12.96 | 15.29 | 16.13 | 7.53 | 16.28 | 8.35 | 14.60 | 9.04 | 8.41 | 26.14 | 9.47 | 9.47 | 9.47 | 36.84 | 30.71 | 9.76 | 6.97 | 36.84 |
| VA | 10.22 | 7.61 | 9.05 | 11.32 | 5.11 | 4.92 | 7.70 | 7.70 | 10.13 | 7.82 | 11.06 | 8.34 | 9.02 | 9.49 | 9.78 | 5.63 | 22.11 | 6.32 | 6.90 | 6.90 | 32.08 | 20.56 | 5.08 | 2.91 | 32.08 |
| WA | 7.94 | 7.94 | 7.94 | 7.29 | 7.29 | 3.15 | 6.88 | 6.88 | 12.21 | 8.54 | 7.94 | 9.48 | 11.84 | 16.40 | 10.06 | 4.30 | 17.24 | 3.92 | 7.61 | 7.61 | 7.61 | 7.61 | 8.83 | 17.24 | 7.61 |
| WV | 14.45 | 9.91 | 13.88 | 11.18 | 5.99 | 6.38 | 8.45 | 8.45 | 10.70 | 9.85 | 8.29 | 10.83 | 10.72 | 16.15 | 10.77 | 6.65 | 24.50 | 7.80 | 7.57 | 7.57 | 32.81 | 7.91 | 7.67 | 3.60 | 17.91 |
| WI | 10.46 | 10.33 | 15.46 | 11.52 | 9.18 | 5.80 | 8.13 | 8.13 | 11.32 | 12.60 | 5.84 | 14.90 | 14.06 | 19.42 | 10.64 | 6.15 | 34.47 | 7.77 | 9.80 | 9.80 | 22.52 | 48.12 | 15.46 | 4.83 | 22.52 |
| WY | 4.77 | 4.77 | 4.77 | 4.77 | 4.77 | 4.77 | 4.77 | 4.77 | 4.77 | 4.77 | 4.77 | 4.77 | 4.77 | 4.77 | 4.77 | 4.77 | 4.77 | 4.77 | 4.77 | 4.77 | 4.77 | 4.77 | 4.77 | 4.77 | 4.77 |
| AVG. | 15.47 | 11.27 | 16.88 | 13.72 | 8.74 | 6.38 | 9.42 | 9.42 | 13.27 | 13.11 | 9.79 | 13.47 | 11.46 | 18.54 | 11.92 | 7.62 | 28.89 | 9.14 | 10.07 | 10.07 | 35.99 | 20.79 | 8.78 | 6.48 | 30.31 |

## R013113-60 Workers' Compensation (cont.) (Canada in Canadian dollars)

**Reference Tables**

| Province | | Alberta | British Columbia | Manitoba | Ontario | New Brunswick | Newfndld. & Labrador | Northwest Territories | Nova Scotia | Prince Edward Island | Quebec | Saskat-chewan | Yukon |
|---|---|---|---|---|---|---|---|---|---|---|---|---|---|
| Carpentry—3 stories or less | Rate | 5.99 | 3.64 | 4.17 | 4.35 | 5.05 | 11.00 | 3.40 | 9.23 | 6.23 | 13.26 | 4.37 | 9.42 |
| | Code | 42143 | 721028 | 40102 | 723 | 238130 | 4226 | 4-41 | 4226 | 401 | 80110 | 1226 | 202 |
| Carpentry—interior cab. work | Rate | 1.86 | 2.62 | 4.17 | 4.35 | 4.59 | 4.37 | 3.40 | 4.33 | 3.82 | 13.26 | 2.57 | 9.42 |
| | Code | 42133 | 721021 | 40102 | 723 | 238350 | 4279 | 4-41 | 4274 | 402 | 80110 | B1127 | 202 |
| CARPENTRY—general | Rate | 5.99 | 3.64 | 4.17 | 4.35 | 5.05 | 4.37 | 3.40 | 9.23 | 6.23 | 13.26 | 4.37 | 9.42 |
| | Code | 42143 | 721028 | 40102 | 723 | 238130 | 4299 | 4-41 | 4226 | 401 | 80110 | 12.02 | 202 |
| CONCRETE WORK—NOC | Rate | 4.01 | 3.87 | 7.01 | 16.50 | 5.05 | 11.00 | 3.40 | 5.19 | 6.23 | 15.41 | 5.44 | 5.23 |
| | Code | 42104 | 721010 | 40110 | 748 | 238110 | 4224 | 4-41 | 4224 | 401 | 80100 | B1314 | 203 |
| CONCRETE WORK—flat (flr. sidewalk) | Rate | 4.01 | 3.87 | 7.01 | 16.50 | 5.05 | 11.00 | 3.40 | 5.19 | 6.23 | 15.41 | 5.44 | 5.23 |
| | Code | 42104 | 721010 | 40110 | 748 | 238110 | 4224 | 4-41 | 4224 | 401 | 80100 | B1314 | 203 |
| ELECTRICAL Wiring—inside | Rate | 1.95 | 1.41 | 1.90 | 3.25 | 2.45 | 2.91 | 2.76 | 2.66 | 3.82 | 5.92 | 2.57 | 5.23 |
| | Code | 42124 | 721019 | 40203 | 704 | 238210 | 4261 | 4-46 | 4261 | 402 | 80170 | B1105 | 206 |
| EXCAVATION—earth NOC | Rate | 2.34 | 3.25 | 4.02 | 4.68 | 5.05 | 3.84 | 3.57 | 2.88 | 3.13 | 7.55 | 2.76 | 5.23 |
| | Code | 40604 | 721031 | 40706 | 711 | 238190 | 4214 | 4-43 | 4214 | 404 | 80030 | R1106 | 207 |
| EXCAVATION—rock | Rate | 2.34 | 3.25 | 4.02 | 4.68 | 5.05 | 3.84 | 3.57 | 2.88 | 3.13 | 7.55 | 2.76 | 5.23 |
| | Code | 40604 | 721031 | 40706 | 711 | 238190 | 4214 | 4-43 | 4214 | 404 | 80030 | R1106 | 207 |
| GLAZIERS | Rate | 2.56 | 3.05 | 4.17 | 9.25 | 5.05 | 6.11 | 3.40 | 5.19 | 3.82 | 14.17 | 5.44 | 5.23 |
| | Code | 42121 | 715020 | 40109 | 751 | 238150 | 4233 | 4-41 | 4233 | 402 | 80150 | B1304 | 212 |
| INSULATION WORK | Rate | 2.05 | 6.91 | 4.17 | 9.25 | 4.59 | 6.11 | 3.40 | 5.19 | 6.23 | 13.26 | 4.37 | 9.42 |
| | Code | 42184 | 721029 | 40102 | 751 | 238310 | 4234 | 4-41 | 4234 | 401 | 80110 | B1207 | 202 |
| LATHING | Rate | 4.67 | 6.27 | 4.17 | 4.35 | 4.59 | 4.37 | 3.40 | 4.33 | 3.82 | 13.26 | 5.44 | 9.42 |
| | Code | 42135 | 721042 | 40102 | 723 | 238390 | 4279 | 4-41 | 4271 | 402 | 80110 | B1316 | 202 |
| MASONRY | Rate | 4.01 | 3.50 | 4.17 | 11.15 | 5.05 | 6.11 | 3.40 | 5.19 | 6.23 | 15.41 | 5.44 | 9.42 |
| | Code | 42102 | 721037 | 40102 | 741 | 238140 | 4231 | 4-41 | 4231 | 401 | 80100 | B1318 | 202 |
| PAINTING & DECORATING | Rate | 3.30 | 3.36 | 3.28 | 6.75 | 4.59 | 4.37 | 3.40 | 4.33 | 3.82 | 13.26 | 4.37 | 9.42 |
| | Code | 42111 | 721041 | 40105 | 719 | 238320 | 4275 | 4-41 | 4275 | 402 | 80110 | B1201 | 202 |
| PILE DRIVING | Rate | 3.95 | 3.82 | 4.02 | 6.34 | 5.05 | 3.84 | 3.57 | 5.19 | 6.23 | 7.55 | 5.44 | 9.42 |
| | Code | 42159 | 722004 | 40706 | 732 | 238190 | 4129 | 4-43 | 4221 | 401 | 80030 | B1310 | 202 |
| PLASTERING | Rate | 4.67 | 6.27 | 4.59 | 6.75 | 4.59 | 4.37 | 3.40 | 4.33 | 3.82 | 13.26 | 4.37 | 9.42 |
| | Code | 42135 | 721042 | 40108 | 719 | 238390 | 4271 | 4-41 | 4271 | 402 | 80110 | B1221 | 202 |
| PLUMBING | Rate | 1.95 | 1.90 | 3.04 | 3.98 | 2.45 | 3.08 | 2.76 | 2.52 | 3.82 | 6.19 | 2.57 | 5.23 |
| | Code | 42122 | 721043 | 40204 | 707 | 238220 | 4241 | 4-46 | 4241 | 402 | 80160 | B1101 | 214 |
| ROOFING | Rate | 6.41 | 6.18 | 7.37 | 13.30 | 5.05 | 11.00 | 3.40 | 9.23 | 6.23 | 19.71 | 5.44 | 9.42 |
| | Code | 42118 | 721036 | 40403 | 728 | 238160 | 4236 | 4-41 | 4236 | 401 | 80130 | B1320 | 202 |
| SHEET METAL WORK (HVAC) | Rate | 1.95 | 1.90 | 7.37 | 3.98 | 2.45 | 3.08 | 2.76 | 2.52 | 3.82 | 6.19 | 2.57 | 5.23 |
| | Code | 42117 | 721043 | 40402 | 707 | 238220 | 4244 | 4-46 | 4244 | 402 | 80160 | B1107 | 208 |
| STEEL ERECTION—door & sash | Rate | 2.05 | 12.66 | 10.05 | 16.50 | 5.05 | 11.00 | 3.40 | 5.19 | 6.23 | 21.98 | 5.44 | 9.42 |
| | Code | 42106 | 722005 | 40502 | 748 | 238120 | 4227 | 4-41 | 4227 | 401 | 80080 | B1322 | 202 |
| STEEL ERECTION—inter., ornam. | Rate | 2.05 | 12.66 | 10.05 | 16.50 | 5.05 | 11.00 | 3.40 | 5.19 | 6.23 | 21.98 | 5.44 | 9.42 |
| | Code | 42106 | 722005 | 40502 | 748 | 238120 | 4227 | 4-41 | 4227 | 401 | 80080 | B1322 | 202 |
| STEEL ERECTION—structure | Rate | 2.05 | 12.66 | 10.05 | 16.50 | 5.05 | 11.00 | 3.40 | 5.19 | 6.23 | 21.98 | 5.44 | 9.42 |
| | Code | 42106 | 722005 | 40502 | 748 | 238120 | 4227 | 4-41 | 4227 | 401 | 80080 | B1322 | 202 |
| STEEL ERECTION—NOC | Rate | 2.05 | 12.66 | 10.05 | 16.50 | 5.05 | 11.00 | 3.40 | 5.19 | 6.23 | 21.98 | 5.44 | 9.42 |
| | Code | 42106 | 722005 | 40502 | 748 | 238120 | 4227 | 4-41 | 4227 | 401 | 80080 | B1322 | 202 |
| TILE WORK—inter. (ceramic) | Rate | 2.89 | 3.62 | 1.95 | 6.75 | 4.59 | 4.37 | 3.40 | 4.33 | 3.82 | 13.26 | 5.44 | 9.42 |
| | Code | 42113 | 721054 | 40103 | 719 | 238340 | 4276 | 4-41 | 4276 | 402 | 80110 | B1301 | 202 |
| WATERPROOFING | Rate | 3.30 | 3.35 | 4.17 | 4.35 | 5.05 | 4.37 | 3.40 | 5.19 | 3.82 | 19.71 | 4.37 | 9.42 |
| | Code | 42139 | 721016 | 40102 | 723 | 238190 | 4299 | 4-41 | 4239 | 402 | 80130 | B1217 | 202 |
| WRECKING | Rate | 2.34 | 4.44 | 6.37 | 16.50 | 5.05 | 3.84 | 3.57 | 2.88 | 6.23 | 13.26 | 2.76 | 9.42 |
| | Code | 40604 | 721005 | 40106 | 748 | 238190 | 4211 | 4-43 | 4211 | 401 | 80110 | R1125 | 202 |

## R015423-10　Steel Tubular Scaffolding

On new construction, tubular scaffolding is efficient up to 60' high or five stories. Above this it is usually better to use a hung scaffolding if construction permits. Swing scaffolding operations may interfere with tenants. In this case, the tubular is more practical at all heights.

In repairing or cleaning the front of an existing building the cost of tubular scaffolding per S.F. of building front increases as the height increases above the first tier. The first tier cost is relatively high due to leveling and alignment.

The minimum efficient crew for erecting and dismantling is three workers. They can set up and remove 18 frame sections per day up to 5 stories high. For 6 to 12 stories high, a crew of four is most efficient. Use two or more on top and two on the bottom for handing up or hoisting. They can also set up and remove 18 frame sections per day. At 7' horizontal spacing, this will run about 800 S.F. per day of erecting and dismantling. Time for placing and removing planks must be added to the above. A crew of three can place and remove 72 planks per day up to 5 stories. For over 5 stories, a crew of four can place and remove 80 planks per day.

The table below shows the number of pieces required to erect tubular steel scaffolding for 1000 S.F. of building frontage. This area is made up of a scaffolding system that is 12 frames (11 bays) long by 2 frames high.

For jobs under twenty-five frames, add 50% to rental cost. Rental rates will be lower for jobs over three months duration. Large quantities for long periods can reduce rental rates by 20%.

| Description of Component | Number of Pieces for 1000 S.F. of Building Front | Unit |
|---|---|---|
| 5' Wide Standard Frame, 6'-4" High | 24 | Ea. |
| Leveling Jack & Plate | 24 | |
| Cross Brace | 44 | |
| Side Arm Bracket, 21" | 12 | |
| Guardrail Post | 12 | |
| Guardrail, 7' section | 22 | |
| Stairway Section | 2 | |
| Stairway Starter Bar | 1 | |
| Stairway Inside Handrail | 2 | |
| Stairway Outside Handrail | 2 | |
| Walk-Thru Frame Guardrail | 2 | ↓ |

Scaffolding is often used as falsework over 15' high during construction of cast-in-place concrete beams and slabs. Two foot wide scaffolding is generally used for heavy beam construction. The span between frames depends upon the load to be carried with a maximum span of 5'.

Heavy duty shoring frames with a capacity of 10,000#/leg can be spaced up to 10' O.C. depending upon form support design and loading.

Scaffolding used as horizontal shoring requires less than half the material required with conventional shoring.

On new construction, erection is done by carpenters.

Rolling towers supporting horizontal shores can reduce labor and speed the job. For maintenance work, catwalks with spans up to 70' can be supported by the rolling towers.

## R015423-20　Pump Staging

Pump staging is generally not available for rent. The table below shows the number of pieces required to erect pump staging for 2400 S.F. of building frontage. This area is made up of a pump jack system that is 3 poles (2 bays) wide by 2 poles high.

| Item | Number of Pieces for 2400 S.F. of Building Front | Unit |
|---|---|---|
| Aluminum pole section, 24' long | 6 | Ea. |
| Aluminum splice joint, 6' long | 3 | |
| Aluminum foldable brace | 3 | |
| Aluminum pump jack | 3 | |
| Aluminum support for workbench/back safety rail | 3 | |
| Aluminum scaffold plank/workbench, 14" wide x 24' long | 4 | |
| Safety net, 22' long | 2 | |
| Aluminum plank end safety rail | 2 | ↓ |

The cost in place for this 2400 S.F. will depend on how many uses are realized during the life of the equipment.

## R024119-10 Demolition Defined

**Whole Building Demolition** - Demolition of the whole building with no concern for any particular building element, component, or material type being demolished. This type of demolition is accomplished with large pieces of construction equipment that break up the structure, load it into trucks and haul it to a disposal site, but disposal or dump fees are not included. Demolition of below-grade foundation elements, such as footings, foundation walls, grade beams, slabs on grade, etc., is not included. Certain mechanical equipment containing flammable liquids or ozone-depleting refrigerants, electric lighting elements, communication equipment components, and other building elements may contain hazardous waste, and must be removed, either selectively or carefully, as hazardous waste before the building can be demolished.

**Foundation Demolition** - Demolition of below-grade foundation footings, foundation walls, grade beams, and slabs on grade. This type of demolition is accomplished by hand or pneumatic hand tools, and does not include saw cutting, or handling, loading, hauling, or disposal of the debris.

**Gutting** - Removal of building interior finishes and electrical/mechanical systems down to the load-bearing and sub-floor elements of the rough building frame, with no concern for any particular building element, component, or material type being demolished. This type of demolition is accomplished by hand or pneumatic hand tools, and includes loading into trucks, but not hauling, disposal or dump fees, scaffolding, or shoring. Certain mechanical equipment containing flammable liquids or ozone-depleting refrigerants, electric lighting elements, communication equipment components, and other building elements may contain hazardous waste, and must be removed, either selectively or carefully, as hazardous waste, before the building is gutted.

**Selective Demolition** - Demolition of a selected building element, component, or finish, with some concern for surrounding or adjacent elements, components, or finishes (see the first Subdivision (s) at the beginning of appropriate Divisions). This type of demolition is accomplished by hand or pneumatic hand tools, and does not include handling, loading,

storing, hauling, or disposal of the debris, scaffolding, or shoring. "Gutting" methods may be used in order to save time, but damage that is caused to surrounding or adjacent elements, components, or finishes may have to be repaired at a later time.

**Careful Removal** - Removal of a piece of service equipment, building element or component, or material type, with great concern for both the removed item and surrounding or adjacent elements, components or finishes. The purpose of careful removal may be to protect the removed item for later re-use, preserve a higher salvage value of the removed item, or replace an item while taking care to protect surrounding or adjacent elements, components, connections, or finishes from cosmetic and/or structural damage. An approximation of the time required to perform this type of removal is 1/3 to 1/2 the time it would take to install a new item of like kind. This type of removal is accomplished by hand or pneumatic hand tools, and does not include loading, hauling, or storing the removed item, scaffolding, shoring, or lifting equipment.

**Cutout Demolition** - Demolition of a small quantity of floor, wall, roof, or other assembly, with concern for the appearance and structural integrity of the surrounding materials. This type of demolition is accomplished by hand or pneumatic hand tools, and does not include saw cutting, handling, loading, hauling, or disposal of debris, scaffolding, or shoring.

**Rubbish Handling** - Work activities that involve handling, loading or hauling of debris. Generally, the cost of rubbish handling must be added to the cost of all types of demolition, with the exception of whole building demolition.

**Minor Site Demolition** - Demolition of site elements outside the footprint of a building. This type of demolition is accomplished by hand or pneumatic hand tools, or with larger pieces of construction equipment, and may include loading a removed item onto a truck (check the Crew for equipment used). It does not include saw cutting, hauling or disposal of debris, and, sometimes, handling or loading.

## R024119-20 Dumpsters

Dumpster rental costs on construction sites are presented in two ways.

The cost per week rental includes the delivery of the dumpster; its pulling or emptying once per week, and its final removal. The assumption is made that the dumpster contractor could choose to empty a dumpster by simply bringing in an empty unit and removing the full one. These costs also include the disposal of the materials in the dumpster.

The Alternate Pricing can be used when actual planned conditions are not approximated by the weekly numbers. For example, these lines can be used when a dumpster is needed for 4 weeks and will need to be emptied 2 or 3 times per week. Conversely the Alternate Pricing lines can be used when a dumpster will be rented for several weeks or months but needs to be emptied only a few times over this period.

## R040130-10    Cleaning Face Brick

On smooth brick a person can clean 70 S.F. an hour; on rough brick 50 S.F. per hour. Use one gallon muriatic acid to 20 gallons of water for 1000 S.F. Do not use acid solution until wall is at least seven days old, but a mild soap solution may be used after two days.

Time has been allowed for clean-up in brick prices.

## R040513-10    Cement Mortar (material only)

Type N - 1:1:6 mix by volume. Use everywhere above grade except as noted below. - 1:3 mix using conventional masonry cement which saves handling two separate bagged materials.

Type M - 1:1/4:3 mix by volume, or 1 part cement, 1/4 (10% by wt.) lime, 3 parts sand. Use for heavy loads and where earthquakes or hurricanes may occur. Also for reinforced brick, sewers, manholes and everywhere below grade.

Mix Proportions by Volume and Compressive Strength of Mortar

| Where Used | Mortar Type | Allowable Proportions by Volume | | | | Compressive Strength @ 28 days |
|---|---|---|---|---|---|---|
| | | Portland Cement | Masonry Cement | Hydrated Lime | Masonry Sand | |
| Plain Masonry | M | 1 | 1 | — | 6 | |
| | | 1 | — | 1/4 | 3 | 2500 psi |
| | S | 1/2 | 1 | — | 4 | |
| | | 1 | — | 1/4 to 1/2 | 4 | 1800 psi |
| | N | — | 1 | — | 3 | |
| | | 1 | — | 1/2 to 1-1/4 | 6 | 750 psi |
| | O | — | 1 | — | 3 | |
| | | 1 | — | 1-1/4 to 2-1/2 | 9 | 350 psi |
| | K | 1 | — | 2-1/2 to 4 | 12 | 75 psi |
| Reinforced Masonry | PM | 1 | 1 | — | 6 | 2500 psi |
| | PL | 1 | — | 1/4 to 1/2 | 4 | 2500 psi |

Note: The total aggregate should be between 2.25 to 3 times the sum of the cement and lime used.

The labor cost to mix the mortar is included in the productivity and labor cost of unit price lines in unit cost sections for brickwork, blockwork and stonework.

The material cost of mixed mortar is included in the material cost of those same unit price lines and includes the cost of renting and operating a 10 C.F. mixer at the rate of 200 C.F. per day.

There are two types of mortar color used. One type is the inert additive type with about 100 lbs. per M brick as the typical quantity required. These colors are also available in smaller-batch-sized bags (1 lb. to 15 lb.) which can be placed directly into the mixer without measuring. The other type is premixed and replaces the masonry cement. Dark green color has the highest cost.

## R040519-50    Masonry Reinforcing

Horizontal joint reinforcing helps prevent wall cracks where wall movement may occur and in many locations is required by code. Horizontal joint reinforcing is generally not considered to be structural reinforcing and an unreinforced wall may still contain joint reinforcing.

Reinforcing strips come in 10′ and 12′ lengths and in truss and ladder shapes, with and without drips. Field labor runs between 2.7 to 5.3 hours per 1000 L.F. for wall thicknesses up to 12″.

The wire meets ASTM A82 for cold drawn steel wire and the typical size is 9 ga. sides and ties with 3/16″ diameter also available. Typical finish is mill galvanized with zinc coating at .10 oz. per S.F. Class I (.40 oz. per S.F.) and Class III (.80 oz per S.F.) are also available, as is hot dipped galvanizing at 1.50 oz. per S.F.

## R042110-10 Economy in Bricklaying

Have adequate supervision. Be sure bricklayers are always supplied with materials so there is no waiting. Place best bricklayers at corners and openings.

Use only screened sand for mortar. Otherwise, labor time will be wasted picking out pebbles. Use seamless metal tubs for mortar as they do not leak or catch the trowel. Locate stack and mortar for easy wheeling.

Have brick delivered for stacking. This makes for faster handling, reduces chipping and breakage, and requires less storage space. Many dealers will deliver select common in 2' x 3' x 4' pallets or face brick packaged. This affords quick handling with a crane or forklift and easy tonging in units of ten, which reduces waste.

Use wider bricks for one wythe wall construction. Keep scaffolding away from wall to allow mortar to fall clear and not stain wall.

On large jobs develop specialized crews for each type of masonry unit.

Consider designing for prefabricated panel construction on high rise projects.

Avoid excessive corners or openings. Each opening adds about 50% to labor cost for area of opening.

Bolting stone panels and using window frames as stops reduces labor costs and speeds up erection.

## R042110-20 Common and Face Brick

Common building brick manufactured according to ASTM C62 and facing brick manufactured according to ASTM C216 are the two standard bricks available for general building use.

Building brick is made in three grades; SW, where high resistance to damage caused by cyclic freezing is required; MW, where moderate resistance to cyclic freezing is needed; and NW, where little resistance to cyclic freezing is needed. Facing brick is made in only the two grades SW and MW. Additionally, facing brick is available in three types; FBS, for general use; FBX, for general use where a higher degree of precision and lower permissible variation in size than FBS is needed; and FBA, for general use to produce characteristic architectural effects resulting from non-uniformity in size and texture of the units.

In figuring the material cost of brickwork, an allowance of 25% mortar waste and 3% brick breakage was included. If bricks are delivered palletized

with 280 to 300 per pallet, or packaged, allow only 1-1/2% for breakage. Packaged or palletized delivery is practical when a job is big enough to have a crane or other equipment available to handle a package of brick. This is so on all industrial work but not always true on small commercial buildings.

The use of buff and gray face is increasing, and there is a continuing trend to the Norman, Roman, Jumbo and SCR brick.

Common red clay brick for backup is not used that often. Concrete block is the most usual backup material with occasional use of sand lime or cement brick. Building brick is commonly used in solid walls for strength and as a fire stop.

Brick panels built on the ground and then crane erected to the upper floors have proven to be economical. This allows the work to be done under cover and without scaffolding.

## R042110-50 Brick, Block & Mortar Quantities

| Type Brick | Nominal Size (incl. mortar) L H W | Modular Coursing | Number of Brick per S.F. | C.F. of Mortar per M Bricks, Waste Included 3/8" Joint | 1/2" Joint |
|---|---|---|---|---|---|
| Standard | 8 x 2-2/3 x 4 | 3C=8" | 6.75 | 10.3 | 12.9 |
| Economy | 8 x 4 x 4 | 1C=4" | 4.50 | 11.4 | 14.6 |
| Engineer | 8 x 3-1/5 x 4 | 5C=16" | 5.63 | 10.6 | 13.6 |
| Fire | 9 x 2-1/2 x 4-1/2 | 2C=5" | 6.40 | 550 # Fireclay | — |
| Jumbo | 12 x 4 x 6 or 8 | 1C=4" | 3.00 | 23.8 | 30.8 |
| Norman | 12 x 2-2/3 x 4 | 3C=8" | 4.50 | 14.0 | 17.9 |
| Norwegian | 12 x 3-1/5 x 4 | 5C=16" | 3.75 | 14.6 | 18.6 |
| Roman | 12 x 2 x 4 | 2C=4" | 6.00 | 13.4 | 17.0 |
| SCR | 12 x 2-2/3 x 6 | 3C=8" | 4.50 | 21.8 | 28.0 |
| Utility | 12 x 4 x 4 | 1C=4" | 3.00 | 15.4 | 19.6 |

For Other Bonds Standard Size Add to S.F. Quantities in Table to Left

| Bond Type | Description | Factor |
|---|---|---|
| Common | full header every fifth course | +20% |
| | full header every sixth course | +16.7% |
| English | full header every second course | +50% |
| Flemish | alternate headers every course | +33.3% |
| | every sixth course | +5.6% |
| | Header = W x H exposed | +100% |
| | Rowlock = H x W exposed | +100% |
| | Rowlock stretcher = L x W exposed | +33.3% |
| | Soldier = H x L exposed | — |
| | Sailor = W x L exposed | -33.3% |

| Concrete Blocks Nominal Size | Approximate Weight per S.F. Standard | Lightweight | Blocks per 100 S.F. | Mortar per M block, waste included Partitions | Back up |
|---|---|---|---|---|---|
| 2" x 8" x 16" | 20 PSF | 15 PSF | 113 | 27 C.F. | 36 C.F. |
| 4" | 30 | 20 | | 41 | 51 |
| 6" | 42 | 30 | | 56 | 66 |
| 8" | 55 | 38 | | 72 | 82 |
| 10" | 70 | 47 | | 87 | 97 |
| 12" | 85 | 55 | | 102 | 112 |

## R042210-20 Concrete Block

The material cost of special block such as corner, jamb and head block can be figured at the same price as ordinary block of same size. Labor on specials is about the same as equal-sized regular block.

Bond beam and 16″ high lintel blocks are more expensive than regular units of equal size. Lintel blocks are 8″ long and either 8″ or 16″ high.

Use of motorized mortar spreader box will speed construction of continuous walls.

Hollow non-load-bearing units are made according to ASTM C129 and hollow load-bearing units according to ASTM C90.

## R053100-10 Decking Descriptions

### General - All Deck Products

Steel deck is made by cold forming structural grade sheet steel into a repeating pattern of parallel ribs. The strength and stiffness of the panels are the result of the ribs and the material properties of the steel. Deck lengths can be varied to suit job conditions, but because of shipping considerations, are usually less than 40 feet. Standard deck width varies with the product used but full sheets are usually 12″, 18″, 24″, 30″, or 36″. Deck is typically furnished in a standard width with the ends cut square. Any cutting for width, such as at openings or for angular fit, is done at the job site.

Deck is typically attached to the building frame with arc puddle welds, self-drilling screws, or powder or pneumatically driven pins. Sheet to sheet fastening is done with screws, button punching (crimping), or welds.

### Composite Floor Deck

After installation and adequate fastening, floor deck serves several purposes. It (a) acts as a working platform, (b) stabilizes the frame, (c) serves as a concrete form for the slab, and (d) reinforces the slab to carry the design loads applied during the life of the building. Composite decks are distinguished by the presence of shear connector devices as part of the deck. These devices are designed to mechanically lock the concrete and deck together so that the concrete and the deck work together to carry subsequent floor loads. These shear connector devices can be rolled-in embossments, lugs, holes, or wires welded to the panels. The deck profile can also be used to interlock concrete and steel.

Composite deck finishes are either galvanized (zinc coated) or phosphatized/painted. Galvanized deck has a zinc coating on both the top and bottom surfaces. The phosphatized/painted deck has a bare (phosphatized) top surface that will come into contact with the concrete. This bare top surface can be expected to develop rust before the concrete is placed. The bottom side of the deck has a primer coat of paint.

Composite floor deck is normally installed so the panel ends do not overlap on the supporting beams. Shear lugs or panel profile shape often prevent a tight metal to metal fit if the panel ends overlap; the air gap caused by overlapping will prevent proper fusion with the structural steel supports when the panel end laps are shear stud welded.

Adequate end bearing of the deck must be obtained as shown on the drawings. If bearing is actually less in the field than shown on the drawings, further investigation is required.

### Roof Deck

Roof deck is not designed to act compositely with other materials. Roof deck acts alone in transferring horizontal and vertical loads into the building frame. Roof deck rib openings are usually narrower than floor deck rib openings. This provides adequate support of rigid thermal insulation board.

Roof deck is typically installed to endlap approximately 2″ over supports. However, it can be butted (or lapped more than 2″) to solve field fit problems. Since designers frequently use the installed deck system as part of the horizontal bracing system (the deck as a diaphragm), any fastening substitution or change should be approved by the designer. Continuous perimeter support of the deck is necessary to limit edge deflection in the finished roof and may be required for diaphragm shear transfer.

Standard roof deck finishes are galvanized or primer painted. The standard factory applied paint for roof deck is a primer paint and is not intended to weather for extended periods of time. Field painting or touching up of abrasions and deterioration of the primer coat or other protective finishes is the responsibility of the contractor.

### Cellular Deck

Cellular deck is made by attaching a bottom steel sheet to a roof deck or composite floor deck panel. Cellular deck can be used in the same manner as floor deck. Electrical, telephone, and data wires are easily run through the chase created between the deck panel and the bottom sheet.

When used as part of the electrical distribution system, the cellular deck must be installed so that the ribs line up and create a smooth cell transition at abutting ends. The joint that occurs at butting cell ends must be taped or otherwise sealed to prevent wet concrete from seeping into the cell. Cell interiors must be free of welding burrs, or other sharp intrusions, to prevent damage to wires.

When used as a roof deck, the bottom flat plate is usually left exposed to view. Care must be maintained during erection to keep good alignment and prevent damage.

Cellular deck is sometimes used with the flat plate on the top side to provide a flat working surface. Installation of the deck for this purpose requires special methods for attachment to the frame because the flat plate, now on the top, can prevent direct access to the deck material that is bearing on the structural steel. It may be advisable to treat the flat top surface to prevent slipping.

Cellular deck is always furnished galvanized or painted over galvanized.

### Form Deck

Form deck can be any floor or roof deck product used as a concrete form. Connections to the frame are by the same methods used to anchor floor and roof deck. Welding washers are recommended when welding deck that is less than 20 gauge thickness.

Form deck is furnished galvanized, prime painted, or uncoated. Galvanized deck must be used for those roof deck systems where form deck is used to carry a lightweight insulating concrete fill.

## Wood, Plastics & Comp.　　R0611 Wood Framing

### R061110-30　Lumber Product Material Prices

The price of forest products fluctuates widely from location to location and from season to season depending upon economic conditions. The bare material prices in the unit cost sections of the book show the National Average material prices in effect Jan. 1 of this book year. It must be noted that lumber prices in general may change significantly during the year.

Availability of certain items depends upon geographic location and must be checked prior to firm-price bidding.

## Wood, Plastics & Comp.　　R0616 Sheathing

### R061636-20　Plywood

There are two types of plywood used in construction: interior, which is moisture-resistant but not waterproofed, and exterior, which is waterproofed.

The grade of the exterior surface of the plywood sheets is designated by the first letter: A, for smooth surface with patches allowed; B, for solid surface with patches and plugs allowed; C, which may be surface plugged or may have knot holes up to 1″ wide; and D, which is used only for interior type plywood and may have knot holes up to 2-1/2″ wide. "Structural Grade" is specifically designed for engineered applications such as box beams. All CC & DD grades have roof and floor spans marked on them.

Underlayment-grade plywood runs from 1/4″ to 1-1/4″ thick. Thicknesses 5/8″ and over have optional tongue and groove joints which eliminate the need for blocking the edges. Underlayment 19/32″ and over may be referred to as Sturd-i-Floor.

The price of plywood can fluctuate widely due to geographic and economic conditions.

Typical uses for various plywood grades are as follows:

AA-AD Interior — cupboards, shelving, paneling, furniture

BB Plyform — concrete form plywood

CDX — wall and roof sheathing

Structural — box beams, girders, stressed skin panels

AA-AC Exterior — fences, signs, siding, soffits, etc.

Underlayment — base for resilient floor coverings

Overlaid HDO — high density for concrete forms & highway signs

Overlaid MDO — medium density for painting, siding, soffits & signs

303 Siding — exterior siding, textured, striated, embossed, etc.

## Thermal & Moist. Protec.　　R0731 Shingles & Shakes

### R073126-20　Roof Slate

16″, 18″ and 20″ are standard lengths, and slate usually comes in random widths. For standard 3/16″ thickness use 1-1/2″ copper nails. Allow for 3% breakage.

## Thermal & Moist. Protec.　　R0752 Modified Bituminous Membrane Roofing

### R075213-30　Modified Bitumen Roofing

The cost of modified bitumen roofing is highly dependent on the type of installation that is planned. Installation is based on the type of modifier used in the bitumen. The two most popular modifiers are atactic polypropylene (APP) and styrene butadiene styrene (SBS). The modifiers are added to heated bitumen during the manufacturing process to change its characteristics. A polyethylene, polyester or fiberglass reinforcing sheet is then sandwiched between layers of this bitumen. When completed, the result is a pre-assembled, built-up roof that has increased elasticity and weatherablility. Some manufacturers include a surfacing material such as ceramic or mineral granules, metal particles or sand.

The preferred method of adhering SBS-modified bitumen roofing to the substrate is with hot-mopped asphalt (much the same as built-up roofing). This installation method requires a tar kettle/pot to heat the asphalt, as well as the labor, tools and equipment necessary to distribute and spread the hot asphalt.

The alternative method for applying APP and SBS modified bitumen is as follows. A skilled installer uses a torch to melt a small pool of bitumen off the membrane. This pool must form across the entire roll for proper adhesion. The installer must unroll the roofing at a pace slow enough to melt the bitumen, but fast enough to prevent damage to the rest of the membrane.

Modified bitumen roofing provides the advantages of both built-up and single-ply roofing. Labor costs are reduced over those of built-up roofing because only a single ply is necessary. The elasticity of single-ply roofing is attained with the reinforcing sheet and polymer modifiers. Modifieds have some self-healing characteristics and because of their multi-layer construction, they offer the reliability and safety of built-up roofing.

## Openings | R0813 Metal Doors

### R081313-20   Steel Door Selection Guide

Standard steel doors are classified into four levels, as recommended by the Steel Door Institute in the chart below. Each of the four levels offers a range of construction models and designs, to meet architectural requirements for preference and appearance, including full flush, seamless, and stile & rail. Recommended minimum gauge requirements are also included.

For complete standard steel door construction specifications and available sizes, refer to the Steel Door Institute Technical Data Series, ANSI A250.8-98 (SDI-100), and ANSI A250.4-94 Test Procedure and Acceptance Criteria for Physical Endurance of Steel Door and Hardware Reinforcements.

| Level | | Model | Construction | For Full Flush or Seamless | | |
|---|---|---|---|---|---|---|
| | | | | Min. Gauge | Thickness (in) | Thickness (mm) |
| I | Standard Duty | 1 | Full Flush | | | |
| | | 2 | Seamless | 20 | 0.032 | 0.8 |
| II | Heavy Duty | 1 | Full Flush | | | |
| | | 2 | Seamless | 18 | 0.042 | 1.0 |
| III | Extra Heavy Duty | 1 | Full Flush | | | |
| | | 2 | Seamless | | | |
| | | 3 | *Stile & Rail | 16 | 0.053 | 1.3 |
| IV | Maximum Duty | 1 | Full Flush | | | |
| | | 2 | Seamless | 14 | 0.067 | 1.6 |

*Stiles & rails are 16 gauge; flush panels, when specified, are 18 gauge.

## Openings | R0852 Wood Windows

### RQ85216-10   Window Estimates

To ensure a complete window estimate, be sure to include the material and labor costs for each window, as well as the material and labor costs for an interior wood trim set.

## Openings | R0853 Plastic Windows

### R085313-20   Replacement Windows

Replacement windows are typically measured per United Inch.

United Inches are calculated by rounding the width and height of the window opening up to the nearest inch, then adding the two figures.

The labor cost for replacement windows includes removal of sash, existing sash balance or weights, parting bead where necessary and installation of new window.

Debris hauling and dump fees are not included.

## R087120-10 Hinges

All closer equipped doors should have ball bearing hinges. Lead lined or extremely heavy doors require special strength hinges. Usually 1-1/2 pair of hinges are used per door up to 7'-6" high openings. Table below shows typical hinge requirements.

| Use Frequency | Type Hinge Required | Type of Opening | Type of Structure |
|---|---|---|---|
| High | Heavy weight ball bearing | Entrances | Banks, Office buildings, Schools, Stores & Theaters |
| | | Toilet Rooms | Office buildings and Schools |
| Average | Standard weight ball bearing | Entrances | Dwellings |
| | | Corridors | Office buildings and Schools |
| | | Toilet Rooms | Stores |
| Low | Plain bearing | Interior | Dwellings |

| Door Thickness | Weight of Doors in Pounds per Square Foot | | | | |
|---|---|---|---|---|---|
| | White Pine | Oak | Hollow Core | Solid Core | Hollow Metal |
| 1-3/8" | 3psf | 6psf | 1-1/2psf | 3-1/2 — 4psf | 6-1/2psf |
| 1-3/4" | 3-1/2 | 7 | 2-1/2 | 4-1/2 — 5-1/4 | 6-1/2 |
| 2-1/4" | 4-1/2 | 9 | — | 5-1/2 — 6-3/4 | 6-1/2 |

## R092000-50   Lath, Plaster and Gypsum Board

**Gypsum board lath** is available in 3/8″ thick x 16″ wide x 4′ long sheets as a base material for multi-layer plaster applications. It is also available as a base for either multi-layer or veneer plaster applications in 1/2″ and 5/8″ thick—4′ wide x 8′, 10′ or 12′ long sheets. Fasteners are screws or blued ring shank nails for wood framing and screws for metal framing.

**Metal lath** is available in diamond mesh pattern with flat or self-furring profiles. Paper backing is available for applications where excessive plaster waste needs to be avoided. A slotted mesh ribbed lath should be used in areas where the span between structural supports is greater than normal. Most metal lath comes in 27″ x 96″ sheets. Diamond mesh weighs 1.75, 2.5 or 3.4 pounds per square yard, slotted mesh lath weighs 2.75 or 3.4 pounds per square yard. Metal lath can be nailed, screwed or tied in place.

Many **accessories** are available. Corner beads, flat reinforcing strips, casing beads, control and expansion joints, furring brackets and channels are some examples. Note that accessories are not included in plaster or stucco line items.

**Plaster** is defined as a material or combination of materials that when mixed with a suitable amount of water, forms a plastic mass or paste. When applied to a surface, the paste adheres to it and subsequently hardens, preserving in a rigid state the form or texture imposed during the period of elasticity.

**Gypsum plaster** is made from ground calcined gypsum. It is mixed with aggregates and water for use as a base coat plaster.

**Vermiculite plaster** is a fire-retardant plaster covering used on steel beams, concrete slabs and other heavy construction materials. Vermiculite is a group name for certain clay minerals, hydrous silicates or aluminum, magnesium and iron that have been expanded by heat.

**Perlite plaster** is a plaster using perlite as an aggregate instead of sand. Perlite is a volcanic glass that has been expanded by heat.

**Gauging plaster** is a mix of gypsum plaster and lime putty that when applied produces a quick drying finish coat.

**Veneer plaster** is a one or two component gypsum plaster used as a thin finish coat over special gypsum board.

**Keenes cement** is a white cementitious material manufactured from gypsum that has been burned at a high temperature and ground to a fine powder. Alum is added to accelerate the set. The resulting plaster is hard and strong and accepts and maintains a high polish, hence it is used as a finishing plaster.

**Stucco** is a Portland cement based plaster used primarily as an exterior finish.

Plaster is used on both interior and exterior surfaces. Generally it is applied in multiple-coat systems. A three-coat system uses the terms scratch, brown and finish to identify each coat. A two-coat system uses base and finish to describe each coat. Each type of plaster and application system has attributes that are chosen by the designer to best fit the intended use.

| Gypsum Plaster Quantities for 100 S.Y. | 2 Coat, 5/8″ Thick | | 3 Coat, 3/4″ Thick | | |
|---|---|---|---|---|---|
| | Base | Finish | Scratch | Brown | Finish |
| | 1:3 Mix | 2:1 Mix | 1:2 Mix | 1:3 Mix | 2:1 Mix |
| Gypsum plaster | 1,300 lb. | | 1,350 lb. | 650 lb. | |
| Sand | 1.75 C.Y. | | 1.85 C.Y. | 1.35 C.Y. | |
| Finish hydrated lime | | 340 lb. | | | 340 lb. |
| Gauging plaster | | 170 lb. | | | 170 lb. |

| Vermiculite or Perlite Plaster Quantities for 100 S.Y. | 2 Coat, 5/8″ Thick | | 3 Coat, 3/4″ Thick | | |
|---|---|---|---|---|---|
| | Base | Finish | Scratch | Brown | Finish |
| Gypsum plaster | 1,250 lb. | | 1,450 lb. | 800 lb. | |
| Vermiculite or perlite | 7.8 bags | | 8.0 bags | 3.3 bags | |
| Finish hydrated lime | | 340 lb. | | | 340 lb. |
| Gauging plaster | | 170 lb. | | | 170 lb. |

| Stucco–Three-Coat System Quantities for 100 S.Y. | On Wood Frame | On Masonry |
|---|---|---|
| Portland cement | 29 bags | 21 bags |
| Sand | 2.6 C.Y. | 2.0 C.Y. |
| Hydrated lime | 180 lb. | 120 lb. |

## R092910-10 Levels of Gypsum Drywall Finish

In the past, contract documents often used phrases such as "industry standard" and "workmanlike finish" to specify the expected quality of gypsum board wall and ceiling installations. The vagueness of these descriptions led to unacceptable work and disputes.

In order to resolve this problem, four major trade associations concerned with the manufacture, erection, finish and decoration of gypsum board wall and ceiling systems have developed an industry-wide *Recommended Levels of Gypsum Board Finish*.

The finish of gypsum board walls and ceilings for specific final decoration is dependent on a number of factors. A primary consideration is the location of the surface and the degree of decorative treatment desired. Painted and unpainted surfaces in warehouses and other areas where appearance is normally not critical may simply require the taping of wallboard joints and 'spotting' of fastener heads. Blemish-free, smooth, monolithic surfaces often intended for painted and decorated walls and ceilings in habitated structures, ranging from single-family dwellings through monumental buildings, require additional finishing prior to the application of the final decoration.

Other factors to be considered in determining the level of finish of the gypsum board surface are (1) the type of angle of surface illumination (both natural and artificial lighting), and (2) the paint and method of application or the type and finish of wallcovering specified as the final decoration. Critical lighting conditions, gloss paints, and thin wall coverings require a higher level of gypsum board finish than do heavily textured surfaces which are subsequently painted or surfaces which are to be decorated with heavy grade wall coverings.

The following descriptions were developed jointly by the Association of the Wall and Ceiling Industries-International (AWCI), Ceiling & Interior Systems Construction Association (CISCA), Gypsum Association (GA), and Painting and Decorating Contractors of America (PDCA) as a guide.

**Level 0: Used in temporary construction or wherever the final decoration has not been determined. Unfinished. No taping, finishing or corner beads are required.** Also could be used where non-predecorated panels will be used in demountable-type partitions that are to be painted as a final finish. .

**Level 1 Frequently used in plenum areas above ceilings, in attics, in areas where the assembly would generally be concealed, or in building service corridors and other areas not normally open to public view. Some degree of sound and smoke control is provided; in some geographic areas, this level is referred to as "fire-taping," although this level of finish does not typically meet fire-resistant assembly requirements.** Where a fire resistance rating is required for the gypsum board assembly, details of construction should be in accordance with reports of fire tests of assemblies that have met the requirements of the fire rating acceptable.

All joints and interior angles shall have tape embedded in joint compound. Accessories are optional at specifier discretion in corridors and other areas with pedestrian traffic. Tape and fastener heads need not be covered with joint compound. Surface shall be free of excess joint compound. Tool marks and ridges are acceptable.

**Level 2 It may be specified for standard gypsum board surfaces in garages, warehouse storage, or other similar areas where surface appearance is not of primary importance.**

All joints and interior angles shall have tape embedded in joint compound and shall be immediately wiped with a joint knife or trowel, leaving a thin coating of joint compound over all joints and interior angles. Fastener heads and accessories shall be covered with a coat of joint compound. Surface shall be free of excess joint compound. Tool marks and ridges are acceptable.

**Level 3 Typically used in areas that are to receive heavy texture (spray or hand applied) finishes before final painting, or where**

**commercial-grade (heavy duty) wall coverings are to be applied as the final decoration.** This level of finish should not be used where smooth painted surfaces or where lighter weight wall coverings are specified. The prepared surface shall be coated with a drywall primer prior to the application of final finishes.

All joints and interior angles shall have tape embedded in joint compound and shall be immediately wiped with a joint knife or trowel, leaving a thin coating of joint compound over all joints and interior angles. One additional coat of joint compound shall be applied over all joints and interior angles. Fastener heads and accessories shall be covered with two separate coats of joint compound. All joint compounds shall be smooth and free of tool marks and ridges. The prepared surface shall be covered with a drywall primer prior to the application of the final decoration.

**Level 4 This level should be used where residential grade (light duty) wall coverings, flat paints, or light textures are to be applied. The prepared surface shall be coated with a drywall primer prior to the application of final finishes. Release agents for wall coverings are specifically formulated to minimize damage if coverings are subsequently removed.**

The weight, texture, and sheen level of the wall covering material selected should be taken into consideration when specifying wall coverings over this level of drywall treatment. Joints and fasteners must be sufficiently concealed if the wall covering material is lightweight, contains limited pattern, has a glossy finish, or has any combination of these features. In critical lighting areas, flat paints applied over light textures tend to reduce joint photographing. Gloss, semi-gloss, and enamel paints are not recommended over this level of finish.

All joints and interior angles shall have tape embedded in joint compound and shall be immediately wiped with a joint knife or trowel, leaving a thin coating of joint compound over all joints and interior angles. In addition, two separate coats of joint compound shall be applied over all flat joints and one separate coat of joint compound applied over interior angles. Fastener heads and accessories shall be covered with three separate coats of joint compound. All joint compounds shall be smooth and free of tool marks and ridges. The prepared surface shall be covered with a drywall primer like Sheetrock first coat prior to the application of the final decoration.

**Level 5 The highest quality finish is the most effective method to provide a uniform surface and minimize the possibility of joint photographing and of fasteners showing through the final decoration.** This level of finish is required where gloss, semi-gloss, or enamel is specified; when flat joints are specified over an untextured surface; or where critical lighting conditions occur. The prepared surface shall be coated with a drywall primer prior to the application of final decoration.

All joints and interior angles shall have tape embedded in joint compound and be immediately wiped with a joint knife or trowel, leaving a thin coating of joint compound over all joints and interior angles. Two separate coats of joint compound shall be applied over all flat joints and one separate coat of joint compound applied over interior angles. Fastener heads and accessories shall be covered with three separate coats of joint compound.

A thin skim coat of joint compound shall be trowel applied to the entire surface. Excess compound is immediately troweled off, leaving a film or skim coating of compound completely covering the paper. As an alternative to a skim coat, a material manufactured especially for this purpose may be applied such as Sheetrock Tuff-Hide primer surfacer. The surface must be smooth and free of tool marks and ridges. The prepared surface shall be covered with a drywall primer prior to the application of the final decoration.

## R097223-10   Wall Covering

The table below lists the quantities required for 100 S.F. of wall covering.

| Description | Medium-Priced Paper | Expensive Paper |
|---|---|---|
| Paper | 1.6 dbl. rolls | 1.6 dbl. rolls |
| Wall sizing | 0.25 gallon | 0.25 gallon |
| Vinyl wall paste | 0.6 gallon | 0.6 gallon |
| Apply sizing | 0.3 hour | 0.3 hour |
| Apply paper | 1.2 hours | 1.5 hours |

Most wallpapers now come in double rolls only.
To remove old paper, allow 1.3 hours per 100 S.F.

## R099100-10   Painting Estimating Techniques

Proper estimating methodology is needed to obtain an accurate painting estimate. There is no known reliable shortcut or square foot method. The following steps should be followed:

• List all surfaces to be painted, with an accurate quantity (area) of each. Items having similar surface condition, finish, application method and accessibility may be grouped together.

• List all the tasks required for each surface to be painted, including surface preparation, masking, and protection of adjacent surfaces. Surface preparation may include minor repairs, washing, sanding and puttying.

• Select the proper Means line for each task. Review and consider all adjustments to labor and materials for type of paint and location of work. Apply the height adjustment carefully. For instance, when applying the adjustment for work over 8' high to a wall that is 12' high, apply the adjustment only to the area between 8' and 12' high, and not to the entire wall.

When applying more than one percent (%) adjustment, apply each to the base cost of the data, rather than applying one percentage adjustment on top of the other.

When estimating the cost of painting walls and ceilings remember to add the brushwork for all cut-ins at inside corners and around windows and doors as a LF measure. One linear foot of cut-in with brush equals one square foot of painting.

All items for spray painting include the labor for roll-back.

Deduct for openings greater than 100 SF, or openings that extend from floor to ceiling and are greater than 5' wide. Do not deduct small openings.

The cost of brushes, rollers, ladders and spray equipment are considered to be part of a painting contractor's overhead, and should not be added to the estimate. The cost of rented equipment such as scaffolding and swing staging should be added to the estimate.

## R099100-20   Painting

| Item | Coat | One Gallon Covers | | | In 8 Hours a Laborer Covers | | | Labor-Hours per 100 S.F. | | |
|---|---|---|---|---|---|---|---|---|---|---|
| | | Brush | Roller | Spray | Brush | Roller | Spray | Brush | Roller | Spray |
| Paint wood siding | prime | 250 S.F. | 225 S.F. | 290 S.F. | 1150 S.F. | 1300 S.F. | 2275 S.F. | .695 | .615 | .351 |
| | others | 270 | 250 | 290 | 1300 | 1625 | 2600 | .615 | .492 | .307 |
| Paint exterior trim | prime | 400 | — | — | 650 | — | — | 1.230 | — | — |
| | 1st | 475 | — | — | 800 | — | — | 1.000 | — | — |
| | 2nd | 520 | — | — | 975 | — | — | .820 | — | — |
| Paint shingle siding | prime | 270 | 255 | 300 | 650 | 975 | 1950 | 1.230 | .820 | .410 |
| | others | 360 | 340 | 380 | 800 | 1150 | 2275 | 1.000 | .695 | .351 |
| Stain shingle siding | 1st | 180 | 170 | 200 | 750 | 1125 | 2250 | 1.068 | .711 | .355 |
| | 2nd | 270 | 250 | 290 | 900 | 1325 | 2600 | .888 | .603 | .307 |
| Paint brick masonry | prime | 180 | 135 | 160 | 750 | 800 | 1800 | 1.066 | 1.000 | .444 |
| | 1st | 270 | 225 | 290 | 815 | 975 | 2275 | .981 | .820 | .351 |
| | 2nd | 340 | 305 | 360 | 815 | 1150 | 2925 | .981 | .695 | .273 |
| Paint interior plaster or drywall | prime | 400 | 380 | 495 | 1150 | 2000 | 3250 | .695 | .400 | .246 |
| | others | 450 | 425 | 495 | 1300 | 2300 | 4000 | .615 | .347 | .200 |
| Paint interior doors and windows | prime | 400 | — | — | 650 | — | — | 1.230 | — | — |
| | 1st | 425 | — | — | 800 | — | — | 1.000 | — | — |
| | 2nd | 450 | — | — | 975 | — | — | .820 | — | — |

## R131113-20    Swimming Pools

Pool prices given per square foot of surface area include pool structure, filter and chlorination equipment, pumps, related piping, ladders/steps, maintenance kit, skimmer and vacuum system. Decks and electrical service to equipment are not included.

Residential in-ground pool construction can be divided into two categories: vinyl lined and gunite. Vinyl lined pool walls are constructed of different materials including wood, concrete, plastic or metal. The bottom is often graded with sand over which the vinyl liner is installed. Vermiculite or soil cement bottoms may be substituted for an added cost.

Gunite pool construction is used both in residential and municipal installations. These structures are steel reinforced for strength and finished with a white cement limestone plaster.

Municipal pools will have a higher cost because plumbing codes require more expensive materials, chlorination equipment and higher filtration rates.

Municipal pools greater than 1,800 S.F. require gutter systems to control waves. This gutter may be formed into the concrete wall. Often a vinyl/stainless steel gutter or gutter/wall system is specified, which will raise the pool cost.

Competition pools usually require tile bottoms and sides with contrasting lane striping, which will also raise the pool cost.

# Plumbing · R2211 Facility Water Distribution

## R221113-50   Pipe Material Considerations

1. Malleable fittings should be used for gas service.
2. Malleable fittings are used where there are stresses/strains due to expansion and vibration.
3. Cast fittings may be broken as an aid to disassembling of heating lines frozen by long use, temperature and minerals.
4. Cast iron pipe is extensively used for underground and submerged service.
5. Type M (light wall) copper tubing is available in hard temper only and is used for nonpressure and less severe applications than K and L.
6. Type L (medium wall) copper tubing, available hard or soft for interior service.
7. Type K (heavy wall) copper tubing, available in hard or soft temper for use where conditions are severe. For underground and interior service.
8. Hard drawn tubing requires fewer hangers or supports but should not be bent. Silver brazed fittings are recommended, however soft solder is normally used.
9. Type DMV (very light wall) copper tubing designed for drainage, waste and vent plus other non-critical pressure services.

### Domestic/Imported Pipe and Fittings Cost

The prices shown in this publication for steel/cast iron pipe and steel, cast iron, malleable iron fittings are based on domestic production sold at the normal trade discounts. The above listed items of foreign manufacture may be available at prices of 1/3 to 1/2 those shown. Some imported items after minor machining or finishing operations are being sold as domestic to further complicate the system.

**Caution:** Most pipe prices in this book also include a coupling and pipe hangers which for the larger sizes can add significantly to the per foot cost and should be taken into account when comparing "book cost" with quoted supplier's cost.

# Plumbing · R2240 Plumbing Fixtures

## R224000-40   Plumbing Fixture Installation Time

| Item | Rough-In | Set | Total Hours | Item | Rough-In | Set | Total Hours |
|---|---|---|---|---|---|---|---|
| Bathtub | 5 | 5 | 10 | Shower head only | 2 | 1 | 3 |
| Bathtub and shower, cast iron | 6 | 6 | 12 | Shower drain | 3 | 1 | 4 |
| Fire hose reel and cabinet | 4 | 2 | 6 | Shower stall, slate | | 15 | 15 |
| Floor drain to 4 inch diameter | 3 | 1 | 4 | Slop sink | 5 | 3 | 8 |
| Grease trap, single, cast iron | 5 | 3 | 8 | Test 6 fixtures | | | 14 |
| Kitchen gas range | | 4 | 4 | Urinal, wall | 6 | 2 | 8 |
| Kitchen sink, single | 4 | 4 | 8 | Urinal, pedestal or floor | 6 | 4 | 10 |
| Kitchen sink, double | 6 | 6 | 12 | Water closet and tank | 4 | 3 | 7 |
| Laundry tubs | 4 | 2 | 6 | Water closet and tank, wall hung | 5 | 3 | 8 |
| Lavatory wall hung | 5 | 3 | 8 | Water heater, 45 gals. gas, automatic | 5 | 2 | 7 |
| Lavatory pedestal | 5 | 3 | 8 | Water heaters, 65 gals. gas, automatic | 5 | 2 | 7 |
| Shower and stall | 6 | 4 | 10 | Water heaters, electric, plumbing only | 4 | 2 | 6 |

Fixture prices in front of book are based on the cost per fixture set in place. The rough-in cost, which must be added for each fixture, includes carrier, if required, some supply, waste and vent pipe connecting fittings and stops. The lengths of rough-in pipe are nominal runs which would connect to the larger runs and stacks. The supply runs and DWV runs and stacks must be accounted for in separate entries. In the eastern half of the United States it is common for the plumber to carry these to a point 5' outside the building.

# Exterior Improvements · R3292 Turf & Grasses

## R329219-50   Seeding

The type of grass is determined by light, shade and moisture content of soil plus intended use. Fertilizer should be disked 4" before seeding. For steep slopes disk five tons of mulch and lay two tons of hay or straw on surface per acre after seeding. Surface mulch can be staked, lightly disked or tar emulsion sprayed. Material for mulch can be wood chips, peat moss, partially rotted hay or straw, wood fibers and sprayed emulsions. Hemp seed blankets with fertilizer are also available. For spring seeding, watering is necessary. Late fall seeding may have to be reseeded in the spring. Hydraulic seeding, power mulching, and aerial seeding can be used on large areas.

## R331113-80   Piping Designations

There are several systems currently in use to describe pipe and fittings. The following paragraphs will help to identify and clarify classifications of piping systems used for water distribution.

Piping may be classified by schedule. Piping schedules include 5S, 10S, 10, 20, 30, Standard, 40, 60, Extra Strong, 80, 100, 120, 140, 160 and Double Extra Strong. These schedules are dependent upon the pipe wall thickness. The wall thickness of a particular schedule may vary with pipe size.

**Ductile iron pipe** for water distribution is classified by Pressure Classes such as Class 150, 200, 250, 300 and 350. These classes are actually the rated water working pressure of the pipe in pounds per square inch (psi). The pipe in these pressure classes is designed to withstand the rated water working pressure plus a surge allowance of 100 psi.

The American Water Works Association (AWWA) provides standards for various types of **plastic pipe.** C-900 is the specification for polyvinyl chloride (PVC) piping used for water distribution in sizes ranging from 4″ through 12″. C-901 is the specification for polyethylene (PE) pressure pipe, tubing and fittings used for water distribution in sizes ranging from 1/2″ through 3″. C-905 is the specification for PVC piping sizes 14″ and greater.

**PVC pressure-rated pipe** is identified using the standard dimensional ratio (SDR) method. This method is defined by the American Society for Testing and Materials (ASTM) Standard D 2241. This pipe is available in SDR numbers 64, 41, 32.5, 26, 21, 17, and 13.5. Pipe with an SDR of 64 will have the thinnest wall while pipe with an SDR of 13.5 will have the thickest wall. When the pressure rating (PR) of a pipe is given in psi, it is based on a line supplying water at 73 degrees F.

The National Sanitation Foundation (NSF) seal of approval is applied to products that can be used with potable water. These products have been tested to ANSI/NSF Standard 14.

**Valves and strainers** are classified by American National Standards Institute (ANSI) Classes. These Classes are 125, 150, 200, 250, 300, 400, 600, 900, 1500 and 2500. Within each class there is an operating pressure range dependent upon temperature. Design parameters should be compared to the appropriate material dependent, pressure-temperature rating chart for accurate valve selection.

# Abbreviations

| | |
|---|---|
| A | Area Square Feet; Ampere |
| ABS | Acrylonitrile Butadiene Stryrene; Asbestos Bonded Steel |
| A.C. | Alternating Current; Air-Conditioning; Asbestos Cement; Plywood Grade A & C |
| A.C.I. | American Concrete Institute |
| AD | Plywood, Grade A & D |
| Addit. | Additional |
| Adj. | Adjustable |
| af | Audio-frequency |
| A.G.A. | American Gas Association |
| Agg. | Aggregate |
| A.H. | Ampere Hours |
| A hr. | Ampere-hour |
| A.H.U. | Air Handling Unit |
| A.I.A. | American Institute of Architects |
| AIC | Ampere Interrupting Capacity |
| Allow. | Allowance |
| alt. | Altitude |
| Alum. | Aluminum |
| a.m. | Ante Meridiem |
| Amp. | Ampere |
| Anod. | Anodized |
| Approx. | Approximate |
| Apt. | Apartment |
| Asb. | Asbestos |
| A.S.B.C. | American Standard Building Code |
| Asbe. | Asbestos Worker |
| ASCE. | American Society of Civil Engineers |
| A.S.H.R.A.E. | American Society of Heating, Refrig. & AC Engineers |
| A.S.M.E. | American Society of Mechanical Engineers |
| A.S.T.M. | American Society for Testing and Materials |
| Attchmt. | Attachment |
| Avg., Ave. | Average |
| A.W.G. | American Wire Gauge |
| AWWA | American Water Works Assoc. |
| Bbl. | Barrel |
| B&B | Grade B and Better; Balled & Burlapped |
| B.&S. | Bell and Spigot |
| B.&W. | Black and White |
| b.c.c. | Body-centered Cubic |
| B.C.Y. | Bank Cubic Yards |
| BE | Bevel End |
| B.F. | Board Feet |
| Bg. cem. | Bag of Cement |
| BHP | Boiler Horsepower; Brake Horsepower |
| B.I. | Black Iron |
| Bit., Bitum. | Bituminous |
| Bit., Conc. | Bituminous Concrete |
| Bk. | Backed |
| Bkrs. | Breakers |
| Bldg. | Building |
| Blk. | Block |
| Bm. | Beam |
| Boil. | Boilermaker |
| B.P.M. | Blows per Minute |
| BR | Bedroom |
| Brg. | Bearing |
| Brhe. | Bricklayer Helper |
| Bric. | Bricklayer |
| Brk. | Brick |
| Brng. | Bearing |
| Brs. | Brass |
| Brz. | Bronze |
| Bsn. | Basin |
| Btr. | Better |
| Btu | British Thermal Unit |

| | |
|---|---|
| BTUH | BTU per Hour |
| B.U.R. | Built-up Roofing |
| BX | Interlocked Armored Cable |
| °C | degree centigrade |
| c | Conductivity, Copper Sweat |
| C | Hundred; Centigrade |
| C/C | Center to Center, Cedar on Cedar |
| C-C | Center to Center |
| Cab. | Cabinet |
| Cair. | Air Tool Laborer |
| Calc | Calculated |
| Cap. | Capacity |
| Carp. | Carpenter |
| C.B. | Circuit Breaker |
| C.C.A. | Chromate Copper Arsenate |
| C.C.F. | Hundred Cubic Feet |
| cd | Candela |
| cd/sf | Candela per Square Foot |
| CD | Grade of Plywood Face & Back |
| CDX | Plywood, Grade C & D, exterior glue |
| Cefi. | Cement Finisher |
| Cem. | Cement |
| CF | Hundred Feet |
| C.F. | Cubic Feet |
| CFM | Cubic Feet per Minute |
| c.g. | Center of Gravity |
| CHW | Chilled Water; Commercial Hot Water |
| C.I. | Cast Iron |
| C.I.P. | Cast in Place |
| Circ. | Circuit |
| C.L. | Carload Lot |
| Clab. | Common Laborer |
| Clam | Common maintenance laborer |
| C.L.F. | Hundred Linear Feet |
| CLF | Current Limiting Fuse |
| CLP | Cross Linked Polyethylene |
| cm | Centimeter |
| CMP | Corr. Metal Pipe |
| C.M.U. | Concrete Masonry Unit |
| CN | Change Notice |
| Col. | Column |
| $CO_2$ | Carbon Dioxide |
| Comb. | Combination |
| Compr. | Compressor |
| Conc. | Concrete |
| Cont. | Continuous; Continued, Container |
| Corr. | Corrugated |
| Cos | Cosine |
| Cot | Cotangent |
| Cov. | Cover |
| C/P | Cedar on Paneling |
| CPA | Control Point Adjustment |
| Cplg. | Coupling |
| C.P.M. | Critical Path Method |
| CPVC | Chlorinated Polyvinyl Chloride |
| C.Pr. | Hundred Pair |
| CRC | Cold Rolled Channel |
| Creos. | Creosote |
| Crpt. | Carpet & Linoleum Layer |
| CRT | Cathode-ray Tube |
| CS | Carbon Steel, Constant Shear Bar Joist |
| Csc | Cosecant |
| C.S.F. | Hundred Square Feet |
| CSI | Construction Specifications Institute |
| C.T. | Current Transformer |
| CTS | Copper Tube Size |
| Cu | Copper, Cubic |
| Cu. Ft. | Cubic Foot |
| cw | Continuous Wave |
| C.W. | Cool White; Cold Water |

| | |
|---|---|
| Cwt. | 100 Pounds |
| C.W.X. | Cool White Deluxe |
| C.Y. | Cubic Yard (27 cubic feet) |
| C.Y./Hr. | Cubic Yard per Hour |
| Cyl. | Cylinder |
| d | Penny (nail size) |
| D | Deep; Depth; Discharge |
| Dis., Disch. | Discharge |
| Db. | Decibel |
| Dbl. | Double |
| DC | Direct Current |
| DDC | Direct Digital Control |
| Demob. | Demobilization |
| d.f.u. | Drainage Fixture Units |
| D.H. | Double Hung |
| DHW | Domestic Hot Water |
| DI | Ductile Iron |
| Diag. | Diagonal |
| Diam., Dia | Diameter |
| Distrib. | Distribution |
| Div. | Division |
| Dk. | Deck |
| D.L. | Dead Load; Diesel |
| DLH | Deep Long Span Bar Joist |
| Do. | Ditto |
| Dp. | Depth |
| D.P.S.T. | Double Pole, Single Throw |
| Dr. | Drive |
| Drink. | Drinking |
| D.S. | Double Strength |
| D.S.A. | Double Strength A Grade |
| D.S.B. | Double Strength B Grade |
| Dty. | Duty |
| DWV | Drain Waste Vent |
| DX | Deluxe White, Direct Expansion |
| dyn | Dyne |
| e | Eccentricity |
| E | Equipment Only; East |
| Ea. | Each |
| E.B. | Encased Burial |
| Econ. | Economy |
| E.C.Y | Embankment Cubic Yards |
| EDP | Electronic Data Processing |
| EIFS | Exterior Insulation Finish System |
| E.D.R. | Equiv. Direct Radiation |
| Eq. | Equation |
| EL | elevation |
| Elec. | Electrician; Electrical |
| Elev. | Elevator; Elevating |
| EMT | Electrical Metallic Conduit; Thin Wall Conduit |
| Eng. | Engine, Engineered |
| EPDM | Ethylene Propylene Diene Monomer |
| EPS | Expanded Polystyrene |
| Eqhv. | Equip. Oper., Heavy |
| Eqlt. | Equip. Oper., Light |
| Eqmd. | Equip. Oper., Medium |
| Eqmm. | Equip. Oper., Master Mechanic |
| Eqol. | Equip. Oper., Oilers |
| Equip. | Equipment |
| ERW | Electric Resistance Welded |
| E.S. | Energy Saver |
| Est. | Estimated |
| esu | Electrostatic Units |
| E.W. | Each Way |
| EWT | Entering Water Temperature |
| Excav. | Excavation |
| Exp. | Expansion, Exposure |
| Ext. | Exterior |
| Extru. | Extrusion |
| f. | Fiber stress |
| F | Fahrenheit; Female; Fill |
| Fab. | Fabricated |

# Abbreviations

| | | | | | |
|---|---|---|---|---|---|
| FBGS | Fiberglass | H.P. | Horsepower; High Pressure | LE | Lead Equivalent |
| F.C. | Footcandles | H.P.F. | High Power Factor | LED | Light Emitting Diode |
| f.c.c. | Face-centered Cubic | Hr. | Hour | L.F. | Linear Foot |
| f'c. | Compressive Stress in Concrete; Extreme Compressive Stress | Hrs./Day | Hours per Day | L.F. Nose | Linear Foot of Stair Nosing |
| | | HSC | High Short Circuit | L.F. Rsr | Linear Foot of Stair Riser |
| F.E. | Front End | Ht. | Height | Lg. | Long; Length; Large |
| FEP | Fluorinated Ethylene Propylene (Teflon) | Htg. | Heating | L & H | Light and Heat |
| | | Htrs. | Heaters | LH | Long Span Bar Joist |
| F.G. | Flat Grain | HVAC | Heating, Ventilation & Air-Conditioning | L.H. | Labor Hours |
| F.H.A. | Federal Housing Administration | | | L.L. | Live Load |
| Fig. | Figure | Hvy. | Heavy | L.L.D. | Lamp Lumen Depreciation |
| Fin. | Finished | HW | Hot Water | lm | Lumen |
| Fixt. | Fixture | Hyd.;Hydr. | Hydraulic | lm/sf | Lumen per Square Foot |
| Fl. Oz. | Fluid Ounces | Hz. | Hertz (cycles) | lm/W | Lumen per Watt |
| Flr. | Floor | I. | Moment of Inertia | L.O.A. | Length Over All |
| F.M. | Frequency Modulation; Factory Mutual | IBC | International Building Code | log | Logarithm |
| | | I.C. | Interrupting Capacity | L-O-L | Lateralolet |
| Fmg. | Framing | ID | Inside Diameter | long. | longitude |
| Fdn. | Foundation | I.D. | Inside Dimension; Identification | L.P. | Liquefied Petroleum; Low Pressure |
| Fori. | Foreman, Inside | I.F. | Inside Frosted | L.P.F. | Low Power Factor |
| Foro. | Foreman, Outside | I.M.C. | Intermediate Metal Conduit | LR | Long Radius |
| Fount. | Fountain | In. | Inch | L.S. | Lump Sum |
| fpm | Feet per Minute | Incan. | Incandescent | Lt. | Light |
| FPT | Female Pipe Thread | Incl. | Included; Including | Lt. Ga. | Light Gauge |
| Fr. | Frame | Int. | Interior | L.T.L. | Less than Truckload Lot |
| F.R. | Fire Rating | Inst. | Installation | Lt. Wt. | Lightweight |
| FRK | Foil Reinforced Kraft | Insul. | Insulation/Insulated | L.V. | Low Voltage |
| FRP | Fiberglass Reinforced Plastic | I.P. | Iron Pipe | M | Thousand; Material; Male; Light Wall Copper Tubing |
| FS | Forged Steel | I.P.S. | Iron Pipe Size | | |
| FSC | Cast Body; Cast Switch Box | I.P.T. | Iron Pipe Threaded | M²CA | Meters Squared Contact Area |
| Ft. | Foot; Feet | I.W. | Indirect Waste | m/hr.; M.H. | Man-hour |
| Ftng. | Fitting | J | Joule | mA | Milliampere |
| Ftg. | Footing | J.I.C. | Joint Industrial Council | Mach. | Machine |
| Ft lb. | Foot Pound | K | Thousand; Thousand Pounds; Heavy Wall Copper Tubing, Kelvin | Mag. Str. | Magnetic Starter |
| Furn. | Furniture | | | Maint. | Maintenance |
| FVNR | Full Voltage Non-Reversing | K.A.H. | Thousand Amp. Hours | Marb. | Marble Setter |
| FXM | Female by Male | KCMIL | Thousand Circular Mils | Mat; Mat'l. | Material |
| Fy. | Minimum Yield Stress of Steel | KD | Knock Down | Max. | Maximum |
| g | Gram | K.D.A.T. | Kiln Dried After Treatment | MBF | Thousand Board Feet |
| G | Gauss | kg | Kilogram | MBH | Thousand BTU's per hr. |
| Ga. | Gauge | kG | Kilogauss | MC | Metal Clad Cable |
| Gal., gal. | Gallon | kgf | Kilogram Force | M.C.F. | Thousand Cubic Feet |
| gpm, GPM | Gallon per Minute | kHz | Kilohertz | M.C.F.M. | Thousand Cubic Feet per Minute |
| Galv. | Galvanized | Kip. | 1000 Pounds | M.C.M. | Thousand Circular Mils |
| Gen. | General | KJ | Kiljoule | M.C.P. | Motor Circuit Protector |
| G.F.I. | Ground Fault Interrupter | K.L. | Effective Length Factor | MD | Medium Duty |
| Glaz. | Glazier | K.L.F. | Kips per Linear Foot | M.D.O. | Medium Density Overlaid |
| GPD | Gallons per Day | Km | Kilometer | Med. | Medium |
| GPH | Gallons per Hour | K.S.F. | Kips per Square Foot | MF | Thousand Feet |
| GPM | Gallons per Minute | K.S.I. | Kips per Square Inch | M.F.B.M. | Thousand Feet Board Measure |
| GR | Grade | kV | Kilovolt | Mfg. | Manufacturing |
| Gran. | Granular | kVA | Kilovolt Ampere | Mfrs. | Manufacturers |
| Grnd. | Ground | K.V.A.R. | Kilovar (Reactance) | mg | Milligram |
| H | High Henry | KW | Kilowatt | MGD | Million Gallons per Day |
| H.C. | High Capacity | KWh | Kilowatt-hour | MGPH | Thousand Gallons per Hour |
| H.D. | Heavy Duty; High Density | L | Labor Only; Length; Long; Medium Wall Copper Tubing | MH, M.H. | Manhole; Metal Halide; Man-Hour |
| H.D.O. | High Density Overlaid | | | MHz | Megahertz |
| H.D.P.E. | high density polyethelene | Lab. | Labor | Mi. | Mile |
| Hdr. | Header | lat | Latitude | MI | Malleable Iron; Mineral Insulated |
| Hdwe. | Hardware | Lath. | Lather | mm | Millimeter |
| Help. | Helper Average | Lav. | Lavatory | Mill. | Millwright |
| HEPA | High Efficiency Particulate Air Filter | lb.; # | Pound | Min., min. | Minimum, minute |
| | | L.B. | Load Bearing; L Conduit Body | Misc. | Miscellaneous |
| Hg | Mercury | L. & E. | Labor & Equipment | ml | Milliliter, Mainline |
| HIC | High Interrupting Capacity | lb./hr. | Pounds per Hour | M.L.F. | Thousand Linear Feet |
| HM | Hollow Metal | lb./L.F. | Pounds per Linear Foot | Mo. | Month |
| HMWPE | high molecular weight polyethylene | lbf/sq.in. | Pound-force per Square Inch | Mobil. | Mobilization |
| | | L.C.L. | Less than Carload Lot | Mog. | Mogul Base |
| H.O. | High Output | L.C.Y. | Loose Cubic Yard | MPH | Miles per Hour |
| Horiz. | Horizontal | Ld. | Load | MPT | Male Pipe Thread |

# Abbreviations

| | | | | | |
|---|---|---|---|---|---|
| MRT | Mile Round Trip | Pl. | Plate | S.F.C.A. | Square Foot Contact Area |
| ms | Millisecond | Plah. | Plasterer Helper | S.F. Flr. | Square Foot of Floor |
| M.S.F. | Thousand Square Feet | Plas. | Plasterer | S.F.G. | Square Foot of Ground |
| Mstz. | Mosaic & Terrazzo Worker | Pluh. | Plumbers Helper | S.F. Hor. | Square Foot Horizontal |
| M.S.Y. | Thousand Square Yards | Plum. | Plumber | S.F.R. | Square Feet of Radiation |
| Mtd., mtd. | Mounted | Ply. | Plywood | S.F. Shlf. | Square Foot of Shelf |
| Mthe. | Mosaic & Terrazzo Helper | p.m. | Post Meridiem | S4S | Surface 4 Sides |
| Mtng. | Mounting | Pntd. | Painted | Shee. | Sheet Metal Worker |
| Mult. | Multi; Multiply | Pord. | Painter, Ordinary | Sin. | Sine |
| M.V.A. | Million Volt Amperes | pp | Pages | Skwk. | Skilled Worker |
| M.V.A.R. | Million Volt Amperes Reactance | PP, PPL | Polypropylene | SL | Saran Lined |
| MV | Megavolt | P.P.M. | Parts per Million | S.L. | Slimline |
| MW | Megawatt | Pr. | Pair | Sldr. | Solder |
| MXM | Male by Male | P.E.S.B. | Pre-engineered Steel Building | SLH | Super Long Span Bar Joist |
| MYD | Thousand Yards | Prefab. | Prefabricated | S.N. | Solid Neutral |
| N | Natural; North | Prefin. | Prefinished | S-O-L | Socketolet |
| nA | Nanoampere | Prop. | Propelled | sp | Standpipe |
| NA | Not Available; Not Applicable | PSF, psf | Pounds per Square Foot | S.P. | Static Pressure; Single Pole; Self- |
| N.B.C. | National Building Code | PSI, psi | Pounds per Square Inch | | Propelled |
| NC | Normally Closed | PSIG | Pounds per Square Inch Gauge | Spri. | Sprinkler Installer |
| N.E.M.A. | National Electrical Manufacturers | PSP | Plastic Sewer Pipe | spwg | Static Pressure Water Gauge |
| | Assoc. | Pspr. | Painter, Spray | S.P.D.T. | Single Pole, Double Throw |
| NEHB | Bolted Circuit Breaker to 600V. | Psst. | Painter, Structural Steel | SPF | Spruce Pine Fir |
| N.L.B. | Non-Load-Bearing | P.T. | Potential Transformer | S.P.S.T. | Single Pole, Single Throw |
| NM | Non-Metallic Cable | P. & T. | Pressure & Temperature | SPT | Standard Pipe Thread |
| nm | Nanometer | Ptd. | Painted | Sq. | Square; 100 Square Feet |
| No. | Number | Ptns. | Partitions | Sq. Hd. | Square Head |
| NO | Normally Open | Pu | Ultimate Load | Sq. In. | Square Inch |
| N.O.C. | Not Otherwise Classified | PVC | Polyvinyl Chloride | S.S. | Single Strength; Stainless Steel |
| Nose. | Nosing | Pvmt. | Pavement | S.S.B. | Single Strength B Grade |
| N.P.T. | National Pipe Thread | Pwr. | Power | sst, ss | Stainless Steel |
| NQOD | Combination Plug-on/Bolt on | Q | Quantity Heat Flow | Sswk. | Structural Steel Worker |
| | Circuit Breaker to 240V. | Qt. | Quart | Sswl. | Structural Steel Welder |
| N.R.C. | Noise Reduction Coefficient/ | Quan., Qty. | Quantity | St.;Stl. | Steel |
| | Nuclear Regulator Commission | Q.C. | Quick Coupling | S.T.C. | Sound Transmission Coefficient |
| N.R.S. | Non Rising Stem | r | Radius of Gyration | Std. | Standard |
| ns | Nanosecond | R | Resistance | Stg. | Staging |
| nW | Nanowatt | R.C.P. | Reinforced Concrete Pipe | STK | Select Tight Knot |
| OB | Opposing Blade | Rect. | Rectangle | STP | Standard Temperature & Pressure |
| OC | On Center | Reg. | Regular | Stpi. | Steamfitter, Pipefitter |
| OD | Outside Diameter | Reinf. | Reinforced | Str. | Strength; Starter; Straight |
| O.D. | Outside Dimension | Req'd. | Required | Strd. | Stranded |
| ODS | Overhead Distribution System | Res. | Resistant | Struct. | Structural |
| O.G. | Ogee | Resi. | Residential | Sty. | Story |
| O.H. | Overhead | Rgh. | Rough | Subj. | Subject |
| O&P | Overhead and Profit | RGS | Rigid Galvanized Steel | Subs. | Subcontractors |
| Oper. | Operator | R.H.W. | Rubber, Heat & Water Resistant; | Surf. | Surface |
| Opng. | Opening | | Residential Hot Water | Sw. | Switch |
| Orna. | Ornamental | rms | Root Mean Square | Swbd. | Switchboard |
| OSB | Oriented Strand Board | Rnd. | Round | S.Y. | Square Yard |
| O.S.&Y. | Outside Screw and Yoke | Rodm. | Rodman | Syn. | Synthetic |
| Ovhd. | Overhead | Rofc. | Roofer, Composition | S.Y.P. | Southern Yellow Pine |
| OWG | Oil, Water or Gas | Rofp. | Roofer, Precast | Sys. | System |
| Oz. | Ounce | Rohe. | Roofer Helpers (Composition) | t. | Thickness |
| P. | Pole; Applied Load; Projection | Rots. | Roofer, Tile & Slate | T | Temperature; Ton |
| p. | Page | R.O.W. | Right of Way | Tan | Tangent |
| Pape. | Paperhanger | RPM | Revolutions per Minute | T.C. | Terra Cotta |
| P.A.P.R. | Powered Air Purifying Respirator | R.S. | Rapid Start | T & C | Threaded and Coupled |
| PAR | Parabolic Reflector | Rsr | Riser | T.D. | Temperature Difference |
| Pc., Pcs. | Piece, Pieces | RT | Round Trip | Tdd | Telecommunications Device for |
| P.C. | Portland Cement; Power Connector | S. | Suction; Single Entrance; South | | the Deaf |
| P.C.F. | Pounds per Cubic Foot | SC | Screw Cover | T.E.M. | Transmission Electron Microscopy |
| P.C.M. | Phase Contrast Microscopy | SCFM | Standard Cubic Feet per Minute | TFE | Tetrafluoroethylene (Teflon) |
| P.E. | Professional Engineer; | Scaf. | Scaffold | T. & G. | Tongue & Groove; |
| | Porcelain Enamel; | Sch., Sched. | Schedule | | Tar & Gravel |
| | Polyethylene; Plain End | S.C.R. | Modular Brick | Th., Thk. | Thick |
| Perf. | Perforated | S.D. | Sound Deadening | Thn. | Thin |
| PEX | Cross linked polyethylene | S.D.R. | Standard Dimension Ratio | Thrded | Threaded |
| Ph. | Phase | S.E. | Surfaced Edge | Tilf. | Tile Layer, Floor |
| P.I. | Pressure Injected | Sel. | Select | Tilh. | Tile Layer, Helper |
| Pile. | Pile Driver | S.E.R., S.E.U. | Service Entrance Cable | THHN | Nylon Jacketed Wire |
| Pkg. | Package | S.F. | Square Foot | THW. | Insulated Strand Wire |

# Abbreviations

| | | | | | |
|---|---|---|---|---|---|
| THWN | Nylon Jacketed Wire | USP | United States Primed | Wrck. | Wrecker |
| T.L. | Truckload | UTP | Unshielded Twisted Pair | W.S.P. | Water, Steam, Petroleum |
| T.M. | Track Mounted | V | Volt | WT., Wt. | Weight |
| Tot. | Total | V.A. | Volt Amperes | WWF | Welded Wire Fabric |
| T-O-L | Threadolet | V.C.T. | Vinyl Composition Tile | XFER | Transfer |
| T.S. | Trigger Start | VAV | Variable Air Volume | XFMR | Transformer |
| Tr. | Trade | VC | Veneer Core | XHD | Extra Heavy Duty |
| Transf. | Transformer | Vent. | Ventilation | XHHW, XLPE | Cross-Linked Polyethylene Wire |
| Trhv. | Truck Driver, Heavy | Vert. | Vertical | | Insulation |
| Trlr | Trailer | V.F. | Vinyl Faced | XLP | Cross-linked Polyethylene |
| Trlt. | Truck Driver, Light | V.G. | Vertical Grain | Y | Wye |
| TTY | Teletypewriter | V.H.F. | Very High Frequency | yd | Yard |
| TV | Television | VHO | Very High Output | yr | Year |
| T.W. | Thermoplastic Water Resistant | Vib. | Vibrating | Δ | Delta |
| | Wire | V.L.F. | Vertical Linear Foot | % | Percent |
| UCI | Uniform Construction Index | Vol. | Volume | ~ | Approximately |
| UF | Underground Feeder | VRP | Vinyl Reinforced Polyester | Ø | Phase; diameter |
| UGND | Underground Feeder | W | Wire; Watt; Wide; West | @ | At |
| U.H.F. | Ultra High Frequency | w/ | With | # | Pound; Number |
| U.I. | United Inch | W.C. | Water Column; Water Closet | < | Less Than |
| U.L. | Underwriters Laboratory | W.F. | Wide Flange | > | Greater Than |
| Uld. | unloading | W.G. | Water Gauge | Z | zone |
| Unfin. | Unfinished | Wldg. | Welding | | |
| URD | Underground Residential | W. Mile | Wire Mile | | |
| | Distribution | W-O-L | Weldolet | | |
| US | United States | W.R. | Water Resistant | | |

## RESIDENTIAL
## COST ESTIMATE

OWNER'S NAME: _____  APPRAISER: _____

RESIDENCE ADDRESS: _____  PROJECT: _____

CITY, STATE, ZIP CODE: _____  DATE: _____

| CLASS OF CONSTRUCTION | RESIDENCE TYPE | CONFIGURATION | EXTERIOR WALL SYSTEM |
|---|---|---|---|
| ☐ ECONOMY | ☐ 1 STORY | ☐ DETACHED | ☐ WOOD SIDING—WOOD FRAME |
| ☐ AVERAGE | ☐ 1-1/2 STORY | ☐ TOWN/ROW HOUSE | ☐ BRICK VENEER—WOOD FRAME |
| ☐ CUSTOM | ☐ 2 STORY | ☐ SEMI-DETACHED | ☐ STUCCO ON WOOD FRAME |
| ☐ LUXURY | ☐ 2-1/2 STORY | | ☐ PAINTED CONCRETE BLOCK |
| | ☐ 3 STORY | OCCUPANCY | ☐ SOLID MASONRY (AVERAGE & CUSTOM) |
| | ☐ BI-LEVEL | ☐ ONE STORY | ☐ STONE VENEER—WOOD FRAME |
| | ☐ TRI-LEVEL | ☐ TWO FAMILY | ☐ SOLID BRICK (LUXURY) |
| | | ☐ THREE FAMILY | ☐ SOLID STONE (LUXURY) |
| | | ☐ OTHER _____ | |

| *LIVING AREA (Main Building) | *LIVING AREA (Wing or Ell) (     ) | *LIVING AREA (Wing or Ell) (     ) |
|---|---|---|
| First Level _____ S.F. | First Level _____ S.F. | First Level _____ S.F. |
| Second Level _____ S.F. | Second Level _____ S.F. | Second Level _____ S.F. |
| Third Level _____ S.F. | Third Level _____ S.F. | Third Level _____ S.F. |
| Total _____ S.F. | Total _____ S.F. | Total _____ S.F. |

*Basement Area is not part of living area.

| MAIN BUILDING | COSTS PER S.F. LIVING AREA |
|---|---|
| Cost per Square Foot of Living Area, from Page _____ | $ |
| Basement Addition: _____ % Finished, _____ % Unfinished | + |
| Roof Cover Adjustment: _____ Type, Page _____ (Add or Deduct) | (     ) |
| Central Air Conditioning: ☐ Separate Ducts ☐ Heating Ducts, Page _____ | + |
| Heating System Adjustment: _____ Type, Page _____ (Add or Deduct) | (     ) |
| Main Building: Adjusted Cost per S.F. of Living Area | $ |

| MAIN BUILDING TOTAL COST | $ _____ /S.F. Cost per S.F. Living Area | x | _____ S.F. Living Area | x | _____ Town/Row House Multiplier (Use 1 for Detached) | = | $ _____ TOTAL COST |

| WING OR ELL (     ) _____ STORY | COSTS PER S.F. LIVING AREA |
|---|---|
| Cost per Square Foot of Living Area, from Page _____ | $ |
| Basement Addition: _____ % Finished, _____ % Unfinished | + |
| Roof Cover Adjustment: _____ Type, Page _____ (Add or Deduct) | (     ) |
| Central Air Conditioning: ☐ Separate Ducts ☐ Heating Ducts, Page _____ | + |
| Heating System Adjustment: _____ Type, Page _____ (Add or Deduct) | (     ) |
| Wing or Ell (     ): Adjusted Cost per S.F. of Living Area | $ |

| WING OR ELL (     ) TOTAL COST | $ _____ /S.F. Cost per S.F. Living Area | x | _____ S.F. Living Area | = | $ _____ TOTAL COST |

| WING OR ELL (     ) _____ STORY | COSTS PER S.F. LIVING AREA |
|---|---|
| Cost per Square Foot of Living Area, from Page _____ | $ |
| Basement Addition: _____ % Finished, _____ % Unfinished | + |
| Roof Cover Adjustment: _____ Type, Page _____ (Add or Deduct) | (     ) |
| Central Air Conditioning: ☐ Separate Ducts ☐ Heating Ducts, Page _____ | + |
| Heating System Adjustment: _____ Type, Page _____ (Add or Deduct) | (     ) |
| Wing or Ell (     ): Adjusted Cost per S.F. of Living Area | $ |

| WING OR ELL (     ) TOTAL COST | $ _____ /S.F. Cost per S.F. Living Area | x | _____ S.F. Living Area | = | $ _____ TOTAL COST |

TOTAL THIS PAGE [ _____ ]

Page 1 of 2

683

## RESIDENTIAL
## COST ESTIMATE

| Total Page 1 | | | $ |
|---|---|---|---|
| | QUANTITY | UNIT COST | |
| Additional Bathrooms: _____ Full, _____ Half | | | |
| Finished Attic: _____ Ft. x _____ Ft. | S.F. | | + |
| Breezeway: ☐ Open ☐ Enclosed _____ Ft. x _____ Ft. | S.F. | | + |
| Covered Porch: ☐ Open ☐ Enclosed _____ Ft. x _____ Ft. | S.F. | | + |
| Fireplace: ☐ Interior Chimney ☐ Exterior Chimney     ☐ No. of Flues ☐ Additional Fireplaces | | | + |
| Appliances: | | | + |
| Kitchen Cabinets Adjustment:     (+/−) | | | |
| ☐ Garage ☐ Carport: _____ Car(s) Description _____ (+/−) | | | |
| Miscellaneous: | | | + |

ADJUSTED TOTAL BUILDING COST     $ _____

| REPLACEMENT COST |
|---|
| ADJUSTED TOTAL BUILDING COST     $ _____ |
| Site Improvements |
|     (A) Paving & Sidewalks     $ _____ |
|     (B) Landscaping     $ _____ |
|     (C) Fences     $ _____ |
|     (D) Swimming Pool     $ _____ |
|     (E) Miscellaneous     $ _____ |
| TOTAL     $ _____ |
| Location Factor     x _____ |
| Location Replacement Cost     $ _____ |
| Depreciation     −$ _____ |
| LOCAL DEPRECIATED COST     $ _____ |

| INSURANCE COST |
|---|
| ADJUSTED TOTAL BUILDING COST     $ _____ |
| Insurance Exclusions |
|     (A) Footings, Site Work, Underground Piping     −$ _____ |
|     (B) Architects' Fees     −$ _____ |
| Total Building Cost Less Exclusion     $ _____ |
| Location Factor     x _____ |
| LOCAL INSURABLE REPLACEMENT COST     $ _____ |

**SKETCH AND ADDITIONAL CALCULATIONS**

# Index

# Index

# Index

# Index

# Index

699

# Division Notes

| | CREW | DAILY OUTPUT | LABOR-HOURS | UNIT | 2010 BARE COSTS | | | | TOTAL INCL O&P |
|---|---|---|---|---|---|---|---|---|---|
| | | | | | MAT. | LABOR | EQUIP. | TOTAL | |
| | | | | | | | | | |
| | | | | | | | | | |
| | | | | | | | | | |
| | | | | | | | | | |
| | | | | | | | | | |
| | | | | | | | | | |
| | | | | | | | | | |
| | | | | | | | | | |
| | | | | | | | | | |
| | | | | | | | | | |
| | | | | | | | | | |
| | | | | | | | | | |
| | | | | | | | | | |
| | | | | | | | | | |
| | | | | | | | | | |
| | | | | | | | | | |
| | | | | | | | | | |
| | | | | | | | | | |
| | | | | | | | | | |
| | | | | | | | | | |
| | | | | | | | | | |
| | | | | | | | | | |

# Division Notes

| | CREW | DAILY OUTPUT | LABOR-HOURS | UNIT | 2010 BARE COSTS | | | | TOTAL INCL O&P |
|---|---|---|---|---|---|---|---|---|---|
| | | | | | MAT. | LABOR | EQUIP. | TOTAL | |
| | | | | | | | | | |
| | | | | | | | | | |
| | | | | | | | | | |
| | | | | | | | | | |
| | | | | | | | | | |
| | | | | | | | | | |
| | | | | | | | | | |
| | | | | | | | | | |
| | | | | | | | | | |
| | | | | | | | | | |
| | | | | | | | | | |
| | | | | | | | | | |
| | | | | | | | | | |
| | | | | | | | | | |
| | | | | | | | | | |
| | | | | | | | | | |
| | | | | | | | | | |
| | | | | | | | | | |
| | | | | | | | | | |
| | | | | | | | | | |
| | | | | | | | | | |
| | | | | | | | | | |
| | | | | | | | | | |

# Division Notes

| | CREW | DAILY OUTPUT | LABOR-HOURS | UNIT | 2010 BARE COSTS | | | | TOTAL INCL O&P |
|---|---|---|---|---|---|---|---|---|---|
| | | | | | MAT. | LABOR | EQUIP. | TOTAL | |
| | | | | | | | | | |
| | | | | | | | | | |
| | | | | | | | | | |
| | | | | | | | | | |
| | | | | | | | | | |
| | | | | | | | | | |
| | | | | | | | | | |
| | | | | | | | | | |
| | | | | | | | | | |
| | | | | | | | | | |
| | | | | | | | | | |
| | | | | | | | | | |
| | | | | | | | | | |
| | | | | | | | | | |
| | | | | | | | | | |
| | | | | | | | | | |
| | | | | | | | | | |
| | | | | | | | | | |
| | | | | | | | | | |
| | | | | | | | | | |
| | | | | | | | | | |
| | | | | | | | | | |

# Division Notes

| | CREW | DAILY OUTPUT | LABOR-HOURS | UNIT | 2010 BARE COSTS | | | | TOTAL INCL O&P |
|---|---|---|---|---|---|---|---|---|---|
| | | | | | MAT. | LABOR | EQUIP. | TOTAL | |
| | | | | | | | | | |
| | | | | | | | | | |
| | | | | | | | | | |
| | | | | | | | | | |
| | | | | | | | | | |
| | | | | | | | | | |
| | | | | | | | | | |
| | | | | | | | | | |
| | | | | | | | | | |
| | | | | | | | | | |
| | | | | | | | | | |
| | | | | | | | | | |
| | | | | | | | | | |
| | | | | | | | | | |
| | | | | | | | | | |
| | | | | | | | | | |
| | | | | | | | | | |
| | | | | | | | | | |
| | | | | | | | | | |
| | | | | | | | | | |
| | | | | | | | | | |
| | | | | | | | | | |

# Division Notes

| | CREW | DAILY OUTPUT | LABOR-HOURS | UNIT | 2010 BARE COSTS | | | | TOTAL INCL O&P |
|---|---|---|---|---|---|---|---|---|---|
| | | | | | MAT. | LABOR | EQUIP. | TOTAL | |
| | | | | | | | | | |
| | | | | | | | | | |
| | | | | | | | | | |
| | | | | | | | | | |
| | | | | | | | | | |
| | | | | | | | | | |
| | | | | | | | | | |
| | | | | | | | | | |
| | | | | | | | | | |
| | | | | | | | | | |
| | | | | | | | | | |
| | | | | | | | | | |
| | | | | | | | | | |
| | | | | | | | | | |
| | | | | | | | | | |
| | | | | | | | | | |
| | | | | | | | | | |
| | | | | | | | | | |
| | | | | | | | | | |
| | | | | | | | | | |
| | | | | | | | | | |
| | | | | | | | | | |

# Reed Construction Data/RSMeans— a tradition of excellence in construction cost information and services since 1942

**For more information visit the RSMeans website at www.rsmeans.com**

## Book Selection Guide

The following table provides definitive information on the content of each cost data publication. The number of lines of data provided in each unit price or assemblies division, as well as the number of reference tables and crews, is listed for each book. The presence of other elements such as equipment rental costs, historical cost indexes, city cost indexes, square foot models, or cross-referenced indexes is also indicated. You can use the table to help select the RSMeans book that has the quantity and type of information you most need in your work.

| Unit Cost Divisions | Building Construction Costs | Mechanical | Electrical | Repair & Remodel | Square Foot | Site Work Landsc. | Assemblies | Interior | Concrete Masonry | Open Shop | Heavy Construction | Light Commercial | Facilities Construction | Plumbing | Residential |
|---|---|---|---|---|---|---|---|---|---|---|---|---|---|---|---|
| 1 | 553 | 372 | 385 | 474 | | 489 | | 301 | 437 | 552 | 483 | 220 | 967 | 386 | 157 |
| 2 | 737 | 264 | 85 | 676 | | 964 | | 358 | 215 | 734 | 706 | 434 | 1154 | 288 | 242 |
| 3 | 1506 | 213 | 201 | 850 | | 1357 | | 277 | 1837 | 1506 | 1497 | 347 | 1422 | 182 | 359 |
| 4 | 897 | 24 | 0 | 697 | | 699 | | 572 | 1105 | 873 | 592 | 489 | 1145 | 0 | 405 |
| 5 | 1851 | 201 | 156 | 958 | | 795 | | 1021 | 758 | 1838 | 1050 | 826 | 1841 | 276 | 722 |
| 6 | 1841 | 67 | 69 | 1429 | | 449 | | 1160 | 299 | 1820 | 384 | 1530 | 1453 | 22 | 2043 |
| 7 | 1438 | 209 | 125 | 1462 | | 524 | | 546 | 466 | 1436 | 0 | 1143 | 1500 | 218 | 905 |
| 8 | 2048 | 61 | 10 | 2118 | | 294 | | 1737 | 694 | 1974 | 0 | 1527 | 2320 | 0 | 1397 |
| 9 | 1783 | 72 | 26 | 1598 | | 268 | | 1875 | 367 | 1737 | 15 | 1511 | 2027 | 54 | 1331 |
| 10 | 986 | 17 | 10 | 597 | | 224 | | 800 | 157 | 986 | 29 | 481 | 1072 | 231 | 214 |
| 11 | 1020 | 214 | 163 | 487 | | 126 | | 865 | 30 | 1005 | 0 | 231 | 1034 | 173 | 110 |
| 12 | 547 | 0 | 2 | 303 | | 248 | | 1691 | 12 | 536 | 19 | 349 | 1736 | 23 | 317 |
| 13 | 733 | 119 | 111 | 247 | | 344 | | 255 | 69 | 732 | 256 | 80 | 743 | 74 | 79 |
| 14 | 280 | 36 | 0 | 229 | | 28 | | 259 | 0 | 279 | 0 | 12 | 299 | 21 | 6 |
| 21 | 78 | 0 | 16 | 30 | | 0 | | 250 | 0 | 78 | 0 | 60 | 368 | 373 | 0 |
| 22 | 1148 | 7031 | 155 | 1106 | | 1466 | | 622 | 20 | 1103 | 1648 | 823 | 6940 | 8763 | 634 |
| 23 | 1185 | 7032 | 609 | 774 | | 158 | | 679 | 38 | 1105 | 110 | 660 | 5089 | 1869 | 418 |
| 26 | 1246 | 493 | 9875 | 1003 | | 739 | | 1053 | 55 | 1234 | 523 | 1080 | 9811 | 438 | 559 |
| 27 | 67 | 0 | 210 | 34 | | 9 | | 59 | 0 | 67 | 35 | 48 | 212 | 0 | 4 |
| 28 | 86 | 58 | 107 | 61 | | 0 | | 68 | 0 | 71 | 0 | 40 | 122 | 44 | 25 |
| 31 | 1477 | 735 | 608 | 798 | | 2793 | | 7 | 1208 | 1421 | 2865 | 600 | 1538 | 660 | 606 |
| 32 | 811 | 114 | 0 | 675 | | 3967 | | 359 | 274 | 784 | 1481 | 373 | 1443 | 226 | 422 |
| 33 | 519 | 1025 | 465 | 201 | | 1967 | | 0 | 225 | 518 | 1890 | 117 | 1553 | 1196 | 115 |
| 34 | 109 | 0 | 20 | 4 | | 144 | | 0 | 31 | 64 | 122 | 0 | 129 | 115 | 0 |
| 35 | 18 | 0 | 0 | 0 | | 166 | | 0 | 0 | 18 | 281 | 0 | 83 | 0 | 0 |
| 41 | 52 | 0 | 0 | 24 | | 7 | | 22 | 0 | 52 | 30 | 0 | 59 | 14 | 0 |
| 44 | 98 | 90 | 0 | 0 | | 32 | | 0 | 0 | 23 | 32 | 0 | 98 | 105 | 0 |
| **Totals** | 23114 | 18447 | 13408 | 16835 | | 18257. | | 14836 | 8297 | 22546 | 14048 | 12981 | 46158 | 15636 | 11070 |

| Assembly Divisions | Building Construction Costs | Mechanical | Electrical | Repair & Remodel | Square Foot | Site Work Landscape | Assemblies | Interior | Concrete Masonry | Open Shop | Heavy Construction | Light Commercial | Facilities Construction | Plumbing | Asm Div | Residential |
|---|---|---|---|---|---|---|---|---|---|---|---|---|---|---|---|---|
| A | | 15 | 0 | 182 | 150 | 530 | 598 | 0 | 536 | | 570 | 154 | 24 | 0 | 1 | 374 |
| B | | 0 | 0 | 809 | 2471 | 0 | 5577 | 329 | 1914 | | 368 | 2031 | 143 | 0 | 2 | 217 |
| C | | 0 | 0 | 635 | 865 | 0 | 1235 | 1567 | 146 | | 0 | 765 | 247 | 0 | 3 | 588 |
| D | | 1066 | 811 | 694 | 1793 | 0 | 2422 | 767 | 0 | | 0 | 1271 | 1025 | 1078 | 4 | 861 |
| E | | 0 | 0 | 85 | 260 | 0 | 297 | 5 | 0 | | 0 | 257 | 5 | 0 | 5 | 392 |
| F | | 0 | 0 | 0 | 123 | 0 | 124 | 0 | 0 | | 0 | 123 | 3 | 0 | 6 | 358 |
| G | | 527 | 294 | 311 | 202 | 2366 | 668 | 0 | 535 | | 1194 | 200 | 293 | 685 | 7 | 300 |
| | | | | | | | | | | | | | | | 8 | 760 |
| | | | | | | | | | | | | | | | 9 | 80 |
| | | | | | | | | | | | | | | | 10 | 0 |
| | | | | | | | | | | | | | | | 11 | 0 |
| | | | | | | | | | | | | | | | 12 | 0 |
| **Totals** | | 1608 | 1105 | 2716 | 5864 | 2896 | 10921 | 2668 | 3131 | | 2132 | 4801 | 1740 | 1763 | | 3932 |

| Reference Section | Building Construction Costs | Mechanical | Electrical | Repair & Remodel | Square Foot | Site Work Landscape | Assemblies | Interior | Concrete Masonry | Open Shop | Heavy Construction | Light Commercial | Facilities Construction | Plumbing | Residential |
|---|---|---|---|---|---|---|---|---|---|---|---|---|---|---|---|
| Reference Tables | yes | yes | yes | yes | no | yes | yes | yes | yes | yes | yes | yes | yes | yes | yes |
| Models | | | | | 107 | | | | | | | 46 | | | 28 |
| Crews | 487 | 487 | 487 | 467 | | 487 | | 487 | 487 | 465 | 487 | 465 | 467 | 487 | 465 |
| Equipment Rental Costs | yes | yes | yes | yes | | yes | | yes | yes | yes | yes | yes | yes | yes | yes |
| Historical Cost Indexes | yes | yes | yes | yes | yes | yes | yes | yes | yes | yes | yes | yes | yes | yes | no |
| City Cost Indexes | yes | yes | yes | yes | yes | yes | yes | yes | yes | yes | yes | yes | yes | yes | yes |

# Annual Cost Guides

For more information
visit the RSMeans website
at www.rsmeans.com

## RSMeans Building Construction Cost Data 2010

Offers you unchallenged unit price reliability in an easy-to-use format. Whether used for verifying complete, finished estimates or for periodic checks, it supplies more cost facts better and faster than any comparable source. Over 1,000 unit prices have been updated for 2010. The City Cost Indexes and Location Factors cover over 930 areas, for indexing to any project location in North America. Order and get *RSMeans Quarterly Update Service* FREE. You'll have year-long access to the RSMeans estimating **HOTLINE** FREE with your subscription. Expert assistance when using RSMeans data is just a phone call away.

$169.95 per copy
Available Sept. 2009
Catalog no. 60010

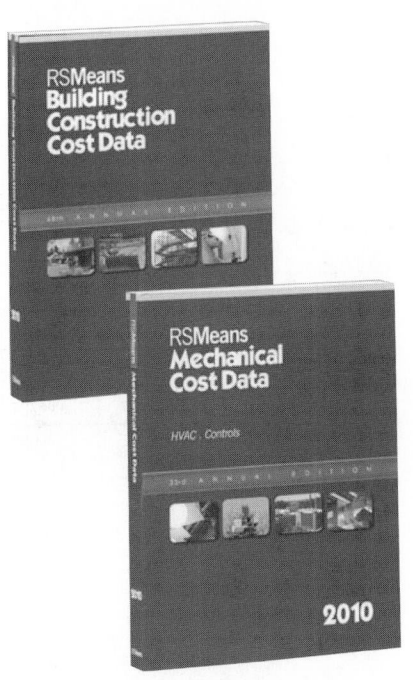

**Unit prices organized according to the latest MasterFormat!**

## RSMeans Mechanical Cost Data 2010

- **HVAC**
- **Controls**

Total unit and systems price guidance for mechanical construction. . . materials, parts, fittings, and complete labor cost information. Includes prices for piping, heating, air conditioning, ventilation, and all related construction.

Plus new 2010 unit costs for:

- Thousands of installed HVAC/controls assemblies components
- "On-site" Location Factors for over 930 cities and towns in the U.S. and Canada
- Crews, labor, and equipment

$169.95 per copy
Available Oct. 2009
Catalog no. 60020

## RSMeans Plumbing Cost Data 2010

Comprehensive unit prices and assemblies for plumbing, irrigation systems, commercial and residential fire protection, point-of-use water heaters, and the latest approved materials. This publication and its companion, *RSMeans Mechanical Cost Data*, provide full-range cost estimating coverage for all the mechanical trades.

Now contains updated costs for potable water and radiant heat systems and high efficiency fixtures.

$169.95 per copy
Available Oct. 2009
Catalog no. 60210

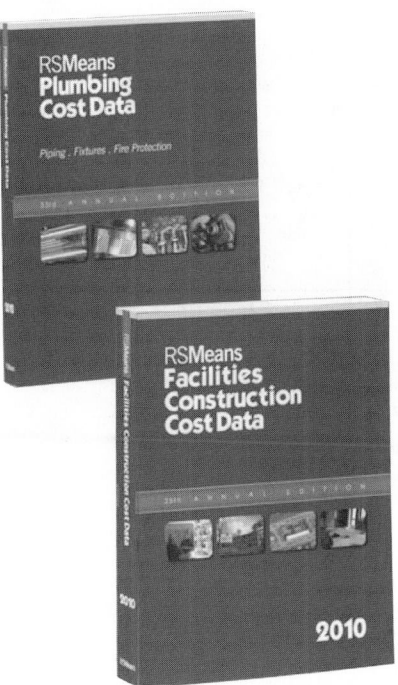

**Unit prices organized according to the latest MasterFormat!**

## RSMeans Facilities Construction Cost Data 2010

For the maintenance and construction of commercial, industrial, municipal, and institutional properties. Costs are shown for new and remodeling construction and are broken down into materials, labor, equipment, and overhead and profit. Special emphasis is given to sections on mechanical, electrical, furnishings, site work, building maintenance, finish work, and demolition.

More than 43,000 unit costs, plus assemblies costs and a comprehensive Reference Section are included.

$419.95 per copy
Available Nov. 2009
Catalog no. 60200

For more information
visit the RSMeans website
at www.rsmeans.com

# Annual Cost Guides

## RSMeans Square Foot Costs 2010

*It's Accurate and Easy To Use!*

- **Updated price information** based on nationwide figures from suppliers, estimators, labor experts, and contractors

- "How-to-Use" sections, with **clear examples** of commercial, residential, industrial, and institutional structures

- Realistic graphics, offering true-to-life illustrations of building projects

- Extensive information on using square foot cost data, including sample estimates and alternate pricing methods

$184.95 per copy
Available Oct. 2009
Catalog no. 60050

## RSMeans Repair & Remodeling Cost Data 2010

### Commercial/Residential

Use this valuable tool to estimate commercial and residential renovation and remodeling.

**Includes: New costs for hundreds of unique methods, materials, and conditions that only come up in repair and remodeling, PLUS:**

- Unit costs for over 15,000 construction components
- Installed costs for over 90 assemblies
- Over 930 "on-site" localization factors for the U.S. and Canada.

**Unit prices organized according to the latest MasterFormat!**

$144.95 per copy
Available Oct. 2009
Catalog no. 60040

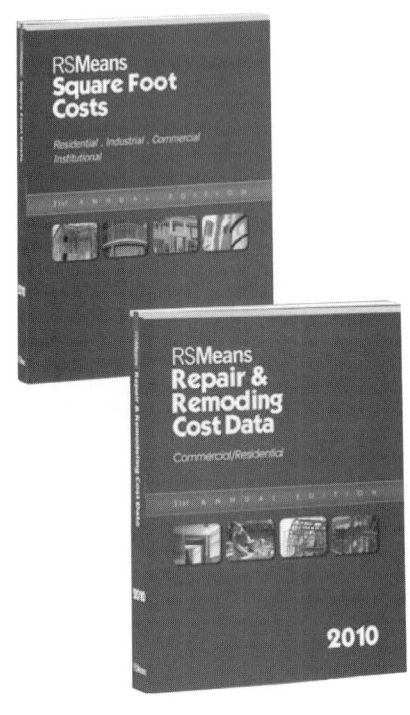

## RSMeans Electrical Cost Data 2010

Pricing information for every part of electrical cost planning. More than 13,000 unit and systems costs with design tables; clear specifications and drawings; engineering guides; illustrated estimating procedures; complete labor-hour and materials costs for better scheduling and procurement; and the latest electrical products and construction methods.

- A variety of special electrical systems including cathodic protection

- Costs for maintenance, demolition, HVAC/mechanical, specialties, equipment, and more

$169.95 per copy
Available Oct. 2009
Catalog no. 60030

## RSMeans Electrical Change Order Cost Data 2010

*RSMeans Electrical Change Order Cost Data* provides you with electrical unit prices exclusively for pricing change orders—based on the recent, direct experience of contractors and suppliers. Analyze and check your own change order estimates against the experience others have had doing the same work. It also covers productivity analysis and change order cost justifications. With useful information for calculating the effects of change orders and dealing with their administration.

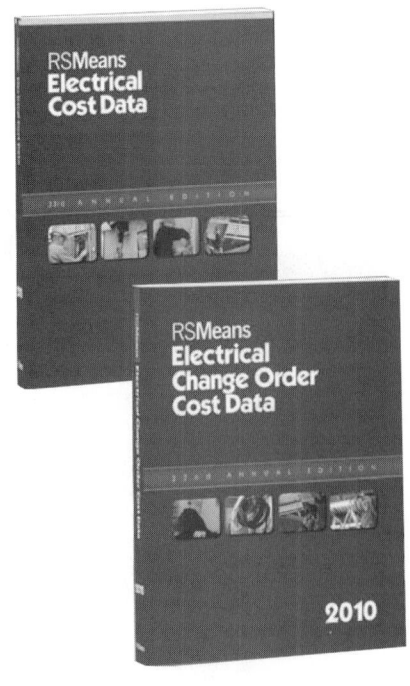

**Unit prices organized according to the latest MasterFormat!**

$169.95 per copy
Available Dec. 2009
Catalog no. 60230

## RSMeans Assemblies Cost Data 2010

*RSMeans Assemblies Cost Data* takes the guesswork out of preliminary or conceptual estimates. Now you don't have to try to calculate the assembled cost by working up individual component costs. We've done all the work for you.

Presents detailed illustrations, descriptions, specifications, and costs for every conceivable building assembly—240 types in all—arranged in the easy-to-use UNIFORMAT II system. Each illustrated "assembled" cost includes a complete grouping of materials and associated installation costs, including the installing contractor's overhead and profit.

$279.95 per copy
Available Sept. 2009
Catalog no. 60060

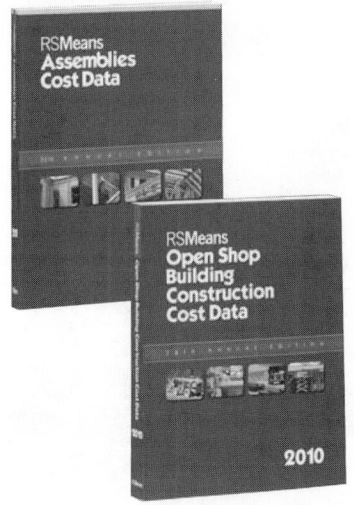

## RSMeans Open Shop Building Construction Cost Data 2010

The latest costs for accurate budgeting and estimating of new commercial and residential construction. . . renovation work. . . change orders. . . cost engineering.

*RSMeans Open Shop "BCCD"* will assist you to:
• Develop benchmark prices for change orders
• Plug gaps in preliminary estimates and budgets
• Estimate complex projects
• Substantiate invoices on contracts
• Price ADA-related renovations

**Unit prices organized according to the latest MasterFormat!**

$169.95 per copy
Available Dec. 2009
Catalog no. 60150

## RSMeans Residential Cost Data 2010

Contains square foot costs for 30 basic home models with the look of today, plus hundreds of custom additions and modifications you can quote right off the page. With costs for the 100 residential systems you're most likely to use in the year ahead. Complete with blank estimating forms, sample estimates, and step-by-step instructions.

Now contains line items for cultured stone and brick, PVC trim lumber, and TPO roofing.

$144.95 per copy
Available Oct. 2009
Catalog no. 60170

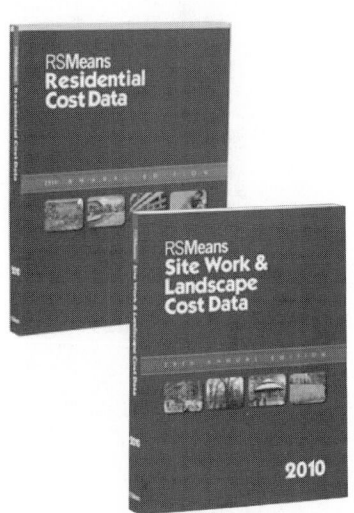

**Unit prices organized according to the latest MasterFormat!**

## RSMeans Site Work & Landscape Cost Data 2010

Includes unit and assemblies costs for earthwork, sewerage, piped utilities, site improvements, drainage, paving, trees & shrubs, street openings/repairs, underground tanks, and more. Contains 57 tables of assemblies costs for accurate conceptual estimates.

Includes:
• Estimating for infrastructure improvements
• Environmentally-oriented construction
• ADA-mandated handicapped access
• Hazardous waste line items

$169.95 per copy
Available Nov. 2009
Catalog no. 60280

## RSMeans Facilities Maintenance & Repair Cost Data 2010

*RSMeans Facilities Maintenance & Repair Cost Data* gives you a complete system to manage and plan your facility repair and maintenance costs and budget efficiently. Guidelines for auditing a facility and developing an annual maintenance plan. Budgeting is included, along with reference tables on cost and management, and information on frequency and productivity of maintenance operations.

The only nationally recognized source of maintenance and repair costs. Developed in cooperation with the Civil Engineering Research Laboratory (CERL) of the Army Corps of Engineers.

$379.95 per copy
Available Nov. 2009
Catalog no. 60300

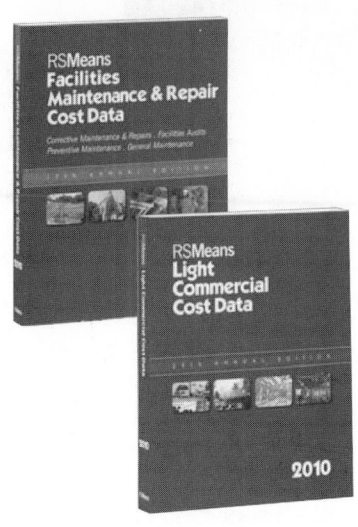

## RSMeans Light Commercial Cost Data 2010

Specifically addresses the light commercial market, which is a specialized niche in the construction industry. Aids you, the owner/designer/contractor, in preparing all types of estimates—from budgets to detailed bids. Includes new advances in methods and materials.

Assemblies Section allows you to evaluate alternatives in the early stages of design/planning.

Over 11,000 unit costs ensure that you have the prices you need. . . when you need them.

**Unit prices organized according to the latest MasterFormat !**

$144.95 per copy
Available Nov. 2009
Catalog no. 60180

For more information
visit the RSMeans website
at www.rsmeans.com

# Annual Cost Guides

## RSMeans Concrete & Masonry Cost Data 2010

Provides you with cost facts for virtually all concrete/masonry estimating needs, from complicated formwork to various sizes and face finishes of brick and block—all in great detail. The comprehensive Unit Price Section contains more than 7,500 selected entries. Also contains an Assemblies [Cost] Section, and a detailed Reference Section that supplements the cost data.

**Unit prices organized according to the latest MasterFormat !**

$154.95 per copy
Available Dec. 2009
Catalog no. 60110

## RSMeans Labor Rates for the Construction Industry 2010

Complete information for estimating labor costs, making comparisons, and negotiating wage rates by trade for over 300 U.S. and Canadian cities. With 46 construction trades listed by local union number in each city, and historical wage rates included for comparison. Each city chart lists the county and is alphabetically arranged with handy visual flip tabs for quick reference.

$379.95 per copy
Available Dec. 2009
Catalog no. 60120

## RSMeans Construction Cost Indexes 2010

What materials and labor costs will change unexpectedly this year? By how much?
• Breakdowns for 316 major cities
• National averages for 30 key cities
• Expanded five major city indexes
• Historical construction cost indexes

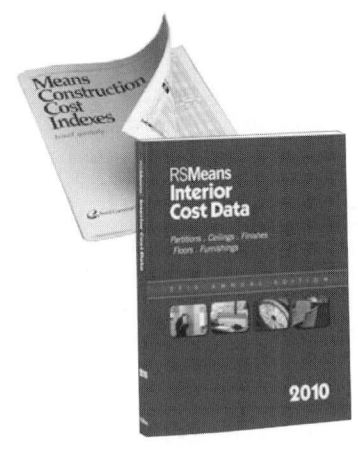

$362.00 per year (subscription)
Catalog no. 50140

$90.50 individual quarters
Catalog no. 60140 A,B,C,D

## RSMeans Interior Cost Data 2010

Provides you with prices and guidance needed to make accurate interior work estimates. Contains costs on materials, equipment, hardware, custom installations, furnishings, and labor costs. . . for new and remodel commercial and industrial interior construction, including updated information on office furnishings, and reference information.

**Unit prices organized according to the latest MasterFormat !**

$169.95 per copy
Available Nov. 2009
Catalog no. 60090

## RSMeans Heavy Construction Cost Data 2010

A comprehensive guide to heavy construction costs. Includes costs for highly specialized projects such as tunnels, dams, highways, airports, and waterways. Information on labor rates, equipment, and materials costs is included. Features unit price costs, systems costs, and numerous reference tables for costs and design.

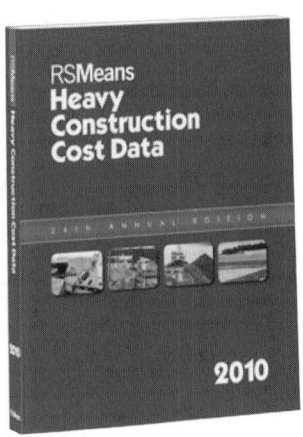

$169.95 per copy
Available Nov. 2009
Catalog no. 60160

**Unit prices organized according to the latest MasterFormat!**

# Reference Books

For more information
visit the RSMeans website
at www.rsmeans.com

## Value Engineering: Practical Applications

*...Design, Construction, Maintenance & Operations*

**by Alphonse Dell'Isola, PE**

...tool for immediate application—for engineers, ...hitects, facility managers, owners, and contractors. ...cludes making the case for VE—the management ...efing; integrating VE into planning, budgeting, ...d design; conducting life cycle costing; using VE ...ethodology in design review and consultant selection; ...se studies; VE workbook; and a life cycle costing ...ogram on disk.

...9.95 per copy
...er 450 pages, illustrated, softcover
...talog no. 67319A

## Facilities Operations & Engineering Reference

**by the Association for Facilities Engineering and RSMeans**

An all-in-one technical reference for planning and managing facility projects and solving day-to-day operations problems. Selected as the official certified plant engineer reference, this handbook covers financial analysis, maintenance, HVAC and energy efficiency, and more.

$54.98 per copy
Over 700 pages, illustrated, hardcover
Catalog no. 67318

## The Building Professional's Guide to Contract Documents

**...rd Edition**

**by Waller S. Poage, AIA, CSI, CVS**

...comprehensive reference for owners, design ...ofessionals, contractors, and students

Structure your documents for maximum efficiency.
Effectively communicate construction requirements.
Understand the roles and responsibilities of construction professionals.
Improve methods of project delivery.

...4.95 per copy, 400 pages
...iagrams and construction forms, hardcover
...atalog no. 67261A

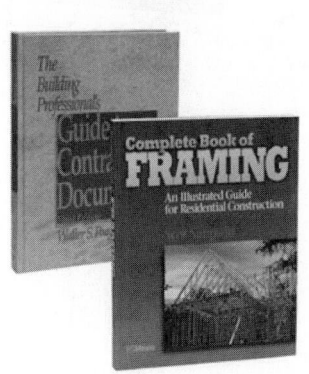

## Complete Book of Framing

**by Scot Simpson**

This straightforward, easy-to-learn method will help framers, carpenters, and handy homeowners build their skills in rough carpentry and framing. Shows how to frame all the parts of a house: floors, walls, roofs, door & window openings, and stairs—with hundreds of color photographs and drawings that show every detail.

The book gives beginners all the basics they need to go from zero framing knowledge to a journeyman level.

$29.95 per copy
352 pages, softcover
Catalog no. 67353

## Cost Planning & Estimating for Facilities Maintenance

...this unique book, a team of facilities management ...thorities shares their expertise on:

Evaluating and budgeting maintenance operations
Maintaining and repairing key building components
Applying *RSMeans Facilities Maintenance & Repair Cost Data* to your estimating

...overs special maintenance requirements of the ten ...ajor building types.

...9.95 per copy
...er 475 pages, hardcover
...talog no. 67314

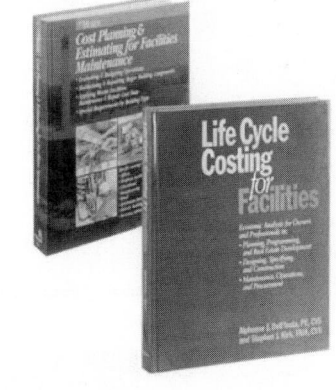

## Life Cycle Costing for Facilities

**by Alphonse Dell'Isola and Dr. Steven Kirk**

Guidance for achieving higher quality design and construction projects at lower costs! Cost-cutting efforts often sacrifice quality to yield the cheapest product. Life cycle costing enables building designers and owners to achieve both. The authors of this book show how LCC can work for a variety of projects — from roads to HVAC upgrades to different types of buildings.

$99.95 per copy
450 pages, hardcover
Catalog no. 67341

## Planning & Managing Interior Projects 2nd Edition

**by Carol E. Farren, CFM**

*...xpert guidance on managing renovation & relocation ...ojects*

...is book guides you through every step in relocating ...a new space or renovating an old one. From initial ...eeting through design and construction, to post-project ...ministration, it helps you get the most for your ...mpany or client. Includes sample forms, spec lists, ...reements, drawings, and much more!

...4.98 per copy
...0 pages, softcover
...talog no. 67245A

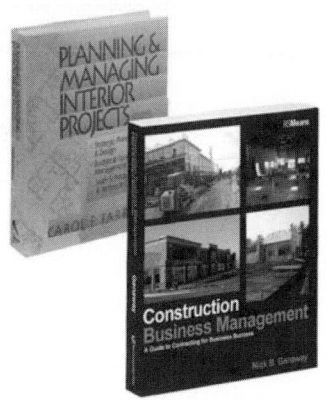

## Construction Business Management

**by Nick Ganaway**

Only 43% of construction firms stay in business after four years. Make sure your company thrives with valuable guidance from a pro with 25 years of success as a commercial contractor. Find out what it takes to build all aspects of a business that is profitable, enjoyable, and enduring. With a bonus chapter on retail construction.

$49.95 per copy
200 pages, softcover
Catalog no. 67352

For more information
visit the RSMeans website
at www.rsmeans.com

# Reference Books

## Interior Home Improvement Costs 9th Edition

Updated estimates for the most popular remodeling and repair projects—from small, do-it-yourself jobs to major renovations and new construction. Includes: kitchens & baths; new living space from your attic, basement, or garage; new floors, paint, and wallpaper; tearing out or building new walls; closets, stairs, and fireplaces; new energy-saving improvements, home theaters, and more!

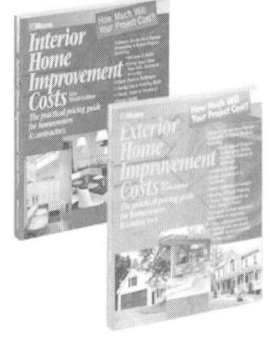

$24.95 per copy
250 pages, illustrated, softcover
Catalog no. 67308E

## Exterior Home Improvement Costs 9th Edition

Updated estimates for the most popular remodeling and repair projects—from small, do-it-yourself jobs, to major renovations and new construction. Includes: curb appeal projects—landscaping, patios, porches, driveways, and walkways; new windows and doors; decks, greenhouses, an sunrooms; room additions and garages; roofing, siding, and painting; "green" improvements to save energy & water.

$24.95 per copy
Over 275 pages, illustrated, softcover
Catalog no. 67309E

## Builder's Essentials: Plan Reading & Material Takeoff

*For Residential and Light Commercial Construction*

### by Wayne J. DelPico

A valuable tool for understanding plans and specs, and accurately calculating material quantities. Step-by-step instructions and takeoff procedures based on a full set of working drawings.

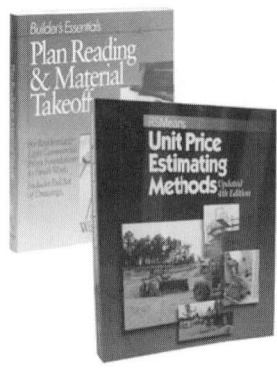

$35.95 per copy
Over 420 pages, softcover
Catalog no. 67307

## Means Unit Price Estimating Methods

### New 4th Edition

This new edition includes up-to-date cost data and estimating examples, updated to reflect changes to the CSI numbering system and new features of RSMeans cost data. It describes the most productive, universally accepted ways to estimate, and uses checklists and forms to illustrate shortcuts and timesavers. A model estimate demonstrates procedures. A new chapter explores computer estimating alternatives.

$59.95 per copy
Over 350 pages, illustrated, softcover
Catalog no. 67303B

## Total Productive Facilities Management

### by Richard W. Sievert, Jr.

Today, facilities are viewed as strategic resources. . . elevating the facility manager to the role of asset manager supporting the organization's overall business goals. Now, Richard Sievert Jr., in this well-articulated guidebook, sets forth a new operational standard for the facility manager's emerging role. . . a comprehensive program for managing facilities as a true profit center.

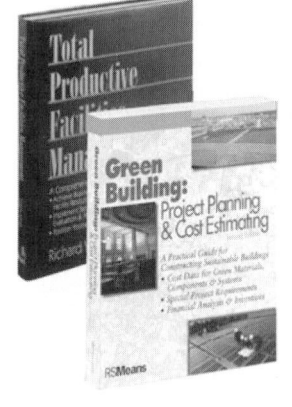

$29.98 per copy
275 pages, softcover
Catalog no. 67321

## Green Building: Project Planning & Cost Estimating 2nd Edition

This new edition has been completely updated with the latest in green building technologies, design concepts, standards, and costs. Now includes a 2010 Green Building *CostWorks* CD with more than 300 green building assemblies and over 5,000 unit price line items for sustainable building. The new edition is also full-color with all new case studies—plus a new chapter on deconstruction, a key aspect of green building.

$129.95 per copy
350 pages, softcover
Catalog no. 67338A

## Concrete Repair and Maintenance Illustrated

### by Peter Emmons

Hundreds of illustrations show users how to analyze, repair, clean, and maintain concrete structures for optimal performance and cost effectiveness. From parking garages to roads and bridges to structural concrete, this comprehensive book describes the causes, effects, and remedies for concrete wear and failure. Invaluable for planning jobs, selecting materials, and training employees, this book is a must-have for concrete specialists, general contractors, facility managers, civil and structural engineers, and architects.

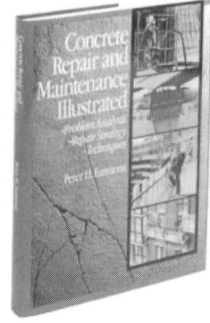

$69.95 per copy
300 pages, illustrated, softcover
Catalog no. 67146

# Reference Books

For more information
visit the RSMeans website
at www.rsmeans.com

## Means Illustrated Construction Dictionary Condensed, 2nd Edition

The best portable dictionary for office or field use—an essential tool for contractors, architects, insurance and real estate personnel, facility managers, homeowners, and anyone who needs quick, clear definitions for construction terms. The second edition has been further enhanced with updates and hundreds of new terms and illustrations . . . keeping with the most recent developments in the construction industry.

Now with a quick-reference Spanish section. Includes tools and equipment, materials, tasks, and more!

$9.95 per copy
Over 500 pages, softcover
Catalog no. 67282A

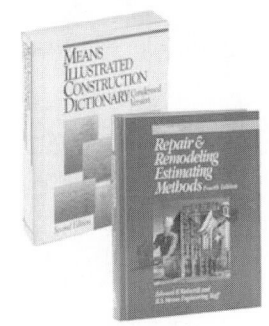

## Means Repair & Remodeling Estimating 4th Edition

### By Edward B. Wetherill and RSMeans

This important reference focuses on the unique problems of estimating renovations of existing structures, and helps you determine the true costs of remodeling through careful evaluation of architectural details and a site visit.

*New section on disaster restoration costs.*

$69.95 per copy
Over 450 pages, illustrated, hardcover
Catalog no. 67265B

## Facilities Planning & Relocation

### by David D. Owen

A complete system for planning space needs and managing relocations. Includes step-by-step manual, over 50 forms, and extensive reference section on materials and furnishings.

*New lower price and user-friendly format.*

$9.98 per copy
Over 450 pages, softcover
Catalog no. 67301

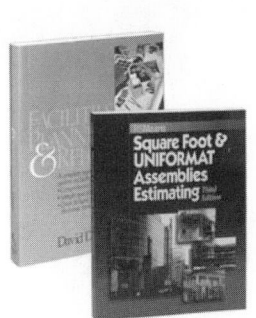

## Means Square Foot & UNIFORMAT Assemblies Estimating Methods 3rd Edition

Develop realistic square foot and assemblies costs for budgeting and construction funding. The new edition features updated guidance on square foot and assemblies estimating using UNIFORMAT II. An essential reference for anyone who performs conceptual estimates.

$69.95 per copy
Over 300 pages, illustrated, softcover
Catalog no. 67145B

## Means Electrical Estimating Methods 3rd Edition

Expanded edition includes sample estimates and cost information in keeping with the latest version of the CSI MasterFormat and UNIFORMAT II. Complete coverage of fiber optic and uninterruptible power supply electrical systems, broken down by components, and explained in detail. Includes a new chapter on computerized estimating methods. A practical companion to *RSMeans Electrical Cost Data.*

$4.95 per copy
Over 325 pages, hardcover
Catalog no. 67230B

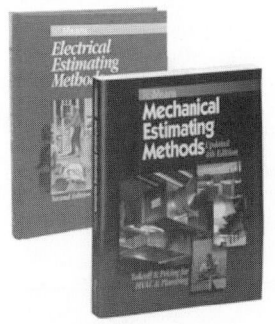

## Means Mechanical Estimating Methods 4th Edition

Completely updated, this guide assists you in making a review of plans, specs, and bid packages, with suggestions for takeoff procedures, listings, substitutions, and pre-bid scheduling for all components of HVAC. Includes suggestions for budgeting labor and equipment usage. Compares materials and construction methods to allow you to select the best option.

$64.95 per copy
Over 350 pages, illustrated, softcover
Catalog no. 67294B

## Means ADA Compliance Pricing Guide 2nd Edition

### by Adaptive Environments and RSMeans

Completely updated and revised to the new 2004 *Americans with Disabilities Act Accessibility Guidelines,* this book features more than 70 of the most commonly needed modifications for ADA compliance. Projects range from installing ramps and walkways, widening doorways and entryways, and installing and refitting elevators, to relocating light switches and signage.

$9.95 per copy
Over 350 pages, illustrated, softcover
Catalog no. 67310A

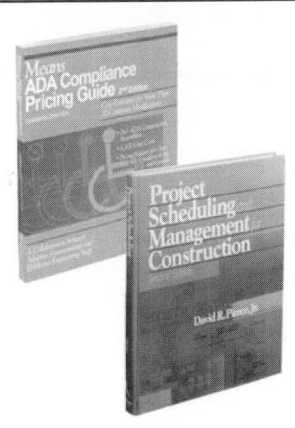

## Project Scheduling & Management for Construction 3rd Edition

### by David R. Pierce, Jr.

A comprehensive yet easy-to-follow guide to construction project scheduling and control—from vital project management principles through the latest scheduling, tracking, and controlling techniques. The author is a leading authority on scheduling, with years of field and teaching experience at leading academic institutions. Spend a few hours with this book and come away with a solid understanding of this essential management topic.

$64.95 per copy
Over 300 pages, illustrated, hardcover
Catalog no. 67247B

For more information
visit the RSMeans website
at www.rsmeans.com

# Reference Books

## The Practice of Cost Segregation Analysis

### by Bruce A. Desrosiers and Wayne J. DelPico

This expert guide walks you through the practice of cost segregation analysis, which enables property owners to defer taxes and benefit from "accelerated cost recovery" through depreciation deductions on assets that are properly identified and classified.

With a glossary of terms, sample cost segregation estimates for various building types, key information resources, and updates via a dedicated website, this book is a critical resource for anyone involved in cost segregation analysis.

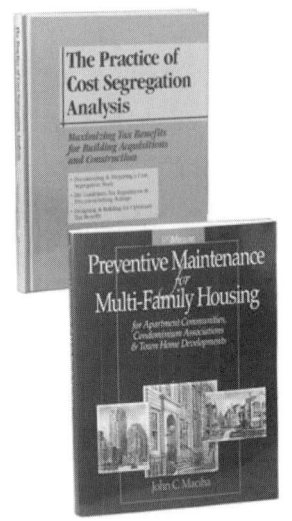

$99.95 per copy
Over 225 pages
Catalog no. 67345

## Preventive Maintenance for Multi-Family Housing

### by John C. Maciha

Prepared by one of the nation's leading experts on multi-family housing.

This complete PM system for apartment and condominium communities features expert guidance, checklists for buildings and grounds maintenance tasks and their frequencies, a reusable wall chart to track maintenance, and a dedicated website featuring customizable electronic forms. A must-have for anyone involved with multi-family housing maintenance and upkeep.

$89.95 per copy
225 pages
Catalog no. 67346

## How to Estimate with Means Data & CostWorks

### New 3rd Edition

### by RSMeans and Saleh A. Mubarak, Ph.D.

New 3rd Edition—fully updated with new chapters, plus new CD with updated *CostWorks* cost data and MasterFormat organization. Includes all major construction items—with more than 300 exercises and two sets of plans that show how to estimate for a broad range of construction items and systems—including general conditions and equipment costs.

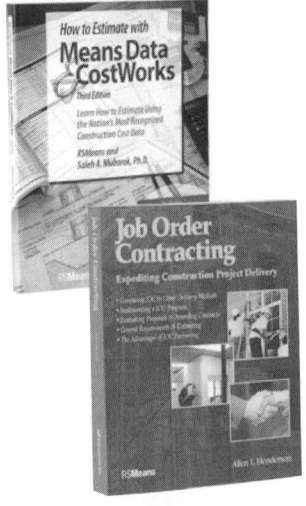

$59.95  per copy
272 pages, softcover
Includes CostWorks CD
Catalog no. 67324B

## Job Order Contracting

### Expediting Construction Project Delivery

### by Allen Henderson

Expert guidance to help you implement JOC—fast becoming the preferred project delivery method for repair and renovation, minor new construction, and maintenance projects in the public sector and in many states and municipalities. The author, a leading JOC expert and practitioner, shows how to:

• Establish a JOC program
• Evaluate proposals and award contracts
• Handle general requirements and estimating
• Partner for maximum benefits

$89.95 per copy
192 pages, illustrated, hardcover
Catalog no. 67348

## Builder's Essentials: Estimating Building Costs

### For the Residential & Light Commercial Contractor

### by Wayne J. DelPico

Step-by-step estimating methods for residential and light commercial contractors. Includes a detailed look at every construction specialty—explaining all the components, takeoff units, and labor needed for well-organized, complete estimates. Covers correctly interpreting plans and specifications, and developing accurate and complete labor and material costs.

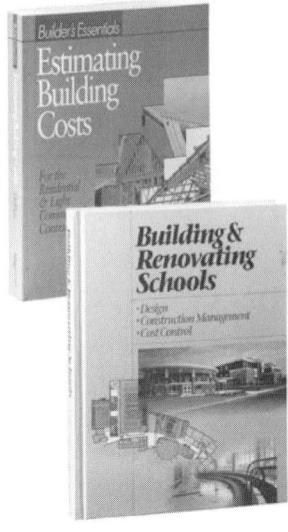

$29.95 per copy
Over 400 pages, illustrated, softcover
Catalog no. 67343

## Building & Renovating Schools

This all-inclusive guide covers every step of the school construction process—from initial planning, needs assessment, and design, right through moving into the new facility. A must-have resource for anyone concerned with new school construction or renovation. With square foot cost models for elementary, middle, and high school facilities, and real-life case studies of recently completed school projects.

The contributors to this book—architects, construction project managers, contractors, and estimators who specialize in school construction—provide start-to-finish, expert guidance on the process.

$69.98 per copy
Over 425 pages, hardcover
Catalog no. 67342

# Reference Books

For more information
visit the RSMeans website
at www.rsmeans.com

## The Homeowner's Guide to Mold By Michael Pugliese

Expert guidance to protect your health and your home.

Mold, whether caused by leaks, humidity or flooding, is a real health and financial issue—for homeowners and contractors. This full-color book explains:
- Construction and maintenance practices to prevent mold
- How to inspect for and remove mold
- Mold remediation procedures and costs
- What to do after a flood
- How to deal with insurance companies

$21.95 per copy
144 pages, softcover
Catalog no. 67344

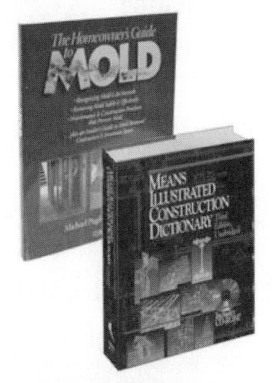

## Means Illustrated Construction Dictionary
### Unabridged 3rd Edition, with CD-ROM

Long regarded as the industry's finest, *Means Illustrated Construction Dictionary* is now even better. With the addition of over 1,000 new terms and hundreds of new illustrations, it is the clear choice for the most comprehensive and current information. The companion CD-ROM that comes with this new edition adds many extra features: larger graphics, expanded definitions, and links to both CSI MasterFormat numbers and product information.

$99.95 per copy
Over 790 pages, illustrated, hardcover
Catalog no. 67292A

## Means Landscape Estimating Methods
### New 5th Edition

Answers questions about preparing competitive landscape construction estimates, with up-to-date cost estimates and the new MasterFormat classification system. Expanded and revised to address the latest materials and methods, including new coverage on approaches to green building. Includes:
- Step-by-step explanation of the estimating process
- Sample forms and worksheets that save time and prevent errors

$64.95 per copy
Over 350 pages, softcover
Catalog no. 67295C

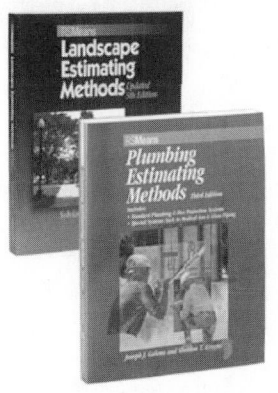

## Means Plumbing Estimating Methods 3rd Edition
### by Joseph Galeno and Sheldon Greene

Updated and revised! This practical guide walks you through a plumbing estimate, from basic materials and installation methods through change order analysis. *Plumbing Estimating Methods* covers residential, commercial, industrial, and medical systems, and features sample takeoff and estimate forms and detailed illustrations of systems and components.

$29.98 per copy
330+ pages, softcover
Catalog no. 67283B

## Understanding & Negotiating Construction Contracts
### by Kit Werremeyer

Take advantage of the author's 30 years' experience in small-to-large (including international) construction projects. Learn how to identify, understand, and evaluate high risk terms and conditions typically found in all construction contracts—then negotiate to lower or eliminate the risk, improve terms of payment, and reduce exposure to claims and disputes. The author avoids "legalese" and gives real-life examples from actual projects.

$59.95 per copy
300 pages, softcover
Catalog no. 67350

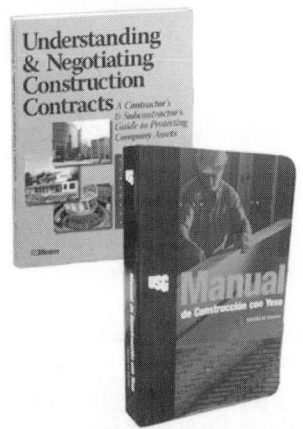

## The Gypsum Construction Handbook (Spanish)

*The Gypsum Construction Handbook*, Spanish edition, is an illustrated, comprehensive, and authoritative guide on all facets of gypsum construction. You'll find comprehensive guidance on available products, installation methods, fire- and sound-rated construction information, illustrated framing-to-finish application instructions, estimating and planning information, and more.

$29.95 per copy
Over 450 pages, softcover
Catalog No. 67357S

## Means Spanish/English Construction Dictionary 2nd Edition
### by RSMeans and the International Code Council

This expanded edition features thousands of the most common words and useful phrases in the construction industry with easy-to-follow pronunciations in both Spanish and English. Over 800 new terms, phrases, and illustrations have been added. It also features a new stand-alone "Safety & Emergencies" section, with colored pages for quick access.

Unique to this dictionary are the systems illustrations showing the relationship of components in the most common building systems for all major trades.

$43.95 per copy
Over 400 pages
Catalog no. 67327A

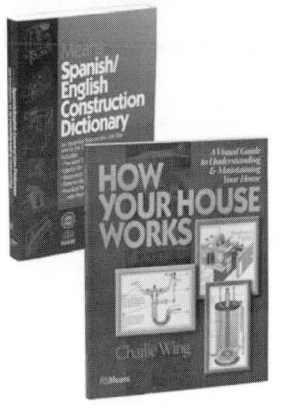

## How Your House Works
### by Charlie Wing

A must-have reference for every homeowner, handyman, and contractor—for repair, remodeling, and new construction. This book uncovers the mysteries behind just about every major appliance and building element in your house—from electrical, heating and AC, to plumbing, framing, foundations and appliances. Clear, "exploded" drawings show exactly how things should be put together and how they function—what to check if they don't work, and what you can do that might save you having to call in a professional.

$21.95 per copy
160 pages, softcover
Catalog no. 67351

719

For more information
visit the RSMeans website
at www.rsmeans.com

# Professional Development

## *Means CostWorks*® CD Training

This one-day course helps users become more
familiar with the functionality of *Means CostWorks*
program. Each menu, icon, screen, and function
found in the program is explained in depth. Time is
devoted to hands-on estimating exercises.

**Some of what you'll learn:**
- Searching the database utilizing all navigation
  methods
- Exporting RSMeans Data to your preferred
  spreadsheet format
- Viewing crews, assembly components, and much
  more!
- Automatically regionalizing the database

You are required to bring your own laptop computer
for this course.

When you register for this course you will receive
an outline for your laptop requirements.

**Also offering web training for CostWorks CD!**

## Unit Price Estimating

This interactive *two-day* seminar teaches attendees
how to interpret project information and process
it into final, detailed estimates with the greatest
accuracy level.

The most important credential an estimator
can take to the job is the ability to visualize
construction, and estimate accurately.

**Some of what you'll learn:**
- Interpreting the design in terms of cost
- The most detailed, time-tested methodology for
  accurate pricing
- Key cost drivers—material, labor, equipment,
  staging, and subcontracts
- Understanding direct and indirect costs for
  accurate job cost accounting and change order
  management

**Who should attend:** Corporate and government
estimators and purchasers, architects, engineers…
and others needing to produce accurate project
estimates.

## Square Foot & Assemblies Estimating

This *two-day* course teaches attendees how to
quickly deliver accurate square foot estimates
using limited budget and design information.

**Some of what you'll learn:**
- How square foot costing gets the estimate
  done faster
- Taking advantage of a "systems" or
  "assemblies" format
- The RSMeans "building assemblies/square
  foot cost approach"
- How to create a reliable preliminary
  systems estimate using bare-bones
  design information

**Who should attend:** Facilities managers, facilities
engineers, estimators, planners, developers,
construction finance professionals… and others
needing to make quick, accurate construction cost
estimates at commercial, government,
educational, and medical facilities.

## Repair & Remodeling Estimating

This *two-day* seminar emphasizes all the
underlying considerations unique to repair/
remodeling estimating and presents the correct
methods for generating accurate, reliable R&R
project costs using the unit price and assemblies
methods.

**Some of what you'll learn:**
- Estimating considerations—like labor-hours,
  building code compliance, working within
  existing structures, purchasing materials in
  smaller quantities, unforeseen deficiencies
- Identifying problems and providing solutions to
  estimating building alterations
- Rules for factoring in minimum labor costs,
  accurate productivity estimates, and allowances
  for project contingencies
- R&R estimating examples calculated using
  unit price and assemblies data

**Who should attend:** Facilities managers, plant
engineers, architects, contractors, estimators,
builders… and others who are concerned with the
proper preparation and/or evaluation of repair and
remodeling estimates.

## Mechanical & Electrical Estimating

This *two-day* course teaches attendees how to
prepare more accurate and complete mechanical/
electrical estimates, avoiding the pitfalls of omission
and double-counting, while understanding the
composition and rationale within the RSMeans
Mechanical/Electrical database.

**Some of what you'll learn:**
- The unique way mechanical and electrical systems
  are interrelated
- M&E estimates–conceptual, planning, budgeting,
  and bidding stages
- Order of magnitude, square foot, assemblies, and
  unit price estimating
- Comparative cost analysis of equipment and
  design alternatives

**Who should attend:** Architects, engineers, facilities
managers, mechanical and electrical contractors…
and others needing a highly reliable method
for developing, understanding, and evaluating
mechanical and electrical contracts.

## Green Building: Planning & Construction

In this *two-day* course, learn about tailoring a
building and its placement on the site to the local
climate, site conditions, culture, and community.
Includes information to reduce resource
consumption and augment resource supply.

**Some of what you'll learn:**
- Green technologies, materials, systems, and
  standards
- Modeling tools and how to use them
- Cost vs. value of green products over their life
  cycle
- Low-cost green strategies, and economic
  incentives and funding
- Health, comfort, and productivity

**Who should attend:** Contractors, project managers,
building owners, building officials, healthcare and
insurance professionals.

## Facilities Maintenance & Repair Estimating

This *two-day* course teaches attendees how to
plan, budget, and estimate the cost of ongoing and
preventive maintenance and repair for existing
buildings and grounds.

**Some of what you'll learn:**
- The most financially favorable maintenance,
  repair, and replacement scheduling and estimating
- Auditing and value engineering facilities
- Preventive planning and facilities upgrading
- Determining both in-house and contract-out
  service costs
- Annual, asset-protecting M&R plan

**Who should attend:** Facility managers,
maintenance supervisors, buildings and grounds
superintendents, plant managers, planners,
estimators… and others involved in facilities
planning and budgeting.

## Practical Project Management for Construction Professionals

In this *two-day* course, acquire the essential
knowledge and develop the skills to effectively and
efficiently execute the day-to-day responsibilities of
the construction project manager.

**Covers:**
- General conditions of the construction contract
- Contract modifications: change orders and
  construction change directives
- Negotiations with subcontractors and vendors
- Effective writing: notification and
  communications
- Dispute resolution: claims and liens

**Who should attend:** Architects, engineers, owner's
representatives, project managers.

## Facilities Construction Estimating

In this *two-day* course, professionals working in
facilities management can get help with their daily
challenges to establish budgets for all phase of a
project

**Some of what you'll learn:**
- Determine the full scope of a project
- Identify the scope of risks & opportunities
- Creative solutions to estimating issues
- Organizing estimates for presentation &
  discussion
- Special techniques for repair/remodel and
  maintenance projects
- Negotiating project change orders

**Who should attend:** Facility managers, engineers,
contractors, facility trades-people, planners &
project managers

# Professional Development

For more information
visit the RSMeans website
at www.rsmeans.com

## Scheduling and Project Management

This *two-day* course teaches attendees the most current and proven scheduling and management techniques needed to bring projects in on time and on budget.

**Some of what you'll learn:**
- Crucial phases of planning and scheduling
- How to establish project priorities and develop realistic schedules and management techniques
- Critical Path and Precedence Methods
- Special emphasis on cost control

**Who should attend:** Construction project managers, supervisors, engineers, estimators, contractors... and others who want to improve their project planning, scheduling, and management skills.

## Assessing Scope of Work for Facility Construction Estimating

This *two-day* practical training program addresses the vital importance of understanding the SCOPE of projects in order to produce accurate cost estimates for facility repair and remodeling.

**Some of what you'll learn:**
- Discussions of site visits, plans/specs, record drawings of facilities, and site-specific lists
- Review of CSI divisions, including means, methods, materials, and the challenges of scoping each topic
- Exercises in SCOPE identification and SCOPE writing for accurate estimating of projects
- Hands-on exercises that require SCOPE, take-off, and pricing

**Who should attend:** Corporate and government estimators, planners, facility managers, and others who need to produce accurate project estimates.

## Site Work & Heavy Construction Estimating

This *two-day* course teaches attendees how to estimate earthwork, site utilities, foundations, and site improvements, using the assemblies and the unit price methods.

**Some of what you'll learn:**
- Basic site work and heavy construction estimating skills
- Estimating foundations, utilities, earthwork, and site improvements
- Correct equipment usage, quality control, and site investigation for estimating purposes

**Who should attend:** Project managers, design engineers, estimators, and contractors doing site work and heavy construction.

# 2010 RSMeans Seminar Schedule

Note: call for exact dates and details.

| Location | Dates |
|---|---|
| Las Vegas, NV | March |
| Washington, DC | April |
| Denver, CO | May |
| San Francisco, CA | June |
| Washington, DC | September |
| Dallas, TX | September |
| Las Vegas, NV | October |
| Atlantic City, NJ | October |
| Orlando, FL | November |
| San Diego, CA | December |

# 2010 Regional Seminar Schedule

| Location | Dates | Location | Dates |
|---|---|---|---|
| Seattle, WA | January and August | St. Louis, MO | August |
| Dallas/Ft. Worth, TX | January | Houston, TX | October |
| Austin, TX | February | Colorado Springs, CO | October |
| Anchorage, AK | March and September | Baltimore, MD | November |
| Oklahoma City, OK | March | Sacramento, CA | November |
| Phoenix, AZ | March | San Antonio, TX | December |
| Aiea, HI | May | Raleigh, NC | December |
| Kansas City, MO | May | | |
| Bethesda, MD | June | | |
| Columbus, GA | June | | |
| El Segundo, CA | August | | |

**1-800-334-3509, ext. 5115**

For more information
visit the RSMeans website
at www.rsmeans.com

# Professional Development

## Registration Information

**Register early... Save up to $100!** Register 30 days before the start date of a seminar and save $100 off your total fee. *Note: This discount can be applied only once per order. It cannot be applied to team discount registrations or any other special offer.*

**How to register** Register by phone today! The RSMeans toll-free number for making reservations is **1-800-334-3509, ext. 5115.**

**Individual seminar registration fee - $935.** *Means CostWorks®* **training registration fee - $375.** To register by mail, complete the registration form and return, with your full fee, to: RSMeans Seminars, 63 Smiths Lane, Kingston, MA 02364.

**Government pricing** All federal government employees save off the regular seminar price. Other promotional discounts cannot be combined with the government discount.

**Team discount program** for two to four seminar registrations. Call for pricing: 1-800-334-3509, ext. 5115

**Multiple course discounts** When signing up for two or more courses, call for pricing.

**Refund policy** Cancellations will be accepted up to ten business days prior to the seminar start. There are no refunds for cancellations received later than ten working days prior to the first day of the seminar. A $150 processing fee will be applied for all cancellations. Written notice of cancellation is required. Substitutions can be made at any time before the session starts. **No-shows are subject to the full seminar fee.**

**AACE approved courses** Many seminars described and offered here have been approved for 14 hours (1.4 recertification credits) of credit by the AACE

International Certification Board toward meeting the continuing education requirements for recertification as a Certified Cost Engineer/Certified Cost Consultant.

**AIA Continuing Education** We are registered with the AIA Continuing Education System (AIA/CES) and are committed to developing quality learning activities in accordance with the CES criteria. Many seminars meet the AIA/CES criteria for Quality Level 2. AIA members may receive (14) learning units (LUs) fc each two-day RSMeans course.

**Daily course schedule** The first day of each seminar session begins at 8:30 a.m. and ends at 4:30 p.m. The second day begins at 8:00 a.m. and ends at 4:00 p.r Participants are urged to bring a hand-held calculator, since many actual problem will be worked out in each session.

**Continental breakfast** Your registration includes the cost of a continental breakfast, and a morning and afternoon refreshment break. These informal segments allow you to discuss topics of mutual interest with other seminar attendees. (You are free to make your own lunch and dinner arrangements.)

**Hotel/transportation arrangements** RSMeans arranges to hold a block of rooms at most host hotels. To take advantage of special group rates when making your reservation, be sure to mention that you are attending the RSMeans seminar. You are, of course, free to stay at the lodging place of your choice. (**Hotel reservations and transportation arrangements should be made directly by seminar attendees.**)

**Important** Class sizes are limited, so please register as soon as possible.

*Note: Pricing subject to change.*

## Registration Form

**ADDS-1000**

**Call 1-800-334-3509, ext. 5115 to register or FAX this form 1-800-632-6732. Visit our Web site: www.rsmeans.com**

Please register the following people for the RSMeans construction seminars as shown here. We understand that we must make our own hotel reservations if overnight stays are necessary.

☐ Full payment of $_____enclosed.

☐ Bill me

Please print name of registrant(s)

(To appear on certificate of completion)

_____

_____

_____

_____

P.O. #: _____
GOVERNMENT AGENCIES MUST SUPPLY PURCHASE ORDER NUMBER OR TRAINING FORM.

Firm name_____

Address_____

City/State/Zip_____

Telephone no._____ Fax no._____

E-mail address_____

Charge registration(s) to: ☐ MasterCard ☐ VISA ☐ American Express

Account no._____ Exp. date_____

Cardholder's signature_____

Seminar name_____

Seminar City _____

**Please mail check to: RSMeans Seminars, 63 Smiths Lane, P.O. Box 800, Kingston, MA 02364 USA**

CONSTRUCTION COST INFORMATION... PRODUCTS & SERVICES

For more information
visit the RSMeans website
at www.rsmeans.com

# New Titles

## The Gypsum Construction Handbook by USG

An invaluable reference of construction procedures for gypsum drywall, cement board, veneer plaster, and conventional plaster. This new edition includes the newest product developments, installation methods, fire- and sound-rated construction information, illustrated framing-to-finish application instructions, estimating and planning information, and more. Great for architects and engineers; contractors, builders, and dealers; apprentices and training programs; building inspectors and code officials; and anyone interested in gypsum construction. Features information on tools and safety practices, a glossary of construction terms, and a list of important agencies and associations. Also available in Spanish.

**$29.95**
**Over 575 pages, illustrated, softcover**
**Catalog no. 67357A**

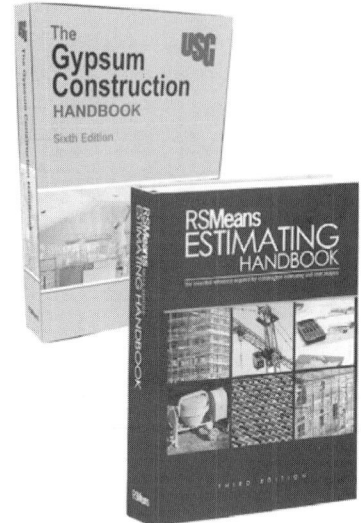

## RSMeans Estimating Handbook, 3rd Edition

Widely used in the industry for tasks ranging from routine estimates to special cost analysis projects, this handbook has been completely updated and reorganized with new and expanded technical information.

*RSMeans Estimating Handbook* will help construction professionals:

• Evaluate architectural plans and specifications
• Prepare accurate quantity takeoffs
• Compare design alternatives and costs
• Perform value engineering
• Double-check estimates and quotes
• Estimate change orders

**$99.95 per copy**
**Over 900 pages, hardcover**
**Catalog No. 67276B**

## BIM Handbook
### A Guide to Building Information Modeling for Owners, Managers, Designers, Engineers and Contractors
**by Chuck Eastman, Paul Teicholz, Rafael Sacks, Kathleen Liston**

Building Information Modeling (BIM) is a new approach to design, construction, and facility management where a digital depiction of the building process is used to facilitate the exchange of information in digital format.

The BIM Handbook provides an in-depth understanding of BIM technologies, the business and organizational issues associated with its implementation, and the profound advantages that effective use of BIM can provide to all members of a project team. Also includes a rich set of informative BIM case studies.

**$85.00**
**504 pages**
**Catalog no. 67356**

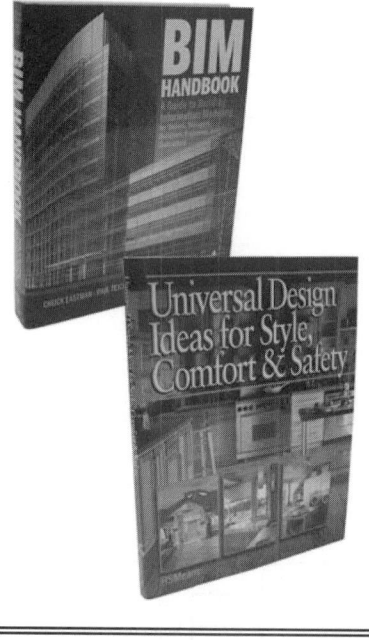

## Universal Design Ideas for Style, Comfort & Safety
**by RSMeans and Lexicon Consulting, Inc.**

Incorporating universal design when building or remodeling helps people of any age and physical ability more fully and safely enjoy their living spaces. This book shows how universal design can be artfully blended into the most attractive homes. It discusses specialized products like adjustable countertops and chair lifts, as well as simple ways to enhance a home's safety and comfort. With color photos and expert guidance, every area of the home is covered. Includes budget estimates that give an idea how much projects will cost.

**$21.95**
**160 pages, illustrated, softcover**
**Catalog no. 67354**

## Green Home Improvement
**by Daniel D. Chiras, PhD**

With energy costs rising and environmental awareness increasing, many people are looking to make their homes greener. This book makes it easy, with 65 projects and actual costs and projected savings that will help homeowners prioritize their green improvements.

Projects range from simple water savers that cost only a few dollars, to bigger-ticket items such as efficient appliances and HVAC systems, green roofing, flooring, landscaping, and much more. With color photos and cost estimates, each project compares options and describes the work involved, the benefits, and the savings.

**$24.95**
**320 pages, illustrated, softcover**
**Catalog no. 67355**

## Residential & Light Commercial Construction Standards, 3rd Edition, Updated
**by RSMeans and contributing authors**

This book provides authoritative requirements and recommendations compiled from leading professional associations, industry publications, and building code organizations. This all-in-one reference helps establish a standard for workmanship, quickly resolve disputes, and avoid defect claims. Updated third edition includes new coverage of green building, seismic, hurricane, and mold-resistant construction.

**$59.95**
**Over 550 pages, illustrated, softcover**
**Catalog no. 67322B**

# 2010 Order Form

| Qty. | Book no. | COST ESTIMATING BOOKS | Unit Price | Total |
|---|---|---|---|---|
| | 60060 | Assemblies Cost Data 2010 | $279.95 | |
| | 60010 | Building Construction Cost Data 2010 | 169.95 | |
| | 60110 | Concrete & Masonry Cost Data 2010 | 154.95 | |
| | 50140 | Construction Cost Indexes 2010 (subscription) | 362.00 | |
| | 60140A | Construction Cost Index–January 2010 | 90.50 | |
| | 60140B | Construction Cost Index–April 2010 | 90.50 | |
| | 60140C | Construction Cost Index–July 2010 | 90.50 | |
| | 60140D | Construction Cost Index–October 2010 | 90.50 | |
| | 60340 | Contr. Pricing Guide: Resid. R & R Costs 2010 | 39.95 | |
| | 60330 | Contr. Pricing Guide: Resid. Detailed 2010 | 39.95 | |
| | 60320 | Contr. Pricing Guide: Resid. Sq. Ft. 2010 | 39.95 | |
| | 60230 | Electrical Change Order Cost Data 2010 | 169.95 | |
| | 60030 | Electrical Cost Data 2010 | 169.95 | |
| | 60200 | Facilities Construction Cost Data 2010 | 419.95 | |
| | 60300 | Facilities Maintenance & Repair Cost Data 2010 | 379.95 | |
| | 60160 | Heavy Construction Cost Data 2010 | 169.95 | |
| | 60090 | Interior Cost Data 2010 | 169.95 | |
| | 60120 | Labor Rates for the Const. Industry 2010 | 379.95 | |
| | 60180 | Light Commercial Cost Data 2010 | 144.95 | |
| | 60020 | Mechanical Cost Data 2010 | 169.95 | |
| | 60150 | Open Shop Building Const. Cost Data 2010 | 169.95 | |
| | 60210 | Plumbing Cost Data 2010 | 169.95 | |
| | 60040 | Repair & Remodeling Cost Data 2010 | 144.95 | |
| | 60170 | Residential Cost Data 2010 | 144.95 | |
| | 60280 | Site Work & Landscape Cost Data 2010 | 169.95 | |
| | 60050 | Square Foot Costs 2010 | 184.95 | |
| | 62019 | Yardsticks for Costing (2009) | 154.95 | |
| | 62010 | Yardsticks for Costing (2010) | 169.95 | |
| | | **REFERENCE BOOKS** | | |
| | 67310A | ADA Compliance Pricing Guide, 2nd Ed. | 79.95 | |
| | 67356 | BIM Handbook | 85.00 | |
| | 67330 | Bldrs Essentials: Adv. Framing Methods | 12.98 | |
| | 67329 | Bldrs Essentials: Best Bus. Practices for Bldrs | 29.95 | |
| | 67298A | Bldrs Essentials: Framing/Carpentry 2nd Ed. | 15.98 | |
| | 67298AS | Bldrs Essentials: Framing/Carpentry Spanish | 15.98 | |
| | 67307 | Bldrs Essentials: Plan Reading & Takeoff | 35.95 | |
| | 67342 | Building & Renovating Schools | 69.98 | |
| | 67339 | Building Security: Strategies & Costs | 44.98 | |
| | 67353 | Complete Book of Framing | 29.95 | |
| | 67146 | Concrete Repair & Maintenance Illustrated | 69.95 | |
| | 67352 | Construction Business Management | 49.95 | |
| | 67314 | Cost Planning & Est. for Facil. Maint. | 89.95 | |
| | 67328A | Designing & Building with the IBC, 2nd Ed. | 99.95 | |
| | 67230B | Electrical Estimating Methods, 3rd Ed. | 64.95 | |
| | 64777A | Environmental Remediation Est. Methods, 2nd Ed. | 49.98 | |
| | 67343 | Estimating Bldg. Costs for Resi. & Lt. Comm. | 29.95 | |
| | 67276B | Estimating Handbook, 3rd Ed. | $99.95 | |
| | 67318 | Facilities Operations & Engineering Reference | 54.98 | |
| | 67301 | Facilities Planning & Relocation | 49.98 | |
| | 67338A | Green Building: Proj. Planning & Cost Est., 2nd Ed. | 129.95 | |
| | 67355 | Green Home Improvement | 24.95 | |

| Qty. | Book no. | REFERENCE BOOKS (Cont.) | Unit Price | Total |
|---|---|---|---|---|
| | 67357A | The Gypsum Construction Handbook | 29.95 | |
| | 67357S | The Gypsum Construction Handbook (Spanish) | 29.95 | |
| | 67323 | Historic Preservation: Proj. Planning & Est. | 49.98 | |
| | 67308E | Home Improvement Costs–Int. Projects, 9th Ed. | 24.95 | |
| | 67309E | Home Improvement Costs–Ext. Projects, 9th Ed. | 24.95 | |
| | 67344 | Homeowner's Guide to Mold | 21.95 | |
| | 67324B | How to Est.w/Means Data & CostWorks, 3rd Ed. | 59.95 | |
| | 67351 | How Your House Works | 21.95 | |
| | 67282A | Illustrated Const. Dictionary, Condensed, 2nd Ed. | 59.95 | |
| | 67292A | Illustrated Const. Dictionary, w/CD-ROM, 3rd Ed. | 99.95 | |
| | 67348 | Job Order Contracting | 89.95 | |
| | 67347 | Kitchen & Bath Project Costs | 19.98 | |
| | 67295C | Landscape Estimating Methods, 5th Ed. | 64.95 | |
| | 67341 | Life Cycle Costing for Facilities | 99.95 | |
| | 67294B | Mechanical Estimating Methods, 4th Ed. | 64.95 | |
| | 67245A | Planning & Managing Interior Projects, 2nd Ed. | 34.98 | |
| | 67283B | Plumbing Estimating Methods, 3rd Ed. | 29.98 | |
| | 67345 | Practice of Cost Segregation Analysis | 99.95 | |
| | 67337 | Preventive Maint. for Higher Education Facilities | 149.95 | |
| | 67346 | Preventive Maint. for Multi-Family Housing | 89.95 | |
| | 67326 | Preventive Maint. Guidelines for School Facil. | 149.95 | |
| | 67247B | Project Scheduling & Management for Constr. 3rd Ed. | 64.95 | |
| | 67265B | Repair & Remodeling Estimating Methods, 4th Ed. | 69.95 | |
| | 67322B | Resi. & Light Commercial Const. Stds., 3rd Ed. | 59.95 | |
| | 67327A | Spanish/English Construction Dictionary, 2nd Ed. | 23.95 | |
| | 67145B | Sq. Ft. & Assem. Estimating Methods, 3rd Ed. | 69.95 | |
| | 67321 | Total Productive Facilities Management | 29.98 | |
| | 67350 | Understanding and Negotiating Const. Contracts | 69.95 | |
| | 67303B | Unit Price Estimating Methods, 4th Ed. | 59.95 | |
| | 67354 | Universal Design | 21.95 | |
| | 67319A | Value Engineering: Practical Applications | 79.95 | |

| | |
|---|---|
| MA residents add 6.25% state sales tax | |
| Shipping & Handling** | |
| Total (U.S. Funds)* | |

Prices are subject to change and are for U.S. delivery only. *Canadian customers may call for current prices. **Shipping & handling charges: Add 7% of total order for check and credit card payments. Add 9% of total order for invoiced orders.

**Send order to:**  **ADDV-1000**

Name (please print) _____

Company _____

☐ **Company**

☐ **Home   Address** _____

_____

City/State/Zip _____

Phone # _____  P.O. # _____

(Must accompany all orders being billed)

# RSMeans Project Cost Report

By filling out this report, your project data will contribute to the database that supports the RSMeans Project Cost Square Foot Data. When you fill out this form, RSMeans will provide a $30 discount off one of the RSMeans products advertised in the preceding pages. Please complete the form including all items where you have cost data, and all the items marked (✔).

---

## $30.00 Discount per product for each report you submit.

---

## Project Description (No remodeling projects, please.)

✔ Building Use (Office, School...) _____

✔ Address (City, State) _____

_____

✔ Total Building Area (SF) _____

✔ Ground Floor (SF) _____

✔ Frame (Wood, Steel...) _____

✔ Exterior Wall (Brick, Tilt-up...) _____

✔ Basement: (check one) ☐ Full ☐ Partial ☐ None

✔ Number Stories _____

✔ Floor-to-Floor Height _____

✔ Volume (C.F.) _____

% Air Conditioned _____ Tons _____

**Total Project Cost** $ _____

Owner _____

Architect _____

General Contractor _____

✔ Bid Date _____

✔ Typical Bay Size _____

✔ Capacity _____

✔ Labor Force: _____ % Union _____ % Non-Union

✔ Project Description (Circle one number in each line)

1. Economy  2. Average  3. Custom  4. Luxury
1. Square  2. Rectangular  3. Irregular  4. Very Irregular

Comments _____

_____

| | | |
|---|---|---|
| A ✔ General Conditions | $ | |
| B ✔ Site Work | $ | |
| C ✔ Concrete | $ | |
| D ✔ Masonry | $ | |
| E ✔ Metals | $ | |
| F ✔ Wood & Plastics | $ | |
| G ✔ Thermal & Moisture Protection | $ | |
| GR     Roofing & Flashing | $ | |
| H ✔ Doors and Windows | $ | |
| J ✔ Finishes | $ | |
| JP     Painting & Wall Covering | $ | |

| | | |
|---|---|---|
| K ✔ Specialties | $ | |
| L ✔ Equipment | $ | |
| M ✔ Furnishings | $ | |
| N ✔ Special Construction | $ | |
| P ✔ Conveying Systems | $ | |
| Q ✔ Mechanical | $ | |
| QP     Plumbing | $ | |
| QB     HVAC | $ | |
| R ✔ Electrical | $ | |
| S ✔ Mech./Elec. Combined | $ | |

Please specify the RSMeans product you wish to receive. Complete the address information.

Product Name _____

Product Number _____

Your Name _____

Title _____

Company _____
☐ Company
☐ Home    Street Address _____

City, State, Zip _____

Return by mail or Fax 888-492-6770.

Method of Payment:

Credit Card # _____

Expiration Date _____

Check _____

Purchase Order _____

**RSMeans**
**a division of Reed Construction Data**
Square Foot Costs Department
P.O. Box 800
Kingston, MA 02364-3008